ᴇORGIA *continued*

ᴀU Atlanta University, Atlanta.
ᴀuA Augusta College, Augusta.
ColuC Columbus College, Columbus.
CuA Andrews College, Cuthbert.
DC Columbia Theological Seminary, Decatur.
DS Agnes Scott College, Decatur.
DecA* Agnes Scott College, Decatur.
DecCT* Columbia Theological Seminary, Decatur.
DoS South Georgia College, Douglas.
EU Emory University, Atlanta.
Hi Georgia Historical Society, Savannah.
MM Mercer University, Macon.
MW Wesleyan College, Macon.
MiW Woman's College of Georgia, Milledgeville.
MilvC* Woman's College of Georgia, Milledgeville.
OgU Oglethorpe University, Oglethorpe University.
De* University of Georgia, DeRenne Library.
J University of Georgia, Athens.
J-De — DeRenne Georgia Library.
J-Ex — Georgia State College of Business Administration Library, Atlanta.

HAWAII

J University of Hawaii, Honolulu.
J-EWC Center for Cultural and Technical Interchange between East and West, Honolulu.

ILLINOIS

Illinois State Library, Springfield.
Chicago Public Library.
A Art Institute of Chicago, Chicago.
F Chicago Natural History Museum, Chicago.
F-A — Edward E. Ayer Ornithological Library.
Hi Chicago Historical Society, Chicago.
IP Institute for Psychoanalysis, Chicago.
J John Crerar Library, Chicago.
MILC* Center for Research Libraries, Chicago.
McC McCormick Theological Seminary, Chicago.
N Newberry Library, Chicago.
RL Center for Research Libraries, Chicago.
U University of Chicago, Chicago.
arbS Southern Illinois University, Carbondale.
G Garrett Theological Seminary, Evanston.
N Northwestern University, Evanston.
dS Southern Illinois University, Edwardsville.
K Knox College, Galesburg.
i Illinois State Historical Library, Springfield.
S St. Procopius College, Lisle.
unS Saint Mary of the Lake Seminary, Mundelein.
S Illinois State University, Normal.
A Augustana College Library, Rock Island.
ivfR Rosary College, River Forest.
University of Illinois, Urbana.
-M — Medical Sciences Library, Chicago.
-U — Chicago Undergraduate Division, Chicago.

IOWA

AS Iowa State University of Science and Technology, Ames.
DL Luther College, Decorah.
DuC Loras College, Dubuque.
DuU University of Dubuque, Dubuque.
DuU-S — Theological Seminary Library.
DuW Wartburg Theological Seminary, Dubuque.
U University of Iowa, Iowa City.

IDAHO

B Boise Public Library.
PI Idaho State University, Pocatello.
PS* Idaho State University, Pocatello.
U University of Idaho, Moscow.

INDIANA

Indiana State Library, Indianapolis.
AndC Anderson College, Anderson.
CollS* St. Joseph's College, Rensselaer.
Go Goshen College Biblical Seminary Library, Goshen.
Hi Indiana Historical Society, Indianapolis.
IB Butler University, Indianapolis.

INDIANA *continued*

InLP Purdue University, Lafayette.
InNd University of Notre Dame, Notre Dame.
InOlH* St. Leonard College Library, Dayton, Ohio.
InRE Earlham College, Richmond.
InRenS St. Joseph's College, Rensselaer.
InStme St. Meinrad's College & Seminary, St. Meinrad.
InU Indiana University, Bloomington.

KANSAS

K Kansas State Library, Topeka.
KAS St. Benedict's College, Atchison.
KAStB* St. Benedict's College, Atchison.
KHi Kansas State Historical Society, Topeka.
KKcB Central Baptist Theological Seminary, Kansas City.
KMK Kansas State University, Manhattan.
KStMC* St. Louis University, School of Divinity Library, St. Louis, Mo.
KU University of Kansas, Lawrence.
KU-M — Medical Center Library, Kansas City.
KWiU Wichita State University, Wichita.

KENTUCKY

Ky-LE Library Extension Division, Frankfort.
KyBgW Western Kentucky State College, Bowling Green
KyHi Kentucky Historical Society, Frankfort.
KyLo Louisville Free Public Library.
KyLoS Southern Baptist Theological Seminary, Louisville.
KyLoU University of Louisville, Louisville.
KyLx Lexington Public Library.
KyLxCB Lexington Theological Seminary, Lexington. (Formerly College of the Bible)
KyLxT Transylvania College, Lexington.
KyMoreT Morehead State College, Morehead.
KyU University of Kentucky, Lexington.
KyWA Asbury College Library, Wilmore.
KyWAT Asbury Theological Seminary, Wilmore.

LOUISIANA

L Louisiana State Library, Baton Rouge.
L-M Louisiana State Museum Library, New Orleans.
LCA Not a library symbol.
LCS Not a library symbol.
LHi Louisiana History Society, New Orleans.
LNHT Tulane University Library, New Orleans.
LNT-MA Tulane University, Latin American Library, New Orleans.
LU Louisiana State University, Baton Rouge.
LU-M — Medical Center Library, New Orleans.
LU-NO — Louisiana State University in New Orleans.

MASSACHUSETTS

M Massachusetts State Library, Boston.
MA Amherst College, Amherst.
MB Boston Public Library.
MBAt Boston Athenaeum, Boston.
MBBC* Boston College, Chestnut Hill.
MBCo Countway Library of Medicine. (Harvard-Boston Medical Libraries)
MBH Massachusetts Horticultural Society, Boston.
MBHo* Massachusetts Horticultural Society, Boston.
MBM* Countway Library of Medicine (Harvard-Boston Medical Libraries).
MBMu Museum of Fine Arts, Boston.
MBU Boston University.
MBdAF U.S. Air Force Cambridge Research Center, Bedford.
MBrZ Zion Research Library, Brookline.
MBrigStJ* St. John's Seminary, Brighton.
MBtS St. John's Seminary Library, Brighton.
MCM Massachusetts Institute of Technology, Cambridge.
MCR Radcliffe College, Cambridge.
MCSA Smithsonian Institution, Astrophysical Observatory, Cambridge.
MChB Boston College, Chestnut Hill.
MH Harvard University, Cambridge.
MH-A — Arnold Arboretum.
MH-AH — Andover-Harvard Theological Library.
MH-BA — Graduate School of Business Administration Library.
MH-FA — Fine Arts Library. (Formerly Fogg Art Museum)
MH-G — Gray Herbarium Library.
MH-HY — Harvard-Yenching Institute. (Chinese-Japanese Library)

MASSACHUSETTS *continued*

MH-L — Law School Library.
MH-P — Peabody Museum Library.
MH-PR — Physics Research Library.
MHi Massachusetts Historical Society, Boston.
MMeT Tufts University, Medford.
MNF Forbes Library, Northampton.
MNS Smith College, Northampton.
MNoeS Stonehill College Library, North Easton.
MNtcA Andover Newton Theological School, Newton Center.
MSaE Essex Institute, Salem.
MShM Mount Holyoke College, South Hadley.
MU University of Massachusetts, Amherst.
MWA American Antiquarian Society, Worcester.
MWAC Assumption College, Worcester.
MWC Clark University, Worcester.
MWH College of the Holy Cross, Worcester.
MWalB Brandeis University, Waltham.
MWelC Wellesley College, Wellesley.
MWhB Marine Biological Laboratory, Woods Hole.
MWiW Williams College, Williamstown.
MWiW-C — Chapin Library.

MARYLAND

MdAN U.S. Naval Academy, Annapolis.
MdBE Enoch Pratt Free Library, Baltimore.
MdBG Goucher College, Baltimore.
MdBJ Johns Hopkins University, Baltimore.
MdBJ-G — John Work Garrett Library.
MdBP Peabody Institute, Baltimore.
MdBWA Walters Art Gallery, Baltimore.
MdU University of Maryland, College Park.
MdW Woodstock College, Woodstock.

MAINE

MeB Bowdoin College, Brunswick.
MeBa Bangor Public Library.
MeU University of Maine, Orono.
MeWC Colby College, Waterville.
MeWaC* Colby College, Waterville.

MICHIGAN

Mi Michigan State Library, Lansing.
MiAC Alma College, Alma.
MiD Detroit Public Library.
MiD-B — Burton Historical Collection.
MiDA Detroit Institute of Arts, Detroit.
MiDU University of Detroit, Detroit.
MiDW Wayne State University, Detroit.
MiEM Michigan State University, East Lansing.
MiEalC* Michigan State University, East Lansing.
MiGr Grand Rapids Public Library.
MiH* Michigan College of Mining and Technology, Houghton.
MiHM Michigan College of Mining and Technology, Houghton.
MiU University of Michigan, Ann Arbor.
MiU-C — William L. Clements Library.

MINNESOTA

MnCS St. John's University, Collegeville.
MnH* Minnesota Historical Society, St. Paul.
MnHi Minnesota Historical Society, St. Paul.
MnRM Mayo Clinic and Foundation Library, Rochester.
MnSJ James Jerome Hill Reference Library, St. Paul.
MnSSC College of St. Catherine, St. Paul.
MnU University of Minnesota, Minneapolis.

MISSOURI

MoHi Missouri State Historical Society, Columbia
MoK Kansas City Public Library.
MoKL Linda Hall Library, Kansas City
MoKU University of Missouri at Kansas City, Kansas City.
MoS St. Louis Public Library.
MoSB Missouri Botanical Garden, St. Louis.
MoSC* Concordia Seminary Library, St. Louis.
MoSCS Concordia Seminary Library, St. Louis.
MoSM Mercantile Library Association, St. Louis.
MoSU St. Louis University, St. Louis.
MoSU-D — School of Divinity Library, St. Louis.
MoSW Washington University, St. Louis.
MoU University of Missouri, Columbia.

The National Union Catalog

Pre-1956 Imprints

The National Union Catalog

Pre-1956 Imprints

A cumulative author list representing Library of Congress printed cards and titles reported by other American libraries. Compiled and edited with the cooperation of the Library of Congress and the National Union Catalog Subcommittee of the Resources Committee of the Resources and Technical Services Division, American Library Association

Volume 337

LIVON, MARIUS - LOCKYER, HERBERT

Mansell 1974

Mansell Information/Publishing Limited
3 Bloomsbury Place, London WC1

The American Library Association
50 East Huron Street, Chicago, Illinois 60611

The paper on which this catalog has been printed is supplied by P. F. Bingham Limited and has been specially manufactured by the Guard Bridge Paper Company Limited of Fife, Scotland. Based on requirements established by the late William J. Barrow for a permanent/durable book paper it is laboratory certified to meet or exceed the following values:

Substance 89 gsm
pH cold extract 9·4
Fold endurance (MIT ½kg. tension) 1200
Tear resistance (Elmendorf) 73 (or 67 × 3)
Opacity 90·3%

Library of Congress Card Number: 67–30001
ISBN: 0 7201 0416 5

Printed by Balding & Mansell Limited, London and Wisbech, England
Bound by Bemrose & Sons Limited, Derby, England

American Library Association

Resources and Technical Services Division

RESOURCES COMMITTEE

SUBCOMMITTEE ON THE NATIONAL UNION CATALOG

Chairman GORDON R. WILLIAMS
Director CENTER FOR RESEARCH LIBRARIES
5721 Cottage Grove Avenue, Chicago, Illinois 60637

Members

DOUGLAS W. BRYANT *University Librarian*
Widener Library, Harvard University
Cambridge, Massachusetts 02138

VERNER W. CLAPP 1901-1972 *formerly*
Consultant Council on Library Resources, Inc.

JOHN W. CRONIN *formerly*
Director Processing Department
Library of Congress
2129 32nd Place, S.E.
Washington, D.C. 20020

CHARLES W. DAVID *formerly*
Director of Library Development
Marine Historical Association
854 Radnor Road
St. Davids, Pennsylvania 19087

WILLIAM S. DIX *University Librarian*
Princeton University
Princeton, New Jersey 08540

RALPH E. ELLSWORTH *formerly*
Director University of Colorado Libraries
Boulder, Colorado 80302

HERMAN H. FUSSLER *Professor*
Graduate Library School
University of Chicago
Chicago, Illinois 60637

WARREN J. HAAS *Vice President*
for Libraries and Information Services
Columbia University
New York City, New York 10027

RUTHERFORD D. ROGERS *University Librarian*
Yale University
New Haven, Connecticut 06520

GEORGE A. SCHWEGMANN, JR. *formerly*
Chief Union Catalog Division
3534 Porter Street, N.W.
Washington, D.C. 20016

FREDERICK H. WAGMAN *Director*
University of Michigan Libraries
Ann Arbor, Michigan 48104

WILLIAM J. WELSH *Director*
Processing Department
Library of Congress
Washington, D.C. 20540

Publisher's Note

Because of the large number of sources from which the information in the National Union Catalog has been collected over a long period of time an understanding of its scope and an acquaintance with its methods is necessary for the best use to be made of it. Users are therefore earnestly advised to make themselves familiar with the introductory matter in Volume 1. This fully defines the scope of the Catalog and sets out the basis on which the material reported to the National Union Catalog has been edited for publication in book form.

National Union Catalog Designation

Each main entry in the Catalog has been ascribed a unique identifying designation. This alphanumeric combination appears uniformly after the last line of the entry itself and consists of:

1 The letter N, signifying National Union Catalog.
2 The initial letter under which the entry is filed.
3 A number representing the position of the entry within the sequence under its initial letter.

This National Union Catalog designator is sufficient both to identify any main entry in the Catalog and to establish its position within the sequence of volumes. It is, however, recommended that when referring to titles by the National Union Catalog designation a checking element, such as the key word or initials of the title, be added.

Reported Locations

Alphabetic symbols which represent libraries in the United States and Canada follow the National Union Catalog designation. These groups of letters signify which libraries have reported holding copies of the work. The first library so represented usually is the one that provided the catalog information.

Printed on the end sheets of each volume is a list of most frequently used symbols, each followed by the full name of the library. *List of Symbols*, containing a comprehensive list of symbols used, is published as a separate volume with the Catalog. The Library of Congress has also issued *Symbols Used in the National Union Catalog of the Library of Congress*. In cases where a symbol is not identified in these lists the National Union Catalog Division of the Library of Congress will, on enquiry, attempt to identify the library concerned.

Other Developments

Under the terms of their agreement with the American Library Association, the publishers have undertaken to apply, as far as is practicable, new developments in library science and techniques which may have the effect of further enhancing the value of the Catalog. To this end, the publishers will be pleased to receive suggestions and enquiries relating to technical and production aspects of the Catalog and will be glad to consider proposals calculated to improve its utility and amenity. Mansell Information/Publishing Limited will be pleased also to advise libraries on possible applications of the methods and techniques developed for this and similar projects to their own requirements.

J.C.
London, *August 1968*

VOLUME 337

Liveon (Marius). *De l'omoplate et de ses indices de largeur dans les races humaines. 64 pp. 4°. *Paris*, 1879, No. 346.

NL 0422705 DNLM

PT19 .L75 Rare bk room
Livona. Ein historisch-poetisches taschenbuch für die deutsch-russischen ostseeprovinzen. 1812₍–16₎ Riga und Dorpat, F. Meinshausen ₍1812?–16?₎
2 v. fronts., plates, ports. 13½cm.
Includes music.
Edited by G. T. Tielemann.

1. German literature—Baltic Provinces—Collections.

NL 0422706 ICU NN MH PPLT

41.2 L762
Livoni, P
Mastitisbekaempelse; eksperimentelle undersøgelser specielt med henblik på gennemførelse af kollektive bekaempelsesforanstaltninger. With an English summary. Århus, 1955.
193 p.
Afhandling - Veterinaer- og landbohøjskole, Copenhagen.
1. Mastitis.

NL 0422707 DNAL

Livoni de Saavedra, Yolanda.
La marmita. Santiago de Chile ₍Impreso por Stanley, 1943₎
1 p. l., 5-648 p. 19cm.
On cover: 1000 recetas.
Advertising matter interspersed.

1. Cookery, Chilean.
New York. Public library for Library of Congress A 46-258
TX725.L54
₍2₎† 641.5

NL 0422708 NN DLC

Livoni de Saavedra, Yolanda.
La marmita ₍1.000 recetas₎ La Paz, Bolivia ₍cover 1952₎
448 p. 18 cm.

1. Cookery, Chilean.
TX725.L54 1952 641.5 53-34188 ‡

NL 0422709 DLC

Livonia.
Adressbuch für das Gouvernement Livland, zum Gebrauch für Behörden
see under Klingenberg, Adolph, comp.

Livonia.
Akten und Recesse der Livländischen Stäendetage
see under title

Livonia.
Allgemeines Adress-Buch für das Gouvernement Livland und die Provinz Oesel
see under Budberg, Karl, Freiherr, ed.

Z943.8 Z1 1583:1
Livonia.
Constitvtiones Livonicae, post submotum ex Livonia Moschum, à Serenissimo Stephano Poloniae rege, sancitae. Cracoviae, in officina Nicolai Scharffenberger, 1583.
₍20₎ p. 21 cm. ₍Polish history pamphlets. 1583:1₎
Signatures: A-B 4, C 2

NL 0422712 MnU

Livonia.
Лифляндскія губернскія вѣдомости. Годъ
Рига, 18
v. 46½cm. 3 nos. a week.
Established 1853, and published in German, until 1886, after which date it was published in Russian and German under Russian title. cf. N. M. Lisovskii.—Русская періодическая печать. 1703–1900. Petrograd, 1915, p. 122.
Volume for 1888 lettered on cover: Livländische gouvernements zeitung.
Editor: 18 A. Klingenberg.
1. Livonia—Pol. & govt.—Period. I. Klingenberg, A., ed. II. Title. III. Title: Livländische gouvernements zeitung.
32-6763
Library of Congress J7.R7L5
₍2₎ 352.0474

NL 0422713 DLC

Livonia.
Patente der livlaendischen Gouvernements-Regierung.
Riga, 8° – f°.
Title varies slightly.
1801–58, issued without t.-p.

NL 0422714 NN

HD 1536 .L 7 A5
LIVONIA. Commission zur Durchsicht der bäuerlichen Verhältnisse in Livland
Vorschläge der auf Allerhöchsten Befehl zur Durchsicht der bäuerlichen Verhältnisse in Livland niedergesetzten Commission. Riga, Gedr. bei W. F. Häcker, 1847.
15+378 p. tables.
Abgedruckt zum Behuf der auf den 25 August einstehenden Landtags-Berathung.

NL 0422715 InU

Livonia. Gubernskiĭ statisticheskiĭ komitet.
Resultate der am 3. März 1867 in den Städten Livlands ausgeführten Volkszählung, zusammengestellt und hrsg. mit Genehmigung des livländischen Statistischen Comité's vom Secretair R. Eckhardt... Riga: Druck der livländischen Gouvernements-Typographie, 1871. xi, 400 p. f°.
Title-page and text in German and Russian.

1. Livonia—Census, 1867.
N. Y. P. L. October 23, 1934

NL 0422716 NN

Livonia. Gubernskiĭ statisticheskiĭ komitet.
Сборникъ статистическихъ свѣдѣній по Лифляндской губерніи, изданный Лифляндскимъ губернскимъ статистическимъ комитетомъ. Подъ ред. Н. Карлберга. Рига, 1886.
88 p. 28 cm.

1. Livonia—Statistics. I. Karlberg, N., ed. II. Title.
Title romanized: Sbornik statisticheskikh svîedîeniĭ po Liflîandskoĭ gubernii.
HA1448.L55A5 72-223317

NL 0422717 DLC

Livonia. Landeskultur-bureau
see Liv-Estländisches Bureau für Landeskultur.

4HD 1960
Livonia. Landraths-Collegium.
Materialien zur Kenntniss der livländischen Agrarverhältnisse mit besonderer Berücksichtigung der Knechts- und Tagelöhner-Bevölkerung. Riga, Gedruckt in der Müllerschen Buchdr., 1885.
244 p.
Bound with its Materialien zur Kenntniss der livländischen Bauer-Verhältnisse. Riga, 1883.
Library of Congress DLC

NL 0422719 DLC-P4

4HD 1960
Livonia. Landraths-Collegium.
Materialien zur Kenntniss der livländischen Bauer-Verhältnisse. Riga, Gedruckt in der Müllerschen Buchdr., 1883.
39 p.

NL 0422720 DLC-P4

Livonia. Landtag
see Livonia. Ständetage.

Livonia. *Laws, statutes, etc.*
Altlivlands rechtsbücher. Zum theil nach bisher unbenutzten texten herausgegeben von dr. F. G. v. Bunge. Leipzig, Breitkopf und Härtel, 1879.
vi, 264 p. 22cm.
"Litteraturnotizen": p. 42–44.
Contents.—Einleitung.—Die texte: Das Waldemar-Erich'sche lehnrecht. Das älteste livländische ritterrecht. Der spiegel land- und lehnrechts. Das stück vom musstheil. Die artikel vom lehngut und lehnrecht. Fabri's Formulare procuratorum.
1. Feudal law—Livonia. 2. Law—Livonia. I. Bunge, Friedrich Georg von, 1802–1897, ed. II. Title.
13-24746 Revised

NL 0422722 DLC MH MH-L CtY ICU CLSU PU

Livonia. Laws, statutes, etc.
Arbusow, Leonid, 1882– ed.
... Das bauernrecht des sog. Budberg-Schraderschen landrechtsentwurfs von 1740 in ursprünglicher gestalt. Herausgegeben von Leonid Arbusow. Riga, E. Bruhns, 1937.

Livonia. Laws, statutes, etc.
HD 719 .B19 E6
ENTWURF EINER LANDGEMEINDE-ORDNUNG FÜR DIE Ostsee-Gouvernements. Riga, Druck der Livländischen Gouvernements-Typographie, 1866.
206 p.
Interleaved with blank pages.

NL 0422724 InU

Livonia. Laws, statutes, etc.
Bunge, Friedrich Georg von, 1802–1897.
Entwurf einer ordnung des gerichtlichen verfahrens in civilrechtssachen für Liv-, Est- und Curland. Von d. Friedrich Georg von Bunge... Reval, F. Kluge, 1864.

Livonia. Laws, statutes, etc.
Nielsen, Christian Heinrich, 1759–1829.
Handbuch zur kenntniss der polizeygesetze und anderer verordnungen für güterbesitzer und einwohner auf dem lande in Lief- und Ehstland. Von C. H. Nielsen ... Dorpat, M. G. Grenzius, 1794–95.

VOLUME 337

Livonia. *Laws, statutes, etc.*
Liefflåndische landes-ordnungen / nebst darzu gehörigen placaten und stadgen ... Riga, G. M. Nöller, 1705.
778, ₍36₎ p. 19½cm.
Title vignette (coat of arms)

I. Title.
27-11335
Library of Congress

NL 0422727 DLC MnU

Livonia. Laws, statutes, etc.
Liefflåndische landes-ordnungen, nebst darzu gehörigen placaten und stadgen. Riga, 1707.
Also another title-page dated 1705.

NL 0422728 MH-L

Livonia. *Laws, statutes, etc.*
Liefländisches allergnädigst confirmirtes landschaftliches credit-reglement vom 15. october 1802. Mit beygefügten general-detaxations-principien und eidesformeln. Mitau, Gedruckt bey J. F. Steffenhagen und sohn, 1803.
184, ₍12₎, xiv p. fold. form. 19cm.

1. Credit—Livonia. 2. Agricultural credit—Livonia. I. Title.
30-16221
Library of Congress HG2051.L5A4 1802

NL 0422729 DLC

Livonia. Laws, statutes, etc.
Liv-, est- und curlaendisches privatrecht. Zusammengestellt auf befehl des herrn und kaisers Alexander II. St. Petersburg, Buchdr. der Zweiten abtheilung Seiner Kaiserlichen Majestät eigener kanzlei, 1864.

Livonia. *Laws, statutes, etc.*
Livländische Agrar- und Bauern-Verordnung, in Uebereinstimmung mit der vom dirigirenden Senat im Jahre 1849 erlassenen Original-Druckschrift in russischer Sprache. Riga, Gedruckte bei W. F. Häcker, 1850.
294 p. 27 cm.

1. Peasantry—Livonia. 2. Land tenure—Livonia—Law. 3. Agricultural laws and legislation—Livonia. I. Russia. Laws, statutes, etc. II. Title.
64-58680

NL 0422731 DLC InU MH

Livonia. *Laws, statutes, etc.*
Livländische bauer-verordnung am 13. november 1860 allerhöchst bestätigt. In uebereinstimmung mit dem bei dem ukase des Dirigirenden senats vom 10. januar 1861, nr. 1569, emanirten original-texte, nach zuvoriger approbation der deutschen uebersetzung ... von der livländischen gouvernements-regierung publicirt. Riga, Livländische gouvernements-typographie, 1861.
5 p. l., 291, ₍1₎ p. 24½cm.
—— Alphabetisches sach- und wort-register zu der Livländischen bauer-verordnung vom jahre 1860. Riga, Livländische gouvernements-typographie, 1862.
1 p. l., 116 p. 24cm. ₍With Livländische bauer-verordnung ... Riga, 1861₎
1. Law—Livonia. 2. Agricultural laws and legislation—Livonia. I. Title.
Library of Congress ₍2₎ 30-20922

NL 0422732 DLC NN

Livonia. *Laws, statutes, etc.* Livländische Bauer-Verordnung. (*Indexes*)
Alphabetisches Sach- und Wort-Register zur allerhöchst bestätigten neuen Livländischen Bauer-Verordnung. Entworfen von dem wendenschen Herrn Kreis-Richter, Collegien-Assessor von Hagemeister und dem Herrn Kirchspiels-Richter von Samson. Zusammengetragen, ergänzt und approbirt durch die allerhöchstverordnete Commission zur Einführung der neuen Bauer-Verordnung in Livland. Dorpat, Gedruckt bei J. C. Schünmann, 1821.
146 p. 21 cm.

1. Peasantry—Livonia—Indexes. 2. Agricultural laws and legislation—Livonia—Indexes. I. Hagemeister, Heinrich von, 1784–1845. II. Samson von Himmelstiern, Georg Friedrich, 1783– III. Title: Alphabetisches Sach- und Wort-Register bur neuen Livländischen Bauer-Verordnung.
59-55621

NL 0422734 DLC InU

HD 719 .L 7 A3 1821
LIVONIA—Laws,statutes,etc.
Sammlung der Gesetze, welche das heutige livländische Landrecht enthalten, kritisch bearb. von Gustav Johann von Buddenbrock. Mitau, Gedr. von J.F. Steffenhagen; Riga, Gedr. von W.F. Häcker, 1802-1821.
2v. in 4.
Contents:
1. Bd. Angestammte livländische Landes-Rechte.
2. Bd. Aeltere hinzugekommene Landesrecht. 3 pts.
I. Buddenbrock, Gustav Johann von,1758-1821,ed. II. Tc.

NL 0422735 InU MH-L

Livonia. Laws, statutes, etc.
Vidzemes 1638. gada arklu revizia, latviesu novadi
see under Dunsdorfs, Edgars, ed.

Livonia. Schwedisches Generalgouverneur-Archiv
see Latvia. Valsts centralais archivs. Zviedru ģeneral-gubernatora archivs.

Livonia. Ständetage.
Akten und Rezesse der Livländischen Ständetage
see under title

JN 6733 .A23 S3
LIVONIA. Ständetage.
Die Recesse der livländischen Landtage aus den Jahren 1681 bis 1711. Theils im Wortlaute, theils im Auszuge. Hrsg. von C. Schirren. Dorpat, E. J. Karow, 1865.
447 p.

I. Schirren,Carl Christian Gerhard, 1826-1919,ed.

NL 0422739 InU

Livonia. Statisticheski komitet
see Livonia. Gubernskiĭ statisticheskiĭ komitet.

Law
Livonia. Treaties, etc., 1561.
Courland. *Laws, statutes, etc.*
Formula regiminis de anno MDCXVII. Pacta subjectionis inter Regem Sigismundum Augustum et Magistrum Gotthardum Kettler, inita Vilnae die XXVIII. Novembris anni MDLXI. et privilegium Sigismundi Augusti datum Vilnae nobilitati Livoniae feria VI. post festum S. Catharinae, MDLXI. Regierungs-Formel vom Jahre 1617. Unterwerfungs-Verträge zwischen dem Könige Sigismund August und dem Heermeister Gotthard Kettler, abgeschlossen zu Wilna den 28. November 1561 und das Privilegium, welches der König Sigismund August dem lieflandischen Adel im Jahre 1561, sechs Tage nach dem Feste der heiligen Catharina, in Wilna ertheilet. Uebersetzt von Heinrich Ludwig Birkel. Mitau, Gedruckt bey J. F. Stessenhagen, 1807.

Livonia of Venice; or, The wife of seven husbands. A remarkable tale. London, Printed by T. Maiden for A. Lemoine and J. Roe ₍1807₎ 60 p. front. 15cm.
Signatures K₂–O₂.
"Madeline of Brittany. An ancient tale," p. ₍50₎–60.

1. No subject. I. Title: The wife of seven husbands. II. Title: Madeline of Brittany.
N. Y. P. L. June 26, 1947

NL 0422743 NN

Livoniae historia in compendium ex annalibus ...
see under Horner, Thomas, 15th cent.

A Livonian.
Aus dem Tagebuche eines Livländers
see under [Lenz, Wilhelm von] 1808-1883. [Supplement]

Livonian tales. The deponent. The wolves. The Jewess
see under [Eastlake, Elizabeth (Rigby) lady] 1809-1893.

Livonica. Oder, Einiger zu mehrer erläuterung der mit anfang des 1700. jahres in Liefland entstandenen unruhe dienlicher stücke und actorum publicorum. Fasciculus 1.₍–10.₎ ₍Riga? 1700–02?₎
10 pt. in 1 v. 18½cm.
Each part with separate t.-p. and paging.
Warmholtz (Bibl. hist. sveo-gothica) gives 11 parts, Riga (?) 1700–03.

1. Livonia—Hist. 2. Courland—Hist. 3. Sweden—Hist.—Charles XII, 1697–1718.
17-11618
Library of Congress DK511.L3L5

NL 0422747 DLC

Livonicus, *pseud.*
see
Paeglit, Adolf.

Livonius,
Das preussische Eisenbahnnetz, mit besonderer Beziehung auf die östlichen Provinzen, von Livonius und Mertens. Berlin, B. Behr, 1846.
88 p. nar. 8°.

NL 0422749 NN

VOLUME 337

Livonius, Dr.
Ludwig van Beethoven. Ein Gedenkblatt zum 75. Todestage des unsterblichen Meisters, 1827, 26. März, 1902. Von Dr. Livonius. Mit einem Anhang: Beethovens Missa solemnis. Kiel [etc.] Lipsius & Tischer, 1902. 52 p. 22½cm.

1. Beethoven, Ludwig van, 1770-1827.
N. Y. P. L. December 16, 1942

NL 0422750 NN

HB41 .W77 no.75 Livonius, Eberhard von.
Die wirtschaftliche Entwicklung des Rittergutes Grumkow in Pommern, 1679-1926. Leipzig, A. Deichert, 1927.
viii, 95 p. map, plans, tables. (Wirtschafts- und Verwaltungsstudien mit besonderer Berücksichtigung Bayerns, 75)
Includes bibliography.

1. Agriculture--Economic aspects--Pomerania. I. Title: Rittergut Grumbkow in Pommern.

NL 0422751 ICU CtY MH NN ICJ ICRL

JX 4044 L76 Livonius, Ernst Manfred von
Die völkerrechtliche anerkennung unter besonderer berücksichtigung Sowjet-Russlands ... vorgelegt von ... Ernst Manfred v. Livonius ... Charlottenburg, Druck studentenwerk, 1934.
xi, 118 p. 29 cm.

Thesis, Würzburg, 1933.
Lithoprinted.
Bibliography.

NL 0422752 NNC ICRL CtY CLSU

Livonius, O.
Colonialfragen, von O. Livonius... Berlin: R. Wilhelmi, 1885. 2 p.l., 68 p. 8°.

1. Colonies and colonization. 2. Colonies and colonization (German).
N. Y. P. L. November 19, 1920.

NL 0422753 NN CtY

Livonius, O.
Unsere flotte im deutsch-französischen kriege. Von O. Livonius ... Berlin, E. S. Mittler und sohn, 1871.
49 p. 22cm.
Imperfect: t.-p. mutilated.

1. Franco-German war, 1870-1871. 2. Germany—Navy—Hist. I. Title.
Library of Congress DC298.L77 42-39600

NL 0422754 DLC NN

Livonius, Otto.
Vom Schwarzen Meer nach Pommerns Küste; aus dem Tagebuch des Rittmeisters Livonius... Stolp: O. Eulitz, 1926. 24 p. 8°.
p. 23-24, advertising matter.

1. European war, 1914-1918—Personal narratives, German.
N. Y. P. L. February 9, 1927

NL 0422755 NN

Livonius, W. von.
Die feldausrustung des officiers ... Berlin, 1913. 60 p.

NL 0422756 DNW

Livonnière, Claude Pocquet de
see Pocquet de Livonnière, Claude, 1652-1726.

H 91 L78 Livonnière, Jean de.
Scènes de la vie sociale; petit traité de science sociale par l'image [par] Jean de Livonnière [et] Marcel Clément. Préface de Louis de Calan. Beaumont-Monteux, Centre français de sociologie [1955]
191 p. illus. 23cm.

1. Social sciences--Pictorial works. I. Clément, Marcel, joint author.

NL 0422758 NIC NNC

Livonnière, Marin de, d. 1865.
Lisa, par Marin de Livonnière. Paris, P. Brunet, 1867.
2 p. l., 283 p. 17cm.

I. Title.
18-16962
Library of Congress PQ2338.L67L5 1867

NL 0422759 DLC

Livor, J.
The peoples' hand book of homeopathic practice, by J. Livor, M. D. [New York?] ©1882.
cover-title, 37, [3] p. 16cm.

1. Homeopathy—Popular works.
Library of Congress RX76.L78 7-13818†

NL 0422760 DLC DNLM

Livor, John
A new system of English grammar on the oral method, to which is added a key to the exercises. By John Livor, 2d stereotype ed. New York, L. W. Schmidt, 1851.
iv, 79, [1] p. 18cm.

1. English language - Grammar - 1800-1870.

NL 0422761 NNC

Livorno, Lodovico da
see Lodovico da Livorno, Padre Lettore, Cap.

Livorno
see Leghorn.

Livorno a Vittorio Emanuele II e ad Amedeo di Savoia, duca d'Aosta
see under Leghorn. Comitato per le feste dell'agosto, 1892.

Livorno, 1904
see Guida-album di Livorno e dintorni 1904.

LIVORNO: stradario e notizie utili. Livorno, Societa' editrice Tirrena [195-] 111 p. 16cm.

1. Leghorn, Italy (City)--Streets--Direct.

NL 0422766 NN

W 4 P23 1941 Livory, Marcel, 1911-
La résection recto-sigmoïdienne avec intubation colo-rectale ... Paris, Foulon, 1941.
83 p. illus. (Paris. [Université. Faculté de médecine. Thèse. 1941. no. [41])

NL 0422767 DNLM MnU

Livoti, Paul L 1899-
A compilation and analysis of the laws of the state of New York relating to the administration of the jury system, by Paul Livoti ... [Jamaica, N. Y., Jamaica law printing co., inc.] ©1939.
cover-title, 2 p. l., 134 p. 27cm.

1. Jury—New York (State) I. New York (State) Laws, statutes, etc.
Library of Congress 41-24016

NL 0422768 DLC

WD 375 L788m 1955 LI VOTI, Pietro
Le mesenchimopatie chirurgiche; considerazioni cliniche e ricerche sperimentali. Palermo, D. E. L. F. [1955]
122 p. illus. (Collana di monografie mediche D. E. L. F.)
1. Collagen diseases

NL 0422769 DNLM ICJ

Livovschi, Victor.
... Contribution à l'étude des oxindoles ... Paris, Jouve & cie, 1937.
3 p. l., [3]-79, [1] p. 24cm.
Thèse—Univ. de Paris.
Bibliographical foot-notes.

1. Oxindols.
Library of Congress QD401.L795 41-18870
[2] 547.8

NL 0422770 DLC CtY

[Livoy, Timothée de] 1715-1777.
Dictionnaire de synonimes françois. Paris, Saillant, 1767.
xv, [1], 566, [2] p. 21cm.

1. French language—Synonyms. I. Title.
11-2866
Library of Congress PC2591.A2L7

NL 0422771 DLC CSt PKsL

PC2591 L5 1788 Livoy, Timothée de, 1715-1777.
Dictionnaire de synonymes françois. Nouv. éd. Rev., corr., & considérablement augmentée par M. Beauzée. Paris, Nyon, 1788.
xii, 700 p.

1. French language - Synonyms.

NL 0422772 CU

VOLUME 337

PC2591 L5 1740 Livoy, Timothée de, 1715-1777.
Dictionnaire de synonymes françois. Nouv. éd. rev., corr., & considérablement augm. par M. Beauzée. Paris, Nyon, 1740.
viii, 700 p.

1. French language - Synonyms.

NL 0422773 CU

PC2591 L5 1828 Livoy, Timothée de, 1715-1777.
Dictionnaire de synonymes françois, par Timothée de Livoy, augmenté par Beauzée. 3. éd. rev. et dégagée d'un grand nombre de mots inusités par M. Lepan. Paris, chez l'éditeur, 1828.
vii, 508 p.

1. French language - Synonyms and antonyms. I. Beauzée, Nicolas, 1717-1789, ed. II. Title.

NL 0422774 CU

FC7 A1CO 3760p [Livoy, Timothée de, 1715-1777.
Dissertation sur les interdits arbitraires des confesseurs, pour servir de supplément à l'ecrit posthume de m. l'abbé Gueret, intitulé, Droit des curés, &c.
[Paris?]M.DCC.LIX.
12°. 62p. 17cm.
Also attributed to Jérôme Besoigne.
Guéret's work appeared under the title: Droits qu'ont les curés de commettre leurs vicaires & les confesseurs dans leurs paroisses.

Occasioned by the controversy over acceptance of the bull Unigenitus.
No.3 in a volume labeled on spine: Pieces divers[es] 1759, 1760.

NL 0422776 MH ICN

Livoy, Timothee de, 1715-1777, ed.
Voyage d'Espagne fait en l'annee 1755
see under Caimo, Norberto.

Livramento, Affonso Cavalcanti.
Projecto de reforma do calendario civil.
Rio de Janeiro;1909. 16 pp.

NL 0422778 DCU-IA

Livramento, Barao do.
Discurso pronunciado na primeira sessao macna da sodiedade emancipadors de Pernambuco...
Recife, 1870.
17p.

NL 0422779 DCU-IA

Livraria Barateira, Lisboa.
Catalogo do leilão da preciosa biblioteca que na sua quasi totalidade pertenceram ao ilustre bibliofilo e grande latinista Barão de Vila Nova de Foscôa e ultimamente ao Conde de Pinhel, Lisboa, 1940.
352p. 22cm.

NL 0422780 IEN

Livraria Bertrand
see Bertrand e Filhos, Firm, Booksellers, Lisbon.

Lilly Z 999 .L 98 Mendel LIVRARIA COELHO, Lisbon
Catalogo de alguns livros raros e curiosos dos seculos XVI e XVII ...
Lisboa, 1931.
165 p. illus, (facsims.) 22.5 cm.

Contains also its Catalogo de alguns livros e manuscriptos ... Lisboa, 1930.
Bound in quarter leather.
From the library of C. R. Boxer.

NL 0422782 InU

Livraria de Manuel dos Santos, *Lisbon*
see Livraria Manuel dos Santos, *Lisbon*

Livraria do globo, *Porto Alegre*.
Album da Livraria do globo, Barcellos, Bertaso & c^ia. Porto Alegre, 1925. 44 p. illus., pl., port. f°.

Cover-title.

NL 0422784 NN

Livraria do globo, Porto Alegre.

Nova e definitiva tabella de cambio globo, de 1 a 13 pence por 1$000 unica em fracções de 1/512, 1/256 e 1/128 avos. Revista e ampliada ... Porto Alegre, Livraria do globo, 1931.

Livraria do globo, *Porto Alegre.*
... 60 years of work. Pôrto Alegre, Livraria do globo [1943?]
1 p. l., [8] p. of illus. (incl. ports.) 22cm.
At head of title: 1883-1943.

Library of Congress Z564.L55 45-19279
[2] 655.181

NL 0422786 DLC

1517 Livraria H. Garnier, Rio de Janeiro.
... Supplemento ao catalogo geral ...
Rio de Janeiro.

NL 0422787 DPU

Livraria José Olympio, Rio de Janeiro.
Brazilian medical contributions
see under [Ribeiro, Leonidio] comp.

Livraria José Olympio, Rio de Janeiro.
... Vida dos livros ... Rio de Janeiro.
Semi-monthly.

NL 0422789 CU

Z 999 .L78 LIVRARIA LUSITANA
Catálogo de livros raros e curiosos, dos séculos XV a XX, impressos e manuscritos em diversas línguas, à venda na Livraria Lusitana. Organisado e anotado por José dos Santos.
Lisboa, Tip. Viana, 1937-38.
2 v. in 1 facsims.

1. Catalogs--Booksellers'--Portugal.
2. Bibliography--Rare books. I. Santos, José dos, 1881-

NL 0422790 InU ICN

1517 Livraria Magalhães.
Catalogo, 1918-1919. S. Paulo.

NL 0422791 DPU

Livraria Manuel dos Santos, *Lisbon.*
Bibliografia geral ou descripção bibliografica de livros tanto de autores portuguezes como brasileiros e muitos de outras nacionalidades impressos desde o seculo xv até a actualidade, com a marcação dos respectivos preços de venda. Dá'se igualmente noticia de muitos manuscritos de evidente interesse para a historia do Brasil e das possessões portuguesas, etc. Lisboa, Tip. Mendonça, 1914-17-1918-25.
2 v. illus., plates (part col.) ports., facsims. 23 cm. (v. 2: 25 cm.)
At head of title: Manoel dos Santos.
Consists of catalogs no. 1-12 (1914-17) and no. 1-6 (1918-21) combined in 2 v., with addition of general t. p., preface, and index.
1. Portuguese literature—Bibl.—Catalogs. 2. Brazilian literature—Bibl.—Catalogs. 3. Catalogs, Booksellers'—Portugal. I. Title.

Z2739.Z9L58 016.869 32-30304 rev*

NL 0422792 DLC CU ICN MH

Livraria Manuel dos Santos, *Lisbon.*
Bibliografia por Manoel dos Santos. Ilustrada com gravuras, algumas coloridas, reproduzindo os frontispicios, fechos e encadernaçoes de varias obras estimadas e raras. Lisboa, Tip. de A. de Mendonça, 1915.
142 p. illus., col. plates, facsims. 24 cm.
"Alguns manuscritos estimaveis, entre os quais um muito importante para a historia do Brasil. Livros pouco vulgares, raros e rarissimos, que fizeram parte da biblioteca do Mosteiro de Palme, pertença de d. Antonio Bernardo da Fonseca Moniz (bispo do Porto), e que serão vendidos em leilão ... na Rua do Ouro ... pelas 21 horas (9 da noite) 1153 items.
1. Portuguese literature—Bibl.—Catalogs.

Z999.L79 42-26244 rev*

NL 0422793 DLC

Greenlee 4A 216 LIVRARIA MANUEL DOS SANTOS, Lisbon.
Catálogo das magníficas livrarias que pertenceram ao ilustre pintor Adriano de Sousa Lopes e ao escritor e arqueólogo Francisco Nogueira de Brito. Orgânizado por Arnaldo de Oliveira. Para venda em leilão...21 de Junho de 1948 [e] 12 de Julho de 1948, no Salão de Vendas da Liquidadora Fuertes. Lisboa, Antiga Livraria Manuel dos Santos, 1948.
2 v. in 1. 22cm. (Leilãos, no.139-140)

NL 0422794 ICN

Livraria Manuel dos Santos, Lisbon.
Catálogo duma importante livraria que será vendida em leilão sob a direcção de Manoel dos Santos, com um prefácio por Henrique de Campos Ferreira Lima. Obras antigas e modernas (de 1476 até á actualidade), muitas das quais referentes ao Brasil, Japão, China, India, etc., etc... á venda... começará a 6 de outubro de 1924... Porto, Portugal: Sociedade de papelaria, Lda., 1924. xv, 535 p. incl. facsims. 8°.

1. Bibliography—Catalogues, Booksellers'. 2. Bibliography, Portuguese.
N. Y. P. L. October 15, 1925

NL 0422795 NN MH

Greenlee 4A 201 LIVRARIA MANUEL DOS SANTOS, Lisbon.
Catalogos de leilos da "Liquadadora do Livro." Lisboa, Livraria Manuel dos Santos, 1932-1947.
22 v. 24cm.

Consists of catalogs no. 1-135.

NL 0422796 ICN

VOLUME 337

Livraria Manuel dos Santos, Lisbon.
Guia do turista em Lisboa
see under title

LIVRARIA MANUEL DOS SANTOS, Lisbon.
Revista bibliografica camiliana e reproducão facsimile dos frontispicios de todas as obras e edições, cartas autografas, retratos, folhetos, folhas avulsas, etc., etc. do romancista Camillo Castello Branco e de outros livros que lhe digam respeito, preços por que teem sido vendidos tanto em leilão como em livreiro, descritos bibliograficamente por Manoel dos Santos, com uma noticia sobre Camillo pelo Theophilo Braga. Lisboa, 1916-26 (cover (v.1) 1917, (v.2) 1923]

2 v., 1 pt. illus., ports., 26cm.

Vol. [1]-3, fasc. 1.
Issued in parts, 1916-26.

1. Castello Branco, Camillo, 1825-1890--Bibl. I. Title. II. Santos, Manoel dos.

NL 0422799 NN MH

Livraria Martins Editôra, São Paulo.
Album de familia, 1932
see under title

Livraria Moraes, Lisboa
see Araujo Moraes, João d', bookseller, Lisbon.

Livraria Pereira da Silva
see Pereira da Silva & ca., Booksellers, Lisbon.

---

q015.469 Livraria Portugal, Lisbon--Servicos Bibliograficos.
L766 Publicações recebidas.

Lisboa.
no. 34cm. monthly.

NL 0422803 IU CU

Livraria Portugália.
[Lista de alguns jornais e publicações periódicas portuguesas revista até 30 de Nov.de 1944] Lisboa, 1945.

[13] p.

NL 0422804 MH

Livrauw, François, joint author.

JN6271
.H4
[Henry, Albert] 1870–
La Chambre des représentants en 1894–1895. Bruxelles, Société belge de librairie, 1896.

25.8
5165
Livrauw, François.
Le senat belge en 1894-1898, par François Livraux et Albert Henry. Bruxelles, 1897.

NL 0422806 DLC

Livré, Eustache
Décret de l'Assemblée nationale, du 14 avril 1791, sanctionné par le roi le 17 du même mois, rendu sur le rapport fait au nom du Comité de salubrité; par M. Livré. Imprimé par ordre de L'Assemblée nationale ... [Paris, Imprimerie nationale, 179-?]
4 p. 19½cm.

I. France. Assemblée nationale constituante, 1789-1791.

NL 0422807 NNC CtY-M

Livré, Eustache.
——— Exposé de la nécessité de la réduction des districts du département de la Sarthe; [à l'Assemblée nationale, oct. 1790].
n. t.-p. [Paris, 1790.] 22h. pp. 16.

NL 0422808 NIC

Livre, Nicolas de, tr.

QE533
.M19
Rare bk.
coll.
Maggio, Lucio.
Discovrs dv tremblement de terre en forme de dialogue. Pris de l'italien de Lucio Maggio ... Paris, Denys du Val, 1675.

Le Livre; revue du monde littéraire—archives des écrits de ce temps—1.–10. année; 1880–89. Paris, A. Quantin, 1880–86; Maison Quantin, 1887–89.

21 v. illus., plates (part col.) ports. 29½cm. monthly.

Title varies: 1880–81, Le Livre, revue mensuelle.
1882–89, Le Livre, revue du monde littéraire ...
Title in red and black. Initials, head and tail pieces, vignettes, borders, colored plates, engraved portraits, facsimiles of bindings, etc.
In two parallel series: "Bibliographie moderne" and "Bibliographie rétrospective," one number of each being published monthly; the first volume of the "Bibliographie rétrospective" has title "Bibliographie ancienne."
The "Table décennale" announced in the last number was not published.

"Curiosités littéraires, études singulières, lettres inédites, dissertations bibliographiques, comptes rendus de livres nouveaux, d'événements bibliophiliques, d'enchères à sensation ..."
First of a series of three periodicals edited by Octave Uzanne and published under his direction. Succeeded by Le Livre moderne (janv. 1890–déc. 1891); in turn succeeded by L'Art et l'idée (janv.–déc. 1892) Le Livre et l'image (mars 1893–juin 1894) by John Grand-Carteret, similar in style, scope and tendency, may be regarded as a fourth series, intended to fill the place made vacant by the discontinuation of L'Art et l'idée.

1. Bibliography—Period. 2. Books. 3. Book collecting. 4. Bookbinding. I. Uzanne, Louis Octave, 1852–

2—13667.

Library of Congress Z1007.L775

TxU NcD MdBWA NN ICJ MiU OCl OU MB
NL 0422811 DLC NbU CU ViU NcU ICN ICU MH PU PPL

Le Livre; revue générale de l'édition. no. 1– mai 1948–
[Paris]
no. in v. illus. 19 cm. monthly (irregular)

subtitle varies

1. Bibliography—Period.

Z1007.L814 53–19923 ‡

NL 0422812 DLC LU IU

Wing
Z
0
.514
Le LIVRE.
[Bruges, Desclée de Brouwer, 1955]
14p. col.front., plates(part col.) 19cm.
(Collection Prière de l'art)

"Paru sous le titre 'Das Buch' dans la collection 'Bilderkreis'."
"Introduction par Paul Doncoeur."

NL 0422813 ICN

Le livre à la mode
see under [Caraccioli, Louis Antoine de] 1721–1803.

Le livre abominable de 1665, qui courait en manuscrit parmi le monde, sous le nom de Molière (comédie politique en vers sur le procès de Foucquet), découvert & pub. sur une copie du temps par Louis-Auguste Ménard. Paris, Firmin-Didot & cie, 1883.

2 v. in 1. 18cm.

"Tiré à petit nombre sur Hollande Van Gelder."

I. Molière, Jean Baptiste Poquelin, 1622–1673, supposed author. II. Ménard, Louis Auguste, ed.

12–11660

Library of Congress PQ1844.L6 1883

NL 0422815 DLC IU CtY NN

Le livre admirable
see under Mirabilis liber.

Livre allemand-français de l'A, B, C et de lecture, avec une choix particulière de telles noms qui s'écrivent par la même lettre initiale dans chacune de ces langues. Cadeau pour des enfants bien diligens, avec 75 gravures et autant de descriptions allemandes et françaises. Vienne: A. Paterno[, 18—?]. 98 p. col'd front., col'd plates. 21cm.

Schatzki Coll. of Children's Books.

646760A. 1. German language—Exercises and readers. 2. French language—Exercises and readers.
N. Y. P. L. September 12, 1934

NL 0422817 NN

Un livre americain sur l'enseignement du français
see under [Bezard, Julien]

Un LIVRE ayant appartenu à Montaigne. Sauveterre. 1880.

pp.7 [5].
"20 exemplaires."
"Extrait de la Revue des bibliophiles."

NL 0422819 MH

Le LIVRE belge. Het Boek in België. Année 1-3, no. 4/6; juil./août, 1947-[jan.? 1954]
Bruxelles. 3 v. in 2. illus. 24cm.

Bimonthly, July, 1947-July, 1948; irregular, 1949-54.
Not published between v. 3, no. 3/4, 1951/52 and v. 3, no. 4/6, Jan. 1954?
Published by the Syndicat des éditeurs belges (Syndicaat der belgische uitgevers).

Vol. 1-3, no. 3/4, contributions in Flemish or French; v. 3, no. 4/6, in French.
Vols. 1-3, no. 3/4 in two separately paged sections; section 2 comprises: Bulletin bibliographique publié par le Syndicat des éditeurs belges. Bibliografisch bulletijn door het Syndicaat der belgische uitgevers.
Vol. 3, no. 4/6, undated, is "Numéro édité à l'occasion de l'exposition Le Livre scientifique et le livre d'art dans les pays du Benelux. Paris. Fevrier 1954" (p. 13-65 are "Catalogue de la participation belge et luxembourgoise à l'exposition").

1. Bibliography, Belgian--Per. and soc. publ. I. Syndicat des éditeurs belges. II. Syndicat des éditeurs belges. Bulletin bibliographique. III. Syndicat des editeurs belges. Bibliografisch bulletijn. IV. Title: Het Boek en België.

NL 0422822 NN CU NN ICU LU IU NNC PU

VOLUME 337

Livre belge. Pub. par le Cercle de la librairie, de l'imprimerie et de toutes les professions qui s'y rattachent. [Bruxelles, 1888-89]
21 v. in 1. illus. (part col.) plates (part col.) port., facsims., double tab. 35cm.
General t.-p., illus. in colors.
Specimens of printing by members of the Cercle belge de la librairie.

1. Book industries and trade—Belgium. 2. Printing—Specimens. I. Cercle belge de la librairie, Brussels.
14-16708
Library of Congress Z348.L65

NL 0422823 DLC ICRL

Le livre belge, au cours d'un siècle d'histoire
see under Copenhagen. Danske Kunstindustrimuseum.

"Le **Livre** blanc"; formulaire médical ... Les spécialités pharmaceutiques présentées sous tous les classements utiles ...
Paris, H. Perrier, 19
v. 14 cm. annual.
Publication began in 1931.
"Créé sous le contrôle d'un groupe d'anciens internes en médecine des hôpitaux de Paris."

1. Medicine—Formulae, receipts, prescriptions.
RS125.L74 615.13 44-48193 rev

NL 0422825 DLC DNLM PPCPh CU-M

Le livre blanc. Paris. 1928.
see under [Cocteau, Jean] 1889-1963.

Le livre blanc. [Paris] P. Morihien [195-?]
86 p. illus.

NL 0422827 NNC CtY

Le **livre** blanc austro-allemand sur les assassinats des 30 juin et 25 juillet 1934. (Weissbuch über die erschiessungen des 30. juni 1934) Traduit de l'allemand par Georges Lefort. Avec une préface de m. Georg Branting ... [Paris] Éditions de la Nouvelle revue critique [c1935]
2 p. l., [7]-254 p., 1 l. 19cm. (Collection "La vie d'aujourd'hui". 40)
CONTENTS.—1. ptie. Les événements du 30 juin en Allemagne.—2. ptie. L'aventure autrichienne.—Conclusion: La mort de Hindenburg.
1. Germany—History—1933- 2. Austria—History—Revolution, 1918- 3. Germany—Foreign relations—Austria. 4. Austria—Foreign relations—Germany. 5. Nationalsozialistische deutsche arbeiterpartei. I. Lefort, Georges, tr. II. Title: Weissbuch über die erschiessungen des 30. juni 1934.
A C 35-2897
Title from N. Y. Pub. Libr. Printed by L. C.

NL 0422828 NN MH

Le livre blanc de l'intervention italienne en Espagne
see under Comité franco-espagnol, Paris.

Livre blanc du Saint-Siège
see under Catholic Church. Pope, 1903-1914 (Pius X)

Le livre blanc grec. Paris, Berger-Levrault, 1918.
136 p.

NL 0422831 OClW

949.3
L7881
Livre blanc; ou, Revolution gordune. [Gand] 1790.
226p. 18cm.

Attributed to Charles Louis Maximilien Dierickx, to Bernard Coppens, and to Jean Baptiste Vervier.

1. Belgium. History. Revolution, 1789-1790.

NL 0422832 IEN

Le Livre blanc, précédé d'un front. et accompagné de 17 dessins de Jean Cocteau
see under Cocteau, Jean, 1889-1963.

Livre blanc; quatre années de lutte pour la défense de l'Église hongroise; documents publiés sur la demande du cardinal Josef Mindszenty, primat de Hongrie, précédés des protestations des cardinaux français. Paris, Amiot-Dumont [c1949]
191 p. 19 cm. (Archives d'histoire contemporaine)
A translation of papers selected from those sent out of Hungary by Cardinal Mindszenty.

1. Catholic Church in Hungary—Hist.—Sources. 2. Church and state in Hungary. 3. Hungary—Pol. & govt.—1918- I. Mindszenty, József, Cardinal, 1892-
BX1519.W422 282.4391 50-3600

NL 0422834 DLC NN NcU

LIVRE blanc sur Buchenwald [lettres et documents autographes émanant des rescapés de Buchenwald. Paris] Les Éditions de la déportation et de la résistance [1955?] 448 p. facsims. 31cm.
Cover title.
At head of title: Un secteur de la résistance française.
Letters and documents also in facsimile.
1. Buchenwald, Weimar, Germany (Concentration camp). 2. World war, 1939-1945--Free and resistance movements, French. 3. World war, 1939-1945--Prisoners and prisons, German.

NL 0422835 NN MH

HV8964
.T8I6
Livre blanc sur la détention politique en Tunisie.
International Commission against Concentration Camp Practices.
Livre blanc sur la détention politique en Tunisie. [Paris, Le Pavois, 1953]

Livre blanc, traduction autorisée; documents sur les préliminaires de la guerre augmentés de documents nouveaux
see under Germany. Auswärtiges Amt.

Livre blanc tunisien des événements qui amenèrent la déposition, la déportation et l'exil de Son Altesse Sidi Mohamed Moncef Pacha Bey. Présenté au Gouvernement provisoire de la République française par L. A. les princes husséinites ... MM. Habib Bourguiba [et al.] Tunis, 1946.
56 p. ports. 25 cm.

1. Mohammed el-Moncef, Bey of Tunis, 1881-1948. I. Bourguiba, Habib, Pres. Tunisia, 1903-
DT264.3.M6L5 N.E. 66-440

NL 0422838 DLC

Livre blanc tunisien des événements qui amenèrent la déposition, la déportation et l'exil de Son Altesse Sidi Mohamed Moncef Pacha Bey. Présenté au Gouvernement provisoire de la République française par L. A. les princes husséinites ... [MM.] Habib Bourguiba [et al.] Tunis, 1946.
56 p. ports. 25 cm.
Photoreproduction of copy in Library of Congress.

NL 0422839 MH

Le **Livre** bleu; recueil biographique. 1950-
Bruxelles, F. Larcier.
v. 22 cm.

1. Belgium—Biog.
DH513.L58 52-19212

NL 0422840 DLC CaBVaU OCl NN DNLM NcU PPT MiU TxU

Le **Livre** bleu, véritable guide du textile
see **Annuaire** général textile.

Livre bleu d'Haiti
see Haiti, 1919-1920, livre bleu d'Haiti.

Celt 64.2
Livre brediah er fé eit chervige d'er Vretonèd a escobty Guénèd. Guénèd [Vannes] 1843-1844.
Breton translation of the Annales de la propagation de la foi.

NL 0422843 MH

Le livre chrétien. Paris, Fayard.

NL 0422844 DCU DLC

Livre complet du jubilé de 1865 spécial au diocèse de Bayeux
see under Bayeux, France (Diocese) [supplemen

Le **Livre** contemporain.
v. 1-
Boston: Schoenhof Book Co., 1918- 16°.
v.
Irregular.

1. Bibliography (French).—Per. and soc. publ. 2. Literature.—Per. and soc. publ.
N. Y. P. L. October 9, 1923.

NL 0422846 NN OClW PU

Livre contenant les prieres publiques, l'administration des sacremens ...
see under Protestant Episcopal Church in the U.S.A. Book of Common Prayer. French.

Livre curieux contenant la naifue representation des habits des femmes
see under [Hollar, Wenceslaus] 1607-1677.

VOLUME 337

Livre d'adresses de la ville d'Anvers et communes limitrophes
see **Adresboek** van de stad Antwerpen en randgemeenten.

... Le **Livre** d'adresses de madame; répertoire des principaux fournisseurs parisiens pour tout ce qui intéresse la femme et la maîtresse de maison ...
Paris, Mme Jeanne Bredeville
v. 20^cm.
At head of title: Annuaire de la Parisienne.
Advertising matter interspersed.

1. Paris—Direct. I. Title: Annuaire de la Parisienne.

Library of Congress DC704.L5 20-16508 Revised

NL 0422850 DLC ICRL NN

Livre d'adresses des entreprises industrielles belges & françaises en Russie.
1911.
Bruxelles [1911 4°.
no. folded map.
Published by the Société d'études belgo-russe.

1. Corporations (Foreign), Russia. —Directories. 2. Commerce, Russia.—Directories.
N. Y. P. L. April 17, 1922.

NL 0422851 NN

Livre d'adresses et relevé des automobiles et des avions.
1.— éd.; 1951—
Luxembourg, T. Jungblut.
v. 20 cm.
At head of title, 1951— : Grand-Duché de Luxembourg.

1. Luxemburg—Comm.—Direct. 2. Automobiles—Direct.—Luxemburg.
HF5189.5.L5 55-58127

NL 0422852 DLC

Le livre d'airain
see under Bricaire de La Dixmerie, Nicolas, d. 1791.

Livre d'airs à boire. *4053.61
= Manuscript. [18—?] 2 v. Sm. 4°.
Contains music.

F5574 — Manuscripts in this Library. Music. — Drinking songs. — Songs. With music. Coll.

NL 0422854 MB

PJ466 .L5 1912 Le Livre d'amour de l'Orient. [Introduction et notes par B. de Villeneuve [pseud.]
Paris, Bibliothèque des Curieux, 1912—
v. tables, diagrs. 23cm. (Les Maitres de l'amour)
CONTENTS.—1 ptie. Ananga-ranga; traité hindou de l'amour conjugal. La fleur lascive orientale.—Le livre de volupte. 1912.—2. ptie. Le jardin parfumé du cheikh Nefzaoui. 1912.—3. ptie. Les Kama sutra de Vatsyayana. 1912.
1. Erotic literature. 2. Oriental literature—Translations into French. 3. French literature—Translations from oriental literature. I. Kalyānamalla. Ananga-ranga. II. 'Umar ibn Muhammad, al-Nafzāwi, fl. 16th cent. III. Vātsyāyana, called Malla-nāga. Kāma sūtra. IV. Vèze, Raoul, 1864— ed.

NL 0422855 ViU

... **Le Livre d'amour de l'Orient ... Introduction et notes par B. de Villeneuve** [*pseud.*] **Paris, Bibliothèque des curieux,** 1912-1921.
4 v. tables, diagrs. 23^cm. (Les Maitres de l'amour)
CONTENTS.—1. ptie. Ananga-ranga; traité hindou de l'amour conjugal, par Kalyana Malla. La fleur lascive orientale. Le livre de volupté. 1921.—2. ptie. Le jardin parfumé du cheikh Nefzaoui. 1912.—3. ptie. Les Kama sutra de Vatsyayana. 1912.—4. ptie. Le bréviaire de la courtisane, par Ksemendra. Les leçons de l'entremetteuse, par Damadaragapta. 1920.

NL 0422856 CtY

HQ 461 L5 Le Livre d'amour de l'Orient. Paris, Bibliothèque des curieux, 1920-22.
4 v. 23 cm. (Les Maitres de l'amour)

Contents. - 1. ptie. Kalyānamalla. Ananga-ranga. 1921. - 2. ptie. 'Umar ibn Muhammad, al-Nafzawi. Le jardin parfumé du Cheikh Nafzaoui. 1922. - 3. ptie. Vatsyayana, called Malla-nāga. Les kama sutra de Vatsyayana. 1921. - 4. ptie. Ksemendra. La brévicare de la courtisane. 1920.
1. Erotic literature.

NL 0422857 OU

... Le **Livre** d'amour de l'Orient ... Introduction et notes par B. de Villeneuve [*pseud.*] Paris, Bibliothèque des curieux, 1920-28.
4 v. tables, diagrs. 23^cm. (Les Maitres de l'amour)
CONTENTS.—1. ptie. Ananga-ranga; traité hindou de l'amour conjugal, par Kalyana Malla. La fleur lascive orientale. Le livre de volupté. 1921.—2. ptie. Le jardin parfumé du cheikh Nefzaoui. 1922.—3. ptie. Les Kama sutra de Vatsyayana. 1928.—4. ptie. Le bréviaire de la courtisane, par Ksemendra. Les leçons de l'entremetteuse, par Damadaragapta. 1920.
1. Erotic literature. 2. Oriental literature—Translations into French. 3. French literature—Translations from oriental literature. I. Kalyāṇamalla. Anaṅga-raṅga. II. 'Umar ibn Muḥammad, al-Nafzāwī, fl. 16th cent. III. Vātsyāyana, called Malla-nāga. Kāma sūtra. IV. Kshemendra, fl. 1050. Samayamātṛkā. V. Dāmodaragupta, fl. ca. 790. Kuṭṭanimata. VI. Vèze, Raoul, 1864— ed.
Library of Congress PJ466.L5 43-37208

NL 0422858 DLC IU MH

Gtl2 58 Le livre d'amour des anciens. Amours des dieux. Amour conjugal. La science de l'amour, d'après le "De figuris Veneris" de Forberg. Le livre d'amour de Plutarque. La muse de Straton ou la couronne de Sodome. Le livre d'amour de Martial, Catulle, Pétrone, Ausone, etc. Paris, Bibliothèque des curieux, 1911.
3p.ℓ., [3]-317p., 1ℓ. 22½cm. (Les Maitres de l'amour)

NL 0422859 CtY MH ICN NjP

... Le **Livre** d'amour des anciens: Amours des dieux. Amour conjugal. La science de l'amour en Grèce et à Rome. Le livre d'amour de Plutarque. La muse de Straton; ou, La couronne de Sodome. Le livre d'amour de Martial, Catulle, Pétrone, Ausone, etc. Paris, Bibliothèque des curieux, 1927.
3 p. l., [3]-245 p., 1 l. 23^cm. (Les Maitres de l'amour)

1. Greece—Moral conditions. 2. Rome—Moral conditions. 3. Sex in literature.
Library of Congress HQ13.L5 43-36818

NL 0422860 DLC

Le Livre d'art international. [Paris, Arts et métiers graphiques, 1931]
cover-title, 100p. illus., plates (part mounted, part col.) facsims. 31cm.

At head of title: "Arts et metiers graphiques, Paris. [v.]26. Numero spécial, 15 novembre, 1931.

1. Illustration of books. 2. Illustrated books. I. Arts et métiers graphiques.

NL 0422861 IEN MWelC PPD

Livre d'Artus. Inhaltsangabe der version P des Livre d'Arthus.
(In Freymond, Émile. Beiträge zur kenntnis der altfranzösischen Artusromane in prosa)

NL 0422862 MH

---

*7910.174.7
Livre, Le, d'Artus of the MS. no. 337 at the Bibliothèque nationale, ff. 115a to 294d. A unique fragment. [With glossary.]
— Washington. 1913. (2), 370 pp. [Carnegie Institution of Washington. Publication no. 74. The vulgate version of the Arthurian romances edited from manuscripts in the British Museum. Vol. 7.] 29½ cm.

K1521 — Arthurian romances. — S.r.c. — Ed. ref. made.

NL 0422863 MB

LIVRE d'église à l'usage de ceux qui fréquentent leur paroisse. 343
Paris, 1765. (24), 860 pp. 12°.

NL 0422864 MB

Livre d'église à l'usage de Chartres ...
see under Catholic Church. Liturgy and ritual. Chartres.

Livre d'église latin-françois
see under Catholic Church. Liturgy and ritual. Breviary. French & Latin. [Miscellaneous]

Livre d'Enanchet.
... Das "Livre d'Enanchet", nach der einzigen handschrift 2585 der Wiener nationalbibliothek herausgegeben von Werner Fiebig. Jena und Leipzig, W. Gronau, 1938.
xlviii, 160 p. 24½^cm. (Berliner beiträge zur romanischen philologie, hrsg. von Ernst Gamillscheg und Emil Winkler. Bd. VIII, 3/4)
The author's thesis, Berlin.
"Literatur": p. viii-xiii.

I. Fiebig, Werner, ed. II. Vienna. Nationalbibliothek. Mss. (2585)
Library of Congress PC13.B47 bd. 8, hft. 3/4 42-15666
[3] (479.082) 848.1

NL 0422867 DLC CtY PPT PBm MH

Le Livre d'heures de Henri II
see under [Quentin-Bauchart, Ernest] 1830-1910.

Un livre d'heures de l'école de Jean Bourdichon
see under Lafond, Jean, 1888-

Livre d'heures de Notre Dame ...
see under [Destree, Joseph] 1853-1932.

Un livre d'heures rouennais enluminé d'après le Speculum humanae salvationis
see under Lafond, Jean, 1888-

VOLUME 337

Livre d'hommage à la mémoire du Dr. Samuel Poznański (1864–1921), offert par les amis et les compagnons du travail scientifique. Varsovie: Édit par le Comité de la Grande Synagogue à Varsovie, 1927. xlvii, 216, 214 p. front. (port.) f°.

Articles in English, German, Polish and Hebrew; the last, 214 p., paged separately and with added Hebrew t.-p.
Added t.-p. in Polish.
Contents: Balaban, M. Dr. Samuel Poznański. Marx, A., et E. Poznanski. Bibliographie de tous les ouvrages et articles du Dr. Samuel Poznański (1889–1926). Abrahams, I. The words of Gad the Seer. Adler, E. N. The divan of El'azar ha Babli. Balaban, M. Studien und Quellen zur Geschichte der frankistischen Bewegung in Polen. Büchler, A. The induction of the bride and the bridegroom into the חופה in the first and the second centuries in Palestine. Duschinsky, C. The Yekum Purkan (יקום פורקן) Ginzberg, L. Die Haggada bei den Kirchenvätern. Kokowzoff, P. The date of life of Bahya ibn Paqoda. Krauss, S. Beiträge zur Geschichte der Geonim. Marx, A. Der arabische Bustanai-Bericht und Nathan ha-Babli. Obermann, J. Drei Kontextglossen zum Deboraliede. Schorr, M. Les composés dans les langues sémitiques. Schwarz, A. Muss Lev. 16, 23 umgestellt werden? Seeligmann, S. Ein Originalbrief der Vierländersynode nach Amsterdam aus 1677. Simonsen, D. Vier arabische Gutachten des R. Mose ben Maimon.

347425A. 1. Poznanski, Samuel, 1864–1921. 2. Poznanski, Samuel—Bibl. 3. Essays, Jewish—Collections.
N. Y. P. L. May 22, 1928

NL 0422873 NN NjP OCH MH CtY CU PPDrop

Bo79
681

Livre d'hommage des lettres françaises à Émile Zola ... Collaborateurs: Paul Alexis, Ph.Dubois, Ch.Duclaux, Yves Guyot [e. a.] Bruxelles,G.Balat;[etc.,etc.]1898.
vip.,1l.,261p. 21½cm.
Preface (p.v-vi) signed: Mecislas Golberg, Léon Parsons, Henri van de Putte.
Tributes and documents relating to Zola's part in the Dreyfus affair.

NL 0422874 CtY RPB IU MiDW

---

*FC9
D8262
Z898l

Livre d'hommage des lettres françaises a Émile Zola ...
Paris,Société libre d'édition des gens de lettres.Bruxelles,Georges Balat,éditeur.1898.
vip.,1l.,207,261p. 21cm.,in case 22.5cm.
Desachy 457.
Dedicatory letter signed: Mecislas Golberg, Léon Parsons, Henri van de Putte.
"Le proces d'Émile Zola (7-24 février 1898). Impressions d'audiences par Séverine [pseud.]": p.[135]-207 of pt.1.

"Plaidoirie de me Labori": p.115-257 of pt.2.
Original printed white wrappers; in cloth case.

NL 0422876 MH NN OU RPB

...Le livre d'honneur des cent villes de France... Paris, D'Honneur, 1839. 194 p. DLC: YA 1732

NL 0422877 DLC

Livre d'or à l'occasion du jubilé de vingt-cinq ans d'activité chirurgicale du docteur Théodore L. Papayoannou ... Le Caire, le 8 mai 1932. Naumburg-Saale, Lippert & co., buchdruckerei, 1932.

xi p., 1 l., 278 p. front. (port.) illus. (part col.) fold. tab., diagrs. 28 cm.

Foreword signed: Le comité: Prof. dr. Jean Koumaris. Dr. F. Rosenauer. Dr. B. Sackarnd.
Preface in Greek and French, contributions by various authors in German, French, and English.

1. Medicine—Collected works. 2. Surgery—Collected works. 3. Papayoannou, Théodore L. I. Koumaris, Jean, ed. II. Rosenauer, Fritz, joint ed. III. Sackarnd, Bernard, 1888– joint ed.

R111.P28 617.04 33—2705

NL 0422878 DLC OU

Le LIVRE d'or de Bayonne; textes gascons du XIIIe siècle. [Edited by J.Bidache] Pau.1906.

Facsims.
"150 exemplaires." Rom 182.3

NL 0422879 MH IU

Le LIVRE d'or de Bayonne; textes latins et gascons du Xe au XIVe siècle. [Edited by J.Bidache and published, with a biographical sketch of the editor, by Victor Dubarat.] Pau, [G. Lescher-Moutoué, imp.], 1906.

Facsimile plates. Rom. 182.3.5

NL 0422880 MH

Le livre d'or de J.-F. Millet, par un ancien ami; illustré de dix-sept eaux-fortes originales par Frédéric Jacque. Paris, A. Ferroud; [etc., etc., 1891]

2 p. l., 164, [4] p. front. (port.) illus., 9 pl. 33½cm.

Title vignette and illustrations etched.
"Il a été tiré cinq cent cinquante exemplaires numérotés à la presse, savoir ... nos 51 à 550.—Cinq cents exemplaires sur papier de Hollande teinté. Exemplaire no 546."

1. Millet, Jean François, 1814–1875. I. Jacque, Frédéric, 1859– illus.

22–14086

Library of Congress ND553.M6L5

NL 0422881 DLC MH CtY NN PPPM

Le livre d'or de J.-F. Millet
see also Le livre d'or de L'angelus de Millet.

PQ2609
.L52Z8

Le Livre d'or de Josélia; avec le concours de Luigia et Huguette Soueix [et al. Paris, Éditions de "Psyché," 1952]

90 p. port. 19 cm.

Imprint on mounted label.
"Quelques poèmes écrits en l'honneur de Josélia de: Émile Pignot [et al.]": p. [57]–75.

1. Élie, Joseph, 1892 or 3–1951. I. Soueix, Luigia.

A 53–5370

Illinois. Univ. Library
for Library of Congress [1]

NL 0422883 IU DLC

Le livre d'or de l'Académie Commerciale Catholique de Montréal
see under Leblond de Brumath, Adrien.

Livre d'or de l'activité française
see
Le Guide professionnel des provinces françaises.

Livre d'or de l'Afrique noire française. Casablanca, Éditions C. E. P. [1949–
v. illus. 25 x 31 cm.

1. Africa, French West—Descr. & trav.

DT527.L7 54–27669 ‡

NL 0422886 DLC DAU

Le livre d'or de l'Alsace. Nos généraux: Général Taufflieb, commandant le 37e corps d'armée, né à Strasbourg. [Strasbourg, 19—] 63 p. illus. 19cm.

Text in French and German.

1. Taufflieb, Émile Adolphe, 1857–1938.
N. Y. P. L. December 30, 1943

NL 0422887 NN MH

Le livre d'or de l'Alsace; pages choisies ... 1916
see under Devire, Maurice.

Le livre d'or de l'Angelus de Millet, par un ancien ami; illustré de dix-sept eaux-fortes originales par Frédéric Jacque. Paris, A.Ferroud, n.d.
164p.illus.pl.por.34cm.

1. Bookplates.Individual.Stettinius, Mary Burton. 2. Millet, Jean François, 1814-1875. I. Jacque, Frédéric, 1859- illus.

NL 0422889 OC OCU

Le livre d'or de L'angelus de Millet
see also Le livre d'or de J.-F. Millet.

TL67
.L5

Livre d'or de l'automobile et de la motocyclette. un demi siècle d'efforts et d'initiatives des industriels belges. [Liège] Royal Motor Union, 1951.

257 p. illus. (part col.) 32 cm.

1. Automobiles—Hist. 2. Automobile industry and trade. 3. Motorcycles.

A 52–3406

Detroit. Public Library
for Library of Congress [1]

NL 0422891 MiD DLC

...**Le livre** d'or de l'enseignement religieux (depuis l'an de grace 1900...). Brochure de propagande, avec une préface par un groupe d'instituteurs français. [no.] 1– Havre: Les Éditions à bon marché, 191–?–]. v. 16°.

Cover-title.

1. Catholic Church, Roman—France—Clergy.
N. Y. P. L. June 16, 1926

NL 0422892 NN

972.94
L788

Livre d'or de l'évolution, 1901. Directeur-Fondateur: Jules Rosemond... [Port-au-Prince] H. Chauvet [1901?]
18 p. mounted ports. 27cm.

At head of title: Patrie. Fraternité. Union.

1. Haiti. 2. Haiti - Biog. I. Rosemond, Jules, 1874-1928.

NL 0422893 FU

Livre d'or de l'exil français
see under Fédération nationale des prisonniers de guerre.

Le Livre d'or de l'Exposition de 1900. [v. 1–2; 1900] Paris, E. Cornély, 1900.

2 v. in 1. illus., double plates (part col.) 32½cm. weekly.
No more published.

1. Paris. Exposition universelle, 1900.

16-8396

Library of Congress T804.B1L5

NL 0422895 DLC

VOLUME 337

Le livre d'or de l'horlogerie
see under Journal suisse d'horlogerie et de bijouterie.

Le livre d'or de l'ordre de Léopold et de la Croix de fer
see under Veldekens, Ferdinand Jean Josse, 1815-1883.

DR442 .L78
Livre d'or de l'Orient: notices historiques et biographiques illustrées articles variés ... Paris, F. Levé,
plates, ports. 18 x 10 cm.
Cover-title.
"Ce volume-bijou [nouv. sér., 1. v.] souvenir de la 14e Fête nationale ottomane, donnée en l'honneur de l'anniversaire de S.M.I. le sultan Abdul-Hamid Khan II, est offert à titre gracieux."
Editor: N. Nicolaïdes.

NL 0422898 DLC

Le Livre d'or de la cinematographie de France... album annuel. [no.]

Paris: Edition d'Herdo-Film [192 4°.
v. illus., ports.

1. Moving pictures.—Yearbooks.
N. Y. P. L. July 22, 1924

NL 0422899 NN

Le livre d'or de la comtesse Diane
see under [Beausacq, Marie Josephine (de Suin) comtesse de, 1829-1899] comp.

L629.19 Q904
Livre d'or de la conquête de l'air. Bruxelles, L'agence Dechenne,
110197 1909.
[8], vi, [2], 342, [2] p. illus. (incl. ports., maps), 10 pl. (part col., part fold.) 33½cm.
"Ont collaboré à cet ouvrage: pour le texte MM. C. Ader, E. Archdeacon, G. Besançon, L. Bleriot, H. Farman, le capitaine Ferber, C. Flammarion, C. Humbert, H. Kapferer, le comte de Lambert, H. Latham, A. Leblanc, le commandant Renard, A. Santos-Dumont, le capitaine E. Spelterini, le comte H. de La Vaulx, W. & O. Wright, etc., etc.; pour les gravures: MM. E. Grasset, A. Johanson, H. Lanos, R. Lelong, Macchiati, L. Simont, G. Scott."
"Il a été tiré de cet ouvrage cinq cents exemplaires numérotés .... Exemplaire nº 485."

NL 0422901 ICJ

Livre d'or de la conquête de l'air. [Paris] P. Lafitte & cie, 1909.
4 p. l., vi p., 1 l., 342 p., 1 l. illus. (incl. ports.) col. plates (part double) 32½ x 24½cm.
"Il a été tiré de cet ouvrage cinq cents exemplaires numérotés à la presse de 1 à 500 et revêtus du timbre de contrôle du Bureau spécial du Cercle de la librairie. Exemplaire nº 231."

1. Aeronautics—Hist.

31-22477

Library of Congress TL515.L5 629.1309

NL 0422902 DLC DSI

Le Livre d'or de la cuisine françoise. [Paris] 1912.
48 p. illus. 32cm.
Supplement to Le Temps, Nov. 1912.

1. Cookery, French. I. Le Temps. Supplement.

15-3113

Library of Congress TX719.L5

NL 0422903 DLC

Le livre d'or de la faculté de droit de Paris
see under Paris. Université. Faculté de droit.

DC 216 .L78
Le livre d'or de la famille Bonaparte; études historiques, biographies et portraits Napoléoniens, publiés d'après des documents authentiques et des notes particulières, recueillies et mises en ordre avec le plus grand soin par une société de littérateurs et de publicistes. Paris, Administration générale des publications illustrées, 1855-56.
4 v. illus.
Vols.3-4 published by A.Bouret, Paris.

1.Bonaparte family.

NL 0422905 MiU NN FTaSU

LIVRE d'or de la foire de Paris, 1949. Paris [1949]
67 p. illus., map. 31cm.

"Palmares; revue periodique [no. 1]"
Includes advertising matter.

1. Fairs—France—Paris. I. Palmares.

NL 0422906 NN

TX637 C545 1937
Le livre d'or de la gastronomie en Suisse. Edition 1937-1938. Lausanne, Editions novos [1938?]
192 p. illus.

NL 0422907 CU

...Livre d'or de la gendarmerie, 1913-1916. Paris: H. Charles-Lavauzelle, 1918. 142 p. incl. tables. 8°.
At head of title: Mémorial de la gendarmerie.

1. European war, 1914- —Biography. 2. Police, France.
N. Y. P. L. October 3, 1919.

NL 0422908 NN

Livre d'or de la grande famille médicale, médecins—vétérinaires—pharmaciens, guerre 1914— pub. par la Revue de pathologie comparée ... Paris, A. Maloine et fils, 1915—
v. illus. 25cm.

1. European war, 1914- —France. 2. European war, 1914- —Registers, lists, etc. 3. Physicians—France. 4. Veterinarians—France. 5. Pharmacists—France. I. Revue de pathologie comparée.

18-23037

Library of Congress D629.F8L5

NL 0422909 DLC DNLM CSt-H PPC

Livre d'or de la guerre de 1914-1918. Agents et ouvriers de la Cie des Chemins de Fer de l'Hérault morts pour la patrie, blessés — décorés — cités. [Montpellier: Roumégous et Déhan, 1921?] 23 p. illus. 8°.

1. European war, 1914- —Registers, lists, etc. 2. European war, 1914- —Registers of dead, wounded and missing.
N. Y. P. L. April 3, 1922.

NL 0422910 NN

DT 782 F121
Livre d'or de la mission du Lessouto. Soixante-quinze ans de l'histoire d'une tribu Sud-Africaine, 1833-1908. Préface de A. Boegner. Paris, Maison de Missions Évangéliques, 1912.
xviii, 689p. illus. fold. map.

1. Société des missions évangéliques chez des peuples non chretiens, Paris. I. Boegner, Alfred, 1851-1912

NL 0422911 MBU CtY ICU IEN WU

Livre d'or de la noblesse de France
see under Magny, Claude Drigon, marquis de, 1797-1879.

Livre d'or de la noblesse européenne, precedé d'une histoire de l'origine et des privileges de la noblesse
see under Givodan, Léon, comte de.

Livre d'or de la noblesse phanariote et des familles princières de Valachie et de Moldavie
see under [Rangabé, Eugenios Rizo] 1851-

4DC 1424
Livre d'or de la Picardie; 25e anniversaire de la création de la Foire-Exposition de Picardie, 1926-1951. [ ] Fédération des foires françaises [1951]
71 p.

NL 0422915 DLC-P4

Livre d'or de la Résistance Belge
see under Belgium. Commission de l'historique de la résistance.

D811 L5L78
Le Livre d'or de la résistance liégoise aux bombardements par "V." Ce livre contient la liste complète des victimes et leur état civil. [Liége, M. Corombelle, 1944]
32 p. illus., fold. map. 25cm.
Cover title: Liége sous les "V," novembre 1944 à janvier 1945.

1. World War, 1939-1945 - Belgium - Liége. 2. World War, 1939-1945 - Registers of dead - Belgium. 3. World War, 1939-1945 - Destruction and pillage - Belgium - Liége. I.Title: Liége sous les "V."

NL 0422917 CSt-H

Livre d'or de la Société française Hispano-Suiza ...
see under [Massuger, Louis]

VOLUME 337

Livre d'Or de la ville de Soultz en Haute-Alsace
see under Gasser, A[uguste] comp.

DC801
.M28L5

Livre d'or de la ville du Mans. Paris, Régie française de propagande [1955]
136p. illus.

1. A17 (Mans, Le) - Description.

NL 0422920 DS

Le livre d'or de nos légionnaires, 1914-1918
see under [Comité du monument du souvenir à Luxembourg]

Le Livre d'or de quelques 5000 familles du Velay, etc., 1910
see under Brun, Louis , bookseller, Lyrns.

848
B438Dl

Livre d'or de Remy Belleau, avec illustrations de Bellier de la Chavignerie, Brisard, Cazals, Delbanne, Oury, Piébourg; phototypies de J. Royer. Nogent-le-Rotrou, Veuve Gouhier-Delouche, 1900.
317,35,67p. front.(port.) illus.,plates.
O.

Preface signed Émile Hinzelin.

Contents: 1.ptie. Préface (Émile Hinzelin). Extraits de Remy Belleau. Notice sur Camille Gaté (Émile Hinzelin). Hommage des poetes. Le parnasse percheron (Louis Duval). Hommage des poetes normands et percherons.- 2.ptie. Nogent et son chateau (Lucien Devaux). L'amitie et Remy Belleau (Antony Rocher). Comite de la statue de Remy Belleau. L'oeuvre du comité (Pierre Bruyant) Les fêtes de Nogent-le-Rotrou. Liste de souscripteurs au monument de Remy Belleau.

NL 0422924 IaU IU Mi CtY

BQ7469
.E56Z56

Le livre d'or de Renan. Paris, A. Joanin [1903]
218p.

Includes material relevant to the erection of a statue of Renan in Treguier.

1. Renan, Ernest, 1823-1892.

NL 0422925 TNJ-R TxDaM MWelC IU MH NNCoCi ICN IU

Le livre d'or de Sainte-Beuve, publié à l'occasion du centenaire de sa naissance, 1804-1904. Paris, Aux bureaux du Journal des débats, 1904.
4 p. l., [iii]-xxi p., 1 l., 462 p., 1 l. front., plates, ports. 28½cm.
"Tirage à deux mille exemplaires."
"Bibliographie": p. [353]-440.
CONTENTS.—Brunetière, F. Discours à la cérémonie du centenaire.—I. L'œuvre: Boissier, G. L'étude sur Virgile de Sainte-Beuve. Appendice par H. Martin. Bourget, P. Sainte-Beuve poète. Claretie, J. Sainte-Beuve et la Comédie-Française. Michaut, G. La confession de Sainte-Beuve. Lemaître, J. Sainte-Beuve fut-il "envieux"? Bourdeau, J. La psychologie et la philosophie de Sainte-Beuve. Audebrand, P. Les critiques de 1830. Dorez, L. Sainte-Beuve et la Bibliothèque nationale. Lettres à Jules Ravenel (1845-1865) Malo, C. Sainte-Beuve critique militaire. Chaumeix. A. Sainte-Beuve et le Journal des dé-

Continued in next column

Continued from preceding column

bats. Roz, F. Sainte-Beuve à Lausanne. Thier, C. de. Sainte-Beuve à Liège. Lefranc, A. Sainte-Beuve professeur au Collège de France. Essarts, E. des. Sainte-Beuve professeur à l'École normale (1859-1861) Thomas, L. Sainte-Beuve et Madame Lemercier. Sakellaridès, E. Lettres de Sainte-Beuve à Prosper Enfantin. Chambon, F. Lettres inédites de Sainte-Beuve à Villemain. Lettres boulonnaises.—II. L'homme: Troubat, J. Sainte-Beuve intime. Bournon, F. Les origines. Les premières années de Boulogne. Hamy, E. T. Le premier maître de Sainte-Beuve, Louis Blériot (1813-1818) Lefebvre, A. Premières amours de Sainte-Beuve au pays natal. Hallays, A. Sainte-Beuve et Ondine Desbordes-Valmore. Bournon, F. Les logis parisiens de Sainte-Beuve. Tourneux, M. Les portraits de Sainte-Beuve. La bibliothèque de Sainte-Beuve. Une profession de foi de Sainte-Beuve. Bibliographie. Commémoration du centenaire de le naissance de Sainte-Beuve: I. Boulogne-sur-Mer. II. Liège. III. Lausanne.
1. Sainte-Beuve, Charles Augustin, 1804-1869.
5-1580‡

Library of Congress PQ2391.Z5L4

NL 0422927 DLC TxU NcD NIC CtY NjP

14094
.13
.01
.592

Livre d'or des anciens élèves et professeurs du collège d'Autun (morts pour la France pendant la guerre (1914-1918)) Ed. par les soins de l'Association des anciens élèves du collège d'Autun. [Autun, P. Poirson] 1923.
94 p. 26 cm.

On cover: Livre d'or du collège d'Autun.

1. EUROPEAN WAR, 1914-1918 - FRANCE - AUTUN 2. EUROPEAN WAR, 1914-1918 - REGISTERS, LISTS, ETC. I. Association des anciens élèves, Autun, France. II. Title Livre d'or du collège d'Autun.

NL 0422928 NjP

Le LIVRE d'or des Annales politiques et littéraires. Paris, 1893.

f°. Portrs, plates, facsimiles, and other illustr.

NL 0422929 MH

971.4
fL767

Le Livre d'or des Canadiens. Serie nouvelle de portraits et de biographies. Montreal, La Compagnie de Publication Mont Royal, 1912-
v. illus., ports. 31cm.

Includes advertising matter.

1. French-Canadians. 2. French-Canadians. Biography.

NL 0422930 MnU NN

2309.229

Livre d'or, Le, des Canadiens. [Publié à l'occasion de la Fête nationale des Canadiens-Français.] 24 juin, 1915. 7e année.
— Montréal. La Compagnie de publication. [1915.] Mont-Royal
v. Portraits. Plates. Maps. Autograph facsimiles. 22 cm.
The issue for 1915 relates solely to the European War.

K7315 — French in Canada.— European War, 1914-.— Fête nationale des Canadiens-Français.

NL 0422931 MB CSt-H

LIVRE d'or des Carabiniers, par le capitaine Bué. Illustré par Éd. Detaille, Titeux, Van Muyden. [Paris, C. Blot, 1898] xviii, 449 p. illus. (part col.), ports. 33cm.

One of 400 copies printed.

1. Army, French—Regt. hist. I. Bué, Alphonse, b. 1829.

NL 0422932 NN

LIVRE d'or des Carabiniers, par le capitaine Bué. Illustré par Éd. Detaille, Titeux, Van Muyden. [Paris, C. Blot, 1898?] 45 p. 26cm.

A brief account of the publishing by a committee of carabiniers of the Livre d'or des carabiniers, Paris, 1898. (33cm.)

1. Army, French—Regt. hist.

NL 0422933 NN MH

BX
1815
.L78

Livre d'or des Congrégations françaises, 1939-1945. Préf. par S. Exc. Mgr. Théas. Paris, D. R. A. C. [1948]

493 p. 25cm.

1. Monasticism and religious orders--France. 2. World War, 1939-45--France. 3. World War, 1939-45--Religious aspects. 4. World War, 1939-45--Catholic Church.

NL 0422934 DCU

Le livre d'or des enfants
see under Lonlay, Eugène, marquis de, 1815-1866.

Le livre d'or des familles; ou, La Terre-sainte illustrée
see under Luthereau, Jean Guillaume Antoine, b. 1810.

D639
E45F82

Le livre d'or des Francs-Bourgeois pendant la guerre de 1914-1918. Paris [Imp. J. Langlois, 1919?]
141, [1] p. XVIII pl. (group ports.) 31cm.
On cover: Guerre de 1914-1918. Le livre d'or des Francs-Bourgeois.
"Pieux hommage d'admiration et de gratitude de la Maison des Francs-Bourgeois à ceux de ses enfants qui donnèrent leur vie pour le salut de tous."
1. European war, 1914-1918 - Registers of dead. 2. France - Biography. 3. European war, 1914-1918 - France. I. Paris. École des Francs-Bourgeois. II. Title: Guerre de 1914-1918.

NL 0422937 CSt-H

Le livre d'or des legendes Francaises et Etrangeres.
Paris: 1912-1913. 248 pp.

NL 0422938 DCU-IA

Livre d'or des notaires et des clercs de notaires de l'arrondissement de Mamers, morts pour la France, blessés ou cités à l'ordre pendant la grande guerre de 1914-1918. Mamers: G. Enault [1921]. 38 p. 12°.

1. European war, 1914- .—Registers of dead, wounded and missing. 2. European war, 1914- .—France: Mamers.
N. Y. P. L. February 10, 1922.

NL 0422939 NN

Le Livre d'or des peintres exposants...
ed.
Paris, 19 8°.
v. illus., plates, ports.

1. Painters (French). 2. Painting (French), 20th century.—Exhibitions, France: Paris.
N. Y. P. L. April 13, 1920.

NL 0422940 NN MB

VOLUME 337

Le LIVRE d'or des petits enfants. [Paris] Lebrun [18--] 108 p. illus. 20cm.

1. Primers, French

NL 0422941 NN

Le LIVRE d'or des peuples, Plutarque universel, sous la direction de Pierre Lefranc. [Paris, 1866?] 1 v. illus., ports. 30cm.

[Tome 1?]
Imperfect: t.-p. mutilated; title completed from Bib. nat. cat.

1. Biography. I. Lefranc, Pierre, b.1815, ed.

NL 0422942 NN

Le Livre d'or des salons ... Carnet de visites. Liste alphabétique des rues ... Paris, F. Bender [1885?- v. 17cm.

1. Paris - Streets.

NL 0422943 NcU

Livre d'or des souverains, suite de l'Annuaire des maisons souveraines ...
see under Hiort-Lorenzen, Hans Rudolf, 1832-1917, ed.

Le LIVRE d'or des tirailleurs indigènes de la province d'Alger, devenus 1er régiment de tirailleurs algériens, (1866-1878). Alger, A.Jourdan, 1879.

Vols. 1. Fr. 351.1

NL 0422945 MH

Le livre d'or des Troupes du Levant 1918-1936. [Beyrouth? 1937]
210, vii p. illus., group port., maps (part fold.) plans. 25 cm.

1. France. Armée. Troupes du Levant. 2. Syria—Hist. 3. Lebanon—Hist.

DS98.L5 56-50671

NL 0422946 DLC

Livre d'or du bibliophile. 1.- année; 1925-
Paris [1926]-
v. illus. (part col.) 32½ cm.
Vol. 2 covers the years 1926/27; v. 1928/29.
"Édité par la Chambre syndicale des éditeurs de livres d'art et de publications à tirage limité."
"La composition et le tirage du titre, de la préface et de la table méthodique ont été exécutés par Ducros et Colas."
Consists of specimens of recently published French works, including title-pages and illustrations.
1. French literature—Bibl.—Period. 2. Bibliography—Period. 3. Bibliography — Limited editions. 4. Publishers and publishing — France. 5. Illustrated books. 6. Printing—Specimens. 7. Title-page. I. Chambre syndicale des éditeurs de livres d'art et de publications à tirage limité, Paris.

Z2161.L78 010.5 31—6103

NL 0422947 DLC WaSp OrU LU CtY TxDaM NjR NcU

Bs41g 037 Livre d'or du bimillénaire Genève ... Genève, Editions P.-F.Perret-Gentil,1942.
4p.ℓ.,11-307,[1]p. illus.(incl.ports.,maps, plans,facsim.,diagrs.) 27cm.

NL 0422948 CtY NN CU MU

Livre d'or du canton de Fribourg. Nomenclature des bourgeois de la ville de Fribourg des anciennes familles patriciennes et des notabilités et célébrités du canton. Fribourg, Impr. E. Bonny, 1898.
91 p. 5 col. pl. 28cm.
Preface signed: Alfred Raemy.

1. Heraldry—Switzerland—Fribourg. 2. Fribourg (Canton)—Biog. 3. Fribourg (Canton)—Nobility.

Library of Congress DQ432.L7 5-15633†

NL 0422949 DLC

Le Livre d'or du centenaire d'Anatole France, 1844-1944. Paris, Calmann-Lévy [1949]
304 p. illus., ports. 26 cm.
"Ce livre d'or a été établi sur l'initiative et par les soins de M. Claude Aveline, président de la Société Anatole France."
"Bibliographie": p. [283]-297.

1. France, Anatole, 1844-1924—Anniversaries, etc. I. Aveline, Claude, 1901- ed.
PQ2254.Z5L5 928.4 A 50-1987
Illinois. Univ. Library for Library of Congress [1]†

NL 0422950 IU LU GEU NcD NIC NN MB DLC

Le Livre d'or du centenaire d'Hector Berlioz. Paris, G. Petit; [etc., etc., 1907]
vi, 224, [2] p. front., plates, ports., fold. geneal. tab. 32½ cm.
"Il a été tiré de cet ouvrage 325 exemplaires sur papier vélin de cuve numérotés à la presse. Exemplaire n° 41."
Frontispiece and each plate accompanied by guard sheet with descriptive letterpress.
Contributions in French, English and German.
"English bibliography of Berlioz": p. 154-156.
"Catalogue de l'Exposition Hector Berlioz organisée par M. Nicolas Manskopf, dans son musée musical à Francfort-sur-le-Main (Allemagne), au mois de janvier 1901": p. [216]-222.
1. *Berlioz, Hector, 1803-1869—Anniversaries, etc., 1903. I. Grenoble. Comité du centenaire Berlioz.

ML410.B5L59 28—4198

NL 0422951 DLC CtY ICU CU CtY-M NN NNC NIC

... Livre d'or du centenaire de l'independance belge. Sous le haut patronage de S.M. le roi Albert. Bruxelles [etc.] Leclercq, De Ridder et De Haas [1930-31]
722 p., 2 l. front., illus. (part. col., incl. maps), plates (part. col., part. mounted, incl. ports.) 41 cm.
At head of title: 1830-1930.
Edition of 300 copies.
1. Belgium. I. Title: 1830-1930.

NL 0422952 CU

... Livre d'or du centenaire de l'indépendence belge; sous le haut patronage de S. M. le roi Albert. Bruxelles-Anvers, Leclercq, de Ridder et de Haas [1931]
722 p., 2 l. front., illus. (part col., incl. maps, plans) plates (part col., part mounted) ports. (part col. mounted) diagrs. 42½cm.
At head of title: 1830-1930.
Head and tail pieces, initials.
"Ouvrage publié sous la direction de René Leclercq avec la collaboration de Camille Puylaert."

1. Belgium. I. Leclercq, René, ed. II. Puylaert, Camille, joint ed.

Library of Congress DH645.L5 33-25084
[2] 949.3

NL 0422953 DLC CU-S CtY CU NN

Livre d'or du centenaire de la fanfare royale grand-ducale Luxembourg-grund, 1852-1952. [Luxembourg, Saint Paul, 1952]
320p. 24cm.

1. Luxemburg - Hist. - Sources.

NL 0422954 TNJ

Livre d'or du centenaire de Marcelin Berthelot
see Centenaire de Marcelin Berthelot.

Le Livre d'or du cinéma français.
Paris, Agence d'information cinégraphique.
v. illus. 28 cm.
Director: M. Pascal.

1. Moving-pictures—France. I. Pascal, Marc.
PN1993.5.F7L57 52-38798 ‡

NL 0422956 DLC ICU FU CLSU NN

Le Livre d'or du cinquantenaire de l'École regionale des Beaux-Arts de Rennes. [Vizzanova, n.d.]

NL 0422957 NN

LIVRE d'or du cinquantenaire de la fondation de l'Université Catholique de Lille, 1877-1927. Lille, Impr.du Nouvelliste et de La Dépêche, 1927.

Ports.-and plates.
"Le memorial des étudiants morts pour la France", pp. 305-333.

NL 0422958 MH

Livre d'or du clergé diocésain de Lyon pendant la guerre 1914-1918
see under [Bornet, Étienne Marie, Bp.] 1882-

Livre d'or du clergé et des congrégations, 1914-1922... Tome 1- Paris: Bonne presse, 1925- v. 4°.
At head of title: La preuve du sang.
"Introduction," signed: C. B.
"Préface: Le sang des prêtres," by Henry Bordeaux.

1. European war, 1914-1918—Registers, lists, etc. 2. European war, 1914-1918—Biog. 3. Clergy—France, 1914-1918. 4. B., C., editor. 5. Bordeaux, Henry, 1870-
N. Y. P. L. October 21, 1925

NL 0422960 NN

914.49 L788 Le Livre d'or du Dauphiné, 1349-1949. Grenoble, Roissard [19 -52]
2v. 22cm.

"Conférences du lundi organisées avec le concours de l'Académie delphinale et de la Société des écrivains dauphinois..."

1. Dauphiné. 2. Dauphiné. Intellectual life.

NL 0422961 IEN

VOLUME 337

Le livre d'or du Dauphiné (1349-1949) Conférences du lundi, organisées avec le concours de l'Académie delphinale et de la Société des écrivains dauphinois en la Chambre de Commerce de Grenoble du 13 decembre 1948 au 16 mai 1949 à l'occasion du vi[e] centenaire du rattachement du Dauphiné à la France. Grenoble, Roissard [1949]
241 p.
1. Le Dauphiné.

NL 0422962 MChB

Le LIVRE d'or du Dauphiné (1349-1949); conférences du lundi organisées avec le concours de l'Académie delphinale et de la Société des écrivains dauphinois en la Chambre de Commerce de Grenoble du 13 décembre 1948 au 16 mai 1949 à l'occasion du VIe centenaire du rattachement du Dauphiné à la France. Grenoble, Roissard [1951] 1 v. ports. 23cm.
[Tome 1]
Includes bibliographies.

1. Dauphiné, France—Hist. I. Société des écrivains dauphinois. II. Académie delphinale, Grenoble.

NL 0422963 NN

Le Livre d'or du Dauphiné, 1349-1949; conférences du lundi organisées avec le concours de l'Académie delphinale et de la Société des écrivains dauphinois en la Chambre de commerce de Grenoble du 13 décembre 1948 au 16 mai 1949 à l'occasion du vi[e] centenaire du rattachement du Dauphiné à la France. Grenoble, Roissard ₍1952–
v. illus., ports, music. 23 cm.
Errata slip inserted.
CONTENTS.
2. Conférences artistiques et littéraires: Le théâtre dauphinois, par L.-A. Robert. La poésie dauphinoise, par A. Bachelard. Louis le Cardonnel, par R. Fernandat. Stendhal et Barnave, par F. Vermale. Chants et danses du Dauphiné, par P. Pittion. Réflexions berlioziennes, par J. Giroud. Henri Fantin-Latour, par A. Sainson. Jules Flandrin, par G. Gariel. Champollion, par G. Gariel et P. Tresson. Vienne entre 1349 et 1949, par M. Faure.

1. Dauphiné.

DC611.D247L5 62-31648

NL 0422965 DLC

Livre d'or du Dr. Theodore L. Papayoannov. Naumburg, Lippert, 1932.

NL 0422966 DNLM

Livre d'or du Grand hôtel et Bernerhof, Berne... see under Bernerhof, Bern.

Livre d'or du grand Lausanne. Lausanne, P.-F. Perret-Gentil ₍1955₎
398 p. illus. 25 cm.

1. Lausanne.

DQ729.L5 57-23391 ‡

NL 0422968 DLC MdBJ NjP

Livre d'or du jubilé littéraire de Charles Maurras. Paris ₍L'Action française₎ 1937.
1 p. l., 72, ₍1₎ p., 1 l. front. (port.) facsim. 28½cm.
"Il a été tiré, de ce Livre d'or du jubilé littéraire de Charles Maurras, 251 exemplaires ... Exemplaire no. 198."
"Les deux premiers articles de Charles Maurras": p. 53-₍73₎

1. *Maurras, Charles, 1868–

A C 38-1085

Illinois. Univ. Library for Library of Congress ₍2₎

NL 0422969 IU

Le livre d'or du Lyonnais du Forez et du Beaujolais see under [Monfalcon, Jean Baptiste] 1792-1874.

Livre d'or du monde horticole. 1913.

NL 0422971 MBH

Edia 901L Le livre d'or du Mont-Blanc. Thonon-les-Bains (Haute-Savoie)Imprimerie Raffin & cie.[1901]
89,[1]p.incl.plates,ports. fold.plate. 16x24cm.
On cover: Mont-Blanc. Livre d'Or. 1901.

1. Mont Blanc.

NL 0422972 CtY

Le LIVRE d'or du pontificat de Léon XIII. Bruxelles Société belge de Librairie,etc.,etc., [1888.]
4°. C 4621.21F

NL 0422973 MH

Le livre d'or du Salon de peinture et de sculpture see under Lafenestre, Georges Edouard, 1837-1919, ed.

Le Livre d'or du Tour de France, 1903-1947; l'histoire du maillot jaune. ₍n. p., 1948?₎
112 p. illus. 22 cm.
Cover title.
Advertising matter interspersed.
"1947 (25 juin-20 juillet)-₍1948 (30 juin-26 juillet)₎": folder (16 p.) inserted at end.

1. Cycling—France. I. Title: Tour de France, 1903-1947.

A50-2280

New York. Public Libr. for Library of Congress ₍1₎

NL 0422975 NN

TL 721.4 .L79 Livre d'or du tourisme aérien. Pref.de Étienne Riché,ancien sous-secrétaire d'état au Ministère de l'air. Introd.de André Wateau,Président de l'Aéro-club de France. Illus.de Gustave Alaux,Lucien Cavé,Durandeau,Geneviève Gallibert, Geo.Ham,R.Naly,Theunissen,Jacques Weismann. Paris, Édilux, 1935.
₍245₎ p. illus.(part col.) plates,ports., facsims. 39 cm.
Issued in slipcase.
210 copies printed. "150 exemplaires sur vélin d'arches numérotés de 51 à 200 ... Exemplaire no 54,imprimé spécialement pour Monsieur Emile Dubonnet."
1.Aeronautics--France. 2.Aeronautical societies. 3 Air pilots--France. I. Aéro-club de France. II.Title: Tourisme aérien.

NL 0422976 MiU

Livre d'or du 3e régiment de spahis ... see under [Jullian, David Raymond Martin]

DB205.7 L58 Livre d'or du voyage de Monsieur T.G.Masaryk en France, en Belgique et en Grande Bretagne, Octobre, 1923. Prague ₍Impr. par la Průmyslová tiskárna₎ 1924.
141 p. illus.,ports. 29cm.
English edition has title: President Masaryk in Paris, Brussels and London in October, 1924.
1.Czechoslovak Republic - Relations (general) with Europe. 2.Masaryk, Tomáš Garrigue, Pres. Czechoslovak Republic, 1850-1937. I.Masaryk, Tomáš Garrigue, Pres. Czechoslovak Republic, 1850-1937.

NL 0422978 CSt CtY MB DLC-P4 IU IEN

WE 800 L788 1947 Livre d'or, en l'honneur du professeur Jörgen Schaumann. ₍Stockholm, 1947₎
1 v. (various pagings) illus. (part col.) port.

Consists of articles by various authors reprinted chiefly from Acta medica scandinavica and Acta dermato-venereologica.
Includes bibliographies

1. Dermatology - Collected works
2. Sarcoidosis I. Schaumann, Jörgen N 1879-

NL 0422979 DNLM NNC IU-M

R111 .S35 Livre d'or en l'honneur du Professeur Jörgen Schaumann. Avant-propos du Professeur Henri Gougerot. ₍Stockholm, I. Haeggström, 1948₎
1 v.(v.p.) front.(port.) illus. 23cm.

1. Schaumann, Jörgen. 2. Medicine - Collections.

NL 0422980 NNU MnU

GV943 L5 Le Livre d'or jubilaire de l'U. R. B. S. F. A., 1895-1945. Texte et présentation de Victor Boin, dessins de Paul Daxhelet. Bruxelles, Leclercq & De Haas ₍1950₎
583 p. illus., ports. (part col.) 33 cm.
Cover title: Histoire du football en Belgique et au Congo Belge.

1. Soccer. 2. Union royale belge dés sociétés de football-association. I. Boin, Victor.

A 51-6573

Illinois Univ. Library for Library of Congress ₍1₎

NL 0422981 IU DLC

Livre d'or. L'Égypte nouvelle. ₍Le Caire, L'Imprimerie Paul Barbey₎ 1938.
₍252₎ p. illus., ports., map, diagrs. 34½cm.
Advertising matter included in paging.
On cover: L'Égypte nouvelle. Golden book 1938.
The contributions are in French and English.
Charles Papadopoulo, manager; Alexandre Adopol, chief editor.

1. Egypt. I. Papadopoulo, Charles. II. Adopol, Alexandre. III. Title: L'Égypte nouvelle.

S D 41-12 Provisional

U. S. Dept. of state. Libr. for Library of Congress DT100.L5 ₍2₎

NL 0422982 DS NN PP

Livre d'or, notariat, magistrature, barreau au champ d'honneur, 1914–
₍Angers, Imp. Burdin, Gaultiers et Thébert, succ^rs, 19
v. 24cm.
Cover-title.
"Supplément à l'Revue généalogique."

1. European war, 1914– —France. 2. Notaries—France. 3. Magistrates. 4. Lawyers—France. I. Revue généalogique. Supplement.

19-18517

Library of Congress D609.F8L4

NL 0422983 DLC NN

VOLUME 337

WP qL786 1906 LIVRE d'or offert au Professeur S. Pozzi en souvenir de vingt années d'enseignement à l'Hôpital Broca., 8 juillet 1906. [Paris, 1906]
420 p. illus., port.
Autograph presentation copy of S. Pozzi. Signed.
1. Pozzi, Samuel Jean, 1846-1918

NL 0422984 DNLM NNC-M NNC

Le livre d'or, ou Livre des vassaux de l'abbaye de Saint-Claude
see under Saint-Claude, France. Benedictine Abbey.

Livre d'or, Le. Poésies choisies extraites du Parnasse. 4699.70
Paris. Autbureau du Parnasse. 1879. 212 pp. [Bibliothèque du Parnasse.] 18°.

E2177 — France. Lit. Poetry. Coll. — S.r.

NL 0422986 MB

Livre d'or; recueil sélectionné de sonnets composés en l'honneur de Martin-Saint René à l'occasion de son cinquantenaire littéraire, 1902–1952. Publication commémorative de la Bibliothèque des études poétiques. [Paris, 1953]
55 p. 19 cm.

1. French poetry—20th cent. 2. Martin Saint-René, pseud.—Poetry.
A 53-6551
Illinois. Univ. Librar.
for Library of Congress [1]

NL 0422987 IU NN

Le livre d'or; révélations de l'archange saint Michel
see under [Charvoz, Alexandre]

M7 .L786 Le Livre d'orgue du Père Pingré. Anonymes français du XVIIIe siècle. [Restitution: J. Bonfils] Paris, Éditions musicales de la Schola Cantorum [19--]
32 p. (L'Organiste liturgique, 45-46)
Caption title: Pièces de différents auteurs copiées par le Père Pingré.
Transcribed from ms. no.2372, Bibliothèque Sainte-Geneviève, Paris.
1. Organ music. 2. Suites (Organ) I. Paris. Bibliothèque Sainte-Geneviève. Mss. (2372) II. Pingré, Alexandre Guy, 1711-1796, comp.

NL 0422989 ICU

Le livre d'un inconnu. Paris, A. Lemerre, 1879.
99 p.
Poems

NL 0422990 CU

Le "Livre de ballades" de Jehan et Charles Bocquet
see under Bocquet, Jean, 1510 (ca.)-1569.

Le livre de bourgeoisie de la ville de Strasbourg, 1440-1530
see under Strassburg.

Livre de cantiques avec les parties qui y appartiennent ... 2de éd., augm. Stockholm, 1734.
12°. (Bd. with it: Les Evangiles et les Epitres ... 1734)

NL 0422993 CtY

Le Livre de ce qu'il y a dans l'Hades
see
Book of that which is in the nether world.

Livre de cent et un; oder, Hundert und ein Epigramm auf den grossen Kopf des kleinen Unbekannten E. C. F. A.
see under [Adam, E C F]

Livre de César
see
Faits des Romains.

Le livre de chasse du roy Modus
see under Livre du roy Modus.

Le livre de Ciperis de Vignevaulx
see Ciperis de Vignevaulx (*Chanson de geste*)

Livre de clergie
see
Image du monde.

Le livre de comptes de la caravane russe à Pékin en 1727-1728...
see under [Lange, Lorenz]

Le livre de cuisine des petites filles
see under [Ambroise-Thomas, Josy]

Wing ZW 6461 605 LIVRE de divers assortes d'escritures le plus usitées en la chrestienté. [Netherlands? ca.1605?]
[31] l. 19x26cm.
One plate dated 1603.

NL 0423002 ICN

Livre de famille. [Angers] Jacques-Petit, 1947.
2 v. col. illus. 27 cm.
Title from colophon of v. 1; each vol. has special t.-p.

1. Genealogy. 2. Genealogy—Forms, blanks, etc.
CS17.L5 929.2 48-19484*‡

NL 0423003 DLC

Le livre de jade
see under Gautier, Mme. Judith, 1846-1917, comp. and tr.

Livre de Job
see
L'hystore Job.

Le livre de joie
see
Le livre joyeux

Livre de jostice et de plet.
see
Li Livres de jostice et de plet.

[Le LIVRE de jugement d'astrologie selon Aristote. Le livre Messchallach astrologien des conionctions et recepcions et interrogacions, etc.].

Manuscript, 15th cent. 4°. ff.(112). Diagrs. ff. 5-22 are bland. After f.(91) 2 pages of later manuscript are inserted.
With ornamental initials in blue and red and rubricated throughout.
A note on f.(1) states that the original wor] was probably in Arabi translated into Latin then into French by order of Charles, duke of Normandy.

NL 0423009 MH

... Le livre de l'amour miséricordieux. [Arras (Pas-de-Calais) Imprimerie moderne, 1934]
v. col. plates. 22 x 17cm.
At head of title, t. 1- : Μονολόγοι.
"Copyright 1934 by Chanoine F. Caron."

1. Lord's supper. I. Caron, François, 1881-
Library of Congress BX2169.L57 35-606
Copyright A—Foreign 25568
[2] 264.025

NL 0423010 DLC

VOLUME 337

Le Livre de l'année.
Montréal, Société Grolier Québec.
v. illus. 25 cm.

I. Société Grolier Québec limitée.

AP21.L53 52-20762 ‡

NL 0423011 DLC

Le livre de l'épervier, cartulaire de la commune de Millau
see under Millau.

Livre de l'estat et mutation ...
see under [Roussat, Richard]

Le Livre de l'étudiant, collection dirigee par Paul Hazard. no. 1- Paris, Boivin & cie [c1939]-

NL 0423014 OO DLC AAP

Livre de l'internelle consolacion
see Imitatio Christi. French. (editions: Paris, Jannet, 1856; Paris, Helleu et Sergent, 1926)

Le Livre de la chasse du grand sénéschal de Normandye
see under [Brézé, Jacques de] d. 1494.

Le livre de la conqueste de Constantinople et de l'empire de Romanie
see
Chronicle of Morea.

Le Livre de la conqueste de la princée de l'Amorée
see under Chronicle of Morea.

Livre de la conqueste de la Toison d'or, par le prince Jason de Tessalie, faict par figures avec l'explication d'icelles
see under Gohory, Jacques, d. 1576.

Livre de la diablerie
see under Amerval, Eloy d', fl. 1463-1508.

FC5 .100 519ℓ

[Le livre de la discipline de lamour divine, la repetition de la disciple, avec les proprietes damour seraphique.]
[Paris,1519]
8p.ℓ.,176 numb.ℓ. 17cm.
Colophon: Cy finist le liure de la discipline damour diuine et de la repetition de la disciple ... Fait a paris ce .xxviii. iour de nouēbre pour regnault chaudiere libraire demourant a lenseigne de lhomme sauuaige en la rue saīct iacques. Lan mil.v.cxix.

Caption on 2d prelim. leaf: Sensuyt la table du liure intitule la discipline damour diuine faict, cōpose, et escript ou monastere des celestīs de nostre dame dābert es forestz dorleans lan mil quatre cens soixante et dix.
Numerous errors in foliation.
Imperfect: t.-p., 8th prelim. leaf, & leaves 1, 161, 168, 176 wanting; title transcribed from Brunet v.3, col.1120.
Prelim. leaves misbound in order: 2, 4, 3, 6, 5, 7.

NL 0423022 MH

Le liure de la femme forte et vertueuse declaratif du catique de salomon es prouerbes au chapitre final qui ce comence.
See under
[Le Roy, Francois, fl. 1499-1512.]

Le livre de la ferme et des maisons de campagne .. 1865
see under Joigneaux, Pierre, 1815-1892.

Hfa22 7

Livre De La Fontaine Perilleuse, Avec La Chartre D'Amours: autrement intitulé, le songe du verger. Oeuure tres excellent, de poësie antique contenant la Steganographie des mysteres secrets de la science minerale. Auec commentaire de I.G[ohory]. P[arisien]. ...
A Paris,Pour Iean Ruelle,1572.
48 numb.ℓ. 16cm.
Signatures: A-F8.
Originally published, without imprint, under title: La Fōtaie peril'euse auec la chartre damours.

NL 0423025 CtY WU

D501 .L7

"Le livre de la fraternité héroique." Les heros de la guerre. Paris, J. Tallandière, 1916-
v. illus. 33.5 cm.
Cover-title.
Fasc. 1-3 have title: Le livre de la fraternité heroique rédigé sous la direction de Henri Levêque.

NL 0423026 DLC

Le livre de la jeune femme chrétienne
see under Letissier, Marie Benigne Esther. [Supplement]

Le liure de la musique d'Euclide
see under [Cleonides]

Livre de la passion (*Old French poem, 14th cent.*)
... Le livre de la passion, poème narratif du XIVe siècle, édité par Grace Frank. Paris, É. Champion, 1930.
xxvii, 122, [2] p. $18\frac{1}{2}^{cm}$. (Les Classiques français du moyen âge ... [64])
Based on manuscript in Bibliothèque nationale, fonds français 1555, fol. 154 r°-192r°.
A "centon des traditions apocryphes et des interprétations symboliques du temps". *cf.* p. vi.

1. Jesus Christ—Poetry. I. Frank, Grace, 1886- ed.

Library of Congress PQ1489.L48 1930 31-15478

ScC CU MoSU
OCU OCl OOxM ViU KyU MH NBuU GU GDS CU-S OU NIC
NL 0423029 DLC MsSM CaBVaU TU MH NcU PHC PSC PBm

Le livre de la 15ème brigade internationale. Nos combats contre le fascisme. Madrid [Diana (U. G. T.)] 1937.
320 p. incl. illus., plates, ports., facsims. $23\frac{1}{2}^{cm}$.

1. Spain—Army—15. brigada internacional. 2. Spain — Hist. — Civil war, 1936-1939—Personal narratives.

Library of Congress DP269.L52 41-22733
[2] 946.08

NL 0423030 DLC TxU

Livre de la taille de Paris l'an de grace 1313
see under Paris.

HV L788 1901

Le LIVRE de la tempérance, recueil de lectures, dictées, etc. Tournai, Delcourt-Vasseur, 1901.
122 p.
Awarded a prize at the Concours national pour l'enseignement antialcoolique, opened in 1899 by the province of Hainaut.

NL 0423032 DNLM

Livre de la ville de Linz
see Linz heute.

Le livre de Lazare
see under [Heine, Heinrich] 1797-1856.

LE livre de lecture. Lond., Nelson, 1875-82. 3 v. illus. 16-17 cm. Royal school series.

NL 0423035 CaNSWA

---

8 6670

LIVRE de lecture pour les classes supérieures du 1r corps des cadets. Tome 2.
St. Pétersbourg, de l'imprimerie du dit corps. 1807. (3) pp. 8°.

NL 0423036 MB

275.81 L784

Livre de lecture syrienne. 3d ed.
1 v.

NL 0423037 DCU-H

VOLUME 337

LIVRE de madame. Édité pour John Wanamaker, par Maquet à Paris. [Paris, Imprimé par Maquet, graveur, 1917] 150 p., 4 l. illus., plates. 12cm.

Plates in the calendar signed G. Barbier.
Bound in white satin over paper covers; girl's figure in pencil within floriated frame printed in blue lines, and colored by hand; signed G.B. 1912. Issued in box with same printed ornament on satin.
Contains calendar, pages for notes, and collection of poems.
With bookplate of Frank Weitenkampf.

NL 0423038 NN

Livre de Maguelonne
see
Pierre de Provence et Maguelonne.

Le livre de Marc Avrele, emperevr, et eloqvent oratevr
see under [Guevara, Antonio de] bp. d. 1545?

Livre de Metz
Blonde mss. 43 bis, table du Livre de Metz. [35]p. [18-]

Cover-title.
Problems in Polish checkers.

NL 0423041 OCl

Livre de Metz
Poirson-Prugneaux mss., table du Livre de Metz. [11]p. [1830?]

Cover-title.
Problems in Polish checkers.

NL 0423042 OCl

Le Livre de mon ami
see under France, Anatole, 1844-1924.

Le Livre de Mormon
see under Book of Mormon. French.

Case MS VM 145 .L 788

LIVRE de musique. [n.p., 16--]
289[i.e. 290] l. 13x26cm.

Binder's title.
Manuscript in ink, in at least two hands, on printed staffs. Probably of French origin.
A collection of miscellaneous pieces, probably for the musette.
Written in the French violin clef; many of the pieces have words.
Number 58 repeated in numbering.
Imperfect: leaves 1, 67-69, 72-73, 76-77, 88-89, 116-119, 122-129, 131, 136-142, 159-191, 219-225, 253-265, 284-286 wanting.

NL 0423045 ICN

Livre de notions élémentaires de français
see under [Degosserie, H]

AW 2 F74

Une livre de pain. [Paris, Imp. de la veuve d'Ant.-J. Gorsas [1795?]
8p. 20cm.

Micro-opaque

NL 0423047 CaBVaU NNC

Le livre de piété du jeune homme, par l'auteur des "Paillettes d'or". Avignon, Aubanel frères [1927]
2 p. l., [vii]-ix, 301, [1] p. 15cm.

1. Catholic church—Prayer-books and devotions. 2. Christian life. I. Paillettes d'or, Author of.

Library of Congress BX2151.L5 28-18410

NL 0423048 DLC

Microfilm H609

[Livre]
Le liure de plusieurs pièces, c'est à dire, faict & recueilly de diuers autheurs cōme Clemēt Marot & autres... Lyon, T. Payen, 1549.
127 l.

Colophon: Imprimé à Lyon par Nicolas Bacquenois.
Microfilm (negative) of the original in the British Museum. London, British Museum Photographic Service, 1965? 1 reel. 35mm.
1.French literature - 16th cent.

NL 0423049 MiDW

Hfm.22

Le livre de Pochi, écrit pour Judith Cladel et ses petites amies par Paul Arène, Jean-Bernard, Jules Claretie, Alphonse Daudet, C.Delon, Hector France, Camille Lemonnier, Lugol,Catulle Mendès, Mullem, Henri Passerieu, Edmond Picard, Ernest Pouvillon, Marie Sever des Moulins, Armand Silvestre, Maurice Talmeyr. Illustrations de Ary Gambard et Lunel. Décorations de Calice et Stein. Paris,Ed.Monnier,de Brunhoff et c^ie^ [1885]
22p.l.,iv,168p. illus.(part col.) 23cm.
Title in red and black.

NL 0423050 CtY

Livre de poésie à l'usage des jeunes filles chrétiennes...
see under [Lenormant, Amélie (Cyvoct)] d. 1893, comp.

---

383 L767

Livre de poste; ou, État général des postes de l'Italie et des pays voisins avec les réglemens et tarifs, suivi de la carte itinéraire des routes desservies en poste. Milan, J. P. Giegler,1826.
72p. fold.map.

1. Postal service--Italy.

NL 0423052 IU

Le livre de preuve; edited by Louis Brandin.
Romania, v. 42, p. 204-254.

NL 0423053 OO

Livre de priere; lumiere, flamme, parfums
see under [Monod, Wilfred] 1867-

BX2170 .I6L5

Livre de prières indulgenciées, uniquement composé de prières enrichiés d'indulgences authentiques. Einsiedeln, Benziger & co., 1890.
356 p. front. 24°.

NL 0423055 DLC

Safe 2 W 9281 .5

Livre de prières, tissé [sur soie] d'après les enluminures des manuscrits du XIVe au XVIe siècle. Lyon,1886. sq.D.

Bound in leather chiseled and modeled with burin in Gothic style; title on cover in imitation of the mss. of the middle ages. Gothic text (within ornamental borders) initials and illustrations woven in black threads on a grey ground in Lyons silk. This is the first example of this kind of work as applied to a book.
"Achevé...sur les dessins du R.P.I. Hervier...par J.A.Henry, fabricant."

NL 0423057 ICN

Le livre de quatre couleurs ...
see under [Caraccioli, Louis Antoine de] 1721-1803.

Livre de raison.
Paris, Alsatia, 19
v. plates. 18cm.

Publication began with issue for 1943.
Issued for 19 under the direction of Louis Chaigne, Victor Bindel and Raymond Postal.

1. Almanacs, French. 2. Youth—France. I. Chaigne, Louis, 1899- II. Bindel, Victor. III. Postal, Raymond.

Library of Congress AY836.L5 45-32109
[2] 529.43

NL 0423059 DLC NN IU

Le livre de raison. Bruxelles, 1939
see under [Degée, Olivier]

Livre de raison de la famille Dudrot de Capdebosc (1522-1675)/ publié et annoté par Philippe Tamizey de Larroque. Paris, A.Picard, 1891.
47 p. 24cm.
"Extrait,à cent-vingt exemplaires,de la Revue de Gascogne."
Inserted (25 p.,1 l.,at end): H.D.-de Grammont. [Alger, Typ.A.Jourdan, 1893?] With portrait and bibliography.
With this is bound Tamizey de Larroque,Philippe,1828-1898,ed. ... Deux livres de raison de l'Agenais. 1893.
1.Grammont,Henri Delmas de,1830-1892. I.Tamizey de Larroque,Philippe,1828-1898, ed. II.Title.

NL 0423061 MiU

Le livre de sang, ou Calcul abrégé des assassinats commis ou occasionnés par les prêtres. [Paris, Impr. de Martin, 1790?]
8 p. 21 cm.

NL 0423062 MH

VOLUME 337

Le livre de santé. Contenant le regime & gouuernement que toutes personnes doiuent garder pour s'entretenir en santé. Auec le moyen de guarir ceux qui sont desia malades. Plus le temps est eu pour se faire seigner, purger, & mediciner, selon les douze moys & saisons de l'année.
A Troyes, C. Garnier, 1581.
[48] p. 15 cm.
Title vignette.
Signatures: A-A^8, B-B^8, C-C^2, C^4-C^8, 1 l.

NL 0423063 CtY-M

Case MS 7Q 5
[Livre]
LIURE de tablature. [n.p., 16--?]
187(i.e.188)p. 17x23cm.
Manuscript in ink.
Title from cover.
One page between 116 and 117 omitted in numbering.
Collection of dances for the lute, in French lute tablature.
Bookplate of Alfred Cortot.

NL 0423064 ICN

Livre de Tertullien du Mantua
see under Tertullianus, Quintus Septimius Florens.

NE 647 L767
Livre de têtes antiques, gravées d'après les pierres & cornalines du cabinet du roy. Dedié aux amateurs de dessein. Paris, F. Chereau, 1754.
18 plates.
Engraved t. p. signed: P. Aveline.

1. Engravings, French. I. Aveline, P.

NL 0423066 CLU

Livre de Thot
see under Alliette.

C 9558.68
Le livre de tous les saints. Paris, H. Casterman, etc. etc., 1868.
pp. 72. Illus. (Nouvelle bibliothèque morale et amusante, 2e série, 1.)

NL 0423068 MH

Livre de tout ce qui s'est passe pandant la guerre de Paris, 1649. [Paris? 1649?] 4 v. 22cm.
Binder's title.
Collection of political pamphlets.

1. Fronde. 2. Mazarinades—Collections.
N. Y. P. L. May 12, 1948

NL 0423069 NN

4AG 36
Le livre de tout le monde; ou, Instructions, recettes et découvertes sur les arts et métiers, l'agriculture, les fabriques...les moeurs, etc., par MM. Boquillon [et al.] Paris, Société universelle philantropique, 1837.
287 p.

NL 0423070 DLC-P4 ICRL

Le livre de Vêsandâr
see under Jātakas.

Le LIVRE de vie de la ville de Bergerac, publié pour la première fois,avec une introduction et des notes par Charles Durand. Périgueux, E. Laporte, 1887.

Facsimile plate and other illustr.
Text in the dialect of Périgord, and French translation, on opposite pages.

NL 0423072 MH

Typ 515 28.526
[Livre]
Le liure de vraye et parfaicte oraison ... [Paris,1528]
[325]p. 14.5cm.
Signatures: A^{10},a-b^8,c^2,Aa^8,[2d]A^{10},A^8,[2d] b-c^8,+2,[3d]a-b^8,[4th]a-i^8,k^6 (Aa7-8 blank; k6 blank?, wanting).
Colophon: Imprime a Paris par maistre Simon du bois, pour Chrestiē Wechel, libraire iure de luniuersite de Paris: demourant en la rue sainct Jaques a lenseigne de lescu de Basle. Mil v.c. xxviii. au mois de juillet.
Illus. on t.-p.
Imperfect: leaves $\underset{4}{c}$ 1 & 8 wanting.

NL 0423073 MH

Beinecke Library 1971 1063
Le Livre de vraye et parfaicte oraison, auquel est compris ce qui est contenu en la page suiuante. A Lyon, Par Iean de Tournes, 1543.
320 p. illus. 8^{12} cm.
Signatures: a-v^8.
"Le Livre de vraye et parfaicte oraison, inspiré du texte latin du Betbuchlein et des Psaumes pénitentiaux de Luther, est une traduction, avec commentaires, des textes indiqués à la table..."- cf. A. Cartier. Bibl.des éditions des De Tournes, I, p.176.

First published in Paris, 1529.

1. Prayer-books.

NL 0423075 CtY

... Livre dédié à Gaston Bonnier par ses élèves et ses amis à l'occasion du vingt-cinquième anniversaire de la fondation du Laboratoire de biologie végétale de Fontainebleau et de la création de la Revue générale de botanique. Paris, Librairie générale de l'enseignement, 1914.
4 p. l., [xii]-xvi, 678 p. front., illus., plates, port. $25\frac{1}{2}^{cm}$. (Revue générale de botanique. [t. 25 bis] Travaux de biologie végétale)
Bibliographies interspersed.
1. Bonnier, Gaston Eugène Marie, 1853– 2. Botany—Physiology. 3. Botany—Anatomy. [2, 3. Botany, Physiological and structural] 4. [Fontainebleau. Laboratoire de biologie végétale]

Library, U. S. Dept. of Agriculture 450R326 vol. 25 bis Agr 15-287

NL 0423076 DNAL

Livre del juise
see Li ver del juïse en fornfransk predikan.

Livre des airs a boire (MS., Obl. 4o.)
94p.

Printed, illus. extra t.-p.(putti playing assorted instruments, "H. Pola del P. Bouttats sculp.") has imprint á La Haye. Chez Louis et Henry van Dole, marchands libraires, ou l'on vende toute sorte de musique, et de papier reglé.
Contents(most for two voices): De touttes les beautez.-Que ton sort est digne d'envie.-Tambour battant.-Jeune Philis.-au secours cher Bachus.-

Contents (cont.):Benes dieux de plaisirs.-En vain pour oublier.-Versez moy.-Quand l'amour attaque mon coeur.-Dans cet agreable sejour.-Suive qui voudra.-Le vin charmante.-Fuyer le vin.-Ma bergere vient de changer.-Depuis que l'amour s'est glissé.-Pour goutter des plaisirs.-L'on observe par tout.-Un genereux heros.-Pour pleurer plus longtemps.-L'on ne scait.-Le roy d'egypte.-Rien ne trouble.-Verse verse verse.-Parma figue. Impitoyable, Celimeine.-Quoy pauvre amant.-Prenons tous le panier.-Je sens que cupidon.-

Contents (cont.):Bachus a moy.-Tout est contraire -L'amour te fait souffrir.-Pour vivre heureux.-Iris chantoit.-Craignons les plus douces chaines -Je veux boire.-Reveillez vous.-

NL 0423079 MBCo

Le livre des animaux; illustrations de Pierre Zénobel. [Paris]: Éditions de Cluny, 1930?]. col'd illus. sq. f°.
Unpaged.

1. Animals. 2. Zénobel, Pierre, illustrator.
N. Y. P. L. September 10, 1932

NL 0423080 NN OC1

Le livre des assises et pleas del' corone, moves & dependants devant les justices sibien en lour circuit come aylours, ...
see under Gt. Brit. Year books, 1327-1377. (Edward III)

Le livre des ballades; soixante ballades choisies. Paris, A. Lemerre, 1876.
2 p. l., [iii]-xxxii p., 1 l., 185, [1] p., 1 l. $20\frac{1}{2}^{cm}$. [Bibliothèque illustrée]
Title in red and black; red line borders.
Not illustrated; included by Lemerre in the "Bibliothèque illustrée" because he had previously published portraits of all the authors represented in the volume, which could easily be added. cf. Vicaire's Manuel.
"Avertissement" signed: Alphonse Lemerre.
"Histoire de la ballade" by Charles Asselineau: p. [v]-xxxii.
1. Ballades. 2. French poetry (Collections) I. Lemerre, Alphonse, 1838-1912. II. *Asselineau, Charles, 1820-1874. Histoire de la ballade.
27-11998
Library of Congress PQ1191.B3L5 1876

NL 0423082 DLC NSyU MdBP MH

Le livre des bêtes
see under Golschmann, Léon, 1861- ed. and tr.

Le Livre des bourgeois de l'ancienne république de Genève
see under Geneva.

VOLUME 337

Le Livre des cent ballades.

Les cent ballades, poème du XIVe siècle composé par Jean le Seneschal avec la collaboration de Philippe d'Artois, comte d'Eu, de Boucicaut le jeune et de Jean de Crésecque, pub. avec deux reproductions phototypiques, par Gaston Raynaud. Paris, Firmin-Didot et cie, 1905.

2 p. l., lxx, 260 p. 2 facsim. 23½cm. (*Half-title:* Société des anciens textes français)

I. Jean de Saint-Pierre, sénéchal d'Eu, d. 1396. II. Philippe d'Artois, comte d'Eu, d. 1397. III. Crésecque, Jean, sire de, d. 1396. IV. Boucicaut, Jean Le Maingre de, maréchal de France, d. 1421. V. Raynaud, Gaston, 1850–1911, ed.

Library of Congress PQ1489.L53 1905 7–9514

PBm ViU
OOxM MB INS CaBVaU OrU CU FU PU NcD PSC PU PP PHC
NL 0423085 DLC GU WaU OU MiU NBuU OO PPL OCl NcD

Le Livre des cent ballades.

Le Livre des cent ballades, contenant des conseils à un chevalier pour aimer loialement & les responses aux ballades, pub. d'après trois manuscrits de la Bibliothèque impériale de Paris & de la Bibliothèque de Bourgogne de Bruxelles, avec une introduction, des notes historiques & un glossaire, par le marquis de Queux de Saint-Hilaire. Paris, E. Maillet, 1868.

3 p. l., [iii]–xxxix, 282 p., 1 l. 22cm.

Authorship ascribed to Jean de Saint-Pierre, assisted by Philippe d'Artois, comte d'Eu, Jean de Crésecque, and Jean Le Maingre de Boucicaut.

"[516 exemplaires; 500 exemplaires papier vergé ... n° 307."

I. Jean de Saint-Pierre, sénéchal d'Eu, d. 1396. II. Philippe d'Artois, comte d'Eu, d. 1397. III. Crésecque, Jean, sire de, d. 1396. IV. Boucicaut, Jean Le Maingre de, maréchal de France, d. 1421. V. Queux de Saint-Hilaire, Auguste Henry Édouard, marquis de, 1837–1889, ed.

15–12755

Library of Congress PQ1489.L53 1868

NL 0423087 DLC TNJ CLSU WaU CtY MB MdBP NNU NN OCl

Le Livre des cent ballades.

[Le Livre des cent ballades and a collection of poetry attributed to Othon de Granson, reproduced from ms. français 2201, fol. 1–105a in the Bibliothèque nationale, Paris]

(*In* The Modern language association of America. Collection of photographic facsimiles. 1927. 17 x 28½cm. no. 67. facsim.: 106 sheets mounted on 53 l.)

Negative. Deposited in the Library of Congress by the M. L. A. Committee on the reproduction of manuscripts and rare printed books.

Each sheet of the facsimile represents two pages of the original (a verso and the opposite recto) beginning with the verso of the first leaf and the recto of the second leaf.

Collation of original (as represented by facsimile): verso of p. l., numb. l. 1–99, 99–105 (recto) 15½ x 10½cm. 8 miniatures. Initials.

The original is a 15th century vellum manuscript.

Described in Catalogue des manuscrits français. Ancien fonds. t. 1, 1868.

For a discussion of the poems attributed to Granson, *cf.* Romania, v. 19, 1890. p. [237]–259.

The authorship of Le Livre des cent ballades is ascribed to Jean de Saint-Pierre, assisted by Philippe d'Artois, comte d'Eu, Jean de Crésecque, and Jean Le Maingre de Boucicaut.

Le Livre des cent ballads is incomplete at end.

CONTENTS.—Le Livre des cent ballades, numb. l. 1–70.—A collection of poetry attributed to Othon de Granson, numb. l. 71–105 (recto)

1. Manuscripts, French—Facsimiles. 2. Ballads. I. Jean de Saint-Pierre, sénéchal d'Eu, d. 1396. II. Philippe d'Artois, comte d'Eu, d. 1397. III. Crésecque, Jean, sire de, d. 1396. IV. Boucicaut, Jean Le Maingre de, maréchal de France, d. 1421. V. Granson, Oton de, d. 1397. VI. Paris. Bibliothèque nationale. Mss. (Fr. 2201)

Pho M 30–27

Library of Congress (Card Division)

NL 0423089 DLC

Le LIVRE des cent-et-un, Paris.

See PARIS; ou Le livre des cent-et-un.

Livre (Le) des charades . . . contenant plus de 525 devinettes amusantes . . . 18 pp., 3l. *Gand: Snoeck-Ducaju et fils,* [189-?] 24°.

NL 0423091 NN

Le livre des charmes, où sont cités quelques-uns des plus jolis textes écrits à la louange du corps féminin par Salomon—Doctor Mardrus—Lucien—Cyre de Foucault ... [e. a.] Cet ouvrage est illustré de vingt-neuf planches dans le texte et hors-texte. Paris, Aux Éditions La Bourdonnais, 1937.

[60] p. incl. illus., plates. front. 27½cm.

1. Human figure in art. 2. Anatomy, Artistic. 3. Women in literature and art.

A C 39-1470

Grosvenor library for Library of Congress HQ1219.L5 [2]

NL 0423092 NBuG

Le livre des comptes-faits
see under Barreme, François Bertrand de, 1640?–1703.

Livre des connoilles

see

Évangiles des quenouilles

Le Livre des conteurs. Bruxelles, J. P. Meline, 1833.

3 v. 15cm.

CONTENTS.—t. I. La pleiade des conteurs, par M. X. B. Saintine. Une demoiselle de compagnie, par M. Ancelot. Mariette, par M. J. Janin. Fragment du journal d'un inconnu, publié par M. Eugène Sue. Riche et pauvre, par Jonathan-le-Visionnaire. (M. X. B. Saintine.) Générosa, par M. A. Jal.—t. II. Les réciprocités, par Michel Raymond. Le capucin, par M. le comte de Peyronnet. Lucrèce, par M. Aloysius Block. C'était son droit, par M. V. Schœlcher. Le loup-garou, par le bibliophile Jacob. Trésor des fèves et fleur des pois, par M. Ch. Nodier. L'âme en peine, par M. Ferdinand Langlé.—t. III. René-Paul et Paul-René, par M. Émile Deschamps. Un jour de coquetterie, par M. Ancelot. L'honnête homme, par M. Michel Masson. Catherine, par le comte Jules de Resseguier. Blanca, par M. Jules de Saint-Felix. Une joute, par M. Alexander Dumas. Justice à Naples, par M. Paul de Julvécourt.

18–22845

Library of Congress PQ1269.L5

NL 0423095 DLC

Livre des coutumes. Bordeaux, 1890
see under Bordeaux. Laws, statutes, etc.

Livre des deduis du roi Modus et de la reine Ratio.

See

Livre du roy Modus.

Le livre des droits de Verdun, publié par E.-M. Meijers ... et J.-J. Salverda de Grave ... Haarlem, H. D. Tjeenk Willink & zoon n. v., 1940.

3 p. l., xiii, 191 p. 25½cm. (*Added t.-p.:* Rechtshistorisch instituut. Institut historique de droit, Leiden. [Publicaties] ser. II, 10)

"Manuscrit nouv. acq. franç. 11836 de la Bibliothèque nationale ... Le Livre des droits est une réunion assez confuse de règles concernant le droit coutumier en vigueur à Verdun au XIIIe et au XIVe siècle, et l'administration urbaine. Il se divise en deux parties, dont la première est en vers."—p. i.

"Bibliographie": p. xiii.

1. Customary law—Verdun, France. I. Meijers, Eduard Maurits, 1880– ed. II. Salverda de Grave, Jean Jacques, 1863– joint ed. III. Verdun, France. Laws, statutes, etc. IV. Paris. Bibliothèque nationale. Mss. (Nouv. acq. fr. 11836)

41–24316

NL 0423098 DLC NN NIC IEN OU

Le livre des droiz et des commandemens d'office de justice, publié d'après le manuscrit inédit de la Bibliothèque de l'Arsenal par C. J. Beautemps-Beaupré ... Paris, A. Durand, 1865.

2 v. 23cm.

"Ce manuscrit ... copié en 1424 ... nous donne ... l'état de la jurisprudence au commencement du quinzième siècle dans une des provinces importantes de la France [Poitou] et même dans quelques pays voisins."—Préface.

I. Beautemps-Beaupré, Charles Jean, 1823–1899, ed. II. Paris. Bibliothèque de l'Arsenal.

11–12316

Library of Congress

NL 0423099 DLC OO CtY MH

Fr 1340.09.4

Le Livre des écoles primaires contenant la déclaration des droits et des devoirs de l'homme et du citoyen. Le catéchisme français par La Chabeaussière. L'institution des enfants par N. François. Lyon, Librairie des Ecoles primaires, an 7

31 p.

NL 0423100 MH

Le livre des Eneydes

see

Eneydes.

Le LIVRE des enfans. Québec, Imprimé par Thomas Cary & cie, 1834. 24 p. illus. 18cm.

In original illustrated yellow paper covers, with publisher's advertisement on back.

784530. 1. Primers, Canadian-French.

NL 0423102 NN CtY CaOTP

Franklin
381
L76
h1781

Le livre des enfans et des jeunes gens sans études, ou Idées générales des choses qu'ils ne doivent pas ignorer; suivie d'Élémens de chronologie pour l'histoire ancienne; Des devoirs de l'homme, ou Abrégé de la science du salut; De l'economie politique [par Moreau, curé de Buzancy]; D'un entretien moral, adressé à la jeune noblesse; Des commandemens de l'honnête homme [par A.A.J. Feutry], & De la science du bon-homme Richard [par B. Franklin]. Nouvelle édition, publiée

par M. Feutry ... A Paris, Chez Charles-Pierre Berton, libraire, rue Saint-Victor, au Soleil levant, 1781.
xii, 420 p. 13 cm.

I. Moreau, curé de Buzancy Les devoirs de l'homme. II. Feutry, Aimé Ambroise Joseph, 1720-1789, ed. III. Franklin, Benjamin, 1706-1790. Way to wealth. Fr. tr. Chron. cd.

NL 0423104 CtY

AG
196
F8
L5

Le livre des enfans; ou, Idées generales & définitions des choses dont les enfans doivent être instruits. Nouv. ed., rev., corr. & augm. Paris, Osmont, 1728.
187 p. 16 cm.

1. Children's questions and answers.

NL 0423105 WU

Le livre des enfans, ou, Idées générales & définitions des choses, dont les enfans doivent être instruits. Ouvrage très-utile aux personnes qui sont chargées du soin de les élever. Nouv. éd., rév., corr. & augm. Paris, P. Prault, 1732. 187 p. 16cm.

Dedication signed: F. G.

DLC: YA2416

260423B. 1. Textbooks—France.
N. Y. P. L.

SCHATZKI CHILDREN'S BOOKS COLL.
I. G., F.
February 16, 1944

NL 0423106 NN DLC

VOLUME 337

Le livre des faicts du bon messire Jean Le Maingre, dit Boucicaut, mareschal de France et gouverneur de Gennes.

(*In* Petitot, Claude B., ed. Collection complète des mémoires relatifs à l'histoire de France ... Paris, 1819–29. 22cm. [sér. 1] t. VI (1819) p. [373]–t. VII (1819) p. 234)

Reprinted from the 1st ed., 1620, published by Théodore Godefroy. *cf.* Avertissement, t. VI, p. 169.

1. France—Hist.—Charles V, 1364–1380. 2. France—Hist.—Charles VI, 1380–1422. 3. Boucicaut, Jean Le Maingre de, d. 1421. I. Godefroy, Théodore, 1580–1649, ed.

A 45–1436

New York. Public library for Library of Congress DC3.P49 ser. 1, t. 6–7

NL 0423107 NN OC1W DLC

Livre des faicts du bon Messire Jean Le Maingre, dit Boucicaut, maréchal de France et gouverneur de Gennes.

(In Michaud, J.F., ed. Nouvelle collection des memoires pour servir à l'histoire de France. Paris, 1836–39. 26 cm. v. 2 (1836) p. [203]–332)

I. Boucicaut, Jean Le Maingre de, maréchal de France, d. 1412.

NL 0423108 NIC MdBP

Le Livre des faits de Messire Jacques de Lalaing see Chastellan, Georges, 1405?–1475. Chronique de J. de Lalain.

Livre des faits et des conquêtes de la principauté de Moreé see Chronicle of Morea.

Le livre des femmes see under Saint-Mars, Gabrielle Anne (Cisterne de Courtiras) vicomtesse de, 1804–1872.

Livre des fiefs de Guillaume de Blaye see under Guillaume de Blaye, Bp., d. 1307.

Le livre des fiefs du marquisat de Franchimont see under Franchimont (Marquisate)

Le livre des instituteurs see under [Soleil, Joseph]

Le **livre** des jeunes braves, ou Étrennes militaires, recueil d'anecdotes remarquables, de beaux-faits d'armes, de traits généreux, etc.... Paris, Rapilly [etc.] 1823. 132 p. illus. 15 x 22cm.

273540B. 1. France—Hist., Juvenile 2. Military history—France. I. Title: Étrennes militaires. N. Y. P. L. August 22, 1944

NL 0423115 NN

Le Livre des jeunes filles; conseils aux jeunes personnes qui ont terminé leur éducation. Par une religieuse de la Nativité. 3. éd., revue avec soin. Lyon, Girard & Josserand, 1863.

xii, 380 p. 18 cm.

NL 0423116 PLatS

Le Livre des lettres.

[Marseille, R. Laffont.

v. 19 cm. irregular.

At head of title : Fusées.

AP20.L585 805 49-56066*‡

NL 0423117 DLC NN OU NNC PU

Livre des lettres (Girk T'lt'oc) see under Tallon, Maurice.

Le livre des manifestes ... see under Chais de Sourcesol, Guillaume.

BX 1763 L5 1555

Le livre des marchans fort vtile à toutes gens: pour cognoistre de quelles marchandises on se doit garder d'estre trompé. Nouuellement reueu, & augm. par son autheur. Lisez et profitez. A Geneve, Par Iean de Laon & Lucas de Mortiere, 1555.

[48] p. 11 cm.

Signatures: A-C8.

1. Catholic Church - Doctrinal and controversial works.

NL 0423120 OU

DA 460 .L79

Livre des marches faits par les armées de Sa Majesté de la Grande Brittagne depuis l'an 1689 jusques a la fin de la campagne 1695 [i.e.1697] [n.p., 17--]

2 v. 23½ x 19 cm.

In manuscript.

Armorial book-plate: Bibliotheca Lindesiana.

1.Gt.Brit.--History,Military--1689-1714.

NL 0423121 MiU

Le livre des mères. Paris, Éditions familiales de France [1947]

252 p. illus. 25 cm.

1. Woman—Biog. 2. Catholic Church—Biog.

BX4667.L5 922.2 49-16185*

NL 0423122 DLC OC1

Le livre des merveilles du monde see under Zakariya ibn Muhammad, al-Kazwini, d. 1283.

Livre des merveilles; Marco Polo, Odoric de Pordenone, Mandeville, Hayton, etc. see under Paris. Bibliotheque nationale. Departement des manuscrits.

Livre des messes. [Paris, Au bureau d'édition de la schola cantorum, n.d.] 183p. 34½cm. (Anthologie des maitres religieux primitifs des 15., 16. 17. siècles. 1.année)

Édition populaire par Charles Bordes.

NL 0423125 MWelC

Livre des mestiers.

Het Brugsche Livre des mestiers en zijn navolgingen. Vier aloude conversatieboekjes om fransch te leeren nieuwe uitgave en ingeleid door dr. Jan Gessler ... En door een consortium van Brugsche drukkers uitgevoerd, met de ondersteuning van de Universitaire stichting van België. Brugge, 1931

6 pts. in 2 v. diagr. 26 cm.

"Deze uitgave ... werd gedrukt op ... zes honderd exemplaren op "Tennyson" genummerd van 1 tot 600 ... Exemplaar no. 207."

NL 0423126 CU

Livre des mestiers.

Caxton, William, *ca.* 1422–1491.

Dialogues in French and English. By William Caxton. (Adapted from a fourteenth-century book of dialogues in French and Flemish.) Ed. from Caxton's printed text (about 1483), with introduction, notes, and word lists, by Henry Bradley ... London, Pub. for the Early English text society, by K. Paul, Trench, Trübner & co., ltd., 1900.

Livre des mestiers

Le livre des mestiers; dialogues français-flamands composés au XIVe siècle par un maitre d'école de la ville de Broges. Publié par H. Michelant. Paris, Tross, 1875

vi,[47] p.

1 Michelant, Henri, 1811-1890, ed.

NL 0423128 MH IU WU CtY MdBP

PC2827 .L58

Livre des mestiers.

Le Livre des mestiers de Bruges et ses dérivés; quatre ancien. manuels de conversation publiés par Jean Gessler ... avec le concours des maîtres imprimeurs brugeois et de la Fondation universitaire de Belgique. Bruges, 1931.

6 pt. 26cm.

Texts in parallel columns: pt. 1–2, 4, French and Flemish; pt. 3, French and English.

"Du présent ouvrage ... il a été tiré ... six cents exemplaires sur papier Tennyson numérotés 1 à 600 ... Exemplaire n° 157."

Contents.—Introduction. Inleiding.—I. Le Livre des mestiers. De bouc vanden ambachten.—II. Gesprächbüchlein, romanisch & flämisch.—III. Caxton's dialogues. Tres bonne doctrine pour aprendre briefment fransoys et engloys. Ryght good lernyng for to lerne shortly frenssh and englyssh.—IV. Vocabulair pour aprendre romain et flameng. Vocabulaer om te leerne walsch ende vlaemsch.

1. French language—Old French—Conversation and phrase books. 2. Flemish language—Conversation and phrase books. I. Gessler, Jean, ed. II. Fondation universitaire.

A C 33–1366

Princeton univ. Library for Library of Congress

DLC
NL 0423130 NjP CaBVaU OrPR NcD ICU NN MH MiU CtY

VOLUME 337

Livre des mille et une images: album des récréations. Cette intéressante et nombreuse collection de gravures offre, aux jeunes gens, un délassement utile et sans danger; aux jeunes dessinateurs, un choix étonnant et varié de modeles tout genre; aux coloristes, une suite inépuisable de sujets ... Tournai, Typographie de J. Casterman [ca. 1835]
3 v. in 1. illus. 24½ cm.

Vol.2-3 have title: Album des récréations. "Collection of nearly two thousand wood engravings by well-known English and French engravers of the period and including many cuts of much earlier date. Many of the blocks are those used in "The Penny magazine." 1832, and similar popular illustrated magazines, both French and English." cf.Birrell & Garnett, ltd. Popular woodcuts, XVIIIth & XIXth centuries. Catalogue 35.

1.Wood-engravings, English.2.Wood-engravings, French.

NL 0423132 NNC

Le Livre des morts
see Book of the dead.

Le Livre des morts des anciens Egyptiens
see under Book of the dead.

Livre des mystères du ciel et de la terre
see under Bakhaila Mīkā'ēl.

Livre, Le, des nouvelles. Anthologie. Série 1, no. 1
Paris: Édition du livre des nouvelles [1898- v. 12°.
Série 2, no. 1, lacks p. 35-36.

1. Fiction (French).—Collections.
N. Y. P. L. January 29, 1912.

NL 0423136 NN

Livre des perles enfouies et du mystère précieux au sujet des indications des cachettes, des trouvailles et des trésors
see Kitāb al-durr al-maknūz.

Le livre des petits enfants; nouvel alphabet, contenant des alphabets variés, des exercices gradués jusqu'à la lecture courante, un choix de maximes et de proverbes appropriés à l'enfance, un petit recueil de notions usuelles, des contes moraux, historiettes, fables, poésies, par Fénelon, Florian, La Fontaine ... [et autres] Illustré de 90 vignettes par mm. Gérard Séguin, Meissonnier, Grandville, Steinheil [!], Français. Paris, J. Hetzel, éditeur 1843.
4 p. l., [5]-115 p. illus. 20cm.
1. French language - Chrestomathies and readers.

NL 0423138 NNC NN

Le Livre des petits enfants. Ire partie.—Un alphabet complet —des alphabets variés des exercices gradués jusqu'à la lecture courante—un choix de maximes et de proverbes appropriés à l'enfance. IIme partie.—Un recueil de notions usuelles—trente contes moraux—historiettes—fables—poésies. Par Fénelon [et autres]... 3e éd. rev. et augm. Paris, J. Hetzel, 1853.
119p. incl. front., illus. 18½cm.

1. French language. Readers.

Printed by the Wesleyan University Library, 1936

NL 0423139 CtW

Le livre des petits enfants, ou recueil de recits, mis a la portee du premier age, avec vocabulaire. N.Y., Wiley & Putnam, 1844.
216 p.

NL 0423140 OCX

Le LIVRE des petits enfants, ou Recueil de récits mis à la portée du premier âge. Nouvelle éd., américaine. New York, George R.Lockwood, [1846].

sq. 12°.

NL 0423141 MH

Le livre des petits enfants; ou, Recueil de récits mis à la portée du premier âge, avec vocabulaire. 2. éd. americaine. New York, Wiley et Putnam, 1846.
1 p. l., ii, [3]-240 p. 16cm.

1. French language—Chrestomathies and readers.

11-18015

Library of Congress PC2115.L7

NL 0423142 DLC NcU

Le livre des petits enfants, ou, Recueil de recits mis a la portee du premier age, avec vocabulaire. New ed. N.Y., Lockwood, c1848.
240 p.

NL 0423143 PPD

Le livre des petits enfants; ou, Recueil de récits mis à la portée du premier âge, avec vocabulaire... New York: R. Lockwood & Son, 1853. 240 p. 16°.
Nouvelle édition américaine.

138900A. 1. French language—Exercises and readers.
N. Y. P. L. January 27, 1925

NL 0423144 NN ViU

Le livre des petits enfants, ou Recueil de récits mis à la portée du premier age, avec vocabulaire. Nouvelle éd. américaine. New York, R.Lockwood & son, 1857.

NL 0423145 MH CtY

Le livre des petits enfants, ou Recueil de récits mis à la portée du premier âge avec vocabulaire. Nouvelle édition américaine. New York, R.Lockwood & son, 1861.

NL 0423146 MH

1883 Le Livre des petits enfants, ou recueil de récits mis à la portée du premier âge. Avec vocabulaire. Nouv. éd. amér. New York, G.R. Lockwood [1865?]
1 p.l., 240 p. sq. 18°.
Toner collection.

NL 0423147 DLC

Le livre des petits enfants; ou, Recueil de récits mis a la portée du premier âge, avec vocabulaire. Nouvelle éd. américaine. New York, G. R. Lockwood [1871]
1 p. l., ii, [3]-240 p. 16½cm.

1. French language—Chrestomathies and readers.

33-8167

Library of Congress PC2115.L7 1871 448.6

NL 0423148 DLC ViU

Le livre des petits garçons; recueil de monologues. Paris, Librairie théâtrale, 1897.
3 p. l., [3]-204 p. 18½cm.
Cover dated 1898.

1. Monologues.

42-8723

Library of Congress PN4338.M6L5
[2]

NL 0423149 DLC

Le livre des prières communes
see under Church of England. Book of Common Prayer. French. [Supplement]

Le livre des prodiges, ou Histoires et aventures merveilleuses et remarquables de spectres, revenans, esprits, fantomes, demons, etc., rapportees par des personnes dignes de foi. Nouv. éd. Paris, Masson, 1821.
191 p. front. 17 cm.

NL 0423151 PV

Le livre des prophéties ou Recueil des prophéties les plus curieuses connues jusqu'à ce jour. Passé, présent, futur. Prophéties de Blois, du solitaire d'Orval, du P. Souffrant, etc., etc. Rennes, Lib. générale de l'Ouest, [187-?]
Cover: 3e éd.

NL 0423152 MH

Le livre des pseaumes de David
see Church of England. Book of Common Prayer. French. La liturgie angloise.

VOLUME 337

Le livre des quatre maitres
see under Annals of the four masters.

Le Livre des quenouilles
see Les évangiles des quenouilles.

Livre des quererts
see
Book of caverns.

Le livre des récompenses et des peines
see under [Lao Tzu]

Livre des rois d'Égypte
see Book of the Kings of Egypt.

Le Livre des Rois du Nouveau Testament, ou Correspondance du Lond***, avec M. Plut .. [Préliminaire, & 1e Lettre]
8 p. 8°.
And 4e suite du Livre des Rois de l'Ancien Testament, & .. 5e Lettre. 26 p. 8°.
[In vol. labeled "French Revolution Tracts, v. 12]

NL 0423159 CtY

Le livre des rondeaux galants et satyriques du XVIIe siècle
see under Bever, Adolphe van, 1871-1925, ed.

G 1964 L59 Livre des routes d'Italie a' l'usage des seigneurs qui voyagent par la poste ou' l'on trouve la description des villes, bourgs, villages, & rivières, & l'explication des vues à quelques milles de la route sur la droite & sur la gauche en vingt-trois cartes géographiques. Avec une note exacte des postes, du prix des chevaux, & de toutes les meilleures auberges tant dans les villes que sur la route avec leur juste prix & beaucoup d'autres choses nécessaires & utiles. [n.p., n.d.]
3 v. in 1. 23 fold. maps. 19cm.

An English edition, printed in Italy and having the title: A brief account of the roads of Italy... was published in London in 1775.

NL 0423162 PPT MiU

Le Livre des sauvages, au point de vue de la civilisation française
see under [Petzholdt, Julius] 1812-1891.

Livre des secrets aux philosophes
see Placides et Timeo.

Le Livre des Sept nations, 1865
see [Cuoq, Jean Andre] 1821-1898.
Tsiatak nihonon8entsiake onk8e on8e akoiatonser Les livre des Sept...

Le livre des signaux de la flotte de l'ancienne regence d'Alger
see under Devoulx, Albert, 1826-

Le livre des sonnets; dix dizains de sonnets choisis. Paris, A. Lemerre, 1874.
2 p. l., xxxv, [1] p., 1 l., 156 p., 2 l. 20½cm. [Bibliothèque illustrée]
Title in red and black; red line borders.
Not illustrated; included by Lemerre in the "Bibliothèque illustrée" because he had previously published portraits of all the authors represented in the volume, which could easily be added. *cf.* Vicaire's Manuel.
"Avertissement" signed: Alphonse Lemerre.
The "Histoire du sonnet" by Charles Asselineau (p. [iii]-xxxv) was published separately in an edition of 23 copies in 1855; a 2d edition (150 copies) appeared in 1856, and a reprint, with facsimile signatures of sonnet writers, in the "Amateur d'autographes", 1872.
1. Sonnets, French. I. Lemerre, Alphonse, 1838-1912. II. *Asselineau, Charles, 1820-1874. Histoire du sonnet.

27-11999

Library of Congress PQ1191.S7L5 1874

NL 0423167 DLC CLSU

Le livre des sonnets; quatorze dizains de sonnets choisis. Paris, A. Lemerre, 1875.
3 p. l., xxxvii p., 1 l., 208 p. 16cm. [Petite bibliothèque littéraire]
Added t.-p., engraved.
"Avertissement" signed: Alphonse Lemerre.
"Histoire du sonnet", by Charles Asselineau: p. [v]-xxxvii.

1. Sonnets, French. I. Lemerre, Alphonse, 1838-1912. II. *Asselineau, Charles, 1820-1874. Histoire du sonnet.

11-31675 Revised

Library of Congress PQ1191.S7L5 1875

NL 0423168 DLC OrPR

(Le) livre des sonnets;seize dizains de sonnets choisis. 228p. Paris,A. Le-merre,1875.

"Avertissement" signed:Alphonse Lemerre
"Histoire du sonnet",by Charles Asselineau:preface p.[7]-34.

NL 0423169 OrP

Le livre des sonnets; seize dizains de sonnets choisis Paris, A. Lemerre éditeur, 1893. xxxiv,228 p 15cm

Avertissement signed: A L.
"Histoire du sonnet," p.[v]- xxxiv signed: Charles Asselineau.
1. Sonnets, French--Collections I Lemerre Alphonse, 1838-1912, ed II Asselineau Charles, 1820-1874. Histoire du sonnet

NL 0423170 NN

Le livre des sonnets; seize dizains et sonnets choisis. Paris, Lemerre [1949]

xxxiv, 228 p. (Petite bibliothèque littéraire)
Histoire du sonnet, par Charles Asselineau: p.[vii]-xxxiv

NL 0423171 MH OCl

Le livre des sports athlétiques et des jeux de plein air
see under Claremont, Henry.

Le livre des Tetes de bois. Paris, G. Charpentier, 1883.
5 p.l., [v]-xv p., 1 l., 445 p., 1 l. illus., plates, music. 25 cm.
Illustrated title-page.
"Preface" signed: Saint-Juirs [pseud., of René Delorme]
1. French literature (Selections: Extracts, etc.) I. Delorme, René, 1848-1890.

NL 0423173 RPB NN

Le livre des trahisons de France envers la maison de Bourgogne.
Chroniques relatives à l'histoire de la Belgique sous la domination des ducs de Bourgogne ... Publiées par m. le baron Kervyn de Lettenhove ... Bruxelles, F. Hayez, impr., 1870-76.

Le Livre des vacances. Nouvelle série. Recueil de contes par Jean d'Agraives, Henriette Celarié, J. Girardin [e. a.] ... [Paris] Hachette [1931]
158, [2] p. illus. 23½cm.

1. Children's stories, French. I. Agraives, Jean d'.

33-8655

Library of Congress PZ21.L5
Copyright A—Foreign 15039
[2] 843.910822

NL 0423175 DLC MB

Livre des vassaux du comté de Champagne et de Brie 1172-1222, pub. d'après le manuscrit unique des Archives de l'empire, par Auguste Longnon. Paris, Franck, 1869.
2 p. l., iii, 151, 414, [2] p. 22½cm.
On verso of 1st prelim. leaf: En 1869 le Livre des vassaux du comté de Champagne et de Brie a obtenu de l'Académie des inscriptions et belles-lettres une des médailles décernées au concours des antiquités de la France.
"Forme le tome VII de 'l'Histoire des ducs et des comtes de Champagne' pub. par Arbois de Jubainville."—Lorenz, Catal. général.
1. Champagne—Hist.—Sources. 2. Brie—Hist.—Sources. I. Longnon, Auguste Honoré, 1844-1911, ed. II. France. Archives nationales. Mss. (P. 1114) III. Arbois de Jubainville, Henry *i. e.* Marie Henry d', 1827-1910. Histoire des ducs et des comtes de Champagne.

18-601

Library of Congress DC611.C47L7

NL 0423176 DLC PU NIC CtY

PQ 2338 .L58 Le livre des veillées. Paris, Société bibliographique, 1837.
164p. fronts. 13cm.

Contents.- L'orphelin.- Lettre sur Paris [par] Mathurin Bruno.- Michel Carroll.- L'impie de village [par] L'abbé A. Devoille.- La jactance d'un monsieur de la ville [par] d'Exauvillez.- Le pauvre [par] d'Exauvillez.- Le mari [par] d'Exauvillez.- Le mystificateur mystifié [par] d'Exauvillez.- Victor, ou la prière [par] Gorse. - L'utile lecon [par] d'Exauvillez.

NL 0423177 TNJ

Liure dore de Marc Aurele ...
see under [Guevara, Antonio de] d. 1545.

Le livre du bibliophile. Paris, G. & R. Briffaut, [192-
v. 28.5 cm.

NL 0423179 DLC MiU

VOLUME 337

Le livre du bibliophile. Paris, A. Lemerre, 1874
see under [France, Anatole] 1844-1924.

Le livre du centenaire: cent ans de vie française à la Revue des deux mondes
see under Revue des deux mondes.

QA29 P6L5 Le livre du centenaire de la naissance de Henri Poincaré, 1854-1954. Paris, Gauthier-Villars, 1955.
304 p. plates, ports., facsims.

Poincaré, Henri, 1854-1912. 2. Mathematics - Addresses, essays, lectures.

NL 0423182 CU RPB PPAmP CLSU

Le livre du centenaire du Journal des débats, 1789-1889
see under Journal des débats politiques et littéraires.

Le Livre du Chastel de Labour
see under Bruyant, Jean, 14th cent.

Le livre du collège
see under Geneva. Université.

Livre du Conseil
see
Popol vuh.

Le livre du faulcon.

Le livre du faulcon. London, From the Shakspeare press, by W. Bulmer and co., 1817.
4 p. l., [69] p., 1 l. 25½cm.
Presented to the Roxburghe club by Robert Lang. Listed as no. 14 in the "Catalogue of books presented to and printed by the Club," 1898.
The original edition, of which only one copy is known, bears no imprint, but was probably printed for Antoine Vérard, Paris, about 1500. Other editions appeared under titles: Le livre du faulcon des dames, and Faulcon damours. *cf.* Brit. mus. Catalogue, and Brunet, Manuel du libraire.
Reprint ([69] p.): gothic type; initials (title and prologue) Signatures: A-D[8], E[8]; verso of last leaf blank.
The initial capitals of the lines of an acrostic rondeau on the verso of the original title-page form the name, Isabeau Faucon.

I. Faucon, Isabeau. II. Roxburghe club, London. III. Title: Faulcon damours. IV. Lang, Robert.

Library of Congress PR1105.R7 1817 g 14-6529

NL 0423187 DLC TxU CtY MoU OU ICN

Le Livre du gradé d'artillerie à l'usage des élèves brigadiers, brigadiers et sous-officiers d'artillerie de campagne, contenant toutes les matières nécessaires à l'exercice de leurs fonctions et conforme à tous les règlements parus jusqu'à ce jour. Paris, Berger [1917] 946 p. illus., plates(1 fold., 1 col.) maps(1 double)diagrs. 19 cm.
"Édition pour 1918."

1. France-Army-Artillery.

NL 0423188 NjP

Le livre du gradé d'artillerie à l'usage des élèves brigadiers, brigadiers et sous-officiers d'artillerie de campagne, contenant toutes les matières nécessaires à l'exercice de leurs fonctions et conforme à tous les règlements parus jusqu'à ce jour. Édition pour 1918. Paris, Nancy, Berger-Levrault, 1918.
19 cm.
1. Artillery - Handbooks, manuals, etc.

NL 0423189 CtY DNW NjP

Le LIVRE du gradé d'artillerie, à l'usage des élèves brigadiers, brigadiers et sour-officiers d'artillerie de campagne. Contenant toutes les matières nécessaires à l'exercice de leurs fonctions, et conforme à tous les règlements parus jusqu'à ce jour. 15 jium 1922. Éd. pour 1922. Nancy, etc., Berget-Levrault, 1922.

Nar. 12°. Plates and other illustr.

NL 0423190 MH

Le livre du grade d'infanterie a l'usage des eleves caporaux, caporaux et sous-officiers de l'infanterie et du genie contenant toutes les matieres necessaires a l'exercice de leurs fonctions et conforme a tous les reglements parus jusqu'a ce jour. Ed. completement remaniee et mise a jour (octobre, 1913) Paris, Nancy, Berger-Levrault, 1913.
xlviii, 980 p. illus., plates. 16½cm.

NL 0423191 DNW

Soc UD 155 F8 L5 1913 Le Livre du gradé d'infanterie; a l'usage des élèves caporaux, caporaux et sous-officiers de l'infanterie et du génie. Édition complètement remaniée et mise a jour (October 1913) Paris, Berger-Levrault [1913?]
977p. illus.

Année d'instruction 1913-1914.

1. France. Armée. Infanterie - Non-commissioned officers' handbooks.

NL 0423192 FTaSU

Le livre du gradé d'infanterie à l'usage des élèves caporaux, caporaux et sous-officiers de l'infanterie et du génie; contenant toutes les matières nécessaires à l'exercice de leurs fonctions et conforme à tous les règlements parus jusqu'à ce jour. Édition complètement remaniée et mise à jour (Novembre 1914) Paris, Berger-Levrault, 1914.
942 p. S.

NL 0423193 NcD

Uxl34 F6 916l Le livre du gradé d'unfanterie à l'usage des élèves caporaux, caporaux et sous-officiers de l'infanterie et du génie, contenant toutes les matières nécessaires à l'exercice de leurs fonctions et conforme à tous les règlements parus jusqu'à ce jour. Ed. complètement remaniée et mise à jour (octobre 1916) Paris, Berger-Levrault, 1916.
xxxi, 804p. illus., maps. 19cm.
On cover: Edition 1916-1917.

NL 0423194 CtY

Le livre du gradé d'infanterie à l'usage des élèves-caporaux, caporaux et sous-officiers de l'infanterie et du génie, contenant toutes les matières nécessaires à l'exercice de leurs fonctions et conforme à tous les règlements parus jusqu'à ce jour... Paris: Berger-Levrault, 1917. xxviii, 752 p., 4 col'd maps, 1 col'd pl. illus. (incl. diagr., maps, plans, tables. rev. ed. 12°.

Colored maps printed on both sides.

1. Infantry.—Manuals, France. 2. Military art and science.—Manuals, France, 1917.
N. Y. P. L. September 6, 1917.

NL 0423195 NN NjP

Le livre du grade d'infanterie. A l'usage des eleves caporaux, caporaux et sous-officiers de l'infanterie et du genie. Content toutes les matieres necessaires a l'exercice de leurs fonctions et conforme a tous les reglements parus jusqu'a ce jour. Edition mise a jour au 15 mai 1921. Paris, Berger-Levrault, 1921.
4 p. l., 1019 p. illus. 19 cm.

NL 0423196 DNW

842L767 01 Livre du lax d'amour, contemplacion pour l'ame devote sur la passion.
28 l.

Photographic reproduction of leaves 27-81 of 15th century ms. in the Bibliothèque nationale, Paris. Ms. nouv. acq. fr.10032.

NL 0423197 IU

Le Livre du médecin, l'examen du malade et son traitement. ... . Paris, A. Poinat, [1912-].
Vol illus. 18cm.
Cover-title.

NL 0423198 ICJ DLC

Le livre du millénaire d'Avicenne
see under
Congrès d'Avicenne, Teheran, 1954.

Le livre du nouveau Tristan ...
see under Maugin, Jean, 16th cent.

Le livre du paumier, von Karl Christ... Ein Beitrag zur Kenntnis der altfranzösischen Mystik. (In: Mittelalterliche Handschriften. Leipzig, 1926. 4°. p. [57-]81.)

Caption-title.

305057A. 1. Sermons, Latin. 2. Christ, Karl, 1878- editor.
N. Y. P. L. September 8, 1927

NL 0423201 NN

Le livre du pays noir; anthologie de littérature africaine
see under Lebel, Roland, 1893-

Le livre du pêcheur
see under Fisch-Hook, psued.

VOLUME 337

Livre du préfet
see
Byzantine Empire. *Laws, statutes, etc., 886-911 (Leo VI, the Wise)*

Le livre du principe lumineux et du principe passif, Shang thsing tsing king
see under Ko-hsüan, supposed author.

Le livre du IVme centenaire des Capucins
see under Capuchins. Province suisse.

Le livre du recteur; catalogue des étudiants de l'Académie de Genève de 1559 à 1859
see under Geneva. Université.

Le livre du roi Dancus
see under Dancus rex.

Livre du roy Modus.
Kung Praktiks och drottning Teoris jaktbok
see under
Nordenfalk, Carl Adam Johan, 1907-

Livre du roy Modus.
Le livre de chasse du roy Modus; transcrit en français moderne avec une introduction et des notes par Gunnar Tilander ... Illustré de 51 figures d'après les miniatures du manuscrit français 12399 de la Bibliothèque nationale. Paris, É. Nourry, 1931.

xxviii, 204 p. illus. 28½cm. (*Half-title:* Les maîtres de la vénerie. I)

1. Hunting. 2. Falconry. I. *Tilander, Gunnar, 1894- ed.

Library of Congress SK25.L5 31-31107

NL 0423210 DLC

Livre du roy Modus.
Le livre du roy Modus. Chambéry, Antoine Neyret, 20 Oct. 1486.

[104] l., the first (blank) wanting, the last supplied in facsim. woodcuts: illus. f°. 28.4 cm.
The authorship is now generally ascribed to Henri de Ferrières. *cf.* Thiébaud, J. Bibl. des ouvrages français sur la chasse. Paris, 1934, col. 388-396.
Hain. Repertorium (with Copinger's Supplement) 11447. Morgan. Cat. of mss. and early pr. books, 620 (variations) Thiébaud (variation; *cf.* also for provenance of this copy) Goff M-739
Bound by Trautz-Bauzonnet. Book-plates of C. F. G. R. Schwerdt and H. Gallice.

1. Hunting. 2. Falconry. I. Ferrières, Henri de, fl. 1370, supposed author.

Incun. 1486.L76 Rosenwald Coll. 47-43829

NL 0423211 DLC

Livre du roy Modus.
Le livre du roy Modus et de la rayne Racio Nouvelle édition, conforme aux manuscrits de la Bibliothèque royale, ornée de gravures faites d'après les vignettes de ces manuscrits fidèlement reproduito avec une préface par Elzéar Blaze, ... Paris, 1839.
26.5 cm.
Attributed to Henri de Ferrières.

NL 0423212 CtY MH NN OkU

Livre du roy Modus.
Les livres du roy Modus et de la royne Ratio, publiés avec introduction, notes et glossaire par Gunnar Tilander ... Paris, Société des anciens textes français, 1932.

2 v. 14 pl. (facsims.) 23½cm. (*Half-title:* Société des anciens textes français)

Text of manuscript. Paris, Bibl. nat., fr. 12399, supplemented by Bibl. nat., fr. 1299.
The facsimiles (of miniatures) are printed on both sides.
The "rosace" in which the author concealed his name, has been variously interpreted; the solution of Chassant, generally accepted, ascribed the work to Henri de Fer(r)ières. *cf.* Introd., p. 1-lvi.

CONTENTS.—t. I. Introduction. Le livre des deduis du roy Modus.—t. II. Le songe de pestilence. Glossaire. Tables des noms propres.

1. Hunting. 2. Falconry. 3. France—Soc. life & cust. 4. Illumination of books and manuscripts—Specimens, reproductions, etc. I. Ferrières, Henri de, fl. 1370, supposed author. II. Tilander, Gunnar, 1894- ed. III. Société des anciens textes français. IV. Paris. Bibliothèque nationale. Mss. (Fr. 12399) V. Title: Livre des deduis. VI. Title: Songe de pestilence.

Library of Congress PQ1489.L6 1932 34-2670
[5] [799.2] 848.1

MiU ViU PU NcU WaU PBm CU FU ScU
NL 0423214 DLC CaBVaU ICU NBuU GU PPT PHC MB OO

Hfa35
43w

Livre du roy Modus.
Le roy Modvs des dedvitz de la chace, venerie et favconnerie. Avec privilege. A Paris Par Guillaume le Noir, rue Sainct Iaques, à la Rose Blanche Couronnee. 1560.
8p.ℓ., 104numb.ℓ. illus. 15½cm.
Signatures: [ornament]⁸ ^{8}A-N^{8}.
Attributed to Henri de Ferrières.

NL 0423215 CtY MH

Le livre du second age, ou, instructions amusantes sur l'histoire naturelle des animaux
see under [Pujoulx, Jean Baptiste] 1762-1821.

Livre du très chevalereux comte d'Artois et de sa femme.
Les aventures romanesques d'un comte d'Artois, d'après un ancien manuscrit, orné de dessins, de la Bibliothèque nationale, par Alice Hurtrel. Paris, G. Hurtrel, 1883.

viii, 232 p. illus. (part col.) 16 cm.

"Tirée d'un ancien manuscrit de la Bibliothèque nationale, fonds français no 11610, et intitulé: Le livre du comte d'Artois ... Quant au texte, nous avons dû le modifier et le rapprocher du français moderne."

1. Hurtrel, Alice. II. Title.

PQ1571.L6 1883 25-21925 rev

NL 0423217 DLC PV

Livre du tres chevalereux comte d'Artois et de sa femme.
Le livre du très chevalereux comte d'Artois et de sa femme, fille au comte de Boulogne; pub. d'après les manuscrits et pour la première fois. Paris, Techener, 1837.

xxviii, 207 p. 28 pl. 4°.

Introduction by J. Barrois.
Plates are reproduced from the ms. miniatures.

Library of Congress 1-F-3609

NL 0423218 DLC TNJ ICN MdBP OCl MB

Le Livre du vaillant des habitants de Lyon en 1388; **estimation des biens meubles et immeubles par servir à l'assiette de la taille, publié par Édouard Philipon** ... avec une introduction de Charles Perrat ... Lyon, Impressions de M. Audin et cie., 1927.

3 p. l., xvi, 224 p., 1 l. fold. plan. 23 x 17½cm.

"Ce livre publié sous les auspices de la Commission municipale du vieux Lyon a été tiré à 250 ex. sur vélin teinté et 50 sur Montgolfier."

1. Taxation — Lyons — Lists. 2. France — Hist. — Charles VI, 1380-1422—Sources. 3. Lyons—Hist.—Sources. I. Philipon, Édouard Paul Lucien, 1851- II. Perrat, Charles.

Library of Congress HJ9470.L82L5 29-19933

NL 0423219 DLC UU

Livre du vingt-cinquieme anniversaire de l'École française de droit de Beyrouth
see Beirut. Université Saint-Joseph. Faculté de droit et des sciences économiques. Melanges à la memoire de Paul Huvelin.

Le livre égyptien ./. Que mon nom fleurisse, publié et traduit par J. Lieblein... Leipzig: I. C. Hinrichs, 1895. 47, lxxiii p. facsim. 8°.

Includes also the texts and translations of papyri from the British Museum, Turin, Gizeh, Lepsius' Denkmäler and the Musée du Louvre.

J. S. BILLINGS MEM. COLL.

1. Egyptian literature, Religious. 2. Lieblein, Jens Daniel Carolus, 1827-1911, translator.
N. Y. P. L. April 12, 1927

NL 0423221 NN

Bonaparte
Collection No.1613

LIVRE en quatre langues... The book of four languages. St.Petersbourg, F.Meyer, 1796.
355p. 20½cm.

Added t.-p. in Russian and German.
Text in Russian, German, French and English, in parallel columns across two pages.

NL 0423222 ICN

Le Livre en Suisse
see **Das Schweizer buch.**

Le livre en Suisse: bulletin bibliographique de la Bibliotheque nationale suisse
see Das Schweizer buch.

Livre et document; études sur le livre, les bibliothèques et la documentation, pub. sous la direction de Georgette de Grolier. Saint-Cloud, Revue du livre et des bibliothèques, 1948.

94 p. illus., maps (part col.) 24 cm.

1. Bibliography. 2. Library science. I. Grolier, Georgette de, ed.

A 49-2964*

Yale Univ. Library
for Library of Congress [1]

NL 0423225 CtY PU ICU

Le Livre et l'estampe.
Année 1, no. 1-9 (jan. - nov., 1923)
Paris: Albert Morancé, 1923. v. illus. 12°.

Monthly.
Editor: Pierre Gusman.
No more published.

1. Prints.—Per. and soc. publ. 2. Gusman, Pierre, 1862- editor.
N. Y. P. L. July 30, 1924

NL 0423226 NN

VOLUME 337

Le Livre et l'estampe. no 1- ; déc, 1954.
Bruxelles.

no. in v. illus., ports., facsims. 22 cm. quarterly.
"Revue de la Société des bibliophiles et iconophiles de Belgique."

1. Bibliomania—Period. 2. Engravings—Period. I. Société des bibliophiles et iconophiles de Belgique.

Z990.L5 57-25076

NL 0423227 DLC TxU NN

Le Livre & l'image; revue documentaire illustrée, mensuelle. Directeur littéraire: J. Grand-Carteret. Directeur-gérant: Émile Rondeau. t. 1[-3]; mars 1893[-juin 1894] ... Paris, É. Rondeau, 1893-[94]
3 v. illus., plates (part col.) ports., facsims. 25cm.
Title in red and black. Initials, head and tail pieces, vignettes, colored plates, engraved portraits, facsimiles of bindings, etc.
"Curiosités littéraires, études singulières, lettres inédites, dissertations bibliographiques, comptes rendus de livres nouveaux d'événements bibliophiliques, d'enchères à sensation ..."
May be regarded as a continuation of the series of three periodicals edited by Octave Uzanne and published under his direction, being similar in style, scope, and tendency: Le Livre, 1880-89; Le Livre moderne, janv. 1890-déc. 1891; L'Art et l'idée, 1892.
1. Bibliography—Period. 2. Books. 3. Book collecting—Period. 4. Art. I. Grand-Carteret, John, 1850-1927.

Library of Congress Z1007.L8 2—13670

NL 0423228 DLC ICN MiU TU NcU MH MoU OCl MB ICJ

Le livre et ses amis; revue mensuelle de l'art du livre. 1.- année (no. 1-); nov. 1945-
Paris.

v. illus., facsims. 29 cm.
Director: Nov. 1945- Paul Massonnet.

1. Bibliography—Period. I. Massonnet, Paul, ed.

Z1007.L82 010.5 48-13276*

CLU NN ICU MU MiU CLSU
NL 0423229 DLC TU OU ICN IEN ICRL NjR GU IU IEN

Le liure et traicte de toute vraye noblesse
see under [Clichtove, Josse van] d. 1543.

Le Livre fait par force, ou le Mystificateur mystifié et corrigé. Par un Persiffleur Persifflé. C'est a-peu-près ainsi que se sont tant de livres! [Ornament] A Mystificatopolis, chez Momus, a la Marotte. [Berlin?] MMMM.DCC.LXXXIV.
xvi, 286 p. front. 20cm.

Edited by A. R. C. D. L.
Bound in blue paper, margins untrimmed.
Brit. Mus. gen. cat. v.127, col. 790.

1. Authors, French. I. L., A. R. C. D. II. Persiffleur Persifflé.

NL 0423232 FU ICN

Le Livre français. 1.- année; avril 1905-
Paris.

v. in 23 cm.

Monthly (except Aug.-Sept.) 1905-09; monthly, 1910-
Title varies: Apr.-July 1905, Bulletin bibliographique de l'Action sociale de la femme.—Oct.-Nov. 1905, Bibliographie de l'Action sociale de la femme.—Dec. 1905-Dec. 1908, Bibliographie du bon livre français.—Jan. 1909- Bibliographie du livre français.
Issues for Apr. 1905-Aug. 1914, Jan. 1919- also in, and issues for Sept. 1914-Dec. 1918 only in, Action sociale de la femme et le livre français.
Supplements accompany some numbers.

1. French literature—Bibl.—Period.

Z2165.L75 9-25308 rev*

NL 0423233 DLC CaBViP RP MB MnU

---

*ZAN-1074
Film Reproduction.
Le LIVRE français; bulletin de bibliographie critique. Année 43-date (no. [1]-date): nov./dec. 1945-date
Paris. v. 22cm.
Film reproduction. Negative.
CURRENT IN PERIODICALS DIVISION
Quarterly (irregular).
Founded 1902 as a bibliographical section included in Action sociale de la femme. Revue mensuele (later its Bulletin mensuel; see that entry) in which it continued through Sept./Nov. 1939. With Apr. 1905 (v. 1, no. 1)

also began independent publication under title: Action sociale de la femme. Bulletin bibliographique. Slight variations in title until v. 9, no. 4, Apr. 1913, when it became Le livre français (cf. Union list of serials). The independent file previous to Nov./Dec. 1945 is not in the library.
Suspended independent publication during World war I; suspended all publication during World war II in which period a total of 15 no., published 3 or 4 times a year, was issued clandestinely for distribution in Paris (not in the library). Revived solely as an independent publication with v. 43, no. 1, Nov./Dec. 1945. -cf. v. 43, no. 1.
Published by Les Amis du livre français.
1. Bibliography, French-- Per. and soc. publ. Amis du livre français.

NL 0423235 NN

Z
88
515
LIVRES français choisis à l'intention des bibliothèques étrangères et des bibliothèques françaises à l'étranger. [Paris, Didot, 1937]
144p.

NL 0423236 ICN

Wing
ZB
2739
.5159
Le LIVRE français des origines à la fin du second empire. Exposition au Pavillon de Marsan 4 au avril 1923. Paris, A. Morancé [1923]
ix, 115p. illus. (1 col.) 19cm.

At head of title: Congrès des bibliothécaires et bibliophiles.
"Comité de l'exposition: Paul Durrieu, Charles Mortet, Amédée Boinet, Frantz Callot; Henry Martin, president du Congrès International des bibliothecaires et des bibliophiles."

NL 0423237 ICN CtY-M

Le livre français des origines à la fin du second empire par Henry Martin, André Blum, Ch. Mortet, mlle J. Duportal, Louis Réau, Frantz Calot, Amédée Boinet et le comte Durrieu. Exposition du Pavillon de Marsan avril 1923. Paris et Bruxelles, G. van Oest et cie, 1924.
ix, 184 p., 1 l. CIV pl. (4 col.) 29½ x 23cm.
Introduction signed: Henry Martin, président du Congrès international des bibliothécaires & des bibliophiles ...
CONTENTS.—Introduction, par H. Martin.—Les manuscrits à peintures, par H. Martin.—Le livre à gravures: du XVe siècle, par A. Blum; du XVIe siècle, par Ch. Mortet; du XVIIe siècle, par mlle J. Duportal; du XVIIIe siècle, par L. Réau.—Le livre illustré du XIXe siècle, par Fr. Calot.—La reliure, par A. Boinet.—Les amateurs de livres en France depuis le moyen âge jusqu'à la fin du second empire, par le comte P. Durrieu.

1. Illumination of books and manuscripts—France. 2. Illustration of books—France—Hist. 3. Engraving—France—Hist. 4. Bookbinding—France. 5. Book collectors—France. I. Martin, Henry Marie Radegonde, 1852-1927. II. Blum, André, 1881- III. *Mortet, Charles, 1852-1927. IV. Duportal, Jeanne, 1866- V. Réau, Louis, 1881- VI. Calot, Frantz. VII. Boinet, Amédée, 1881- VIII. *Durrieu, Paul, comte, 1855-1925. IX. Congrès des bibliothécaires & des bibliophiles. Paris, 1923.

Library of Congress Z1023.L79 25—823

NNGr WU MB CtY WU ICN MH NjP
NL 0423239 DLC MoSW FTaSU WaSp IaU CLU OOxM NcU

[Livre français en Alsace et Lorraine, *Strasbourg*]
Un siècle de livres français sur l'Alsace, 1830-1930 ... volumes et brochures—manuscrits et documents ... Catalogue. [Strasbourg, Imprimerie des Dernières nouvelles de Strasbourg, 1937]
116 p., 1 l. 19½cm.
On cover: ... Exposition organisée du 15 juin au 1er juillet 1937 par l'œuvre du "Livre français en Alsace et Lorraine" à la Maison de la jeune Alsace ... Strasbourg.

1. Alsace—Bibl. I. Title.

Library of Congress Z2244.A46L7 39-30139
015.44383

NL 0423240 DLC

Livre généalogique de la race française de chevaux de selle bretons; publié avec la documentation de l'administration des haras: chevaux de selle de Corlay. [St-Brieuc, Les Presses bretonnes] 1943.
130 p. illus. 23 cm.

1. Breton horse. 2. Horses—France—Corlay (Côtes-du-Nord) I. Title: Chevaux de selle de Corlay.

SF293.B7L5 70-245078

NL 0423241 DLC

Livre généalogique des Colomb. Lille, Société de Saint-Augustin, Desclée, De Brouwer et cie, 1891.
91 p., 1 l. coats of arms. 31 x 24cm.
Large-paper copy.
Title in red and black, within ornamental borders.
"Ma vie politique. Par Pierre-François de Colomb": p. [81]-91.

1. Colombo, Cristoforo. 2. Colomb family. I. Société de Saint-Augustin. II. Colomb, Pierre François.

A 25-569

Harvard univ. Library
for Library of Congress [a37b1-]

NL 0423242 MH MiU-C

Livre généalogique indiquant la parenté qui existe entre les membres vivants d'une même famille. Livre 1. Roubaix-Tourcoing.
Roubaix, V. Hache.
v. 22 cm.
Cover title, : Généalogies des familles de Roubaix-Tourcoing et environs.

1. France—Geneal.

CS598.L49 56-17951

NL 0423243 DLC

Livre généalogique indiquant la parenté qui existe entre les membres vivants d'une même famille. Livre III. Cambrai, Douai, Valenciennes, Arras et la Flandre.
[Roubaix] V. Hache.
v. 22 cm.
Cover title, : Généalogies des familles de Cambrai, Douai, Valenciennes, Arras et la Flandre.

1. France—Geneal.

CS598.L5 56-17359

NL 0423244 DLC NN

4A
4705
. LIVRE général des postes et relais...sur le continent européen... Bruxelles, Berthot, 1825.
312p. 19cm.

NL 0423245 ICN

Le livre illustré des patiences
see under Blancoeur, Comtesse de, pseud.

Le liure intitule le Jouuencel
see under [Bueil, Jean de, comte de Sancerre] 1406-1477.

Le livre jaune sur la crise syrienne et libanaise
see under Correspondance d'Orient.

VOLUME 337

Le livre joyeux.
Paris, c192-

PN6185
.L5

NL 0423249 DLC

Livre jubilaire, édité par le Groupement belge d'etudes oto-neuro-ophtalmologiques et neuro-chirurgicales à l'occasion du XXVme anniversaire de sa fondation, 1925-1950
see under Groupement belge d'études oto-neuro-ophtalmologiques et neuro-chirurgicales.

WP 100 qL788 1952
LIVRE jubilaire; mémoires originaux dédiés au professeur Amédée Laffont.
Paris, Encyclopédie médico-chirurgicale, 1952.
328 p. illus., port.
1. Gynecology - Collected works
2. Laffont, Amédée, 1883-
3. Obstetrics - Collected works

NL 0423251 DNLM

WP 100 qL786 1949
LIVRE jubilaire; mémoires originaux dédiés au professeur Gaston Cotte. Lyon, Audin, 1949.
548 p. illus., port.
1. Cotte, Gaston, 1879- 2. Gynecology - Collected works

NL 0423252 DNLM

Livre jubilaire Albert Lemaire, publié par la Revue belge des sciences médicales. Collaborateurs: F. Arloing, E. Aubertin, F. Bezançon [et autres] ... Louvain, Secrétariat de la Revue belge des sciences médicales, 1931.
xxii, 607, [1] p. front. (port.) illus., plates (2 col.) diagrs. (1 fold.) 25½cm.
Includes bibliographies.
CONTENTS.—Maldague, L. Discours prononcé à la manifestation A. Lemaire.—Mauriac, Pierre. Que les explications simplistes ne peuvent convenir aux problèmes biologiques.—Arloing, Fernand. Sur le virus tuberculeux filtrable.—Aubertin, E. Étude sur la virulence du virus filtrant tuberculeux transmis par passages successifs de ganglions à ganglions chez le cobaye.—Bezançon, Fernand. L'éosinophilie sputaire dans l'asthme.—Étienne, Georges et Verain, M. Nos recherches sur le pH du sang. Sa technique et quelques applications cliniques.—Fiessinger, Noël. Le syndrome d'intoxication cérébro-méningée au cours des cirrhoses.—Labbé, Marcel. Les diabètes insulino-résistants.—Langeron, L. Sur quelques faits cliniques et thérapeutiques intéressant la pathologie vasomotrice et sur leur interprétation générale.—Lian, Camille. De l'angine de poitrine compliquant les névralgies thoraco-brachiales gauches.—Merklen, P. Esquisse de l'évolution de la question du chlore néphritique.—Mouriquand, Georges. Clinique expérimentale: Fixateurs, antifixateurs et défixateurs du calcium.—Vallery-Radot, Pasteur, Dérot, M. et Gauthier-Villars, P. Reproduction expérimentale des néphrites aiguës et chroniques par l'injection de sels de bismuth.—Sabrazès, J. et Bonnel, F. Quelques particularités nouvelles de la myélo-leucémie aiguë à propos de l'agranulocytose.—Sergent, Émile. Les enseignements apportés à l'étude de la dilatation des bronches par la méthode d'opacification par le lipiodol.—Nanta, A. Aspergilloses spléniques et inoculation intrasplénique.—Hymans van den Bergh, A. A. (avec ... dr. Rehorst) A propos des hématies elliptiques (l'ovalocytose).—Danielopolu, D. Le traitement chirurgical de l'angine de poitrine par la méthode de la suppression du réflex presseur. Bases physiologiques et cliniques de cette méthode.—Naegeli, O. Wesen und begriffsfassung der perniziösen anaemie.—Roch, M. La douleur provoquée par une affection viscérale peut-elle être la conséquence d'une modification humorale des téguments voisins?—Béco, Lucien de. Ouabaïne. Digitaline. (Pharmacodynamie et clinique)—Bessemans, A. et Lambin, P. Les modifications de la formule leucocytaire du lapin au cours de son infection par "*Treponema pallidum*" ou "*Treponema cuniculi*".—Dulière, W.-L. La fonction physiologique de la créatine dans le muscle strié.—Dupont, Adolphe. Aspects atypiques des tumeurs glomiques.—Firket, Jean. Tuberculose miliaire traumatique; étude pathogénique et médico-légale.—Govaerts, P. et Gratia, A. Contribution à l'étude de l'hémophilie.—Haibe, A. L'asthme bronchique et son traitement.—Nolf, P. Le mécanisme de la chute de la pression artérielle générale dans le choc peptonique.—Rodhain, J. et Dubois, A. Observations de cas de parasitisme par *Onchocerca volvulus* chez l'Européen. Réactions cutanées. Allergie dans la filariose volvulus et la filariose loa.—Rome, Marie. Contribution à l'étude des sympathomes embryonnaires.—Roskam, Jacques. Le dépistage des saigneurs latents et des petits saigneurs.—Thérasse, G. et Willaert, L. Notes sur la vitesse de sédimentation des globules rouges au cours de la tuberculose pulmonaire.—Verhoogen, René. Sur le diagnostic et le traitement de la fièvre typhoïde.—Vernieuwe, J. Troubles pathologiques de l'oreille en rapport avec des lésions dentaires.—Appelmans, R. et Picard, E. Le cancer de l'intestin grêle.—Arcq, J. A propos de la fixation du galactose.—Bruynoghe, R., Tan, J. et Cavires, K. La parenté des oiseaux

Continued in next column

Continued from preceding column

d'après les essais sérologiques.—Ide, M. Signification du bios.—Maisin, J. [et autres] Le traitement des hyperthyroïdies par la rœntgenthérapie et la Curiethérapie.—Morelle, Jean. Mutations calciques dans la guérison du rachitisme expérimental.—Schillings, M. Les angiomes de la vessie.—Simonart, André. Contribution à l'étude de l'hydrolyse de l'acétyl-choline par voie fermentaire.—Wildenberg, L. van den, et Dupont, A. A propos des glandes thyroïdes aberrantes latérales.—Gehuchten, Paul van. Tumeur frontale gauche avec aphasie amnésique; contribution à l'étude de l'aphasie motrice.—Yernaux, N. La cure bismuthée, ses possibilités, ses modalités, ses représentations graphiques.—Lambin, P. et Gerard, M.-J. Les modifications du nombre des réticulocytes au cours des anémies aplastiques.—Morelle, Léon. Les réactions érythroblastiques causées par les sulfures colloïdaux.—Wuyts, A. Sur l'origine de la métaplasie myéloïde dans l'intoxication par la saponine.
1. Lemaire, Albert, 1875-1933. 2. Medicine—Addresses, essays, lectures. 3. Chest—Diseases. I. Arloing, Fernand, 1876- II. Revue belge des sciences médicales. 39-2138
Library of Congress R111.L57
[3] 610.4

NL 0423257 DLC CtY PPC

550.4 J15
Livre jubilaire Charles Jacob. [Paris, 1949.
410 p. illus., maps(part fold.) profiles (part fold.) port. 25cm. (Annales Hébert et Haug, t.7)
"A l'occasion de sa quarantième année d'enseignement et de son passage à la double présidence de l'Académie des sciences et de l'Institut de France."
Includes bibliographies.

1. Geology - Addresses, essays, lectures. 2. Jacobs, Charles. 3. Festschriften.

NL 0423258 CSt

Livre jubilaire de m. Eugène-Louis Bouvier, membre de l'Institut, professeur honoraire au Muséum. Paris, Firmin-Didot et cie, 1936.
379 p., 1 l. incl. front. (port.) illus., XVI plates (2 col.) diagrs. 28½cm.
French and English.
Contains bibliographies.
CONTENTS.—Portrait de m. E.-L. Bouvier.—Liste des souscripteurs.—Cétacés: Neuville, Henri. Le pancréas des cétacés et les théories insulaires.—Mollusques: Fischer-Piette, E. Sur la distribution de *Patella intermedia* et sur les répartitions dites capricieuses.—Lamy, Ed. Quelques mots sur le rôle joué par les arthropodes dans la dissémination des mollusques.—Péripates: Gravier, Ch. et Fage, L. La collection des onychopores (péripates) du Muséum national d'histoire naturelle de Paris.—Crustacés: Beauchamp, P. de. Sur la faune des sources du plateau de Langres.—Guiart, Jules. Les crustacés parasites de *Mola mola*.—Legendre, R. Les stades larvaires et post-larvaires de *Palinurus vulgaris* et de *Scyllarus arctus*, au large du golfe de Gascogne.—Mathias, Paul. L'accouplement chez *Chirocephalus diaphanus*, crustacé phyllopode.—Pérez, Charles. Bourgeons de régénération des appendices thoraciques chez les *Æglea*.—Quidor, A. Sur *Leposphilus labrei* et *Mesoglicola delagei*.—Arachnides: André, Marc. Victor Hugo acarologiste.—Denis, Jacques. Quelques observations sur la biologie d'*Antistea elegans*.—Fage, Louis. Une araignée termitophile. *Andromma bouvieri*, n. sp.—Vachon, Max. Les stades du développement chez les pseudoscorpions.—Rabaud, Étienne. Notes sur le comportement maternel de *Pisaura mirabilis*.—Sergent, Edm. Habitat des tiques pendant leur vie libre.—Insectes: Badonnel, A. Sur les gonapophyses des femelles du genre *Ectopsocus*.—Barbey, A. L'insecte, élément de dislocation de la forêt européenne.—Bayard, A. Caractères spécifiques de l'armure génitale des *Aricia* du groupe *Medon*.—Berland, Lucien. Deux observations sur l'orientation chez les hyménoptères.—Bernard, Francis. Changements de taille au cours de la croissance larvaire chez *Notonecta maculata*.—Bertrand, Henri. Note sur une larve inédite de *Dryopini* de la collection Grouvelle.—Biedermann, R. Sur trois formes d'*Agrias pericles*.—Bodenheimer, F. S. Les grillons en Orient.—Bohn, Georges. Intervention du facteur masse d'animaux dans les tropismes.—Boursin, Ch. Contributions à l'étude des *Noctuidæ trifinæ*. La *Scotogramma stigmosa* se trouve-t-elle en France?—Bugnion, E. Les organes buccaux du *Pheropsophus bimaculatus*, carabique cingalais de la tribu des *Aptini*.—Cappe de Baillon, P. L'œuf des insectes. Technique microscopique.—Chopard, L. Un remarquable genre d'orthoptères de l'ambre de la Baltique.—Colas, G. et Reymond, A. Note sur la forêt d'Iraty et sur l'extension d'espèces espagnoles sur le versant français des Pyrénées.—Costa-Lima, A. da. Sur un nouveau chryside (*Duckeia cyanea*), parasite des œufs de phasmide.—Cotte, J. *Deilephila livornica* (lépid.) et la loi de Riley.—Cros, Auguste. Le *Julodis onopordi* var. *algirica*.—Cuénot, L. Sur le mode de fixation de l'œuf de *Paniscus*, ichneumonide ectoparasite d'une chenille.—Demaison, Louis. *Rhyparioides metelkana* en France.—Didier, Robert. Description d'un *Cladognathus* nouveau.—Ferrière, Ch. Note sur un nouvel eupelmide de Madagascar.—Fleutiaux, E. Mes souvenirs d'entomologiste.—Galliard, Henri. La ponte de *Triatoma protracta*.—Houard, C. Vue d'ensemble sur la collection cécidologique du Muséum national d'histoire naturelle de Paris.—Jeannel, R. Sur le *Feronia spinicollis* de Dejean.—Laboissière, V. Coup d'œil sur les *Galerucinæ* aptères.—Lameere, Auguste. Évolution des orthoptères.—Lathy, Percy J. *Thecla* nouveaux d'Amérique du Sud.—Le Cerf, F. Sur la nymphe des *Eriocraniidæ*.—Lesne, P. Nouvelles données sur les coléoptères de la famille des *Sphæriidæ*.—Lhoste, Jean. L'organe copulateur mâle dans la famille des *Scydmænidæ*.—Magnan, A. La cinématographie ultra-rapide pour l'étude du vol des oiseaux et des insectes.—Orchymont, A. d'. *Anacæna lævis*, espèce nouvelle du nord de l'Inde.—Paillot, A. Problèmes posés par l'étude de l'entomologie appliquée.—Pictet, Arnold. Quelques problèmes de faunistique résolus par la zoogéographie expérimentale.—Piéron, H. Sens du temps et horloge chimique de l'abeille à l'homme.—Poisson, Raymond. Sur une nouvelle espèce africaine du genre *Laccocoris*.—Praviel, G. Observations sur la *Lithina scutularia* et description d'une nouvelle sous-espèce.—Richet, Charles. Un instinct des chenilles processionnaires.—Rymer Roberts, A. W. Observations on the spiracles of curculionid larvæ in the first instar.—Roubaud, E. Le besoin de vol dans le comportement sexuel chez les insectes ptérygotes.—Rousseau-Decelle, G. Des variations parallèles chez les morphos des espèces *hecuba* et *perseus*.—Rungs, Ch. Un bu-

Continued in next column

Continued from preceding column

preste nouveau du Maroc.—Séguy, E. Un nouveau conopide marocain et synopsis générique des conopides de la région holarctique.—Semichon, Louis. Observations sur les larves de *Colletes daviesanus*.—Seurat, L. G. Mode respiratoire et appareil trachéen de la larve du *Trichocladius seurati*.—Seyrig, André. Un mutillide parasite d'un lépidoptère: *Stenomutilla Freyi*.—Sollaud, E. Sur quelques formes endémiques de la faune cavernicole du Jura.—Stempffer, H. Note sur la systématique de *Lycæna eleusis*.—Strohl, Jean. L'embryogénie physiologique et l'organisation des insectes, suivi de propos sur la métamorphose.—Teissier, Georges. La loi de Dyar et la croissance des arthropodes.—Théry, André. *Pachyschelus* du Tonkin.—Vayssière, Paul. Remarques sur la morphologie et la biogéographie des *Stictococcinæ*.—Venet, H. De l'atrophie des élytres chez les *Carabus*.—Verrier, Marie-Louise. Observations préliminaires sur les cécidies des régions montagneuses.—Vincent, J. La variation homogéne des *Catocala*.—Willemse, C. Description of some new *Acrididæ* from Celebes.—Wittmer, W. Un nouveau *Cephaloncus* tripolitain.

1. Arachnida. 2. Bouvier, Eugène Louis, 1856- 3. Cetacea. 4. Crustacea. 5. Insects. [5. Entomology] 6. Mollusks. [6. Mollusca] 7. Peripatus.
Agr 36-901
Library, U. S. Dept. of Agriculture 411B663
[QL3.L]

NL 0423266 DNAL NIC PPAN NNC

Livre jubiliare dédié à Charles van Bambeke, professeur à l'Université de Gand, à l'occasion du 70e anniversaire de sa naissance, par ses élèves et anciens élèves, 6 février 1899. Bruxelles, H. Lamertin, 1899.
x, [2], 335 p. front. (port.) illus., plates (part double) 28cm.
"Liste des travaux publiés par M. le prof. Ch. van Bambeke": p. vii-x.
Includes bibliographies.
Contents.—Verschaffelt, E. Galton's "Regression to mediocrity" bij ongeslachtelijke voortplanting.—Sabbe, H. Sur l'ectrodactylie symétrique.—Broeckaert, J. Sur l'étiologie de certaines anomalies congénitales du voile du palais.—Waele, H. de. Recherches sur le rôle des globules blancs dans l'ab sorption chez les vertébrés.—Duyse, D. van. Contribution à l'étude du crypt ophtalmos.—Verstraeten, C. Note sur la résistance de la paroi gastro-intesti nale chez le chien.—Vandevelde, A. J. J. Over het opnemen van water en het afscheiden van oplosbare stoffen door de zaden van *Pisum sativum*.—Fredericq, L. Sur un sel de cuisine provenant du Congo.—Leboucq, H. Recherches sur la morphologie de l'aile du murin (*Vespertilio murinus*)—Nuel, J. P. De certaines malformations (congénitales) du cristallin.—Willem, V., & Minne, A. Recherches sur la digestion et l'absorption intestinale chez le lombric.—Stricht, O. van der. Étude de plusieurs anomalies intéressantes lors de la formation des globules polaires.—*Same*. Étude de la sphere attractive ovulaire à l'état pathologique.—Buck, D. de, & Moor, L. de. Considérations sur le sang leucémique.—Fredericq, L. Note sur le sang de l'écrevisse.—Bruyne, C. de. Contribution à l'étude physiologique de l'amitose.—MacLeod, J. Over de correlatie tusschen het aantal meeldraden en het aantal stampers bij het speenkruid (*Ficaria ranunduloides*)

NL 0423269 ICJ DNLM CU

L616.054-N41 v.14-15.
95267 ... Livre jubilaire dédié à M. A. van Gehuchten, professeur à l'Université de Louvain à l'occasion du 25me anniversaire de son professorat. ... . Louvain, A. Uystpruyst, [etc., etc.], 1913.
641, [2] p. front. (port.), illus. 26½cm. (*In* Le Névraxe, volumes XIV-XV.)

NL 0423270 ICJ DNLM

Livre jubilaire du professeur Henri Roger
Actualités de neuro-psychiatrie
see under title

Livre jubilaire en l'honneur du professeur Georges Dubreuil. Strasbourg, Librairie "Alsatia", 1952.
484 p. illus., port. 25cm. (Archives d'anatomie, d'histologie et d'embryologie, t. 34, année 1951/52)

Includes bibliographies.

I. Dubreuil, Georges

NL 0423272 NNC NNC-M

VOLUME 337

618.9 Livre jubilaire du professeur Paul Rohmer
R738l Actualités de médecine infantile. Paris, G. Doin, 1948.
346p. illus., diagrs. 25cm.

Includes bibliographies.

1. Pediatrics. Rohmer, Paul.

NL 0423273 IU-M

Serial
A Livre jubilaire en l'honneur du professeur Louis Bounoure. Strasbourg, Librairie "Alsatia", 1954.
cover-title, xiv, 198 p. illus., port. (Archives d'anatomie, d'histologie et d'embryologie, t. 37, 1954, 2. ptie., fasc. 4/8)

I. Bounoure, Louis, 1885- II. Title.

NL 0423274 NNC-M

Livre jubilaire offert à G.-H. Roger ... par ses collègues, ses élèves et ses amis. Paris, Masson et c^ie, 1932.
1 p. l., 242 p., 1 l. front. (port.) illus., diagrs. 28½^cm.

CONTENTS.—Achard, C. Introduction.—Arnaudet, A. et Marquis, Mlle. Sur la toxicité de l'urée.—Aubertin, C. L'insuffisance de la moelle osseuse.—Bachrach, Eudoxie. La biologie des diatomées et les problèmes qu'elle pose.—Bénard, H. Échanges gazeux au niveau du tissu cellulaire sous-cutané.—Biancani, E. et H. Hydrophilie colloïdale. Imbibition cellulaire et agents physiques.—Binet, L. La réanimation du centre respiratoire.—Blum, P. La cyanose intermittente.—Bory, L. Considération et recherches sur le rôle physiologique de la mélanine.—Brocq, P. Le syndrome humoral de la pancréatite hémorragique.—Cardot, H. Les organes contractiles rythmiques des mollusques dans l'expérimentation.—Chabanier, H. Jeûne et hyperglycémie provoquée.—Chevallier, P. Le phagédénisme.—Chiray, M. La mésure de la lipase pancréatique dans le sérum sanguin humain.—Clerc, A. Sur certaines modifications cliniques présentées par le sens de l'onde électrique auriculaire.—Comte, A. Quelques réflexions à propos d'un cas de congestion cérébrale active.—Demanche, R. La floculation des sérums syphilitiques.—Fabre, R. L'action du foie sur les poisons.—Garrelon, L. et Thuillant, R. Le traitement par l'atropine des syncopes cardiaques secondaires chloroformiques.—Garnier, M. et Marek, J. Les différentes actions pathogènes exercées par le nitrate d'urane.—Girard, R. Quelques recherches sur les variations du rapport $\frac{\text{globuline}}{\text{sérine}}$ du sérum sanguin au cours de la syphilis.—Godlewski, H. Hydratation et déshydratation.—Goldsmith, Marie. Un réflexe conditionnel chez les chenilles de Galleria melonella.—Gosset, A. et Petit-Dutaillis, D. La rechloruration dans l'occlusion intestinale. Indications de la méthode et résultats.—Lasseur, P. Phénomène de Charrin et Roger.—Laudat, M. Variations de l'indice réfractométrique subles par le sérum sanguin du fait de la traversée pulmonaire.—Lebon, J. L'exploration du pancréas par l'épreuve de la sécrétion glandulaire provoquée.—Le Clerc, R. et Benda, R. Techniques instrumentales pour la pratique de l'hémoculture et de la transfusion sanguine.—Lévy-Valensi, J. Claude Perrault, physiologiste.—Meyer, J. La perspiration de l'eau.—Piédelièvre, R. L'étude expérimentale des orifices d'entrée des balles dans la peau.—Porak, R. Le rythme de la diurèse.—Rathery, F. Le rôle du glycogène hépatique dans le métabolisme des glucides.—Régnier, J. et Valette, G. Étude du mode de fixation de la cocaïne sur les fibres nerveuses mise en évidence d'une adsorption normale.—Salomon, M. De l'utilité en clinique de prendre systématiquement la tension artérielle aux deux bras.—Sartory, A. Quelques parasites des mycoses osseuses.—Touraine, A. A côté.—Tournade, A. Sur les troubles cardio-vasculaires engendrés par l'inhalation de fumée de tabac.—Trémolières, F. Pathogénie de l'entéro-colite mucomembraneuse.—Vacquez, H. et Donzelot, E. Le surrénalome hypertensif.—Verne, J. Lipides et réaction aldéhydique au niveau de la cellule pulmonaire in vivo et en culture.—Villaret, M. et Justin-Besançon, L. Recherches sur les effets circulatoires de l'embolie cérébrale.—Weil, E. Les hémorragies hémotrypsiques chez la femme.

1. Roger, Georges Eugène Henri, 1860- 2. Medicine—Addresses, essays, lectures.

33-24129

Library of Congress R111.R75
[2] 610.4

NL 0423278 DLC

Livre jubilaire offert à Maurice Zimmermann, professeur honoraire de géographie à l'Université de Lyon, par ses élèves et ses amis à l'occasion de ses quatre-vingts ans, 4 mars 1949. Géographie naturelle, géographie humaine générale, géographie régionale, géographie historique et divers. Lyon, Université de Lyon, Institut des études rhodaniennes, Institut de géographie, 1949.

xvii, 425 p. illus., ports., maps (part fold.) 30 cm.

"Bibliographie ... des principaux ouvrages et articles de M. Maurice Zimmermann, par M. Laferrère et J. Thibaudet": p. [xiii]-xvii.

1. Geography—Addresses, essays, lectures. 2. Zimmermann, Maurice, 1869-

G58.L55 910.04 A 51-1451

Harvard Univ. Library for Library of Congress [3]†

NL 0423279 MH DLC PU IEN

Livre jubilaire offert au docteur Albin Lambotte par ses amis et ses élèves. Bruxelles, Vromant & c^o, 1936.
578 p. incl. illus., plates, tables, diagrs. front. (port.) 24½^cm.
Includes bibliographies.

CONTENTS.—Albin Lambotte.—Hustin, A. Discours prononcé à la séance académique du 1er juin 1935 à Anvers.—Leriche, René. Conférence faite à la séance académique du 1er juin 1935 à Anvers: L'avenir de la chirurgie osseuse.—Sauerbruch, F. Conférence faite à la séance académique du 1er juin 1935 à Anvers: Historique de la chirurgie osseuse.—Albee, F. H. Intracapsular fracture of the neck of the femur.—Alglave, P. Contribution à l'ostéosynthèse métallique appliquée aux fractures fermées.—Bastos, Manuel. Sobre el tratamiento de las seudoartrosis y en especial las del humero.—Bérard, Félix. Ostéosynthèse axiale des os longs par auto-greffe locale.—Chaklin, V. D. An intra-extramedullary method of treating pseudarthrosis and some types of improperly united fractures.—Charbonnel, M. Indications et technique générale du traitement des fractures récentes.—Cuendet, S. Procédé de réduction des fractures de la diaphyse des deux os de l'avant-bras à l'aide de l'appareil à broches jumelées.—Dahl-Iversen, E. Réduction simple, sanglante, des fractures condyliennes irréductibles du coude.—Danis, R. La maladie du plâtre.—Darrach, William. Derangements of the inferior radio-ulnar articulation.—Beule, Fritz de. Le traitement de certaines fractures par l'enclouage transcutané.—Delchef, J. Redites sur l'ostéosynthèse. Sa place dans le traitement des fractures.—Demel, R. Erfolg der sprunggelenksumdrehplastik.—Harcourt, J. y M. d'. Normas para el tratamiento quirúrgico de las fracturas recientes del cuello del femur.—Dupuy de Frenelle. De la tolérance à longue échéance du matériel métallique ostéosynthésique.—Esser, J. F. S. Moignons incapables.—Fairbank, H. A. T. Extension in the treatment of fractures with special reference to skeletal traction.—Blanc Fortacín, José. Regeneración osea y protesis metalica.—Fredet, Pierre. La suture précoce et le traitement ambulatoire des fractures de la rotule.—Grimault, L. Les résultats éloignés de l'ostéosynthèse.—Hey-Groves, E. W. Organization, the most important factor in the treatment of fractures.—Hustin, A. A propos du mécanisme de la claudication intermittente de la jambe. A propos du traitement opératoire des fractures du cou-de-pied vicieusement consolidées.—Johansson, Sven. Osteosynthesetechnik.—Lenormant, Ch. Sur le traitement des fractures du corps du calcanéum.—Leonte, C. Quelques considérations sur l'ostéosynthèse des fractures diaphysaires.—Mathieu, Paul. Reconstruction de la mortaise tibiopéronière dans le traitement des fractures malléolaires.—Mayer, Léo. Treatment of femoral neck fractures by wire screw fixation.—Moreira, Godoy. Nouvelle agrafe à trois lames.—Orell, Svante. Transplantation of "os novum" (osteosynthesis in tuberculous spondylitis).—Patel, Maurice. Considérations sur le traitement de la pseudarthrose du col fémoral.—Picot, Gaston. L'intervention chirurgicale dans les fractures marginales postérieures du tibia.—Putti, V. Sul cerchaiggio a nastro.—Robineau, M. L'ostéosynthèse est-elle une bonne opération?—Rouvillois, H. Main bote radiale par blessure de guerre traitée par ostéosynthèse après raccourcissement du cubitus sain et greffe ostéopériostique du radius.—Schoemaker, J. Een richtingsinstrument voor de behandeling van de fractura colli femoris.—Sherman, W. O. The operative treatment of fractures.—Simon, René. La place actuelle de l'ostéosynthèse dans le traitement des fractures.—Smith-Petersen, M. N. Tuberculosis of the sacro-iliac joint.—Spehl, Georges. L'arthrodèse extra-articulaire de la hanche dans la coxalgie chez l'adulte.—Steindler, Arthur. Treatment of osseous clubhand.—Tamini, L. A. Fractures et ostéomyélite.—Tavernier, L. L'ostéosynthèse des fractures du fémur chez l'enfant.—Valls, José, Ottolenghi, C. E. y Lagomarsino, E. H. "La osteosintesis en las fracturas del cuello del pie", algunos resultados.—Verbrugge, Jean. L'utilisation du magnésium dans le traitement chirurgical des fractures.—Verhoogen, Jean et Van der Beken, Ch. Étude de 194 ostéosynthèses pratiquées dans le service de clinique chirurgicale du professeur Verhoogen de 1904 à 1930.—Frisch, Otto von. Meine erfahrungen mit der osteosynthese nach Lane.

1. Lambotte, Albin, 1866- 2. Fractures. 3. Bones—Surgery. 4. Bones—Diseases.

Library of Congress RD11.L47 39-33132
[2] 617.04

NL 0423284 DLC DNLM

Livre jubilaire offert au professeur Hartmann par ses amis et ses élèves. Paris, Masson et c^ie, 1932.

2 p. l., xxxvi, 679, [1] p. front. (port.) illus. 28½^cm.

Contributions by various authors in French, English, and Spanish.
"L'oeuvre du professeur Hartmann, par le docteur Bernard Cunéo": p. [ix]-xxxvi.
Contains bibliographies.

1. Surgery—Addresses, essays, lectures. 2. Hartmann, Henri Albert Charles Antoine, 1860- I. Cunéo, Bernard, 1873-

32-30276

Library of Congress RD11.L5

Copyright A—Foreign 18103
[2] 617.04

NL 0423285 DLC

Livre jubilaire publié à l'occasion du xxve anniversaire académique [1929-1954] du professeur Paul van Gehuchten à Louvain. Bruxelles, Impr. des sciences, 1955.

1 v. (various pagings) illus., port., diagrs. 24 cm.

French or Flemish, with summaries in English, Flemish, French, and German.
Includes bibliographies.

1. Neurology—Collected works. 2. Gehuchten, Paul van, 1893-

RC332.L5 58-17167

CU DCU ICU
NL 0423286 DLC ICRL IU OU PPC CtY-M MiU DNLM NIC

W 5 LIVRE jubilaire publié en l'honneur du
D427L docteur Paul Dérache. Bruxelles
1933 [Vromans] 1933.
xxvi, 148 p. illus., port.

1. Dérache, Paul 2. Medicine - Addresses

NL 0423287 DNLM DAL

Livre jubilaire publié en l'honneur du professeur Jean Verhoogen. Bruxelles, 1929.
3 p. l., vi, 747, [1] p. front. (port.) illus. 27^cm.
Contains bibliographies and bibliographical foot-notes.

CONTENTS.

Notice biographique.—Achard, Ch. Le liquide des kystes du rein et de l'hydronéphrose expérimentale.—Alessandri, Roberto. Quelques considérations sur les tumeurs médullaires.—Bazy, Pierre. Technique de l'adénomectomie prostatique.—Beer, Edwin. Développement et progrès de la chirurgie de la rate.—Berard, Léon et Mallet-Guy, Pierre. De quelques formes anatomo-cliniques des pancréatites chroniques chirurgicales (à propos de huit observations inédites)—Boeckel, André. Six cas de néoplasme inopérable de la vessie traités par l'étincelage à vessie ouverte.—Brohee, Georges. Deux cas d'hypertrophie massive des seins.—Brongersma, N. Résultat éloigné d'une cystectomie totale.—Cahen, Jean. a) L'emploi de la rachi-anesthésie dans le service du prof. J. Verhoogen (1914-1928) b) Arthroplastie pour tumeur blanche ancienne du genou.—Cifuentes, P. Le prostatisme précoce.—E. F. Chocholka. Les prostatites chroniques. Essai d'un système clinique.—Compan, Vicente. Contribution à l'étude de la chirurgie du kyste hydatique du rein.—Coppez, Henry. Les traumatismes du chiasma des nerfs optiques.—Coquelet, Oct. Introduction à l'étude des suppurations pulmonaires.—Covisa, Isidro. Sur les fistules urétro-rectales, à propos de deux cas cliniques.—Danis, Robert et Loicq, René. Les incisions transversales franches de l'abdomen.—Degraeuwe, A. De l'importance de l'examen du fonctionnement rénal en chirurgie abdominale.—D'Haenens, Ant. Hématurie essentielle profuse. Anémie grave. Transfusion sanguine pré-opératoire. Néphrectomie. Guérison.—De Moor, Paul. Deux cas de rupture spontanée de la vessie.—Des Cressonnieres, J. L'hyperleucocytose dans le diagnostic de la grossesse extra-utérine rompue.—Desmeth, Jean. Les polypes du col vésical chez la femme.—Dordu, Fabien. Hétéroplasties et autoplasties.—Dustin, A. P. Guérison réelle et guérison apparente des tumeurs malignes irradiées.—François, Jules. Le diagnostic précoce des tumeurs du rein. Valeur de la pyélographie dans le diagnostic des tumeurs rénales.—Gayet, G. Le sarcome du vagin chez l'enfant.—Giordano. D. Sympathie génito-mammaire.—Guisy, Barthélémy. Deux cas mortels d'embolie gazeuse observés pendant le remplissage de la cavité vésicale au moyen d'air.—Hartmann, Henry. Que faut-il penser de la fréquence de l'ulcéro-cancer de l'estomac.—Hendrix, G. L'extirpation du péroné chez les amputés au dessous du genou.—Hicguet, G. De la thyrotomie comme moyen diagnostique et thérapeutique des néoplasies laryngées.—Hogge, Albert. Les barrières défensives des appareils urinaire et génital contre les ennemis du dehors.—Hustin, A. Thermomètre enregistreur lumineux.—Janet, Jules. Quelques principes de petite urologie qui me sont chers.—Keyes, Edward L. Le traitement du carcinome de la vessie par l'implantation d'émanation de radium.—Kidd, Frank. La chylurie et son traitement chirurgical.—Kummer, Ernest. Tumeur lymphomateuse de la prostate, manifestation d'une lymphadénomatose aleucémique.—Lambotte, A. Contribution à la chirurgie conservatrice de la main dans les traumatismes.—Le Fur, René. De la part respective du rein et de la vessie dans les infections urinaires à colibacilles.—Legueu, F. L'incontinence d'urine d'origine urétérale.—Lemoine, Georges. Thyroïdectomie ou sympathectomie dans le traitement du goitre exophtalmique.—Lepoutre, C. De la lithiase urinarie survenant chez les malades longtemps immobilisés pour diverses affections osseuses et articulaires.—Lorthioir, J. Note sur le traitement des rétrécissements de l'œsophage chez l'enfant.—Marion. Reconstitution d'un urétre continent chez la femme.—Martin, Paul. Thérapeutique des traumatismes fermés cranio-encéphaliques.—Michon, Edouard. Réflexions sur les grands kystes du rein.—Moreau, Jules. Les erreurs du diagnostic de l'ulcère gastrique et duodénal. (Erreurs cliniques, chirurgicales, radiographiques)—Neumann et Coryn. Les tendances actuelles dans le traitement du cancer du rectum.—Nogues, Paul. Quelques causes de fausses cystites chez la femme.—Œconomos, Spyridon. A propos d'un cas de mouvement rétrograde des calculs urétéraux.—Papin. Traitement chirurgical des diverticules vésicaux.—Pousson. Ce que peut la chirurgie dans les néphrites médicales.—Rafin. Disjonction pubienne, accidents urinaires tardifs.—Ravasini, Carlo. Contribution à l'interprétation de la pyélographie.—Renard-Dethy, H. Les coliques néphrétiques d'origine prostatique.—Rouffart-Thiriar, M. A propos de 6 observations d'ostéo-synthèse pour fracture diaphysaire du fémur.—Slosse, Aug. Note sur l'intervention du phosphore inorganique dans le métabolisme des glucides.—Strominger, L. Sur la rachianesthésie dans les maladies des voies urinaires.—Thevenot, Léon. Tumeur du vestibule chez un enfant de 2 ans et demi.—Sir Thomson-Walker, John. Ma méthode pour la prostatectomie.—Vandenbranden, F. Y a-t-il un danger à employer la méthode de Beer dans le traitement des papillomes vésicaux?—Vandeput, Eugène. Traitement des ulcères duodénaux par la gastro-jéjunostomie associée a l'exclusion duodénale (ligature du pylore)—Vander Elst. L'exploration radiologique au lipiodol en gynécologie.—Van Houtum. A propos des rétrécissements inflammatoires de l'uretère.

1. Verhoogen, Jean, 1864- 2. Medicine—Addresses, essays, lectures.

S G 36-14

Library, U. S. Surgeon-General's Office [R111]
[2]

NL 0423294 DNLM MiU PPC

RC902
L76
1955 Livre jubilaire publié en l'honneur du Professeur Paul Govaerts. [Bruxelles, Imprimerie Médicale et Scientifique] 1955.
756 p. illus.

Includes bibliographies.

1. Kidneys - Diseases - Addresses, essays, lectures. I. Govaerts, Paul, 1889- II. Brussels. Université Libre. Clinique Médicale.

NL 0423295 NNC NNU MiU ICJ DNLM ICRL

Livre jubilaire publié par la Société de médecine de Gand
see under Société de médecine de Gand.

VOLUME 337

Le livre, l'estampe, l'édition en Brabant du XVe au XIIe siècle
see under Brussels. Exposition d'art ancien, 1935.

NL 0423297

...Le livre; les plus beaux exemplaires de la Bibliothèque nationale. Paris, Éditions du Chêne, 1942. 170 p. illus. (part col.) 32cm. (La Tradition française; collection dirigée par André Lejard.)
"Avertissement" signed A. L.
Articles by E. A. Van Moë, Robert Brun and others.
"Bibliographie," p. 165-166.

155561B. 1. Illumination of books and manuscripts—Specimens, reproductions, etc. 2. Illustration of books. 3. Bookbinding—Hist. and illustration. I. Ser.
N. Y. P. L. May 7, 1942

NL 0423298 NN ICU WaS CU-A MH NcU

Le Livre; les plus beaux exemplaires de la Bibliothèque nationale. [Nouv. éd. mise à jour] Paris, Éditions du Chêne, 1949.
166 p. illus. (part col.) 32 cm. (La Tradition française)
CONTENTS.—Les manuscrits, par É. A. van Moë.—Le livre aux xve et xvie siècles, par R. Brun.—Le livre aux xviie et xviiie siècles, par J. Wilhelm.—Le livre au xixe siècle (de 1801 à 1870) par P. H. Michel.—Le livre au xxe siècle, par J. Guignard.—La reliure, par R. Brun.—Bibliographie (p. 165-166)
1. Illustration of books—France. 2. Illumination of books and manuscripts—France. 3. Bookbinding—France.
NC980.L5 1949 096.1 50-4233 rev

NL 0423299 DLC NNGr MoSW OCU

BF 1612 .L44 Le Livre magique, histoire des événements et des personnages surnaturels; contenant des détails sur la démologie, l'astrologie et la chiromancie; sur les lutins, les fantômes, les spectres, le sabbat, les maléfices, les talismans, les peines et les supplices de l'Inquisition, etc., etc. Ouvrage composé d'après les plus célèbres démonographes et cabalistes: les deux Albert [et al.] Paris, Corbet ainé, 1835.
244 p. 17cm.

NL 0423300 NNC NIC

Le Livre mignard, ou la fleur des fabliaux
see under Malo, Charles, 1790-1871, ed.

NL 0423301

Le Livre moderne; revue du monde littéraire et des bibliophiles contemporains, publiée par Octave Uzanne. 1.-4. v.; jan. 1890-déc. 1891. Paris, Maison Quantin.
5 v. illus. (part col.) ports., facsims. 24 cm. monthly.
"Tirage à mille cinquante exemplaires: mille, sur vergé des Vosges (numérotés de 1 à 1000); vingt, sur papier du Japon (de I à XX); quinze, sur papier de Chine (de XXI à XXXV); quinze, sur papier Whatmann (de XXXVI à L) Exemplaire no. 726." ("Le tome premier est numéroté")
Supersedes Le Livre; revue du monde littéraire.
Superseded by L'Art et l'idée.
Includes index.
1. Bibliography—Period. 2. Books. 3. Book collecting—Period. I. Uzanne, Louis Octave, 1852-1931.
Z1007.L78 2-13668 rev*

NL 0423302 MiU OU ICJ DLC NhD ICU IEN ICU ICJ MB CtY PPL PP

Le Livre National, Collections Populaires. Paris, Jules Tallandier.

NL 0423303 DLC

Livre noir. Bruges, J.Bogaert & c., [1790?]
At head of title: N° 1.

NL 0423304 MH

Le livre noir de la Commune de Paris (dossier complet) L'Internationale dévoilée. Bruxelles, Office de publicité, 1871.
396 p. 19cm.
1. Paris—Hist.—Commune, 1871. 2. The International.
18-21496
Library of Congress DC316.L6

NL 0423305 DLC NcD

Le livre noir de la Commune de Paris (dossier complet). L'Internationale dévoilée. 2. éd. Bruxelles, Office de publicité 46, rue de la Madeleine, 1871.
395, [1] p. 19cm.
1. Paris—Hist.—Commune, 1871. 2. The International.
Library of Congress DC316.L83 5-16079

NL 0423306 DLC GU ICU

Le livre noir de la Commune de Paris (dossier complet). L'Internationale dévoilée. 3. éd. Bruxelles, Office de publicité, 46 rue de la Madeleine, 1871.
395, [1] p. 18cm.
1. Paris—Hist.—Commune, 1871. 2. The International.
6-40176†* Cancel
Library of Congress DC316.L84

NL 0423307 DLC CaBVaU ICJ MB

Livre noir de la dictature autrichienne
see under Labor and Socialist International. Commission of Enquiry into the Conditions of Political Prisoners.

NL 0423308

Le LIVRE noir des médecins grecs; une page de la persécution de l'hellénisme en Turquie. Paris, P. Thévoz, 1920. 43 p. 24cm.
Film reproduction. Positive.
1. Physicians--Turkey. 2. Greeks in Turkey.

NL 0423309 NN UU

Un livre noir, diplomatie d'avant guerre d'après les documents des archives russes...
see under Marchand, René, 1888-

NL 0423310

Beinecke Library European Tracts N3 1790 L767 Livre noir du Comté de Namur, ou Correspondance du ci-devant gouvernement autrichien de Bruxelles, avec ses agens subalternes dans le Comté de Namur. A Bruxelles, Chez Lemaire, imprimeur-libraire, rue de l'Impératrice, 1790.
2 p.l., 140 p. 20 cm.
The Etats souverains played a trick on Stassart de Noirmont by publishing his official correspondence as president of the Conseil de Namur.- cf. Biographie nationale de l'Académie royale des sciences, des lettres et des beaux arts de Belgique, Brussels, v.23, 699-702.
1. Namur - History - Sources. I. Namur (Comté) Etats. II. Namur (Province) Conseil provincial.

NL 0423312 CtY

... Le Livre noir du Vercors, précédé d'un poème de Pierre Emmanuel. Neuchâtel, Ides et calendes [1944]
5 p. l., [13]-119 p., 2 l. incl. plates. 21½cm.
At head of title: Albert Béguin ... [etc.]
CONTENTS.—Menkès, Georges. Faits et témoignages.—Courthion, Pierre. L'atmosphère.—Heyd, Richard. Du mémorial de l'oppression aux charniers de Bron.—Béguin, Albert. Au seuil de l'enfer.—Du Bochet, Paul. Nos conclusions.—Tronchet, Lucien. Reconstruire.
1. World war, 1939-1945—Atrocities. 2. World war, 1939-1945—France—Vercors. I. Béguin, Albert.
45-10748
Library of Congress D804.G4L5
[2] 940.54056

NL 0423313 DLC IaU CtY OCl CSt

Livre nouveav de l'art d'architectvre des cinq ordres et de plusieurs recueils de cette science ...
see under Lavergne, de architect.

NL 0423315

Typ 515 33.526 Liure nouueau, dict patrõs de lingerie: cestassauoir a deux endroitz, a point croise, poĩt couche & point picque, en fil dor, dargẽt, de soye, ou aultre, en quelque ouurage que ce soit: en cõprenant lart de broderie et tissuterie.
On les vend a Lyõ,chez Pierre de saĩcte Lucie,pres nostre dame de Confort.[after 1533]
4°. [48]p. illus. 19.5cm.
Signatures: A-F⁴.
Title within ornamental border containing devices of C. Nourry; p.[3-47] are lace patterns; printer's mark of P. de Sainte Lucie on p.[48].
Imperfect: leaves B2-3,C2-4,D1-2 wanting, replaced by patterns from other series (2 genuine leaves, the others pen-and-ink facsimiles).
With this is bound Antoine Belin's Patrons [after 1533].

NL 0423316 MH

Livre pour les femmes mariees
see under Gasparin, Catherine Valérie (Boissier), comtesse de, 1813-1894.

NL 0423317

Bo57 3 Livre rouge ... Paris,Baudouin,1790.
vi,7-43p. 23cm.
Title vignette: Imprimerie nationale.
Published by the Comité des pensions of the Assemblée nationale.
1.Pensions - France. 2.France - Court and courtiers. I.France. Assemblée nationale constituante, 1789-1791. Comité des pensions.

NL 0423318 CtY NN

VOLUME 337

Le Livre rouge
Livre rouge [avec Addition]. Paris, Chez Baudouin, 1790.
39, 8 p. 20 cm.

"Addition au Livre rouge, ou Démonstration de la vérité de ce qui a été dit dans l'avertissement imprimé en tête au dépouillement de ce livre" on last 8 pages.
With this are bound: [Sauvageot, Olivier] Réponse aux observations du comte de Ségur. [1790]; France. Assemblée nationale constituante, 1789-1791. Comité des pensions. Réponse aux observations de m. Necker. 1790; France. Assemblée nationale constituante, 1789-1791. Comité des pensions. Rapports, 1790.

NL 0423320 MB-BA MH NN NNC CU MnU

LIVRE ROUGE.
Le livre rouge. Conclusions du Mémoire Madrolle, ou Rêve d'un royaliste quand même. Publié par J. D. A-Paris, Chez tous les marchands de nouveautés, 1830. 52 p. 20cm.

1. Pensions, Personal--France. 1715-1793. 3. Madrolle, cour royale de Paris. 2. France--Court and courtiers. Antoine. Memoire a la I. D.

NL 0423321 NN

Livre rouge.
... 1.-3. registre des dépenses secrètes de la cour, connu sous le nom de Livre rouge, apporté par des députés des corps administratifs de Versailles, le 28 février 1793, l'an deuxième de la république, déposé aux archives, & imprimé par ordre de la Convention nationale. Paris, Imprimerie nationale, 1793.
3 v. in 1. 22cm.
At head of title: Convention nationale.
Covers the time from the 10th of January 1750 to the 16th of August 1789.
1. France — Court and courtiers. 2. France — Hist. — Revolution—Sources. I. France. Convention nationale, 1792–1795. II. Title: Registre des dépenses secrètes de la cour.
10—21229
Library of Congress DC142.L7

NL 0423322 DLC IaU WaU CtY NN CaBVaU

Le livre rouge d'Eu
see under Eu, France.

Le livre rouge des atrocités allemandes d'après
see under Domergue, Jean Gabriel, 1889- illus.

Le Livre rouge, histoire de l'échafaud en France, etc.
see under Dupray de la Mahérie, Paul Valentin, ed.

Le livre rouge, or Red book: being a list of secret pensions, paid out of the public treasure of France; and containing characters of the persons pensioned, anecdotes of their lives, an account of their services and observations tending to shew the reasons for which the pensions were granted. Translated from the 8th Paris ed. London, Printed for G. Kearsley, 1790.
2 p. l., [3]-163 p. 22cm.
Printed in red.
1. Pensions—France. 2. France—Court and courtiers.
9-33274
Library of Congress JN2344 1790.L6
——— Copy 2. [With Calonne, C. A. de. The speech delivered ... the 22d of February, 1787. London, 1787] HJ1082.C27 1787 [a44b1]

CU-A NIC PU
NL 0423326 DLC MiDW GU KyU MH-BA CtY NjP NN InU

Le livre rouge, or Red book; being a list of private pensions paid from the public treasury of France. Containing the names of the pensioners, the nature of their services, with observations on their respective merits. Tr. from the French eds. printed at Paris in 1790. New-York, Printed by G. Forman for J. Fellows, 1794.
25 p. 20cm.

1. Pensions—France. 2. France—Court and courtiers.
9-33273†
Library of Congress JN2344.1790.L62

NL 0423327 DLC NN MiU-C PPAmP MBAt NN

Le livre rouge, ou, Liste des pensions secrettes, sur le tresor public; contenant les noms & qualités des pensionnaires, l'état de leurs services, & des observations sur les motifs qui leur ont mérité leur traitement ... [Paris?] De l'imprimerie royale, 1790.
172 p. 21½cm. [With Calonne, C. A. de. The speech delivered ... the 22d of February, 1787. London, 1787]
Contains 11 livraisons issued in 7 parts, each part with special t.-p.
1. Pensions—France. 2. France—Court and courtiers.
44-12355
Library of Congress HJ1082.C27 1787

NL 0423328 DLC CtY NjP NN NIC MH MH-BA ViU MiU

Le Livre rouge; ou, Soirées d'hiver de quelques paysans des provinces Rhénanes. Traduit de l'allemand, à l'occasion de l'affaire de l'archevèque de Cologne. 2. éd., enrichie d'une notice biographique de ce prélat et de plusiers notes. Paris, Librairie de la Société de l'enseignement catholique, 1838.
131 p. 14 cm.

NL 0423329 PLatS

Livre sans nom
see under [Cotolendi, Charles] d. ca. 1710.

Livre sans nom, 1933
see under [Madan, Geoffrey] comp.

... Le livre scolaire catholique français
see under Labelle, Eugène.

Le livre secret des grands exorcismes et benedictions

see under

[Houssay, Ernest Louis, 1844-1912.

Livre-souvenir de la famille Blanchet, publié à l'occasion de la célébration du troisième centenaire de naissance de Pierre Blanchet. Québec, 1946. 296 p. plates, ports. 25cm.
Cover-title: 1646-1946, 3ième centenaire de naissance de Pierre Blanchet. Famille Blanchet: Canada et États-Unis.
On spine: Les Blanchet au Canada et aux États-Unis (notes historiques).
1. Blanchet family. I. Title: Les Blanchet au Canada et aux États-Unis.

NL 0423334 NN WaSpG

929.2
G122
Livre-souvenir des fêtes du troisième centenaire des Gagnon, 1640-1940. [1942,
171 p., 1 l. front., illus.

I. Title.

NL 0423335 NNC

Le Livre suisse
see Das Schweizer buch.

Le livre, suivi du Catalogue illustré des éditions Édouard Pelletan
see under [Pelletan, Édouard] 1854-1912.

Livre vert; actes et documents concernant la question carélienne, 1922
see under Finland. Délégation carélienne.

Livre vert de l'archevêché de Narbonne ...
see under Narbonne, France (Archdiocese)

Le livre vert de Lacaune (Tarn)
see under [Gautrand]

QU
4
L788n
1948
LIVREA, Gaetano
Nozioni di chimica biologica. Roma, Studio editoriale degli Istituti universitari Socrate Bucciarelli, 1948.
435 p.
1. Biochemistry

NL 0423341 DNLM ICJ OU

Livrelli (Baptiste) [1889-]. *Du choix d'un traitement pour les fractures de l'humérus. 39 pp. 8°. Montpellier, 1914. No. 52.

NL 0423342 DNLM CtY

Livrelli, J A
L'occupation italienne en Corse. Préf. de maître V. de Moro-Giafferri. Hors-texte dessiné par Gabriel Giner. Paris, P. Fieschi [1949]
246 p. illus. 24 cm.
"Annexes": p. 219-244.

1. World War, 1939-1945—Corsica. 2. Corsica—Hist. I. Title.
A 52-5529
New York. Public Libr. for Library of Congress [1]

NL 0423343 NN

Livrenteog forsørgelsesanstalten af 1842.
Foreløbig beretning om opgjørelsen af dødeligheden i Livrente- og forsørgelses-anstalten af 1842 samt Livsforsikkrings-anstalten i Kjøbenhavr i aarene 1842 til 1868, og disse anstalters status den 31te dec. 1868. Kjøbenhavn, Trykt hos J. H. Schultz, 1870.

VOLUME 337

LIVRERA, PIETRO.
...La Passione di Cristo; dramma sacro. Torino: Tip. editrice La Salute, 1938. 141 p. 21cm.

At head of title: P. Livrera—B. Filetto.
Copy no. 466. With autograph of author.

1. Passion plays—Italy. I. Filetto, Basilio, jt.au.

N. Y. P. L.

NL 0423345 NN

Livres à gravures imprimés à Lyon au xve siècle ... Lyon, Association Guillaume Le Roy ⌊1924–
v. illus., facsims. 28 x 23½cm.
At head of title, vol. III– : Claude Dalbanne.
Imprint, vol. III– : Lyon.
"Donner, dans la grandeur des originaux, la reproduction de toutes les gravures, ornements et lettres gravées des livres imprimés à Lyon au xve siècle, tel est le but des publications de notre association. Avec la description du volume étudié, chaque fascicule contiendra la reproduction du titre et du colophon, ainsi que les alphabets des caractères qui y sont employés et les filigranes qui s'y touvent."—Publisher's announcement.
1. Wood-engravings, French. 2. Illustrated books—15th and 16th cent.—Facsimiles. 3. Printing—Hist.—Lyons. I. Dalbanne, Claude, 1877– ed. II. Association Guillaume Le Roy, Lyons.

30-27805

Library of Congress ⌊2⌋

NL 0423346 DLC ViU MnU CaOTP MnU MiU

Livres Américains traduits en français et livres français sur les États-Unis d'Amérique (Répertoire d'ouvrages disponibles en librairie au 1er Mai 1951); American books in French translation and French books about the United States of America (A bibliography of books available on May 1, 1951). Paris, Services Américains d'information, 1951.
xiv,123p.

NL 0423347 ScU ScCleU

015.493
L76
1940-45

Livres belges parus de 1940 a 1945. Bruxelles, L'Office International de Librairie, S.P.R.L. [1946?]
cover-title, 24p. 22cm.

1. Belgium--Bibl. I. Office International de Librairie.

NL 0423348 LU

Z
1033
.M6
P49
ser.1

Livres-bijoux, précurseurs des Cazins. Bibliconographie historique des premières collections fondées de 1773 à 1779 à Lille, à Lyon et à Orléans. ⌊Paris, 1894⌋
108 p. 16 cm. (Petits joyaux bibliophiliques. Collections precieuses publiées au dixhuitième siècle, 1. sér.)

1. Cazin, Hubert Marin, 1724-1795. 2. Bibliography - Microscopic and miniature editions.

NL 0423349 DCU

Livres catholiques; catalogue collectif. 1945/51–
Paris, Syndicat des éditeurs.
v. 22 cm.

1. Catholic literature—Bibl.—Catalogs. 2. Catholic Church—Bibl.—Catalogs. I. Syndicat national des éditeurs (France)

Z7837.L59 53-17407 rev

NL 0423350 DLC OrStbM DDO MH NN DCU ICarbS

Livres Catholiques; Catalogue collectif
for later editions see *also* Catalogue collectif des livres religieux.

Les livres chez les Egyptiens
see under [Lenormant, François] 1837-1883.

Livres classiques.
Paris, Cercle de la librairie.
v. illus. annual.

Ceased 1922.
Continued by Livres et matériel d'enseignement.
Supplement to Bibliographie de la France.
Vol.72 has title: Catalogue des livres classiques.
Vol.111 has title: Livres classiques et matériel d'enseignement.

NL 0423353 ICRL

Les livres classiques de l'empire de la Chine, recueillis par le père Noël
see under [Ssu Shu]

Livres curieux
see under Garrigue, Rudolph Peter (Bookseller)

Case
VM
1730
L 78

LIVRE⌊S⌋ d'airs de differents avthevrs à deux parties. A Paris, R. Ballard, 1660-68.
8v. 17cm.

Books 3-7, 9-11.
Titles within illustrated borders; initials.
Melodies unaccompanied; diamond-shaped notes.

NL 0423356 ICN

Le livres d'amours de Drouart La Vache
see under [André, le Chapelain]

Livres d'Aquitaine; essai d'inventaire littéraire
see under [Got, Armand]

Z2165
.B58Et

... Livres d'étrennes et publications périodiques ... 1909–
Paris [1908–
v. illus. (part. col.) 26½cm.

Supplement to Bibliographie de la France. 1909-1929 bound with Bibliographie de la France, 1908-1928 (Z2165. B58)

1. French literature--Bibl.--Period.
I. Bibliographie de la France.

HU NBuG ICRL NcD DNAL
NL 0423359 DLC IU NjP NN NcU MiU OU PPPM PPULC DCU

Livres de chasseur. Notes bibliographiques.
[Compiègne, 1885]
64 p. 22 cm.
A bibliographic fragment containing a list of books on hunting under the letters A, B, & C through Carlos, and published as a specimen of a forthcoming "Bibliographie complète des ouvrages sur la chasse." Notes by R. Souhart. Cf. Brit. mus.
[Bound with Baguenault de Puchesse, G. Jean et Jacques de la Taille. Orléans, 1889]

NL 0423360 CtY

Les livres de divination
see under Nikolaides, Ioannes.

Livres de France. 1.–
année; mai 1950–
⌊Paris, Hachette, etc.⌋
v. in illus., ports. 27 cm. 10 no. a year.

1. French literature—Book reviews—Periodicals. 2. French literature—Bibliography—Periodicals. 3. French literature—History and criticism—Periodicals.

Z2165.L77 71-233417

NL 0423362 DLC CaBVaU NNC OrU DAL NN DCU CtY

Li Livres de jostice et de plet.
Li Livres de jostice et de plet, publié pour la première fois d'après le manuscrit unique de la Bibliothèque nationale, par Rapetti, avec un glossaire des mots hors d'usage, par P. Chabaille. Paris, Typographie de Firmin Didot frères, 1850.
2 p. l., lii, 451, ⌊1⌋ p. 28½cm. (*Half-title:* Collection de documents inédits sur l'histoire de France ... 1. sér. Histoire politique)
The work of editing the manuscript was commenced by H. Klimrath.
"Glossaire du Livre de jostice et de plet": p. ⌊361⌋–421.
1. Justice, Administration of—France. 2. Civil law—France. 3. French language—Old French—Glossaries, vocabularies, etc. I. Rapetti, Louis Nicolas, 1812–1885, ed. II. Chabaille, François Adrien Polycarpe, 1796–1863. III. Klimrath, Henri, 1807–1837.

30—1977

Library of Congress

ViU PU NN MiU OCU OClW ICU CaBVaU
NL 0423363 DLC PU OU NIC CaTOP TNJ IEN MdBP MH

Les Livres de l'année; table méthodique des livres et publications annoncés dans la Bibliographie de la France ... 1922–
Paris, Cercle de la librairie, Bibliographie de la France, 1922–
v. 24½cm.
Each volume is in five parts. I. Belles-lettres. Littérature générale. Romans, contes, nouvelles. Poésies. Théâtre.—II. Droit. Philosophie. Sociologie. Religions.—III. Technologie. Agriculture. Commerce. Finances. Mathématiques. Armée. Marine. Annuaires. Agendas. Dictionnaires.—IV. Histoire. Géographie. Voyages. Beaux-arts. Musique.—V. Médicine. Éducation physique. Sports. Sciences physiques, chimiques et naturelles.
1. French literature—Bibl.—Period. 2. Bibliography—Period. I. Bibliographie de la France. II. Cercle de la librairie, Paris.

28-13032

Library of Congress Z2165.B58L

NL 0423364 DLC NBuU DS WaS OrCS DAU PSt OU IEdS PU

Les livres de l'enfance du XVe au XIXe siècle
see under Gumuchian et compagnie, booksellers, Paris.

Les livres de la guerre, août 1914, août 1916; préface en vers de Edmond Rostand ... Paris, Agence générale de librairie et de publications ⌊1916⌋
ix p., 1 l., ⌊13⌋–178 p., 1 l. plates, ports. 22cm.

1. European war, 1914– —Bibl. I. Rostand, Edmond, 1868–1918.

18–26485

Library of Congress Z6207.E8L5

ICJ MdBP MeB CtY
NL 0423366 DLC IU TU FMU OCl MB NjP PU-B PP PPC

VOLUME 337

Livres de la Trésorerie des chartes du Hainaut. 1435. Inventaire des meubles de l'hôtel de Guillaume IV, duc de Bavière, à Paris. 1409. Mons, E. Hoyois, 1842.

25 p. 23½cm. (*Half-title:* Société des bibliophiles belges, séant à Mons. no. 12 des Publications)

"Tiré à 100 exemplaires destinés au commerce. no. quatorze."
Preface signed: Aug. Lacroix, Ad. Mathieu.

1. Literature, Medieval—Bibl. 2. Manuscripts—Catalogs. 3. Guillaume IV, comte de Hainaut, 1366–1417. 4. Furniture—France—Catalogs. I. Lacroix, Augustin François, 1793–1875, ed. II. Mathieu, Adolphe Charles Ghislain, 1804–1876, joint ed.

17-23999

Library of Congress DH801.H2S6 no. 12

NL 0423367 DLC

Livres de médecine; bibliographie metnodique.

Paris, Librairie Maloine ⌊
In v. 20-22cm.

1. Medicine - Bibliography - Catalogs.
I. Maloine, A

NL 0423368 NNC NNC-M

ZWB 100 L788 1936

LIVRES de médecine; bibliographie-méthodique, 1935. ⌊Strasbourg, Impr. des Dernières Nouvelles, 1936?⌋
126 p.
Caption title.
1. Medicine - France - Bibl.

NL 0423369 DNLM

Livres de médecine, contenant les auteurs de l'accouchement, de l'anatomie, de la chirurgie, de la botanique, de la chymie, pharmacie, etc. 30 pp. [interleaved]. sm. 8°. [*n. p., n. d.*]
Incomplete.
Bound with: CATALOGUS librorum medicorum, etc. sm. 8°. *Argentorati.* 1768.

NL 0423370 DNLM

PQ 1173 L5 Cage

Le livres de plusieurs pieces, dont le contenu se treuve en la page suyante...Paris, Par Arnoul l'Angelier, 1548.

199 l. 16mo
A miscellaneous collection of minor French literary works of the 16th century.

NL 0423371 DFo

Livres des XV & XVI siècles.
Paris, Frazier-Soye, 1914

Lond. Cat. (supplement) 1:441

NL 0423372 NcU

Livres des respirations

see

Book of opening the mouth

Les livres du mois; tables mensuelles des nouveaux ouvrages publiés ... dans la Bibliographie de la France, journal général et officiel de la librairie et de l'imprimerie. 1- 1912-
Paris, Librairie des presses universitaires de France.
v. 24cm.
Caption title: Bibliographie de la France, supplément.
1. French literature - Bibl. - Period. I. Bibliographie de la France. Supplement.

NL 0423374 DCU PPPM DNAL MiD AzTeS CStbS DLC CU OU

Z 2165 .B582

Les livres du semestre. 1952-
Paris, Cercle de la librairie.
v. 24 cm.
Supplement to Bibliographie de la France.

1. French literature - Bibl. - Period. I. Bibliographie de la France. / Supplement.

NL 0423375 DCU

Z 2165 .B583

Les livres du trimestre. Jan./Mar. 1952-
Paris, Cercle de la librairie.
v. 24 cm.
Supplement to Bibliographie de la France.

1. French literature - Bibl. - Period. I. Bibliographie de la France. / Supplement.

NL 0423376 DCU

.. Les **Livres** en 1881- études critiques et analytiques par MM. Gaston d'Hailly, A. Le-Clère & Henri Litou, rédacteurs de la Revue des livres nouveaux, publiées dans ce recueil pendant l'année 1881-
t. 1- 1881-
Paris, 1883-

v. 25cm. monthly.

At head of title: Romans, poésies, théâtre, musique, philosophie, histoire, biographies, mémoires, voyages, etc., etc.

I. Hailly, Gaston d', 1837- II. Le Clère, A. III. Litou, Henri. IV. Revue des livres nouveaux.

11-11417

Library of Congress AP20.L6

NL 0423377 DLC CaOTU MH

Les livres et des pamphlets sur le concordat. Paris, chez A.Dubrey, 1919.

45 p.

NL 0423378 MH

Livres et matériel d'enseignement. v.112- 1923-
Paris, Cercle de la librairie.
v. illus. annual.

No volume numbering after v.125.
Continues Livres classiques.
Supplement to Bibliographie de la France.

NL 0423379 ICRL NBuG

Livres français choisis à l'intention des bibliothèques étrangères et des bibliothèques françaises à l'étranger. ⌊Paris, Firmin-Didot et cie, 1937⌋

1 p. l., ⌊v⌋–xv, 144 p. 27½cm.

Classified and priced.
"Cette liste de livres et de périodiques a été dressée, à la demande du Ministère des affaires étrangères, par un comité composé d'écrivains et de savants dont l'autorité et la compétence sont universellement reconnues."—Avertissement.

1. French literature—Bibl. 2. Bibliography—Best books—French literature. I. France. Ministère des affaires étrangères.

38-24736

Library of Congress Z1035.2.L78
⌊3⌋ [016] 015.44

NL 0423380 DLC ViU PSt OCl MB NNC OClW

Livres français choisis à l'intention des bibliothèques étrangères et des bibliothèques françaises à l'étranger. ⌊Paris, 1947⌋
248 p.
"Ce catalogue ... est édité par l'Association pour la diffusion de la pensée française, à la demande de la Direction générale des relations culturelles du Ministère des affaires étrangères."

1. French literature—Bibl. 2. Bibliography—Best books—French literature.

CU IU CSt
NL 0423381 ICU MtU ICN NIC LU CU NNC PBL MiU PPT

Livres français parus en Amérique de 1940 à 1944. Rio de Janeiro, 1944.

48 p. 23 cm. (Documents bibliographiques, no 1)

——— Supplément. no. 1-
septembre 1944-
⌊Rio de Janeiro, 1944-

v. 23 cm. (Documents bibliographiques, no 1)

Z2161.L6932

1. French literature—Bibl.

Z2161.L693 50-52908

NL 0423382 DLC

Livres illustrés des XVIe et XVIIIe; somptueuses reliures romantiques mosaïquées . . . éditions originales . . . très beaux livres modernes illustrés, importantes reliures . . . provenant de la bibliothèque d'un amateur. Vente du 28 février, 1939. Paris: A. Blaizot & fils, 1939. 56 p. col'd front., plates. 27cm.

42493B. 1. Bookbinding, French—Collections, Private. 2. Illustrated books—Bibl.—Catalogues. I. Blaizot, Auguste, &' fils, Paris.
N. Y. P. L. September 30, 1940

NL 0423383 NN

Livres modernes; ouvrages avec le portrait des auteurs ... oeuvres des Goncourt ...
see under [Goncourt, Louis Antoine Huot de] 1822-1896.

Livres rares et précieux, manuscrits, dessins, peintures, etc.
see under Grosseuvre,

Livres religieux
see Catalogue collectif des livres religieux.

Les livres roses pour la jeunesse.
Paris, 19-

Analyzed

NL 0423387 DLC ScU

Les livres secrets des confesseurs dévoilés aux pères de famille
see under [Jogand-Pagès, Gabriel Antoine] 1854-1907.

VOLUME 337

Livres sur les établissements français de l'Océanie et sur les mers adjacentes, dans la collection Kroepelien
see under Kroepelien, Bjarne.

Le Livret c'est le servage
see under Democratie Pacifique.

15
9445 Livret-chaix continental (services franco-internationaux et etrangers) Guide officiel des voyageurs sur tous les chemins de fer de l'Europe. [Etc. parais sant tous les mois] 35e annee. Janv. Juillet, 1880. Paris, A. Chaix & cie, [1880]
2 v. 16°.

NL 0423391 DLC

Livret-Chaix, continental (services franco-internationaux et étrangers) Guide officiel des voyageurs sur tous les chemins de fer de l'Europe. Paris, [1913]

NL 0423392 NjP

... Livret-Chaix colonial; guide officiel pour le transport des passagers et des marchandises à destinations des colonies françaises et dans l'intérieur de ces colonies, pub. sous le haut patronage du Ministère des colonies ... Paris, Librairie Chaix, 19
v. tables, maps. 27cm.

Cover-title.
Published in January and July.

1. France—Comm.—Direct. 2. France—Colonies—Comm. 3. Shippers' guides—France.

8-24656

Library of Congress HE9.F8L6

NL 0423393 DLC

Livret-Chaix; guide du visiteur à l'Exposition universelle de 1878
see under [Chaix, Napoleon] 1807-1869.

...Livret-Chaix, guide officiel des voyageurs spécial pour les chemins de fer de Paris à Lyon et à la Méditerranée; services entre Lyon, la Suisse et l'Italie... Paris: Chaix [1888]. xii, xxviii, 201-288 p. double map. 16°.

Cover-title.
At head of title: Service d'hiver. — Tirage du 1er avril 1888.
Advertising matter, p. viii-xii, i-xxviii.
With bookplate of T. B. M. Mason.
In: * C p. v. 1608, no. 2.

MYERS COLLECTION.

1. Railways.—Timetables, Europe.
N. Y. P. L. December 1, 1919.

NL 0423395 NN

Livret-Chaix. Guide officiel des voyageurs sur tous les chemins de fer français et les principaux chemins de fer étrangers ...

Paris, A. Chaix et cie., 18
v. maps. 17½cm.

After June 1879 this work appeared in 2 parts: "Livret-Chaix continental, partie étrangère," and "Livret-Chaix spécial pour la France." cf. Brit. mus. Catalogue.

1. Railroads — Europe — Time-tables. 2. Railroads — France — Time-tables. 3. Europe—Descr. & trav.—Guide-books.

CA 7—1048 Unrev'd

Library of Congress HE3004.L78

NL 0423396 DLC MBAt PPL NjP MH

LIVRET Chaix. Guide officiel sur le chemin de fer de ceinture et le reseau des environs. de Paris, Aout,1880. P. 1880.

Plans.

NL 0423397 MH

Livret-Chaix des environs de Paris, indiquant, pour toutes les localités
see under [Chaix, Napoléon] 1807-1865.

~~Fr 1633.02.70~~
Livret chrétien à l'usage des militaires pour le temps des missions. [Montpellier, 1921]

23 p.

NL 0423399 MH

Livret de commandemens en tableaux synoptiques de l'ordonnance de l'infanterie du 4 mars 1831
see under [France. Ministère de la guerre]

Le livret de l'etudiant de Montpellier publ sous les auspices du Conseil general des Facultes..

see

Montpellior, France. Universite. Annuaire et livret de l'etudiant...

Livret de l'Exposition de la jeunesse chez le peintre-expert J.-B. Lebrun en 1791
see under [Furcy-Raynaud, Marc] 1872-1922, ed.

Livret de l'exposition du Colisée, 1776
see under Paris. Colisée.

LIVRET de tempérance. Annee III.-V. Bruxelles,n.d.

3 vol. sm.8°.
At head of title: Ligue patriotique contre l'alcoolisme.

NL 0423404 MH

Le livret des ana
see under [Ludewig, Hermann Ernst] 1809-1856.

Livret des rues de Paris, carrefours, cours et passages
see under [Chaix, Napoléon] 1807-1865.

DT545
.L5 Livret-guide de la Côte d'Ivoire, publié à l'occasion de la cinquième conférence des Africanistes de l'Ouest, Abidjan et Adjopodoumé, décembre 1953. [Abidjan, Imp. de la Côte d'Ivoire, 1953]
78 p. illus., maps.

1. Ivory Coast.

NL 0423407 DS

Livret-guide du chargeur
see under Compagnie maritime des chargeurs reunis.

Livret-guide du Japon, 1923. 1923
see under Japan. Tetsudōshō.

Livret. Guide no. 1-10
see under [International geological congress. 12th, Toronto, 1913]

...Le livret medical et sanitaire (carnet de sante, individuel et prive) 1 ed...
RC4L
.L5 Paris, c1923
1 pam.12°

NL 0423411 DLC

LIVRET nouveau auquel sont contenuz. xxv. receptez esprouves de prendre poissons,canes et oyseaulx avec les mains,moclars,filetz et marses,etc., [Lyons,J.Moderne, cir,1530. Facsimile reprint, Paris, Goupil,1913.]

pp.50. Vign.
100 copies printed, no.20.
Text printed both in facsimile and in modern type.
Sait to be the first book on fishing published in French. It is a version of a Flemish tract,the "Boe..tken",published about 1492, which is the earliest printed work on fishing, an edition of Oppian excepted

NL 0423413 MH

LIVRET ou Guide a l'usage des voyageurs de Bayonne en Espagne. Bayonne, T.Detroyat, [18-?]

24°. pp.30.

NL 0423414 MH

Livrets des expositions de l'Académie...
see under Guiffrey, Jules Marie Joseph, 1840-1918.

Livrets des salons de Lille (1773-1788)
see under [Lille. Académie des arts]

VOLUME 337

Les livrets du bibliophile, publiés sous la direction de A.A.M. Stols. ⌈Maestricht, Éditions A.A.M. Stols, etc., etc., 1926⌉
10 v. 18cm.
"Il a été tiré ... 350 exx. numerótés ... ⌈no. XXII⌉"
Each volume has also special t.-p.
Contents. - no. 1. Nodier, C. Le bibliomane; conte fantastique. - no. 2. Claudel, P. La philosophie du livre. - no. 3. France, A. Le livre du bibliophile. no. 4. Aveline. C."Les désires"; ou, Le livre égaré. - no. 5. Mallarmé, S. Quant au livre. - no. 6. Valery, P. Notes sur le livre et le manuscrit. - no. 7. Flaubert, G. Bibliomanie; conte. - no. 8. Larbaud, V. Ce vice impuni, la lecture. - no. 9. Asselineau, C. L'enfer du bibliophile, vu et décrit par Charles Asselineau. - no. 10. Duhamel, G. Lettre sur les bibliophiles.
1.Bibliomania. I.Stols, Alexander Alphonse Marius, 1900-

NL 0423418 MnU DLC

PQ 1141 L76 Les Livrets du mandarin. 1. sér., no.1-10, 1923-24., 2. sér.,no.1-10, 1931-32; 3. sér., no.1-10, 1932-35; 4. sér., no.1-10, 1936-45.
Paris, "La Connaissance", 1923-
v. 21cm.
Supersedes Connaissance; revue des lettres et idées.
1. French literature - Collections.

NL 0423419 CLU MiU

Um livro. 1854.
see under [Castello Branco, Camillo] 1825-1890.

Z 8 .P8L79 O livro. Lisboa, Empreza do Diario de Noticias, 1925-
illus. (Collecção Patricia, 20, 43)
Edited by Albino Forjaz de Sampaio.
Includes bibliographies.
Contents.--[v.1, pt.1] Ex-libris.--[v.1, pt.2] História trágico-marítima.
1. Gomes de Brito, Bernardo, 1688 b., comp. História trágico-marítima. 2. Books--Hist.--Portugal. 3. Book-plates, Portuguese. I. Forjaz de Sampaio, Albino, 1884-, ed. II. Series.

NL 0423421 ICU

Livro azul; indicador commercial e profissional ⌈do Estado de Pernambuco⌉
⌈Recife⌉
v. illus. 29cm. annual.
1. Pernambuco, Brazil (State)—Comm.—Direct.
HF3409.P4L5 53-31305 ‡

NL 0423422 DLC

SP PQ 9151 L59 1803 LIVRO curiozo; anno de MDCCCIII. [1803?]
694, 28 [i.e. 56] p. (l. 27-28 blank)
Holograph.
Cover title.
Title burnt into cover.
1. Portuguese poetry - Selections: Extracts, etc.

NL 0423423 CaBVaU

... O livro da Corte imperial. Porto, Typ. Progresso de D. A. da Silva & c.ia, 1910.
16 p. l., 274 p., 1 l. 24cm. (Real bibliotheca publica municipal do Porto. Collecção de manuscriptos ineditos agora dados à estampa, I)
Half-title: Corte enperial.
Title-page of ms. (with red initial) reads: Este liuro he chamado Corte enperial o qual liuro he Dafonso Uaasquez de Caluos morador na çidade do Porto. Vasquez de Calvos is considered the owner, not the author of the book. cf. Introd. (signed: José Pereira de Sampaio)
I. Pereira de Sampaio, José, 1857- ed. II. Title: Corte enperial.
Library of Congress BX1750.L65 21-9899

NL 0423424 DLC NNH MoU OU MiU PU

Livro da homenagem ao grande pintor, José Malhôa, realizada, com a exposição das sua ⌈!⌉ obras, na Sociedade nacional de belas-artes em junho de 1928; com 100 reproduções de obras do mestre e mais 3 ilustrações. Lisboa, 1928.
112 p., 1 l. front., xcviii pl., ports. 25cm.
"Catálogo da grande exposição de homenagem a José Malhôa na Sociedade nacional de belas artes em junho de 1928": p. ⌈103⌉-112.
1. Malhôa, José, 1860- I. Sociedade nacional de belas artes, Lisbon.
Library of Congress ND833.M28L5 42-49002

NL 0423425 DLC NN MH

Livro da queima das fitas ...
see under Lisbon. Universidade técnica. Escola superior de medicina veterinária.

O Livro das creanças portuguezas e brazileiras, coordenado por D. João da Camara ⌈et al.⌉ Lisboa, Livraria Ferreira, 1909.
370 p. illus., ports. 21 cm.
Includes unsigned selections and a compilation of poetry and prose by various authors.
1. Children's literature. I. Camara, João da, 1852-1908.
PZ81.L5 49-30838*

NL 0423427 DLC NBuU

HG4109 .L5 O Livro das sociedades anonimas brasileiras; periodo de 1943 a 1945, historicos, relatorios, balanços de 4.500 companhias de todo o territorio nacional, 1946. Suplemento: "Que é o senhor" na industria e no comercio? Com indicações sobre 35.000 diretores e membros dos conselhos fiscais. São Paulo, Agencia Siciliano ⌈1946⌉
cxl, 1554 p. 27 cm.
1. Corporations—Brazil—Direct. 2. Directors of corporations—Brazil—Direct.
HG4109.L5 58-21089

NL 0423428 DLC WaS

LIVRO de cabeceira da mulher.
Rio de Janeiro, Editôa civilizaçao brasileira.
v. 21cm.
1. Periodicals--Brazil.

NL 0423429 NN

Livro de como se fazen as cores
see under Blondheim, David Simon, 1884-1934, ed.

"Livro de homenagem" aos professores Alvaro e Miguel Ozorio de Almeida. Editado por collegas, amigos, assistentes e discipulos em honra ás suas actividades scientificas. Rio de Janeiro, Brasil ⌈Typographia do Instituto Oswaldo Cruz⌉ 1939.
2 p. l., ⌈iii⌉-xlviii, 649, ⌈1⌉ p. illus., 8 pl., ports., tables (1 fold.) diagrs. 28cm.
German, Portuguese, English or French.
"Titulos e trabalhos scientificos dos professores Alvaro e Miguel Ozorio de Almeida": p. ⌈iii⌉-xx.
Includes bibliographies.
1. Physiology — Addresses, essays, lectures. 2. Ozorio de Almeida, Alvaro. 3. Ozorio de Almeida, Miguel, 1890-
U. S. Dept. of agr. Library for Library of Congress 444L76 QP71.O9 ⌈3⌉ Agr 41-526 612.04

NL 0423431 DNAL MnU-B ICRL NIC NNC MH ICJ CU

Livro de homenagem Romualdo Ferreira d'Almeida. Sao Paulo, 1946.

NL 0423432 DNAL

4BJ 338 Livro de instrucção e recreio. Com huma estampa fina. Dado á luz e publicado em Portuguez pela primeira vez. Lisboa, Impressão Regia, 1819.
188 p.

NL 0423433 DLC-P4

LIVRO de leitura para uso das escolas indigenas da provincia de Moçambique. 3a e 4a classe. Lourenço. Marques, Imp. nacional,1908.
"Vocabulario portuguez-ronga," pp.[I]-XLVI, at end.

NL 0423434 MH

Livro de marinharia de Bernardo Fernandes (cêrca de 1548) Pref. e notas por A. Fontoura da Costa. ⌈Lisboa⌉ Divisão de Publicações e Biblioteca, Agência Geral das Colónias, 1940.
242 p. illus. (part col.) 23 cm.
First ed. of a Vatican ms. (Borg. lat. 153) a part of which was written by Bernardo Fernandes. The compilation of the entire ms. also has been attributed to him.
1. Navigation—Early works to 1800. I. Fernandes, Bernardo, fl. 1548. II. Fontoura da Costa, Abel, 1869- ed.
VK144.L5 49-55803*

NL 0423435 DLC NSyU NN CSt IEN

Livro de marinharia; roteiros, sondas e outros conhecimentos relativos à navegação
see under Brito Rebello, Jacintho Ignacio de, 1830-1920.

VOLUME 337

... Livro de ouro; commemorativo da visita de Sua Magestade el-rei D. Carlos 1.º aos Estados Unidos do Brazil e da abertura dos portos ao commercio mundial. Lisboa, Escola typ. das Officinas de S. José, 1908.
xxxix, 296 p. illus., plates, ports. 35½cm.
Title and text within ornamental borders.
At head of title: Homenagem ao Brazil e Portugal.
"Tiragem especial 1050 exemplares. Exemplar nº. 0843."
1. Portugal—For. rel.—Brazil. 2. Brazil—For. rel.—Portugal. 3. Carlos I, king of Portugal, 1863-1908. 4. Portugal—Biog. 5. Brazil—Biog. 6. Portuguese in Brazil.
Library of Congress F2508.L78 9—2383

NL 0423437 DLC ICN CSt

O livro de Reporter X; obsequiosa colaboração de Adelino Mendes, Aguinaldo Escaleira, Belo Redondo [and others] Lisboa, Agencia Editorial Brasileira [193- ?]

NL 0423438 MH

O livro do Aglais
see under Brandão, Julio, 1870-

PQ9217 .C80P5
Livro do centenario de Camões em 1880.
Pinheiro Chagas, Manuel, 1842-1895.
Festas do centenario em Lisboa e da Academia das Sciencias. [Lisboa, E. Riché, 1880?]

O Livro do centenario de Camões (prospecto)
see under [Riche, Emilio] ed.

Livro do centenário de Eça de Queiroz. Lisboa, Rio [de Janeiro] Edições Dois mundos [1945]
717 p., 1 l. incl. front. pl., ports., facsims. 24½cm.
On cover: Organizado por Lúcia Migual Pereira e Câmara Reyes.
Bibliographical foot-notes.
1. Eça de Queiroz, José Maria, 1845-1900. I. Miguel Pereira, Lucia, ed.
PQ9261.E3Z732 928.69 A 47-3157
Yale univ. Library for Library of Congress [2]

NL 0423442 CtY CaBVaU NcU PSt TxU MH NN DLC NNC MiU InU TNJ MoSU KU

Livro do centenario dos cursos juridicos [1827-1927]
see under Rio de Janeiro. Universidade. Faculdade de direito.

Livro do instrucção e Recreio com huma estempa fina...dado à luz e publicado em Portuguez pela primeria vez. Lisboa, Na Impressão Regia, 1819.

NL 0423444 DLC

HJ 9531 .L5 L53
Livro do lançamento e serviço que a Cidade de Lisboa fez el Rei Nosso Senhor no ano de 1565; documentos para a historia da Cidade de Lisboa. Lisboa, Câmara Municipal, 1947-48.
4 v. 27 cm.
Cover title.
"Um códice quinhentista que se guarda no Arquivo Histórico da Câmara Municipal de Lisboa."
1. Taxation—Lisbon—Lists. I. Lisbon. Camara Municipal.
HJ9531.L5L53 51-17629 rev

NL 0423445 DLC ICU MH I OrU

Livro dos municípios do estado de São Paulo. 1950- São Paulo, Livraria Martins.
v. 28 cm.
1. Cities and towns—Brazil—São Paulo (State) 2. São Paulo, Brazil (State)—Direct.
F2631.L685 52-28093

NL 0423446 DLC CU

Greenlee 4582 L69 1941
O LIVRO grande de Sampayo; ou, Livro dos vedores de Ceuta (1505-1670) Coimbra, 1941.
419p. facsims. 25cm.
At head of title: José de Bsaguy.
"Separata de O Instituto, vols.93, 94, 97, 99 e 101."

NL 0423447 ICN CU InU

Livro insigne das Flores e perfeicoens das vidas dos gloriosos sanctos do velho e nouo testamento
see under Marulus, Marcus, 1450-1524.

Livro jubilar do professor Lauro Travassos, editado para commemorar o 25° anniversario de suas actividades scientificas (1913-1938) Rio de Janeiro, Brasil [Typographia do Instituto Oswaldo Cruz] 1938.
1 p. l., xx, 589, [1] p. illus., plates, map, port., tables (part fold.) diagrs. 27½cm.
Articles in English, Portuguese, French, Spanish, Italian, and German.
Descriptive letterpress on versos facing plates.
Bibliography at end of most of the articles.
1. Travassos, Lauro. 2. Parasites.
A 42-4999
Cornell univ. Library for Library of Congress [3]

NL 0423449 NIC CU NcRS DNAL NcU PPAN CtY-M LU NNC PU-BZ CtY ICU DPU ICJ

Livro I [i. e. primeiro] de misticos de reis. Libro II dos reis D. Dinis, D. Afonso IV, D. Pedro I; documentos para a historia da cidade de Lisboa. [Lisboa, Camara Municipal, 1947]
viii, 270 p. facsims. 28 cm.
1. Lisbon—Hist.—Sources.
DP752.L54 57-24300

NL 0423450 DLC IU CU ICU MH

Livro I [i. e. primeiro] de misticos. Livro II [i. e. segundo] del rei dom Fernando. Documentos para a história da cidade de Lisboa. [Lisboa, Câmara Municipal de Lisboa, 1949]
vii, 316 p. facsims. 27 cm.
Documents belonging to the historical archives of the Câmara Municipal de Lisboa.
1. Lisbon — History — Sources. I. Lisbon. Câmara Municipal. II. Title: Livro segundo del rei dom Fernando. II. Title: Documentos para a história da cidade de Lisboa.
DP756.L53 73-203310

NL 0423451 DLC MH

Livro primeiro- de Tombo das propriedades foreiras à Camara desta muy insigne cidade de Lisboa; documentos para a historia da cidade de Lisboa. [Lisboa, Camara Municipal, 1950-
v. facsims. 28 cm.
1. Lisbon—Hist.—Sources.
DP752.L56 57-24308

NL 0423452 DLC CaBVaU OrU MH

Rare Book Dept. *XG .3656 .11 no.1
[Livron, de]
Faits justificatifs du sieur de Livron, accusé de crime de leze-nation, & détenu dans les prisons depuis le 6 octobre.
[Paris] De l'impr.de Letellier & André,rue de Savoie,nº.10. [1790]
14p. 21.5cm.(8vo)
Half-title; imprint from p.14.

NL 0423453 MB

Livron, Andreĭ Karlovich de.
Anglo-Russian marine dictionary. Containing a collection of technical sea-terms and commanding words. By Capt. A. de Livron... London: S. Low, Marston & co. [etc., etc.] 1894. 162 p. 24cm.
223612B. N. Y. P. L. 1. Nautical dictionaries, English-Russian. April 16, 1943

NL 0423454 NN DNW DN

M1503 L54F13
Livron, P de
Fabius; ou, Les martyrs. Paris, Le Bailly [1883?]
Pl. no. L. B. 2296.
15 p.
Imperfect copy: t. p. wanting.
Composer's name in ink on first page.
I. Title. II. Les martyrs.

NL 0423455 CU

Livros; mensário da vida literária portuguesa ... no. 1- março 1925-
Lisboa, F. Machadó & c.ª l.da, 1925-
v. illus. (incl. ports.) 26cm.
Editors: Mar. 1925- Salvador Saboya and others.
1. Portuguese literature—Bibl.—Period. 2. Bibliography—Period. I. Saboya, Salvador, ed.
Library of Congress Z2715.L78 34-20118
[2] 015.469

NL 0423456 DLC

VOLUME 337

CS 964 .L78
Livros de linhagens. Lisboa, Eds.Biblion, 1937-
v.

CS 964 .L78 Index
CONTENTS.--Livro velho 1.--Livro velho 2. ---Indice onomástico. Lisboa ⌜Horus, 1964- v. (Gabinete de Estudos Heráldicos e genealógicos. Caderno de estudos)

1.Portugal--Geneal. 2.Portugal--Nobility. I.Title: Livro velho.

NL 0423457 MiU CU

Livros de Portugal.

Lisboa.

v. in illus. 23 cm. monthly.

Began publication in 1941?
"Menário bibliográfico do Gremio Nacional dos Editores e Livreiros."

1. Portuguese literature—Bibl.—Period. I. Gremio Nacional dos Editores e Livreiros.

Z2715.L783 49-40106*

ICN PU CU-I
NL 0423458 DLC CU IaU MiU IU NN OU FTaSU WaU CStbS

Livros de Portugal, ltda., *Rio de Janeiro.*
Catálogo da exposição do livro português, apresentado por Livros de Portugal, ltda ⌜na Biblioteca Nacional⌝ Rio de Janeiro ⌜194-⌝
vii, 268 p. 18 cm.

1. Portuguese literature—Bibl.—Catalogs. I. Title.

Z2739.Z9L6 48-42479*

NL 0423459 DLC CU

Livros do Brasil. Colleção de obras-primas da literatura national dirigida por Afrânio Peixoto.
v. 1

São Paulo ⌜etc.⌝ Companhia editora nacional, 1942 20cm.
v. in ports.

1. Brazilian literature—Collections. I. Peixoto, Afrânio, 1876- , ed.
N. Y. P. L. November 6, 1942

NL 0423460 NN OO

Os liuros quarto & quĩto da Historia do descobrimento & cõquista da India pelos Portugueses ...
see under [Lopes de Castanheda, Fernão] d. 1559.

Livrustkammaren, *Stockholm*
see **Stockholm. Livrustkammaren.**

Livrustkammaren; journal of the Royal Armoury.

Stockholm.

v. illus., ports. 22 cm. irregular.

Began publication in 1937. Cf. Sweden. Riksdagen. Bibliotek. Arsbibliografi över sveriges offentliga publikationer.
Chiefly Swedish and English.

1. Arms and armour—Period. I. Stockholm. Livrustkammaren.

U800.A1L5 52-25306

NL 0423463 DLC NN DS

[Livry, Charles, marquis de] 1802-1867.
Le coup de pistolet; comedie-vaudeville en un acte, ... Paris, 1828.
35 p. 8°. [In Bibl. dram., 2e sér, t. 44]
I. Ribbing, Adolphe, comte.

NL 0423464 CtY

Livry, Charles, marquis de, 1802–1867.
Madame Peterhoff, vaudeville-anecdote en un acte, par MM. Charles de Livry, Antonin D. ⌜pseud.⌝ et Roche, représenté pour la première fois, à Paris, sur le théâtre des Variétés, le 16 août 1836. ⌜Paris: Marchant, 1836⌝ 14 p. 25cm. (Magasin théâtral. Tome 14 ⌜no. 5⌝)

Caption-title.
Tunes of the incidental songs and choruses indicated by title.

38583B. 1. Drama, French. I. Petitjean, Ernest Georges, jt. au. II. Roche, Eugène, jt. au. III. Title. IV. Ser.
N. Y. P. L. May 13, 1941

NL 0423465 NN CU ICRL NNC

Micro-card 57-11 ser.2 no.2055
Livry, Charles de, 1802-1867.
Madame Peterhoff, vaudeville-anecdote en un acte, par MM. Charles de Livry, Antonin D. et Roche. ⌜Paris, Marchant, 1836. Louisville, Ky., Falls City Press, 1962⌝
1 card. ⌜Three centuries of French drama. ser.2: 17th, 18th and 19th centuries, no.2055⌝
Microcard edition.
Collation of original: 14 p.
I. D , Antonin, joint author. II. Roche, Eugène, joint author. III. Title.

NL 0423466 AU

[Livry, Charles, marquis de] 1802-1867.
Um naufragio nas costas da Bretanha. Drama em 4 actos. Traduzido do francez, por Joaquim Jose Annaya. Lisboa, V.A. dos Santos, 1866.
87 p. 8°.
In: NQM p. v. 88, no. 10.
I. Ambroise.

NL 0423467 NN

Livry, Charles, marquis de, 1802-1867.
Polichinelle vampire;grande pantomime dans le genre italien,à grand spectacle,en 15 tableaux, mêlée de dialogues,de métamorphoses,de travestissements et de danses. Par MM.Charles et Vautier. Représentée,pour la première fois,a Paris,sur le Théatre des Funambules,le 25 mai 1850. Paris,Dechaume,[18-].

sq.16°. pp.8.

NL 0423468 MH

---

ar W 7250
Livry, Charles, marquis de, 1802-1867.
La salamandre, comédie-vaudeville en quatre actes, par MM. Ch. de Livry, de Forges et Ad. de Leuven. ... Paris, Barba, 1834.
30 p. 24cm.

No. 7 in vol. lettered: Théatre parisien.

NL 0423469 NIC

Livry, Charles, marquis de, 1802-1867.
La salamandre; comédie-vaudeville en quatre actes, par M.M. Ch. de Livry, de Forges [pseud.] et Ad. de Leuven [pseud.] ... Bruxelles, 1840.
p. 16°. [In Bibl. dram., 4esér., t. 62]
I. Pitaud (Philippe Auguste Alfred. II. Ribbing (Adolphe, comte)]

NL 0423470 CtY

Livry,Charles,marquis de,1802-1867.
Le tir au pistolet,vaudeville en un acte et en deux tableaux; par mm.Charles ⌜pseud.⌝ Adolphe ⌜pseud⌝ et Masson ... Paris, J.-N. Barba, 1829.

2 p.l.,⌜3⌝-34 p. 20cm.

No.16 in volume lettered Théatre du vaudeville ⌜v.38⌝

I.Leuvin,Adolphe de,1800-1884, joint author. II. Masson,Michel,1800-1883, joint author. III.Title.

NL 0423471 MiU

Livry, Charles, marquis de, 1802-1867, joint author.
Théaulon de Lambert, Marie Emmanuel Guillaume Marguerite, 1787-1841.
La Tyrolienne, comédie-vaudeville en un acte, imitée de Goethe; par MM. Théaulon, Adolphe ⌜*pseud.*⌝ et Charles ⌜*pseud.*⌝ Représentée, pour la première fois, sur le Théatre des nouveautés, le 7 juillet 1829 ... Paris, J. N. Barba, 1829.

Music ML 410 G83L5
Livry, Hippolyte, comte de, 1771-1822.
Recueil de mes réponses aux journalistes, et de mes rebuts des journaux. [Paris,1807]
1v. (various paging) 22cm.

Bound with the author's Recueil de lettres écrites à Grétry ou a son sujet [Paris, 1809?]

1. Grétry, André Ernest Modeste, 1741-1813. I. Title.

NL 0423473 MU

Livry, Hippolyte, *comte* **de,** 1771-1822.
Recueil de lettres écrites à Grétry ou à son sujet par Hypolite de Livry ... Paris, Ogier ⌜1809?⌝
vij, 157 p. 21½cm.

1. Grétry, André Ernest Modeste, 1741-1813.

17-1370

Library of Congress ML410.G83L5

NL 0423474 DLC MU

Music ML 410 G83L5
Livry, Hippolyte, comte de, 1771-1822.
Reflexions morales, et probablement fort inutiles. Paris,Ogier,1807.
80p. 22cm.

Bound with the author's Recueil de lettres écrites à Grétry ou à son sujet [Paris, 1809?]

1. Ethics. 2. Social ethics. I. Title.

NL 0423475 MU

Livry, Hippolyte, comte de, 1771-1822.
Retour de l'empereur.
Paris, 1815

[Napoleon pamphlets, v. 16, no. 12]

DC197 .N2

NL 0423476 DLC

Livry, Hippolyte, comte de, 1771-1822.
Seconde suite au Retour de l'empereur.
Paris, 1815

[Napoleon pamphlets, v. 16, no. 14]

DC197 .N2

NL 0423477 DLC

VOLUME 337

Livry, Hippolyte, comte de, 1771-1822.
Suite au Retour de l'empereur.
Paris, 1815

[Napoleon pamphlets, v. 16, no. 13]

DC197
.N2

NL 0423478 DLC

Livry-Level, Philippe, pseud.
see
Renault-Roulier, Gilbert, 1904-

BX8079
.L5

Livsbilleder fra den lutherske kirke i Amerika. Decorah, Iowa, Norske synodes forlag ₍19--?₎
315 p. ports. 23 cm.

Contents.--Dr. C.F.W. Walther.--Herman Amberg Preus.--Friedrich C.D. Wyneken.--Nils Thorbjørnsen Ylvisaker.--Jakob M. Buehler.--Knut Ellefsen Bergh.--Jacob Aall Ottesen.

NL 0423480 MnHi NdU

274.8
L767

Livsbilleder fra kirken i Norden... Chicago. Lutherforeningen, 1888.
2v. in 1.

Contents.- 1.del. Ansgarius. Olaf den Hellige Thomas von Westen. Hans Egede.- 2.del. Thomas Kingo. Hans Adolph Bronson. Peder Dass. Erik Pontoppidan.

1. Scandinavia--Church history. 2. Scandinavia--Biog.

NL 0423481 IU NdU

Livschitz, Nahum.
Ueber das Romershausen'sche inductorium ... Uster, Druck von A. Diggelmann, 1886.
36 p. illus., diagrs. on 2 pl. 22½cm.
Inaug.-diss.—Zürich.

1. Induction coils.

9-20589

Library of Congress QC645.L7

NL 0423482 DLC

Livsey, Richard, ed.
The prisoners of 1776; a relic of the Revolution. Comp. from the journal of Charles Herbert, of Newburyport, Mass. (1777-1780), who was taken prisoner, Dec. 1776. 1847.

NL 0423483 RP

021.7
L7881

Livsey, Rosemary Earnshaw, 1898-
... Library news and reviews ... [Chicago, Ill., American library association, 1940]
9 numb.l.
Caption title.
Mimeographed.
At head of title: Written by Rosemary Livsey of Los Angeles public library. Adapted for Wichita city library. Wichita city library, Kansas, March 16,1939 ...

1. Libraries. 2. Publicity. I. Wichita, Kan. Public library.

NL 0423484 IU

Livsey, Stella Morse.
. . . Children's musical moments. A new natural method for the pianoforte especially adapted to children from six to eight years of age, by Stella Morse Livsey. Boston ₍etc.₎ The B. F. Wood music co. ₍c1910₎ Publ. pl. no. B. F. W. 3788. 43 p. 31cm. (On cover: Edition Wood. no. 614.)

For piano with interlinear words.

1. Children's music—Piano. 2. Piano—Methods. 3. Children's music—Songs, U. S. I. Title.
N. Y. P. L. June 25, 1942

NL 0423485 NN

Livsey, Stella Morse.
Pleasant paths to piano playing, by Stella Morse Livsey. Boston: O. Ditson Co. ₍1921.₎ Publ. pl. no. 74018. 48 p. f°.

1. Piano.
N. Y. P. L. March 28, 1922.

NL 0423486 NN

Livsforsikringsanstalten i Kjøbenhavn.

Foreløbig beretning om opgjørelsen af dødeligheden i Livrente- og forsørgelses-anstalten af 1842 samt Livsforsikkrings-anstalten i Kjøbenhavn i aarene 1842 til 1868, og disse anstalters status den 31te dec. 1868. Kjøbenhavn, Trykt hos J. H. Schultz, 1870.

Livsforsikringsselskapet Gjensidige.
Gjensidige gjennom hundre år, 1847-1947. Oslo, Grøndahl, 1947.
2 v. in 1. illus., ports., plan.

NL 0423488 MH-BA

QA1
.A526
no.44
1951

Livshits, A Kh
On the Jordan-Hölder theorem in structures, by A. H. Livšic₍!₎ New York, American Mathematical Society, 1951.
15 p. 23cm. (American Mathematical Society. Translation, no. 44)
Translated from his O teoreme Zhordana-Gel'dera v strukturakh <Matematicheskii sbornik (n. s.) 24(66), 227-235 (1949 >
Bibliography: p. 15.
I. Title: Jordan-Hölder theorem in structures. II. Ser.

NL 0423489 ViU MH CaBVaU NIC

DK268
.3
.L58

Livshiťs, A L
Повышение материального и культурного уровня жизни народа—непреложный закон социализма. Стенограмма публичной лекции, прочитанной в Москве. Москва ₍Правда₎ 1950.
31 p. 22 cm.
At head of title: Всесоюзное общество по распространению политических и научных знаний.

1. Russia—Soc. condit. I. Title.
Title transliterated: Povyshenie material'nogo i kul'turnogo urovnia zhizni naroda.

DK268.3.L58 52-42871

NL 0423490 DLC

---

q620.17 L76p

Livshits, B G
Plastic deformation of cementite in steel, by B. G. Livshits and B. N. Orlov. ₍Altadena, Calif., H. Brutcher Technical Translations, 1950?₎
4l. diagrs. 30cm. (Brutcher translation no. 2523)
Caption title.
"Translated from Doklady Akademii nauk SSSR, vol. 70, 1950, no.2, pages 229-230)
Bibliography: leaf 4.

NL 0423491 IU

Livshiťs, B. O., ed.

HJ1210
.K35

Карманная книжка финработника.

Ленинград, Госфиниздат СССР.

PG3476
.B83E5

Livshiťs, Benedikt Konstantinovich, 1886- 1939.
Гилея. ₍New York₎ М. Бурлюк, 1931.
15 p. illus., ports. 32 cm.
Bound with Burliuk, D. D. Энтелехизм. New York ₍1930₎
Bibliography: p. ₍2₎

1. Burliuk, David Davidovich, 1882- I. Title.
Title transliterated: Gileia.

PG3476.B83E5 53-54083

NL 0423493 DLC

Livshiťs, Benedikt Konstantinovich, 1886-
От романтиков до сюрреалистов; антология французской поэзии. Ленинград, Время ₍1934₎
190 p. 16 cm.
At head of title: Бенедикт Лившиц.

1. French poetry—Translations into Russian. 2. Russian poetry—Translations from French. I. Title.
Title romanized: Ot romantikov do siurrealistov.

PQ1170.R8L5 68-34391

NL 0423494 DLC

PG
3065
.F8L5

Livshiťs, Benedikt Konstantinovich, 1886-
Polutoraglazyĭ strelets. [Leningrad] Izd-vo pisateleĭ v Leningrade [1933]
295p. illus.
At head of title: Benedikt Livshits.
In Cyrillic characters.
Photocopy. Ann Arbor, Mich., University Microfilms, 1972. 21cm.

1. Futurism. 2. Russian poetry--20th century--History and criticism. I. Title

NL 0423495 NhD WU

TN140
.C5L5

Livshiťs, Boris Grigor'evich.
Д. К. Чернов и мировое значение его работ по металловедению; стенограмма публичной лекции, прочитанной в Москве. Москва ₍Правда₎ 1949.
23 p. diagrs. 22 cm.
At head of title: Всесоюзное общество по распространению политических и научных знаний.

1. Chernov, Dmitriĭ Konstantinovich, 1839-1921. 2. Iron—Metallography.
Title transliterated: D. K. Chernov.

TN140.C5L5 50-24142 rev

NL 0423496 DLC

TA490
.L5
1946

Livshiťs, Boris Grigor'evich.
Физические свойства сплавов. Утверждено в качестве учебника для металлургических вузов. 2. перер. изд. Москва, Гос. научно-техн. изд-во лит-ры по черной и цветной металлургии, 1946.
320 p. diagrs. 23 cm.
Errata slip inserted.

1. Alloys. I. Title.
Title transliterated: Fizicheskie svoĭstva splavov.

TA490.L5 1946 52-25476 rev

NL 0423497 DLC

VOLUME 337

TN140 .M6L5
Livshit͡s, Boris Grigor'evich, ed.
Н. А. Минкевич—выдающийся ученый-инженер. Москва, Гос. научно-техн. изд-во машиностроит. лит-ры, 1955.
185, [3] p. ports., diagrs., facsims. 23 cm.
Bibliography: p. 168–[180]
1. Minkevich, Nikolaĭ Anatol'evich, 1883–1942.
Title transliterated: N. A. Minkevich—vydai͡ushchiĭsi͡a uchenyĭ-inzhener.
TN140.M6L5 56–32721
NL 0423498 DLC

TA490 .L53
Livshit͡s, Boris Grigor'evich.
Высококоэрцитивные сплавы. Москва, Гос. научно-техн. изд-во лит-ры по черной и цветной металлургии, 1945.
121, [3] p. diagrs. 22 cm.
Errata slip inserted.
Bibliography: p. 120–[122]
1. Alloys. I. Title.
Title transliterated: Vysokokoėrt͡sitivnye splavy
TA490.L53 54–53460
NL 0423499 DLC

Livshit͡s, Boris Samoĭlovich.
Автоматизация внутрирайонной телефонной связи. Москва, Гос. изд-во лит-ры по вопросам связи и радио, 1953.
44, [4] p. diagrs. 23 cm. (Лекции по технике связи)
Bibliography: p. [46]
1. Telephone, Automatic. I. Title.
Title transliterated: Avtomatizat͡sii͡a vnutriraĭonnoĭ telefonnoĭ svi͡azi.
TK6397.L5 54–23722 rev
NL 0423500 DLC

Livshit͡s, E. O., joint author.
Bakhareva, M A
... Français. Часть v; учебник французского языка для 9 и 10 класса средней школы. Под методической редакцией Н. Тенновой ... Москва, Государственное учебно-педагогическое издательство Наркомпроса РСФСР, 1940.

Livshit͡s, E S
Детская беспризорность и новые формы борьбы с нею; методическое письмо работникам социально-правовой охраны. Москва, Работник просвещения, 1924–
v. 24 cm.
At head of title, v. 1– : Е. С. Лившиц.
Includes bibliographical references.
1. Children — Institutional care — Russia. 2. Juvenile delinquency—Russia. I. Title.
Title romanized: Detskai͡a besprizornost' i novye formy bor'by s nei͡u.
HV1213.L57 72–218104
NL 0423502 DLC

HG3124 .L58
Livshit͡s, Fedor Davydovich.
Банки Союза СССР. Москва, Фин. изд-во, 1925.
80 p. 19 cm. (Банковская библиотека, вып. 2)
1. Banks and banking—Russia. I. Title. (Series: Bankovskai͡a biblioteka, vyp. 2)
Title transliterated: Banki Soi͡uza SSR.
HG3124.L58 50–51288 rev
NL 0423503 DLC

Livshit͡s, Fedor Davydovich.
Банковая статистика, с основами общей теории. [2. перер. изд.] Москва, Госфиниздат, 1948.
424 p. 23 cm.
Bibliography: p. [414]–420.
1. Banks and banking—Stat. 2. Banks and banking—Russia—Stat. I. Title.
Title transliterated: Bankovai͡a statistika.
HG1588.L5 1948 50–16526 rev
NL 0423504 DLC OrU

Livshit͡s, Fedor Davydovich, joint author.
HF5693 .I 53
Isakov, Vasiliĭ Ivanovich.
Финансовые вычисления. Допущено в качестве учеб. пособия для финансовых и финансово-кредитных техникумов. Москва, Госфиниздат, 1955.

QA73 .L55
Livshit͡s, Fedor Davydovich.
Счетная линейка для экономистов; пособие для работников статистики, учета и планирования. Москва, Гос. статистическое изд-во, 1954.
174 p. illus. 22 cm.
——— Microfilm copy (negative)
Made in 1955 by the Library of Congress.
Microfilm Slavic 590 AC
1. Slide-rule. I. Title.
Title transliterated: Schetnai͡a lineĭka dli͡a ėkonomistov.
QA73.L55 55–29989 rev
NL 0423506 DLC

HD8529 .G43L5
Livshit͡s, I
Орденоносцы легкой промышленности Грузии; вступ. статья Г. А. Джабуа. Москва, Гос. изд-во легкой промышл., 1941.
23 p. illus., ports. 23 cm.
1. Labor and laboring classes—Georgia (Transcaucasia) 2. Socialist competition. I. Title.
Title transliterated: Ordenonost͡sy legkoĭ promyshlennosti.
HD8529.G43L5 49–57787*
NL 0423507 DLC

HD8039 .T42R86
Livshit͡s, I
Передовые текстильщики Грузии. Вступ. статья Л. А. Рухадзе. Москва, Гос. изд-во легкой промышл., 1941.
19 p. illus. 23 cm.
1. Textile workers—Georgia (Transcaucasia) I. Title.
Title transliterated: Peredovye tekstil'shchiki Gruzii.
HD8039.T42R86 61–57683 ‡
NL 0423508 DLC

Livshit͡s, I. I., ed.
TN343 .K46
Kharkov. T͡Sentral'nyĭ zaochnyĭ gornyĭ institut.
Горная электротехника и механика. Под ред. И. И. Лившица. Харьков, Гос. научно-техн. изд-во Украины, 1934.

Livshit͡s, I. I͡A., ed.
Law
Russia (1923– U. S. S. R.) *Laws, statutes, etc.*
Договоры и арбитраж в местной промышленности; сборник руководящих материалов. [Составитель И. А. Лившиц] Москва, Гос. изд-во местной промышл., 1948–

Livshit͡s, I͡A L *writer on military history.*
Первая гвардейская танковая бригада в боях за Москву. Москва, Воен. изд-во, 1948.
258 p. plates, ports. 21 cm.
1. Moscow, Battle of, 1941–1942. 2. Russia (1923– U. S. S. R.). Armii͡a. 1. gvardeĭskai͡a tankovai͡a brigada.
Title transliterated: Pervai͡a gvardeĭskai͡a tankovai͡a brigada.
D764.3.M6L5 49–25821 rev*
NL 0423511 DLC

Livshit͡s, I͡Akov Borisovich, joint ed.
Весь Петроград. 1922 г. Под редакцией А. И. Гессена и Я. Б. Лившица. [Петроград] Издательство "Петроград" [1922?]

TL671 .2 .L5
Livshit͡s, I͡Akov Davidovich.
Строительная механика самолета. Допущено в качестве учеб. пособия для авиационных ин-тов. Москва, Глав. ред. авиационной лит-ры, 1946.
403 p. diagrs., tables. 23 cm.
Bibliography: p. 397–[398]
——— Microfilm.
Negative film in the Library of Congress.
Microfilm Slavic 150 AC
Call No.———
1. Aeroplanes—Design and construction. I. Title.
Title transliterated: Stroitel'nai͡a mekhanika samoleta.
TL671.2.L5 54–18025 rev
NL 0423513 DLC CLSU

Livshit͡s, Iosif I͡Ul'evich.
Панська Польща—аванпост інтервенції. [Харків] Пролетар, 1931.
52 p. 18 cm.
Author's pseud., В. Юльський, at head of title.
1. Poland—Hist.—1918–1945. I. Title. II. Title: Pol'shcha—avanpost interventsiï.
Title transliterated: Pans'ka Pol'shcha—avanpost interventsiï.
DK440.L5 55–52293 rev ‡
NL 0423514 DLC

Livshit͡s, Isaak Grigor'evich, ed.
PJ1095 .C44
Champollion, Jean François, 1790–1832.
О египетском иероглифическом алфавите. Перевод, ред. и комментарии И. Г. Лившица. [Москва] Изд-во Академии наук СССР, 1950.

HF5439 .E4L5
Livshit͡s, I͡U L
Электротовары бытового назначения; пособие для продавцов. Москва, Госторгиздат, 1947.
46 p. illus. 22 cm. (В помощь продавцу)
1. Salesmen and salesmanship. 2. Electric apparatus and appliances. I. Title.
Title transliterated: Ėlektrotovary.
HF5439.E4L5 49–19590*
NL 0423516 DLC

VOLUME 337

HF5845 .L5
Livshit͡s, I͡U L
Витрина магазина. Москва, Госторгиздат, 1946.
39 p. illus. 20 cm.
Bibliography on p. [3] of cover.

1. Show-windows. I. Title.
Title transliterated: Vitrina magazina.

HF5845.L5 51-32548

NL 0423517 DLC

SD207 .L5
Livshit͡s, M D
Промышленное освоение лесов [СССР] итоги и перспективы. Москва, Гос. лесное техн. изд-во, 1933.
55 p. 18 cm.
Errata slip inserted.

1. Forests and forestry—Russia. 2. Lumber trade—Russia.
Title transliterated: Promyshlennoe osvoenie lesov.

SD207.L5 50-43874

NL 0423518 DLC

Livshit͡s, Mark L'vovich.
Окраска и отделка изделий массового потребления. Под ред. В. С. Киселева. Москва, Гос. изд-во местной промышл. РСФСР, 1955.
295 p. illus. 22 cm.
At head of title: М. Л. Лившиц и И. Н. Колотухин.
Bibliography: p. 193-[194]

1. Painting, Industrial. I. Kolotukhin, I. N.
Title transliterated: Okraska i otdelka izdelii massovogo potreblenii͡a.

TT305.L48 56-35267 rev

NL 0423519 DLC

Livshit͡s, Moiseĭ L'vovich.
Быстроходные дизели Д6. В помощь механикам и мотористам. Изд. 2., доп. и испр. Москва, Гос. научно-техн. изд-во машиностроит. лит-ры, 1954.
262 p. illus. 23 cm.

1. Diesel motor. I. Title.
Title transliterated: Bystrokhodnye dizeli D6.

TJ795.5.L58 1954 55-27666 rev

NL 0423520 DLC

Livshit͡s, Raisa Solomonovna.
Очерки по размещению промышленности СССР. [Ленинград] Гос. изд-во полит. лит-ры, 1954.
358 p. 21 cm.
At head of title: Академия наук СССР. Институт экономики.
——— Microfilm copy (negative)
Microfilm Slavic 781 AC

1. Russia—Indus. 2. Industries, Location of—Russia. I. Title.
Title transliterated: Ocherki po razmeshchenii͡u promyshlennosti SSSR.

HC335.L585 54-42275 rev

NL 0423521 DLC CaBVaU CtY

HC333 .L54
Livshit͡s, Raisa Solomonovna.
Размещение промышленности в дореволюционной России. Москва, Изд-во Академии наук СССР, 1955.
293, [3] p. map, diagrs. 20 cm.
At head of title: Академия наук СССР. Институт экономики.
Bibliography: p. 287-[294]

1. Russia—Indus.—Hist. I. Title.
Title transliterated: Razmeshchenie promyshlennosti v dorevoli͡ut͡sionnoĭ Rossii.

HC333.L54 56-34170 rev

NL 0423522 DLC

Livshit͡s, S I͡A
Феррорезонансные стабилизаторы напряжения. Рекомендовано в качестве пособия для радиоклубов. Москва, Гос. энерг. изд-во, 1951.
47 p. diagrs. 20 cm. (Массовая радиобиблиотека, вып. 91)

1. Voltage regulators. I. Title.
Title transliterated: Ferrorezonansnye stabilizatory.

TK6565.V6L5 54-17509

NL 0423523 DLC

Livshit͡s, S V *comp.*
... Кадры специалистов; сборник законодательных и ведомственных постановлений о подготовке специалистов и о снабжении ими народного хозяйства. Москва, Советское законодательство, 1931.
169, [4] p. 17cm.
At head of title: С. Лившиц.

1. Educational law and legislation—Russia. 2. Technical education—Russia. 3. Vocational education—Russia. I. Russia (1923- U. S. S. R.) Laws, statutes, etc. II. Russia (1917- R. S. F. S. R.) Laws, statutes, etc. III. Title.

34-39023

NL 0423524 DLC

Livshit͡s, S V *comp.*
... Рабочие кадры; сборник действующего законодательства и ведомственных распоряжений о подготовке рабочих кадров и о снабжении ими народного хозяйства. Москва, Советское законодательство, 1931.
215 p. 17½cm.
At head of title: С. Лившиц.

1. Labor laws and legislation—Russia. 2. Vocational education—Russia. 3. Educational law and legislation—Russia. I. Russia (1923- U. S. S. R.) Laws, statutes, etc. II. Russia (1917- R. S. F. S. R.) Laws, statutes, etc. III. Title.

34-39024

NL 0423525 DLC

Livshit͡s, Samuil Il'ich, 1902–
Партийные университеты подполья: Капри, 1909 г., Болонья, 1910-11 гг., Лонжюмо, 1911 г. Москва, Изд-во Всес. об-ва политкаторжан и сс.-поселенцев, 1929.
148 p. 18 cm. (Научно-популярная библиотека по истории революционного движения в очерках, воспоминаниях и биографиях, № 7)
At head of title: С. Лившиц.
Bibliographical footnotes.

1. Rossiĭskai͡a sot͡sial-demokraticheskai͡a rabochai͡a partii͡a—History. I. Title.
Title romanized: Partiĭnye universitety podpol'i͡a.

JN6598.S6L58 72-278351

NL 0423526 DLC

Livshit͡s, V I͡A
Принцип непосредственности в советском уголовном процессе. Москва, Изд-во Академии наук СССР, 1949.
205 p. 22 cm.
At head of title: Академия наук СССР. Институт права.

1. Evidence, Criminal—Russia. I. Title.
Title transliterated: Prinfsip neposredstvennosti v sovetskom ugolovnom prot͡sesse.

50-25662

NL 0423527 DLC

Livshit͡s, Zinovii Aleksandrovich, joint tr.
PQ4696 S7B83
Goldoni, Carlo, 1707-1793.
Лжец; комедия в 3 действиях; пер. в стихах З. Калик и Зин. Лившица. Москва, "Искусство"; [etc.] 1936.

Livshyts', I͡A D
see
Livshit͡s, I͡Akov Davidovich.

Livšic, A H
see Livshit͡s, A Kh

Livson, Mikael.
Epävarsinainen laiminlyöntirikos (Delictum commissivum per omissionem) Rikosoikeudellinen tutkimus. [Helsinki] Suomalainen Lakimiesyhdistys [jakaja: Akateeminen Kirjakauppa, 1949]
xx, 235 p. 25 cm. (Suomalaisen Lakimiesyhdistyksen julkaisuja. A-sarja, n:o 36)
Thesis—Helsingin Yliopisto.
Summary in German.
Bibliography: p. [xiii]-xx.

1. Omission, Criminal. 2. Omission, Criminal—Finland. I. Title. (Series: Suomalainen Lakimiesyhdistys, Helsingfors. Julkaisuja. A-sarja, n:o 36)

51-40787

NL 0423531 DLC OrU NIC

4K 5094
Livson, Mikael
Näennäinen rikoskonkurrenssi. Vammala [ ] 1954.
117 p.
(Suomalaisen Lakimiesyhdistyksen julkaisuja; B-sarja, n:o 64)

NL 0423532 DLC-P4 CtY-L

BF241 L5
Livson, Norman Herman, 1924-
After-effects of prolonged inspection of apparent movement. [Berkeley, 1951]
ii,89 l. tables.
Thesis (Ph.D.) - Univ. of California, Sept. 1951.
Bibliography: p.87-89.

NL 0423533 CU

Et livssyn to radioforedrag, med bidrag av Biskop Eivind Berggrav - Prof. dr. Kristine Bonnevie, [and others] Oslo, utgitt av norsk rikskringkasting i kommisjon hos J.M. Stenersens 1939.
113p.
Norwegian.

NL 0423534 OCl

*fGC8 L7675 869l
Livtschak, Joseph.
Die Lösung des aëronautischen Problems (der Luftschiffahrts-Frage) von Joseph Livtschak. Mit vier dem Texte eingedruckten Holzschnitten ...
Wien, 1869. Druck und Papier von Leopold Sommer. Eigenthum des Verfassers.
35p. illus. 28.5cm.

NL 0423535 MH CoCA

VOLUME 337

Livy, pseud.

see

Livingston, Charles Adolphe.

Livy, Milton Ives.
Divorce reform; an article on divorce and a proposed bill advocating a liberal, logical divorce reform law in the state of New York, by Milton Ives Livy... New York City₍, 192–?₎. 30 p. 12°.

1. Divorce—Jurisp.—U. S.
N. Y. P. L. September 12, 1927

NL 0423537 NN OO

LIVY, MILTON IVES
Marriage and divorce: with a complete compilation of divorce and marriage laws of 48 states and territories of the United States. 233 Broadway, New York, Author, 1924.
63 p.

NL 0423538 OrU OrPR NN

Livy, Milton Ives.
Wills; how to make and break them; with a complete compilation of the laws on wills and testaments of 48 states and territories of United States, and complete legal forms of wills. By Milton Ives Livy... New York, N. Y.₍, 1925?₎ 71 p. 8°.

1. Wills.
N. Y. P. L. May 25, 1926

NL 0423539 NN

Livy, Titus

see

Livius, Titus

Liw, Poland (Villiage)
Liw; dawne i nowe pamiatki stolecznego miasta ziemi liwskiej
see under Leszczynski, Karol Rafal, ed.

اللواء. السنة الاولى– (العدد الأول–)؛
٤ كانون الثانى ١٩٦٢ –
₍بيروت₎

v. illus. (part col.) ports. 33 cm. weekly.

Title transliterated: al-Liwā'.

AP95.A6L55 N E 64-3373

PL 480: UAR-B-39

NL 0423542 DLC NSyU

Liwa ben Bezaleel
see
Judah Löw ben Bezaleel, *d.* 1609.

ZP
L767

Liwanag (Light) no. 1-5; Dec. 1942-Apr. 1943.
₍Manila₎
1 v. illus. 30 cm. monthly.

"Published by the Federation of Evangelical Churches in the Philippines."
English and/or Tagalog.
Photocopy.

1. Philippine Islands - Missions - Period. 2. Protestantism in the Philippine Islands. 3 Missions - Period. I. Philippine Federation of Christian Churches (2) x General catalogue II. Title: Light (2) SA(2)

NL 0423544 CtY-D

Liwanowa, T
see
Livanova, Tamara Nikolaevna.

Fyd
T121
+L76

Liwayway. v.1-
Nov. 18, 1922-
Manila, Liwayway Publications.
illus. 30 cm. weekly.

Issues for 1942- Sept. 2, 1944, published during the Japanese occupation, called v.1-3, no.3; April 25, 1945-Oct. 17, 1949 called v.1-5, no.18.
Tagalog and English.
Supplement with title Suplemento ng mgn balita inserted in some issues.

NL 0423546 CtY NN NIC

Liweh, Theodor, 1858-
Anglesit, cerussit und linarit von der grube "Hausbaden" ...
Inaug. diss. Strassburg, 1884 (Leipzig)
Bibl.

NL 0423547 ICRL MH

Liwehr, August.
Die anfechtbarkeit von erfindungen; mit tabellen und auszügen aus den bestimmungen des internationalen patentrechts, von dr. ing. h. c. August Liwehr. Charlottenburg, F. Huth, 1930.

80, ₍4₎ p. 21cm.
"Benutzte literatur": p. 75–76.

1. Patents. 2. Patent laws and legislation. I. Title.

35-30940

NL 0423548 DLC

Liwehr, August.
Die verwertung von erfindungen, mit tabellen der wichtigsten bestimmungen aus dem internationalen privatrecht, von dr. ing. h. c. August Liwehr. Berlin-Charlottenburg, F. Huth, 1930.

104 p. 21cm.
"Benutzte literatur": p. 104.

1. Inventions. 2. Patents. 3. Patent laws and legislation. I. Title.
33-12402

Library of Congress T339.L55
Copyright A—Foreign 9600
₍2₎ 608

NL 0423549 DLC

Liwehr, August Eugen, 1886–
Die Aufbereitung von Kohle und Erzen. Zusammengestellt und bearbeitet von Bergingenieur August Eugen Liwehr... Bd. 1– Leipzig: A. Felix, 1917– v. diagrs., tables. 4°.

"Benützte Literatur," Bd. 1, on verso of p. vii.

1. Ores.—Dressing. 2. Coal.—Dressing.
N. Y. P. L. August 6, 1920.

NL 0423550 NN ICJ

Liwehr, August Eugen, 1886–
...Mit meinen Augen durch unsere Kultur. Leipzig: A. Felix, 1917. vii, 248 p. 8°.

1. Civilization. 2. Culture (German).
N. Y. P. L. April 30, 1920.

NL 0423551 NN

Liwehr, August Eugen, 1886–
Die Verwendung von Pressluft im Bergbaubetriebe, von... August Eugen Liwehr... Weimar: C. Steinert, 1915. 1 p.l., ii p., 1 l., 258 p., 3 pl. (1 double), 1 fold. table. diagr. 12°.

1. Air (Compressed) in mining.
N. Y. P. L. March 23, 1916.

NL 0423552 NN ICJ

Liwenagel
see **Leraren in Wiskunde en Natuurwetenschappen aan Gymnasia en Lycea.**

Liwer, David.
עיר המתים (הטסדת היהודים באיזור זגלמביה) תירגם מכתב׳
יד. א. ש. שטיין. תל־אביב, נ. מברסקי, תש״ו.
₍Tel-Aviv, 1945/46₎

215 p. illus., ports. 19 cm.

1. Jews in Będzin. 2. World War, 1939–1945—Poland—Będzin. I. Stein, A. S., tr. II. Title. *Title transliterated:* 'Ir ha-metim.

DS135.P62B38 55-55414

NL 0423554 DLC MH

Y78
L788k
1926

LIWIN, Zacharias, 1726-1788.
Kyrkostoetoschopia saebyensis. Eller Eric Jonssons, kyrko-waektares, brodfogdes, samt orgel-trampares, lefwernes beskrifning. Foersta delen. Tranaas, Tranaas Typografiska Anstalts Foerlag [1926]
5p., 151p. 24.5cm.

Facsimile reprint.
No. more published.

NL 0423555 MH-AH NN

Liwlēchian, Tōnapet Karapet, 1875–1917.
Հասկաքաղ. Բրոֆ. Տ. Կ. Լիւլէճեանի (Բաղդատ) դրական վաստակը եւ 1915-ի թանոքի յուշերը: Ֆրէզնօ, Քալիֆ., Տպարան Crown Print. ₍1955₎

691 p. illus., facsim., ports. 26 cm.
Includes bibliographical references.

1. Armenian massacres, 1915–1923—Personal narratives. I. Title.
Title romanized: Haskak'agh.

PK8548.L5 1955 72-279229

NL 0423556 DLC

4DK
Rus
381

Liwoff, Grégoire
Michel Katkoff et son époque; quelques pages d'histoire contemporaine en Russie 1855-1887. Paris, E. Plon, Nourrit, 1897.
318 p.

NL 0423557 DLC-P4 WU MH CtY NIC KU InU IU

VOLUME 337

Liwschitz, Boris 1882-
Tachographische untersuchungen ueber die wirkung kohlensaeurehaltiger soolbaeder.
Inaug. Diss. Tuebingen, 1907 (Berlin)

NL 0423558 ICRL DNLM

Liwschitz (Gitta). *Zur Frage über die Funktionen und die Lage des Magens bei Chlorose. [Zürich.] 36 pp. 8°. Berlin, S. Karger, 1908.

NL 0423559 DNLM

DS125 .R75 Liwschitz, J., tr.

Rubaschow, Salman, 1889–
... Privatwirtschaftliche und genossenschaftliche kolonisation in Palästina. Berlin, F. Ostertag, 1922.

Liwschitz (Lisa). *Ueber Adrenalinbehandlung bei subjektiven Ohrgeräuschen. 21 pp. 8°. Bern. 1910.

NL 0423561 DNLM

Liwschitz, Michael
see
Liwschitz-Garik, Michael, 1883–

Liwschitz (Osip). *Ueber den Einfluss des Kaffees auf den Eiweisstoffwechsel beim Menschen. 20 pp. 8°. Basel, Brin & Co., 1914.

NL 0423563 DNLM MH CtY

Liwschitz, Selman: Die spontanen Gehirnblutungen nach dem Sektionsmaterial des Pathologischen Instituts zu Leipzig aus den Jahren 1905—12. Leipzig 1914: Lehmann. 54 S. 8°
Leipzig, Med. Diss. v. 18. April 1914, Ref. Marchand
[Geb. 1. Jan. 88 Alexandrinka; Wohnort: Leipzig; Staatsangeh.: Rußland; Vorbildung: G. Mariupol Reife 08; Studium: Leipzig 10 S.; Rig. 18. April 14.]
[U 14. 2329

NL 0423564 ICRL DNLM CtY

Liwschitz (Selmann) [1881–]. *Zwei Fälle von multipler Sklerose. 42 pp. 8°. Freiburg i. B., E. A. Günther, 1906.

NL 0423565 DNLM ICRL

QD281 .P6L58 (Hebr) **Liwschitz, Yecheskel.**
מחקרים בשטח הפילימריזציה של חומצות אמינו. ירושלים,
תשי"ב. ‏[Jerusalem, 1952]

58 l. 34 cm.

Added t. p.: Researches on the polymerisation of amino acids.
Thesis—Hebrew University, Jerusalem.
Summary in English.
Bibliography: leaves 52–54.

1. Amino acids. 2. Polymers and polymerization.
Title transliterated: Meḥkarim be-shetaḥ ha-polimerizatsyah shel ḥumtsot amino.

QD281.P6L58 56–48592

NL 0423566 DLC

Liwschitz-Garik, Michael, 1883–
D-C and A-C machines, based on fundamental laws, by Michael Liwschitz-Garik assisted by Robert T. Weil, Jr. New York, Van Nostrand [1952]

508 p. illus. 24 cm.

1. Electric machinery. I. Title.

TK2181.L47 621.313 52–6380 rev]

MiHM FMU CU FTaSU MiU CaBVa CaBViP
NL 0423567 DLC Wa NIC NcRS TxU MB PU OU NcD FU

Liwschitz-Garik, Michael, 1883-
Electric machinery, by Michael Liwschitz-Garik ... assisted by Clyde C. Whipple ... New York, D. Van Nostrand company, inc., 1946.
2 v. illus., diagrs. 23½cm.
"The basis for this work ... is a book [Die elektrischen maschinen] in three volumes published in German by the author during the years 1926 to 1934 ... In order to achieve suitability as a textbook, the material has been brought up to date and adapted to the conditions of this country."—Pref.
"References": v. 1, p. 283–285; v. 2, p. 563–571.
CONTENTS.—v. 1. Fundamentals and D-C machines.—v. 2. A-C machines.
1. Electric machinery. I. Whipple, Clyde Colburn, 1892– joint author.

46–7430
Library of Congress TK2181.L48
[6] 621.313

PPT TU NcGU WaS WaT TxU OrU FU OU OrCS
NL 0423568 DLC CaBVa CU PV PCM TxU MiHM PPD PSt PP

Liwschitz-Garik, Michael, 1883-
Electric machinery, by Michael Liwschitz-Garik ... assisted by Clyde C. Whipple ... New York, D. Van Nostrand company, inc., [1947]
2 v. illus., diagrs. 23½cm.
"The basis for this work ... is a book [Die elektrischen maschinen] in three volumes published in German by the author during the years 1926 to 1934 ... In order to achieve suitability as a textbook, the material has been brought up to date and adapted to the conditions of this country."—Pref.
"References": v. 1, p. 283–285; v. 2, p. 563–571.
CONTENTS.—v. 1. Fundamentals and D-C machines.—v. 2. A-C machines.

NL 0423569 ViU

Liwschitz-Garik, Michael, 1883-
Electric machinery, by Michael Liwschitz-Garik ... assisted by Clyde C. Whipple ... New York, D. Van Nostrand Co. [1946]
2 v. illus., diagrs. 23 1/2cm.
"The basis for this work ... is a book [Die elektrischen maschinen] in three volumes published in German by the author during the years 1926 to 1934 ... in order to achieve suitability as a textbook, the material has been brought up to date and adapted to the conditions of this country."—Pref.
"References": v. 1, p. 283-285; v. 2, p. 563-571.
CONTENTS.—v. 1. Fundamentals and D-C machines. —v. 2. A-C machines.
1. Electric machinery. I. Whipple, Clyde Colburn, 1892- joint author.

NL 0423571 MB

Liwschitz-Garik, Michael, 1883-
Električne mašine. Preveli s nemačkog Miodrag Ranojević i Mirko Lazić. Beograd, Naučna Knjiga, 1950.
3v. in 1. illus., diagrs.

Serbian

NL 0423572 OCl

Liwschitz-Garik, Michael, 1883-
... Die elektrischen maschinen; einführung in ihre theorie und praxis, von dr.-ing. M. Liwschitz ... Mit 284 abbildungen und 13 tafeln. Leipzig und Berlin, B. G. Teubner, 1926.

viii, 336 p., 1 l. XIII pl., diagrs. 21½cm. (Teubners technische leitfäden. bd. 24)

"Literaturverzeichnis": p. [325]-331.

1. Electric machinery.

NL 0423573 MiU

Liwschitz-Garik, Michael, 1883–
Die elektrischen Maschinen. Leipzig, B. G. Teubner, 1931–34.

3 v. illus., diagrs. 23 cm.

Bd. 1: 2. erweiterte und verb. Aufl.
Bd. 2: Von M. Liwschitz [und] H. Glöckner.

CONTENTS.—Bd. 1. Allgemeine Grundlagen.—Bd. 2. Konstruktion und Isolierung.—Bd. 3. Berechnung und Bemessung.
Includes bibliographies.

1. Electric machinery. I. Glöckner, Hugo.

TK2181.L5 1931 621.313 32–2012 rev*

NL 0423574 DLC PPF OU

Liwschitz-Garik, Michael, 1883–
Winding alternating-current machines; a book for winders, repairmen, and designers of electric machines, by Michael Liwschitz-Garik assisted by Celso Gentilini. New York, Van Nostrand [1950]

xv, 766 p. illus. 24 cm.

Bibliography: p. 750–751.

1. Armatures. 2. Electric machinery—Alternating current. I. Title.

TK2477.L5 1950 621.316 50–11541 rev

ViU WaT IdU MiU MiHM CU CoU
NL 0423575 DLC PSC TxU PPF MB AAP ICJ OrP MtBC WaS

Liwschitz (Schlema) [1888–]. *Biologische Untersuchungen zur Caseinfrage. 60 pp. 8°. München, R. Müller & Steinicke, 1913.

NL 0423576 DNLM PPWI CtY MiU

W 6 P3 LIWSZYC, Stanisław
Rola czynników nerwowo-wegetatywnych w patogenezie gruźlicy płuc. [Wyd. 1.] Warszawa, Państwowy Zakład Wydawn. Lekarskich, 1954.
79 p. illus.
1. Nervous system - Autonomic
2. Tuberculosis

NL 0423577 DNLM

Lix, F., illus.
Les explorations inconnues. Le roi de prairies.
see under Biart, Lucien, 1828-1897.

PQ2338 L788A7 Lix, Tony
À Paris et en province, recueil de nouvelles. Tours, Mame, 1889.
139 p. illus. 21cm.

NL 0423579 GU

Lix Klett, Carlo, 1851–
... Consigli pratici agli agricoltori della Repubblica argentina, per il Signor Carlo Lix Klett ... Buenos Aires [etc.] "La Rural", compagnia d'assicurazioni contro la grandine, 1903.

16 p. 25cm.

At head of title: "La Rural."

1. Agriculture—Argentine Republic. I. Title.

30–17375

Library of Congress S517.A7L5

NL 0423580 DLC

VOLUME 337

Lix Klett, Cárlo, 1851-
Estudios sobre producción, comercio, finanzas é intereses generales de la República Argentina, por Cárlos Lix Klett ... Con una introducción de Enrique M. Nelson ... Buenos Aires, Est. tip. de Tailhade y Rosselli, 1900.
2 v. plates (part col., part fold.) ports., maps (part fold.) diagrs. (part fold.) 27cm.

1. Argentine Republic.

A 14-1544

Title from Univ. of Calif. HC175.L5 Printed by L. C.

NL 0423581 CU DPU ICJ

Lix Klett, Carlo, 1851-
Étude technique sur la race ovine, 2e éd. 1889.

NL 0423582 DPU DNAL PPF

Lix Klett, Carlo, 1851-
La rural. Consejos prácticos a los agricultores de la república argentina... Villa María (Córdoba) La Rural, 1903.
Binder's title "Agriculture. Miscellaneous."
4 v.

NL 0423583 DPU

Lix Rotis
La prediction d'Ita-pa, ...
Paris, [c1915]

PQ2623 .I9P7 1915

NL 0423584 DLC

Lixaldius, Franciscus, *fl.* 1567.
... Le registre de Franciscus Lixaldius, trésorier général de l'armée espagnole aux Pays-Bas, de 1567 à 1576, publié par m. F. Rachfahl ... Bruxelles, Kiessling et cie, 1902.
2 p. l., viii, 187 p. 22½ cm. [Académie royale des sciences, des lettres et des beaux-arts de Belgique, Brussels. Commission royale d'histoire. Publications in octavo. 24]
At head of title: Commission royale d'histoire.
Edited from a ms. in the Royal archives, Dresden, a Latin translation of the original Spanish manuscript.
1. Spain. Ejército—Hist. 2. Spain—Hist.—Philip II, 1556-1598—Sources. 3. Netherlands—Hist.—Wars of independence, 1556-1648. I. Rachfahl, Felix, 1867-1925, ed.

DH191.7.L7 3-16641 rev

NL 0423585 DLC GU MoU CtY MiU PU IaU MB CU NIC

Lixaute, Auguste.
Der Strassen-, Eisenbahn-, Canal-, Brücken-, Küstendamm-, Deich- und Hafenbau, sowie die Bewässerungsarbeiten ... Nach dem französischen mit beständiger Rücksicht auf deutsche Art und Bedürfniss von Friedrich Harzer. Weimar, B. F. Voigt, 1851.
xx, 653 p. 18 cm. and atlas (20 plates) 23 cm. (Neuer Schauplatz der Künste und Handwerke, 189. Bd.)
Translation of Le guide du constructeur des travaux publics.

1. Civil engineering. 2. Public works. (Series)

P O 51-151

U. S. Patent Office. for Library of Congress Library TA145.L5 [2]

NL 0423586 DP NN

Lixaute, Auguste.
...Der Strassen-, Eisenbahn-, Canal-, Brücken-, Küstendamm-, Deich- und Hafenbau, sowie Bemerkungen über Bewässerungsarbeiten...Nach dem Französischen, deutschen Zuständen angepasst, von Friedrich Harzer. Zweite Auflage mit Ergänzungen von W. A. Hertel... Weimar: B. F. Voigt, 1862. xvi, 690 p. incl. tables. 12° and atlas of 20 fold. pl. obl. 8°. (Neuer Schauplatz der Künste und Handwerke. Bd. 189.)

204448A. 1. Building. 2. Harzer, Friedrich, translator. 3. Hertel, W. A., editor. 4. Ser.
N. Y. P. L. December 13, 1927

NL 0423587 NN

Lixfeld, Else, 1907-
... Zur Frage der Nierenschädigungen durch Avertin bei chirurgischer Behandlung der Lungentuberkulose ... Quakenbrück, 1936.
Inaug.-Diss. - Kiel.
Lebenslauf.
"Literaturverzeichnis": p. 22-24.

NL 0423588 CtY

Lixon, Camille Louis, 1894-
... De l'action des protéines toxiques sur la respiration ... Lille, [1922]
24.5 cm.
Thèse - Univ. de Lille.

NL 0423589 CtY

4PQ Span 664
Lixtanov, I
El peque, relato. [Traducido del ruso por J.L. Salado] Moscú, Ediciones en Lenguas Extranjeras, 1950.
359 p.

NL 0423590 DLC-P4

Liyanage, Martheniz W
El té, su cultivo y beneficio, por Martheniz W. Liyanage ... [Huanuco? Perú, Imprenta americana, 1942.
2 p. l., [iii]-viii, 136 p., 1 l. plates (1 col., 1 fold.) 25½cm.
"Bibliografía consultada": p. 136.

1. Tea. 2. Tea—Peru. 3. Tea trade.

44-19762

Library of Congress SB271.L67 [3] 633.72

NL 0423591 DLC TxU

Liyo Catalán, Bictoriano, 1892-
see
Lillo Catalán, Victoriano, 1892-

Liyūnārdū Dāvinshī
see
Leonardo da Vinci, 1452-1519.

Liyūtī,
see
Lyautey, Louis Hubert Gonzalve, 1854-1934.

Liz, Buenaventura Fernández de
see
Fernández de Liz, Buenaventura, *fl.* 1777.

Liz, José Honorio Vázquez
see Vazquez Liz, José Honorio.

Liz Ferreira, Antonio José de
see
Ferreira, Antonio José de Liz, 1905-

'Liza Jane, the girl miner
see [Wheeler, Edward L]
Dumb Dick's pard; or, 'Liza Jane ...

Lizabe, María Ausunción.
Deseo cumplido. Madrid, Ediciones Rumbos [1955]
216 p. 19 cm. (Colección Jupiter y Danae, no. 5)
A novel.

I. Title.

A 56-1577

Illinois. Univ. Library for Library of Congress [3]

NL 0423599 IU

Lizabeth, pseud
see
Wallace, Kathryn

Bw51 N8 771L
Lizakevits, J G de
Essai abrégé de l'histoire de Nowgorod. Contenant l'origine de cette ville, de ses princes et leurs actions les plus mémorables, tiré des monuments russes. Copenhague, Pierre Steinmann, 1771.
188 p. 20cm.

1. Novgorod, Russia (City) - Hist.

NL 0423601 CtY MH

Lizalde, Daniel Hidalgo-
see Hidalgo-Lizalde, Daniel, 1899-

S 917.26 L768e
Lizama Escoffié, Homero.
... En las riberas del Caribe. Bosquejo histórico-geográfico del territorio federal Q. Roo, 1920-23. Merida, Impr. "Oriente", 1927.
8 p.l., vii, 216 p. plates, (incl. ports.).

1. Yucatan, Mexico - Description and travel

NL 0423603 WaPS DLC-P4

VOLUME 337

W 4
G91
1946

LIZAMA RUBIO, Carlos
Tratamiento de la fiebre tifoidea por el neosalvarsán. [Guatemala] Sánchez & de Guise [1946?]
29 p. illus.
Tesis - Guatemala.
1. Neoarsphenamine 2. Typhoid - Treatment

NL 0423604 DNLM

Lizan, José Pavón
see
Pavón Lizan, José.

Lizan, L., pseud
see
Lanzi, L.

Lizana, Bernardo de, d. 1631. Del principio y fundacion destos cuyos omules deste sitio y pueblo de Ytzmal. [Fr. and Span.] 18 pp. (Col. doc. de l'Amérique ancienne, v. 3, p. 318.)

NL 0423607 MdBP

Lizana, Bernardo de, *d.* 1631.
Historia de Yucatán. Devocionario de Ntra. Sra. de Izmal y conquista espiritual, por el P. Fr. Bernardo de Lizana ... Impresa en 1633 y ahora nuevamente por el Museo nacional de México. México, Impr. del Museo nacional, 1893.
12 p. l., 127 numb. l., [2] p. 2 facsim. 23½cm.
Includes facsimile of t.-p. of original edition, Valladolid, 1633.

1. Yucatan—Church history. 2. Indians of Mexico—Yucatan. 3. Catholic church in Yucatan—Biog. I. Mexico. Museo nacional.

6-43077

Library of Congress F1376.L78

NNH
NL 0423608 DLC CoU WU NNH CU-B CtY DSI PU-Mu PPAmP

Gz
972.64
L768h
1892

LIZANA, BERNARDO DE, d. 1631.
Historia y conquista espiritual de Yucatán, por el p. fr. Bernardo de Lizana ... Impresa en 1633 y ahora nuevamente por el Museo nacional de Mexico. México, Impr. del Museo nacional, 1892.
6p.l.,123 numb.l.,1l. facsim. 23½cm.
Published also under title: Historia de Yucatán.
1. Yucatan - Church history. 2. Indians of Mexico - Yucatan. 3. Catholic church in Yucatan - Biog. I. Mexico. Museo nacional. II. Lizana, Bernardo de, d. 1631. Historia de Yucatán.

NL 0423609 TxU MiU-C

Lizana, Manuel de Salinas y
see
Salinas y Lizana, Manuel de

Lizana Bravo, Pedro.
... Comentario sobre el artículo 7 del Código de derecho internacional privado; memoria de prueba para optar al grado de licenciado en la Facultad de ciencias jurídicas y sociales de la Universidad de Chile. Santiago de Chile, Talleres gráficos "Gutenburg," 1941.
72, [2] p. 26cm.
"Bibliografía": p. [71]-72.

1. International law, Private—America. 2. International law, Private—Chile.

45-26464

Library of Congress JX6110.L5
[3] 341.5

NL 0423611 DLC

Lizana Droguett, Desiderio, *d.* 1922.
... Cómo se canta la poesía popular, trabajo leído por su autor en las sesiones de 22 de julio y 15 de setiembre de 1911 de la Sociedad de folklore chileno ... Santiago de Chile, Imprenta universitaria, 1912.
73 p. 25½ cm.
"Trabajo publicado en la 'Revista' de la Sociedad chilena de historia y geografía. Año II. Tomo III. Núm. 5."

1. Folk-songs, Chilean—Hist. & crit. I. Title.

ML3575.C5L5 784.4983 30-34133 rev

NL 0423612 DLC DPU

Lizana Droguett, Desiderio, *d.* 1922.
Sancho en el cielo, poema joco-satírico [por] Pedro Recio (Desiderio Lizana D.) Santiago de Chile, Impr., Litografía y Encuadernación La Ilustración, 1916.
31 p. illus. 28 cm.

1. Cervantes Saavedra, Miguel de—Characters—Sancho Panza. 2. Cervantes Saavedra, Miguel de—Anniversaries, etc., 1916. 3. Cervantes in fiction, drama, poetry, etc. I. Title.

PQ8097.L69S3 55-54595 ‡

NL 0423613 DLC

G868.81
L766s

Lizana Droguett, Desiderio, d. 1922.
Sancho en el cielo, poema joco-satírico [por] Pedro Recio (Desiderio Lizana Droguett) Santiago de Chile, Impr. Universitaria, 1916.
48p. port. 19cm.

1. Cervantes Saavedra, Miguel de - Characters Sancho Panza. 2. Cervantes Saavedra, Miguel de - Anniversaries, etc., 1916. 3. Cervantes in fiction, drama, poetry, etc. I. Title.

NL 0423614 TxU DLC

Lizana Hidalgo, José J
... De la incompetencia como causal de casación de forma en material civil (n.° 1 y 2 del artículo 942 del Código de p. civil) Memoria de prueba para optar al grado de licenciado en la Facultad de ciencias jurídicas y sociales de la Universidad de Chile. Santiago de Chile, Dirección general de prisiones, imp., 1942.
107 p. 26cm.
"Bibliografía": p. [101]

1. Jurisdiction—Chile. 2. Appellate procedure—Chile.

43-18799

NL 0423615 DLC

F3091
.S23

Lizana M., Elías, comp.

Santiago de Chile (*Archdiocese*)
Colección de documentos históricos, recopilados del arch. del arz. de Stgo. ... Santiago de Chile, Impr. de San José, 1919-

---

Lizana Pizarro, Oscar, 1905-
... El duelo; memoria de prueba para optar al grado de licenciado en la Facultad de ciencias jurídicas y sociales de la Universidad de Chile. [Santiago de Chile] Imp. La Bolsa, 1929.
3 p. l., [5]-98 p., 1 l. 26½cm.
"Bibliografía": 3d prelim. leaf.

1. Dueling. 2. Dueling—Chile. I. Title.

45-48837

NL 0423617 DLC

LIZANA Y BEAUMONT, Francisco Javier de, 1750-1811.

This Library has a collection of pastoral letters, proclamations, and sermons of Francisco Xavier de Lizanay Beaumont, archbishop of Mexico, issued during the years 1807 to 1809 (Call-number:-SA 3398.16)

NL 0423618 MH

Lizana y Beaumont, Francisco Javier de, abp., 1750-1811.
Aviso paternal que el Illmô. señor doctor D. Francisco Xavier de Lizana y Beaumont, arzobispo de México, del consejo de Su Magestad &c. dirige a sus eclesiasticos, manifestándoles que las comedias no son diversiones conformes á su estado. México: M. de Zúñiga y Ontiveros, 1803. 19 p. 8°.

1. Catholic Church, Roman—Mexico —Clergy. 2. Pastoral letters—Mexico.
N. Y. P. L. November 24, 1925

NL 0423619 NN CU-B

RBC
972.511
(282)
L789c

Lizana y Beaumont, Francisco Javier de, Abp., 1750-1811.
Carta gratulatoria del Exmô. é Illmô. Sr. Arzobispo de México al clero secular y regular de la Capital. [México, 1810]
[4]p. 20 cm.
Caption title.
Dated and signed: México y octubre 9 de 1810. Francisco Arzobispo de México.
Medina. La imprenta en México (1539-1821). 10478.
1. Mexico (Archdiocese). 2. Catholic Church - Pastoral letters and charges.

NL 0423620 LNHT CU-B

Lizana y Beaumont, Francisco Javier de, Abp., 1750-1811.
Carta pastoral, en la que el Illmô. señor don Francisco Xavier de Lizana y Beaumont, Arzobispo de Mexico, del consejo de S.M. &c. instruye á sus súbditos sobre los desengaños y frutos que han debido sacar de los exercicios espirituales que acaban de practicar. Mexico, por D. Mariano de Zúñiga y Ontiveros, 1804.
1 p.l.,17 p. 19 cm.

Medina, Impr. en Mexico, 9709.
Disbound.

NL 0423621 InU CU-B

Lizana y Beaumont, Francisco Javier de, abp., 1750-1811.

—— Carta pastoral que ... dirige á sus diocesanos sobre la santidad de nuestra sagrada religion, y las obligaciones que nos impone. Mexico, Oficina de la calle de Santo Domingo, 1807. 28p. 19cm. (Pastorales de Lizana. 7)

NL 0423622 CU-B PBL

VOLUME 337

Lizana y Beaumont, Francisco Javier de, abp., 1750-1811.
Carta pastoral que á las RR. MM. superioras y súbditas de los conventos de religiosas del arzobispado de Mexico dirige el Illmô. Señor Dôr. D. Francisco Xavier de Lizana y Beaumont. México: Imprenta madrileña, 1803. 42 p. 8°.

Badly worm-eaten.

1. Pastoral letters, Mexican.
N. Y. P. L. September 1, 1925

NL 0423623 NN InU CU-B

Lizana y Beaumont, Francisco Javier de, Abp., 1750-1811
Carta Pastoral que el Exmô. é Illmô. señor Dr. D. Francisco Xavier de Lizana y Beaumont, dirige á sus fieles súbditos sobre la falsedad de las promesas de Napoleon y su hermano Josef. [Mexico,1810] 15 p. 20 cm.

Medina, Impr. en Mexico, 10476.
Dated at end, Mexico, July 8, 1810.
In wrapper.

NL 0423624 InU CU-B RPJCB

Gz 282.25 L768c
Lizana y Beaumont, Francisco Xavier de, abp.-d. 1811.
Carta pastoral que el illmo. señor doctor d. Francisco Xavier de Lizana y Beaumont, arzobispo de México, del Consejo de Su Mag. &c., dirige á los fieles de su Arzobispado sobre al grandeza de nuestra santa religión, en lo que enseña, manda creer y practicar. México, Imprenta madrileña, 1803.
41p. 21cm.

1. Catholic church - Pastoral letters and charges.

NL 0423625 TxU NN RPJCB InU CU-B ICN

Lilly
Lizana y Beaumont, Francisco Javier de, Abp, 1750-1811.
Carta Pastoral que el Illmô. señor D. Francisco Xavier de Lizana y Beaumont, Arzobispo de Mexico, del consejo de S.M. &c. dirige á todos los fieles de su Arzobispado con ocasion de los calamidades de España. Mexico, por Don Mariano de Zúñiga y Ontiveros, 1805.
1 p.l.,19 p. 18 cm.

Medina,Impr. en Mexico, 9797.
Disbound.

NL 0423626 InU CU-B

Lilly Mendel
Lizana y Beaumont, Francisco Javier de, Abp., 1750-1811.
Carta Pastoral que el Illmô. señor D.D. Francisco Xavier de Lizana y Beaumont por la gracia de Dios, y de la santa sede apostolica, Arzobispo de Mexico, del consejo de S.M. &c. dirige a su clero sobre la santidad del estado Sacerdotál y obligaciones inseparables de el, Mexico,Oficina de la calle de Santo Domingo, 1807.
42 p. 20 cm.

Medina,Impr en Mexico, 9963.
In wrapper.

NL 0423627 InU DLC CU-B

Gz 282.25 L768ca
Lizana y Beaumont, Francisco Xavier de, abp., d. 1811.
Carta pastoral que el ilustrisimo señor don Francisco Xavier de Lizana y Beaumont, del Consejo de S.M., arzobispo de Mexico, dirije á sus diocesanos sobre el modo de santificar el tiempo de quaresma. [México] Impresa en la Oficina de doña María Fernández de Jáuregui, 1809.
27p. 21cm.
1. Lent. 2. Catholic church - Pastoral letters and charges.

NL 0423628 TxU CtY RPJCB CU-B

Lizana y Beaumont, Francisco Xavier de, Abp., d. 1811.
Constituciones de la congregacion de los sacerdotes
see under title

Lizana y Beaumont, Francisco Javier de, Abp., 1750-1811.
Elogios latino y castellano del excelentisimo e ilustrisimo señor don Francisco Xavier de Lizana y Beaumont, arzobispo y virey de México...
see under Mexico (City) Catedral. Cabildo.

Lizana y Beaumont, Francisco Javier de, abp. of Mexico, 1750-1811
Epistola familiaris quam ego, Franciscus Xaverius a Lizana et Beaumont, archiepiscopus Mexicanus...mitto ad vos omnes verbum Dei evangelizantes, qui estis gaudium & corona mea, circa altissimum ministerii vestri munus, in annuntiando evangelio populo Dei. Mexici: Marianus de Zunniga & Ontiveros, 1805. 2 p.l., 24 p. 12°.

1. Catholic Church (Roman), Mexico, 1805.
N. Y. P. L. September 23, 1913.

NL 0423631 NN InU

Lilly Mendel
Lizana y Beaumont, Francisco Javier de, Abp., 1750-1811.
Exhortacion del Illmo. Señor Don Francisco Xavier de Lizana y Beaumont, Arzobispo de Mèxico,en que manifiesta la obligación de socorrer á la Nacion española en la actual guerra con la Francia. Reimpresa en Cadiz, por Don Manuel Ximenez Carreño, [1808?]
16 p. 19 cm.

See Medina,Impr. en Mexico, 10090.
Dated at end Mexico, Sept. 13, 1808.
Disbound

NL 0423632 InU RPJCB CU-B

Lizana y Beaumont, Francisco Javier de, abp., d. 1811.
Exhortacion del Exmô. Illmô. Sr. Don Francisco Xavier de Lizana y Beaumont, arzobispo de México, a sus fieles y demas habitantes de este reyno. [México:] M. de Zúñiga y Ontiveros, 1810. 10 p. 8°.

1. Sermons, Spanish-American.
N. Y. P. L. September 1, 1925

NL 0423633 NN CtY CU-B TxU CSmH InU NcU

Lizana y Beaumont, Francisco Javier de, Abp., d. 1811.
Habitantes de la Nueva España
see under Mexico (Viceroyalty)

Lizana y Beaumont, Francisco Tavier de, abp., 1750-1811.
Instruccion pastoral del...Francisco Xavier Lizana y Beaumont...sobre la costumbra de llevar las señoras el pecho y brazos desnudos. Mexico, Oficina de Doña Maria Fernandez de Jauregui, 1808.
42 p. 20 cm.
Bound with: Ceballos, Pedro de. Exposicion...1808.

NL 0423635 PBL CU-B RPJCB

---

17 1063
Lizana y Beaumont, Francisco Javier de, abp. 1750-1811.
Instruccion pastoral del illmo. Senot Don Francisco Xavier de Lizana y Beaumont, arzobispo de Mexico... En Mexico, en la oficina de Dona Maria Fernandez de Jauregui, calle de Santo Domingo, 1808.

NL 0423636 DLC CtY

Lizana y Beaumont, Francisco Javier de, abp., d. 1811.
Nos d. Francisco Xavier de Lizana y Beaumont, por la gracia de Dios y de la Santa sede apostólica arzobispo de México ... A los curas, coadjutores, vicarios, y eclesiásticos de ésta nuestra diocesi ... Bendito sea el Padre de las misericordias ... Dos son los puntos á que nos ceñirémos ... El uno será poner en vuestras manos nuevos instrumentos para beneficiar ésta viña: el otro, avisaros de algunos medios de que os debeis valer ... [México, 1803?]
12 p. 29½cm.
Caption title.
Dated: México y marzo 5. de 1803.
1. Mexico (Archdiocese) 2. Catholic church — Pastoral letters and charges.
Library of Congress BX874.L58N6 38-19885

NL 0423637 DLC InU RPJCB

---

fF1203 M194 no. 22 x
Lizana y Beaumont, Francisco Xavier de, Abp. 1750-1811.
Nos Don Francisco Xavier de Lizana y Beaumont... Habiendo llegado á nuestra noticia, que varias personas de esta Ciudad de México y otras poblaciones del Arzobispado... [Mexico] 1810.
broadside 42x31cm. [Mexican Viceregal miscellany, no. 22]
Signed: Francisco Arzobispo de México. Rubric. Por mandado de S.E. Illmâ. el Arzobispo mi Señor. Dr. D. Domingo Hernandez, Secretario. Rubric.
Dated: á once dias del mes de Octubre del año de mil ochocientos diez.
With the official seal of the Archbishop.
Provenance: H. H. Bancroft.

1. Roman Catholic Church in Mexico. Mexico (Archdiocese) 2. Roman Catholic Church in Mexico. Morelia (Archdiocese) 3. Abad Queipo, Manuel, Bp. of Michoacan, 1751-1825. 4. Excommunication. (Series)

NL 0423639 CU-B InU RPJCB

Lizana y Beaumont, Francisco Javier de, Abp., d. 1811.
Proclama del arzobispo virey de México, contra los engaños perfidos de los Bonapartes
see under Mexico (Viceroyalty)

Lizana y Beaumont, Francisco Javier de, Abp., d. 1811.
Proclama del arzobispo virey de Nueva España a los fieles vasallos de Fernando VII
see under Mexico (Viceroyalty)

VOLUME 337

[Lizana y Beaumont, Francisco Javier de] abp., 1750-1811.
Señores Curas y Vicarios de la Iglesias de este Arzobispado. Saben vms. muy bien, que sin embargo de la enorme distancia que dividia a los Israelitas... [Mexico, 1805]
[4] p.
Dated (at end): Hacienda de Santa Clara en Santa Visita de Xonacatepec 15 Jan., 1805.
Signed: Francisco Arzobispo de Mexico.

NL 0423642 RPJCB CtY

Lizana y Beaumont, Francisco Javier de abp., 1750-1811.
—— Sentimientos religiosos, con los que ... desea instruir á sus amados diocesanos en la Semana santa, visitas y estaciones que en ella se practican en las iglesias. Mexico, Doña María Fernandez de Jauregui, 1808. 28p. 19cm. (Pastorales de Lizana. 9)

NL 0423643 CU-B RPJCB

Lizana y Beaumont, Francisco Javier de, abp., 1750-1811.
Sermon moral que en la solemne accion de gracias, que se hace anualmente en el sagrario de esta sta. Iglesia metropolitana de Mexico por los beneficios recibidos de la Divina Piedad, predicó la noche del dia 31 de diciembre de 1805. el illmõ. señor don Francisco Xavier de Lizana y Beaumont ... Mexico, Impreso en la oficina de Maria Fernandez Jauregui, 1806.
F1207 542 v.38:6 x
xxiii p. 20cm. (Sermones varios. v. 38, no. 6)

NL 0423644 CU-B InU

Lilly
Mendel
Lizana y Beaumont, Francisco Javier de, Abp., 1750-1811.
Sermon que en las solemnes Rogativos que se hicieron en la Santa Iglesia Metropolitana de México implorando el auxilio divino en las actuales occurencias de la Monarquia Española predicó en el dia 18 de Agosto de 1808. El Illmõ. Sr. don Francisco Xavier de Lizana y Beaumont ... lo dá á luz la noblisima ciudad de México, y le dedica á Maria Santisima de Guadalupe. Mexico, en la oficina de Doña Maria

NL 0423645 InU

Lilly
BX 1
.M62
Mendel
Lizana y Beaumont, Francisco Javier de, Abp., 1750-1811.
... Sermon que en las solemnes Rogativos [1808] (Card 2)
Fernandez de Jauregui, [1808].
3 p.l.,25,[1] p. 19 cm.
Medina, Impr. en Mexico, 10088.
In wrapper.
1. Sermons,Spanish--Mexico. 2. Guadalupe, Nuestra Señora de 3. Church and state in Mexico. I. Mendel imprint: Mexico, 1808.

NL 0423646 InU CtY PBL CU-B RPJCB

Lizana y Beaumont, Francisco Javier de, Abp., 1750-1811.
see also
Mexico (Archdiocese) Archbishop, 1803-1811 (Lizana y Beaumont)

Lizano, Miguel Obregón
see
Obregón Lizano, Miguel, 1861-1935.

Lizano, Zacarias Aguayo
see
Aguayo Lizano, Zacarias.

W 4
M61
1950
LIZANO AGUIAR, Eduardo
Sinopsis clínica sobre paludismo y tosferina en la población de San Nicolás del Sitio, Badiraguato, Sinoloa. México, 1950.
63 p.
Tesis - Univ. de México.
1. Malaria - Mexico - Sinaloa (State)
2. Whooping cough - Mexico

NL 0423650 DNLM

Lizano H , Víctor, *comp.*
... Leyendas de Costa Rica, compiladas por Víctor Lizano H. ... San José, C. R., Editorial "Soley y Valverde," 1941.
167, [2] p. 23cm. (Serie escolar Costa Rica, no. 3)
CONTENTS.—Conquistadores y caciques, tesoros y piratas.—Volcanes, cerros, piedras y aguas.—Leyendas de la Virgen y casos de la fe.—El cadejos, la llorona y otros personajes (supersticiones populares)—Del tiempo viejo.
1. Legends—Costa Rica. 2. Folk-lore—Costa Rica. I. Title.
43-48437
Library of Congress GR118.C6L5
[3] 398.22

NL 0423651 DLC IU MH-P KU CU-B OCl TxU CU IaU IEN

Lizano Ríos, Félix.
La flor y la sombra. Madrid, Ediciones Ensayos, 1953.
49 p. 16 cm. (Colección Años y leguas, v. 12)
Poems.
I. Title.
PQ6621.I 45F55 59-48565 ‡

NL 0423652 DLC

W 4
M61
1952
LIZANO VARGAS, Edgar
Informe médico sanitario sobre Nueva Italia, municipio de Zaragoza, Mich. Un nuevo tratamiento de la tricocefalosis. México, 1952.
57 p.
Tesis - Univ. de México.
1. Public health- Mexico - Michoacán

NL 0423653 DNLM

Lizaranzu, [J. V.] de.
La Compagnie du chemin de fer Victor-Emmanuel devant ses actionnaires, depuis 1853 jusqu'à nos jours, 1er janvier 1867. Paris: L'auteur, 1867. 3 p.l., (1)4-63(1) p. 8°.
1. Railways, Italy.
N. Y. P. L. May 14, 1913

NL 0423654 NN

Lizarazo, Jose Antonio Osorio
see
Osorio Lizarazo, Jose Antonio, 1900-

Lizarazu de Anzola Toro, Beatriz.
La expropiación. Bogotá, 1952.
59 p. 24 cm.
Tesis—Pontificia Universidad Católica Javeriana.
1. Eminent domain—Colombia. I. Title.
55-38038 ‡

NL 0423656 DLC TxU MH-L

Lizardi (F. de) and Company, London.
Conversion of Mexican bonds. abstract of the decree of the Mexican government...
see under Mexico. Laws, statutes, etc.

Lizardi, José Joaquin Fernandez de
see Fernández de Lizardi, José Joaquín, ca. 1776-1827.

Lizardi, Manuel. Opinión que al Sr. ingeniero D. Francisco Glennie presenta en consulta ... México, Díaz de León, 1882. 16p. 23cm.

NL 0423659 CU-B NN

Lizardi, Miguel G. de.
Vallarta, Ignacio Luis, 1830-1893.
Ocurso presentado a la Suprema corte de justicia y formulado por el lic. Ignacio L. Vallarta pidiendole que se sirva mandar se le dé el debido cumplimiento á su ejecutoria de 27 de noviembre de 1883. Mexico, Impr. de Dublan y c.ª, 1886.

W 4
M61
1934
LIZARDI, Octavio
Diagnóstico de la enfermedad de Nicolas y Favre. México, 1934.
74 p. illus.
Tesis - Univ. de México.
1. Lymphogranuloma venereum - Diagnosis

NL 0423661 DNLM

Lizardi, Rafael Sanhueza
see Sanhueza Lizardi, Rafael.

Lizardi Albarrán, Fernando.
Las regiones árticas en la geopolítica y en las relaciones internacionales. México, 1950.
153 p. 20 cm.
Tesis (licenciatura en derecho)—Universidad National Autónoma de México.
1. Arctic regions. I. Title.
55-33899

NL 0423663 DLC

Lizardi Albarrán, Manuel.
... Ensayo sobre la naturaleza jurídica del fideicomiso, tesis de licenciatura en derecho. México, D. F., 1945.
2 p. l., 7-208 p., 2 l. 23cm.
At head of title: Universidad nacional autónoma de México. Escuela nacional de jurisprudencia.
1. Trusts and trustees—Mexico.
45-19493

NL 0423664 DLC

Lizardi Ramos, César.
Exploraciones en Quintana Roo [por] César Lizardi Ramos. México, 1940.
1 p. l., 44, [2] p. illus. (incl. map, plans) 19½cm.
"Bibliografía": p. 40-41.
1. Mayas—Antiq. 2. Yucatan—Antiq. I. Title.
41-9101
Library of Congress F1435.L797
[2] 972.015

NL 0423665 DLC InU CU LNHT CU-B PBm MH

VOLUME 337

[Lizardi Ramos, César] *ed.*
Los mayas antiguos; monografías de arqueología, etnografía y lingüística mayas, publicadas con motivo del centenario de la exploración de Yucatán por John L. Stephens y Frederick Catherwood en los años 1841–42. [México] El Colegio de México [1941]
2 p. l., [7]–361 p., 1 l. illus. (incl. map, plans, music) 2 col. pl. (1 fold.) 23cm.
"Prefacio" signed: César Lizardi Ramos.
"Primera edición, 1941."
"Bibliografía de John Lloyd Stephens, por Arthur E. Gropp": p. [17]–32.
Includes bibliographies.
1. Mayas—Antiq. 2. Stephens, John Lloyd, 1805–1852—Bibl. I. Stephens, John Lloyd, 1805–1852. II. Catherwood, Frederick. III. Gropp, Arthur Eric, 1902– IV. Title.
Harvard univ. Library for Library of Congress [3]† A 43-3450
F1435.L57 972.015
DLC PU-Mu
NL 0423666 MH OrU OCl CU FMU NcU NNCoCi CtY ICN

Lizardi Ramos, César.
El orden de los katunes de la cuenta corta, por César Lizardi Ramos ... México, D. F., Talleres de Excelsior, 1937.
1 p. l., 14 p. 20cm.
"Trabajo presentado a la Academia nacional de ciencias 'Antonio Alzate', en su sesión del 23 de noviembre de 1936."
"Bibliografía": p. 14.
1. Chronology, Maya. I. Title.
41-21603
Library of Congress F1435.3.C14L58
[2] 529.3
NL 0423667 DLC CU-B CSt

Lizardi Ramos, César.
...Pensamiento y acción... México, Excélsior, 1943. 6 p. illus. 17cm.
"Reimpresión de un artículo publicado en el Suplemento de 'Excélsior' el 25 de julio ...1943."
1. Thought and thinking.
N. Y. P. L. November 30, 1949
NL 0423668 NN

Lizardi Ramos, César.
Recurrencias de las fechas mayas, por César Lizardi Ramos; trabajo presentado al segundo Congreso mexicano de historia, inaugurado en Mérida, Yucatán, el 20 de noviembre de 1935. México, D. F., Tip. "Excélsior," 1936.
15, [1] p. 20cm.
1. Calendar, Maya. I. Congreso mexicano de historia. 2d, Merida, 1935. II. Title.
42-13635
Library of Congress F1435.3.C14L59
[2] 529.3
NL 0423669 DLC CU-B LNHT

Lizardi Ramos, César.
... Tenayuca, the pyramid of the rattlesnakes. 2d ed., rev. Mexico [Excélsior printing office] 1943.
cover-title, 16 p. illus. 19½cm.
Text on p. [3] of cover.
1. Tenayuca San Bartolo, Mexico. 2. Pyramids.
44-19558
Library of Congres: F1219.1.T24L5 1943
[3] 913.725
NL 0423670 DLC CU PBm

W 4 M61 1950 LIZARDI ROMERO, Rubén
Informe sanitario; aspectos clínicos de la fiebre tifoidea y su tratamiento en villa del Pueblito', Querétaro. México, Ortega, 1950.
50 p.
Tesis - Univ. de México.
1. Public health - Mexico - Querétaro (State) 2. Typhoid - Mexico - Querétaro (State)
NL 0423671 DNLM

Lizardo, César.
Clima del sueño, poemas. Caracas, Avila Gráfica, 1952.
106 p. illus. 21 cm.
I. Title.
PQ8549.L553C6 861.6 52-44901 ‡
NL 0423672 DLC

Lizardo, César.
Espacio y voz del paisaje. Caracas, Tip. Garrido [1954]
87 p. illus. 32 cm.
1. Venezuela—Descr. & trav.—1950– I. Title.
PQ8549.L553E8 55-26822 ‡
NL 0423673 DLC NcU TxU NN

Lizardo, César.
Eternidad del júbilo, poemas. Caracas, Tip. Garrido, 1955.
85 p. illus. 24 cm.
I. Title.
PQ8549.L553E83 57-34812 ‡
NL 0423674 DLC FU DPU NcU NN

Lizardo, Pedro.
... Crónicas de Dos Puntos. Valencia [Venezuela] 1923.
118 p. 21.5 cm.
NL 0423676 CtY

[Lizardo, Pedro]
... El forastero. Valencia [Venezuela] Imp. "Unión," 1916.
129 p. port. 16cm.
At head of title: Dos puntos [pseudonym of the author]
NL 0423677 CU-B CtY

F2341 .C2M3 Lizardo, Pedro Francisco.
Matiz, Leo.
Algo de Caracas. [Fotografías de Leo Matiz. Texto de Pedro F. Lizardo. Caracas? 195–]

Lizardo, Pedro Francisco.
... Canción del agua clara (poesía) Caracas, Coop. de artes gráficas, 1939.
176 p. incl. port. 23½cm. [Publicaciones auspiciadas por el Ateneo de Valencia. 2]
I. Title.
A 41-4095
Harvard univ. Library for Library of Congress [2]
NL 0423679 MH OCl

Lizardo, Pedro Francisco.
... Comarca de amor (1939–1940) Valencia, Venezuela, Grupo "Estudios," 1941.
7 p. l., 19–69 p., 2 l. mounted port. 23½cm.
Poems.
I. Title.
42-20822
Library of Congress PQ8549.L56C6
[2] 861.6
NL 0423680 DLC KMK IU

Lizardo, Pedro Francisco.
El tiempo derramado (poemas 1947–1952) Caracas, Ediciones Garrido, 1954.
106 p. illus. 22 cm.
I. Title.
PQ8549.L56T5 55-30880 ‡
NL 0423681 DLC MH NN CU

PQ8549 .L56 V5 Lizardo, Pedro Francisco
La viva elegía (1943) Valencia, Venezuela, Editorial "Tierra Firme", 1944.
88p. 21cm.
Poems.
"300 ejemplares ... 100 ejemplares numerados ... N° 38."
Author's autograph presentation copy.
I. Title. Autograph
NL 0423682 PSt KMK TxU

Lizardo Díaz, José
see
Lizardo Díaz O , J

Lizardo Díaz O , J
De la democracia a la dictadura. Guatemala, Impr. Hispania, 1946.
133 p. illus. 22 cm.
1. Guatemala—History—1821–1945. I. Title.
F1466.45.L49 70-247982
NL 0423684 DLC TxU DPU TU IU NN CU-B LNHT

W 4 S23 1946 LIZARDO Y VIDAL, Francis
Iritis tuberculosa. [Ciudad Trujillo, 1946]
68 ℓ. (Santo Domingo. Universidad. Facultad de Medicina. Tesis, 1945-1946, no. 16)
Typewritten copy.
Contains author's signature.
1. Eye - Tuberculosis 2. Iris - Diseases
NL 0423685 DNLM

Lizarra, A de.
... Los vascos y la República española, contribución a la historia de la guerra civil, 1936–1939. Buenos Aires, Editorial vasca Ekin, s. r. l., 1944.
300 p., 1 l. 18½cm.
Bibliographical foot-notes.
1. Spain—Hist.—Civil war, 1936–1939. 2. Basques. I. Title.
DP269.L523 A 47-214
New York. Public library for Library of Congress [3]†
WaS TU Wa GU WaSpG WaPS WaT WaSp CaBVaU WaWW WaTC OrSaW IdPI IdU IC InU OrCS MtU MtBC Or OU DLC WaE NcU OCl OrU NBuU OrP OrPR MtBuM OrStbM
NL 0423686 NN OrU-M IdB CoU CtY NcD MB ScU ViU TxU

Lizarra, A de.
Los vascos y las cruzadas; prólogo del R. P. Sánchez de Gamarra. Gráficos de Kerman Ortiz de Zarate. Buenos Aires, Editorial Vasca Ekin, 1946.
149 p. maps. 18 cm. (Biblioteca de cultura vasca, 26)
"Bibliografía": p. 143–148.
1. Crusades. 2. Navarre (Kingdom)—Hist. I. Title. (Series)
D161.5.N3L58 49-25990*
NL 0423687 DLC ICRL ICN OCl PU CU FU IdU

VOLUME 337

Lizárraga, Francisco.
Diccionario técnico inglés-español y español-inglés para uso de los ejércitos de tierra, mar y aire. Madrid, Compañía Bibliográfica Española ₍1953?₎
706 p. 18 cm.

1. Military art and science—Dictionaries. 2. English language—Dictionaries—Spanish. 3. Military art and science—Dictionaries—Spanish. 4. Spanish language—Dictionaries—English. I. Title.

U25.L68 54-33732

NL 0423688 DLC DPU NcU CtY GU MH NN

JX2787 .E6 1876 Lizárraga, Gabino, tr.
Heffter, August Wilhelm, 1796-1880.
Derecho internacional público de Europa, por A.-G. Heffter. Traduccion de G. Lizarraga ... Madrid, Librería de V. Suárez, 1875.

Lizarraga, Jacinto, y ca., plaintiff.
Cirerol, Manuel, *defendant.*
Constancias relativas al incidente de desembargo de la finca San Diego Azcorra promovido en el juicio ejecutivo, que los Señores Jacinto Lizarraga y cª. siguen contra el Sr. Lic. D. Manuel Cirerol por suma de pesos, comentadas por un abogado. Merida de Yucatan, Impr. del "Eco de comercio", 1887.

Lizarraga, Jacinto, y compania, plaintiff.
₍Patrón, Joaquín₎
Instruccion comunicada por los magistrados que la suscriben, al C. juez de primera instancia Lic. José E. Castillo, para informar al juzgado de distrito en el juicio de amparo promovido por Jacinto Lizarraga y compañía contra actos de dicho juez como ejecutor del fallo dictado por la Sala de revision del H. Tribunal superior de justicia, en el incidente promovido por la Sra. Amada Villamil de Cirerol, sobre disembargo de la hacienda San Diego Azcorra. Mérida, "Imprenta mercantil", á cargo de J. Gamboa Guzmán, 1888.

Bonaparte Collection No.13785 LIZARRAGA, JOAQUÍN.
Jesus. Copla guisa batzuc molde gutitacoac, celebratus Jesus Jaunaren amoreac ta favoreac. Don Joaquin Lizarragac componduac, ta Luis Luciano Bonaparte principeac arguitara emanac. Londresen,1868.
₍246₎p. 15cm.

Vinson 392.

NL 0423692 ICN NN

Bonaparte Collection No.1079 LIZARRAGA, JOAQUÍN.
Urteco igande guztietaraco platicac edo itzaldiac Nafarroan, Elcano deritzan errian... Donostian,I.R.Baroja,1846.
447p. 22½cm.

Vinson 235.

NL 0423693 ICN

Lizarraga, Jorge Cervera
see **Cervera Lizarraga, Jorge.**

Lizarraga, Juan de
see
Leicarraga, Ioannes, f. 1571

Lizárraga, Reginaldo de, *ca.* 1545-1615.
Descripción colonial, por Fr. Reginaldo de Lizárraga ... Buenos Aires, J. Roldán, 1916.
2 v. 19 cm. (Biblioteca argentina; publicación mensual de los mejores libros nacionales, 13-14)
Half-title: Descripción breve de toda la tierra del Perú, Tucumán, Río de la Plata y Chile, para el Excmo. Sr. conde de Lemos y Andrada, presidente del Consejo real de Indias, por Fr. Reginaldo de Lizárraga.
Taken from the edition of Serrano y Sans, Madrid, 1909, which was based on the MS. copy in the Biblioteca nacional, Madrid, having title "Descripción y población de las Indias." The original MS. of the work is preserved in the library of San Lázaro, in Zaragoza. cf. v. 1, p. 16.

An edition edited by Carlos A. Romero was published at Lima, 1908, with title "Descripción y población de las Indias."
"Noticia preliminar por Ricardo Rojas": v. 1, p. ₍9₎-35.

1. America—Early accounts to 1600. 2. South America—Description and travel. I. Rojas, Ricardo, 1882-1957, ed. (Series)

E141.L782 19-6838

NL 0423697 WU MB NIC OU TxU NcD DLC

980 L768 Lizárraga, Reginaldo de, 1545-1615.
... Descripción colonial, por fr. Reginaldo de Lizárraga ... 2. edición. Buenos Aires, "La Facultad", 1928.
2 v. 19ᶜᵐ. (Biblioteca argentina; publicación mensual de los mejores libros nacionales; director: Ricardo Rojas. 13-14)

Taken from the edition of Serrano y Sans, Madrid, 1909, which was based on the ms. copy in the Biblioteca nacional, Madrid, having title "Descripción y población de las Indias." The original ms. of the work is preserved in the library of San Lázaro, in Zaragoza. cf. v. 1, p. 18-19.
An edition edited by Carlos A. Romero was published at Lima, 1908, with title "Descripción y población de las Indias."
"Noticia preliminar ₍por Ricardo Rojas₎": v. 1, p. ₍13₎-37.

NL 0423699 NNC MH TxU CtY

Lizárraga, Reginaldo de, ca. 1545-1615.
Descripción de las indias, crónica sobre el antiguo Perú, concebida y escrita entre los años 1560 a 1602. Estudio biobibliográfico sobre el autor por Carlos A. Romero. Introd. y notas breves por Francisco A. Loayza. Lima, 1946.
252 p. port., facsims. 19 cm. (Los Pequeños grandes libros de historia americana, ser. 1, t. 12)
Pub., 1908, under title: Descripción y población de las indias.

1. America—Early accounts to 1600. 2. South America—Descr. & trav. (Series)

E141.L782 1946 980 49-48251*

NL 0423700 DLC CU NcD NNC MnU MH ICN IEN TxU WU

Lizárraga, Reginaldo de, ca. 1545-1615
Descripción y población de las Indias, por Fr. Reginaldo de Lizárraga, dominico, obispo de la Concepción y del Paraguay; publicada en la Revista del Instituto histórico del Perú, con un prologo y noticia biografica del autor, por Carlos A. Romero. Lima, Imprenta americana, 1908.
2 p. l., viii, 209 p. port. 25ᶜᵐ.

1. America—Early accounts to 1600. 2. South America—Descr. & trav. I. Romero, Carlos Alberto. II. Title.

17-16349

Library of Congress E141.L78

NL 0423701 DLC PSt DPU NcD TxU CtY MH-P

F1411 .H67 Lizárraga, Reginaldo de, ca.1545-1615.
... **Historiadores** de Indias ... Por M. Serrano y Sanz Madrid, Bailly, Bailliére é hijos, 1909-

G631.8 L768c Lizárraga Aramburo, Pablo Aquiles.
Control químico de la fertilidad de las tierras del ingenio de Costa Rica, Sinaloa. México, 1951.
31p. diagrs. 24cm.
Tesis (químico) - Universidad Nacional Autónoma de México.
Bibliography: p.31.

1. Agricultural chemistry. 2. Soil fertility. 3. Soil chemistry. 4. Soils - Mexico - Costa Rica. I. Title.

NL 0423703 TxU

Lizárraga-Bengoa, Martín Ursúa y Arizmendi, *conde* **de.**
Conquista del Ytza en la Nueva España. Publicado de la edición de 1714 por Vicente Fontavella. Valencia, 1943.
79 p. facsim. 17 cm. (Colección aneja de Saitabi. Serie 4: Textos, no. 1)
At head of title: Universidad Literaria de Valencia. Facultad de Filosofía y Letras.
Previously published in Nobiliario de el valle el la Valdorba, by Francisco de Elorza y Rada.

1. Itza Indians. I. Fontavella, Vicente, ed. II. Title. (Series)

F1376.L79 52-52444

NL 0423704 DLC

Lizárraga-Bengoa, Martín Ursúa y Arizmendi, conde de.
A narrative of the conquest of the province of the Ytzas in New Spain ...
see under Elorza y Rada, Francisco de, fl. 1714.

Lizarraga Fischer, V. E., tr.
Armstrong, Martin Donisthorpe, 1882-
Circo español (Godoy y los Borbones de España) por Martin Armstrong; traducción directa del inglés por V. E. Lizarraga Fischer. ₍Santiago de Chile₎ Ediciones Ultra ₍1938₎

W 4 M61 1953 LIZARRAGA GARCIA, Benjamin
El bloqueo del ganglio estrellado en la práctica médica. México, 1953.
59 p. illus.
Tesis - Univ. de México.
1. Stellate ganglion

NL 0423707 DNLM

Lizarralde, Alvaro Copete
see
Copete Lizarralde, Alvaro.

Lizarralde, Daniel.
Alteraciones de la voz, nódulos de los cantores Buenos Aires, [n.p.] 1917.
53 p. pl. 18 cm.

NL 0423709 NcU

Lizarralde, Fernando.
... Ceniza de sueños; poesías. Buenos Aires, Librería y editorial "La Facultad," de Bernabé y cía. ₍1942₎
3 p. l., 9-105 p., 3 l. front. (port.) 18½ᶜᵐ.

I. Title.

43-18529

Library of Congress PQ7797.L545C4
₍2₎ 861.6

NL 0423710 DLC

VOLUME 337

Lizarralde, Fernando.
El Ollantay argentino; ensayo sobre la tragedia andina de Ricardo Rojas. [Eva Perón, República Argentina] Ediciones Término [1953]
118 p. illus. 21 cm.
Tesis—Universidad Nacional de Buenos Aires.
Includes bibliography.
1. Ollanta. 2. Rojas, Ricardo, 1882–
Full name: Fernando María Lizarralde.
PM6308.O6L5 56-17838 ‡

NL 0423711 DLC RPB MoU ViU CU-S NBuU IU NN TxU

Lizarralde, Fernando.
... Senda de amor ... Buenos Aires, Librería y editorial: "La Facultad" de J. Roldán y cía. [1929]
84 p., 2 l. incl. front. (port.) 16cm.
On cover: Poesías.
I. Title.
34-32505
Library of Congress PQ7797.L54584 861.6

NL 0423712 DLC

Basqu BT 645 L59 Lizarralde, José A
Andra Mari. Reseña histórica del culto de la Virgen Santísima en la provincia [de Guipúzcoa y] la provincia de Vizcaya. Bilbao, Imprenta C. Dochao de Urigüen, 1926-34.
2 v. illus. 21½cm.
Prologo de v.1 por Dr. D. Narciso de Estenaga.
Prologo de v.2 por Dr. D. Mateo Múgica.
Contents.- v.1. Semblanza religiosa de la provincia de Guipúzcoa, ensayo iconográfico, legendario, e histórico.- v.2. Ensayo iconografico legendario, e histórico. Reseña histórica del culto de la Virgen Santísima en la provincia de Vizcaya.

NL 0423714 IdU

Lizarralde, José A.
Historia de la Universidad de Sancti Spiritus de Oñate. por el r. p. José A. Lizarralde ... Tolosa, Impr. de I. López Mendizábal, 1930.
xv, 530 (i. e. 526) p. illus. (facsim.) plates, plans. 18½cm.
Error in paging: no. 261-262 and 283-284 omitted.
1. Oñate, Spain. Universidad de Sancti Spiritus.
33-17182
Library of Congress LF4823.O56L5 378.46

NL 0423715 DLC NcD

Lizarralde A , Eduardo.
... Consideraciones sobre cirugía experimental; tesis presentada a la Junta directiva de la Facultad de ciencias médicas de la Universidad nacional por Eduardo Lizarralde A. ... en el acto de su investidura de médico y cirujano ... Guatemala, Tipografía Sánchez & de Guise, 1944.
46 p., 1 l. illus. 27½cm.
At head of title: Facultad de ciencias médicas de la Universidad nacional. República de Guatemala, Centro América.
"Bibliografía": p. [45]-46.
1. Surgery, Experimental.
45-16794
Library of Congress RD61.L5

NL 0423716 DLC

Lizarralde, Pelegrin Calle
see Calle Lizarralde, Pelegrin.

Lizarralde Arrillaga, José.
La importancia de los estados financieros para la obtención de crédito, su aplicación en Guatemala. Guatemala, 1955.
60 p. 23 cm.
Tesis (contador-auditor público)—Universidad de San Carlos de Guatemala.
1. Credit—Guatemala. 2. Financial statements—Guatemala.
HG3729.G92L5 59-48347 ‡

NL 0423718 DLC MH-L

QS L788e 1844 **LIZARS, Alexander Jardine**
Elements of anatomy, intended as a text-book for students. Edinburgh, Bell & Bradfute, 1844.
2 v. illus.

NL 0423719 DNLM

Lizars (Alexander Jardine). A probationary essay on the knee joint. 38 pp. 8°. *Edinburgh, J. Walker.* 1831. [*Also, in:* P., v. 1062; 1191; 1273.]

NL 0423720 DNLM

Lizars, Alexander Jardine
——. Syllabus of the course of lectures on the anatomy of the human body, delivered by ... v, 8-49 pp. 8°. *Edinburgh, J. Walker,* [n. d.]

NL 0423721 DNLM

QS L788t **LIZARS, Alexander Jardine**
Text-book of anatomy for junior students. Edinburgh, Bell & Bradfute [1844]-
v.

NL 0423722 DNLM

Lizars, Daniel, *d.* 1812.
The Edinburgh geographical and historical atlas, comprehending a sketch of the history of geography; a view of the principles of mathematical, physical, civil, and political geography; an account of the geography, statistics, and history of each continent, state, and kingdom, delineated. And a tabular view of the principal mountain chains in the world. Engraved on sixty-nine copper plates, and compiled from materials drawn from the newest and most authentic sources. Edinburgh, J. Hamilton, successor to D. Lizars; London, Whittaker, Treacher, & co., [etc., etc., 1831?]
6 p. l., 16, 288, 4 p. LXIX (i. e. 58) fold. pl. (col. maps) 47½cm.
Some maps are numbered as two or four plates each; plate 32 omitted in numbering.
1. Atlases. [2]† Map 46-397
Library of Congress G1019.L55

NL 0423723 DLC NN OCl

LIZARS, DANIEL, *d.* 1876.
Information addressed to the board of directors of the City of Toronto and Lake Huron Railway Company, London, on the superior advantages of Goderich, the district town of the Huron, on Lake Huron, compared with the village of Sarnia, on the river St. Clair, as the Lake Huron terminus of the projected railway. By Daniel Lizars, esq., Clerk of the Peace of the Huron District, Director of the direct Ontario and Huron Junction Railway Company, formed at Goderich, C.W., 3rd June, 1845, and Delegate from the Inhabitants of the said District. *London: William Stevens, printer, Bell yard, Temple Bar. MDCCCXLV. (For Private Circulation.)*
2 p.l., 48 p. 8vo. 21.2 x 13.5 cm.

NL 0423724 CaOTP

Lizars, John, 1787?-1860.
Anatomy of the brain, from the celebrated dissections of John Lizars ... comprising fifteen engravings (colored after nature) with accompanying explanations. Ed. by Landon Rives, M. D. Cincinnati, H. W. Derby, 1854.
2 p. l., xv col. pl. 47cm.
Page of letterpress opposite each plate.
1. Brain. I. Rives, Landon, ed.
6-2385
Library of Congress QM455.L78

NL 0423725 DLC WU-M ICU OU CtY-M PPWI PU DNLM

Lizars, John, 1787?-1860.
Anatomy of the brain, from the celebrated dissections of John Lizars... comprising 15 engravings (colored from nature)...Ed. by Landon Rives... Cincinnati, 1860.
47 cm.

NL 0423726 CtY

Lizars, John, 1787?-1860.
Beobachtungen über die Exstirpation krankhafter Ovarien. Mit nach der Natur colorirten Kupfertafeln. Aus dem Englischen. eimar, Grossherzogl. Sächs. priv. Landes-Industrie-Comptoirs, 1826.
14 p. 5 plates. 40 1/2 cm.
Ex libris Edgar Goldschmid, no. B609.
1. Ovarian Diseases. I. Title.

NL 0423727 WU-M ICJ

Lizars, John, 1787-1860.
——. Elements of anatomy, intended as a text-book for students. 2 v., paged consecutively and interleaved. xxxv, 900 pp., 2 pl. 16°. *Edinburgh, Bell & Bradfute,* 1844.

NL 0423728 DNLM

Lizars, John, 1787?-1860, defender.

Syme, James, 1799-1870, *pursuer.*
A full report of the jury cause, Syme *v.* Lizars, on Thursday, March 12, 1840. Taken in shorthand by Mr. Simon Macgregor. [Edinburgh] Edinburgh printing & publishing company: London, Smith, Elder, & co.; [etc., etc.] 1840.

Lizars, John, 1787?-1860, *pursuer.*
Jury court—First division. John Lizars, esq., surgeon, against James Syme, esq., surgeon. Monday, 26th July, 1852. (Before the lord justice-general and a jury.) [Edinburgh, Printed by W. H. Lizars, 1852]
55 p. 21½cm. [*With* Syme, James, pursuer. A full report of the jury cause, Syme *v.* Lizars ... [Edinburgh] London [etc.] 1840]
Caption title.
Action for libel.
I. Syme, James, 1799-1870, defender. II. Scotland. Jury court.
28-22053

NL 0423730 DLC DNLM CtY-M

RG481 f.L75 LIZARS,JOHN,1787?-1860.
Observations on extraction of diseased ovaria; illustrated by plates coloured after nature. By John Lizars... Edinburgh,D.Lizars;[etc.,etc.]1825.
[4],24 p. 5 col.pl. 44½cm.
1.Ovariotomy.

MnU CtY-M
NL 0423731 ICU MBCo PPPH PPC NN MiU DNLM NNNAM

Lizars, John, 1787-1860.
——. Observations on hernia. 8 pp. 8°. [*Edinburgh,* 1831.] [P., v. 1056.]

NL 0423732 DNLM

Lizars, John, 1787-1860.
——. Operation for the cure of club-foot ... being an appendix to a system of practical surgery. 14 pp., 4 pl. 8°. *Edinburgh, W. H. Lizars,* 1842. [*Also, in:* P., v. 918; 1300.]

NL 0423733 DNLM

Lizars, John, 1787-1860.
——. Operation for the cure of squinting; being an appendix to a system of practical surgery. 7 pp., 3 pl. 8°. *Edinburgh, W. H. Lizars,* 1840.

NL 0423734 DNLM

VOLUME 337

Lizars, John, 1787?-1860.
Plates on anatomy of brain, from his system of anatomical plates. [Cincinnati, 18--]

NL 0423735 NjP

RD783 L76 1853 Lizars, John, 1787?-1860.
Practical observations on the treatment of clubfoot, with cases illustrated by explanatory plates, the drawings after nature. 2d ed. ... Edinburgh, W. H. Lizars, 1853.
20 p. V plates.

1. Foot - Abnormities and deformities.

NL 0423736 NNC MBCo DNLM

WE L789p 1855 **LIZARS, John, 1787?-1860**
Practical observations on the treatmen of clubfoot with cases illustrated by explanatory plates, the drawings after nature. 3d ed. Edinburgh, Lizars, 1855.
38 p. illus.

NL 0423737 DNLM

Lizars, John, 1787?-1860.
Practical observations on the treatment of stricture of the urethra and fistula in perineo... Edinburgh, Lizars, 1851.
91 p.

NL 0423738 PPC

Lizars, John, 1787?-1860.
Practical observations on the treatment of stricture of the urethra and fistula in perineo, illustrated with cases and drawings of these affections. To this edition there is annexed a copious appendix, which contains the opinions and observations of the most eminent London surgeons and others, on the subject of the operation of the perineal section ... 3d ed., greatly improved and enl. By John Lizars ... Edinburgh, W. H. Lizars; London, S. Highley, 1853.
7 p. l., [v]-xxxviii p., 1 l., 249p. XV pl. (part col.) 23½cm.
1. Urethra. 2. Perineum.

Printed by Wesleyan University Library

NL 0423739 CtW MBCo WU-M CtY-M DNLM PPC

LIZARS, John, 1787?-1860.
Practical observations on the use and abuse of tobacco. Edinburgh, W. H. Lizars, 1854.

Pamphlet.

NL 0423740 MH

RC567 .L59 1856 Lizars John, 1787?-1860.
Practical observations on the use and abuse of tobacco, greatly enlarged from the original communication on the effects of tobacco smoking, which appeared in Medical times and gazette, Aug. 5, 1854. 4th ed. Edinburgh, 1856.
30 p. 23 cm.

1. Tobacco habit. I. Title.

NL 0423741 NjR DNLM KyU

Lizars, John, 1787?-1860.
Practical observations on the use and abuse of tobacco. Greatly enl. from the original communication on the Effects of tobacco smoking which appeared in the Medical times and gazette, August 5, 1854. 5th ed. Edinburgh, W. H. Lizars; London, George Philip, 1856.
32p. 22cm.

1.Smoking. 2.Tobacco. I.Title: Observations on the use and abuse of tobacco. II.Title: Effects of tobacco smoking.

NL 0423742 NcD-MC

Lizars, John, 1787?-1860.
Practical observations on the use and abuse of tobacco, greatly enlarged from the original communication on the effects of tobacco smoking, which appeared in Medical times and gazette, August 5, 1854. Accompanied with cases, illustrated by coloured plates, the drawings after nature. By John Lizars, ... Sixth edition. ... . Edinburgh, W. H. Lizars; [etc., etc.], 1857.
42 p. 2 col. pl. (incl. front.) 22½cm.

NL 0423743 ICJ

Lizars, John, 1787-1860.
——. Practical observations on the use and abuse of tobacco, greatly enlarged from the original communication on the effects of tobacco smoking which appeared in Medical Times and Gazette, August 5, 1854; accompanied with cases. 7. ed. 64, 3 pp. 8°. *Edinburgh, W. H. Lizars,* 1857.

NL 0423744 DNLM

Lizars (John) [1787-1860]. A probationary surgical essay on gonorrhœa virulenta. 1 p. l., 28 pp. 8°. *Edinburgh, W. Blair,* [1815]. [P., v. 1270.]

NL 0423745 DNLM

Lizars, John, 1787-1860.
——. Substance of the investigations regarding cholera asphyxia; with cases and dissections, communicated by Prof. Delpech and Dr. Coste, of Montpellier, and Dr. Lowenhayn, of Moscow, during their residence in this country. To which are added observations on the disease in Edinburgh and the neighbouring districts, with numerous cases and dissections. 3 p. l., 72 pp. 8°. *Edinburgh, J. Hamilton,* 1832. [P., v. 1040; 1214.]

NL 0423746 DNLM

Toner **Lizars, John,** 1787?-1860.
Substance of the investigations regarding cholera asphyxia in 1832: with cases and dissections, communicated by Professor Delpech, and Dr. Coste of Montpelier, and Dr. Lowenhayn of Moscow, during their residence in this country. To which are added observations on the disease in Edinburgh and the neighbouring districts, with numerous cases and dissections. By John Lizars ... 2d ed. ... Edinburgh, W. H. Lizars; [etc. etc.], 1848]
4 p. l., 77 p. 23cm.
"Professor Delpech's communication on cholera": p. [1]-18.
1. Cholera, Asiatic. I. Delpech, Jacques Mathieu, 1777-1832. II. Title.

35-36252

Library of Congress RC126.L7 1848

NL 0423747 DLC DNLM OClW-H

WO qL789sa 1830 **LIZARS, John, 1787?-1860**
Surgery. [Edinburgh? 1830?] p. [421]-492. illus.

Author's autograph presentation copy. Signed.
Reprinted from the Edinburgh encyclopaedia.

NL 0423748 DNLM

Lizars, John, 1787?-1860.
A system of anatomical plates; accompanied with descriptions, and physiological, pathological, and surgical observations. By John Lizars ... Edinburgh, D. Lizars; [etc., etc.] 1822-26.
12 pts. in 1 v. 21½cm. and atlas of 101 col. pl. 45cm.
Atlas has engr. t.-p. with title vignette.

1. Anatomy, Human—Atlases. 6—1582

——— Copy 2. Imperfect: Atlas wanting.
Library of Congress QM25.L76 [a42b1]

NL 0423749 PPHa CaBVaU MiU NjP MB WU ViU DNLM ICJ DLC OClW-H KU-M CtY-M CU OrU-M NcD IU-M

QS fL789s 1840 **LIZARS, John, 1787?-1860**
A system of anatomical plates of the human body, accompanied with descriptions, and physiological, pathological, and surgical observations. Edinburgh, Lizars, [1804?]
xxii, 241, xxxvi p., 101 plates.

Contains signature of Louis A. Edwards.

NL 0423750 DNLM

Lizars, John, 1787?-1860.
A system of anatomical plates of the human body accompanied with descriptions, and physiological, pathological, and surgical observations, by John Lizars, ... Edinburgh, W.H. Lizars, [etc., etc., 1841?]
[6, v]-xxii, [4] 341, xxxvi p. col. pl. 43.5 cm.
Title vignette.

NL 0423751 CtY WU

Lizars, John, 1787-1860.
——. A system of anatomical plates of the human body, accompanied with descriptions and physiological, pathological, and surgical observations. 3 p. l., xv, 241 pp., 101 pl., xxiv, 6, vii, 10 pl. fol. *Edinburgh, W. H. Lizars,* 1856,
For Biography, see Dict. Nat. Biog., Lond., 1893, xxxiii, 405 (T. Seccombe).

NL 0423752 DNLM ViRA

WO L789s 1847 **LIZARS, John, 1787?-1860**
A system of practical surgery, including all the recent discoveries and operations. 2d ed. Edinburgh, Lizars, 1847.
503 p. illus.

NL 0423753 DNLM WU-M

Lizars, John, 1787?-1860.
A system of practical surgery, with numerous explanatory plates, the drawings after nature. Edinburgh, W. H. Lizars [etc.] 1838-39.
2 pts. in 1 v. illus. 23 cm.
Author's presentation copy to the Royal Medical Society of Edinburgh.

1. Surgery. I. Title.

NL 0423754 WU-M N KU-M KyU DNLM MBCo OClW-H

Lizars, John, 1787?-1860.
The use and abuse of tobacco. By John Lizars ... From the 8th Edinburgh ed. Philadelphia, Lindsay & Blakiston, 1859.
1 p. l., ix-xi, 13-138 p. 26½cm.

1. Tobacco habit.

7—34677

Library of Congress RC371.T6L7

NL 0423755 DLC CaBViP DNLM PPC MH ViU

Lizars, John, 1787-1860.
The use and abuse of tobacco. Phila., Lindsay & Blakiston, 1867.

Bound with Alcohol: its place and power, by James Miller.

NL 0423756 OCl

Lizars, John, 1787-1860.
The use and abuse of tobacco... From the eighth Edinburgh edition. Philadelphia, Lindsay & Blakiston, 1873.
2 p. l., ix-xi, 13-138 p. 16°.

NL 0423757 NN

VOLUME 337

Lizars, John, 1787-1860.
Use and abuse of tobacco. New York, 1875.

NL 0423758 NjP

Lizars, John, 1787?-1860.
The use and abuse of tobacco. From the 8th Edinburgh ed. Philadelphia, P. Blakiston, 1883.
[2], ix-xi, 13-138 p. + 13[3] p. (advertisements)

1. Tobacco - Physiological effect. 2. Smoking. I. Title. II. Imprint date: 1883.

NL 0423759 KU-M OCl ICJ CtY-M

Lizars, Kathleen Macfarlane, joint author.
Lizars, Robina.
Humours of '37, grave, gay and grim; rebellion times in the Canadas. By Robina and Kathleen Macfarlane Lizars ... Toronto, W. Briggs; [etc., etc.] 1897.

Lizars, Kathleen Macfarlane.
Lizars, Robina.
In the days of the Canada company: the story of the settlement of the Huron tract and a view of the social life of the period. 1825-1850. By Robina and Kathleen Macfarlane Lizars. With an introduction by G. M. Grant ... Toronto, W. Briggs; Montreal, C. W. Coates [etc.] 1896.

Lizars, Kathleen Macfarlane.
The valley of the Humber, 1615-1913, by K. M. Lizars ... Toronto, W. Briggs, 1913.
x p., 1 l., 170 p. plates (1 col.) maps, plan. 23½cm.
"Authorities cited": p. 165-170.

1. Humber River and Valley, Ont.—Hist. I. Title.

15-1690

Library of Congress F1059.H9L8

NL 0423762 DLC CaBVaU CaBVa NN

WB 37167

Lizars, Robina
Committed to his charge; a Canadian chronicle, by R. & K. M. Lizars. Toronto, G. N. Morang, 1900.
311 p.

I. Lizars, Kathleen Macfarlane, joint author. II. Title (1)

NL 0423763 CtY TxU CaBVaU

Lizars, Robina.
Humours of '37, grave, gay and grim; rebellion times in the Canadas. By Robina and Kathleen Macfarlane Lizars ... Toronto, W. Briggs; [etc., etc.] 1897.
3 p. l., [5]-369, [1] p. illus. (facsim.) fold. map. 19½cm.

1. Canada—Hist.—Rebellion, 1837-1838. I. Lizars, Kathleen Macfarlane, joint author. II. Title.

16-9473

Library of Congress F1032.L78

CaOTU
NL 0423764 DLC CaBVaU NBuHi CaNSWA CU TxU NIC MB

Lizars, Robina.
In the days of the Canada company: the story of the settlement of the Huron tract and a view of the social life of the period. 1825-1850. By Robina and Kathleen Macfarlane Lizars. With an introduction by G. M. Grant ... Toronto, W. Briggs; Montreal, C. W. Coates [etc.] 1896.
xiv, [2], [17]-494 p. front., illus., pl., port., plans, facsim. 22½cm.

1. Canada company, London. 2. Ontario—Hist. I. Title.

Library of Congress F1058.L78 2-19052

NL 0423765 DLC CaBVaU UU OrU CaOTU OCl CaNSWA CU

Lizars, William Home, 1788-1859, illus.

Audubon, John James, 1785-1851.
The birds of America; from original drawings by John James Audubon ... London. Pub. by the author, 1827-38.

Lizars, William Home, 1788-1859.
Edinburgh geographical general atlas: containing maps of every empire, state, and kingdom; with a tabular view of the heights of the great mountain chains, and a very copious and comprehensive consulting index. Compiled, drawn and engr. from the latest and most authentic sources. The maps of the new British colonies upon an extra large scale; and the whole engr. upon sixty-nine plates. Edinburgh, W.H. Lizars [183-?] [2] l.,68 double col.maps,[4] l., 16 p. 49cm.

Maps were incorrectly numbered to 69—cf. Publisher's note.

1. Geography—Atlases, 183- .

NL 0423768 NN

Lizars, William Home, 1788-1859.
Lizars' Edinburgh geographical general atlas: containing maps of every empire, state, and kingdom; with a tabular view of the heights of the great mountain chains, and a very copious and comprehensive consulting index. Compiled, drawn, and engraved, from the latest and most authentic sources. The maps of the new British colonies upon an extra large scale; and the whole engraved upon sixty-nine plates. Edinburgh, W. H. Lizars; London, S. Highley; [etc., etc., 1842?]
2 p. l., 29 p. LXIX (i. e. 68) fold. pl. (col. maps) 49cm.
Plate 32 omitted in numbering.
1. Atlases.

Map 46-393

Library of Congress G1019.L56 [2]†

NL 0423769 DLC

Lizars, William Home, 178?-1859.
... The Edinburgh penman, a new set of copy lines. Edinburgh, Designed & engraved by W. H. Lizars [ca. 1840?]
1 pt. 7 x 18 cm. (No. 27)

Cover-title.
Designated as "Set 18" on plate [1].

NL 0423770 NNC

Kress Room

Lizars, William Home, 1788-1859.
Lizars' guide to the Caledonian railway, forming a full description of the line and its scenery from Edinburgh to Carlisle, and back from Carlisle to Glasgow ... Opened 1847. 2d ed. Edinburgh, W.H. Lizars [etc., etc.] 1848.
36 p. front. (fold map) 16 cm.

Title vignette.
1. Railroads - Early works to 1850. 2. Caledonian rail- way. 3. Railroads - Scotland.

NL 0423771 MH-BA

Lizars, William Home, 1788-1859.

Segar, *Sir* **William,** *d.* 1633.
Original institutions of the princely orders of collars, by Sir William Segar. Edinburgh, Printed for W. H. Lizars [etc.] 1823.

Lizars, William Home, 1788-1859.
Plan of Edinburgh drawn & engraved for McDowall's Guide to the City.
Edinburgh. T. & W. McDowall. [184-?] Size, 9 × 10⅜ inches.
Scale, none. Folded.
Submap. — Plan of Leith.

G3430 — Edinburgh. Descr. Maps. — ...Dowall [McDowall], T. & W., publishers.

NL 0423773 MB

LIZARS, William Home, 1788-1859.
Plan of the city of Dublin. Drawn and engraved for Johnston & Deas' New pictures of Dublin,by W.H. Lizars, Edinburgh, [18..]

18 1/2 x 11 3/4 in.

NL 0423774 MH

Lizars, William Home, 1788-1859.
Lizars' Scottish tourist. A guide to the picturesque scenery, antiquities, etc. (the original work)... Edinburgh: W. H. Lizars, 1850. 438 p. facsim., front., illus., maps, plan, plates. 18. ed. 12°.
Added, engr. t.-p.

272896A. 1. Scotland—Guidebooks, 1850.
N. Y. P. L. February 25, 1927

NL 0423775 NN

Lizars, William Home, 1788-1859.

The Scottish tourist's portable guide to the land of Burns, with an excursion from Dumfries through the stewartry of Kirkcudbright. Illustrated with views, maps, etc. Edinburgh, W. H. Lizars; [etc., etc.] 1848.

TypTS 805 49.526

Lizars, William Home, 1788-1859.
Specimens of engraving, lithography & typography.
W.H.Lizars,3,St James' square,Edinburgh.1849 ...

2 pts.in 1v. 22x29cm.
Cover-title.
Pt.2 has special t.-p.: Specimens of plain and ornamental types, etc., etc., for letter-press printing.
Original half red morocco & decorated gray boards.

NL 0423777 MH

TypTS 805 49.526

Lizars, William Home, 1788-1859.
Specimens of plain and ornamental types, etc., etc., for letter-press printing.
W.H.Lizars,St.James' square,Edinburgh. MDCCCXLIX.

5p.ℓ.,16 numb.ℓ.,lℓ.,17-46 numb.ℓ. 22x29cm.
(Pt.2 of his Specimens of engraving, lithography & typography, 1849)
Leaves printed on 1 side only.

NL 0423778 MH

Lizarte Martínez, Angel.
... Dios, espíritu y materia, esencia, función, coordinación; origen y evolución del cosmos de la tierra y de la vida. 2. ed. [Montevideo, Editorial Florensa & Lafon] 1944.
183 p., 3 l. 18½cm.
"Dificultades de todo orden ... me decidieron en el año 1934 a realizar una 1.ª edición, muy restringida, abreviando y suprimiendo problemas completamente resueltos ... Hoy sale a la luz esta 2.ª edición, tal como fué concebida y desarrollada en el original, aspirando a su mayor divulgación."—p. [7]

1. Cosmology—Curiosa and miscellany. 2. Life. I. Title.

45-10787

Library of Congress BD701.L6 1944

113

NL 0423779 DLC MH

Lizarza, Adolfo Portela y.

see

Portela y Lizarza, Adolfo.

VOLUME 337

Pamphlet Mexico 1811 L76 Lizarza, Facundo de
Discurso ... vindicando al excelentícimo señor don José Iturrigaray, de las falcas imputaciones de un quaderno títulado, por ironía, Verdad sabida, y buena fe guardada. Cadiz,1811.

NL 0423781 CtY

Lizarza, Facundo de
Discurso...vindicando al Excelentísimo Señor Don José Iturrigaray. de las falsas imputaciones de un quaderno titulado, por ironía Verdad sabida, y buena fe guardada.En Cadiz en la oficina de D. Nicolas Gomez de Requena...año de 1811. Reimpreso en Mexico: por D.Manuel Antonio Valdés, año de 1812.
71p. 20cm.
1.Lopez Cancelada, Juan, b.1765. Verdad sabida y buena fe guardada. 2. Mexico---Hist.---Wars of independence, 1810-1821. 3. Iturrigaray, Jose de, Viceroy of Mexico.

NL 0423782 LNHT CtY CU-B IEN

Lizarza, Francisco Xavier
see
Lizarza Inda, Francisco Javier.

Lizarza, Manuel Ventura de.
Panegyrico en alabança de n. seraphico padre s. Francisco: patente el santissimo sacramento. Dixole el dia qvatro de octvbre, de el año de 1673. en el convento de Mexico el r. p. fr. Manuel Ventura de Lizarza ... Dedicale a n. r[mo] p. fr. Francisco Trebiño ... Con licencia: en Mexico, Por Francisco Rodriguez Lupercio. Año de 1674.
Film copy, made in 1941, of the original in the Medina collection, Biblioteca nacional de Santiago de Chile. Positive.

Negative film in Brown university library.
Collation of the original, as determined from the film: [40] p. illus. (coat of arms)
Privileges signed: Ioan de San Miguel; doctor, y maestro d. Antonio de la Torre, y Arellano; d[or] d. Antonio de Cardenas, y Salazar; Francisco de Villena; fr. Miguel de Aguilera.
Medina, La imprenta en México, 1107.

1. Francesco d'Assisi, Saint, 1182-1226. 2. Sermons, Spanish—Mexico.
A 44-4902
Brown univ. Library for Library of Congress Film AC-2 reel 15, no. 7
[3]†

NL 0423785 RPB InU DLC RPJCB

Lizarza Inda, Francisco Javier.
La sucesión legítima a la corona de España. 2. ed. Pamplona, 1951.
110 p. 17 cm.

1. Spain—Kings and rulers—Succession. I. Title.
54-28608 ‡

NL 0423786 DLC

946.08 L768m 1954 Lizarza Iribarren, Antonio.
Memorias de la conspiración; cómo se preparó en Navarra la cruzada, 1931-1936. 3.ed. Pamplona, Gómez, 1954.
224p. plates, ports., facsims. 21cm.

1. Spain.--Hist.--Republic, 1931-1939. 2. Carlists. 3. Spain--Hist.--Civil War, 1936-1939. I. Title.

NL 0423787 IU CU NN CSt-H MCM

Lizaso, Domingo de.
Nobiliario de los palacios, casas solares y linajes nobles de la M. N. y M. L. provincia de Guipúzcoa por D. Domingo de Lizaso ... con una introducción de D. Juan Carlos de Guerra ... San Sebastián, Imprenta de la provincia, 1901.
2 v. in 1. 31½cm. 3-21916

NL 0423788 DLC TNJ MH

Lizaso, Felix, 1891-
...Biografia. La Habane, Molina y cia. 1933.
22 p.

NL 0423789 PHC

Lizaso, Félix, 1891- ed.
... Breve antología del 10 de octubre; discursos y artículos de Carlos Manuel de Céspedes, José Manuel Mestre, Enrique Piñeyro, Antonio Zambrana, Eugenio M. Hostos, José Martí, Manuel Sanguily, Enrique José Varona. Publicaciones de la Secretaría de educación, Dirección de cultura. La Habana [Cárdenas y cía.] 1938.

qG972.91 M362Yl.c
Lizaso, Félix, 1891-
Camino de Martí, por Félix Lizaso ... [La Habana] 1953.
cover-title, 14 numb.l. 29cm.
"Contribución de la Sociedad colombista panamericana al año centenario de Martí."

1. Martí, José, 1853-1895. I. Sociedad colombista panamericana. II. Title.

NL 0423791 TxU NN NcU DLC-P4 NcD CU-B MH

868.79 M362Zg Lizaso, Félix, 1891-
...La casa de Martí... Habana, Imprenta "El Siglo XX", 1944.
34p. 25cm.
At head of title: Academia de la Historia de Cuba.
Thesis:- Cuba. 1944.

1. Martí, José, 1853-1895. I. Academia de la Historia de Cuba, Havana. II. Title.

NL 0423792 LU IU OKentU

Lizaso, Félix, 1891-
Cosme de la Torriente, un orgullo de Cuba, un ejemplo para los cubanos. Habana, Comisión del Homenaje Nacional, 1951.
68 p. 20 cm.

1. Torriente y Peraza, Cosme de la, 1872-
Full name: Félix Lizaso y González.
F1787.T715L5 923.27291 51-35854 ‡

NL 0423793 DLC CtY NN NBuU TxU NcD CU NcU DPU

Lizaso, Félix, 1891-

Martí, José, 1853-1895.
... Educación. Publicaciones de la Secretaría de educación, Dirección de cultura. La Habana [Talleres de Cultural, s. a.] 1935.

Lizaso, Félix, 1891-
... Ensayistas contemporáneos, 1900-1920. La Habana, Editorial Trópico, 1938.
281 p., 1 l. 20½cm. (Antologías cubanas, 2)
"Fichas bio-bibliográficas": p. [239]-281.

1. Cuban literature—Hist. & crit. 2. Authors, Cuban. 3. Cuban essays. I. Title.
39-15249
Library of Congress PQ7378.L5
[2] 864.60822

NL 0423795 DLC CU AU MoSU FU NBuU LU NcU NcD NjP DPU

Lizaso, Félix, 1891- ed.

Martí, José, 1853-1895.
... Epistolario de José Martí: arreglado cronologicamente con introducción y notas por Félix Lizaso ... Habana, Cultural, s. a., 1930-31.

Lizaso, Félix, 1891- ed.

Martí, José, 1853-1895.
... Espíritu de América. Publicaciones de la Secretaría de educación, Dirección de cultura. La Habana [Montalvo-Cárdenas] 1937.

Lizaso, Félix, 1891- , ed.
Feria del libro; gaceta mensual literaria y artistica ...
see under title

Lizaso, Félix, 1891-
José Martí; recuento de centenario. Habana, Impr. Ucar García, 1953.
2 v. 22 cm.

1. Martí, José, 1853-1895. *Full name:* Félix Lizaso y González.
F1783.M38L47 928.6 53-33592 rev ‡

NL 0423799 DLC OKentU FU NBuU MB NN CU TxU OOxM

PQ 7389 M2Z68 Lizaso, Félix, 1891-
Martí, crítico de arte. Habana,1953.
24p. 22cm. (Cuadernos de divulgacion cultural de la comisión Nacional Cubana de la UNESCO, no.7)
At head of title: Año del centenario de Jose Martí.
1. Martí, José, 1853-1895.

NL 0423800 MU NNC NN FMU MH IU

Lizaso, Félix, 1891-
... Martí, espíritu de la guerra justa ... La Habana [Ucar, García y cía.] 1944.
2 p. l., 7-79 p. 17cm. (Colección Ensayos)
"Conferencia leída el 27 de agosto de 1942 en el 'Lyceum'."—p. [10]
First published in "Revista de la Habana," September, 1942. *cf.* p. 7.

1. Martí, José, 1853-1895. [Full name: Félix Lizaso y González]
45-14329
Library of Congress F1783.M38L48
[2] 928.6

NL 0423801 DLC FU NcU NNC NjP DPU PU

Lizaso, Félix, 1891-
Martí, martyr of Cuban independence; translated by Esther Elise Shuler. [Albuquerque] University of New Mexico Press [1953]
vii, 260 p. mounted port. 24 cm.
Translation of Martí, místico del deber.

Continued in next column

VOLUME 337

Continued from preceding column

1. Martí, José, 1853–1895.
Full name: Félix Lizaso y González.
F1783.M38L492 928.6 53–12559

IdPI WaT OrU IU MB TU Or CaOTP MtU WaWW MtBuM OrCS WaS OrPR WaPS WaSp OrP CaBVaU WaS Wa KU TxU ViU CLU PSt CoGjM KEmT OrStbM OrSaW OrU-M MtBC
NL 0423802 DLC IdU WaSpG ODW OCl OOxM PP CU-B NN

Lizaso, Félix, 1891–
... Martí, místico del deber. Buenos Aires, Editorial Losada, s. a. [1940]
330 p. incl. front. (port.) 23cm. (*Half-title:* Biografías, históricas y novelescas)
Bibliography included in "Camino de Martí" (p. 317–327)

1. *Martí, José, 1853–1895.
A 41–1663
Harvard univ. Library for Library of Congress F1783.L59 [2] 928.6

FMU OCU OU CSt
NL 0423803 MH OrU GU NBuU UU NcD OCl NcU GU WaU

G972.91
M362Ll.ma
1946 **Lizaso, Félix,** 1891–
Martí, místico del deber. 2. ed. Buenos Aires, Editorial Losada [1946]
330p. port. 23cm. (Biografías históricas y novelescas)

1. Martí, José, 1853–1895. I. Title. II. Series.

NL 0423804 TxU

F1788
.L54 Lizaso, Félix, 1891–
Martí, místico del deber. 3. ed.
Buenos Aires, Editorial Losada, s.a. [1952]
267 p., incl. front. (port.) 23cm. (Half-title: Biografías historicas y novelescas)
Bibliography included in "Camino de Marti" (p. 317–327)

1. Martí, José, 1858–1895.

NL 0423805 ViU IaU LU MU

Lizaso, Félix, 1891–
... Martí y la Utopía de América ... La Habana [Úcar, García y cía.] 1942.
2 p. l., 7–46 p. 16½cm. (Colección Ensayos)

1. *Martí José, 1853–1895. 2. America—Civilization.
42–24684
Library of Congress F1783.M38L5 [3] 928.6

NL 0423806 DLC WaS LU NcD NcU NN

Lizaso, Félix, 1891–
Panorama de la cultura cubana. [1. ed.] México, Fondo de Cultura Económica [1949]
155 p. 22 cm. (Colección Tierra firme, 47)
"En este libro recogemos, ampliándolos, los trabajos que preparamos para el curso de conferencias que ofrecimos en Buenos Aires en el mes de octubre de 1946."

1. Cuba—Intellectual life. 2. Cuba—Civilization.
Full name: Félix Lizaso y González.
F1778.L58 917.291 50–2810*

ICU ViU OCl NcD CU NN NcU MiU IdPI GU LU
NL 0423807 DLC ScU MU CSt IaU PBm OOxM TxU PU OCU

Lizaso, Félix, 1891–
... Pasión de Martí. La Habana [Imp. Ucar, García y cía.] 1938.
2 p. l., 7–202 p., 2 l. 18cm.
CONTENTS.—Pasión de Martí.—Signo.—El hombre.—El hombre en sus cartas.—La intimidad literaria.—Posibilidades filosóficas.—Hombre para el hombre.—Educación.—Espíritu de América.—Vida del espíritu.—Voz y rumbo.

1. *Martí, José, 1853–1895. I. Title.
39–24112
Library of Congress PQ7389.M2Z717 [2] 928.6

NL 0423808 DLC CU MB NcD OCl NcU CtY NjP NN IU DPU

3177
.785
.792 Lizaso, Félix, 1891–
El pensamiento vivo de Varona. Buenos Aires, Editorial Losada [1949]
218 p. illus. 19 cm. (Biblioteca del pensamiento vivo,37)

1.Varona y Pera, Enrique José, 1849–1933. I.Title.

NL 0423809 NjP NcU

PQ7389
M2Z69 **Lizaso, Félix, 1891–**
Personalidad de José Martí. Habána [Ucar García] 1954.
39p. 19cm.

1. Martí, José, 1853–1895. I. Title.

NL 0423810 IaU NcU OOxM TxU MH MoSW

Lizaso, Félix, 1891–
Personalidad e ideas de José Martí [por] Félix Lizaso [y] Ernesto Ardura. Habana, 1954.
73 p. 18 cm.
CONTENTS.—La personalidad de Martí, por F. Lizaso.—Las ideas de José Martí, por E. Ardura.

1. Martí, José, 1853–1895. I. Ardura, Ernesto. II. Title.
Full name: Félix Lizaso y González.
A 55–3666
Florida. Univ. Library for Library of Congress [1]

NL 0423811 FU

Lizaso, Félix, 1891– *ed.*
La poesía moderna en Cuba (1882–1925) antología crítica, ordenada y publicada por Félix Lizaso y José Antonio Fernández de Castro. Madrid, Hernando, 1926.
406 p. 19cm.
Each group of poems preceded by a bio-bibliographical sketch of the author.

1. Cuban poetry (Collections) 2. Cuban literature—Bio-bibl. I. Fernández de Castro, José Antonio, joint ed. II. Title.
38–20053
Library of Congress PQ7384.L55

MiU CLSU NN MsU
NL 0423812 DLC CU IU NN MH TxU NBuU PSt CtY PBm

Lizaso, Félix, 1891–
... Posibilidades filosóficas en Martí. La Habana, Molina y cía, 1935.
28 p. 23½cm.

1. *Martí, José, 1853–1895.
A 40–1267
Stanford univ. Library for Library of Congress [2]

NL 0423813 CSt

Lizaso, Félix, 1891–
Proyección humana de Martí. Buenos Aires, Editorial Raigal [1953]
160 p. 20 cm.

1. Martí, José, 1853–1895. I. Title.
PQ7389.M2Z718 55–40049

NN IaU KU CSt-H ViU CU-S TNJ AU OU CtY NcD
NL 0423814 DLC TxU MiU ICU FMU WaU NcU MU IEN CU

Lizaso, Félix, 1891–
Rafael Ma. de Mendive, el maestro de Martí, por Félix Lizaso.
(In Havana (city) Historiador. Habaneros ilustres. 1ª series, tomo i, p. [75]–93)

NL 0423815 DPU

Lizaso y Azcárate, Domingo, 1841–
Manual para el empleo del material de puentes modelo Danés, redactado por el coronel de ingenieros D. Domingo de Lizaso y Azcarate y el capitán del mismo cuerpo D. Antonio Mayandía y Gómez. Aprobado y declarado reglamentario para la instrucción y servicio del regimiento de pontoneros por real orden de 28 de mayo de 1895. Madrid, Imprenta del memorial de ingenieros, 1895.
xv, 381 p. incl. tables. illus., diagrs. 18cm.

1. Military bridges. I. Mayandía y Gómez, Antonio, 1860–
22–25669
Library of Congress UG335.L5

NL 0423816 DLC DNW ICU

Lizaso y González, Félix
see
Lizaso, Félix, 1891–

Lizasoain, Ignacio María de Echaide
see
Echaide Lizasoain, Ignacio María de.

Lizasoain, J Manuel.
Quelques aperçus sur l'agriculture de la province de Guipuzcoa [Espagne]. Une ferme dans la même province. ... Par J. Manuel Lizasoain. ... [Paris-Auteuil, Imprimerie des Orphelins-apprentis d'Auteuil, 1903.]
184 p. 23cm.
Thèse—Institut agricole de Beauvais.

NL 0423819 ICJ

S
342.46
L768c **Lizaur y Laeave, Ignacio de**
La carta otorgada de 1808 ... Madrid, Imprenta Helénica, 1916.
81, [3] p.

1. Spain - Constitutional history. 2. Spain - Politics and government. 3. Spain - Constitution. I. For. auth. cd. II. Title.

NL 0423820 WaPS

556.718
L789e **Lizaur y Roldán, Juan de.**
Expedición del Museo Nacional de Ciencias Naturales de Madrid a la Guinea continental española en el verano de 1940. Madrid, S. Aguirre, 1941.
26p. plates, fold. map. 23cm. (Publicaciones de la Real Sociedad geográfica. Serie B, núm. 97)

NL 0423821 IEN

Lizazo, Ramón García
see García Lizazo, Ramón.

WP
L789c
1909 **LIZCANO GONZALEZ, Policarpo**
Cirurgía abdominal ginecológica. Madrid, Bailly-Baillière, 1909.
501 p. illus.

NL 0423823 DNLM CU

VOLUME 337

WP L789ca 1906 LIZCANO GONZÁLEZ, Policarpo
Clínica ginecológica; casos clínicos de la consulta de ginecología de la casa de socorro de la inclusa. Madrid, Teodoro, 1906.
319 p.

NL 0423824 DNLM

WP L789m 1903 LIZCANO GONZÁLEZ, Policarpo
Las metritis. Madrid, Cruzado, 1903.
288 p. illus.

NL 0423825 DNLM

G355.86 L768o Lizcano Mariño, Efraim.
La obra revolucionaria del Ejército; indiscreciones necesarias a militares y civiles. Bogotá, Editorial Antena, 1944-
v. 17cm.

1. Colombia. Ejército - Addresses, essays, lectures. I. Title.

NL 0423826 TxU

Lizcano y Alaminos, Francisco.
Historia de la verdadera cuna de Miguel de Cervantes Saavedra y López, autor del Don Quijote de la Mancha, con las metamórfosis bucólicas y geórgicas de dicha obra. Vida y hechos del príncipe de los ingenios españoles, con una refutación analítica de las biografías que de este autor se han impreso hasta el día. Con un juicio crítico del célebre escritor Jacinto Octavio Picón. Madrid, Impr. de J. Gil y Navarro, 1892.
464 p. illus. 19 cm.

1. Cervantes Saavedra, Miguel de—Homes and haunts—Alcázar de San Juan, Spain.

PQ6338.A4L5 59-57781

IU WU
NL 0423827 DLC MH CtY CU ViU NNH MB ICU CU NN MiU

Lizcano y Gonzalez, Policarpo
see Lizcano González, Policarpo.

Lizé,
Catalogue des objets d'art, de curiosité et d'ameublement de la renaissance et du XVIIIe siècle ... composant la collection de feu m. Lize, de Rouen, et dont la vente aura lieu, a Paris ... 25 ... 26 ... 27 et ... 28 mars, 1901 ... Commissaire-priseur: m[e] P. Chevallier ... Experts: mm. Mannheim ... m. A. Bloche ... [Paris, Imp. de l'art, E. Moreau et cie, 1901]
64 p. plates. 31cm. Tan cloth. Uncut.

1. Art--Private collections.

NL 0423829 CSmH

Lizé (Adolphe). *Sur la rupture de la matrice pendant l'accouchement. 24 pp. 4°. Paris, 1848, No. 129, v. 474.

NL 0423830 DNLM

DD901 .S7L78 LIZEL, GEORG, 1694-1761.
M. Georg Litzels...Beschreibung der römischen todten-töpffe und anderer heidnischen leichengefässe, welche ... bey Speyer ausgegraben werden, nebst einer beschreibung eines steinernen sarges worinn eine edle Römerin in kalch liegend, und eine fibvla ... gefunden worden... Speyer, J.H. Zeuner; [etc., etc.] 1749.
[6], 71 p. 2 fold.pl. 18½cm.

1. Urns. 2. Spires, Ger.--Antiquities, Roman.

NL 0423831 ICU CLU

[Lizel, Georg] 1694-1761, comp.
Deutsche jesuiten-poesie; oder, Eine sammlung catholischer gedichte, welche zur verbesserung allen reimenschmiden wohlmeinend vorleget Megalissvs [pseud.] Franckfurth und Leipzig, J.E. Müller, 1731.
6 p.l., 148 p. 17 cm.
1. Religious poetry - German.

NL 0423832 CU

LIZEL, Georg, 1694-1761.
Historia Poetarum Graecorum Germaniae. Francofurti et Lipsiae, 1730.
pp. 333

NL 0423833 MH NjP PU

Lizel, Georg, 1694-1761.
Studiosus modulans; sive, cantica. Argentorati, 1727.

NL 0423834 NjP

Lizelius, Johan, respondent.
... Undersökning om lagskipningen uti Finland i de äldre tider...
see under Bilmark, Johan, 1728-1801, praeses.

Lizell (Anders Daniel)
*De origine astronomiæ apud Orientales. Lundae, [1796]. 18 pp. 4°.

NL 0423836 NN

Lizell, Gustaf Vilhelm, 1874-
Den kateketiska undervisningen; med särskild hänsyn till Konfirmandskolan. Historisk-principiell framställning. Uppsala, Edv. Berlings Boktryckeri, 1920.
5v. 24cm.

1. Catechetics - Lutheran church. 2. Confirmation - Lutheran church. i. Title.

NL 0423837 MoSCS

Lizell, Gustaf Vilhelm, 1874-
... Om den gamla kyrkans kristendomsundervisning; liturgisk-kateketisk studie, af Gustaf Lizell ... Uppsala, A.-b Akademiska bokhandeln [1920]
123 p. 24[cm]. (Uppsala universitets årsskrift 1920. Teologi. 1)
Running title: Kristendomsundervisningens historia i gamla tiden.

1. Religious education—History. 2. Church history—Primitive and early church. 3. Baptism—History.

A C 39-2063
Minnesota. Univ. Library for Library of Congress [AS284.U7 1920] [4] (378.485)

NL 0423838 MnU MoU IEG PU

Lizell, Gustaf Vilhelm, 1874-
Svedberg och Nohrborg, en homiletisk studie ... af Gustaf Lizell ... Uppsala, A.-b. Akademiska bokförlaget [1910]
viii p., 1 l., 260, 47 p. 23½[cm].
Akademisk afhandling—Uppsala.
"Litteratur": p. [vii]-viii.

1. Swedberg, Jesper, bp., 1653-1735. 2. Nohrborg, Anders, 1725-1767. 3. Preaching—Hist.—Sweden.

11-31407
Library of Congress BV4208.S8L5

NL 0423839 DLC CtY PBa PU CU

Lizell, Gustaf Vilhelm, 1874-
Svenska högmessoritualet 1614-1811. Af Gustaf Lizell. Uppsala, Akademiska boktryckeriet, E. Berling, 1911.
v. 24½[cm]. (Uppsala universitets årsskrift, 1911, bd. 1)
"Källor och litteratur": t, p. [vii]-xii.

1. Lutheran church in Sweden—Liturgy and ritual.

13-14954
Library of Congress AS284.U7

NL 0423840 DLC NN IEG ICJ

Lizell, Gustaf Vilhelm, 1874-
Uppsaliensiskt studentliv kring sekelskiftet, några minnen och intryck, av Gustaf Lizell. Uppsala: Almqvist & Wiksell[, 1924]. 44 p. plates. 4°.

1. Student life—Sweden—Upsala.
N. Y. P. L. August 26, 1925

NL 0423841 NN

Lizell, Johannes Freder, respondent.
Dissertationum academicarum ...
see under Boëthius, Daniel, 1751-1810, praeses.

Lizell, Sven.
Richard Andersson, 1851-1918; minnesteckning av Sven Lizell. Stockholm, Wibergh [1919]
cover-title, 15, [1] p. 21½[cm].
Portrait on cover.

1. Andersson, Richard, 1851-1918.

20-23808
Library of Congress ML410.A56L4

NL 0423843 DLC

Lizenzen-Handbuch deutscher Verlage; Zeitungen Zeitschriften, Buchverlage. 1.- 1947-
Berlin, W. de Gruyter.
v. 24 cm.
Title varies: v. 1, Handbuch der Lizenzen deutscher Verlage.

1. German periodicals—Direct. 2. German newspapers—Direct. 3. Publishers and publishing—Germany—Direct.

Z317.L5 053 51-20390 rev

NIC
NL 0423844 DLC OCl NN NNUN NNC CSt-H CtY DNLM PU

Lizer, Carlos.
El "Ceroplastas grandis", nuevo para la fauna argentina. 1916.

NL 0423845 PPAmE

Lizer, Carlos.
Coccido asiatico nuevo para la Republica Argentina "Chrysomphalus dictyospermi" 1916.

NL 0423846 PPAmE

Lizer, Carlos.
... Estudio químico de la mezcla sulfo-calcica empleada como insecticida-fungicida. Buenos Aires [Talleres graficos "Damiano"] 1914.
1 p. l., [5]-40 p. incl. tables, diagr. 26[cm].
At head of title: Carlos Lizer.
Bibliographical foot-notes.

1. Lime-sulphur spray. [1. Lime-sulphur wash]

Agr 15—1256
U. S. Dept. of agr. Library for Library of Congress 464.4L76 [a41b1]

NL 0423847 DNAL

VOLUME 337

Lizer, Carlos
Informe sobre la expedición al Chaco boliviano. Prensetado [!] a la 1ª Comisión de Defensa Agrícola. Buenos Aires, Talleres Gráficos del Ministerio de Agricultura de la Nación, 1919.
47 p. maps (part fold.)

At head of title: Extracto del Boletín del Ministerio de Agricultura de la Nación.

NL 0423848 NNC NN

LIZER, Carlos
Legislacion nacional sobre policia sanitaria de los vegetales en la Republica Argentina. Recopilacion y concordancia de leyes de reglamentos. Buenos Aires, 1923.

By Carlos Lizer and Raul Bazzi.

NL 0423849 MH-L

Lizer, Carlos.
Nueva subespecie de "Ceroplastes" de la Republica Argentina. (Ceroplastes grandis, hempeli) 1919.

NL 0423850 PPAmE

Lizer, Carlos.
Primer ensayo bibliográfico de entomología argentina, por Carlos Lizer ... Buenos Aires, "Coni," 1919.
1 p. l., p. [351]-380. 26½cm.
"De la Primera reunión nacional de la Sociedad argentina de ciencias naturales: Tucumán, 1916 (pág. 351-380)"

1. Insects—Argentine Republic—Bibl.

Library of Congress Z5859.A6L7 20-15019

NL 0423851 DLC

Lizer, Carlos.
Sobre la presencia del "Chrysomphalus paulistus", en el delta del Paraná. 1916.

NL 0423852 PPAmE

Lizer y Trelles, Carlos A.
... Insectos y otros enemigos de la quinta. Buenos Aires, Editorial sudamericana [1941]
2 p. l., [9]-214 p., 3 l. illus. 18cm. (Enciclopedia agropecuaria argentina, 2)

1. Insects, Injurious and beneficial. 2. Agricultural pests. 3. Vegetables—Diseases and pests. I. Title.

Library of Congress SB931.L76 42-16336
[2] 632.7

NL 0423853 DLC DNAL

Lizer y Trelles, Carlos A
... La lucha moderna contra la langosta en el país, por el prof. ing. Carlos A. Lizer y Trelles ... Buenos Aires, 1940.
31 p. plates, diagrs. 22½cm. (Academia nacional de agronomía y veterinaria ... [Publicaciones] 5)

1. Locusts. I. Title.

Library of Congress SB945.L7L5 42-47354

NL 0423854 DLC DNAL

DG338 .A4L7 Lizerand, Georges, 1877-
Aetius ... Paris, Hachette et cie, 1910.
138, [6] p. 22½cm.
Thèse—Univ. de Paris.
"Liste des ouvrages consultés et cités": p. 7-14.

1. Aetius, d. 454.

NL 0423855 ICU CaBVaU

944.024 L76c Lizerand, Georges, 1877-
Clément V et Philippe IV le Bel. Paris, Hachette, 1910.
xlviii, 508p. 23cm.

Bibliography: p.xxxiii-xlviii.

1. Clemens V, Pope, 1263?-1314. 2. Philippe IV, le Bel, King of France, 1268-1314. 3. Catholic church. For. rel. France. 4. France. For. rel. Catholic church.

NL 0423856 KU MnCS PHC MB CtY

Lizerand, Georges, 1877-
... Clément v et Philippe le Bel. Paris, Hachette et cie, 1911.
398 p., 1 l. 19cm.

1. Clemens v, pope, 1263?-1314. 2. Philippe IV, le Bel, king of France, 1268-1314. 3. Catholic church—For. rel.—France. 4. France—For. rel.—Catholic church.

12-23972

Library of Congress DC92.L6

NL 0423857 DLC IaU

Lizerand, Georges, 1877-

Yonne, *France (Dept.)*
Documents sur la révolution française. Département de l'Yonne. Procès-verbaux de l'administration départementale de 1790 à 1800. Publiés sous les auspices du Conseil général ... Auxerre, Impr. A. Gallot [etc.] 1889-19

Lizerand, Georges, 1877-
... Le dossier de l'affaire des Templiers, éd. et tr. par Georges Lizerand ... Paris, H. Champion, 1923.
2 p. l., xxiv, 229 p. 18½cm. (Les classiques de l'histoire de France au moyen âge ... [2])
"Addition" (p. [214*]-214****) laid in.
Latin and French on opposite pages.

1. Templars in France. I. Title.
Library of Congress CR4755.F7L5 24-22134

OC1W MiU OCU PBm NN MH PU NcU NjR
NL 0423859 DLC MoU IdU CU InU MBtS NIC DCU NcD OU

DC130 B35 L5 Lizerand, Georges, 1877-
Le duc de Beauvillier, 1648-1714. Paris, Société d'Edition "Les Belles Lettres", 1933.
vii, 625p. 19cm.

Letters and documents included in appendix (p.[397]-593.
Bibliographical footnotes.

NL 0423860 RPB MiU GU NjP IaU

---

944 L768 Lizerand, Georges, 1877-
Études d'histoire rurale. Paris, Delalain [1951?]
181 p. maps. 19cm.
Contents.- Aménagement des domaines du clergé régulier de la guerre de Cent ans à 1789.- Le régime rural de la France au XVIIe et au XVIIIe siècle.-La suppression des droits féodaux.-Evolution d'un finage rural.-A propos du remembrement rural.
1. Country life in France. 2. Land tenure in France. Hist. I. Title.

NL 0423861 MnU NN CSt NIC MH InU

Lizerand, Georges, 1877-
... Le régime rural de l'ancienne France. Paris, Presses universitaires de France, 1942.
vii, 190 p., 1 l. illus. (plans) II pl. (1 double) 23cm.
"1re édition."
"Ouvrages à consulter": p. [187]-190.

1. Agriculture—France—Hist. 2. Land tenure—France.
44-23631
Library of Congress HD644.L5
[2] 333.76

NL 0423862 DLC WaU NIC MiU PBm NcD CU LU NIC ICU PU

Lizerand, Georges, 1877-
... Robespierre. Paris, Fustier [1937]
2 p. l., [7]-226 p., 2 l. 19cm.

1. Robespierre, Maximilien Marie Isidore de, 1758-1794.
Library of Congress DC146.R6L66 37-18084
Copyright A—Foreign 35630
[2] 923.244

NL 0423863 DLC FTaSU

Lizerand, Georges, 1877-
Un siècle de l'histoire d'une commune rurale, Vergigny. Paris, Delalain [1950]
126 p. maps. 22 cm.

1. Vergigny, France—Hist.

DC801.V46L5 944.41 50-56787

NL 0423864 DLC NBuU NN

41.2 L76 Lizerand, Jean Philippe, 1926-
Maladies du gibier à plumes. Paris, Foulon, 1953.
102 p.

Thèse - École nationale vétérinaire, Alfort.

1. Game-birds. Diseases.

NL 0423865 DNAL

B 981 .51 Lizeray, Henri, 1844-
Bases de l'église druidique et nationale; le druidisme restauré... Paris, 1885.

Bibliographical foot-notes.

NL 0423866 ICN

LIZERAY, Henri, 1844-
Explication des gloses malbergiques contenues dans la loi salique. Fasc. 1. Paris, E.Thorin, 1886.

NL 0423867 MH

LIZERAY, Henri, 1844-
Fondation du pan-celtisme. Les Francs, nation celtique. Paris, chez l'auteur, 1884.

NL 0423868 MH

[LIZERAY, Henri] 1844-
Les Francs, originaires de Tongres et descendants des Cimbres./ [Saint-Armand, imp. Destenay, 1885?]

pp.7.
"Ecrite pour rectifier l'erreur de date qui s'est glisée dans notre recherche precedente sur les Francs."

NL 0423869 MH

VOLUME 337

Lizeray, Henri, 1844- *ed.*
Leabhar gabala. Livres des invasions ...
see under Leabhar gabhála.

LIZERAY, H[enri] 1844-
Ogmios ou Orphee. Paris, Vigot freres, 1903.
pp. 44.

NL 0423871 MH

DC 63 .L79 Lizeray, Henri, 1844-
Les traditions nationales retrouvées, par Henri Lizeray ... Paris, Carré, 1892.
31 p. 24cm.
Contents.--Préface.--Le peuple Atlante.--Etymologie des mots Atlantes.--Origine, langue et religion des Francs.

NL 0423872 MiU CU

Lizeray, Pierre de.
Les méthodes d'impression des timbres-poste. Paris, Le Monde des philatélistes [1955]
31 p. illus. 21 cm. (Étude no 8)
Cover title.
1. Postage-stamp printing. I. Title.
HE6183.L5 57-39493

NL 0423873 DLC

Lizerolles, Pierre-Marie
Dans l'intimité de personnages illustres, 1845-1890. [n.p., n.d.]
[12] p. (chiefly illus.)
Album of photographs with handwritten captions started by Pierre-Marie Lizerolles and completed by J.M.Dufrenoy, his grandson.

NL 0423874 MH

Lizet (A.) *Sur la rage communiquée. 22 pp. 4°. Paris, 1827, No. 186, v. 209.

NL 0423875 DNLM PPC

Lizet, Pierre.
Contribution à l'étude de la syphilis tertiaire du corps de l'utérus. Paris, M. Vigné, 1934.
101
Thèse.

NL 0423876 DNLM NNC

Case 5A 166 LIZET, PIERRE, 1482-1554.
...Aduersum pseudoeuãgelicam hæresim libri seu commentarij nouem, duobus excusi uoluminibus. Lvtetiae, Apud M.Vascosanum, 1551.
[1], 288, [22] l. 25cm.

NL 0423877 ICN

Case 4A 1488 no.3 LIZET, PIERRE, 1482-1554.
Petri Lizetii ... De auriculari confessione, lib. I. De monastico instituto, lib. I. De huiusce seculi caecitate, ac circumuentione, dialogus inter Spiritalem & Mundanum. Lvgdvni, Apvd S. Gryphivm, 1552.
154p., [1] l. 26cm. (with his De sacris utriusq; instrumenti ... 1552)
Title vignette (printer's device) A different device on verso of last leaf.

NL 0423878 ICN

Case 4A 1488 no.1 LIZET, PIERRE, 1482-1554.
Petri Lizetii ... De sacris utriusq; instrumenti libris in uualgare eloquium minimè uertendis, rudiq; plebi haudquaquam inuulgandis, dialogvs inter Pantarchevm et Neotervm. Lvgdvni, Apvd S. Gryphivm, 1552.
123, [1] p. 26cm.
Caption title on p.3: Dialogvs, de sacris libri in vvalgare eloqvivm minime vertendis...
Title vignette (printer's device) A different device on p. [124]
With this are bound his: Tractatus, De mobilibus Ecclesiae ... 1552; and De auriculari confessione ... 1552.

NL 0423880 ICN

Lizet, Pierre, 1482-1554. Douët d'Arcq, L. Prisée de la bibliothèque du Président L. en 1554. 23 pp. (Biblioth. École des Chartes, v. 37, 1876, p. 358.)

NL 0423881 MdBP

Case 4A 1488 no.2 LIZET, PIERRE, 1482-1554.
Petri Lizetii ... Tractatus, De mobilibus Ecclesiae praeceptionibus. Sex libros continens. Lvgdvni, Apvd S. Gryphivm, 1552.
234(i.e.214)p., [1] l. 26cm. (with his De sacris utriusq; instrumenti ... 1552)
Nos. 129-148 omitted in paging.
Title vignette (printer's device) A different device on verso of last leaf.

NL 0423882 ICN

Lizet, Pierre, 1908-
... Contribution à l'étude de la syphilis tertiaire du corps de l'utérus ... Paris, 1934.
Thèse - Univ. de Paris.
"Bibliographie": p. [93]-101.

NL 0423883 CtY

Lizeux, Antoine
Les évêques devant la loi. P, 1861
16 p.

NL 0423884 MH

S464 M232 L5 Liziard, Paul
La Gauloisière, domaine soumis au métayage. [Laval, Impr. Mayennaise] 1896.
119 p. illus., 4 fold. plans.
Thèse agricole- Institut agricole de Beauvais.
1. Agriculture- Maine, France. I. Title.

NL 0423885 CU-A

Lizier, Augusto, 1870-
Augusto Serena. Omaggio della famiglia nell anniversario dell'acerbissimo lutto, si ristampa, col gentile consenso dell'autore, il necrologio del caro estinto, pubblicato a cura della Deputazione di storia patria (Vol. XXXVI XXXVII dell'Archivio Veneto) Treviso, Industri Poligrafiche Longo & Zoppelli [1947?]
8 p.
1. Serena, Augusto, 1868-

NL 0423886 NNC

Lizier, Augusto, 1870-
... L'economia rurale dell'età prenormanna nell'Italia meridionale. (Studii su documenti editi dei secoli IX-XI) Palermo, A. Reber, 1907.
xvi, 189 p., 1 l. illus., diagr. 24½cm.
"Bibliografia": p. [xi]-xvi.
1. Agriculture—Economic aspects—[Italy]
Agr 31-748
Library, U. S. Dept. of Agriculture 281.176L76

NL 0423887 DNAL MH

Lizier, Augusto, 1870-
... Lezioni di storia per le scuole secondarie di avviamento professionale ... Palermo, Industrie riunite editoriali siciliane, 1936.
v. illus. (incl. ports., map) 22cm. (On cover: Collezione IRES per le scuole secondarie di avviamento professionale)
Contents.—
II. Per la seconda classe (dal 1500 ai nostri giorni)
1. Italy—Hist.—Juvenile literature.
44-30441
Library of Congress DG468.L5
[2] 945

NL 0423888 DLC

Lizier, Augusto, 1870-
... Note intorno alla storia del comune di Treviso, dalle origini al principio del XIII secolo, Modona, Forghieri, 1901.
viii, 103 p. 25 cm.
Bibliography: p. [73]-103.
1. Treviso - History.

NL 0423889 NNC

373.45 L76s Lizier, Augusto, 1870-
... La scuola media in Novara nei suoi principali momenti dalle origini ai giorni nostri. Discorso pronunciato nella solenne festa centenaria del R. Convitto nazionale di Novara (7 giugno 1908) Novara Stabilimento tipografico G. Parzini, 1908.
30p.
"Estratto dall'opuscolo commemorativo della festa centennaria del R. Convitto nazionale di Novara."
1. Novara. R. Convitto nazionale.

NL 0423890 IU

Lizier, Augusto, 1870-
Le scuole di Novara ed il Liceo-convitto; monografia storica. Novara, Stab. G. Parzini, 1908.
xix, 329 p. illus. 29 cm.
At head of title: Nel primo centenario del regio Convitto nazionale di Novara, 1808-1908.
"Edizione ... di trecento esemplari numerati. Esemplare N. 290."
Includes bibliographical references.
1. Convito nazionale di Novara. 2. Education. Italy. Novara. History.

NL 0423892 NcD

PQ4218 S5L5 Lizio-Bruno, Letterio, 1837-1908.
Canti popolari delle Isole Eolie, e di altri luoghi di Sicilia; messi in prosa italiana ed illustrati dal L.Lizio-Bruno. Messia, I. d'Amico, 1871.
vi.243p. 20cm.
I. Italian poetry - Sicily. 2. Italian poetry - Collections. I. Title.

NL 0423893 IaU ICU PU ICN OCl MH NN

VOLUME 337

Lizio-Bruno, Letterio, 1837-1908, comp.
Canti scelti del popolo siciliano posti in versi italiani... Aggiuntavi una traduzione francese di anonimo autore. Messina, D'Amico, 1867.
131 p. 22½ cm.
Poems in Sicilian dialect, Italian and French. The French translations are by Tommaso Cannizzaro. cf.Pitrè. Bibliografia delle tradizioni popolari d'Italia.
1.Folk-songs of Sicily. I.Cannizzaro, Tommaso,1838-1916,tr.

NL 0423894 NjP ICN MH OCl NN

LIZIO-BRUNO, Letterio, 1837-1908.
Dante e la chiesa di Roma; discorso letto per la Societa Dante Alighieri il 20 settembre 1896. Marsala, L.Giliberti,1897.
pp.36.

NL 0423895 MH RPB NN NIC

Lizio-Bruno, Letterio, 1837-1908.
Della Gemma Donati consorte dell'Allighieri; lettera al sig. G. Corsini. [Firenze, 1864]
(3) p. 8°.
In Il primo canto dell Inferno...1886.

NL 0423896 RPB NIC

Lizio-Bruno, Letterio, 1837-1908.

[Cannizzaro, Tommaso] 1838-1916.
Ore segrete; saggi lirici ... Messina, Stamperia I. d'Amico, 1862.

[LIZIO-BRUNO,Letterio.] 1837-1908.
Per l'attentato contro S.M.Umberto I,22 april 1897. [Trapani? Tip.Frat.Missina & C.,1897?].
1.8°. pp.(4).
Without title-page. Caption title.
A poem.
Signed at end:L.Lizio-Bruno.

NL 0423898 MH

PQ4005 .L76 Lizio-Bruno, Letterio, 1837-
Scritti vari. Messina, Tip. I. d'Amico, 1865.
158 p.

1. Italian literature--Addresses, essays, lectures.

NL 0423899 ICU

Lizioli, Adelaide.
...Monologhi e commediole per le alunne delle scuole femminili. Torino: Società editrice internazionale[, 1927]. 95 p. 19cm.

677661A. 1. Juvenile literature—Monologues, Italian. 2. Juvenile literature—Drama, Italian.
N. Y. P. L. December 12, 1933

NL 0423900 NN

Lizioli, Adelaide.
...Il più forte; commedia per ragazzi. Milano: "Alba"[, 1926]. 33 p. 12°. (Arte e artisti.)

1. Juvenile literature—Drama, Italian. 2. Title.
N. Y. P. L. November 15, 1927

NL 0423901 NN

Lizioli, Adelaide.
...La vittoria di Meneghino; commediola in tre atti per fanciulli. Milano: "Alba"[, 1926]. 25 p. 12°. (Arte e artisti. no. 1.)

1. Juvenile literature—Drama, Italian. 2. Title.
N. Y. P. L. November 15, 1927

NL 0423902 NN

Lizi͡ukov, Aleksandr Il'ich.
... Что надо знать бойцам при наступлении на немцев из боевого опыта фронтовика. Москва, Военное издательство Народного комиссариата обороны Союза ССР, 1942.
23, [1] p. 14ᶜᵐ.
At head of title: Герой Советского союза генерал-майор А. И. Лизюков.

1. Russia—Army—Handbooks, manuals, etc. 2. Germany — Army — Drill and tactics. I. Title. *Title transliterated:* Chto nado znat' boĭtsam pri nastuplenii na nemt͡sev.
43-41279
Library of Congress U115.R9L5
[2]

NL 0423903 DLC

Lizi͡ukov, Aleksandr Il'ich.
... Что надо знать воину красной армии о боевых приемах немцев; из боевого опыта фронтовика. Москва, Военное издательство Народного комиссариата обороны Союза ССР, 1942.
38, [2] p. 14½ x 11ᶜᵐ.
At head of title: Герой Советского Союза генерал-майор А. И. Лизюков.

1. Russia—Army—Handbooks, manuals, etc. 2. Germany — Army — Drill and tactics. I. Title. *Title transliterated:* Chto nado znat' voinu krasnoĭ armii.
43-43434
Library of Congress
[2]

NL 0423904 DLC

Lizius, Charles Bernhard, tr.

Navin, John Nicholson.
Navin's thier-arznei-buch und landwirthschaftliche thierheilkunde. Ein vollständiges handbuch der zucht, wartung, dressur, behandlung und verpflegung der landwirthschaftlichen hausthiere ... Von John Nicholson Navin ... Aus dem englischen übers. von Carl Bernhard Lizius. Indianapolis, Navin und Lizius, 1879.

Lizius, M.
Handbuch des forstlichen Wege- und Eisenbahnbaues. Nach dem Nachlasse des kgl. bayr. Forstmeisters M. Lizius bearbeitet von K. Dotzel. Berlin: P. Parey, 1898. x, 290 p., 1 pl. illus. 8°.

1. Forestry and railways. 2. Railways.—Engineering and construction. 3. Dotzel, K.
N. Y. P. L. May 9, 1912.

NL 0423906 NN

LIZIUS, Maxim [ ].
Kinder aus geschiedenen Ehen.
Inaug. diss., Würzburg, Aschaffeubung, 1908.

NL 0423907 MH-L ICRL

Lizius, Maximilian.
Am Hüttenherd; Plaudereien eines alten bayerischen Jägers und Bergsteigers, von Maximilian Lizius. München, Bayerischer Landwirtschafts-Verlag [c1949] 196 p. illus. 21cm.

550373B. 1. Hunting—Germany—Bavaria. 2. Mountaineering—Germany—Bavaria.
N. Y. P. L. December 27, 1950

NL 0423908 NN DLC-P4

Lizius, Maximilian.
Anleitung zur Vornahme von Kassenprüfungen bei den Amtskassen der Reichsfinanzverwaltung, hrsg. von Maximilian Lizius [und] Otto Zwiebel. 3., erweiterte und ergänzte Aufl. München, C. Gerber [1939]
190 p. 21 cm.

1. Finance, Public—Germany—Accounting.
HJ9925.G15L5 1939 52-56224 ‡

NL 0423909 DLC

Lizius, Maximilian.
Handbuch der Reichssteuerverwaltung. 2. neubearb. Aufl. München, J. Schweitzer, 1940 [i. e. 1938]-
1 v. (loose-leaf) 24 cm.

1. Taxation—Germany.
HJ3484.A4L59 52-54745

NL 0423910 DLC IU MH

Liznar, Josef, 1852-1932.
Anleitung zur Messung und Berechnung der Elemente des Erdmagnetismus. Von J. Liznar, ... Wien, Verlag des Verfassers, 1883.
77, [3] p. diagrs. 22½ᶜᵐ.

NL 0423911 ICJ DAS

Liznar, Josef, 1852-
Die barometrische Höhenmessung. Mit neuen Tafeln, welche den Höhenunterschied ohne Zuhilfenahme von Logarithmentafeln zu berechnen gestatten. Von J. Liznar ... Leipzig und Wien, F. Deuticke, 1904.
[4], 43 p. incl. tables. 25½ᶜᵐ.

NL 0423912 ICJ DAS

Liznar, Josef, 1852-
Ein Beitrag zur Kenntniss der 26tägigen Periode des Erdmagnetismus, von J. Liznar... (Vorgelegt in der Sitzung am 25. Mai 1894.) Wien: F. Tempsky, 1894. 13 p., 1 diagr. Tables. 8°.
Cover-title.
Repr.: Kaiserliche Akad. der Wissenschaften in Wien. Mathematisch-naturwissenschaftliche Classe. Sitzungsb. Bd. 103, Abt. 2.

1. Magnetism (Terrestrial), 1894.
N. Y. P. L. September 29, 1916.

NL 0423913 NN

Liznar, Josef, 1852-
Das Klima von Batavia nach Dr. van der Stok's "Observations made at Batavia," vol. VI. Von J. Liznar. [Berlin,] 1886. p. 145-153. Tables. 4°.
Caption-title.
Repr.: Meteorologische Zeitschrift, April 1886.

1. Meteorology, Java: Batavia. 2. Stok, Johannes Paulus van der, 1851-
N. Y. P. L. October 10, 1917.

NL 0423914 NN

Liznar, Josef, 1852-1932.
Eine Methode zur graphischen Darstellung der Richtungsänderungen der erdmagnetischen Kraft...
Wien, 1891
2 pl. 14 p. 25cm.

Wien, Sitz. Ber., 100 (Abth. 2a), 1891, p. 1153-1166.

NL 0423915 DN-Ob

Liznar, Josef, 1852-1932.
Eine neue magnetische Aufnahme Österreichs. 3-5.
Wien, 1891-94
3 nos. 25cm.

Wien, Sitz. Ber., 100 (Abth. 2a), 1891, p. 1320-1329, 101, 1892, p. 1613-1619; 103, 1894, p. 43-49.

NL 0423916 DN-Ob

VOLUME 337

Liznar, Josef, 1852-1932.
Die 26 tägige Periode des Nordlichtes. Wien. 1888.
16 p. 8.

NL 0423917 DAS

Liznar, Josef, 1852-1932.
Ueber das Klima von Brunn. Brunn. 1886.
70 p.

NL 0423918 DAS

Liznar, Josef, 1852-1932.
Über den Stand des Normalbarometers des meteorologischen Institutes in Wien gegenüber den Normalbarometern der anderen meteorologischen Centralstellen Europa's. Wien. 1886.
23p. 8°.

NL 0423919 DAS

Liznar, Josef, 1852-1932.
Über die Bestimmung der bei den Variationen des Erdmagnetismus auftretenden ablenkenden Kraft, nebst einem Beitrage zur eilfjährigen Periode des Erdmagnetismus. Vorleuf.
Wien, 1892
1 pl. 16 p. 25cm.
Wien, Sitz. Ber., 101 (Abth. 2a), 1892, p. 87-102.

NL 0423920 DN-Ob

Liznar, Josef, 1852-
Über die Darstellung der Verteilung der erdmagnetischen Kraft auf einem Gebiete auf Grund von Messungen an wenigen Orten, von J. Liznar. (In: Meteorologische Zeitschrift. Hann-Band. Braunschweig, 1906. 4°. p. 181-186.)

1. Magnetism (Terrestrial), 1906.
N. Y. P. L. January 4, 1915.

NL 0423921 NN

Liznar, Josef, 1852-1932.
Über die 26 tägige Periode der erdmagnetischen Elements in hohen magnetischen Breiten. Wien. 1887.
18 p. plate. 8.
P.2811

NL 0423922 DAS

13545 Y v.62 Liznar, Josef, 1852-1932.
Die Vertheilung der erdmagnetischen Kraft in Österreich-Ungarn zur Epoche 1890.0 nach den in den Jahren 1889 bis 1894 ausgeführten Messungen. I. Theil. Erdmagnetische Messungen in Österreich. [Wien, K.K. Hof- und Staatsdruckerei, 1895]
137-368 p. 29cm. (Akademie der Wissenschaften, Vienna. Mathematisch-naturwissenschaftliche Klasse. Denkschriften, Bd. 62)

NL 0423923 NIC

13545 Y v.67 Liznar, Josef, 1852-1932.
Die Vertheilung der Erdmagnetischen Kraft in Österreich-Ungarn zur Epoche 1890.0 nach den in den Jahren 1889 bis 1894 ausgeführten Messungen. II. Theil. [Wien, K.K. Hof- und Staatsdruckerei, 1899]
96 p. 8 maps. 29cm. (Akademie der Wissenschaften, Vienna. Mathematisch-naturwissenschaftliche Klasse. Denkschriften, Bd. 67)

1. Magneti sm, Terrestrial.

NL 0423924 NIC

Lizón, Adolfo
see Lizón Gadea, Adolfo.

Lizón Gadea, Adolfo.
... Brigadas internacionales en España. [Madrid] Editora nacional, 1940.
94 p., 1 l. xiv pl. (incl. ports., facsim.) on 7 l. 22cm.
"Indice bibliográfico": p. [91]-92.

1. Spain—Hist.—Civil war, 1936-1939—Foreign participation. I. Title.
41-16581
Library of Congress DP269.L525
[2] 946.08

NL 0423926 DLC NcD IaU IEN MiU GU

865B38 OcYL Lizón Gadea, Adolfo.
Ensayo crítico sobre las Cartas desde mi celda. Murcia, Imp. sucesores de Nogués, 1936.
58p. 22cm. (Publicaciones de la Universidad de Murcia)

At head of title: Centenario de Bécquer.
"Notas" (bibliographical): p.[51]-58.
1. Bécquer, Gustavo Adolfo, 1836-1870. Cartas desde mi celda. //(Series: Murcia, Spain (City) Universidad. Publicaciones)

NL 0423927 IU

PQ6623 .I7Z76 Lizón Gadea, Adolfo.
Gabriel Miró y los de su tiempo. Madrid, 1944.
150 p. illus. 17 cm.

1. Miró Ferrer, Gabriel, 1879-1930.
PQ6623.I 7Z77 53-49949

InU WU CU
NL 0423928 DLC NcD MH MsSM PPT DGW MWelC CtY MeWC

Lizón Gadea, Adolfo.
Gente de letras, cuentos de la mala uva. Dibujos de Eduardo Vicente. Madrid, 1944.
175 p. illus. 17 cm.

I. Title.
PQ6621.I 7G4 53-50292

NL 0423929 DLC

Lizón Gadea, Adolfo.
Historia de una sonrisa; novela. Madrid, A. Aguado [1951]
118 p. 20 cm.

I. Title.
A 52-2642
Illinois. Univ. Library for Library of Congress [1]

NL 0423930 IU

PQ6621 L19983 Lizón Gadea, Adolfo
Saulo, el leproso; novela. Madrid, A. Aguado, 1947.
235 p.

NL 0423931 CU ICU

Lizondo, Estratón J
... Monteagudo, el pasionario de la libertad, su vida y sus obras. Tucumán, Rep. argentina, Editorial La Raza, 1943.
225 p., 3 l. incl. mounted port. 26cm.
"Bibliografía": p. [219]-225.

1. Monteagudo, Bernardo, 1785?-1825. 2. Spanish America—Hist.—Wars of independence, 1806-1830.
44-32935
Library of Congress F2845.M767
[3] 923.282

NL 0423932 DLC Ia NIC NcD NcU CU TxU

Lizondo Borda, Manuel, 1889-
... Descubrimiento del Tucumán; el pasaje de Almagro, la entrada de Rojas, el itinerario de Matienzo ... Tucumán, Argentina, 1943.
3 p. l., [9]-99 p., 3 l. fold. map. 24 cm. (Universidad nacional de Tucumán. Departamento de investigaciones regionales. Instituto de historia, lingüística y folklore. [Publicaciones especiales] XI)
"Publicación hecha en conmemoración del cuarto centenario de la entrada de Diego de Rojas en el Tucumán (1543-1943)"
"Bibliografía": p. [89]-91.

1. Tucumán (Gobernación)—Hist. 2. Almagro, Diego de, d. 1538. 3. Rojas, Diego de, d. 1544. 4. Matienzo, Juan de, d. 1587. I. Title.
F2991.L76 982 A 44-2090 rev
Harvard Univ. Library for Library of Congress [r52d1]†

OU TxU CoU
NL 0423933 MH DPU ICN NcU NNC PU ViU OCU DLC CU

Lizondo Borda, Manuel, 1889-

Tucumán, *Argentine republic (Province) Gobernador, 1832-1838 (Alejandro Heredia)*
... Documentos argentinos. Gobierno de Alejandro Heredia (su acción en Tucumán, en las provincias del norte y en la guerra con Bolivia) 1832-1838. Introducción y notas de Manuel Lizondo Borda ... Tucumán, Argentina [Buenos Aires, Imprenta López] 1939.

Lizondo Borda, Manuel, 1889.

Tucumán, *Argentine republic (Province) Junta conservadora del Archivo histórico.*
... Documentos argentinos ... Prólogo y notas de Manuel Lizondo Borda ... Tucumán, Argentina, 1939-

Lizondo Borda, Manuel, 1889- ed.

F3011 .T89A48 Tucumán, *Argentine Republic. Cabildo.*
Documentos coloniales. Actas capitulares de San Miguel de Tucumán. Prólogo y comentarios de Manuel Lizondo Borda. Tucumán, 1946-

Lizondo Borda, Manuel, 1889- ed.

Tucuman, *Argentine republic (Province) Junta conservadora del Archivo histórico.*
... Documentos coloniales relativos a San Miguel de Tucumán y a la gobernación de Tucumán, siglo XVI; introducción y comentarios de Manuel Lizondo Borda ... Tucumán (R[e]pública] argentina) Imprenta López, 1936.

Lizondo Borda, Manuel, 1889-

Tucumán, *Argentine republic. Cabildo.*
... Documentos tucumanos. Actas del Cabildo ... Introducción y notas de Manuel Lizondo Borda ... Tucumán, Argentina [Talleres graficos de M. Violetto] 1939-40.

Lizondo Borda, Manuel, 1889-
... Estudios de voces tucumanas ... Tucuman (R. Argentina) M. Violetto & cia., impresores, 1927-
v. 23cm. (Publicacion de la Universidad de Tucuman)

1. Spanish language—Provincialisms—Argentine Republic. 2. Spanish language—Foreign words and phrases—Kechua. 3. Kechua language—Etymology.
28-22925
Library of Congress PC4872.L5

NL 0423939 DLC CU FU NcU CtY ICU ViU PU NN

PQ 7797 H3 M353 LAC Lizondo Borda, Manuel, 1889-
Expresiones del Martín Fierro; sobre unas glosas de Tiscornia. [Buenos Aires, 1926?]
[79]-87p. 22cm.

Detached from Nosotros, Buenos Aires, no. 208, Sept. 1926.

1. Hernandez, José, 1834-1886. Martín Fierro. I. Title. Sp.: Martínez Reales Collection.

NL 0423940 TxU

VOLUME 337

Lizondo Borda, Manuel, 1889- , ed.
...Gobierno de Alejandro Heredia (su acción en Tucumán, en las provincias del Norte y en la guerra con Bolivia) 1832-1838; introducción y notas de Manuel Lizondo Borda...
see Tucumán, Argentine republic (Province) Gobernador, 1832-1838 (Alejandro Heredia)
...Documentos argentinos.

Lizondo Borda, Manuel, 1889–
... Goethe, la casa de Goethe, pensamientos de Goethe. Tucumán, República argentina [Impr. de "La Gaceta"] 1932.
3 p. l., 9–149, [1] p., 1 l. pl., ports. 18½cm.
At head of title: M. Lizondo Borda.
"Bibliografía": p. 147–[150]
1. Goethe, Johann Wolfgang von—Biog. 2. Goethe, Johann Wolfgang von—Homes and haunts. 3. Goethe, Johann Wolfgang von—Quotations.
Library of Congress PT2053.L5 33-38237
[2] 928.3

NL 0423942 DLC TxU

Lizondo Borda, Manuel, 1889–
Historia de la gobernación del Tucumán (siglo XVI) por Manuel Lizondo Borda. Publicación de la Universidad de Tucumán. Buenos Aires, "Coni", 1928.
292 p. 19cm.
"Bibliografía": p. [271]–289.
1. Tucumán (Gobernación)—Hist.
Library of Congress F2991.L77 29-9328

MH-A PU NN MB NcU
NL 0423943 DLC OCl CU TxU LNHT DSI CtY MiU MU WU

Lizondo Borda, Manuel, 1889–
Historia de Tucumán (siglo XIX) Tucumán, 1948.
300 p. 26 cm. (Universidad Nacional de Tucumán. Facultad de Ciencias Culturales y Artes. Instituto de Historia. [Publicaciones especiales] 14)
Universidad Nacional de Tucumán. Publicación no. 452.
Bibliography: p. 273–282.
1. Tucumán, Argentine Republic (Province)—Hist. (Series: Tucumán, Argentine Republic. Universidad. Instituto de Historia, Lingüística y Folklore. Publicaciones especiales, 14)
F2991.L777 982 50-13654

NcU OClW
NL 0423944 DLC IaU PU CoU MH LU CtY CU TxU ViU

Lizondo Borda, Manuel, 1889–
... Historia del Tucumán (siglos XVII y XVIII) Tucumán, Argentina [Talleres gráficos M. Violetto] 1941.
3 p. l., [9]–204 p., 3 l. 24cm. (Universidad nacional de Tucumán. Departamento de investigaciones regionales. Instituto de historia, lingüística y folklore. [Publicaciones especiales] VI)
"Bibliografía": p. [189]–193.
1. Tucumán (Gobernación)—Hist.
Library of Congress F2991.L775 43-6616
[3] 982

NL 0423945 DLC IU WaU CU MiEM NcU MH PU

Lizondo Borda, Manuel, 1889–
Historia del Tucumán, siglo XVI. 2. ed., corr. de la "Historia de la Gobernación del Tucumán (siglo XVI)." Tucumán, 1942.
233 p. 25 cm. (Universidad Nacional de Tucumán. Departamento de Investigaciones Regionales. Instituto de Historia. Lingüística y Folklore. Publicaciones especiales, 8)
Universidad Nacional de Tucumán. Publicación no. 314.
"Bibliografía": p. [205]–216.
1. Tucumán (Gobernación)—Hist. (Series: Tucumán, Argentine Republic. Universidad. Instituto de Historia, Lingüística y Folklore. Publicaciones especiales, 8. Series: Tucumán, Argentine Republic. Universidad. Publicaciones, no. 314)
F2991.L77 1942 982 48-37189 rev*

NL 0423946 DLC MH PU CoU LU WaU CU DPU

Lizondo Borda, Manuel, 1889-
Monumentos históricos de Tucumán
see under Lanziuto, Ernesto, 1911-

PQ7797 Lizondo Borda, Manuel, 1889-
L54P6 El poema del auga. Nueva ed. Tucumon,
1946 Argentina [El Progress, 1946.
43p. 19cm.

NL 0423948 IaU

F Lizondo Borda, Manuel, 1889-
2235.4 San Martin y Tucumán. Tucumán, 1950.
+L5 109p. illus. 28cm. (Publicaciones de la Junta Conservadora del Archivo Histórico de Tucumán, 11. Serie 4: Documentos argentinos, publ. 3)
Bibliographical footnotes.
1. San Martín, José de, 1778-1850 2. Tucumán, Battle of, 1812 I. Title

NL 0423949 WU

Lizondo Borda, Manuel, 1889–
... Temas de ética y literatura. Tucumán, Argentina [Buenos Aires, Imprenta López] 1939.
2 p. l., 7–240 p., 1 l. 18½cm.
"Los trabajos que forman el presente volumen—artículos, conferencias discursos—, han sido entresacados de una producción desperdigada y varia que va de 1913 a 1932."—Prólogo.
Contents.—Reflexiones tucumanas.—Consideraciones didácticas.—Comentarios americanos.—Evocaciones literarias.—Valoraciones argentinas.
I. Title.
Library of Congress PQ7797.L547T4 42-3208
[2] 864.6

NL 0423950 DLC NcD NcU NNC

Lizondo Borda, Manuel, 1889–
... Tucuman al traves de la historia; el Tucuman de los poetas; compilación hecha por orden de la Comisión provincial del 1er centenario de la independencia argentina, 1816—9 de julio—1916. (Publicación oficial) Tucuman, Imp. Prebisch & Violetto, 1916.
2 v. 27cm.
1. Tucuman, Argentine republic (Province)—Hist. 2. Argentine poetry (Collections) I. Tucuman, Argentine republic (Province) Comisión provincial del 1er centenario de la independencia argentina. II. Title.
Library of Congress F2991.L78 17—10755

NL 0423951 DLC LNHT CtY NIC MB MoU CU

Lizondo Borda, Manuel, 1889–
... Tucumán indígena; diaguitas, lules y tonocotés, pueblos y lenguas (siglo XVI) A manera de prólogo por Juan B. Terán. Tucumán, República argentina [Talleres gráficos Miguel Violetto] 1938.
2 p. l., [7]–94 p., 3 l. 24cm. (Universidad nacional de Tucumán. Departamento de investigaciones regionales. Instituto de historia, lingüística y folklore. [Publicaciones especiales] II)
Universidad nacional de Tucumán. Publicación nº 238.
"Bibliografía": p. [91]–92.
1. Indians of South America—Argentine republic—Tucumán (Province) 2. Diaguita Indians. 3. Lule Indians. 4. Tonocote Indians. 5. Indians of South America—Languages—Argentine republic. I. Title.
Library of Congress F2821.1.T89L58 41-11747
[2] 980.4

NL 0423952 DLC CU NIC CoU MB NN MH PU ViU DPU

498 Lizondo Borda, Manuel, 1889-
L76v ...Voces tucumanas, derivadas del Quichua. Publicacion de la unversidad de Tucuman. Tucuman, Argentina, M. Violetto & cia, 1927.
2 p.l., [7]-400 [1]p. 23cm. (Tucuman. Ur versidad Estudios de voces Tucumanas, no.1)
1. Kechua language. I. Title.

NL 0423953 LU

Lizondo Gascueña, Julián.
Espejo y gloria de España (figuras, momentos, evocaciones); lecturas patrióticas escolares, por Julián Lizondo Gascueña... Prólogo de Manuel Machado... Ilus. de Fortunato Julián. Burgos, Hijos de S. Rodríguez [1939] 202 p. illus. 19cm.
2. ed.
349650B. 1. Spain—Hist.
N. Y. P. L. April 29, 1947

NL 0423954 NN

DC Lizop, Raymond.
611 Le Comminges et le Couserans avant la
P99L77 domination romaine. Toulouse, E. Privat, 1931.
xxiv,287 p. illus., map. 25cm.
1. Pyrenees, France—Antiquities. 1. Comminges—Antiquities. 3. Couserans—Antiquities.

NL 0423955 NIC MoU O MH

Lizop, Raymond.
Les Convenae et les Consoranni (Comminges et Couserans) Toulouse, Édouard Privat, etc., etc., 1931.
Maps, plans and plates.
Thèse - Paris.
At head of title: Histoire de deux cités gallo-romaines.
"Bibliographie", p. [xvii]-xxx.

NL 0423956 MH

Lizop, Raymond, joint author.

Lavedan, Pierre.
... Les fouilles de Saint-Bertrand de Comminges (Lugdunum Convenarum) avec 7 figures dans le texte et 20 planches hors texte, par Pierre Lavedan ... Raymond Lizop ... Bertrand Sapène ... Toulouse, É. Privat, 1929.

Lizop, Raymond.
... Histoire de deux cités gallo-romaines; les Convenae et les Consoranni (Comminges et Couserans) par Raymond Lizop ... Toulouse, É. Privat; Paris, H. Didier, 1931.
3 p. l., [ix]–xxxix, 552 p. plates, 2 fold. maps, plans (1 fold.) 25½cm. (Bibliothèque méridionale ... 2. sér., t. XXV)
"Bibliographie": p. [xvii]–xxix.
1. Comminges, France—Hist. 2. Couserans, France—Hist. 3. Comminges, France—Antiq. 4. Couserans, France—Antiq. I. Title: Les Convenae et les Consoranni.
Library of Congress DC801.C685L5 33-13839
[2] 944.8

NNC
NL 0423958 DLC CaBVaU OU MiU NNC LU MoU CtY NN MH

LIZOP, RAYMOND.
Le message de Mistral. Avant-propos par Philadelphe de Gerde. [Toulouse? Éditions de l'Escolo deras Pireneos, 1941] 199 p. 23cm.
Includes numerous excerpts from the works of Mistral.
1. Mistral, Frédéric, 1830-1914.

NL 0423959 NN NjP

Lizot (Emile-Alexis). Sur l'amygdalite, ou inflammation des amygdales. 20 pp. 4°. Paris, 1829, No. 109, v. 224.

NL 0423960 DNLM

VOLUME 337

DK265 .4 .L59 Hebr **Lizov, Boris.**
דער בלוטיקער אפשיין. פון די געוועזענע אינטערווענציעס קעגן
סר"ר—און די געפאר פון די קומענדיקע. כארקאוו, מעלוכע-פאר-
לאג פאר די נאציאנאלע מינדערהייטן אין אוס"רר.
[Kharkov] 1932.
181 p. illus. 17 cm.

1. Russia—Hist.—Allied intervention, 1918–1920.
Title transliterated: Der blutiker opshayn.

DK265.4.L59 60-56471 ‡

NL 0423961 DLC

Lizovius, Joachimus, respondent.
De descensu Christi ad Inferos
see under
Affelmann, Joannes, praeses.

Lizza, Irene.
...Villa Rossa agli Eucalipti; romanzo. [Milano] Editori associati [1948] 198 p. 19cm.

1. ed.

NL 0423963 NN DLC-P4

Lizza, Zofia, joint ed.

M2 .C616M82 **Chomiński, Józef M** *ed.*
Music of the Polish Renaissance; a selection of works from the xvith and the beginning of the xviith century. Edited by Józef M. Chominski and Zofia Lissa. [Translation from the Polish: Claire Grece Dąbrowska; English translation of the Polish songs: Przemysław Mroczkowski. Kraków] Polskie Wydawn. Muzyczene, 1955.

Lizzadri, Oreste.
Migliorare ed estendere la sicurezza sociale a tutti i lavoratori. Relazione al III Congresso della CGIL, Napoli, 26 novembre–3 dicembre 1952. In appendice, Risoluzione delle commissioni della protezione sociale, del collocamento e della ricreazione. A cura dell'Ufficio stampa e propaganda della C. G. I. L. [Roma, 1953?]
39 p. 21 cm. (Atti e documenti del III Congresso della C. G. I. L.)

1. Insurance, Social—Italy. 2. Public welfare—Italy. I. Title. (Series: Confederazione generale italiana del lavoro. 3. congresso, 1952. Atti e documenti)

HD7184.L5 54-38594

NL 0423965 DLC IU

Lizzani, Carlo.
Il cinema italiano. Firenze, Parenti [1953]
319 p. illus. 24 cm. (Saggi di cultura moderna, v. 2)
"In appendice: Indicazioni metodologiche e una filmografia, a cura di Leopoldo Paciscopi e Giorgio Signorini."

1. Moving-pictures—Italy. I. Paciscopi, Leopoldo.

PN1993.5.I 88L5 A 53-7601

Southern Calif., Univ. of. for Library of Congress Library [a58b½]†

NL 0423966 CLSU DLC

Lizzani, Carlo.
Il cinema italiano. 2. ed. Firenze, Parenti [1954]
442 p. illus. 23 cm. (Saggi di cultura moderna, v. 2)
"In appendice: Indicazioni metodologiche, filmografia, documenti, note, a cura di Leopoldo Paciscopi e Giorgio Signorini."

1. Moving-pictures—Italy. I. Paciscopi, Leopoldo.

A 55-375

Southern Calif., Univ. of. for Library of Congress Library [½]

NL 0423967 MB CLSU OrU MiU KMK IU IEG CtY MH PU TxU

Lizzani, Mario
... Le terme. Roma, Palombi, 1938.
cover-title, 20 p. illus. (Piccola biblioteca "Roma". 21)

1. Baths - Rome. 2. Rome (City) - Antiquities.

NL 0423968 NNC

Lizzani, Mario
... Il Tevere ... [Roma, 1936]
cover-title, 19 p. illus. (Piccola biblioteca "Roma". 8)

1. Tiber river and valley - Description and travel. 2. Rome (City) - Description.

NL 0423969 NNC

Lizzardi, Oreste
Il problema del mezzogiorno, problema nazionale. Discorso pronunziato al XXX Congresso del P. S. I. a Milano il 13 gennaio 1953. [Roma, Tip. E.I.I., 1953]
39 p. 17cm.

NL 0423970 WU

Lizzari. Antonio
——. Dissertazione epistolare ad un amico, relativa a due osservazioni in istampa recentemente pubblicate, in cui coll' autorità di alcune antiche e moderne dottrine, e osservazioni si accredita l' operazione cerusica detta paracentesi nell' idropisie, ascitiche, cistiche, e del peritoneo. Si tocca ancora di passagio all' altra operazione cerusica, detta nefrotomia. 168 pp. 12°. *Venezia, A. Zatta*, 1761.

NL 0423971 DNLM

Lizzari. Antonio
——. Lettera apologetica ad un amico, contenente una storia medica. 224 pp. 8°. *Venezia, A. Zatta*, 1770.

NL 0423972 DNLM

Lizzari. Antonio
——. Lettera riguardante la storia delle malattie acute occorse negli anni 1761 e 1762, non pure nella città di Venezia che quasi in tutta l' Italia, scritta ad un amico. 168 pp. 12°. *Venezia, G. Bettinelli*, 1762.

NL 0423973 DNLM

Lizzari (Antonio). Lettera riguardante una rara tardezza di polso in un complesso non volgare di mali, ed indiritta all' ... Lottario Giuseppe Lotti.
In: Rac. d' opusc. scient. e filol. 16°. Venezia, 1753, xlix, 267-315.

NL 0423974 DNLM

---

33 **Lizzie Braham's sweet by and by songster.** New York, A.J. Fisher, [1877]
Ill. tit. 60 p. 18°. [Fisher, A.J. publisher. 18 mo. dime song books no. 115]

NL 0423975 DLC

RA386.224 fL789c Lizzie Cassel (Steamboat)
Cash book covering the period October 21, 1888 through March 1, 1894. n.p., 1888-94.
1v.42cm.

Morgan, Davis and Martin, owners.

NL 0423976 OC

PZ260 .L85 18— Lizzie Claire; or, The last penny. Philadelphia, American Sunday-School Union [18--]
24 p. illus.

NL 0423977 ICU

Lizzie French; or, Pleasant memories
see under [French, Sarah Abigail]

Lizzie Lee's daughter; or, A rich father's remorse; ... Truly a most romantic incident of real life in Fifth avenue, New York city. [New York? 18—?] 62 p. illus. 23cm.

NL 0423979 NN

Lizzie Leigh, a domestic tale
see under [Gaskell, Elizabeth Cleghorn (Stevenson)] 1810-1865.

PR 3541 L53+ 1895 **Lizzie Lindsay (Ballad)**
The ballad, Lizzie Lindsay, written from memory by George Mitchell, at Mrs. Dawson Rowley's request, 1891. Brighton [Eng.] Priv. Print., J. Beal, 1895.
[15] p. illus. 27cm.

"Notes of the Mitchell family, and George Mitchell's recollection of the song,": p. [13-15]

I. Mitchell, George, 1823-

NL 0423981 NIC

---

* M1 .S444 v.112 no. 57 Lizzie Lindsay & My heart is sair; favorite Scotch ballads [London, Musical Bouquet Office 192 High Holborn; & J. Allen, 20 Warwick Lane, Paternoster Row, 18—?]
[81]-84 p. 34cm. [Sheet music collection, v. 112, no. 57]
Caption title
"Musical bouquet [no. 309]"
Bottom of p. [81] cut off.

1. Songs, Scottish. I. Title: My heart is sair.

NL 0423982 ViU

Lizzie Lovell; or, What a little girl can do
see under American Baptist Publication Society.

Lizzie Maitland
see under [Clarke, Mrs. De Witt C.]

Lizzie Nutt's sad experience. A heart broken, and a family plunged in grief. Wreck and ruin! The shooting and tragic death of noble-hearted Captain Nutt, Lizzie's brave father... Philadelphia,[c1883.] YA 16397
64p.

NL 0423985 DLC CSmH NN

VOLUME 337

Lizzie Nutt's sad experience. A heart broken, and a family plunged in grief... The shooting and tragic death of noble-hearted Captain Nutt, Lizzie's brave father, who flinched not ...to die in defence of his daughter's honor. The great Dukes trial at Uniontown, Pa. Full account... [Uniontown? Pa.: Barclay & co., 1886] p. 19–79. illus. (incl. ports.) 24cm.

Cover-title.
Imperfect: cover mutilated.
Includes the trial of James Nutt for the killing of N. L. Dukes.

EDMUND LESTER PEARSON COLL. Purchased for J. S. Billings Mem. Coll.

1. Murder—Trials—U. S.—Pennsylvania. 2. Nutt, Adam Clark, 1839–1882. 3. Dukes, Nicholas Lyman, d. 1883. 4. Nutt, James, 1862–
N. Y. P. L. September 26, 1939

NL 0423986 NN

Unclass. Lizzie's cook book edited by "The Bachelette." San Jose, California, Smith & Wilcox, 1891. 114 p. 21 cm.

NL 0423987 DLC

JUV. 813.49 L789 Lizzie's visit to New-York, by the author of "Addie and her turtle" ... etc. New York, Protestant Episcopal Society for the Promotion of Evangelical Knowledge [1864] 137 p. front. 16 cm.

Addie and her turtle, author of.

NL 0423988 NcD

L101 .I8A55 Lizzo, Luigi, ed.
Almanacco del maestro. 1950/51–
Sant'Agata di Puglia, Tip. casa Sacro Cuore di Gesù.

945.11 L768o2 Lizzoli, L
Osservazioni sul dipartimento dell' Agogna ... 2.ed., cor. ed accresciuta. Milano, 1802. 179p. fold.tab.

NL 0423990 IU

Lizzy's poems and pictures for her young friends. London, Darton & co., 1857.

NL 0423991 MH

Ljackij, Evgenij
see Liatskii, Evgenii Aleksandrovich, 1868-

Ljackij, Evžen
see Liaťskiĭ, Evgeniĭ Aleksandrovich, 1868–

Ljadow, Anatoly
see Liadov, Anatoliĭ Konstantinovich, 1855–1914.

Ljalikov, K S
see Lialikov, K S

Ljapin, A
see Liapin, Andrei Pavlovich.

Ljapin, A. P.
see Liapin, A P

Ljapunov, B V
see Liapunov, Boris Valerianovich.

Ljapunow, A A
see Liapunov, Aleksei Andreevich.

Ljapunow, Alexander Michailowitsch
see Liapunov, Aleksandr Mikhaĭlovich, 1857–1918.

Ljapunow, B W
see Liapunov, Boris Valerianovich.

Ljaschtschenko, P
see Liashchenko, Petr Ivanovich, 1876–

Ljass, A M
see Liass, A M

Ljau, Gai-lung
see Liao, Kai-lung.

Ljenharður og Blandína.
see under [Bürger, Gottfried August] 1747-1794

Ljermontov, Mihail Jurjević
see Lermontov, Mikhail IUr'evich, 1814-1841.

Ljeskow, Nikolai
see Leskov, Nikolaĭ Semenovich, 1831–1895.

336.2 L76s Ljessinoff, Panayot, 1884-
Das system der veranlagten steuern in Bulgarien (mit besonderer berücksichtigung der wirtschaftlichen, sozialen und politischen verhältnisse) ... München, 1909.
161p.

Inaug.-diss.--Munich.
Lebenslauf.
"Literatur": p.[5]-7.

1. Taxation--Bulgaria.

NL 0424009 IU PU

Ljesskow, Nikolaj
see Leskov, Nikolaĭ Semenovich, 1831–1895.

Ljevarstvo.
[Zagreb]
v. in illus., ports. 29 cm. 6 no. a year.

Began in 1955.
Organ of Društvo ljevača SR Hrvatske (called 19 -62 Društvo ljevača NR Hrvatske)

1. Founding—Period. I. Društvo ljevača SR Hrvatske.

TS200.L58 68-122628

NL 0424011 DLC IU ICRL

Ljevin, D. M.
see Levin, D M

JS6939 .L5A54 Ljig, *Serbia (District)* *Charters.*
Статут Народног одбора Среза Љишког у Љигу. Љиг, 1953.
39 p. 20 cm.

1. Ljig, Serbia (District) Narodni odbor. I. Title.
Title transliterated: Statut Narodnog odbora Sreza Ljiškog u Ljigu.

JS6939.L5A54 54-33428 ‡

NL 0424013 DLC

Ljočić (Draga). *Ein Beitrag zur operativen Therapie der Fibromyome des Uterus. 1 p. l., 115 pp., 1 l. 8°. *Zürich, O. Füssli u. Comp.,* 1878.

NL 0424014 DNLM

Ljóðabók
see
Strengleikar.

LJØSNE, KNUT.
Minneord om Kristen Holbø, av Knut og Halvdan Ljøsne. (IN: Årbok for Gudbrandsdalen. Otta. 22cm. årg. 22 (1954) p. 46-53. illus., port)

1. Holbø, Kristen, 1869-1953.

NL 0424016 NN

Ljone, Oddmund, 1917–
Grønt lys for eventyret. [Bergen] J. W. Eide [1954]
381 p. illus. 22 cm.

1. Aadnesen, Gunnar, 1881– 2. South America—Descr. & trav. I. Title.

F2223.L73G7 55-19261 ‡

NL 0424017 DLC MnU

Ljone, Oddmund, 1917–
Kaptein Toralf Andersen og hans menn. Med forord av sjøfartsdirektøren. [Bergen] J. W. Eide [1953]
204 p. illus. 22 cm.

1. Andersen, Toralf, 1900– 2. Ferncastle (Tanker) I. Title.

VK140.A45L5 54-16845 ‡

NL 0424018 DLC MnU C

VOLUME 337

Ljono, Anders, 1901–
Hva Oseberghaugen gjemte. ₍Tønsberg₎ 1952.
35 p. illus. 21 cm. (Vestfold historielags småskrifter)
Includes bibliography.

1. Oseberg, Norway—Antiq. 2. Ship burial. I. Title.

GT3380.L52 54-24747 ‡

NL 0424019 DLC MnU

Ljós í myrkri. Til sjúklinga frá sjúkling. [Reykjavík], Aldar-prentsm., [1905.] 16°. pp. 8. IcH17T769

NL 0424020 NIC

Ljós og sannleikur. I. árgangur. Útgefandi: Páll Jónsson. Reykjavík, Félagsprentsmiðjan, 1920. fol. IcH41L781
Monthly, publ. from March 1919 to Feb. 1920.
Covertitle.

NL 0424021 NIC

Ljósberinn. I.–V. árgangur. Útgefandi: Jón Helgason prentari. Reykjavík, 1921–25. 5 *vols.* 8°. IcH41L61–
Weekly. Each number has the subtitle: Smárit barnanna.

NL 0424022 NIC

Ljósberinn. VI., VIII.–XIV. árgangur. Útgefandi: Jón Helgason, prentari. [Vol. VIII: Útgefandi: Bókaverzlunin Emaus.] Reykjavík, 1926, 1928–30; Prentsmiðja Jóns Helgasonar, 1931–34. sm. 8°. (vol. vi) and la. 8°. IcH41L6, 8–14
Semi-monthly.

NL 0424023 NIC

Ljósið
see under Jochumsson, Einar, 1842-1923.

W 1 LJ787J
LJÓSMÆÐRABLAÐIÐ.
arg. 1- 1932-
Reykjavik, Ljósmæðrafélag Íslands.
v. illus., ports.

1. Obstetrics - period. I. Ljósmæðrafélag Íslands

NL 0424025 DNLM NIC

Ljósvetninga saga.
Ljosavandsfolkenes Saga.
(Billeder af Livet paa Island. Samling 3, p. 101-185. Kjøbenhavn, 1876)

NL 0424026 MB

Y 9164 .43 v.2
Ljósvetninga saga.
Ljósvetníngasaga. (in Íslendínga sögur. 1829-30. v.2, p.5-6, [1]-112)

"Written about 1200; the saga now embodies three tales which presumably were not in the original saga."-Islandica, v.l.
Ed. from ms.485. 4°, Arna Magnæan collection, Copenhagen, by Þorgeir Guðmundsson and Þorsteinn Helgason.-cf. Islandica, v.l.

NL 0424027 ICN MB

Ljósvetninga saga.
Ljósvetninga saga. Búið hefir til prentunar Vald. Ásmundarson. Reykjavík, S. Kristjánsson, 1896.
2 p. l., 150 p., 1 l. 18cm. (Íslendinga sögur, 14.)

I. Ásmundarson, Valdimar, 1852-1902, ed.

NL 0424028 MiU PBm NN NdU NjP NIC PU CaBVaU

Ljósvetninga saga,
Ljósvetninga saga, búið hefir til prentunar Benedikt Sveinsson. Reykjavík, Sigurður Kristjánsson, 1921.
xxiv, 149 p. 18cm. (On cover: Íslendinga sögur. 14)

I. Sveinsson, Benedikt, ed. II. Ser.

NL 0424029 ViU MH NIC

Ljosvetninga saga.
Ranisch, Wilhelm, 1865- tr.
Fünf geschichten aus dem östlichen Nordland. Mit einer übersichtskarte. Übertragen von Wilh. Ranisch und Walter H. Vogt. Jena, E. Diederichs, 1921.

Ljosvetninga saga.
Íslenzkar fornsögur, gernar út af hinu Íslenzka bókmentafélagi ... Kaupmannahöfn, Í prentsmiðju S. L. Möllers, 1880-83.

PT7269 .L78S6
LJÓSVETNINGA SAGA.
Ljósvetninga saga, med þáttum Reykdoela saga ok Víga-Skútu, Hreiðars þáttr; Bjorn Sigfússon gaf út. Reykjavík, Hið Íslenzka fornritafélag, 1940.
xcv, 282 p. illus., map, geneal. tables. (Íslenzk fornrit, bindi 10)

I. Reykdoela saga. II. Sigfússon, Björn, 1905- ed. Series.

NL 0424032 ICU NcD ViU FU PU WaU NIC

Ic F65 Lj491
Ljósvetninga saga.
Soga om Ljosvetningane, omsett til nynorsk av Hallvard Magerøy. Oslo, Det norske samlaget, 1950.
147, ₍1₎ p. 21cm. (Norrøne bokverk, 37)

I. Magerøy, Hallvard, tr. II. Title. III. Series.

NL 0424033 NIC

Ljósvetninga saga med tháttum.
Gudmund der Mächtige.₍ Übertragen und mit einer Einführung herausgegeben von Ludwig Meyn. Hamburg, Hanseatische Verlagsanstalt, 1927. 8°. pp. 132, 4 *pls.*, *map*. IcF65Lj441
"Bauern und Helden. VIII. Band."

NL 0424034 NIC

Ljotić, Dimitrije V., 1891-1945.
Из мога живота. ₍München₎ 1952.
229 p. 21 cm.

1. Yugoslavia—Pol. & govt.—1918-1945—Addresses, essays, lectures. I. Title.
Title transliterated: Iz moga života.

DR359.L5A3 1952 65-52703

NL 0424035 DLC CaBVaU MH CSt ICU MiU NBuU

Ljotić, Dimitrije V., 1891-1945.
Svetska revolucija; izvodi iz spisa. ₍München, Iskra, 1949₎
240 p. 15 cm.

1. Propaganda, Communist—Yugoslavia. 2. Communism—Russia. I. Title.
HX365.5.A6L5 1949 66-54821

NL 0424036 DLC MH ICU CaBVaU

Ljouwert
see
Leeuwarden.

Lju, Bai-jü
see
Liu, Pai-yü.

Lju, Da-njän
see
Liu, Ta-nien.

Ljubarsky, E
see
Liubarskiĭ, E I

4TS 184
Ljubasevszkij, I F
A gumiabroncs korszerű gyártastechnológiája ₍irta₎ I. F. Ljubasevszkij, L. G. Margulisz, B. Ja. Nyiszelovszkij. ₍ ₎ Nehezipari Könyv, 1953.
407 p.

NL 0424041 DLC-P4

4HC Yugo 10
Ljubenović, Svetozar.
Naše delo, naš ponos; reportaže iz borbe za petoletku. [Beograd] Izd. Borbe, 1948.
68 p.

NL 0424042 DLC-P4

D 513 .S4 L79
LJUBIĆ,JOSIP
Neprijatelj jugoslovenstva; protiv Sitona-Vatsona. ₍Sarajevo, Štamp. Gaković, 1927₎
52 p.

At head of title: Ild Bogdanov (Josip Ljubić)

1. European War, 1914-1918--Causes. 2. Seton-Watson, Robert William, 1879-1951.

NL 0424043 InU

[Ljubić, Josip]
Poziv Dalmaciji;preporogjaj hrvatske narodne stranke u Dalmaciji i njezina programa./ U Spljetu, Štamp. Narodne tiskare, 1901
23 p.

NL 0424044 MH

Ljubić, Josip.
Seljaštvo Švicarske. Napisao Josip Ljubić. Zagreb₍: "Tipografija," D. D.₎, 1928. 211 p. incl. tables. illus. 12°.

546331A. 1. Agriculture—Economics —Switzerland.
N. Y. P. L. October 13, 1931

NL 0424045 NN

VOLUME 337

Ljubić, Sime, 1822-1896, ed.
Commissiones et relationes Venetae 1433-[1571]. Zagrabiae, sumptibus Academiae Scientiarum et Artium, 1876-80.
3 vol. (Monumenta spectantia historiam Slavorum Meridionalium, 6, 8, 11.)

NL 0424046 MH MdBP IU NN

Ljubić, Sime, 1822-1896.
Dizionario biografico degli uomini illustri della Dalmazia, compilato dall' Ab. Simeone Gliubich ... Vienna, R. Lechner, 1856.
2 p. l., [iii]-viii, 325 p. 23 cm.

1. Dalmatia—Bio-bibl. 2. Italian literature—Dalmatia—Bibl.

Z2124.D2L5 5-29484 rev

NL 0424047 DLC NIC NNC

LJUBIC, Sime, 1822-1896.
Krizobojnici u Zadru. Ulomak iz mletačkoga krizoboja 1202-1204. Progr. U.Osieku, brzotisk D.Lehmanna i druga, 1862.
pp.14.

NL 0424048 MH

F 591 .58 v.1-5, 9,12, 17,21-22
LJUBIĆ, SIME, 1822-1896, ed.
Listine o odnošajih izmedju južnoga slavenstva i mletačke republike, skupio Sime Ljubić... Na sviet izdala Jugoslavenska akademija znanosti i umjetnosti. U Zagrebu, 1868-91.
10v. (Monumenta spectantia historiam Slavorum meridionalium... v.1-5, 9, 12, 17, 21-22)
Text in Latin.
Contents.—kn.I. 960-1335.—kn.II. 1336-1347. —kn.III. 1347-1358.—kn.IV. 1358-1403.—kn.V. 1403-1409.—kn.VI. 1409-1412.—kn.VII. 1412-1420. —kn.VIII. 1420- 1424.—kn.IX. 1423-1452. —kn.X. 1453-1469.

Index rerum, personarum et locorum in voluminibus I-V Monumentorum spectantium historiam Slavorum meridionalium. Opera S.Ljubić... Edidit Academia scientiarum et artium Slavorum meridionalium. Zagrabiae, 1893.
393p. (Monumenta spectantia historiam Slavorum meridionalium. v.24)

NL 0424050 ICN IU CLU NN MH MdBP

Bonaparte Collection No. 13,235
Ljubić, Sime, 1822-1896, ed.
Običaji kod Morlakah u Dalmacii; sakupio i izdao S.Ljubić. U Zadru, 1846.

Text in the Croatian language.
Title translated: Customs of the Morlaks in Dalmatia.

NL 0424051 ICN MH

Ljubić, Sime, 1822-1896.
Ogledalo književne poviesti jugoslavjanske Na podučavanje mladeži nacrtao Šime Ljubić. [Rieka] Riečki E. Mohovića tiskarski kamen. zavod, 1864-69.
2 v. in 1. 18 cm.

1. Yugoslav literature—Hist. & crit. 2. Slavs, Southern. I. Title.

PG561.L53 67-116095

NL 0424052 DLC MiEM MH CtY MiU ICU IU InU ICN

Ljubić, Šime, 1822-1896.
Opis jugoslavenskih novaca. Izd. umnoženo. U Zagrebu, Artističko-tipografički zavod D. Albrechta, 1875.
xxvii, 235 p. illus., 17 plates. 30 cm.

1. Coins, Yugoslav. 2. Numismatics—Yugoslavia. I. Title.

CJ3356.L5 55-51927

NL 0424053 DLC PPiU FTaSU DDO NN CtY

891.83109 L789p
Ljubić, Sime, 1822-1896.
Pregled hrvatske poviesti. Riečki, E.Mohovića, 1864.
359p. 18cm.

1. Serbo-Croatian poetry - Hist. and crit.

NL 0424054 NcU

Ljubić, Sime, 1822-1896, ed.
Budua, *Dalmatia. Laws, statutes, etc.*
Statuta et leges civitatis Buduae, civitatis Scardonae, et civitatis et insulae Lesinae. Opera prof. Simeonis Ljubić. Zagrabiae, officina Societatis typographicae, 1882-3.

LJUBIC, TONE, ed.
Ljudske pripovedke iz Dobrēpolj. Ljubljana, 1944.
93 p. illus. 21cm. (Narodopisna knjižnica. 3.zv.)

Film reproduction. Master negative. Positive in *ZQ-376.

NL 0424056 NN

Ljubimov, B
see Liubimov, B

Ljubimowa, W W
see
Liubimova, V V

Ljubinković, Mirjana Ćorović-
see
Ćorović-Ljubinković, Mirjana.

LJUBINKOVIĆ, RADIVOJE.
Srpski crkveni spomenici u klisuri reke Treske. Skoplje, "Nemanja", 1940.
36 p. illus. (Biblioteka "Hrišćanskog dela; knj.24)

NL 0424060 DDO

PG1418 .L5 1900z
Ljubiša, Stjepan Mitrov, 1824-1878.
Целокупна дела. [Београд, Народна просвета, 19—]
2 v. illus. 20 cm. (Библиотека српских писаца)

Title transliterated: Celokupna dela.

PG1418.L5 54-47757 ‡

NL 0424061 DLC CSt CaBVaU

---

tPG1418 L5K2 1950
Ljubiša, Stjepan Mitrov, 1824-1878.
Kanjoš Macedonović; priča paštrovska iz petnaestog vijeka. [Ilustrirao Albert Kinert. Zagreb, Izdavačko poduzeće Mladost, 195-?]
39 p. illus. (Mala knjižnica sv. 5)

NL 0424062 CU

PG1418 .L5K7
Ljubiša, Stjepan Mitrov, 1824-1878.
Крађа и прекрађа звона; приповетке. Београд, Просвета, 1949.
41 p. 17 cm. (Мала библиотека, 30)

I. Title. *Title transliterated:* Krađa i prekrađa zvona.

PG1418.L5K7 52-42237 ‡

NL 0424063 DLC

PG1418 .L5A6 1948
Ljubiša, Stjepan Mitrov, 1824-1878.
Одабране приповијести. [Београд] Новое поколење, 1948.
xxix, 148, xvi p. port. 21 cm. (Југословенски класици, 10)

(Series: Jugoslovenski klasici, 10)
Title transliterated: Odabrane pripovijesti.

PG1418.L5A6 1948 52-15873

NL 0424064 DLC

Ljubiša, Stjepan Mitrov, 1824-1878, *comp.*
Причања Вука Дојчевића. Београд, Штампано у Држ. штампарији Краљевине Србије, 1902-03.
2 v. 20 cm. (Српска књижевна задруга. [Издања] 67, 81)

I. Title. *Title transliterated:* Pričanja Vuka Dojčevića.

PG1418.L5P68 60-58188 ‡

NL 0424065 DLC CaBVaU FTaSU CtY

Hag37 L77
Ljubiša, Stjepan Mitrov, 1824-1878, comp.
Pripovijesti crnogorske i primorske. Skupio, složio i pregledao Sćepan Mitrov Ljubiša. U Dubrovniku, Nakladom tiskarne D.Pretnera, 1875.
iv,277,[3]p. 19½cm. (Narodna biblioteka.III)

NL 0424066 CtY MH

Ljubiša, Sćepan Mitrov, editor.
Pripovijesti crnogorske i primorske. 2° izdanje. U Dubrovniku, nakladom knjižare Dragutina Pretnera, 1889.
pp. iv, 277 +. (Narodna biblioteka, 3.)

Folklore–Montenegro |Do.–Dalmatia||

NL 0424067 MH InU OCl MiU

PG1418 .L5P7 1924
Ljubiša, Stjepan Mitrov, 1824-1878, *ed.*
Приповијести црногорске и приморске. Београд, Графички ин-т "Народна мисао," 1924.
268 p. 20 cm. (Српска књижевна задруга. [Издања; коло 27, бр. 177)

I. Title. *Title transliterated:* Pripovijesti crnogorske i primorske.

PG1418.L5P7 1924 55-46715 ‡

NL 0424068 DLC FTaSU CoU

PG1418 .L5P7
Ljubiša, Stjepan Mitrov, 1824-1878.
Приповијести црногорске и приморске. Предговор написно Видо Латковић. [Уредио В. Живојиновић] Београд, Просвета, 1948.
xviii, 247 p. port. 21 cm. (Југословенски старији писци. Одабрана дела)

I. Title. *Title transliterated:* Pripovijesti crnogorske i primorske.

PG1418.L5P7 52-44435 ‡

NL 0424069 DLC

Ljubiša, Stjepan Mitrov, 1824-1878.
Pripovijesti i pričanja. Beograd, Jugoslovenska knjiga, 1949.
254 p. illus. 28 cm.

I. Title.

PG1618.L5P7 54-36002 ‡

NL 0424070 DLC OCl TxU CLU MH MiU

VOLUME 337

PG1418
.L5P73
Ljubiša, Stjepan Mitrov, 1824-1878.
Приповиjести и причања. Београд, Југословенска књига, 1949.
266 p. illus. 28 cm.

Title transliterated: Pripovijesti i pričanja.

PG1418.L5P73 55-25074 ‡

NL 0424071 DLC

Ljubisavljević, K.M.
see Ĺubisavlević, Kosta M.

W 6
P3
LJUBISAVLJEVIĆ, Sava
Antituberkulozni dispanzer kao zdravstvena ustanova i centar regionalne antituberkulozne službe. Beograd, 1955.
20 p. illus.
Report read at the tenth Kongres ftiziologa Jugoslavije, Sarajevo, Oct. 5-7, 1955.
1. Tuberculosis - Clinics - Yugoslavia 2. Tuberculosis - Prevention

NL 0424073 DNLM

Ljubišić. Lj P
DR345
L5
Šesta godina srpskog ustanka; vojna studija. Beograd, 1910.
182,iv p. 25ᶜᵐ.

1.Serbia - History - Insurrection, 1804-1813

NL 0424074 CSt

Ljubitsch, David, 1890-
Die goldsolreaktion im liquor cerebrospinalis beigfrühsyphilis. Leipzig, 1918.
Inaug. diss.
Bibl.

NL 0424075 ICRL DNLM CtY

Ljubitsch, Noah, 1892-
Zur charakterisierung von cellulosepraeparaten. Berlin, 1926.
In. Diss.

NL 0424076 ICRL CtY

Ljubitzkaja, L.I.
see Savich, Liubitskaia Lidiia Ivanovna, 1886-

Ljublinski, W S
see
Lûblinskiĭ, Vladimir Sergeevich.

Ljubljana. Akademija znanosti in umetnosti
see Slovenska akademija znanosti in umetnosti, *Ljubljana.*

Ljubljana. Avtomobilsko-motociklistična zveza Slovenije
see Avto-moto zvenza Slovenije.

Ljubljana. Babiška šola.
Dvesto let Ljubljanske babiške šole (1753-1953)
see under [Lavrič, Vito] ed.

Ljubljana. Bogoslovski fakultet
see
Ljubljana. Teološka fakulteta.

Ljubljana. Centralni higienski zavod.
RA299
.Y8Z4
Zdravstvena služba Slovenije.
Ljubljana.

Ljubljana. Centralni higienski zavod.
Law
Yugoslavia. *Laws, statutes, etc.*
Zbirka predpisov o higieni živil. Izdal in uredil Centralni higienski zavod v Ljubljani, Oddelek za higieno prehrane. Ljubljana, 1954.

Ljubljana. Cirilmetodijsko društvo katoliških duhovnikov LR Slovenije
see
Cirilmetodijsko društvo katoliških duhovnikov LR Slovenije.

Ljubljana, Jugoslavia. Comte national pour la defense des pays occupes.
see
Comite national pour la defense des pays occupes Ljubljana, Jugoslavia

---

Ljubljana. Deželni muzej
see
Ljubljana. Narodni muzej.

Ljubljana. Direkcija pošte, telegrafa in telefona
see
Yugoslavia. *Direkcija pošta, telegrafa i telefona Ljubljana.*

Ljubljana. Društvo arhitektov Slovenije
see
Društvo arhitektov Slovenije.

Ljubljana. Društvo ekonomistov Slovenije
see
Zveza ekonomistov Slovenije.

Ljubljana. Društvo inženirjev in tehnikov gozdarstva in lesne industrije LRS
see
Društvo inženirjev in tehnikov gozdarstva in lesne industrije LRS.

Ljubljana. Društvo pravnika NR Slovenije
see
Društvo pravnikov LR Slovenije.

Ljubljana. Društvo pravnikov
see
Društvo pravnikov LR Slovenije.

Ljubljana. Društvo pravnikov LR Slovenije
see
Društvo pravnikov LR Slovenije.

4HG
346
Ljubljana. Državni zavarovalni zavod.
Navodila za poslovanje DOZ-ovega poverjenika v podjetjih, ustanovah in uradih, kjer se premije za življenjsko zavarovanje odtegujejo od prejemkov zavarovanih članov delovnih kolektivov. Ljubljana, 1951.
11 p.

NL 0424095 DLC-P4

Ljubljana. Etnografski muzej.
Bulletino
see
Etnolog.

Ljubljana. Etnografski muzej.
DR381
.S6E8
Etnolog. knjiga 1-17; 1926/27-44. Ljubljana.

Ljubljana. Etnografski muzej.
La revue
see
Etnolog.

Ljubljana. Etnografski muzej.
GN1
.S5
Slovenski etnograf. letnik 1- 1948-
Ljubljana.

Ljubljana. Fizikalni institut "J. Stefan"
see
Slovenska akademija znanosti in umetnosti, *Ljubljana. Fizikalni institut "J. Stefan."*

Ljubljana. Forest Institute of Slovenia
see
Ljubljana. Gozdarski institut Slovenije.

Ljubljana. Galerie Moderne
see
Ljubjana. Moderna galerija.

Ljubljana. Galerie nationale
see
Ljubljana. Narodna galerija.

VOLUME 337

Ljubljana. Geodetski zavod.
Seznam mest, okrajev, mestnih občin, kat. občin in naselij h karti upravne razdelitve LR Slovenije. Ljubljana, 1952.
101 p. 20 cm.

1. Slovenia—Administrative and political divisions. I. Title.

JS6949.S6L56 59-42151

NL 0424104 DLC NNC

Ljubljana. Geografski institut
see Ljubljana. Univerza. Geografski institut.

Ljubljana. Geografsko drustvo
see Geografsko drustvo, Ljubljana.

QE287 .G423

Ljubljana. Geoloski zavod.
Geologija; razprave in poročila. knjiga 1- 1953-
Ljubljana, Državna založba Slovenije.

Ljubljana. Glasbena Matica
see
Glasbena Matica v Ljubljani.

Ljubljana. Glavna zadružna zveza LR Slovenije
see
Glavna zadružna zveza LR Slovenije.

Ljublana. Gostinska zbornica za LRS
see
Gostinska zbornica za LR Slovenijo.

Ljubljana. Gozdarski institut Slovenije.
Gozdarski in lesnoindustrijski priročnik. Ljubljana [Kmečka knjiga] 1952-
v. tables. 17 cm. (*Its* Strokovna in znanstvena dela)
CONTENTS.—1. del. Tablice.

1. Forests and forestry—Slovenia. I. Title.

SD217.S6L56 57-21532 ‡

NL 0424111 DLC

SD217 .S6154

Ljubljana. Gozdarski institut Slovenije.
Reports.
Inštitut za gozdno in lesno gospodarstvo Slovenije.
Zbornik. Proceedings. 1- 1947/49-
Ljubljana.

Ljubljana. Gozdarski institut Slovenije
see also Institut za gozdno in lesno gospodarstvo Slovenije.

Ljubljana. Hermes, Železničarsko športno društvo
see
Slovensko športno društvo Železničar, *Ljubljana.*

W 6 P3

LJUBLJANA. Higienski zavod
Rešimo mladino pred alkoholizmom.
Ljubljana, 1939.
79 p.
1. Alcoholism Title

NL 0424115 DNLM

Ljubljana. Histolosko-embrioloski institut
see Ljubljana. Medicinska visoka sola. Histolosko-embrioloski institut.

Ljubljana. Historischer Verein für Krain
see Historischer Verein für Krain, Ljubljana.

QC1 .L74

Ljubljana. Institut "Jožef Stefan."
Reports. v. 1-
Ljubljana, 1953-
v. illus., ports. 24 cm.
Vol. 1 issued by "J. Stefan" Institute of Physics of the Slovenian Academy of Sciences and Arts.
English or German.

1. Physics—Societies, etc.

QC1.L74 58-38271

NL 0424118 DLC ICRL IU CLSU

Ljubljana. Institut "Jožef Stefan"
see also
Slovenska akademija znanosti in umetnosti, *Ljubljana. Fizikalni institut "J. Stefan."*

Ljubljana. Inštitut za biologijo
see **Slovenska akademija znanosti in umetnosti,** *Ljubljana. Inštitut za biologijo.*

Ljubljana. Inštitut za geografijo
see **Slovenska akademija znanosti in umetnosti,** *Ljubljana. Inštitut za geografijo.*

Ljubljana. Inštitut za gozdno in lesno gospodarstvo Slovenije
see Inštitut za gozdno in lesno gospodarstvo Slovenije.

Ljubljana. Inštitut za literature
see
Slovenska akademija znanosti in umetnosti, *Ljubljana. Institut za literature.*

Ljubljana. Institut za narodnostna vprašanja
see
Ljubljana. Univerza. *Institut za narodnostna vprašanja.*

Ljubljana. Inštitut za raziskovanje krasa
see
Slovenska akademija znanosti in umetnosti, *Ljubljana. Inštitut za raziskovanje krasa.*

Ljubljana. Institute for Questions of Nationality
see
Ljubljana. Univerza. *Institut za narodnostna vprašanja.*

Ljubljana. Institutum Biologiae
see **Slovenska akademija znanosti in umetnosti,** *Ljubljana. Inštitut za biologijo.*

Ljubljana. Institutum Carsologicum
see
Slovenska akademija znanosti in umetnosti, *Ljubljana. Inštitut za raziskovanje krasa.*

Ljubljana. Institutum Litterarum
see
Slovenska akademija znanosti in umetnosti, *Ljubljana. Institut za literature.*

Ljubljana. "J. Stefan" Institut
see
Ljubljana. Institut "Jožef Stefan."

Ljubljana. "J. Stefan" Institute of Physics
see
Slovenska akademija znanosti in umetnosti, *Ljubljana. Fizikalni institut "J. Stefan."*

Ljubljana, Yugoslavia. Juridicki fakultet
see
Ljubljana, Yugoslavia. Univerza. Juridicki fakultet

Ljubljana.
Kaiserlich-koenigliche Staats-Oberrealschule.
Jahresbericht.
1
Laibach, 1
no. 8°.

1. Education, Higher—Austria— Laibach.
N. Y. P. L. May 19, 1925

NL 0424133 NN

Ljubljana. Katehetsko društvo
see
Katehetsko društvo v Ljubljani.

Ljubljana. Kmetijska zbornica
see
Slovenia. Kmetijska zbornica.

Ljubljana. Komora za trgovinu, obrt i industriju
see
Ljubljana. Zbornica za trgovino, obrt in industrijo.

Ljubljana. Krainisches landes-museum Rudolfinum
see
Ljubljana. Narodni muzej.

Ljubljana. Kraljevi etnografski muzej
see **Ljubljana. Etnografski muzej.**

VOLUME 337

Ljubljana. Landes-museum im herzogthume Krain
see
Ljubljana. Narodni muzej.

Ljubljana. Leonova družba
see
Leonova družba, *Ljubljana.*

Ljubljana. Lesnoi institut
see
Ljubljana. Gozdarski institut Slovenije.

Ljubljana. Manjšinski institut
see
Manjšinski institut, *Ljubljana.*

Ljubljana. Matica slovenska
see Slovenska Matica v Ljubljani.

W 1
LJ789
LJUBLJANA. Medicinska visoka šola.
Histološko-embriološki inštitut
[Izdaje] 1; 1954. Ljubljana.
14 p. illus.
Summaries in English.
Continued by the Izdaje of the institute under its later name: Ljubljana. Univerza. Histološko-embiološki institut.
1. Medicine - Period.

NL 0424144 DNLM

Ljubljana. Medicinska visoka šola. Histološko-embriološki inštitut.
Stetje retikulocitov
see under
Kališnik, M

Ljubljana. Medicinska visoka šola.
Kirurgična klinika. Zbornik kirurgične klinike...
see under Lavrič, Božidar.

TK7802
.L55
Ljubljana. Mednarodni sejem radia, televizije, telekomunikacij in avtomatizacije.
Katalog.
Ljubljana, Gospodarskó raztavišče.
v. illus. 20 cm.
In Slovenian, Serbocroatian, English, and German.

TK7802.L55 62-44988

NL 0424147 DLC

HJ9448
.L82A3
Ljubljana. Mestni ljudski odbor.
Ljubljana. *Ordinances, etc.*
Proračun.
[V Ljubljani]

Law
Ljubljana. Mestni ljudski odbor.
Ljubljana. *Ordinances, etc.*
Sklep zbora proizvajalcev MLO v Ljubljani o določitvi volilnih enot in odločba Mestne volilne komisije v Ljubljani o zborih volivcev. [Ljubljana, 1953]

Ljubljana. *Mestni ljudski odbor*
see also
Ljubljana (*District*) *Okrajni ljudski odbor.*

Ljubljana. *Mestni ljudski odbor. Urad za statistiko in evidenco*
see
Ljubljana. *Urad za statistiko.*

ND953
.G7L4
Ljubljana. Mestni muzej.
Grohar, Ivan, 1867-1911.
Ivan Grohar; študijska razstava. Besedilo napisala in katalog uredila Marija Levstek. V. Ljubljani, Mestni muzej, 1954.

Ljubljana. Mestni muzej.
Vprašanja Mestnega muzeja v Ljubljani. Ljubljana, 1954.
35 p. 20 cm.

I. Title.

AM101.L598 56-15825 ‡

NL 0424153 DLC

Ljubljana. Mestni muzej
see also
Ljubljana. Narodni muzej

Law
Ljubljana. Mestna volilna komisija.
Ljubljana. *Ordinances, etc.*
Sklep zbora proizvajalcev MLO v Ljubljani o določitvi volilnih enot in odločba Mestne volilne komisije v Ljubljani o zborih volivcev. [Ljubljana, 1953]

Ljubljana. Minorities institute
see Manjšinski institut, Ljubljana.

Ljubljana. Moderna Galerija.
... Angleški akvarel in Risba. April 1954.
Ljubljana, 1954.
pamph. illus.

NL 0424157 PPPM

Ljubljana. Moderna Galerija.
Henry Moore; skulptura in Risba.
Ljubljana, 1955.
pamph. illus.

NL 0424158 PPPM

Ljubljana. Moderna Galerija.
Karla Bulovceva-Mrak; risbe. April 1954.
Ljubljana, 1954.
pamph. illus.

NL 0424159 PPPM

NE40
.L5
Ljubljana. Moderna galerija.
Mednarodna grafična razstava. Exposition internationale de gravure. 1.- 1955-
Ljubljana [Sekretarijat za organizacijo mednarodnih grafičnih razstav]

Ljubljana. Moderna galerija.
Mednarodna razstava barvne litografije. Ljubljana, 1953.
12 p. (chiefly illus.) 25 cm.

1. Art, Modern—20th cent. 2. Art—Exhibitions. I. Title.

N6490.L57 55-15796

NL 0424161 DLC

Ljubljana. Moderna galerija.
Mednarodna razstava lesorezov Xylon. Ljubljana, 1954.
28 p. illus. 24 cm.

1. Wood-engravings—Exhibitions. I. Xylon. II. Title.

NE1010.L63 59-45660 ‡

NL 0424162 DLC PPPM

Fogg Art Mus.
Ljubljana. Moderna galerija
Moderna Austrijska risba in grafika. Ljubljana, 1955.
19 p. 24 plates
At head of title: Graficna Zbirka Albertina, Dunaj.

NL 0424163 MH-FA

Ljubljana. Moderna Galerija.
Nikolaj Pirnat; spominska razstava.
Junij - Julij 1954. Ljubljana, 1954.
36 p. [26] illus. 24 cm.

NL 0424164 PPPM

Ljubljana. Moderna Galerija.
... Les peintres slovenes de Trieste...
18. Okbobre isdala Decembru 1953.
Ljubljana, 1953.
pamph. illus.

NL 0424165 PPPM

4-NC-65 Ljubljana. Moderna galerija.
Razstava slikarskih in grafičnih del tržaških umetnikov. V Ljubljani, 1950.
1 v. (unpaged)

NL 0424166 DLC-P4 NN

Ljubljana. Moderna galerija.
Razstava slovenskega slikarstva v dobi realizma. [V Ljubljani] 1950.
[36] p. illus. 24 cm.

1. Paintings, Slovenian—Exhibitions. I. Title.

ND948.L55 55-23657 ‡

NL 0424167 DLC

VOLUME 337

Ljubljana. Moderna galerija.
Razstava sodobnega jugoslovanskega kiparstva Zveze upodabljajočih umetnikov FLR Jugoslavije, februar-marec 1951. ₍Katalog uredila: Kalin Zdenko in Maleš Miha₎ Ljubljana ₍1951₎
unpaged (chiefly illus.) 25 cm.

1. Sculpture, Yugoslav—Exhibitions. I. Kalin, Zdenko. II. Maleš, Miha. III. Savez likovnih umetnika Jugoslavije. IV. Title.
NB949.L5 59-41665 ‡

NL 0424168 DLC

Ljubljana. Moderna galerija.
Slovenski impresionisti: Grohar, Jakopič, Jama, Sternen. ₍Izložbu priredila: Moderna i Narodna galerija u Ljubljani. Tekst: France Stelè; katalog: Zoran Kržišnik₎ U Ljubljani, 1952.
29 p. illus. 24 cm.

1. Painters, Slovenian. 2. Impressionism (Art) I. Stele, Franc, 1886- II. Kržišnik, Zoran. III. Ljubljana. Narodna galerija. IV. Title.
ND952.L55 58-35954 ‡

NL 0424169 DLC NN

ND 949 S55L76 Ljubljana. Moderna galerija.
Slovenski impresionisti: Ivan Grohar, Rihard Jakopič, Matija Jama, Matej Sternen. Ob razstavi del slovenskih impresionistov v Moderni Galeriji v Ljubljani April - Maj 1949. [Ljubljana, 1949]
22 p. illus.

1. Impressionism (Art) - Slovenia. I. Title.

NL 0424170 CLU

Ljubljana. Moderna Galerija.
... Sodobna Roroska Grafika. November-December 1954. Ljubljana, 1954.
pamph. illus.

NL 0424171 PPPM OC1MA

4ND-233 Ljubljana. Moderna galerija.
Stane Kregar; retrospektivna umetnostna razstava. V Ljubljani, Moderna galerija, 1950.
7 p.
I. Kregar, Stane

NL 0424172 DLC-P4

Ljubljana. Moderna galerija.
Tržaški slovenski slikarji. ₍Uredil in sestavil življenjepisne podatke Karel Dobida₎ Ljubljana, 1953.
19 p. illus. 24 cm.

1. Paintings, Slovenian—Exhibitions. 2. Painters, Slovenian. I. Dobida, Karel, ed.
ND1943.L55 55-23658 ‡

NL 0424173 DLC MB OC1MA CU MiU ICU MH NN IU

Ljubljana. Moderna Galerija.
Umetnostna Razstava... Maj 1954. Ljubljana, 1954.
pamph. illus.

NL 0424174 PPPM OC1MA

Ljubljana. Moderna galerija
Veno Pilon, grafika in risba. Ljubljana, Moderna galerija, 1954.
31p. front. (port.) pl. 20cm.

Text in Slovenian, French summary: p. 19-20.
Exhibition held in October 1954.

NL 0424175 PPPM OC1MA

Ljubljana. Musée ethnographique royal
see
Ljubljana. Etnografski muzej.

Ljubljana. Musée royal d'ethnographie
see
Ljubljana. Etnografski muzej.

Ljubljana. Museo d'etnografia
see
Ljubljana. Etnografski muzej.

Ljubljana. Museum Nationale
see
Ljubljana. Narodni muzej.

Ljubljana. Muzejsko društvo za Slovenijo
see
Muzejsko društvo za Slovenijo, *Ljubljana.*

Ljubljana. Narodna glaerija.
Fortunat Bergant
see under Cevc, Anica.

Fogg Art Mus.
Ljubljana. Narodna galerija
Gvidon Birolla. [Uvod: Jelisava Čopič] Ljubljana, Narodna galerija, 1952
[17] p. port., illus., 12 plates
"Izdano ob kolektivni razstavi slikarjevih del prirejeni v počastitev njegove sedemdesetletnice"
1.Birolla, Gvidon, 1881- I.Birolla, Gvidon, 1881- II.Čopič, Jelisava

NL 0424182 MH-FA

Ljubljana. Narodna galerija.
Hinko Smrekar, 1883-1942. ₍Uvod in katalog: Karel Dobida₎ V Ljubljani, 1952.
53 p. illus. 24 cm.

1. Smrekar, Hinko, 1883-1942. I. Dobida, Karel.
ND538.S62L5 56-29039 ‡

NL 0424183 DLC

ND949 .S55L55 Ljubliana. Narodna galerija.
Klasicizem in romantika na Slovenskem. ₍Uvod: Izidor Cankar. Biografski podatki in katalog: Čopić Jelisava₎ V Ljubljani, 1954.
57 p. illus. 25 cm.
Slovenian and French.

1. Painting, Slovenian—History. 2. Classicism in art. 3. Romanticism in art. I. Čopič, Jelisava. II. Title.
ND949.S55L55 78-212199

NL 0424184 DLC OC1MA DNGA PPPM

Ljubljana. Narodna galerija Knjižnica

3 (1939) - Mesesnel, France
Janez in Jurij Šubic

NL 0424185 MH

Ljubljana. Narodna galerija.
Maksim Gaspari. ₍Izdano ob kolektivni razstavi umetnikovih del, prirejeni v počastitev njegove sedemsetletnice rojstva. V Ljubljani₎ 1953.
36 p. illus., plates, port. 24 cm.

1. Gaspari, Maksim, 1883-
ND953.G3L6 59-35733

NL 0424186 DLC MH

Ljubljana. Narodna galerija.
Slovenska moderna umetnost. [v.1-]
Ljubljana, Narodne galerija, n.d.

Preface in v.1 signed : Izidor Cankar.

NL 0424187 OC1

ND952 .L55 Ljubljana. Narodna galerija.

Ljubljana. Moderna galerija.
Slovenski impresionisti: Grohar, Jakopič, Jama, Sternen. ₍Izložbu priredila: Moderna i Narodna galerija u Ljubljani. Tekst: France Stelè; katalog: Zoran Kržišnik₎ U Ljubljani, 1952.

Ljubljana, Yugoslavia. Narodna galerija.
Začetki slovenskega impresionizma. Jakopičev paviljon, 1955. ₍Katalog: Karel Dobida. Ljubljana, 1955₎ 31 p. 13 plates, ports. 24cm.
"Les débuts de la peinture impressioniste slovène" (₍2₎ p.) inserted.

1. Grohar, Ivan, 1867-1911. 2. Jakopič, Rihard, 1869-1943. 3. Jama, Matija, 1872-1947. 4. Sternen, Matej, 1870-1949. I. Dobida, Karel.

NL 0424189 NN

Z2957 .S6S55 Ljubljana. Narodna in univerzitetna knjižnica.

Slovenska bibliografija. 1- 1945/47-
Ljubljana, Državna založba Slovenije.

A44Y L769J Ljubljana. Narodni Muzej.
Izvestja. 1- letnik; 1891-
Ljubljana, Kranjsko.
illus. 22cm. annual.

NL 0424191 CtY

Ljubljana. Narodni muzej.
Jahresbericht.

Laibach, 18
v. 20cm.

Publication began with report for 1837?
Vols. for 18 issued under an earlier name of the museum: Landesmuseum im herzogthume Krain.
Report for 1838 has supplement: Notizen über Georg freiherrn v. Vega.

Q44.L34 46-44090

NL 0424192 DLC

VOLUME 337

Ljubljana. Narodni muzej.

ND1335
.Z3

Zagreb. Muzej za umjetnost i obrt.
Razstava miniatur na Hrvatskem od XVI. do XIX. stoletja. ₍Slovenski tekst kataloga priredil Tone Potokar₎ Ljubljana, Narodni muzej, 1954.

Ljubljana. Narodni muzej
Vodnik po zbirkah Narodnega muzeja v Ljubljani. Ljubljana, 1931-33

2 v. illus.
Contents: - 1. Kulturno zgodovinski del. - 2. Prirodopisni del

NL 0424194 MH WaU

Ljubljana. Narodni muzej
see also
Ljubljana. Mestni muzej.

Ljubljana. National minorities institute
see
Manjšinski institut, *Ljubljana.*

Ljubljana. National Museum
see
Ljubljana. Narodni muzej.

Ljubljana. Nuklearni institut "Jožef Stefan"
see
Ljubljana. Institut "Jožef Stefan."

Ljubljana. Obrtna zbornica LR Slovenije
see
Obrtna zbornica LR Slovenije.

4K
Yugo
190

Ljubljana. Ordinances, etc.
Odloki o javnem redu in miru, tržnem in sejemskem redu, ter o hišnem redu. [V Ljubljani, Izdaja Uradnega vestnika MLO, 1951]
20 p.

NL 0424200 DLC-P4

4K
Yugo
78

Ljubljana. Ordinances, etc.
Priročnik za šoferje in sprevodnike v javnem avtomobilskem prometu. Ljubljana, Glavna direkcija za cestni promet, 1951.
121 p.

NL 0424201 DLC-P4

HJ9448
.L82A3

Ljubljana. *Ordinances, etc.*
Proračun.
₍V Ljubljani₎
v. tables. 24 cm. annual.
Issued, 19 by the Mestni ljudski odbor.

1. Ljubljana—Budget. I. Ljubljana. Mestni ljudski odbor.

HJ9448.L82A3 61-36462 rev

NL 0424202 DLC NN

Ljubljana. Ordinances, etc.
Provinzial-gesetzsammlung des laibacher gouvernements für das jahr 1819 ... Laibach, L. Eger, 1820.
viii, 143 p. fold. table. 19cm.
"Herausgegeben auf allerhöchsten Befehl unter der Aufsicht des k. k. Laibacher Landesguberniums."
No more published?

NL 0424203 MH-L

Ljubljana. Ordinances, etc.
... Raccolta delle norme forestali vigenti nella Provincia di Lubiana. Traduzioni italiane dal testo iugoslavo. Lubiana, 1941.
2 p.l., 100 numb. l. 33½ x 21cm.
At head of title: Regno d'Italia. Alto commissariato per la Provincia di Lubiana. Milizia nazionale forestale.

Each law also separately paged.
Reproduced from typewritten copy.

NL 0424205 MH-L

Ljubljana. *Ordinances, etc.*
Sklep zbora proizvajalcev MLO v Ljubljani o določitvi volilnih enot in odločba Mestne volilne komisije v Ljubljani o zborih volivcev. ₍Ljubljana, 1953₎
35 p. 21 cm.

I. Ljubljana. Mestni ljudski odbor. II. Ljubljana. Mestna volilna komisija.

56-40180 ‡

NL 0424206 DLC

Ljubljana. Pensioni zavod za službenike
see
Pokojninski zavod za nameščence v Ljubljani.

Ljubljana. Planinska zveza Slovenije
see
Planinska zveza Slovenije.

Ljubljana. Pokojninski zavod za nameščence
see
Pokojninski zavod za nameščence v Ljubljani.

Ljubljana. Prešernova knjižnica
see
Prešernova knjižnica, *Ljubljana.*

Ljubljana. Prirodoslovni muzej.

QH7
.P668

Prirodoslovna izvestja. knjiga 1-
Ljubljana, 1944-

Ljubljana. Prirodoslovno društvo
see
Prirodoslovno društvo, *Ljubljana.*

HJ
9063
Y8L4

Ljubljana. Rajonski ljudski odbor.
Predlog proračuna rajonskega ljudskega odbora.
19 -
Ljubljana.
v.

1. Budget - Ljubljana.

NL 0424213 CLU

Ljubljana. *Rajonski ljudski odbor.*
Zapisnik.
Ljubljana.
v. 24 cm.

1. Ljubljana—Pol. & govt. I. Title.

JS31.L74 53-27838

NL 0424214 DLC

Ljubljana. Republiška zveza kmetijskih zadrug
see
Republiška zveza kmetijskih zadrug.

Ljubljana. Research Institute
see
Ljubljana. Znanstveni institut.

PN2856
L4L4

Ljubljana (City) Šentjakobsko gledališče.
Jubilejni zbornik Šentjakobskega gledališča, 1920-1950. [Uredili Anča Grgurević et al.] V Ljubljani. Tiskarna "Toneta Tomšiča," 1950?]
70 p. illus., ports.

1. Ljubljana (City) Šentjakobsko gledališče. I. Grgurević, Anča, ed.

NL 0424217 CU

Ljubljana. Sindikat prosvetnih delavcev Slovenije
see
Sindikat prosvetnih delavcev Slovenije.

Ljubljana. Slavistično društvo
see Slavistično društvo, *Ljubljana.*

Ljubljana. Slovene Chemical Society
see
Slovensko kemijsko društvo.

Ljubljana. Slovenian National Opera
see
Ljubljana. Slovensko narodno gledališče.

Ljubljana. Slovenska akademija znanosti in umetnosti
see **Slovenska akademija znanosti in umetnosti,** *Ljubljana.*

Ljubljana. Slovenska izseljenska matica
see
Slovenska izseljenska matica, *Ljubljana.*

VOLUME 337

Ljubljana. Slovenska književna zadruga
see
Slovenska književna zadruga, *Ljubljana.*

Ljubljana. Slovensko kemijsko društvo
see
Slovensko kemijsko društvo.

ML420
.B38P5
Ljubljana. Slovensko narodno gledališče.
50 ⌈i. e. Petdeset⌉ let umetniškega dela Julija Betetta. ⌈V Ljubljani, Posebna izd. Gledališkega lista Opere, 1954⌉

Ljubljana. Slovensko športno društvo Železničar
see
Slovensko športno društvo Železničar, *Ljubljana.*

Ljubljana. Socialno-ekonomski institut.
Socialni problemi slovenske vasi
see under Pirc, Ivo.

Ljubljana. Socialno-Ekonomski Institut.
Zbirka študij. št. 1-
Ljubljana, 19

NL 0424229 CtY MH

Ljubljana. Société chimique slovène
see
Slovensko kemijsko društvo.

Ljubljana. Société d'ethnographie
see
Etnografsko društvo, *Ljubljana.*

Ljubljana. Société touristique
see
Turistično društvo, *Ljubljana.*

Ljubljana. Srednja technicna sola
see
Ljubljana. Tehniška srednja šola.

Ljubljana. Strokovna zadruga koncesijoniranih elektrotehnikov
see
Združenje elektrotehniških obrti za Dravsko banovino, *Ljubljana.*

Ljubljana. Šumarski institut Slovenije
see
Ljubljana. Gozdarski institut Slovenije.

T173
.L7937L4
Ljubljana. Tehniška srednja šola.
Letno poročilo Tehniške srednje šole, Delovodske šole, Nadzorniške rudarske šole in Delavskega tehhikuma ⌈i. e. tehnikuma⌉ 1949/50–
⌈Ljubljana⌉

BR9
.S5B6
Ljubljana. Teološka fakulteta.
Bogoslovni vestnik.
Ljubljana, Teološka fakulteta.

HF5167
.L5L5
Ljubljana. Trgovska in obrtniška zbornica.
Seznam industrijskih in večjih obrtnih podjetij v okraju Trgovsko in obrtniške zbornice v Ljubljani. ⌈V Ljubljani, 19—⌉
79 p. 21 cm.
Slovenian and French.

1. Ljubljana—Comm.—Direct. I. Title.

HF5167.L5L5 59-28264

NL 0424238 DLC

Ljubljana. Trgovsko predstavništvo Jugoslovanske cone Svobodnega tržaškega ozemlja
see
Trgovsko predstavništvo Jugoslovanske cone Svobodnega tržaškega ozemlja.

Ljubljana. Trgovinska zbornica za LR Slovenijo
see
Trgovinska zbornica za LR Slovenijo, *Ljubljana.*

Ljubljana. *Turistični urad.*
Gospodarski adresar glavnega mesta Ljubljane. Ljubljana, 1953.
xvi, 156 p. fold. col. map (in pocket) 14 cm.

1. Ljubljana—Direct.

DR396.L55A56 60-38548

NL 0424241 DLC

Ljubljana. Turistično društvo
see
Turistično društvo, *Ljubljana.*

Ljubljana. Umetnosto zgodovinsko društvo
see
Umetnosto zgodovinsko društvo, *Ljubljana.*

Ljubljana, Yugoslavia. Univerza.
... Ksiega pamiatkowa ku czci jego ekscelencji x. biskupa Mariana Leona Fulmana ... Lublin, ⌈"Narodowa"⌉ 1939.
3 v. tables. 24cm. (Towarzystwo naukowe katolickiego uniwersytetu lubelskiego, tom 30-32)
Bibliographical footnotes.
Contents.- I. Wydział kościelne.- II. Wydział prawa i nauk społeczno-ekonomicznych.- III. Wydział nauk humanistycznych.

NL 0424245 MH-L

Slav 9035.1.870
Ljubljana. Univerza
Prešernova razstava 1946; seznam predmetov, za Prešernov teden priredila Ljubljanska univerza. [V Ljubljani, 1946]
24 p.

NL 0424246 MH

Ljubljana, Yugoslavia. Univerza.
...Seznam predavanj na Univerzi kralja Aleksandra I. v Ljubljani...
V Ljubljani, 1 no. 23½cm.
At head of title: Catalogus lectionum Universitatis Alexandrinae...

NL 0424247 NN DLC CU

LH5
L5T7
Ljubljana. Univerza.
Tribuna; list študentov Ljubljanske univerze. leto 1- 8 dec. 1951-
Ljubljana.

LF
+5475
+L55
A63
Ljubljana. Univerza
Zgodovina Slovenske Univerze v Ljubljani do leta 1929. ⌈V Ljubljani, Izd. Rektorat Univerze, 1929⌉
533p. illus. 31cm.

1. Ljubljana. Univerza - Hist. I. Title

NL 0424249 WU MH MB IU NN CaBVaU ICU NjP CU

Ljubljana. Univerza. *Biotehniška fakulteta.*
Zbornik. Research reports. zv. 1.–
Ljubljana, 1953–
v. illus., maps. 24 cm.
Title varies: v. 1– Zbornik za kmetijstvo in gozdarstvo. Review of agriculture and forestry.— v. -9, Zbornik za kmetijstvo in gozdarstvo.
In Slovenian, with summaries in English or German.
Vol. 1 issued by Agronomska in gozdarska fakulteta.
1. Agriculture—Collected works. 2. Forests and forestry—Collected works. 3. Veterinary medicine—Collected works. I. Agronomska in gozdarska fakulteta. II. Ljubljana. Univerza. Biotehniška fakulteta. Research reports. III. Title: Zbornik za kmetijstvo in gozdarstvo. IV. Title: Review of agriculture and forestry.

S13.L55 75-492315

NL 0424250 DLC IU NcRS

Ljubljana. Univerza. *Elektrotechnische Fakultät*
see
Ljubljana. Univerza. *Fakulteta za elektrotehniko.*

Ljubljana. Univerza. *Faculté d'électrotechnique*
see
Ljubljana. Univerza. *Fakulteta za elektrotehniko.*

Ljubljana. Univerza. *Faculty of Electrical Engineering*
see
Ljubljana. Univerza. *Fakulteta za elektrotehniko.*

Ljubljana. Univerza. *Faculty of Mechanical Engineering*
see
Ljubljana. Univerza. *Fakulteta za strojništvo.*

Ljubljana. Univerza. *Faculty of Mining, Metallurgy and Chemical Technology*
see
Ljubljana. Univerza. *Fakulteta za rudarstvo, metalurgijo in kemijsko tehnologijo.*

VOLUME 337

Ljubljana. Univerza. Fakulteta za Agronomijo, Gozdarstvo in Veterinarstvo. Zbornik.
Ljubljana [Yugoslavia]
v. illus. 24cm.
Title changes: v.1-7, 1953-60, Zbornik za kmetijstvo in gozdarstvo.- v.8- 1961- Zbornik.
Summaries in English, French or German.
1.Agriculture - forestry - Soc. 2.Forest and Soc. 3.Agriculture - Yugo-
NL 0424256 OrCS

TK4 .E7474
Ljubljana. Univerza. Fakulteta za elektrotehniko.
Elektrotehniški vestnik. okt. 1931-
[Ljubljana, Elektrotehniška prosveta]

QC989 .Y6P6
Ljubljana, Univerza. Fakulteta za naravoslovje in tehnologijo.
Poseben prikaz vremena v Sloveniji. A special presentation of weather in Slovenia.
Ljubljana.

Ljubljana. Univerza. *Fakulteta za rudarstvo, metalurgijo in kemijsko tehnologijo. Department of Mining and Metallurgy*
see
Ljubljana. Univerza. *Fakulteta za rudarstvo, metalurgijo in kemijsko tehnologijo. Oddelek za rudarstvo in metalurgijo.*

TN4 .R843
Ljubljana. Univerza. Fakulteta za rudarstvo, metalurgijo in kemijsko tehnologijo. Oddelek za rudarstvo in metalurgijo.
Rudarsko-metalurški zbornik. 1952-
Ljubljana.

TJ4 .L55
Ljubljana. Univerza. *Fakulteta za strojništvo.*
Izvestje Fakultete za strojništvo Univerze v Ljubljani
Ljubljana.
v. 29 cm.
TJ4.L55 65-83644
NL 0424261 DLC

Ljubljana. Univerza. *Filozofska fakulteta.*
Zbornik. 1- 1950-
Ljubljana.
v. illus. 25 cm.
Vols. 1- have also title: Recueil de [sic] travaux.
Tables of contents and summaries also in French, English, or other languages.
I. Title: Ljubljana. Univerza. Filozofska fakulteta. Recueil des travaux.
AS346.L55 64-43240
NL 0424262 DLC ICU MoU MiU

HC 407 .Y8 L 9
LJUBLJANA--Univerza--Geografski institut
Gospodarska struktura Slovenije v luči poklicne statistike in delavskega zavarovanja. Izdelal: Geografski institut na Univerzi Kralja Aleksandra V Ljubljani. Ljubljana,1939.
37 p. maps.
At head of title: Socialno ekonomski institut v Ljubljani. Zbirka študij,št.5.
1. Slovenia--Econ.cond. I. Ilešič,Svetozar. II. Title.
NL 0424263 InU CtY ICU

Ljubljana. Univerza. *Institut za narodnostna vprašanja.*
Who should have Trieste? Ljubljana, 1953.
43 p. illus. 20 cm.
1. Trieste. I. Title.
DB321.L6 55-33648
NL 0424264 DLC NIC CU IU

Ljubljana. Univerza. *Institute for Questions of Nationality*
see
Ljubljana. Univerza. *Institut za narodnostna vprašanja.*

Ljubljana. Univerza. *Juridična fakulteta.* Raccolta di studi scientifici
see its Zbornik znanstvenih razprav.

Ljubljana. Univerza. Juridična fakulteta.
Razlastitev v pravne, sistemu Federativne Ljudske Republike Jugoslavije
see under Strobl, Majda.

Ljubljana. Univerza. *Juridična fakulteta.* Travaux et articles
see its Zbornik znanstvenih razprav.

Ljubljana, Yugoslavia. Univerza. Juridicna fakulteta.
Ucbeniki. Yugoslavia, Serbocroat, Univ. Ljubljana, 1925.
NL 0424269 DDO

Ljubljana. Univerza. *Juridična fakulteta.*
Zbornik znanstvenih razprav.
V Ljubljani.
v. ports., diagrs. 24 cm.
Began publication with issue for 1920/21.
Vols. have title pages in French: Travaux et articles; v. 18-19 (1941/42-42/43) in Italian: Raccolta di studi scientifici.
Summaries in English, French, and other languages.
1. Law — Societies, etc. 2. Law — Addresses, essays, lectures. 3. Law—Yugoslavia—Addresses, essays, lectures. I. Title.
53-34682
NL 0424270 DLC CaOTU CU KU NNC ICU FTaSU ViU NSyU

Ljubljana. Univerza. *Ljudska študentska mladina.*
O današnjih glavnih nalogah študentov. Ljubljana, Mladinska knjiga, 1946.
40 p. illus. 21 cm.
At head of title: III. konferenca LŠM Ljubljanske univerze.
1. Ljubljana. Univerza—Students. I. Title.
LF5475.L59A6 56-34382
NL 0424271 DLC

Ljubljana. Univerza. *Medicinska fakulteta*
see also
Ljubljana. Medicinska visoka šola.

Ljubljana. Univerza. *Pravna fakulteta*
see
Ljubljana. Univerza. *Juridična fakulteta.*

PG1801 .C3
Ljubljana. Univerza. Seminar za slovansko filologijo.
Časopis za slovenski jezik, književnost in zgodovino.
Ljubljana.

Ljubljana. Univerza. *Teološka fakulteta*
see also
Ljubljana. Teološka fakulteta.

W 2 GS5.2 L7U8L
LJUBLJANA. Uprava kliničnih bolnic
Letno poročilo o delu kliničnih bolnic
Ljubljana, 19
v. illus.
NL 0424276 DNLM

HA1189 .L53A35
Ljubljana. Urad za statistiko.
Tromesečni statistični pregled mesta Ljubljana.
Ljubljana.

Ljubljana. Urbanistični inštitut
see
Urbanistični institut, Ljubljana.

Ljubljana. Vrhovni sud
see
Yugoslavia. *Vrhovno sodišče (Ljubljana)*

Ljubljana. Vrhovno sodišče
see
Yugoslavia. *Vrhovno sodišče (Ljubljana)*

HV 2850. 4. S5 L789j 1950
LJUBLJANA. Zavod za gluho mladino
Jubilejni zbornik Zavoda za gluho mladino v Ljubljani, 1900-1950. [Zbornik uredili: Ermenc Zvonko [et al.] Ljubljana, 1950.
117 p. illus., port.
1. Deaf - Institutions - Slovenia I. Ermenc, Zvonko, ed. Title
NL 0424281 DNLM

L53 .L562
Ljubljana. Zavod za proučevanje šolstva LRS.
Zbornik.
[V Ljubljani, Drž. založba Slovenije]
v. illus., tables. 24 cm.
1. Education — Slovenia — Societies, etc. 2. Education — Societies, etc.
L53.L562 64-51835
NL 0424282 DLC

Ljubljana. Zavod za spomeniško varstvo SRS
see
Zavod za spomeniško varstvo SRS.

Ljubljana. *Zavod za statistiko*
see
Ljubljana. *Urad za statistiko.*

VOLUME 337

HF304 .L8

Ljubljana. Zbornica za trgovino, obrt in industrijo.
Razprave Zbornice za trgovino, obrt in industrijo v Ljubljani. [Ljubljana?]
v. 19 cm. 2 no. a year.

1. Boards of trade—Yugoslavia—Ljubljana.

HF304.L8 65-72536

NL 0424285 DLC

Ljubljana. Združenje elektrotehniških obrti za Dravsko banovino
see
Združenje elektrotehniških obrti za Dravsko banovino, *Ljubljana*.

Ljubljana. Združenje grafičnih podjetij LRS
see
Združenje grafičnih podjetij LRS.

Ljubljana. Železničarsko športno društvo Hermes
see
Slovensko športno društvo Železničar, *Ljubljana*.

Ljubljana. Zgodovinsko društvo za Slovenijo
see
Zgodovinsko društvo za Slovenijo.

Ljubljana. Znanstveni institut.
Allied airmen and prisoners of war rescued by the Slovene partisans. Compiled after the records of the Head-quarter [sic] of Slovenia. Ljubljana, 1946.
88 p. illus., fold. col. map. 24 cm.

1. World War, 1939-1945—Prisoners and prisons, German. 2. World War, 1939-1945—Yugoslavia. I. Title.

D805.Y8L5 *949.7 940.53497 54-16877

NL 0424290 DLC MH CSt-H

Ljubljana. Znanstveno društvo
see **Znanstveno društvo v Ljubljani.**

Ljubljana. Znanstveno društvo za humanistične vede
see
Znanstveno društvo za humanistične vede v Ljubljani.

Ljubljana. Zavod za proučevanje varnosti pri delu LRS.
Priročnik k razstavi higiensko-tehnične zaščitne službe. Ljubljana, 1955.
117 p. illus. 17 cm.

1. Hygiene, Public—Addresses, essays, lectures. 2. Industrial hygiene. I. Title.

RA436.L53 59-22540 ‡

NL 0424293 DLC

Ljubljana. Zavod za raziskavo materiala in konstrukcij.
Zavod za raziskavo materiala in konstrukcij, njegov obseg in delo. Ljubljana, 1953.
38 p. illus. 30 cm.

1. Building materials—Testing. I. Title.

TA416.L58 55-19054 rev ‡

NL 0424294 DLC CU

Ljubljana. Zveza borcev narodnoosvobodilne borbe za Slovenijo
see
Zveza borcev narodnoosvobodilne borbe za Slovenijo.

Ljubljana. Zveza ekonomistov Slovenije
see
Zveza ekonomistov Slovenije.

Ljubljana. Zveza ljudskoprosvetnih društev
see
Zveza ljudskoprosvetnih društev.

Ljubljana. Zveza pionirjev Slovenije
see
Zveza pionirjev Slovenije.

Ljubljana. Zveza prijateljev mladine Slovenije
see
Zveza prijateljev mladine Slovenije.

Ljubljana (*District*) *Okrajni ljudski odbor.*
Nekateri današnji in jutrišnji problemi Ljubljane; stanje njenih komunalnih in prometnih naprav, potrebe po stanovanjih, zdravstvenih, socialnih, kulturnih in prosvetnih ustanovah. Ljubljana, 1955.
75 p. illus. 34 cm.

1. Ljubljana. I. Title.

DR396.L55A53 57-17441 ‡

NL 0424300 DLC

Ljubljana (*District*) *Okrajni ljudski odbor*
see also
Ljubljana. *Mestni ljudski odbor.*

Law

Ljubljana (Oblast) Laws, statutes, etc.

Samouprava; uradni list Ljubljanske in Mariborske oblasti. letnik 1-2, 1928-29. Ljubljana [Ljubljanski oblastni odbor]

Ljubljana (*Oblast*)
see also **Slovenia.**

Ljubljana (Pokrajina)
Krajevni leksikon dravske bonovine.
see under title

Ljubljana (*Pokrajina*)
see also **Slovenia.**

Ljubljana (*Pokrajina*)
see also **Slovenia (*Federated Republic, 1945-*)**

Ljubljana (*Pokrajina*) *Laws, statutes, etc.*
Amtsblatt
see
Ljubljana (*Pokrajina*) *Laws, statutes, etc.*
Službeni list.

Ljubljana (*Pokrajina*) *Laws, statutes, etc.*
Bollettino ufficiale
see
Ljubljana (*Pokrajina*) *Laws, statutes, etc.*
Službeni list.

Ljubljana (*Pokrajina*) *Laws, statutes, etc.*
Službeni list. [letnik 1] kos 33-
23 apr. 1941-
V Ljubljani.
v. 31 m. semiweekly (irregular)
Supersedes Službeni list of Slovenia and continues the numbering for the year.
Called also Bollettino ufficiale, with text in Italian and Slovenian, Apr. 23, 1941-Sept. 22, 1943; Amtsblatt, with text in German and Slovenian, Sept. 25, 1943-
Ceased publication in 1945.
Superseded by Uradni list of Slovenia (Federated Republic, 1945-)
Numbered supplements accompany most issues.
Vol. 1, 1941, bound with Službeni list of Slovenia, v. 12, 1941.

53-55726

NL 0424309 DLC

Ljubljana okolica
see
Ljubljana (*District*)

Ljubljanska opera
see
Ljubljana. Slovensko narodno gledališče.

Ljubljanska pokrajina
see **Ljubljana (*Pokrajina*)**

AP58 .S55L5

Ljubljanski zvon. leto 1-61, zv. 1/2; jan. 1881-1941. Ljubljana.
61 v. 25 cm. monthly.
Vol. for 1900 includes a separately numbered monthly supplement: Slovenska knjigarna.

Indexes:
Vols. 1-61, 1881-1941. (Issued as Biblioteka, no. 3 of the Slovenska akademija znanosti in umetnosti) 1 v.
I. Title: Slovenska knjigarna.

AP58.S55L5 56-54407

KU MoU FTaSU NcD IU NjP
NL 0424313 DLC CSt P NNC NIC TxU ViAsR NN IEdS

Ljubo Wiesner; spomenica o 50-godišnjici. Zagreb, 1936.
84 p. port. 23 cm.
Serbo-Croatian or Slovenian.
Includes bibliographical references.
CONTENTS.—Krnic, I. 1885-1935.—Barac, A. Pedesetgodišnjica Ljube Wiesnera.—Krleža, M. Lirika Ljube Wiesnera.—Borko, B. Ljubo Wiesner.—Šimić, S. Ikarov odgovor.

1. Vizner, Ljubo, 1885-1951.

PG1618.V58Z7 74-234447

NL 0424314 DLC OU

Ljubojević, July Liebbald
see Liebbald-Ljubojevic, July.

Ljubomyrshyj, Stepan
see Ljubomyrs'kyi, Stepan.

Ljubovič, J. O.
see **Lîubovich, IÛ O**

VOLUME 337

LJUBŠA, MATTHIAS.
Die Christianisierung der heutigen Diözese Seckau. Graz, Styria, 1911.
xv, 247 p.

NL 0424318 DDO

Ljubša, Matthias , comp. Slav 8462.25.11
Slovenske gorice; opis. Maribor, Tisk in zaloge Tiskarne sv.Cirila, 1925
78 p. (Cirilova knjižnica, XIV.zvezek)

NL 0424319 MH

Ljubtschenko, Arkadij.
Erzählung von einer Flucht und andere Erzählungen. Aus dem Ukrainischen übersetzt von E. Bönike. Charkiw, etc., Literatura i Misteztwo, 1933.

NL 0424320 MH

LJUBUNČIĆ, HASAN.
Put na hadž u 1954 godini. Sarajevo, Štamparski zavod "Veselin Masleša," 1955. 100 p. illus. 24cm.
"Separat iz Glasnika Vrhovnog islamskog starješinstva za 1955 g."

1. Muhammadanism--Pilgrimages.

NL 0424321 NN

Ljubunčić, Salih Slav 8238.82.35
Davorin Trstenjak, 1848-1921; studija. Zagreb, Tisak Nadb.skupske tiskare, 1931
102 p. illus.

NL 0424322 MH

Ljubunčić, Salih.
Vidovićeva škola kao kulturno-etički i socijalno pedagoški pokret. Napisao Salih Ljubunčić. Sarajevo: Štamparija "Obod," 1925. 150 p. front. (port.), illus. 8°. (Nakladna biblioteka "Uzgajatelj." Knjiga 1.)

1. Vidovićeva škola za uzgoj odraslih. 2. Vidović, Miljenko, 1884- 3. Education, Adult—Jugoslavia.
N. Y. P. L. March 8, 1927

NL 0424323 NN

Ljubušak, Mehmed, beg Kapetanovič-
see Kapetanovič, Mehmed, bey, 1839-1902.

Bonaparte Collection No. 13,190
Ljubuški, Lovrjenc.
Grammatica latino-illyrica ex Emmanuelis; aliorumque approbatorum grammaticorum libris, juventuti illyricæ studiosè accommodata... Venetiis,1742.

NL 0424325 ICN

D766 .6 .A2L5
Ljudi i događaji koji se ne zaboravljaju. Zagreb, Novinarsko izdavačko poduzeće [1953]-
v. illus. 20 cm.
Vols. 1- edited by Slava Ogrizović.

1. Yugoslavia—Hist.—Axis occupation, 1941-1945. I. Ogrizović, Slava, ed.
D766.6.A2L5 59-41396 ‡

NL 0424326 DLC CaBVaU

Ljudi na radilištima; knjiga reportaža. Zagreb, Glas rada, 1950.
142 p. illus. 20 cm. (Graditelji socijalizma)

1. Labor and laboring classes—Yugoslavia.
HD8631.L5 55-27420 ‡

NL 0424327 DLC

Ljudska fronta. leto 1- avg. 1949-
[V Ljubljani]
v. in tables. 23 cm. monthly.
Organ of Zvezni odbor za organizacijska vprašanja of the Ljudska fronta Jugoslavije.
Vols. 1- called also no. 1-

1. Narodni front Jugoslavije—Period. I. Narodni front Jugoslavije. Savezni odbor za organizaciona pitanja.
JN9679.A5N38 58-45877

NL 0424328 DLC

Ljudska fronta Jugoslavije
see Narodni front Jugoslavije.

HQ799 Y8L5
Ljudska mladina Slovenije.
[Izvestje kongresa]
Ljubljana.
v. illus., ports. 17 cm.

1. Youth—Slovenia—Congresses.
HQ799.Y8L5 57-48872

NL 0424330 DLC

AP215 .S55M5
Ljudska mladina Slovenije.
Mlada pota.
[Ljubljana]

HQ799 .Y82S6
Ljudska mladina Slovenije.
Mladina.
Ljubljana.

Ljudska mladina Slovenije.
Od Doboja do Banjaluke: mladinska proga 1951. Ljubljana, CK LMS, 1951.
66 p. illus. 30 cm.

I. Title.
HQ799.Y8L53 58-33904

NL 0424333 DLC

HQ799 Y82S63
Ljudska mladina Slovenije.
Priročnik za mlade aktiviste.
[Ljubljana]

Ljudska mladina Slovenije.
III. [i. e. Treti] Kongres. Ljubljana, Mladinska knj., 1947.
115 p. illus., ports. 20 cm.

1. Youth—Slovenia—Congresses.
HQ799.Y8L54 70-264376

NL 0424335 DLC

HX 8 .L 79
LJUDSKA PRAVICA; GLASILO KOMUNISTIČNE PARTIJE Slovenije,leto 7,1943. Ponatis ilegalnih izdaj ob peti obletnici Osvobodilne fronte. Ljubljana Cankarjeva založba,1946.
133 p. illus.,facsims.

1. Communism--Slovenia--Period.

NL 0424336 InU MH

DR381 .S6L5
Ljudska prosveta. leto 1- jan. 4, 1952-
Ljubljana [Ljudska prosveta Slovenije]
v. illus., ports. 30 cm. biweekly.
Journal of Zveza ljudskoprosvetnih društev.

1. Slovenia—Intellectual life—Period. I. Zveza ljudskoprosvetnih društev.
DR381.S6L5 58-34592

NL 0424337 DLC

AP58 .S55O2
Ljudska prosveta.
Obzornik; mesečnik za ljudsko prosveto.
V Ljubljani, Ljudska prosveta.

Ljudska republika Slovenija
see Slovenia (*Federated Republic, 1945-*)

Ljudska študentska mladina Ljubljanske univerze
see
Ljubljana. Univerza. *Ljudska študentska mladina.*

Ljudska tehnika Slovenije.
1. [i. e. Prvi] kongres Ljudske tehnike Slovenije, Ljubljana 17.-18. vi. 1950. [Ljubljana, 1950]
16 p. illus. 20 cm.

1. Technology—Slovenia.
T26.S52L5 59-34612 ‡

NL 0424341 DLC

Ljudska uprava. letnik 1-11; 1948-58. Ljubljana.
11 v. 25 cm. monthly.
Issued by various agencies of the Izvršni svet of the Ljudska skupščina of Slovenia.
Superseded by Javna uprava.

1. Slovenia—Pol. & govt.—Period. I. Slovenia (Federated Republic, 1945-) Izvršni svet.
JN9679.S6L5 58-24874 rev

NL 0424342 DLC MH-L CU

VOLUME 337

HV7551 .L55

Ljudski miličnik. (Ml. 4 C; 1951-52)
Ljubljana.
(2)v. in(1) illus., ports., maps. 52 cm.
Frequency varies.
Published 1948-52.
Journal of Ljudska milica Slovenije.
(L.C. set incomplete: v.1-3 and scatter issues wanting.)

1. Police—Slovenia—Period. I. Slovenia (Federated Republic, 1945-) Ljudska milica.

HV7551.L55 59-54965

NL 0424343 DLC

Ljudski pravnik
see
Pravnik.

Ljung, Anders Scan 3049.2
Ur Falkenbergs stads historia. [Halmstad, Tidn. Hallands boktr., 1945]
355 p. illus.

NL 0424345 MH

Ljung, Erik W.
... Studier och iakttagelser rörande rågodling, rågförädling och lokala sortförsök. Reseberättelse af Erik W. Ljung. Malmö, Skånska lith. aktiebolaget, 1909.
35 p. 23cm. (Meddelanden från Kungl. landtbruksstyrelsen. n:r 142. n:r 2 år 1909)

1. Rye.

Agr 10-583

Library, U. S. Dept. of Agriculture 11Sw3 no. 142

NL 0424346 DNAL

Ljung, Harvey Albert. Chapel Hill, 1928
Reduction of nitro-compounds.

NL 0424347 NcU

Ljung, Harvey Albert.
A system of qualitative analysis for the anions. Chapel Hill, 1931.
53 p. tables, Q.
Thesis (Ph.D.) - University of North Carolina, 1931.
Carbon copy of typewritten manuscript.
Bibliography: p. 53.
N.C.-Univ.-Theses.

NL 0424348 NcU

Ljung, Ragnar, ed.
I Värmland; läsebok för skolor, cirklar och resenärer. Utgiven av Ragnar Ljung och Bengt Redell. [Karlstad, Nermans Trycksaker, 1950]
403p. illus.

Swedish.

NL 0424349 OCl PPAmSwA

DL991 .A7L54

Ljung, Sven, 1906–
Arboga stads historia. Arboga [Tryckt hos Arboga boktr., 1949–
v. illus., maps (1 fold.) 26 cm. (Stadsmonografier utg. i samarbete med Institutet för folklivsforskning, Stockholm, v. 2:A)
Bibliography: v. 1, p. 406–413.
CONTENTS.—1. delen. Tiden intill 1551. Med ett byggnadshistoriskt bidrag av Bengt Söderberg.

1. Arboga, Sweden. (Series: Stadsmonografier, v. 2:A)
Full name: Sven Johan Gustaf Ljung.

A 50-7749

Minnesota. Univ. Libr. for Library of Congress [3]

NL 0424350 MnU MH NN

LJUNG, Sven, 1906 -
Erik Jöransson Tegel. En biografisk-historiografisk studie. Lund 1939. 8:o.
XIX, 234 s.
Diss. Lund. phil.

NL 0424351 ICRL

Ljung, Sven, 1906–
Erik Jöransson Tegel; en biografisk-historiografisk studie, av Sven Ljung. Lund, A.-b. Gleerupska univ.-bokhandeln [1939]
xix, 234 p. 25½cm.
"Källor och litteratur": p. [viii]–xix.

1. Tegel, Erik Göransson, 1560?–1636.
[Full name: Sven Johan Gustaf Ljung]

A C 40-954

New York. Public library for Library of Congress [2]

NL 0424352 NN CtY ViU MH

DL991 .S595L4

Ljung, Sven, 1906–
Söderköpings historia. Söderköping, S:t Ragnhilds gille, 1949–
v. illus., map. 25 cm. (Stadsmonografier utg. i samarbete med Institutet för folklivsforskning, Stockholm, v. 1:A)
Bibliography: v. 1, pt. [vii]–xvii.
CONTENTS.—1. delen. Tiden till 1568. Med ett byggnadshistoriskt bidrag av Sigurd Erixon.

1. Söderköping, Sweden. (Series: Stadsmonografier, v. 1:A)
Full name: Sven Johan Gustaf Ljung.

A 50-7750

Minnesota. Univ. Libr. for Library of Congress [3]

NL 0424353 MnU DLC ICU NN MH

JS6275 .A3A3 1929

Ljung, Sven, 1906-

Stockholm. *Rådet.*
Stockholms stads tänkebok 1524–29 m. m., av m:r Olauus Petri Phase, utg. genom Ludvig Larsson. Lund, C. Bloms boktr., 1929–40.

Ljung, Sven, 1906-
Uppsala under yngre medeltid och Vasatid. [Uppsala, Almqvist & Wiksell, 1954]
xiii,463 p. 26cm. (Uppsala, Sweden. Historiekommittén. Uppsala stads historia. 2)

Bibliography, p. 433-443.

NL 0424355 NN MH

Ljung, W., joint author.
Bersell, Anders Olof, 1853–1903.
Församlingsskolans läsebok. Utarb. af A. O. Bersell under medverkan af S. P. A. Lindahl och W. Ljung. Rock Island, Ill., The Lutheran Augustana book concern [°1890]

Ljungberg, Ann Margret Dahlquist-
see Dahlquist-Ljungberg, Ann Margret, 1915–

DL971 .U5L5

Ljungberg, Axel.
Uppländska bilder. [En bilderbok om Uppland utg. i anslutning till Upsala sparbanks 125-årsjubileum] Uppsala, 1955.
107 p. (chiefly illus. (part col.)) 30 cm.

1. Uppland, Sweden—Descr. & trav.—Views. I. Title.

A 56-3863

Minnesota. Univ. Libr. for Library of Congress [3]

NL 0424358 MnU DLC

Ljungberg, Bror Edvard
see Ljungberg, Edvard, 1905–

Ljungberg, Carl Fredrik.
Svenska språkets redighet. Strängnäs, Tryckt af L.A. Collin, 1756.
199 p. 17 cm.
Contents.-Orthographia, skrifsätt. - Etymologia, skiljesätt. - Syntaxi, bindesätt. - Prosodia, rimsätt.
1. Swedish language - Grammar.

NL 0424360 CU

Ljungberg, Carl Fredr. August, respondent.
Om arten af Molieres lustspel ...
see under Hagberg, Jakob Theodor, 1825-1893, praeses.

Ljungberg, Cecilia.
Ur fröken Ursulas skrin; dikter i obunden form... Stockholm, A. Bonnier [1939]
139 p. 20cm.

NL 0424362 MnU

Ljungberg, Edvard, 1905–
On the reabsorption of chlorides in the kidney of rabbit. Lund, H. Ohlssons boktr., 1947.
189 p. illus. 24 cm.
Akademisk avhandling—Lund.
Extra t.-p., with thesis statement, inserted.
Translated by Maja Abdon.
"Also appears as Supplementum [186] to Acta medica Scandinavica."
"References": p. [184]–189.

1. Kidneys. 2. Chlorides—Physiological effect. I. Abdon, Maja, tr.
Full name: Bror Edvard Ljungberg.

QP211.L52 1947 612.46 49-13829*

NL 0424363 DLC ViU

Ljungberg, Edvard, 1905–
On the reabsorption of chlorides in the kidney of rabbit. Lund, H. Ohlssons boktr., 1947.
189 p. illus. 24 cm. (Acta medica Scandinavica. Supplementum 186)
Translated by Maja Abdon.
Issued also as thesis, Lund.
"References": p. [184]–189.

1. Kidneys. 2. Chlorides—Physiological effect. I. Abdon, Maja, tr. (Series)
Full name: Bror Edvard Ljungberg.

612.46 A 49-1050*

John Crerar Library for Library of Congress [1]

NL 0424364 ICJ OU

Ljungberg, Einar, 1880 -
Carl Michael Bellman som nykterhetsvän och skönhetsapostel. Stockholm, Ljungbergs förlag [1927]
124 p. illus.

1. Bellman, Carl Michael, 1740-1795.

NL 0424365 WaU NN CU MnU

Ljungberg, Einar, 1880–
Olyckliga från fängelser, sjukhus, krogar och natthärbergen. [Stockholm, Frams förlag (i distribution), 1915]
62 p. illus. 20 cm.
L. C. copy replaced by microfilm.
——— Microfilm.
Microfilm 28722 PT

I. Title.

[PT9875.L6367O4] 75-21215

NL 0424366 DLC

VOLUME 337

HX 337 L55 A3
Ljungberg, Einar, 1880–
På uppviglarstråt; färdminnen av Texas [pseud.] Stockholm, Fram [1917]
58p. 20cm.

1. Socialists, Swedish I. Title

NL 0424367 WU

Ljungberg, Einar, 1880–
Den sköna synderskan; Stockholmsroman från våra dagar. Stockholm, Ljungbergs förlag ₍1930₎
271 p.

NL 0424368 WaU

Ljungberg, Eva.
Något om diakoniss-werksamheten, af E. L. Helsingfors, Folkupplysnings-sällskapet, 1889.
37 p. 19 cm. (Folkupplysnings-sällskapets skrifter, 66)

1. Deaconesses—Finland. I. E. L. II. L., E. III. Title. IV. Series: Kansanvalistusseura. Skrifter, 66.

BV4423.L58 77-262278

NL 0424369 DLC

Ljungberg, Eva.
Systrar. Helsingfors, Söderström ₍1905₎
122 p.

NL 0424370 WaU

839.7369 L789R
Ljungberg, Eva Charlotta, 1850-1919.
Raumo historier och andra berättelser. Helsingfors, Söderström, 1910-11.
2 v. 20 cm.

NL 0424371 NcD MH

TP315 .I 55
Ljungberg, Gregory, 1907- ed.

Ingeniörsvetenskapsakademien, *Stockholm.*
IVA:s försöksstation; ett nytt laboratorium vid Drottning Kristinas väg avsett för bränsletekniskt forskning. Utg. med anledning av Ingeniörsvetenskapsakademiens tjugofemte högtidsdag den 24 oktober 1944. ₍Redaktör: Gregory Ljungberg. Stockholm₎ 1944.

Ljungberg, Hans, *comp.*
Typografisk ordlista; facktuttryck på svenska, tyska, engelska och franska. 3. omarb. och väsentligt utökade uppl. Stockholm, Bröderna Lagerström, 1948.
134 p. 22 cm. (Nordisk boktryckarekonsts fackbibliotek, 7)

1. Printing—Dictionaries—Polyglot. 2. Dictionaries, Polyglot. I. Title. (Series)

Z118.L7 1948 50-19369

NL 0424373 DLC MH PU IU

WB 34591
Ljungberg, Helge, 1904-
Ansgar och Björkö. Stockholm, Svenska Kyrkans Diakonistyrelses Bokförlag [1945]
181 p. illus.

1. Ansgar, Saint, Abp. of Hamburg and Bremen, 801-865. 2. Björko, Sweden (Uppland) cdu

NL 0424374 CtY MnU

4DL 102
Ljungberg, Helge, 1904-
Fornnordisk livsåskådning. Stockholm, Föreningen Norden, KF:s bokförlag i distribution, 1943.
44 p.

(Nordens serie, 4)

NL 0424375 DLC-P4 MH

BR 1014 .L5
Ljungberg, Helge, 1904-
Hur kristendomen kom till Sverige. Stockholm, A. Bonnier ₍1946₎
58 p. 18 cm. (in binder, 19 cm.) (Studentföreningen verdandis småskrifter, nr. 485)

1. Sweden - Church hist. I. Title

NL 0424376 WU MH

Ljungberg, Helge, 1904–
Die nordische Religion und das Christentum; Studien über den nordischen Religionswechsel zur Wirkingerzeit. Aus dem Schwedischen übers. von Hilko Wiardo Schomerus. Gütersloh, C. Bertelsmann, 1940.
vii, 325 p. 24 cm.
Bibliographical footnotes.

1. Scandinavia—Church history. 2. Scandinavia—Religion. I. Title.
Full name: Helge David Ljungberg.

BR974.L615 274.8 48-42508*‡

NL 0424377 DLC NIC NNC DCU OCU

Ljungberg, Helge, 1904–
... Den nordiska religionen och kristendomen; studier över det nordiska religionsskiftet under vikingatiden av Helge Ljungberg. Stockholm, H. Geber; Köpenhamn, Levin & Munksgaard ₍1938₎
ix, 342 p. illus. (map) 24cm. (Nordiska texter och undersökningar, utgivna i Uppsala av Bengt Hesselman. 11)
Akademisk avhandling—Uppsala.
Added t.-p., with thesis note, inserted.
"Bibliografi": p. ₍317₎–342.

1. Scandinavia—Church history. 2. Scandinavia—Religion. I. Title.
₍*Full name:* Helge David Ljungberg₎

Library of Congress PD1513.N64 vol. 11 40-30447
₍2₎ (439.5082) 274.8

NL 0424378 DLC MnU FMU NcD NjP IU

Ljungberg, Helge, 1904–
Tor; undersökningar i indoeuropeisk och nordisk religionshistoria. Uppsala, Lundequistska bokhandeln ₍1947–
v. illus. 25 cm. (Uppsala universitets årsskrift 1947: 9
Summary in French.
CONTENTS.—1. Den nordiske åskguden och besläktade indoeuropeiska gudar. Den nordiske åskguden i bild och myt.
1. Thor. 2. Mythology, Aryan. 3. Mythology, Norse. (Series: Uppsala. Universitet. Årsskrift, 1947: 9)
Full name: Helge David Ljungberg.

AS284.U7 1947, no. 9, etc. A 49-3883*

Minnesota. Univ. Libr. for Library of Congress ₍2₎†

NL 0424379 MnU MoU PU NIC IEG TxU DLC

4PT Swed.- 118
Ljungberg, Helge, 1904-
Vara högtider, text av Helge Ljungberg, originallitografier av Björn Jonson. Stockholm, L. Hökerberg [1948]
125 p.

NL 0424380 DLC-P4

Ljungberg, K₍arl₎ E₍dvard₎ 1820–
La Suède, son développement moral, industriel & commercial; d'après des documents officiels par C.-E. Ljungberg ... Tr. par L. de Lilliehöök ... Paris, Impr. de Dubuisson et cᵉ, 1867.
vi, ₍7₎-176 p., 1 l. tables. 25cm.

1. Sweden—Economic conditions. I. Lilliehöök, L. de, tr.
4-19675

Library of Congress HC375.L78

NL 0424381 DLC CtY NcD MiU MH

Ljungberg, Kurt.
Mozart-musik i musikcirkeln; studiehandledning för instrumentalcirklar, sångkörer och lyssnarcirklar. ₍Göteborg₎ Godtemplarordens studieförbund ₍1955₎
23 p. 19 cm.

1. Mozart, Johann Chrysostom Wolfgang Amadeus, 1756-1791. 2. Mozart, Johann Chrysostom Wolfgang Amadeus—Bibl. I. Title.

ML410.M9L45 56-27669 ‡

NL 0424382 DLC

Ljungberg, Kurt.
Musikorientering; en kortfattad framställning av musikens historia och den musikaliska formläran. Stockholm, Ehlin ₍1950₎
192 p. illus., ports., music. 19 cm. (Folkbildningsserien)

1. Music—Hist. & crit. 2. Music—Sweden—Hist. & crit. 3. Music—Manuals, text-books, etc. I. Title.

ML160.L66 A 51-2093 rev

Oregon. Univ. Library for Library of Congress ₍r51b1₎†

NL 0424383 OrU DLC

Ljungberg, Laurentius, respondent.
Dissertatio de Christianae religionis in Svecia initiis et effectibus...
see under Fant, Erik Mikael, 1754-1817, praeses.

Ljungberg, Laurentius, respondent.
Dissertatio de Georgio Petri Salaemontano...
see under Fant, Erik Mikael, 1754-1817, praeses.

DL644 .Z52L7
LJUNGBERG, LEIF TORE BERTIL, 1900–
Malmösläkten Bergh, personhistoriska anteckningar, utgivna av Leif Ljungberg och Th. C. Bergh. ₍Malmo, Lundgrens Söners, 1936₎ 132p. Illus. Ports. Map.

NL 0424386 InU

Ljungberg, Leif Tore Bertil, 1900–
Ur djupa källarvalven; kulturhistoriska skisser från Malmö och annorstädes. ₍Redigerad av Einar Bager₎ Malmö, Sydsvenska dagbladet ₍1950₎
150 p. illus., ports. 26 cm.
"Leif Ljungberg ägnas denna hyllning på 50-årsdagen den 11. april 1950 av vänner till honom och hans gärning."

1. Malmö, Sweden—Civilization. 2. Sweden—Civilization. I. Title.

DL991.M2L5 51-24530

NL 0424387 DLC NN

QH9 .T6 no. 204-205 Rare bk. coll.
Ljungberg, Nils Jonas, 1793-1870, respondent.
Thunberg, Karl Peter, 1743-1828, *praeses.*
De plantis venenatis ... Upsaliæ, excudebant Regiæ academiæ typographi ₍1822₎

Ljungberg, Nils Wilhelm, 1818-1872.
Chronologie de la vie de Jésus. Deux études. Lund: Imprimerie Derling. 1878.
1/2 Cloth: xii. 94.

NL 0424389 ICMcC

Ljungberg, Nils Wilhelm, 1818–1872.
Die hebräische Chronologie von Saul bis zur babylonischen Gefangenschaft, von N. W. Ljungberg. Braunschweig: F. Bosse, 1922. xv, 46 p. 8°.

SCHIFF COLLECTION.
137611A. 1. Bible.—Old Testament. —Chronology.
N. Y. P. L. October 6, 1924

NL 0424390 NN PPDrop MH

VOLUME 337

LJUNGBERG, Nils Wilhelm, 1818-1872.
Ny kritisk bearbetning af Livius och Horatii Oder, anmäld och genom upplysande prof askadliggjord af N.W.Ljungberg. Göteborg. Heldung & Lindskog,1858.

pp.96.
Aftryck ur Goteborgs Kongl.Vetenskaps-och Vitterhets-Samhälles Handlingar, 4, de hälftet.

NL 0424391 MH

P 27 .L 5 1918

Ljungberg, Nils Wilhelm, 1818-1872.
Ur Nils Wilhelm Ljungbergs ... Efterlämnade papper ... Lund, C. W. K. Gleerups förlag [1918-
v. front. (ports.) 27½cm.
Bibliographical references included in footnotes.
1. Chronology, Roman. 2. Roman emperors. I. Wulff, Fredrik Amadeus, 1845-1930, ed. II. Title: De romerska kejsarnas kronologi.

NL 0424392 MdBJ

Ljungberg, Olof.
Beskattning av inkomst av skogsbruk [av] Olof Ljungberg. Lagstiftningen om skogskonto [av] Carl Åbjörnsson. [Stockholm] Taxeringsnämndsordförandenas riksförbund, 1954.
32 p. 24 cm. (Skattenytts skriftserie, 1)
Cover title.

1. Forests and forestry—Sweden—Taxation. I. Åbjörnsson, Carl. Lagstiftningen om skogskonto. II. Title. (Series)

56-21037

NL 0424393 DLC MH-L

Ljungberg, Petrus Adolphus, respondent.
Calculi variationum integralium...
see under Björling, Emanuel, Gabriel, 1808-1872, praeses.

Ljungberg, Petrus Ericus, respondent.
De vi et indole mythi oedipici...
see under Bergstedt, Carl Fredrik, 1817- praeses.

Ljungberg, Valdemar.
...Göteborgs befästningar och garnison. Göteborg: Göteborgs litografiska aktiebolag, 1924. 728 p. illus. (incl. maps), plans (1 col'd). 4°. (Gothenburg «city». Jubileumsutställningens publikationskommitté. Skrifter utgivna till Göteborgs stads trehundraårsjubileum. [bd.] 8.)
Cover date: 1926.

1. Fortifications—Sweden—Gothenburg. 2. Ser.
N. Y. P. L. September 13, 1927

NL 0424396 NN NNC

Ljungberg, Valdemar
Göteborgsporträtt [av] Valdemar Ljungberg och Evald E'son Uggla. Göteborg, Göteborgs litografiska aktiebolag, 1923.
223 p. illus. (Skrifter utgivna till Göteborgs stads trehundraarsjubileum genom Jubileumsutställningens publikationskommitté. 11)

No. 93 of 200 copies.

NL 0424397 NNC NN

Ljungberger, Erik.
... Carl Barcklind. Stockholm, H. W. Tullberg, 1916.
39 p. incl. ports. 24cm. (Sceniska konstnärer. [4])

1. Barcklind, Carl, 1873-

22-11071

Library of Congress PN2777.S4 vol. 4

NL 0424398 DLC

Ljungberger, Erik.
... Emma Meissner. Stockholm, H. W. Tullberg, 1916.
39 p. incl. ports. 24cm. (Sceniska konstnärer. [2])

1. Meissner, Fru Emma Olivia (Ekström) 1866-

22-11069

Library of Congress PN2777.S4 vol. 2

NL 0424399 DLC

Ljungberger, Erik.
... Harriet Bosse. Stockholm, H. W. Tullberg, 1917.
43 p. incl. ports. 24cm. (Sceniska konstnärer. [5])

1. Bosse, Fru Harriet Sofie, 1878-

22-11072

Library of Congress PN2777.S4 vol. 5

NL 0424400 DLC CU MnU MH

Ljungberger, Erik.
... John Forsell. Stockholm, H. W. Tullberg, 1916.
43 p. incl. ports. 24cm. (Sceniska konstnärer. [1])

1. *Forsell, John, 1868-

22-11068

Library of Congress PN2777.S4 vol. 1

NL 0424401 DLC

Ljungberger, Erik.
... Nils Personne. Stockholm, H. W. Tullberg, 1916.
43 p. incl. ports. 24cm. (Sceniska konstnärer. [3])

1. Personne, Nils Edvard, 1850-

22-11070

Library of Congress PN2777.S4 vol. 3

NL 0424402 DLC

[Ljungblad, Sverre G] ed.
Rudolf Nilsen, dikteren og mennesket. Oslo: Internasjonalt arbeiderforlag, 1936. 75 p. plates, ports. 24½cm.
Forord signed: Sverre G. Ljungblad.
CONTENTS.—Øverland, Arnulf. Ved Rudolf Nilsens båre.—Ljungblad, S. G. Rudolf Nilsen, dikteren og mennesket.—Hilt, Christian. Rudolf Nilsen, en revolusjonens sønn ok sanger.—Ljungblad, S. G. Rudolf Nilsen, et minnedikt.

877138A. 1. Nilsen, Rudolf, 1901-1929.
N. Y. P. L. April 21, 1937

NL 0424403 NN

Ljungblom (Carolus A.) *Tussis sciagraphia ætiologica. 1 p. l., 8 pp. 4°. Upsaliæ, 1823.

NL 0424404 DNLM

WX 2 GS8 L8L1a

LJUNGBY, Sweden. Länslasarettet
Årsberättelse.
Ljungby [1870?]-
v.

NL 0424405 DNLM

Ljungbyslākten Sandbergs släktförening.
Ljungbysläkten Sandberg; biografiska uppgifter till och med den 1. juli 1955. [4. uppl., redigerats av Sven Malmquist. Eslöv, 1955]
61 p. ports. 21 cm.

1. Sandberg family. I. Malmquist, Sven, ed.

CS929.S3 1955 57-42980

NL 0424406 DLC

Ljungdahl, Axel.
Studie över möjligheterna för hemortsbekämpning genom flygstridskrafter mot bakgrunden av erfarenheterna från det Andra världskriget. [Linköping, 1954]
125 p. illus. 21 cm.
Cover title: Luftkrig mot hemorten.
"Särtryck ur Kungl. Krigsvetenskapsakademiens handl. nr. 2, 1954."

1. Air warfare. 2. World War, 1939-1945—Aerial operations. I. Title. II. Title: Luftkrig mot hemorten.

UG630.L58 56-16333 ‡

NL 0424407 DLC

Ljungdahl, David.
Fjäriln vingad, svenska storfjärilar i färg efter originalmålningar av David Ljungdahl. [Stockholm] Sohlamns [1953]
50 plates.

NL 0424408 InLP

Ljungdahl, David, illus.
Nordström, Frithiof.
Svenska fjärilar; systematisk bearbetning av sveriges storfjärilar, *Macrolepidoptera*, av Frithiof Nordström och Einar Wahlgren i samarbete med och under redaktion av Albert Tullgren. Med 50 planscher efter originalmålningar av David Ljungdahl ... Stockholm, Aktiebolaget familjeboken [1935?-

---

Re24 0138 10

Ljungdahl, Gustaf Samuel, 1882 -
... Earth magnetic researches along the coasts of Sweden ... Stockholm, Statens reproduktionsanstalt, 1936-
v. maps, tables. 31cm. ([Sweden] Kungl. Sjökarteverket. Jordmagnetiska publikationer, nr.10)
"References": p.9.
Contents. - pt.I. Magnetic declination at the epoch July 1, 1929. -

NL 0424410 CtY

Ljungdahl, Gustaf Samuel, 1882-
... Jordmagnetisk översiktskarta över Sverige 1930...Magnetic general chart of Sweden, 1930. Stockholm, 1930.
cover-title, [4] p., incl. 3 charts. 31 cm. (Sweden. Sjökarteverket. Jordmagnetiska publikationer, nr. 7)
Text in Swedish and English in parallel columns.

NL 0424411 CtY DAS

Ljungdahl, Gustaf Samuel, 1882-
... Jordmagnetiska undersökningar i norra och mellersta sverige åren 1913-1921 ... English summary. Stockholm, Statens reproduktionsanstalt, 1925.
75 p., 1 l. illus. VI plates (fold.) in pocket on back cover. 20.5 cm. (Sweden. Sjökarteverket. Jordmagnetiska publikationer, nr. 4)

NL 0424412 CtY

VOLUME 337

Ljungdahl, Gustaf Samuel, 1882-
... Jordmagnetiska undersökningar i södra Sverige, åren 1917 och 1922 (with an English summary) av Gustaf S. Ljungdahl ... Magnetiska deklinationsbestämningar i Blekinge, åren 1914-1915, av Helge Odelsiö. Stockholm, 1924.
66 p. illus. 6 plates (5 fold.) 30.5 cm. (Sweden. Sjökarteverket. Jordmagnetiska publikationer, nr. 3)

NL 0424413 CtY

Re24 0158 13
Ljungdahl, Gustaf Samuel, 1882-
Magnetic measurements on the Kompass in the Baltic Sea 1938. Stockholm, Statens Reprodukt-tionsanstalt, 1940.
21p. illus., maps, tables. 31cm. (Sweden. Sjökarteverket. Jordmagnetiska publikationer, no.13)

NL 0424414 CtY

Ljungdahl, Gustaf Samuel, 1882-
...Magnetiska deklinationsbestämningar år 1919 på Gottland... Stockholm, 1922.
21 p. II pl. 31 cm. (Sweden. Sjökarteverket. Jordmagnetiska publikationer, nr. 1)

NL 0424415 CtY

Ljungdahl, Gustaf Samuel, 1882-
... Note on the average range of magnetic anomalies in Sweden, by Gustaf S. Ljungdahl ... [Uppsala, Almqvist & Wiksells boktryckeri-a.-b., 1936]
6 p. 2 illus. (charts) 23cm. (Arkiv för matematik, astronomi och fysik. bd. 25B, no 12)
Caption title.

NL 0424416 ICJ

Re24 0158 12
Ljungdahl, Gustaf Samuel, 1882-
The re-survey of the magnetic main repeat-stations in Sweden for the epoch July 1, 1936. Stockholm, Statens Reproduktionsanstalt, 1939.
25p. maps, tables. 31cm. (Sweden. Sjökarteverket. Jordmagnetiska publikationer, no. 12)

NL 0424417 CtY

Ljungdahl, Gustaf Samuel, 1882-
... Stormfloden i Skagerrak-Kattegat den 4 december 1914 och därmed sammanhängande vattenståndsfluktuationer. (The storm-flood in Skagerrak-Kattegat on December 4th, 1914 and connected fluctuations of water-level) ... Av Gustaf S. Ljungdahl. [Göteborg, W. Zachrissons boktryckeri a.-b., 1921]
cover-title, 7, [5] p. incl. tables. 14 pl. (maps, charts, diagrs.) on 7 l. 45 x 32cm.
Akademisk avhandling—Uppsala.
At head of title: Ur Svenska hydrografisk-biologiska kommissionens skrifter 1921.
Summary in English.
"Litteraturförteckning": p. [8]
1. Tides—Skagerrak. 2. Tides—Cattegat.
QB416.L5 47-36717

NL 0424418 DLC ICRL CtY IU PU

Ljungdahl, Gustaf Samuel, 1882-
Kartografiska sällskapet, *Stockholm.*
Sveriges kartläggning; en översikt, utg. av Kartografiska sällskapet. [Stockholm] Generalstabens litografiska anstalt [1922]

Ljungdahl, Gustaf Samuel, 1882-
... Undersökning av magnetiska deklinationen inom anomalierna vid Vänern, åren 1914, 1916 och 1917. (With an English summary) ... Stockholm, 1922.
28 p. illus. V pl. (incl. 1 fold.) 31 cm. (Sweden. Sjökarteverket. Jordmagnetiska publikationer, nr. 2)

NL 0424420 CtY

Ljungdahl, Johan, 1883-
...Krigargravarna i Trälleborg; ett minne från världskrigets dagar. Trälleborg: Tryckeri a.-b. Allehanda, 1932. 31 p. illus. 22cm.

787238A. 1. Cemeteries—Sweden—Trälleborg.
N. Y. P. L. November 8, 1935

NL 0424421 NN

Ljungdahl, Karl Gustaf, 1892-
Bränsle och kraft; orientering rörande Sveriges energiförsörjning. Publicerad på föranstaltande av Bränsleutredningen 1951. Stockholm, Gummessons boktr., 1951.
72 p. 24 cm. (Statens offentliga utredningar 1951: 32)
At head of title: Handelsdepartementet.

1. Power resources—Sweden. I. Title. (Series: Sweden. Statens offentliga utredningar 1951: 32)
J406.R15 1951: 32 55-31092 rev

NL 0424422 DLC

QV 740 GS8 L7r 1953
LJUNGDAHL, Malte, ed.
Recepthandbok på grundval av de nordiska ländernas farmakopéer, utarb. av Malte Ljungdahl, under medverkan av Eric Flodmark [och] Karin Östberg. [Malmö] Gleerup [1953]
658 p.
1. Formularies Title

NL 0424423 DNLM

Ljungdahl, Malte.
Untersuchungen über die arteriosklerose des kleinen kreislaufs; aus der medizinischen Universitätsklinik zu Lund, von Malte Ljungdahl ... mit einem vorwort von prof. K. Petren, Lund; mit 17 abbildungen auf tafel I-IV. Wiesbaden, J. F. Bergmann, 1915.
vi p., 1 l., 106 p. IV pl. 26cm.
"Literaturverzeichnis": p. [189]-194.

1. Arteries—Diseases. [1. Arteriosclerosis] 2. [Sclerosis, Pulmonary]
Library, U. S. Surgeon-General's Office S G 18-206

NL 0424424 DNLM CtY ICJ PPC OC1W-H ICRL

BL 225 L54
Ljungdahl, O
Naturens evangelium, och Skapelsesagor, af O. Ljungdahl. [Stockholm] Frihetsförbundets förlog [1908]
31p. 20cm.

1. Natural theology 2. Creation I. Title II. Title: Skapelsesagor

NL 0424425 WU

Ljungdahl, Samuel Laurentius.
De transeundi generibus, quibus utitur Isocrates, commentatio. Scripsit Samuel Ljungdahl... Upsaliae: Typis exscripserunt Edquist et Berglund, 1871. 70 p. 8°. (Upsala. Universitet. Upsala universitets årsskrift. Philosophi, språkvetenskap och historiska vetenskaper. 1871, [nr.] 3.)

Latin and Greek text.
Bibliography, p. 7.

1. Isocrates.
N. Y. P. L. March 29, 1927

NL 0424426 NN NIC CtY NjP PBm ICRL

Ljungdahl, Samuel Laurentius, respondent.
Paroeclae thorstunensis antiquarie
see under Berggren, Jonas.

Ljungdal, Arnold, 1901- comp.
Ett decennium ung svensk lyrik; antologi sammanställd av Arnold Ljungdal. Stockholm, Universal press [1935]
166, [4] p., 2 l. 22 x 18cm.

1. Swedish poetry (Collections) I. Title.
[Full name: Arnold Gottfrid Ljungdal]
36-35893
Library of Congress PT9583.L5
[2] 839.7160822

NL 0424428 DLC MnU IEN

Ljungdal, Arnold, 1901-
Fanorna; dikter. Stockholm, Bonnier [1928]
72 p. 20cm.

Full name: Arnold Gottfred Ljungdal.

NL 0424429 WU

Ljungdal, Arnold, 1901-
Farväl till Don Juan; roman. Stockholm, Wahlström & Widstrand [1941]
301 p. 21cm.

Full name: Arnold Gottfried Ljungdal

NL 0424430 WU

Ljungdal, Arnold, 1901-
Katedral; dikter. Stockholm, Norstedt [1950]
98 p. 23 cm.

I. Title. *Full name:* Arnold Gottfried Ljungdal.
A 51-3893
Minnesota. Univ. Libr. for Library of Congress [1]

NL 0424431 MnU NN MH

Ljungdal, Arnold, 1901-
Kulturen i fara, av Arnold Ljungdal. Stockholm, A. Bonnier [1927]
108 p., 1 l. 19½cm.
CONTENT.—Marx och Spengler.—Socialismen som kulturuppgift.—Erövringen av maskinerna.—Modern kollektivpsykologi.—Folkets teater och arbetarnas.—Den nya svenska dikten och tiden.—Ur Amerikas moderna lyrik.—Ny tysk diktning.—Diktaren bakom fängelsemurarna.—Cement—romanen om det nya Ryssland.—Marxism och religion.—Teologi och modern religiositet.—Moderna religionssurrogat.—Professor Böök och pingströrelsen.
1. Literature—Addresses, essays, lectures. 2. Socialism—Addresses, essays, lectures. I. Title.
[Full name: Arnold Gottfrid Ljungdal]
35-25225
Library of Congress PN516.L57 [839.746] 804

NL 0424432 DLC

Ljungdal, Arnold, 1901-
Lyriskt bokslut; ett dikturval. Stockholm, Steinsviks bokförlag [1945]
127 p.

NL 0424433 WaU

Ljungdal, Arnold, 1901-
Marxismens världsbild. Stockholm, P. A. Norstedt [1947]
337 p. 20 cm.
"Litteratur": p. 324-332.

1. Socialism. 2. Dialectic (Economics) I. Title.
Full name: Arnold Gottfried Ljungdal.
HX56.L58 335 48-18259*

NL 0424434 DLC NN

PT9875 L62M6 1927
Ljungdal, Arnold, 1901-
Morgonrodnad, skådespel i fem akter. Stockholm, A. Bonnier [1927]
156 p. [Svenska teatern, n:r 408]

NL 0424435 CU NN

VOLUME 337

Ljungdal, Arnold, 1901 -
...Tiden och tron, av Arnold Ljungdal... Stockholm: A. Bonnier [, 1926]. 99 p. 12°. (Bonniers små handböcker i vetenskapliga ämnen.)

Bibliography, p. 99.

1. Faith.
N. Y. P. L. June 15, 1927

NL 0424436 NN

Ljungdal, Arnold, 1901 -
...Till den nya tiden; dikter. Stockholm: Tidens förlag, 1926. 121 p. 12°.

1. Poetry, Swedish. 2. Drama, Swedish.
N. Y. P. L. June 15, 1927

NL 0424437 NN MH

PT9875
.L637T5

Ljungdal, Arnold, 1901-
Till mänska klarnad; dikter. Stockholm, Norstedt [1953]
92 p. 23 cm.

I. Title.
Full name: Arnold Gottfrid Ljungdal.
A 54-2
Minnesota. Univ. Libr. for Library of Congress [2]

NL 0424438 MnU DLC

Ljungdal, Arnold, 1901 -
...Trå kvinnospel. Malmö: Aktiebolaget Framtidens Bokförlag [1922]. 55 p. 12°.

Contents: Uppgörelse, drama i en akt. Simson och Delila, en fabel om dikt och kvinnan.

1. Drama, Swedish. 2. Title. 3. Title: Uppgörelse. 4. Title: Simson och Delila.
N. Y. P. L. January 14, 1925

NL 0424439 NN

Ljungdal, Arnold, 1901-
Ungdom; dikter. Stockholm, A. Bonnier [1931]
77 p. sm. 4°.

NL 0424440 MH

PN
511
L55
MAIN

Ljungdell, Ragna.
Det oforstorbara; studier, skisser, profiler. Stockholm, New York, Ljus [1945]
279p. 20cm.

1. Literature, Modern - Addresses, essays, lectures. 2. Women as authors. I. Title.

NL 0424441 TxU

Ljungdell, Ragna, *ed.*
Modern finsk lyrik, ett urval i svensk tolkning jämte inledning. Stockholm, A. Bonnier [1947]
186 p. 20 cm.

1. Finnish poetry—Translations into Swedish. 2. Swedish poetry—Translations from Finnish. I. Title.

PH401.S3L5 49-28540*

NL 0424442 DLC NN MnU

Ljungdorff, Per Johan Vilhelm
see Ljungdorff, Vilhelm, 1876-

Ljungdorff, Vilhelm, 1876-
E. T. A. Hoffmann och ursprunget till hans konstnärskap, af V. Ljungdorff. Lund, Gleerupska univ.-bokhandeln [1924]
431, [2] p., 2 l. 21½cm.

Akademisk avhandling—Lund.
Extra t.-p., with thesis note, inserted.
"Litteratur": p. [429]-431.

1. Hoffmann, Ernst Theodor Amadeus, 1776-1822.
[Full name: Per Johan Vilhelm Ljungdorff]
36-30127
Library of Congress PT2361.Z5L5 1924
[2] 928.3

NL 0424444 DLC CtY MiU ICU NjP

Ljunge, Andreas Peter
see
Liunge, Andreas Peter, 1798-1879

Ljungerud, Ivar.
Zur Nominalflexion in der deutschen Literatursprache nach 1900. Lund, C. W. K. Gleerup [1955]
350 p. 25 cm. (Lunder germanistische Forschungen, 31)

Bibliography: p. [336]-340.

1. German language—Inflection. (Series)

PF3171.L5 56-19870

NL 0424446 ICU NcD NN ViU OU MU RPB GU TU CU-S DLC CaBVaU NbU MoU CSt FTaSU OCU CU TxU

Ljungfelt, Joel, 1870-
Med m/s Annie Johnson från Göteborg till Centralamerika och Nordamerikas Pacifik-kust. Efter dagboksanteckningar, av Joel Ljungfelt... Lund: C.-W. Lindströms bokhandel [1936] 167 p. illus. (incl. ports.), map. 22½cm.

877238A. 1. Pacific coast—Descr. and trav. 2. Panama—Descr. and trav., 1900- . 3. West Indies—Descr. and trav., 1900- . 4. England—Descr. and trav., 1914- .
N. Y. P. L. April 20, 1937

NL 0424447 NN MnHi

Ljungfors, Åke.
Bidrag till svensk diplomatik före 1350. Lund, C. W. K. Gleerup [1955]
xxviii, 234 p. facsims., tables. 24 cm.

Akademisk avhandling—Lund.
Extra t. p., with thesis statement, inserted.
Bibliography: p. xv-xxvi.

1. Sweden—Hist.—Sources. 2. Diplomatics. I. Title.

CD79.S8L5 56-29139

NL 0424448 DLC WaU MiU NNC MnU CtY NN

Ljungfors, Vilhelm.
Helsingborgs-Landskrona nation i Lund under professor Martin Weibulls inspektorat; biografiska anteckningar. Lund, Skånska centraltryckeriet, 1903. x,185 p. port. 22cm.

1. Lund, Sweden. Universitet—Registers. 2. Sweden—Biog. I. Lund, Sweden. Universitet. Helsingborgs-Landskrona nation.

NL 0424449 NN

Ljungfors, Vilhelm.
Svenska släkter. Under medverkan af Personhistoriska Samfundet utgifna af V. Ljungfors. Heft Lund: H. Ohlsson, 19 v. 8°.

Title from cover.

1. Genealogy, Sweden. 2. Personhistoriska Samfundet.
N. Y. P. L. September 17, 1913.

NL 0424450 NN

Ljunggirst, J.E.
Meastermyr in vaextikologisk studie, 1914.
Uppsala Univ. Ph.D. Diss. 1914.

NL 0424451 PU

WCA
L791f
1867

LJUNGGREN, Alrik, 1827-
Fall af visceral-syfilis. Stockholm, Haeggström, 1867.
128 p.
Afhandling såsom specimen för e. o. professionen i syfilidologi - Karolinska institutet, Stockholm.

NL 0424452 DNLM

W 4
U68
1865

LJUNGGREN, Alrik, 1827-
Försök till en kritisk framställning af de olika methoderna att behandla syphilis. 1. afd. Inledning, eller en kort framställning öfver de vigtigaste lärorna om syphilis nosologi och pathologi. Stockholm, Nisbeth, 1865.
79 p.
On cover: Behandlings - methoderna mot syphilis. 1. häftet. Inledning.
No more published?

Afhandling - Uppsala.
Without thesis statement.
Published also under title: Studier i syfilidologi.

NL 0424454 DNLM

Ljunggren (Alrik) [1827-]. *Studier e syphilidologi. [Upsal.] 79 pp. 8°. Stockholm, H. Nisbeth, 1865.

NL 0424455 DNLM

Ljunggren, Anders Ragnar Sigurd
see
Ljunggren, Ragnar, 1889-

Ljunggren, Carl August, 1860 -
Om bruket af sig och sin i svenskan; historisk framställning. Lund, Gleerup, 1901

NL 0424457 MH

Ljunggren, Carl August, 1860-
Om käksvulster med ursprung ifrån tandepitelgroddlisten. ... Af Carl Aug. Ljunggren ... Med 4 taflor och 16 autotypier. Stockholm, Kungl. boktryckeriet P. A. Norstedt & söner, 1894.
[2], 97 p. illus., 4 pl. (part double). 23½cm.
Akademisk afhandling—Lund.
Published also in Nordiskt medicinskt arkiv, årg. 1895.
Bibliographical foot-notes.

NL 0424458 ICJ DNLM

Ljunggren, Carl August, 1860-
The poetical gender of the substantives in the works of Ben Jonson ... Lund, Collin & Zickerman, 1892.
1 p. l., 62 p., 1 l. 27cm.
Thesis—Lund.

1. Jonson, Ben, 1573?-1637. 2. English language—Gender. I. Title.

Library of Congress PR2646.L5 15-16818

NL 0424459 DLC OCl

VOLUME 337

PD 5410 L53 1931 MAIN
Ljunggren, Carl August 1860–
Stilarter och språkriktighetsregler; ett försök till hjälpreda vid modersmålets skriftliga behandling. 2. uppl. Lund, Gleerup [1919]
76p. cm.

1. Swedish language - Grammar. 2. Swedish language - Style. I. Title.

NL 0424460 TxU

439.75 L76s 1931
Ljunggren, Carl August, 1860 –
Stilarter och språkriktighetsregler; ett försök till hjälpreda vid modersmålets skriftliga behandling av C. A. Ljunggren 5.upplagan. Lund, Gleerupska univ.-bokhandeln [1931]
88p.

1. Swedish language--Grammar. 2. Swedish language--Style.

NL 0424461 IU

PD 5420 L82 S 1941
Ljunggren, Carl August, 1860 –
Stilarter och språkriktighetsregler ett försök till hjälpreda vid modersmålets skriftliga behandling. Attonde upplagan. Lund, Gleerup [1941]
96p. 18cm.

NL 0424462 WU

PD5460 L53 1950
Ljunggren, Carl August, 1860-
Stilarter och språkriktighetsregler; ett försök till hjälpreda vid modersmålets riktiga behandling. [11.uppl.] Lund, Gleerupska universitetsbokhandeln [1950]
96 p.

1. Swedish language - Idioms, corrections, errors.

NL 0424463 CU WU

4DL 129
Ljunggren, Carl Johan
Minnes-anteckningar under 1813 och 1814 årens kampagner uti Tyskland och Norge. Jemte tillägg, innefattande kort öfversigt af svenska arméens verksamhet i fälttågen uti Tyskland och Norge 1813 och 1814. Stockholm, A. Bonnier, 1855.
346 p.

NL 0424464 DLC-P4

4DL Swed. 559
Ljunggren, Carl Johan
Skildring af krigshändelserna i Oster-och Västerbotten, 1808-1809. Utgifven af Reinh. Hausen. Helsingfors, 1903.
153 p.

(Skrifter utgivna af Svenska litteratursällskapet i Finland, 58)

NIC NcD NN
NL 0424465 DLC-P4 MH ICU MnU GU OU ICU NNC MdBJ

Ljunggren, Einar Jordan Carlsson, 1896–
... Studien über klinik und prognose der Grawitzschen nierentumoren; zugleich ein beitrag zur frage nach der genese der hämaturie, von Einar Ljunggren. Stockholm, Kungl. boktryckeriet, P. A. Norstedt & söner, 1930.
1 p. l., [v]–vii (*i. e.* viii), 363 p. incl. illus. (part col.) tables. 24[cm]. (*On cover:* Acta chirurgica scandinavica. vol. LXVI. Supplementum XVI)
At head of title: Aus der Chirurgischen klinik des Maria krankenhauses in Stockholm.
Translated from the Swedish by Fräulein M. Carmesin and Dr. Med. Rudolf Popper.
"Literaturverzeichnis": p. [358]–363.

1. Kidneys—Tumors. 2. Hematuria. I. Carmesin, M., tr. II. Popper, Rudolf, joint tr.

A C 33-1579

Title from John Crerar Libr. Printed by ?

NL 0424466 ICJ ViU PPC

Ljunggren, Erik Gustaf.
Atlas öfver Sveriges städer med deras alla egor och jordar, jemte areal-beskrifningar, innefattande 89 kartor, upprättade under åren 1853-1861 ... Stockholm, 1862.
Folio. 62 x 49 cm.

NL 0424467 CtY

W 4 B72 1936/37
Ljunggren, Erik Karl Victor, 1910-
Contribution à la thérapeutique des fractures récentes du col du fémur par la méthode de "Royal Whitmann," Bordeaux, Bière, 1936.
80 p. (Bordeaux. Université. Faculté de médecine et de pharmacie. Thèse. 1936/37. no. 44)

NL 0424468 DNLM CtY NNC

Ljunggren, Evald Jordan, 1865-1935, ed.

PT9605 .L5
Lejonkulans dramer efter Löberödshandskriften, utg. av Ewald Ljunggren, Camille Polack och Erik Noreen. [Uppsala, Almquist & Wiksells boktr., 1908-41]

439.83 D131oYl
Ljunggren, Evald Jordan, 1865-1935.
Ordbog over det danske sprog, grundlagt af Verner Dahlerup ... København, 1918-22 ... [Lund, C. W. K. Gleerup; etc., etc., 1923]
p.278-297.
Caption title.
Signed: Evald Ljunggren.
A review of bd.1-4.
Reprinted from Arkiv för nordisk filologi XXXIX, ny följd XXXV.

1. Dahlerup, Verner, 1859- Ordbog over det danske sprog.

NL 0424470 IU

PD 5625 S9oZ5 1
Ljunggren, Evald Jordan, 1865-1935.
Svenska akademiens ordbok. Ett genmäle af Evald Ljunggren ... Lund, C. W. K. Gleerup [1904]
47 p.

A reply to criticisms by R. G. Berg.
----- ----- Genmäle r:r2, af Evald Ljunggren. Lund, H. Ohlssons boktryckeri, 1905.
56 p.

1. Svenska akademien. Ordbog öfver svenska språket. 2. Berg, Ruben Gustafsson, 1876-

NL 0424471 CLSU

DS41 L5 Public Affairs Library
Ljunggren, Florence, ed.
An international directory of institutes and societies interested in the Middle East. Edited by Florence Ljunggren and Charles L. Geddes.
159p. 22cm.

1. Near East - Societies, etc. - Direct. I. Geddes, Charles L., joint ed. II. Title.

NL 0424472 TxU

Ljunggren, Florence, tr.

AS284 .G7 föl. 5, ser. A, bd. 5, no. 1
Izikowitz, Karl Gustav, 1903–
Musical and other sound instruments of the South American Indians, a comparative ethnographical study. Göteborg, Elanders boktr., 1935.

Ljunggren, Gustaf.
Gasskyddets kemi, av Gustaf Ljunggren ... 2. tryckningen ... Stockholm [Lund, H. Ohlssons boktryckeri, 1939]
cover-title, 18 p. 21½ cm.
"Särtryck ur Elementa. [Mars 1939]"
CONTENTS. — De viktigaste stridsgaserna. — Påvisandet av stridsgaser.—Provtagning och behandling av proven.—Oskadliggörande, sanering av stridsgaser.—Gasmasken

1. Gases, Asphyxiating and poisonous—War use. I. Title.

UG447.L54 1939 43-48907 rev

NL 0424474 DLC

---

ar V 12997
Ljunggren, Gustaf.
Hemliga vapen. Stockholm, Riksförbundet för sveriges försvar [1946]
60 p. illus. 19cm. (Medborgarkunskap om riksförsvaret, 25/26)

1. Arms and armor. I. Title.

NL 0424475 NIC

4QD 186
Ljunggren, Gustaf
Katalytisk kolsyreavspjälkning ur ketokarbonsyror; kinetiska studier över acetättiksyrans sönderdelning. Mit deutscher Zusammenfassung. Lund, Gleerupska Univ.-bokhandeln [1925]
157 p.

NL 0424476 DLC-P4 ICU CtY

Ljunggren, Gustaf.
Katalytisk kolsyreavspjaelkning ur ketokarbonsyror kinetiska...
Inaug. diss. Lund,1925.
Bibl.

NL 0424477 ICRL

Ljunggren, Gustaf.
Stridsgaser och gasskydd. Med illustrationer av S. G. Blohm. [Stockholm, 1950]
20 p. illus. 21 cm. (Civilförsvarsstyrelsens småskrifter)

1. Gases, Asphyxiating and poisonous—War use. I. Title. (Series: Sweden. Civilförsvarsstyrelsen. Småskrifter)

UG447.L56 53-28888

NL 0424478 DLC

LJUNGGREN, Gustaf. War gases and the development of warfare. 190p. 4° [n. p.] 1931.
Transl. from Norsk techr. mil med., 1931, 35: 11-23.

NL 0424479 DNLM

Ljunggren, Gustaf Hakan Jordan, 1823-1905.
Bellman och Fredmans epistlar; en studie af Gustaf Ljunggren. Lund, F. Berlings Förlag, 1867.
275p. 21cm.

1. Bellman, Carl Michael, 1740-1795. Fredmans epistlar.

NL 0424480 IEN MnU

PR 2808 .L79
Ljunggren,Gustaf Håkan Jordan,1823-1905.
Caesars-karakteren i Shakespeares Julius Caesar. Inbjudningsskrift till den högtidlighet hvarmed professoren i zoologi,fil. doktorn herr August Wilhelm Qvennerstedt kommer att i embetet installas af Kongl. Carolinska universitetets rector. [Lund, 1880?]
1 p.ℓ.,28 p. 27 x 21[cm].
Signed: Gustaf Ljunggren.
From Lunds universitets års-skrift,t.XVII.
1.Shakespeare,William--Characters--Julius Caesar.

NL 0424481 MiU

VOLUME 337

[Ljunggren, Gustaf Hakan Jordan]
Carl v. Linnés vistande i Lund och bref till E. G. Lidbeck. Inbjudningsskrift. Lund, 1878.
[2], 18 p. l. 8°.
Reprinted from Lunds universitets arsskrift, 1878, xiv.

NL 0424482 MH-A

Edh 869L
Ljunggren, Gustaf Håkan Jordan, 1823-1905.
Från en resa, af Gustaf Ljunggren ... Lund, C.W.K.Glerrup's sortiment[1871]
2p.ℓ.,277,[1]p. front. 19½cm.

NL 0424483 CtY

LJUNGGREN, Gustaf Håkan Jordan, 1823-1905.
Framstallning af de Fornamsta esthetiska systemerna. Lund, 1856.
2 v.

NL 0424484 MH

Ljunggren, Gustaf Håkan Jordan, 1823-1905.
Framställning af de förnämsta esthetiska systemerna. Af Gustaf Ljunggren ... 2. öfwersedda uppl. Lund, C. W. K. Gleerup, 1869-[83]
2 v. in 1. 22cm.
CONTENTS.—1. del. Från och med Kant till och med Hegel.—2. del. Vischers system.

1. Esthetics.

36-2546

Library of Congress N69.L5 1869 701

NL 0424485 DLC

Ljunggren, Gustaf [Håkan Jordan] 1823- *praeses.*
Några punkter ur läran om det naturskönа ... Lund, Berlingska boktryckeriet, 1852.
2 p. l., 16 p., 1 l., 17-29 p. 20cm.
Akademisk afhandling.—Lund.
Respondents: Hjalmar Christierson and Carl Lewenhaupt.
Separate t.-p. inserted between p. 16 and 17 for the second part of the dissertation, defended by Carl Lewenhaupt.

I. Christierson, Hjalmar, respondent. II. Lewenhaupt, Carl, grefve, respondent.

Library of Congress 4-34753†

NL 0424486 DLC

F 52 .845 v.28
Ljunggren, Gustaf Hakan Jordan, b.1823.
Den nationella rörelsen inom svenska vitterheten, år 1811... [Stockholm, 1877?] (K. Vitterhets historie och antikvitets akademiens Handlingar. 28. del. n.f.8:[3])

Half-title.
On verso half-title: Uppläst som inträdestal i Kongl. Vitterhets historie och antiqvitets akademien den 19 december 1877.

NL 0424487 ICN

Ljunggren, Gustaf Håkan Jordan, 1823-1905, ed.

Nordisk universitets-tidskrift. -10. aarg.; -1864.
Kjöbenhavn, Lund, Christiania, Upsala, 18 -[66]

DL971 .S8S6
Ljunggren, Gustaf Håkan Jordan, 1823-1905.
Skånska herregårdar. Tecknade af Fr. Richardt, beskrifna af Gustaf Ljunggren. Lund, C. W. K. Gleerup, 1852-63.

Ljunggren, Gustaf Håkan Jordan, 1823-1905.
Smärre skrifter. Lund, C. W. K. Gleerup, 1872-1881.
3 v. in 1.

1. Swedish literature - History and criticism. I. Title.

NL 0424490 WaU RP NcD MH CU

PT 8090 .L789
LJUNGGREN,GUSTAF HAKAN JORDAN,1823-1905
Studier öfver Holberg, I. Lund, 1864.
[26]-52 p.

Detached from Nordisk universitets-tidskrift, v. 9, no. 2, 1864.

1. Holberg, Ludvig, baron, 1684-1754. I. Nordisk universitets-tidskrift, v. 9, no. 2.

NL 0424491 InU MH

4AS 53
Ljunggren, Gustaf Håkan Jordan, 1823-1905.
Svenska adademiens historia, 1786-1886. På Akademiens uppdrag författad. Stockholm, Kongl. boktr., 1886.

NL 0424492 DLC-P4

Ljunggren, Gustaf Håkan Jordan, 1823-1905.
Svenska dramat intill slutet af sjuttonde århundradet. Af Gustaf Ljunggren ... Lund, C. W. K. Gleerup; [etc., etc.] 1864.
1 p. l., iv, [2], 582, [2] p. 21½cm.

1. Swedish drama—Hist. & crit.

17-3842

Library of Congress PT9415.L5

NL 0424493 DLC ICU IU CtY PU NN

4PT Swed. 621
Ljunggren, Gustaf Håkan Jordan, 1823-1905.
Svenska vitterhetens häfder efter Gustaf IIIs död. Lund, C. W. K. Gleerup, 1873-90.
4 v.

NL 0424494 DLC-P4 IU MH NN PU CU

AS284 G7 3
Ljunggren, Gustaf Håkan Jordan, 1823-1905
Tegnérs "Axel"; literaturhistorisk skiss. Göteborg, W. Zachrisson, 1897.
12 p. 25 cm. (Göteborgs högskolas årsskrift. III bd., 1897:1)

1. Tegnér, Esaias, 1782-1846--Axel. (Series)

NL 0424495 RPB NN

Ljunggren, Gustaf Karl, 1889-1950
Från predikstol och altare; efterlämnade predikningar och tal. Stockholm, Svenska kyrkans diakonistyrelses bokförlag [1951]

NL 0424496 MH

Ljunggren, Gustaf Karl, 1889-
Det kristna syndmedvetandet intill Luther, en dogmhistorisk studie av d. Gustaf Ljunggren ... Uppsala, Almqvist & Wiksells boktryckeri-a.-b. in kommission; [etc., etc., 1924]
2 p. l., 352 p. 25½cm. (On cover: Arbeten utg. med understöd av Vilhelm Ekmans universitetsfond. Uppsala. 31)

24-21119

Library of Congress BT715.L5

NL 0424497 DLC IEG MiU CU ICU PU

GT6 L769s
Ljunggren, Gustaf Karl, 1889-
Synd och skuld i Luthers teologi. Stockholm, Svenska kyrkans diakonistyrelses bokförlag [1928]
vii, 493 p. 24 cm.

Bibliographical footnotes.

1. Luther, Martin, 1483-1546. I. Title.

NL 0424498 CtY-D IEG MH

Ljunggren, Gustaf Karl, 1889-
Zur geschichte der christlichen heilsgewissheit von Augustin bis zur hochscholastik ... Uppsala [Gedruckt bei Hubert & co., g. m. b. h., in Göttingen] 1920.
8°, 328 p. 24½cm.
Inaug.-diss.—Upsala.
"Die im buchhandel käufliche ausgabe des werkes ist im verlage von Vandenhoeck & Ruprecht in Göttingen erschienen."
"Zitierte literatur": p. 327-328.

1. Salvation.

24-25218

Library of Congress BT752.L5

NL 0424499 DLC DDO TxFTC CtY PU ICU

JE L769z
Ljunggren, Gustaf Karl, 1889-
Zur geschichte der christlichen heilsgewissheit von Augustin bis zur hochscholastik. Göttingen, Vandenhoeck & Ruprecht, 1921.
7*, 328 p. 25 cm.

Issued also as diss., Uppsala.
Bibliography: p. 327-328.

NL 0424500 CtY-D IEG NcD IaU TxFTC GEU-T OU

Ljunggren, Hjalmar.
Ägirs gästabud [av] Jol Strand [pseud. Stockholm, LTs förlag [1953]
310 p. 20 cm.

I. Title.

A 54-2659

Minnesota. Univ. Libr. for Library of Congress [3]

NL 0424501 MnU

Ljunggren, Hjalmar.
Finnpastorn; roman [av] Jol Strand [pseud.] Stockholm, LT:s förlag [1950]
296 p. 20 cm.

I. Title.

A 51-6726

Minnesota. Univ. Lib for Library of Congress [1]

NL 0424502 MnU

[Ljunggren, Hjalmar]
Jussinaho—Finnbyn; roman. [Av] Jol Strand [pseud.] Stockholm, LT:s förlag [1948]
197 p. 20 cm.

I. Title.

A 49-6625*

Minnesota. Univ. Lib for Library of Congress [1]

NL 0424503 MnU

VOLUME 337

[Ljunggren, Hjalmar]
Lång-Kristoffer, av Jol Strand [pseud.] Stockholm, A. Bonnier [1939]
275 p. 21 cm.

I. Title.

PT9875.L64L3 839.736 40-19677 rev*

NL 0424504 DLC

Ljunggren, Hjalmar.
Lokes äventyr. [Av] Jol Strand [pseud. Stockholm] LTs förlag [1954]
201 p. 20 cm.

I. Title.

A 55-3993

Minnesota. Univ. Libr. for Library of Congress [2]

NL 0424505 MnU

Ljunggren, Hjalmar.
Timmerkojan; roman [av] Jol Strand [pseud.] Stockholm, LTs förlag [1951]
262 p. 20 cm.

I. Title.

A 52-4713

Minnesota. Univ. Libr. for Library of Congress [2]

NL 0424506 MnU

Ljunggren, Karl Gustav, 1906-
... Adjektivering av substantiv i svenskan; undersökningar i svensk ordbildnings- och betydelselära, av Karl Gustav Ljunggren. Lund, C. W. K. Gleerup; [etc., etc., 1939]
2 p. l., 321 p. diagr. 25½ᶜᵐ. (Lunds universitets årsskrift. n. f., avd. 1, bd. 35, nr. 3)
"Käll- och litteraturförteckning, viktigare förkortningar": p. [307]-317.

1. Swedish language—Word formation. 2. Swedish language—Noun. 3. Swedish language—Adjective. I. Title.

A 40-2151

Chicago. Univ. Library for Library of Congress AS284.L96 n. f., avd. 1, bd. 35 [AS284.L8 n. f., avd. 1, bd. 35]
[2] (378.485)

NL 0424507 ICU NcU PU

Ljunggren, Karl Gustav, 1906-
Almanackorna och det svenska ordförrådet, bidrag til svensk ordhistoria, av K. G. Ljunggren. Lund, H. Ohlssons boktryckeri, 1944.
155, [1] p. illus. (facsims.) 24ᶜᵐ. (Added t.-p.: Skrifter utgivna av Vetenskaps-societeten i Lund. Publications of the New society of letters at Lund. 28)

1. Swedish language—Hist. 2. Almanacs, Swedish.

46-19347

Library of Congress PD5075.L53
[2] 439.709

NL 0424508 DLC TxU NIC ICU NcD

PD1514 .S3

Ljunggren, Karl Gustav, 1906- ed.
Festskrift till Jöran Sahlgren 1884/1944. [Redigerad med biträde av E. Noreen, I. Modéer och H. Ståhl. Lund, Gleerup, 1944]
530 p. illus., port., map. 25 cm.
Contains 47 articles in various languages.
Includes bibliographies.

1. Sahlgren, Jöran, 1884- 2. Scandinavian languages—Addresses, essays, lectures. 3. Scandinavian literature—Addresses, essays, lectures.

PD1514.S3 51-46864

NL 0424509 DLC CoU GU TU CU MdBJ ICU TxU MH

Ljunggren, Karl Gustav, 1906-
De främmande orden i svenskan; synpunkter och ståndpunkter. Lund, C. W. K. Gleerup [1945]
21 p. 25 cm. (Lunds universitets årsskrift, n. f., avd. 1, bd. 41, nr. 3)
"Medföljde Inbjudning till doktorspromotioner vid universitet i Lund 1945."

1. Swedish language—Foreign words and phrases. I. Title. (Series: Lund. Universitet. Acta Universitatis Lundensis, n. s. Lunds universitets årsskrift, n. f., avd. 1, bd. 41, nr. 3)

AS284.L8 n. f., avd. 1, bd. 41, nr. 3 A 48-4414*

Chicago. Univ. Libr. for Library of Congress [2]†

NL 0424510 ICU PU NIC TxU NcU DLC

Ljunggren, Karl Gustav, 1906-
... Objekt och adverbial; studier i svensk syntax, av Karl Gustav Ljunggren. Lund, C. W. K. Gleerup; Leipzig, O. Harrassowitz [1942]
211, [1] p. 25ᶜᵐ. (Lunds universitets årsskrift, n. f., avd. 1, bd. 38, nr. 3)
"Litteratur": p. [195]-199.

1. Swedish language—Syntax. I. Title.

A 45-3044

Chicago. Univ. Library for Library of Congress [AS284.L8 n. f., avd. 1, bd. 38]
[3] (378.485)

NL 0424511 ICU TxU PU NcU

Ljunggren, Karl Gustav, 1906-

PT9550 .S8 Haft 85, etc.

Söderwall, Knut Fredrik, 1842-1924.
Ordbok öfver svenska medeltids-språket. Lund, Berlingska boktryckeri- och stilgjuteri-aktiebolaget, 1884-1918.

Ljunggren, Karl Gustav, 1906-
Språkvård och språkforskning. Lund, C. W. K. Gleerup [1946]
192 p. 21 cm.

1. Scandinavian philology—Addresses, essays, lectures. I. Title.

PD1515.L8 56-43697

NL 0424513 DLC NN CU TxU MdBJ WU

PD5774 L5

Ljunggren, Karl Gustav, 1906-
Studier över förhållandet mellan verbalpartikel och verb i fornsvenskan. Lund, H. Ohlssons boktryckeri, 1932.
xii,246 p.

Akademisk avhandling - Lund.
Added t.p. with theses note.
Bibliography: p.[ix]-xii.

1. Swedish language - Old Swedish - Verb.

NL 0424514 CU PU CtY MH OU ICRL TxU

Ljunggren, Karl Gustav, 1906-
Studier över sydsvenska ortnamn. Mit deutscher Zusammenfassung. Lund, Gleerup [1948]
75 p. 25 cm. (Lundastudier i nordisk språkvetenskap, 5)
"Detta arbete, som även ingår i Sydsvenska ortnamnssällskapets årsskrift 1946-48, har tryckts med bidrag från Humanistiska fonden."
Bibliographical footnotes.

1. Names, Geographical—Sweden. 2. Swedish language—Etymology. (Series)

DL605.L55 929.4 50-21535

NL 0424515 DLC LU CtY TxU PU MnU CU

Ljunggren, Karl Gustav, 1906-
... Studier över verbalsammansättningen i 1500-talets svenska, av K. G. Ljunggren. Lund, C. W. K. Gleerup; [etc., etc., 1937]
x, 191 p. 25½ᶜᵐ. (Lunds universitets årsskrift. n. f., avd. 1, bd. 32, nr. 6)
"Källor och förkortningar": p. [v]-x.

1. Swedish language—Old Swedish—Verb.

A 39-124

Chicago. Univ. Library for Library of Congress AS284.L96 n. f., avd. 1, bd. 32 [AS284.L8 n. f., avd. 1, bd. 32]
[2] (378.485)

NL 0424516 ICU NcU DLC PU

AS284 .L8 bd. 37, nr. 3-4;

Ljunggren, Karl Gustav, 1906-
... Studier till 1541 års Bibel ... Lund, C. W. K. Gleerup; Leipzig, O. Harrassowitz [1941-

---

Ljunggren, Karl Gustav, 1906-
... Undersökningar över nordiska ortnamns behandling i medellågtyskan och medellågtyska drag i gamla nordiska ortnamn, av K. G. Ljunggren. Lund, C. W. K. Gleerup; [etc., etc., 1937]
169 p. 25ᶜᵐ. (Lunds universitets årsskrift. n. f., avd. 1, bd. 33, nr. 7)
Summary in German.
Bibliography: p. [5]-6.

1. Scandinavian languages—Etymology—Names. 2. Names, Geographical—Scandinavia. I. Title.

A 42-4865

Chicago. Univ. Library for Library of Congress [AS284.L8 n. f., avd. 1, bd. 33, nr. 7]
[3] (378.485)

NL 0424518 ICU NcU TxU

WB 130 L789c 1917

LJUNGGREN, Knut
Cellernas uppror, medicinska kåserier. Stockholm, Bonniers [1917]
143 p. illus., port.

NL 0424519 DNLM

Ljunggren, Nils Peter, respondent.
Numismata Anglo-Saxonica Musei Academiae Lundensis ordinata & descripta ...
see under Hildebrand, Bror Emil, 1806-1884, praeses.

BV207 .L78 1914

Ljunggren, Olof
Bönen i gamla Testamentet. Lund, Håkan Ohlssons Boktryckeri, 1914.
xi, 458p. 25cm.
Bibliography: p.[vii]-xi.

1. Prayer--Biblical teaching. I. Title.

NL 0424521 IEG NjP ICU NN ICRL PPDrop

Ljunggren, Pontus.
The region of Hälia in Dalecarlia, Sweden; an investigation of regional transformations leading to meta-sediments and igneous-looking rocks. Göteborg, 1954.
141 p. illus., maps (1 fold. col.) 25 cm.
Thesis—Lund.
Extra t. p., with thesis statement, inserted.
Bibliography: p. 111-112.

1. Petrology—Sweden—Dalecarlia. I. Title.

QE451.S5L59 55-39367

NL 0424522 DLC CU MiU CtY

Ljunggren, Ragnar 1889-
Om den opersonliga konstruktionen.
Inaug. Diss. Upsala, 1926
Bibl.

NL 0424523 ICRL IU PU

Ljunggren, Ragnar, 1889-
... Om den opersonliga konstruktionen ... av Ragnar Ljunggren. Uppsala, A.-b. Lundequistska bokhandeln [1926]
xix, 354 p., 1 l. 24ᶜᵐ. (Uppsala universitets årsskrift 1926 [bd. 2] Filosofi, språkvetenskap och historiska vetenskaper, 6)
The author's thesis, Uppsala; issued also without series title.
"Citerade arbeten": p. [v]-x.

1. Language and languages. 2. Swedish language. I. Title: Den opersonliga konstruktionen.

[Full name: Anders Ragnar Sigurd Ljunggren]

A 42-1959

Minnesota. Univ. Libr. for Library of Congress [AS284.U7 1926]
[2] (378.485)

NL 0424524 MnU CU CtY MoU ICU MH

VOLUME 337

Ljunggren, Ragnar, 1889–
... Supinum och dubbelsupinum; syntaktiska studier, av Ragnar Ljunggren. Uppsala, A.-b. Lundequistska bokhandeln [1934]
iv, 103 p. 24½cm. (Uppsala universitets årsskrift 1934. Filosofi, språkvetenskap och historiska vetenskaper. 4)
"Citerade arbeten": p. [102]–103.
1. Swedish language—Verb. 2. Swedish language—Syntax. I. Title.
[Full name: Anders Ragnar Sigurd Ljunggren]
A C 38-1343
Minnesota. Univ. Library for Library of Congress [AS284.U7 1934] [4] (378.485)

NL 0424525 MnU CU MoU DLC PU

Ljunggren, Reinhold, illus.
PT9875 .S27T7
Sandgren, Gustav Emil, 1904–
Trosa, av Gustav Sandgren. Målningar av Reinhold Ljunggren. Stockholm, A. Bonnier, 1948.

Ljunggren, S.
... Majsen och jordbruket; nutids- och framtidsbilder efter officiella uppgifter, af S. Ljunggren. Stockholm, Centraltryckeriet, 1902.
47 p. 18½cm.
Medföljer Göteborgs handels- och sjöfarts-tidning.
1. Denmark. Agriculture. 2. Maize. 3. Sweden. Agriculture.
Agr 3-218
Library, U. S. Dept. of Agriculture 33L76

NL 0424527 DNAL

Ljunggren, S. A.
De gente patricia claudiorum nonulla. I. Per spatium liberae civitatis.
Inaug. diss. Upsala, 1898.

NL 0424528 ICRL

Ljunggren, T
QC 310 1949
Contributions of the theory of diffraction of electromagnetic waves by spherical particles. [II] Uppsala, 1949.
Arkiv för fysik", bd. 1, nr. 1 with thesis statement (4p) inserted.

NL 0424529 CtY

Ljunggren, Thuro, respondent.
... Versio svecana selectorum ex paulinis epistolis locorum ad examen revocata dissertatione academica...
see under Floder, Johann, praeses.

Ljunggren, Torsten.
Lorenzo Hammarsköld som kritiker, med särskild hänsyn till hans förhållande till Tegnér. Lund, C. W. K. Gleerup, 1952.
688 p. illus., col. port., facsims. 25 cm.
Akademisk avhandling—Stockholms högskola.
Extra t. p., with thesis statement, inserted.
Bibliography: p. [652]–667.
1. Hammarsköld, Lorenzo, 1785–1827. 2. Tegnér, Esaias, Bp., 1782–1846. 3. Swedish literature—Hist. & crit.
PT9753.L5 839.709 53-28653

NL 0424531 DLC CLSU CtY IEN MH NN NIC ViU MnU WU

Ljunggren, W P F.
On the auxiliaries shall and will in the English language, especially with regard to modern English. Academical dissertation. Carlskrona, printed at Länsboktryckeriet, 1893–94.
2 pt.
Eng. lang.-Verb||.

NL 0424532 MH ICRL NcU

Ljunggren, Wilhelm, 1905–
Einige eigenschaften der einheiten reeller quadratischer und rein-biquadratischer zahlkörper, mit anwendung auf die lösung einer klasse unbestimmter gleichungen vierten grades, von Wilhelm Ljunggren ... Oslo, I kommisjon hos J. Dybwad, 1937.
73, [1] p. 27½ cm. (Norsk videnskaps-akademi i Oslo. Skrifter. I. Mat.-naturv. klasse, 1936, no. 12)
"Utgitt for Fridtjof Nansens fond."
1. Forms (Mathematics) 2. Numbers, Theory of. 3. Equations, Quartic.
AS283.O56 1936, no. 12 A 48-4913
John Crerar Library for Library of Congress [2]†

NL 0424533 ICJ DLC

Ljunggren, Wilhelm, 1905–
Einige Sätze über unbestimmte Gleichungen von der Form $Ax^4+Bx^2+C=Dy^2$. Oslo, I kommisjon hos J. Dybwad, 1943.
53 p. 27 cm. (Skrifter utgitt av det Norske videnskaps-akademi i Oslo. I. Mat.-naturv. klasse. 1942, no. 9)
"Trykt for Oslo kommunes fond."
"Literaturverzeichnis": p. 53.
1. Diophantine analysis. (Series: Norske videnskaps-akademi i Oslo. Matematisk-naturvidenskapelig klasse. Skrifter, 1942, no. 9)
AS283.O56 1942, no. 9 A 54-3207
John Crerar Library for Library of Congress [1]†

NL 0424534 ICJ DLC

Ljungh, Anders Theodor.
Über isoptische und orthoptische kurven ... Lund, H. Ohlsson's buchdruckerei, 1895.
2 p. l., 49 p., 1 l. diagrs. on fold. pl. 24cm.
Akademisk afhandling—Lund.
"Angewandte arbeiten": 2d prelim. leaf.
1. Curves, Plane.
Library of Congress QA567.L78 5-31318†

NL 0424535 DLC

Ljungh, Hjalmar, 1874–
Bergman, Folke.
... Archaeological researches in Sinkiang, especially the Lop-nor region, by Folke Bergman; descriptive lists of textiles by Vivi Sylwan, appendices by Sten Konow and Hjalmar Ljungh; with 20 half tone plates, 2 coloured plates, 36 collotype plates, and 52 illustrations and maps in the text. Stockholm, Bokförlags aktiebolaget Thule, 1939.

Ljunghall, Arvid
QC 065 125
The intensity of twilight and its connection with the density of the atmosphere Hälsingborg, 1949.
171p. charts, tables. 25cm. (Lund. Universitet Observatoriet. Meddelanden, ser.2, nr.125)
Diss. - Lund.
Extra t.-p. with thesis statement inserted.
Bibliography: p.165-170.

NL 0424537 CtY

Ljunghoff, Aina
... Fritt ur hjärtat om katekesen; en diskussion och ett förslag. Lund, C.W.K. Gleerup [1948]
92p., 1l. 20cm.
At head of title: Aina och Johannes Ljunghoff.

NL 0424538 NNUT

Ljunghoff, Johannes
Bergspredikan; handledning och studieuppgifter. 2. omarbetade uppl. Lund, Gleerup [1954]
62 p.

NL 0424539 MH

LJUNGHOFF, Johannes.
Christopher Jacob Boström Sveriges Platon. Uppsala, L. Norblad, [1916].

NL 0424540 MH

LJUNGHOFF, Johannes Nathanaol, 1887-
Jesus som undervisare. Lund, C.W.K. Gleerups Foerlag [1939]
42p. 19.5cm. (Skrifter i Teologiska och Kyrkliga Aemnen, 14)

NL 0424541 MH-AH

LJUNGHOFF, Johannes Nathanael, 1887-
Katekesen i kyrka och skola; ett aktuellt problem. Lund, C.W.K. Gleerups Foerlag [1946?]
46p. 20.5cm. (Skrifter i Teologiska och Kyrkliga Aemnen, 26)

NL 0424542 MH-AH

Ljungholm, Carl Anders, 1877– *ed.*
Apoteksvarustadgan med utdrag ur riksdagshandlingarna, förklarande anmärkningar och register. Utgiven av Carl Ljungholm. ... Stockholm, A. Bonnier, [1914].
[2], 92 p. 19½cm.

NL 0424543 ICJ

Ljungholm, Carl Anders, 1877– ed.
HJ8734 .F6
Försäkringsaktiebolaget Skandia, *plaintiff.*
Guldklausulmålet. Svea hovrätts protokoll i mål mellan Försäkringsaktiebolaget Skandia och Riksgäldskontoret angående tillämpningen av guldklausulen i svenska statens dollarobligationer av år 1924. Stockholm, Kungl. boktryckeriet, P. A. Norstedt & söner, 1935.

Ljungholm, Carl Anders, 1877– ed.
Svensk juristtidning. 1.– årg.; 1916– Stockholm, A.-b. Nordiska bokhandeln i distribution [1916–

LJUNGLUND, Leon.
Lifvets bejakande några tankar om viljan och kärleken. Stockholm, Wahlström Widstrand, [1914].

NL 0424546 MH

Ljunglund, Leon.
De politiska åskådningarna: konservatismen, liberalismen, socialismen, kommunismen, fascismen, den nya rättsstaten. Av Leon Ljunglund [and others] Stockholm, Natur och kultur [1931]
184 p. (Natur och kultur, 111)

NL 0424547 MH

Ljunglund, Leon.
De tre frestelserna; reflexioner vid en världshistorisk vändpunkt. Stockholm, Natur och kultur [1936]

NL 0424548 MH

VOLUME 337

Ljungman (Axel Vilhelm) 1841-1901.
Anteckningar rörande sillsaltning, sillvrakning och sillhandel. 176 pp. *Uddevalla: Bohusläns boktryckeri-aktiebolag,* 1882. 12°.

NL 0424549 NN

Ljungman, Axel Vilhelm, 1841-1901.
Berättelse öfver med kanonånbaten Gunhild, under sommaren 1871 företagen expedition för anställande af atskilliga undersökningar till hafsfiskets befrämjande uti Skagerrach och Kattegat. Upsala, 1873.

28 p. 8°.

NL 0424550 MH-Z

Ljungman, Axel Vilhelm, 1841–1901.
The Bohus-län sea fisheries and their future. By Axel V. Ljungman. ⌈Tr. by Herman Jacobson⌉

(*In* Report of the commissioner of fish and fisheries for 1880. Washington, 1883. 22cm. p. 89-98)

"From Aftonbladet, nos. 6 and 43, January 9 and February 21, 1882."

1. Fisheries—Sweden. I. Jacobson, Herman, tr.

F 16-290

Library, U. S. Bur. of Fisheries

NL 0424551 DI OO

LJUNGMAN, Axel Vilh[elm], 1841-1901.
Bohus läns hafsfisken och de vetenskapliga hafsfiskeundersökningarna. II.Göteborg Göteborgs handels-tidnings aktiebolags. tryckeri,1878.

101 p.

NL 0424552 MH

Ljungman, Axel Vilhelm, 1841–1901.
Contribution towards solving the question of the secular periodicity of the great herring fisheries. By Axel Ljungman. ⌈Tr. by Herman Jacobson⌉

(*In* Report of the commissioner of fish and fisheries for 1879. Washington, 1882. 22cm. p. 497-503)

1. Herring-fisheries. I. Jacobson, Herman, tr.

F 17-6

Library, U. S. Bur. of Fisheries

NL 0424553 DI CaBVaU OO

Ljungman, Axel Vilhelm, 1841–1901.
Contributions towards a more correct knowledge of the herring's mode of life. By Axel Ljungman. ⌈Tr. by Herman Jacobson⌉

(*In* Report of the commissioner of fish and fisheries for 1879. Washington, 1882. 22cm. p. 505-513)

1. Herring-fisheries. 2. Fishes—Food. I. Jacobson, Herman, tr.

F 17-7

Library, U. S. Bur. of Fisheries

NL 0424554 DI CaBVaU

Ljungman, Axel Vilhelm, 1841–1901.
The future of the herring fisheries on the coast of Bohuslan. By Axel V. Ljungman. ⌈Tr. by Herman Jacobson⌉

(*In* Report of the commissioner of fish and fisheries for 1884. Washington, 1886. 22cm. p. 399-409)

1. Herring-fisheries—Bohuslän. I. Jacobson, Herman, tr.

F 17-132

Library, U. S. Bur. of Fisheries

NL 0424555 DI CaBVaU OO

Ljungman, Axel Vilhelm, 1841–1901.
The great Bohuslan herring-fisheries. By Axel V. Ljungman. ⌈Tr. by H. Jacobson⌉

(*In* Report of the commissioner of fish and fisheries for 1878. Washington, 1880. 22cm. p. 221-239)

1. Herring-fisheries—Bohuslan. I. Jacobson, Herman, tr.

F 16-158

Library, U. S. Bur. of Fisheries

NL 0424556 DI OO CaBVaU

Ljungman, Axel Vilhelm, 1841–1901.
The great herring fisheries considered from an economical point of view. By Axel Vilhelm Ljungman. ⌈Tr. by Herman Jacobson⌉

(*In* Report of the commissioner of fish and fisheries for 1883. Washington, 1885. 22cm. p. 341-357)

A paper read before the Swedish economic society, February 1883.

1. Herring-fisheries—Sweden. I. Jacobson, Herman, tr.

F 17-30

Library, U. S. Bur. of Fisheries

NL 0424557 DI CaBVaU OO

Ljungman, Axel Vilhelm, 1841-1901.
Die Härings-Fischerei. Die Abhängigkeit des Härings von äusseren physikalischen und biologischen Verhältnissen. Stettin, 1880.

52 p. 8°.

NL 0424558 MH-Z

Ljungman (Axel Vilhelm) 1841-1901.
Kortfattad berättelse öfver de under artiondet 1873–'83 utförda vetenskapliga undersökningarna, Zörande sillen och sillfisket vid Sveriges vestkust. 104 pp., 1l. *Göteborg: Handelstidnings Aktiebolags Tryckeri,* 1883 12°.

NL 0424559 NN MH

Ljungman, Axel Vilhelm, 1841-1901.
Några geologiska iakttagelser gjorda under en resa i mellersta Bohuslän sommaren 1870. Upsala, 1870.

22 p. 8°.

NL 0424560 MH-Z

Zool. Mus.

Ljungman, Axel Vilhelm, 1841-1901.
Några ord om de stora bohuslänska sillfiskena. Göteborg, 1877.

31 p. 8°.

NL 0424561 MH-Z

Ljungman, Axel Vilhelm, 1841-1901.
Några ord om den unionella frågans lösning, jämte utkast till tvänne författningsförslag, af A. V. L. Göteborg, Göteborgs handelstidnings aktiebolags tryckeri, 1895.

71, 48, 42 p. 21cm. (The union of Norway with Sweden; a collection of pamphlets. v. 2)

NL 0424562 MnU NN

4LF
174

Ljungman, Axel Vilhelm, 1841-1901.
Några ord om det tillämnade universitetet i Göteborg . Tvänne smärre uppsatser. Göteborg, Göteborgs handelstidnings aktiebolags tryckeri, 1880.
22 p.

NL 0424563 DLC-P4 MH

LJUNGMAN, Axel Vilhelm, 1841-1901.
Om de stora sillfiskena betraktade fran nationalekonsnomisk synpunkt, etc., Stockholm, 1884.

1 pam.

NL 0424564 MH-Z

Ljungman, Axel Vilhelm, 1841-1901.
Om offentliga atgärder med hänsyn till det rika bohuslänska sillfisket. Göteborg, 1882.

48 p. 16°.

NL 0424565 MH-Z

Ljungman, Axel Vilhelm, 1841-1901.
Om sillens och skarpsillens racer med serskild hänsyn till Sveriges vestkust. Kjøbenhavn, 1881.

137 p. 8°.
Tidsskrift for Fiskeri.

NL 0424566 MH-Z

Ljungman, A⌈xel Vilhelm⌉ 1841–1901.
... *Ophiuroidea* viventia huc usque cognita enumerat A. Ljungman. Holmiæ, P. A. Norstedt & filii, 1867.

2 p. l., 303–336 p. 21½cm.

At head of title: Öfversigt af Kgl. Vetenskaps-akademiens förhandlingar 1866. ⌈no. 9⌉

1. Ophiuroidea.

Library of Congress QL384.O6L7 6-15589†

NL 0424567 DLC

Ljungman, Axel Vilhelm, 1841-1901.
Preliminär berättelse för 1873–74 öfver de beträffande sillen och sillfisket vid Sveriges vestkust anställda undersökningarna. Af Axel Vilh. Ljungman. .... Upsala, E. Berling, 1874.

[4], 74, [2] p. 21½cm.
"Tryckt såsom handskrift."
Bibliographical foot-notes.

NL 0424568 ICJ MH

Ljungman, Axel Vilhelm, 1841-1901.
Preliminary report for 1873–74 on the herring and the herring-fisheries on the west coast of Sweden. By Axel Vilhelm Ljungman. ⌈Tr. from the Swedish by H. Jacobson⌉

(*In* Report of the commissioner of fish and fisheries for 1873-4 and 1874-5. Washington, 1876. 22cm. p. 123-168)

1. Herring. 2. Herring fisheries. I. Jacobson, H., tr.

F 16-8

Library, U. S. Bur. of Fisheries

NL 0424569 DI CaBVaU OO

Ljungman, Axel Vilhelm, 1841–1901.
The propagation and growth of the herring and small-herring, with special regard to the coast of Bohuslan. By Axel V. Ljungman. Tr. by Herman Jacobson.

(*In* Report of the commissioner of fish and fisheries for 1878. Washington, 1880. 22cm. p. 639-659)

"From Nordisk tidsskrift for fiskeri, 5th year, part 4, Copenhagen, 1879."

1. Fishes—⌈Breeding habits⌉ 2. Temperature, Physiological effect of. I. Jacobson, Herman, tr.

F 16-122

Library, U. S. Bur. of Fisheries

NL 0424570 DI CaBVaU

VOLUME 337

LJUNGMAN, Axel Vilhelm,1841-1901.
The salt-water fisheries of Bohuslän and the scientific investigations of the salt-water fisheries. n.p., [18-?]
pp.(97).
Caption serves as title.
Running title reads:-Report of Commissioner of fish and fiheries. pp. 143-239.

NL 0424571 MH

Ljungman, Axel Vilhelm, 1841-1901.
The salt-water fisheries of Bohuslan and the scientific investigations of the salt-water fisheries. By Axel V. Ljungman. [Tr. by H. Jacobson]
(In Report of the commissioner [of fish and fisheries] for 1878. Washington, 1880. 22cm. p. 143-220)

1. Fisheries—Bohuslan. 2. Herring-fisheries. 3. [Reaction to stimuli] I. Jacobson, Herman, tr.

F 16-157

Library, U. S. Bur. of Fisheries

NL 0424572 DI CaBVaU

Ljungman, Axel Vilhelm, 1841-1901.
Special results of the investigations relating to the herring and herring fisheries on the west coast of Sweden made during the years 1873-1883. By A. V. Ljungman. [Tr. by Herman Jacobson]
(In Report of the commissioner of fish and fisheries for 1883. Washington, 1885. 22cm. p. 729-745)

1. Reproduction—[Fishes] 2. Herring-fisheries. I. Jacobson, Herman, tr.

F 17-34

Library, U. S. Bur. of Fisheries

NL 0424573 DI CaBVaU

Ljungman, Axel Vilhelm, 1841-1901.
Sweden at the Great international fishery exposition at London, 1883. By Axel Vilhelm Ljungman.
(In Bulletin of the United States fish commission for 1883. Washington, 1883. 22½cm. vol. III, p. 231-239)

1. London. International fishery exposition, 1883—Sweden. 2. Fisheries—Sweden.

F 18-128

Library, U. S. Bur. of Fisheries

NL 0424574 DI CaBVaU

Ljungman (Axel Vilhelm) 1841 - 1901.
Utkast till förslag till föreningsgrundlag för Konungarikena Sverige och Norge . . . 49 pp. *Göteborg: Göteborgs Handelstidnings Aktiebolags Tryckeri*, 1895. 8°.

NL 0424575 NN InU

Ljungman, Axel Vilhelm, 1841-1901.
What should be done by the government with regard to the great Bohus-län herring fisheries. A memorial addressed to the Council of state and the head of the Royal civil department [of Sweden] by Alex V. Ljungman. [Tr. by Herman Jacobson]
(In Report of the commissioner of fish and fisheries for 1880. Washington, 1883. 22cm. p. 99-126)

1. Herring fisheries—Sweden. 2. [Fishing methods]

F 16-291

Library, U. S. Bur. of Fisheries

NL 0424576 DI OO

LJUNGMAN,Carl Fredrich.
Beskrifning om Gripsholms Slott; som innefatter dess åtskilliga förändringar ifrån sitt första til närvarande tid,så långt som svenska historien,publique handlingar och tilförlåtelige vittnesbörd gifva anledning;med bifogad förteckning,på de portraiter,af kejsare,konungar, furstar,prinsar och prinsessor [etc.]. Stockholm,A.Zetterberg,1790.
18 cm. Folded plan and other illustr.
Gripsholms Slott is situated in Södermanland,Sweden.

NL 0424577 MH

WA 29114 Ljungman, Carl Fredrich
En kort beskrifning, om Gripsholms Slott, som innefattar dess åtskilliga förändringar ifrån sitt första til närwarande tid, så långt, som Swenska historien, publique handlingar och tilförlatelige Wittnesbörd gifwer anledning, med bifogad förteckning, på de contersaits af Kajsare, konungar, drottningar, prinsar och prinsessor ... som therstädes finnas ... samt det år 1745 uprättade inventarium ... Stockholm, Tryckt af P.J. Nyström, 1755.
135 p. 18 cm.

NL 0424578 CtY

Ljungman, Henrik.
Das Gesetz erfüllen. Matth. 5, 17 ff. und 3, 15 untersucht. Lund, Gleerup [1954]
140 p. 26 cm. (Lunds universitets årsskrift, n. f., avd. 1, bd. 50, nr. 6)
Bibliography: p. [127]-133.

1. Bible. N. T. Matthew v, 17-48—Criticism, interpretation, etc. 2. Bible. N. T. Matthew III, 15—Criticism, interpretation, etc. (Series: Lund. Universitet. Acta Universitatis Lundensis, n. s. Lunds universitets årsskrift, n. f., avd. 1, bd. 50, nr. 6)
[AS284.L8 bd. 50, nr. 6] A 55-2721

Chicago. Univ. Libr. for Library of Congress [2]

IaU MBu-T ICMcC
NL 0424579 ICU PU NjPT PPLT CtY-D GDecCT NjNbS GU

Ljungman, Henrik.
Guds barmhärtighet och dom, fariséernas lära om de två 'måtten.' Lund, Gleerup [1950]
190 p. 23 cm.
Akademisk avhandling—Lund.
Extra t. p., with thesis statement, inserted.
Summary in English.
Bibliography: p. [172]-178.

1. God—Mercy. 2. Judaism. I. Title.
BT153.M4L5 A 51-3236

Yale Univ. Library for Library of Congress [1]†

NL 0424580 CtY DLC NNUT ICU MH-AH

Ljungman, John, ed.
Författningar och bestämmelser rörande Stockholms folkskolor. Utgivna av John Ljungman, ... Stockholm, P. A. Norstedt & söner, [1911].
vi, 342 p. incl. tables. 19cm.

NL 0424581 ICJ MnU

Ljungman, John.
En förmyndares åligganden enligt de nya förmynderskapslagarna av den 27 juni 1924; kort handledning med praktiska anvisningar; av John Ljungman... Som bilagor: Lagtexter och formulär. Stockholm: A.-B. Svenska handelsbankens notariatavdelning[, 1924]. 63 p. incl. forms. 2. ed. 8°.

1. Guardianship—Jurisp.—Sweden, 1924.
N. Y. P. L. July 27, 1925

NL 0424582 NN

Ljungman, John.
När och hur bör man göra testamente? Populär framställning av delar av svensk testamentsrätt jämte praktiska anvisningar, av John Ljungman... Stockholm: Svenska Handelsbankens Notariatavdelning[, 1923]. 20 p. 8°.

1. Wills—Jurisp.—Sweden.
N. Y. P. L. January 21, 1925

NL 0424583 NN

Ljungman, Karl Severin Beth
see Ljungman, Seve, 1909-

Ljungman, Kjerstin Gertrud Elisabeth Göransson-
see
Göransson-Ljungman, Kjerstin Gertrud Elisabeth, 1901-

Ljungman, Seve, 1909-
Om prestation in natura. Uppsala, Almqvist & Wiksells boktr., 1948-
v. 25 cm.
"Citerad litteratur": v. 1, p. [67]-69.
Contents.—1. Särskilt vid köp av lös egendom.

1. Specific performance—Sweden. I. Title. II. Title: Prestation in natura.
Full name: Karl Severin Beth Ljungman.
A 49-7659*

Minnesota. Univ. Libr for Library of Congress [3]†

NL 0424586 MnU DLC MH-L ICU

Ljungman, Seve, 1909-
Om skada och olägenhet från grannfastighet, ett bidrag till läran om immissionernas rättsliga behandling ... av Seve Ljungman ... Uppsala, Almqvist & Wiksells boktryckeri ab, 1943.
4 p. l., 294 p. 24cm.
Akademisk avhandling—Uppsala.
Added t.-p., without thesis note.
"Källförteckning": p. [274]-286.
1. Nuisances. 2. Nuisances—Sweden. I. Title.
[Full name: Karl Severin Beth Ljungman]
47-35700

NL 0424587 DLC CU-L NNC NIC

Ljungman, Seve, 1909-
Om skattefordran och skatterestitution. Uppsala, Almqvist & Wiksells boktr., 1947.
186 p. 25 cm.
Bibliography: p. [176]-180.

1. Tax collection—Sweden. I. Title.
Full name: Karl Severin Beth Ljungman.
50-22290

NL 0424588 DLC

Ljungman, Seve, 1909-
Speciell fastighetsrätt
see under
Eberstein, Gösta, 1880-

LJUNGMAN, SEVE, 1909 -
L'unificazione del diritto privato Scandinavo. Rome Estratto dalla Rivista trimestrale di Diritto e Procedura Civile, 1949. n.4.
912-918 p. (Istituto Internazionale per l'unificazione del Diritto Privato. Pub. 1949)

NL 0424590 WaU-L

VOLUME 337

Ljungner, Erik, 1892–
East-West balance of the Quaternary ice caps in Patagonia and Scandinavia. [Uppsala, 1949]
12–96 p. illus., maps (1 fold.) profiles. 25 cm. (Report of the Swedish Expedition to Patagonia, no. 10)
Cover title.
"Reprinted from Bull. of the Geol. Inst. of Upsala, vol. xxxiii."
Bibliography: p. 87–95.
1. Glacial epoch. 2. Glaciers—Patagonia. 3. Glaciers—Scandinavia. I. Title. (Series: Patagonienexpeditionen, 1932–1934. Rapport n:o 10)
QE697.L68 551.31 52-39144

NL 0424591 DLC

QE282 .L75 LJUNGNER, ERIK, 1892–
Spaltentektonik und morphologie der schwedischen Skagerrak-küste. Uppsala, 1927.
254 p. illus., VII pl. (part fold.) diagrs. 25cm.
Inaug.-diss.--Upsala.
Reprinted from Bulletin of the Geological institute of Upsala, vol. 21.
1. Geology--Sweden.

NL 0424592 ICU ICRL MH CtY

Ljungner, Erik, 1892–
see also Patagonienexpeditionen, *1932–1934.*

Ljungquist, Adolf Ivar
see
Ljungquist, Ivar, 1892–

Ljungquist, Anna.
Zur Qualität in der Ernährung; Rezepte für die vegetarische Küche. Mit einer Einleitung zur Ernährungsfrage von Gerhard Schmidt, und einem Anhang: Landbau und Ernährung. von Erika Riese; Ernährung und Gewürzpflanzen, von Marie Wundt. Dornach, R. Geering [1955]
191 p. 23 cm.
1. Cookery (Vegetables)
A 56-5417
Purdue Univ. Library for Library of Congress [1]

NL 0424595 InLP

Ljungquist, Carolus, respondent.
... Dissertatio academica, de notionibus... see under Christiernin, Peter Nikolai, praeses.

Ljungquist, Carl, 1771-1811, respondent
Fant, Erik Mikael, 1754–1817, *praeses.*
Observationes quædam historicæ antiquam juris svecani faciem illustrantes ... Upsaliæ, litteris J. F. Edman [1797]

PN5299 .S83D3 Ljungquist, Ivar, 1892– ed.
Dagens nyheter, *Stockholm.*
Bakom spalterna; ur Dagens nyheters historia. Utgivare: Ivar Ljungquist. Stockholm, Bonnier [1952–

Ljungquist, Ivar, 1892–
Bittenbergarna; roman. Stockholm, A. Bonnier [1948]
357 p. 20 cm.
I. Title. *Full name:* Adolf Ivar Ljungquist.
A 49-2677*
Minnesota. Univ. Libr. for Library of Congress [1]

NL 0424599 MnU PU

Ljungquist, Ivar, 1892 –
Kampen om läsarna, ur Dagens nyhesters historia, 1889-1921. Del II. Stockholm, Bonniers [1953]
1 v.

NL 0424600 MnU

Ljungquist, Ivar, 1892–
Det mörka småland. Andra upplagan. Stockholm, Wahlström, 1921.
226 p.
Contents: Flitens monument. - Katrina. - Den gamla lyktan. - Sammels enepåk. - En otidig telning. - Vad alla visste. - Huvudet och begynnelsen till allt ont. - Prinsessan av det undangömda landet. - Folkets präster. - Det allra heligaste. - Böndernas barn. - Duraeus den siste.

NL 0424601 CaBVa

Ljungquist, Ivar, 1892–
Nils Dacke; roman, av Ivar Ljungquist. Stockholm: A. Bonniers förlag[, 1927]. 423 p. 8°.
1. Fiction, Swedish. 2. Dacke, Niels, fl. 1542—Drama. 3. Title.
N. Y. P. L. August 9, 1928

NL 0424602 NN WU

Ljungquist, Ivar, 1892–
... "Smålänning, guhjälp!" Stockholm, A. Bonnier [1941]
367, [1] p. fold. map. 19ᶜᵐ.
1. Småland, Sweden. 2. Småland, Sweden—Civilization. I. Title.
[Full name: Adolf Ivar Ljungquist]
43-50484
Library of Congress DL971.S55L54
[2] 948.6

NL 0424603 DLC

Ljungquist, Ivar, 1892–
Tidningsmästare och -gesäller. Stockholm, Bonnier [1955]
217 p. illus., ports. 21 cm.
1. Journalists—Correspondence, reminiscences, etc. I. Title.
Full name: Adolf Ivar Ljungquist.
A 57-725
Minnesota. Univ. Libr. for Library of Congress [1]

NL 0424604 MnU

Ljungquist, Ivar, 1892–
Ur Dagens nyheters historia. Stockholm, Bonnier [1952–54]
3 v. illus., ports., facsims. 22 cm.
Contents.—del 1. 1889–1921. Bakom spalterna. Minnesanteckningar av Otto v. Zweigbergk och andra.—del 2. 1889–1921. Kampen om läsarna.—del 3. 1922–1946.
1. Dagens nyheter, Stockholm. I. Title. II. Title: Bakom spalterna. III. Title: Kampen om läsarna.
PN5309.S83D35 55-57834 rev

NL 0424605 DLC IEN NN

LJUNGQUIST, Jakob Erhard.
Mastermyr. En växtekologisk studie. 1. Akad. avh. av J.E.Ljungquist. Karlstad 1914.
57 s. 6 pl. (Ur. Redog. F. Karlstads h. allm. läroverk, 1913/14.
Diss. Uppsal. Phil.

NL 0424606 MH ICRL CtY

4BR 1416 Ljungquist, Ragnar
När eld kommer lös. 3. uppl. Orebro, Evangeliipress [1951]
80 p.

NL 0424607 DLC-P4

Ljungquist, Walter Bertil, 1900–
Azalea. Stockholm, A. Bonnier [1948]
350 p. 20 cm.
I. Title.
A 49-5404*
Minnesota. Univ. Libr. for Library of Congress [1]

NL 0424608 MnU

Ljungquist, Walter Bertil, 1900–
Brevet från Casper. Stockholm, Bonnier [1955]
225 p. 20 cm.
I. Title.
PT9875.L65B7 55-34957 ‡

NL 0424609 DLC WU CU MnU

Ljungquist, Walter Bertil, 1900–
En dörr står på glänt; noveller av Walter Ljungquist. Stockholm, A. Bonnier [1937]
252 p., 1 l. 20ᶜᵐ.
Contents.—Godnattkyssen.—Flyktingar.—Jan, Gunilla och hästarna.—Marie-Louise är i sitt rum.—En dörr står på glänt.—Bitter bilaga.—Vind i natten.
I. Title.
37-38560 Revised
Library of Congress PT9875.L65D6 1937
[r46c2] 839.736

NL 0424610 DLC CtY

Ljungquist, Walter Bertil, 1900–
Farväl, sommar! Roman av Walter Ljungquist. Stockholm, A. Bonnier [1940]
218 p. 19½ᶜᵐ.
I. Title.
A 46-2549
Harvard univ. Library for Library of Congress [2]

NL 0424611 MH

Ljungquist, Walter Bertil, 1900–
Kammarorgel. [Roman] Stockholm, Bonnier [1954]
287 p. 20 cm.
I. Title.
PT9875.L65K3 54-27517 ‡

NL 0424612 DLC OrP MnU NN OCl

VOLUME 337

Ljungquist, Walter Bertil, 1900–
Liljor i Saron (Kanske inte en roman) Stockholm, Bonnier [1952]
178 p. 20 cm.

I. Title.

PT9875.L65L5 53-18132 ‡

NL 0424613 DLC MH MnU PP

Ljungquist, Walter Bertil, 1900–
Nycklar till okänt rum. Stockholm, Bonnier [1950]
231 p. 20 cm.

I. Title.
PT9875.L65N9 A 51-3365
Minnesota. Univ. Libr. for Library of Congress [2]†

NL 0424614 MnU WU MH DLC

Ljungquist, Walter Bertil, 1900–
Ombyte av tåg, av Walter Ljungquist. Stockholm, Albert Bonniers förlag [1933]
183 p. 19cm.
A novel.

I. Title.

A C 34-3966 rev
Minnesota. Univ. Libr. for Library of Congress [r46c2]

NL 0424615 MnU CtY MB

Ljungquist, Walter Bertil, 1900-
Ombyte av tåg. Stockholm, Bonnier [1945]
183 p.

NL 0424616 MH

Ljungquist, Walter Bertil, 1900–
Resande med okänt bagage, av Walter Ljungquist. Stockholm, A. Bonnier [1938]
377 p. 19½cm.
A novel.

I. Title.

40-6972 Revised
Library of Congress PT9875.L65R4 1938
[r46c2] 839.736

NL 0424617 DLC MnU

Ljungquist, Walter Bertil, 1900–
Revolt i grönska. Stockholm, Bonnier [1951]
285 p. 20 cm.

I. Title.

PT9875.L65R44 52-25359 ‡

NL 0424618 DLC NcD MnU MH NN

PT9875 .L65S6 1935 Ljungquist, Walter Bertil, 1900-
Släkten står på trappan. Stockholm, A. Bonnier [1935]
315 p. 20 cm.

NL 0424619 MB

Ljungquist, Walter Bertil, 1900-
Vägskäl. [Stockholm] Bonnier [1943]
523 p. 20cm.

NL 0424620 WU MnU OCl

PT9875 .L62V3 1941 Ljungquist, Walter Bertil, 1900 –
Vandring med månen; roman ... Stockholm, A. Bonnier [1941]
403 p.

NL 0424621 ICU

Ljungquist, Walter Bertil, 1900-
Vandring med månen. [Oversatt av Eva Mathisen. Oslo] Bokkommisjon, 1947.

NL 0424622 MH

Ljungstedt, Anders, 1759-1835.
A brief account of an ophthalmic institution...
see under title

[Ljungstedt, Anders] 1759-1836.
Contribution to an historical sketch of the Portuguese settlements in China, principally of Macao, of the Portuguese envoys & ambassadors to China, of the Roman Catholic mission in China and of the papal legates to China. By A. L., knt. Macao, China, 1832.
2 p. l., [vii]-xii p., 1 l., 174 p., 1 l. 19½cm.
"One hundred copies struck off for distribution."

1. Portuguese in China. 2. Macao, China. 3. Missions—China. 4. Catholic church—Missions.

Library of Congress DS740.5.P7L7 5—7192

NL 0424624 DLC

[Ljungstedt, Anders] 1759–1835.
Contribution to an historical sketch of the Roman Catholic church at Macao; and the domestic and foreign relations of Macao. By A. L., knt. Canton, China, 1834.
2 p. l., 53 p. 20½cm.

1. Catholic church in Macao. 2. Macao. I. Title.

Library of Congress BX1667.M3L52 43-39278

NL 0424625 DLC MH

Ljungstedt, Anders, 1759–1835.
An historical sketch of the Portuguese settlements in China; and of the Roman Catholic church and mission in China. By Sir Andrew Lungstedt ... A supplementary chapter, description of the city of Canton, republished from the Chinese repository, with the editor's permission. Boston, J. Munroe & co., 1836.
xv, 323, xviii p. 2 fold. pl. (incl. front.) fold. map, 2 fold. plans. 22½ cm.

1. Portuguese in China. 2. Macao. 3. Missions—China. 4. Catholic church—Missions. 5. Canton, China—Descr.

DS740.5.P7L72 5–7191 rev

DCU-IA InU CU OU
NL 0424626 DLC PKsL MB CtY CtY-AO NN MSaE ViU WaU

Ljungstedt, Gustav Christer, 1799-1832, respondent.
Agardh, Karl Adolf, 1785–1859, praeses.
Aphorismi botanici ... Lundæ, literis Berlingianis, 1817.

Ljungstedt, Gustaf Christer, 1799- 1832, resp.
Schedulae [-Novae schedulae] criticae de lichenibus exsiccatis Sueciae
see under Fries, Elias Magnus, 1794-1787, pr.

Ljungstedt, Hannah Milnor Robinson
see
Ljungstedt, Milnor, 1858-1942.

H19 79 Ljungstedt, Karl, 1856-
Anmärkningar till det starka preteritum i germanska språk. Upsala, Akademiska boktryckeriet, E. Berlin, 1887.
148p. 25cm.

1. Germanic languages - Tense.

NL 0424630 CtY NcD ICRL MH

PT7235 L5 Ljungstedt, Karl, 1856-
Eddan; om och ur de fornnordiska guda- och hjältesångerna, en populär framställning, af Karl Ljungstedt. Stockholm, J. Seligmann [1898]
[8],248 p. 20cm.

Largely commentary with selections in Swedish translation interspersed.
Contents.- Handskrifter af Eddadikterna.- Gudasånger.- Hjältesånger.- Tillägg.

NL 0424631 CU CtY NcU

439.7 L76g Ljungstedt, Karl, 1856-1916.
Grunddragen af modersmålets historia; en populär framställning ... Stockholm, J. Seligmann [1898]
204p.

1. Swedish language--Hist.

NL 0424632 IU PU

PD5075 .L75 Ljungstedt, Karl, 1856–
... Modersmålet och dess utvecklingsskeden, av Karl Ljungstedt ... 5. upplagan, genomsedd av Natan Lindqvist. Stockholm, A. Bonnier [1927]
47 p. illus. (incl. ports.) 24cm. (Studentföreningen Verdandis småskrifter. 46)

1. Swedish language—Hist.

NL 0424633 ICU CU

Ljungstedt, Karl, 1856–
... Språket, dess lif och ursprung, af Karl Ljungstedt ... (2. tusendet.) Stockholm, A. Bonnier [1891]
38 p. 20cm. (Studentföreningen Verdandis småskrifter. 30)
On cover: 1.-4. tusendet.

1. Language and languages.

12-28755
Library of Congress P105.L6

NL 0424634 DLC

AS284 S74 no.30 Ljungstedt, Karl, 1856-
Språket, dess liv och ursprung. 3. uppl. rev. av Natan Lindqvist. Stockholm, A. Bonnier [1920]
48 p. (Studentföreningen Verdandis småskrifter, 30)

NL 0424635 CU

Ljungstedt, Karl, 1856-
Språkets lif; inledning till den jämförande språkvetenskapen. Populär framställning. Stockholm, J. Seligmann [1899]
153 p.

1. Language and languages. I. Title.

NL 0424636 WaU CU

Ljungstedt, Karl, 1856-1916, tr.
Valda sånger ur den poetiska Eddan...
see under Edda Saemundar. [Complete and partial editions. Swedish. 1904]

VOLUME 337

Ljungstedt, Milnor, 1858–1942, ed.
Ancestral proofs & probabilities; an occasional bulletin, no. 1–4. Milnor Ljungstedt, editor and publisher. [Bethesda, Md.] 1935–36.
4 v. 28 cm.
"Items gathered from original court and church records of the colonial states."—no. 1, p. 20.
This material was originally compiled for publication in the now discontinued "County court note-book." cf. no. 1, p. [1]
1. United States—Genealogy. I. Title.
CS68.L5 35-16191

NL 0424638 DLC PHi MiD NN

Ljungstedt, Mrs. Milnor, ed.
The County court note-book; a little bulletin of history and genealogy. v. 1–10; Oct. 1921–Dec. 1931. [Bethesda, Md., 1921–31]

G3702 .C3 1932 .U54
Ljungstedt, Olof Axel.
U. S. *Geological survey.*
Geologic map of the United States, by the United States Geological survey, W. C. Mendenhall, director. Compiled by George W. Stose assisted by O. A. Ljungstedt ... [Washington; Engraved and printed by the U. S. Geological survey, 1932.

Ljungström, Barbro.
...Du skall icke...roman. Stockholm: Natur och kultur [1935] 238 p. 20½cm.
833848A. 1. Fiction, Swedish. I. Title.
N. Y. P. L. August 10, 1936

NL 0424641 NN

Ljungström, Barbro.
...Styvmor; roman. Stockholm: Bokförlaget Natur och kultur [1937] 207 p. 20½cm.
75466B. 1. Fiction, Swedish. I. Title.
N. Y. P. L. November 12, 1940

NL 0424642 NN

Ljungstroem, Claës Johan, 1819-1882.
Åhs och Wedens härader samt staden Borås beskrifna. Stockholm, 1865.
168 p., 5 pls. 4°.
For references to runes, see p. 57-61 (with 3 pls.)

NL 0424643 NIC

Ljungström, Claës Joh. Förteckning på en del ord, hvilka i dagligt tal af Westgötaalmogen begagnas och i fornnordiskan återfinnas, men hvilka antingen sällan eller ock aldrig förekomma i svenska skriftspråket. *Extr. fr.* Westergötlands Fornminnesföreningens Tidskrift. I. häftet. 1869. pp. 25-36. IcE45L788

NL 0424644 NIC

Ljungstroem, Claës Johan, 1819-1882.
Kinnefjerdings och Kållands härader samt Staden Lidköping beskrifne. Lund, 1871.
(4) + 212 p., 15 pls. 4°.
For runic inscriptions, see p. 49-60 (with 11 pls.)

NL 0424645 NIC

Ljungstroem, Claës Johan, 1819-1882.
Kinnefjerdings och Kallands härader samt Staden Lidköping beskrifne. 2. upplagan. Lund, 1875.
(4) - 13 - (2) p., 2 pls. 8°.

NL 0424646 NIC

Ljungström, Claës Johan, 1819-1882.
Runa-list eller konsten att läsa runor, folkskolorna och menige man meddelad. Lund, 1866.
(4) + 12 p. 8°.

NL 0424647 NIC

Ljungström, Claës Johan, 1819–1882.
Rúna-list, eller Konsten att läsa runor, folkskolorna och folket meddelad af Claës Joh. Ljungström. 2. uppl. ... Lund, F. Berlings boktryckeri, 1875.
2 p. l., 13, [2] p. 4 pl. on 2 l. 21cm.
Plates printed on both sides.
1. Runes.
23-3856
Library of Congress PD2014.L5

NL 0424648 DLC CtY NIC

Ljungström, Claës Johan, 1819-1882, ed.
Vestergötlands fornminnesförening.
Vestergötlands fornminnesförenings tidskrift. [1.]–
Lund [etc.] 1869–

Ljungström, David.
Vad ska vi säga om filmen. Stockholm, Missionsförbundets förlag [1953]
62 p. 20 cm. (Ungdomen diskuterar, 5)
"Litteraturförteckning": p. 62.
1. Moving-pictures—Moral and religious aspects. I. Svenska missionsförbundet. II. Title. (Series)
A 54-4254
Southern Calif., Univ. of. Library for Library of Congress [1]

NL 0424650 CLSU

Ljungström, Ernst. Bladets bygnad inom familjen Ericinese. i. Ericese. Akademisk afhandling. Lund. 1883. 4°. pp. [2], 47. 2 plates. (Arbeten från Lunds botaniska institution, 6.)
"Aftryck ur Lunds universitets årsskrift, tom. xix."

NL 0424651 MH-A

Ljungström, Georg, 1861-
Mellan de stora världskrigen, det gangna och det kommande; strödda tankar. Stockholm, Litteraturförlaget [1921]

NL 0424652 MH

Ljungström, Georg, 1861–
Nostradamus och Anton Johanssons profetior om nu stundande världshändelser, analyserade av Georg Ljungström. Stockholm: A.-B. Seelig & Co., 1928. 99 p. port. 8°.
Contents: Anton Johanssons syner. Nostradamus. Indianen. När faller franska republiken. Annie Besants Krishnamurti-Kristus.
401729A. 1. Prophecies. 2. Johansson, Anton, fl. 1913–14. 3. Notredame, Michel de, 1503–1566. 4. Besant, Annie (Wood), 1847– 5. Krishnamurti.
N. Y. P. L. February 25, 1929

NL 0424653 NN

Ljungström, John.
...Tecken, som bebåda tidsåldrarnas slut, utvecklingens kulmen, slutet på mänsklighetens historia, af John Ljungström... Stockholm: A. V. Carlson [1916]. 95 p. 8°.
At head of title: Fullkomligt och totalt olik alla andra böcker i samma ämne.

NL 0424654 NN

Ljungstroem, Klas Johan
see
Ljungstroem, Claes Johan, 1819-1882

Ljungström, Olle
The stress distribution in a 23°.5 swept back wing with rectangular cross section. Study of some important secondary effects. Linköping, Sweden, Saab Aircraft Company, 1951.
16 ℓ. diagrs. 29 cm.
Caption title.
Photostat (Positive)
SAAB MEMO No. IHC-0-531;TIP no. U18008.
1. Aeroplanes--Wings, swept-back.

NL 0424656 RPB

Ljungström, Oscar, 1868?–
..."The esoteric tradition;" false prophets. [Lund: H. Ohlssons boktryckeri, 1936] 12 p. 22½cm.
Cover-title.
1. Theosophy. 2. Purucker, Gottfried de, 1874– The esoteric tradition.
N. Y. P. L. March 2, 1938

NL 0424657 NN CtY

[Ljungström, Oscar] 1868–
... Graded lessons in theosophy (under the auspices of Theosophical university, Point Loma, California, U. S. A.) [Lund, Berlingska boktr., 1934]
[28] p. 23cm.
Caption title.
At head of title: No. 1–[13]
Signed: Oscar Ljungström.
1. Theosophy. I. Point Loma, Calif. Theosophical university. II. Title.
39-20821
Library of Congress BP565.L75
[2] 212

NL 0424658 DLC CtY NN

Mbz41 1 1935ℓ
[Ljungström, Oscar] 1868-
Karma, a reply to Mr. J.H.Fussell ...
[Lund,1935]
Caption title.
1.Fussell, Joseph Hall, 1863-

NL 0424659 CtY

Ljungström, Oscar, 1868–
Karma in ancient and modern thought, by Oscar Ljungström. Lund, Printed by H. Ohlsson, 1938.
37 (*i. e.* 39) p. 20½cm.
Leaf inserted between p. 18 and 19.
1. Karma. I. Title.
40-16562
Library of Congress BJ1499.K3L5
[2] 294

NL 0424660 DLC CtY NN CLSU CU

VOLUME 337

Ljungström, Oscar, 1868?–
Motrevolution; socialismens nedkämpande, av Oscar Ljungström. Stockholm: A. V. Carlson [1917]. 47 p. 8°.

1. Socialism (Contra).
N. Y. P. L. January 21, 1920.

NL 0424661 NN

Ljungström, Oscar, 1868–
A philosophical overhaul, by Oscar Ljungström. A first chapter. [Lund, Printed by H. Ohlsson, 1937]
118 p. diagrs. 20½cm.
"Printed as manuscript."
"No. 30."

I. Title.
37-12682
Library of Congress B4495.L53P5
[2] 198.5

NL 0424662 DLC CtY CLSU PU NN MH

Mbz41
1
1935ℓ
[Ljungström, Oscar] 1868-
Was Judge's plan right? ... [Lund,1935]
Caption title.

1.Judge, William Quan, 1851-1896.

NL 0424663 CtY

Ljungstrom aircraft Diesel engine. n. p. [1934?]
[30] ℓ., illus.

NL 0424664 MiD

Ljungvik,Herman,1896-
... Beiträge zur syntax der spätgriechischen volkssprache von Herman Ljungvik. Uppsala, Almqvist & Wiksell; [etc.,etc., 1932]
vii,[1],110 p. (Skrifter utgivna av K.Humanistiska vetenskaps-samfundet i Uppsala. 27:3)
"Literatur": p.[iv]-vii.

1.Greek language,Hellenistic (B.C.300-A.D.600)—Syntax [Full name: o Herman Ljungvik]

NL 0424665 MiU DDO CLSU IaU OU NIC

Ljungvik, Herman, 1896–
... Studien zur sprache der apokryphen Apostelgeschichten ... von Herman Ljungvik. Uppsala, A.-b. Lundequistska bokhandeln [1926]
xi, 106 p. 24cm. (Uppsala universitets årsskrift 1926 [bd. 2] Filosofi, språkvetenskap och historiska vetenskaper. 8)
The author's thesis, Uppsala; issued also without series title.
"Literatur": p. [vii]-xi.
1. Greek language, Hellenistic (B. C. 300–A. D. 600) 2. Greek language Biblical. 3. Bible. N. T. Apocryphal books. Acts. Greek—Language style.
[Full name: Otto Herman Ljungvik]
A 42-1961
Minnesota. Univ. Libr. for Library of Congress [AS284.U7 1926] [2] (378.485)

NL 0424666 MnU

Ljungvik, Herman, 1896–
Studien zur sprache der apokryphen Apostelgeschichten ... Uppsala, Appelbergs boktryckeri aktiebolag, 1926.
xi, 106 p. 25cm.
Inaug.-diss.—Upsala.
"Literatur": p. [vii]-xi.

1. Greek language, Hellenistic (B. C. 300–A. D. 600) 2. Greek language, Biblical. 3. Bible. N. T. Apocryphal books.
[Full name: Otto Herman Ljungvik]
28-29863
Library of Congress PA895.B6L5

NL 0424667 DLC MoU CtY DDO IU PU MnU

Ljungvik, Otto Herman
see
Ljungvik, Herman, 1896–

Ljungwaldh, Ruben.
Fastighetsköp, inteckning i fast egendom; några vinkar och råd vid fastighetsförvärv med kortfattad framställning av inteckningsrätten. [Stockholm] Forum [1945]
118 p. illus. 23 cm.

1. Real property—Sweden. I. Title.
54-20871 ‡

NL 0424669 DLC

Ljungwaldh, Ruben
Fastighetsköp. Inteckning i fast egendom. Några vinkar och råd vid fastighetsförvärv med kortfattad framställning av intecknings-rätten, av Ruben Ljungwaldh. [Stockholm, Svenska tryckeriaktiebolaget, 1945]
118, [2] p. tables, diagrs. 22½cm.

NL 0424670 MH-L

Ljungwaldh, Ruben.
Fastighetsköp; inteckning i fast egendom. Några vinkar och råd vid fastighetsförvärv med kortfattad framställning av inteckningsrätten. Ny, av författaren omarb. uppl. [Stockholm] Forum [1953]
125 p. diagrs. 20 cm.

1. Real property—Sweden. I. Title.
A 54-2029
New York Univ. Wash. Sq. Library for Library of Congress [1]†

NL 0424671 NNU-W DLC

Ljungzell, Nils J
Skeppsbyggnad och båtkonstruktion. Stockholm, Norstedt [1931]
696-1082 p. illus., map. 25 cm.
Detached from Uppfinningarnas bok.

1. Ship-building.
VM145.L5 51-54819

NL 0424672 DLC

Ljus och frihet
see under Lennstrand, Viktor Emanuel, 1861-1895, comp.

---

*BX
4800
.L5
Ljus på vägen. årg. 1, n:o 1- jan.- Minneapolis.
v. 21 cm. bimonthly.

"En hvarannan månad utkommande tidskrift, innehållande predikningar och kortare stycken till uppbyggelse i tron, kärleken och hoppet. Light on the way, a Swedish bi-monthly magazine."
Editor: J. G. Princell.

NL 0424674 MnHi

Ljusberg, Nicolaus, respondent.
Initia imperii R. Johannis III...
see under Fant, Erik Mikael, 1754-1817, praeses.

Ljusglimtar från Mongoliet; tidskrift för Svenska mongolmissionen.
Stockholm.
v. illus. 22 cm.

NL 0424676 CtY-D

Ljuskova, A E
see Līūskova, Aleksandra Evgen'evna.

Ljuskultur. v. 42
[Stockholm]
v. in illus. 26 cm. quarterly.
Began publication in 1929. Cf. Svensk bok-katalog, 1926–30.
Title varies: —Oct.-Dec. 1951, Tidskrift för ljuskultur.
Issued by Svenska förening för ljuskultur.
Organ of Svenska belysningssällskapet, Lysteknisk selskab i Danmark, and Selskapet for lyskultur i Norge.

1. Lighting—Period. I. Svenska föreningen för ljuskultur.
TH7700.L53 54-16534

NL 0424678 DLC PPF

Ljusne, Sweden. Sjukhus.
Årsberättelse.
Söderhamn, A. Hammarströms boktr.
v. 23 cm.

RA989.S84L55 52-18301

NL 0424679 DLC

Ljusterdal, Walter, joint ed.

Edling, Nils Gustav Sebastian, 1880– *ed.*
Vendels sockens dombok. Uppsala, Almqvist & Wiksells boktr. [1925–

Ljusternik, L A
see
Līūsternik, Lazar' Aronovich, 1899–

Ljutostanski, J. J.
see Līūtostanskiĭ, Ippolit Iosifovich, 1835–1915.

SD539
.L55
Lkhota, Otakar.
Как изнасяме дървените материали от горите. София, Земиздат, 1951.
90 p. illus. 17 cm.

1. Lumber—Transportation. I. Title.
Title transliterated: Kak iznasiāme dŭrvenite materiali ot gorite.
SD539.L55 59-34034

NL 0424683 DLC

Ll., A.R., tr.

Farnés, Sebastián.
Narraciones populares catalanas, recogidas por Sebastián Farnés, tr. libremente por A. R. Ll., ilustraciones de M. Durán. Barcelona, Biblioteca universal ilustrada, 1893.

VOLUME 337

[Barnes, Almont]
Administrative organization: a consideration of the principal executive departments of the United States government, in relation to administration. By Ll. B. Washington, D. C., W. H. Morrison, 1884.

Ll., B.
La independencia de Napoles...
see under title [Supplement]

Ll., B., barrister-at-law, pseud.
A new guide to the bar... 1907
see under title

Ll., B. of Harvard College, sometime commoner of Magdalen Hall, Oxford.
The English universities in the North American review; an essay
see [Rich, William Alexander]

Ll., C.
La cuestion de Italia...
see under title

Ll., C., Rev.
Observations on the choice of a school...
see under title

Ll., F.
La cabeza y el corazon
see under title [Supplement]

Ll., G. A., tr.

Ledit, Joseph Henry, 1898–
... Religión y comunismo, traducido por G. A. Ll. s. J. Buenos Aires, Editorial Difusión, 1938.

Ll., H.
Hindu women...
see Lloyd, Helen.

Ll., J.
The death of God's Moses's considered...
see under title

Ll., J.S.
La Pesca como esport.
see under title

LL., M.
Cartilla del Federalista...
see Llanos, Mateo.

Ll., M.
Men-miracles...
see
Lluelyn, Martin, 1616-82

LL. Z, J.E.
Preliminar, y cartas, que preceden al tomo I. de las Memorias historico-physicas
see under [Llano y Zapata, José, Eusebio del fl. 1744-1769.

QL 427 .L79 Llabador, Francis, 1906–
Les mollusques testacés marins, fluviatiles et terrestres de l'Ouest Algérien, depuis la frontière marocaine jusqu'à la Tafna. Alger, Imprimeries "La Typo-litho" et J. Carbonel réunies, 1935.
179 p. map, tables. 24 cm.
Thèse--Algiers.
Bibliography: p. [172]-175.

1. Mollusca--Algeria.

NL 0424699 MiU CtY

Llabería, Antonio.
La muerte de Romea. Loa drámatica escrita en honor de D. Julian Romea, por D. Antonio Llaberia. Barcelona: S. Manero, 1868. 2 p.l., 4-10 f. 8°.

1. Drama (Spanish). 2. Title.
N. Y. P. L. October 3, 1919.

NL 0424700 NN

Llabia, Ramón de
see Ramón *de Llavia, 15th cent.*

Llabres, Alejandro Bérgamo
see Bérgamo Llabres, Alejandro.

Llabrés, Gabriel
see Llabrés y Quintana, Gabriel, 1858-

Llabrés, Juan
see Llabrés Bernal, Juan.

Llabrés, Miquel Puigserver
see
Puigserver Llabrés, Miquel.

Span 3412.5
Llabrés Bernal, Juan
El archivo de la audiencia de Mallorca; noticia histórico descriptiva. Con un apéndice extracto de 280 documentos en pergamino de los siglos XIII a XVII. Palma de Mallorca, Impr. de Guasp, 1923

121 p.
Tirada aparte del Bolletí de la Societat Arqueológica Luliana, año XXXIX, tomo XXI, núms. 515-516 y 517-518.

NL 0424706 MH

Llabrés Bernal, Juan.
Breve noticia de la labor científica del capitán de navío don Felipe Bauzá y de sus papeles sobre América, 1764–1834; publicada con motivo del centenario de su muerte, por Juan Llabrés Bernal ... Palma de Mallorca, Imprenta Guasp, 1934.
1 p. l., [5]–76 p. port. 19½cm.

1. *Bauzá, Felipe, 1764?–1834—Bibliography.
A C 35-2635
Title from N. Y. Pub. Libr. Printed by L. C.

NL 0424707 NN

LLABRÉS BERNAL, JUAN.
De la marina de antaño; notas para la historia de Menorca (1769-1905). Artículos publicados en la prensa. Palma de Mallorca, 1955. 1 v. illus., ports. 25cm.

[Tomo] 1.

1. Minorca--Hist. 2. Mediterranean sea--Political and economic aspects.

NL 0424708 NN

Law
Llabrés Bernal, Juan, joint author.

Puértolas, E
Nociones de estiba y transporte de carga en los buques de comercio; técnica y legislación, de utilidad para los alumnos de náutica, por E. Puértolas y J. Llabrés. Palma de Mallorca, 1947.

Llabrés Bernal, Juan.
Notas de bibliografía extranjera sobre las Baleares y sus naturales a partir de 1931, por Juan Llabres ... Palma, Imp. politécnica, 1941.
cover-title, 26 p. 24cm.

1. Balearic islands—Bibl.
A 45-3971
New York. Public library for Library of Congress [2]

NL 0424710 NN

Llabrés Bernal, Juan.
Noticias y relaciones históricas de Mallorca (1801-1850). [Palma de Mallorca, 1945-53?]
13 pts. in 8. illus., ports. 26cm.

Pliego 1-4, 6-7, 17-23.
Issued in 8 parts.
Cover-title.
At head of title: Boletín de la Sociedad arqueológia Luliana, Palma de Mallorca.

NL 0424711 NN

Llabrés Rubio, Pedro.
... Rosa, la pantalonera ...
see under Alonso López, Francisco, 1887-1948.

DP 130.7 .C9L77 LLABRÉS Y QUINTANA, GABRIEL, 1858-
Bernardo Dez-Coll es el autor de la crónica catalana de Pedro IV el ceremonioso de Aragón que fue escrita por los años de 1365 a 1390, tesis doctoral. Madrid, Tip. de la Revista de Archivos, Bibliotecas y Museos, 1903.
46 p.

"De la Revista de Archivos, Bibliotecas, y Museos."

1. Descoll, Bernat

NL 0424713 InU

Llabrés y Quintana, Gabriel, ed.

Sociedad arqueológica Luliana, *Palma, Majorca.*
Boletin de la Sociedad arqueológica Luliana; revista de estudios históricos ... t. 1–
años 1885-86–
Palma de Mallorca, 1886–

VOLUME 337

Llabrés y Quintana, Gabriel, 1858- ed.

Cançoner dels comtes d'Urgell.
Cançoner dels comtes d'Urgell. [Barcelona] 1906.

Llabrés y Quintana, Gabriel, 1858-
Catálogo de los objetos que contiene el Museo provincial de Huesca
see under Huesca, Spain (Province) Museo provincial.

FILM 12102 Z Library School
Llabrés y Quintana, Gabriel, 1858-
La dinastía de impresores más antigua de Europa; ó sea, El pié de imprenta Guasp (1579 á 1879 - Palma) Noticias y documentos. Mahón, Fábregues, 1897.
22 p. On film (Negative)

Microfilm. Original in British Museum.
"Extraido de la 'Revista de Menorca'."

1. Guasp, family of printers. 2. Printing - Hist. - Palma, Majorca. I. Title.

NL 0424717 CU NNC NNH

Llabrés y Quintana, Gabriel, 1858-
Estudi históric y literari escrit per En Gabriel Llabrés sobre'l Cançoner dels comtes d'Urgell, publicat per la Societat catalana de bibliófils. Barcelona, Societat catalana de bibliófils, 1907.
3 p. l., lxxviii p., 4 l. incl. 2 geneal. tab. double pl., 2 double facsim. 28cm.
"Exemplar n. 91."

1. Cançoner dels comtes d'Urgell. 2. Catalan poetry—Hist. & crit. I. Societat catalana de bibliófils, Barcelona.

Library of Congress PC3913.L3 30-2101

NL 0424718 DLC MH OCl CU

PC3937 .C528 L8
Llabrés y Quintana, Gabriel, 1858-
Estudi históric y literari escrit per En Gabriel Llabrés sobre'l Cançoner dels comtes d'Urgell, publicat per la Societat catalana de bibliófils. Oliva, Impressor Vilanova y Geltrú, 1907.
3 p. l., lxxviii p., 4 l. incl. 2 geneal. tab. double pl., 2 double facsim. 28cm.

1. Cançoner dels comtes d'Urgell. 2. Catalan poetry—Hist. & crit. I. Societat catalana de bibliófils, Barcelona.

NL 0424719 ICU

Llabrés y Quintana, Gabriel, 1858- ed.
Libre de saviesa. 1. ed., feta estampar ab un estudi preliminar ... 1908
see under Jaime I, King of Aragon, 1208-1276.

PC 3927 L55
Llabres y Quintana, Gabriel, 1858-
Poéticas catalanas d'en Berenguer de Noya y Francesch de Olesa, ara novament estampades per en Gabriel Llabres y Quintana. Barcelona, Verdaguer, 1909.
xxiii,103p. (Biblioteca catalana; segle XIV)
Contains Lo mirall de trovar of Berenguer de Noya and La nova art de trovar of Francesch de Olesa.

NL 0424721 UU TU MH ICN

He27 1
Llabrés y Quintana, Gabriel, 1858-
... Repertorio de "consuetas" representadas en las iglesias de Mallorca (siglos XV y XVI).
Pamphlet
From Revista de archivos, bibliotecas y museos, (3.época) año 5, p.920-927, diciembre, 1901.

NL 0424722 CtY

Llaca, Enrique Bustamante-
see Bustamante-Llaca, Enrique.

Llaca y Argudin, Francisco, 1878-

Trelles y Govín, Carlos Manuel, 1866-
Bibliografía cubana del siglo XIX, por Carlos M. Trelles ... Matanzas, Impr. de Quirós y Estrada, 1911-15.

Llaca y Argudín, Francisco, 1878 -
Legislacion notarial de Cuba. Compilacion de disposiciones oficiales concordadas y anotadas, por Francisco Llaca y Argudín ... Habana, Impr. "Avisador comercial," 1917.
226 p. 24cm.

I. Title.

19-19798

NL 0424725 DLC CtY FU

Llaca y Argudín, Francisco, 1878 -
... Legislación notarial de Cuba. Compilación de disposiciones oficiales concordadas y anotadas, por el dr. Francisco Llaca y Argudín ... 2. ed. ... Habana, Impr. y papelería de Rambla, Bouza y ca., 1931.
410 p. 24cm. (Biblioteca del "Repertorio judicial")

1. Notaries—Cuba. I. Title.

32-13023

NL 0424726 DLC

Llaca y Argudín, Francisco, 1878- ed.
... Legislación sobre amnistías e indultos de la república de Cuba; recopilación y notas aclaratorias por el dr. Francisco Llaca y Argudín ... Habana, Cultural, s. a., 1933.
66 p. 23cm. (Biblioteca del "Repertorio judicial")

1. Amnesty—Cuba. 2. Pardon—Cuba. I. Cuba. Laws, statutes, etc. II. Title.

34-25281

NL 0424727 DLC

Llaca y Argudín, Francisco, 1878 -
... Legislación sobre el divorcio en Cuba; compilación de disposiciones oficiales concordadas y anotadas por Francisco Llaca y Argudín ... Publicación autorizada por el gobierno ... Habana, Impr. de Rambla, Bouza y ca., 1931.
197 p. 23½cm. (Biblioteca del "Repertorio judicial")

1. Divorce—Cuba. 2. Marriage law—Cuba. [2. Marriage—Cuba] I. Cuba. Laws, statutes, etc. II. Title.

31-18654

NL 0424728 DLC

Law
Llaca y Argudín, Francisco, 1878- ed.
FOR OTHER EDITIONS SEE MAIN ENTRY

Cuba. *Laws, statutes, etc.*
Legislación sobre el registro del estado civil en Cuba; compilación de disposiciones oficiales concordadas y anotadas, por Francisco Llaca y Argudín. 3. ed. corr. y aumentada. Habana, Impr. de Rambla, Bouza, 1930.

Llaca y Argudín, Francisco, 1878- *ed.*
... Legislación sobre jubilaciones y pensiones de funcionarios y empleados públicos; compilación de disposiciones oficiales concordadas y anotadas por Francisco Llaca y Argudín ... Habana, Impr. y papelería de Rambla, Bouza y ca., 1926-36.
2 v. 25cm. (Biblioteca del "Repertorio judicial")
"Publicación autorizada por el gobierno."

1. Civil service pensions—Cuba. I. Cuba. Laws, statutes, etc.

Library of Congress JL1012.Z2L52 43-46252
[2] 351.5

NL 0424730 DLC

Llaca y Argudín, Francisco, 1878-
... El libro del procurador; compilación de disposiciones oficiales, concordadas y anotadas por Francisco Llaca y Argudín ... Habana, Impr. de Rambla, Bouza y ca., 1937.
3 p. l., [5]-242 p. 22½cm. (Biblioteca del "Repertorio judicial")

1. Lawyers—Cuba. I. Title.

42-46286

NL 0424731 DLC

Llaca y Argudín, Francisco, 1878-
El libro del procurador; compilación de disposiciones oficiales concordadas y anotadas. 2. ed., ampliada, corr. y puesta al corriente con la legislación y jurisprudencia, por Juan J. E. Casasús. Habana, Impr. Berea, 1951.
319 p. 23 cm. (Biblioteca del "Repertorio judicial")

1. Lawyers—Cuba. I. Casasús, Juan José Expósito, 1899- II. Title. (Series)

55-19972

NL 0424732 DLC

Llaca y Argudín, Francisco, 1878 -
Organizacion de los tribunales de Cuba y su personal, desde 1°. de enero de 1899 hasta 31 de diciembre de 1917, por el Dr. Francisco Llaca y Argudin ... Habana, Impr. de Rambla, Bouza y c.ª, 1918.
223 p. 22cm.
Errata slip mounted on p. 2 of cover.

1. Courts—Cuba. 2. Cuba—Biog.

Library of Congress JL1015.L6 19-16978

NL 0424733 DLC

Llaca y Argudín, Francisco, 1878 -
Organizacion de los tribunales de Cuba y su personal desde 1° de enero de 1899 hasta 31 de julio de 1919, por el Dr. Francisco Llaca y Argudin ... Habana, Impr. de Rambla, Bouza y c.ª, 1919.
243 p. 23½cm.

1. Courts—Cuba. 2. Cuba—Biog.

Library of Congress JL1015.L6 1919 20-22750

NL 0424734 DLC CtY

Llaca y Argudín, Francisco, 1878 -
Organizacion de los tribunales de Cuba y su personal desde 1°. de enero de 1899 hasta 31 de diciembre de 1922, por el Dr. Francisco Llaca y Argudin ... 3. ed. ... Habana, Impr. de Rambla, Bouza y c.ª, 1923.
321 p., 1 l. 24½cm.

1. Courts—Cuba. 2. Lawyers—Cuba. 3. Cuba—Biog. [4. Biography] I. Title.

26-5266

NL 0424735 DLC

Llaca y Argudín, Francisco, 1878-
El procedimiento correccional en Cuba, compilación de disposiciones oficiales concordadas y anotadas por Francisco Llaca y Argudín ... Publicación autorizada por el gobierno ... Habana, Impr. de Rambla, Bouza y ca., 1924-
v. 24cm.

—— Apéndice primero (1929-1937) ... Habana, Impr. de Rambla, Bouza y ca., 1937.
4, 807 p. 24cm.

1. Criminal procedure—Cuba. 2. Courts—Cuba. I. Title.

26-5261 Revised

NL 0424736 DLC

VOLUME 337

4K Cuba 40 Llaca y Argudín, Francisco, 1878-1949
El procedimiento correccional en Cuba, compilacion de disposiciones oficiales concordadas y anotadas. Publicacion autorizada por el gobierno. 2. ed., corregida y aumentada. Habana, Impr. y papeleria de Rambla, Bouza, 1929.
3 v. in 2.

NL 0424737 DLC-P4

Llaca y Escoto, Francisco, ed.
Repertorio judicial: revista ... fundada bajo los auspicios del Colegio de abogados de la Habana ... año 1- marzo 1925-
Habana, Impr. de Rambla, Bouza y ca., 1925-

Llacar, Perfecto E
Of clouds and silver lines, selected poems, by Perfecto E. Llacar ... Laoag, Ilocos Norte, 1946.
3 p. l., viii p., 1 l., 82 p. 22 cm.

I. Title.

PS9993.L5O3 821.91 47-25151

NL 0424739 DLC

Llacayo y Santa María, Augusto
Escorial. Biblioteca.
... Antiguos manuscritos de historia, ciencia y arte militar, medicina y literarios existentes en la biblioteca del Monasterio de San Lorenzo del Escorial; por D. Augusto Llacayo y Santa María ... Sevilla, F. Alvarez y ca., 1878.

DP402 .B8 .L5 Llacayo y Santamaría, Augusto.
Burgos: catedral, Cartuja, huelgas; monumentos religiosos, artísticos e históricos, curiosidades, cosas notables de Burgos y sus cercanías. 2. ed. Burgos, R. Arnaiz, 1887.
236p. illus. 21cm.

1. Burgos, Spain - Descr.

NL 0424741 NNU-W

Wason DS548 L79 Llacayo y Santa Maria, Augusto.
Cochinchina y el Tonkin; España y Francia en el reino de Annam. Búrgos, Impr. de D. Timoteo Arnaiz, 1883.
114 p. 19cm.

1. French in Cochin China. 2. Spanish in Cochin China. 3. French in Tonkin. 4. Spanish in Tonkin.

NL 0424742 NIC

Llacayo y Santa Maria, Augusto.
Un nó sé qué! y un qué sé yó! Comedia en un acto y en verso, original. Madrid: C. Lopez, 1859. 2 p.l., 31 p. 8°. (Galeria dramática.)

In: NPL p. v. 374, no. 3.

By Augusto Llacayo and E. Larroga

1. Drama (Spanish). 2. Larroga, Eugenio, jt. au. 3. Title.
N. Y. P. L. April 17, 1912.

NL 0424743 NN

Llacayo y Santa María, Augusto.
Un so sé qué! y un que sé yo! Comedia en un acto y en verso, original de Don Augusto Llacayo y Don Eugenio Larroca. Madrid, Cipriano López, 1859.
31p.

Microcard edition.

NL 0424744 ICRL LU OrU

Llach, Emilio.
Emilio Llach migajas (articulos y pequeñas narraciones...) Sevilla, 1896.

NL 0424745 NNH

Llach, Guillermo
... De la indignidad y de la incapacidad sucesoria ...

(In Bogotà. Universidad Javeriana. Tesis. 1943, v. II, p. ⌊249⌋-290)

NL 0424746 MH-L

Llach, Leonor.
... Cuadros conocidos (cuentos). México, Editorial "Cvltvra", 1933.
223 p., 1 l. 18½cm.

I. Title.

35-11511

Library of Congress PQ7297.L55C8 863.6

NL 0424747 DLC ICarbS TxU CU OOxM

Llach, Leonor.
... Retratos de almas. México ⌊La Impresora, S. Turanzas del Valle⌋ 1939.
105 p. 19½cm.
Short stories.

I. Title.

41-16318

Library of Congress PQ7297.L55R4
⌊2⌋ 863.6

NL 0424748 DLC

Llach Carreras, Juan.
A través de España, por d. Juan Llach Carreras ... Nueva ed. Gerona-Madrid, Dalmáu Carles, Pla, s. a., 1935.
2 p. l., 7-281 p. illus. 18cm.

1. Spanish language—Chrestomathies and readers. 2. Spain—Descr. & trav. I. Title.

36-24427

Library of Congress PC4127.G4L6 1935
⌊2⌋ [914.6] 468.6

NL 0424749 DLC

Llach Trevoux, Guillermina
... Patronatos para reos libertados ... ⌊por⌋ Guillermina Llach Trevoux. Mexico, 1946.
53 p., 1 l. 22½cm.

Tesis (abogado) - Univ. de Mexico.
"Reglamento del patronato para reos libertados, publicado en el diario oficial el 14 de junio de 1934": p. 49-53.
Bibliographical footnotes.

NL 0424750 MH-L

Llactacúyac, *pseud.*
see
Cordero Palacios, Octavio.

Llacuna, Joan.
Aurora de l'aragall. Il·lustrat amb 11 aiguaforts de Grau Sala. Barcelona, 1947.
118 p. illus. 26 cm.
Poems.

I. Title.

PC3941.L47A9 55-31648 ‡

NL 0424752 DLC

Llacuna, José Pablo
see Gómez Llacuna, José Pablo.

Llado, Antonio Cortés
see Cortés Llado, Antonio.

Llado, Cristián Cortes
see Cortes Llado, Cristián.

Lladó, Elma Mabel Marchisio
see Marchisio Lladó, Elma Mabel.

849.98 L791 Lladó, Francesc de B
Els dos poders. Pròleg del Joan Tusquets. Barcelona, Llibreria Catalònia ⌊1929⌋
204 p. (Biblioteca horitzons, v.5)

NL 0424757 MiU

4PQ Span 676 Lladó, Francesc de B
En tot lloc i en tot moment, poemes eucarístics. Il·lustracions de J. Artigas Basté. Barcelona, Editorial Estel [1952]
127 p.

NL 0424758 DLC-P4

Lladó, Francesc de B
Llibret de sant Josep Oriol; poemes. 1. ed. Barcelona, M. Montserrat Borrat ⌊1950⌋
183 p. illus. 13 cm.

1. Oriol, José, Saint, 1650-1702—Poetry. I. Title.

PC3941.L48L5 55-26828 ‡

NL 0424759 DLC

B 4568 B24L62 Llado, Juan.
Balmes; notas biográficas y crítica general sobre su personalidad y sus obras. Traducción del catalán arreglada y editada por el semanario Ausetania con un prólogo del excmo. sr. d. Manuel Polo Peyrolón. Vich, Imprenta Ausetana, 1910.
xv, 120 p. illus. 19 cm.

1. Balmes, Jaime Luciano, 1810-1848. I. Title.

NL 0424760 NBuU

Lladó, Juan Bérgamo y
see
Bérgamo y Lladó, Juan.

VOLUME 337

Lladó, L
... España; la riqueza artística del Palacio nacional. [Barcelona, Los Talleres huecograbado de S. Mumbrú, 1935]
xxv p. 128 pl. on 64 l. 17½ x 24½cm.
Text in Spanish, French, English and German.

1. Madrid. Palacio nacional. I. Title.

A 43-1058

New York. Public library for Library of Congress [2]

NL 0424762 NN

Lladó, Luis.
Tomás G. Masaryk; prólogo del doctor Eduardo Benes ... Textos y traducciones del prof. Luis Lladó; fragmentos seleccionados y ordenados de varias obras del famoso escritor checo, Carlos Capek. México, Ediciones Minerva, 1942.
3 p. l., 11-189, [1] p., 1 l. front. (coat of arms) plates (incl. music) ports., map. 23½cm.

1. Masaryk, Tomáš Garrigue, pres. Czechoslovak republic, 1850-1937. 2. Czechoslovak republic. I. Čapek, Karel, 1890-1938.

43-6461

Library of Congress DB217.M3L5
[2] 923.1437

NL 0424763 DLC

Llado, Mario Cortes
see Cortes Llado, Mario.

Span 745.139.727

Llado, Mateo
Las chekas de Barcelona, forjaremos una sociedad más justa, más humana. Reportaje por Mateo Lladó, fotografias de Carlos Perez de Rozas. Barcelona, Editorial Alas [1939]
34 p. (Biblioteca Victoria, Año 1, Num. 2)
Photoreproduction of Harvard College Library copy

1. Spain. Servicio de Investigación Militar

NL 0424765 MH

4PQ Span. Am. 154

Lladó, Miguel.
Yo y mi perro. [1. edición] Lérida Editora Leridana, 1947.
120 p. (Biblioteca de escritores Leridanos, 1)

NL 0424766 DLC-P4 IU

Lladó, Miquel, 1919-
Els anys, els dies i les hores. [1. ed.] Lleida, Impr. Abardia [1952]
64 p. illus. 21 cm.
Poems.

I. Title.

PC3941.L485A7 55-57703 ‡

NL 0424767 DLC

Lladó, N Llopis
see Llopis Lladó, Noel.

Lladó, Pedro.
El triunfo de la justicia antes un mercat esgarrat; comedia en dos actos y en prosa original de D. Pedro Lladó... Torroella de Montgrí, 1893. iv, (i)6-55 p. 12°.

1. Drama (Spanish). 2. Title.
N. Y. P. L. October 3, 1919.

NL 0424769 NN

Lladó, Pedro.
El triunfo de la justicia; antes, Un mercat esgarrat, comedia en dos actos y en prosa. Torroella de Montgrí, 1893.
55p.
Microcard edition.

NL 0424770 ICRL

Llado, Victor Faura y
see
Faura y Llado, Victor

Lladó de Cosso, José.
Izaguirre, el poeta místico de "Desiertos y campiñas." [Tegucigalpa] Talleres Tipo-litográficos "Aristón," 1949.
174, xxii p. 22 cm.
"Máximas": p. [i]-xxii.

1. Izaguirre, Carlos.

PQ7509.I 8Z7 A 51-10492

New York. Public Libr. for Library of Congress [1]†

NL 0424772 NN CSt IU CtY TxU LU DLC

Llado de Cosso, José, ed.
Mercurio [revista mensual illustrada dé actualidades, ciencias, artes, crítica, viajes, politica, industrias, modas, etc.]
[New Orleans, The Mercurio publishing company] 19

---

48 1035

Llado Figueras, José
Breves biografias intimas de grandes filosofos [ ]
Editorial Molino [1952]
235 p.

NL 0424774 DLC-P4

Lladó i Figueres, Josep Maria.
14 [i. e. Catorce] de abril, Cataluña es una democracia [por] J. M. Lladó y Figueras. [Barcelona] Biblioteca Política de Catalunya, 1938.
60 p. 20 cm.
On cover: Fechas históricas.

1. Catalonia—Pol. & govt. I. Title. II. Title: Cataluña es una democracia.

DP302.C68L5 946.7 39-16061 rev*

NL 0424775 DLC PPiU

Lladó i Figueres, Josep Maria.
El 19 [i. e. diecinueve] de julio en Barcelona [por] J. M. Lladó y Figueres. [Barcelona] Biblioteca Política de Catalunya, 1938.
110 p. 20 cm.
On cover: Fechas históricas.

1. Spain—Hist.—Civil War, 1936-1939. 2. Barcelona—Hist. I. Title.

DP269.L53 946.08 39-16060 rev*

NL 0424776 DLC IEN NN

Lladó y Ferragut, Jaime.
El archivo de la Real y Pontificia Universidad Literaria y Estudio General Luliano del antiguo Reino de Mallorca. Con un prólogo del P. Miguel Batllori. Palma de Mallorca, Impr. Vda. F. Soler, 1946.
viii, 78, xiv p. illus., ports. 24 cm.

1. Palma, Majorca. Real y Pontificia Universidad Literaria—Bibl.—Sources.

CD1879.P3L6 49-57683*

NL 0424777 DLC

Lladó y Ferragut, Jaime
El Archivo municipal de la villa de Alaró. Catálogo de su sección historica, documentos y noticias
see under Alaró, Majorca. Archivo municipal.

Lladó y Ferragut, Jaime, *ed.*
Catálogo de la sección histórica del Archivo Municipal de la ciudad de Lluchmayor (Baleares) Documentos y noticias por Jaime Lladó y Ferragut. Prólogo por Jaime Sastre Vidal. Palma de Mallorca, Imp. SS. Corazones, 1955.
83 p. illus., port., fold. map. 22 cm.
"Bibliografía referente a Lluchmayor": p. 82-83.

1. Lluchmayor, Majorca—Bibl. 2. Archives—Majorca. I. Lluchmayor, Majorca. Archivo Municipal. II. Title.

CD1877.L54L54 57-48026

NL 0424779 DLC

Lladó y Ferragut, Jaime.
Catálogo de la sección histórica del Archivo Municipal de la villa de Binisalem (Baleares); documentos y noticias. Prólogo por Juan Vich Salom. Palma de Mallorca, Imp. SS. Corazones, 1953.
xxii, 58 p. illus., ports., facsims., music. 22 cm.
"Bibliografía referente a Binisalem": p. 56-57.

1. Archives—Majorca. 2. Binisalem, Majorca—Hist.—Sources—Bibl. I. Binisalem, Majorca. Archivo Municipal.

CD1877.B5L55 57-58667

NL 0424780 DLC

Lladó y Ferragut, Jaime.
El régimen municipal en los pueblos de Mallorca desde Jaime I de Aragón, por d. Jaime Lladó y Ferragut ... 1. ed. Palma de Mallorca, J. Tous, impresor, 1933.
59 p., 1 l. 20½cm.
"Bibliografía histórico local": p. 7-10.

1. Municipal government—Majorca. I. Title.

34-11184

Library of Congress JS6320.M3L5 1933
[2] 352.0467

NL 0424781 DLC NcD

Lladó y Ferragut, Jaime.
Rincones de Palma ... por don Jaime Lladó y Ferragut ... Mallorca [Impr. de la Librería politécnica] 1930-
v. illus. 21½cm.

1. Architecture, Domestic—Palma, Majorca. I. Title.

32-30044

Library of Congress NA7387.P3L6
[2] 728.09467

NL 0424782 DLC

Lladó y Figueres, José María y
see
Lladó i Figueres, Josep Maria.

Lladonosa, Josep
see
Lladonosa Pujol, José.

BX4636 .L6S2L8

Lladonosa Pujol, José.
La antigua parroquia de San Martín de Lérida. Ilustraciones de Ricardo Calvet y Miguel Portugués. Lérida, Artes Gráficas Ilerda, 1944.
138 p. illus., plans.
Includes bibliography.

1. Lérida. San Martín (Church)

NL 0424785 ICU CtY NN

VOLUME 337

Lladonosa Pujol, José.
La ciutat de Lleida. Barcelona, Editorial Barcino, 1955–
v. illus. 19 cm. (Enciclopèdia catalunya. Biblioteca per a l'estudi de Catalunya, València i les Balears en tots els aspectes, v. 26
Includes bibliography.
1. Lérida, Spain.
DP402.L33L58 56-18965 ‡
NL 0424786 DLC InU NN NcU

Lladonosa Pujol, José.
Compendio de historia de Lérida. ⌊1. ed.⌋ Lérida, Editora Leridana, 1948.
210 p. 17 cm. (Biblioteca de escritores leridanos, 10)
Bibliographical references included in "Notas" (p. 195-208)
1. Lérida, Spain—Hist. (Series)
DP402.L33L6 51-25659
NL 0424787 DLC

Lladonosa Pujol, José.
Manuel de Montsuar, 1410–1491; la historia de un gran carácter al servicio de las instituciones leridanas. Prólogo del Dr. J. Ernesto Martínez Ferrando. Lérida, Imprenta Escuela Provincial, 1950 ⌊i. e. 1952⌋
323, lvi p. illus., port. 24 cm.
At head of title: Instituto de Estudios Ilerdenses de la Excma. Diputación Provincial de Lérida. Delegación del Consejo Superior de Investigaciones Científicas.
1. Montsaur, Manuel de, 1410-1491. 2. Catalonia—Hist.
DP302.C65L56 65-66973
NL 0424788 DLC NNC CU MH ICN

Lladró, Ramón.
See
Lladró y Mallí, Ramón, 1825–1896.

Bonaparte Collection No.4585
LLADRÓ Y MALLI, RAMÓN, 1825-1896.
La demanà de una novia. Cuadrét de costums valensianes en un acte y en vèrs. Valencia, C.Mariana,1858.
30p. 22½cm.
Binder's title: R.Lladro y Malli.
NL 0424790 ICN

Lladró y Mallí, Ramon, 1825–1896.
A deshora de la nit: sainete escrit en Valensiá y en prosa y vers. Valencia: Impr. de la casa de beneficencia, 1888.
29 p. 8°. (Adm. lirico-dram de E. Hidalgo)
NL 0424791 NN

Lladró y Mallí, Ramón, 1825–1896.
Diciembre y enero. Revista del año 1870. Cuadro cómico-lirico-histórico-plástico, original y en verso del ciudadano Ramon Lladró y Malli; música de D. José Jordá... Valencia: V. Leon, 1871. 24 p. 8°.
Without music.
1. Drama (Spanish). 2. Title.
N. Y. P. L. December 11, 1919.
NL 0424792 NN

PQ 6226 .T4 v.1
Lladró y Malli, Ramón, 1825-1896.
A falta de buenos, ó Rafela la filanera; choguét escrit en dialecte valensiá, en un acte y en vers, orichinal de R. LL. y M. Valensia, Imp. de D. E. Mariana, 1855.
24 p. (In Teatro español. ⌊Madrid, etc., 1787-1935⌋ v. 1, ⌊4⌋)
NL 0424793 MiEM ICN

Lladró y Malli, Ramon.
Lo ideal. Tres tratados afines... Valencia, 1889.
NL 0424794 NNH

Bonaparte Collection No.4583
LLADRÓ Y MALLI, RAMÓN, 1825-1896.
El mejor marido, ó Sènto el de Meliana. Comedia en un acto y en verso Valensia, C.Mariana,1858.
32p. 22½cm.
Binder's title: R.Lladro y Malli.
NL 0424795 ICN

Bonaparte Collection No.4584
LLADRÓ Y MALLI, RAMÓN, 1825-1896.
El sereno d'Alfafar. Choguét del chènero bilingüe en un acte y en vèrs. Valensia,C. Mariana,1858.
24p. 22½cm.
Binder's title: R.Lladro y Malli.
NL 0424796 ICN

Llagas, Juan de las
see Juan de las Llagas.

Llagostera, Daniel Girona
see Girona Llagostera, Daniel.

4DL Nor. 35
Llagostera, Lluis
Noruega y Spitzberg, records de viatge, 1909. Barcelona, Tip. "L'Avenç", 1910.
51 p.
NL 0424799 DLC-P4

Llagostera y Sala, Francesch.
Aforística catalana, ó sia Col-lecció de refranis populars catalans. 2ª ed. Barcelona, A. Verdaguer, 1883.
pp. 48.
Proverbs-Catalan||AcS 186599
NL 0424800 MH NNH

Llaguet (Bastien) [1870–]. *Contribution à l'étude de la bile comparativement dans l'urine et les matières fécales à l'état normal et à l'état pathologique. 116 pp., 2 pl. 8°. Bordeaux, 1910. No. 69.
NL 0424801 DNLM

Llaguno, Alberto Fuentes
see
Fuentes Llaguno, Alberto.

Llaguno, J O.
... Frondas poéticas. Guayaquil, Librería "Gutenberg" de Uzcátegui & cía., 1909.
171 p. 18cm.
I. Title.
22-4295
Library of Congress PQ8219.L5F7
NL 0424803 DLC DPU NN

---

789 L789 fro 1919
Llaguno, J O
... Frondas poéticas. Guayaquil, 1919.
203,iii p. port. 17cm.
With author's autograph.
NL 0424804 CU

Llaguno, Joaquin, plaintiff.
Sánchez, Pedro.
Alegato de buena prueba, que el lic. d. Pedro Sanchez, apoderado de d. Joaquin Llaguno en el negocio que sigue contra el lic. d. Francisco B. Belaunzarán sobre la propiedad de un camino en terrenos de la hacienda de Santa Cruz, presentó ante el sr. juez de primera instancia de Fresnillo. Zacatecas, Impreso en la tip. del gobierno, 1857.

Llaguno, Joaquín
Esposicion que hace al publico Joaquin Llaguno sobre el embargo de la hacienda de San Jacinto. Zacatecas, Imprenta del Supremo Gobierno, 1862.
28 p. 19½cm.
NL 0424806 MH-L

Llaguno, Joaquin.
Exmo. señor. Los que suscribimos, individuos del comercio y minería de Zacatecas... hacemos presente.
see under [Compañía Zacatecana]

Llaguno, Joaquin.
Zamora, Victoriano.
Informe hecho a la exma. 2.ª sala, por el c. Victoriano Zamora, relativo a los ruidosos autos del denuncio de San Clemente. El que para su vindicacion publica Joaquin Llaguno. Zacatecas, Impr. a cargo de A. Villagrana, 1839.

Llaguno, Joaquín, plaintiff.
Fernández Monjardín, Antonio, *d.* 1870.
Informe que hizo en la Primera sala de la Suprema corte de justicia el licenciado d. Antonio Fernandez Monjardin, fundando el recurso de nulidad que interpuso don Joaquin Llaguno en el juicio sobre denuncio de la mina de San Clemente, seguido en la ciudad de Zacatecas. Mégico, Oficina de Galvan, a cargo de M. Arevalo, 1840.

Llaguno, Leonardo Tariche
see Tariche Llaguno, Leonardo.

Llaguno, Manuel, defendant.
⌊Moctezuma, Manuel Andrés⌋
Documentos falsificados presentados en juicio. ¿En qué tiempo puede denunciarse su falsedad? Negocia Dávila-Llaguno. ⌊n. p.⌋ Tip. popular de María de la Rosa vda. de Baer s. l. p. ⌊1910?⌋

VOLUME 337

Llaguno, Pablo.
See
Llaguno y de Cardenas, Pablo.

[Llaguno y Amírola, Eugenio] d. 1799, editor.
Claros varones de Castilla, y letras de Fernando de[l] Pulgar... Madrid, 1789.
16°.

NL 0424813 CtY

Llaguno y Amírola, Eugenio, d. 1799.
Historia de los movimientos, separacion y guerra de Cataluña, en tiempo de Felipe IV
see under Mello, Francisco Manuel de, 1611-1666.

Llaguno y Amirola, Eugenio, d. 1799.
López de Ayala, Pedro, 1332–1407.
Cronicas de los reyes de Castilla, don Pedro, don Enrique II. don Juan I, don Enrique III. por don Pedro Lopez de Ayala ... con las enmiendas del secretario Geronimo Zurita: y las correcciones y notas añadidas por don Eugenio de Llaguno Amirola ... Madrid, Impr. de A. de Sancha, 1779–80.

Llaguno y Amírola, Eugenio, *d.* 1799.
Noticias de los arquitectos y arquitectura de España desde su restauración, por ... D. Eugenio Llaguno y Amirola, ilustradas y acrecentadas con notas, adiciones y documentos, por D. Juan Agustin Cean-Bermudez ... Madrid, En la Imprenta real, 1829.
4 v. in 2. 22½cm.
8-11184
Library of Congress, no.

NL 0424816 DLC CtY IaU MiU PBm CU MB

Llaguno y Amirola, Eugenio, d. 1799, ed.
Sumario de los reyes de España por el despensero mayor de la reyna doña Leonor, muger del rey don Juan el Primero de Castilla, con las alteraciones y adiciones que posteriormente le hizo un anonimo: publicado por don Eugenio de Llaguno Amirola ... Madrid, Impr .de A. de Sancha, 1781.

Llaguno y Amirola, Eugenio, *-1799.*
Vida de Fernan Perez de Guzman.
(*In* Perez de Guzman, Fernan. Generaciones, semblanzas e obras de los excelentes reyes de España D. Enrique III. y D. Juan II. Pp. 185-193. Madrid. 1775.)

M5787a — Perez de Guzman, Fernan.

NL 0424818 MB

Llaguno y Amirola, Eugenio, *-1799.*
Vida de Fernando de Pulgar.
(*In* Pulgar, Hernando del. Claros varones de Castilla, y letras. Pp. (3)-(8). Madrid. 1775.)

M5787a — Pulgar, Hernando del.

NL 0424819 MB

Cuba
HD415
.L6

Llaguno y de Cardenas, Pablo.
Asunto cubano; reparto de tierras ociosas, estudio agro-social, por el ingeniero Pablo Llaguno y de Cardenas. [Habana?] Empresa editora de publicaciones, 1936.
2 p.l., 3-90 p. fold. diagr. 22.5 cm.

NL 0424820 DPU

4F
Cuba
25

Llaguno y de Cárdenas, Pablo
La Isla de Pinos, pequeño bosquejo histórico de la isla y sus aguas medico medicinales. Habana, Impr. "La Impresora Nacional" [19]
47 p.

NL 0424821 DLC-P4 MH

Film
396
no. 9

LLAGUNO Y DE CARDENAS, Pablo
La Isla de Pinos; pequeño bosquejo histórico de la Isla y sus aguas médico medicinales. Habana, Impresora Nacional [1915?]
47 p. illus., port.
Film copy.
Contains errata slip.

NL 0424822 DNLM

LLAGUNO Y DE CARDENAS, PABLO.
El tabaco; correspondiente a un estudio sobre el cultivo del tabaco habano y las probables de subplantaciones exoticas. Habana, 1945. 47 p. illus., fold. map. 24cm.

At head of title: Asuntos cubanos.

1. Tobacco--Culture and curing--Cuba.

NL 0424823 NN

Law

Llaguno y Ubieta, Pedro Pablo.
Cuba. *Laws, statutes, etc.*
Código notarial y legislación complementaria; recopilado y anotado por Pedro Pablo Llaguno. Prólogo de Miguel González Ferregur. Habana, J. Montero, 1950.

Llaguno y Ubieta, Pedro Pablo.
... Formularios notariales y jurisprudencia; prólogo del doctor Mario Recio Forns ... La Habana, Editorial Lex, 1945.
102 p., 1 l. 24cm.

1. Forms (Law)—Cuba. 2. Notaries—Cuba.

46-4260

NL 0424825 DLC

Llaguno y Ubieta, Pedro Pablo.
Formularios notariales y jurisprudencia; con breves comentarios sobre redacción de intsrumentos públicos según el Código notarial y sentencias del Tribunal Supremo en materia notarial. Prólogo del doctor Bernardo Caramés Camacho. Habana, 1953.
348 p. 24 cm.

1. Forms (Law)—Cuba. 2. Notaries—Cuba.

54-34268 ‡

NL 0424826 DLC

Llaguno y Ubieta, Pedro Pablo.
La masonería ante el momento político-constitucional cubano, por el hermano dr. Pedro Pablo Llaguno y Ubieta .. Habana, Cuba [Impreso Standard, aguacate y progreso] 1937 [*i. e.* 1938]
cover-title, 12 p. 21cm.

1. Cuba. Constitution. I. Title.

41-26952

Library of Congress JL1003.1938.L55

NL 0424827 DLC

Chi
PQ
8097
.L69H7

Llaima, Lautaro.
Hojas de otoño; poemas. Santiago, Chile, Impr. Nascimento, 1952.
165 p. 19 cm.

NL 0424828 DPU

Llais Cyfeillion Cymru.
Daffodils under the snow; being the publication in book form of the leading articles previously printed in "Llais Cyfeillion Cymru," the quarterly news letter of Cyfeillion Cymru (the Apostolate of the Welsh missions) during the years 1942 to 1946. With illustrations by Gerald Cross. [Liverpool, Cyfeillion Cymru, 1946]

NL 0424829 MH

Llais o'r Dyffryn, *bardic name*
see
Williams, Daniel, "*Llais o'r Dyffryn.*"

Y Llais Rhybuddiawl. [Llundain, argraphwyd dros Gymdeithas y Traethodau Crefyddol, 17]
12 p. 16°.
Too closely trimmed.
Without title-page. Caption title.
At head of title: Rhif. 45.

NL 0424831 MH

Y Llais Rhybuddiwl. Llundain, Cymdeithas y Traethodau Crefyddol, a sefydlwyd, 1799.

Pp. 12.
Rhif. 45.
The Religious Tract Society.

NL 0424832 MH

Llais yr oes at yr Eglwys...
see under [Ellis, Moses]

LLAM, -----.
La revolucio a judici; drama serio-jocos en un acte en vers y en catala del que ara s'parla compost per lo senyor LLam. n.p., [18-?]

f°. pp. 7.
Without title-page. Caption title.

NL 0424834 MH

Llama Lois, Ramón.
La papa no es tan suave; antecedentes y comentarios. [Habana, P. Fernández] 1955.
103 p. 23 cm.

1. Potatoes—Marketing. 2. Potatoes—Cuba. I. Title.

A 60-718

Florida. Univ. Library
for Library of Congress [1]

NL 0424835 FU

Llama Lois, Ramón.
La papa no es tan suave. La Habana, Ed. Lex, 1955-59.
2 v. illus. 23cm.

NL 0424836 FU DNAL

Llamada de atención a la conciencia nacional. [México] 1940.
18 p. 17cm.
Signed: Concepción Michel... [and 34 other women]

1. Woman—Social position—Mexico. I. Michel, Concepción.
N.Y.P.L. April 12, 1948

NL 0424837 NN

VOLUME 337

La Llamada movilización de 1920 (Antecedentes y documentos) Santiago de Chile, Escuela tip. "La Gratitud nacional", 1923.
xxxii, 387, [1] p. fold. map. 18 cm.
1. Tacna-Arica question.

NL 0424838 CU

Llamamiento de la Isla de Cuba
see under [Madan, Cristóbal F.] 1807-1899.

Llamamiento que a la nación mejicana hacen varios republicanos de corazón, para salvar sus instituciones y derrocar el poder usurpador de D. Benito Juárez. San Luis Potosí, 1871. 12p. 20cm.

NL 0424840 CU-B

Bon.
E
5
B 4587
Llamamiento religioso-patriótico á nombre de Berrio-Ochoa. Por un Vizcaíno. Bilbao,1889.

NL 0424841 ICN

Llamamiento respetuoso. [New York? 1868?] 13 p. 8°.
Caption-title.
Signed by José Vilches and three others.
Full title: Voto imparcial de varios españoles, europeos y americanos, en la cuestión Cuba-Ordoñez.—cf. Trelles, 1856–68, p. 343.

1. Ordoñez y Romero, Agustín. 2. Cuba.—History: Insurrection. 1849–51. 3. Vilches, José. 4. Title: Voto imparcial de varios españoles, europeos y americanos, en la cuestión Cuba-Ordoñez.
N. Y. P. L. October 9, 1923.

NL 0424842 NN

The ... Llamarada; yearbook of the Ellettsville high school ... 1927-
[Ellettsville, Ind., °1927-
v. illus. (incl. ports.) plates. 28cm.

I. Ellettsville, Ind. High school.
CA 27-319 Unrev'd
Library of Congress LD7501.E47655

NL 0424843 DLC

The Llamarada...
v.
[South Hadley, Mass., 18 4°.
v. illus., plates, ports.
Published by the Junior class of Mount Holyoke College.

1. Colleges and universities.—Student publications: Annuals.
N. Y. P. L. October 29, 1923.

NL 0424844 NN MB DHEW OO

G498
L77u
Llamas, A de
Uakambabelté o Vilela, lenguas indígenas aborígenes; mi contribución primera al estudio de la historia antigua, 1909. Corrientes, Tip. y Enc. de T. Heinecke, 1910.
94p. illus. 18cm.

1. Indians of South America - Languages - Argentine Republic. 2. Vilela language. I. Title.

NL 0424845 TxU MH MiU

615.135
L79p
Llamas, Antonio G
Pharmacal arithmetic. Manila, Philippines, Manila college of pharmacy [c1935]
234p. tables. D.

NL 0424846 IaU PPPCPh

Llamas, Atenógnes.

Vallarta, Ignacio Luis, 1830-1893.
... Informe á la vista pronunciado por el Lic. Ignacio L. Vallarta en el recurso de súplica interpuesto por D. Atenógenes Llamas contra la sentencia del Tribunal de circuito de Guadalajara, que declaró incompetente á la jurisdicción federal para conocer de la demanda contra los dueños de la hacienda de Huacasco, sobre pago de un capital nacionalizado. México, Impr. de F. Diaz de Leon, 1891.

Llamas, Aurelio.
El hambre hace toreros; sainete cómico-lírico-dramático-taurino en un acto y en prosa, original. Música del maestro Adolfo del Rey. Sevilla: E. Bergali, 1888. 27(1) p. 8°. (Biblioteca lírico-dramática.)

In: NPL p. v. 284, no. 15.

1. Drama (Spanish). 2. Rey, Adolfo del, composer. 3. Title.
N. Y. P. L. March 9, 1911.

NL 0424848 NN

Llamas, C. L. de, ed.

Chutro, Pedro.
Clínica quirúrgica; conferencias del profesor Dr. Chutro, resumidas por C. L. de Llamas. Ulcera cancerosa y diagnóstico diferencial—Forúnculos, antrax y panadizos—Aparato de Pedro Delbet—Várices—Flegmacia alba dolens—Coxalgia—El coxálgico—Hernias inguinales—Artritis tuberculosas de la rodilla—Apendicitis. Buenos Aires, Impresores: Silla hnos., 1926.

Llamas, Diego Osorio de Escobar y
see
Osorio de Escobar y Llamas, Diego, bp., d. 1673.

Llamas, Enrique.
Essential hypertension, by Enrique Llamas. [New York? 1945]
cover-title, 20 p. 24½cm.
"References": p. 20.

1. Blood—Pressure. 2. Sulphapyridine. I. Title.
A 45-4902
Wm. H. Welch med. library for Library of Congress RC669.L79

NL 0424851 MdBJ-W DLC

Llamas, Enrique.
El virus del hombre. Bogota, Editorial ABC [1946]
154 p.

NL 0424852 ICJ CtY-M

WM
40
L791v
1950
LLAMAS, Enrique
El virus del hombre. Bogota, Editorial ABC [1950?]
154 p.
1. Mental disorders - Case reports
2. Virus diseases

NL 0424853 DNLM

Llamas (Francisco). *La sábila. 19 pp. 8°. México, 1881.

NL 0424854 DNLM

Llamas, Germán Flórez
see
Flórez Llamas, Germán.

Llamas, Jaime de Anesagasti
see Anesagasti y Llamas, Jaime de, 1863-1910.

BS
998
.L4
Llamas, José
Antigua Biblia judía medieval romanceada. [n. p.] 1951.
cover-title, [289]-304 p. facsims.

"De 'Sefarad', XI."

NL 0424857 NNC

BS
67.5
.L53
Llamas, José
Biblia latina interlineal, inédita. [Madrid, Imp. del Real Monasterio de el Escorial, 1951.
23 p. 24cm.

"Separata de 'La Ciudad de Díos' (vol. CLXIII, págs. 257-275)."
Bibliographical footnotes.

NL 0424858 NNC

Llamas, José, ed.

BS998
L55
Bible. O. T. Spanish (Old Spanish) 1950-55.
Biblia medieval romanceada judío-cristiana; versión del Antiguo Testamento en el siglo XIV, sobre los textos hebreo y latino. Edición y estudio introductorio por José Llamas. Madrid, Instituto "Francisco Suárez," 1950-55.

Z6621
.E77H4
Or
Llamas, José.
Catálogo de los manuscritos hebreos de la real biblioteca de San Lorenzo del Escorial. El Escorial, 1944.
1 v. (various pagings) plates.
"Estudio publicado en la revista 'Sefarad' y adaptado por el autor en tres fascículos para su uso en bibliotecas."

1. Manuscripts, Hebrew--Catalogs. 2. Manuscripts--Spain--Catalogs. I. Escorial. Biblioteca.

NL 0424860 ICU

Ref.
223.2
L791e
Llamas, José.
Los epígrafes de los salmos en las Biblias castellanas judías medievales. Madrid, 1953.
[239]-256 p.

"De Sefarad, XIII"
On t. p. Consejo Superior de Investigaciones Científicas "Instituto Arias Montano"

1. Bible. O. T. Psalms. Spanish--Criticism, interpretation, etc. I. Spain. Consejo Superior de Investigaciones Científicas. Instituto Arias Montano. II. Title.

NL 0424861 PrU

VOLUME 337

Llamas, José.
... Maimónides, siglo XII. Madrid, M. Aguilar [1935]
284, [2] p., 1 l. incl. front. (port.) illus. (facsim.) pl. 17cm. (Half-title: Biblioteca de la cultura española)
CONTENTS.—Maimónides: Su vida. Sus obras. Su ideario. Bibliografía. Antología.

1. Moses ben Maimon, 1135–1204. I. Moses ben Maimon, 1135–1204.
Library of Congress B759.M34L6 36-23144
[2] 181.3

NL 0424862 DLC OCH NcD OrPS CtY CoU CSt NcU OU PBm

Llamas, José
Mártires agustinos de El Escorial. El Escorial, Impr.del Real Monasterio, 1940
32 p. ports.
Span 745.19.39.15 - xerox reproduction

1. Escorial, Spain. 2. Spain - Hist. -, 1936-39 - Campaigns and battles

NL 0424863 MH

R128 .I 818 Llamas, José, ed. and tr.

Israeli, Isaac, *ca.* 832–*ca.* 932.
... Tratado de las fiebres. Ed. de la versión castellana y estudio por ... José Llamas ... Madrid [etc.] Instituto "Arias montano," 1945.

[Llamas, José Gregorio de] *plaintiff.*
Demanda personalmente presentada por quien en ella se espresa al juez de 1a instancia del distrito de Jeréz, lic. d. J. Cecilio Acosta. Zacatecas, Impresa por A. Villegrana, 1841.
cover-title, 24 p. 19½cm.
Signed: J. Gregorio de Llamas.
"D. José Manuel de Amozurrutia dueño de la hacienda nombrada la Labor de Santa Gertrudis ... convierte en el provecho esclusivo de su hacienda toda la agua del rio de esta ciudad ... causándome graves perjuicios y daños que protesto reclamar."—p. 3.

1. Water-rights—Mexico—Zacatecas (State) I. Amozurrutia, José Manuel de, defendant. II. Title.
34-42193

NL 0424865 DLC

Llamas, José Joaquín Ayala y
see Ayala y Llamas, José Joaquín.

WB 100 qL791o 1942 LLAMAS, Lulio de
Orientación diagnóstica y terapéutica, sintomatología topográfica y esquemas sindrómicos de la patología humana, etiopatogenia y terapéutica sinóptica de las enfermedades. Buenos Aires, 1942.
xvi, 1433 p. illus.
1. Medicine - Clinical

NL 0424867 DNLM

Llamas, Matias de Escobar y
see Escobar, Matias, d. 1748.

Llamas, Menas Alonso
see
Alonso Llamas, Menas

UF620 .A2P15 1940 Llamas, R., ed.

Paille, François Joseph Georges.
... Tiro de ametralladoras; adaptación y ampliación de la obra "Tirs lointains de mitrailleuses," del comandante G. Paillé ... 2. ed., corr. Madrid, Editorial bibliográfica militar, 1940.

Write on slip words underlined below and class mark —

Llamas, Roberto.
...Valor alimenticio del huevo, por Roberto Llamas... Chapultepec, D. F.: Impr. del Instituto de biología, 1935. 18 p. 20½cm. (Mexico «City». Universidad nacional. Instituto de biología. Folletos de divulgacion cientifca. [no.] 16.)

1. Eggs as food. I. Ser.
N. Y. P. L. May 25, 1936

NL 0424871 NN

Llamas, Santiago Ibanez
see Ibañez Llamas, Santiago.

Llamas, Tomás Gil
see
Gil Llamas, Tomás.

Llamas Amaya, Ismael.
... Hipoclorhidria y anacidez en las colitis parasitarias crónicas; tesis que presenta para su examen profesional de médico cirujano y partero Ismael Llamas Amaya. México, D. F., 1943.
92, [1] p. 23 x 17½cm.
At head of title: Universidad nacional autónoma de México. Facultad de medicina.
"Bibliografía": p. 89–[93]

1. Colitis. 2. Gastric juice. 3. Metabolism, Disorders of. I. Title.
45-17869
Library of Congress RC862.L5
[2] 616.34

NL 0424874 DLC

Llamas Noriega, Francisco.
Informe a la vista producido ante el supremo tribunal de justicia, por el lic. Francisco Llamas Noriega, como apoderado de los sres. d. Juan Rincon Gallardo y Da. Carlota C. de R. Gallardo en el juicio ejecutivo seguido en su contra por el lic. don Benito Garza, como apoderado del señor don Antonio Llaguno, sobre pretendidos daños y perjuicios Zacatecas, Imp. de "La Rosa", 1895.
44 p. 21 cm.
(No. 3 in a vol. lettered: Nulidad, venta bienes, sociedad conyugal. Herencia, hijos naturales, v.36)

NL 0424875 DLC

Law Llamas Pérez, Angel, ed.

Spain. *Laws, statutes, etc.*
Ley de arrendamientos urbanos de 31 de diciembre de 1946; exposición y comentarios [por] R. Llanas de Niubó [y] A. Llamas Pérez. Barcelona, 1947.

Law Llamas Pérez, Angel, joint author.

Llanas de Niubó, Renato.
Ley de arrendamientos urbanos de 31 de diciembre de 1946; sinopsis de la ley y apéndice conteniendo las disposiciones legales que la completan [por] R. Llanas de Niubó [y] A. Llamas Pérez. Barcelona [Distribuidor: Librería Bosch] 1947.

Law Llamas y Molina, Sancho de. FOR OTHER EDITIONS SEE MAIN ENTRY

Castile. Laws, statutes, etc., 1504–1516 (Juana la Loca)
[Leyes de Toro]
Comentario crítico-jurídico-literal á las ochenta y tres Leyes de Toro. Su autor: Sancho de Llamas y Molina. Madrid, Impr. de Repullés, 1827.

Llamas y Molina, Sancho, fl.1800.
Disertacion histórico-crítica sobre la edición de las partidas del Rey Don Alonso el Sábio, que publicó la Real Academia de la Historia en el año de 1806. Madrid, Impr. de Repullés, 1820.
x,148 p. 20 cm.

1. Law - Castile - History and criticism. I. T.

NL 0424879 NjP C NcD WaPS

Llamas y Molina, Sancho, fl. 1800.

Robbins, Lloyd McCullough, 1875– *ed. and tr.*
Laws of community property (bienes gananciales) **Laws of Toro, 1505, by Lloyd M. Bobbins[!] ... [and] Bernardine M. Murphy ... Lausanne (Switzerland) Imprimerie des arts et métiers s. a., 1929.**

Llamazares, Andrés G.
El seguro contra incendio ante la jurisprudencia argentina ... Buenos Aires, Est. tip. J. Carbone, 1914.
204 p. 26½cm.
Thesis—Buenos Aires.
"Bibliografía": p. [203]–204.
17-9940
Library of Congress

NL 0424881 DLC

Llamazares, Jose Fernandez
see Fernandez Llamazares, Jose.

Llamazares, Juan.
... La Argentina en el comercio ibero-americano, por Juan Llamazares ... Buenos Aires, Editorial Guillermo Kraft, ltda., 1941.
2 p. l., 7–8, xiv, 9–328 p., 1 l. diagrs. 26cm.
At head of title: Bolsa de comercio de Buenos Aires. Instituto de estudios económicos, jurídicos y sociales. Atilio Dell' Oro Maini, director.
"Bibliografía": p. 303–306.

1. Argentine republic—Comm.—Spanish America. 2. Spanish America—Comm.—Argentine republic. I. Buenos Aires. Bolsa de comercio. Instituto de estudios económicos, jurídicos y sociales. II. Title.
41-17570
Library of Congress HF3388.S85L6
[3] 382.0982

NL 0424883 DLC WU MB NSyU CU IU MiEM NcU DPU

Llamazares, Juan.
Empresas modernas, ensayos sobre dirección y organización. Buenos Aires, Instituto Argentino de Relaciones Industriales, 1955.
180 p. diagrs. 23 cm. (Colección Organización de empresas, v. 1)
Includes bibliographies.

1. Industrial management. I. Title. (Series)
HD37.L6 57-15911

NL 0424884 DLC NN DS

VOLUME 337

Llamazares, Juan.
Examen del problema industrial argentino, aspectos de política económica y social. Buenos Aires, 1943.
318 l. 28 cm.
Tesis—Univ. de Buenos Aires.
"Bibliografía principal": leaves 309-317.

1. Argentine Republic—Indus. I. Title.
HC175.L7 338 48-38755*

NL 0424885 DLC TxU

4HD 2462 Llamazares, Juan
Examen del problema industrial argentino; aspectos de política económica y social. Buenos Aires, Facultad de Ciencias Económicas, 1946.
298 p.

NL 0424886 DLC-P4 MH TxU ICU

Llamazares, Juan.
... La situación bancaria en 1937, por Juan Ll. Llamazares ... nota preliminar del director del Instituto dr. Pedro J. Baiocco. Buenos Aires, 1938.
3 p. l., ⌊9⌋-74 p., 3 l. diagrs. 25½cm.
At head of title: Universidad de Buenos Aires. Facultad de ciencias económicas. Instituto de economía bancaria.
"En los concursos universitarios 1937-38 de la Institución Mitre, este trabajo mereció el premio 'Ireneo Cucullu' de ciencias económicas."
"Bibliografía": p. ⌊71⌋-74.
1. Banks and banking—Argentine republic. I. Buenos Aires. Universidad nacional. Instituto de economía bancaria. II. Title.
42-45828
Library of Congress HG2864.L6

NL 0424887 DLC TxU NN

Llamazares, Julio Perez
see
Perez Llamazares, Julio

LLAMAZARES, Thomas de.
Apophthegmas en romanze, notables dichos, y sentencias de sanctos padres de la iglesia, de philosophos, y otros varones illustres. Leon de Francia, [Lyons], J.A.Huguetan y G. Barbier, 1670.

NL 0424889 MH

RARE BOOK DEPT.
Llamazares, Tomás de, 17th cent.
Cornv-copia sacro-profana. Con dos cartas, o tratados doctrinales al fin. Burgos, 1685.

NL 0424890 WU

WF 658 L791c 1942
LLAMBES, Juan J
Carcinoma primitivo del pulmón, por Juan J. Llambés ⌊et al.⌋ ⌊La Habana, 1942⌋
507 p. illus. (Biblioteca médica de autores cubanos, v. 4)
1. Lungs - Cancer

NL 0424891 DNLM

Llambi-Campbell, P.
... Abriss des staats- und verwaltungsrechts der Argentinischen Republik, von dr. P. Llambi-Campbell ... übers. von amtsgerichtsrat R. Bartolomäus ... Hannover, M. Jänecke, 1911.
viii, 252 p. 17½cm. (Bibliothek des öffentlichen rechts ... 20. bd.)
On cover: Jäneckes bibliotheken, reihe C.
"Literatur": p. ⌊vi⌋-viii.

1. Argentine Republic. Laws, statutes, etc. II. Bartolomäus, Richard, tr.
12-15794

NL 0424892 DLC CU NN ICJ

Llambi-Campbell, Paulino.
... Le grand secret de l'univers; la gravitation expliquée par la radiopression des ondes ultra microscopiques. ⌊Paris⌋ Hachette ⌊1934⌋
3 p. l., ⌊5⌋-216 p., 1 l. diagrs. 19cm.
At head of title: P. Llambi Campbell.

1. Gravitation. 2. Radiation. I. Title.
36-9896
Library of Congress QC178.L7
⌊2⌋ 531.5

NL 0424893 DLC CU PU NN

Llambías, Alfonso
see
Llambías de Azevedo, Alfonso.

W 4 B92 no. 4550
LLAMBIAS, Alfredo
Luxación de la articulación de Lisfranc. Buenos Aires, 1931.
38 p. illus. (Buenos Aires. Universidad Nacional. Facultad de Ciencias Médicas. Tesis, año 1931, no. 4550)
1. Foot - Dislocation

NL 0424895 DNLM

Llambías, Héctor.
... La dialéctica comunista y el concepto de la libertad. Buenos Aires, Gladium, 1938.
3 p. l., 9-82, ⌊1⌋ p., 2 l. 18cm.

1. Liberalism. 2. Communism. 3. Socialism. I. Title.
42-42710
Library of Congress HX184.L6
⌊2⌋ 335.4

NL 0424896 DLC CSt NN

Llambías, Joaquín.
... Contribución al estudio del cáncer de la ampolla de Vater, por los doctores J. Llambías, D. Brachetto-Brian y G. Orosco. ... Buenos Aires, "La Semana médica", imp. de E. Spinelli, 1928.
56 p. illus. 24cm.
At head of title: Instituto de anatomía y fisiología patológicas de la Facultad de medicina ...
"De La Semana médica, n.° 37, 1928."
"Bibliografía," p. [55]-56.

NL 0424897 ICJ

---

*Llambías, Joaquín. Lecciones de anatomía patológica ... Buenos Aires, Coni, 1921.
595p. illus. 26cm.

NL 0424898 CU

SF995 L77
Llambías, Joaquin
El sarcoma infeccioso de la gallina; contribución al estudio experimental de los tumores conjuntivos malignos, por Joaquin Llambías ... y D. Brachetto-Brian ... Buenos Aires, "La Semana médica", 1924.
179 p. illus. 27cm.
1. Cancer, Experimental. 2. Poultry - Diseases I. Brachetto-Brian, D jt. au. II. Title.

NL 0424899 NNC CU ICJ DNLM

Law
Llambías, Jorge Joaquín.

Arauz Castex, Manuel.
Derecho civil, parte general ⌊por⌋ Manuel Arauz Castex ⌊y⌋ Jorge Joaquín Llambías. ⌊1. ed.⌋ Buenos Aires, Editorial Perrot, 1955.

Llambías, Jorge Joaquín.
Efectos de la nulidad y de la anulación de los actos jurídicos. Buenos Aires, Ediciones Arayú ⌊1953⌋
206 p. 24 cm.

1. Juristic acts—Argentine Republic. 2. Nullity—Argentine Republic. I. Title.
55-16208 ‡

NL 0424901 DLC CtY-L

Llambías de Azevedo, Alfonso.
... El alba lograda, y otras permanencias. Paysandú ⌊Talleres gráficos de la Librería Firpo⌋ 1936.
⌊53⌋ p. 24cm.
Poems.

I. Title.
38-33303
Library of Congress PQ8519.L55A7
⌊2⌋ 861.6

NL 0424902 DLC TxU

F2701 .A813
Llambías de Azevedo, Alfonso, ed.

Ateneo del Uruguay. Anales. (*Indexes*)
Los "Anales del Ateneo del Uruguay." Introd., índice y notas ⌊por⌋ Alfonso Llambías de Azevedo. Montevideo, 1950.

Llambías de Azevedo, Alfonso.
... Canto para una noche del sur ... Montevideo ⌊Talleres gráficos Stella⌋ 1940.
⌊9⌋ p. 23½cm. (Nebli, 2)

I. Title.
42-45996
Library of Congress PQ8519.L55C3
⌊2⌋ 861.6

NL 0424904 DLC TxU

Llambías de Azevedo, Alfonso.
... Cuatro poemas de guerra, y un epílogo de Emilio Oribe. Montevideo, "Casa A. Barreiro y Ramos," s. a., 1942.
1 p. l., 5-18 p., 1 l. 24cm.
"La edición consta de quinientos ejemplares, de los cuales ciento cincuenta están numerados a mano por el autor. Ejemplar nº sesenta y siete."

43-1336
Library of Congress PQ8519.L55C8
⌊2⌋ 861.6

NL 0424905 DLC NcU TxU

Llambías de Azevedo, Alfonso.
... Las eternas presencias. Montevideo, C. García & cía., 1942.
94 p., 1 l. 18cm.
At head of title: Alfonso Llambías.
Poems.

I. Title.
44-1154
Library of Congress PQ8519.L55E75
⌊2⌋ 861.6

NL 0424906 DLC CtY

Llambías de Azevedo, Alfonso.
El modernismo. Montevideo, Casa del Estudiante, 1950.
31 p. 25 cm.

1. Spanish literature—Hist. & crit. 2. Spanish-American literature—Hist. & crit. I. Title.
PQ6046.M6L5 860.9 51-34178 ‡

NL 0424907 DLC TxU IU TU MH

VOLUME 337

Llambías de Azevedo, Alfonso.
El modernismo. [Montevideo? Imprenta Nacional? 1950]
[163]-189 p. 25 cm. (Anales de la Universidad de Montevideo, no. 166, 1950, p. 163-189)

NL 0424908 NcD

Llambías de Azevedo, Alfonso, *ed.*
... Poetas y prosistas españoles. De acuerdo con el nuevo programa de idioma español, 3er. curso de la enseñanza secundaria ... Montevideo, M. García, 1939.
2 v. 19½cm.

1. Spanish literature (Selections: Extracts, etc.) I. Title.
43-45927
Library of Congress PQ6172.L56
[2] 860.82

NL 0424909 DLC

Llambías de Azevedo, Juan.
... Eidética y aporética del derecho; prolegómenos a la filosofía del derecho. [Buenos Aires] Espasa-Calpe argentina s. a. [1940]
2 p. l., 7-134 p., 4 l. 19cm. (*On cover:* Biblioteca filosófica)

1. Law—Philosophy. I. Title.
41-10052

NL 0424910 DLC

Llambías de Azevedo, Juan.
... La filosofía del derecho de Hugo Grocio. Montevideo, Peña & cía., impresores, 1935.
85 p. 24½cm. (Biblioteca de publicaciones oficiales de la Facultad de derecho y ciencias sociales de la Universidad de Montevideo. Sección III. VIII)
"Bibliografía": p. [83]-85.

1. Grotius, Hugo, 1583-1645. 2. Law—Philosophy. I. Title.
Library of Congress 37-15534
——— Copy 2. [3] 340.1

NL 0424911 DLC CtY MH-L

G340.1
L77ℓ

LLAMBIAS DE AZEVEDO, JUAN
Lecciones sobre la justicia dictadas por el Dr. Juan Llambias de Azevedo y tomada por el Br. Amadeo Molina; versión taquigráfica. Montevideo, Organización Taquigráfica Medina, 1942.
123p. 22cm.
"Bibliografía": p.2-5.

1. Justice. I. Molina, Amadeo. II. Title.

NL 0424912 TxU

Llambías de Azevedo, Juan.
... Sobre la distinción entre las normas de los usos sociales y el derecho ... Montevideo, "Impresora uruguaya", s. a., 1938.
16 p. 22½cm. (Ediciones de "La Revista de derecho, jurisprudencia y administración". III)
"Apartado del t. XXXVI, núm. 2 de 'Rev. d. j. a.' y del volumen de Estudios de doctrina en honor del dr. José A. de Freitas."

1. Manners and customs. 2. Law. I. Title.
39-19923

NL 0424913 DLC

Llambías de Olivar, Antonio.
... Contribución al conocimiento de los minerales de manganeso en el Uruguay, por A. Llambías de Olivar ... Montevideo, Imprenta nacional, 1921.
36 p. illus., maps, tables, diagrs. 23½cm. (Uruguay. Instituto de geología y perforaciones. Boletin no. 5)
At head of title: Republica Oriental del Uruguay. Ministerio de industrias. Instituto de geologia y perforaciones. A. Llambias de Olivar, director.

1. Manganese ores—Uruguay. I. Title.
G S 22-13
Library, U. S. Geological Survey (490) B no. 5

NL 0424914 DI-GS DPU

Llambías de Olivar, Antonio.
... Relación de un viaje a la barra del Pirahy, relacionado con la pulverización del carbón ... Informe acerca de la investigación geológica efectuada en la república. Informe referente a los estudios efectuados de las principales cuencas carboníferas de Río Grande del Sur ... por Antonio Llambías de Olivar ... Montevideo, Imprenta nacional, 1918.
1 p. l., 71 p. illus., map, 2 fold. diagr. 23½cm. (Uruguay. Instituto de geología y perforaciones. Boletín n.° 3)
At head of title: República O. del Uruguay. Ministerio de industrias ...
1. Coal—Uruguay. 2. Geology—Uruguay. I. Title.
G S 20-306 Revised
U. S. Geol. survey. Library for Library of Congress QE231.L5

NL 0424915 DI-GS ViU

KG 13481
Llambias de Olivar, José
Consideraciones sobre la teoria de Einstein. Montevideo, Lit. e imp.del Comercio, 1926
84 p.

NL 0424916 MH

Llambias de Olivar, José.
... Ensayo sobre el "origen de las rocas." Montevideo [Esc. tip. "Talleres Don Bosco"] 1909.
53 p., 1 l. incl. tables. 20½cm.
Loose leaf of "Errata."

1. Petrology. 2. Rocks—Analysis.
12-1713
Library of Congress QE431.L6

NL 0424917 DLC MH

LLAMBIAS DE OLIVAR,José.
Observacion del eclipse anular del 3de diciembre de 1918 en Montevideo. Montevideo tableres de "La buena prensa", 1919.
pp.26+. 1 Illustr.

NL 0424918 MH DPU

Llambias de Olivar, Jose.
Origen de las manchas solares. Prevision del tiempo para todo el ano de 1920. Montivideo, Talleres de La Buena Prensa... 1919.
51 p. 23.5 cm.

NL 0424919 DN-Ob

CS
389
A7
L562
LAC

Llambías de Olivar, R
Ensayo sobre el linaje de los Artigas en el Uruguay [por] R. Llambías de Olivar. Montevideo, Casa A. Barreiro y Ramos, 1925.
2v. illus. 26cm.

MC 1. Artigas family. Sp.: Lucuix Collection.

NL 0424920 TxU

XPA 6683
Llamby, Charles de
Officio do engenheiro Llamby ao administrador delegado da Companhia de Moçambique [remettido ao governo em officio do Commissario Regio, de 7 Fevereiro de 1891] I. Lisboa, Imprensa Nacional, 1891
10 p.
Text in French
Report signed: Ch.de Llamby
1. Manica. II. Companhia de Moçambique. I. Companhia de Moçambique

NL 0424921 MH

Llamea, José Gotianos
see Gotianos Llamea, José.

232.932 Llamera, Bonifacio.
L77t
Teología de San José; y ed. bilingüe, versión e introducción por el mismo autor de la Suma de los dones de San José, por Isidoro de Isolano. Madrid, [Editorial Católica] 1953.
xxvii, 662p. illus. 20cm. (Biblioteca de autores cristianos, 108. Sección II: Teología y canones)
Bibliography: p.[xvii]-xxvii.

NL 0424923 IU IaU

BT
1075
F2
L7

Llameras, Marceliano, O.P.
Fatima: the rosary and the heart of Mary ... Translated by Matthias Mueller, O.P. [n.p.] 1950.
75 p. 23cm.
"Reprinted from The Thomist, vol. xiii, no. 4, October, 1950."
1. Fatima, Nossa Senhora da. I. Title.

NL 0424924 DCU

Llames Massini, J C
... Antecedentes, títulos, trabajos y actuación docente, presentados a la Facultad de ciencias médicas para optar a la cátedra de obstetricia vacante por jubilación del prof. dr. Miguel Z. O'Farrell. Buenos Aires, "Las Ciencias", 1932.
60 p., 1 l. 24cm.
At head of title: Dr. J. C. Llames Massini.

NL 0424925 ICJ

LLAMES MASSINI,J.C.
La partera de Buenos Aires y la escuela de parteras. Buenos Aires, Flaiban y Camilloni,1915
Ports., facsim, and other illustr.

NL 0424926 MBCo CtY MdBJ PU NjP

Llames Morán, Ramón.
La declaración del justo. Estudios contemporáneos, por Mario Lomas y Alirmenni... Puerto Principe: A. Morales, 1892. 246 p. 12°.

1. Cuba.—Politics. 2. Political science.—Essays.
N. Y. P. L. October 10, 1923.

NL 0424927 NN ICU

Llames Moran, Ramon.
El 12 de Agosto de 1887. Apuntes administrativos. Habana, P. Fernandez y Compañia, 1891.
17 p. 8°.

NL 0424928 NN

VOLUME 337

Llamosa, Francisco.
Memorias de un camarero letrado, novela. México, Impresora Mexicana, 1955.
392 p. 21 cm.

I. Title.

PQ7297.L56M4 57-37009 ‡

NL 0424929 DLC NN CU-B TxU

Llamosa, José Luis Bravo
see Bravo Llamosa, José Luis.

Llamosas, Lorenzo de las.
Manifiesto apologetico, en qve se tratan las principales materias del reyno del Perù, y las primeras operaciones, que hizo en los ocho años de su govierno, el excelentissimo señor Don Melchor de Navarra, y Rocafull, Hijar, Vique, Manrique, y Moncada...virrey, governador, y capitan general de los reynos del Perù, Tierra-Firme, y Chile... Sacale a lvz...Don Lorenzo de las Llamosas, sv avtor. [Madrid?] 1692. 3 p.l., 20 f. 30cm. (f°.)

See: Palau y Dulcet, IV, 305.

312466B. 1. Peru—Hist., 1548-1820. 2. Navarra y Rocafull, Melchor de, 1626-1691.
N. Y. P. L. July 18, 1945

NL 0424931 NN

Llamosas, Lorenzo de las.
Obras. Introd. y notas de Rubén Vargas Ugarte. Lima, 1950.
xxxi, 215 p. 22 cm. (Clásicos peruanos, v. 3)
Bibliography: p. [xxix]-xxxi.

(Series)

PQ8497.L5 1950 861.39 51-20657

MiU KyU NN NcU TNJ ICN CtY
NL 0424932 DLC ViU CaBVaU CSt MiU CU TxU IU IaU

LLAMOSAS, LORENZO DE LAS.
Obras. Introd. y notas de Rubén Vargas Ugarte. Lima, 1950. xxxi, 215 p. 22cm. (Clásicos peruanos, v. 3)

Film reproduction. Positive.
Bibliography: p. [xxix]-xxxi.

1. Poetry, Peruvian. I. Vargas Ugarte, Rubén, 1886-

NL 0424933 NN

Llamosas, Lorenzo de las. Paris, 1705
Pequeno panegirico a la magestad christianisin

NL 0424934 NNH

Peru
Cwpr
k692l

[Llamosas, Lorenzo de las]
[Relación en que se tratan las principales materias del Reyno del Perú. [n.p.,1692]
2p.l.,20 numb.l. 29½cm.
Binder's title: Llamosas - Relación del royno del Perú 1692.
Signed: Don Lorenço de las Llamosas.
No title-page; title taken from A.Palau y Dulcet's Manual del librero hispano-americano, t.4,p.305.

NL 0424935 CtY

Llamosas, Manuel V. Rodríguez.
See
Rodríguez Llamosas, Manuel V., 1889-

Llamosas Herrera, Raúl.
Proceso de investigación en los conflictos colectivos de orden económico en el derecho laboral mexicano. México, 1952.
95 p. 21 cm.
Tesis (licenciatura en derecho)—Universidad Nacional Autónoma de México.
Bibliography: p. [93]

1. Labor disputes—Mexico. 2. Arbitration, Industrial—Mexico. I. Title.

55-38049

NL 0424937 DLC MH-L

Llamozas, Héctor Esteves
see Esteves Llamozas, Héctor.

LLAMOSAS Y DE CEPEDA, Antonio.
Lo que sucededespues; poema.
Habana, J.Valdepares,1885.

pp. 25.

NL 0424939 MH NN

Llamozas, Salvador N.
Capricho popular. Para piano.
= Caracas. Llamozas & Co. [191-?] 7 pp. Decorated title-page. 34.5 cm.

E1639 — T.r. — Pianoforte. Music.

NL 0424940 MB

1508 Llamozas, Salvador N.
Siempre tú... Caracas, Llamozas.
2. a ed.

NL 0424941 DPU

Llamozas González, Paulo.
Cartilla ganadera. 3. ed., corr. y aumentada. Caracas, Impr. Nacional, 1948.
137 p. illus. 23 cm.

1. Stock and stock-breeding—Venezuela. I. Title.

SF75.L55 1948 54-34677 ‡

NL 0424942 DLC ViU

LLAMOZAS GONZALEZ, PAULO.

Cartilla ganadera; 4 ed. corr. y aum.
Caracas, Ministerio de Agricultura y Cria, 1953.
137 p. illus.
Title translated: Cattle-breeding note.
(20) 1. Domestic animals. Breeding.
2. Venezuela. Domestic animals.
I. Venezuela. Dirreccion de Ganaderia.
II. Title.

NL 0424943 DNAL

W 4
M61
1955

LLAMOZAS HERRERA, José Lorenzo
Toxemias del embarazo preeclampsia y eclampsia. México, 1955.
76 p.
Tesis - Univ. de México.
1. Eclampsia

NL 0424944 DNLM

Llampallas, Guillermo Mitjans
see
Mitjans Llampallas, Guillermo.

DP140
.3
.L78

Llampayas, José.
Alfonso X, el hombre, el rey y el sabio. Madrid, Biblioteca Nueva, 1947.
253 p. (Españoles famosos)

1. Alfonso X, el Sabio, King of Castile and Leon, 1221-1284.

CU-S
NL 0424946 ICU InU WU IEN IU CLSU CtY PU NcD NcU

Sp.
946.02
A38.LL

LLampayas, José
Alfonso X; el hombre, el rey, y el sabio.
Madrid, Nueva, 1947.
256 p.

1. Alfonso X, El Sabio, Rey de Castilla y León, 1221-1284. 2. España - Historia.
I. Título.

NL 0424947 LN

Llampayas, José.
...Elena y los tres arqueros (novela del año uno), por José Llampayas. Madrid, Ed. Plutarco, 1941. 134 p. 16cm. (La Novela de la paz.)

NL 0424948 NN

Llampayas, José.
... Fernando el Católico, por José Llampayas. Madrid, Biblioteca nueva, 1941.
258 p. incl. front. (port.) 19½cm. (La España imperial)

1. Fernando v, el Católico, king of Spain, 1452-1516.
[Full name: José Llampayas Lluveres]
44-27659
Library of Congress DP163.5.L5
[2] 946.03

NL 0424949 DLC WaU WU CLU

Llampayas, José.
... Goya (su vida, su arte y su mundo) por José Llampayas. Madrid, Biblioteca nueva, 1943.
4 p. l., 11-238 p., 2 l. 20½cm. (Españoles famosos)

1. Goya y Lucientes, Francisco José de, 1746-1828.
[Full name: José Llampayas Lluveres]
44-23362
Library of Congress ND813.G7L57
[2] 927.5

NL 0424950 DLC CtY CLU

Llampayas, José.
... Jaime I, el conquistador, por José Llampayas. Madrid, Biblioteca nueva, 1942.
234, [2] p. 20cm. (Españoles famosos)

1. Jaime I, king of Aragon, 1208-1276.
[Full name: José Llampayas Lluveres]
46-29190
Library of Congress DP129.L5
[2] 923.1465

NL 0424951 DLC ScU NN CLU

863.6
L791

Llampayas, José.
Mosen Bruno Fierro, cuadros del alto Aragón.
[Madrid] Coleccion Argensola, 1924.
202p.

NL 0424952 ICarbS

Llampayas Lluveres, José
see
Llampayas, José.

VOLUME 337

Llampillas, Francisco Xavier, 1731-1810.
Ensayo historico-apologetico de la literatura española contra las opiniones preocupadas de algunos escritores modernos italianos...Tr. del italiano al español por Josefa Amar y Borbon... Zaragoza, 1783-1784.
4 v. in 2. 20 cm.
Contents.-
Parte 2. de la literatura moderna. 4 v. in 2.

NL 0424954 CtY

Llampillas, Francisco Xavier, 1731-1810.
Ensayo historico-apologetico de la literatura española contra las opiniones preocupadas de algunos escritores modernos italianos. Disertaciones del abate Don Xavier Lampillas ... Tr. del italiano por Doña Josefa Amar, y Borbon ... 2. ed., corr., enmendada, é ilustrada con notas, por la misma traductora ... Madrid, Impr. de P. Marin, 1789.
7 v. 21cm.

Contents.—t. 1-2. Literatura antigua.—t. 3-6. Literatura moderna.—t. 7. Respuesta del Señor abate Don Xavier Lampillas a los cargos recopilados por el Señor abate Tiraboschi en su carta al Señor abate N. N. sobre el Ensayo historico-apologetico de la literatura española ... Va añadida un indice alfabetico de los principales autores, y materias que comprenden los seis tomos de la obra del abate Lampillas (with special t.-p. only)

1. Spanish literature—Hist. & crit. 2. Latin literature—Spain. 3. Literature, Comparative—Spanish and Italian. 4. Literature, Comparative—Italian and Spanish. 5. Learning and scholarship—Spain. 6. Tiraboschi, Girolamo, 1731-1794. I. Amar y Borbón, Josefa, b. 1753, tr. II. Title.

Library of Congress PQ6031.L3 19-9715

NL 0424956 DLC TxU OrU MiDW MoU MoSU ViU NN OCU NcD

860.9
L788sa Llampillas,Francisco Xavier,1731-1810.
Saggio storico-apologetico della letteratura spagnuola contro le pregiudicate opinioni di alcuni moderni scrittori italiani. Genova, Presso F.Repetto,1778-81.
2 v.in 6.

1.Spanish literature--Hist.& crit. I.Title.

NL 0424958 MiU PBm ICN

Llampillas, Francisco Xavier, 1731-1810.
Tiraboschi, Girolamo, 1731-1794. FOR OTHER EDITIONS SEE MAIN ENTRY
Storia della letteratura italiana del cavaliere abate Girolamo Tiraboschi ... 1. ed. veneta, dopo la seconda di Modena, riv., cor. ed accresciuta dall' autore. ... Venezia. 1795-96.

Llana, Eduardo A Pérez
see Pérez Llana, Eduardo A

Llana, Emilio González
see González Llana, Emilio-

Llana, Félix González.
See
González Llana, Félix.

Llana, Francisco Murcia de la
see
Murcia de la Llana, Francisco.

Llana, J González
see González Llana, J

Llana, José González-
see
González-Llana, José.

Llana, Lorenzo Fuster y
see Fuster y Llana, Lorenzo.

Llana, M. G. Political parties in Spain. 15 pp.
(Fortn. Rev. n. s. v. 39, 1886, p. 106.)

NL 0424967 MdBP

Llana, Manuel Gonzalez
see
Gonzalez de la Llana, Manuel

Llana, Pedro de la.
A book of comment and criticism (being a collection of miscellaneous writings and addresses), by Pedro de la Llana... Manila, P. I., 1926. xi, 175 p. front. (port.) 12°.

436887A. 1. Philippine Islands. 2. Philippine Islands—Govt.
N. Y. P. L. October 11, 1929

NL 0424969 NN DPU NNC MiU

Llana, Pedro de la, *ed.*
The Philippine Commonwealth handbook, a cultural and economic survey of present-day Philippines, with sketches of the outstanding builders of the Commonwealth. Pedro de la Llana, ed. and pub., F. B. Icasiano, associate ed. Manila, 1936.
xii, 522 p. 21 cm.

1. Philippine Islands. I. Icasiano, F. B., ed. II. Title.

DS686.L55 919.14 48-30742*

NL 0424970 DLC NN InU WU

991.4
L791 Llana, Pedro de la, ed.
The Philippine Commonwealth handbook (A cultural and economic survey of present-day Philippines with sketches of the outstanding builders of the Commonwealth. Pedro de la Llana, editor and publisher. F.B. Icasiano, associate editor. Manila, Printed by General Printing Press, 1936.
xii, 522 p. 20cm.

NL 0424971 CSt

Llana Barrios, María Esther.
... Rondas de muerte y vida. Montevideo [Talleres gráficos "Sur"] 1939.
3 p. l., 9-62 p. 20cm.
Poems.

I. Title.

Library of Congress PQ8519.L56R6 42-45907
[2] 861.6

NL 0424972 DLC

Llana Barrios, María Esther.
Tierra y sol. [Montevideo] 1948.
77 p. 17 cm.
Poems.

I. Title.

PQ8519.L56T5 54-34561

NL 0424973 DLC NN

Llana Barrios, Mario.
... El juicio político; estudio constitucional e histórico-político. Montevideo, Impresora moderna, 1942.
146 p., 3 l. 24½cm.

1. Impeachments. 2. Impeachments—Uruguay. 3. Constitutional law. I. Title.

Library of Congress JF295.L5 44-20472
[3] 351.345

NL 0424974 DLC TU FU NcD NcU

Llanarth, Monmouthshire, England.
Catholic registers . . . 1781-1838. Contributed by J. Hobson Matthews.
(In Catholic Record Society. Miscellanea. Vol. 3, pp. 144-180. London. 1906.)

G3880 -- Matthews, John Hobson, ed. — Registers. Parish.

NL 0424975 MB

Llanas, A
L'anada a Montserrat
see under Aules Garriga, Eduardo, 1839-191

LLANAS, Alberto, 1847-1915.
Don Gonzalo, o l'orgull del gecn; comedia catallana. Barcelona. biblioteca de "L'Atlantida" 1879.

Port.

NL 0424977 MH

Llanas, Alberto, 1847-1915.
Don "Gonzalo", o L'orgull del Gec; comèdia catalana en tres actes, de costums catalanes... [Barcelona, Bonavía, 1919]
24 p. 28 cm. (La Escena catalana, Any II [2a época] núm. 34)

NL 0424978 NcU

Llanas, Alberto, 1847-1915.
Don "Gonzalo", o L'orgull del gec; comèdia en tres actes, de costums catalanas... Barcelona, Millà [1932]
79 p. 20 cm. (Catalunya teatral. Any I, no. 5)

NL 0424979 NcU

LLANAS, Alberto, 1847-1915.
Els raigs Y; idili fi de sigl en un acte. Barcelona, "Lo Teatro Regional". 1900.

On cover:- Biblioteca de Lo Teatro Regional 150.

NL 0424980 MH

PC
4460
.L55 Llanas, Alberto, 1847-1915
Reglas gramaticales ilustradas. Dibujos de Antonio Utrillo. Barcelona, B. Miralles [ca. 1900]
1 v. (chiefly illus.) 10 x 15 cm.

1. Spanish language - Idioms, corrections, errors. I. Title.

NL 0424981 WU NNH

VOLUME 337

Llanas, Eduardo, 1843–1904.

Escolapios insignes por su piedad religiosa desde el origen de las escuelas pías hasta nuestras días. Se publica por disposición del Rmo. P. vicario general de las escuelas pías de España ... Madrid, Impr. de San Francisco de Sales, 1899–1900.

BX +1585 +L55 Llanas, Eduardo, 1843-1904.
El laicismo; ó, Vindicación del sacerdocio contra los ataques del Correo catalán. [Barcelona?] Villanueva y Geltrú [1884]
43 p. 27 cm. (in binder, 31 cm.)

1. Catholic Church in Spain. 2. Correo catalán, Barcelona. I. Title.

NL 0424983 WU

---

550 L791s Llanas, Eduardo, 1843-1904.
Los seis dias de la creación. Barcelona, Biblioteca de la Sociedad Cristiana, 1889.
ix,180p. illus. 16cm.

1.Geology. 2.Bible and geology. 3. Creation. I.Title. √IC

NL 0424984 CLSU

Llanas, Ignacio Esparza
see
Esparza Llanas, Ignacio.

Llanas, Manuel de Lasala
see
Lasala Llanas, Manuel de.

Q868.73 L77c Llanas, Pedro L
Caridad y recompensa; novela original. Mexico, Impr. del Cinco de Mayo, 1874.
2v. in 1. plates. 23cm.

TxU copy imperfect: t.p. of v.1 wanting.

I. Title. Sp.: García Collection.

NL 0424987 TxU CSt CLSU

Llanas-Aguilaniedo, Jesus.
... Investigaciones sobre la invertasa... Zaragoza, 1920.
Thesis - Zaragoza.

NL 0424988 CtY

Llanas Aguilaniedo, José María, 1875-1921.
—— ... Navegar pintoresco. Madrid, F. Fé [etc.] 1903. 320p. 19cm.

NL 0424989 CU

3175 .1379 .372 Llanas Aguilaniedo, Jose Maria, 1875-1921.
Pityusa; novela. Madrid, Libreria de Fernando Fe [1908]
306 p. 19 cm.

NL 0424990 NjP

Law

Llanas de Niubó, Renato, ed.

Spain. *Laws, statutes, etc.*
Ley de arrendamientos urbanos de 31 de diciembre de 1946; exposición y comentarios [por] R. Llanas de Niubó [y] A. Llamas Pérez. Barcelona, 1947.

Llanas de Niubó, Renato.
Ley de arrendamientos urbanos de 31 de diciembre de 1946; sinopsis de la ley y apéndice conteniendo las disposiciones legales que la completan [por] R. Llanas de Niubó [y] A. Llamas Pérez. Barcelona [Distribuidor: Librería Bosch] 1947.
44 p. 25 cm.

1. Landlord and tenant—Spain. 2. Leases—Spain.

53-18162 ‡

NL 0424992 DLC

4BT 180 Llanas de Niubó, Renato
La pasión de Nuestro Señor Jesucristo. [1. ed.] Barcelona, L. de Caralt [1953]
363 p.

NL 0424993 DLC-P4 DCU

Llanas de Niubó, René.
... El judaísmo, por René Llanas de Niubó. Barcelona, J. Vilamala, 1935.
3 p. l., [9]–215 p. plates, port., map. 19cm. (Las sectas; biblioteca trimestral ... n.º 14)

"Judaísmo y cristianismo, sermones predicados en el adviento de 1933 por el cardenal Faulhaber, arzobispo de Munich (Baviera)": p. [189]–215.

1. Jewish question. 2. Christianity and other religions—Judaism. 3. Advent sermons. 4. Catholic church—Sermons. 5. Sermons, German—Translations into Spanish. 6. Sermons, Spanish—Translations from German. I. Faulhaber, Michael von, cardinal, 1869– Judentum, christentum, germanentum. II. Title.

36-29208

Library of Congress DS141.L73
[2] 296

NL 0424994 DLC

Llanas y Castells, Alberto de Sicilia
see Llanas, Alberto, 1847–1915.

Llanas y Rabassa, Salvador, 1862–
El alfiler de oro. Drama en tres actos y un prólogo. En prosa, original de Salvador Llanas Rabassa... Gracia: P. Lladó, 1884. 2 p.l., (1)8–66 p. 12°.

1. Drama (Spanish). 2. Title.
N. Y. P. L. October 1, 1919.

NL 0424996 NN

Llanas y Rabassa, Salvador, 1862 –
¡Entre mi hijo y mi honra! Drama trágico en tres actos, en verso, original de Salvador Llanas Rabassa... Barcelona: I. López, 1882. 78 p. 8°.

1. Drama (Spanish). 2. Title.
N. Y. P. L. April 4, 1916.

NL 0424997 NN

Llanas y Rabassa, Salvador, 1862–
La mujer de Urias; drama en tres actos, prólogo y epilogo en prosa, original de Salvador Llanas Rabassa... Barcelona: Libreria "La Universitaria" de S. Durán, 1884. 2 p.l., (1)8–67 p. 12°.

1. Drama (Spanish). 2. Title.
N. Y. P. L. October 1, 1919.

NL 0424998 NN

Llanas y Rabassa, Salvador, 1862 –
La mujer de Urías, drama en tres actos, prólogo y epílogo en prosa, original de Salvador Llanas Rabassa. Barcelona, Librería "La Universitaria" de S. Durán, 1884.
67p.

Microcard edition.

NL 0424999 ICRL MoU LU FU OrU

Llanbaddock, *Eng.* (*Parish*)
Registrum antiquum de Llanbadog in comitatu Monumethensi. 1582–1709. Transcribed from the copy in the public library at Cardiff and edited by Joseph Alfred Bradney ... London, Mitchell, Hughes and Clarke, 1919.
vii, 32 p. 26½cm.

"The register here printed is from a copy ... which was made in the year 1839 [!] by Lady Phillipps, the wife of Sir Thomas Phillipps of Middle hill, baronet."—Introd.

1. Registers of births, etc.—Llanbaddock, Eng. I. Phillipps, Harriet (Molyneux) lady, d. 1832. II. Bradney, Sir Joseph Alfred, 1859– III. Title.

30-30166

Library of Congress CS436.L52
[2] 929.3094243

NL 0425000 DLC NN MH MiU

[Llanbehr. - 1835]
see under [Hunt, Leigh] 1784-1859.

Llancarvan, Caradog of
see
Caradog, *of Llancarvan.*

Llancol, Rodrigo
see Alexander VI, pope, 1431-1505.

Llandaff, bp. of, 1739-1740
see
Mawson, Matthias, bp. of Ely, 1683-1770

Llandaff, Alfred Ollivant, bp. of.
see
Ollivant, Alfred, bp. of Llandaff, 1798-1882

Llandaff, Charles Richard Sumner, *Bp. of*
see Sumner, Charles Richard, *Bp. of Winchester,* 1790–1874.

Llandaff, Edward Copleston, *Bp. of*
see Copleston, Edward, *Bp. of Llandaff,* 1776–1849.

Llandaff, Herbert Marsh, *Bp. of*
see Marsh, Herbert, *Bp. of Peterborough,* 1757–1839.

Llandaff, John, bp. of
see Ewer, John, bp. of Bangor, d. 1774.

VOLUME 337

Llandaff, Jonathan Shipley, bishop of.
See
Shipley, Jonathan, bishop of St. Asaph, 1714-1788.

Llandaff, Richard, bp. of
see Watson, Richard, bp. of Llandaff, 1737-1816.

Llandaff, Richard Newcome, *Bp. of*
see Newcome, Richard, *Bp. of St. Asaph, d.* 1769.

Llandaff, Richard Watson, bp. of
see Watson, Richard, bp. of Llandaff, 1737-1816.

Llandaff, Robert Clavering, bp. of
see Clavering, Robert, bp. of Peterborough, 1671-1745.

Reference card

Llandaff, William, *bp. of*
see
Van Mildert, William, *bp. of Durham*, 1765-1836.

Llandaff, William Morgan, bp. of
see Morgan, William, of St. Asaph, 1540?-1604.

Llandaff, William Van Mildert, *Bp. of*
see Van Mildert, William, *Bp. of Durham*, 1765-1836.

HV L791r LLANDAFF, Wales. School for the Deaf and Dumb
Report.
1st- 1864-
London.
v. illus., ports.

NL 0425018 DNLM

Llandaff (*Diocese*)
... Acts of the bishops of Llandaff. Actorum episcoporum landavensium liber a 5to die decembris, 1660, usque ad ... ex originali manu-scripto ... transcriptus, cum notis nonnullis, per Josephum Alfredum Bradney de Tal-y-coed in Comitatu monumethensi. Prepared and issued by the Committee appointed under the authority of the Llandaff diocesan conference ... Cardiff, W. Lewis, 1908-
v. 23½cm. (Llandaff records. vol. II)
1. Llandaff (Diocese)—Hist.—Sources. I. Bradney, Joseph Alfred, 1859- ed.
9-25992
Library of Congress DA740.L7A3 vol. 2

NL 0425019 DLC FU NcD CtY

Llandaff, Diocese of.
Anglica Sacra
see under Wharton, Henry, 1664-1695.

DA740 .G5C48 Llandaff (Diocese)

Clark, George Thomas, 1809-1898, *comp.*
Cartæ et alia munimenta quæ ad dominium de Glamorgan pertinent ... Curante Geo. T. Clark. Dowlais [Priv. print.] 1885-93.

X325 L77 887 Llandaff. Cathedral. Library.
Catalogue of the Cathedral Library. Cardiff, W. Lewis, 1887.
99 p. 22 cm.
At head of title: Diocese of Llandaff.

1. Christian literature - Bibl. 2. Church history - Bibl.

NL 0425022 CtY

Llandaff (Diocese)
Catalogue of the Cathedral Library
see under Llandaff. Cathedral. Library.

Llandaff (*Diocese*)
A digest of the parish registers within the diocese of Llandaff previous to 1836, together with a table of the bishop's transcripts, to 1812, now in existence in the bishop's registry, with inventories of the act books of the bishops of Llandaff since 1660; and those of the dean and chapter since 1575. Prepared and issued by the Committee appointed under the authority of the Llandaff diocesan conference. 1905 ... Cardiff, W. Lewis, printer [1905?-
x, 93 p. 23½cm. (Lettered: Llandaff records. vol. I)
Mr. Robert Rickards, chairman of committee.
1. Registers of births, etc.—Llandaff.
9-25991
Library of Congress DA740.L7A3 vol. 1

NL 0425024 DLC NIC FU NcD MH

FILM FP 1101 Llandaff (Diocese) Bishop,1601-1617 (Francis Godwin)
To the parson,vicar or curate,of and to everie of them. [Oxford, 1603]
Caption title.
At end: Matherne. Sept.30.1602. Fr.Landaven [i.e.Francis Godwin,Bp.of Llandaff,later Bp.of Hereford]
Orders of the Bishop of Llandaff for the reformation of the abuses in his diocese.
Short-title catalogue no.11948 (carton 1101)
I.Godwin,Francis, Bp.of Hereford,1562-1633.

NL 0425025 MiU NNC

DA 740 L7 A3 Llandaff records. v. 1-5. London [etc.] F. Griffiths [etc.] 1905-14?
5 v. 24 cm.
Prepared and issued by a committee appointed by the Llandaff Diocesan Conference.

1. Llandaff (Diocese) - Hist. - Sources I. Llandaff (Diocese)

NL 0425026 Vi NN DCU DLC

Llanddewi Rhydderch, Eng.
see
Llanthewy Rytherch, Eng. (Parish)

G868.8208 Ar37 no.285 Llanderas, Nicolás de las.
Así es la vida; comedia asainetada en tres actos, original de Nicolás de las Llanderas y Arnaldo M. Malfatti. [Buenos Aires, Sociedad General de Autores de la Argentina, 1952]
56p. ports. 27cm. (Argentores, 2. época, año 15, no.285)

I. Malfatti, Arnaldo, joint author. II. Title. Series (contents)

NL 0425028 TxU

Llandinabo, Eng. (Parish)
The register books of Llandihabo, Pencoyd...
see under Parry, Joseph Henry.

Llandoff, Herbert Marsh, successively bp. of Llandoff and Peterborough
see Marsh, Herbert, bp. of Peterborough, 1757-1839.

Llandovery, and other poems; with a play, The battle of souls; by F. A. C., author of Shadows and other poems. London: The C. W. Daniel Co. [, 1930.] 48 p. 12°.

517644A. 1. Poetry, English. 2. Drama, English. I. C., F. A. II. Title: The battle of souls.
March 25, 1931

NL 0425031 NN MH

WX 2 FW3 L6S3r LLANDUDNO, Wales. Llandudno Sanatorium and Convalescent Home for Women
Report.
Llandudno, 18
v.

NL 0425032 DNLM

Llandudno, Wales. Public library.
...Librarian's report.

[Llandudno] 33½cm.

Annual.
Report year ends March 31st.
Reproduced from typewritten copy; cover printed.

1. Libraries—Gt. Br.—Wales— Llandudno.
June 14, 1940

NL 0425033 NN

Llandudno Cottage Hospital. Annual reports by the board of management to the subscribers, etc. 1.-3., 1881-4. 8°. *Llandudno*, 1882-4.

NL 0425034 DNLM

Llaneces, José, 1863-
Exposición Llaneces, "Salón Witcomb," año 1907, Buenos Aires. [Madrid: Lit. Mateu, 1907.] 2 l. 30 plates, ports. obl. 16°.
Prefatory note signed: Mariano de Cávia.

1. Paintings (Spanish). 2. Cávia, Mariano de, 1855-
November 15, 1920.

NL 0425035 NN

VOLUME 337

Llanelly (Wales). Charter.
Charter of incorporation. Llanelly: J. Davies & Co., Ltd., 1914. 7 f. f°.
At head of title: Dated 14th August, 1913.

1. Municipal charters and ordinances. Gt. Br.: Wales: Llanelly.
January 25, 1918.

NL 0425036 NN

Llanelly (Wales). Ordinances.
Bye-laws for regulating, cleansing, occupying, and using the Llanelly market... Llanelly: "Mercury" offices, 1908. 8 p. 8°.

1. Markets.—Jurisprudence, Gt. Br.: Wales: Llanelly. February 13, 1918.

NL 0425037 NN

Llanelly (Wales.). Ordinances.
Bye-laws for the good rule and government of the borough of Llanelly. Llanelly: "Mercury" offices, 1915. 8 p. 8°.

1. Municipal charters and ordinances, Gt. Br.: Wales: Llanelly.
December 26, 1917.

NL 0425038 NN

Llanelly (Wales). Ordinances.
Bye-laws... with respect to new buildings... Llanelly: J. Davies & Co. Ltd., 1912. 2 l. 8°.
Cover-title.

1. Building construction.—Jurisprudence, Gt. Br.: Wales: Llanelly.
March 12, 1918.

NL 0425039 NN

Llanelly (Wales). Ordinances.
Bye-laws... with respect to new streets and buildings... Llanelly: W. Davies, 1899. 61(1) p. 8°.

1. Streets.—Jurisprudence, Gt. Br.: Wales: Llanelly. 2. Building construction.—Jurisprudence, Gt. Br.: Wales: Llanelly.
March 13, 1918.

NL 0425040 NN

Llanelly (Wales). Ordinances.
Bye-laws... with respect to the pleasure ground known as "Parc Howard," Llanelly. Llanelly: "Mercury" Co., Ltd., 1912. 10 p. 8°.

1. Parks.—Jurisprudence. Gt. Br.: Wales: Llanelly.
March 12, 1918.

NL 0425041 NN

Llanelly Railway and Dock Company.
Half-yearly report.

London, no. f°.

1. Railways, Gt. Br.: Wales (Indiv.): Llanelly Railway and Dock Company.
January 17, 1922.

NL 0425042 NN

LLANERAS, MARCO ANTONIO.
Ensayos caricaturescos, por Marco Antonio Llaneras jr. [La Habana? Propiedad del autor, 1932] 96 f., 97-99 p. illus. (incl. ports.) 21½cm.

Folios 5-6, 12-95 are full page illus.

819415A. 1. Caricature and comic art, Cuban. I. Title.

NL 0425043 NN

Llaneras de Sierra, Marco A
Evocación martiana; homenaje a nuestro apóstol. Habana, Editorial "El Sol," 1947.
58 p. port. 18 cm.

1. Martí, José, 1853-1895. I. Title.
A 48-8634

Yale Univ. Library for Library of Congress

NL 0425044 CtY NcU NN

El llanero (estudio de sociología venezolana)
see under [Bolívar Coronado, Rafael] 1884-

Llanes, Carlos Antonio.
Conferencias pronunciadas en la Escuela de comercio de la Asociacion de dependientes del comercio de la Habana...
see under Asociación de dependientes del comercio de la Habana.

Llanes, Fernando Antonio, *ed.*
En el día de la madre. [Recopilaciones] San Salvador, Ministerio de Cultura [1950]
82 p. 18 cm. (Biblioteca del pueblo, 9)
Poems.

1. Mothers. I. Title.

PN6071.M7L6 52-19221

NL 0425047 DLC TxU

Llanes, Héctor Silva
see Silva Llanes, Héctor, 1903-

Llanes, José Calderon y
see Calderon y Llanes, José.

Llanes, José L
The constitutional question on the writ of habeas corpus, by José L. Llanes. Foreword by Vicente Llanes. Manila, Archipelago Pub. House [©1951]
xix, 200 p.

1. Habeas corpus--Philippine Islands. I. Title.

NL 0425050 NSyU

PQ 7409 .L5F8

Llanes, Manuel.
El fuego. Ciudad Trujillo, La Española [1953]
25 p. (Colección La Isla necesaria, 4)

A poem.

El fuego.

NL 0425051 MoU NN

Llanes, Ricardo M
La Avenida de Mayo, media centuria entre recuerdos y evocaciones. Buenos Aires, G. Kraft [1955]
340 p. illus. 21 cm. (Colección Cúpula)

1. Buenos Aires—Streets—Avenida de Mayo. I. Title.

F3001.L6 56-46400 ‡

NL 0425052 DLC PSt NIC InU TxU CU NN IU

Llanes, Ricardo M
Señor ministro: Buenos Aires [Tall. Gráf. de D. Cersosimo] 1948.
135, [5] p. 24 cm.
Bibliography: p. [139]

1. Argentine Republic—Hist.—Study and teaching. I. Title.
A 52-555

New York. Public Libr. for Library of Congress

NL 0425053 NN ICarbS

Llanes Campomanes, Juan
see Juan de la Anunciación, d. 1701.

350.946 L79 1918

Llanes, Spain. Charters.
El fuero de llanes. Madrid [Impr. de Fortanet] 1918.
62 p. facsim. 25 cm.
At head of title: Adolfo Bonilla y San Martin.
Bibliographical footnotes.
Errata slip inserted.
Author's autograph presentation copy.

I. Bonilla y San Martin Adolfo, 1875-1926.

NL 0425055 MiU

DP402 .L45D6

Llanes, Spain. Laws, statutes, etc. Fuero de Llanes.
Documentos raros y curiosos para la historia de Llanes. [Madrid?], Chimalistac, 1955.

Llaneza, Luis.
¡Buena noche! Pasa-calle cómico-lirico pascual en un cuadro y en prosa, original de Luis Llaneza, música de Manuel M. Faixá ... Madrid: R. Velasco, 1915. 22 p., 1 l. 12°.
On cover: Madrid: Soc. de autores españoles.

1. Drama (Spanish). 2. Title.
September 26, 1916.

NL 0425057 NN MH

VOLUME 337

Llaneza, Maximino.
Bibliografía del V. P. M. Fr. Luis de Granada de la Orden de predicadores, por Fr. Maximino Llaneza ... Salamanca, Establecimiento typográfico de Calatrava, 1926–
v. port., facsims. 25cm.

1. Luis de Granada, 1504–1588—Bibl.

Library of Congress Z8527.5.L79 28–21365

NL 0425058 DLC CU MH NcD NN ICU

Llanfair Discoed, Eng.
see
Llanvair Discoed, Eng. (Parish)

Llanfihangel Ystern Llewern, *Eng. (Parish)*
Registrum antiquum de Llanfihangel Ystern Llewern in comitatu Monumethensi. 1685–1812. Transcribed from the original register books and edited by Joseph Alfred Bradney ... To which is added a short account of the parish, together with list of rectors and monumental inscriptions. London, Mitchell, Hughes and Clarke, 1920.
xii, 46 p. pl. 26cm.

1. Registers of births, etc.—Llanfihangel Ystern Llewern, Eng. I. Bradney, Sir Joseph Alfred, 1859– II. Title.

Library of Congress CS436.L54 30–30167
929.3094243

NL 0425060 DLC NN

WX 2 FW3 L7C8r LLANGOLLEN, Wales. Cottage Hospital
Report. 1st- 1876-
Llangollen.
v.

NL 0425061 DNLM

Ib55 Td1 L77
Llangunnor Hill; a loco-descriptive poem. With notes. Humbly dedicated by the author, to the public at large. Carmarthen, Printed and sold for the author by J. Daniel [Pref. 1794]
xii, 28 p. 20 cm.
Added t.-p. Imprint varies.
Attributed to John Bethell. - cf. Aubin, Robert A. Topographical poetry, p.101, 305.

I. Bethell, John supposed author.

NL 0425062 CtY

Llano, Ramiro
see
Ramiro Llano,

Llano, Agustin E. Callejas
see Callejas Llano, Agustin E.

Llano, Alberto.
Compendio de historia de España, por Alberto Llano. Barcelona, I. G. Seix y Barral hnos., s. a., 1932.
114 p. illus. (incl. ports., maps) 17 x 13cm. [Colección Compendios]

1. Spain—Hist. I. Title.

Library of Congress DP68.L6 33–8352
946

NL 0425065 DLC

Llano, Alberto Restrepo
see
Restrepo Llano, Alberto.

Llano, Ambrosio.
Nos el licenciado d. Ambrosio Llano tesorero de esta santa Iglesia metropolitana provisor vicario general y gobernador de èste arzobispado por el illustrisimo sr. d. Juan Felix de Villegas arzobispo del mismo ... Por quanto S. M. Dios le guarde, deseoso de que sus amados vasallos logren las gracias y jubileos ... [Guatemala, 1799]
Microfilm copy, made in 1942, of the original broadside in the Medina collection, Biblioteca nacional de Santiago de Chile. Positive. Negative film in Brown university library.
Caption and part of text used as title.

Signed: Ambrocio Llano. Por mandado de s. sria. Josè Francisco Gabarrete.
Dated in Nueva Guatemala, Nov. 28, 1799.
"Sobre publicación y recibimiento de la Bula de cruzada."—Medina, La imprenta en Guatemala, 986.

1. Indulgences.
Microfilm AC–2 reel 185, no. 2 Mic A 49–1134

Brown Univ. Library for Library of Congress †

NL 0425068 RPB DLC

Llano, Antonio.
Álgebra elemental, con numerosas aplicaciones prácticas, libro de texto para la enseñanza secundaria y las escuelas de artes y oficios, por Antonio Llano. Boston, Nueva York [etc.] D. C. Heath y compañía [c1931]
xxiii, [1], 445 p. illus., diagrs. 19cm.

1. Algebra. 2. Algebra—Problems, exercises, etc.

Library of Congress QA152.L79 31–15927
Copyright A 37775 512

NL 0425069 DLC

Llano, Antonio, ed. FOR OTHER EDITIONS SEE MAIN ENTRY

Cuyás, Arturo, 1845–1925.
Appleton's new English-Spanish and Spanish-English dictionary, containing more than six thousand modern words and twenty-five thousand acceptations, idioms and technical terms not found in any other similar work: with a pronouncing key and the fundamental tenses of irregular verbs, by Arturo Cuyás; revised and enlarged by Antonio Llano ... New York, London, D. Appleton-Century company, incorporated, 1940.

Llano, Antonio, tr.

Butler, Nicholas Murray, 1862–
Democracia y seudodemocracia, por Nicholas Murray Butler ... traducida del inglés por Antonio Llano. New York, C. Scribner's sons, 1940.

PS111 .S6P3 Llano, Antonio, tr.

Parrington, Vernon Louis, 1871–1929.
... El desarrollo de las ideas en los Estados Unidos ... por Vernon Louis Parrington. Traducción de Antonio Llano. Lancaster, Pa., Lancaster press, inc., 1941–

Llano, Antonio, tr.

Fairgrieve, James, 1870–
Geografía humana por grados ... por Jaime Fairgrieve y Ernesto Young; versión española del inglés por Antonio Llano. Nueva York, D. Appleton y compañía [c1930–

Llano, Antonio, tr.

Young, Jacob William Albert, 1865–
Geometría plana, por J. W. A. Young y Lambert L. Jackson; refundida y adaptada al español por Antonio Llano. Nueva York, Londres, D. Appleton y compañia, 1927.

Llano, Antonio

[**Cuyás, Arturo**] 1845–1925.
Noble's new Spanish-English and English-Spanish dictionary; containing more than six thousand modern and twenty-five thousand common words, idioms, scientific and commercial terms not found in any other similar work, together with a key to the correct pronunciation of both the Spanish and English words; also the fundamental tenses of irregular verbs. New rev. and enl. ed., printed from new plates with new type arrangement. New York, Translation publishing company, inc. [c1928]

Llano, Antonio, tr.

Angell, *Sir* Norman, 1874–
... La paz y el pueblo, por Norman Angell, traducción de Antonio Llano ... Barcelona, G. Gili, 1936.

Llano, Antonio, tr.

American society for testing materials.
... Pliego [!] de condiciones normales para fundición para moldeo. Forma adoptada por la Sociedad americana de ensayos de materiales. Ed. corr. de 1909. Ed. española-inglesa preparada bajo la dirección de la Oficina de normas <Bureau of standards> durante la presidencia de S. W. Stratton ... Wáshington. Imprenta del gobierno, 1919.

Llano, Antonio, tr.

American society for testing materials.
... Pliego de condiciones normales cadenas de hierro y de acero. Forma adoptada por la Sociedad americana de ensayos de materiales. Ed. corr. de 1918. Ed. española-inglesa preparada bajo la dirección de la Oficina de normas <Bureau of standards> durante la presidencia de S. W. Stratton ... Wáshington, Imprenta del gobierno, 1919.

Llano, Antonio, tr.

American society for testing materials.
... Pliego de condiciones normales para acero Béssemer estirado en frío para la fabricación de tornillos en máquinas automáticas de roscar. Forma adoptada por la Sociedad americana de ensayos de materiales. Adoptado en 1914. Ed. española-inglesa preparada bajo la dirección de la Oficina de normas <Bureau of standards> durante la presidencia de S. W. Stratton ... Wáshington, Imprenta del gobierno, 1919.

VOLUME 337

Llano, Antonio, tr.

American society of testing materials.
... Pliego de condiciones normales para acero carbono y de aleación para automóviles. Forma adoptada por la Sociedad americana de ensayos de materials. Ed. corr. de 1918. Ed. española-inglesa preparada bajo la dirección de la Oficina de normas <Bureau of standards> durante la presidencia de S.W.Stratton... Washington, Imprenta del gobierno, 1919.

Llano, Antonio, tr.

American society for testing materials.
... Pliego de condiciones normales para acero de calderas y hogares de locomotora. Forma adoptada por la Sociedad americana de ensayos de materiales. Ed. corr de 1918. Ed. española-inglesa preparada bajo la dirección de la Oficina de normas <Bureau of standards> durante la presidencia de S. W. Stratton ... Wáshington Imprenta del gobierno, 1919.

Llano, Antonio, tr.

American society for testing materials.
... Pliego de condiciones normales para acero de construcciones para buques. Forma adoptada por la Sociedad americana de ensayos de materiales. Ed. corr. de 1916. Ed. española-inglesa preparada bajo la dirección de la Oficina de normas <Bureau of standards> durante la presidencia de S. W. Stratton ... Wáshington, Imprenta del gobierno, 1919.

Llano, Antonio, tr.

American society for testing materials.
... Pliego de condiciones normales para acero de construcciones para edificios. Forma adoptada por la Sociedad americana de ensayos de materiales. Ed. corr. de 1916. Ed. española-inglesa preparada bajo la dirección de la Oficina de normas <Bureau of standards> durante la presidencia de S. W. Stratton ... Wáshington, Imprenta del gobierno, 1918.

Llano, Antonio, tr.

American society for testing materials.
... Pliego de condiciones normales para acero de construcciones para locomotoras. Forma adoptada por la Sociedad americana de ensayos de materiales. Ed. corr. de 1916. Ed. española-inglesa preparada bajo la dirección de la Oficina de normas <Bureau of standards> durante la presidencia de S. W. Stratton ... Wáshington, Imprenta del gobierno, 1918.

Llano, Antonio, tr.

American society for testing materials.
... Pliego de condiciones normales para acero de construcciones para vagones. Forma adoptada por la Sociedad americana de ensayos de materiales. Ed. corr. de 1916. Ed. española-inglesa preparada bajo la dirección de la Oficina de normas <Bureau of standards> durante la presidencia de S. W. Stratton ... Wáshington, Imprenta del gobierno, 1919.

Llano, Antonio, tr.

American society for testing materials.
... Pliego de condiciones normales para acero de remaches para buques. Forma adoptada por la Sociedad americana de ensayos de materiales. Ed. corr. de 1914. Ed. española-inglesa preparada bajo la dirección de la Oficina de normas <Bureau of standards> durante la presidencia de S. W. Stratton ... Wáshington, Imprenta del gobierno, 1919.

Llano, Antonio, tr.

American society for testing materials.
... Pliego de condiciones normales para acero de remaches para calderas. Forma adoptada por la Sociedad americana de ensayos de materiales. Ed. corr. en 1914. Ed. española-inglesa preparada bajo la dirección de la Oficina de normas <Bureau of standards> durante la presidencia de S. W. Stratton ... Wáshington, Imprenta del gobierno, 1919.

Llano, Antonio, tr.

American society for testing materials.
... Pliego de condiciones normales para acero níquel de construcciones. Forma adoptada por la Sociedad americana de ensayos de materiales. Ed. corr. de 1916. Ed. española-inglesa preparada bajo la dirección de la Oficina de normas <Bureau of standards> durante la presidencia de S. W. Stratton ... Wáshington, Imprenta del gobierno, 1919.

Llano, Antonio, tr.

American society for testing materials.
...Pliego de condiciones normales para acero Siemens-Martín estirado en frío para la fabricación de tortillos en máquinas automáticas de roscar. Forma adoptada por la Sociedad americana de ensayos de materiales. Adoptado en 1915. Ed. española-inglesa preparada bajo la dirección de la Oficina de normas <Bureau of standards> durante la presidencia de S. W. Stratton ... Wáshington, Imprenta del gobierno, 1919.

Llano, Antonio, tr.

American society for testing materials.
... Pliego de condiciones normales para alambre de cobre dulce o recocido. Forma adoptada por la Sociedad americana de ensayos de materiales. Ed. corr. de 1915. Ed. española-inglesa preparada bajo la dirección de la Oficina de normas <Bureau of standards> durante la presidencia de S. W. Stratton... Wáshington, Imprenta del gobierno, 1919.

Llano, Antonio, tr.

American society for testing materials.
... Pliego de condiciones normales para alambre de cobre estirado en frío. Forma adoptada por la Sociedad americana de ensayos de materiales. Ed. corr. de 1915. Ed. española-inglesa preparada bajo la dirección de la Oficina de normas <Bureau of standards> durante la presidencia de S. W. Stratton ... Wáshington, Imprenta del gobierno, 1919.

Llano, Antonio, tr.

American society for testing materials.
... Pliego de condiciones normales para alambre de cobre semiduro. Forma adoptada por la Sociedad americana de ensayos de materiales. Ed. corr. de 1915. Ed. española-inglesa preparada bajo la dirección de la Oficina de normas <Bureau of standards> durante la presidencia de S. W. Stratton ... Wáshington, Imprenta del gobierno, 1919.

Llano, Antonio, tr.

American society for testing materials.
... Pliego de condiciones normales para armaduras para hormigón hechas de acero en billets. Forma adoptada por la Sociedad americana de ensayos de materiales. Ed. corr. de 1914. Ed. española-inglesa preparada bajo la dirección de la Oficina de normas <Bureau of standards> durante la presidencia de S. W. Stratton ... Wáshington, Imprenta del gobierno, 1919.

Llano, Antonio, tr.

American society for testing materials.
... Pliego de condiciones normales para armaduras para hormigón hechas de rieles de acero. Forma adoptada por la Sociedad americana de ensayos de materiales, Ed. corr. de 1914. Ed. española-inglesa preparada bajo la dirección de la Oficina de normas <Bureau of standards> durante la presidencia de S. W. Stratton ... Wáshington, Imprenta del gobierno, 1919.

Llano, Antonio, tr.

American society for testing materials.
... Pliego de condiciones normales para aros de acero para ruedas de ferrocarril. Forma adoptada por la Sociedad americana de ensayos de materiales. Ed. corr. de 1916. Ed. española-inglesa preparada bajo la dirección de la Oficina de normas <Bureau of standards> durante la presidencia de S. W. Stratton ... Wáshington, Imprenta del gobierno, 1919.

TA469 .A5 1919 Llano, Antonio, tr.

American society for testing materials.
... Pliego de condiciones normales para barras de hierro dulce de calidad. Forma adoptada por la Sociedad americana de ensayos ed [!] materiales. Ed. corr. de 1918. Ed. española-inglesa preparada bajo la dirección de la Oficina de normas <Bureau of standards> durante la presidencia de S. W. Stratton ... Wáshington, Imprenta del gobierno, 1919.

Llano, Antonio, tr.

American society for testing materials.
... Pliego de condiciones normales para barras y planchas a medio acabar de acero carbono y aceros de aleación para piezas forjadas. Forma adoptada por la Sociedad americana de ensayos de materiales. Ed. corr. de 1918. Ed. española-inglesa preparada bajo la dirección de la Oficina de normas <Bureau of standards> durante la presidencia de S. W. Stratton ... Wáshington, Imprenta del gobierno, 1919.

Llano, Antonio, tr.

American society for testing materials.
... Pliego de condiciones normales para bridas de acero dulce. Forma adoptada por la Sociedad americana de ensayos de materiales. Ed. corr. de 1914. Ed. española-inglesa preparada bajo la dirección de la Oficina de normas <Bureau of standards> durante la presidencia de S. W. Stratton ... Wáshington, Imprenta del gobierno, 1918.

Llano, Antonio, tr.

American society for testing materials.
... Pliego de condiciones normales para bridas de acero duro. Forma adoptada por la Sociedad americana de ensayos de materiales. Ed. corr. de 1914. Ed. española-inglesa preparada bajo la dirección de la Oficina de normas <Bureau of standards> durante la presidencia de S. W. Stratton ... Wáshington, Imprenta del gobierno, 1918.

Llano, Antonio, tr.

American society for testing materials.
... Pliego de condiciones normales para bridas de acero duro templado. Forma adoptada por la Sociedad americana de ensayos de materiales. Adoptado en 1915. Ed. española-inglesa preparada bajo la dirección de la Oficina de normas (Bureau of standards) durante la presidencia de S. W. Stratton ... Wáshington, Imprenta del gobierno, 1919.

VOLUME 337

Llano, Antonio, tr.

American society for testing materials.
... Pliego de condiciones normales para bridas de acero extradulce. Forma adoptada por la Sociedad americana de ensayos de materiales. Ed. corr. de 1914. Ed. española-inglesa preparada bajo la dirección de la Oficina de normas ⟨Bureau of standards⟩ durante la presidencia de S. W. Stratton ... Wáshington, Imprenta del gobierno, 1918.

Llano, Antonio, tr.

American society for testing materials.
... Pliego de condiciones normales para bridas de acero extraduro. Forma adoptada por la Sociedad americana de ensayos de materiales. Ed. corr. de 1914. Ed. española-inglesa preparada bajo la dirección de la Oficina de normas ⟨Bureau of standards⟩ durante la presidencia de S. W. Stratton ... Wáshington, Imprenta del gobierno, 1919.

Llano, Antonio, tr.

American society for testing materials.
... Pliego de condiciones normales para cilindros de fundición para locomotoras. Forma adoptada por la Sociedad americana de ensayos de materiales. Ed. corr. de 1914. Ed. española-inglesa preparada bajo la dirección de la Oficina de normas ⟨Bureau of standards⟩ durante la presidencia de S. W. Stratton ... Wáshington, Imprenta del gobierno, 1919.

TA480
.C7A5
1919

Llano, Antonio, tr.

American society for testing materials.
... Pliego de condiciones normales para cobre del Michigán en barras para alambre y en tortas, planchas, barras redondas para tubos, lingotes y barras de lingotes. Forma adoptada por la Sociedad americana de ensayos de materiales. Ed. corr. de 1913. Ed. española-inglesa preparada bajo la dirección de la Oficina de normas ⟨Bureau of standards⟩ durante la presidencia de S. W. Stratton ... Wáshington, Imprenta del gobierno, 1919.

TA480
.C7A53
1919

Llano, Antonio, tr.

American society for testing materials.
... Pliego de condiciones normales para cobre electrolítico en barras para alambre y en tortas, planchas, barras redondas para tubos, lingotes y barras de lingotes. Forma adoptada por la Sociedad americana de ensayos de materiales. Ed. corr. de 1913. Ed. española-inglesa preparada bajo la dirección de la Oficina de normas ⟨Bureau of standards⟩ durante la presidencia de S. W. Stratton ... Wáshington, Imprenta del gobierno, 1919.

Llano, Antonio, tr.

American society for testing materials.
... Pliego de condiciones normales para ejes, barras y otras piezas forjadas de acero templado y recocido para locomotoras y vagones. Forma adoptada por la Sociedad americana de ensayos de materiales. Ed. corr. de 1918 Ed. española-inglesa preparada bajo la dirección de la Oficina de normas ⟨Bureau of standards⟩ durante la presidencia de S. W. Stratton ... Wáshington, Imprenta del gobierno, 1918.

Llano, Antonio, tr.

American society for testing materials.
... Pliego de condiciones normales para ejes, barras y otras piezas forjadas de acero de aleación templado y recocido para locomotoras y vagones. Forma adoptada por la Sociedad americana de ensayos de materiales. Ed. corr. de 1918. Ed. española-inglesa preparada bajo la dirección de la Oficina de normas ⟨Bureau of standards⟩ durante la presidencia de S. W. Stratton ... Wáshington, Imprenta del gobierno, 1919.

Llano, Antonio, tr.

American society for testing materials.
... Pliego de condiciones normales para ejes de acero laminados en frío. Forma adoptada por la Sociedad americana de ensayos de materiales. Ed. corr. de 1916. Ed. española-inglesa preparada bajo la dirección de la Oficina de normas ⟨Bureau of standards⟩ durante la presidencia de S. W. Stratton ... Wáshington, Imprenta del gobierno, 1919.

Llano, Antonio, tr.

American society for testing materials.
... Pliego de condiciones normales para ejes de acero para vagones y ténderes. Forma adoptada por la Sociedad americana de ensayos de materiales. Ed. corr. de 1918. Ed. española-inglesa preparada bajo la dirección de la Oficina de normas ⟨Bureau of standards⟩ durante la presidencia de S. W. Stratton ... Wáshington, Imprenta del gobierno, 1919.

Llano, Antonio, tr.

American society for testing materials.
... Pliego de condiciones normales para hierro de virotillos. Forma adoptada por la Sociedad americana de ensayos de materiales. Ed. corr. de 1918. Ed. española-inglesa preparada bajo la dirección de la Oficina de normas ⟨Bureau of standards⟩ durante la presidencia de S. W. Stratton ... Wáshington, Imprenta del gobierno, 1919.

TJ1330
.A5
1918

Llano, Antonio, tr.

American society for testing materials.
... Pliego de condiciones normales para hierro para pernos de máquinas de vapor. Forma adoptada por la Sociedad americana de ensayos de materiales. Ed. corr. de 1918. Ed. española-inglesa preparada bajo la dirección de la Oficina de normas ⟨Bureau of standards⟩ durante la presidencia de S. W. Stratton ... Wáshington, Imprenta del gobierno, 1918.

Llano, Antonio, tr.

American society for testing materials.
... Pliego de condiciones normales para la pureza de aceite de linaza crudo de semilla norteamericana. Forma adoptada por la Sociedad americana de ensayos de materiales. Ed. corr. de 1915. Ed. española-inglesa preparada bajo la dirección de la Oficina de normas ⟨Bureau of standards⟩ durante la presidencia de S. W. Stratton ... Wáshington, Govt. print. off., 1919.

Llano, Antonio, tr.

American society for testing materials.
... Pliego de condiciones normales para la pureza del aceite de linaza hervido de semilla norteamericana. Forma adoptada por la Sociedad americana de ensayos de materiales. Adoptado en 1915. Ed. española-inglesa preparada bajo la dirección de la Oficina de normas ⟨Bureau of standards⟩ durante la presidencia de S. W. Stratton ... Wáshington, Imprenta del gobierno, 1919.

Llano, Antonio, tr.

American society for testing materials.
... Pliego de condiciones normales para la trementina. Forma adoptada por la Sociedad americana de ensayos de materiales. Adoptado en 1915. Ed. española-inglesa preparada bajo la dirreción de la Oficina de normas ⟨Bureau of standards⟩ durante la presidencia de S. W. Stratton ... Wáshington, Imprenta del gobierno, 1919.

TA490
.A5
1919

Llano, Antonio, tr.

American society for testing materials.
... Pliego de condiciones normales para lingotes de bronce manganesado para moldes en arena. Forma adoptada por la Sociedad americana de ensayos de materiales. Ed. corr. de 1914. Ed. española-inglesa preparada bajo la dirección de la Oficina de normas ⟨Bureau of standards⟩ durante la presidencia de S. W. Stratton ... Wáshington, Imprenta del gobierno, 1919.

TA480
.Z6A5
1919

Llano, Antonio, tr.

American society for testing materials.
... Pliego de condiciones normales para peltre o zinc del comercio. Forma adoptada por la Sociedad americana de ensayos de materiales. Ed corr. de 1918. Ed. española-inglesa preparada bajo la dirección de la Oficina de normas ⟨Bureau of standards⟩ durante la presidencia de S. W. Stratton ... Wáshington, Imprenta del gobierno, 1919.

Llano, Antonio, tr.

American society for testing materials.
... Pliego de condiciones normales para pernos de acero templado de aleación para ferrocarriles. Forma adoptada por la Sociedad americana de ensayos de materiales. Ed. corr. de 1916. Ed. española-inglesa preparada bajo la dirección de la Oficina de normas ⟨Bureau of standards⟩ durante la presidencia de S. W. Stratton ... Wáshington, Imprenta del gobierno, 1919.

Llano, Antonio, tr.

American society for testing materials.
... Pliego de condiciones normales para pernos de acero templado para ferrocarriles. Forma adoptada por la Sociedad americana de ensayos de materiales. Ed. corr. de 1916. Ed. española-inglesa preparada bajo la dirección de la Oficina de normas ⟨Bureau of standards⟩ durante la presidencia de S. W. Stratton ... Wáshington, Imprenta del gobierno, 1919.

Llano, Antonio, tr.

American society for testing materials.
... Pliego de condiciones normales para piezas forjadas de acero ordinario y de aceros de aleación. Forma adoptada por la Sociedad americana de ensayos de materiales. Ed. corr. de 1918. Ed. española-inglesa preparada bajo la dirección de la Oficina de normas ⟨Bureau of standards⟩ durante la presidencia de S. W. Stratton ... Wáshington, Imprenta del gobierno, 1918.

Llano, Antonio, tr.

American society for testing materials.
... Pliego de condiciones normales para piezas forjadas de acero para locomotoras. Forma adoptada por la Sociedad americana de ensayos de materiales. Ed. corr. de 1916. Ed. española-inglesa preparada bajo la dirección de la Oficina de normas ⟨Bureau of standards⟩ durante la presidencia de S. W. Stratton ... Wáshington, Imprenta del gobierno, 1918.

Llano, Antonio, tr.

American society for testing materials.
... Pliego de condiciones normales para piezas fundidas de acero. Forma adoptada por la Sociedad americana de ensayos de materiales. Ed. corr. de 1916. Ed. española-inglesa preparada bajo la dirección de la Oficina de normas ⟨Bureau of standards⟩ durante la presidencia de S. W. Stratton ... Wáshington, Imprenta del gobierno, 1919.

VOLUME 337

TA474 .A5 1919 Llano, Antonio, tr.

American society for testing materials.
... Pliego de condiciones normales para piezas vaciadas de fundición dulce de moldes. Forma adoptada por la Sociedad americana de ensayos de materiales. Ed. corr. de 1915. Ed. española-inglesa preparada bajo la dirección de la Oficina de normas <Bureau of standards> durante la presidencia de S. W. Stratton ... Wáshington, Imprenta del gobierno, 1919.

TA474 .A52 1919 Llano, Antonio, tr.

American society for testing materials.
... Pliego de condiciones normales para piezas vaciadas de fundición gris. Forma adoptada por la Sociedad americana de ensayos de materiales. Ed. corr. de 1918. Ed. española-inglesa preparada bajo la dirección de la Oficina de normas <Bureau of standards> durante la presidencia de S. W. Stratton ... Wáshington, Imprenta del gobierno, 1919.

TA469 .A52 1919 Llano, Antonio, tr.

American society for testing materials.
... Pliego de condiciones normales para planchas de hierro dulce. Forma adoptada por la Sociedad americana de ensayos de materiales. Ed. corr. de 1918. Ed. española-inglesa preparada bajo la dirección de la Oficina de normas <Bureau of standards> durante la presidencia de S. W. Stratton ... Wáshington. Imprenta del gobierno, 1919.

Llano, Antonio, tr.

American society for testing materials.
... Pliego de condiciones normales para rieles de acero. Forma adoptada por la Sociedad americana de ensayos de materiales. Ed. corr. de 1914. Ed. española-inglesa preparada bajo la dirección de la Oficina de normas <Bureau of standards> durante la presidencia de S. W. Stratton ... Wáshington, Imprenta del gobierno, 1918.

Llano, Antonio, tr.

American society for testing materials.
... Pliego de condiciones normales para rieles de tranvía y rieles altos vignole de acero siemens-martín. Forma adoptada por la Sociedad americana de ensayos de materiales. Adoptado en 1912. Ed. española-inglesa preparada bajo la dirección de la Oficina de normas <Bureau of standards> durante la presidencia de S. W. Stratton ... Wáshington, Imprenta del gobierno, 1918.

Llano, Antonio, tr.

American society for testing materials.
... Pliego de condiciones normales para ruedas de fundición para vagones. Forma adoptada por la Sociedad americana de ensayos de materiales. Adoptado en 1905. Ed. española-inglesa preparada bajo la dirección de la Oficina de normas <Bureau of standards> durante la presidencia de S. W. Stratton ... Wáshington, Imprenta del gobierno, 1919.

Llano, Antonio, tr.

American society for testing materials.
... Pliego de condiciones normales para ruedas macizas de acero forjado para ferrocarriles de vapor. Forma adoptada por la Sociedad americana de ensayos de materiales. Ed. corr. de 1916. Ed. española-inglesa preparado bajo la dirección de la Oficina de normas (Bureau of standards) durante la presidencia de S. W. Stratton ... Wáshington, Imprenta del gobierno, 1919.

Llano, Antonio, tr.

American society for testing materials.
... Pliego de condiciones normales para ruedas macizas de acero para servicio de ferrocarriles eléctricos. Forma adoptada por la Sociedad americana de ensayos de materiales. Ed. corr. de 1916. Ed. española-inglesa preparada bajo la dirección de la Oficina de normas <Bureau of standards> durante la presidencia de S. W. Stratton ... Wáshington, Imprenta del gobierno, 1919.

Llano, Antonio, tr.

American society for testing materials.
... Pliego de condiciones normales para tubos de acero o de hierro dulce soldados por recubrimiento o sin soldadura para calderas de máquinas fijas. Forma adoptada por la Sociedad americana de ensayos de materiales. Ed. corr. de 1918. Ed. española-inglesa preparada bajo la dirección de la Oficina de normas (Bureau of standards) durante la presidencia de S. W. Stratton ... Wáshington, Imprenta del gobierno, 1919.

Llano, Antonio, tr.

American society for testing materials.
... Pliego de condiciones normales para tubos de acero para calderas de locomotora soldados por recubrimiento y sin soldadura. Forma adoptada por la Sociedad americana de ensayos de materiales. Ed. corr. de 1918. Ed. española-inglesa preparada bajo la dirección de la Oficina de normas ⟨Bureau of standards⟩ durante la presidencia de S. W. Stratton ... Wáshington, Imprenta del gobierno, 1919.

Llano, Antonio, tr.

American society for testing materials.
... Pliego de condiciones normales para tubos de fundición para abastecimiento de agua. Forma adoptada por la Sociedad americana de ensayos de materiales. Adoptado en 1904. Ed. española-inglesa preparada bajo la dirección de la Oficina de normas ⟨Bureau of standards⟩ durante la presidencia de S. W. Stratton ... Wáshington, Imprenta del gobierno, 1919.

Llano, Antonio, tr.

American society for testing materials.
... Pliego de condiciones normales para tubos de hierro de carbón vegetal para calderas de locomotora soldados por recubrimiento. Forma adoptada por la Sociedad americana de ensayos de materiales. Ed. corr. de 1918. Ed. española-inglesa preparada bajo la dirección de la Oficina de normas ⟨Bureau of standards⟩ durante la presidencia de S. W. Statton ... Wáshington, Imprenta del gobierno, 1919.

Llano, Antonio, tr.

American society for testing materials.
... Pliego de condiciones normales para tubos soldados de acero. Forma adoptada por la Sociedad americana de ensayos de materiales. Ed. corr. de 1918 Ed. española-inglesa preparada bajo la dirección de la Oficina de normas ⟨Bureau of standards⟩ durante la presidencia de S. W. Stratton ... Wáshington, Imprenta del gobierno, 1919.

Llano, Antonio, tr.

American society for testing materials.
... Pliego de condiciones normales para tubos soldados de hierro dulce. Forma adoptada por la Sociedad americana de ensayos de materiales. Adoptado en 1918. Ed. española-inglesa preparada bajo la dirección de la Oficina de normas ⟨Bureau of standards⟩ durante la presidencia de S. W. Stratton... Wáshington, Imprenta del gobierno, 1919.

Llano, Antonio, tr.

American society for testing materials.
... Pliego de condiciones normales para varillas de acero para resortes de ferrocarril. Forma adoptada por la Sociedad americana de ensayos de materiales. Ed. corr. de 1916. Ed. española-inglesa preparada bajo la dirección de la Oficina de normas ⟨Bureau of standards⟩ durante la presidencia de S. W. Stratton ... Wáshington, Imprenta del gobierno, 1918.

TA435 .U55 Llano, Antonio, tr.

U.S. *Bureau of foreign and domestic commerce.*
... Pliego de condiciones y ensayos normales referentes al cemento Pórtland. Forma adoptada por la Sociedad americana de ensayos de materiales y por el gobierno de los Estados Unidos. Ed. corr. de 1917. Ed. española-inglesa preparada bajo la dirección de la Oficina de normas (Bureau of standards) durante la presidencia de S. W. Stratton. Wáshington, Imprenta del gobierno, 1918.

Llano, Antonio, tr.
Standard specifications for...
see under American society for testing materials.

[Llano, Antonio.]
...Trabajos en el rio Misisipi para contener las aguas y ampliar el cauce... Wáshington, D. C.: La Unión panamericana[, 1926]. ii, 8 p. 8°. (Pan American Union. Finanzas, industria, comercio. no. 17.)

"Por Antonio Llano," p. 1.
Repr.: Pan Am... Union. Boletín.

1. Mississippi river—Improvement and control. 2. Se... January 18, 1928

NL 0425139 NN

LLANO, Antonio, tr. 1891.
El cristianismo ante la filosofía, la moral y la historia. Nueva York, Imp. "El Polígloto", 1891.

NL 0425140 MH PU

Llano, Antonio Prast y Rodriguez de
see Prast y Rodriguez de Llano, Antonio.

Llano, Antonio Valle
see Valle Llano, Antonio.

Llano, Ataulfo Fernández
see
Fernández Llano, Ataulfo.

Llano, Ciriaco del.
Viva el grande Egercito imperial megicano de las tres garantias. Capitulacion acordada para la evacuacion de la ciudad de Puebla ...
see under Iturbide, Agustín de, emperor of Mexico, 1783-1824.

VOLUME 337

Llano, Enrique.
Danses indiennes du Mexique ₍par₎ Enrique Llano et Marcel de Clerck. 10 lithographies de Giner. Bruxelles ₍M. Hayez₎ 1939.
138 p. illus. 22 cm.
Includes bibliography.

1. Indians of Mexico—Dances. I. Clerck, Marcel de, joint author. II. Title.

F1219.3.D2L6 61-58057 ‡

NL 0425145 DLC CU MH-P NN CtY CU-B DSI CSt MiU

Llano, Enrique de
¿Donde empieza la decencia? [Novela. México] Editorial Alrededor de América, Sección de México. [n.d.]
F1203 T4L53 x 139 p. 18cm. [Terrazas collection]

NL 0425146 CU-B CoU

Llano, Enrique Emilio del, ed.
Cárlos V
see under title

4Ra-11 Llano, Fernando.
Principios básicos de la administración sanitaria. [Habana] 1939.
29 p. (Primer Congreso Panamericano de Municipios. Tema no. 28)
At head of title: Municipio de La Habana. Ponencia Problemas Sociales.

NL 0425148 DLC-P4

Llano, Francisco Gómez de
see
Gómez de Llano, Francisco.

Llano, G. Queipo de
see Queipo de Llano, Gonzalo, 1875-

Llano, Gabriel Mateo Menéndez de Luarca y Queipo de
see Menéndez de Luarca, Gabriel, 1742-1812.

Llano, George Albert, 1911-
Airmen against the sea, an analysis of sea survival experiences. Maxwell Air Force Base, Ala., Arctic, Desert, Tropic Information Center, Research Studies Institute ₍1955 or 6₎
vi, 114 p. diagrs., tables. 27 cm. (₍U. S.₎ Arctic, Desert, Tropic Information Center. ADTIC publication G-104)

1. Survival (after aeroplane accidents, shipwrecks, etc.) 2. Search and rescue operations. I. Title. (Series)

GB5.U52 no. G-104 56-62123 rev

NL 0425152 DLC NbU

Llano, George Albert, 1911-
Economic uses of lichens.
(*In* Smithsonian Institution. Annual report, 1950. Washington, 1951. 24 cm. p. 385-422. 8 plates)
"Reprinted ... from Economic botany, vol. 2, no. 1, January-March 1948, with revisions."
Bibliography: p. 421-422.

1. Lichens. I. Title.

Q11.S66 1950 52-4086

NL 0425153 DLC NNBG OClW TxU

Llano, George Albert, 1911-
A monograph of the lichen family Umbilicariaceae in the Western Hemisphere. Washington, Office of Naval Research, Dept. of the Navy, 1950.
vi, 281 p. illus., maps, diagrs. 27 cm.
"Navexos P-831."
Bibliography: p. 214-218.

1. Umbilicariaceae.

QK585.U5L6 57-48426

IEN
NL 0425154 DLC CLSU NNBG KyU ViU WU MiU IaAS NcD

Llano, Humberto Delgado
see
Delgado Llano, Humberto.

Llano, Joaquín G. Lebredo y.
See
Lebredo y Llano, Joaquín G., 1833-1889.

Llaño, José Moreno.
see
Moreno Llaño, José.

Llano, Juan C
Biografia del procer americano Jose Maria Cordoba arreglada de orden de la municipalidad de Concepcion ... Medellin, Imprenta del estado, 1876.
72 p.

NL 0425158 ViU

862.3 L791b Llano, Lope de.
Bernardo del Carpio en Francia, comedia. ₍Madrid, Libreria de Quiroga, 1798₎
24p.

NL 0425159 ICarbS NN

Llano, Lope de.
Bernardo del Carpio en Francia ₍comedia₎ ₍Madrid, 1798₎
24p.

Microcard edition.

NL 0425160 ICRL MoU FU

---

860 L791 tB Llano, Manuel.
La braña. Prólogo de Luys Santa Marina. Santander [Artes Graficas] 1934.
168p. 20cm.

NL 0425161 CLSU

Llano, Manuel.
... Brañaflor; prólogo de Miguel Artigas ... Santander, Imp. y enc. de la Librería moderna, 1931.
4 p. l., xi-xv, 318 p. 21cm.

1. Folk-lore—Spain. I. Title.

32-13615

Library of Congress PQ6621.L3B7 1931 398.20946

NL 0425162 DLC IaU

Llano, Manuel.
... Rabel (leyendas) Santander ₍Aldus, s. a.₎ 1934.
240 p., 1 l. 19cm. (Ediciones literarias montañesas. ₍1₎)

1. Legends—Spain—Santander. I. Title.

36-33859

Library of Congress GR237.S3L6

398.2209463

NL 0425163 DLC

Llano, Manuel.
... El sol de los muertos, novela montañesa. Santander, Librería moderna, 1929.
232, ₍8₎ p. 19cm.

I. Title.

31-7804

Library of Congress PQ6621.L3S6 1929

863.6

NL 0425164 DLC

Llano, Manuel J. de.
Opusculo sobre telegrafia-electro-magnética y apuntes de los sistemas mas usuales en Europa y los Estados Unidos; seguido de una memoria del establecimiento del telegrafo en la republica, y estado que guarda hoy, a la que van agregadas algunas reflexiones para cambiar el sistema actual en uso por otro mas adaptable a las circunstancias, y para manifestar la necesidad que hay de que esta mejora se propague bajo los auspicios del supremo gobierno, por Manuel J. de Llano... México: Andrade y Escalante, 1858. 38 p. 4°.

31899A. 1. Telegraphy.—History. 2. Telegraphy.—History, Mexico.
January 17, 1922.

NL 0425165 NN

Llano, Pedro Nolasco de
see **Nolasco de Llano, Pedro.**

G868.81 L7717e **Llano, Ramiro.**
Emoción. [Poemas] Montevideo, 1944.
75p. port. 21cm.

NL 0425167 TxU

Llano, Rodolfo Arroyo
see
Arroyo Llano, Rodolfo.

VOLUME 337

Llano, Rosario Queipo de
see
Queipo de Llano, Rosario.

Llano, Sergio del.
Los partidos en Cuba y la normalidad politica, por Sergio del Llano. Habana, Impr. el Aerolito, 1893.
22 p. 19½cm.

1. Political parties—Cuba. I. Title.
13-12777
Library of Congress F1783.L79

NL 0425170 DLC NN

Llano, Teodomiro.
Biografía del señor Gabriel Echeverri, E. Bogotá, M. Rivas & ca., 1890.
116 p.

NL 0425171 NcU

Tr.R. Llano, Tomás de
Noviliario de casas, y linages de España ... [n.p.] 1653.
20 p.l., 47 l. 19½cm.

Title vignette.

NL 0425172 NcD

Llano de Gallardo, Lola.
Plato criollo. 4. ed. Medellín, Editorial Bedout [19—]
185 p. 21cm.

On cover: 6. ed.

1. Cookery, Spanish-American. I. Title.

NL 0425173 FU

Llano de San Javier, Jose Maria Palacio y Abarzuza
see Palacio y Abarzuza, José María, marques del Llano de San Javier, conde de las Almenas.

Llano Gómez, Enrique.
Algunos aspectos del contrato de seguros. Bogotá, 1955.
60 p. 24 cm.
Tesis—Pontificia Universidad Católica Javeriana, Bogotá.

1. Insurance law—Colombia. I. Title.
57-30003 ‡

NL 0425175 DLC TxU MH-L

SB267 L57 Agric. Library
Llano Gómez, Enrique
Cultivo del cacao. Bogotá, Ministerio de la Economía Nacional, 1947.
150 p. illus.(part fold.col.) (Publicaciones del Ministerio de la Economía Nacional)

1. Cacao. I. Title.

NL 0425176 CU WaU IU TxU NcD NN MH NcRS

90.11 L77
Llano Gómez, Enrique.
Propagación de plantas. Bogota, Colinagro, 1952.
157 p.

1. Plant propagation.

NL 0425177 DNAL

Llano Roza de Ampudia, Aurelio de.
... Bellezas de Asturias de oriente a occidente, por Aurelio de Llano Roza de Ampudia ... Oviedo, Imprenta "Gutenberg", 1928.
xiii, 542 p., 1 l. incl. front. (port.) illus. 24½cm.
At head of title: Excma. Diputación provincial de Oviedo.

1. Asturias—Descr. & trav. 2. Architecture—Asturias. I. Oviedo (Province) Diputación provincial. II. Title.
30-16271
Library of Congress DP302.A78L6

NL 0425178 DLC

Llano Roza de Ampudia, Aurelio de.
... Cuentos asturianos, recogidos de la tradición oral por Aurelio de Llano Roza de Ampudia. Madrid, Impr. de R. Caro Raggio, 1925.
316 p., 1 l. front. (ports.) 2 pl., fold. map. 23½cm. (Archivo de tradiciones populares. I)
At head of title: Junta para ampliación de estudios e investigaciones científicas. Centro de estudios históricos.

1. Tales, Spanish. 2. Folk-lore—Asturias. I. Madrid. Centro de estudios históricos. II. Title.
30-7247
Library of Congress GR237.A7L6

NL 0425179 TxU DLC OO OCl NjP MB MoU CU GU MH IU NIC

GR 237 A7 L793
Llano Roza de Ampudia, Aurelio de.
Del folklore asturiano, conferencia pronunciada en el paraninfo de la Universidad de Oviedo el día 3 de diciembre de 1920. Oviedo, Tip. el Correo de Asturias, 1921.
52 p. 22cm.

1. Folk-lore--Spain--Asturias. I. Title.

NL 0425180 NIC

Llano Roza de Ampudia, Aurelio de.
Del folklore asturiano: mitos, supersticiones, costumbres; por Aurelio de Llano Roza de Ampudia ... Con un prólogo de R. Menéndez Pidal. Madrid, Talleres de Voluntad, 1922.
xix, [1], 277 p. 20cm.

1. Folk-lore—Asturias. 2. Superstition. 3. Spain—Soc. life & cust. I. Title.
33-5038
Library of Congress GR237.A7L63 398.09461

NL 0425181 NjP IU NN DLC WaU NIC NcD PBm MiU IaU CU MH ICU

PC 4786 .L5
Llano Roza de Ampudia, Aurelio de
Dialectos jergales asturianos; vocabularios de la xiriga y el bron. Recogidos y compuestos por Aurelio de Llano Roza de Ampudia. Oviedo, Tip. El Correo de Asturias, 1921.
19p. 22cm.

Cover title.

1. Spanish languague - Dialects - Asturias. I. Title.

NL 0425182 TNJ PrU

861.04 L77e
Llano Roza de Ampudia, Aurelio de, comp.
Esfoyaza de cantares asturianos, recogidos directamente de boca del pueblo. Oviedo, Imp. "El Carbayon," 1924.
xxx, 327 p.

1. Spanish ballads and songs. I. Title.

NL 0425183 WaU CU

PQ7001 .A83L8
Llano Roza de Ampudia, Aurelio de, *comp.*
Esfoyaza de cantares asturianos, recogidos directamente de boca del pueblo por Aurelio de Llano Roza de Ampudia ... Oviedo, M. Morchón, 1924.
xxx, [1], 327, [1] p. 18cm.
Bibliographical foot-notes.

1. Folk-songs, Spanish—Asturias.

NL 0425184 ICU NjP

Llano Roza de Ampudia, Aurelio de.
La iglesia de San Miguel de Lillo, por Aurelio de Llano Roza de Ampudia ... con un prólogo de Bernardo Acevedo y Huelves ... ilustrada con 60 dibujos, planos y fotografías Oviedo [Spain] Imprenta Gutenberg, 1917.
xi, 95 p., 2 l. illus. (incl. plans) col. pl. 25cm.

1. Naranco, Spain. San Miguel de Lillo (Church)
33-88534
Library of Congress NA5811.N3L6 726.509461

NL 0425185 DLC CU

DP 402 C3 L79
Llano Roza de Ampudia, Aurelio de.
El libro de Caravia, por Aurelio de Llano Roza de Ampudia y de Valle. Oviedo, Gutenberg, 1919.
xi, 242 p. illus. 24cm.

1. Caravia, Spain--Descr. 2. Caravia, Spain--Hist. 3. Caravia, Spain--Soc. life and cust. 4. Folk-lore--Spain--Caravia.

NL 0425186 NIC CU PBm NN NcD

Llano Roza de Ampudia, Aurelio de.
Pequeños anales de quince días; la revolución en Asturias, octubre, 1934, por Aurelio de Llano Roza de Ampudia ... Oviedo, Talleres tipográficos, Altamirano, 5 y 7, 1935.
3 p. l., [xi]-xiii, 213 p. 1 l. front. (port.) illus. (incl. map, plans) 24½cm.

1. Oviedo (Province)—Hist. 2. Spain—Hist.—Republic, 1931- I. Title. II. Title: La revolución en Asturias.
36-33511
Library of Congress DP302.O8L6
946.08

NL 0425187 DLC MH CU

LLANO ROZA DE AMPUDIA, Aurelio de.
Vocabulario de la Tixileira; dialecto jergal asturiano. Oviedo, imp. "La Cruz", 1924.

pp.10.
Cover serves as title-page.

NL 0425188 MH

VOLUME 337

Llano Ruiz de Saravia, Jose Maria Queipo de, conde de Toreno
see Toreno, Jose Maria Queipo de Llano Ruiz de Saravia, conde de, 1786-1843.

F2277 .L43 Llano y López del Castillo, Juan de.
Breve relato de mi ida a Venezuela y de mis trabajos en aquella república. Mis súplicas al Ministerio de Estado. ‹Valencia, Venezuela› Ed. "Diario de Valencia," 1925.
38p. fold. maps(at end)

NL 0425190 NcU

He79 140h Llano y Persi, Manuel de, 1826-1903
García de Paredes, drama en tres actos precedido de un prólogo, original y en verso. Madrid,Estab.Tip.de A.Vicente,1848.
72p. 19cm. (La España dramatica)

1. García de Paredes, Diego, 1466-1530 - Drama. x.ser. CDU

NL 0425191 CtY

Llano y Persi, Manuel de, 1826-1903.
García de Paredes, drama en tres actos, precedido de un prólogo, original y en verso. Madrid, A. Vicente, 1848.
72p.
Microcard edition.

NL 0425192 ICRL MoU LU

862.5 L791n Llano y Persi, Manuel de, 1826-1903.
No hay chanzas con el amor; comedia en un acto, original y en verso. Madrid, J. González, 1848.
32 p. 21 cm.

NL 0425193 ICarbS MiEM NN

Llano y Persi, Manuel de, 1826-1903.
No hay chanzas con el amor, comedia en un acto, original y en verso, por Don Manuel de Llano. Madrid, J. González y A. Vicente, 1848.
32p.
Microcard edition.

NL 0425194 ICRL MoU LU

PQ 6534 L44 N6 1867 Llano y Persi, Manuel de, 1826-1903.
No hay chanzas con el amor; comedia en un acto y en verso, original de Manuel de Llano. Salamanca, Est. tip. del Hospicio, 1867.
32 p. 20 cm. (Círculo literario comercial, 51)

NL 0425195 CU-S CtY

Llano y Persi, Manuel de, 1826-1903.
Un voto y una venganza. Drama trágico en cuatro actos, original y en verso, por Don Manuel de Llano y Don Cayetano Suricalday. Madrid, S. Omaña, 1849.
65p.
Microcard edition.

NL 0425196 ICRL LU OrU

Llano y Raymat, Gregorio de, 1875–
Estudios jurídicos sobre cuestiones prácticas de derecho civil e hipotecario, por Gregorio de Llano y Raymat (doctor Liso) ... Habana, Cultural, s. a., 1928.
212 p., 2 l. 23½cm.
Imprint on cover: Habana, Librería Cervantes.

1. Civil law—Cuba—Addresses, essays, lectures. 2. Mortgages—Cuba.
42-49545

NL 0425197 DLC

W 3 MU571 1938 no. 28 LLANO Y VEGA, Fernando
Principios básicos de la administración sanitaria. [La Habana] 1939.
29 p. (Primer Congreso Panamericano de Municipios. Tema no. 28. Problemas sociales)
1. Public health Series: Inter-American Congress of Municipalities. 1st, Havana, 1938. Tema no. 28

NL 0425198 DNLM

Lilly Library LLANO Y ZAPATA, JOSE EUSEBIO DE, fl.1744-1769
Obras varias de don Joseph Eusebio de Llano y Zapata. ‹n.p., 175-?›
1 v. (various pagings) 4to (18.9 cm.)

Half-title.
See Medina, J. T., BHA, IV, p. 532, for description of a volume with the same title, but variations in content.
In vellum.

‹1› Lessius, L. Hygiasticon. 1743.

‹2› His Resolucion en consulta sobre la irregularidad de las terminaciones exiet, y transiet, 1733?
‹3› His Resolucion physico-mathematica. 1743.
‹4› His Respuesta en que satisface ... a los dos reparos ... 1745.
‹5› His Carta, or diario ... a su ... amigo ... el doctor don Ignacio Chirivoga y Daza. ‹1747?›

‹6› Villegas y Quevedo, D. Carta ... a don Joseph Eusebio de Llano y Zapata. ‹1747?›
‹7› His Carta ... al señor Doct. D. Ignacio Chirivoga y Daza. ‹1747?›
‹8› His Observacion diaria, critico, historico. 1748.
‹9› His Philippi V., hispaniarum et indiarum regis ... epitaphium. 1748.
‹10› His Re- lacion del auto particular de fè. 1750.

NL 0425201 InU

Llano y Zapata, Joseph Eusebio de, fl.1744-1769
Breve coleccion de varias cartas...Cadiz, 1764.

Bd. with his: Carta, o diario...n.p.

NL 0425202 RPJCB

LLANO Y ZAPATA,JOSÉ EUSEBIO DE,fl. 1744-1769
Carta ... al señor Doct. D. Ignacio Chirivoga y Daza ... ‹Lima? 1747?›
‹4› p. 4to (18.9 cm.) (In his Obras varias, no. ‹7›)

Vargas Ugarte, R., Imp. per., 1571 (Note), assigns to the year 1748.
Caption title.
Dated October 16, 1747.

NL 0425203 InU

Llano y Zapata, José Eusebio de, d. 1769.
Carta, o diario que escribe D. Joseph Eusebio de Llano, y Zapata a su mas venerado amigo, y docto correspondiente el doctor Don Ignacio Chirivoga, y Daza, canonigo de la santa iglesia de Quito, en que con la mayor verdad, y critica mas segura le dá cuenta de todo lo acaecido en esta capital dél Perú desde el viernes 28 de octubre de 1746, quando experimentó su mayór ruyna con él grande movimiento de tierra, que padeció á las diez, y media de la noche del mencionado dia, hasta 16 de febrero de 1747 con una tabla en que se dá él calculo exacto de todo él numero de temblores, que se hán sentido en él tragico sucesso, que es lastimoso assumpto de este escrito. Y jvntamente le participa el estrago del presidio del Callao, y sus habitadores con la inundacion del mar, que los tragó en la noche dél primer terremoto. En Lima: Impressa por F. Sobrino[, 1747]. 1 p.l., 33 p. 19½cm. (4°.)
Sabin 41669. Medina IEL 987.
Imperfect: lower edges of p. 1-4 cropped.

1. Earthquakes—Peru, 1746. 2. Chiriboga y Daza, Ignacio de. *Revised* October 9, 1934

NL 0425205 NN RPJCB InU

Pamphlet Peru 1748 L76 Llano y Zapata, Joseph Eusebio de, fl.1744-1769.
Carta, ó diario que escribe D. Joseph Eusebio de Llano y Zapata a su mas venerado amigo y docto correspondiente, el doctor don Ignacio Chirivoga y Daza en que con la mayor verdad, y critica mas segura le dà cuenta de todo lo acaecido en capital de el Perù, desde el viernes 28. de octubre de 1746. quando experimentò su mayor ruina con el grande movimiento de tierra que padeciò à las diez y media de la noche del mencionado dia hasta 16. de febrero de 1747. Con una tabla en que se dà el calculo exacto de todo el numero de temblores que se han sentido en el tragico sucesso, que es lastimoso assumpto de este escrito, y juntamente le participa el estrago del Presidio del Callao y su habitadores con la inundacion del mar que los tragò en la noche del primer terremoto. Madrid,1748.
Medinà, Biblioteca hispano-americana,3467.
1. Chirivoga y Daza, Ignacio.

NL 0425207 CtY RPJCB MB ICN InU

Ayer 1263 L79 1769 LLANO Y ZAPATA, JOSÉ EUSEBIO DE.
Carta-persuasiva al señor don Ignacio de Escandon...sobre assunto de escribir la Historia-literaria de la America meridional... En Cadiz, Por don F.Rioja, 1768,reimpr.Lima,Los Niños Huerfanos,1769.
[6],18p. 19cm.

NL 0425208 ICN

Llano y Zapata, José Eusebio de, fl. 1744-1769.
Carta-persuasiva al señor don Ignacio de Escandon ... Sobre asunto de escribir la historia-literaria de la America Meridional. Sv avtor don Joseph Evsebio de Llano Zapata. Con licencia. En Cadiz: Por don Francisco Rioja, frente de Candelaria. Año de MDCCLXVIII. Y reimpresa en Lima en la Oficina de los niños huerfanos. Año de 1769.
Microfilm copy, made in 1943, of the original in the Medina collection, Biblioteca nacional de Santiago de Chile. Positive.
Negative film in Brown university library.
Collation of the original, as determined from the film: 4 p. l., 3-18 p.

Privilege signed: D. Martin de Martiarena.
Dated: Cadiz, y mayo 8. de 1768.
Poem on p. 18.
Medina, La imprenta en Lima, 1296.

1. Peruvian literature—Addresses, essays, lectures. 2. Escandón, Ignacio de.
Microfilm AC-2 reel 214, no. 21 Mic A 49-1078

Brown Univ. Library for Library of Congress †

NL 0425210 RPB DLC

VOLUME 337

Llano y Zapata, José Eusebio de, fl. 1744-1769.

Micro-film AC-2 reel 241, no. 14

Ríos, Francisco de los, *bp.*
Carta, que el illmo. y rmo. señor d. fr. Francisco de los Rios, obispo electo de Panamà, escribe a nvestro ervdito compatriota don Joseph Eusebio de Llano Zapata, sobre el alto concepto que nuestro exmo. señor virey don Manuel de Amat, y Junient se ha grangeado en la Europa, y ministerio de España, en vista de las sabias resoluciones. y acertadas providencias con que felizmente gobierna los vastos dominios del Perù, &c. Sacala a luz el doct. d. Joseph Morales de Aramburù y Montero ... En Lima: En la oficina de la calle de San Jacinto: año de 1772.

Llano y Zapata, José Eusebio de, tr.

[Lessius, Leonardus] 1554-1623.
Higiasticon, o Verdadero modo de conservar la salvd, tradvcido del idioma latino al castellano, qve dedica ... al ilvstrissimo señor doctor d. Pedro Morcillo, Rubio de Auñon ... sv tradvctor don Joseph Eusebio de Llano, y Zapata ... Impresso en Lima, Por Isidoro Sagrero, 1744.

Llano y Zapata, José Eusebio de.
Memorias histórico-físicas-apologéticas de la América Meridional que a la Majestad del Señor Don Carlos III dedica Don José Eusebio de Llano Zapata. Lima, Impr. y librería de San Pedro, 1904.

xiii p., 2 l., 617 p. 25½cm.

"El manuscrito, que ahora ha pasado á ser propiedad de la Biblioteca de Lima ... es nada menos que la copia que, en 1761, obsequió el autor al rey Carlos III por intermedio del bailéo Don Julián de Arriaga ... Es indudable que [el autor] ... escribió otros dos tomos sobre los reinos animal y vegetal, y uno sobre el Amazonas y sus afluentes. Fatalmente no se encuentra ... el original ó copia."—Preliminar.

The appendix (p. [547]-617) contains three letters by the author to Don Gregorio Mayans y Siscar, the marqués de Villa Orellana, and Don Cayetano Marcellano de Agramonte respectively, reprinted from his "Preliminar y cartas, que preceden al tomo de las Memorias historico-physicas, critico-apologeticas de la America meridional". Cadiz, 1759.

1. South America. 2. Peru. 3. Mines and mineral resources—South America. I. Peru. Biblioteca nacional, Lima.

Library of Congress F2208.L78 5-34155

NL 0425215 DLC NcU CU NcD NIC CtY DPU ICJ MB TxU

[Llano y Zapata, José Eusebio de] fl. 1744-1769.
Narración circunstanciada de la deplorable catastrofe sufrida en la ciudad de Lima e inundación del puerto del Callao. Lima, Impr. de La Libertad [1863] 25, vi p. 20cm.

Cover-title: Memoria de los acontecimientos tristes y lamantables en la corte de Lima y su puerto. Con la ruina total de esta, e inundación del Callao, en el mes de octubre, año de 1746. 2. ed.
CONTENTS.—Carta ó diario que escribe D. José Eusebio de Llano y Zapata, á su ... amigo ... el dr. D. Ignacio de Chirivoga y Daza.—Segunda carta del padre Lozana (sic)

1. Earthquakes—Peru—Lima, 1746. 2. Chiriboga y Daza, Ignacio de. I. Lozano, Pedro, 1697-ca. 1759. II. Title.

January 18, 1946

NL 0425216 NN

Lilly Library

LLANO Y ZAPATA, JOSÉ EUSEBIO DE, fl. 1744-1769
Observacion diaria, critico, historico, metheorologica, contiene todo lo acaecido en Lima, desde primero de Marzo de 1747. hasta 28 de octubre ...y...la historia de las santas imagenes patronas de los temblores... Lima, 1748.
3 p.l., 49 p. 4to (18.9 cm.) (In his Obras varias, no. [8])

Medina, J.T., Impr. en Lima, 998; Vargas Ugarte, R., Imp. per., 1577; Palau y Dulcet, A., Manual, 144672.

NL 0425217 InU CtY

Lilly Library

LLANO Y ZAPATA, JOSE EUSEBIO DE, fl. 1744-1769
Philippi V., hispaniarum et indiarum regis, a D. Iosepho Eusebio de Llano et Zapata, epitaphium. Limae, F. Sobrinum, 1748.
[8] p. 4to (18.9 cm.) (In his Obras varias, no. [9])

Vargas Ugarte, R., Impr. per., 1578.

NL 0425218 InU

Lilly Library

[LLANO Y ZAPATA, JOSÉ EUSEBIO DE] fl. 1744-1769
Preliminar, y cartas, que preceden al tomo I. de las Memorias historico-physicas, critico-apologeticas de la America meridional. Su autor Don J. E. LL. Z. Cadiz, P. Gomez de Requena, 1758.
8 p.l., 93 p. 4to (18.6 cm.)

First edition. Medina, J.T., BHA, 3860.
"Treats upon several...subjects, & incidentally endeavours to defend...the Spaniards against...Las Casas."—Rich, Obadiah. (Continued on next card)

Bibliotheca americana nova.
In half red leather.

NL 0425220 InU RPJCB

Llano y Zapata, José Eusebio de, *fl.* 1744-1769.
Preliminar, y cartas, que preceden al tomo I. de las Memorias historico-physicas, critico-apologeticas de la America meridional. Su autor don Joseph Eusebio Llano Zapàta. Cadiz, P. Gomez de Requèna, 1759.

17 p. l., 283 p. 15cm.

"Treats upon several ... subjects, & incidentally endeavours to defend ... the Spaniards against ... Las Casas."—Rich, Obadiah. Bibliotheca americana nova.

1. South America. 2. Casas, Bartolomé de las, bp. of Chiapa, 1474-1566.

Library of Congress F2208.L79 1-22523 Revised

NL 0425221 DLC CtY MH RPJCB

Lilly Library

LLANO Y ZAPATA, JOSÉ EUSEBIO DE, fl. 1744-1769
Relacion del auto particular de fè que... la Inquisicion...celebró... el dia 19. de octubre de 1749 y breve noticia de la ruyna... que padecieron la capilla, y casas del Sto. Tribunal el dia 28. de octubre de 1746 con el grande terremoto...que escribe d. Joseph Eusebio Llano y Zapata. Lima, Impr. de la Calle de la Barranca, por A. Gutierres de Zevallos, 1750.
1 p.l., 56 p. 4to (18.9 cm.)

Medina, J.T., Impr. en Lima, 1017; Vargas Ugarte, R., Imp. per., 1612; Palau y Dulcet, A., Manual, 144673.
Variant of Relacion del auto particular... 1750, in his Obras varias, no. [10]. See 5-8.
Red cloth with mottled boards.
From the library of Bernardo Mendel.

NL 0425223 InU

LLANO Y ZAPATA, JOSÉ EUSEBIO DE, fl. 1744-1769
Resolucion en consulta sobre la irregularidad de las terminaciones exiet, y transiet, del capitulo 6. de Judith, y 51. de Isaias, que segun reglas de latinidad pedian ser exibit y transibit. Que consagra àl...don Pedro Morcillo...y dà en respuesta àl...don Juan de Avendano... Lima, 1733?
[24] + p. 4to (18.9 cm.) (In his Obras varias, no. [2])

See Medina, J.T., Impr. en Lima, 944; Palau y Dulcet, A., Manual, 144666; Vargas Ugarte, R., Imp. per., 1498, for 1743 ed. with variant t. p.
Dedication dated Nov. 29, 1743.
Imperfect: All after p. 24 wanting.

NL 0425225 InU

Llano y Zapata, José Eusebio de.
Resolvcion en consvlta sobre la irregvlaridad de las terminaciones exiet, y transiet, halladas en los capitulos sexto de Judith, y sinquenta y vno de Isaìas, pidiendo segun reglas de latinidad ser exibit, y transibit. Qve dedica y consagra al ilvstrissimo señor doctor don Pedro Morcillo, Rubio de Auñon ... y da en respvesta. al doctor don Jvan de Auendaño ... don Joseph Evsebio de Llano y Zapata ... Impressa en Lima, 1743.

[28] p. 20½cm. [With [Lessius, Leonardus] Higiasticon ... Lima, 1744]
One of the passages, Judith VI, 4 in the Latin Vulgate corresponds to Judith VI, 6 in the English authorized version.
1. Bible. O. T. Apocrypha. Judith VI, 6. Latin—Criticism, interpretation, etc. 2. Bible. O. T. Isaiah VI, 4. Latin—Criticism, interpretation, etc. 3. Avendaño, Juan de.

Library of Congress RA775.L653 43-44812

NL 0425226 DLC

Llano y Zapata, José Eusebio de, *fl.* 1744-1769.
Resolucion physico-mathematica sobre la formacion de los cometicos cuerpos, y efectos, que causan sus impressiones, que dedica ... al ilvstrissimo señor doct. d. Pedro Morcillo Rubio de Auñon ... d. Joseph Eusebio de Llano, y Zapata ... Impressa en Lima, Por Juan Joseph Morèl, 1744.

[40] p. 20½ cm. [With [Lessius, Leonardus] Higiasticon ... Lima, 1744]
Medina, La imprenta en Lima, 953.
——— Microfilm copy.
Made in 1943 from the original in the Medina collection, Biblioteca nacional de Santiago de Chile. Positive.
Negative film in Brown university library.
Microfilm AC-2 reel 213, no. 7
1. Comets. 2. Astronomy—Early works to 1800.
RA775.L653 43-42889 rev

NL 0425227 DLC InU

[Llano y Zapata, José Eusebio de] *fl.* 1744-1769, *supposed author.*
Respuesta dada al rey nuestro señor d. Fernando el Sexto, sobre una pregunta, que S. M. hizo à un mathematico, y experimentado en las tierras de Lima, sobre el terremoto, acaecido en el dia primero de noviembre de 1755. [Colophon: Con licencia: En Sevilla, En la imprenta real de la viuda de d. Diego Lopez de Haro, en calle Genova] [1756?]

Microfilm copy, made in 1943, of the original in the Medina collection, Biblioteca nacional de Santiago de Chile. Positive.
Negative film in Brown university library.
Collation of the original, as determined from the film: 8 p.

Caption title.
"Es muy posible que [el autor] fuese don José Eusebio Llano y Zapata."—Medina, Biblioteca hispano-americana, 7497.

1. Lima—Earthquake, 1755. I. Title.
Microfilm AC-2 reel 193, no. 27 Mic A 49-53

Brown Univ. Library for Library of Congress †

NL 0425229 RPB NN DLC

Lilly Library

LLANO Y ZAPATA, JOSÉ EUSEBIO DE, fl. 1744-1769
Respuesta en que satisface don Joseph Eusebio de Llano y Zapata a los dos reparos, que a unas cartas latinas, qve escribio, pvso ...don Joseph Mariano de Alcozer... [Lima?] Impressa por un amigo del autor, 1745.
[6] p. 4to (18.9 cm.) (In his Obras varias, no [4])

Vargas Ugarte, R., Imp. per., 1529.

NL 0425230 InU

Llano Zapata, José Eusebio de
see
Llano y Zapata, José Eusebio de, *fl.* 1744-1769.

Llano, Texas. [Insurance map.] ms. 1 sheet. f°.

1. Insurance (Fire).—Maps, U. S.: Texas: Llano. 2. Llano, Texas.—Maps.

May 8, 1923.

NL 0425232 NN

VOLUME 337

Tz 338.2752 L77a Llano-Burnet Granite Association.
Application to the Railroad Commission of Texas for a reduction in rates on rough granite. [Austin, Tex.] 1911.
38p. 22cm.

Cover title.

1. Granite industry and trade - Texas. I. Texas. Railroad Commission. II. Title.

NL 0425233 TxU

334.05 LL Llano colonist. v.1- 1921-
Newllano, La.
v. illus. weekly.

Pub. by the Llano Co-operative Colony. Nov.6, 1937 last published?

NL 0425234 IU CU-B DL MiU NN TxU ICJ

Film 386 Llano colonist, My.7, 1921-[Dec.9,1937?] Newllano, La. Llano Publication, 1921-[1937?]

Microfilm of copies in the Louisiana State Library and Tulane University.
Collation of the original as determined from the film: v. illus. weekly.
For list of editors consult: Historical records survey, Louisiana. Louisiana newspapers, 1794-1940.

NL 0425235 LU WHi

Llano co-operative colony, Leesville, La.
Gateway to freedom. The story of how workers are co-operating in the ownership, management, labor and distribution of products where they own collectively all productive property. Leesville, La., Llano co-operative colony [1924]
cover-title, 36 p. 20½ cm.
Imperfect: p.5-8 wanting.

Foreword signed: Kate Richards O'Hare.

1.Cooperation in Louisiana. I. O'Hare, Kate Richards.

NL 0425237 NjP

JBA83LL .LL Llano Co-operative Colony, Newllano, La.
Detailed information about the Llano Co-operative colony. Newllano, La., Llano co-operative press, July, 1932.
34 p. 20 cm.

Cover title.

1. Utopias — U. S.

NL 0425238 WHi NcD

JBA83LL .LL Llano cooperative colony, Newllano, La.
Our 'constitution and by laws'. Llano, Calif.? n.d.
1 l. 16 x 9 cm.

Caption title.

NL 0425239 WHi

Le Llano de San Lázara et le camp de Cuajimalpa. México, Imprimerie de Andrade et Escalante, 1865. 8p. 22cm. (Papeles varios. 64:14)

NL 0425240 CU-B

Llano del Rio company.
Llano del Rio colony, co-operation in action; a story of the endeavor and achievements of California industrial pioneers in a new field of activity. Los Angeles, Colony press department, 1914.

32 p. illus. 22 cm.
Paper cover: The gateway to freedom: Llano del Rio co-operative colony.

NL 0425241 MH

HX 656 L77L6 Llano del Rio Co-operative Colony, Llano, Calif.
The gateway to freedom. Co-operation in action. A story of the endeavor and achievements of the Llano del Rio Co-operative Colony at Llano, California ... Llano, Colony Press Dept., 1915.
31 p. illus., port.

1. Cooperative societies. 2. Communism. I. Title.

NL 0425242 CLU

Llano Sánchez, Lagarto y Arraiján. Ed. oficial. [Panamá] Tip. "Diario de Panama" [1909?]
1 p. l., 19 p. 17½cm.

"Caserio de Llano Sánchez" signed: La directora de la Escuela alternada, Belermina Soberon. "Lagarto" signed: Camilo Bosques. "Arraiján" signed: Jose Surribas, director de la Escuela de varones de Arraiján.

1. Llano Sánchez, Panama. 2. Lagarto, Panama. 3. Arraiján, Panama. I. Soberón, Belermina. II. Bosques, Camilo. III. Surribas, José.

18-9391

Library of Congress F1576.L7L7

NL 0425243 DLC

Llanos, Adalberto Vara
see
Vara Llanos, Adalberto.

Llanos, Adolfo
see
Llanos y Alcaraz, Adolfo, 1834-1894

Chi PQ 8097 .L695N5 Llanos, Aida.
Nido para mi alma. Santiago, Impr. Rascimento, 1952.
40 p. 19 cm.

NL 0425246 DPU NN

Llanos, Alberto Valenzuela
see
Valenzuela Llanos, Alberto, 1869-1925.

Llanos, Americo, pseud.
see
Vasseur, Alvaro Armando, 1878-

Llanos, Antonio, 1806-1881.
Fragmentos de algunas plantas de Filipinas, no incluidas en la Flora de las islas, de la 1ª. ni 2ª. edición. Dispuestos según el sistema linneano. Por el P. Fr. Antonio Llanos ... Manila, M. Ramirez, 1851.
2 p. l., [3]-125 p. 14½cm.
[Botanical pamphlets, v. 8, no. 1]
Supplementing the Flora de Filipinas, por P. Fr. Manuel Blanco, published in 1837, and 2d edition in 1845.
An appendix was published in 1858 in the Anales de la Academia real de ciencias de Madrid. The two together were reprinted in 1880 in v. 4 of a large paper edition of Blanco's Flora.
1. Botany—Philippine Islands.

1-18572 Revised

Library of Congress QK3.B77 vol. 8, no. 1

NL 0425249 DLC MH-A

Llanos, Antonio, 1806-1881.
Fragmentos de algunas plantas de Filipinas, no incluidas en la Flora de las islas de la primera ni segunda edición, dispuestos segun el sistema linneano, por el P. Fr. Antonio Llanos ... Añadidos con otros trabajos del autor y vertidos al latin por el P. Fr. Celestino Fernández-Villar ...
(In Blanco, Manuel. Flora de Filipinas. Manila, 1877-83. 45½cm. t. 4, 1880, [v]-xviii, 108 p. 3 col. pl.)
First published in 1851, supplementing the Flora de Filipinas, por P. Fr. Manuel Blanco, 1837, 2d edition 1845. An appendix, published in 1858 in Anales de la Academia real de ciencias de Madrid, is also included in this reprint.
1. Botany—Philippine Islands. I. Fernández-Villar, Celestino, tr.

1-18573 Revised

Library of Congress QK358.B64 vol. 4 [r24e2]

NL 0425250 DLC MH-A CU MBH PV

Llanos, Antonio, 1806-1881.
——— Nuevo apéndice ó suplemento a la Flora de Filipinas del Manuel Blanco. [Madrid. 1856.] 4°. Plate.
Memorias de la Real academia de ciencias, 1856, iv, 495-509.

NL 0425251 MH-A

Llanos, Antonio, 1806-1881.
Nueva descripcion del pasac (Mimusops erythroxylon Boj.) arbol de Filipinas. [Madrid, 1873]
Plate. 8°.
Anales de la Sociedad española de historia natural, 1873, ii, 255-256.

NL 0425252 MH-A

Llanos, Antonio, 1841-1906.
See
Llanos y Berete, Antonio, 1841-1906.

4PQ Col. 2 Llanos, Antonio, 1905-
Casa paterna, 1932-1943. [Bogota, 1950]
75 p.

NL 0425254 DLC-P4 NjP TxU

4PQ Col. 3 Llanos, Antonio, 1905-
Rosa secreta (1942) [Bogota, 1950]
94 p.

NL 0425255 DLC-P4 DPU

VOLUME 337

Llanos, Antonio, 1905-
Temblor bajo los ángeles; sonetos, 1937-1938. Bogotá, Librería Siglo XX, 1942.
112p. 18cm. (Ediciones Librería Siglo XX)

I. Title. II. Series.

NL 0425256 TxU NN

Llanos, Antonio, 1905-
[Tierra]
see under Campo-Arana, José.

Llanos, Antonio, 1905-
La voz entre lágrimas, 1941-1943. [Bogota, 1950]
85 p.

NL 0425258 DLC-P4 DPU TxU NjP

Llanos, Augusto C
Ecología de la vizcacha ("Lagostomus maximus maximus" Blainv.) en el nordeste de la provincia de Entre Ríos. Por Augusto C. Llanos y Jorge A. Crespo. Buenos Aires, 1952.
[289]-378 p. illus., plates, fold. map, diagrs., tables. 26 cm.
"De la Revista de investigaciones agricolas, tomo VI, no. 3-4, 1952."
At head of title: Republica Argentina. Ministerio de Agricultura y Ganaderia. Direccion General de Investigaciones Agricolas. Instituto de Sanidad Vegetal.

English summary.
Bibliography: p. 376-378.

1. Rodentia - Ecology. 2. Viscachas. I. Crespo, Jorge A., jt. auth. II. Argentine Republic. Direccion General de Investigaciones Agricolas. Instituto de Sanidad Vegetal. II. Title.

NL 0425260 DI MiU

Llanos, Augusto C
Los mamiferos de la Patagonia. Buenos Aires, 1955.
[167]-177 p. 27 cm. (Argentine Republic. Administracion General de Parques Nacionales. Publicación técnica no. 14)
Cover title.
"De Natura, tomo 1, no. 2, (1955)."

1. Mammals - Patagonia. (Series)

NL 0425261 DI

LLANOS, Belisario
Azoemia, constante de Ambard; la prueba de la fenolsulfonftaleina. Buenos Aires, 1916.
82 p. (Buenos Aires. Universidad Nacional. Facultad de Ciencias Médicas. Tesis, año 1916, no. 3152)

NL 0425262 DNLM

[Llanos, Bernardino de los] 1557-1639.
Aduertencias para mayor noticia de la grammatica, y reducir al vso, y exercicio los preceptos della. Impresso con licencia en Mexico, En casa de Ioan Ruyz. Año de M.DC.XV. Vendese en la tienda de Diego Garrido, à la esquina de la calle de Tacuba.
Film copy, made in 1941, of the original in the Medina collection, Biblioteca nacional de Santiago de Chile. Positive.
Negative film in Brown university library.
Collation of the original, as determined from the film: 1 p. l., 73 numb. l.
Medina, La imprenta en México, 288.

1. Latin language—Grammar—1500-1800. I. Title.

A 43-1670

Brown univ. Library for Library of Congress Film AC-2 reel 2, no. 4 †

NL 0425263 RPB DLC

[Llanos, Bernardino de los] 1557-1639.
Aduertencias para mayor noticia de la grammatica, y reduzir al vso, y exercicio los preceptos della. Con licencia. En Mexico, Por la viuda de Bernardo Calderon. Año de 1645. Vendese en la calle de S. Agustin.
Film copy, made in 1941, of the original in the Medina collection, Biblioteca nacional de Santiago de Chile. Positive.
Negative film in Brown university library.
Collation of the original, as determined from the film: 1 p. l., 73 numb. l.
Errors in foliation: leaves 16, 19, 70 misnumbered 19, 16, 76 respectively.
Leaf 34 badly stained.
Privilege signed, Excellentissimo Señor Conde de Saluatierra.
Medina, La imprenta en México, 501.
1. Latin language—Grammar—1500-1800. I. Title.

A 43-1681 Revised

Brown univ. Library for Library of Congress Film AC-2 reel 4, no. 3 [r45c2]†

NL 0425264 RPB DLC

Llanos, Emma de la Barra de
see
[Barra, Emma de la]

Llanos, Enrique, 1879-
Über das wachstum der diphtheriebacillen auf vegetabilischen nährböden und milch ... Freiburg (Baden) Buchdr. E. Kuttruff, 1903.
38 p. 22cm.
Inaug.-diss.—Freiburg i. B.
Lebenslauf.

1. Bacillus diphtheriae.

8-5739†

Library of Congress QR201.D6L8

NL 0425266 DLC DNLM

Llanos, Estanislao Rendueles
see Rendueles Llanos, Estanislao.

Llanos, Félix Luis Baldasano y de
see
Baldasano y de Llanos, Félix Luis.

Llanos, Florencio.
... De las horas vividas (versos). Ciudad Real, 1940. 189 p. illus. 21cm.
On cover: Poemas de juventud.

NL 0425269 NN

Llanos, Froilán Díaz de los
see
Díaz de los Llanos, Froilán, d. 1709.

---

†LLANOS, Jorge A. Valenzuela.
See VALENZUELA LLANOS, Jorje A.

Llanos, José Cardús
see Cardus Llanos, José.

Llanos, José María de.
Criterios equívocos; charlas para campamentos. Madrid [Departamento Nacional de Propaganda del Frente de Juventudes] 1952.
81 p. 22 cm.
At head of title: Delegación Nacional del Frente de Juventudes.

1. Youth—Conduct of life—Addresses, essays, lectures. I. Title.

BJ1665.L55 66-50395 ‡

NL 0425273 DLC

Llanos, José María de.
Defendiendo y acusando; recopilación de artículos. Madrid, Ediciones Studium de Cultura [1950-
v. 20 cm.

1. Catholic Church in Spain. 2. Catholic Church—Addresses, essays, lectures. I. Title.

BX1585.L55 53-29287

NL 0425274 DLC

Llanos, José María, S.J.
Glosas a la oración del año Santo. Soria Editorial Los Linajes, 1951.
73 p.

NL 0425275 DCU

Llanos, José María de
Nuestra ofrenda; los jesuítas de la provincia de Toledo en la cruzada nacional, por José Mª de Llanos. Madrid, Apostolado de la Prensa [1942]
ix, 286 p.

1. Jesuits - Spain. 2. Spain - Hist. - 1936-39 - Religious aspects

NL 0425276 MH

Llanos, José Maria de.
La oración del trabajo. Madrid, Ediciones Gloria, 1954.
80 p.

NL 0425277 DCU

Llanos, José María de
Reportajes para Cristo. Barcelona, Juan Flors, 1955.
2 v. (Coleccion Remanso. Seccion II, 3, 4.)

NL 0425278 DCU

VOLUME 337

248 Llanos, José María de.
L791t Treinta y cuatro aventuras hacia Dios. Madrid [E.P.E.S.A.] 1948.
460p. 20cm.

1.Vocation (in religious orders, congregations, etc.) I.Title. VE.

NL 0425279 CLSU

Llanos, Juan García Jove
see Jove-Llanos, Juan García.

G868.8
L731a Llanos, Julio.
Arturo Sierra. [Buenos Aires] E. de Marisco, 1884.
193p. 18cm.

NL 0425281 TxU MH

Llanos, Julio.
... La cuestión agraria. La Plata, Taller de impresiones oficiales, 1911.
546 p. 25cm.

1. Agriculture, Cooperative. 2. Agriculture. Economic aspects. 3. Buenos Ayres (Province) Agriculture.

Agr 13-472

Library, U. S. Dept. of Agriculture 31L77

NL 0425282 DNAL MB TxU CU

G868.8
L731B1 Llanos, Julio.
Días de Paris; agosto 1914-agosto 1916. Barcelona, Maucci [1917]
376p. 20cm.

1. European War, 1914-1918 - France. I. Title.

NL 0425283 TxU

Llanos, Julio.
... El Dr. Francia. Buenos Aires, A. Moen y hermano, 1907.
2 p. l., [11]-81 p. pl., port. 19cm.
At head of cover-title: Hacia la historia.

1. Francia, José Gaspar Rodriguez, dictator of Paraguay, d. 1840.

Library of Congress F2686.F72 19-17545

NL 0425284 DLC CU TxU

3151 Llanos, Julio.
Los Yankees del Sud reconocidos por los Yankees del Norte. Roma, Tip. Enrico Voghera, 1909.

NL 0425285 DPU

Llanos, L.
see
Llanos Gutierrez, Valentin.

G913.85
L77e Llanos, Luis A
... Exploraciones arqueológicas en Quimsarumiyoc y Huaccanhuayco.—Calca ... Lima, Imprenta del Museo nacional, 1941.
1p.l.,[240]-261p. pl. 25cm.

"Sobretiro de la Revista del Museo nacional, tomo X, no.2."
"Bibliografía": p.259.

1. Calca, Peru - Antiq.

NL 0425287 TxU

Llanos, M. T. de, tr.
Demaison, André, 1885-
... El libro de los animales llamados salvajes. Buenos Aires-México, Espasa-Calpe argentina, s. a. [1942]

Llanos, Mario E Dihigo y
see Dihigo y Llanos, Mario E

Pamphlet Llanos, Mateo
Mexico Cartilla del Federalista, ó Principios
1833 del derecho político aplicados a la legis-
L77 lacion, por M.LL. Mexico, Impreso por Juan Ojeda, 1833.
20 p.

NL 0425290 CtY

Llanos, Mateo.
Métodos fáciles para aprender los idiomas ingles, frances, y la aritmética. Dispuestos por... Mateo Llanos... Méjico: Imprenta de Galvan a cargo de M. Arevalo, 1833. 90 p. 24°.

1. French language.—Grammar. 2. English language.—Grammar. 3. Arithmetic.—Text books (Elementary), 1833.

December 28, 1918.

NL 0425291 NN

Llanos, Niceforo Enrique Espinoza
see
Espinoza Llanos, Niceforo Enrique, 1915-

Llanos, Tomás de, joint author.

Microfilm
AC-2
reel 234,
no. 26
Grillo, Agustín.
Los fatores del assiento para la introdvccion de negros bozales en estos reynos. Manifiestan las razones qve les asisten, en exclusion de las discurridas por el Consulado. [Lima, 1672]

PC
4111
L5 Llanos, V
A catechism of Spanish grammar, containing the elements, or first principles of the Spanish language; and designed as an easy introduction to the knowledge of that language, by V. Llanos. London, Printed for F. and W. B. Whittaker, 1824.
64 [6] p. 14 cm. (Pinnock's Catechisms of the Arts and Sciences)

1. Spanish language—Grammar—1870-1950—Outlines, sylla bi, etc. I. Title.

NL 0425294 IEdS

Llanos, Valentin
see
Llanos Gutierrez, Valentin.

Llanos Aparicio, Luis.
Vuélvase mañana ... Colección de teatro, tres actos. (Síntesis psicológica de la vida burocrática y de la política criolla del país) [La Paz, 1948?]
98 p. 19 cm.
Cover title.

I. Title.

PQ7819.L55V8 A 51-10289

New York. Public Libr. for Library of Congress †

NL 0425296 NN WU TxU DLC

Llanos Godinez, Ildefonso
Os Jesuitas. Historica secreta da fundacao, propagacao e influencia ... New edition. Rio de Janeiro, Laemmert, 1872.
165 p.

NL 0425297 PU

Llanos González, A de.
Teoría y práctica del derecho usual español. [Madrid] Escelicer [1955]
955 p. 25 cm.

1. Forms (Law)—Spain.

56-20109

NL 0425298 DLC MH-L

Llanos Gutierrez, Valentin
Don Esteban; or, Memoirs of a Spaniard, written by himself. London, H. Colburn, 1825.
3v. 21cm.

NL 0425299 CoD CaBVaU NcU MH OOxM ScU NcU NcD

3829 Llanos Gutierrez, Valentin.
.63
.331 Don Esteban; or, Memoirs of a Spaniard.. 2d ed. London, Colburn, 1826.
3 v. $20\frac{1}{2}$ cm.

NL 0425300 NjP

Llanos Gutierrez, Valentin.
Don Esteban; oder, Memoiren eines Spaniers. [By V. Llanos Gutierrez] Aus dem Englischen nach der zweiten Auflage frei übersetzt von G. Sellen. Theil 1-3. Leipzig, C. Foche, 1827.
3 v. 16°.

NL 0425301 NN

VOLUME 337

Llanos Gutiérrez, Valentín, ed.

D352 .8 .H3A3 Halen, Juan van, 1788-1864.
Narrative of Don Juan van Halen's imprisonment in the dungeons of the Inquisition at Madrid, and his escape in 1817 and 1818; to which are added, his journey to Russia, his campaign with the army of the Caucasus, and his return to Spain in 1821. Edited from the original Spanish manuscript, by the author of "Don Esteban" and "Sandoval." London, H. Colburn, 1827.

HS 435 L79 1826 ⌊Llanos Gutierrez, Valentin⌋
Sandoval; or, The freemason. A Spanish tale, by the author of "Don Esteban". London, Henry Colburn, 1826.
3 v. 19cm.

1. Freemasons--Fiction. I. Title.

NL 0425303 NIC CtY IU TxU

⌊Llanos Gutierrez, Valentin⌋
Sandoval; or. The freemason. A Spanish tale. By the author of "Don Esteban" ... New-York, E. Bliss & E. White ⌊etc.⌋; Philadelphia, H. C. Carey & I. Lea. 1826.
2 v. 18½cm.

I. Title.

7-25437

Library of Congress PZ3.L7718

NL 0425304 DLC MH NcD NcU PU

JC 311 .L53 LLanos Herrera, Leon Pablo
Nacionalidad colombiana. Bogotá Tip. Minerva, 1919.
53p. 21cm.

Thesis - Universidad Nacional. Facultad de Derecho y ciencias politicas.

1. Nationalism - Colombia. I. Title.

NL 0425305 TNJ

Llanos Lecuona, Rafael Díaz-
see
Díaz-Llanos Lecuona, Rafael.

Llanos Lerma, Raúl.
Las finanzas del Estado de Nayarit y la economía regional. México, 1954.
170, ⌊3⌋ p. tables. 23 cm.
Tesis (licenciatura en economía) — Universidad Nacional Autónoma de México.
Bibliography: p. ⌊171⌋

1. Finance, Public—Nayarit, Mexico. 2. Nayarit, Mexico—Econ. condit. I. Title.

HJ805.N3L5 55-30280

NL 0425307 DLC CU-B

Llanos Mansilla, Hugo A joint author.
Los gobiernos
see under
Rámila Gómez, Consuelo.

Llanos Medina, Artemio.
... El principio de la autonomía de la voluntad y sus limitaciones; memoria de prueba para optar al grado de licenciado en la Facultad de ciencias jurídicas y sociales de la Universidad de Chile. ⌊Santiago de Chile⌋ 1944.
2 p. l., ⌊ix⌋-xv, 164 p. 26½cm.
"Bibliografía": p. ⌊155⌋-160.

1. Contracts. 2. Public policy (Law) 3. Capacity and disability. I. Title.

45-15864

NL 0425309 DLC DPU

Llanos V Ulises.
Del estado de quiebra; noticia histórica, definición y caracteres generales, elementos constitutivos del estado de quiebra y modos de provocar su declaración ⌊por⌋ Ulises Llanos V. Santiago de Chile, Imp. y Librería "Cisneros," 1927.
ix, 420 p. 27 cm.
Bibliography: p. ⌊iii⌋-iv.

1. Bankruptcy—Chile. I. Title.

70-296524

NL 0425310 DLC MH-L

Llanos Valenzuela, Gilberto.
... La identificación personal en Chile, por Gilberto Llanos Valenzuela... Santiago de Chile [Imprenta El Esfuerzo] 1937.
74 p. incl. ports. illus., diagrs. 26.5 cm.
At head of title: Dirección de investigaciones, identificación y pasaportes. Ministerio del interior.
"Tirada aparte de la revista Detective correspondiente a los nos. 42-43 junio-julio de 1937, Santiago de Chile."

NL 0425311 DPU

Llanos y Alcaraz, Adolfo, 1834-1894.
Obras dramáticas de Adolfo Llanos y Alcaráz. ⌊Mexico, Impr. de "La Colonia española," 1876⌋
236 p., 1 l. 22½cm.
CONTENT.—¿Quién es el loco? Cuento escrito por Edgardo Poe, encajado en la escena de los Bufos, adornado con música por Don José Rogel ... 2. ed. (with special t.-p.)—El árbol caido.—Un muerto de buen humor, con musica del maestro Rogel ... 2. ed.—La oracion por pasiva.—Las tres Marias. Música de Don José Rogel ... 2. ed.

I. Poe, Edgar Allan, 1809-1849. II. Rogel, José, b. 1829.

18-6374

Library of Congress PQ6534.L45A19 1876

NL 0425312 DLC MoU

NPL p.v.655, no.22
⌊Llanos y Alcaráz, Adolfo,⌋ 1834-1894
...Cambio de gabinete. Comedia en un acto y en verso, original de Z. C. H... ⌊Madrid: G. Alhambra, 1868.⌋ 10 p. 4°. (Biblioteca dramática.)
Caption-title.

1. Drama (Spanish). 2. H., Z. C. 3. Title.

January 18, 1922.

NL 0425313 NN

Llanos y Alcaraz, Adolfo, 1834-1894.
¡Central! Pasillo telefónico en un acto y en prosa, original de Adolfo Llanos ... Madrid, F. Fiscowich, 1886.
40 p. 17cm.

I. Title.

21-4289

Library of Congress PQ6534.C3

NL 0425314 DLC InU CtY MoU OO NN

M1503 L55C7 Llanos y Alcaraz, Adolfo, 1834-1894.
[Cristobal Colon; acc. arr. piano]
Cristobal Colon; opera en 3 actos. Letra de C. L. Cuenca. Música del Mtro. A. Llanos. Madrid, Zozaya [1893?] Pl. nos. Z3559, 3620-3634.
1 v. (various pagings)
Spanish words.

NL 0425315 CU

Llanos y Alcaraz, Adolfo, 1834-1894.
Defensa del libro intitulado "No vengais a America". T. 1-2. Mexico, La Colonia Española, 1877-1878.
2 v. 24°.
Vol. 1, 1878.

NL 0425316 NN

Llanos y Alcaráz, Adolfo, 1834-1894.
La dominacion española en Mexico
see under title

Llanos y Alcaraz, Adolfo, 1834-1894.
Don Carlos de Borbon y el partido carlista. Mexico, Impr. de "La Colonia Española", 1876.
69p. 14cm.

p.33-64 have been lowered by the binder to fit size of "Bound with" entry.
Bound with: D⌊on⌋ Carlos de Borbon en Mexico... 1876.

1. Carlos de Bourton, Luis.

NL 0425318 LNHT MB

PQ 6171 .A195 L791 Llanos y Alcaraz, Adolfo, 1834-1894
Elementos de gramatica parda, para uso de los hombres. 3. ed. Madrid, Librería de F. Fé, 1884.
2 v. illus. 19cm. (Biblioteca Extravagante)

On cover: ¡No leais esto, mujeres!
Vol. 2, although published, is not included in the Porter Collection
I. Title II. Title: ¡No leais esto, mujeres!

NL 0425319 WU

PQ 6534 L45E3 Llanos y Alcaraz, Adolfo, 1834-1894.
Elementos de gramática parda, para uso de los hombres, por Adolfo Llanos. Madrid, F. Fé, 1884-85.
2 v. in 1. 18cm. (Biblioteca extravagante)

NL 0425320 NIC

VOLUME 337

LLANOS [Y ALCARAZ], Adolfo, 1834-1894.
Ensayo general; sainete lirico.
Madrid,1887.

(El teatro).

NL 0425321 MH NN

Llanos y Alcaraz, Adolfo, 1834-1894.
Ensayo general, sainete lírico en un acto, original, letra de Adolfo Llanos, música del maestro inglés Arthur Sullivan. Madrid, M. P. Montoya, 1887.
32p.

Microcard edition.

NL 0425322 ICRL MoU

LLANOS [Y ALCARAZ], Adolfo, 1834-1894.
El figon de las desdichas; sainete lirico.
Madrid,1887.

(El teatro).

NL 0425323 MH OO NN

Llanos y Alcaraz, Adolfo, 1834-1894.
El figon de las desdichas, sainete lírico, original, letra de Adolfo Llanos, música del maestro Chapí. Madrid, M. P. Montoya y Compañia, 1887.
40p.
Microcard edition.

NL 0425324 ICRL MoU LU

Llanos y Alcaraz, Adolfo, 1834-1894.
El figon de las desdichas
For scores see under Chapí y Lorente, Ruperto, 1851-1909.

E 168 .L54 Llanos y Alcaraz, Adolfo, 1834-1894
El gigante americano; descripciones de los Estados Unidos de la América del Norte. Madrid, Tip. de R. Fé, 1886.
267 p. 19 cm.

1. United States - Descr. & trav. - 1865-1900. I. Title.

NL 0425326 WU ICU CU MiDW MB CU

868.708 C697 v.11 Llanos y Alcaraz, Adolfo, 1834-1894.
La guerra civil. Drama en un acto y en verso, original de Adolfo Llanos y Alcaraz ... México, Imprenta de "La Colonia española",1876.
42p. 17cm. (In Collection of Mexican plays, v.11)

On cover: El Teatro, galería dramática escogida.
Contains autograph of author.

I. Title.

NL 0425327 IEN

G972.9105 L77g Llanos y Alcaraz, Adolfo, 1834-1894.
La guerra con los Estados Unidos. Habana, Imp. del Avisador Comercial, 1897.
70p. 22cm.

1. Cuba - Hist. - Revolution, 1895-1898. 2. U.S. - Relations (general) with Spain. 3. Spain - Relations (general) with the U.S. I. Title.

NL 0425328 TxU FU MoU MH WaPS NBC DNW

LLANOS Y ALCARAZ, Adolfo,1834-1894.
Hojas secas; poesias. Mexico, 1876.

pp.84, ix, (2).

NL 0425329 MH

PQ 6534 .L4H8 1875 Llanos y Alcaráz, Adolfo, 1834-1894.
Horas alegres. Poesías festivas de Adolfo Llanos y Alcaráz. México, Impr. de la "Colonia Española", 1875.
77 p.

NL 0425330 ICU NNH

LLANOS Y ALCARAZ, Adolfo, 1834-1894.
Melilla; historia de la campana de Africa en 1893-94, Madrid,1894.

NL 0425331 MH

Llanos y Alcaraz, Adolfo, 1834-1894.
Un muerto de buen humor, cuento del siglo pasado...con música de [José] Rogel... Madrid, J. Rodriguez, 1867.
31 (1) p. 12°. (Repertorio de los Bufos Madrileños)
p. 15 & 16 bound before t.p.
In: NPL. p. v. 68, no. 13.

NL 0425332 NN OO

Llanos y Alcaraz, Adolfo, 1834-1894.
Un muerto de buen humor, cuento del siglo pasado rejuvenecido ... música del maestro Rogel. Madrid, José Rodríguez, 1867.
31p. (Repertorio de los bufos Madrileños)

Microcard edition.

NL 0425333 ICRL MoU

Llanos y Alcaraz, Adolfo, 1834-1894.
La mujer en el siglo diez y nueve. Hojas de un libro originales de Adolfo Llanos y Alcaraz, precedidas de un prologo por Don Manuel Cañete ... Lima, Libreria hispano-francesa, 1865.
xx, 368, (2) p. 16cm.

1. Woman.

9-3492†

Library of Congress HQ1214.L8

NL 0425334 DLC NNH

Llanos y Alcaraz, Adolfo, 1834-1894.
No vengaís á América. Libro dedicado á los pueblos europeos. Por Adolfo Llanos y Alcaráz. México, Impr. de "La Colonia española," de A. Llanos, 1876.
x, 487 p., 2 l., 216 p. 20cm.

"Apéndice. Manifestaciones en favor de Adolfo Llanos y Alcaráz", 216 p. ("Este Apéndice ... sólo acompaña á los ejemplares destinados á repartirse gratis en Europa")

1. Mexico. 2. Mexico—Pol. & govt. I. Title.

3—28381

Library of Congress F1227.L80

NL 0425335 DLC InU CU-S NN NNH

F1227 L57 Llanos y Alcaráz, Adolfo. 1834-1894.
No vengaís á América. Libro dedicado á los pueblos europeos. Por Adolfo Llanos y Alcaráz. México, Impr. de "La Colonia española," de A. Llanos, 1876 [i.e. 1877?]
x, 487 p., 2 l., 223 p. 20cm.

"Apéndice. Manifestaciones en favor de Adolfo Llanos y Alcaráz," 223 p. ("Este Apéndice ... sólo acompaña á los ejemplares destinados á repartirse gratis en Europa")

NL 0425336 CU

Llanos y Alcaráz, Adolfo, 1834-1894.
¿Nos casamos? Perplejidad de dos vecinos, original de Adolfo Llanos... Madrid: Establecimiento tipográfico de M. P. Montoya y Compañia, 1884. 29 p., 3 l. 12°.

On cover: Administración lirico-dramática.

1. Drama (Spanish). 2. Title.

August 25, 1917.

NL 0425337 NN

Llanos y Alcaraz, Adolfo, 1834-1894.
¿Nos casamos? Perplejidad de dos vecinos, original de Adolfo Llanos. Madrid, M. P. Montoya, 1884.
29p.

Microcard edition.

NL 0425338 ICRL FU OrU LU

Llanos y Alcaraz, Adolfo, 1834-1894.
Novisimo diccionario del amor y de otras... Madrid, 1884.

NL 0425339 NNH OCU

[LLANOS Y ALCARAZ, Adolfo,] 1834-1894
Origen del plajio en Mexico; polemica sostenida por el periodico La Colonia Española con varios organos de la prensa mexicana. Mexico, Imp. de "La Colonia Española" de A.Llanos,1877.

NL 0425340 MH LNHT DPU

PQ6534 L45P4 Llanos y Alcaraz, Adolfo, 1834-1894.
Pedreria falsa; colección de guijarros literarios, labrados por Adolfo Llanos y Alcaraz. Mexico, Impr. de "La Colonia Española," 1875.
296p. 22cm.

"Contiene este coleccion varios artículos sueltos, revistas y críticas literarias, publicados... en diferentes periódicos de España y de América."

NL 0425341 IaU NN

VOLUME 337

Llanos y Alcaraz, Adolfo, 1834-1894.
Playeras, zarzuela en un acto y en verso, original de Adolfo Llanos, música del maestro Chapí. Madrid, M. P. Montoya, 1887.
30p.
Microcard edition.
In the MIDWEST INTER-LIBRARY CENTER

NL 0425342 ICRL MoU

LLANOS [Y ALCARAZ], Adolfo, 1834-1894.
Playeras; zarzuela. Madrid,1887.
(El teatro).

NL 0425343 MH InU OO NN

LLANOS Y ALCARAZ, Adolfo, 1834-1894.
Plegarias a la Virgen Maria. Mexico, imp. de "La colonia. española," 1878.

NL 0425344 MH NNH

LLANOS Y ALCARAZ, Adolfo, 1834-1894.
Poemas de la barbarie; apendice de un libro Costumbres barbaras del mundo civilizado. Madrid, [imp. universal,18-?]
Biblioteca economica de instruccion y recreo
On cover:- 4a ed.

NL 0425345 MH

LLANOS Y ALCARAZ, Adolfo, 1834-1894.
El porvenir de España en America. Mexico, impr. de "La Colonia española" 1878.
sq. 16°.
183p.

NL 0425346 MH NN

Llanos y Alcaraz, Adolfo, 1834–1894.
... ¡Quién es el loco? Cuento escrito por Edgardo Poe, encajado en la escena de los bufos por Adolfo Llanos y Alcaráz, y adornado con música por Don José Rogel ... Madrid, Impr. de J. Rodriguez, 1867.
27, [1] p. 20cm. (Repertorio de los Bufos madrileños)
Based on Poe's tale: The system of Dr. Tarr and Prof. Fether.

I. Poe, Edgar Allan, 1809–1849. II. Rogel, José, b. 1829. III. Title.
21-10222
Library of Congress PQ6534.L45O6

NL 0425347 DLC OO NN FMU

Llanos y Alcaraz, Adolfo, 1834–1894.
Recuerdos. Coleccion de poesias, de Adolfo Llanos y Alcaráz. Mexico, Impr. de "La Colonia española", 1876.
3 p. l., viii p., 1 l., [7]–228, [4] p. front. (port.) 31½cm.

I. Title.
25-11693
Library of Congress PQ6534.L45R4 1876

NL 0425348 DLC TxU NNH

Y 722 .L 77
LLANOS Y ALCARAZ, ADOLFO, 1834-1894.
Romancero de don Jaime el Conquistador, por Adolfo Llanos, premiado con medalla de oro en público certamen por la Real academia española é impreso á sus expensas. Madrid,Tello,1889.
189p.

NL 0425349 ICN IU MH NIC NNH CU CLU

Llanos y Alcaraz, Adolfo, 1834-1894.
El suicidio de España. Detalles, episodios y juicios críticos de la guerra hispano-americana en 1898, por varios testigos presenciales. Bajo la dirección de Adolfo Llanos y Alcaraz. Barcelona, R. Molinas, 1899.
4 p. l., 247, [1] p. 19½cm.

1. U. S.—Hist.—War of 1898.
11-2916
Library of Congress E715.L79

NL 0425350 DLC

LLANOS Y ALCARAZ, Adolfo, 1834-1894.
Timepo perdido; coleccion de articulos politicos, criticos y de polemica originales Mexico, imp. de "La colonia española" de A.Llanos, 1876.

NL 0425351 MH NN

LLANOS [Y ALCARAZ], Adolfo, 1834-1894.
Tocador de señoras. Madrid,1887.
Span 4370.9.31

NL 0425352 MH NN

865L772 Ot
Llanos y Alcaraz, Adolfo, 1834–1894.
Los tres refranes; aventuras de un asturiano, relatadas por Adolfo Llanos y Alcaráz. México, Impr. de I. Escalante, 1874-75.
2 v. in 1. front. (port.) 22½cm.
Vol. 2 has imprint: México, Imprenta de "La Colonia Española."
Contents.—La suerte del pobre.—En busca de fortuna.

NL 0425353 IU

Llanos y Alcaraz, Adolfo, 1834–1894.
Los tres refranes; aventuras de un asturiano, relatadas por Adolfo Llanos y Alcaráz. México, Impr. de "La colonia española," 1875.
2 v. in 1. front. (port.) 22½cm.
Vol. 2 has special t.-p.
Contents.—La suerte del pobre.—En busca de fortuna.

I. Title.
43-49693
Library of Congress PQ6534.L45T7

NL 0425354 DLC

Llanos [y Alcaraz] Adolfo, 1834–1894.
La tromepeta: juguete cómico en un acto y en verso... Madrid, M.P. Montoya y Ca. 1885.
33 p. 8°. (Admin. lirico-dramat.)
In NPL p.v. 187, no. 13.

NL 0425355 NN

Llanos y Alcaraz, Adolfo, 1834-1894.
La trompeta, juguete cómico en un acto y en verso, original de Adolfo Llanos. Madrid, M. P. Montoya y Ca., 1885.
33p.
Microcard edition.

NL 0425356 ICRL FU MoU

86L771 Z7
Llanos y Alcaráz, Adolfo, 1834-1894.
Zoa, por Adolfo Llanos y Alcaráz. Mexico [Tip. de "La Colonia espanola"; 1866.
2 p. l., 119 p. 20½cm.
On cover: "Segunda edicion."
I. Title.

NL 0425357 NNC

Llanos y Alcaráz, Adolfo, 1834–1894.
Zoa, por Adolfo Llanos y Alcaráz. México, 1876. 119 p. 20cm.
2. ed.

NL 0425358 NN

Llanos y Berete, Antonio, 1841-1906.
La caridad
For libretti see under Llofriu y Sagrera, Eleuterio, 1835-1880.

Llanos y Berete, Antonio, 1841-1906.
La divina zarzuela
For libretti see under Cuenca, Carlos Luis de, 1849-1927.

Llanos y Berete, Antonio, 1841–1906.
...IIa fantasia sobre cantos populares de España. Por Antonio Llanos... Madrid: Zozaya [, 189–?]. Publ. pl. no. Z. 4079 Z. 20 p. f°.
Spanish words with music for 4 men's voices.

1. Choruses—Men's voices. 2. Folk songs, Spanish.
September 10, 1925

NL 0425361 NN

Llanos y Berete, Antonio, 1841–1906.
...Jota aragonesa, con cantos populares, y Jota estudiantil (conocidas con el nombre de jotas del Manzanares,) por el maestro A. Llanos... Madrid: Zozaya [187–?]. Publ. pl. nos. B. Z. 181–182. 2 v. f°.
Arranged for piano, 2 hands, with superlinear Spanish words.

1. Folk songs, Spanish. 2. Piano.
January 21, 1925

NL 0425362 NN

Llanos y Berete, Antonio, 1841-1906, arr.
Manolito el rayo
For libretti see under Larra, Luis Mariano de, 1830-1901.

VOLUME 337

Llanos y Jaime, Antonio.
... "El Ministerio público y la defensa en nuestro procedimiento penal del orden común"; tesis que para su examen profesional de abogado presenta el alumno Antonio Llanos y Jaime. México, D. F., 1936.
75 p. 20cm.
At head of title: Facultad de derecho y ciencias sociales.
Errata slip mounted on p. [2] of cover.

1. Mexico. Ministerio público federal. 2. Public prosecutors—Mexico. 3. Public defenders—Mexico. 4. Criminal procedure—Mexico. I. Title.
37-23446

NL 0425364 DLC

LLANOS Y MORIEGA, Eulalia de.
Coleccion de composiciones poeticas. Publicadas por su hermana, Teresa. Gijon, Torre y compañia, 1871.

NL 0425365 MH

Llanos y Torriglia, Félix de, 1868–
...La Academia americana de artes y letras de Nueva York; inauguración de un nuevo edificio, discurso leído por Don Félix de Llanos y Torriglia. Madrid: Tipografía de archivos, 1931. 19 p. 24½cm.
At head of title: Academia de la historia.
HAE p.v.94 — — Second copy.

696634A. 1. United States—Rel., Gen., with Spain. 2. Spain—Rel., Gen., with U. S. I. Academia de la historia, Madrid.
November 15, 1934

NL 0425366 NN

N3450
.L5 Llanos y Torriglia, Félix de, 1868-
...Algunos recuerdos de d. Antonio Maura. Madrid, Salvador Cuesta, 1927.
24p. 24cm.
Author's autographed presentation copy to Dr. Cook.
Bound with his Unos autografos de don Bartolomé José Gallardo. 1924.

1.Maura y Montaner, Antonio, 1853-1925.

NL 0425367 NNU-W

897n
L791 Llanos y Torriglia, Félix de, 1868-
Apología de la carta privada como elemento literario; discurso leído por Félix de Llanos y Torriglia ante la Real Academia española con motivo de su recepción, el día 13 de diciembre de 1945. Contestación por Agustín González de Amezúa y Mayo. Madrid, Imp. de E. Maestre, 1945.
76 p. 26cm.
Bibliographical foot-notes.

NL 0425368 CU IU

LLANOS Y TORRIGLIA, Félix de, 1868 -
Apuros de la hacienda y enfermedad de la moneda española en tiempos de Cervantes. Madrid, imp. de la Revista de Legislacion, a cargo de B. Millan, 1905.
pp. 31.

NL 0425369 MH

Llanos y Torriglia, Félix de, 1868–
Así llegó a reinar Isabel la Católica (folios descabales de una crónica que está a medio hacer) por Félix de Llanos y Torriglia ... Madrid, Editorial Voluntad, s. a., 1927.
457 p., 2 l. front. (port.) illus. (incl. ports.) 21½cm.
"Notas" at the end of each chapter.

1. Isabel I, la Católica, queen of Spain, 1451-1504. 2. Spain—Hist.—Ferdinand and Isabella, 1479-1516. I. Title.
30-30153
Library of Congress DP163.L5
923.146

NL 0425370 DLC OU CU NN MH

XPA 6368
Llanos y Torriglia, Félix de, 1868-
Catalina de Aragón, Reina de Inglaterra. Conferencia leida en la Unión de Damas Españolas el dia 9 de Marzo de 1914. Madrid, Impr. Helénica [1914]
54 p. port.

NL 0425371 MH CU WU

Llanos y Torríglia, Félix de, 1868-
... Cataluña e Irlanda; conferencia del ilmo. sr. D. Félix de Llanos y Torríglia leída en la sesión pública de 27 de enero de 1919. Madrid, J. Ratés, 1919.
58 p. 21cm.
At head of title: Real academia de jurisprudencia y legislación.
Bibliographical footnotes.

NL 0425372 MH-L

---

*Llanos y Torriglia, Félix de. ... Cómo se hizo la revolución en Portugal. Conferencias leídas por D. Felix de Llanos y Torriglia en sesiones públicas de los días 25 y 28 de marzo y 3 de abril de 1914. Madrid, Imprenta clásica española, 1914. 103p. 19cm.
At head of title: Real academia de jurisprudencia y legislación.

NL 0425373 CU

949.3
Is1Wll Llanos y Torriglia, Félix de, 1868-
Conferencias pronunciadas en las sesiones públicas de 16 y 19 de enero de 1917. Tema: Los orígenes de la nacionalidad belga: la Infanta de España, Isabel Clara Eugenia, soberana de los Países Bajos. Madrid, Estab. tip. de J. Ratés, 1917.
93p. ports. 22cm.
At head of title: Real Academia de Jurisprudencia y Legislación.

NL 0425374 IU CU

Bnl9A
G134
920L Llanos y Torriglia, Félix de, 1868-
Una consejera de estado: Dª Beatriz Galindo "la Latina." Conferencia. Madrid, Editorial Reus, 1920.
110p. 19cm. (Academia de Jurisprudencia y Legislación, Madrid. Publicaciones, 22)

1. Galindo, Beatriz, 1475-1534. I.Ser. cdu.

NL 0425375 CtY NN MH CU OKentU

Llanos y Torriglia, Félix de, 1868–
Contribución al estudio de la reina de Portugal, hermana de Carlos V, doña Catalina de Austria; discurso leído ante la Real academia de la historia en el acto de su recepción pública el día 2 de mayo de 1923, por el excmo. sr. d. Félix de Llanos y Torriglia, y contestación del excmo. sr. d. Gabriel Maura y Gamazo, conde de la Mortera. Madrid, Imp. de la "Rev. de arch., bibl. y museos," 1923.
134 p. port. 22cm.
Title lettered on back: Estudio de d. Catalina de Austria.
"Bibliografía del discurso": p. [115]-118.
1. Catharina de Austria, queen consort of John III, king of Portugal, 1507-1578. I. Maura y Gamazo, Gabriel, duque de Maura, 1879– II. Academia de la historia, Madrid.
33-4625 Revised
Library of Congress DP610.C3L6
[r43b2] 923.1469

NL 0425376 DLC MH

Llanos y Torriglia, Félix de, 1868–
... Desde la cruz al cielo; vida y muerte de la infanta Isabel Clara Eugenia. 1. ed. Madrid, Ediciones "Fax", 1933.
299 p., 2 l. ports. 18½cm.

1. Isabel, consort of Albert, archduke of Austria, 1566-1633. I. Title.
34-6465
DH602.I 8L47
920.7

NL 0425377 DLC NNH

Llanos y Torriglia, Felix de, 1868-
... Discurso leído por el secretario general, Don Félix de Llanos y Torriglia, en la sesión inaugural del curso de 1897 á 98 celebrada el 26 de noviembre de 1897. Madrid, Tip. de los hijos de M. G. Hernández, 1897.
1 p. l., [5]-61 p. 24 cm.
At head of title: Real academia de jurisprudencia y legislación.

NL 0425378 CU-B

Llanos y Torriglia, Félix de, 1868–
El divorcio de Catalina de Aragón. San Juan Fisher y santo Tomás Moro. Síntesis histórica por Félix de Llanos y Torriglia ... Madrid, 1935.
119 p., 1 l. pl., ports. 23½ cm.
"Conferencias en Acción española (25 de mayo y 3 de abril de 1935)"
"Apéndice[s]: (p. [95]-115): A. Los confesores de Catalina de Aragón. B. Las enseñanzas de Luis Vives. C. Las santa monja de Kent D. La lápida de las Catalinas. E. Bibliografía."
1. Catharine of Aragon, consort of Henry VIII, king of England, 1485-1536. 2. Henry VIII, king of England, 1491-1547—Divorce from Catharine. 3. Fisher, John, Saint, bp. of Rochester, 1459?-1535. 4. More, Sir Thomas, Saint, 1478-1535. I. Title.
DA333.A6L6 923.142 36—29221

NL 0425379 DLC MH

JX
5771
L77 Llanos y Torriglia, Félix de, 1868-
El dominio de lo impalpable (perspectivas jurídicas de la aeronáutica y la teletrasmisión). Discurso leído por Félix de Llanos y Torriglia en su recepción como académico de mérito, y contestación de Adolfo Pons y Umbert a nombre de la Academia. Sesión del día 28 de abril de 1926. Madrid, Editorial Reus, 1926.
87 p. (Publicaciones de la Real Academia de Jurisprudencia y Legislación, 75)

NL 0425380 NNC-L NN

Llanos y Torriglia, Félix de, 1868–
...La emperatriz Eugenia en el archivo del palacio de Liria. Madrid: Tip. de archivos, 1935. 42 p. facsim., illus. 24cm.

1. Eugénie, empress consort of Napoleon III, 1826-1920.
October 27, 1938

NL 0425381 NN

VOLUME 337

Llanos y Torriglia, Félix de, 1868–
... En el hogar de los reyes católicos y Cosas de sus tiempos. Madrid, Ediciones Fax [1943]
207 p., 2 l. illus. (incl. ports.) 20cm.

1. Spain—Hist.—Ferdinand and Isabella, 1479–1516. 2. Spain—Soc. life & cust. I. Title.
45-17961
Library of Congress DP162.L55
946.03

NL 0425382 DLC CLU OU

Llanos y Torriglia, Félix de, 1868–
En el hogar de los Reyes Católicos y Cosas de sus tiempos. Madrid, Ediciones "Fax" [1946]
286 p. illus., ports. 20 cm.
Apéndices (p. [253]–284): Beatriz Galindo, la Latina. Isabel la Católica y Juana la Beltraneja.

1. Spain—Hist.—Ferdinand and Isabella, 1479–1516. 2. Spain—Soc. life & cust. I. Title.
DP162.L55 1946 946.03 48-14371*

NL 0425383 DLC CoU KU

Llanos y Torríglia, Félix de, 1868-
... Ferri y su escuela. Madrid, 1889.
cover-title, [31] p. 23cm.
At head of title: Academia de jurisprudencia.
"El Ateneo; revista científica, literaria y artística."
"Memoria leida el día 12 de Febrero último ... en la primera de las sesiones públicas especiales, á las que ha sido invitada la Academia Médico-Quirúrgica."
Signed at end: F. de Llanos y Torríglia.

NL 0425385 MH-L

DP58 .C7 t.7 Llanos y Torriglia, Félix de, 1868-
Francisco Silvela. Madrid, Editorial Purcalla, 1946.
195p. illus. 21cm. (Colección medio siglo de historia; los presidentes del Consejo de la Monarquía española, t.7)

1. Silvela y de Le Vielleuze, Francisco, 1845-1905. I. Series.

NL 0425386 PSt MH NcD

Llanos y Torriglia, Félix de, 1868–
... Germán Gamazo, el sobrio castellano, por Félix de Llanos y Torriglia. Madrid, Espasa-Calpe, s. a., 1942.
246 p. front., ports., facsim. 19½cm. (Vidas españolas e hispanoamericanas del siglo XIX. 58)

1. Gamazo y Calvo, Germán, 1838–1901. 2. Spain—Pol. & govt.—19th cent.
A 43-1249
Harvard univ. Library for Library of Congress

OCl
NL 0425387 MH MnU CU TNJ CLU MiU IEN NcD FTaSU

4A 3798 LLANOS Y TORRIGLIA, FELIX de, 1868-
La infanta María Ana Victoria de Borbón, Hija de Felipe V. Conferencias pronunciada por ... de las reales Academias españolas y de la historia, el 7 y 21 de Marzo de 1946. [Madrid, Imprenta del Ministerio de Asuntos exteriores, 1946]
59p. 24cm.
Bibliography: p. 59

NL 0425388 ICN

Llanos y Torriglia, Félix de, 1868–
... Isabel Clara Eugenia ... Madrid, Editorial Volvntad, s. a., 1928–
v. ports. 17cm. (Colección de manuales Hispania ... vol. III.—ser. D)
Added t.-p.: Colección "Hispania" dirigida por ... Antonio Ballesteros y Beretta ...
Bibliographical notes: v. 1, p. 237–250.
CONTENTS.—I. La novia de Europa.

1. Isabel, consort of Albrecht, archduke of Austria, 1566–1633.
Library of Congress DH602.I 8L5 32-4702
920.7

NL 0425389 DLC CU

Llanos y Torriglia, Félix de, 1868-

Zarco Cuevas, Eusebio Julián, 1887–
Los jerónimos de San Lorenzo el real de el Escorial; discursos leídos ante la Real academia de la historia en la recepción pública del r. p. fr. Julián Zarco Cuevas ... el día 1.° de junio de 1930. [El Escorial, Impr. del real monasterio San Lorenzo, 1930.

Llanos y Torriglia, Felix de, 1868- joint ed.

Eugénie, *empress consort of Napoleon III*, 1826–1920.
Lettres familières de l'impératrice Eugénie, conservées dans les archives du palais de Liria et publiées par les soins du duc d'Albe avec le concours de F. de Llanos y Torriglia et Pierre Josserand; préface de Gabriel Hanotaux ... Paris, Le Divan, 1935.

Llanos y Torriglia, Félix de, 1868–
María I de Inglaterra ¿La sanguinaria? Reina de España. Madrid, Espasa-Calpe [1946]
492 p. illus. 23 cm. (Grandes biografías)
Includes bibliography.

1. Mary I, Queen of England, 1516–1558.
DA347.L57 53-37151 ‡

NL 0425392 DLC NN IU MnU MH MWelC CU

Llanos y Torriglia, Félix de, 1868–
... María Manuela Kirkpatrick, condesa del Montijo, la gran dama, por Félix de Llanos y Torriglia. 1. ed. Madrid [etc.] Espasa-Calpe, s. a., 1932.
243 p. front., ports. 19cm. (Vidas españolas e hispanoamericanas del siglo XIX. 22)

1. Montijo, María Manuela (Kirkpatrick) condesa de, 1794–1879.
Library of Congress DP202.M6L6 33-9900
920.7

NL 0425393 DLC IdU NcD FTaSU NN OO OCl CtY

Llanos y Torriglia, Félix de, 1868–
... Mirando a Portugal; el interés de España ... Madrid, Imprenta clásica española, 1917.
1 p. l., [5]–194 p., 1 l. 19cm.

1. Portugal. 2. Portugal—Relations (general) with Spain. 3. Spain—Relations (general) with Portugal. I. Title.
18-16469
Library of Congress DP675.L57

NL 0425394 DLC CU

Llanos y Torriglia, Félix de, 1868–
Noticia de las "Deux journées espagnoles" celebradas en Bruselas los dias 16 y 17 de mayo de 1924, redactada por Felix de Llanos y Torriglia... Madrid: "Rev. de arch., bibl. y museos," 1924. 39 p. 8°.
"Publicada en el Boletín de la Real academia de la historia."
Autographed presentation note on fly-leaf.
"Journées hispano-belges, 16–17 mai 1924; catalogue des document exposés aux Archives du royaume," p. 18–39.

592696A. 1. Exhibitions—Brussels, 1924. I. Belgium. Archives générales du royaume.
July 5, 1932

NL 0425395 NN NNU-W

Llanos y Torriglia, Félix de, 1868–
... La novia de Europa, Isabel Clara Eugenia. Ed. rev. Madrid, Ediciones "FAX," 1944.
272 p., 2 l. ports. 19½cm.
Bibliography included in "Notas" (p. [257]–272)

1. Isabel, consort of Albert, archduke of Austria, 1566–1633. I. Title.
A 46-1024
New York. Public library for Library of Congress DH602.I 8L52 1944
†
920.7

NL 0425396 DLC NN IU

Llanos y Torriglia, Félix de, 1868–
... La reina Isabel, fundidora de España, por Félix de Llanos y Torriglia. Barcelona [etc.] Editorial Labor, s. a., 1941.
287 p., 2 l. XIV pl. (incl. ports., facsims.) on 7 l. 18½cm. (Colección Pro ecclesia et patria. [18])
"Nota bibliográfica": p. [285]–287.

I. Isabel I, la Católica, queen of Spain, 1451–1504.
44-34531
Library of Congress DP163.L52
923.146

NL 0425397 DLC WaU CoU ICU

Llanos y Torriglia, Félix de, 1868–
...La Reina Isabel, fundidora de España, por Félix de Llanos y Torriglia. 2. ed. Barcelona [etc.] Editorial Labor, 1949. 267 p. illus. 19cm. (Colleción Pro ecclesia et patria. 18)
"Nota bibliográfica," p. 265–267.

556622B. 1. Isabella I, queen of Spain, 1451–1504. 2. Spain—Hist.—Ferdinand and Isabella, 1497–1516.
April 6, 1951

NL 0425398 NN NBuC NcU MH TxU MB GASU

Llanos y Torriglia, Félix de, 1868–
... Santas y reinas, apuntes biográficos. 2. ed. Madrid, Ediciones FAX, 1943.
888 p., 2 l. illus. (ports.) 20½cm.
Includes bibliographies.
CONTENTS.—Santa Mónica (viñetas de un devocionario)—Santa Isabel de Aragón, reina de Portugal.—Juana de Arco, santa de la patria.—Leonor de Inglaterra, reina de Castilla.—Doña Juana la Loca y Enrique VIII de Inglaterra.—El divorcio de Catalina de Aragón. San Juan Fisher y santo Tomás Moro.—Cuatro reinas españolas que presidieron desde el trono de Portugal la epopeya de los descubrimientos: Doña Isabel de Castilla. Doña María de Castilla. Doña Leonor de Austria. Doña Catalina de Austria.—Contribución al estudio de la reina de Portugal, hermana de Carlos V, doña Catalina de Austria.—El capitán Iñigo de Loyola y la dama de sus pensamientos.—Isabel de la Paz, la reina con quien vino la corte a Madrid.
1. Spain—Queens. 2. Portugal—Queens. 3. Saints.
New York. Public library for Library of Congress ° A 45-936

NL 0425399 NN CLU IU

VOLUME 337

N3450
.L5 Llanos y Torriglia, Félix de, 1868-
Unos autografos de don Bartolomé José Gallardo, por d. Félix de Llanos y Torriglia. Madrid, Tip. de la "Rev. de archivos, bibliotecas y museos", 1924.
35p. 24cm.
Author's autographed presentation copy to Dr. Cook.
With this are bound his Algunos recuerdos de d. Antonio Maura; Portugal en el Museo del Prado; and Noticia de las "Deux journées espagnoles" celebradas en Bruselas los días 16 y 17 de mayo de 1924.
1. Gallardo, Bartolomé José, 1776-1852.

NL 0425400 NNU-W

Llanos y Torriglia, Félix de, 1868–
La vida hogareña a través de los siglos. Las casas del rey prudente. Madrid, Ediciones Fax [1947]
246 p. illus. 20 cm.

1. Spain—Soc. life & cust. 2. Felipe II, King of Spain, 1527–1598
I. Title. II. Title: Las casas del rey prudente.

DP48.L6 914.6 48–23194*

NL 0425401 DLC MiU MChB

Llanover, Augusta (Waddington) Hall, lady, d. 1896, ed.
Delany, *Mrs.* **Mary (Granville) Pendarves,** 1700–1788.
The autobiography and correspondence of Mary Granville, Mrs. Delany: with interesting reminiscences of King George the Third and Queen Charlotte. Ed. by the Right Honourable Lady Llanover ... London, R. Bentley, 1861.

Llanover, Augusta (Waddington) Hall, lady, d. 1896, ed.
Delany, *Mrs.* **Mary (Granville) Pendarves,** 1700–1788.
The autobiography and correspondence of Mrs. Delany. Rev. from Lady Llanover's edition, and ed. by Sarah Chauncey Woolsey ... Boston, Roberts brothers, 1879.

Llanover, Augusta (Waddington) Hall, lady, d. 1896.
The first principles of good cookery illustrated. And recipes communicated by the Welsh hermit of the cell of St. Gover, with various remarks on many things past and present. By the Right Hon. Lady Llanover. London, R. Bentley, 1867. xii, 482 p. illus. 21cm.

358715B. 1. Cookery.

March 18, 1948

NL 0425404 NN

Llanover, Augusta (Waddington) Hall, *lady, d.* 1896.
Good cookery illustrated. And recipes communicated by the Welsh hermit of the cell of St. Gover, with various remarks on many things past and present. By the Right Hon. Lady Llanover. London, R. Bentley, 1867.
xii, 482 p., 1 l. incl. front., illus. xi pl. 20cm.

1. Cookery, Welsh. I. Title.

45-32004

Library of Congress TX717.L55

NL 0425405 DLC

Llanover, Augusta (Waddington) Hall, lady, d. 1896.
...The prize essay on the advantages resulting from the preservation of the Welsh language, and national costumes of Wales ...by Gwenynen Gwent... London, Longman, Rees, Orme, Brown, Green and Longman [etc., etc.] 1836. 18 p. 23cm.

At head of title: Gwent and Dyfed royal eisteddfod, 1834.

1. Welsh. 2. Welsh language. I. Eisteddfod, Gwent and Pembrokeshire, Wales, 1834.

November 22, 1948

NL 0425406 NN ICN MH

Llanover, Augusta (Waddington) Hall, lady, d. 1896, ed.
Delany, *Mrs.* **Mary (Granville) Pendarves, 1700–1788.**
Mrs. Delany at court and among the wits, being the record of a great lady of genius in the art of living .. with an introduction by R. Brimley Johnson ... London, S. Paul & co. ltd. [1925]

Llanover, Augusta (Waddington) Hall, lady, d. 1896.
...Y traethawd buddugol ar y buddioldeb a ddeillia oddiwrth gadwedigaeth y iaith gymraeg, a dullwisgoedd cymru. Gan Gwenynen Gwent. ‹Mrs. Hall, o Llanover.› Caerdydd, W Bird, 1836. 18 p. 23cm.

At head of title: Eisteddfod Gwent a Dyfed, 1834.

1. Welsh. 2. Welsh language. 3. Welsh language—Texts and translations. I. Eisteddfod, Gwent and Pembrokeshire, Wales, 1834.

November 22, 1948

NL 0425408 NN MH

Llanover, Sir Benjamin Hall, baron, 1802-1867.
Speech...in the House of Commons...July 1, 1851, on the motion of the Marquis of Blandford, for church extension out of the resources of the established church. *London: J. Pattie,* [1851] 16 pp. 16°.
In: *C. p. v. 738.

NL 0425409 NN

Llanquihue, Banco de
see
Banco Llanquihue, *Puerto Montt, Chile.*

Llanquihue. (Chile) provincia. Comité de defensa y adelanto regional de Puerto Montt.
Libro de la provincia de Llanquihue. Padre las Casas, Imprenta y Editorial "San Francisco", 1943.
384 p. illustraciones y fotografías.
[Reseña histórica-bibliográfica-administrativa de las diferentes épocas desde la era colonial, colonización alemana, hasta la actualidad. Documentos y antecedentes]

NL 0425411 DPU

Llansannan, *Wales (Parish)*
The registers of the parish of Llansannan 1667–1812. [Transcribed by Robert Ellis] Liverpool, Printed by I. Foulkes, 1904.
xiv p., 1 l., 9–447, [1] p. 27½cm.

1. Registers of births, etc.—Llansannan, Wales. I. Ellis, Robert, transcriber.

10-27526

Library of Congress CS436.L6

NL 0425412 DLC NcD FU CtY CSt IU MH

Llanso, Antonio Garcia
see
Garcia Llanso, Antonio, 1854-1914.

---

x282
C685
v.2 Llansol, Silvestre, father.
Novena de la purisima concepcion ... Guadalaxara, Reimpresa en la oficina de doña Petra Manjarres y Padilla, 1820.
[25]p. illus.
[A collection of religous pamphlets in the Spanish language. 2]

1. Catholic church--Prayer-books and devotions.

NL 0425414 IU

Llanthewy Rytherch, *Eng. (Parish)*
Registrum antiquum de Llanddewi Rhydderch in comitatu Monumethensi. 1670–1783. Transcribed from the original register book and edited by Joseph Alfred Bradney ... London, Mitchell, Hughes and Clarke, 1919.
2 p. l., 36 p. 26cm.

1. Registers of births, etc.—Llanthewy Rytherch, Eng. I. Bradney, Sir Joseph Alfred, 1859– ed.

30-24314

Library of Congress CS436.L57 929.3

NL 0425415 DLC NN ICN

BV312
.L8 **LLANTHONY ABBEY.**
Hymns of Llanthony monastery. Suitable for missions ... London, R. Berkeley, 1891.
cover-title, 23 p.
At head of title: Gwir yn erbyn ŷ byd. Jesus only. Pax.
Preface signed: Ignatius, O.S.B., monk.

1. Hymns, English.

NL 0425416 ICU NBU-T

Llanthony Priory.
The Irish cartularies of Llanthony prima & secunda. Edited from the mss. in the Public Record Office, London, by Eric St. John Brooks. Dublin, Stationery Office, 1953.
xxx, 345 p. 25 cm.
At head of title: Coimisiún Láimhscríbhinní na hÉireann, Irish Manuscripts Commission.

1. Church property—Ireland. I. Brooks, Eric St. John, ed. II. Ireland (Eire) Irish Manuscripts Commission. III. Title.

BX2596.L5A4 56-15577

NL 0425417 DLC NcD WU MB CU MiU CtY MnU NN NNC ICU

Llantilio Crossenny, *Eng. (Parish)*
Registra antiqua de Llantilio Crossenny et Penrhos in comitatu Monumethensi. 1577–1644. Transcribed from the copy in the Bodleian library and ed. by Joseph Alfred Bradney ... London, Mitchell, Hughes and Clarke, 1916.
viii, 46 p., 1 l. 26cm.
The ms. is an exact transcript of the copy of the register made by Walter Powell.
"A brief of the register booke of Penros": p. 21–46.

1. Registers of births, etc.—Llantilio Crossenny, Eng. 2. Registers of births, etc.—Penrose, Eng. I. Powell, Walter, 1581–1655. II. Bradney, Sir Joseph Alfred, 1859– III. Title.

17—19229

Library of Congress CS436.L6A3

NL 0425418 DLC

VOLUME 337

F1210 .2 D48 no.3 x
Llanto de la America por el decreto imperial y real que le quita a Pepe Botellas. [Mexico? 1808?]
7 p. 21cm. [Diversos impresos mejicanos de los años de 1808, 809, 810, 811, y 812, no. 3]

NL 0425419 CU-B

El llanto de las ruinas; la historia, el arte y la religión ultrajados en los templos de Buenos Aires; 16-17 de junio de 1955. Buenos Aires ₍Librería Don Bosco₎ 1955.
96 p. 18 cm.

1. Buenos Aires—Churches. 2. Argentine Republic—Hist.—Revolution, 1955.
F3001.L63 58-17238 ‡

NL 0425420 DLC OKentU MB FMU

Ayer *2143 D75 L7 1733
LLANTO de los astros en el occaso del sol nvestro smo. padre Benedicto XIII, qve en magestvosa pyra, y honorosas exeqvias celebrò el sagrado firmamento dominicano en la ciudad de Manila en las Islas Philipinas. ₍Manila₎ Convento de Nuestra Señora de Los Angeles, 1733.
14 p.l., 96p. 19½cm.
Errors in pagination.
"Oratio fvnebris exeqvialis honor, fvnestra declamatio...per oravit...f. Antonivs del Campo": p.59-72.
"Oración fvne- bre... Dixo la...fr. Diego Saenz: p.73-96.

NL 0425421 ICN

El Llanto de Mexico en los Tiernos y Lugubres Recuerdos que a la Augusta Memoria de el Gran Papa Clemente XIV... Mexico, 1775.
Bound as the 2d of 2.
JCB has another copy.
Medina (Mexico) 5820: Palau (2) 144769; Sabin 13627.

NL 0425422 RPJCB

F1207 L5399 x
El llanto de Mexico en los tiernos y lugubres recuerdos que a la augusta memoria de el gran papa Clemente XIV. consagraron las dos ilustres y religiosissimas provincias de predicadores y menores observantes de Mexico en sus dos maximos titulares conventos de santo Domingo, y s. Francisco de esta corte los dias 27. y 28. de marzo, 3. y 4. de abril de 1775 ... Mexico, F. de Zuñiga y Ontiveros, 1775.
17 p.l., xxi, ₍4₎, 32, ₍4₎, xv, ₍4₎, 33 (i.e.45) ₍2₎ p. 21cm.
Following 16 prelim. leaves of introductory material, are four funeral orations, each with half-title: Oratio ... habita ... ab p. f.

Josepho Raphaele Bonaventura Olmedo. Sacerdote grande ... elogio funebre, que ... dixo ... fr. Joseph Gallegos. Oratio ... dicta ... a r. p. fr. Cosma Enriquez Guerrero. El Maximo entre los sagrados politicos ... sermon funebre que ... predicó ... Antonio Blanco Valdez.

NL 0425424 CU-B RPJCB

Q 960
Llanto sobre los que niegan la providencia. Mexico, 1869.

NL 0425425 MH TxU

Llantos del reyno de Chile por la falta de su gobernador, y captain general Don Manuel de Amat, por haber sido promovido á virrey del Perú &c. [Lima, 1762?]
[7] p. 20 cm. [Coleccion de folletos. Tom. X. Poesias americanas. 1762 á 1847]
Caption title.

NL 0425426 CtY

Llantrithyd, *Wales (Parish)*
The registers of Llantrithyd, Glamorganshire. Christenings, 1597-1810; burials, 1571-1810; marriages, 1571-1752. Ed. by H. Seymour Hughes. London, Mitchell and Hughes, 1888.
2 p. l., 80 p. illus. (facsims.) 27cm.

1. Registers of births, etc.—Llantrithyd, Wales. I. Hughes, H. Seymour, ed.
Library of Congress CS458.L6A2 6-11675

NL 0425427 DLC FU MB CtY NN

Llanvair Discoed, Eng. (Parish)
Caerwent, *Eng. (Parish)*
Registra antiqua de Caerwent (1568-1812) et Llanfair Discoed (1680-1812) in comitatu Monumethensi. Transcribed from the original register books and edited by Joseph Alfred Bradney ... to which is added a short account of the parishes and vicars. London, Mitchell, Hughes and Clarke, 1920.

Llanyblodwell, England (Parish).
The register of Llanyblodwel ₍1695-1812₎. ₍London, 1913.₎ vi, 179, xxiii p. 22½cm. (Shropshire Parish Register Society. Shropshire parish registers. St. Asaph diocese. v. 3, part 2-3.)
Half-title.
Transcribed by T. R. Horton and W. G. D. Fletcher, collated by R. Leighton; indexes compiled by T. M. Carpendale.

559284. 1. Parish registers—Gt. Br.—Eng.—Llanyblodwell. I. Carpendale, T. M. II. Fletcher, William George Dimock, 1851- . III. Horton, T. R. IV. Leighton, Rachel Frances Marion. V. Ser.
Revised November 28, 1934

NL 0425429 NN

Llanymynech, England (Parish).
The register of Llanymynech ₍1666-1812₎. ₍London, 1922.₎ vii, 207, xxvi p. 22½cm. (Shropshire Parish Register Society. Shropshire parish registers. St. Asaph diocese. v. 8, part 1.)
Half-title.
Transcribed by R. Leighton; the index compiled by B. A. Hughes.

104265A. 1. Parish registers—Gt. Br.—Eng.—Llanymynech. I. Hughes, Beatrice A. II. Leighton, Rachel Frances Marion. III. Ser.
Revised November 28, 1934

NL 0425430 NN

Llanza y Esquibel, Benito de.
Centellas y Moncada. Drama trájico en cinco actos, por el exmo. Sr. D. Benito de Llanza y Esquibel, Hurtado de Mendoza, y Don Manuel Tamayo y Baus. Barcelona, A Freixas, 1850.
104p.
Microcard edition.

NL 0425431 ICRL NN LU

Llaque, J Flavio García
see García Llaque, J Flavio.

Llarena, Joaquin Gomez de
see Gomez de Llarena y Pou, Joaquin, 1891-

Llarena, José María.
La colonia alemana en Chile, Santiago de Chile
see under Aranda, Diego.

Llarena y Pou, Joaquín Gómez de
see
Gómez de Llarena y Pou, Joaquín, 1891-

Llarralde, Joaquin, ed. and tr.
₍Chatauvillard, *comte de*₎
... Codigo del duelo, traducido, arreglado y anotado por Joaquin Llarralde y Anselmo Alfaro ... Mexico, Impr. de I. Paz, 1886.

Llasera, A López
see
López Llasera, A

Llasera Diaz, Emilio
... The family law in Spain, by Emilio Llasera Diaz ... Madrid, Consejo general de los ilustres colegios de abogados de España, 1952.
₍7₎ p. 27½cm.
"IV congreso de la International bar association, Madrid, julio de 1952."

NL 0425438 MH-L

Llata, Jose Antonio Septien y
see
Septien y Llata, Jose Antonio

Llata, Luis de la.
Las Juntas Federales de Mejoras Materiales. México, 1952.
98 p. 23 cm.
Tesis (licenciatura en derecho)—Universidad Nacional Autónoma de México.
Bibliography: p. 97-98.

1. Mexico. Juntas federales de Mejoras Materiales. I. Title.
53-15150

NL 0425440 DLC MiU

Llata, Oscar Seiglie y
see
Seiglie y Llata, Oscar.

Llata, René Capistrán de la
see Capistrán de la Llata, René.

Llatas, Miguel Pompido y
see
Pompido y Llatas, Miguel.

VOLUME 337

Llatas, Rossend, joint author.

Serra i Baldó, Alfons.
... Resum de poetica catalana (mètrica i versificació) per Alfons Serra i Baldó i Rossend Llatas. Barcelona, Editorial Barcino, 1932.

Llatchos, Pedro Llorens y
see
Llorens y Llatchos, Pedro

Llates, Rosendo
see
Llates Serrat, Rosendo.

Llates Serrat, Rosendo.
... Las fiestas populares barcelonesas ... Barcelona, Librería Dalmau, 1944.
2 p. l., [7]-138 p., 2 l. plates, facsim. 18cm. (Colección Barcelona y su historia)
At head of title: R. Llates.

1. Barcelona—Festivals, etc. 2. Barcelona—Soc. life & cust. I. Title.
Library of Congress DP402.B3L5 46-21335
914.67

NL 0425447 DLC OCl CtY CLU

4PQ Span 757 **Llates Serrat, Rosendo**
Llibre de l'humor català; antologia literària i anecdòtica. Pròleg, recopilació i ordenació de Rossend Llates. [1. ed.] Barcelona, Editorial Selecta [1953]
237 p.
(Biblioteca Selecta, 135)

NL 0425448 DLC-P4 NN InU

4PC Cat 137 **Llates Serrat, Rosendo**
Teatre popular: els pastorets. Pròleg i recopilació de Rossend Llates. Herodes, de Jaume Piquet; Pastorells, de Bartomeu Ferrà; Camí d'estels, de Miquel Enrich... [1. ed.] Barcelona, Editorial Selecta [1952]
310 p.
(Biblioteca Selecta, 94)

NL 0425449 DLC-P4 InU NN

Llates Serrat, Rosendo.
Vida de san José Oriol. Barcelona, Editorial Barna [1953]
301 p. illus. 20 cm.

1. Oriol, José, Saint, 1650-1702.
BX4700.O65L6 54-34863 ‡

NL 0425450 DLC

Llauder, Manuel, marquís del Valle de Rivas, 1789-1851.
Cauderno de reglas y advertencias para la instruccion del recluta y prevenciones generales para la de los regimientos de infanteria... Madrid, 1829.

NL 0425451 NNH

F 4054 .484 **LLAUDER, MANUEL, marqués DEL VALLE DE RIVAS, 1789-1851.**
Memorias documentadas del teniente general don Manuel Llauder, marqués del Valle de Rivas, en las que se aclaran sucesos importantes de la historia contemporánea, en que ha tenido parte el autor. Madrid, Boix, 1844.
167, 119p.

NL 0425452 ICN IEN MH

Llauradó, Andrés. ... Canales. Conclusiones formuladas sobre el tema y discurso pronunciado en su apoyo ... Madrid, Impr. de Moreno y Rojas, 1889. 12p. 25cm.
At head of title: Congreso económico nacional de Barcelona.

NL 0425453 CU

Llaurado, Andrés.
... Eaux souterraines. [Paris, 1888]
10 p. 24 cm. [With his Los irrigations. 1887]
Caption title.
At head of title: Association française pour l'avancement des sciences...Congrès d'Oran, 1888.
1. Water, Underground.

NL 0425454 CU

Llaurado, Andres.
—— ... Les irrigations dans les terres arables en Espagne. [Paris, 1887] 8p. 24cm.
At head of title: Association française pour l'avancement des sciences ... Congrès de Toulouse. 1887.

NL 0425455 CU DNAL

Llaurado, Andrés.
Les irrigations in Esponage. 1870.

NL 0425456 DNAL

Llaurado, Andrès.
Projet de lao de recours aux entriprisio de canaus et reserves irrigation 1891.

NL 0425457 DNAL

Llauradó, Andrés.
Proyecto de ley de auxilios á los canales y pantanos de riego y exposición de motivos de la ley, por Don Andrés Llauradó ... (Trabajo encomendado al autor por el Excmo. Sr. Ministro de fomento) Madrid, Imprenta de R. Moreno y R. Rojas, 1890.
58 p., 1 l. 25½cm.
"Obras del mismo autor": l. at end.

1. Irrigation. 2. Irrigation. Legislation.
Agr 7-1290
Library, U. S. Dept. of Agriculture 55L77P

NL 0425458 DNAL

Llaurado, Andres.
—— Las queserías pirenaicas francesas y su importancia en la conservacion de los montes .... Madrid, Impr. de Moreno y Rojas, 1888. 8p. 24cm.

NL 0425459 CU DNAL

Llaurado, Andrés.
Tratado de aguas y riegos 1878.

NL 0425460 DNAL

Llauradó, Andrés.
Tratado de aguas y riegos, por Don Andres Llauradó ... 2. ed. corr. y aumentada. Madrid, Impr. de Moreno y Rojas, 1884.
2 v. illus., tables. 22½cm.
"Obras consultadas": v. 1, p. [547]-553.

1. Irrigation—Spain.
Library of Congress TC805.L7 6-36490

NL 0425461 DLC CU PPC

Llauradó, Emilio Morera y
see
Morera y Llauradó, Emilio, 1847-1918.

Llauradó, José Ferrer-Vidal y
see
Ferrer-Vidal y Llauradó, José.

Llausas, José.
Curso teorico y practico de lengua francesa...
see under Anglada, Francisco.

---

xF3052 M39 v.15 no.6 Llausas i Recasens, Carlos
Utilidad e importancia del estudio de la lejislacion comparada. Memoria presentada por Carlos Llausas i Recasens para optar al grado de licenciado en leyes i ciencias políticas ... Santiago, Impr. Nacional, 1879.
18p. 23cm. (In The Máximo del Campo Yávar Collection of Chileana. Santiago, 1843-1895. v.15)

1. Comparative law. I. Title.

NL 0425465 IaU

Llausas y Mata, José. Barcelona, 1850
Cuaderno de poesias y escritos en prosa....

NL 0425466 NNH OrU

PQ8549 .L39 A4 **Llavaneras Carrillo, Jesus Antonio.**
Alma en flor; poesias. Contiene ademas gran parte de las manifestaciones de duelo recibidas con motivo del fallecimiento del poeta, compiladas por su hermano Claudio Llavaneras C. Trujillo, Impr. Santana 1915.
106p. port.

I. Llavaneras Carrillo, Claudio, comp.
II. Title.

NL 0425467 NcU

VOLUME 337

Llave, David Carpintero de la
see Carpintero de la Llave, David.

Llave, Enrique de Benito y de la.
See
Benito y de la Llave, Enrique de.

869.1 Llave, Fernando de la.
L772m Migajas de sol; poemas. México, Editorial "Grecas," 1926.
[87] p. 16cm.

NL 0425470 IU

F1203 Llave, Fernando de la
T4L533 Tanalhia; [cuento de dos gajos. Chihuahua, 1929]
x [10] l. 24cm. [Terrazas collection]

NL 0425471 CU-B

Lilly
F 1232
.L 79 D62
Mendel
LLAVE, PABLO DE LA, 1773-1833
Discurso patriótico pronunciado en la plazuela principal de la Alameda de Mexico ... el 16 de setiembre de 1828, aniversario del Grito de Dolores. Mexico, Impr. del Aguila, 1828.
1 p.l., 16 p. 20.5 cm.

In wrapper.

1. Grito de Dolores.

NL 0425472 InU

Llave, Pablo de la, 1773-1833.

Mexico. *Ministerio de justicia y negocios eclesiásticos.*
Memoria que el secretario de estado y del despacho universal de justicia y negocios eclesiásticos, presenta al soberano Congreso constituyente sobre los ramos del ministerio de su cargo, leida en la sesion de 8 de noviembre de 1823. Impresa de órden del mismo soberano Congreso. Mexico, Impr. del supremo gobierno, en Palacio [1823?]

Llave, Pablo de la, 1773-1833.

Mexico. *Ministerio de justicia y negocios eclesiásticos.*
Memoria que en cumplimiento del articulo 120. de la constitucion federal de los Estados Unidos Mexicanos. Leyó el secretario de estado y del despacho universal de justicia y negocios eclesiásticos, en la Cámara de senadores el dia 5. y en la de Diputados el 7. de enero de 1825. sobre los ramos del ministerio de su cargo. Mexico, Impr. del supremo gobierno de los Estados Unidos Mexicanos, 1825.

Llave, Pablo de la, 1773-1833.
Novorum vegetabilium descriptiones. In lucem prodeunt opera Paulli de La Llave et Ioannis Lexarza Reip. Mexic. civ. Fasciculus I-II. Mexici, apud M. Riveram, 1824-25.
2 v. 29½cm.

1. Mexico. Botany. I. Lexarza, Juan Martinez de, 1785-1824, joint author.

Agr 11-678

Library, U. S. Dept. of Agriculture 452L15

NL 0425475 DNAL CtY CU DSI MH-A

Llave Uriarte, Arturo de la.
Las sociedades mercantiles extranjeras. [México] 1947.
63 p. 23 cm.
Tesis (licenciatura en derecho)—Univ. Nacional Autónoma de México.
"Bibliografía": p. [61]-63.

1. Corporations, Foreign—Mexico. 2. Aliens—Mexico.

50-15939

NL 0425476 DLC

Llave y Bringas, José María de la, respondent.

Microfilm
AC-2
reel 207,
no. 1
Ximénez de las Cuevas, José Antonio, *praeses.*
Certamen teologico, en que con el favor de Dios Nuestro Señor Trino y Uno, de la purisima e inmaculada Virgen Maria Señora Nuestra, de nuestro angelico maestro santo Tomas, y santos patronos de los estudios Juan Nepomuceno, y Luis Gonzaga, se defenderá públicamente la suma teologica del sol de las escuelas en los reales y pontificios colegios de san Pedro y san Juan de esta ciudad de la Puebla de los Angeles, en el acto que llaman de estatuto: a saber, en el dia veinte de Agosto por el colegial b. d. Joseph Maria de la Llave y Bringas, y en el dia veinte y uno por el colegial b. d. Joseph Mariano Moreno, siendo presidente el br. d. Joseph Antonio Ximenes de las Cuevas ... [Lima] Impreso en la oficina de d. Pedro de la Rosa, con privilegio real. (D. l. d. r.) Año de mil setecientos noventa y ocho.

Llave y García, Joaquín de la, 1853-1915.
Balística de las armas portátiles, por el general de brigada d. Joaquín de la Llave y García ... 6. ed., hecha bajo la dirección de los hijos del autor, d. Joaquín de la Llave y Sierra ... y d. Alfonso de la Llave y Sierra ... Texto y tablas. Toledo, Imprenta, librería y encuadernación de Rafael Gómez-Menor, 1942.
4 p. l., 266, 143 p. incl. port., tables. 21½cm.
"Una adaptación de la Balística abreviada de su autor a las necesidades de la enseñanza en la Academia de infantería."—3d prelim. leaf.
"Obra de texto en la Academia de infantería hasta la supresión de las de este carácter en 1928 al crearse la Academia general militar en Zaragoza."

"Bibliografía": p. [251]-261.
L. C. copy imperfect: p. [3]-[4] following p. 266 wanting.

1. Ballistics. I. Llave y Sierra, Joaquín de la, 1882- ed. II. Llave y Sierra, Alfonso de la, joint ed.

45-26751

Library of Congress UF820.L5 1942

623.54

NL 0425480 DLC NN

Llave y García, Joaquín de la, 1853-1915.
Estudio sobre nuestra artillería de plaza (tanteos de armamento) Por ... Don Joaquín de la Llave y García ... Madrid, Impr. del Memorial de ingenieros, 1892.
171 p. incl. tables. pl. 28cm.

1. Spain—Army—Artillery. 2. Artillery.

24-11960

Library of Congress UF485.S8L6

NL 0425481 DLC

Llave y Garcia, Joaquin de la, 1853-1915.
...Fortificacion de campana op el Coronel ...D. Joaquin de la Llave y Garcia. 3.a ed. Barcelona, Revista cientifico-militar y biblioteca militar, 1904.
vii, 360 p. illus. 22 cm.

NL 0425482 DNW

Llave y García, Joaquín de la, 1853-1915.
Lecciones de artillería explicadas en la Escuela superior de guerra, por D. Joaquin de la Llave y Garcia ... 2. ed., corr. Madrid, Impr. del Cuerpo de artillería, 1896.
2 v. in 1. tables. 24½cm. *and* atlas of 27 pl. fol.
Imperfect: atlas wanting in L. C. copy.

1. Artillery.

18-1317

Library of Congress UF145.L67 1896

NL 0425483 DLC

Llave y Garcia, Joaquin de la, 1853-1915.
Marina de guerra, guerra maritima y defensa de las costas... Madrid, Imp. Memorial de Ingenieros, 1899.
234 p. 4°.

NL 0425484 NN

Llave y García, Joaquín de la, 1853-1915.
Nociones de fortificación permanente por el coronel graduado, comandante de ejército D. Joaquín de la Llave y García ... Barcelona, Revista científico-militar y biblioteca militar, 1887-1888.
viii, 277, [2] p. 18cm. (*Lettered on cover:* Publicaciones de la biblioteca militar)

1. Fortification. I. Title.

17-14907

Library of Congress UG405.L6

NL 0425485 DLC NcD

Llave y García, Joaquín de la, 1853-1915.
... Pizarras (programa detallado) de las lecciones de artillería. Nociones fundamentales de artillería. Material de artillería de las principales potencias militares [por] profesor don Joaquín de la Llave y García ... Madrid, Imprenta del Cuerpo de artillería, 1894.
187 p. incl. tables. 25cm.
At head of title: Escuela superior de guerra. Primer año. Primera clase.

1. Spain. Ejército. Artillería. I. Title.

34-21241

Library of Congress UF87.L5
[a45b1]
358.1

NL 0425486 DLC

Llave y Garcia, Joaquin de la, 1853-1915.
Problemes de balistica aplicades a la fortificacion y a la tactica, por el coronel graduade commandante de ingenieros, Don Joaquin dela Llave y Garcia... Madrid, Imprenta del Memorial de ingenieros, 1896.
ix, 184 p. illus., tables.
25½cm.

NL 0425487 DNW

Llave y García, Joaquín de la, 1853-1915.
...Recuerdos de Bulgaria y Rumania desde el punto de vista económico, por el Excmo. Señor Don Joaquín de la Llave y García ... Conferencia pronunciada en el salón de actos del "Fomento del trabajo nacional" el día 20 de septiembre de 1912. Barcelona: F. Altés y Alabart, 1912. 26 p. 8°. (Soc. de geografía comercial, Barcelona. Publicaciones. núm. 5.)

1. Economic history—Bulgaria. 2. Economic history—Rumania. 3. Series.

December 18, 1924

NL 0425488 NN

VOLUME 337

Llave y García, Joaquín de la, 1853–1915.
El sitio de Barcelona en 1713–1714; estudio histórico, por d. Joaquín de la Llave y García ... Madrid, Imprenta del Memorial de ingenieros del ejército, 1903.
viii, 288 p. illus., fold. pl., plans (part fold.) 28cm.
Bibliographical foot-notes.

1. Barcelona—Siege, 1713–1714. I. Title.
42-30028
Library of Congress D283.B3L5

NL 0425489 DLC TxU CU MH WaPS

Llave y Garcia Joaquin de la, 1853-1915.

R. Sociedad geográfica, *Madrid.*
Velada en memoria del excmo. sr. d. Francisco Coello y Quesada, celebrada en la Sociedad geográfica de Madrid la noche del 29 de noviembre de 1998 [i. e. 1898] Discursos de los sres. d. Manuel de Foronda, d. Joaquín de la Llave, d. Rafael Álvarez Sereix y d. Rafael Torres Campos. Madrid, Estab. tip. de Fortanet, 1898.

Llave y Sierra, Alfonso de la, joint ed.

UF820 .L5 1942
Llave y García, Joaquín de la, 1853–1915.
Balística de las armas portátiles, por el general de brigada d. Joaquín de la Llave y García ... 6. ed., hecha bajo la dirección de los hijos del autor, d. Joaquín de la Llave y Sierra ... y d. Alfonso de la Llave y Sierra ... Texto y tablas. Toledo, Imprenta, librería y encuadernación de Rafael Gómez-Menor, 1942.

Llave y Sierra, Joaquin de la, 1882- ed.

UF820 .L5 1942
Llave y García, Joaquín de la, 1853–1915.
Balística de las armas portátiles, por el general de brigada d. Joaquín de la Llave y García ... 6. ed., hecha bajo la dirección de los hijos del autor, d. Joaquín de la Llave y Sierra ... y d. Alfonso de la Llave y Sierra ... Texto y tablas. Toledo, Imprenta, librería y encuadernación de Rafael Gómez-Menor, 1942.

Llave y Sierra, Joaquín de la, 1882–
Biografía de Carlos Ibáñez e Ibáñez de Ibero, marqués de Mulhacén, escrita para el acto de colocar su retrato en la Galería de Catalanes Ilustres. Barcelona, 1953.
16 p. 22 cm.
At head of title: Ayuntamiento de Barcelona.

1. Ibáñez e Ibáñez de Ibero, Carlos, marqués de Mulhacén, 1825–1891.
QB36.I 2L4 56-40578 ‡

NL 0425493 DLC

LLAVE Y SIERRA, Joaquin DE LA, 1882-
Estudio historico-militar sobre el conde de Barcelona, Ramon Berenguer III "el Grande" Barcelona, Tobella y Costa,1903.
pp.94.

NL 0425494 MH

La llave de la gaveta
see under Larrea, José María, 1828-1863.

... La llave de los tesoros. S. Calleja, editor. [Madrid? 19—?]
15, [1] p. illus. 6½cm. (Juguetes instructivos, Serie XV, t. 287)
Illustrated t.-p.
Colored illustrated paper covers with portrait and brief biography of Zorrilla on back cover.

I. Calleja, S ed. II. Ser.

NL 0425496 ViU

La Llave del Saber, Compañía.

PN593 .L52
FOR OTHER EDITIONS SEE MAIN ENTRY
Literatura universal; un estudio completo, que comprende las literaturas de las naciones, desde la aurora de la civilización hasta el momento actual ... Preparado por eminentes profesores y escritores norteamericanos y sudamericanos. [Elsinore? Calif.] Cía La Llave del Saber [1954]

La Llave del saber; una obra comprensiva y sistemática, conteniendo datos de vital importancia en relación con los problemas diarios que confrontan al niño en la escuela, escrita en lenguaje claro y sencillo ... Preparada por prominentes educadores norteamericanos y puertorriqueños ... Chicago, Nueva York, Americana corporation. [°1935]
9 v. fronts. (part col.) illus. (incl. map) plates (part col.) ports., charts, diagrs. 23½cm.
Vols. [2], [3] and [9] have text in English, with Spanish title lettered on cover and with English t.-p.: The Key to knowledge: a comprehensive and systematic presentation of practical and essential knowledge.
Published in 1931, with text entirely in English, under title: Hayward's key to knowledge.

Includes music.
CONTENTS.—[v. 1] Historia de las naciones.—[v. 2] Government and citizenship.—[v. 3] Maravillas del universo.—[v. 4] La naturaleza.—[v. 5] Story of the world's literature.—[v. 6] El mundo de la belleza y del arte.—[v. 7] Educación higiénica.—[v. 8] Invenciónes y descubrimientos.—[v. 9] Stories, books, plays, biographies.

1. Encyclopedias and dictionaries, Spanish. 2. Encyclopedias and dictionaries. I. Title: The Key to knowledge.
35-11036
Library of Congress AG5.H32

Copyright A 84772 031

NL 0425499 DLC

La Llave del saber; una obra comprensiva y sistemática, conteniendo datos de vital importancia en relación con los problemas diarios que confrontan al niño en la escuela, escrita en lenguaje claro y sencillo ... Preparada por prominentes educadores norteamericanos y sudamericanos. [Caracas] La Llave del saber, cía. [°1938]
7 v. fronts. (part col.) illus., plates (part col.) ports., maps (1 double) diagrs. 24cm.
Includes music.
"Impreso en Estados Unidos de América."
Published in 1931, with English text, under title: Hayward's key to knowledge.

CONTENTS.—[v. 1]–[2] Historia de las naciones.—[v. 3] Maravillas del universo.—[v. 4] La naturaleza.—[v. 5] El mundo de la belleza y del arte.—[v. 6] Educación higiénica.—[v. 7] Invenciónes y descubrimientos.

1. Encyclopedias and dictionaries, Spanish. 2. Encyclopedias and dictionaries.
39-1139
Library of Congress AG5.H33

Copyright A 121909 [036] 031

NL 0425501 DLC LU

La Llave del saber; una obra comprensiva y sistemática, conteniendo información educacional, importante y esencial, escrita en lenguaje ameno, claro y sencillo. Tiene como finalidad estimular la ambición, elevar los ideales y desarrollar normas rectas y saludables de vida. Es indispensable para toda persona interesada en la cultura. Preparada por prominentes educadores norteamericanos y sudamericanos. Ampliamente ilustrada. Caracas, La Llave del saber, cía. [°1939]
7 v. fronts. (2 col.) illus., plates (part col.) ports., diagrs. 24cm.
Printed in the United States.

Published in 1931, with text entirely in English, under title: Hayward's key to knowledge.
Includes music.
CONTENTS.—[v. 1–2] Historia de las naciones.—[v. 3] Maravillas del universo.—[v. 4] La naturaleza.—[v. 5] El mundo de la belleza y del arte.—[v. 6] Educación higiénica.—[v. 7] Invenciónes y descubrimientos.

1. Encyclopedias and dictionaries, Spanish. 2. Encyclopedias and dictionaries. I. Title: The Key to knowledge.
Library of Congress AG5.H33 1939 41-37329

NL 0425503 DLC

La Llave del saber; una obra comprensiva y sistemática, conteniendo información educacional, importante y esencial, escrita en lenguaje ameno, claro y sencillo ... Preparado por eminentes profesores norteamericanos y latinoamericanos. [Elsinore, Calif., Cía La Llave del Saber, °1953]
5 v. illus. (part col.) ports., maps. 24 cm.
Published in 1931, with text entirely in English, under title: Hayward's key to knowledge.
CONTENTS.—[1] Maravillas del universo.—[2] La naturaleza.—[3] El mundo de la belleza y del arte.—[4] Educación higiénica.—[5] Invenciones y descubrimientos.
1. Encyclopedias and dictionaries, Spanish.
AG5.H33 195" [036] 031 54-20081

NL 0425504 DLC

La llave falsa, o sea. Los dos hiyos. Drama en tres actos. Barcelona, Juan Francisco Piferer, 1826.
1-33p. [2-4] 23cm.
— Aqui ahora .... Felipe, cuán-
— gratitud, serán su recompensa.

tr. by Bretón de los Herreros.

NL 0425505 NcU

[LLÁVEN, Magin.]
Controversia suscitada con motivo de los atentados cometidos contra la independencia y soberania del estado de Chiapas. Mexico, 1876.
12 p.

NL 0425506 MH-Z

Llavería, Agustín Sardá y
see
Sardá y Llavería, Agustín, 1836-1913.

Llaverías, Amadeo
see Llaverías y Rovirosa, Amadeo, 1870?-1935.

Llaverías, Federico, 1888–
... La aparición de Nuestra Señora de la Altagracia. La milagrosa batalla del Santo Cerro (tradiciones relijiosas) por Federico Llaverías. (21 de enero de 1928) Santo Domingo, R. D., Imp. de J. R. vda. García, sucs., 1928.
20 p. plates. 22cm.

1. Altagracia, Nuestra Señora de la. 2. Santo Cerro, Dominican republic. I. Title.
[*Full name:* Federico Llaverías y Arredondo]
46-39319
Library of Congress BT660.A4L5

NL 0425509 DLC

Llaverías, Federico, 1888–
Bosquejo histórico de la ciudad de Santo Domingo, de los restos de Colón, i del faro de Colón ... Santo Domingo, R. D., J. R. vda. García, 1925.
58 p. illus. 16cm.

1. Colombo, Cristoforo—Tomb. 2. Santo Domingo—Hist. 3. Santo Domingo. Columbus memorial lighthouse.
41-25198
Brief cataloging
Library of Congress E112.L75

NL 0425510 DLC IU

VOLUME 337

420 Llaverias, Federico, 1888-
El Canal de Panama y la república dominicana, por F. Llaverias... Santo Domingo, 1914.

NL 0425511 DPU

F813 .LL Llaverías, Federico, 1888-
Christopher Columbus; the discovery of his remains in Santo Domingo. 4th ed. [Havana, P. Fernandez] 1939.
24 p. illus. 24 x 11 cm.

1. Colombo, Cristoforo - Tomb. I. Title.

NL 0425512 WHi NN

Llaverías, Federico, 1888-
...La ciudad de Santo Domingo i sus monumentos coloniales... Santo Domingo, Garcia, 1927.
55 p. plates. 20½ cm.

At head of title: Republica dominicana..Secretaría de e.de fomento i comunicaciones.
"Opúsculo conmemorativo de la Exposición nacional de Santiago i del día consagrado a la provincia de Santo Domingo: 28 de mayo de 1927."

1.Santo Domingo-Historic houses,etc. Santo Domingo-Churches.

NL 0425514 NjP

PC .L57 Llaverias, Federico, 1888-
Compendio de ortografía y prosodia del idioma castellano, por Federico Llaverias. Santo Domingo, Imp. "El independiente", 1928.
5 p.l., [3]-56 p. 22 cm.

NL 0425515 DPU

Llaverías, Federico, 1888-
Contribución al progreso cívico de la ciudad de Santo Domingo. Santo Domingo [Imp.El Independiente] 1930.

NL 0425516 MH

Llaverias, Federico, 1888-
Cristóbal Colón; el hallazgo de sus restos en Santo Domingo, por el ldo. Federico Llaverias... Cuarta edicion. [Habana: Impresores P. Fernandez y cia.] 1939. 25 p. incl. diagr. illus. (incl. facsims.) 23½cm.

"Aprobado...por la Junta colombina de Santo Domingo."

1. Columbus, Christopher—Tomb.

April 19, 1940

NL 0425517 NN DPU

Llaverías, Federico, 1888- ed.
... Convicción y justicia (recopilación de impresiones que reflejan la elevada y sincera conciencia de Puerto Rico) San Juan, P. R. [Impreso por la Casa Baldrich] 1935.
1 p. l., 7-40 p., 1 l. port. 23½cm.

Articles and interviews of several prominent Puerto Ricans on their impressions of the Dominican republic. cf. p. 7.

1. Dominican republic. I. Title.

42-11463

Library of Congress F1931.L75

NL 0425518 DLC

Pam 972.93 (921) Trujillo-l Llaverías, Federico, 1888-
"El día del benefactor de la patria" discurso pronunciado por el Lic. Federico Llaverías, en el acto celebrado el día 14 de enero de 1945 en el "Teatro Julia" de Ciudad Trujillo." Santiago, República Dominicana, El Diario [1945]
15p. 23 cm.
1. Trujillo Molina, Rafael Leónidas, pres. Dominican republic, 1891-1961.

NL 0425519 LNHT

Llaverias,Federico,1888-
... ¿Es el estado responsable de las pérdidas i los perjuicios sufridos por los extranjeros en tiempos de perturbaciones interiores ó guerras civiles? ... Santo Domingo, Tipografía Listin diario [1917?]
56 p.,1 l. 22½cm.
Tesis - Universidad central de Santo Domingo. Facultad de derecho i ciencias politicas.
Año académico de 1915-1916,núm.3.

"Bibliografía": p.[2]
No.[5] in: Santo Domingo. Universidad. Facultad de derecho. Tesis. 1912-1917.

NL 0425521 MiU-L

Llaverías, Federico, 1888-
Una forma de ceremonial diplomatico (adaptable a la Republica Dominicana) por Federico Llaverias ... Santo Domingo, Imp. Escobar y cia, 1912.
91 p. 25cm.

1. Dominican Republic—Diplomatic and consular service. I. Title

28-7826

Library of Congress JX1752.L5

NL 0425522 DLC

Llaverías, Federico, 1888-
Manual de derecho consular dominicano, por Federico Llaverías ... Santo Domingo, R. D., Impr. de J. R. vda. García, 1925.
138 p. incl. port. 23cm.

1. Consular law. 2. Dominican republic—Diplomatic and consular service. I. Title.

26-23604

NL 0425523 DLC ICU

3146 Llaverias, Federico.
Mi labor pro faro de Colon en Washington, D.C. Santo Domingo, Imprenta Nuevo Diario, 1926.

NL 0425524 DPU

KF 4023 Llaverias, Federico, 1888-
Ofrenda votiva. n.p. [193-]

NL 0425525 MH

Llaverías, Federico, 1888-
... Por España y por su lengua, por el lic. Federico Llaverías ... Ciudad Trujillo, R. D., Imp. J. R. vda. García, sucs., 1941.
184 p. 23cm. (Academia dominicana de la lengua. Publicación núm. 4)

1. Spanish language—Addresses, essays, lectures. 2. Spanish language—Provincialisms—Dominican republic. I. Title.

[Full name: Federico Llaverías y Arredondo]

45-25546

Library of Congress PC4027.L5

460.4

NL 0425526 DLC NNC

F1203 T4L535 x Llaverías, Federico, 1888-
El Primer Congreso Panamericano de Periodistas (impresiones) Con un Apéndice relativo a la República Dominicana. Santo Domingo, Impr. Montalvo, 1927.
130 p. illus.(1 fold.) ports. 22cm. [Terrazas collection]

1. Pan American Congress of Journalists. 1st, Washington, D.C., 1926. 2. Journalism - Congresses. 3. Journalism - Hispanic America. 4. Dominican Republic. I. Title.

NL 0425527 CU-B DPU

Llaverías, Federico, 1888- ed.
La primera misa en América, por el lic. Federico Llaverías ... Trujillo, R. D., Imprenta J. R. vda. García, sucs., 1936.
28 p. 24½cm.

CONTENTS.—¿Fué en Puerto Rico donde se dijo la primera misa en América? Por monseñor Edwin V. Byrne.—Una carta del cónsul dominicano, Federico Llaverías, al obispo Byrne.—El obispo Byrne le contesta al cónsul dominicano.—Otra carta del cónsul Llaverías para el obispo Byrne.—Una lanza por Santo Domingo, por el dr. Víctor Coll y Cuchí.—[Dos cartas a la Academía de la historia]—Conferencia del dr. Víctor Coll y Cuchí en el Ateneo.

1. Haiti—Hist.—To 1791. 2. Catholic church in the West Indies. I. Title.

42-11972

Library of Congress F1911.L6

NL 0425528 DLC TxU ICU

LE 15 .C42 L7 Llaverías,Federico,1888-
La universidad de Santo Domingo y su ciudad universitaria. Asunción,Paraguay, Editorial El País, 1950.
46 p. port. 20 cm.
Cover title.
Talk before the Unión Club in Asunción.

1.Ciudad Trujillo. Universidad de Santo Domingo.

NL 0425529 MiU MH NNC NIC

Llaverías, Federico, 1888-
... Vicios de la dicción castellana, por el lic. Federico Llaverías ... Santo Domingo, R. D., Imprenta de J. R. viuda García, sucesores, 1933.
177 p. port. 25cm. (Academia dominicana de la lengua. (Publicación núm, 1))

1. Spanish language—Idioms, corrections, errors. 2. Spanish language—Glossaries, vocabularies, etc. I. Title.

42-14873

Library of Congress PC4460.L55

NL 0425530 DLC CU FU

VOLUME 337

Llaverías, Federico, 1888–
... Vicios de la dicción castellana, por el lic. Federico Llaverías ... 2. ed., publicada por la Academia dominicana de la lengua (correspondiente de la española). Ciudad Trujillo, República dominicana, Imprenta "Listín diario," 1940.
cover-title, 177 p. 24cm. (Academia dominicana de la lengua. (Publicación núm. 1))

1. Spanish language—Idioms, corrections, errors. 2. Spanish language—Glossaries, vocabularies, etc. I. Title.
43-29056
Library of Congress PC4460.L55 1940
468.3

NL 0425531 DLC OrU NcU LU NN TxU ViU MH

Llaverías, Joaquín
see
Llaverías y Martínez, Joaquín, 1875–1956.

Llaverías Arredondo, Federico
see
Llaverías, Federico, 1888–

Llaverías y Arredondo, Federico
see
Llaverías, Federico, 1888–

Llaverías y Martínez, Joaquín, 1875– *ed.*
... Actas de las asambleas de representantes y del Consejo de gobierno durante la guerra de independencia ... Recopilación e introducción por Joaquín Llaverías y Emeterio S. Santovenia ... La Habana, Imprenta "El Siglo xx", A. Muñiz y hno, 1928–
v. 28cm. (Academia de la historia de Cuba. Colección de documentos. vol. I–
Vol. 1 has imprint: La Habana. Impr. y papelería de Rambla, Bouza y ca., 1928.
1. Cuba—Pol. & govt.—1895–1899. I. Cuba. Asamblea constituyente (Jimaguayú, 1895) II. Cuba. Consejo de gobierno. III. Cuba. Asamblea de representantes de la revolución cubana. IV. Santovenia y Echaide, Emeterio S., 1889– joint ed. V. Title.
34-8768
Library of Congress F1751.A162 vol. 1–
F1786.L79
(972.910082) 972.91

NL 0425535 DLC MH NcU IaU MB NcD FMU OkU NN

Llaverías y Martínez, Joaquín, 1875–
Biografía del Archivo Nacional de Cuba; conferencia leída en la Universidad de la Habana el día 26 de noviembre de 1954. [1. ed.] Habana, 1954.
59 p. port. 27 cm. (Publicaciones del Archivo Nacional de Cuba, 39)

1. Cuba. Archivo Nacional. I. Title.
CD3903.L5 55-57107

MoU KU
NL 0425536 DLC LU NcU MH-L ViU OCI NcD TxU FU NIC

F1783
.M365
Llaverías y Martínez, Joaquín, 1875– ed.

Martí, José, 1853–1895.
Cartas inéditas de Martí, anotadas por Joaquín Llaverías ... Habana, Impr. "El Siglo xx," 1920.

CD3907
.L4
1944
Llaverías y Martínez, Joaquín, 1875–

Cuba. *Archivo nacional.*
... Catálogo de los fondos del Liceo artístico y literario de la Habana; prefacio del capitán Joaquín Llaverías ... La Habana [Talleres del Archivo nacional de Cuba] 1944.

Z6028
.C94
Llaverías y Martínez, Joaquín, 1875–

Cuba. *Archivo Nacional.*
Catálogo de los mapas, planos, croquis y árboles genealógicos existentes en el Archivo Nacional de Cuba. Prefacio del capitán Joaquín Llaverías y Martínez. [1. ed.] Habana, 1951–

Llaverías y Martínez, Joaquín, 1875– ed.

Figarola-Caneda, Domingo, 1852–1926, *ed.*
... Centón epistolario de Domingo del Monte, con un prefacio, anotaciones y una tabla alfabética por Domingo Figarola-Caneda ... Habana, Imprenta "El Siglo xx," 1923–57.

Llaverías y Martínez, Joaquín, 1875–
... La Comisión militar ejecutiva y permanente de la Isla de Cuba; discurso leído por el académico de número capitán Joaquín Llaverías, en la sesión solemne celebrada el 10 de octubre de 1929. La Habana, Imprenta "El Siglo xx", A. Muñiz y hno., 1929.
194 p., 1 l. col. front. 28cm.
At head of title: Academia de la historia de Cuba.

1. Spain. Comisión militar ejecutiva y permanente de la Isla de Cuba. 2. Cuba—Pol. & govt.—1810–1899. I. Academia de la historia de Cuba, Havana.
30-18822
Library of Congress F1783.L81

NL 0425541 DLC MH MB NN IaU NcD ICU CtY DSI

Llaverías y Martínez, Joaquín, 1875–
... El Consejo administrativo de bienes embargados; discurso leído por el académico de número, capitán Joaquín Llaverías, en la sesión solemne celebrada el 10 de octubre de 1941. La Habana, Imprenta "El Siglo xx," A. Muñiz y hno., 1941.
42 p., 1 l. 24½cm.
At head of title: Academia de la historia de Cuba.

1. Cuba. Consejo administrativo de bienes embargados. 2. Cuba—Hist.—Insurrection, 1868–1878. I. Academia de la historia de Cuba, Havana.
42-19154
Library of Congress F1785.L53
972.91

NL 0425542 DLC FMU NIC IU NcD NcU DPU NjP MH

JL1003
1925
.S3
Llaverías y Martínez, Joaquín, 1875–

Santovenia y Echaide, Emeterio Santiago, 1889–
... Las constituciones cubanas de Guaimaro (1869), Jimaguayu (1895) y La Yaya (1897). Discursos pronunciados en la sesión celebrada por el Club rotario de la Habana, el día 10 de octubre de 1925, en honor de los supervivientes de las asambleas que redactaron dichas constituciones, prologo del dr. Fernando Ortiz. Habana, Imp. "La Universal," 1926.

Llaverías y Martínez, Joaquín, 1875– ed.

Márquez, José de Jesús, 1837–1902.
Diccionario geográfico de la isla de Cuba, por Jose de J. Marquez (1875) Publícalo, arreglado, anotado y con una introducción Joaquin Llaverias ... Habana, Imp. Perez, Sierra y co., 1926.

Llaverías y Martinez, Joaquin, 1875–
Discurso en contestación.
(*In* Academia de la historia. Havana. Discursos leidos en la recepción pública . . . 11 de junio de 1926. Pp. 183–207. Habana. 1926.)
Refers to Un precursor de la independencia de Cuba: Don José Álvarez de Toledo, by Carlos M. Trelles y Govin.
Bibliografía del Señor Carlos Manuel Trelles y Govin de 1920 a 1926, pp. 188–190.

D5008 — Trelles y Govin, Carlos M., 1866–. — Álvarez de Toledo, José, 1779–1858.

NL 0425545 MB

Llaverías y Martínez, Joaquín, 1875–
... Discursos leídos en la recepción pública del señor capitán Joaquín Llaverías y Martínez ... la noche del 14 de junio de 1923. Contesta en nombre de la corporación el dr. Francisco de Paula Coronado. Habana, Imprenta "El Siglo xx," 1923.
99, [1] p. plates, ports., facsims. 28½cm.
Half-title: Facciolo y "La Voz del pueblo cubano."
At head of title: Academia de la historia.

1. Facciolo, Eduardo, 1829–1852. 2. La Voz del pueblo cubano. I. Coronado y Alvarado, Francisco de Paula, 1870– II. Academia de la historia de Cuba. Havana.
24—1240
Library of Congress F1784.L79

NL 0425546 DLC MB CtY DPU NcD

Llaverías y Martínez, Joaquín, 1875–1956.

Trelles y Govín, Carlos Manuel, 1866–
... Discursos leídos en la recepción pública del Sr. Carlos M. Trelles y Govín, la noche del 11 de junio de 1926. Contesta en nombre de la corporación el capitán Sr. Joaquín Llaverías ... Habana, Imprenta "El Siglo xx", 1926.

Llaverías y Martínez, Joaquín, 1875–
FOR OTHER EDITIONS SEE MAIN ENTRY

Quesada y Miranda, Gonzalo de, 1900–
... Discursos leídos en la recepción pública del sr. Gonzalo de Quesada y Miranda, la noche del 7 de septiembre de 1939. Contesta en nombre de la corporación el sr. Joaquín Llaverías y Martínez ... La Habana, Imprenta "El Siglo xx," A. Muñiz y hno., 1939.

Llaverías y Martínez, Joaquín, 1875–
. . . Elogio del lcdo. Roque E. Garrigó y Salido, académico de número. Leído por Joaquin Llaverias y Martinez . . . en la sesión solemne celebrada en la noche del 17 de diciembre de 1938. La Habana: Imp. "El Siglo XX", 1938. 40 p. front. (port.) 24½cm.
At head of title: Academia de la historia de Cuba.

1. Garrigó Salido, Roque Eugenio, 1876– I. Academia de la historia de Cuba, Havana.
July 29, 1940

DPU IU MiU
NL 0425549 NN NcD ICU CU-B NjP ICJ ICarbS LU NNC

Llaverías y Martínez, Joaquín, 1875–
Elogio del Dr. Benigno Souza y Rodríguez, académico de número, leído en la sesión solemne celebrada el 21 junio de 1955. Habana, Impr. "El Siglo xx," 1955.
21 p. illus. 24 cm.
At head of title: Academia de la Historia de Cuba.

1. Souza, Benigno, 1873–1954.
R476.S6L55 58-16723 ‡

NL 0425550 DLC IU NcD CSt MH CU-B DPU NNC ICU

VOLUME 337

Llaverías y Martínez, Joaquín, 1875– 1956.
... Elogio del dr. Domingo Méndez Capote ... leído por el capitán Joaquín Llaverías ... en la sesión solemne celebrada en la noche del 16 de junio de 1935. La Habana, Imprenta "El Siglo xx", A. Muñiz y hno., 1935.
50, [2] p. front. (port.) 28½cm.
At head of title: Academia de la historia de Cuba.

1. Méndez Capote, Domingo, 1863–1934. I. Academia de la historia de Cuba, Havana.

Library of Congress F1787.M48 40-37413 923.27291

NL 0425551 DLC

Llaverías y Martínez, Joaquín.
... Elogio del sr. Pedro Mendoza Guerra, individuo de número, leído por el sr. Joaquín Llaverías y Martínez, individuo de número, en la sesión solemne celebrada en la noche del 1.° de diciembre de 1923. Habana, Imprenta "El Siglo xx", 1923.
26 p., 1 l. port. 28½cm.
At head of title: Academia de la historia.

1. Mendoza Guerra, Pedro, 1862–1920. I. Academia de la historia de Cuba, Havana.

Library of Congress F1787.M484 25-15937

NL 0425552 DLC DPU NcD NN

Llaverías y Martínez, Joaquín, 1875 –
Facciolo y "La voz del pueblo cubano." Discurso.
(*In* Academia de la historia, Havana. Discursos leídos en la recepción pública . . . 14 de junio de 1923. Pp. 5-62. Portraits. Plates. Facsimiles. Havana. 1923.)

M6793 — Facciolo y Alba, Eduardo, 1829-1852. — Cuba. Pol. hist.

NL 0425553 MB

Llaverías y Martínez, Joaquín, 1875–
Historia de los archivos de Cuba, por Joaquín Llaverías ... Prólogo de F. de P. Coronado ... Habana, Imp. de Ruiz y comp. (s. en c.) 1912.
xxiv, 382 p., 1 l. illus., fold. plan. 27cm.

1. Archives—Cuba.

Library of Congress CD3901.L6 12-22927

NL 0425554 DLC ICarbS CU CtY ICJ NN MH

Llaverías y Martínez, Joaquín, 1875–
Historia de los archivos de Cuba. Prólogo de la 1. ed. por F. de P. Coronado. Pref. de la 2. ed. por Emeterio S. Santovenia. 2. ed. Habana, 1949.
xx, 429 p. illus., ports. 27 cm. (Publicaciones del Archivo Nacional de Cuba, 24)

1. Archives—Cuba. (Series: Cuba. Archivo Nacional. Publicaciones, 24)

CD3901.L6 1949 972.91 50-23779

TxU MH ICU
NL 0425555 DLC OKentU CU-S MoU PU NcD CLU CU NcU

L972.91
L791hY
F29
Llaverías y Martínez, Joaquín.
History of the archives at Cuba. [New Orleans, 1938]
3 l., 20 numb. l. 28cm.

Typewritten.
"Translated - December 1938, Federal writers project." Portions of chapters 2-4, 6, 12, 15-16 only.
Spanish edition: Historia de los archivos de Cuba. Habana, Imp. "La Universal" de Ruiz y comp. (S. en C.), 1912.

NL 0425556 LNHT

Llaverías y Martínez, Joaquín, 1875–
... Martí en el Archivo nacional; discurso leído por el académico de número, capitán Joaquín Llaverías, en la sesión solemne celebrada el 27 de enero de 1945. La Habana, Imprenta "El Siglo xx," A. Muñiz y hno., 1945.
58 p., 1 l. 24½cm.
At head of title: Academia de la historia de Cuba.

1. *Martí, José, 1853–1895. I. Academia de la historia de Cuba, Havana.

New York. Public library for Library of Congress F1783.M38L55 A 45-5525
† 928.6

NL 0425557 NN IU IEN TxU DPU NNC CtY MB DLC PU OkU

Cuba
F1755
.A35
v. 2
Llaverías y Martínez, Joaquín, 1875-
Miguel Aldama, o la dignidad patriótica por Joaquín Llaverías.
(In Havana (city) Historiador. Habaneros ilustres. 1ª series, tomo ii, p. [7]-66)

NL 0425558 DPU

Llaverías y Martínez, Joaquín, 1875–
... Miguel Aldama, o la dignidad patriótica ... La Habana, Imprenta Molina y cía., 1937.
64 p. 23½cm.
At head of title: Joaquín Llaverías.
"Conferencia leída el 23 de diciembre de 1937, en el Palacio municipal, correspondiente a la serie sobre Habaneros ilustres, y publicada en el número 11 de los Cuadernos de historia habanera."

1. Aldama, Miguel de, 1820–1888. 2. Cuba—Hist.—Insurrection, 1868–1878. I. Title.

Library of Congress F1785.A365 39-5655 923.37291

NL 0425559 DLC NN DPU

Llaverías y Martinez, Joaquin, 1875-ed.
...Papeles existentes en el Archivo general de Indias relativos a Cuba y muy particularmente a la Habana (Donativo Néstor Carbonell)... [1512-1586] La Habana, Impr. "El siglo XX", 1931.
2v. 27cm. (Academia de la historia de Cuba. Colección de documentos, v.7-8)
1. Cuba---Hist.---to 1810---Sources. 2. Havana ---Hist.---Sources. I. Spain. Archivo general de Indias, Sevillo. II. Ser.: Academia de la historia de Cuba, Havana. Colección de docs., v.7-8.

NL 0425560 LNHT MB

Llaverías y Martínez, Joaquín, 1875–
Los periódicos de Martí, por Joaquín Llaverías ... con una carta de los doctores Francisco de Paula Coronado y Emeterio S. Santovenia ... La Habana, Imp. Pèrez, Sierra y comp., 1929.
131, [1] p. front. (port.) illus. (incl. facsims.) 27cm.

1. Martí, José Julián, 1853–1895. 2. Cuban periodicals. I. Title.

Library of Congress PQ7389.M2Z72 30-22702

NL 0425561 DLC OCU NcU OCl PU-M NN FMU

F1751
.A1655
Llaverías y Martínez, Joaquín, 1875–
Cosculluela y Barreras, Juan Antonio.
... La vida de la Academia de la historia (1928–1929) memoria leída por el secretario ing. Juan Antonio Cosculluela. Informes presentados por los señores capitán d. Joaquín Llaverías ... d. Carlos M. Trellas ... dr. José A. Rodríguez García ... dr. Emeterio S. Santovenia ... y Concurso a premio del año de 1929. La Habana, Imprenta "El Siglo xx," 1929.

Llaverías y Rovirosa, Amadeo, 1870?-1935.

Barcelona. Gimnasio Colón. *Biblioteca.*
Catálogo de la biblioteca del Gimnasio Colón, formada por Amadeo Llaverías y Rovirosa ... Barcelona, Librería anticuaria de Antonio Palau y Dulcet [1935]

Llavero, Francisco, 1909-
Thromboendangiitis obliterans des gehirns, neurologisch-psychiatrische syndrome. Basel, Schwabe, 1948.
248 p. illus., fold. plate.

"Bibliographie": p. 237-248.

1. Thrombo-angiitis obliterans. 2. Brain - Diseases.

NL 0425564 NNC-M CtY IU-M DNLM ICJ

Llavero, Francisco, 1909–
Symptom und Kausalität, Grundfragen der Neurologie und Psychiatrie. Mit einem Geleitwort von H. Pette Stuttgart, G. Thieme, 1953.
251 p. illus. 25 cm.

1. Nervous system—Diseases. 2. Psychiatry. 3. Semiology. I. Title.

RC341.L65 616.8 53-26115 ‡

NL 0425565 DLC ICU ICJ DNLM CU-M

Llawlyfr Cymry Llundain. The London Welsh year book. 19

Llundain, 19 12°.
v. illus.

Text in Welsh and English.
Editors: 19 G. W. Jones and E. B. Davies.

1. Welsh in Gt. Br.: England: London. 2. London.—Directories.
June 12, 1923.

NL 0425566 NN DLC

Bonaparte
Collection
No.7879
LLAWLYFR o weddiau beunyddiol i'r sawl sydd yn cael eu mawr attal gan ddyledswyddau eu galwedigaeth... Llundain, H.Hughes a Butler [n.d.]
63p. 11½cm.

NL 0425567 ICN

Llawysgrif Hendregadredd
Llawysgrif Hendregadredd. Copiwyd gan Rhiannon Morris-Jones. Golygwyd gan John Morris-Jones a T.H.Parry-Williams. Caerdydd, Gwasg Prifysgol Cymru, 1933.
xiv, 366 p.

Copy of manuscript of early Welsh poetry from the library of the late John Ignatius Williams of Hendregadredd.

NL 0425568 MH CU ICN CtY

PC3937
.L79
1897
Llealtat catalana purificada d'envejoses calumnies. Traducció y arreglo per un redactor de la Veu de Catalunya. Barcelona, Estampa "La Catalana", 1897.
112 p. (Biblioteca de la Veu de Catalunya)
Translation, by N. F. y S., of Spanish original: Lealtad cathalana purificada de invidiosas calumnias. Villafranca, 1714.

1. Spain--Hist.--Charles II, 1665-1700.

NL 0425569 ICU MH

VOLUME 337

Llebrés y Moportér, Juan.
Memoria instructiva sobre el estado actual de la isla de Mallorca. Madrid, la viuda de Ibarra, hijos y compañia, 1787.
sm. 4°. pp. (6), 58.

Majorca||

NL 0425570 MH

Llebrez, Juan L Fernández-
see
Fernández-Llebrez, Juan L

Llech-Walter, René, comp.
Regards sur la littérature catalane. [n.p.] Editions du G.R.E.C. [i.e., Grup Rossellonès d'Estudis Catalans, 1952?]

44 p. illus.
Introd.in French,p.1-18; poems in Catalan and French, p.19-44

1. Catalan literature. 2. Catalan poetry - Coll. I. Title. X ref.: Walter, René Llech- (See Llech-Walter, René)

NL 0425572 MH

[Lledias, Felipe]
Lima libre. Cancion patriotica. [Lima, Impr. de Rio, 182-?]
[4] p. 20.5 cm.
Caption title.
Signed: F. LL. [i.e. Felipe Lledias]

NL 0425573 CtY

Lledo, Eduardo de Arevalo y
see Arevalo y Lledo, Eduardo de.

Lledo, José.
El sufragio en Europa y en América. Apuntes de legislacion comparada. Madrid, Los Hijos de J.A. Garcia, 1883.
108 p. 16°.
I. Moya, Luis de.

NL 0425575 NN

Lledo, Jose Bores y
see Bores y Lledó, José.

Lledo, Jose Espana
see Espana Lledo, Jose.

Lledó, Manuel García
see García Lledó, Manuel.

Lledó, Pablo García
see García Lledó, Pablo.

Lledó Martín, José
... La participación de los trabajadores en los beneficios de las empresas. Madrid ⌊Ministerio de trabajo, Instituto nacional de previsión⌋ 1949.
394 p., 1 l. 21½cm.
"Premio Marvá 1947."
Bibliography: p. 343-363.

NL 0425580 MH-L

Lledó Martín, José.
... La pesca nacional ... Madrid, Ediciones Pegaso ⌊1943⌋
3 p. l., ⌊9⌋-488 p., 1 l. pl. 22½cm.
"Premio Marvá 1941."

1. Fisheries—Spain. 2. Fishery products. I. Title.
44-27977
Library of Congress HD9465.S72L5
338.372

NL 0425581 DLC

Lledós, Juan Antonio Lanzón
see
Lanzón Lledós, Juan Antonio.

Lleferydd yr asyn
see under [Jones, Robert] 1745-1829.

Pamphlet
Mexico
1820
L77

Llegadita al escrupuloso. Ha señor escrupuloso! Ya conocemos á Vd., y el noble Ayuntamiento à quien Vd. ha denigrado, lo conoce á pesar que Vd. disfrace sus iniciales. Amigo, lei su papel suversivo, injurioso e incendiario ... [Puebla,1820]
Caption and part of text used as title.

NL 0425584 CtY

Llegar a tiempo. Comedia original en prosa, en tres actos. ⌊Madrid?, n.d.⌋
⌊1⌋-28p. ⌊A-D⌋ 23cm.

- Aleanas de Billey
mas lo que vale, llegar á tiempo.

NL 0425585 NcU

La llegenda del llibreter assassí de Barcelona, per R. Miquel y Planas. Barcelona ⌊Prempses de la Casa Miquel-Rius⌋ 1928.
xxvii, 281 p. incl. col. front., col. illus. 14½cm. ⌊Colecció "Amor del llibre." 2⌋
"Tiratge de 500 exemplars en paper guarro y 25 en paper japonès, tots numerats. n.° 9."
The editor inclines to the theory that the first edition of the Llegenda, in French, was the work of Charles Nodier. cf. p. 217.
This volume contains the following versions: the first edition, which appeared anonymously in the Gazette des tribunaux, Paris, Oct. 23, 1836, under the title La bibliomane; ou, Le nouveau Cardillac; a Catalan version, based largely upon the aforementioned and edited by Miquel y Planas; and Flaubert's Bibliomanie.
1. Bibliomania. I. *Nodier, Charles, 1780-1844, supposed author. II. Miquel y Planas, Ramón, 1874- ed. III. Flaubert, Gustave, 1821-1880. Bibliomanie.
Library of Congress Z992.L75 41-25683

NL 0425586 DLC

Llegendari catalá: Historia de la filla del Rey de Ongría.- Historia de la Emperadriu d'Alemanya, falsament acusada d'adulteri.- Mirable aventura del cavaller Sperciue. Segons manuscrits & cróniques dels segels XIV, XV & XVI. 56 p. Barcelona,Estampa de F. X.Altés,1902.

250 copies printed.

NL 0425587 OCl CU MH

PC3937
.L8
1911

Llegendes rimades de la Biblia de Sevilla, ab notes y glosari de E. Moliné y Brasés. Barcelona ⌊Impr. de la Casa provincial de caritat⌋ 1911.
63 p.
"Extret del n.39 del Boletín de la R. Academia de Buenas Letras de Barcelona."
100 copies printed. Num.24.
Anonymous legends contained on folios CXCI-CC of the rimed Bible attributed to Romeu Sa Bruguera in the Biblioteca Colombina, Seville.
1. Legends, Jewish. 2. Catalan language--Texts.

NL 0425588 ICU

Lleget, Mario
see
Lleget Colomer, Mario.

VM981
.R47

Lleget Colomer, Mario, joint author.

Ribera Jordá, Antonio, 1920-
La conquista de las profundidades ⌊por⌋ Antonio Ribera Jordá, con la colaboración de Mario Lleget Colomer. Barcelona, Editorial Hispano-Europea, 1955.

Lleida, Spain
see Lerida, Spain.

LLÊN CYMRU. Cyfrol 1, rhif 2-date; Gorf. 1950-date. [Caerdydd] Gwasg Prifysgol Cymru. v. 24cm.

Semiannual.
At head of title: Bwrdd gwybodau celtaidd Prifysgol Cymru.

1. Welsh language—Texts and translations. I. Wales. University. Board of Celtic studies.

NL 0425591 NN KU MH

Llenas (Alejandro). * Contribution à l'histoire des maladies de Saint-Domingue. 46 pp. 4°. *Paris, 1874*

NL 0425592 DNLM

Llenas, Alejandro.
Les tombes de Colomb, par le Dr Alejandro Llenas .. Nantes, Mme Ve C. Mellinet, impr.; L. Mellinet et cie, succrs 1892.
cover-title, 24 p. 2 double pl. 23cm.

1. Colombo, Cristoforo—Tomb.

Library of Congress E112.L79 4-37277

NL 0425593 DLC

VOLUME 337

Llenas, José M. a Vidal
see Vidal Llenas, Jose M. a.

W 4 LLENAS DIAZ, José Omar
S23 Algunas consideraciones sobre placenta
1945 previa. ₍Ciudad Trujillo, 1945₎
54 l. (Santo Domingo. Universidad. Facultad de Medicina. Tesis, 1944-1945, núm. 1)
Typewritten copy.
Contains author's signature.
1. Placenta previa

NL 0425595 DNLM

QK Llenas y Fernández, Manel.
590 Ensaig d'una flora liquénica de Catalunya.
S7 ₍Barcelona, Institució Catalana d'Historia
L79 Natural?₎ 1908.
39 p. 22 cm.

Caption title.

1. Lichens - Spain - Catalonia.
I. Title.

NL 0425596 NIC

La LLENGUA catalana a l'ajuntament de Barcelona; debat consistorial de 22 de febrer de 1916. Antecedents i consequencies. Barcelona, [Guinart i Pujolar], 1916.

pp.79.

NL 0425597 MH

Y Llenor; cylchgrawn chwarterol dan nawdd cymdeithasau Cymraeg y colegau cenedlaethol...
Cyfrol 1-

Caerdydd: Y Cwmni cyhoeddi addysgol ₍etc., etc.₎ 1922-
v. 25½cm.

Editor : 1922- W. J. Gruffydd.
Cyfrol 2, rhif 4- have imprint: Wrecsam: Hughes a'i fab.
Includes book reviews.

1. Periodicals—Gt. Br.—Wales. I. Gruffydd, William John, 1881- ed.
July 18, 1938

NL 0425598 NN ICN IU

Y Llenor, Caerdydd
Cyfrol goffa William John Gruffydd; yn cynnwys atgofion ac ysgrifau gan nifer o'i cyfeillion. Caerdydd, Hughes, 1955

92 p. port.

NL 0425599 MH

Llensa de Gelcen, S
Consideracions sobre la flora i la vegetació dels encontorns d'Igualada; discurs reglamentari pronunciat el 15 de juny del 1955 en el VIII Ple del Centre d'Estudis Comarcals d'Igualada. Igualada, 1955.
36 p. illus. 23 cm.

1. Botany—Spain—Igualada. 2. Plant communities.

QK329.L55 59-47256 ‡

NL 0425600 DLC

Lleó, Antonio
see Lleó Silvestre, Antonio.

Lleó, Manuel Urrutia
see Urrutia Lleó, Manuel.

Lleó, Vicente
see
Lleó y Balbastre, Vicente, 1870-1922.

Lleó de la Viña, A
Puentes en arco con tablero suspendido por péndolas oblicuas. Madrid, Instituto Técnico de la Construcción ₍1948₎
35 p. illus. 28 cm. (Consejo Superior de Investigaciones Científicas. Instituto Técnico de la Construcción. Publicaciones, no. 66)

1. Arches. 2. Bridges, Suspension. 3. Bridges, Concrete. I. Title. (Series: Spain. Consejo Superior de Investigaciones Científicas. Instituto Técnico de la Construcción y del Cemento. Publicaciones, no. 66)

TG340.L6 57-33113

NL 0425604 DLC

634.9 Lleó Silvestre, Antonio.
L77c La ciudad y los espacios forestales. [Madrid] Sección de Publicaciones, Prensa y Propaganda [1944]
53p. illus. 22cm.

At head of title: Ministerio de Agricultura.
"Esta conferencia, que corresponde al ciclo sobre el 'Futuro Madrid', fué pronunciada el día 16 de marzo de 1944 en el Aula Magna del Instituto de Estudios de Administración Local."

NL 0425605 IU DNAL

Lleó Silvestre, Antonio.
La ciudad y los espacios forestales; ₍conferencia pronunciada el día 16 de marzo de 1944 en el Aula Magna del Instituto de Estudios de Administración Local. Madrid, Ministerio de Agricultura, Sección de Publicaciones, Prensa y Propaganda ₍1945₎
53 p. illus. 22 cm.

1. Reforestation—Spain—Madrid (Province) I. Title.

SD409.L53 57-34572

NL 0425606 DLC OrCS

Lleó Silvestre, Antonio.
... El coto social de previsión, por Antonio Lleó. (2. ed.) Madrid, 1943.
32 p. 22 cm. (Publicaciones del Instituto nacional de previsión. ₍Núm. 567₎)

1. Insurance, Social—Spain. 2. Agricultural societies—Spain. 3. Agricultural laborers—Spain. I. Title.
HD7205.A35 no. 567a 45-17344 rev
(331.254406146) 331.2544

NL 0425607 DLC

Lleó Silvestre, Antonio.
En pro de las mutualidades escolares y cotos de previsión. Madrid, 1954.
295 p. 25 cm.
At head of title: Comisión Nacional de Mutualidades y Cotos Escolares de Previsión.
Includes bibliography.

1. Afforestation—Spain. 2. Tree planting. I. Title.

SD409.L534 61-38143 ‡

NL 0425608 DLC NcU

Lleó Silvestre, Antonio.
En recuerdo de Antonio Martínez Blanco; discurso necrológico pronunciado, en la sesión inaugural celebrada el 5 de octubre 1949. Madrid ₍1949₎
30 p. 24 cm.
At head of title: Escuela Especial de Ingenieros de Montes. Inauguración del curso 1949-50.

1. Martínez Blanco, Antonio, d. 1949.

TA140.M34L55 59-37199

NL 0425609 DLC

Lleo Silvestre, Antonio.
Interes pedagogico y educador de los Cotos escolares de prevision. Madrid, 1945.

34 p. (Publicaciones del Institute nacional de prevision, 607)
Bound with: Andres Bueno, Vicente de. La prevencion de accidentes del trabajo... etc.

NL 0425610 MH-PA

Lleó Silvestre, Antonio.
Los montes y los seguros sociales, por Antonio Lleó ... Madrid, 1946.
cover-title, 28 p. 21½ cm. (Publicaciones del Instituto nacional de previsión. ₍No. 635₎)
"Publicado en el Boletín de información del Instituto nacional de previsión, número 1, de 1946."

1. Forests and forestry—Spain. 2. Forestry law and legislation—Spain. I. Title.
HD7205.A35 núm. 635 47-20936 rev

NL 0425611 DLC

634.92 Lleó Silvestre, Antonio.
L791r Las realidades, las posibilidades y las necesidades forestales de España. Madrid, 1929.
312p. tables (part fold.,part col.), fold.col.map. 20cm. (Sociedad de Estudios Politicos, Sociales y Económicos. Publicación no.6)

1.Forests and forestry - Spain. 2.Forest reserves - Spain. I.Title.

NL 0425612 CLSU

LLEO Y ABAD,Lorenzo.
El angel tutelar; pieza dramatica en un acto en prosa y verso. Habana, La intrepida. 1871.

pp.28.

NL 0425613 MH

VOLUME 337

Lleo y Balbastre, Vicente, 1870-1922.
¡Apaga y vámonos!
For libretti see under Jackson Veyán, José, 1852-1935.

Lleó y Balbastre, Vicente, 1870-1922.
La balsa de aceite
For libretti see under Delgado, Sinesio, 1859-1928.

Lleó y Balbastre, Vicente, 1870-1922.
El bebé de Paris
For libretti see under Delgado, Sinesio, 1859-1928.

LLEÓ y Balbastre, Vicente, 1870-1922
[LOS BORREGOS. LIBRETTO. SPANISH]
Los borregos; zarzuela en un acto, dividido en cuatro cuadros, en prosa, original de Antonio M. Viérgol. Madrid, R. Velasco, imp., 1912. 41 p. 21cm.

Film reproduction. Negative.
"Estrenada en el Teatro Eslava el 10 de mayo de 1912."
I. Zarzuelas--Librettos. I. Viérgol, Antonio M., 1872- . Los borregos. II. Title.

NL 0425617 NN

Lleó y Balabastre, Vicente, 1870-1922.
La carne flaca
For libretti see under Arniches y Barrera, Carlos, 1866-

Lléo y Balbastre, Vicente, 1870-1922.
Colgar los hábitos
For libretti see under Domínguez, Antonio, 1880-

Lleó y Balbastre, Vicente, 1870-1922.
La comisaría; pasillo cómico-lírico ...
For libretti see under García Alvarez, Enrique.

Lleó y Balbastre, Vicente, 1870-1922.
La copa encantada; zarzuela en un acto. Letra de Jacinto Benavente, música de Vicente Lleó... Madrid: Fuentes y Asenjo [1907?]. Publ. pl. nos. F. y A. 816-820. 42 p. f°.

Vocal score. Spanish words.

1. Operas.—Piano and voice. 2. Operas (Comic).—Piano and voice. 3. Benavente y Martínez, Jacinto, 1866- 4. Title
May 29, 1923

NL 0425621 NN

Lleó y Balbastre, Vicente, 1870-1922.
[La corte de Faraón. acc. arr. piano]
La corte de Faraón; opereta bíblica en un acto dividido en cinco cuadros. Letra de Guillermo Perrín y Miguel de Palacios. Madrid, Ildefonso Alier [191-?] Pl. no. I. A. 1854-63.
78 p.

Vocal score with piano acc. Spanish words.

I. Perrín y Vico, Guillermo, 1857-1923. II. Title.

NL 0425622 CU

[Lleó y Balbastre, Vicente] 1870-1922
La corte de Faraón; opereta bíblica en un acto, dividido en cinco cuadros, en verso, original. Música del maestro Vicente Lleo. Madrid: R. Velasco, 1910. 43(1) p. 1 l. 2. ed. 8°.

In: NPL p. v. 302, no. 24.

1. Drama (Spanish). 2. Lleo, Vicente, composer. 3. Palacios, Miguel de. it. au. 4. Title.
March 16, 1911.

NL 0425623 NN OO

LLEÓ y Balbastre, Vicente, 1870-1922
[LA CORTE DE FARAÓN. LIBRETTO. SPANISH]
La corte de Faraón; opereta bíblica en un acto, dividido en cinco cuadros, en verso original de Guillermo Perrín y Miguel de Palacios. Música del maestro Vicente Lleó. 2. ed. Madrid, R. Velasco, 1910. 43 p. 21cm.
Film reproduction. Negative.
I. Perrín, Guillermo, 1857-1923. La corte de Faraón. II. Palacios, Miguel de, 1860- . La corte de Faraón III. Title.

NL 0425624 NN

Lleo y Balbastre, Vicente, 1870-1922.
El crimen pasional
For libretti see under Fernandez Palomero, Manuel, d. 1914.

Lléo y Balbastre, Vicente, 1870-1922.
El cuarteto Pons
For libretti see under Arniches y Barrera Carlos, 1866-

Lleó y Balbastre, Vicente, 1870-1922.
España Nueva
For libretti see under Paso, Antonio, 1870-1906.

Lleó y Balbastre, Vicente, 1870-1922.
Los hombres alegres
For libretti see under Paso, Antonio, 1870-1906.

Lleó y Balabastre, Vicente, 1870-1922.
El método Górritz
For libretti see under Arniches y Barrera, Carlos, 1866-1943.

Lleó y Balbastre, Vicente, 1870-1922.
La moral en peligro
For libretti see under Delgado, Sinesio, 1859-1928.

Lleó y Balbastre, Vicente, 1870-1922.
[Las once mil. Libretto. Spanish]
Las once mil, zarzuela cómica en un acto y en prosa, dividida en dos cuadros, letra de José María de la Torre y Ricardo Aparicio. Música del maestro Vicente Lleó. Barcelona, Impr. "La Catalana", 1895.
32p. 20cm. (Administración lírico-dramática)

Vol.1, no.12, in a collection with binder's title: Spanish plays; Zarzuelas, v.1.

NL 0425631 FMU NN MB

Lleó y Balbastre, Vicente, 1870-1922.

... Los presupuestos de Villapierde, zarzuela cómica en un acto. Letra de los sres. Paso, Granés, y Alvarez, música de los maestros Lleó y Calleja ... Madrid, Zozaya [18—]
cover-title, 39 p. 34½cm.
Publisher's plate nos.: Z 4228 Z-Z 4234 Z.
First performance: Madrid, 1900.

1. Zarzuelas—Vocal scores with piano acc. I. Calleja, Rafael, 1874- Los presupuestos de Villapierde. II. *Paso, Antonio, 1870- Los presupuestos de Villapierde. III. Granés, Salvador María, 1840-1911. Los presupuestos de Villapierde. IV. García Alvarez, Enrique, 1873-1931. Los presupuestos de Villapierde. V. Title.

43-48644

Library of Congress M1503.L7845P7

NL 0425632 DLC

Lleó y Balbastre, Vicente, 1870-1922.
[Los presupuestos de Villapierde, acc. arr.piano]
Los presupuestos de Villapierde, zarzuela cómica en un acto. Letra de los sres. Paso, Granés, y Alvarez. Música de los maestros Lleó y Calleja. Madrid, Zozaya [1902]
Pl.nos. Z 4288 Z-Z 4234 Z.
39 p. 35cm.

Cover title.
Vocal score with piano accompaniment.
Spanish words.

NL 0425633 CU NN

Lleó y Balbastre, Vicente, 1870-1922.
El Principe Sin-Miedo; opereta ...
For libretti see under Jover, Gonzalo, 1858-1922.

Lleo y Balbastre, Vicente, 1870-1922.
La regadera
For libretti see under Casero y Barranco, Antonio, 1874-

Lleó y Balbastre, Vicente, 1870-1922.
El rival de Sherlock Holmes
For libretti see under Córdoba, Ernesto.

Lleó y Balbastre, Vicence, 1870-1922.
!Si las mujeres mandasen!
For libretti see under Fernandez de la Puente, Manuel.

Lleó y Balbastre, Vicente, 1870-1922.
La Tabla de salvacion
For libretti see under Delgado, Sinesio, 1859-1928.

VOLUME 337

Lleó y Balbastre, Vicente, 1870–1922.

... La tiple mimada, zarzuela en un acto. Letra de d. Diego G. Prieto, música del mtro. Vicente Lleó ... Madrid, B. Zozaya [18—]

47 p. 34½cm. (On cover: Repertorio Zarzuelas en uno y dos actos de los maestros más notables)

Caption title.
Publisher's plate nos.: Z 4236 Z-Z 4242 Z.
First performance: Madrid, 1899.

1. Zarzuelas—Vocal scores with piano acc. I. Jiménez Prieto, Diego, d. 1907. La tiple mimada. II. Title.

43-45480

Library of Congress M1503.L7845T5

NL 0425639 DLC MH NN

Lleó y Balbastre, Vicente, 1870-1922
[¡ TÓ ESTÁ PAGAO! LIBRETTO. SPANISH]
¡Tó está pagao! Sainete lírico en un acto, dividido en tres cuadros, original de Pepe Ángeles. Valencia, Impr. de V. Gallego, 1918. 45 p. illus. 21cm.

At head of title: Sociedad de autores españoles.
"Estrenado...en el Teatro Rufafa, de Valencia...[el] 28 de noviembre de 1918."
Imprint on cover: Madrid, Sociedad de autores españoles.
I. Ángeles, José. ¡Tó está pagao!. II. Title.

NL 0425640 NN

Lléo y Balbastre, Vicente, 1870-1922.
La vida alegre
for libretti see under Capella, Jacinto, 1880-

PQ6218 .S6 v.95 Lleó y Balbastre, Vicente, 1870-1922.
[La vuelta de presidio. Libretto. Spanish]
La vuelta de presidio; entremés tragi-cómico en verso, original de José López Silva. Música del maestro Vicente Lleó. Madrid, R. Velasco, Impresor, 1908.
23p. 20cm.

Vol. 95 no. 7 in a collection with binder's title: Spanish plays; Entremeses líricos.
i. López Silva, José, 1861-1925. La vuelta de presidio. ii. Title.

NL 0425642 FMU

Lleonart, Joaquín Marsillach y
see
Marsillach y Lleonart, Joaquín, 1859-1883.

Lleonart, José, 1880–
... Apuntes sobre la vida y las obras de Goethe, por José Lleonart. Barcelona, I. G. Seix y Barral hnos., s. a., 1943.

67 p. illus. (incl. ports.) 17½cm. (Colección Estudio de conocimientos generales. [19])

1. Goethe, Johann Wolfgang von, 1749-1832.

44-32122

Library of Congress PT2053.L55

928.

NL 0425644 DLC

Lleonart, José, 1880- tr.

Zweig, Stefan, 1881-1942.
... Calidoscopio, novelas. Traducción directa del alemán por José Lleonart. Buenos Aires, Barcelona. Editorial Juventud argentina [1941]

Y 7209 .102 v.36 LLEONART, JOSÉ, 1880-
El camí errat; novel·la. Barcelona, Editorial Catalana[192-?]
208p. 19cm. (Biblioteca catalana)

NL 0425646 ICN

Lleonart, José, 1880–
... Cómo hago un curso comentando la historia de la cultura. Barcelona, Comissariat de la propaganda de la generalitat de Catalunya, 1937.

48 p. 17½cm. (Aspectos de la actividad catalana. 2)

CONTENTS.—I. La materia del curso.—II. Qué es la Escuela del trabajo.

1. Civilization — Hist. — Study and teaching. 2. Barcelona. Escola del treball. I. Title.

40-15115

Library of Congress DP302.C57A8 t. 2

(914.67) 901

NL 0425647 DLC

Lleonart, José, 1880–
El conqueridor de València. Pròleg de L. Gassó i Carbonell. Barcelona, Editorial Barcino, 1952.

48 p. 20 cm. (Publicacions de "La Revista," 2. sér. v. 10)

1. Jaime I, King of Aragon, 1208-1276. 2. Valencia—Hist. I. Title.

DP129.L53 55-21826 ‡

NL 0425648 DLC TNJ

Lleonart, José
Les elegies i els jardins. Barcelona, Institució de les Lletres Catalanes, 1938.

NL 0425649 MH

LLEONART, José
Elegies germaniques. [Barcelona, B.Baxarias, 1910].

Presentation copy with author's autograph.

NL 0425650 MH

PN153 L5 Lleonart, José, 1880-
El escritor y su obra. Barcelona, Seix y Barral, 1944.
70 p. illus., ports. 18cm. (Colección Estudio de conocimientos generales, 29)

1. Authorship. I. Title.

NL 0425651 GU

Lleonart, José, 1880–
... El hogar y sus componentes a través del tiempo, por José Lleonart. Barcelona, I. G. Seix y Barral hnos., s. a., 1941.

70 p. illus. 17½cm. (Colección Estudio de conocimientos generales. [8])

1. Dwellings—Hist. I. Title.

44-11821

Library of Congress GT170.L55

571.8

NL 0425652 DLC

Lleonart, José, 1880- tr.

DS810 .L324 Laytha, Edgar, 1910–
... El Japón, ayer, hoy y mañana; traducción directa del alemán por José Lleonart. Barcelona, Editorial Juventud, s. a. [1942]

Lleonart, José, 1880-
Josep Lleonart. Pròleg de Joan d'Arezzo. Barcelona, 1924.
57 p. 13 cm. (Els Poetes d'ara)

Poems.

NL 0425654 NjP CU

Lleonart, José
La merla, i altres cants. Barcelona, Gili, 1914.
91 p. (Biblioteca Illes d'Or, 4)

NL 0425655 MH

Lleonart, José, 1880- tr.

CT3420 .G618 [Gosselin, Louis Léon Théodore] 1857–1935.
... Mujeres (amores desvanecidos) Versión española de José Lleonart. Madrid [etc.] Editorial Juventud, s. a. [1940]

PC3941 .L78R7 1929 Lleonart, José, 1880-
Rondant de nit. Barcelona, Les Ales Esteses, [1929]
120 p. (Col.lecció popular de Les Ales Esteses, 13)

NL 0425657 ICU

Lleonart, José
Un tragipoema i Tisianel-la. Barcelona, La Revista, 1934
127 p.

NL 0425658 MH

Lleonart, José, 1880–
Vida de Mozart. Barcelona, I. G. Seix y Barral Hnos., 1940.

119 p. illus., ports., facsim. 19 cm. (Vidas de grandes hombres)

1. Mozart, Johann Chrysostom Wolfgang Amadeus, 1756-1791. (Series)

ML410.M9L47 50-48164

NL 0425659 MH DLC

Lleonart, Manuel Deulofeu y
see Deulofeu y Lleonart, Manuel.

G868.81 L774h Lleonart, Yolanda.
Hora-luz; poemas. La Habana [P. Fernández] 1940.
156p. 17cm.

CONTENTS.--Motivos de sol.--Motivos de luna.

NL 0425661 TxU NN FU ViU MB CtY IEN NjP

VOLUME 337

qG-J
L77r

LLEONART, YOLANDA
Rondas escolares para los grados primarios; letra de Yolanda Lleonart y Andrés de Piedra-Bueno. Música de Arturo R. Ojea. Habana, Cultural, s.a., 1939.
57p. 25½cm.

1. Rondo. I. Piedra-Bueno, Andrés de, 1903- joint author. II. Ojea, Arturo R.

NL 0425662 TxU

Lleonart, Yolanda.
Rueda-rueda, poemas. Habana, 1941.
74 p. 19 cm.

I. Title.

PZ74.3.L45 861.6 45-25336 rev*

NL 0425663 DLC MU TxU FU CtY MB DPU NjP

Lleonart Maragall, José
see Lleonart, José, 1880-

Lleopart, Luis de Castellarnau y de
see Castellarnau y de Lleopart, Luis de.

Llera, Angel Manuel Mergal
see
Mergal Llera, Angel Manuel, 1909-

Llera, Carlos de la.
La devaluación monetaria y la contabilidad. México, 1949.
97 p. diagrs., forms. 24 cm.
Tesis (contador público y auditor)—Universidad Nacional Autónoma de México.
Bibliography: p. 95.

1. Inflation (Finance) 2. Accounting. I. Title.

HF5657.L55 50-31180

NL 0425667 DLC

Llera, Enrique Suero
see
Montini, Javier de, 1936-

Llera, Evelio.
Ensayo sobre una génesis de la cultura. Habana, 1951.
12 p. illus. 23 cm.
Bibliography: p. 12.

1. Man, Prehistoric. I. Title.

A 52-2450

New York. Public Libr.
for Library of Congress

NL 0425669 NN

Llera, Humberto Piñera
see
Piñera Llera, Humberto.

Llera, Indalecio.
Teoría de la literatura y de las artes, por el P. Indalecio Llera ... Bilbao, Imp. "Graphos"—Rochelt y Martín, 1914.
xxiv, 709 p., 1 l. illus. 24cm.
"Bibliografía": p. [v]-xi.

1. Esthetics. 2. Art—Hist. 3. Music. 4. Literature.

17-17032

Library of Congress BH81.L6

NL 0425671 DLC CU

Llera, Mariano Escandon y
see Escandón y Llera, Mariano.

LLERA, Matías de, fl. 1652-1666
Manus medica dextera quinque digitos continens, quorum primus disputationem in duos Galeni libros de febrium differentiis. Secundus librum, De curandi ratione per sanguinis missionem. Tertius, Controversias de purgatione ... Quartus, Tractatum de crisibus, et diebus decretoriis. Quintus ... Consultandi rationem proponit ... Caesar Augustae, Apud Joannem de Ybar, 1666.
[44], 618, [1] p. front. (port.) 21 cm.

NL 0425673 DNLM

Llera, Víctor Fernández
see Fernández Llera, Víctor, 1850-1923.

Lleras, Alberto
see Lleras Camargo, Alberto, pres. Colombia, 1906-

Lleras, Antonio Alvarez
See
Alvarez Lleras, Antonio, 1892 -

Lleras, Federico
see
Lleras Acosta, Federico, 1877-1938.

Lleras, Gustavo Andrade
see Andrade Lleras, Gustavo.

Lleras, Jorge Alvarez
see
Alvarez Lleras, Jorge, 1885-

Lleras, José Manuel, 1843-1879.
Sáenz Echeverría, Carlos, 1853-1893.
... Piezas de teatro de Carlos Sáenz Echeverría y José Manuel Lleras. [Bogotá, Editorial Minerva, s. a., 1936]

Lleras, José Manuel, 1843-1879.
Variedades literarias, ed. 1879.

NL 0425681 DPU CtY

F
2271.52
L547
LAC-Z

Lleras, Lorenzo María, 1811-1867
Esposición hecha en 18 de noviembre de 1853 al ciudadano Presidente de la República, ...sobre los tratados de amistad i límites, de estradición de reos, i de navegación fluvial, que, como plenipotenciario de la Nueva Granada, celebró con ... Miguel María Lisboa ... en los meses de junio i julio del mismo año. Con un mapa. Bogotá, Impr. del Neo-granadino [1854]
59p. 27cm.

NL 0425682 TxU DCU

PQ8179
L56O3

Lleras, Lorenzo María, 1811-1867
Ocios poéticos. Primera colección, que comprende la "Temora" de Ossian, poema épico en ocho libros, los "Ecos de la prisión" i algunas otras composiciones orijinales i traducidos. Bogotá, Impr. de Echeverría Hnos., 1863.
xiii, 400 p.

I. Macpherson, James, 1736-1796./ Ossian poems. Spanish. II. Title.

NL 0425683 CU

Lleras, Lorenzo María, 1811-1867. tr.
[Gillies, John] M. D.
FOR OTHER EDITIONS SEE MAIN ENTRY
República de Colombia ó noticia de sus límites, extensión, montañas, ríos, producciones, comercio, población, habitantes, educación, leyes, religión é historia. Publicada en la septima edición de la "Enciclopedia británica", traducida al castellano y publicada, con varias notas, por el dr. Lorenzo María Lleras ... Bogotá, Imprenta de Lleras, 1896.

Lleras, Luis, tr.
Passaglia, Carlo, 1812-1887.
Apolojia de la causa italiana, dirijida a los obispos catolicos por un sacerdote catolico, (el padre Passaglia), i tr. de la ed. francesa por Luis Lleras. Bogota, Impr. de la Nacion, 1862.

Lleras, Ricardo
see
Lleras Codazzi, Ricardo, 1869 -

Lleras, Rudesindo López y
see López y Lleras, Rudesindo.

VOLUME 337

Lleras Acosta, Carlos Alberto.
... Conferencias y discursos. Bogota, Impr. de "La Luz", 1918.
238 p. 24½cm.
At head of title: Carlos Alberto Lleras A., presbitero.

1. Social sciences—Addresses, essays, lectures.

Library of Congress AC75.L5 20-6002 Revised
[r27b2]

NL 0425688 DLC TNJ CtY IU

Lleras Acosta, Carlos Alberto
Cuestiones y obras sociales. Bogota, Casís, 1923
228 p. illus.

NL 0425689 MH NcD

Lleras Acosta, Carlos Alberto.
... Instruccion civica. Bogota, Talleres de Ediciones Colombia, 1926.
247 p. fold. tab. 17cm.

1. Colombia—Pol. & govt. I. Title.

Library of Congress JL2831.L6 27-14811

NL 0425690 DLC NN

Lleras Acosta, Federico, 1877-1938.
... Resumen de los estudios de bacteriología y serología de la lepra, por el profesor Federico Lleras Acosta ... Summary of the studies on the bacteriology and serology of leprosy, by Professor Federico Lleras Acosta ... Bogotá, Imprenta nacional, 1938.
28 p. 24cm.
At head of title: República de Colombia. Comunicación a la IV Conferencia internacional de leprología del Cairo.
Spanish, French and English.
"Bibliografía": p. [27]-28.
1. Bacillus leprae. I. International congress of leprosy. 1st. Cairo, 1938.
Library of Congress QR201.L5L53 41-31021
616.01

NL 0425691 DLC DPU CtY

JX
1550
L77
Lleras Camargo, Alberto, pres. Colombia, 1906-
Address of dr. Alberto Lleras, Director General of the Pan American Union, before the Economic Club of Detroit. November 3, 1947. [1947]
10 p.
With this is bound text in Spanish entitled "La conferencia de Rio de Janeiro."

NL 0425692 NNC

Lleras Camargo, Alberto, *pres. Colombia,* 1906-
... Un año de gobierno, 1945-1946, por Alberto Lleras. Discursos y otros documentos. [Bogotá; Imprenta nacional, 1946.
3 p. l., [9]-398 p. 24cm.
At head of title: República de Colombia.

1. Colombia—Pol. & govt.—1886- I. Title.

F2277.L55 986 47-24711

NBuU TxU
NL 0425693 DLC OrU TNJ MU CU NN LU NcU CtY IU MH

Lleras Camargo, Alberto, *Pres. Colombia,* 1906-
The inter-American way of life; selections from the recent addresses and writing of Alberto Lleras. Washington, Pan American Union, 1951.
46 p. 21 cm.

1. Organization of American States. 2. Pan-Americanism. I. Title.

F1402.L6 341.187 51-60508 rev 2

NL 0425694 DLC NcU NN Or IU CU TxU OrU OrCS

G378.86
B636
Ll
Lleras Camargo, Alberto, Pres. Colombia, 1906-
Misión y problema de la universidad [por] Alberto Lleras [y] Mario Laserna. Bogotá [Universidad de los Andes] 1955.
29p. illus. 24cm.
Cover title.
"Discursos pronunciados ... con ocasión del acto de posesión de la Rectoría de la Universidad de los Andes."
1. Bogotá. Universidad de los Andes - Addresses, essays, lectures. I. Laserna, Mario. II. Title.

NL 0425695 TxU

Lleras Camargo, Alberto, Pres. Colombia, 1906-
Nuestra adhesión a la causa de América [por] Manuel Avila Camacho ...
see under Avila Camacho, Manuel, Pres. Mexico, 1897-1955.

Lleras Camargo, Alberto, *Pres. Colombia,* 1906-
The Organization of American States; an example for the world. Lewisburg, Pa., Bucknell University Press, 1954.
16 p. 23 cm.
"An address delivered at Bucknell University on April 29, 1954."

1. Organization of American States.

F1402.L63 55-1901 rev ‡

NL 0425697 DLC AAP NcD TxU WU

JL2815
1944
.A4
Lleras Camargo, Alberto, 1906-
... Reforma constitucional: Discurso del señor ministro de gobierno en el Congreso judicial. Mensajes del presidente López. Exposiciones del presidente de la república y del ministro de gobierno sobre la reforma constitucional. Texto del proyecto de reforma constitucional. Bogotá, Imprenta nacional, 1944.

G106
C76
1946Ll
LLERAS CAMARGO, ALBERTO, pres. Colombia, 1906-
Remarks of Dr. Alberto Lleras ... to the second Inter-American congress of philosophy, New York, December 29, 1947. [New York? 1947?]
3 numb. l. 28cm.
Caption title.
Reproduced from type-written copy.
1. Philosophy - Congresses. I. Inter-American congress of philosophy. 2d, New York, 1947.

NL 0425699 TxU

Lleras Camargo, Alberto, Pres. Colombia, 1906-
F1405
1948
.Z5P36
Pan American Union.
Resultados de la Conferencia de Bogotá; serie de conferencias dictadas en la Unión Panamericana, mayo 24, 25 y 26, 1948. Oradores: Alberto Lleras, William Manger [y] Charles Fenwick. [Washington, 1948]

Lleras Camargo, Alberto, Pres. Colombia, 1906-
F1405
1948
.Z5P36
Pan American Union.
The results of Bogotá; lecture series on the Bogotá Conference held at the Pan American Union May 24, 25 and 26, 1948. Speakers: Alberto Lleras, William Manger [and] Charles Fenwick. [Washington, 1948]

F
1418
Pam
5
Lleras Camargo, Alberto., pres. Colombia, 1906-
El sistema regional americano ... [Bogotá? 1947]
10 l. 28 cm.
Caption title.
"Discurso pronunciado ... al recibir el título de doctor honoris causa de la Universidad nacional de Colombia. "El Tiempo- Domingo 27 de abril de 1946."
Mimeographed.

NL 0425702 DPU

Lleras Camargo, Alberto, *Pres. Colombia,* 1906-
see also
Colombia. *Presidente, 1945-1946 (Lleras Camargo)*

Lleras Codazzi, Ricardo, 1869- ed.
... Catálogo descriptivo de las muestras de algunas minas de Antioquía y Caldas
see under Bogotá. Museo nacional.

Lleras Codazzi, Ricardo, 1869- ed.
Catálogo descriptivo de los minerales de Muzo
see under Bogota. Museo nacional.

Lleras Codazzi, Ricardo, 1869- ed.
Bogota. Museo nacional.
... Catalogo descriptivo de los principales minerales de Tolima y Huila, vitrina I, por Ricardo Lleras Codazzi, conservador del Museo de historia natural. Edicion oficial. Bogota, Imprenta nacional, 1928.

Lleras Codazzi, Ricardo, 1869-
Contribución al estudio de los minerales de Colombia, por Ricardo Lleras Codazzi ... Bogota, Imprenta de la Cruzada, 1915.
18 p. 23½cm.

1. Mines and mineral resources—Colombia.

Library, U. S. Geological Survey GS 16-80

NL 0425707 DI-GS DPU

Lleras Codazzi, Ricardo, 1869-
... Contribución al estudio de los minerales en Colombia, por Ricardo Lleras Codazzi ... Bogotá, Imprenta nacional, 1916.
17 p. 24cm.
At head of title: Republica de Colombia.

1. Mines and mineral resources—Colombia.

Library, U. S. Geological Survey GS 16-541

NL 0425708 DI-GS

VOLUME 337

[Lleras Codazzi, Ricardo] 1869–
Las conversaciones de Papá Rico. Carta-prólogo de Agustín Nieto Caballero. Bogotá, Ediciones Colombia, 1926.
149 p., 1 l. front. (ports.) 18cm. (Half-title: Ediciones Colombia, t. 16)

1. Natural history—Addresses, essays, lectures. I. Title.
38-32478
Library of Congress QH81.L75
574.04

NL 0425709 DLC FU IaU

558.61
L791c
Lleras Codazzi, Ricardo, 1869-
La "Corcovadita" del doctor Sechibe [sic] [Bogotá, 1928]
12 p. 24cm.
At head of title: Ministerio de Industrias Sección de Publicaciones.
"Del 'Boletín de agricultura,' año II, número 5, noviembre de 1928."
1. Geology - Colombia. I. Scheibe, Ernest Albrecht. II. Colombia. Ministerio de Industrias y Trabajo. III. Title.

NL 0425710 FU

Lleras Codazzi, Ricardo.
Estudio comparativo de las regiones de Muzo y Zipaquirá, contribución al estudio de la mineralogía de Colombia. (In: Pan American Scientific Congress, I. Santiago de Chile, 1908-09. Trabajos. Santiago de Chile, 1911. 4°. v. 14, p. 256-259.)

1. Mineralogy, Colombia.
January 29, 1914

NL 0425711 NN

Lleras Codazzi, Ricardo, 1869–
... Los minerales de Colombia, por Ricardo Lleras Codazzi ... edición oficial. Bogotá, Imprenta nacional, 1927.
150 p. 20 pl. (incl. diagrs.) 24cm.
At head of title: República de Colombia. Biblioteca del Museo nacional.

1. Mineralogy—Colombia. I. Bogotá. Museo nacional.
G S 28-34 Revised
U. S. Geol. survey. Library for Library of Congress QE379.C6L52
[r43c2]† 549.986

NL 0425712 DI-GS MtBuM FU CU NcD NN ICJ MiHM DLC

Col QE 379 .C4L54
Lleras Codazzi, Ricardo, 1869-
... Mineralizadores y minerales motálicos de Colombia, por Ricardo Lleras Codazzi... Bogotá, Imprenta nacional, 1905
41 p. 24 cm. (Tratajos de la Oficina de historia natural. Sección de mineralogía y geología.)
At head of title: República de Colombia...

NL 0425713 DPU

Lleras Codazzi, Ricardo, 1869–
... Notas adicionales sobre los minerales y las rocas de Colombia, por Ricardo Lleras Codazzi ... Edicion oficial. Bogota, Imprenta nacional, 1929.
50 p., 1 l. illus., 7 pl., fold. map. 24cm.
At head of title: Republica de Colombia. Biblioteca del Museo nacional.
"Bibliografia": p. 14.

1. Mineralogy—Colombia. 2. Petrology—Colombia. I. Bogota. Museo nacional.
30-13698
Library of Congress QE379.C6L53

NL 0425714 DLC CSt FU TxU DSI

Lleras Codazzi, Ricardo, 1869–
... Notas geográficas y geológicas, por Ricardo Lleras Codazzi ... Ed. oficial. Bogotá, Imprenta nacional, 1926.
125 p., 1 l. plates (2 fold.) 24½ cm.
At head of title: República de Colombia. Biblioteca del Museo nacional.

1. Geology—Colombia. 2. Physical geography—Colombia. I. Title.
QE239.L6 G S 27-326 rev
U. S. Geol. Survey. Libr. for Library of Congress [r50b1]†

DLC
NL 0425715 DI-GS MtBuM CU ICJ MiU PPAmP DSI TxU FU

Lleras Codazzi, Ricardo, 1869–
... Notas mineralogicas y petrograficas, por Ricardo Lleras Codazzi ... Bogota, Imprenta nacional, 1925.
90, [1] p. 12 pl., tables. 24cm.
At head of title: República de Colombia. Biblioteca del museo nacional.

1. Mineralogy—Colombia. 2. Petrology—Colombia. I. Bogota. Museo nacional. Biblioteca. II. Title.
G S 26—238
U. S. Geological survey. Libr. for Library of Congress 103(460) L77bn [a40c1]

NL 0425716 DI-GS DNLM NN ICJ CSt FU CtY IU CU MH

Llera Codazzi, Ricardo, 1869-
Restauración de la colección mineralógica y petrográfica. Bogotá, Imp. del Centenário, 1910.
vi, 68 p. 19cm.
At head of title: Universidad Nacional, Facultad de Matemáticas e Ingeniería.
"Publicación hecha por disposición del consejo directivo de la facultad, como un homenaje en el centenario de la independencia."

Contents. - Prologo. - Catálogo de la colección mineralógica y petrográfica de la Universidad Nacional. - Estudio de las menas colombianas.
1. Mineralogy - Catalogs and Collections. 2. Petrology - Catalogs and collections. 3. Ores - Colombia. I. Colombia. Universidad, Bogotá. Facultad de Matemáticas e Engeniería.

NL 0425718 FU

552
L791ro
[Lleras Codazzi, Ricardo] 1869-
Las rocas andinas en Colombia. Bogotá Sociedad Editorial, 1929.
28 p. 24cm.
"Del 'Boletín de Agricultura,' año II, número 8, Febrero de 1929."
At head of title: Ministerio de Industrias. Sección de Publicaciones.
Signed: R. Ll. C.
1. Petrology - Colombia. I. Colombia. Ministerio de Industrias. II. Title.

NL 0425719 FU

Lleras Codazzi, Ricardo, 1869–
... Las rocas de Colombia, por Ricardo Lleras Codazzi ... Edición oficial. Bogotá, Imprenta nacional, 1928.
102 p. 10 pl. 23½ cm.
At head of title: República de Colombia. Biblioteca del Museo nacional.

1. Petrology—Colombia. I. Title.
QE449.C6L5 G S 29-20
U. S. Geol. Survey. Libr. for Library of Congress [a48c1]†

NL 0425720 DI-GS CSt CU FU IU OU DSI NN DLC NBuU

Lleras Codazzi, Ricardo, 1869-
Las sulfosales de algunas minas colombianas. Bogotá, 1929.
7 p. 24cm.
Cover title.
"Del 'Boletín de agricultura,' año II, número 7, enero de 1929."
At head of title: [Colombia] Ministerio de Industrias. Sección de Publicaciones.
1. Sulphides. I. Colombia. Ministerio de Industrias. II. Title.

NL 0425721 FU

Lleras de Bayona, Inés Alvarez
see Alvarez Lleras de Bayona, Inés.

G056.84
Un4
sup.
no.74
Lleras de Ospina, Isabel.
Isabel Lleras de Ospina. [Poemas. Presentación por Jorge Montoya Toro. Medellín?] Universidad Pontificia Bolivariana [n.d.]
[16]p. 24cm. (Cuadernillo de poesía colombiana, no.74)
Cover title.

NL 0425723 TxU

PQ
8180.22
.L4
L4
Lleras de Ospina, Isabel.
Lejanía. Bogotá, Antares, 1952.
112 p. illus.

NL 0425724 MiEM

Lleras Pizarro, Josefina.
...Palabras de mujer, ilustró Sergio Trujillo Magnenat. Bogotá, 1945. 158 p. illus. 17cm. (Antologías de "Sábado")

338611B. 1. Colombian literature— Misc. I. Title. II. Ser.
September 26, 1950

NL 0425725 NN TxU

Lleras Pizarro, Miguel.
... Derecho de policía, ensayo de una teoría general, por Miguel Lleras Pizarro ... Bogotá, Librería editorial La Gran Colombia, 1943.
3 p. l., [9]-323, [1] p. 20cm. (Colección de códigos y obras de derecho bajo la dirección de C. H. Pareja. [v.])

1. Police. 2. Police—Colombia. 3. Contraventions (Criminal law) 4. Civil rights.
44-22816 Revised
Library of Congress HV7926.L5
[r45d2] 351.74

NL 0425726 DLC CtY

Lleras Restrepo, Carlos, *Pres. Colombia*, 1908–
De la república a la dictadura, testimonio sobre la política colombiana. [Bogotá, Editorial Argra] 1955.
511 p. 24 cm.
Continued by Hacia la restauración democrática y el cambio social.

1. Colombia—Pol. & govt.—1946– 2. Colombia—Pol. & govt.—1930-1946. I. Title.
F2278.L43 61-59553 rev ‡

FU FMU InU OU
NL 0425727 DLC CU ICU CtY NN NcU IU NNC DS TxU MU

VOLUME 337

Lleras Restrepo, Carlos.

HG854
.C33

Caro, Miguel Antonio, *pres. Colombia,* 1843–1909.
... Escritos sobre cuestiones económicas. ⌐Bogotá┐ Imprenta del Banco de la república ⌐1943┐

Lleras Restrepo, Carlos, *Pres. Colombia,* 1908–
... La estadística nacional; su organización, sus problemas ... Bogotá, Imprenta nacional, 1938.
2 p. l., ⌐7┐–415, 8 p. 17 cm. (Contraloría general de la república. Colección de estudios administrativos)

1. Colombia—Stat. 2. Statistics. I. Title. (Series: Colombia. Departamento de Contraloría. Colección de estudios administrativos)

HA37.C82L5 311.3986 39–21713 rev

NL 0425729 DLC TxU OU DPU DNAL NN CU

Lleras Restrepo, Carlos, *Pres. Colombia,* 1908–
Exposiciones sobre la política económica y fiscal del gobierno. Conferencias y discursos pronunciados sobre este tema por el doctor Carlos Lleras Restrepo ... Bogotá, Imprenta nacional, 1941.
1 p. l., 5–47 p. 24 cm.
On cover: Política fiscal y económica del gobierno. 1941. Ministerio de hacienda y crédito público.

1. Colombia—Econ. condit.—1918– 2. Finance, Public—Colombia. I. Colombia. Ministerio de hacienda. II. Title.

HC197.L56 330.986 42–19270 rev

NL 0425730 DLC NcD CtY NN FU

Lleras Restrepo, Carlos.
...Fondo monetario internacional... ⌐Bogotá┐ Impr. del Banco de la república, 1945. 31 p. 28cm.

1. Money—Congresses, Internat., 1944. 2. Banks and banking, International. 3. Exchange, Foreign.
October 11, 1950

NL 0425731 NN NNC

Lleras Restrepo, Carlos.

Colombia (*Republic of Colombia, 1886–*) ***Ministerio de hacienda.***
... Memorandum; relacionado con las negociaciones celebradas entre el gobierno nacional y la "Société nationale de chemins de fer en Colombie." ⌐Bogotá┐ Ministerio de hacienda y crédito público ⌐1941┐

Lleras Restrepo, Carlos, *Pres. Colombia,* 1908–
Política fiscal; conferencia dictada por el ministro de hacienda y crédito público, dr. Carlos Lleras Restrepo, el 16 de febrero de 1939, en el Teatro municipal de Bogotá. Bogotá, Imprenta nacional, 1939.
24 p. 24½ cm.

1. Finance, Public—Colombia. I. Title.

HJ945.L55 336.86 40–32807 rev

NL 0425733 DLC FU DPU

Lleras Restrepo, Isabel.
... Sonetos. ⌐Bogotá, Editorial Minerva, s. a., 1936┐
1 p. l., v–xx p., 62 numb. l., 63–65 p. port. 17cm.

36–28890
Library of Congress PQ8179.L586
861.

NL 0425734 DLC CtY DPU NN NcD IU

G
115
.L6
1881

Lléras T., Federico
Tratado completo de geografía universal, conforme á las últimas divisiones territoriales, seguido de uno de geografía física y otro de cosmografía, trabajado con arreglo á los mejores autores europeos y americanos. 3. ed. notablemente aum. y corr. Bogotá, M. Rivas, 1881.
192 p.

1. Geography. I. Title.

NL 0425735 NBuU

LLERENA, Agustin R. de.
Bocetos; [poesias], Habana, "Los Niños Huerfanos", 1893.

pp. 42.

NL 0425736 MH

Llerena, Baldomero, ed. FOR OTHER EDITIONS SEE MAIN ENTRY

Argentine republic. *Laws, statutes, etc.*
... Concordancias y comentarios del Código civil argentino, por el doctor Baldomero Llerena ... 2. ed., notablemente aumentada ... Buenos Aires, Impr. de J. Peuser, 1899–1903.

Llerena, Baldomero, ed.
Derecho civil; concordancias y comentarios del Código civil argentino
see Argentine republic. Laws, statutes, etc. Concordancias ...

Llerena, Baldomero.
... Estudios jurídicos sobre jurisprudencia argentina por el Dr. Baldomero Llerena ... Buenos Aires, Impr de P. E. Coni é hijos, 1898.
1 p. l., ⌐v┐–viii, 389 p. 25cm.
At head of title: Derecho civil.

17–11324

NL 0425739 DLC

Llerena, Baldomero.
... Estudios sobre el Codigo civil argentino; comprendiendo en este tomo un estudio sobre el proyecto de fé de erratas presentado al Senado por el dr. d. Gerónimo Cortés Fúnes, dr. B. Paz y demas miembros de la Comision de legislacion. Por el doctor B. Llerena. Tomo primero. Córdoba, Imprenta del "Eco de Córdoba", 1879.
1 p. l., x, ⌐11┐–409 p. 22½cm. (*On cover:* Biblioteca selecta argentina)
At head of title: Derecho civil.
No more published.
1. Civil law—Argentine republic. I. Cortés Funes, Gerónimo, d. 1891. II. Paz, Benjamín, d. 1902. III. Argentine republic. Congreso. Cámara de senadores. Comisión de legislación. IV. Title.

38–11712

NL 0425740 DLC

Llerena, Baldomero, ed.

Revista jurídica y de ciencias sociales. año 1–
1884–
Buenos Aires, 1884–19

Llerena, Carlos Moyano
see **Moyano Llerena, Carlos.**

Llerena, Darío Rodríguez
see
Rodríguez Llerena, Darío, 1889–

Llerena, Joaquín.
Zayas frente a Menocal. A la Asamblea nacional del Partido liberal, deseando que interprete mi franca palabra. ⌐Por┐ Joaquín Llerena. Habana: Imp. y lib. "La propagandista," 1916. 164 p. 25cm.

884129A. 1. Cuba—Politics, 1916. 2. Zayas y Alfonso, Alfredo, 1861–1934.
March 29, 1938

NL 0425744 NN MH

Llerena, José.

San Salvador.
El libro de los juegos florales (Centenario de nuestra independencia 15 de septiembre 1821–1921) San Salvador, Imprenta nacional ⌐1921┐

Llerena, José Alfredo, 1912–
Agonía y paisaje del caballo (18 poemas de José Alfredo Llerena) Quito, Imprenta de la Universidad central, 1934.
50 p. 15 x 20cm.

I. Title.
37–34292
Library of Congress PQ8219.L55A7
861.6

NL 0425746 DLC NcD

Llerena, José Alfredo.
... Aspectos de la fe artística. Quito, Ecuador ⌐Editorial Atahuallpa┐ 1938.
4 p. l., 7–104 p. plates. 16cm.
On p. ⌐4┐ of cover: Sindicato de escritores y artistas.
"Arquitectura del acuario, estética de la nueva arquitectura": p. ⌐71┐–104.

1. Art—Philosophy. 2. Architecture. 3. Esthetics. I. Sindicato de escritores y artistas del Ecuador. II. Title.
43–6400
Library of Congress N69.L52
701

NL 0425747 DLC WaU CtY TxU DPU CU

Llerena, José Alfredo.
José Alfredo Llerena: La pintura ecuatoriana del siglo xx. Alfredo Chaves: Primer registro bibliográfico sobre artes plásticas en el Ecuador. Quito, Ecuador, Imp. de la Universidad, 1942.
3 p. l., ⌐9┐–116 p., 1 l. incl. ports. plates. 21½ cm.

1. Painting—Ecuador. 2. Art—Ecuador—Bibl. I. Chaves, Alfredo.
43–13746
Library of Congress ND385.L58
⌐50e½┐
759.986

InU NNC
NL 0425748 DLC WaS WaU OrU CaBVa PU CtY MB TxU

---

404 **Llerena, José Alfredo.**
La lección de Eugenio Espejo, y La causa era la noche. Quito, Imprenta de la Universidad, [1943]
30 p. 21.5 cm.

NL 0425749 DPU

VOLUME 337

Llerena, José Alfredo, 1912–
Oleaje en la tierra. Quito, Edit. Casa de la Cultura Ecuatoriana, 1955.
190 p. 19 cm. (Biblioteca de relatistas ecuatorianos)

I. Title.
PQ8219.L55O4 56-28694 ‡

NL 0425750 DLC NN DPU CU MnU IU IEdS MU TxU

Llerena, José Alfredo.
...Quito colonial y sus tesoros artisticos. [Quito] Departamento de prensa, turismo y relaciones culturales [194-] 24 p. illus. 26cm.

1. Quito, Ecuador—Descr. 2. Architecture—Ecuador—Quito. I. Ecuador. Prensa, turismo y relaciones culturales, Departamento de.

NL 0425751 NN

Llerena, José Alfredo, 1912–
Segunda vida de una santa y otros cuentos. Quito, Edit. Casa de la Cultura Ecuatoriana, 1953.
92 p. 19 cm.

I. Title.
PQ8219.L55S4 56-30585 ‡

NL 0425752 DLC PSt NcD NN CU DPU IU TxU

WP 1213 L791t 1940 Llerena, José Gerardo
Terminología obstétrica. Recopilado del diccionario de medicina. 1. ed. Lima, Taller de Linotipía, 1940.
208 p.

1. Obstetrics - Dictionaries

NL 0425753 DNLM

Llerena, Juan.
Fisiografía y meteorología de los mares del globo; obra formada en sus viajes con acopio de datos los mas variados y recientes, por Juan Llerena ... Buenos Aires, Impr. de P. E. Coni é hijos, 1888–90.
2 v. 26cm.
"Publicado en los 'Anales de Sociedad científica argentina.'"

1. Ocean. 2. Voyages and travels.
7-36821
Library of Congress GC11.L6

NL 0425754 DLC DI-GS OCl OFH

HE2908 L5 Llerena, Juan
Remedio contra la paralisis politica; proyecto de ferro-carril entre las provincias de Cuyo y el Paraná. [Mendoza? Argentine Republic, 1852]
42 p.

1. Railroads - Argentine Republic. I. Title.

NL 0425755 CU

S403 .A69 Llerena, Juan.
Argentine republic. *Comisión sobre la agricultura, ganadería, organización y economía rural.*
Viajes y estudios de la Comisión argentina sobre la agricultura, ganadería, organización y economía rural en Inglaterra, Estados-Unidos y Australia por Ricardo Newton y Juan Llerena, comisionados por el exmo. gobierno de Buenos Aires. Buenos Aires, Imprenta y fundicion de tipos "La República," 1882–84.

330.9729 L77f 1942 **Llerena, Mario**
Los factores geográficos en el desarrollo económico-cultural de los países del Caribe. Conferencia dictada ante la Sociedad de Geografía e Historia de Costa Rica. San José, Imprenta Nacional, 1942.
21p. 22cm.
At head of title: Secretaria de Educación Pública.

1. Caribbean area. Economic conditions. I. Sociedad de Geografía e Historia de Costa Rica. II. Title

NL 0425757 KU

Llerena, Rafael R.
... De las bolsas y mercados de comercio; exposición crítica y comentario del titulo III, libro I del Código de comercio ... Buenos Aires, A. Etchepareborda, 1903.
6 p. l., [9]–118 p., 1 l. 26cm.
Thesis—Buenos Aires.
15-5721

NL 0425758 DLC

Llerena Morán, José.
... "Breves apuntes sobre las compañías mineras." Tesis para el doctorado en jurisprudencia, presentada por José Llerena Morán. Lima, Imprenta peruana de E. Z. Casanova, 1920.
36 p., 1 l. 24cm.
At head of title: Universidad mayor de San Marcos.

1. Mining law.
43-40487
Library of Congress TN215.L6

NL 0425759 DLC

QH 325 qL791p 1923 LLERENA Y F , Agustín
La posibilidad de la abiogenesia; estudio de plasmogenia. Lima, Opinión Nacional, 1923.
30 p.
Cover title.
Tesis - Univ. de San Marcos, Lima.

NL 0425760 DNLM

Llerendi, José María.
... Manual de filatelia. Barcelona, L. Miracle [1940]
3 p. l., [9]–345 p., 2 l. illus. (incl. ports., facsims.) 19cm.
"Primera edición: enero de 1940."

1. Postage-stamps—Collectors and collecting.
44-45892
Library of Congress HE6215.L57
383.22

NL 0425761 DLC

Llergo, Carlos López de
see
López de Llergo, Carlos.

Llergo, G L de.
Morfogenia; ensayo sobre la generación de las formas redondas de los cuerpos, por G. L. de Llergo ... Mexico, Tipografia economica, 1909.
27 p. 24½cm.

I. Title.
24-17464
Library of Congress QC173.L8

NL 0425763 DLC

Llergo, Jorge Herrera López de
see Herrera López de Llergo, Jorge.

Llergo, Sebastián L. de.
Manifesto respecto a la epoca en que ha ejercido el mando principal de las armas. Merida, Pedrera, 1850.
16 p.

NL 0425765 PU-Mu

Lles, Fernando
see Lles y Berdayes, Fernando, 1883-

Lles, Francisco
see
Lles y Berdayes, Francisco, 1887–1921.

Lles y Berdayes, Fernando, 1883–
... Conferencias. Matanzas, Casas y Mercado, 1944.
139 p., 1 l. 22cm.
CONTENTS.—La filosofía contemporánea y los cambios en la estructura social.—Conferencia leída en la solemne velada del teatro "Sauto" de Matanzas, al conmemorar el segundo aniversario de la muerte del Ir. Horacio Díaz Pardo.—La educación rural y la economía cubana.—Medardo Vitier, pedagogo, ensayista y orador.

1. Philosophy, Modern. 2. Díaz Pardo, Horacio, 1881–1940. 3. Vitier, Medardo, 1886– 4. Sociology, Rural.
A 44-2828 †
Harvard univ. Library for Library of Congress PQ7389.L6C6
[a46d1]† 864.6

NL 0425768 MH LNHT CtY TxU NNC PU DLC

Llés y Berdayes, Fernando, 1883– , and **F. Llés y Berdayes.**
Crepúsculos. Poesias, [por] Fernando y Francisco Lles. Matanzas: "El Escritorio," 1909. 131 p. nar. 16°.

1. Poetry (Cuban). 2. Llés y Berdayes, Francisco, jt. au. 3. Title.
August 31, 1923.

NL 0425769 NN RPB MH

Lles y Berdayes, Fernando, 1883–
La escudilla de Diógenes; etopeya del Cínico por Fernando Lles y Berdayes. Habana, Editorial Nuestra novela, 1924.
119 p. incl. port. 18cm.
Errata slip inserted.

1. Diogenes, the Cynic. I. Title.
43-35472
Library of Congress B305.D44L55

NL 0425770 DLC CtY RPB FU TxU IU MB

VOLUME 337

[Lles y Berdayes, Fernando]
La higuera de Timón, consejos al pequeño Antonio ... Matanzas, Imprenta Casas y Mercado, s. en c., 1921.
105 p. 19½cm.
On cover: Fernando Lles y Berdayes. Por la sinceridad del futuro y por la dicha de los mejores. 1922.

I. Title.
22-23421
Library of Congress BJ1585.L6

NL 0425771 DLC TxU NN MH

Lles y Berdayes, Fernando, *1883–*
El individualismo; ensayo sobre el instinto y la conciencia. — Matanzas, Cuba. 1926. 109 pp. 18 cm.

D1407 — Individualism. — Instinct. — Conscience.

NL 0425772 MB CU NNC IU

Llés y Berdayes, Fernando, 1883–
...Individualismo, socialismo y comunismo; los problemas de la conciencia contemporánea, por Fernando Llés y Berdayes. Valencia: L. Morote, 1932. 43 p. 16½cm. (Cuadernos de cultura. [núm.] 59.)

712888A. 1. Individualism. 2. Socialism. 3. Bolshevism. I. Ser.
July 26, 1934

NL 0425773 NN

Lles y Berdayes, Fernando, 1883–
El individuo, la sociedad y el estado [por] Fernando Lles y Berdayes. Habana, Cultural, s. a., 1934.
299, [1] p. 20½cm.
"Bibliografía": p. 291-293.

1. Sociology. 2. Political science. 3. Individualism. I. Title.
34-37159 Revised
Library of Congress HM136.L55
[r44c2] 301

NL 0425774 DLC FU FMU TxU PU

Llés y Berdayes, Fernando, 1883– , and F. Llés y Berdayes.
Limoneros en flor, [por] F. Llés. Matanzas, Cuba: El Radium, 1912. 192 p. 12°.

1. Poetry (Cuban). 2. Llés y Berdayes, Francisco, jt. au. 3. Title.
June 26, 1923.

NL 0425775 NN MH

LLES Y BERDAYES, Fernando.
La metafisica en el arte. Mantanzas, Casas y Mercado S. en C., [1922]

Pamphlet.

NL 0425776 MH

Lles y Berdayes, Fernando, 1883–
Sol de invierno [por] F. y F. Lles. 1. ed. Matanzas, Bertrán y Dulzaides [1911]
2 p. l., 2-239 p., 2 l. 19½cm.
Poems.

I. Lles y Berdayes, Francisco, 1887-1921, joint author. II. Title.
37-10063
Library of Congress PQ7389.L6S56
861.6

NL 0425777 DLC NN MH

Lles y Berdayes, Fernando, 1883–
... La sombra de Heráclito. Habana [Imprenta "El Siglo xx"] 1923.
258 p. 19½cm.

I. Title.
30-355 Revised
Library of Congress PQ7389.L6S6

NL 0425778 DLC TxU CtY IU

Lles y Berdayes, Francisco, 1887-1921, joint author.
Lles y Berdayes, Fernando, 1883–
Sol de invierno [por] F. y F. Lles. 1. ed. Matanzas, Bertrán y Dulzaides [1911]

Lletenul, David Mariano.

F1466 .C745
Consideraciones relativas a los periódicos contrincantes "El Pueblo" y "El Combate" ... acerca de los sucesos bélicos entre Guatemala y El Salvador ... Guatemala, Imprenta "El Porvenir," 1891.

F 1466.45 L448 LAC-Z
Lletenul, David Mariano.
Semblanzas presidenciales y crónicas electorales de 1892 en Guatemala. Guatemala, Tip. El Comercio, 1892?-
pts. 22cm.

1. Guatemala - Hist. - 1821-1945. I. Title. Sp.: Taracena Flores Collection.

NL 0425781 TxU

F 1466.45 L449 LAC-Z
Lletenel, David Mariano.
Semblanzas presidenciales y de sus candidatos frustrados en Guatemala desde cierta época política y los itinerarios razonados de la república. Guatemala, Tip. Americana, 1898.
1v.(various pagings) 2.cm.

1. Guatemala - Hist. - 1821-1945. Sp.: Taracena Flores Collection.

NL 0425782 TxU

Lletget, Augusto Gil
see Gil Lletget, Augusto.

Lletget, Victor, tr.

Barclay, *Mrs.* Florence Louisa (Charlesworth) 1862-1921.
... Pared por medio, novela escrita en inglés; traducción española de Víctor Lletget; cubierta en colores de Federico Ribas. Barcelona, Madrid, Sociedad general de publicaciones, s. a. [°1924]

WBI L791m 1870
LLETGET Y CAYLA, Tomás
Monografía de los baños y aguas termo-medicinales de Fitero. Barcelona, Verdaguer, 1870.
243 p. illus.
Author's autograph presentation copy.

NL 0425785 DNLM

WB 300 L791c 1830
LLETOR CASTROVERDE, José de
Cartas médico-quirúrgicas, sobre los progresos del arte de curar en estos últimos tiempos, escritas a un médico de Madrid. Madrid, Miyár [1830]
232 p.

NL 0425786 DNLM

Lletres; revista literària catalana. no. 1-
maig 1944–
México.
no. in v. illus. 23 cm.
Monthly, May-July 1944; irregular, Oct. 1944–

AP95.C3L5 56-28726

NL 0425787 DLC

Bonaparte Collection No.7880
LLEUAD yr oes; sef Amgeueddfa fisol o wybodaeth mewn crefydd, moes, athroniaeth, a hanes... [llyfr I]-III; 1827-29. Abertawy, J.A.Williams, 1827-29.
3v. 21cm. monthly.

Title varies slightly.
Imprint varies: 1827, Abertawy, J.A.Williams.—1828-29, Aberystwyth, S.Thomas.
Editors: 1827, J.A.Williams.—1828-30, David Owen.
Superseded Yr Oes (1926)

NL 0425788 ICN

Llevóselo todo el diablo. [Mexico,1822]
Signed: D.D.D.
A criticism of those who give a distorted picture of the political and social situation in Mexico.

NL 0425789 CtY

PB2289 .T5E5 no. 9
Llew Hiraethog, pseud.
Yr hosan las sef, Cywydd Castell Dinbych. Rhuthyn, Argraffwyd gan L. Jones [1882]
24 p. 16 cm.
Bound with Thomas, John. Pigion englynion.

NL 0425790 MB

Llew Llwyfo, *bardic name*
see Lewis, Lewis William, 1831-1901.

Llew Tegid, *bardic name*
see Jones, Lewis Davies, 1851-1928.

Llewellin, Charles Alfred.
... "Concise" corn table of relative prices, adapted for the use of grain and provender trade, by C. A. Llewellin ... Liverpool, The Northern publishing co., ltd., 1920.
15, [1] p. 15cm.

1. Grain trade—Tables and ready-reckoners.
Agr 22-1150
Library, U. S. Dept. of Agriculture 59L773

NL 0425793 DNAL

VOLUME 337

Llewellin, Charles Alfred.
..."Concise" corn table of relative prices adapted for the use of grain and provender trade, by C. A. Llewellin... Liverpool: Northern Pub. Co., Ltd., 1926. 15 p. incl. tables. sq. 24°.

1. Prices of grain—Gt. Br., 1926.
August 8, 1928

NL 0425794 NN

Llewelin, David.
A sermon [on Rom.iii.31] preach'd at the assizes at Northampton, August 13. 1677 ... London, S. Carr, 1678.
[4],36 p. 21cm.

Wing L-2620

NL 0425795 CLU-C NNG

Llewellin, Frederick George.
The early British church and the Roman occupation of Britain, by the Rev. F. G. Llewellin ... London, The Protestant truth society (inc.) [1937]
135, [1] p. front., plates. 19cm.

1. Celtic church. I. Title.
40-689
Library of Congress BR748.L4
274.2

NL 0425796 DLC CaBVa CaBVaU KyLxCB

274.2
L77e
Llewellin, Frederick George
The early British church and the Roman occupation of Britain ... London, The Protestant truth society (inc.) [1938]
135p. front., plates, port.

1. Great Britain--Church history. 2. Great Britain--Hist.--Roman period, B.C.55-A.D.449. I. Title.

NL 0425797 IU

Llewellin, Frederick George.
Heroes of the Reformation. Lond., Protestant truth soc.[19] 120p.illus.

Contents: John Wickliffe (1324-1384)- Martin Luther (1483-1546)- John Calvin (1509-1564)- William Tyndale (1484-1536)- Hugh Latimer (1491-1555)- Thomas Cranmer (1489-1556)

NL 0425798 CaBVa

Llewellin, Frederick George.
The history of Saint Clodock: British king and martyr. Being some account of a Welsh borderland church and parish from the sixth century to the present day... By the Rev. F. G. Llewellin ... Manchester, Eng.: J. Heywood, Ltd., 1919. 3 p.l., (1)6-222 p. incl. plates. fold. map. 12°.
Cover-title: St. Clodock; British king and martyr.

1. Clodock, Saint. 2. Clodock, Eng. (parish).
May 24, 1920.

NL 0425799 NN IEG TxU ICU ViU

IR30.9
L770r
Llewellin, Frederick George
Reformers and the reformation. Hereford, Jakeman and Carver, 1921.
247p.

1. Reformation. Biography. 2. Reformation. I. t.

NL 0425800 CMIG

Llewellin, Frederick George.
The Tudor sovereigns and the Reformation. London, Protestant Truth Society [1938?]
138 p.
1. Reformation - England. 2. Gt. Brit. - History - Tudors, 1485-1603.

NL 0425801 TNJ-R CaBVa

389
L774
Llewellin, John Jestyr
The food front.

(In British speeches of the day. New York, 1944. v.2, no.7. July 1944. p.36-43)

1. Food supply. Gt. Brit. 2. Rationing, consumer. Gt. Brit. I. British speeches of the day. v.2, no.7. II. Title.

NL 0425802 DNAL

Llewellin- Taylour, Alfred Robert, 1877-

Bythewood, William Meecham.
Bythewood & Jarman's compendium of precedents in conveyancing. 2d ed. By Stuart L. Bathurst ... Donald C. L. Cree ... assisted by Albert S. Oppé ... A. R. Taylour ... K. Richard A. Hart ... London, Sweet and Maxwell, limited, 1926.

Law
Llewellin-Taylour, Alfred Robert, 1877- joint ed.
FOR OTHER EDITIONS SEE MAIN ENTRY
Palmer, *Sir* Francis Beaufort, 1845-1917.
Company law: a practical handbook for lawyers and business men. With an appendix containing the Companies (consolidation) act, 1908; Companies act, 1913, and other acts and rules. By Sir Francis Beaufort Palmer ... 12th ed., by Alfred F. Topham ... assisted by Alfred R. Taylour ... London, Stevens and sons, limited, 1924.

Llewellin-Taylour, Alfred Robert, 1877- ed.
The Housing act, 1935, with introduction, notes and index by Alfred R. Taylour ... London, Hadden, Best & co., ltd., 1935.
xxxviii, 171, [1] p. 22½cm.

1. Housing—Gt. Brit. I. Gt. Brit. Laws, statutes, etc. II. Title.
36-12004 Revised
Library of Congress [r42c2] 331.8330942

NL 0425805 DLC CtY

Llewellin-Taylour, Alfred Robert, 1877- ed.
The law relating to housing and the Housing acts, with introduction, annotations and index by Alfred R. Taylour ... 2d ed. London, Hadden, Best & co., ltd., 1937.
xcv, 749 p., 1 l. 22½cm.

1. Housing—Gt. Brit. I. Gt. Brit. Laws, statutes, etc. II. Title.
39-32551

NL 0425806 DLC MiU-L

Llewellin-Taylour, Alfred Robert, 1877- ed.
The law relating to public health and the Public health acts, with introduction, annotations and index by Alfred R. Llewellin-Taylour ... London, Hadden, Best & co., ltd., 1937.
lxxxvii p., 1 l., 658 p. 22cm.
On cover: Local government law and legislation, 1936.

1. Hygiene, Public—Gt. Brit. 2. Gt. Brit.—Sanit. affairs. I. Gt. Brit. Laws, statutes, etc. II. Title. III. Title: Local government law and legislation, 1936.
39-32552

NL 0425807 DLC

Llewellin-Taylour, Alfred Robert, 1877- ed.
The Local government act, 1933, with introduction, notes, appendices and index by Alfred R. Taylour ... and John Moss ... London, Hadden, Best & co., ltd., 1934.
2 p. l., iii-xciv, 940 p., 1 l. incl. forms. 22cm.
Supplementary volume to "Local government law and legislation for 1933 ... arranged and edited by W. H. Dumsday."

1. Local government—Gt. Brit. I. Moss, John, joint ed. II. Gt. Brit. Laws, statutes, etc. III. Title.
35-13971 Revised
Library of Congress JS3134.L5
[r42d2] 352.042

NL 0425808 DLC

Llewellin- Taylour, Alfred Robert, joint ed
FOR OTHER EDITIONS SEE MAIN ENTRY
Palmer, *Sir* Francis Beaufort, 1845-1917.
Palmer's Company precedents for use in relation to companies subject to the Companies act, 1929 ... With copious notes. And an appendix containing acts and rules. 14th ed. By Alfred F. Topham ... Alfred R. Taylour ... and A. M. R. Topham ... London, Stevens and sons, limited, 1931-33.

TX724.5
M3
L5
1951
Llewellyn, A E
The Y.W.C.A. of Malaya & Singapore cookery book: a book of culinary information and recipes compiled in Malaya. Ed. by Mrs. A.E Llewellyn. 6th ed. [Kuala Lumpur] Y.W.C.A. of Malaya and Singapore, 1951.
251 p. illus.

Preface signed by Morag Llewellyn.
Cover title: Y.W.C.A. cookery book of Malaya.
"New edition of the Y.W.C.A. international cookery book of Malaya."

NL 0425810 CU-A

Llewellyn, Alun, 1915-1944
Confound their politics, by Alun Llewellyn. [London] Bell [1934]
xi, 253 p. 19½cm.
"Satire of contemporary European affairs."

1. Europe—Politics—1914- I. Title.
34-33846
Library of Congress D443.L53
940.5

NL 0425811 DLC NN TxU

Llewellyn, Alun, 1915-1944.
Jubilee John, being the record of a pilgrim's progress through an Arabian night, by Alun Llewellyn. London, A. Barker, ltd. [1939]
3 p. l., 290 p. 19cm.
"First published in 1939."

I. Title.
39-10377
Library of Congress PZ3.L7713Ju

NL 0425812 DLC PU

VOLUME 337

Y 155 .L 775 LLEWELLYN, ALUN, 1915-1944
The strange invaders... London, G. Bell & sons ltd., 1934.
309p. 19cm.

NL 0425813 ICN NcD

Llewellyn, Arthur J.

Sherwood music school, *Chicago.*
Sherwood music school courses. Piano ... [Chicago, °1928-

Llewellyn, Arthur J.

Sherwood music school, *Chicago.*
Sherwood music school courses. Violin ... [Chicago. °1931-

Llewellyn, Bernard, 1919-
Friends of the China road. London, Friends' Home service committee [1946]
15 p. 19 cm. (Friends in action)

NL 0425816 MH

Llewellyn, Bernard, 1919-
From the back streets of Bengal. London, Allen & Unwin [1955]
286 p. illus. 23 cm.

1. India—Descr. & trav. 2. Friends, Society of—Mission. I. Title.
DS414.L55 915.4 56-1085 ‡

NL 0425817 DLC ICU NBC DS NcD NcU IU OCl PP CU NN TxU CLU MU MiU CtY ViU WaU HU-EWC

Llewellyn, Bernard, 1919-
I left my roots in China. London, Allen & Unwin [1953]
175 p. illus. 22 cm.

1. World War, 1939-1945—China. 2. China—Descr. & trav. I. Title.
DS710.L75 915.1 53-32574 ‡

NL 0425818 DLC CaBVa WaWW NcD PHC PPFr MH KU

Llewellyn, Bernard, 1919-
I left my roots in China. New York, Oxford University Press, 1953.
175 p. illus. 23 cm.

1. World War, 1939-1945—China. 2. China—Descr. & trav. I. Title.
DS710.L75 1953a 915.1 53-4537 ‡

NL 0425819 DLC WaS OOxM NN TU PP PSC-Hi OCl TxU HU OU

C Il6ust Llewellyn, Don.
Poems in Orange and Blue. Champaign, Ill., Stipes Pub. Co., 1938.
[17]p. 23cm.

1. Illinois. University--Poetry. I. Title.

NL 0425820 IU

Llewellyn, E
Little wonders of nature, by E. Llewellyn. [London] J. Crowther [1944]
47 p. 18½cm.
"Questions": p. 42-47.

1. Zoology—Juvenile literature. 2. Animals, Habits and behavior of. I. Title.
Library of Congress QL49.L78 45-2198
590

NL 0425821 DLC

Llewellyn, E L
The dove's nest, and Benny Averet. Philadelphia, Ashmead & Evans [1865]

NL 0425822 OCl

* PZ6 .L54F 18— [Llewellyn, E L]
Fido and Frank, by E. L. L. New York: Dodd & Mead [18—]
110 p. plates. 16cm.

NL 0425823 ViU

813 L772f Llewellyn, E L
Flowers in the grass. Philadelphia, Presbyterian Board of Publication [1866]
214p. illus. 16cm.

NL 0425824 IU

* PR4890 .L75T5 1860 Llewellyn, E L
Title hunting. Philadelphia, J. B. Lippincott & Co., 1860.
357 p. 19cm.

NL 0425825 ViU

PZ265 .L746U5 1869 Llewellyn, E L
Uncle John in the school-room. Philadelphia, D. Ashmead, 1869.
109 p. illus. (Dove's nest series)

NL 0425826 ICU NjR

* PZ6 .L54V 18— [Llewellyn, E L]
A visit to the woods. By E. L. L. New York: Dodd & Mead [18—]
99 p. plates. 16cm.

NL 0425827 ViU

813 L77w Llewellyn, E L
What to do; for the little folks, by E.L. Llewellyn. Philadelphia, Presbyterian Publication Committee [1866]
113p. illus. 16cm. (Sunday school library)

NL 0425828 TxU

Llewellyn, Mrs. E.V.C.
Heavenly dews ... Baltimore, Turnbull brothers, 1875.
viii, 9-125p. 16cm.

NL 0425829 RPB

M 788.2 L77M Llewellyn, Edward
My regards: solo for trombone with piano acc. Ed. by C. P. Lillya. Remick, c1940.
6 p.

NL 0425830 WaT

Llewellyn, Evan Clifford.
... The influence of Low Dutch on the English vocabulary, by E. C. Llewellyn ... London, Oxford university press, H. Milford, 1936.
xii, 223 p. 22½cm. (Publications of the Philological society. XII)
"This book is substantially my dissertation as presented and accepted for the degree of bachelor of letters at Oxford."—Introd.
Bibliography: p. [x]-xii.

1. English language—Etymology. 2. English language—Foreign words and phrases—Flemish. 3. English language—Foreign words and phrases—Dutch. 4. English language—Foreign words and phrases—Friesian. 5. English language—Foreign words and phrases—Low German. I. Title.
Library of Congress PE1582.L7L6 36-15895
422.4

NL 0425831 DLC OrU WaTC CU OU OCl MiU PBm PU NN

Llewellyn, Evan Henry, 1847-

Gt. Brit. *Local government board. Committee on vaccination expenses.*
... Report of the departmental committee appointed by the president of the Local government board to inquire into the subject of vaccination expenses ... London, Printed for H. M. Stationery off., by Wyman & sons, limited, 1905.

Llewellyn, Frederick, 1917-
Investment of endowment care funds. Los Angeles, Interment Association of California, °1951.
29 p. illus. 23 cm.

1. Investments. I. Title.
HG4521.L78 332.67 52-24427 ‡

NL 0425833 DLC

Llewellyn, Frederick Britton, 1897-
Electron-inertia effects, by F. B. Llewellyn ... Cambridge [Eng.] The University press, 1941.
x, 104 p. diagrs. 21½cm. (*Half-title:* Cambridge physical tracts. General editors: M. L. E. Oliphant ... [and] J. A. Ratcliffe)
"References": p. 101-102.

1. Electrons. 2. Vacuum-tubes. I. Title.
Library of Congress QC721.L73 41-12003
537.53

NL 0425834 DLC P PPD PU PBm PSC OO OCU OU MiHM LU NN ICJ NcD CU KEmT PPF

QC 721 L73 1941a Llewellyn, Frederick Britton, 1897-
Electron-inertia effects, by F. B. Llewellyn ... Cambridge [Eng.] The University press, 1941.
x, 104 p. diagrs. 21 cm. (*Half-title:* Cambridge physical tracts. General editors: M. L. E. Oliphant ... [and] J. A. Ratcliffe)
"References": p. 101-102.
Photocopy made by University Microfilms, Ann Arbor, Michigan, 1970.

NL 0425835 NBuC

VOLUME 337

Llewellyn, Frederick Britton, 1897–
Electron-inertia effects, by F. B. Llewellyn ... Cambridge [Eng.] The University press, 1943.
x, 104 p. diagrs. 21½cm. (Half-title: Cambridge physical tracts. General editors: M. L. E. Oliphant ... [and] J. A. Ratcliffe)
"References": p. 101–102.
"Reprinted 1943."

NL 0425836 ViU

Llewellyn, Frederick Britton, 1897–
Operation of thermionic vacuum tube circuits, by Frederick Britton Llewellyn ... New York, N. Y., 1926.
cover-title, 30 p. diagrs. 25½cm.
Thesis (PH. D.)—Columbia university, 1928.
Vita.
"Reprinted from the Bell system technical journal, vol. v, no. 3 ... July, 1926."

1. Vacuum-tubes.

29-12180

Library of Congress TK5865.L55 1928
Columbia Univ. Libr.

NL 0425837 NNC NIC OU DLC

Llewellyn, Frederick Britton, 1897-
...Phase angle of vacuum tube transconductance ... [N.Y., Bell telephone lab. 1934]
10p. (Bell telephone system. Technical pub. Monograph B-805)

NL 0425838 OU

621.37 Llewellyn, Frederick Britton, 1897-
L79v ...Vacuum tube electronics at ultra-high frequencies; analyzing the performance of vacuum tubes including the effect of transit time of the electrons. [n.p., The Institute of radio engineers, 1934]
cover-title, 42p. tables, diagrs. O. (Bell telephone system technical publications. Monograph B-770)
Reprint from the Bell system technical journal, vol.XIII, Jan.1934.

NL 0425839 IaU OU

Llewellyn, Frederick.
Address on light-gage flat-rolled steel in housing at the Annual convention of the American institute of steel construction, White Sulphur Springs, W. Va., October, 1937. [New York, American institute of steel construction [1937?]
35 p. illus., diagrs.

1. Steel, Structural.

NL 0425840 NNC NcRS MiD

Llewellyn, Frederick T.
Standardization of ship materials, by Fred T. Llewellyn... Read at the meeting of the American Iron and Steel Institute, New York...May 23, 1919. [New York? 1919.] 1 p.l., 70 p. 8°.

1. Ships (Iron and steel). 2. Shipbuilding, U. S. 3. American Iron and Steel Institute, New York. 4. Title.

August 30, 1920.

NL 0425841 NN CU

Llewellyn, Griffith [pseud]
The Fantoccini; or, The great public puppet-show ... described in a poetical epistle from Griffith Llewellyn to his cousin, Rice Ap.Shinkins. With ... notes ... by the Curate of Aberistwith ... Lond., 1809.
ix p., 1 l., [9]-91 p.

NL 0425842 CtY

Llewellyn, Gwyn, joint author.

HD9969
.H8G765
Pool, Arthur George.
The British hosiery industry, a study in competition. Report by A. G. Pool and G. Llewellyn. Leicester, University College, 1955–

Llewellyn, Henry Morton.
Foxhunter in pictures; chosen, introduced and captioned by H. M. Llewellyn. London, Hodder and Stoughton [1952]
unpaged. illus. 22 cm.

I. Title.

SF337.L6 798.23 53-23219 ‡

NL 0425844 DLC OKentU

Llewellyn, Herbert Mervyn.
...The decoration of new plaster and cement, by H. M. Llewellyn...and H. J. Eldridge... Teddington, Middlesex: The Paint research station, 1939. 28 p. illus. 21½cm. (Research association of British paint, colour and varnish manufacturers. Bulletin. [no.] 29.)
Page 28–29 left blank for notes.

1. Plaster and plastering. I. Eldridge, Henry James, jt. au. II. Ser.

February 17, 1941

NL 0425845 NN OrP

Llewellyn, Herbert Mervyn.
... The effect of building materials on paint films, by H. M. Llewellyn ... London, H. M. Stationery off. [printed by Harrison and sons, ltd.] 1931.
iii, 4 p. 23cm. ([Gt. Brit.] Dept. of scientific and industrial research. Building research board. Bulletin, no. 11)
At head of title: ... Department of scientific and industrial research. Building research ...

1. Painting, Industrial. 2. Building materials. I. Title.

34-32524

Library of Congress TT305.L5

NL 0425846 DLC CU

Llewellyn, Herbert Mervyn.
... The effect of building materials on paint films, by H. M. Llewellyn ... (Rev. ed.) ... London, H. M. Stationery off. [printed by Harrison and sons, ltd.] 1934.
iii, 8 p. 24½cm. ([Gt. Brit.] Dept. of scientific and industrial research. Building research board. Bulletin, no. 11)
At head of title: Department of scientific and industrial research. Building research ...

1. Painting, Industrial. 2. Building materials. I. Title.

34-41400

Library of Congress TT305.L5 1934

698.1

NL 0425847 DLC

Llewellyn, Joseph Steele.
Bible training for Christian workers, by J. S. Llewellyn ... Cleveland, Tenn., Church of God publishing house [©1925]
3 p. l., 5-214 p., 1 l. 20½cm.

1. Bible—Study. I. Bible. Selections. English. II. Title.

25-7037

Library of Congress BS600.L6

NL 0425848 DLC

Llewellyn, Joseph Steele.
Summarized Bible study, by J. S. Llewellyn ... Cleveland, Tenn., Church of God publishing house [©1925]
121 p. 20½cm.

I. Title.

25-20416

Library of Congress BS418.L5

NL 0425849 DLC

Llewellyn, Karl Nickerson, 1893-1962.
The bar specializes - with what results? 1933.
16 p.

Caption title.
"Reprinted from The Annals of the American Academy of Political and Social Science, Philadelphia, May, 1933. Publication no. 2577."

NL 0425850 NNC

Llewellyn, Karl Nickerson.
Beach plums, by K. N. Llewellyn. New York & London, The Century co. [©1931]
2 p. l., 8 p. 20½cm.
"First printing."
Verse.

I. Title.

CA 31-1108 Unrev'd

Library of Congress PS3523.L4B4 1931

Copyright A 43470 811.5

NL 0425851 DLC

Llewellyn, Karl Nickerson, 1893–
Belleza y estilo en el derecho. Traducción y prólogo por José Puig Brutau. Barcelona, Bosch [1953]
80 p. 18 cm.

1. Law—U. S.—Hist. & crit. 2. Jurisprudence—Hist.—U. S. I. Title.

55-31788 ‡

NL 0425852 DLC NcD MH-L ICU

Llewellyn, Karl Nickerson, 1893–
The bramble bush; on our law and its study. New York, Oceana Publications, 1951.
160 p. 24 cm.
Errata slip inserted.

1. Law—Study and teaching—U. S. 2. Law—U. S.—Addresses, essays, lectures. I. Title.

347.04 51-1727

OrCS OrPR OrU-L WaWW NN NIC FU NcD TxU TU ViU CU-I
NL 0425853 DLC CaBVa CaBVaU IdB IdPI IdU-L MtU CU

Llewellyn, Karl Nickerson, 1893–
The bramble bush; some lectures on law and its study, by K. N. Llewellyn ... New York, 1930.
ix, 158 p. 26½cm.
"Tentative printing for the use of students at Columbia university School of law."

1. Law—Study and teaching—U. S. 2. Law—U. S.—Addresses, essays, lectures. I. Title.

31-3722

NL 0425854 DLC WaU-L NBuU GU-L PPT NcD OClW PU MH

VOLUME 337

KB6852 .L6552 1929 Llewellyn, Karl Nickerson, 1893-1962.
Cases and materials on the law of sales, by Karl N. Llewellyn ... temporary edition, part 1. Chicago, Callaghan and company, 1929.
xxv, 691 p.

1. Sales--Cases. 2. Forms (Law)--U.S.

NL 0425855 ICU

Llewellyn, Karl Nickerson, 1893–
Cases and materials on the law of sales, by Karl N. Llewellyn ... Chicago, Callaghan and company, 1930.
xxxv, 1081 p. 26 cm. (National casebook series; E. M. Morgan, general editor)

1. Sales—Cases. 2. Forms (Law)—U. S. I. Title.

30—6038

WaU-L IdU
NL 0425856 DLC GU-L NcU OClW MH-L NcD PU-L PSC

Llewellyn, Karl Nickerson, 1893–
The Cheyenne way; conflict and case law in primitive jurisprudence, by K. N. Llewellyn and E. Adamson Hoebel. Norman, University of Oklahoma press, 1941.
ix, ⌈1⌉ p., 3 l., ⌈3⌉–360 p., 1 l. front., plates, ports. 23½ cm. (*Half-title:* The Civilization of the American Indian ⌈21⌉)
CONTENTS.—pt. 1. The study of primitive law.—pt. 2. Cheyenne law-ways.—pt. 3. The law-jobs and juristic method.

1. Law, Cheyenne. I. Hoebel, Edward Adamson, 1906– joint author. II. Title.
E99.C53L55 970.634 41-23735 rev

OrU-L ViU-L KEmT CaBVa CaBVaU ScU
NBuC OrU AAP MB UU OrPS WaWW WaT OrPR PU-L MtHi
MtU PU WaS PSC OU OrCS OCU Or OO NcU-L MiU NIC
NL 0425857 DLC NBuU-L TU WaU-L CU-I PPAmP PBm

Llewellyn, Karl Nikerson, 1893-1962.
Commercial code. Preliminary tentative draft
see under American Law Institute.

Llewellyn, Karl Nickerson, 1893-
A "Commercial Law" course of 4 semester hours, for spring, 1948 ... suggestion. May 13, 1947. ⌈New York, 1947⌉
4 l.

At head of title: To the Faculty.
Caption title.

NL 0425859 NNC

Llewellyn, Karl Nickerson, 1893-
Commercial law materials for use by students in Commercial Law, Sections II and III, Harvard University Law School, 1948-49 ⌈and⌉ Commercial Law class, Columbia University Law School, 1949 ... ⌈by⌉ K.N. Llewellyn ⌈and⌉ Soia Mentschikoff. ⌈Cambridge, Mass., Harvard Law School, 1949⌉
1 v. (various pagings). forms, facsims. 28cm.
Reproduced from typewritten copy.

NL 0425860 MH-L NNC

Llewellyn, Karl Nickerson, 1893-
Commercial law supplement: Final examination given at Harvard by Llewellyn in 1949. ⌈Cambridge? 1949⌉
11 l.

Caption title.
Reproduced from typewritten copy.

NL 0425861 NNC

Llewellyn, Karl Nickerson, 1893-
Commercial transactions. ⌈New York⌉ Practising law institute ⌈c1946⌉
33 p. (Association of American law schools. Significant developments in the law during the war years, v. 3)

"A continuation and complement of a paper I wrote shortly after we entered the war, for stay-at-home lawyers: The crafts of law re-valued (1942) 15 Rocky Mt. L. Rev. 1."--p. 1.

1. Commercial law - U. S. I. Title.

NL 0425862 NNC WaU-L ICU CSt ViU-L PU-L MH-BA

Llewellyn, Karl Nickerson
The Constitution as an institution, by K. N. Llewellyn ... ⌈1934⌉
cover-title, 40 p. 25½cm.

"Reprinted from Columbia law review, vol. XXXIV, no. 1 (January 1934)"

1. U. S. - Constitutional law. 2. U. S. Constitution.

NL 0425864 NNC

Llewellyn, Karl Nickerson, 1893-
Courts, quality of goods, and a credit economy; a study of interaction between economic background, legal ideology, social function, and judicial personality. ⌈1937?⌉
cover-title, 115 p.

"Reprinted from Columbia Law Review, Part I, Vol. XXXVI, page 699 (May, 1936) Part II, Vol. XXXVII, page 341 (March, 1937)"
"This paper originally appeared, save for corrections, in 36 Columbia Law Rev. (1936) under the title: On warranty of quality, and society."
Volume of pamphlets.

1. Warranty. I. Title.

NL 0425866 NNC

L791ei 1928 Llewellyn,Karl Nickerson,1893-1962.
Einführung in das amerikanische Präjudizienrechtswesen,von K.N.Llewellyn. ⌈n.p.⌉ 1928.
51 p. 25cm.
"Zum Gebrauch bei praktischen Übungen über Case Law Methodik an der Universität Leipzig,im Winter-Semester 1928-29."
Bibliography: p.⌈5⌉-6.

1.Stare decisis U.S. I.Title.

NL 0425867 MiU-L MH-L CU

LLEWELLYN, KARL NICKERSON, ed.
Fragments in tribute, by K.N.Llewellyn. [New York? 1935] 18 p. 25½cm.

Cover-title.
Tributes to Justice O.W.Holmes, reprinted from various sources.
"Selected bibliography on Mr.Justice Holmes," p. 15-17.

849044A. 1. Holmes, Oliver Wendell, 1841-1935.

NL 0425868 NN WaU-L

Llewellyn, Karl Nickerson, 1893–
How appellate courts decide cases. ⌈Philadelphia, Brandeis Lawyers' Society, 1951⌉
63 p. 24 cm. (Publications of Brandeis Lawyers Society)
Two addresses delivered in Philadelphia at meetings of the Brandeis Lawyers' Society on Jan. 10 and May 10, 1945.

1. Law—U. S.—Interpretation and construction. I. Title. (Series: Brandeis Lawyers' Society. Publications)

347.9 51-2383

NL 0425869 DLC

Llewellyn, Karl Nickerson, 1893-
How the law functions ⌈by⌉ Karl N. Llewellyn, Walter Wheeler Cook ⌈and⌉ Jerome Frank. ⌈Chicago⌉ Univ. of Chicago press ⌈1933⌉
13 p. 23cm. (National Advisory Council on Radio in Education. Law series I, lecture, no. 12)

1. Law—Hist. & crit. I. Cook, Walter Wheeler, 1873-1943, jt. author. II. Frank, Jerome, 1889- jt. author. III. Ser.

NL 0425870 ViU WaU-L

Llewellyn, Karl Nickerson, 1893-
Law and the Modern Mind ...
see under title

Llewellyn, Karl Nickerson, 1893-
Law in our society: a horse-sense theory of the institution of law; topical syllabus (arranged by lectures, weeks, and double-weeks) 1950 ed. ⌈New York, Columbia University, School of Law, 1950⌉
91 l.

Mimeographed.
"For the confidential use of my students. Not published."

NL 0425872 NNC

Llewellyn, Karl Nickerson, 1893-
The limits of sexual law. (In Geddes, Donald Porter. About the Kinsey report. ⌈New York, 1948⌉ p. ⌈113⌉-130)

1. Kinsey, Alfred Charles, 1894- Sexual behavior in the human male. I. Title.

NL 0425873 NNC

Llewellyn, Karl Nickerson, 1893-
The normative, the legal, and the law-jobs: the problem of juristic method; being also an effort to integrate the "legal" into sociological and political theory. 1940.
cover-title, 1355-1400 p.

"Reprinted from the Yale Law Journal, Volume 49, Number 8, June 1940."
Volume of pamphlets.

NL 0425874 NNC

Llewellyn, Karl Nickerson, 1893-1962.
Offer and acceptance.
5 p. mimeographed.

NL 0425875 WaU-L

VOLUME 337

Llewellyn, Karl Nickerson, 1893-
... On philosophy in American law ₍by₎ K. N. Llewellyn. ₍Philadelphia, 1934₎
8 p. 25½ cm.

"Reprinted from the University of Pennsylvania law review, Philadelphia, Pa., U.S.A., January, 1934."
Bound with his On the problem of teaching "private" law. Cambridge, Mass., 1941.

1. Law - U. S. - Addresses, essays, lectures.

NL 0425876 NNC

Llewellyn, Karl Nickerson, 1893-
On the good, the true, the beautiful, in law. ₍1942₎
cover-title, 224-265 p.

Reprinted from the University of Chicago Law Review, v. 9, no. 2, February 1942.
Volume of pamphlets.

1. Jurisprudence and philosophy. I. Title.

NL 0425877 NNC ICU

Llewellyn, Karl Nickerson, 1893-
... On the problem of teaching "private" law, by Karl N. Llewellyn. Cambridge, Mass., Harvard law review association, 1941.
cover-title, 775-810 p. 25½ cm.

"A reprint from Harvard law review, March 1941."

1. Law - Study and teaching.

NL 0425878 NNC

Llewellyn, Karl Nickerson, 1893-1962.
On what is wrong with so-called legal education by K.N. Llewellyn. Reprinted from Columbia law review, Vol. XXXV, No. 5. (May, 1935)
651-678 p. cover title. (Legal pamphlets, v. 31)

NL 0425879 WaU-L

Llewellyn, Karl Nickerson.
Präjudizienrecht und rechtsprechung in Amerika; eine spruchauswahl mit besprechung von K. N. Llewellyn ... unter mithilfe bei der auswahl von William A. Leider ... und bei der verdeutschung von Wolfram v. Metzler ... 2 teile in einem bande. Gedruckt mit unterstützung der Leipziger Juristenfakultät. Leipzig, T. Weicher, 1933.
xv, ₍1₎, 122 p., 1 l., 360 p. 25ᶜᵐ.
"Dieses buch ist aus einem praktikum über aufbau und praxis des amerikanischen case law hervorgegangen, welches ich die ehre hatte, als gastprofessor und gleichzeitig als Carnegie international professor, im wintersemester 1928-29 an der Leipziger Juristenfakultät zu halten."—Vorwort.
"Einiges aus der literatur": 1. pt., p. ₍120₎-122.
1. Law reports, digests, etc.—U. S. 2. Civil procedure—U. S. I. Leider, William A. II. Metzler, Wolfram von. III. Title.
Library of Congress 33-19552

NL 0425880 DLC LU-L CtY NcD PU-L

Llewellyn, Karl Nickerson.
Put in his thumb, by K. N. Llewellyn. New York & London, The Century co. ₍©1931₎
ix, 119 p. 21ᶜᵐ. $1.50
"First printing."
Poems.

I. Title.

Library of Congress PS3523.L4P8 1931 31-31485
——— Copy 2.
Copyright A 43469 811.5

NL 0425881 DLC WaU-L NIC OrU NcD MH-L

Llewellyn, Karl Nickerson, 1893-
A realistic jurisprudence—the next step, by Karl N Llewellyn. ₍New York, 1930₎
cover-title. p. ₍431₎-465. 25½ᶜᵐ.
"Reprinted from Columbia law review. vol. xxx, no. 4 (April 1930)"

1. Law—Addresses, essays, lectures. 2. Law—Philosophy. I. Title.

Title from Illinois Univ. Printed by L. C. A 34-1573

NL 0425882 IU MH

Llewellyn, Karl Nickerson, 1893-
Selected cases and other materials on the law of sales, by Karl N. Llewellyn ... ₍New York₎ 1929-
v. 26½cm.
"Printed by Columbia university law school for the private use of students in the course in Sales".

NL 0425883 MH-L

Law

Llewellyn, Karl Nickerson, 1893-

New York (*State*) *Law Revision Commission.*
Study of Uniform commercial code. General statement to the commission by Karl N. Llewellyn. Bibliography ₍by Lewis W. Morse₎ Albany, Williams Press, 1955.

Llewellyn, Karl Nickerson, 1893-
Through title to contract and a bit beyond, by K. N. Llewellyn ... New York, N. Y., New York university law quarterly review, 1938.
1 p. l., 51 p. 25½ᶜᵐ. (New York university School of law. Contemporary law pamphlets. Ser. 1, no. 5)

1. Sales—U. S. 2. Contracts—U. S.

43-5641

NL 0425885 DLC NBuU-L GU-L CU NcD NNU-W WaU-L

Llewellyn, Karl Nickerson, 1893-1962.

...Ueber den Rechtsunterricht in den Vereinigten Staaten. Ein Vortrag. Von K.N. Llewellyn ... ₍Jena, 1929₎
p.₍233₎-266.
Caption title.
"Abdruck aus Jherings Jahrbücher für die Dogmatik des bürgerlichen Rechts...bd.79/2. folge, bd.43."

NL 0425886 NcD-L

Llewellyn, Karl Nickerson, 1893-1962
The uniform commercial code in Tennessee

see under title

Law

Llewellyn, Karl Nickerson, 1893-

American law institute.
... Uniform revised sales act (sales chapter of proposed Commercial code) Proposed final draft no. 1, submitted by the Council to the members, for consideration at the twenty-second annual meeting, May 9, 10 and 11, 1944. Joint editorial committee, Institute and National conference of commissioners on uniform state laws. Reporters. Karl N. Llewellyn. Soia Mentschikoff, assistant reporter ... April 27, 1944. Philadelphia, Pa., The American law institute ₍1944₎

412.62
L77

Llewellyn, Leonard M
The effect of increased and/or decreased length of daylight on pelt primeness in adult silver foxes. ₍n.p., 1947?₎
₍3₎ p.

1. Silver fox. 2. Fur. 3. Daylight. I. Bassett, Charles F joint author.

NL 0425889 DNAL

Llewellyn, Leonard M joint author.
The effect of increased or decreased length of daylight on pelt primeness in growing foxes...
see under Bassett, Charles Francis, 1899-

Llewellyn, Llewellyn Jones
see
Llewellyn, Richard Llewellyn Jones.

Llewellyn, Margaret.
Design and our homes; a book on design in the home and in the shop, raising ideas for discussion and suggestions for activities in groups and classes in the co-operative movement. Prepared and published by the Education Dept., Co-operative Union and the Council of Industrial Design. Loughborough ₍Eng., 1951₎
99 p. illus. 21 cm.

1. Art industries and trade—Gt. Brit. 2. Design, Industrial. 3. Interior decoration—Gt. Brit. I. Title.

NK928.L5 745.4 56-45714 ‡

NL 0425892 DLC MH

LLEWELLYN, MARGARET.
Design and our homes; a book on design in the home and in the shop, raising ideas for discussion and suggestions for activities in group and classes in the Co-operative movement. [2. ed. Loughborough] Education dept., Co-operative union and Council of industrial design [1952] 99 p. illus. 22cm.
(Co-operative union, ltd., Manchester, Eng. Design for study. [no. 4])

Bibliography, p. 93-99.

1. Design, Industrial--Gt. Br. I. Series.

NL 0425894 NN

Llewellyn, Martin, 1616-1682
see Lluellyn, Martin, 1616-1682.

Llewellyn, Owen John
The south-bound car, by Owen Llewellyn and L. Raven-Hill. London, Methuen ₍1907₎
ix, 281p. illus. 20cm.

I. Raven-Hill, Leonard, 1867- II. Title.

NL 0425896 PSt

VOLUME 337

Llewellyn, Richard, 1906-
Bare den som lengter. Overs. av Arne Johnssen. Oslo, Gyldendal, 1947.
404 p. 22 cm.
"Originalens titel: None but the lonely heart."

I. Title.
Full name: Richard David Vivian Llewellyn Lloyd.
PR6023.L47N66 50-22491

NL 0425897 DLC

Llewelyn, Richard, 1906-
Belo raz zelené údolfe. [Prekladatel Rudolf Koštial] Tranoscius] v Liptovskom St. Mikuláši, 1946]
648 p.
Slovak.

NL 0425898 OCl

Llewellyn, Richard.
Com'era verde la mia vallata; romanzo. [Unica traduzione autorizzata di Anita Rho. 1. ed. Milano, Mondadori, 1945.
533 p. 20 cm. (Medusa, i grandi narratori d'ogni paese, v. 158)

I. Title.
Full name: Richard David Vivian Llewellyn Lloyd.
PR6023.L47H65 50-26071

NL 0425899 DLC

Llewellyn, Richard
Com'era verde la mia vallata ... 1947.
Italian.

NL 0425900 OCl

AC-L
L77fe
1950
Llewellyn, Richard.
A few flowers for Shiner. London, M. Joseph [1950]
398p. 21cm.

NL 0425901 TxU CaBVaU MiU MH

Llewellyn, Richard.
A few flowers for Shiner. New York, Macmillan, 1950.
372 p. 22 cm.

I. Title.
Full name: Richard David Vivian Lewellyn Lloyd.
PZ3.L7714Fe 50-5029

WaS WaSp OrSaW WaSpG WaT WaTC OrU-M MtBuM
OrP OrU Wa OrPS CaOTP CaBVa Or WaE WaPS OrStbM
OCl TxU ViU OCIW OO CaBVaU IdB IdU MtBC MtU OrCS
NL 0425902 DLC FTaSU CoU MB PPA PPL PP PLF OEaC

Llewellyn, Richard.
A flame for doubting Thomas. New York, Macmillan, 1953.
341 p. 22 cm.

I. Title.
Full name: Richard David Vivian Llewellyn Lloyd.
PZ3.L7714Fl 53-12957 ‡

OrP WaT
NL 0425903 DLC IdB OrU OCl OOxM PU TxU TNJ PSt

Llewellyn, Richard, 1906-
A flame for doubting Thomas. London, M. Joseph [1954]
368 p. 20 cm.

NL 0425904 NNC CaBVa MH InU IEN

Llewellyn, Richard.
The flame of Hercules; the story of a fugitive galley slave. [1st ed.] Garden City, N. Y., Doubleday, 1955.
254 p. 22 cm. (Cavalcade books)

I. Title.
PZ3.L7714Fm 55—8408 ‡

WaSp WaT WaE
NL 0425905 DLC NN OCl OOxM IU KyLx TNJ CaBVa Or

Ic
F88
L801
Llewellyn, Richard
Grænn varstu dalur. Snúið hefur Ólafur Jóh. Sigurðsson. Reykjavík, Helgafell, 1949.
480 p. 24cm.
"Bók þessi heitir á frummálinu How green was my valley. Þýðing sú, sem hér birtist, er gerð eftir 30. prentun hennar hjá The Macmillan Company. Þess má geta, að höfundurinn tileinkar söguna föður sínum og landi feðra sinna."

NL 0425906 NIC

Llewellyn, Richard.
... Grøn var min barndoms dal. København, P. Haase & søn, 1941.
421, [1] p. 21cm.
"Oversat fra engelsk efter Richard Llewellyn 'How green was my valley' af Aage Dons."
"1ste oplag august 1941 ... 2det oplag septr. 1941 ..."

I. Dons, Aage, 1903- tr. II. Title.
[Full name: Richard David Vivian Llewellyn Lloyd]
44-18421
Library of Congress PR6023.L47H62
823.91

NL 0425907 DLC

Llewellyn, Richard.
Grøn var min barndoms dal. København, P. Haase, 1947.
419 p. 21 cm.
"Oversat ... efter 'How green was my valley' af Aage Dons."

I. Title.
Full name: Richard David Vivian Llewellyn Lloyd.
PR6023.L47H62 1947 823.91 51-19584

NL 0425908 DLC

Llewellyn, Richard.
Hoe groen was mijn dal, door Richard Llewellyn. Vertaling van Joh. de Molenaar. 3. druk. Amsterdam, "Elsevier" [1941]
497 p. 21½cm.
"Eerste druk juni 1940 ... derde druk september 1941."

I. Molenaar, Joh. de, tr. II. Title.
[Full name: Richard David Vivian Llewellyn Lloyd]
A F 46-94
Illinois. Univ. Library for Library of Congress PR6023.L47H63

NL 0425909 IU DLC CtY

Llewellyn, Richard.
Hoe groen was mijn dal. Vertaling van Joh. de Molenaar. 5. druk. Amsterdam, Elsevier, 1947.
523 p. 21 cm.

I. Molenaar, Joh. de, tr. II. Title.
Full name: Richard David Vivian Llewellyn Lloyd.
PR6023.L47H63 1947 48-18716*

NL 0425910 DLC CaBVa

Llewellyn, Richard.
... How green was my valley. London, M. Joseph ltd. [1939]
651 p., 1 l. 21cm.
"First published in 1939."

I. Title.
39-31685
Library of Congress PZ3.L7714Ho

NL 0425911 DLC CaBVa IU CtY TxU ViU KyLoU

*
AC8
.A6
no.H-259
1940
Llewellyn, Richard.
How green was my valley. New York, Editions for the Armed Services, ©1940.
511 p. 11 x 17cm. (Armed Services ed. H-259)

NL 0425912 ViU

Llewellyn, Richard.
... How green was my valley. New York, The Macmillan company, 1940.
4 p. l., 495 p. 22cm.
"First printing."

I. Title.
[Full name: Richard David Vivian Llewellyn Lloyd]
40—27043
Library of Congress PZ3.L7714Ho 9

Ky-LE MnU KyMdC OrAshS
OrCS WaSpG PP PPL PPM PU PSC NcD ICN OCl OClU
Or OrU Wa WaWW WaS OrMonO WaT IdB MtBuM OrSaW
PWcS ViU OCIW OCU OU NIC MiU KEmT KyU-C MoU MtU
NL 0425913 DLC WaE WaTC OrP PBm PPD PPT PHC PBa

Llewellyn, Richard.
...How green was my valley...Toronto, The Ryerson press [c1940]

NL 0425914 CaBVaU

VOLUME 337

Llewellyn, Richard
How green was my valley. New York, Macmillan, 1941.
494p.

NL 0425915 OClWHi ViU

Llewellyn, Richard, 1906-
How green was my valley. N. Y., Macmillan, 1942.
404 p.

NL 0425916 KyU KyLx

Llewellyn, Richard
... How green was my valley. New York, The Macmillan company, 1943.
4 p.l., 495 p. 22cm.
"Reprinted ... March 1943."

NL 0425917 ViU OU

PR 6023 L47 H6 1944
Llewellyn, Richard.
How green was my valley. New York, Macmillan 1944 c1940.
495 p. 20 cm.

NL 0425918 OU

961 L791 hSw o Scandinavian Dept.
Llewellyn, Richard
Jag minns min gröna dal. Från engelskan av Gösta Olzon. Stockholm, A. Bonnier [1940]
375 p.
Translation of How Green was my valley.

NL 0425919 CU

Llewellyn, Richard, 1906-
Kako je zelena bila moja dolina, roman. S engleskog prevela Ljubica Vuković. Beograd, Rad, 1955.
495 p.
Croatian.

NL 0425920 OCl

Llewellyn, Richard.
Llythyrau malais; drama dair act, sef "Poison pen" [wedi ei chyfieithu i'r Grymraeg] gan Jeremiah Jones. London, New York, S. French [c1948] 109 p. 15cm. (Welsh drama series)

1. Drama, Welsh—Translations into Welsh. 2. Welsh language—Texts and translations. I. Jones. Jeremiah, tr. II. Ser.

NL 0425921 NN

Llewellyn, Richard.
... None but the lonely heart. London, M. Joseph ltd. [1943
360 p. 20cm.
"First published in 1943."

I. Title. [Full name: Richard David Vivian Llewellyn Lloyd]
44-4355
Library of Congress PZ3.L7714No 2

NL 0425922 PBa CaBVaU DLC CLU NIC PU PPGi PSC PPM PP PPL PBm

Llewellyn, Richard.
... None but the lonely heart. New York, The Macmillan company, 1943.
5 p. l., 444 p. 22 cm.
"First printing."

I. Title. Full name: Richard David Vivian Llewellyn Lloyd.
PZ3.L7714No 43—14647

NL 0425923 OrU Wa WaE WaS WaSp WaT IdPI WaTC ViU ODW OO OClW OCU NcD OkU CaBVa MtU Or OrCS OrP DLC KyLx MtBC MoU MB OU CaOTP PU WaWW

Llewellyn, Richard.
Poison pen, a play in three acts, by Richard Llewellyn. London, S. French limited [c1938]
66 p. diagrs. 21½cm. (On cover: French's acting edition. no. 991)

I. Title. [Full name: Richard David Vivian Llewellyn Lloyd]
39-4929
Library of Congress PR6023.L47P6 1938
[a46c1] 822.91

NL 0425924 DLC OrCS WaT NBuG NN OU

Llewellyn, Richard.
... Qu'elle était verte ma vallée! Roman traduit de l'anglais par Berthe Vulliemin. Genève, J.-H. Jeheber, s. a.; [etc., etc., 1942]
2 p. l., [7]-477, [1] p. 18½cm.

I. Vulliemin, Berthe, tr. II. Title.
[Full name: Richard David Vivian Llewellyn Lloyd]
PR6023.L47H64 46-45171

NL 0425925 DLC

Llewellyn, Richard.
Rien qu'une âme solitaire. Roman, tr. de l'anglais par Pierre Lambert. Genève, J.-H. Jeheber [1943]
409 p. 19 cm.

I. Title. Full name: Richard David Vivian Llewellyn Lloyd.
PR6023.L47N63 49-41709*

NL 0425926 DLC

Llewellyn, Richard
...So gruen war mein tal, roman. Zuerich, Humanitas verlag, [c1941]
544p.
Title of English original: How green was my valley.
Translated by Albert Gysin.

NL 0425927 OCl

LLEWELLYN, Richard, 1906-
So grün war mein tal; roman.
Konstanz. Diana verlag. c1950. 478p.

NL 0425928 WaS

PR6023 .L47H63 1950
Llewellyn, Richard.
So grün war mein Tal, Roman. [Deutsche Übertragung von Albert Gysin. 26. Aufl.] Zürich, Diana [1950]
356 p. 22 cm.
Title in English: How green was my valley.

NL 0425929 MB

Llewellyn, Richard.
So grün war mein Tal, Roman. Deutsche Übertragung von Albert Gysin. Frankfurt a.M., Büchergilde Gutenberg 1955. 478p.

NL 0425930 CaBVa

Llewellyn, Richard.
Solo un cuore. [Traduzione di Frida Ballini e Carlo Izzo] Milano, A. Martello [1947]
491 p. 22 cm. (I Grandi romanzi Martello (9))
Translation of None but the lonely heart.

I. Title. Full name: Richard David Vivian Llewellyn Lloyd.
PR6023.L47N65 50-2779

NL 0425931 DLC

823.9 L791s
Llewellyn, Richard.
Sweet witch. London, Joseph [1955].
255p. 20cm.

NL 0425932 IEN MH

Llewellyn, Richard, 1906-
The witch of Merthyn; a tale of smuggling in the time of scarlet capes and the red tricorne. [1st ed.] Garden City, N. Y., Doubleday, 1954.
253 p. illus. 22 cm. (Cavalcade books)

I. Title. Full name: Richard David Vivian Llewellyn Lloyd.
PZ7.L77Wi 54-7669 ‡

NL 0425933 OrMonO OrP WaE WaS WaSp DLC CaBVa Or FMU PBa OCl OOxM PP WaT

616.991 L791a
Llewellyn, Richard Llewellyn Jones,
Arthritis deformans: comprising rheumatoid arthritis, osteo-arthritis, and spondylitis deformans. New York, W. Wood, 1909.
365p. plates. 25cm.
Includes "References".

1. Rheumatism. 2. Arthritis deformans.

NL 0425934 IU-M OClW-H PPC MiU DNLM NN NcD

Llewellyn, Richard Llewellyn Jones,
Aspects of rheumatism and gout, their pathogeny, prevention and control, by Llewellyn Jones Llewellyn ... London, William Heinemann (Medical books) ltd., 1927.
xiii, 295 p. 22cm.

1. Rheumatism. 2. Gout.
[Name originally: Richard Llewellyn Jones]

NL 0425935 ViU PPC

VOLUME 337

Llewellyn, Richard Llewellyn Jones.
Fibrositis (gouty, infective, traumatic); so-called chronic rheumatism, including villous synovitis of knee and hip, and sacro-iliac relaxation. By Ll. Jones Llewellyn ... and A. Bassett Jones ... London, W. Heinemann [1915]
xxxv, 693 p. illus., plates. 25½ cm.

1. Rheumatism. I. Jones, Arthur Bassett, joint author.
[Name originally: Richard Llewellyn Jones]
S G 16—62
U. S. Army Medical Libr. for Library of Congress [a48r22g½]

NL 0425936 DNLM CtY-M CaBVaU NcD PPJ PPC

Llewellyn, Richard Llewellyn Jones
—— & Jones (Arthur Bassett). Fibrositis (gouty, infective, traumatic): so-called chronic rheumatism including villous synovitis of knee and hip, and sacro-iliac relaxation. xxxv, 693 pp., 6 pl. 8°. New York, Rebman Co. [1915].

NL 0425937 DNLM ICJ

Llewellyn, Richard Llewellyn Jones
Fibrositis. (Gouty, infective, traumatic); so called chronic rheumatism including villous synovitis of knee and hip and sacro-iliac relaxation. By LL. Jones Llewellyn and A. Bassett Jones. Rebman. N.Y.,1917.
893 pp. 8°

NL 0425938 OClW-H

Llewellyn, Richard Llewellyn Jones.
Fibrositis (gouty, infective, traumatic); so-called chronic rheumatism, including villous synovitis of knee and hip, and sacro-iliac relaxation. By Ll. Jones Llewellyn ... and A. Bassett Jones ... London, W. Heinemann [1919]
xxxv, 693 p. illus., plates. 25 cm.

NL 0425939 ViU

Llewellyn, Richard Llewellyn Jones.
Gout, by Llewellyn Jones Llewellyn ... with a section on ocular disease in the gouty by W. M. Beaumont ... London, Wm. Heinemann, ltd., 1920.
xviii, 469 p. col. front., pl. 25cm.
Bibliographical foot-notes.

1. Gout. 2. Eye—Diseases and defects. 3. [Eye—Diseases, Gouty] I. Beaumont, William Mardon.
[Name originally: Richard Llewellyn Jones]
S G 21-70 Revised
Library, U. S. Surgeon-General's Office [r22d2]

NL 0425940 DNLM PPC PPT ICJ

Llewellyn, Richard Llewellyn Jones, joint author.
Jones, Arthur Bassett.
Malingering or the simulation of disease, by A. Bassett Jones and Llewellyn J. Llewellyn ... with a chapter on malingering in relation to the eye, by W. M. Beaumont ... London, W. Heinemann [1917]

Llewellyn, Richard Llewellyn Jones.
Pensions and the principles of their evaluation, by Llewellyn J. Llewellyn ... and A. Bassett Jones ... with a section on pensions in relation to the eye, by W. M. Beaumont ... London, W. Heinemann, ltd., 1919.
xxvii, 702 p., 1 l. incl. tables. 25cm.

1. Pensions, Military—Gt. Brit. 2. Pensions—[Evaluation] 3. Medicine, Military. I. Jones, Arthur Bassett, joint author. II. Beaumont, William Mardon.
[Name originally: Richard Llewellyn Jones]
S G 19-202
Library, U. S. Surgeon-General's Office
Library of Congress UB375.G7L5
[a35j1]

NL 0425942 DNLM PPC CtY ICJ NN MiU

Llewellyn, Richard Llewellyn Jones.
Pensions and the principles of their evaluation, by Llewellyn J. Llewellyn, ... and A. Bassett Jones, ... With a section on pensions in relation to the eye, by W. M. Beaumont, ... St. Louis, C. V. Mosby Company, 1919.
xiii, iii, xv-xxvii, 702 p. incl. tables. 25½cm.
"Introduction to American edition, by James Warren Sever," iii p. between p. [xiv] and xv.
Printed in Great Britain.

NL 0425943 ICJ PP MB

Llewellyn, Robert Edgar, 1910 -
L'actualité du bonhomme. Images de Jean Simard. [Montréal] Fides [c1946]
156 p. illus. 32 cm.
"Adaptation d'une série de causeries données à radio-Canada."
I. La Fontaine, Jean de, 1621-1695. Fables. II. Title.

NL 0425944 CaBVaU

Llewellyn, Robert Edgar, 1910-
L'actualité du bonhomme. Images de Jean Simard. [Montréal] Fides [1947]
156 p. illus. 23 cm.
First published 1946.
1. La Fontaine, Jean, de, 1621-1695. Fables. I. Title.

NL 0425945 CaBVaU

Llewellyn, Robert E., ed.
Maupassant, Guy de, 1850–1893.
... Contes. Édition pour tous. Montréal, Canada, Les Éditions Variétés [1943]

Llewellyn, Robert E., ed.
PQ1808 .A1 1943
La Fontaine, Jean de, 1621–1695.
... Fables, édition complète. Montréal, Can., Les Éditions Variétés [1943]

Llewellyn, Robert E
... La sagesse du bonhomme; illustrations de Jean Simard. [Montreal] Éditions Fides [1946]
171 p., 2 l., incl. illus., plates. 23cm.
"Adaptation d'une série de causeries données à radio-Canada."

NL 0425948 CaBVaU CaOTU

Llewellyn, Robert Edgar, 1910-
Ton foyer. Montréal, FIDES, [1947].
168p. (Collection "Ta mission aujourd'hui")

NL 0425949 CaOTU

Llewellyn, Robert Hall.
Adjective suffixes in old Norse; a study in word-formation.
Thesis, Ph.D. - Harvard university, 1946.
Typewritten.

NL 0425950 MH

Llewellyn, Robert W., joint author.
T7 .N6 no. 43
Swerdlove, Charles A
A critical investigation of the continuous and the snap-back methods of taking time studies, by Charles A. Swerdlove and Robert W. Llewellyn. Raleigh, Dept. of Engineering Research, North Carolina State College, 1949.

Llewellyn, Stephan Peter, 1917-
Journey towards Christmas; official history of the 1st ammunition company, Second New Zealand expeditionary force, 1939–45, by S. P. Llewellyn. Wellington, War history branch, Dept. of internal affairs, 1949. xix, 457 p. illus. 22cm.

533054B. 1. World war, 1939-1945—Regt. hist.—New Zealand. 2. World war, 1939-1945—Campaigns—Africa. 3. World war, 1939-1945—Campaigns—Italy. I. New Zealand. Internal affairs department. War history branch.
September 26, 1950

NL 0425952 NN MiU

Llewellyn, Stephan Peter.
Troopships. Wellington, War History Branch, Dept. of Internal Affairs, 1949.
32 p. illus. 27 cm. (New Zealand in the Second World War; official history)

1. World War, 1939-1945—Transportation. 2. World War, 1939-1945—New Zealand. I. Title. (Series)
D810.T8L55 940.545 50-23120

NL 0425953 DLC ICRL MH

Llewellyn, Thomas Lister, 1878-
Medical research council (Gt. Brit.) *Miners' nystagmus committee.*
... First- report of the Miners' nystagmus committee. London, H. M. Stationery off., 1922-

Llewellyn, Thomas Lister, 1878-
Miners' nystagmus, its causes and prevention by T. Lister Llewellyn ... With a preface by Professor J. S. Haldane ... and a legal appendix by Douglas Knocker ... London, The Colliery Guardian Company Limited, 1912.
[4, vii]-xix, 158 p. illus., plates (1 fold.), diagrs. 22cm.
Additional material inserted on slips at p. 107 and 147.
"References and bibliography": p. [151]-154.

NL 0425955 ICJ PSt

Llewellyn, Thomas Lister, 1878- joint author
Collis, Edgar Leigh, 1870-
... Report on miners' 'beat knee', 'beat hand', and 'beat elbow' by Professor E. L. Collis ... and T. L. Llewellyn ... London, H. M. Stationery off. [printed by F. Hall at the University press, Oxford] 1924.

VOLUME 337

Llewellyn Jones, Frank, 1901-
Fundamental processes of electrical contact phenomena. London, H. M. Stationery Off., 1953.
66 p. illus. 25 cm. (Dept. of Scientific and Industrial Research. Radio research. Special report no. 24)

1. Electric contactors. I. Title.

TK5707.G7 no. 24 55-3723 ‡

NL 0425957 DLC OClW PU-El

Llewellyn-Jones, Frederick, 1866-1941
The concert of America. The new world's league of nations. By F. Llewellyn Jones ...
(*In* Grotius society. Problems of peace and war. London, 1926. 22cm. v. 11, p. 117-135)

1. American republics. [1. Pan Americanism] 2. [International law, American] I. Title.
A 26-396 Revised

Title from Carnegie Endow. Int. Peace JX1392.G7 vol. 11
——— Copy 2.
Library of Congress [JX31.G7 vol. 11]

NL 0425958 DGW-C WaU-L

Llewellyn-Jones, Frederick, 1866-
Military occupation of alien territory in time of peace. By F. Llewellyn Jones.
(*In* Grotius society. Problems of peace and war. London, 1924. 22cm. v. 9, p. 149-162)

1. Military occupation. I. Title. II. Title: Alien territory in time of peace, Military occupation of.
A 24-833 Revised

Title from Carnegie Endow. Int. Peace.
——— Copy 2.
Library of Congress [JX31.G7 vol. 9]

NL 0425959 NNCE WaU-L

Llewellyn-Jones, Frederick, 1866-1941.
National minorities in the British empire. By F. Llewellyn-Jones ...
(*In* Grotius society, London. Problems of peace and war. London, 1927. 22cm. v. 12, p. 99-123)
Discussion: p. 121-123.

1. Minorities—Gt. Brit.
A 29-487

Carnegie endow. int. peace. for Library of Congress Library JX31.G7 vol. 12

NL 0425960 NNCE WaU-L DLC

Llewellyn-Jones, Frederick, 1866-1941.
The nationality of married women. By F. Llewellyn-Jones ...
(*In* Grotius society, London. Problems of peace and war. London, 1930. 22cm. v. 15, p. 121-138)
Discussion: p. 136-138.

1. Woman—Legal status, laws, etc. 2. Marriage law. 3. Citizenship. I. Title.
A 30-1258

Carnegie endow. int. peace. for Library of Congress Library JX31.G7 vol. 15

NL 0425961 NNCE WaU-L DLC

Llewellyn-Jones, Frederick, 1866-
Plebiscites, by F. Llewellyn Jones ...
(*In* Grotius society. Problems of peace and war. London, 1928. 22cm. v. 13, p. 165-185)

1. Plebiscite.
A 29-496 Revised

Title from Carnegie Endow. Int. Peace JX1392.G7 vol. 13
Library of Congress [JX31.G7 vol. 13]
[r32c2]

NL 0425962 NNCE WaU-L

Llewellyn-Jones, Frederick, 1866- *ed.*
The Road traffic act, 1930; the complete text of the act and of the regulations issued by the minister of transport, with the "Highway code." Edited with an introduction, notes, tables of cases and statutes, and a detailed index, by F. Llewellyn-Jones ... London, Sweet & Maxwell, limited, 1931.
xv, 409 p. 22cm.

1. Automobiles—Laws and regulations—Gt. Brit. 2. Highway law—Gt. Brit. [2. Streets and highways—Gt. Brit.] I. Gt. Brit. Laws, statutes, etc. II. Gt. Brit. Ministry of transport. III. Title.

32-2122

NL 0425963 DLC MH-L CtY

Llewellyn-Jones, Frederick, 1866-
Treaty revision and art. XIX of the Covenant of the League of nations. By F. Llewellyn-Jones ...
(*In* Grotius society. Problems of peace and war. London, 1934. 22cm. v. 19, p. 13-31)

1. Treaties—[Revision] 2. League of nations. Covenant. Article 19. 3. European war, 1914-1918—Treaties—[Revision]
A 34-1672

Title from Carnegie Endow. Int. Peace
Library of Congress [JX31.G7 vol. 19]

NL 0425964 NNCE WaU-L

Llewellyn-Jones, Frederick, 1866-1941.
Upper Savoy and the free zones around Geneva, and art. 435 of the treaty of Versailles. By F. Llewellyn Jones ...
(*In* Grotius society, London. Problems of peace and war. London, 1925. 22cm. v. 10, p. 173-188)
Bibliography: p. 188.

1. Savoie, Haute-, France (Dept.) 2. Gex, France. 3. France—For. rel.—Switzerland. 4. Switzerland—For. rel.—France. I. Title. II. Title: Free zones around Geneva.
A 25-677

Carnegie endow. int. peace. for Library of Congress Library JX31.G7 vol. 10
[a44r32f1]†

NL 0425965 NNCE WaU-L DLC

Llewellyn Jones, James Rushton John, 1894-1954
An annotated check list of the Macrolepidoptera of British Columbia. [Victoria? B. C.] 1951.
iii, 148 p. 23 cm. (Entomological Society of British Columbia. Occasional paper no. 1)

1. Lepidoptera—British Columbia. I. Title. (Series)

QL552.L55 61-48212

NL 0425966 DLC CtY

Llewellyn-Jones, J[ames] R[ushton] J[ohn], 1894-1954.
Some lepidoptera from the Forbidden Plateau district of British Columbia. [Victoria,B.C]. Provincial museum,1949.
pp.K47-K48,Q.

NL 0425967 CaBViP

Llewellyn-Jones, J[ames] R[ushton] J[ohn], 1894-1954.
Some suggestions for those interested in breeding lepidoptera. [Vancouver,B.C.(?)]British Columbia entomological society,1944.
pp.19-25,O.

NL 0425968 CaBViP

Llewellyn Lloyd, Richard David Vivian
see
Llewellyn, Richard, 1906-

Llewellyn Thomas, Mrs. Frances Beatrice Caroline, 1890-
At a venture; poems by eight writers
see under title

[Llewellyn Thomas, *Mrs.* **Frances Beatrice Caroline]** 1890-
Silent meadows [by] F. H. Dorset [*pseud.*] ... London, Cobden-Sanderson [1932]
319 p. 19½cm.

I. Title.

Library of Congress PZ3.L7715Si 33-1744

NL 0425971 DLC

[Llewellyn Thomas, *Mrs.* **Frances Beatrice Caroline]** 1890-
Surging tide [by] F. H. Dorset [*pseud.*] Garden City, N. Y., Doubleday, Doran & company, inc., 1931.
5 p. l., 307 p. 20cm.
"First edition."

I. Title.

Library of Congress PZ3.L7715Sp 2 31-22901 Revised

NL 0425972 DLC PPD MB OEaC OClh OCl

[Llewellyn Thomas, *Mrs.* **Frances Beatrice Caroline]** 1890-
Surging tide [by] F. H. Dorset [*pseud.*] London, Cobden-Sanderson [1931]
286 p. 20cm.

I. Title.

Library of Congress PZ3.L7715Su 31-13713 Revised
[r31d2]

NL 0425973 DLC CtY NN

[Llewellyn Thomas, *Mrs.* **Frances Beatrice Caroline]** 1890-
The window of the world, by F. H. Dorset [*pseud.*] ... [London] Wright & Brown [1932]
xii p., 1 l., 15-288 p. 19cm.

I. Title.

Library of Congress PZ3.L7715Wi 32-8150

NL 0425974 DLC

Llewellyn Foundation for Astrological Research, *Los Angeles.*
Foundation report. no. 1-
[Los Angeles, 1950-
no. in v. tables. 22 cm.

1. Astrology—Societies, etc.

BF1651.L55 133.5072 53-39076

NL 0425975 DLC

Llewellyn publishing company, Portland, Or.

[George, Llewellyn]
... Planetary daily guide for all, "better than magic" ...
Portland, Or., Llewellyn publishing company

VOLUME 337

Llewelyn, arr.
The Orpheus collection of male quartettes. Winnipeg, Whaley, Royce & co.ltd., c1905. 94p.

NL 0425977 CaBVa

Llewelyn, Michael Gareth, 1888-
The Aleppo merchant, by Michael Gareth Llewelyn. London, J. Murray [1946]
vii, 212 p. 22½cm.
"First edition December 1945 ... Reprinted August 1946."

I. Title.

A 47-3710

New York. Public library for Library of Congress

NL 0425978 NN PU

Llewelyn, Michael Gareth, 1888-
Sand in the glass, by Michael Gareth Llewelyn. London, J. Murray [1943]
v, [1], 242 p. col. front. 22½cm.
Reminiscences.
"First edition, 1943."

1. Wales—Soc. life & cust. 2. Education—Wales. I. Title.

A 43-2788

Harvard univ. Library for Library of Congress DA730.L7 914.29

NL 0425979 MH CaBVa CU CtY DLC CaBViP

Llewelyn, Michael Gareth, 1888-
To fame unknown... London, J. Murray [1949] 315 p. 19cm.
1. ed.

NL 0425980 NN MH

Llewelyn, Thomas, 1720?-1793.
An historical account of the British or Welsh versions and editions of the Bible. With an appendix containing the dedications prefixed to the first impressions. By Thomas Llewelyn ... London: Printed by R. Hett; and sold by J. Buckland in Paternoster row, and T. Becket and co. in the Strand, 1768.
vii, 112 p. 20½cm.

1. Bible—Versions, Welsh.

26-22917

Library of Congress BS460.W3L5

NL 0425981 DLC CtY NN NIC

Llewelyn, Thomas, 1720? -1793
Historical and critical remarks on the British tongue and its connection with other languages, founded on its state in the Welsh Bible. London, printed for J. Buckland, etc. 1769.
pp. (2), 2, 120.

NL 0425982 MH ICN PPL PHi

Llewelyn, Thomas, 1720?-1793.
Tracts, historical and critical. By the late Thomas Llewelyn. Shrewsbury, J. and W. Eddowes, 1793.
xv, 247 p. 23 cm.
Contents. -An historical account of the British or Welsh versions and editions of the Bible ... -Historical and critical remarks on the British tongue and it's connection with other languages, founded on it's state in the Welsh Bible.

NL 0425983 IEG MH

K
C451
.515
LLEWELYN, WILLIAM HENRY.
The lords, the constitution, and the Franchise Bill. A letter addressed to the most noble, the Marquis of Salisbury. London, Harrison & Sons, 1884.
24p. 18cm.

NL 0425984 ICN

Llewelyn, William Henry.
Vivisection: shall it be regulated or suppressed? 4th thousand.
= Liverpool. Brakell. 1876. 26 pp. 12°.

Sept. 12, 1902

E5665 — Vivisection.

NL 0425985 MB MH

Llewelyn-Williams, Alun
see
Llywelyn-Williams, Alun.

Llewelyn [family] [n. p., 19—]
cover-title, 18 l. coats of arms. 29 cm.

Typewritten.
"The pedigree and early history of the Llewelyn family was originally copied from an old book 'Limbus patrum familiarum Morganiae et Glamorganiae' [by George Thomas Clark] in the British museum library."

1. Llewellyn family.

NL 0425987 ViU

1973
150
Llewelyn's heir; or, North Wales: its manners, customs, and superstitions, during the last century. Illustrated by a story founded on fact ... London, Smith, Elder and Co., 1846.
3 v. 21 cm.

Advertising matter: p. [269]-271, [1] at end of v. 3.

1. Bower, Rev. J W - Bookplate. I.Title: North Wales: its manners, customs, and superstitions.

NL 0425988 CtY MH

Lleyda, Spain
see Lerida, Spain.

Lleyn, Gwilym
see
Rowlands, William, 1802-1865

PB
2298
.L79
A17
1909
Lleyn, Owain, fl. ca. 1860.
[Poems]
Gwaith barddonol. O dan olygiad Myrddin Fardd. Pwllheli, R. Jones, 1909.
xi, 103 p. plates. 17 cm.

I. Jones, John, ed.

NL 0425991 DCU

[Lleyn, S]
Marwnad neu goffadwriaeth y brawd Robert Roberts. Caernarfon, Roberts [1802?]
8 p.

NL 0425992 MH

Lleyn, William.
Cynfeirdd Lleyn: 1500-1800
see under Jones, John, called Myrddin Fardd, 1836-1921, ed.

Lleys, Juan.
Tratado teórico práctico de armonía y composicion musical. Estracto de lo mas útil que contienen las obras últimamente publicadas en Europa, con adiciones y un gran número de ejemplos demostrativos de todas las materias tratadas en esta obra por D. Juan Lleys... Barcelona: J. Budó [, 185- or 186-]. 51, 76 p. illus. (music.) 26½cm.
"Ejemplos," no. 1-152, 76 p. at end.

628648A. 1. Harmony.

September 19, 1933

NL 0425994 NN

BR759
.L56
Llfrau Benjamin ... neu ddynoethiad o annibendod, ffolineb, a gwrthuni gweithrediadau y weinyddiaeth bresenol ... Cyfieithedig gan William Williams. Briton Ferry, D. L. Jones, 1879.
47 p. 17 cm.

1. Clergy--Gt. Brit. I. Williams, William, of Samlet, tr

NL 0425995 MB

R10
Gre950
Lliboutry, Louis
L'aimantation des aciers dans les champs magnétiques faibles: effets du temp, des tensions, des chocs, des champs magnétiques transversaux. Paris, 1950.
Thèse - Grenoble.

NL 0425996 CtY

Lliboutry, Luis, 1922-
Estudio cartográfico, geológico y glaciológico de la zona del Fitz Roy. Buenos Aires, 1952.
62 p. 24 plates (1 fold.) maps (part fold.) diagrs. 27 cm. (Universidad de Buenos Aires. Facultad de Filosofía y Letras. Instituto de Geografía. (Publicaciones) Serie A, nº 17)
Bibliography: p. (63)

1. Cartography—Argentine Republic—Monte Fitz Roy. 2. Geology—Argentine Republic—Monte Fitz Roy. 3. Glaciers—Argentine Republic—Monte Fitz Roy. 4. Monte Fitz Roy. (Series: Buenos Aires. Universidad Nacional. Instituto de Geografía. Publicaciones. Serie A, no. 17)

G5.B8 no. 17 54-41940

NL 0425997 DLC CaBVaU NSyU TxU OU

VOLUME 337

Llibre, Luis.
¡Sense argument! Juguet en un acte y en prosa, original de Lluis Llibre... Barcelona: Bib. "Teatro mundial," 1914. 24 p. 12°.

1. Drama (Catalan). 2. Title.
January 21, 1920.

NL 0425998 NN

... **Llibre** d'amoretes, atribüit a un ermità de Montserrat del segle XIV.[a] Monestir de Montserrat, 1930.
2 p. l., [7]-122 p., 2 l. 17cm. (Mistics de Montserrat, vol. V)
"Introducció" signed: Dom Anselm M. Albareda.

I. Albareda, Anselmo María, 1892- ed.
33-23264
Library of Congress BV5080.L55 242

NL 0426001 DLC

Llibre d'or de la moderna poesia catalana. [Barcelona] La Renaixsensa, 1878.

NL 0426002 MH NNH

Llibre d'or del Jochs florals. Valencia, Estampa de Federico Domenech, Editor, 1895
232 p. ports. (Biblioteca Lo Rat-Penat, Societat de Amadors de les Glories Valencianes, 1)

1. Spanish poetry - Valencia - Coll. 2. Valencia, Spain (City) Jochs florals.

NL 0426003 MH

Llibre de Consolat dels fets maritims
see under Consulate of the sea.

LLIBRE de la patria; coleccio de poesias del modern renaixement. Barcelona, estampa de la Renaixensa, 1882.

NL 0426005 MH FU

LLIBRE de la Renaixensa. Barcelona, Imprempta "La Renaixansa", 1888.

NL 0426006 MH PU

LLIBRE del amor, a las noyas catalanas Barcelona, Estampa de la Renaixensa,1876.
pp.60+.

NL 0426007 MH

Llibre del amor; colecció de poesias del modern renaixement. Barcelona: Estampa de La Renaixensa, 1882. 239 p. 20cm.

255170B. 1. Poetry, Catalan—Col' tions.
N. Y. P. L. January 20, 1944

NL 0426008 NN

Llibre del coc de la Canonja de Tarragona [Editat sota la cura de J.Serra Vilaró. Barcelona, 1935]
1 v. illus.
Limited ed.: 105 cop., no.98

NL 0426009 MH

Llibre dels privilegis
see under Majorca (Kingdom) Laws, statutes etc.

Llibre dels set savis de Roma
see under Seven sages. Catalan.

AG 104 .L5
Llibre nou que conté varios secrets de naturalesa útils é importants, tret dels millors autors coneguts fins ara, y á mes anyadits alguns jochs de mans y diferents remeis utils. Traduhit del castellá al catalá per major inteligencia dels que no entenen la llengua castellana. Vich, Impr. de I. Valls, 1825.
16 p. 15 cm.

NL 0426012 WU

Llibreria l'arxíu, Barcelona
see Batlle, Juan Bautista, bookseller, Barcelona.

Llidó Vicente, Ramón.
... El Colegio mayor de Tomás de Villanueva. Valencia, 1944.
248 p. illus. 22.5 cm.
"De esta edición, compuesta a mano e ilustrada con veintiséis dibujos ... se tiraron trescientos ejemplares numerados ... Ejemplar núm. 32."

NL 0426014 NcD

COMP 029.62 LLI
Lliff, John G comp.
Where to read up on racism and human rights'... San Francisco, Northern California branch, American civil liberties union and West Coast regional office, National association for the advancement of colored people, 1954.
cover-title, 78 p. 28cm.

NL 0426015 MH-L

Lliga catalana.
... Lliga catalana, un partit, una política. Barcelona [Tipografía Emporium, s. a.] 1933.
1 p. l., [5]-302 p. 19cm.
At head of title: Assemblea general de la Lliga regionalista.

1. Catalonia—Pol. & govt.
44-17667
Library of Congress JN8395.C3A5
[2] 329.946

NL 0426016 DLC CSt-H

Lliga Catalana.
Les mancomunitats; antecedents, la Mancomunitat catalana, lley de Mancomunitats. Barcelona, Lliga regionalista, 1912.
xxiii, 69 p., 1 l. 22 cm.
1. Catalonia - Pol. & govt. 2. Catalonia (Mancomunitat) I. Title.

NL 0426017 CSt-H

Lliga Catalana.
El pensament català davant del conflicte europeu; conferencies dels parlamentaris regionalistes. Barcelona, 1915.
xix, 352 p. 27 cm.

1. Catalonia—Econ. condit. 2. European War, 1914-1918—Economic aspects—Spain. I. Title.
HC387.C25L5 55-49695

NL 0426018 DLC

HC 387 .C3 L8
Lliga catalana.
... El pensamiento catalán ante el conflicto europeo; conferencias de los Parlamentarios regionalistas: marzo,abril y mayo de 1915. Barcelona [Imprenta Hijos de Domingo Casanovas] 1915.
xxii,339 p.,2 l. illus.,tables,diagrs. 26½cm.
At head of title: Lliga regionalista.
On cover: Edición castellana.
A Catalan edition was also published under title El pensament catalá davant del conflicte europeu. Barcelona, tip.F.Giro,1915.
CONTENTS.—Conferencia 1.ª.Industrialización y exportación,por L.A.Sedó.—Conferencia 2.ª.Organización industrial y comercial,por L.Ferrer-Vidal y Soler.—Conferencia 3.ª.El problema del crédito,por J.Ventosa y Calvell.—Conferencia 4.ª.Transportes terrestres y marítimos,por J.Garriga y Massó.—Conferencia 5.ª. Subsistencias y materias para la industria,por P.Rahola y Molinas.—Conferencia 6.ª.Política agraria,por C. Camps y de Olzinellas.—Conferencia 7.ª.La Banca catalana,por F.Cambo.
1.Spain—Commerce. 2.Spain—Indus. 3.Credit—Spain. 4.Transportation—Spain. 5.Banks and banking—Spain. 6.Agriculture—Spain. I.Title.

NL 0426020 MiU MH NN

Lliga catalana. *Secció de política social.*
[Publicacions] v. 1-
Barcelona, 1934-
v. 19cm.
44-19856

NL 0426021 DLC MH

Lliga regionalista
see
Lliga catalana.

Llimona, Andrés Vidal y
see Vidal y Llimona, Andres, 1844-1912.

Llimoner, A., pseud
see Marinel-lo y Samuntá, Manuel.

Llinas, Abel.
Essai sur le fondement juridique de la contribution pour avaries communes; étude historique et critique, par Abel Llinas ... Montpellier, Imprimerie l'Abeille (coopérative ouvrière) 1922.
227, [1] p. 24cm.
Issued also as author's thesis, Univ. de Montpellier, 1921.
"Bibliographie": p. [225]-227.

1. Average (Maritime law) I. Title.
32-6384

NL 0426025 DLC CtY MH

Llinás, Domingo Ignacio Boria y de
see Boria y de Llinás, Domingo Ignacio.

VOLUME 337

*D.271
.14
no.1
Llinàs, José Antonio.
Oracio evangelica en la solemnissima festividad de Nvestra Señora del Carmen qve en su Real convento de Palma de Mallorca dixo el m. r. p. Ioseph Antonio Llinàs de la Compañia de Iesus. Mallorca, La viuda Frau [1744]
20 p. 20cm.

I. Palma, Majorca. Nuestra Señora del Carmen (Convent)

NL 0426027 MB

DP
302
B36
L5
Llinás, Juan Antonio de.
Manifestacion de la ex-Junta de Vigilancia de Barcelona a las cortes y a sus conciudadanos. Marsella, J. Mossy, 1841.
39 p. 20 cm.

I. Barcelona. Junta de Vigilancia. II. Title.

NL 0426028 CU-S

Llinás, Pablo A
Compendio de medicina legal y de psiquiatría, por el doctor Pablo A. Llinás ... 2. ed. Bogotá, Editorial Minerva, ltda. 1943.
1 p. l., [5]-516 p. 17½cm.
"Biblioteca consultada": p. 505.

1. Medical jurisprudence—Colombia. 2. Insane—Laws and legislation—Colombia. 3. Insanity—Jurisprudence.
44-46184
Library of Congress RA1022.C7L5 1943
[3] 340.6

NL 0426029 DLC CtY

Llinás, Pablo A.
Conferencias de medicina legal y de psiquiatría para estudiantes de jurisprudencia, por el doctor Pablo A. Llinás ... Bogotá, Talleres de Ediciones Colombia, 1928.
521 p. 20cm. (On cover: Biblioteca de estudios jurídicos y sociales. vol. II)
"Biblioteca consultada": p. [509]

1. Medical jurisprudence—Colombia. 2. Insanity—Jurisprudence. I. Title.
40-587
Library of Congress RA1051.L65

NL 0426030 DLC MH-L

Llinas, Raimundo.
Sermon del glorioso Apostol San Pedro en la Catedral con la ereccion del nuevo Seminario ... En Mallorca, Por Miguel Capó Impreffor, 1700.

NL 0426031 NNH

Llinás y Aznar, José de, Abp. of Tarragona, d. 1710.
Bvllarivm coelestis
see under Catholic Church. Pope.

Llinas y Aznar, José de, Abp. of Tarragona, d. 1710
Torneo poetico ...
see under Alegre, Felipe.

Llinas. Observatorio Belloch
see Barcelona. Observatorio Belloch.

Llinaz, Antonio de
see Linaz, Antonio de, 1634 or 5-1693.

Llines, Jose Abril
see Abril Llinés, José

Z
997
L78
Lliό, Joseph Mora y Catà, Marquis de, d. 1763.
La biblioteca del Marqués de Lliό; noticia [por] Antoni Palau. Barcelona, 1909.
61 [i.e. 16] p. illus. 19cm.

No. 25 of an edition of 60.

I. Palau y Dulcet, Antonio, 1867- ed.

NL 0426037 CoU

Llio, Joseph Mora y Catá, Marquis de, d. 1763.
Observaciones sobre los principios elementales de la historia ... (In Barcelona. Academia de buenas letras. Origen, progressos ... part I, pp. 93-263; part 2. Barcelona. [1756.])

N1405 — History. Writing of.

NL 0426038 MB PU

Llirbat, Henri.
Souvenir d'un Kommando, 1940-1944... [Paris, 1944] 20 l. illus. 30cm.

"Dessins et texte d'Henri Llirbat."

1. World war, 1939-1945—Prisoners and prisons, German. 2. Amateur theatricals.

NL 0426039 NN

Llisa, Pedro de.
Confesionario en idioma del choconate paya, tapalisa...hecho en el Darien.
8p. 13cm.

NL 0426040 LNHT ICN

Llisa, Pedro de, tr.
Pequeño catecismo cristiano, Dios onamaque carta chenicua, tr. en la lengua Cuna ...
see under title

Llisa, Pedro de.
A text in the Indian language of Panama-Darien
see under title

Lliteras, Jorge Gámiz
see Gámiz Lliteras, Jorge.

Lliteras, Juan Andrés.
Apuntes de derecho romano, por Juan Andrés Lliteras en colaboración con Mario B. de Rojas. Prólogo del dr. Octavio Averhoff y Plá ... Habana, Imp. y papelería "La Universal" de Ruiz y comp. (s. en c.) 1918.
vi p., 1 l., 237 p., 1 l. 22cm.
"Bibliografía": p. [239]

1. Roman law. I. *Rojas, Mario B. de, joint author. II. Title.
41-41571

NL 0426044 DLC NNC

Lliteras, Juan Andrés.
... Relations between Cuba and the United States, by Juan Andres Lliteras. Relations between Central America and the United States, by Dana G. Munro. Organizations endowed by Andrew Carnegie ... Worcester, Mass., New York city, Carnegie endowment for international peace, Division of intercourse and education [1934]
38 p. 19½cm. (International conciliation ... January, 1934, no. 296)
"Two papers read before the Institute of public affairs at the University of Virginia in July, 1933."—Pref.
Bibliography: p. 33-34.
1. Cuba—For. rel.—U. S. 2. U. S.—For. rel.—Cuba. 3. Central America—For. rel.—U. S. 4. U. S.—For. rel.—Central America. I. Munro, Dana Gardner, 1892- II. Title. III. Title: Relations between Central America and the United States.
34-5153
Library of Congress JX1907.A8 no. 296
[8] (341.6082) 327.73097291

NL 0426045 DLC CaBVaU WaU-L OrPR OU MiU OCl

Lliteras, Juan Laguia
see
Laguia Lliteras, Juan

Lliteras Coll, Antonio
Correo aéreo. Mahón, Tip. Mahonesa [1950] 185 p. tables. (Manuales de legislación postal, 26)

NL 0426047 NNC-L

LLIVI, Francisco de Paula.
Arturo, el hijo del ajusticiado; novela original. Barcelona, M. Borras, 1846[1847]

Front.

NL 0426048 MH

S
946.08
L77d
Llivi, Francisco de Paula
D. Alfonso de Borbon, ante los partidos. ... Barcelona, Impr. de Leopoldo Domenech, 1872.
47 p.

1. Spain - Politics and government. 2. Alfonso XII, king of Spain, 1857-1885. 3. Spain - History - Revolutionary period, 1868-1875. 4. Political parties - Spain.

NL 0426049 WaPS

Llobateras, Francisco Ginot
see
Ginot Llobateras, Francisco.

Llobera, Raúl R
Manual de gases combustibles. Buenos Aires, El Ateneo, 1955.
430 p. illus. 24 cm.
Includes bibliography.

1. Gas as fuel. I. Title.

TP345.L48 59-20670 ‡

NL 0426051 DLC

Llobera Poquet, Jorge.
Mussolini y el fascismo. Escuela Central Superior de Comercio, curso 1940-41. [Madrid, 1941]
65 p. 22 cm. (Publicaciones de la Cátedra de Organización y Administración de Empresas, Escuela Central Superior de Comercio, 2)
"Bibliografía": p. 65.

1. Italy—Pol. & govt.—1922-1945. 2. Mussolini, Benito, 1883-1945. I. Series: Madrid. Escuela Superior de Comercio. Publicaciones, 2.

JN5455 1941.L6 47-40313*

NL 0426052 DLC

VOLUME 337

Llobert y Ferrandiz, Maria de la Purificacion
see Calderon, Camila, pseud.

WO L792o 1898 LLOBET, Andrés Francisco, 1861-1907
Onze années de pratique chirurgicale. Paris, Baillière, 1898.
2 v. illus.

NL 0426054 DNLM

Llobet, Francisco
See
Llobet Mas y Navarro, Francisco.

BX890 .C22 Llobet, Gabriel de, Abp., 1872– ed.

Cabrières, François Marie Anatole de Rovérié de, *Cardinal*, 1830–1921.
Le cardinal de Cabrières, par monseigneur de Llobet. [Paris] La Bonne Presse [1944]

---

ar W 54115 no.6 Llobet, Georges.
Contribution à l'étude de la déchirure centrale du périnée. Toulouse, G. Kollat, 1912.
59 p. illus. 24cm.

Thèse--Toulouse.

NL 0426057 NIC CtY ICRL

Llobet, Isidoro Macabich
see
Macabich, Isidoro.

Llobet, J
... La constitution de l'Uruguay ...
Toulouse, 1926.
25 cm.
Thése - Univ. de Toulouse.
"Texte de la constitution": p. [36]-68.
"Bibliographie": p. [vii]-ix.

NL 0426059 CtY IU MH

Llobet, J.
... La constitution de l'Uruguay, texes et commentaires. [Toulouse] Faculté de droit, 1926.
ix, [1], 138 p. map. 25½cm. (Bibliothèque de l'Institut de législation comparée de Toulouse. Série des constitutions ... v)
"Bibliographie": p. [vii]-ix.

1. Uruguay—Constitutional history. I. Uruguay. Constitution.
A 32-58 Revised
Title from Carnegie Library of Congress Endow. Int. Peace JF12.T6 vol. 5
[r35c2] (342.082) 342.89

NL 0426060 DGW-C NN

LLOBET, Jose´
El notario de Malaga; comedia en un acto. Barcelona, sucesores de Ramirez y ca., 1886.

On cover:- El teatro.
By Jose Llobet and Alfredo Cruset.

NL 0426061 MH

Llobet, José Puiggarí y
see Puiggarí, José, 1821-1903.

LLOBET, Jose Y.
Estrecheces uretrales. Tesis. Buenos Aires, 1902.
1.8°.

NL 0426063 MH

Llobet, María Villangómez
see
Villangómez Llobet, María, 1913–

Llobet, Mariano Villangómez
see
Villangómez, Mariano.

ML29c .L78 case Llobet, Miguel, 1878–1938.

Falla, Manuel de, 1876–1946.
[Canciones populares españolas; arr.]
Sept chansons populaires espagnoles. Transcription pour chant et guitare par Miguel Llobet. 1931.

Llobet, Rafael Bori
see Bori Llobet, Rafael.

ND813 .S42L5 Llobet, Salvador.

Serra, Francisco, 1912–
F. Serra. Introducción de Salvador Llobet, con 60 reproducciones en huecograbado. Barcelona, S. A. Horta de Impresiones y Ediciones [1951]

Llobet, Salvador.
Granollers: estudio geográfico e histórico. [1. ed.] Granollers, Editorial Alpina, 1951.
61 p. illus., fold. col. map, plan. 19 cm. (Compendios de investigación, no. 1. Serie e geografía e historia, no. 1)

1. Granollers, Spain—Descr.

DP402.G84L5 58-43770

NL 0426069 DLC MH NN

Llobet, Salvador.
El límite septentrional de la vid y el olivo en Cataluña. Zaragoza, 1950.
22 p. illus. 24 cm. (Primer Congreso Internacional de Pireneístas del Instituto de Estudios Pirenaicos. [Monografías] no. general 41. Geografía, 7)
Published also in Actas del Primer Congreso Internacional de Pireneístas.
Bibliographical footnotes.
1. Viticulture—Spain—Catalonia. 2. Olive. I. Title. (Series: Spain. Consejo Superior de Investigaciones Científicas. Instituto de Estudios Pirenaicos. Monografías, 41. Series: Spain. Consejo Superior de Investigaciones Científicas. Instituto de Estudios Pirenaicos. Monografías. Geografía, 7)

SB397.L6 53-22341

NL 0426070 DLC NN

Llobet, Salvador.
El medio y la vida en Andorra, estudio geográfico. Barcelona, Consejo Superior de Investigaciones Científicas, Instituto Juan Sebastián Elcano, Estación de Estudios Pirenaicos, 1947.
347 p. illus., maps (part fold. col.) 24 cm.
"Bibliografía": p. [331]-336.

1. Andorra. I. Title.

DC924.L55 914.67 48-22668*

NL 0426071 DLC KU LU NN CaOTP

Llobet, Salvador.
El medio y la vida en el Montseny, estudio geográfico. Prólogo del Dr. D. Luis Solé Sabarís. Barcelona, 1947.
xi, 518 p. illus., maps (1 fold. col.) 25 cm.
At head of title: Consejo Superior de Investigaciones Científicas. Instituto Juan Sebastián Elcano. Estación de Estudios Pirenaicos.
"Premio Menéndez y Pelayo, 1945."
"Bibliografía": p. [491]-505.

1. Montseny. I. Title.

DP302.M59L6 914.67 47-29160*

NL 0426072 DLC ICU LU KU

Llobet, Salvador.
Montnegre: Coll Sa Creu, Orsavinyà, Vall del Tordera, Fuirosos, Vallmanya, Montbrugós y Vallalta; mapa topográfico excursionista, notas explicativas, itinerarios, turismo. Revisión del mapa y notas explicativas por Salvador Llobet y Pedro Montserrat. [1. ed.] Granollers, Editorial Alpina [1949]
23 p. 2 maps (1 fold. col. in pocket) 16 cm. (Cartografía, 5)

1. Montnegre region—Description and travel—Guide-books. I. Montserrat, Pedro, joint author.

DP302.M585L44 72-246948

NL 0426073 DLC

DP302 .M59P8 1955 Llobet, Salvador, joint author.
Puchades, José María.
Montseny: La Calma, Matagalls, Les Agudes, Turó de l'Home, Valls del Congost, Tordera, Riera d'Arbúcies, Riera Major y Gurri: mapa topográfico, notas explicativas, por J. M. Puchades, A. Bescós, y Salvador Llobet. [Nueva ed.] Granollers, Editorial Alpina [1955]

Llobet de Ximénez, Purificación
see Calderón, Camila, pseud.

PQ 6171 .A195 L792 Llobet Mas y Navarro, Francisco
Carta pastoral del muy ilustre señor prior de Meya sobre contrabandos. Barcelona, F. Surià y Burgada [1789]
52 p. 20 cm.

NL 0426076 WU NN

LLOBET Y MARTI, Ramón.
Monografia o breu descripcio historico-geografica de la vila y parroquia de Sant Marti de Malda (provincia de Lleyda y arquebisbat de Tarragona.) Lleyda, Imprempta Mariana, 1907.

NL 0426077 MH

LLOBET Y VALL-LLOSERA, José Antonio, 1799-1861
Cataluña antigua y Cataluña moderna, obra en la que se trata del comercio de los catalanes de la edad media en el levante y del porvenir de Barcelona. Barcelona, J.Jepus Roviralta, 1866.

"Nicrologia de D.Jose´ Antonio Llobet y Vall-Llosera que ..Leyo´ D.Antonio de Bofarull" pp.[7]-41.
Series: Half-title, Biblioteca catalana de autores antiguos y modernos. Seccion Castellana, 1.

NL 0426078 MH

VOLUME 337

Llobregat, José Javier de Barcáiztegui y Manso, conde del, 1881–
... Fuenterrabia, noticias históricas. Madrid, Talleres Voluntad, 1930.
196 p. 18½cm.
At head of title: Conde del Llobregat.
"Bibliografía": p. [189]–193.

1. Fuenterrabia, Spain.

32-29662
Library of Congress DP402.F8L6
[2] 946.8

NL 0426079 DLC

TP 936 L77n 1944 Llobregat González, Bernardo.
Nuevo manual de pinturas. Corregido, aumentado y ordenado por el Comandante de Armas Navales (Q) Bernardo Llobregat Gonzalez. Madrid, Editorial Naval, 1944.
181 p. 21cm.

"Obras consultadas": p. 5.

1. Paint.

NL 0426080 CLU

Llodra, Anibal Cabarrouy
see Cabarrouy Llodra, Anibal.

Llofriu, Gumersindo.
... Tratado práctico de la extracción del aceite de los orujos de oliva y uva por medio del sulfuro de carbono. Fabricación de sulfuro de carbono y jabones blandos y duros de aceite de orujo por Gumersindo Llofriu .... Madrid, Hijos de D. J. Cuesta, 1904.
[4], 174 p. 47 illus. 23½cm. (Monografías industriales.)

NL 0426082 ICJ

Llofriu, Gumersindo. ... Tratado práctico de la extracción del aceite de los orujos de oliva i uva por medio del sulfuro de carbono y jabones blandos y duros de aceite de orujo ... 2. tirada. Madrid, J. Cuesta, 1917. 174p. illus. 23cm.

NL 0426083 CU

Llofriu, Manuel.
Taxidermia; manual práctico del disecador de animales y plantas; caza, pesca y preparacion de aves, mamíferos, reptiles, peces, insectos, crustáceos, moluscos, anélidos y zoófitos; colocacion, trasporte y conservacion de colecciones de todas clases, formacion de herbarios, etc., etc., por Manuel Llofriu. Madrid, Cuesta, 1885.
240 p. illus. 22½cm.

1. Taxidermy.

15-18076
Library of Congress QL63.L6

NL 0426084 DLC

PQ 6226 .T4 v.7 Llofríu y Sagrera, Eleuterio, 1835-1880.
La caridad; comedia en dos actos y en verso. Música de los coros de Antonio Llanos. Madrid, Imp. de J. Morales y Rodriguez, 1868.
36 p. (In Teatro español. [Madrid, etc., 1787-1935] v. 7, [11])

"Representada ... por los alumnos de la Academia Infantil el 8 de Diciembre de 1867."
At head of title: Biblioteca dramatica infantil.

NL 0426085 MiEM NN MH

Llofríu y Sagrera, Eleuterio, 1835–1880.
... Castigo del cielo. Novela original de D. Eleuterio Llofriu y Sagrera. 3. ed. Madrid, Impr. de la Galería literaria, 1872.
128 p. front. 16cm.
At head of title: Galeria literaria—Murcia y Marti.

I. Title.

20-23682
Library of Congress PQ6534.L5C2

NL 0426086 DLC MH

Llofriu y Sagrera, Eleuterio
Fisica recreativa. Madrid, Galería Literaria, 1873
2 v. illus. (Biblioteca madrileña, 52-53)

NL 0426087 MH

He77 26 51 Llofriu y Sagrera, Eleuterio, 1835-1880.
Galileo. Episodio dramático en un acto y en verso, original de D. Eleuterio Llofriu y Sagrera ... Madrid,Impr.de A.Orejas,1875.
32p. 20cm. [Binder's title: Teatro español, 51]
"Estrenado ... en el teatro-Martín, la noche del 15 de enero de 1875."

NL 0426088 CtY NN

Llofiu y Sagrera, Eleuterio
Gloria, dinero y mujer; novela original. Madrid, Galería Literaria, 1872
2 v. illus. (Biblioteca madrileña, 17-18)

NL 0426089 MH

Llofriu y Sagrera, Eleuterio
Heroismo de una madre; novela original. Madrid, Galería Literaria, 1872
128 p. illus. (Biblioteca madrileña, 6)

NL 0426090 MH

Llofriu y Sagrera, Eleuterio.
Historia de la insurreccion y guerra de la isla de Cuba. Escrita en presencia de datos auténticos, descripciones de batallas, proporcionadas por testigos oculares, documentos oficiales y cuantas noticias pueden facilitar el exacto conocimiento de los hechos. Por D. Eleuterio Llofriu y Sagrera. Ed. ilustrada ... Madrid, Impr. de la Galería literaria, 1870-72.
4 v. plates, ports. 25½cm.

1. Cuba—Hist.—Insurrection, 1868-1878.

A 14-1656
Title from Univ. of Calif. F1785.L5 Printed by L. C.

NL 0426091 CU NcD InU NIC NjP TxU

Llofriu y Sagrera, Eleuterio
La madre de los pobres; novela original. Madrid, Galería Literaria, 1872
2 v. illus. (Biblioteca madrileña, 13-14)

NL 0426092 MH KU

Llofriu y Sagrera, Eleuterio
Maldito dinero; novela de costumbres. Madrid, Galería Literaria, 1874
2 v. illus. (Biblioteca madrileña, 89-90)

NL 0426093 MH

Llofriu y Sagrera, Eleuterio
El naufragio del grumente; novela original. Madrid, Galería Literaria, 1872
128 p. illus. (Biblioteca madrileña, 28)

NL 0426094 MH

Llofriu y Sagrera, Eleuterio, 1835-1880.
Tempestades del alma; leyenda de costumbres. Madrid, Galeria Literaria, 1873
127 p. illus. (Biblioteca madrileña, 49)

NL 0426095 MH

Lloga, Antonio.
Frutos verdes; versos y prosa. Habana [Imp. Editorial Neptuno, 195-?]
62 p. illus. 23 cm.

I. Title.

PQ7389.L615F7 55-57698

NL 0426096 DLC

Lloid, Lodowick
see
Lloyd, Lodowick, fl. 1573-1610

Lloid Dzhorzh, David
see **Lloyd George, David Lloyd George,** *1st earl,* 1863–1945.

Lloide, Lodowicke
see Lloyd, Lodowick, fl. 1573-1610.

Llokje runa, *pseud.*
... "Sara cosecho" (La cosecha del maíz) [Por] Llokje runa. [Cuzco, Talleres gráficos de H. G. Rozas sucs., 1940]
326, 14 p. 17½cm.
At head of title: Novela serrana.
"Ruma [!]; simi i serranismos": 14 p. at end.

I. Title.

43-38308 Revised
Library of Congress PQ8497.L53S3
[r45c2] 863.6

NL 0426099 DLC CSt MoU MiU

Llokje runa, *pseud.*
... Sombras de arcilla; cuentos indios. [Cuzco, H. G. Rozas sucs., 1939?]
1 p. l., iii, 143 p. 18cm.
At head of title: Llokje runa.
"Runa simi i serranismos": p. [133]-143.

I. Title.

45-49666
Library of Congress PQ8497.L53S6
[2] 863.6

NL 0426100 DLC

Llokkje runa, *pseud.*
see
Llokje runa, *pseud.*

VOLUME 337

Llollandllaff, Louis, pseud.
The Llollandllaff legends. By Louis Llollandllaff. London: Cassell and Co., 1894. 160 p. 12°.

1. Poetry (English). 2. Legends.
N. Y. P. L. May 24, 1916.

NL 0426102 NN

Llobera, José.
Grammatica classicae latinitatis ad Alvari Institutiones doctrinamque recentiorum conformata scholis hispanis, americanis, philippinis ... Barcinone, E. Subirana, 1919–1920.
3 p. l., [ix]–xxiv, 579 p. 21½cm.
At head of title: P. J. Llobera, s. j.
"Libri aditi sive bibliographia": p. [xv]–xix.

1. Latin language—Grammar—1870– I. Alvarez, Emmanuel, 1526–1582.

Library of Congress PA2085.L6 21–4102

NL 0426103 DLC CU

Llobera, José, ed.

PQ6410 .L3 1932 León, Luis Ponce de, 1528?–1591.
Obra poéticas. Texto y notas del P. José Llobera. Cuenca, Talleres Tipográficos del Seminario, 1931–32 [i. e. 1932–33]

Llobera, Miguel Costa y
see Costa y Llobera, Miguel, 1854-1922.

Llombart, Antonio
see Llombart Rodriquez, Antonio.

PC3897 .V2L8 Llombart, Constantino, 1849-1893
Cabótes y calaveres. Melonar de Valensia; galería de retratos de personaches sélebres, dibuixats á la ploma, en sério y en broma y en llenguache bilingue por Constantino Llombart y Chusep F. Sanmartin y Aguirre. Valensia, Llibrería de P. Aguilar, 1877.
206 p.
Satirical poems.

1. Catalan language--Dialects--Valencia.
I. Sanmartin y Aguirre, José F

NL 0426107 ICU

Llombart, Constantino, ed.

Escrig y Martínez, José, 1791–1867.
Diccionario valenciano-castellano de D. José Escrig y Martínez. 3. ed., corr. y aum. con un considerable caudal de voces ... y precedida además de un nuevo prólogo, la biografía de su autor, y un ensayo de ortografía lemosino-valenciana, por una sociedad de literatos bajo la dirección de D. Constantino Llombart ... Valencia, P. Aguilar, 1887[–96]

Llombart, Constantino.
Los fills de la morta-viva; apunts bio-bibliogràfichs pera la historia del renaiximent lliterari llemosí en Valencia, per en Constantí Llombart. Valencia, E. Pasqual, 1879.
783 p. port.
Cover has date: 1883.
1. Catalan literature - Valencia - Bio-bibl.
2. Valencia - Bio-bibl. I. Title.

NL 0426109 CLU

Llombart, Constantino, 1849-1893.
Matilde historia de una modista ... Valencia, Imprenta y libreria de Ramón Ortega, editor. Bajada de San Francisco, 1884.

NL 0426110 NNH

LLOMBART, Constantino, 1849-1893.
Niu d'abelles; epigrames llemosins.
2a ed. Valencia, Llibreria d'en P.Aguilar, 1876.

NL 0426111 MH

Llombart, [Constantino] 1849-1893.
¡La sombra de Carracuca! Juguete cómico-lírico bilingüe en un acto y en verso; segunda parte del titulado "¡Carracuca!" Música del maestro Cortina. Valencia: C. Vedejo, 1876. 24 p. 12°.
In: NPL p. v. 360, no. 24.
By C. Llombart and Cebrian

1. Drama (Spanish). 2. Cebrian, au. 3. Cortina, composer. 4. Title.
N. Y. P. L. April 10, 1912.

NL 0426112 NN ICRL MoU CtY

Llombart, Eduardo Gómez
see Gómez Llombart, Eduardo.

NL 0426113

RC266.Spl L77 1954 Llombart Rodriguez, Antonio
Lucha contra el cancer; cincuenta años de mortalidad y morbilidad cancerosa española, por Antonio Llombart y Ubaldo Gastaminza. [San Sebastian] Instituto Radio-Quirúrgico de Guipúzcoa, 1954.
190 p. diagrs., tables. 28cm.

Author's autograph presentation copy.
Bibliography: p. 175-179.

1. Cancer - Spain. 2. Spain - Statistics, Medical. I. Gastaminza, Ubaldo, jt. au. II. Title.

NL 0426115 NNC-M ICU DNLM

QZ 200 L792p 1943 LLOMBART RODRÍGUEZ, Antonio
El problema del cáncer en España, medicina social. Madrid, Delegación Nacional de Sanidad, 1943.
151 p.
"Premio 'Agustin de la Fuente,' Delegación Nacional de Sanidad."
1. Cancer - Spain

NL 0426116 DNLM

Llompart, Arturo Ramos
see
Ramos Llompart, Arturo.

Llompart, G. J., tr.
Metodo de piano... 1898
see under Lemoine, Henry, 1786-1854.

Llompart Aulet, Sebastián, ed.

HD9717 .Z3G6 1946 Guinea, Spanish. *Laws, statutes, etc.*
... Legislación del trabajo de los Territorios españoles del golfo de Guinea. Madrid [Selecciones gráficas] 1946.

Llompart Aulet, Sebastián.
...Sa tia remeis; comèdia de bon humor en 3 actes. Palma de Mallorca: "La Esperança" impr., 1935. 72 p. 19½cm.

879381A. 1. Drama, Catalan. 2. Catalan language—Dialects—Majorca. I. Title.
N. Y. P. L. May 12, 1937

NL 0426120 NN

Llona, Alfonso Letelier
see
Letelier Llona, Alfonso, 1912–

Llona, Emiliano.
La obra de Raymondi. Coleccion de articulos publicados en "El Comercio" de Lima. Por Emiliano Llona ... Lima, Impr. de P. Bacigalupi y c.ª, 1884.
2 p. l., 56 p. 28cm.

1. Raimondi, Antonio, 1826–1890.

Library of Congress Q143.R3L5 22–21989

NL 0426122 DLC DPU NcD

Llona, Florence, tr.

Benoit, Pierre.
Salt Lake; a novel by Pierre Benoit, tr. from the French by Florence and Victor Llona ... New York, A. A. Knopf, 1922.

Llona, Florence, tr.

Clermont-Tonnerre, Élisabeth (de Gramont) *duchesse* de, 1875–
Years of plenty, by E. de Gramont, ex-duchesse de Clermont-Tonnerre. Translated by Florence & Victor Llona. New York, J. Cape & H. Smith [1931]

Llona, Gonzalo.
Cantos vespertinos. Orillas del Guayas: colección completa de poesías de Gonzalo Llona. El autor pone esta obra bajo los auspicios del excmo. sr. dr. dn. Gonzalo S. Córdova ... Con motivo del centenario de la gloriosa batalla de Ayacucho. Guayaquil, Casa editorial Jouvin, 1924.
307, [6] p. ports. 22½cm.

I. Title.

Library of Congress PQ8219.L6 1924 861.6 35–24840

NL 0426125 DLC NN DPU

Llona, Gonzalo.
Ecos del alma; himnos i poemas a la patria, por Gonzalo Llona ... Guayaquil, Ecuador, Casa editorial Jouvin, 1921.
142, [2] p. incl. port. 21½cm.
"Autobiografía": p. [139]–142.

I. Title.

Library of Congress PQ8219.L6E3 24–5182

NL 0426126 DLC TNJ PPAmP

Llona, Jenaro.
Catholic church. *Pope, 1922–* (*Pius XI*)
... El matrimonio cristiano; comentarios y glosas a la carta encíclica de s. s., sobre el matrimonio cristiano, por colaboradores de "Razón y fe". Madrid, Editorial "Razón y fe" [1931

VOLUME 337

Llona, Lastenia Larriva de
see
Larriva de Llona, Lastenia, 1848–

Llona, Marcos.
Ni esto ni aquello; novela. Santiago de Chile, Impr. Casa Nac. del Niño ₍pref. 1952₎
510 p. 19 cm.

I. Title.

PQ8097.L7N5 55-20934 ‡

NL 0426129 DLC CU NN

PQ 8219 LLONA, NUMA POMPILIO, 1832-1907
.L63 A52 El amor supremo. Guayaquil, Imp. de "Los Andes", 1886.
49 p.

Poems.

NL 0426130 InU

Llona, Numa Pompilio, 1832-1907.
Ante la estatua de rocafuerte, en la tarde del 10 de enero de 1884. Sonetos ... Quito, "Los Principios" 1884.

NL 0426131 NNH

Llona, Numa Pompilio, 1832–1907.
Bosquejos de literatos colombianos, por Numa P. Llona. Bogota, Impr. de Silvestre y compañía, 1886.
32 p. 24½cm.
Poems.

1. Authors, Colombian. I. Title.

30-24693

Library of Congress PQ8219.L63B6 861.59

NL 0426132 DLC InU TNJ DPU

PQ8219 Llona, Numa Pompilio, 1832-1907.
L63C3 Cantos americanos; colección de poesías. Paris, Impr. de P.A. Bourdier, 1866.
224 p.

NL 0426133 CU ViU MH

LLONA, Numa P[ompilio], 1832-1907.
Clamores del Occidente; cien sonetos nuevos. Lima, Imp. del Universo, de C. Prince, 1880.

1.8°. Port. inserted.
Cover: Obras poeticas . Ser. I.

NL 0426134 MH TxU CtY NNH

Llona, Numa Pompilio, 1832-1907.
Clamores del occidente, interrogaciones poemas filosoficos ... Tercera edicion ... Lima, Carlo Prince, 1881.

NL 0426135 NNH

PQ 8219 LLONA, NUMA POMPILIO, 1832-1907
.L63 C62 Clamores del occidente. De la penumbra á la luz; poesías amatorias y diversas de Numa P. Llona. 2. ed., revisada por el autor. Lima, Imprenta del Universo, de Carlos Prince, 1882.
171 p.

NL 0426136 InU MH MiEM ICarbS

Llona, Numa Pompilio, 1832–1907.
Clamores del occidente; himnos, dianas y elegías, poesías patrióticas y religiosas de Numa P. Llona ... 3. ed., rev. por el autor. Lima, Impr. del universo de C. Prince, 1882.
2 p. l., ₍vii₎–x p., 3 l., ₍5₎–127, xliv p. 25cm.

I. Title.

13—8556

Library of Congress PQ8219.L63C5 1882

NL 0426137 DLC CU InU

Llona, Numa Pompilio, 1832-1907.
En el segundo centenario de la muerte de d. Pedro Calderon de la barca. Sonetos ... Quito, "Los Principios", 1884.

NL 0426138 NNH

Llona, Numa Pompilio, 1832–1907.
La escuadra española en las costas del Perú, composiciones poéticas de D. Numa P. Llona ... Paris, A. Laplace, 1865.
34, ₍1₎ p. 18cm.
Half-title: Con motivo de la toma de las islas de Chincha por la escuadra española.

1. Peru—Hist.—Spanish question, 1864. 2. Chincha Islands. I. Title.

25-5340

Library of Congress PQ8219.L63E7 1865

NL 0426139 DLC CtY

Llona, Numa Pompilio, 1832–1907.
La estela de una vida, poemas líricos de Numa P. Llona ... París, Garnier hermanos ₍1893₎
2 p. l., xlviii, 274 p., 1 l. front. (port.) facsim. 18cm. (*On cover:* Biblioteca poética)
"Numa P. Llona ₍biografía y juicios₎": p. ₍i₎–xxxvi.

I. Title.

30-4305

Library of Congress PQ8219.L63E8

NL 0426140 DLC CU NcD PBm MH NNH IU

LLONA, NUMA P.
Nuevas poesías. Série primera. Ginebra, Vérésoff y Garrigues [1870] 35 p. 18cm.

Film reproduction. Positive.
No more published?

1. Poetry, Ecuadorian.

NL 0426141 NN

Llona, Numa Pompilio, 1832-1907.
Nuevas poesias y articulos en prosa ... Série primera ... [Genève, Imprimera Vérésoff et Garrigues, 1870]

NL 0426142 NNH

Llona, Numa Pompilio, 1832-1907.
Odisea del alma; poema lirico ... 2. ed. hecha á la vista del autor. Lima, Impr. de Masias hermanos, 1877.
76 p. 19 cm.
Binder's title: Poesias. Autores peruanos. 2.
"Leido en el Club literario de Lima, en la sesion del 30 de marzo de 1876."
"Noticia biografica" signed: L. B. C.

NL 0426143 CtY CU MH

Llona, Rosa M.
El sueño de San Martin...
see under Alva, Rumualdo E.

Llona, Scipión E., 1865–
Teoría cosmológica cicloidal, por Scipión E. Llona... Tomo I Lima, Perú: P. Berrio y Cia, 1918– v. diagrs., illus., plates. 8°.

Contents: Tomo 1, parte 1. Movimientos cicloidales. Algunas de las pruebas astronómicas.

1. Cosmology. 2. Geophysics.
N. Y. P. L. March 16, 1923.

NL 0426145 NN WaU DPU ViU

Llona, Teresa María.
Celajes. (Viñetas de Romero Escacena) 1. ed. Madrid, Talleres Poligráficos, 1930.
109 p. port. 19 cm.
Poems.

I. Title.

PQ6621.L5C4 1930 861.6 39-15003 rev*

NL 0426146 DLC CtY

Llona, Teresa María.
Encrucijada ₍por₎ Teresa María Llona. Lima ₍Empresa Editorial Rimac, s. a.₎ 1938.
2 p. l., vii–xiv p., 1 l., 7–162 p., 1 l. 19cm.
Poems.
"Algunos comentarios sobre 'Celajes' ₍de la autora₎": p. 147–162.

I. Title.

Library of Congress PQ8497.L55E5 41-35637
₍2₎ 861.6

NL 0426147 DLC PSt WU MH NcU DPU

Llona, Teresa María.
Intersection. ₍Poems₎ translated by Marie Pope Wallis. Dallas, Story Book Press ₍1950₎
64 p. 20 cm.

I. Title.

PQ8497.L55E53 861.6 50-1403

NL 0426148 DLC NN

Llona, Victor.
...La croix de feu (Le Ku-Klux-Klan). Paris: Éditions Baudinière₍, 1928₎. 250 p. 12°.

407322A. 1. Knights of the Ku Klux Klan. 2. Title.
N. Y. P. L. May 20, 1929

NL 0426149 NN WaS NjP WaPS OCl

E178 Llona, Victor, tr.
.6
.P782 **Prado y Ugarteche, Javier,** 1871–1921.
... The historical destinies of the United States. Translated from the Spanish by Victor Llona. Lima ₍Imprenta T. Aguirre, 1942?₎

Llona, Victor, tr.

Cather, Willa Sibert, 1875–
... Mon Antonia, traduit de l'anglais par Victor Llona ... Paris, Payot, 1924.

Llona, Victor.
...Notes sur Louis Thomas, avec un portrait par Léon Bakst. Paris, Éditions du Siècle ₍1924₎ xiii, 140 p. front. 19cm.
"Bibliographie," p. ₍101₎–109; "A consulter," p. ₍139₎–140.

341324B. 1. Thomas, Louis, 1885–
N. Y. P. L. October 23, 1946

NL 0426152 NN MH

VOLUME 337

Llona, Victor, joint author.

[Tereshchenko, Sergieĭ]
Pierre le Grand, par Dmitri Novik [pseud.] et Victor Llona ... Paris, J. Tallandier [1931]

Llona, Victor.
... Les pirates du whisky, roman. Paris, Baudinière [°1925]
3 p. l., [9]-254 p., 1 l. 18½cm. (Littérature et art français)

I. Title.

Library of Congress PQ2623.L6P5 1925 26-14333

NL 0426154 DLC NN NjP

Llona, Victor, comp. and ed.
Les romanciers américains. Nouvelles . . . Textes choisis par V. Llona. Préfaces et traductions de Victor Llona, Bernard Fay . . . — Paris. Denoël & Steele. [1931.] 414, (1) pp. [Les romanciers étrangers contemporains.] 18 cm., in 8s.
Contents. — Sherwood Anderson: L'œuf. — Louis Bromfield: Allons chez Hinky Dink. — James Branch Cabell: L'histoire de la ratière. — John Dos Passos: L'homme qui disait s'appeler Jones. — Théodore Dreiser: Nègre Jeff. — Ernest Hemingway: Je vous salue Marie. — Sinclair Lewis: Elmer Gantry. — Ludwig Lewisohn: La pauvre dame. — Jack London: Un drame au Klondike. — Upton Sinclair: La mort de Paul Watkins. — Gertrude Stein: Melanchta. — Glenway Wescott: Dans un fourré.

D5100 — T.r. — S.r. — United States. Lit. Colls. — ...ction. Colls.

NL 0426155 MB CU ViU NjR CtY NNC

Llona, Victor, joint tr.

Benoit, Pierre.
Salt Lake; a novel by Pierre Benoit, tr. from the French by Florence and Victor Llona ... New York, A. A. Knopf, 1922.

Llona, Victor
Whisky-piraten, roman. Berlin, Th. Knaur [n.d.]
319p.

NL 0426157 ICRL

Llona, Victor, joint tr.

Clermont-Tonnerre, Élisabeth (de Gramont) *duchesse* **de,** 1875–
Years of plenty, by E. de Gramont, ex-duchesse de Clermont-Tonnerre. Translated by Florence & Victor Llona. New York, J. Cape & H. Smith [1931]

Llona Barros, Pablo
... La controversia contemporanea acerca de la noción de derecho subjetivo. Memoria de prueba para optar al grado de licenciado en ciencias jurídicas y sociales de la Universidad de Chile. [Santiago, "El Imparcial"] 1946.
108 p., 4 l. 27cm.
"Bibliografía principal": p. [109]

NL 0426159 MiU-L

Llona Gastañeta, Teresa María
see
Llona, Teresa María.

TT 708 .L7

Llona Velarde, Aurora.
Curso de lencería, para el primer año de instrucción secundaria técnica; preparado por Aurora Llona Velarde [y] desarrollado en el Instituto Nacional de Ciencias Domésticas y Artes Utiles, bajo la dirección de la Srta. Graciela Valderrama. Lima, Ministerio de Educación Pública, Dirección de Educación Técnica, Politécnico Principal del Perú, 1947.
iii l., 53 p. illus. 33 cm. (Peru. Dirección de E[du]cación Técnica. Serie de educación técni[ca] T 1000 - 6)
Mimeographed

NL 0426161 DPU

---

fF1521 .5 N5 no.18 x

Llonas, José Leocadio
¡Atengion! [sic] ¡Llamar á un hombre, á una Sociedad, á un pueblo, ó á una Nacion en el dia del combate ... Granada, 1856.
broadside 27x23cm. [Nicaraguan miscellany, no.18]

Dated: Junio 25 de 1856.

1. Walker, William, 1824-1860. I. Title.

NL 0426162 CU-B

Llonch, Arnaldo Izard
see Izard Llonch, Arnaldo.

Llongueras, José Jorge, *comp. and arr.*
Morito pitiiion; canciones populares españolas. Barcelona, Spes, 1941.
11 p. 18 x 25 cm.
For voice and piano.

1. Folk-songs, Spanish. I. Title.

M1779.L78M7 52-53143

NL 0426164 DLC MH

Llongueras, José Jorge, *comp. and arr.*
Serrana; canciones populares españolas. Barcelona, Spes, 1942.
11 p. 18 x 25 cm.
For voice and piano.

1. Folk-songs, Spanish. I. Title.

M1779.L78S4 52-53147

NL 0426165 DLC MH

Llongueras, José Jorge, *comp. and arr.*
La Tarara; canciones populares españolas. Barcelona, Spes, 1941.
11 p. 18 x 25 cm.
For voice and piano.

1. Folk-songs, Spanish. I. Title.

M1779.L78T3 52-53146

NL 0426166 DLC MH

Llongueras, José Jorge.
Ven a Belén; villancicos populares españoles. Armonizados por José J.Llongueras. Barcelona, Spes, 1940.

Score [11] p. (Canciones populares españolas, 4)
Piano-vocal score.

NL 0426167 MH

Llongueras, José Jorge, *comp. and arr.*
Ven a Belén; villancicos populares españoles. Barcelona, Spes, 1942.
11 p. 18 x 25 cm.
For voice and piano.

1. Folk-songs, Spanish. I. Title.

M1779.L78V4 52-53145

NL 0426168 DLC

849.98 L788ca 1955

Llongueras, Juan, 1880-
Cançoner popular de Nadal. 3.ed. Barcelona, Balmes, 1955.
223 p. illus. 16 cm.
With music (unaccompanied melodies)

1. Carols. 2. Catalan poetry (Collections) I. Title.

NL 0426169 MiU

783.6 L792c

Llongueras, Juan, 1880- comp.
Les cançons de Nadal: exhortació poemàtica per a ésser dita i predicada en el temps nadalenc [per] Joan Llongueras. Barcelona, L'Avenç, 1917.
195p. illus.(music) 16cm.

1. Carols. 2. Christmas. Poetry. 3. Catalan poetry. Collections. I. Title.

NL 0426170 IEN

Llongueras, Juan, 1880– *comp.*
... Les cançons de Nadal: exhortació poemàtica per a ésser dita i predicada en el temps nadalenc. 2. ed., augm. amb nombroses nadales populars. Barcelona [Tipografia Emporium] 1927.
1 p. l., [5]-277 p., 1 l. illus. 25½cm. [Quaderns de Joan Llongueres. II]
At head of title: Joan Llongueres.
Title vignette.
With music (unaccompanied melodies)
"La present edició sobre paper de fil Guarro consta de 50 exemplars, numerats a màquina i signats per l'autor. També se'n fa una altra edició sobre paper japó, limitada a 10 exemplars. L'edició corrent, sobre paper de la Casa Torras Domènech consta de 1.000 exemplars. Núm. 12."

"La present exhortació fou dita i predicada, per primera vegada durant els dies nadalencs de l'any 1915."—p. 271.
"Del mateix autor": p. 275-277.

1. Carols. 2. Christmas—Poetry. 3. Catalan poetry (Collections) I. Title.
[Full name: Juan Llongueras y Badia]

Library of Congress ML410.L77A1 33-35068
[2] [849.910822] 783.65

NL 0426172 DLC CtY

Llongueras, Juan, 1880– *comp.*
... Els cants de la Passió: exhortació poemàtica per a ésser dita i predicada en el temps de Passió i Setmana santa. Barcelona [Tipografia Emporium] 1928.
1 p. l., [5]-251 p., 1 l. illus. 25½cm. [Quaderns de Joan Llongueres. II]
At head of title: Joan Llongueres.
Title vignette.
With music (unaccompanied melodies)
"La present edició sobre paper de fil Guarro consta de 50 exemplars, numerats a màquina i signats per l'autor. També se'n fa una altra edició sobre paper japó, limitada a 10 exemplars. L'edició corrent, sobre paper de la Casa Torras Domènech consta de 1.000 exemplars. Núm. 12."

"La present exhortació fou dita i predicada, per primera vegada, la tarda del Divendres sant de l'any 1916, en l'Acadèmia de la joventut catòlica de Barcelona."—p. 243.
"Del mateix autor": p. 249-251.

1. Passion-music. 2. Jesus Christ—Poetry. 3. Catalan poetry (Collections) I. Title.
[Full name: Juan Llongueras y Badia]

Library of Congress ML410.L77A1 33-35067
[2] [849.910822] 783.3

NL 0426174 DLC CtY

VOLUME 337

Llongueras, Juan, 1880–
Evocaciones y recuerdos de mi primera vida musical en Barcelona. Barcelona, Librería Dalmau, 1944.
170 p. ports. 19 cm. (Colección Barcelona y su historia)

1. Musicians—Correspondence, reminiscences, etc. (Series)
Full name: Juan Llongueras y Badía.
ML410.L77A3 927.8 A 48-4964*
New York. Public Libr. for Library of Congress ₍1₎†

NL 0426175 NN DLC

Llongueras, Juan, 1880–
... L'istiu al cor, poesies; pròleg d'Amadeu Vives. Barcelona ₍Tipografia Emporium₎ 1928.
4 p. l., 11–156 p., 1 l. incl. front. 25½cm. ₍Quaderns de Joan Llongueres. III₎
At head of title: Joan Llongueres.
Title vignette.
"La present edició sobre paper de fil Guarro consta de 50 exemplars, numerats a màquina i signats per l'autor. També se'n fa una altra edició sobre paper japó, limitada a 10 exemplars. L'edició corrent, sobre paper de la Casa Torras Domè-nech consta de 700 exemplars. núm. 12."
"Del mateix autor": p. 153–156.
I. Title.
₍Full name: Juan Llongueras y Badía₎
33-17017
Library of Congress PC3941.L55 I 7 849.91

NL 0426176 DLC

LLONGUERAS, Juan, 1880-
Memories de missions de recerca, estudis monografics, croniques per Joan Llongueres, Higini Angles, Pere Bohigas, etc., Barcelona, [Imp. Elzeviriana,], 1928.
2 vol.
1.8°. Ports. and other illustr.
At head of title: Fundacio Concepcio Rabell i Cibils, vds. Romaguera. Obra del Cançoner popular de Catalunya. Materials. Vol. I, fasc. 2, II.

NL 0426177 MH

Llongueras, Juan, 1880–
Pau Casals, per Joan Llongueras, Joan ₍*i. e.* Josep₎ Ramón i Maria Carratalà ... Barcelona, Edicions de "La Nova revista," 1927.
63 p. illus., plates, ports. 18cm. (*Half-title:* Els Homes i les obres, n.° 1)

1. *Casals, Pablo, 1876– I. Ramón i Blanc, Josep. II. Carratalà, María, 1899–
₍Full name: Juan Llongueras y Badía₎
45-30774
Library of Congress ML418.C4L53

NL 0426178 DLC

Llongueras, Juan, 1880–
... Per la nostra sardana. Barcelona ₍Tipografia Emporivm₎ 1933.
2 p. l., 7–132 p., 1 l. 19cm.
At head of title: Joan Llongueres.
Illustrated t.-p.
Prose and poems.
"Del mateix autor": p. 129–132.

1. Sardana. I. Title.
₍Full name: Juan Llongueras y Badía₎
33-37609
Library of Congress GV1796.S3L6
₍2₎ 793.3109467

NL 0426179 DLC

Llongueras, Juan, 1880–
... El ritmo en la educación y formación general de la infancia. Barcelona ₍etc.₎ Editorial Labor, s. a. ₍1942₎
3 p. l., ₍5₎–198 p., 1 l. illus. (incl. music) XII pl. on 6 l., diagrs. 18½cm ₍Colección Labor. Sección II: Educación. N.° 406₎
"Bibliografía": p. ₍197₎–198.

1. Jaques-Dalcroze, Émile, 1865– 2. Music—Instruction and study 3. Musical meter and rhythm. I. Title.
₍Full name: Juan Llongueras y Badía
44-35937
Library of Congress MT22.L5
₍2₎ 780.7:

NL 0426180 DLC FMU

He74
50
Llontisca y Ribas, Antonio
Observaciones criticas, joco-serias sobre ciertos memoriales del ultimo impugnador del Theatro critico, el R.P.Fr. Francisco Soto y Marne ... Lisboa, M.Manescal da Costa, 1751.
40p. 20cm.

1.Feijóo y Montenegro, Benito Jerónimo, 1676-1764. 2.Soto y Marne, Francisco de

NL 0426181 CtY

Llontop Amorós, Carlos.
Sociedades anónimas; régimen legal en el Perú. Lima, 1954.
64 p. illus. 25 cm.

1. Corporation law—Peru. I. Title.
60-33220 ‡

NL 0426182 DLC MH-L MiU-L DS TxU

Llontop Amoros, Carlos.
Timbre fiscal único
see under
Peru. Laws, statutes, etc.

Llonze, Nofre.
El Tenorio en broma animalasia en siete actes ... Barcelona, Millà [1933]
80 p. 20 cm. (Catalunya teatral. Any II, núm. 39)

NL 0426184 NcU

Llop, Enrique Edo y
see Edo y Llop, Enrique, d. 1913.

QA103
L792
1877
Llop, F.
Tratado de arithmetica explicada para uso de las esculas primarias por F. Llop...
Mexico: tip. de J.M.Aguilar Oritz, 1877.
207 p. 15.5 cm.

NL 0426186 DAU

868.9925
L792m
Llop, Francisco
Maximiliano; drama en cuarto actos.
Mexico, Aguilar é Hijos, 1888.
96p.

NL 0426187 ICarbS

Llop, Francisco Broch y
see
Broch y Llop, Francisco.

Llop, Tomás Roig y
see
Roig y Llop, Tomás.

Llopart, Joaquín María de Castellarnau y de
see
Castellarnau y de Lleopart, Joaquín María de.

Llopart, Leopold Gil i
see Gil i Llopart, Leopold.

Llopart, Pedro.
Erfahrungen ueber vergiftungen durch "nitrose-gase" Inaug. diss. Zuerich, 1912.
Bibl.

NL 0426192 ICRL DNLM

Llopart y B., J.
¡Esperant contestació! Monòlech en vers y original, de J. Llopart y B... Barcelona: Lo Teatro regional, 1896. 2 p.l., (1)8–14 p. 8°.

1. Drama (Catalan). 2. Title.
N. Y. P. L. August 11, 1919.

NL 0426193 NN

Llopet (Céleste) [187–]. *Contribution à l'étude des troubles gastriques, consécutifs aux inflammations des organes génitaux de la femme. Sur le rôle du grand épiploon dans la pathogénie de ces troubles; leur thérapeutique. 70 pp. 8°. Lyon, 1901.

NL 0426194 DNLM

Llopis, Arturo, 1909-
Cómo conservar la memoria. [Barcelona, Ayma, 1955]

NL 0426195 MH

862
L792c
Llopis, Carlos
Con la vida del otro, farsa en un prologo y dos actos, el segundo dividido en dos cuadros. Madrid, Alfil c1953.
64p. (Coleccion teatro, 83)

"Premio Nacional de Teatro, 1952."

NL 0426196 FTaSU NN

Llopis, Carlos.
. . . Dos puntos de vista; humorada en tres actos. . . ¡Ahora si que son dos puntos! Apropósito hecho a propósito para Davó-Alfayate. . . Madrid, Las Máscaras, 1946. 83 p. 19cm. (Colección Las Máscaras. no. 3)

1. Drama, Spanish. I. Title. II. Title: ¡Ahora si que son dos puntos!
N. Y. P. L. August 23, 1950

NL 0426197 NN ICU

Llopis, Carlos.
Lo que no dijo Guillermo; aclaración en tres actos, divididoes en siete cuadros. ₍Madrid₎ Ediciones Alfil ₍°1953₎
70 p. 15 cm. (Colección Teatro, 69)

I. Title.
PQ6621.L54L6 56-34446 ‡

NL 0426198 DLC FTaSU NN LU FMU NcU WU

Llopis, Carlos.
Nosotros, ellas ... y el duende; conflicto familiar en un prologo y tres actos. Estrenado en el teatro Reina Victoria, de Madrid el día 3 de mayo de 1946. Madrid, Las Máscaras, 1946.
80 p. 20 cm. (Colección Las Máscaras, no. 5)

I. Title. II. Series.
PQ6621.L54N6 862.6 47-29195*

NL 0426199 DLC FTaSU KEmT MsSM TU NN NcU WU LU ICU

Llopis, Carlos Ruano
see Ruano Llopis, Carlos, 1879-1950.

VOLUME 337

Llopis, Felipe.
Hämophilie und ihre Behandlung (wissenschaftliche Grundlagen), von Felipe Llopis ... Mit 14 Abbildungen im Text und 4 Tafeln. Leipzig, J. A. Barth, 1929.
95 p. IV pl., diagrs. 23cm.

NL 0426201 ICJ PPC DNLM

Llopis, Felipe Mateu y
see
Mateu y Llopis, Felipe, 1901-

Llopis, Fernando Richart.
La salvasió de Salvilla; comòdia en un acte y en pròsa. Valencia, Ed. "Arte y Letras" ₍n.d.₎
29p. 18cm.

In: Teatre valencià. v.3, no.15.
Estrená en el "Salón Novedades", de Valensia, el día 10 de chuñ de 1927.

NL 0426203 NcU

Llopis, Jorge
see
Llopis Establier, Jorge, 1919

Llopis, Manuel Cano
see Cano Llopis, Manuel.

Llopis, Manuel G.
Alicia; opereta en un acto ...
For libretti see under Jover, Gonzalo, 1858-1922.

Llopis, Manuel G.
De Sevilla a los Corrales ...
For libretti see under Jover, Gonzalo, 1858-1922.

Llopis, Manuel G.
Los hombres feos; aventura
For libretti see under Jover, Gonzalo, 1858-1922.

Llopis, Onofre Carrasquer
see Carrasquer Llopis, Onofre.

Llopis, Rodolfo, 1895- joint ed
Alvarez Villamil, V ed.
Cartas de conspiradores ... por V. Álvarez Villamil y Rodolfo Llopis. Madrid ₍etc.₎ Espasa-Calpe, s. a., 1929-

Llopis, Rodolfo, 1895-
...El desarme moral, por Rodolfo Llopis. Valencia: E. Vich, 1931. 42 p. 17cm. (Cuadernos de cultura. ₍núm.₎ 34.)

724793A. 1. Disarmament. I. Ser.
N. Y. P. L. September 19, 1934

NL 0426211 NN

HX344 Z5L5 Llopis, Rodolfo, 1895-
Discurso pronunciado en la clausura del congreso de los jóvenes socialistas españoles en Toulouse (Francia) México, Federación de Juventudes Socialistas de España ₍1945?₎
21 p. 20cm.

1. Socialism in Spain - Addresses, essays, lectures. 2. Partido Socialista Obrero Español.

NL 0426212 GU MiU

Llopis, Rodolfo, 1895-
... Hacia una escuela más humana. Madrid, Editorial España, 1934.
205 p., 1 l. 20cm.

1. Education—Aims and objectives. I. Title.
₍Full name: Rodolfo Llopis Ferrándis₎
35-15239
Library of Congress LB775.L6
₍2₎ 370.1

NL 0426213 DLC

Llopis, Rodolfo, 1895- joint author.
... La revolución de septiembre...
see under Alvarez Villamil, V.

Llopis, Rodolfo, 1895-
... La revolución en la escuela; dos años en la Dirección general de primera enseñanza. Madrid, M. Aguilar, 1933.
275 p., 3 l. 19cm.

1. Education—Spain. I. Title.
₍Full name: Rodolfo Llopis Ferrándis₎
34-17559
Library of Congress LA912.L55
₍2₎ 372.946

NL 0426215 DLC

Llopis, Rodolfo, 1895-
Le Saint-Siège et Franco. Paris, Société universitaire d'éditions et de librairie ₍1955₎
78 p. illus. 18 cm. (L'Esprit laïque; revue trimestrielle d'idées et de documentation, no 4)

1. Church and state in Spain. I. Title.
Full name: Rodolfo Llopis Ferrándis.
BR1026.L56 57-28314 ‡

NL 0426216 DLC NIC CtY-D

862.6 L772f Llopis, Tono.
Federica de Bramante; o, Las florecillas del fango. Drama de capa y bigote con un poco de estrambote en un prólogo y tres actos con dos ricos entreactos [por] Tono y Jorge Llopis. [Madrid] Ediciones Alfil [c1954]
123 p. (Colección teatro, 99)

NL 0426217 KEmT ScU MsSM MiU

Llopis de Peinado, Luz.
La inteligencia de los escolares mexicanos. México, Ediciones Magisterio; distribución exclusiva Librería "La Educación," 1951.
148 p. 20 cm.

1. Intelligence levels—Mexico. I. Title.
LB1131.L57 52-17663 ‡

NL 0426218 DLC CU TxU

862 L7923e Llopis Establier, Jorge, 1919-
¡Enriqueta sí, Enriqueta no!, enigma policiaquísimo en tres actos. ₍Madrid₎ Alfil ₍c1955₎
86p. (Coleccion teatro,123)

"Premio Nacional de Teatro, 1952."

NL 0426219 FTaSU NN MiU ScU MsSM

PQ6621 A64V5 Llopis Establier, Jorge, 1919- joint author.
Lara, Antonio de.
La viuda es sueño; función en tres actos, original de Tono ₍pseud.₎ y Jorge Llopis. ₍Madrid₎ Ediciones Alfil ₍c1952₎

Llopis Ferrándiz, Rodolfo
see Llopis, Rodolfo, 1895-

Llopis Lladó, Noel.
Alto valle de Carançá. ₍1. ed.₎ Barcelona, Editorial Alpina ₍1946₎
64 p. illus. 16 cm. (Guías monográficas)

1. Ruisseau Carença Valley. I. Title.
DC611.R88L5 55-26043 ‡

NL 0426222 DLC

Llopis Lladó, Noel.
Andorra; Valira, d'Ordino, Tristaina, Estanyó, Casamanya, El Serrat, Comapedrosa, Pal. Mapa excursionista, texto español i texte française ₍per₎ N. Llopis Lladó. ₍1. ed.₎ Granollers, Editorial Alpina ₍1951₎
47 p. fold. col. map (inserted) 27 cm. (Editorial Alpina. Cartografía, 9)

1. Andorra—Description and travel.
DC928.L55 78-242464

NL 0426223 DLC

Llopis Lladó, Noel.
Contribución al conocimiento de la morfoestructura de los Catalánides; estudio geológico. Barcelona, Consejo Superior de Investigaciones Científicas, Instituto Lucas Mallada, Sección de Geomorfología, 1947.
372 p. illus., maps (part fold., part col.) 24 cm. and atlas (4 fold. col. maps) 25 cm.
Bibliography: p. ₍353₎-364.

1. Geology—Spain—Catalonia. 2. Geology, Structural.
QE283.L6 551.8 50-21557 rev 2

NL 0426224 DLC

QE 283 .O9 v.1 no.1 Llopis Llado, Noel
Estudio geológico de la caverna de Troskaetakokobea (Ataun-Guipuzcoa) por N. Llopis Llado y J.G. de Llarena. Oviedo, 1950.
27 p. illus., maps (1.fold.) diagrs. 24 cm. (Oviedo. Universidad. Instituto de Geología. Trabajos y memorias, año 1, num. 1)
Cover title.
Reprint from De Munibe, año 1, núm.4, p.153-179.
Bibliografía, p. 27.

1. Geology - Spain. 2. Caves - Spain. I. Llarena J.G. de., jt.auth. II. Title. III. Title: Troskaetako-kobea, Caverna de. (Series)

NL 0426225 DI

VOLUME 337

Llopis Lladó, Noel.
Estudio geológico de la cueva de Troskaeta, Ataun (Guipúzcoa) ₍por₎ Noel Llopis Lladó y Joaquín Gómez de Llarena. San Sebastián, 1949.
27 p. illus., map. 21 cm.
Cover title.
"Publicado en Munibe, revista del Grupo de Ciencias Naturales 'Aranzadi' della Real Sociedad Vascongada de Amigos del País."
Summary in French.
Bibliography: p. 27.
1. Troskaeta Cave, Spain. I. Gómez de Llarena y Pou, Joaquín, 1891- joint author.
GB608.61.L55 53-26085

NL 0426226 DLC

Llopis Lladó, Noel.
Garraf: La Morella, Montau, Vallbona, Les Agulles, Jafra, Aramprunyà, y Sant Ramon; mapa excursionista, notas explicativas, itinerarios, espeleología, turismo. Revisión y notas explicativas por N. Llopis Lladó y Antonio Bescós. ₍1. ed.₎ Granollers, Editorial Alpina ₍1949₎
23, ₍1₎ p. 2 maps (1 fold. col. in pocket) 16 cm. (Cartografía 6)
Bibliography: p. ₍24₎
1. Garraf region—Description and travel—Guide-books. I. Bescós, Antonio, joint author.
DP302.G205L46 74-246718

NL 0426227 DLC

Llopis Lladó, Noel.
Nociones de espeleología. ₍Con la descripción de la zona de la piedra de San Martín. 1. ed.₎ Granollers, Editorial Alpina, 1954.
72 p. illus. 19 cm. (Compendios de investigación, no. 3. Serie de geografía e historia, no. 3)
Includes bibliographies.
1. Speleology. I. Title.
GB601.L6 57-35535 ‡

NL 0426228 DLC MH CLU

Llopis Lladó, Noel.
Ordal: L'Aragall, Sant Jaume, Montcau, Puig d'Agulles, Puig Bernat, Sant Ponç, Pla d'Ardenya; montañismo, espeleología, turismo. Gráficos y notas explicativas por Noel Llopis Lladó. ₍1. ed.₎ Granollers, Editoria Alpina ₍1950₎
22, ₍2₎ p. 2 maps (1 fold. col. in pocket) 16 cm. (Cartografía 8)
Bibliography: p. ₍24₎
1. Ordal region—Description and travel—Guide-books. I. Title.
DP302.O58L6 70-246603

NL 0426229 DLC

Llopis Lladó, Noel.
La paleogeografía y el paisaje fósil de la Provincia de Lérida, por N. Llopis Lladó. Lérida, Imp. La Editora Leridana, 1948.
26 p. illus., maps. 25 cm.
At head of title: Instituto de Estudios Ilerdenses de la Excma. Diputación Provincial de Lérida. Delegación del Consejo Superior de Investigaciones Científicas.
"Se han editado 125 ejemplares como separata del trabajo que con el mismo título ha publicado la revista Ilerda ... en su número VII, fascículo único."
1. Paleogeography—Spain—Lérida (Province) I. Title.
QE501.L58 65-76947

NL 0426230 DLC

Llopis Lladó, Noel.
Problemas de tectónica alpídica del Pirineo. Primer Congreso Internacional de Pireneístas del Instituto de Estudios Pirenaicos. Zaragoza, 1950-
v. illus. 25 cm. (Consejo Superior de Investigaciones Científicas. ₍Instituto de Estudios Pirenaicos. Monografías; Geología, 2; no. general, 43)
Bibliography: v. 1, p. 37-44.
CONTENTS.—1. Sobre el tipo de cuenca de sedimentación.
1. Geology—Pyrenees. 2. Geophysics. (Series: Spain. Consejo Superior de Investigaciones Científicas. Instituto de Estudios Pirenaicos. Monografías. Geología, 2. Series: Spain. Consejo Superior de Investigaciones Científicas. Instituto de Estudios Pirenaicos. Monografías, 43)
QE283.L65 52-41731

NL 0426231 DLC DI NN CSt

QE263
O9
v. 2
no. 1
Llopis Lladó, Noel
Los rasgos morfologicos y geologicos de la cordillera Cantabro-Asturica. Oviedo, 1951.
p. [9]-51. 23 cm. (Oviedo. Universidad. Facultad de ciencias. Trabajos y memorias del Laboratorio de Geologia, ano 2, num. 1)
Cover title.
Bibliografia: p. [49]-51.
With this is bound his Problemas de tectonica alpidica del Pirineo. 1950.
1. Geology - Spain. I. Title. (Series: Oviedo. Universidad. Laboratorio de Geologia. Trabajos y memorias, v. 2, no. 1)

NL 0426232 DI

Llopis Lloret, Bartolomé, tr.
RC622
.B518
Bleuler, Eugen, 1857-1939.
... Afectividad, sugestibilidad, paranoia; versión española de la última edición alemana por el dr. Bartolomé Llopis Lloret. 1. ed. Madrid ₍etc.₎ Ediciones Morata, 1942.

Llopis Lloret, Bartolomé, tr.
RC602
.S24
Schneider, Kurt, 1887-
... Las personalidades psicopáticas; versión española del dr. Bartolomé Llopis. 1. ed. Madrid, Ediciones Morata, 1943.

Llopis Lloret, Bartolomé.
La psicosis pelagrosa; un análisis estructural de los trastornos psíquicos ... Barcelona ₍etc.₎ Editorial científico médica, 1946.
206 p. 22cm.
1. Pellagra. I. Title.
Med 47-824
U. S. Army medical library for Library of Congress ₍WC926L792p 1946₎ ₍2₎

NL 0426235 DNLM ICJ PPC

Llopis Pérez, Francisco
972.9105
L792C
... La cuestión antillana; orígenes del relevo del General Martínez Campos ... Almeria, Tip. de Fernández Múrcia, 1896.
47 p. 22 cm.
1. Cuba. Politics and government. 1875-1895. 2. Spain. Politics and government. 1886-1931. I. Title.

NL 0426236 NcD

Llopis Sancho, Antonio.
...En mis soledades. Prólogo de Felipe Cortines y Murube. Xilografías de Julio Pérez Palacio. Sevilla, Impr. "Los Remedios," 1945. 18cm.
Poems.

NL 0426237 NN

LLOPIS Y BOFILL, Joan.
Ensaig historich sobre la vila de Sitges. Barcelona, Imprempta de "La Hormiga de Oro." 1891.
Illustr.

NL 0426238 MH

Llopis y Pérez, Antonio
923.246
S171L
Historia política y parlamentaria de D. Nicolás Salmerón y Alonso, con sus más notables discursos en el Congreso, en las asambleas de los partidos republicanos y reuniones públicas y descripción del momento parlamentario y político en que los pronunció. Madrid. Impr. de Ediciones España, 1915.
xv, 844 p. port. 26 cm.
At head of title: Congreso de los Diputados.
"Pensamientos de D. Nicolás Salmerón": p. ₍739₎-740. "Apéndice" (p. ₍741₎-838): Otros trabajos filosoficos de Salmerón.
1. Salmerón y Alonso, Nicolás, 1838-1908. 2. Spain. Pol. & govt. 19th cent. Addresses, essays, lectures. I. Salmerón y Alonso, Nicolás, 1838-1908. Historia politica y parlamentaria.

NL 0426240 NcD MH CaBVaU

Lloque runa, *pseud.*
see
Llokje runa, *pseud.*

Llor, Martí Rodón
see
Rodón Llor, Martí.

Llor, Miquel
see **Llor Forcada, Miguel,** 1894-

PQ
6621
L86A2
Llor Forcada, Miguel, 1894-
Abismos, novela; traducción de José M. A. Paya. Barcelona, Ameller ₍19--?₎
194 p. 18cm.
I. Paya. José M. A., tr. II. Title.

NL 0426244 NIC

Llor Forcada, Miguel, 1894-
Cinc contes. Gravats a l'aiguafort de Manuel Humbert. Barcelona, 1935.
133 p. illus. 23 cm.
Issued in portfolio.
150 copies printed. "Tots ells sobre paper de fil especial de la Casa Guarro, compostos a mà en lletra elzeviriana clàsica, de la Casa Gans, i amb aiguaforts tirats a tòrcul. Exemplar no. 99."
CONTENTS.—Entreacte.—Deu minuts de conversa.—Idil·li sota el paraigua.—Una taca de tinta.—Oasi.
PC3941.L56C5 52-51326

NL 0426245 DLC

PC3941
L56H5
Llor Forcada, Miguel, 1894-
Història gris. Barcelona, Llibreria Catalònia, 1925.
230 p. (Biblioteca literària)

NL 0426246 CU

Hec58
L773
H5
1954
Llor Forcada, Miguel, 1894-
Història grisa. Pròleg de Carles Soldevila. [2.ed.] Barcelona, Editorial Selecta [1954]
264 p. port. 14 cm. (Biblioteca Selecta, 159. Secció: novel-la)
At head of title: Miquel Llor.

NL 0426247 CtY MoU IU NN InU

VOLUME 337

PC3946 .B3L8
Llor Forcada, Miguel, 1894- comp.
L'humor a la Barcelona del noucents. Il-lustracions inèdites de Xavier Nogués, preàmbul de Francesc Pujols. Barcelona, Aymà [1949]
245 p. illus.

1. Catalan wit and humor. I. Title.

NL 0426248 ICU MH

PC3941 L56J6
Llor Forcada, Miguel, 1894-
Jocs d'infants. [1.ed.] Barcelona, Editorial Ancora [1950]
237 p. (Col·lecció El Doff)

NL 0426249 CU KU IU InU CLU

Hec58 L773 L3 1954
Llor Forcada, Miguel, 1894-
Laura a la ciutat dels sants.[6. ed.]
Barcelona, Editorial Selecta [1951]
312 p. port. 14cm. (Biblioteca selecta, 91)

NL 0426250 CtY OCU NN

PC 3941 .L56 .S6
Llor Forcada, Miguel, 1894-
El Somriure dels Sants. [2. ed.]
Barcelona, Editorial Selecta [1952]
235 p. (Biblioteca Selecta, 97)
(A) El Somriure dels Sants.

NL 0426251 MoU NN CtY InU NcU

PC 3941 .L56T6
Llor Forcada, Miguel, 1894-
Tots els contes, 1925-1950. Barcelona, Editorial Selecta [1952]
288 p. (Biblioteca Selecta, 95)

NL 0426252 MoU NcU NN CtY

Llorach, Agustin Antich de
see Antich de Llorach, Agustin, 1698-1752.

Llorach, E Alarcos
see Alarcos Llorach, Emilio.

Llorach (Esteban). *Sur l'hygiène de la première enfance. 46 pp. 4°. *Paris*, 1859.

NL 0426255 DNLM

LLORACH, Ezequiel.
Vibraciones del sentimiento; poesias. 2a ed. Madrid, tip. estereotipia Perojo,1878.

NL 0426256 MH PU

Micro-card
Llorar por los muertos, y suspirar por los vicos, ó Las lagrimas engañadoras de una viuda; comedia en tres actos. Valencia, José Gimeno, 1824. [Louisville, Ky., Falls City Microcards, 1961]
1 card. [Four Centuries of Spanish Drama]

Microprint copy.
Collation of the original: 61 p. 16 cm.

I. Title: Las lagrimas engañadoras de una viuda. II. Series.

NL 0426258 LU MoU ICRL

Llorca, Alonso de, *ed.*
El declamador mexicano, recitaciones patrióticas, cívicas y folklóricas [antología. 1. ed.] México, Librería Ariel [1947]
412 p. 20 cm.
Poems.

1. Poetry—Collections. 2. Mexican poetry (Collections) I. Title.

PN6108.L55 861.082 48-17542*

NL 0426259 DLC NN CtY

Llorca, Angel
Más lecciones de cosas. Gerona, Dalmáu Carles, 1912.
295 p. illus.

NL 0426260 MiD

PC 4065 L6
Llorca, Angel.
El primer año de lenguaje; conversación, dibujo, escritura, lectura de lo escrito, trozos en prosa y verso de buenos autores para recitarlos, para frasearlos y para servir de modelo en las lecturas del maestro; canto, gramática, dictado-composición, etc. Madrid, Jiménez Fraud,1923.
216p. 19cm. (His Programas graduados de edución primaria)

1. Spanish language - Study and teaching. I. Title.

NL 0426261 MU

Llorca, Angel.
... El primer año de lenguaje; conversación, dibujo, escritura, lectura de lo escrito, trozos en prosa y verso de buenos autores para recitarlos, para frasearlos y para servir de modelo en las lecturas del maestro; canto, gramática, dictado-composición, etc. 2. ed., corr. y ampliada para que pueda orientar la enseñanza del lenguaje en todos los años de escuela primaria. Madrid, Hernando, 1933.
305 p. illus. 19cm. (*His* Libros de orientación escolar)

1. Spanish language—Study and teaching. I. Title.

Library of Congress PC4065.L6 1933 34-19285
[2] 468.2

NL 0426262 DLC

G270 L773a
LLORCA, BERNARDINO, 1898-
... Atlas y cuadros sincrónicos de historia eclesiástica. Barcelona, Buenos Aires [etc.] Editorial Labor, s.a. [1950]
112p. maps. 28cm.

Bibliography: p.13-14.

1. Ecclesiastical geography - Maps. 2. Church history. I. Title.

NL 0426263 TxU WU IaU GU

BX1735 A5
Llorca, Bernardino, 1898- ed.

Catholic Church. *Pope.*
Bulario pontificio de la Inquisición española en su período constitucional (1478-1525), según los fondos del Archivo Histórico Nacional de Madrid. Ed. crítica por Bernardino Llorca. Roma, Pontificia Università gregoriana, 1949.

BX 81 .L79
Llorca, Bernardino, S.J., 1898-
Compendio de historia de la iglesia catolica. Madrid, Editorial Razon y Fe, S.A., 1951.
632 p. 16 cm.

1. Catholic Church - History.

NL 0426265 DCU

BV 15 L79
Llorca, Bernardino, 1898-
Historia de la Iglesia Católica en sus cuatro grandes edades: antigua, media, nueva, moderna. Madrid, Biblioteca de Autores Cristianos, 1955.
4 v. 21 cm.
Vol. 1: 2a. ed.; v.4: por Francisco J. Montalban, revisada y completada por B. Llorca y Ricardo G. Villoslada.
1. Church history. I. Garcia Villoslada, Ricardo, 1900. II. Leturia, P. de. III. Montalban, Francisco J., 1895-1945.

NL 0426266 IMunS IU PU NcD WU

Llorca, Bernardino.
... La inquisición en España, por Bernardino Llorca, s. J. Barcelona [etc.] Editorial Labor, s. a., 1936.
317 p., 2 l. xx pl. (incl. port., facsims.) 18½cm. (Colección Pro ecclesia et patria. [12])
"Bibliografía de las obras más importantes sobre la inquisición": p. [315]-317.

1. Inquisition. Spain.

Library of Congress BX1735.L55 41-1285
[2] 272.20946

NL 0426267 DLC ViU OU NcD NcU IU

272.2 L7721 1946
LLORCA, BERNARDINO
... La inquisición en España, por Bernardino Llorca, S.J. 2d ed. Barcelona [etc.] Editorial Labor, s.a., 1946.
319p.,1l. XI pl.(incl. port.,facsims.) 18½cm. (Colección Pro ecclesia et patria. [12]
"Bibliografía selecta sobre la inquisición": p.[317]-319.
"Primera edición: 1936. Segunda edición: 1946."

1. Inquisition. Spain. I. Series

NL 0426268 TxU DLC

BX1735 .L67
Llorca, Bernardino, 1898-
La Inquisicion en España. 3.ed. Barcelona, Editorial Labor, 1954.
319 p., 11 plates (incl. port., facsims.)
(Coleccion Pro Ecclesia et Patria, 12)
Includes bibliography.

1. Inquisition. Spain.
Series.

NL 0426269 ICU NNC NBuC MB WU MiU IaU CU NBuU

Llorca, Bernardino, 1898-
La Inquisición Española; estudio crítico. Comillas, Universidad Pontificia, 1953.
190, [5] p. 18 cm.
Bibliography: p. [196]-[195]

1. Inquisition. Spain. I. Title.

BX1735.L56 55-25268

NNJ IU
NL 0426270 DLC CoU DAU NcD MU OCH NN PU CtY PSt

BX945 .L5
Llorca, Bernardino, 1898-
Manual de historia eclesiástica, por el p. Bernardino Llorca ... Barcelona [etc.] Editorial Labor, s. a., 1942.
xxiv, 899, [1] p. 22½cm.
Includes bibliographies.

1. Church history. 2. Catholic church—Hist.

Library of Congress BX945.L5 45-17071
[2] 282

NL 0426271 DLC NN MB

VOLUME 337

282
L773m
1946 LLORCA, BERNARDINO, 1898-
Manual de historia eclesiástica, por el p. Bernardino Llorca ... 2. éd. revisada. Barcelona, Madrid [etc.] Editorial Labor, s.a., 1946.
xxxii, 921p.,1l. 2 fold. maps. 22cm.
Includes bibliographies.
1. Church history. 2. Catholic church - Hist.

NL 0426272 TxU

Llorca, Bernardino, 1898-
Problemas religiosos y eclesiásticos de los Reyes católicos. Zaragoza, Institución "Fernando el católico" (C.S.I.C.) 1952.
24 p. 25 cm. (V congreso de historia de la corona de Aragón. Ponencia, 13)
1. Church and state in Spain. 2. Catholic Church in Spain. I. Title.

NL 0426273 CU-S KU OU

BX 4700
V75 L4 Llorca, Bernardino, 1898-
San Vicente Ferrer y su labor en la conversion de los judios; en el centenario de su canonizacion. [Madrid? 1955?]
[277]-296 p. 23 cm.
Includes bibliographical references.
1. Vincentius Ferrerius, Saint, ca. 1350-1419 2. Jews--Conversion to Christianity I. Title

NL 0426274 OU

Llorca, Bernardino, 1898-
Die spanische inquisition und die "Alumbrados" (1509-1667) nach den originalakten in Madrid und in anderen archiven ... von Bernardino Llorca ... Berlin und Bonn, F. Dümmler, 1934.
xvi, 138 p., 1 l. 24cm.
Inaug.-diss.—Munich.
Lebenslauf.
Published also without thesis note.
"Verzeichnis der benutzten ungedruckten aktenstücke": p. viii-x.
"Literaturverzeichnis": p. xi-xvi.
1. Alumbrados. 2. Inquisition. Spain. I. Title.
41-33953
Library of Congress BX1735.L57 1934 a
[2] 272.20946

NL 0426275 DLC CtY MiU PU PBm NjP

Llorca, Bernardino, 1898-
Die spanische inquisition und die "Alumbrados" (1509-1667) nach den originalakten in Madrid und in anderen archiven, von Bernardino Llorca, s. J. Berlin und Bonn, F. Dümmler, 1934.
xvi, 138 p., 1 l. 25cm.
"Wichtige berichtigungen" slip inserted.
"Verzeichnis der benutzten ungedrucken aktenstücke": p. viii-x; "Literaturverzeichnis": p. xi-xvi.
1. Alumbrados. 2. Inquisition. Spain. I. Title.
34-38705
Library of Congress BX1735.L57
[2] 272.20946

NL 0426276 DLC

Llorca, Blas Vives
see
Vives Llorca, Blas.

Llorca, Carmen
see
Llorca Vilaplana, Carmen.

Llorca, Enrique González
see González Llorca, Enrique.

Llorca, Fernando, ed
Lo que cantan los niños; canciones de cuna, de corro, coplillas, adivinanzas, relaciones, juegos y otras cosas infantiles, anotadas y recopiladas por Fernando Llorca. Ilus. de R. Manchón. Madrid, Llorca y Co. [1914]
199 p. illus., diagrs. 19cm.
1.Children's songs, Spanish. 2.Nursery rhymes. 3.Games. I.Title.

NL 0426280 CSt CU CtY OO ODW NjP PU MdBJ

Llorca, Fernando, ed.
Lo que cantan los niños; canciones de cuna, de corro, coplillas, adivinanzas, relaciones, juegos y otras cosas infantiles, anotadas y recopiladas por Fernando Llorca. Ilustraciones de R. Manchon. 4. ed. Valencia, Prometeo [192-?]
199, [1] p. illus., diagrs. 19cm.
Without music.
1. Children's songs, Spanish. 2. Games. I. Title.
29-12828
Library of Congress PZ74.3.L5

NL 0426281 DLC PBm

Llorca, Fernando.
... Sublevación del infante don Jaime de Aragón seguida de la de su hijo del mismo nombre (1462-1477) Valencia [Prometeo, 1931?]
102 p., 1 l. plates, map. 25cm.
On cover: Contribución al estudio de la acción militar de la ciudad [Valencia] durante la época foral.
"Visita á Villahermosa": p. [99]-102.
1. Jaime, infante of Aragon, d. 1465. 2. Jaime, infante of Aragon, d. 1477. 3. Valencia (City)—Hist. 4. Aragon—Hist. 5. Villahermosa, Spain—Descr. I. Title.
32-31241
Library of Congress DP133.4.L6
[2] 946.02

NL 0426282 DLC

Llorca, Francisco.
Algunos comentarios en el campo experimental del seguro de vida, rol social que desempeña el agente de seguros. Prólogo del doctor Pedro Smolensky. Rosario, Tipo-lito "Pomponio," 1941.
81 p. 23cm.
1. Insurance, Life. I. Title.
HG8771.L57 47-39459*

NL 0426283 DLC

Llorca, Francisco Orts
see Orts Llorca, Francisco.

Llorca, José, comp.
Z7882
.A73
Argentine republic. *Instituto nacional del tabaco.*
... Bibliografía sobre fitotecnia del tabaco; compilada por José Llorca ... ayudante técnico Dep. Experimentación. [Buenos Aires, 1942?]

Llorca, José, comp.
Z7882
.A74
Argentine republic. *Instituto nacional del tabaco.*
... Ensayo de una bibliografía argentina del tabaco, por José Llorca, ingº agrº., técnico del Departamento de experimentación. [Buenos Aires, 1943?]

Llorca, José María Vives
see Vives Llorca, José María.

Llorca, Rodolfo González
see González Llorca, Rodolfo.

Llorca, Vicenç Riera
see Riera Llorca, Vicenç.

330.9
L773g Llorca García, Enrique.
Geografía económico-comercial. Madrid, "Instituto Editorial Reus," Centro de Enseñanza y publicaciones, 1942.
953p. 23cm.
1. Geography, Economic.

NL 0426290 IU

Llorca Linares, Juan Francisco.
... Manual practico de los tribunales industriales con arreglo a la ley de 19 de mayo de 1908 ... Madrid, 1909.
384 p.

NL 0426291 DL

940
L77e Llorca Vilaplana, Carmen
Europa ¿en decadencia? Prólogo de Lain Entralgo. Madrid, Impr. "Prensa Española" [1949]
127p. 20cm.
Bibliographical footnotes.
1. Europe--Hist. 2. Europe--Hist.--Philosophy. 3. Europe--For. rel. 4. Europe--Politics.

NL 0426292 IU NN

Llorca Vilaplana, Carmen.
El mariscal Bazaine en Madrid. Prólogo del Dr. D. Jesús Pabón. Madrid, 1951.
321 p. illus., ports., fold. map. 23 cm.
Tesis—Universidad de Madrid.
Bibliography: p. 313-[320]
1. Bazaine, Achille François, 1811-1888.
DC280.5.B3L5 55-23488

NL 0426293 DLC IU MH CU NcD TxU

Llorca Vives, Bernardino
see
Llorca, Bernardino, 1898-

Llord, Josep
Campanya montemolinista de Catalunya o guerra dels matiners, setembre de 1846 a maig de 1849. Comprén també el moviment republicà de 1848-1849. [Barcelona, Impr. Altés, 1926]
212 p. illus.

NL 0426295 MH ICN

VOLUME 337

Llord O'Lawlor, Manuel.
Apuntes de derecho administrativo del Protectorado de España en Marruecos. Adaptado al programa oficial del Centro de Estudios Marroquíes. Tetuán, Editora Marroquí, 1952.
208, [1] p. 21 cm.
At head of title: Delegación de Educación y Cultura. Centro de Estudios Marroquíes.
Bibliography: p. [209]
1. Administrative law—Morocco (Spanish Zone) I. Tetuán. Centro de Estudios Marroquíes. II. Title.
55-18896

NL 0426296 DLC

Llord y Gamboa, Ramon.
Estudios de quimica y geologia hidrológicas. Memoria premiada por la Real academia de medicina de Madrid ... por Ramon Llord y Gamboa ... Madrid, Imprenta de R. Rojas, 1903.
307 p., 1 l. illus. 19½cm.
1. Water, Composition of.
G S 8-380
Library, U. S. Geol. survey 797 L77

NL 0426297 DI-GS ICJ

Llorden, Andrés
Apuntes histor. de los conventos Sevillanos d. Religiosas Ag. Escorial, 1944.

NL 0426298 NNAHI

Llordén, Andrés.
Biografía del excelentísimo y reverendísimo P. fray Martín de León y Cárdenas, religioso agustino y arzobispo de Palermo, Sicilia. [Málaga] 1947.
131 p. illus. 16 cm. (Excma. Diputación Provincial de Málaga. Publicaciones del Instituto de Cultura, ser. B, v. 5)
"Notas bibliográficas": p. 123-124.
1. León y Cárdenas, Martín de, Abp., 1585 (ca.)-1655. (Series: Málaga, Spain (Province) Instituto de Cultura. Publicaciones, ser. B, v. 5)
BX4705.L543L55 922.245 49-28466*

NL 0426299 DLC NNAHI

Llordon, Andres
El colegio de San acacio y la biblioteca... fundo el...Cardanal Gaspar de Molina y Oviedo, Agustio (extr. Ciuda de Dios 1942/3.

NL 0426300 NNAHI

Llordén, Andrés.
Ensayo histórico-documental de los maestros plateros malagueños en los siglos XVI y XVII; datos inéditos del archivo de protocolos para la historia del arte de la platería en la ciudad de Málaga. Málaga, R. Sánchez, 1947.
xxi, 243 p. facsims. 26 cm. (Libros malagueños, v. 3)
At head of title: Excmo. Ayuntamiento de Málaga. Delegación de Cultura.
1. Silversmithing—Spain—Málaga (City) (Series)
NK7162.L55 52-28812

NL 0426301 DLC NNAHI OU

Ec LE 46 .C82L5
[Llore Mosquera, Víctor]
La Universidad de Cuenca: apuntes para su historia. [Cuenca, 1951]
56 p. 22 cm.

NL 0426302 DPU

Lloreda, Gustavo.
... El arbitraje internacional y la Liga de las naciones ... Bogota, Tipografía Minerva, 1919.
107 p. 24cm.
Tesis—Colombia. Universidad. Bogota.
1. Arbitration, International. 2. League of nations.
Library of Congress JX1952.L65 19-19822

NL 0426303 DLC NBuU

Llorenç, Gracia B. de
see Llorens, Gracia B. de.

BX3344 .M3L7
Llorens, Antoni.
Real Cartuja de Jesús Nazareno de Valldemosa en la Isla de Mallorca. Palma de Mallorca, Francisco Soler Prats, 1929.
96p. VIII plates. 18cm.

NL 0426305 NNU-W

Llorens, Antoni, *ed.*
... Santa Catarina Thomasa i els seus amics. Palma de Mallorca [Casa d'En Francesc Soler i Prats] 1930.
1 p. l., [5]-220 p., 2 l. 17½cm.
"Además de l'edició en paper corrent d'aqueste obra, l'en he fet un tiratje especial de cinc exemplars en paper de fil, numerats i signats per l'autor. nº 5": manuscript note on fly-leaf.
CONTENTS.—Santa Catarina Thomasa.—Els escrits del canonge Abrines.—Les adicions als plecs del canonage Abrines. Les atestacións de sor Margarida Sant Joan. Una carta de fra Domingo de Larez.—El p. d. Vicens Mas. Tres capitols sobre la vida de sor Thomasa.—El prior d. Pere Caldés. L'instrucció para oir la santa missa. La vida inacabada de sor Thomasa. Vida del canonge Abrines.—Fra Antoni Castañeda.
1. Catarina Thomasa, Saint, 1531?-1574. I. Title.
Library of Congress BX4700.C255L6 33-12714
[2] 922.246

NL 0426306 DLC

Micro-card
[Lloréns, B]
La independencia de Nápoles, ó El pirata levantino. Drama de espectáculo, en cuatro actos y un prólogo, escrito en verso. Barcelona, Manero, 1869. [Louisville, Ky., Falls City Microcards, 1960]
2 cards. [Four Centuries of Spanish Drama]
Microprint copy.
Collation of the original: 127 p. 21 cm.
I. Title. II. Title: El pirata levantino III. Series.

NL 0426307 LU OrU FU ICRL

Llorens, Bartolomé.
Secreta fuente. Prólogo de Carlos Bousoño. [1. ed.] Madrid, 1948.
87 p. 15 cm. (Adonais, 48)
I. Title.
PQ6621.L56S4 861.6 50-25965 rev

NL 0426308 DLC MH IU

Llorens, D. Carlos.
Por balcones y ventanas
For libretti see under Blasco y Moreno, Rafael, 1836-1884.

Llorens, Eduardo F **Lores y**
see
Lores y Llorens, Eduardo F

Llorens, Eduardo L., 1886- joint ed.

Johannsen, Gustav Kurt, *ed.*
Actividades mundiales de Hamburgo; edición preparada por G. Kurt Johannsen [y] E. L. Llorens. Hamburgo, Sociedad hamburguesa de publicaciones [193-]

Llorens, Eduardo L 1886-
La autonomía en la integración política, por Eduardo L. Llorens ... 1. ed. Madrid, Editorial Revista de derecho privado [°1932]
xi, 370 p. 20cm.
"Apéndice, textos relativos a la autonomía regional en España": p. [317]-370.
1. State, The. 2. Political science. 3. Autonomy. 4. Spain—Constitutional law. I. Title.
Library of Congress JC271.L6 33-19892
[2] 320.1

NL 0426312 DLC

Llorens, Eduardo L.
La guerra y el derecho by Eduardo L. Llorens Hamburgo Broschel & cie, editores, 1916
91 p. 22 cm.
50827

NL 0426313 DNW MH

JX 4521 L568 LAC
Llorens, Eudardo L , 1886-
La guerra y el derecho, por Eduardo L. Llorens. Quito, Impreso por P.A. Garzón, 1916.
48p. 22cm.
1. War (International law) I. Title.

NL 0426314 TxU DNW

Llorens, Eduardo L 1886-
... La igualdad ante la ley, por E. L. Llorens ... Murcia [Instituto de estudios políticos de la Universidad de Murcia] 1934.
174 p. 22½cm.
At head of title: Instituto de estudios políticos de la Universidad de Murcia.
"Abreviaturas bibliográficas": p. [169]-171.
1. Equality. 2. Constitutional law. 3. Comparative law. I. Murcia, Spain. Universidad. Instituto de estudios políticos. II. Title.
42-44215

NL 0426315 DLC

Llorens, Eduardo L.
... Der krieg und das recht, aus dem spanischen übers. von Aug. Strube. Einzige berechtigte übersetzung. Hamburg, Broschek & co., 1916.
111, [1] p. 22cm.
1. European war, 1914-1918. 2. War (International law) I. Strube, Aug., tr. II. Title.
Library of Congress JX1392.L65 21-18918

NL 0426316 DLC CtY NcD

Llorens, Eduardo L.
... Monroismus panamerikanismus. Einzige berechtigte übersetzung aus dem spanischen von Aug. Strube. Hamburg, Broschek & co., 1918.
80 p. 22cm.
1. American republics. 2. Monroe doctrine. I. Strube, Aug., tr. II. Title.
Library of Congress F1418.L79 21-8422

NL 0426317 DLC

VOLUME 337

Llorens, Eduardo L 1886–
... La negación en español antiguo con referencias a otros idiomas, por E. L. Llorens. Madrid, J. Molina, impresor, 1929.
198 p., 1 l. 24½cm. (Revista de filología española.—Anejo XI)
At head of title: Junta para ampliación de estudios.—Centro de estudios históricos.
"Obras citadas en abreviatura": p. 193–198.
1. Spanish language—Old Spanish—Negatives. 2. Grammar, Comparative and general—Negatives. I. Title.
31-4048
Library of Congress PC4715.L6
[465.9] 467.0159

NL 0426318 DLC KyU OrU PSt MU PPT NcU OU OCU OClW MiU PU PBm FMU GU CU KU NBuU MoSU NcD IaU

Llorens, Eduardo L 1886–
... Qué es la tecnocracia? 1. ed. Madrid, Editorial Revista de derecho privado [°1933]
2 p. l., 114 p., 1 l. 19½ cm. ([Biblioteca de la Revista de derecho privado] ser. E, v. 1)
1. Technocracy.
HB87.L5 330.1 34—16485

NL 0426319 DLC IEN

Llorens, Edward, tr. & ed.
Balades i contes japonesos. Barcelona, Llibr L'avenq.,1909.
91 p.

NL 0426320 PU

Llorens, Emilio, ed.

Anuario geográfico argentino. 1941–
Buenos Aires, Comité nacional de geografía [1942–

Llorens, Emilio.
La Argentina debe industrializarse. Buenos Aires, 1947.
74 p. illus. 27 cm.
At head of title: Universidad de Buenos Aires. Facultad de Ciencias Económicas.
"Monografía presentada en noviembre de 1945 para aspirar al cargo de profesor adjunto de geografía económica nacional."
1. Argentine Republic—Indus. I. Title.
HC175.L74 68-51532

NL 0426322 DLC

Llorens, Emilio, joint author.
FOR OTHER EDITIONS SEE MAIN ENTRY

García-Mata, Rafael.
Argentina económica, por Rafael García-Mata y Emilio Llorens ... 2. ed. Buenos Aires, Compañía impresora argentina, s. a., 1940.

HB3560 .A7L7 (SPR)
Llorens, Emilio.
Demografía Argentina; esbozo de una política demográfica [por] Emilio Llorens [y] Carlos Correa Avila. Buenos Aires, 1948.
141 p. illus. 26 cm.
At head of title: Universidad Nacional de Buenos Aires. Facultad de Ciencias Económicas.
Bibliography: p.139-[141]
1.Argentine republic - Population. I. Correa Avila, Carlos, jt.auth. II.Buenos Aires, Universidad Nacional. Facultad de Ciencias Económicas.

NL 0426324 NjP CSt

Llorens, Emilio, joint author.

García Mata, Rafael.
Geografía económica argentina; síntesis gráfica, por Rafael García Mata ... y Emilio Llorens ... prólogo del ing. Alejandro E. Bunge. Buenos Aires, Compañía impresora argentina, s. a., 1936.

Llorens, Emilio.
Geografía económica general; versiones taquigráficas de las clases dictadas en la Facultad de Ciencias Económicas de la Universidad de Buenos Aires. Compiladas y publicadas, con autorización del profesor, por Alfredo Carballude. [Buenos Aires, Editorial Ergon, 1955.
512 p. illus. 23 cm.
1. Geography, Economic. I. Carballude, Alfredo, ed.
HF1025.L58 57-16581 ‡

NL 0426326 DLC

Llorens, Emilio, joint author.

Francioni, Manuel J
... Ritmo de la economía argentina en los últimos 30 años, por Manuel J. Francioni [y] Emilio Llorens; prólogo del dr. Alejandro E. Shaw. Buenos Aires, Editorial Perlado [1941]

Llorens, Emilio.
... El subconsumo de alimentos en América del Sur. Buenos Aires, Editorial sudamericana [1942]
2 p. l., [7]–262 p., 1 l. illus. (map) diagrs. 19cm. [Biblioteca de orientación económica. Economía de América]
On cover: Confederación argentina del comercio, de la industria y de la producción.
"Bibliografía": p. [249]–250.
1. Food supply—Spanish America. 2. Nutrition. I. Confederación argentina del comercio, de la industria y de la producción. II. Title.
42-23956 Revised
Library of Congress TX360.A5L55
[r43d2] 338.1

NL 0426328 DLC NcU MiU OCl NNUN

467 L7918n
Llorens, Emilio
La negación en español antiguo, con referencias a otros idiomas. Madrid, J.Molina, 1929.
198p. 25cm. (Revista de filología española. Anejo, 11)
Bibliography: p.193-198.
1. Spanish language. Old Spanish. Negatives. I. Title. (Series)

NL 0426329 IEN

Lloréns, Emilio Saleta y
see
Saleta y Lloréns, Emilio.

LLORENS, Francisco.
Informe a la magestad del rey nuestro senõr don Felipe el Grande,Tercero de la corona de Aragon. Que propuso Francisco Llorens ciudadano iurado en Cap de la leal, y coronada ciudad de Valencia su embaxador. En iustificacion de haver resuelto su embaxada la ciudad y concejo general y de las otras deliberaciones que fueron medio para su execucion. [Aragon,1656?]
f°. pp.(2). 34. Coat-of-arms on title-page.

NL 0426331 MH

Llorens, Gracia B de.
... Branca florida. Barcelona, Llibreria Catalonia, 1933.
2 p. l., 7-155 p., 2 l. 20cm.
At head of title: Gracia B. de Llorenç.
Poems.
I. Title.
34-23953
Library of Congress PC3941.L57B7 1933 849.91

NL 0426332 DLC

Llorens, Ignacio de.
Vicios fin de siglo. (In Carbó, Lorenzo. La morfinomanía en Juana Díaz. Ponce, P.R., 1895)

NL 0426333 PrU

Llorens, James A
Spanish royal finances in the 16th century
Thesis - Harvard, 1951

NL 0426334 MH

Llorens, Joaquin Segarra
see Segarra Llorens, Joaquin.

Llorens, José Font
see Font-Llorens, José.

Llorens, José Gassiot
see Gassiot Llorens, José.

Llorens, José Silvimo
See
Llorens y Mabeo, José Silvimo.

Llorens, Josep Maria.
Teoria de la música, per Josep Ma. Llorens... Pròleg de Lluis Millet... Amb més de 250 exemples autògrafs. Lleida [Arts gràfiques ilerda] 1933. v, 245 p. incl. diagrs. illus. (music.) 22cm.
JUILLIARD FOUNDATION FUND.
781815A. 1. Music—Theory.
N. Y. P. L. November 14, 1935

NL 0426339 NN

Llorens, Juan Gassiot
see Gassiot Llorens, Juan.

Llorens, Julian García
see
García Llorens, Julian.

Llorens, M. Massó
see Massó y Llorens, Manuel.

VOLUME 337

Llorens, M. Thous
See
Thous Llorens, M.

Llorens, Manuel García
see García Llorens, Manuel.

Llorens, Modesto
See
Llorens y Torres, Modesto, 1835-

Llorens, Peregrín Luis
see
Llorens y Raga, Peregrín Luis.

42846 .592 Lloréns, Rafael.
Torneo internacional de Barcelona, 1946. Organizado por el Club Ajedrez Barcelona en conmemoración de sus bodas de plata. [n.p., 1946]
213 p. illus. 25 cm.

1.Chess - Tournaments, 1946. I.Club de Ajedrez Barcelona.

NL 0426347 NjP

Lloréns, Rafael.
Torneo internacional de Barcelona, 1946,organizado por el Club Ajedrez, Barcelona, en conmemoración de sus bodas de plata, por Rafael Lloréns. [Barcelona, 1947]
213,[10]p.

NL 0426348 OCl NN

Lloréns, Rafael Segarra
see Segarra Lloréns, Rafael.

4PQ Span. 1017 Llorens, Regina de
Nuestra tía Evelyn. [l. ed.] Buenos Aires, Editorial Molino Argentina [1954]
110 p.

(Coleccion violeta, no. 86)

NL 0426350 DLC-P4

Llorens, Roque Chabás y
see
Chabás y Llorens, Roque, 1844-1912.

Lloréns, Vicente, tr.

HM57 .T557 1946
FOR OTHER EDITIONS SEE MAIN ENTRY

Tönnies, Ferdinand, 1855-1936.
... Principios de sociología; versión española de Vicente Lloréns. México, Fondo de cultura económica [1946]

Llorens, Vicente, 1869-1930,
see
Llorens y Asensio, Vicente, 1869-1930

Llorens Artigas, José.
Formulario y práticas de cerámica. Barcelona, G. Gili, 1947.
452 p. illus. 18 cm.

1. Pottery—Formulae, tables, etc.

A 51-5446

New York. Public Libr. for Library of Congress [1]

NL 0426354 NN

Llorens Castillo, Vicente.
Don Quijote y los libros; discurso pronunciado en la cuadragésima tercera colación de grados de la Universidad de Puerto Rico el 12 de junio de 1947. [Río Piedras, Universidad de Puerto Rico [cover 1947]
33 p. 22 cm.

1. Cervantes Saavedra, Miguel de. Don Quixote. I. Title.

PQ6353.L5 57-32646 ‡

NL 0426355 DLC MB MH RPB MiU NN

Llorens Castillo, Vicente.
Liberales y románticos; una emigración española en Inglaterra, 1823-1834. [1. ed.] México [Colegio de México] 1954.
382 p. illus. 22 cm. (Publicaciones de la Nueva revista de filología hispánica, 3)

1. Refugees, Spanish. 2. Spaniards in Great Britain. I. Title.

DA125.S62L52 56-25511 ‡

PHC IU PSC ICU NcD ViU DCU TxU InU IaU NcU PSt ScU WRU OrU OC1W OU TU CU-S CU MoU NjP NBuU NN NNC MiU
NL 0426356 DLC CaBVaU OCU KyU FU OCl ICN VtMiM GU

Llorens de Serra, Sara, 1881- comp.
... El cançoner de Pineda, 238 cançons populars amb 210 tonades. Barcelona, J. Horta, 1931.
2 p. l., 7-359 p. plates, ports., facsims. 22½cm. (Folklore de La Maresma, per Sara Llorens de Serra. I)

1. Folk-songs, Catalan—Pineda. I. Title.

Library of Congress M1779.L79 33-35096
784.49467

NL 0426357 DLC WaS TU IU NN

Llorens de Serra, Sara
Monolegs per a infants. Barcelona, Horta, 1918

NL 0426358 MH

849.98 L792p Llorens de Serra,Sara,1881- comp.
... Petit aplech d'exemples morals,recullits y cotejats per la srta.Sara Llorens y Carreras, ab una noticia preliminar d'en Rossend Serra y Pagés. Barcelona, Impr.de F.Giró, 1906.
54,[2] p. 18½cm. (Biblioteca folk-lórica catalana. vol.I)
"D'aquesta obreta se'n han estampat 260 exemplars."
Author's autograph presentation copy to Mr.Handman.

1.Exempla. 2.Folk-lore—Catalonia.

NL 0426359 MiU

Llorens García, Jorge.
Derecho social y legislación del trabajo; principios de derecho del trabajo, repertorio de legislación, jurisprudencia y formularios. [1. ed.] Lérida, Editora Leridana, 1947.
183 p. 16 cm. (Biblioteca de escritores leridanos, 7)

1. Labor laws and legislation — Spain. 2. Insurance, Social — Spain. I. Title. (Series)

54-26840

NL 0426360 DLC

862.6 L792v Lloréns Martínez, Juan.
Vida de ensueño, comedia dramática. Valencia, Impr. de J. Soler, 1919.
118p. illus.,port. 19cm.

NL 0426361 IEN

Llorens Raga, Peregrín
see
Llorens y Raga, Peregrín Luis.

Llorens Torres, Luis, 1878-1944.
Al pie de la Alhambra versos precedidos de un estudio critico acerca de Granada y sus principales literatos ... Granada, Madrid, Barcelona, 1899.

NL 0426363 NNH

Lloréns Torres, Luis, 1878-
... Alturas de América; poemas. San Juan de Puerto Rico [Talleres tipográficos Baldrich & co.] 1940.
199, [1] p. port. 22½cm.

I. Title. 41-5610

Library of Congress PQ7439.L6A75
[2] 861.6

NL 0426364 DLC KU PSt OCl CtY TxU TU IdU

Llorens Torres, Luis, 1878-
Alturas de América; poemas. Río Piedras, P. R., Editorial Librería Cultural [1954]
203 p. facsim. 23 cm.

I. Title.

PQ7439.L6A75 1954 57-31264

NL 0426365 DLC NcU NIC NN LU FU OU

Lloréns Torres, Luis.
América (estudios históricos y filológicos) ... Colección de artículos escritos y ordenados por d. Luís Lloréns Torres, con una carta-prólogo de d. Antonio Cortón. Madrid, V. Suárez; [etc., etc., 1898]
204 p. 21cm.
CONTENTS.—Las Antillas.—Descripción de la isla de Puerto Rico.—Los héroes del descubrimiento.—Primer viaje de Colón.—Martín Alonso Pinzón y el descubrimiento de Puerto Rico.—Nombre indiano de esta isla.—Estudios filológicos.—Bibliografía.

NL 0426366 NN MB MH OCU ViU

Microfilm 10025 F Lloréns Torres, Luis, 1878-1944.
América (estudios históricos y filológicos) ... Colección de artículos escritos y ordenados por d. Luís Lloréns Torres, con una carta-prólogo de d. Antonio Cortón. Madrid, V. Suárez; [etc., etc., 1898]
204 p. 21cm. L. C. Copy Replaced by Microfilm
CONTENTS.—Las Antillas.—Descripción de la isla de Puerto Rico.—Los héroes del descubrimiento.—Primer viaje de Colón.—Martín Alonso Pinzón y el descubrimiento de Puerto Rico.—Nombre indiano de esta isla.—Estudios filológicos.—Bibliografía.
1. West Indies—Descr. & trav. 2. Puerto Rico—Hist. 3. Colombo, Cristoforo. 4. Pinzón, Martín Alonso, 1440?-1493. 5. Indians—Languages. 6. Puerto Rico—Bibl. I. Title.

3-2734

Library of Congress [F1971.L79]

NL 0426367 DLC UU

VOLUME 337

LLORÉNS TORRES, Luís, 1878-
La canción de las Antillas y otros poemas. San Juan, P.R., Negociado de materiales, imprenta y transporte, 1929.

pp.27.

NL 0426368 MH

Llorens Torres, Luis, 1878-
Discurso pronunciado el 28 de Octubre de 1893

see under

Martí, José, 1853-1895.

Lloréns Torres, Luis, 1878-
El grito de Lares; drama histórico-poético... por Luis Lloréns Torres, con un prólogo por Luis Muñoz Rivera. Aguadilla, P. R., Tip. Libertad [1927?] 120 p. 18cm.

With autograph of author.

1. Drama, Puerto Rican. I. Title.
N. Y. P. L. April 10, 1946

NL 0426370 NN PBm

Lloréns Torres, Luis, 1878-
...Sonetos sinfónicos, por Luis Lloréns Torres. San Juan de Puerto Rico: Compañía editorial antillana [, 1914]. 110 p. 18½cm. (Biblioteca americana. Tomo 1.)

651428A. 1. Poetry, Porto Rican. I. Title.
N. Y. P. L. July 5, 1933

NL 0426371 NN NRU MH CtY

Llorens Torres, Luis, 1878-
Voces de la campana mayor. 2. ed. Río Piedras, P.R., Editorial Cultrual [n.d.]
252 p. 21 cm.

NL 0426372 TU FU

Llorens Torres, Luis, 1878-1944
Voces de la campana mayor, versos de Luis Llorens Torres. San Juan de Puerto Rico, Editorial puertorriqueña [1935]
4 p. l., 11-254 p., 1 l. 17cm.
Illustrated t.-p.

I. Title.
41-11405 Revised
Library of Congress PQ7439.L6V6
[r41c2] 861.6

NL 0426373 DLC

868.792 L773a Llorens Torres, Soledad.
...Antares mío. [San Juan] Univ. de Puerto Rico, 1946.
84 p., 4 l. 23 cm. (Puerto Rico. Universidad. Arte y letras, 4)

1. Puerto Rican poetry. I. Title.

NL 0426374 LU ICU TxU NjP CtY CU CLSU

Llorens y Asensio, Vicente, 1869-1930,
Spain. *Archivo general de Indias, Seville.*
... Catálogo de la sección 1.: Real patronato ... redactado por Vicente Lloréns Asensio ... Sevilla, Tip. Zarzuela, 1924-

---

Llorens y Asensio, Vicente, 1869-1930.
Historia general de las islas Filipinas desde su descubrimiento hasta nuestros días y Catálogo de los documentos referentes á dichas islas que se conservan en el Archivo general de Indias, por Vicente Llorens Asensio ... Sevilla, Tip. de Rodríguez y López, 1898-
ports. 24cm.

1. Philippine islands—Hist. 2. Philippine islands—Bibl. I. Spain. Archivo general de Indias, Sevilla.
23—5243
Library of Congress DS668.L6

NL 0426376 DLC

Llorens y Asensio, Vicente, 1869-1930.
La primera vuelta al mundo. Relación documentada del viaje de Hernando de Magallanes y Juan Sebastián del Cano.—1519-1522; por Vicente Llorens Asensio ... Sevilla, Impr. de la "Guía comercial," 1903.
179, [1] p. facsims. 16½cm.
"Catálogo de los documentos referentes al viaje de Magallanes y del Cano que se conservan en el Archivo general de Indias": p. 89-179.

1. Magalhães, Fernão de, d. 1521. 2. Cano, Juan Sebastián del, d. 1526. 3. Voyages around the world. I. Spain. Archivo general de Indias, Seville. II. Title.
3—25977
Library of Congress G420.M2L7

NL 0426377 DLC IaU NN NcD CU PU NNH MH MiU-C

Llorens y Asensio, Vicente, 1869-1930.
Los restos de Colón; defensa de la autenticidad de los que reposan en la catedral de Sevilla, por Vicente Llorens Asensio. Sevilla, Tip. de E. López y c.a, 1899.
88 p. 15½cm.

1. Colombo, Cristoforo—Tomb.
5—41663
Library of Congress E112.L82

NL 0426378 DLC NNH MH

Llorens y Barba, Francisco Javier, 1820-1872
Lecciones de filosofía, explicadas en la Universidad Literaria de Barcelona durante los cursos de 1864-65 y 1867-68, por Francisco Javier Llorens y Barba. Taquigrafiadas por José Balari y Jovany. Barcelona, Impr. Elzeviriana, 1920.
3 v. 23 cm. (Publicaciones de la Facultad de Filosofía y Letras de la Universidad de Barcelona)

1. Philosophy.
BD35.L6 57-56122 ‡

NL 0426379 DLC NjP

Llorens y Barba, Francisco Javier, 1820-1872.
...La metafísica de Francesc Xavier Llorens... (Edició adaptada a la Collecció Minerva.) Barcelona: Bonavia & Duràn [1918?]. 31(1) p. 12°. (Minerva; collecció popular dels coneixements indispensables. v. 13.)

1. Metaphysics.
N. Y. P. L. December 13, 1920.

NL 0426380 NN

Llorens y Barba, Francisco Javier, 1820-1872
Oracion inaugural que en le solemne apertura de estudios del año 1854 a 1855 dijo en la Universidad de Barcelona. Barcelona, Impr. de Gorchs, 1854

26 p.

NL 0426381 MH

Llorens y Barba, Javier
See
Llorens y Barba, Francisco Javier, 1820-1872.

Llorens y Bono, Severiano.
El crisol de una amistad. De don Severiano Llorens y Bono. [Alicante, Imprenta de los herederos de Andres Clemente, n. d.]
41 p. 22 cm.
In: Teatro antiguo Borrás. v. 24, no. 24.
At head of title: Comedia nueva.

NL 0426383 NcU

WBH qL792t 1904 LLORENS Y GALLARD, Ignacio de
Topografía médica de Calaf. Barcelona, Impr. Elzeviriana de Borrás y Mestres, 1904.
281 p. illus., ports.
"Laureada por la Real Academia de Medicina y Cirugía de Barcelona con su premio, Medalla de Oro, en el concurso de 1903."
Author's autograph presentation copy.

NL 0426384 DNLM

Llorens y Jordana, Rodolfo.
Servidumbre y grandeza de la filosofía. Buenos Aires, J. Serra, 1949.
217 p. 21 cm.
Errata slip inserted.

1. Philosophy. I. Title.
B1034.L45S45 52-67002

NL 0426385 DLC DPU CtY MH NN TxU

Llorens y Llatchós, Pedro.
Procedimientos para la enseñanza literaria y musical de los ciegos en la Exposición universal de Barcelona, por D. Pedro Llorens y Llatchós ... Procédés pour l'enseignement littéraire et musical des aveugles á l'Exposition universelle de Barcelone, par M. Pierre Llorens y Llatchós ... [Barcelona?] Tipo-lit. de los sucesores de N. Ramírez y ca [1888]
35 p. 21cm.
Spanish and French on opposite pages.
1. Blind—Asylums and education. 2. Blind, Music for the. I. Barcelona. Exposición universal, 1888.
17-1245
Library of Congress HV1576 1888 d

NL 0426386 DLC

Llorens y Maceo, José Silvino
Con Maceo en la invasión. Habana [Duarte y Uriarte] 1928.

205 p. ports. 24cm.

1. Maceo, Antonio, 1845-1896. 2. Cuba - Hist. - Revolution, 1895-1898.

NL 0426387 FU NN MH

Llorens y Martínez, Bernardo.
La mujer que mata; ó, La jaula del monstruo. Drama en cinco actos divididos en 11 cuadros, original de Bernardo Llorens y Martínez... Barcelona: F. Borrás, 1917. 127 p. 16°.

1. Drama (Spanish). 2. Title.
N. Y. P. L. October 1, 1919.

NL 0426388 NN

LLORENS Y PALLEJA, Matías.
Del derecho de laudemio en la enfiteusis de Cataluña. Barcelona, 1901.

Memoria--Universidad Central Barcelona.

NL 0426389 MH

VOLUME 337

Llorens y Raga, Peregrín Luis.
Fray Bonifacio Ferrer, como religioso y como literato. Castellón de la Plana, Sociedad Castellonense de Cultura, 1955.
34 p. 22 cm. (Obras de investigación histórica, 32)

1. Ferrer, Bonifacio, 1355-1417.

BX4705.F425L4 60-33138 ‡

NL 0426390 DLC CtY DCU NN

He77 Llorens y Torres, Modesto, 1835-
026 ... El casado casa quiere, comedia en dos
3 actos y en prosa por D. Modesto Llorens. [Barcelona, 186-?]
16p. 1 illus. 27cm. (Museo dramatico ilustrado)
Binder's titlo: Teatro español, 3.
Caption title.

NL 0426391 CtY NN

Llorens y Torres, Modesto, 1835-
Un episódio de amor, comedia original en un acto y en verso, por D. Modesto Llorens... Barcelona: J. Jepús y R. Villegas, 1859. 49(1) p. 12°.

1. Drama (Spanish). 2. Title.
N. Y. P. L. October 9, 1919.

NL 0426392 NN MoU

Llorens y Torres, Modesto, 1835-
Un episódio de amor, comedia original en un acto y en verso. Barcelona, Jaime Jepus y Ramon Villegas, 1859.
49p.

Microcard edition.

NL 0426393 ICRL FU

[**Llorent, José**]
Lecciones de agricultura para las escuelas de la republica. Panama: Tip. Casis y cia., 1907. 110 p. 20½cm.
"Prologo" signed: Jose Llorent.

1. Agriculture—Textbooks, 1907. I. Title.
N. Y. P. L. September 3, 1940

NL 0426394 NN TxU

Llorente, Alejandro, 1814-1901.
see
Llorente y Lannas, Alejandro, 1814-1901

Llorente, Aniceto
Los Abonos. 2d ed. Burgos. 1892. Sucesor de Arnaiz.
8, 368p.

NL 0426396 MiU

Llorente, Aniceto.
Los abonos, por Aniceto Llorente ... Mexico, Oficina tip. de la Secretaria de fomento, 1894.
379 p., 1 l. 22cm. (Biblioteca agricola de la Secretaría de fomento)

1. Fertilizers and manures.

13-12111

Library of Congress S633.L6

NL 0426397 DLC DNAL

Llorente, Aniceto.
Cartilla que ensena a los agricultores a preparar por si mismos los abonos minerales. 1900.

NL 0426398 DNAL

[**Llorente, Aniceto.**]
El federalismo integral; ó, La federación de los pueblos y las clases sociales y la reducción del poder público. Tortosa: Monclús, 1919. 82 p., 1 l. 12°.
Author's name on cover.

1. Spain.—Government. 2. Decentralization, Spain. 3. Government (Federal), Spain. 4. Syndicalism, Spain. 5. Title.
N. Y. P. L. September 16, 1920.

NL 0426399 NN

Llorente, Aniceto.
Guia practice para elcultivo de la remolacha azucarera. Madrid, Hernandez, 1899.
121 p.

NL 0426400 PPF

Llorente, Antonio Gonzalez Ponce de
see
Gonzalez Ponce de Llorente, Antonio

Llorente, Antonio Tovar
see **Tovar, Antonio.**

Llorente, Daniel Benavides
see
Benavides Llorente, Daniel.

PC3886 Llorente, Euphemia.
.5 Studi etymològic dels noms Cathalunya e cathalà
.L8 (historia, incidents e continuatió d'una polemica). 1.ed. amb el retrat de l'auctora. Madrid, Impr. de R. Medina, 1930.
91 p. port.

1. Catalan language—Etymology—Names.
2. Catalonia (Word)

NL 0426404 ICU

Llorente, Evaristo
Hazañas de un solteron; novela de costumbres. Madrid, Galería Literaria, 1872
2 v. illus. (Biblioteca madrileña, 22-23)

NL 0426405 MH

Llorente, Florencio Porpeta y
see
Porpeta y Llorente, Florencio

Llorente, Francisco Alcalá
see **Alcalá Llorente, Francisco.**

Llorente, Francisco Martín
see
Martín Llorente, Francisco, 1869-

Llorente, Isaac Muñoz
See
Muñoz Llorente, Isaac, 1885-

Llorente, Jorge Casals
see
Casals Llorente, Jorge, 1893-

Llorente, José María Arboleda
see **Arboleda Llorente, José María.**

Llorente, José Mariano Llorente y
see Llorente y Llorente, José Mariano.

BX Llorente, Juan Antonio, 1756-1823
1735 Anales de la Inquisición de España.
.L565 Madrid, Impr. de Ibarra, 1812-13.
2 v. illus. 16 cm.

Bibliographical footnotes.
Contents. - t. 1. Desde el establecimiento de la Inquisición por los reyes católicos hasta el año 1508. - t. 2. Desde el año de 1509 hasta el de 1530.

1. Inquisition. Spain. I. Title.

NL 0426413 WU NIC PU NNH ICU

272.2 Llorente, Juan Antonio, 1756-1823.
L77a ... Anales secretos de la inquisicion española (memoria historica sobre la inquisicion española) Madrid, Libreria Bergua [193-?]
214p.

1. Inquisition--Spain. I. Title.

NL 0426414 IU NNI

BX 1758 LLORENTE, JUAN ANTONIO, 1756-1823
.L77 Apología católica del proyecto de Constitución Religiosa, escrito por un americano; su autor, Don Juan Antonio Llorente. Gerona, A. Oliva, impresor de S.M., 1821.
342 p.

1. Catholic Church--Doctrinal and controversial works--Catholic authors. I. Title.

NL 0426415 InU NjP NNC PV

Llorente, Juan Antonio, 1756-1823.
Apologia católica del Proyecto de Constitucion religiosa, escrito por un Americano, [y publicado por don J. A. Llorente: o bien sea, Respuesta de Llorente á la censura teológica dada por fray Roque Olsinellas y fray Jose Tapias] ... Madrid, 1822.
2 v. in 1. 15.5 cm.
Proyecto de una Constitution religiosa, considerada como parte de la Constitucion civil ... su autor un Americano ... v. 2.

NL 0426416 CtY

VOLUME 337

Llorente, Juan Antonio, 1756-1823, ed.

Casas, Bartolomé de las, *bp. of Chiapa*, 1474-1566.
Colección de las obras del venerable obispo de Chiapa, don Bartolomé de las Casas ... Da todo á luz el doctor don Juan Antonio Llorente ... Paris, En casa de Rosa, 1822.

[LLORENTE, JUAN ANTONIO] 1756-1823, ed.
Colección diplomática de varios papeles antiguos y modernos sobre dispensas matrimoniales y otros puntos de disciplina eclesiástica.../ Madrid: Impr. de Ibarra, 1809. xii, 272, 8 p. 22½cm.

"Discurso preliminar" signed: Juan Antonio Llorente.

689889A. 1. Marriage and the church. I. Title.

NL 0426418 NN DLC-P4 CaBVaU PU IU TxU WU CU InU NNUT

BX1939 D6L4 Llorente, Juan Antonio, 1756-1853.
Colección diplomática de varios papeles antiguos y modernos sobre dispensas matrimoniales y otros puntos de disciplina eclesiástica. 2. ed. Madrid, Impr. de T. Alban, 1822.
272, 8 p. 22cm.

1. Marriage - Dispensations. 2. Dispensations (Canon law)

NL 0426419 CoU MWelC

Llorente, Juan Antonio, 1756-1823.
Colección diplomática de varios papeles antiguos y modernos sobre dispensas matrimoniales y otros puntos de disciplina eclesiastica. 3. ed. Mexico, Impr. de Galvan, 1827.
viii, 276 p.

NL 0426420 NNC MH

Llorente, Juan Antonio, 1756-1823.
Compendio de la historia crítica de la Inquisición de España, precedido de una noticia biográfica de D. Juan Antonio Llorente, traducido del francés, y aumentado de un extracto de los procesos más célebres qui ha formado la Inquisición, por Rodriguez Burón. Tomo 1- Paris: Tournachon-Molin, 1823- v. 24°.

1. Inquisition.—History, Spain. 2. Rodriguez Burón, Tomás.
N. Y. P. L. July 6, 1915.

NL 0426421 NN TxU MH-AH CtY ICN

BX 1735 .L567 Llorente, Juan Antonio, 1756-1823
Consultas del Real y Supremo Consejo de Castilla, y otros papeles sobre atentados y usurpaciones contra la soberanía del rey y su real jurisdición. Obra muy util á los abogados y jueces, como tambien á los aficianados á la historia de España. La da a luz don Astreófilo Hispáno [pseud. Paris, Impr. de A. Bobée, 1818.
403 p. 18cm.

1. Inquisition. Spain I. Title

NL 0426422 WU NjP MH

1526 .182 .592 Llorente, Juan Antonio, 1756-1823
Conversaciones entre Cándido y Prudencio, sobre el estado actual de España. Madrid, García, 1820
62 p. 17 cm

1. SPAIN - POL. & GOVT. - 1813-1833 I.T.

NL 0426423 NjP NNH

[LLORENTE, Juan Antonio, 1756-1823.
Defensa canonica y politica contra injustas acusaciones de fingidos crimenes. Paris. Imp. del Senor Plassan, [1816].

NL 0426424 MH

BX 1426 L5 Llorente, Juan Antonio
Discursos sobre una constitucion religiosa considerada como parte de la civil nacional. Paris, Impr. de Stahl, 1820.
223p. 15cm.
Bound with Grassot y Gispert, J. A. de. Defensa de la obra intitulada projet d'une constitution religieuse. Barcelona, 1821.
1. Catholic Church in Latin America 2. Church and state in Latin America 3. Church and state in Spain 4. Catholic Church - Doctrinal and controversial works I. Title

NL 0426425 WU WaPS InU

Llorente, Juan Antonio, 1756-1823.
Discursos sobre una constitucion religiosa, considerada como parte de la civil nacional ... Nueva ed, adicionada con la Defensa de dicha constitucion verificada por D. José Antonio de Grassot y Gispert. Barcelona, 1837.
16 cm.

NL 0426426 CtY

Llorente, Juan Antonio, 1756-1823.
Disertacion sobre el poder que los reyes españoles ejercieron hasta el siglo duodecimo en la division de obispados, y otros puntos conecsos de disciplina eclesiastica; con un apendice de escrituras en que constan los hechos citados en la disertacion. Madrid, Impr. de Ibarra, 1810.
xvi, 246 p. 22 cm.

1. Ecclesiastical law—Spain. 2. Church and state in Spain. 3. Ecclesiastical geography—Spain.

55-53180

NL 0426427 DLC CoU MH NNH ICN

BX 1584 L5 1822 Llorente, Juan Antonio, 1756-1823.
Disertación sobre el poder que los reyes españoles ejercieron hasta el siglo duodécimo en la division de obispaolos y otros puntos conexos de disciplina eclesiástica, con un apéndice de escrituras en que constan los hechos citados en la disertación. 2. ed. Madrid, Imp. de Alban y Compania, 1822.
211p. 21cm.

Text in Latin and Spanish.

NL 0426428 MU IaU

DP89 L5 1826 Llorente, Juan Antonio, 1756-1823.
Disertacion sobre el poder que los reyes españoles ejercieron hasta el siglo duodecimo en la division de obispados y otros puntos conecsos de disciplina eclesiástica; con un apéndice de escrituras en que constan los hechos citados en la disertacion. Méjico. Impresa en Madrid, y reimpresa en la oficina [de] Alejandro Valdés, 1826.
iv, 276 [10] p. 21cm.

1. Ecclesiastical law - Spain. 2. Church and state - Spain. 3. Ecclesiastical geography - Spain. I. Title.

NL 0426429 CU-B NN WaPS CtY OCl

Llorente, Juan Antonio, 1756-1823.
Dr. Johann Anton Llorente's ... Geschichte der spanischen inquisition. Nach der 3., verb., und mit einem schreiben des französischen bischoffs Gregoire an den spanischen grosinquisitor verm. aufl. des von Leonard Gallois gemachten auszuges deutsch bearb., und bereichert mit ergänzungen und berichtigungen aus dem grösseren werke. Nebst Llorente's leben und angabe seiner schriften. Stuttgart, J. B. Metzler, 1824.
xiv, 242 p. 21cm.
"Vorrede des uebersetzers" signed: H. F. E. [d. e. H. F. Eisenbach]
1. Inquisition. Spain. I. *Gallois, Léonard, 1789-1851, ed. II. Eisenbach, Heinrich Friedrich, b. 1795, tr.

35-22747

Library of Congress BX1735.L64 1824 272.20946

NL 0426430 DLC OO OCH

BX 1735 L6.15 1855 Llorente, Juan Antonio, 1756-1823.
Geschichte der spanischen Inquisition, von Llorente und Gallois. 4.Aufl. Leipzig, O. Wigand, 1855.
2 v. in 1. (254 p.) 16 cm. (Ausgewählte Bibliothek des Auslandes, 1)
Translation of Historia critica de la Inquisicion de Espana.

1. Inquisition. Spain. I. Gallois, Léonard, 1789-1851, ed. II. Title

NL 0426431 OCH

BX 1735 .L57 1823 Llorente, Juan Antonio, 1756-1823.
Histoire abrégée de l'Inquisition d'Espagne précédée d'une analyse de cette histoire par le Comte de Ségur. 2. ed. Bruxelles, Arnold Lacrosse, 1823.
xxxi, 264 p.

1. Inquisition - Spain - Hist. I. Ségur, Philippe Paul, comte de, 1780-1873. II. T.

NL 0426432 NBuU ODW MH NN

Llorente, Juan Antonio, 1756-1823.
Histoire abrégée de l'inquisition d'Espagne; par Léonard Gallois. Paris, Chasseriau, 1823.
398 p. 13½cm.

1. Inquisition - Spain

NL 0426433 NCH

[Llorente, Juan Antonio] 1756-1823.
Histoire abrégée de l'inquisition d'Espagne. par Léonard Gallois. Troisieme édition, précédé d'une notice sur la vie et les écrits de Llorente, et augmenteé d'une lettre de M. Grégoire, ancien évêque de Blois, à Don Ramond-Joseph de Arce, grand inquisiteur général d'Espagne. À Paris, Chez Chasseriau, 1824.
xi, lxxij, [13]-398 p. 13½cm.

A French abridgment of Llorente's Historia critica de la inquisicion de España.

NL 0426434 NNC

[Llorente, Juan Antonio] 1756-1823.
Histoire abrégée de l'inquisition d'Espagne. Par Léonard Gallois. 4. éd., augmentée d'une lettre de m. Grégoire, ancien évêque de Blois, à don Ramon-Joseph de Arce, grand-inquisiteur général d'Espagne. Paris, Peytieux [etc.] 1824.
xlviii, 311 p. 21cm.

1. Inquisition. Spain. I. *Gallois, Léonard, 1789-1851, ed. II. Grégoire, Henri, constitutional bp. of Blois, 1750-1831. III. Title.

38-33070

Library of Congress BX1735.L6 1824

NL 0426435 DLC MdBP CU NBuG ScU

Llorente, Juan Antonio, 1756-1823.
Histoire abrégée de l'inquisition d'Espagne; par Léonard Gallois. 6. éd., précédée d'une notice sur la vie et les écrits de Llorente, et augmentée d'une lettre de M. Grégoire, ancien évêque de Blois, à Don Ramond-Joseph de Arce ... Paris, Brissot-Thivars et cie, 1828.
xii, 384 p. 14cm.

1. Inquisition. Spain. I. Gallois, Léonard, 1789-1851, ed. II. Grégoire, Henri, constitutional bp. of Blois, 1750-1831.

27-3782

Library of Congress BX1735.L6 1828

NL 0426436 DLC PU PPL

D 4940 .519 LLORENTE, JUAN ANTONIO, 1756-1823.
Histoire abrégée de l'Inquisition d'Espagne. Précédée d'un discours sur cette histoire par le comte de Ségur. 4.éd. Bruxelles, A. Lacrosse, 1838.
291p. plates. 23cm.

NL 0426437 ICN

VOLUME 337

Llorente, Juan Antonio, 1756-1823.
Histoire critique de l'inquisition d'Espagne, depuis l'époque de son établissement par Ferdinand v, jusqu'au règne de Ferdinand vii, tirée des pièces originales des archives du Conseil de la Suprême et de celles des tribunaux subalternes du Saint-office. Par d. Jean-Antoine Llorente ... traduite de l'espagnol sur le manuscrit et sous les yeux de l'auteur; par Alexis Pellier ... Paris, Treuttel et Wurtz [etc.] 1817-18.
4 v. front. (port.) illus. (coat of arms) 22½ cm.
"Catalogue des manuscrits qui n'ont pas encore été publiés, et qui ont servi pour composer l'Histoire critique de l'inquisition d'Espagne": v. 1, p. [xxix]-xxxiv.
1. Inquisition. Spain. I. Pellier, Alexis, tr.
BX1735.L6 1817 17-2158

NL 0426438 DLC MU AAP DCU-IA MoSCS MdBP CtY NN NNH

272.2 L77hFp 1818
Llorente, Juan Antonio, 1756-1823.
Histoire critique de l'Inquisition d'Espagne, depuis l'époque de son établissement par Ferdinand V, jusqu'au règne de Ferdinand VII; tirée des pièces originales des archives du Conseil de la Suprême et de celles des tribunaux subalternes du Saint-office. Tr. de l'espagnol, sur le manuscrit et sous les yeux de l'auteur, par Alexis Pellier. 2.éd. Paris, Treuttel et Würtz, 1818.
4v. front.(port.) illus.(coat of arms) 22cm.

"Catalogue des manuscrits qui n'ont pas encore été publiés, et qui ont servi pour composer l'Histoire critique de l'Inquisition d'Espagne": v.1, p.xxxj-xxxvj.

1. Spain--Hist.--House of Austria, 1518-1700. 2. Inquisition--Spain.

MdBP
NL 0426440 IU NIC PU CBPac PPL PPAmP ICU MH RPB

LLORENTE, JUAN ANTONIO, 1756-1823.
Historia critica de la Inquisicion de España. Obra original conforme á lo que resulta de los archivos del consejo de la Suprema, y de los tribunales de provincias. Su autor don Juan Antonio Llorente... Madrid, Imprenta del censor, 1822.
10v. port. 14cm.

"Catalogo de los manuscritos ineditos donde constan las noti- cias": v.1, p.[28]-36.

"Explicacion de las palabras y frases tecnicas que se usan en el Santo-oficio": v.1, p.[37]-58.
"Compendio cronológico de los hechos mas notables que han sido referido en esta historia": v.10, p.1-121.
"Piezas justificativas": v.10, p.[123]-250.
Bookplate of Thomas Forrest Betton, German Town, Pa.

NL 0426442 PU PCC NWM IaU MH CtY MdBP

Llorente, Juan Antonio, 1756-1823.
Historia critica da la Inquisicion de España; obra original conforme á lo que resulta de los archivos del Consejo de la Suprema, y de los tribunales de provincia. Barcelona, De Oliva, 1835-36.
8 v. in 4. port. 16 cm.

NL 0426443 CU-S KU NjP NcD NNH NcU TxU MiU MiDW InU

Llorente, Juan Antonio, 1756-1823.
Historia critica de la Inquisición de España. Obra original conforme lo que resulta de los Archivos del Consejo de la Suprema y de los tribunales de provincia, ordenada y corr. por Juan Landa. Ed. ilus. con magníficas láminas del reputado artista Mariano Teruel. Barcelona, J. Pons, 1870-80.
2 v. plates, ports. 27 cm.

1. Inquisition. Spain.
BX1735.L58 55-49069

NL 0426444 DLC CoU MH CtY OCH OU CU IU

Hum BX 1735 L67 1968
Llorente, Juan Antonio, 1756-1823.
Historia crítica de la inquisicion de España, por don Juan Antonio Llorente ... Obra original conforme lo que resulta de los archivos del Consejo de la Suprema y de los tribunales de provincia. ordenada y corregida por d. Juan Landa ... Barcelona, J. Pons, 1870 [Ann Arbor, Mich., University Microfilms, 1968]
2v.

"Catálogo de los manuscritos inéditos donde constan las noti- cias": t.2, p.[564]-568.

NL 0426445 FTaSU

[Llorente, Juan Antonio] 1756-1823.
Historia general de la inquisicion, escrita en francés por Mr. Leonardo Gallois. Version castellana de Don Francisco Nacente. Barcelona, Administracion, Ronda del Norte, núm. 128; [etc., etc.] 1869-70.
2 v. in 1. 17½ᶜᵐ.
An abridgment of the author's "Historia critica de la inquisición de España".

1. Inquisition. Spain. I. *Gallois, Léonard, 1789-1851, ed. II. Nacente, Francisco, tr. III. Title.
6-22423 Revised
Library of Congress BX1735.L66 1869

NL 0426446 DLC NN

Llorente, Juan Antonio, 1756-1823.
The history of the Inquisition of Spain, from the time of its establishment to the reign of Ferdinand vii., composed from the original documents of the Archives of the Supreme council and from those of subordinate tribunals of the Holy office. Abridge and translated from the original works of d. Jean Antoine Llorente ... London, Printed for G. B. Whittaker, 1826.
xx, 583, [1] p. 21½ᶜᵐ.

1. Inquisition. Spain.
27-4898
Library of Congress BX1735.L63 1826

CaOTP WaWW MtBuM WaT CaBViP WaTC Or OrU-M MtBC MtU OrCS OrPR OrU Wa WaE WaPS WaS WaSpG PV PPL CtY PCA IdPI MoSCS IdB MH CaBVaU NNJ OrP
NL 0426447 DLC OrSaW WaS CSmH OCl OrStbM MiU IdU

Llorente, Juan Antonio, 1756-1823.
The history of the Inquisition of Spain, from the time of its establishment to the reign of Ferdinand vii., composed from the original documents of the Archives of the Supreme council and from those of subordinate tribunals of the Holy office. Abridge and translated from the original works of d. Jean Antoine Llorente ... Philadelphia, T. B. Peterson and brothers [1826]
xx, 583, [1] p. 21½ᶜᵐ.

NL 0426448 FMU

Llorente, Juan Antonio, 1756-1823.
The history of the inquisition of Spain, from the time of its establishment to the reign of Ferdinand vii. Composed from the original documents of the Archives of the Supreme council, and from those of subordinate tribunals of the Holy office. Abridged and translated from the original works of D. Juan Antonio Llorente ... 2d. ed. London, Printed for G. B. Whittaker, 1827.
xx, 583, [1] p. 21½ᶜᵐ.

1. Inquisition. Spain.
27-4904
Library of Congress BX1735.L63 1827

PV PU PPL IU ViU
NL 0426449 DLC WaU-L KU ICU MoS NIC NjNbS PHi PPM

BX1735 .L7
Llorente, Juan Antonio, 1756-1823.
The history of the inquisition of Spain, from the time of its establishment to the reign of Ferdinand vii. Composed from the original documents of the archives of the Supreme council, and from those of subordinate tribunals of the Holy office. Abridged and tr. from the original works of D. Juan Antonio Llorente ... Philadelphia, J. M. Campbell & co.; [etc., etc.] 1843.
6, vii-viii, 9-208 p. 23½ᶜᵐ.

1. Inquisition—Spain.

PPPD PHi PNt PU PHC PPLT CtY I IEN
NL 0426450 ICU PPRETS ViU MnHi MB NN MH NBuG MiD

Llorente, Juan Antonio.
History of the Inquistion of Spain, from the time of its establishment to the reign of Ferdinand VII...from ... original documents...abridged & tr... Phila., [etc.] Campbell, [etc.] 1845.
308 p.

NL 0426451 PPLT OCX

Llorente, Juan Antonio.
History of the Inqiusition of Spain. Ed.2. London, 1877.

NL 0426452 PWcS

Llorente, Juan Antonio, 1756-1823.
History of the Spanish inquisition; abridged from the original work of M. Llorente, late secretary of that institution; by Leonard Gallois. Translated by an American. New York, G. C. Morgan [etc.] 1826.
271, [2] p. front. 17ᶜᵐ.

1. Inquisition. Spain. I. Gallois, Léonard, 1789-1851, ed. II. An American, tr.
27-3783
Library of Congress BX1735.L63 1826 a

NL 0426453 DLC DGU

UB43 L792
Llorente, Juan Antonio, 1756-1823.
Die Kirchenverbesserung im neunzehnten Jahrhundert nach Llorente Projet d'une constitution réligieuse frei bearbeitet [von Ignaz Paul Vitalis Troxler] Aarau, H.R.Sauerländer, 1822.
292p. 21cm.

NL 0426454 NNUT

Mgt33 L773
Llorente, Juan Antonio, 1756-1823.
D.Johann Anton Llorente's ... Kritische Geschichte der spanischen Inquisition, von ihrer Einführung durch Ferdinand V. an bis zur Regierung Ferdinand's VII. Aus Originalakten der Archive des Raths der Oberinquisition und der untergeordneten Tribunale des heiligen Officiums. Uebersetzt und mit Anmerkungen begleitet von Johann Karl Höck ... Gmünd, Ritter, 1819-22.
4v. 18cm.

NL 0426455 CtY InU MoSCS PBa

BX1735 L73
Llorente, Juan Antonio, 1756-1823.
D.Johann Anton Llorente's...Kritische geschichte der spanischen inquisition, von ihrer einführung durch Ferdinand V. an bis zur regierung Ferdinand's VII. Aus originalakten der archive des raths der oberinquisition und der untergeordneten tribunale des heiligen officiums. Uebersetzt und mit anmerkungen begleitet von Johann Karl Höck... Gmünd, Ritter, 1820-22.
4 v. 18cm.

NL 0426456 ICU

Llorente, Juan Antonio.
Lettre à Clausel de Coussergues sur l'Inquisition d'Espagne. Paris, Delaunay, 1817.
42 p.

NL 0426457 PU

Llorente, Juan Antonio, 1756-1823, ed.
Leyes del Fuero-juzgo, ó recopilacion de las leyes de los Wisi-godos españoles ... 1792
see under Visigoths. Laws, statutes, etc.

---

946 L79m
Llorente, Juan Antonio, 1756-1823.
Mémoires pour servir a l'histoire de la révolution d'Espagne, avec des pièces justificatives. Par M.Nellerto[pseud.]... Paris, J.G.Dentu, 1814-1819.
3 v. 21 cm.
Vol.2 was pub.by Plassan, v.3 by Trewttel et Wurtz.

NL 0426459 Mi NWM CU-S FTaSU MH MdBP

VOLUME 337

BX 1735 .L58 Llorente, Juan Antonio, 1756-1823
Memoria histórica sobre qual ha sido la opinion nacional de España acerca del Tribunal de la Inquisicion. Leida en la Real Academia de la Historia en las juntas ordinarias de los dias 25 de octubre, 1, 8 y 15 de noviembre de 1811. [n.p., 1811?]
204 p. 22 cm.

U.W. copy imperfect: t.p. and p. 1-36 wanting. Signatures marked: tom. V. N. 2.

NL 0426460 WU

Llorente, Juan Antonio, 1756-1823.
Memoria histórica sobre qual ha sido la opinión nacional de España acerca del tribunal de la Inquisición, leida en la Real academia de la historia por el excelentisimo Señor Don Juan Antonio Llorente... Madrid: Impr. de Sancha, 1812. 324 p. 20cm.

255009B. 1. Inquisition—Spain.
N. Y. P. L. January 20, 1944

NL 0426461 NN NcD MH MiU CU IU NNH PU PPL NNUW

Llorente, Juan Antonio, 1756-1823.
Memorias para la historia de la revolucion española, con documentos justificativos, recogidas y compiladas por d. Juan Nellerto [pseud.] ... Paris, Plassan, 1814-16.
3 v. 21cm.

1. Spain - History - Napoleonic conquest, 1808-1813. 2. Peninsular war, 1807-1814. I. Title.

NL 0426462 NNC NN ICN

BV 386 .L79 Llorente, Juan Antonio, 1756-1823.
Monumens historiques concernant les deux pragmatiques-sanctions de France, avec des notes, suivis d'un catéchisme sur la matière des concordats. Paris, A. Bobée, 1818.
viii, 190, 16 p. 22cm.

1. Pragmatic Sanction of Charles VII, 1438. 2. Church and state in France. 3. Concordats - France. I. Title.

NL 0426463 DCU MH MH-L

CE46 L56 Llorente, Juan Antonio, 1756-1823.
Monumento romano descubierto en Calahorra a 4 de marzo de 1788, con cuya ilustración se demuestra el uso del computo de la era espaňola antes de la venida de los godos y aún del Redentor ... Madrid, B. Roman, 1789.
101 p. illus.

1. Chronology, Roman. 2. Inscriptions, Latin - Spain.

NL 0426464 CU

Llorente, Juan Antonio, 1756-1823.
Notas al Dictámen de la Comision eclesiástica, encargada del arreglo definitivo del clero de España, impreso de órden de las Córtes; por don Juan Antonio Llorente ... Madrid, Impr. de T. Alban y compañia, 1823.
F1203 F16 v.40:7a x 23 p. 21cm. [Papeles varios. v. 40, no. 7a]

NL 0426465 CU-B

Llorente, Juan Antonio. 1756-1823.
Noticia biografica de D. Juan Antonio Llorente, o memorias para la historia de su vida escritas por el mismo.
Paris, 1818. xxiv, 239 p.
Bound with this: Llorente, Juan Antonio: Defensa canonico y politica de Don Juan Antonio Llorente contre injustas acusaciones de fingidos crimenes...Paris, Imprenta del Senor Plassan, n.d. 177 (1) p.

NL 0426466 DCU-IA

LLORENTE, Juan Antonio.
Noticias historicas de la stres provincias vascongadas, en que se procura investigar el estado civil antiguo de Alava, Guipuzcoa, y Vizcaya, y el origen de sus fueros.
Madrid, Imp. real, 1806-08.

5 vol. sm. 4°.

NL 0426467 MH NN ICU MiU

Llorente, Juan Antonio, 1756-1823.
Observaciones críticas sobre el romance de Gil Blas de Santillana, en las cuales se hace ver que mr. Le Sage lo desmembró del de El bachiller de Salamanca, entónces manuscrito español inédito; y se satisface a todos los argumentos contrarios publicados por el conde de Neufchateau ... Su autor don Juan Antonio Llorente ... Madrid, Impr. de d. T. Alban y compañía, 1822.
408 p. 15cm.

"Yo me propongo probar que el romance de Gil Blas de Santillana y el del Bachiller de Salamanca fueron en su principio una sola obra, escrita ... por un autor natural de Castilla ... El autor original me parece haber sido don Antonio Solis"—p. 7

"Refutacion del nuevo exámen del conde de Neufchateau, ó bien sea Respuesta de Llorente á lo que el señor conde objetó á las Observaciones críticas sobre los romances de Gil Blas y del Bachiller de Salamanca": p. [307]-403.

1. Le Sage, Alain René, 1668-1747. Histoire de Gil Blas. 2. François de Neufchâteau, Nicolas Louis, comte, 1750-1828. 3. Solís y Rivadeneyra, Antonio de, 1610-1686. I. Title.

32-33093

Library of Congress PQ1997.G7L6 843.5

NL 0426469 DLC CaBVaU CU MoU OCl PPL PSC CU MH NNH

PQ1997 G7L6 1837 Llorente, Juan Antonio, 1756-1823.
Observaciones críticas sobre el romance de Gil Blas de Santillana, en las cuales se hace ver que mr. Le Sage lo desmenbró del de El bachiller de Salamanca, entónces manuscrito español inédito; y se satisface a todos los argumentos contrarios publicados por el conde de Neufchâteau ... Barcelona, La viuda è hijos de Gorchs, 1837.
432 p.

"Yo me propongo probar que el romance de Gil Blas de Santillana y el del Bachiller de Salamanca fueron en su principio una sola obra, escrita ... por un autor natural de Castilla ... don Antonio Solis." -- p. 9-10.

NL 0426470 CU MiU MH InU TxU

LLORENTE, Juan Antonio.
Observaciones criticas sobre el romance de Gil Blas de Santillana.

(Appended to LE SAGE, A.R. Historia de Gil Blas, 1840, pp. 897-1034).

NL 0426471 MH

Llorente, Juan Antonio, 1756-1823
Observations critiques sur le roman de Gil Blas de Santillane...On y fait voir que le roman de Gil Blas n'est pas un ouvrage original, mais un démembrement des Aventures du Bachelier de Salamanque, manuscript espagnol, alors inédit, que M. Le Sage dépouilla des parties les plus précieuses. Paris, Moreau, 1822. viii+ 309p.

NL 0426472 InU GEU MH NjP PPL

F1411 .C44 Llorente, Juan Antonio, 1756-1823, ed.
Casas, Bartolomé de las, *bp. of Chiapa*, 1474-1566.
Œuvres de don Barthélemi de las Casas, évêque de Chiapa, défenseur de la liberté des naturels de l'Amérique; précédées de sa vie, et accompagnées de notes historiques, additions, développemens, etc., etc.; avec portrait; par J.-A. Llorente ... Paris, A. Eymery; [etc., etc.] 1822.

Llorente, Juan Antonio, 1756-1823.
Pequeño catecismo sobre la materia de concordatos. Escrito en francés ... y traducido al español por Jose Mariano Ramirez Hermosa. Mexico, Galvan Rivera, 1826.
71 p. 15cm.

1. Concordats.

42-34900
Brief cataloging

Library of Congress BX1790.L55

NL 0426474 DLC MiU-L

Llorente, Juan Antonio, 1756-1823.
Portrait politique des papes, considérés comme princes temporels et comme chefs de l'église, depuis l'établissement du Saint-Siége à Rome, jusqu'en 1822, par Juan-Antonio Llorenté ... Paris, Béchet ainé; Rouen, Béchet jeune, 1822.
2 v. 23 cm.

"Liste chronologique des papes, après Saint-Pierre": v. 2, p. [305]-320.

1. Popes. I. Title.

NL 0426475 NSchU MH TU NCH CtY NN IU OrU

Llorente, Juan Antonio, 1756-1823.
Projet d'une constitution religieuse, considérée comme faisant partie de la constitution civile d'une nation libre indépendante, écrit par un Américain. Publié avec une préface, par Dom Jean-Antoine Llorente... Paris, L.-E. Herhan [1820] xii, 162 p. 22cm.

"Un Américain" is really J. A. Llorente, *cf. British museum catalogue.*

529946B. 1. Church and state. I. Un Américain. II. Title.
N. Y. P. L. September 15, 1950

NL 0426476 NN MH MiU

BX 955 .L55 Llorente, Juan Antonio, 1756-1823
Retrato político de los papas, desde S. Pedro hasta Pio VII inclusive. Con espresión del principio y fin de cada pontificado y reflexiones críticas en los que dan ocasión á ello; formado con presencia de las historias eclesiásticas escritas por el cardenal Fleuri, Natal, Alejandro, y otras muchas acreditadas de muy exactas y verídicas entre los literatos mas críticos. Madrid, Impr. de Alban, 1823.
2 v. 16cm.

1. Popes 2. Papacy - Hist.
I. Title

NL 0426477 WU MH CLSU

922.2 L77pI 1865 Llorente, Juan Antonio, 1756-1823.
Ritratto politico dei papi considerati come principe temporali e come capi della chiesa. Dall'origine della Santa Sede in Roma, fino a Pio VII. Opera di d. G. A. Llorente ... Prima versione italiana con prefazione e cenni storici sulla vita dell'autore. Milano, Presso l'Ufficio della Gazzetta di Milano [etc.] 1865.
420p.

A translation of the author's Portrait politique des papes first pub. in Paris, 1822.

NL 0426478 IU

LLORENTE, JUAN ANTONIO, 1756-1823.
Storia critica della Inquisizione di Spagna, scritta dal sig. D.Gio.Ant.Llorente... compendiata in lingua italiana dal sig.Stefano Ticozzi. Milano, Tip.di commercio al Bocchetto, 1820.
6v. fronts.(v.1:port.) fold.plates. 18cm.

NL 0426479 PU

Llorente, Luis Orcasitas
see
Orcasitas, Luis.

VOLUME 337

Llorente, Manuel G., tr.

CB19 .S65 1940z **Spengler, Oswald,** 1880–1936.
El hombre y la técnica, contribución a la filosofía de la vida. Traducción del alemán por Manuel G. Llorente. Buenos Aires, Luz [194–]

[Llorente, Mariano]
Saggio apologetico degli storici e conquistatori spagnuoli dell' America. Parma, L. Mussi, 1804.
91, [1] p. 18½cm.
Dedication signed: Mariano Llorente.
Includes criticism of statements in Francesco Bartolozzi's Ricerche istorico-critiche circa alle scoperte d'Amerigo Vespucci ... Firenze, 1789.
1. America—Disc. & explor.—Spanish. 2. Spanish America—Hist.—Historiography. 3. Bartolozzi, Francesco, fl. 1789. Ricerche istorico-critiche circa alle scoperte d'Amerigo Vespucci. I. Title.
18-14493
Library of Congress F1411.L78

NL 0426482 DLC CU-B

Llorente, Máximo, tr.

PT2653 .W42 V5816 **Zweig, Stefan,** 1881–1942.
Veinticuatro horas de la vida de una mujer, traducción de Máximo Llorente, prólogo de José Manuel Ripamonti. Buenos Aires, Editorial Tor [1936]

Llorente, Máximo, tr.

Olaf, Michael.
... Vida y muerte de Etiopía, el último imperio africano; versión de Máximo Llorente. Buenos Aires, Editorial Tor [1936?]

Llorente, Miguel de la Pinta
see Pinta Llorente, Miguel de la, 1906–

Llorente, Pedro Gonzalez
see
Gonzalez Llorente, Pedro, 1827-1905

Llorente, Ricardo Martínez
see Martínez Llorente, Ricardo.

Llorente, Rodrigo
see
Llorente Martínez, Rodrigo.

F 909 L826 Llorente, Segundo.
A orillas del "Kusko." Balbao, Editori El Siglo de las Misiones [1951]
275 p. 19 cm. (Coleccion Luz de las Gentes)
1. Alaska--Descr. & trav. 2. Missions--Alaska. I. Title.

NL 0426489 AkU

Llorente, Segundo.
Alaska a través de las cartas del P. Segundo Llorente... Prólogo, introducción biográfica, edición y notas, por Angel Santos Hernández... Palencia, Secretariado de Anking [1948] 326 p. 17cm. (Biblioteca Anking)
554499B. 1. Alaska—Descr. and trav., 1900– 2. Eskimos—Missions.

NL 0426490 NN

F 909 L823 Llorente, Segundo.
Aventureros del circulo polar, por el P. Segundo Llorente. Bilbao, Editorial El Siglo de las Misiones, 1952.
174 p. 19 cm. (Coleccion luz de las gentes)
1. Missions--Alaska. 2. Alaska--Descr. & trav. I. Title.

NL 0426491 AkU

F909 L56 1954 Llorente, Segundo
Cartas de Alaska. Prólogo, introducción biográfica y notas por Angel Santos Hernández. 2. ed. México, Buena Prensa [1954]
445 p. 21cm.
1. Alaska - Descr. & trav. 2. Missions - Alaska. 3. Jesuits in Alaska. I. Title.

NL 0426492 CU-B

Llorente, Segundo.
En el país de los eternos hielos, Alaska boreal; vida del misionero en los hielos polares, por Segundo Llorente ... Buenos Aires, Editorial Difusión, s. a., 1941.
253, [3] p. plates, ports., map. 17½cm.
1. Alaska—Descr. & trav. 2. Missions—Alaska. 3. Jesuits—Missions. I. Title.
44-24456
Library of Congress F909.L8
[3] 917.98

NL 0426493 DLC

N 979.85 L773el **Llorente, Segundo**
En las lomas del Polo Norte, Alaska Boreal; vida del misionero al norte del Círculo Polar Artico. Bs. Aires, Editorial Difusion [1943]
211 p.
1. Alaska - Description and travel. 2. Missions - Alaska. 3. Jesuits - Missions. I. Title.

NL 0426494 WaU

Llorente, Teodoro, 1836-1911
see Llorente y Olivares, Teodoro, 1836-1911.

Llorente, Teodoro, 1879–
see
Llorente Falcó, Teodoro, 1879–

Llorente (Vicente). Conferencia dada el día 22 de octubre 1896 en el Colegio de médicos de Madrid; como contestación al folleto publicado por Camilo Calleja, sobre el suero antidiftérico. 20 pp. 8°. *Madrid, J. A. García,* 1896.

NL 0426497 DNLM

WCC L792d 1899 **LLORENTE, Vicente**
Del diagnóstico, pronóstico y tratamiento de la difteria y el croup ó garrotillo. Madrid, Marqués, 1899.
164 p. illus.
Lectures given at the Instituto Microbiológico, Madrid.

NL 0426498 DNLM

Llorente, Vicente Daniel.
Flores del corazon. Ensayos poeticos de Vicente Daniel Llorente, Veracruz, Tip. de J. Ledesma, 1877.
40 p.
Bound with: La batalla del Callao.

NL 0426499 WaPS

Llorente Falcó, Teodoro, 1879–
Cuentos maravillosos recogidos en Mallorca...
see under Alcover Sureda, Antonio Maria, 1862-1932.

Llorente Falcó, Teodoro, 1879–
De mi Valencia de otros tiempos; memorias de un setentón (artículos publicados en "Las Provincias") por T. Llorente Falcó; prólogo del excmo. Sr. D. Federico García Sanchiz ... Valencia, F. Domenech, 1942–45. 4 v. in 2. 21cm.
332260-1B. 1. Valencia, Spain (City)—Hist.
N. Y. P. L. September 26, 1946

NL 0426501 NN

Llorente Falcó, Teodoro, 1879–
De mi Valencia de otros tiempos; memorias de un setentón (artículos publicados en "Las Provincias") por T. Llorente Falcó, prólogo del excmo. sr. d. Federico García Sanchiz ... 2. ed. ... Valencia, Editorial F. Domenech, s. a., 1943–
v. 21cm.
1. Valencia (City)—Hist. 2. Valencia (City)—Soc. life & cust. I. Title.
46-14253
Library of Congress DP402.V19L57
[2] 946.7

NL 0426502 DLC

Llorente Falcó, Teodor.

Fullana Mira, Luis, 1871–
... Gramática elemental de la llengua valenciana per lo R. P. Lluis Fullana Mira ... prólec d'En Teodor Llorente Falcó ... Valencia, Estab. tip. Domenech, 1915.

Llorente Falcó, Teodoro, 1879–
... Mistral i Llorente (recull de noticies i impressions) per T. Llorente Falcó. Valencia [Renovación tipográfica, 1932?]
177 p., 2 l. illus. (facsims.) plates, ports. 19cm. (L'estel. [Sér. literària. v. 8])
At head of title: Amb motiu d'un centenari.
I. *Mistral, Frédéric, 1830–1914. II. Llorente y Olivares, Teodoro, 1836–1911. III. Title.
34-8873
Library of Congress PC3402.M5Z74
[2] 928.49

NL 0426504 DLC

Llorente Falcó, Teodoro, 1879–
Nuevos cuentos maravillosos...
see under Alcover Sureda, Antonio Maria, 1862-1932.

VOLUME 337

DP402 Llorente Falcó, Teodoro, 1879-
32L79 Los Valencianos en San Sebastián, por Teodoro Llorente Falcó. Valencia, Imp. F. Domenech, 1942.
172 p. 18½cm.

1.San Sebastián, Spain - Hist. 2.Spain - Hist. - Civil war, 1936-1939. I.Title.

NL 0426506 CSt-H

PN Llorente Federico, Daniel, comp.
6095 Ramillete de pensamientos para catequistas
.S5 y educadores. Barcelona, J. Vilamala, 1913.
L6 109 p. 19 cm.

1. Quotations, Spanish. I. Title.

NL 0426507 WU

F LLORENTE FERNÁNDEZ, ILDEFONSO.
409392 Recuerdos de Liébana. Madrid, Imp.y Fund.
.51 de M.Tello, 1882.
398p. 23cm.

Catalogo biográfico-bibliográfico de lebaniegos notables desde los siglos más remotos hasta hoy": p.[349]-388.

NL 0426508 ICN

[Llorente González, Arturo]
... Derechos de autor, escritores y artistas, tesis de licenciatura.] México, Editorial Bolívar, 1944.
5 p. l., 13-92 p., 1 l. 21½ x 17cm.
At head of title: Universidad nacional autónoma de México. Facultad de derecho y ciencias sociales.
Author's name on cover.
"Bibliografía": p. 91-92.

1. Copyright—Mexico.
45-4012
Library of Congress Z609.L6
[3] 655.672

NL 0426509 DLC

Llorente Lázaro, Ramon.
Compendio de farmacologia; ó, Materia medica veterinaria, por D. Ramon Llorente Lázaro ... Madrid [etc.] A. Calleja; [etc., etc., 1857]
2 p.l., iv, 293 p. 19 cm.
With this is bound his Compendio de las generalidades de patologia terapeutica. 1869.
1. Veterinary materia medica and pharmacy.

NL 0426510 CU

ZSF LLORENTE LAZARO, Ramón
615 Compendio de la bibliografía de la
L792c veterinaria española, con algunas
1856 noticias históricas de esta ciencia en nuestra patria, y con las reglas de moral á que debe el veterinario ajustar su conducta facultativa. Madrid, Calleja, 1856.
viii, 204 p.
1. Veterinary medicine - Bibl.

NL 0426511 DNLM WaPS CU

Llorente Lázaro, Ramon.
Compendio de las generalidades de patologia terapeutica y policia sanitaria veterinarias ... por Don Ramon Llorente y Lázaro ... 3. ed., corr. y aum. Madrid, P. Calleja, 1869.
2 p.l., 441 p. fold. table. 19 cm. [With his Compendio de farmacologia. [1857]
1. Veterinary materia medica and pharmacy.

NL 0426512 CU

Llorente Maldonado de Guevara, Antonio.
Estudio sobre el habla de La Ribera (comarca salmantina ribereña del Duero) Salamanca, Colegio Trilingüe de la Universidad, Consejo Superior de Investigaciones Científicas, 1947.
248 p. col. maps. 26 cm. (Tesis y estudios salmantinos, 5)
Tesis—Universidad de Madrid.
Bibliography: p. 48-52.

1. Spanish language—Dialects—Salamanca (Province) (Series)
PC4815.S3L5 58-37666

MoU KU NcU MH DCU IaU TU TxU RPB NRU
NL 0426513 DLC IEN CtY ICU IU InU PU LU CU TxHR FU

Llorente Maldonado de Guevara, Antonio.
Morfología y sintaxis; el problema de la división de la gramática. [Granada] Universidad de Granada, 1955.
299 p. 21 cm. (Colección filológica de la Universidad de Granada, 13)
Bibliography: p. [271]-290.

1. Language and languages. 2. Grammar, Comparative and general—Syntax. (Series: Granada (City) Universidad. Colección filológica, 13)
A 56-1067
Chicago. Univ. Libr. for Library of Congress

MoSU LU NN
NL 0426514 ICU CaBVaU NcD IEN TxU CU CtY MiU MH NcU

---

400 Llorente Maldonado de Guevara, Antonio.
L775pl Los "Principios de gramática general" de
1953 Hjelmslev y la linguística. Introducción a la ciencia del lenguaje. [Granada] Universidad de Granada, 1953.
245p. 21cm. (Colección filológica de la Universidad de Granada, 5)

1. Hjelmslev, Louis, 1899- Omkring sprogteoriens Grundlaeggelse. 2. Language and languages. I. Title. (Series: Granada (City) Universidad. Colección filológica, 5)

CaBVaU
NL 0426515 KU MiU WU TxU CU PU MH CtY LU NN IU

Llorente Martínez, Rodrigo.
Indices de comercio exterior y equilibrio orgánico de la balanza comercial de Colombia. Bogotá, 1952.
55 p. 25 cm.
Tesis—Pontificia Universidad Católica Javeriana.

1. Balance of trade—Colombia. 2. Colombia—Comm. I. Title.
HF3426.L55 55-40625 ‡

NL 0426516 DLC TxU MH

Llorente Monleón, Teodoro, 1906?-
Piadosa evocación; selección de articulos publicados en "Las Provincias" durante los años de 1928 y 1929, por Teodoro Llorente Monleón. Precedidas de un prólogo de Teodoro Llorente Falcó. Valencia, F. Domenech [193-?] 213 p. 18cm.

308933B. 1. No subject. I. Title.
N. Y. P. L. December 11, 1945

NL 0426517 NN

Llorente Olivares, Teodoro
see Llorente y Olivares, Teodoro, 1836-1911.

Llorente Vázquez, Manuel.
Cuadros americanos: Venezuela, Brasil, California, Guatemala, Montevideo y Ecuador, por Manuel Llorente Vázquez ... con un prólogo de Luis Vidart. Madrid, F. Fe, 1891.
xxiii, 432 p. 18½cm.

1. South America — Descr. & trav. 2. Guatemala — Descr. & trav. 3. San Francisco—Descr. I. Vidart, Luis, 1833-1897.
Library of Congress F2223.L79 1—28289

FU WaU
NL 0426519 DLC ICarbS NN ViU IU CU CtY MiU TNJ TxU

Llorente Vázquez, Manuel.
Cuadros americanos: Venezuela, Brasil, California, Guatemala, Montevideo y Ecuador, por Manuel Llorente Vazquez ... con un prólogo de Luis Vidart. Madrid, F. Fe, 1891.
xxiii, 432 p.
Microfilm (positive) (Travel literature. Ser. 1: The Americas. Part 1: Mexico. Reel 131, no. 7)

NL 0426520 UU

LLORENTE VAZQUEZ, Manuel.
E pluribus unum; viajes, costumbres, tradiciones, etc., Con un prologo del Marques de Rojas. Madrid, F-Fe . 1893.

NL 0426521 MH

868.708 Llorente y Azcaray, Eduardo
C697 ... La china poblana y el charro.
v.11 Comedia en un acto, original de Eduardo Llorente y Azcaray ... Puebla, A.Nieto [n.d.]
16p. 14cm. (In Collection of Mexican plays, v.11)

At head of title: [Ediciones de la casa "Nieto"] Serie X.
"Escrita expresamente para la casa 'Nieto'."

NL 0426522 IEN

868.708 Llorente y Azcaray, Eduardo
C697 ... Los pantalones. Juguete cómico
v.11 en un acto, original de Eduardo Llorente y Azcaray ... Puebla, A. Nieto [n.d.]
16p. 14cm. (In Collection of Mexican plays, v.11)

At head of title: [Ediciones de la casa "Nieto"] Serie X.
"Escrito expresamente para la casa 'Nieto'."

NL 0426523 IEN

Llorente y de las Casas, Luis G.
La cueva de la cómica .... Eleha, M. Santamaria, 1864.

NL 0426524 NNH

Llorente y Falcó, María.
Homenaje á María Llorente y Falco
see under title

Llorente y Falcó, Teodoro
see
Llorente Falcó, Teodoro, 1879-

F1546 Llorente y Lafuente, Anselmo, Bp., 1799-1872.
.6 Alocucion del ilustrisimo Sr. Obispo a las tropas del Ejercito
L5 expedicionario. [San José? Costa Rica, 1856]
x broadside. 35x23cm.

Provenance: H.H. Bancroft.

1. Costa Rica - History - 1821-1948. 2. Walker, William, 1824-1860. 3. Filibusters. 4. Church history - Costa Rica - Catholic Church. I. Title.

NL 0426527 CU-B

VOLUME 337

Llorente y Lafuente, Anselmo, Bp. 1799-1872.
Pastoral dada en 12 de octubre de 1867. C. de la Laguna, Impr. de la Paz [1867?]
20 p. 21 cm.

1. Catholic Church—Pastoral letters and charges.

BX874.L62P3 51-51561

NL 0426528 DLC

Llorente y Lannas, Alejandro, 1814-1901.
Catálogo de los libros escogidos del difunto Excmo. Sr.D.Alejandro Llorente. Madrid, Tip. de Fortanet, 1902

159 p.

NL 0426529 MH

Llorente y Lannas, Alejandro, 1814-1901, ed.

Villalobos y Benavides, Diego de, fl. 1598.
Comentarios de las cosas sucedidas en los Paises Baxos de Flandes desde el año de 1594 hasta el de 1598; compuesto por D. Diego de Villalobos y Benavides ... con una introduccion, notas é ilustraciones por D. Alejandro Llorente ... Madrid, A. Durán, 1876.

863C33 Od Y ll
Llorente y Llorente, José Mariano.
Algunas ideas del Quijote aplicadas a la doctrina fundamental de la administración; trabajo para la cátedra de derecho administrativo de Valladolid. Valladolid, Impr. y Lib. de J. Montero, 1905.
72p. 24cm. (Biblioteca de Derecho Administrativo. Publicación, 2)
"Primer premio en el curso de 1903 a 1904."

NL 0426531 IU

Llorente y Matos (Vicente). Datos para el diagnóstico de la difteria y su complicación el crup o garrotillo. Conferencia. 38 pp. 8°. Madrid, J. Perales y Martínez, 1904.

NL 0426532 DNLM

LLORENTE Y MATOS, Vicente, and Julio ROBERT.
La sueroterapia en el tratamiento de la difteria.
Madrid. Anales de obstetrica [etc.]. 1894. 29 pp. 8°

NL 0426533 MB

[Llorente y Olivares, Teodoro] 1836-1911, comp.
Album de poesías de escritores valencianos. Valencia, 1895.
213 p. 22 cm.
Preface signed: Teodoro Llorente.

NL 0426534 CU NNH

He78 127t
Llorente y Olivares, Teodoro, 1836-1911, comp.
... Amorosas. Poesías de los principales autores modernos puestas en rima castellana. 3.ed., corregida poh[!] el autor. Valencia, P.Aguilar[pref.1876]
xvii,[19]-214,[2]p. 15cm. (Biblioteca selecta, 8)
At head of title: T.Llorente.

NL 0426535 CtY

Llorente y Olivares, Teodoro.
—— tr. ... Amorosas; poesías de los principales autores modernos puestas en rima castellana. [2.ed.] Valencia, P. Aguilas, 1882. 192p. 14cm

NL 0426536 CU

Llorente y Olivares, Teodoro, 1836-1911
Epistolari Llorente; correspondència rebuda de 1861 a 1911. Ordenada i anotada per T.Llorente Falcó. Barcelona, Biblioteca Balmes, 1928-

(Biblioteca literària de l'Oficina romànica 1-2)

NL 0426537 MH

Llorente y Olivares, Teodoro, 1836-1911, tr.

La Fontaine, Jean de, 1621-1695.
Fábulas de La Fontaine; ilustradas por Gustavo Doré, traduccion de don Teodoro Llorente. Barcelona, Montaner y Simon. 1885.

Llorente y Olivares, Teodoro, 1836-1911, tr.
Fausto, tragedia
see under Goethe, Johan Wolfgang von, 1749-1832. Faust. Part I. Spanish.

Llorente y Olivares, Teodoro.
— ... Leyendas de oro, poesías de los principales autores modernos vertidas en rima castellana. 2.ed. ... Valencia, P. Aguilar [n.d.] 188p. 14cm.

NL 0426540 CU

He78 127l
Llorente y Olivares, Teodoro, 1836-1911, tr.
... Leyendas de oro; poesías de los principales autores modernos, vertidas en rima castellana. 4.ed., aumentada y corregida por el autor. Valencia,Librería de Aguilar [pref.1875]
xi,[13]-256p. 15½cm. (Biblioteca selecta, V)
At head of title: Teodoro Llorente.

NL 0426541 CtY

PN 6108 .L55
Llorente y Olivares, Teodoro, 1836-1911,tr.
Leyendas de oro. Poesías de los principales autores modernos vertidas en rima castellana. Valencia, Querol y Domenech [1877]
188 p. 15 cm. (Biblioteca selecta, 5)

1. Spanish poetry - Translations from foreign literature I. Title.

NL 0426542 WU NN

Llorente y Olivares, Teodoro, 1836-1911, tr.
Teodoro Llorente leyendas de oro. Valencia, Aguilar, 1889.

NL 0426543 NNH

He78 127p
Llorente y Olivares, Teodoro, 1836-1911, tr.
... Leyendas de oro. Poesías de autores modernos vertidas en rima castellana. 2.ser. Valencia,Librería de Aguilar[1903]
vi,[7]-256p. 15cm. (Biblioteca selecta, XCVII)
At head of title: Teodoro Llorente.

NL 0426544 CtY

Llorente y Olivares, Teodoro, 1836-1911, tr

Heine, Heinrich, 1797-1856.
... Libro de los cantares (Buch der lieder) Traducción en verso de Teodoro Llorente. Buenos Aires, Editorial Sopena argentina, s. r. l., 1941

PQ6621 .L8A17 1885
Llorente y Olivares, Teodoro, 1836-1911.
Llibret de versos. Valencia, T. Llorente, 1885.
198 p.

NL 0426546 ICU CU-S MH CU NNH

Llorente y Olivares, Teodoro, 1836-1911.
Meditaciones de color claro y preludios poéticos por Valentiono. Madrid, Calle de Velarde, 1864.

NL 0426547 NNH

Llorente y Olivares, Teodoro, 1836-1911.

Llorente Falcó, Teodoro, 1879-
... Mistral i Llorente (recull de noticies i impressions) per T. Llorente Falcó. Valencia [Renovación tipográfica, 1932?]

Llorente y Olivares, Teodoro, 1836-1911.
Nou llibret de versos escrit per Teodor Llorente. Valencia, Estampa de Federich Domenech, Editor, 1902

xvi, 268 p. port. (Biblioteca "Lo Rat-Penat", Societat de Amadors de les Glories Valencianes, 6)

NL 0426549 MH CU ICU

Llorente y Olivares, Teodoro, 1836-1911.
Nou llibret de versos. Preàmbul de M.Menéndez y Pelayo. 2.ed. molt aumentada. Valencia, Impr. de Domenech, 1909

xxvii, 378 p.

NL 0426550 MH

PC3802 .B6 no.56
Llorente y Olivares, Teodoro, 1836-1911.
Poesies triades. Barcelona, 1906.
97 p. (Biblioteca popular de "L'Avenç", no.56)

NL 0426551 ICU CtY

Llorente y Olivares, Teodoro, 1836-1911.
Poesies valencianes. Prolec de M.Menéndez y Pelayo. 5.ed., aumentada ab una nova part de poesies no compresgudes en anteriors edicions. Valencia, Establiment Tipografic F.Domenech, 1936

428 p. port. (His Obras completas)

NL 0426552 MH

Hfk 80
Llorente y Olivares, Teodoro, 1836-1911,tr.
... Poetas franceses del siglo XIX; traducción en verso castellano por D. Teodoro Llorente. Edición ilustrada. Barcelona,Montaner y Simón,1906.
398p.,1l. illus. 24cm. (Biblioteca universal)

NL 0426553 CtY

Llorente y Olivares, Teodoro, 1836-1911.
Teodoro Llorente; su vida y sus obras, florilegio de sus poesías. [Edited by Juan Navarro Reverter.] Barcelona, etc., F. Granada y ca. [1909].
pp. 453 +. Port.

NL 0426554 MH CU ICarbS IU

3175 .L387 .1910
Llorente y Olivares, Teodoro, 1836-1911
Teodoro Llorente, su vida y sus obras. Florilegio de sus poesías [Compilado por Juan Navarro Reverter] Barcelona, Granada [1910]
453 p. illus. 21 cm.

I.Navarro Reverter, Juan, comp.

NL 0426555 NjP

VOLUME 337

DP 22 E77 v.25-26 Llorente y Olivares, Teodoro, 1836-1911.
Valencia. Clichés de A. García. Grabados de Joarizti y Mariezcurrena. Barcelona, D. Cortezo, 1887-1889.
2 v. illus., mounted plates. 25cm.
(España, sus monumentos y artes, su naturaleza e historia, v.25-26)

1. Valencia, Spain - Descr. & trav. (Series)

NL 0426556 NIC NN CU TNJ CoU NNC CtY MiU PBm WU MiU NjP MWelC

PQ 6534 L55V5 1907 Llorente y Olivares, Teodoro, 1836-1911.
Versos de la juventud, 1854-66. Madrid, F. Fe [1907]
viii, 286 p. port. 16cm.

NL 0426557 NIC CU MoU CtY

Lloret, Antonio M., joint ed.

[Pantoja, José María] *ed.*
[Ley hipotecaria, comentada y explicada, concordada con las leyes y códigos extranjeros, comparada con las disposiciones de la legislacion española, que han servido de precedente para redactarla ... precedida de una introduccion histórica y de la exposicion de sus motivos y fundamentos; y seguida del reglamento para su ejecucion, etc. (y de un Diccionario completa [!] de la nueva legislacion, etc.) Madrid, 1861-63]

Lloret, Bartolomé Llopis
see
Llopis Lloret, Bartolomé.

Lloret, Isidre.
Dret organic municipal; resum de les lliçons esplicades. [Badalona] 1914.
549 p. 21 cm.
At head of title: Escola de Funcionaris d'Administració Local creada per la Diputació Provincial de Barcelona.

1. Municipal corporations—Spain. I. Title.

55-50438 ‡

NL 0426560 DLC

Lloret, J. Just
see Just Lloret, J.

Lloret, Javier de Ferrer y de
see Ferrer y de Lloret, Javier de.

Lloret, Jeroni, 1506 or 07-1571.
Sylva allegoriarvm sacrae scripturae. Barcinone, In aedibus Pauli Cortey & Petri Mali, 1570.

NL 0426563 NNH

Lloret, Jeroni, 1506 or 07-1571.
Sylva allegoriarvm totivs Sacrae Scriptvrae mysticos eivs sensvs, et magna etiam ex parte l iterales complectens, syncerae theologiae condidatis perutilis, ac necessaria ... Venetiis, Apud Gasparem Bindonum, & Petrum Longum, socios. MDLXXV.
10p.*l.*, 566numb.*l.* 22cm.
Title within ornamental border.

NL 0426564 MH-AH IMunS CU-A

Lloret, Jeroni, 1506 or 07-1571.
Sylva allegoriarvm totius Sacrae Scripturae. Mysticos eivs sensvs, & magna etiam ex parte litterales complectens, syncerae theologiae candidatis perutilis, ac necessaria ... Venetiis, Ex officina G. Bindoni, 1587.
2 v. 22 cm.

NL 0426565 OU FU

Lloret, Jeroni, 1506 or 07-1571.
Sylva allegoriarvm totivs sacrae scriptvrae, mysticos eivs sensvs, et magna etiam ex parte literales complectens, syncerae theologiae candidatis perutilis ac necessaria quae loco integrae bibliothecae cuilibet sacrarum literarum studioso seruire poterit ... cum indice materiarum & dictionum secundum allegorias scripturae enodatarum locupletissimo ... Lvgdvni, Ant. de Harsy, & Petri Rauaud, 1622.
827 p. 37 cm.

NL 0426566 NcD

Lloret, Jeroni, 1506 or 07-1571.
Sylva, seu potius hortus floridus ... n. p., n. d.

NL 0426567 NjNbS

Lloret, Jeroni, 1506 or 07-1571.
Sylva, seu potius hortus floridus allegoriarvm totivs Sacrae Scriptvrae. Mysticos eivs sensvs, et magna etiam ex parte literales complectens ... Cum indice materiarum & dictionum ... locupletissimo. Hac verò postrema et vltima editione accessit ad marginem diligentissima adnotatio authorum ... Coloniae Agrippinae, Apud Joannem Gymnicum, 1612.
[12], 1096, [82] p. 32cm.
Title vignet te, engraved.

NL 0426568 NIC

Lloret, Jeroni, 1506 or 07-1571.
Sylva, seu potius Hortus floridus allegoriarum totius Sacrae Scripturae kysticos ejus sensus et magna etiam ex parte literales complectens, sincerae Theologiae candidatis perutilis ac necessarius, qui loco integrae Bibliothecae cuilibet Sacrarum literarum studioso poterir ... Cum indice materiarum et dictionum secundum Allegorias S. Scripturae enodatarum locupletissimo. Hac vero postrema et ultima editione accesit ad marginem diligentissima adnotatio authorum et praecipue SS. PP. quibus singula locis allegorias quasquo explanarint, hactenus desiderata.

Coloniae Agrippinae, apud Hermannum Demen, 1681.
[8], 1096, [72] p. 35 cm.
Title vignette. Printer's device. Title page in red and black. Head pices. Intials. Bound in boards with clasps.

NL 0426570 PLatS

Lloret, Jeroni, 1506 or 07-1571.
Sylva, seu potius hortus floridus allegoriarum totius Sacrae Scripturae; mysticos ejus sensus, & magna etiam ex parte litterales complectans... Coloniae Agripinae, Hermann Deman, 1701.
4p.*l.*, 1096p. 36cm.

Title page vignette.

1. Bible - Dictionaries. I.Title.

NL 0426571 KAS

Lloret, Jeroni, 1506 or 07-1571.
Sylva, seu potius hortus floridus, allegoriarum totius Sacrae Scripturae ... Coloniae Agrippinae, Apud J. Huisch, 1744.
1096 p. 36 cm.
"Hac vero postrema & ultima editione accessit ad marginem diligentissima adnotatio authorum & praecipue SS. PP. quibus singuli locis allegorias quasque explanarint, hactenus desiderata."

1. Bible—Criticism, interpretation, etc. 2. Allegories. I. Title.

BS505.L6 1744 72-282013

NL 0426572 DLC

Lloret, Jesús.
Reglamento taurino; commentado y puesto al día por Jesús Lloret, "Recorte," y Antonio Bellveser, "Don Gil." Madrid, Insula [n. d.]
73 p. illus. 21 cm.
Cover title.

1. Bull-fighting. I. Bellveser, Antonio, joint author. II. Title.

A 53-3866

Indiana. Univ. Libr. for Library of Congress GV1107.L7 [2]

NL 0426573 InU

Lloret, Jesús.
Reglamento taurino; commentado y puesto al día por Jesús Lloret, "Recorte," y Antonio Bellveser, "Don Gil." [Valencia, 1953] 73 p. illus. 22cm.
Cover-title.

1. Bull-fights. I Bellveser, Antonio, joint author.

NL 0426574 NN

LLORET, JOSÉ.
[NOCHECITA DE SAN JUAN. LIBRETTO. SPANISH]
Nochecita de San Juan; cuento lírico-fantástico inspirado en El sueño de una noche de verano, de Shakespeare, escrito en un acto, dividido en un prólogo y dos cuadros, por José Ramos Martín y Emilio Ferraz Revenga. Madrid, R. Velasco impr., 1919. 34 p. 20cm.

Microfiche (neg.) 1 sheet. 11 x 15cm. (NYPL FSN 11,270)
"Estrenado en el Teatro de la zarzuela la noche del 12 de novembre de 1919."

I. Ramos Martín, José, 1892- ,Nochecita de San Juan. II. Ferraz Revenga, Emilio. Nochecita de San Juan. III. Title. IV. Shakespeare William. Plays. A midsummer night's dream.

NL 0426576 NN

LLORET, José
La vision roja; comedia lirica. Madrid, 1909.

(Sociedad de autores españoles)
By José Lloret and Juan Casero.

NL 0426577 MH NN

Lloret, José Luis.
El miserere. Poema sinfónico para coros y orquesta. Op. 20. Partitura.
— Madrid. Lloret. 1918. (1), 83 pp. 49½ cm.

M21 — T.r. — Symphonic poems.

NL 0426578 MH MB

Lloret, José Maria de Ferrer y de
see Ferrer y de Lloret, José Maria de.

VOLUME 337

Lloret, Ricardo Gonzalez
see
Gonzalez Lloret, Ricardo, 1886-

Lloret Bastidas, Antonio.
Parábola del corazón cardinal. Cuenca, Editorial "Amazonas," 1948.
53 p. 20 cm.
Poems.

I. Title.
PQ8219.L65P3 861.6 53-24512 ‡

NL 0426581 DLC MH DPU WaU

Lloret y de Yepes, José, 1844–
Con razon y sin derecho, comedia en tres actos y en verso, original de D. José Lloret y Yepes... Madrid: J. M. Ducazcal, 1883. 67 p. 8°.
With autograph of author.

1. Drama (Spanish). 2. Title.
N. Y. P. L. July 9, 1920.

NL 0426582 NN FMU MH

Lloret y Gregori, Juan.
Con sus mismas armas; drama en tres actos y en verso, por Juan Lloret y Gregori. Águilas: S. Alarcon, 1903. 67 p. 8°.
With autograph of author.

1. Drama (Spanish). 2. Title.
N. Y. P. L. May 23, 1921.

NL 0426583 NN

He88 Lloret y Gregori, Juan
L773 Margarita, drama en 3 actos y en verso. 2.ed.
M33 Aguilas, Impr.de S.Alarcon, 1906.
61p. 21cm.

NL 0426584 CtY

T233 Lloret y Román, Manuel, ed.
.C9T4
1940 **Cuba.** *Laws, statutes, etc.*
Ley de propiedad industrial (marcas y patentes) vigente en la república de Cuba, explicada y comentada por Manuel Lloret y Román y Jorge Ameller y Escobar ... 1. ed. ₍Habana, Imp. Fiallo y García, 1940.

Llori, Antonio Alomía
see Alomía Llori, Antonio, 1867-

PQ6621
.L57A63
Lloria, Matilde.
Aleluya. Ilus. de Fernando Escrivá. ₍Valencia₎ Institución Alfonso el Magnánimo, Diputación Provincial de Valencia, 1953.
108 p. illus. 18 cm. (Instituto de Literatura y Estudios Filológicos. Colección Murta, 9)
Poems.

I. Title.
A 54-4673

Illinois. Univ. Library for Library of Congress

NL 0426587 IU DLC NN NBuU

WB LLORIA PEREZ, Mateo
960 Nuevo método para el tratamiento y
L792n curación de las enfermedades en general
1922 y especialmente las infecciosas, incluso la tuberculosis pulmonar y el cáncer. Valencia, Pascual, 1922.
174 p. illus., ports.

NL 0426588 DNLM

F1210
.1 La Llorona; o, El espectro de la media noche. San Antonio,
L5 Texas, Editorial Quiroga [c1916]
96 p. 21cm.

NL 0426589 CU-B

La Llorona; o, El expectro [sic] de la media noche. San Antonio, Tex., Librería de Quiroga [c1916]
T1203 88 p. 22cm. [Terrazas collection]
T4L55
x

NL 0426590 CU-B

Llosa, Carlos A Torres de la
see
Torres de la Llosa, Carlos A

Llosa, Francisco
Exposicion que el prefecto de Arequipa durante la revolucion del Peru en 1854 hace a la nacion y al gobierno en elogio del patriotico comportamento de su departamento y en representacion de sus necesidades. Arequipa, Mariano Nicolas Madueño, 1855.
22 p. 19cm.
Signed: Francisco Llosa.

NL 0426592 MH-L

Llosa, Jorge Guillermo
see
Llosa P , Jorge Guillermo.

Llosa, José Antonio
see
Llosa M , José Antonio.

Llosa, José Mariano
see Llosa Benavides, José Mariano.

Llosa, Manín de la, *pseud.*
see
Muñiz García Robés, Gabino.

Llosa, M[ariano] E[stevan] de la.
Proyecto de constitución política prsentado por el ciudadano M.E. de la Llosa, diputado del congreso jeneral constituyente, con un discurso preliminar, mandado imprimir por su autor. Lima, Imprenta de la instrucción primaria, 1827.
19,(1),21 p.
8°

NL 0426597 MH-L CtY

Llosá, Ricardo San Juan
see
San Juan Llosá, Ricardo.

Llosa Benavides, José Mariano.
Poesías patrias y americanas de José Mariano Llosa, dedicadas a la juventud arequipeña. Arequipa, P. Miranda, 1864.
40 p. 19.5 cm.

NL 0426599 CtY

Llosa M , José Antonio.
Revolución agraria; análisis doctrinal, tesis de la Central Obrera Boliviana, Decreto ley de reforma agraria, Reglamento del Servicio de R. A. Con autorización oficial. ₍La Paz₎ Ediciones Nueva Bolivia, 1953.
98 p. ports. 19 cm.

1. Land tenure—Bolivia—Law. I. Bolivia. Laws, statutes, etc. Decreto ley de la reforma agraria. II. Title.
56-25296 rev ‡

NL 0426600 DLC PPiU NcD NN NNC

B Llosa P , Jorge Guillermo
121 Historia del humanismo; India y China
L79 ₍por₎ Jorge Guillermo Llosa P. Bogotá, Editorial Minerva, 1951.
105 p. 24cm.

1. Philosophy, Hindu. 2. Philosophy, Chinese. 3. Humanism.

NL 0426601 NIC TxU CU-S

Llosa P , Teobaldo.
... Enfermedades del trigo (instrucciones para el control de la "carie", el "carbón" y el "tizón del nudo"), por el ingeniero agrónomo Teobaldo Llosa P ... Lima, Peru, Estación experimental agrícola de La Molina, 1937.
10 p., 1 l. 8 plates on 4 l. 24 cm. (Estación experimental agrícola. Lima. Circular no. 40)
Cover-title

NL 0426602 DPU

Llosa P , Teobaldo.
... Informe sobre las enfermedades del palto y del naranjo en la zona de Chanchamayo, por el ing. agrónomo Teobaldo Llosa P. ... Lima, 1939.
33 p. plates. 24 cm. (Estación experimental agrícola. Lima. Informe no. 50. Abril de 1939)
At head of title: Ministerio de fomento. Dirección de agricultura y ganaderia ...

NL 0426603 DPU

Llosa P , Teobaldo.
... El problema de la roya del trigo en el departamento de Ancash, por Teobaldo Llosa P. ... Lima, Sección técnica de propaganda agropecuaria, 1942.
cover-title, 21 p. 24½cm.
At head of title: República del Perú. Ministerio de fomento. Dirección de agricultura y ganadería.

1. Wheat—Diseases and pests. 2. Puccinia. I. Peru. Dirección de agricultura y ganadería.
43-16509
Library of Congress SB608.W5L55

NL 0426604 DLC CtY DNAL

Llosellas, Leopoldo Rius y de
See
Rius y de Llosellas, Leopoldo, 1840-1898.

VOLUME 337

Llosent y Maranón, Eduardo.
Ortega Muñoz. Traducción al inglés de David G. Rowlands. [1. ed.] Madrid, 1952.
87 p. plates (part col.) port. 26 cm.
Spanish and English.

1. Ortega Muñoz, Godofredo M., 1905-

ND813.O7L5 [759.6] 927.5 54-17840

NL 0426606 DLC MH NN

Llosera, José Antonio Llobet y Vall-
see Llobet y Vall-Llosera, José Antonio, 1799-1861.

Lloubes (Edouard-August-Christian) [1883-].
*A propos d'un cas de scarlatine apyrétique. 50 pp. 8°. Lille, 1909.

NL 0426608 DNLM

Llouquet, Louis, 1910-
... L'assistance obstétricale en Algérie ... Alger [1936]
Thèse - Univ. d'Alger.
"Bibliographie": p. [87]

NL 0426609 CtY

Llovera, Bernabé Llovera
see
Llovera Llovera, Bernabé, 1916-

Llovera, Carlos Martínez de Campos y Serrano, conde de
see
Martínez de Campos y Serrano, Carlos, duque de la Torre, 1887-

Llovera, Domingo.
Playas de Cataluña de Cap de Creus al Ebro, descripción sumaria. Información y datos facilitados por Domingo Llovera y Sección Técnica de Editorial Alpina. Con un mapa anecdótico orginal de A. Bescós. [1. ed.] Granollers, Editorial Alpina [1952]
47 p. illus. 17 cm. (Colección popular)
Editorial Alpina. Publicación nº 27.

1. Catalonia—Descr. & trav. 2. Beaches. 3. Coasts—Spain—Catalonia. I. Editorial Alpina, Granollers, Spain. II. Title.

DP302.C61L55 61-35274 ‡

NL 0426612 DLC

Llovera, Fernando.
La columna Uribarry; crónicas de guerra, por Fernando Llovera, "Homitio". Valencia, Gráficas Turia [1936?]
204 p., 1 l. 19½cm.

1. Spain—Hist.—Civil war, 1936- I. Title.

Library of Congress DP269.L6 37-13083
[2] 946.08

NL 0426613 DLC MB

Llovera, José Maria, tr.

Alfonso X, el Sabio, king of Castile and Leon, 1221-1284.
Les "Cantigas" del rei N'Anfós el Savi, per Mn. Higini Anglès; amb la versió catalana pel Dr. Josep M.ª Llovera ... Barcelona, Impr. d'E. Subirana, 1927.

Llovera, José María, tr.

Vianney, Jean Baptiste Marie, Saint, 1786-1859.
Sermones de san Juan Bta. M.ª Vianney ... version y prólogo por el M. Iltre. Dr. D. José M.ª Llovera ... Barcelona, E. Subirana, 1927.

Llovera, José María, tr.

Bible. N. T. Gospels. Catalan. Harmonies. 1927.
Sinopsi evangèlica; text grec de M.-J. Lagrange, o. p., versió catalana i notes de Ll. Carreras i J. M. Llovera ... Barcelona, Editorial Alpha, s. a., 1927.

G301
L774t
Llovera, José Maria
... Tratado de sociología. México, D.F., Editora nacional, s.a., 1952.
3p.l.,[v]-xi, 471p. 23cm.

1. Sociology. I. Title.

NL 0426617 TxU

Llovera, José Maria
Tratado de sociología. México, Editora Nacional, 1955.
471p.

NL 0426618 OCl

Llovera, José M[aria]
Tratado elemental de la sociología cristiana ... Barcelona; Acción Social Popular, 1909.
xv, 426, vii p., 1 l. 8°.

NL 0426619 NN

Llovera, José María.
Tratado elemental de sociología cristiana, por el Dr. D. José M.ª Llovera... Barcelona: "Acción social popular," 1916. xi, 364 p. 3. ed., enl. 8°.

1. Sociology (Christian).
N. Y. P. L. November 15, 1917.

NL 0426620 NN

Llovera, José Maria.
Verdaguer, aspecto sacerdotal de su obra poética. Conferencia leida en la Balmesiana el 1 de junio de 1945, como última de la serie en el homenaje a Verdaguer en conmemoración del aniversario de su nacimiento. Barcelona, L. Gili, 1946.

NL 0426621 MH

Llovera, Miguel.
Ana de Tamar, marquesa de Bellaflor; drama en tres actos divididos en cinco cuadros y en prosa, por Miguel Llovera. Barcelona: Gassó hermanos, 1914. 64 p. 16°.

1. Drama (Spanish). 2. Title.
N. Y. P. L. October 3, 1919.

NL 0426622 NN

Llovera, Patricio Prieto y
see Prieto y Llovera, Patricio.

Llovera Aznar, Humberto
Financiamiento de empresas industriales. México, D. F., 1949.
98 p.

Thesis (Contador público y auditor) Universidad Nacional Autónoma de México.
Includes bibliography.

NL 0426624 NNC

Ven
PQ
8549
.L56V4
Llovera Ezeiza, Vicente.
Versos de entonces. Caracas, Editorial Avila Gráfica, 1949.
143 p. port. 23 cm.

NL 0426625 DPU

Llovera Llovera, Bernabé, 1916-
Agua salada. Caracas [Editorial "Canaima"] 1952.
101 p. 23 cm.

I. Title.

PQ8549.L568A7 67-56246 ‡

NL 0426626 DLC TxU NIC

Llovera Majem, Camilo.
Gramática italiana del siglo xx, por el dr. Camilo Llovera Majem ... Prólogo del iltre. prof. dr. Antonio Gasparetti ... Barcelona, Bosch [1942]
viii, 382 p. 22½cm.
"Bibliografía": p. [371]

1. Italian language—Grammar—1870- 2. Italian language—Textbooks for foreigners—Spaniards.

Library of Congress PC1129.S6L5 45-33386
[2] 458.246

NL 0426627 DLC

Llovera Solano, Rafael
... Discursos. Carupano, Emp. tip. Lyon & Lujan, 1922.
1 p.l.,38 p. 20cm.

NL 0426628 CU-B

Llovera Solano, Rafael.
Hojas de mi album. Ciudad Bolívar, Tip. de. J.S.Machado, 1899-
v. 22cm.

NL 0426629 IEN

G336.222
L774c
Lloveras, Alberto M
El catastro territorial. Córdoba, Impr. de la Universidad, 1951.
114p. map. 27cm.
"De la Revista de la Facultad de Ciencias Exactas, Físicas y Naturales, ano XIII no.3-4, 1950."
Includes bibliography.

1. Cadasters - Argentine Republic. 2. Land - Taxation - Argentine Republic. 3. Real property Argentine Republic. I. Title.

NL 0426630 TxU

WE
170
L792o
1927
LLOVERAS, Carlos V
Operatoria; apuntes de la cátedra, por Carlos V. Lloveras y Juan L. Barros. Buenos Aires, La Clínica, 1927.
129 p. illus.
I. Barros, Juan L

NL 0426631 DNLM

VOLUME 337

Lloveras, Federico, 1912–
Federico Lloveras, Barcelona. [Barcelona, Archivo de arte, 1946] 2 p.l., 10 col. pl. 38cm. (Figuras cumbres del arte contemporaneo español. v. 13)
Issued in portfolio.
Biographical note signed: Fernando Gutiérrez.
Portrait on cover.
566163B. I. Gutiérrez, Fernando. II. Ser.
N. Y. P. L. March 28, 1951
NL 0426632 NN

Lloveras, José Argemí
see
Argemí Lloveras, José.

W 4 B92 no.1258
LLOVERAS, Ventura
Enterectomía y su técnica. Buenos Aires, 1902.
91 p. (Buenos Aires. Universidad Nacional. Facultad de Ciencias Médicas. Tesis, año 1902, no. 1258)
NL 0426634 DNLM MH

282.2 L77
Llovet, Eduardo.
Comentarios sobre colonización. [Montevideo, 1949]
24 p.
1. Colonization, Agricultural. Uruguay. Law. I. Uruguay. Instituto Nacional de Colonización.
NL 0426635 DNAL

SF 488 U8 L79 1930
Llovet, Eduardo.
La industria avícola en el Uruguay. Montevideo, Castro & Pizarro, 1930.
212 p. illus. 23 cm.
1. Poultry - Uruguay. I. Title.
NL 0426636 NIC

Llovet, Enrique, 1917–
Ballet espanol
see under Gyenes, Juan.

Llovet, Enrique, 1917–
... Cartas a unos jóvenes americanos. Madrid, 1942.
2 p.l., 7-66 p., 2 l. 18cm.
"Editado por la Delegación nacional del servicio exterior [de la Falange española tradicionalista]"—Flap of front cover.
1. Spain—Relations (general) with Spanish America. 2. Spanish America—Relations (general) with Spain. I. Falange española tradicionalista y de las juntas ofensivas nacional-sindicalistas. Delegación nacional del servicio exterior. II. Title.
Library of Congress F1414.L58 44-48115
[2] 327.80946
NL 0426638 DLC

PN2784 .G9
Llovet, Enrique, 1917–
Gyenes, Juan.
Don Juan y el teatro en España. Fotografías de Juan Gyenes. Presentación de Luis Escobar, introducción de Enrique Llovet, comentarios de Joaquín Argamasilla de la Cerda [et al.] Madrid, Ediciones Mundo Hispánico [1955]

Llovet, Enrique, 1917–
Los últimos de Filipinas. [Madrid, 1954]
64 p. 15 cm. (La Novela del sábado, año 2, núm. 89)
I. Title.
PQ6621.L58U4 56-30135 ‡
Library of Congress
NL 0426640 DLC CtY NIC

Llovet, J
see Llovet Montros, José, 1907–

Llovet, Juan Jose.
Pegaso encadenado, poemas. Madrid, Saez. 1914.
152 p.
NL 0426642 PU

Llovet, Juan Jose.
El rosal de la leyenda, poemas. Madrid, Imprenta Helenica, 1913.
124 p.
NL 0426643 PU

Llovet, Mariano del Villar y
see Villar y Llovet, Mariano del.

Llovet, Patricio Palomar
see
Palomar Llovet, Patricio.

Llovet, R. Ribera
see Ribera Llovet, R.

Llovet, Ricardo Marín
see
Marín Llovet, Ricardo, 1874–

Llovet Montros, José, 1907–
... Las industrias de la leche, por J. Llovet ... Primera edición ... Barcelona, Salvat editores, s. a., 1931.
2 p. l., iv, [5]-269 p. illus., plans, diagrs. 21cm. (Biblioteca agrícola Salvat)
1. Cheese. 2. Milk.
Library, U. S. Dept. of Agriculture 44L772 Agr 31-1324
NL 0426648 DNAL

Llowarch, Wilfred.
Practical physics. London, New York, Longmans, Green [c1952]
xii, 266 p. illus. 22cm.
1.Physics - Textbooks. I.Title.
NL 0426649 DCU NcGW PSt

"Lloyd", *pseud.*
see
Coe, Lloyd, 1899–

E211 .B99
Lloyd, ———, captain, fl. 1779.
[**Burke, William**] 1730–1798, *supposed author.*
The letters of Valens, (which originally appeared in the London evening post) with corrections, explanatory notes, and a preface, by the author. London, Printed for J. Almon, 1777.

Lloyd, Captain, fl. 1779.
Lists of the forces of the sovereigns of Europe &c. viz. ranks, uniforms, number of officers, private men &c. of each nation. From the original of Capt. Lloyd. Methodized by J. Millan, & engraved by the best hands. London: Printed for J. Millan, 1761. 1 p.l., 30 [i. e. 29] tables on 25 l. 20½cm.
Plates are numbered: 1-8, 11-23, 28-30. 5 are unnumbered.
Engraved throughout.
With bookplate of George R. Dyer.
990676A. 1. Armies—Europe, 1761. 2. Armies, 1761. 3. Seven years' war, 1756-1763. I. Millan, John.
N. Y. P. L. January 15, 1943
NL 0426652 NN

Lloyd, Colonel
see Lloyd, Thomas, 1750-1828.

LLoyd, General
SEE
Lloyd, Henry, 1720?-83.

Lloyd, Ven. archdeacon
see Lloyd, Thomas Bucknall.

Lloyd, A L tr.
Lament
see under Garcia Lorca, Federico, 1899-1936.

LLoyd, Aaron N.Y. 1853
Sermon...
NL 0426657 NjNbS

[**Lloyd, Abigail Parkman**]
Genealogy. Family of Aaron and Sarah Bradley, of Guilford, Conn. ... [Hartford, Conn., Press of the Case, Lockwood & Brainard co., 1879.
46 p. 1 illus. (coat of arms) 23½cm.
Pages at end for insertion of photographs.
1. Bradley family. 2. Bradley family (Aaron Bradley, 1741-1802)
12-17722
Library of Congress CS71.B811 1879
NL 0426658 DLC MWA OCl PBm MnHi

Lloyd, Adele Towson.
"And ne'er forget will I" [by] Adele Towson Lloyd. Chicago, Priv. print., 1912.
viii, 62 p., 1 l. 18cm.
I. Title.
Library of Congress PS3523.L5A5 1912 13-661
NL 0426659 DLC

VOLUME 337

Lloyd, Alan
see
Lloyd, Herbert Alan.

Lloyd, Alan C., joint author.

Z49 .R877 1953a
Rowe, John L 1914–
FOR OTHER EDITIONS SEE MAIN ENTRY
Gregg typing, new series; complete course. The authors: John L. Rowe ₍and₎ Alan C. Lloyd. Consulting editor: Harold H. Smith. New York, Gregg Pub. Division, McGraw-Hill, °1953.

652.302 L793p
Lloyd, Alan C
Personal typing; a complete manual of instruction for writers, students, and others who desire to develop typewriting skill for their personal use. New York, Gregg Pub. Co. ₍1947₎
46p. illus.

1. Typewriting. I. Title.

NL 0426662 ICarbS

---

652 L77p 1950
Lloyd, Alan C
Personal typing; a complete manual of instruction for writers, students, and others who desire to develop typewriting skill for their personal use. New York, Gregg Pub. Co. ₍1950, c1947₎
vi, 90p. illus. 29 x 21cm.

1. Typewriting. I. Title.

NL 0426663 IU N OrCS

Lloyd, Alan Charles Gore
The first product of the printing press in South Africa

(In the South African bookman. ₍Maritzburg₎ 1910. 25cm. vol.1. p.36-57. facsim.)

1. Printing. History. Africa, South. I. South African Bookman. II. Title.

NL 0426664 IEN

Lloyd, Alan Charles Gore.
A list of the serial publications available for consultation in the libraries and scientific institutions of the Union of South Africa, comp. for the Research grant board of the Department of mines and industries, by A. C. G. Lloyd ... New and rev. ed. Cape Town ₍Printed by M. Miller, ltd.₎ 1927.

Lloyd, Alan Hubert, 1883–
Engineering for forest rangers in tropical countries, with special reference to Burma, by A. H. Lloyd ... Oxford, Clarendon press, 1929.
xvi, 228 p. xxxii pl. (incl. front.) on 24 l., plans, diagrs. 25ᶜᵐ.
Bibliography: p. ₍222₎

1. ₍Forestry—Engineering₎ 2. Forests and forestry—Tropics. ₍2. Tropics—Forestry₎

Agr 29-1695

Library, U. S. Dept. of Agriculture 98.74L77

NL 0426666 DNAL OrCS CaBVaU NIC CU CtY NcD

Lloyd, Alan Stredwick.
A digest of the cases reported in the New South Wales State reports and Weekly notes, and of the cases reported on appeal from the Supreme court to the High court and the Privy council, and of the cases decided by the Land appeal court and the Land valuation court during the period 1921-1925, compiled by Alan S. Lloyd ... Sydney ₍etc.₎ The Law book company of Australasia, ltd., 1926.
xix p., 486 (i. e. 490) col. 24½ᶜᵐ.

With extra numbered columns; addenda slips inserted.
Lettered on cover: N. S. W. digest. 1921-25.

1. Law reports, digests, etc.—New South Wales. I. The State reports, New South Wales. II. New South Wales weekly notes. III. New South Wales. Supreme court. IV. New South Wales. Courts. V. Australia. High court. VI. Gt. Brit. Privy council. Judicial committee. VII. New South Wales. Land appeal court. VIII. New South Wales. Land and valuation court. IX. Title: New South Wales digest.

30-6476

NL 0426668 DLC MH

Lloyd, Alan Stredwick, *comp.*
Index of New South Wales cases, 1825-1920, judiciall noticed in the judgments of the Supreme court of N. S. W., the High court of Australia, or the Judicial committee of the Privy council on appeal therefrom, together with a statement of the manner in which each case is dealt with in its place of citation, comp. by Alan S. Lloyd ... and B. V. Stacy ... Sydney, The Law book co. of Australasia ltd.; ₍etc., etc.₎ 1921.
vii p., 113 numb. l. 25ᶜᵐ.
Printed on rectos of leaves only.
1. Annotations and citations (Law)—New South Wales. I. Stacy, Bertie Vandeleur, joint comp. II. New South Wales. Supreme court. III. Australia. High court. IV. Gt. Brit. Privy council. Judicial committee. V. Title.

22-15284

NL 0426669 DLC

Lloyd, Alan Stredwick.
The remuneration of commission agents, by Alan S. Lloyd ... and Percy Ernest Joske ... Sydney ₍etc.₎ The Law book co. of Australasia, limited, 1924.
xii, 198 p. 22ᶜᵐ.

1. Agency (Law) I. Joske, Percy Ernest, joint author. II. Title. III. Title: Commission agents.

27-22643

NL 0426670 DLC

Lloyd, Alan Stredwick.
The remuneration of commission agents in Australia and New Zealand, by Alan S. Lloyd ... and Percy Ernest Joske ... 2d ed. Sydney, Australia ₍etc.₎ The Law book co. of Australasia pty ltd., 1943.
xvi, 304 p. 22½ᶜᵐ.
Addendum slip inserted.

1. Commission merchants—Australia. 2. Commission merchants—New Zealand. 3. Agency (Law)—Australia. 4. Agency (Law)—New Zealand. I. Joske, Percy Ernest, 1895– joint author. II. Title. III. Title: Commission agents.

44-23299

NL 0426671 DLC

Lloyd, Alan Stredwick, reporter.
The State reports, New South Wales, 1901– ... ₍New series₎ v. 1– Sydney ₍etc.₎ The Law book company of Australasia, limited, 1901–

276.761 L775a
Lloyd, Albert Bushnell.
Apolo of the Pygmy forest. London, Chruch Missionary Society, 191-.
62p. illus.

1. Kivebulaya, Apolo. 2. Missions--Uganda. I. Title.

NL 0426673 TxFTC

---

921 K6582LL
Lloyd, Albert Bushnell
Apolo of the pygmy forest; with foreword by J. J. Willis. London, Church Missionary Society ₍1923₎
62 p. illus.

1. Kivebulaya, Apolo, 1864?- 2. Uganda - Description and travel. 3. Missions - Uganda. I. Title.

NL 0426674 WaU CSt TNF CtY

Lloyd, Albert B
Apolo of the pygmy forest. With a foreword by the Right Rev. J. J. Willis. 4th impression. London, Church Missionary Society ₍1926₎
62 p. plates, port.

1. Kivebulaya, Apolo I. Title.

NL 0426675 NNC

Lloyd, Albert Bushnell.
Apolo of the pygmy forest ... with foreword by the Rt. Rev. J.J. Willis. London Church missionary soc. [1931]
62 p. pl. map. D.

NL 0426676 NcD

BV3625 .U4K56
Lloyd, Albert B
Apolo of the Pygmy Forest. With foreword by J. J. Willis, Bishop of Uganda. London, Church Missionary Society [1933]
62 p. illus., ports., map. 19 cm.

1. Kivebulaya, Apolo, 1864?-1933. 2. Missions—Uganda. I. Title.

NL 0426677 MB

LLOYD, ALBERT BUSHNELL.
Apolo of the Pygmy forest. New and enl. ed. London, Church missionary society, 1936. 82 p. illus., ports., map (on lining papers) 19cm.

1. African tribes--Pygmies. 2. Missions, Foreign--Africa. 3. Kivebulaya, Apolo, 1864?-1933.

NL 0426678 NN MH

BV 3625 .C63 K5
Lloyd, Albert Bushnell
Apolo of the pygmy forest. New and enl. ed. London, Church Missionary Society, 1937.
82 p. illus. 19cm.

1. Kivebulaya, Apolo 2. Missions - Congo, Belgian I. Title

NL 0426679 WU

BV 3625 .C63 K53
Lloyd, Albert Bushnell
Apolo the pathfinder; who follows? By A. B. Lloyd; with a pref. by J. J. Willis. London, Church Missionary Society ₍1935₎
68 p. illus. 19 cm.

Sequel to More about Apolo.

1. Kivebulaya, Apolo 2. Missions - Congo (Leopoldville) I. Title

NL 0426680 WU InU CtY MBU

VOLUME 337

PL8704 Z962L5
Lloyd, Albert Bushnell.
Apolo wa mwitu wa mbilikimo; kimeandikwa na A.B.Lloyd. Nairobi, Highway Press, London, New York, Longmans, Green [1950]
64 p. port. 18cm (Watu wenye maana,2)
Title translated: Apolo of the pygmy forests.

1.Christian biography. 2.Africa, Central - Descr. I.Title.

NL 0426681 CSt

Lloyd, Albert Bushnell
Dayspring in Uganda. With introduction by C. Mollan Williams. London, Church Missionary Society, 1921.
xii, 120 p. plates, map.

1. Uganda - Descr. & trav.

NL 0426682 NNC IEG PPPrHi WU CSt-H

Lloyd, A[lbert] B.
In dwarf land and cannibal country; a record of travel and discovery in central Africa. London, T. F. Unwin, 1899.
pp. xxiv, 385 +. Maps, plates, ports., and other illus.

NL 0426683 MH ICJ MB OrU NcU PPL PBa IEN

Lloyd, A[lbert] B.
In dwarf land and cannibal country; a record of travel and discovery in central Africa, with introduction by the Rt. Hon. Sir John H. Kennaway. New York: Charles Scribner's Sons, 1899. xxiv, 385(1) p., 2 fold. maps, 1 port. illus., map. 8°.

1. Uganda. 2. Title.
N. Y. P. L. July 8, 1912.

NL 0426684 NN DNW CtY

---

351 .L55 1899
Lloyd, Albert Bushnell.
In dwarf land and cannibal country; a record of travel and discovery in Central Africa, by A.B. Lloyd. With introduction by Sir John H. Kennaway. New York, Scribner's Sons [1899]
318 p. 3 maps (2 fold.), plates, ports. 21 cm.

1. Africa, Central--Descr. & trav.
2. Uganda--Descr. & trav. I. Title.

NL 0426685 OkU

DT 351 L791
Lloyd, Albert B
In dwarf land and cannibal country; a record of travel and discovery in Central Africa. With introd.by Sir John H.Kennaway. London, T.F.Unwin, 1900.
xxiv,385p. illus.,ports.,3 maps(2 fold.) 21cm.

1. Africa, Central - Descr.& trav. 2. Uganda - Descr.& trav. 3. Negrillos. I. Title.

NL 0426686 NRU PSC MH OO CU

Lloyd, Albert B.
In dwarf land and cannibal country; a record of travel and discovery in Central Africa, by A. B. Lloyd ... With introduction by the Rt. Hon. Sir John H. Kennaway ... With illustrations and maps. 3d impression. London, T. F. Unwin, 1907.
318 p., 1 l. front., plates, ports., 3 maps (2 fold.) 22½cm.
CONTENTS.—England to Uganda.—Uganda.—The Soudanese war.—Uganda to the west coast.

1. Africa, Central — Descr. & trav. 2. Uganda — Descr. & trav. 3. Dwarfs. I. Title.

Library of Congress DT351.L55 8—3120

WaU NjP
NL 0426687 DLC PU-Mu CaBVaU CtY NBuU CU CtY-D NcD

Lloyd, A[lbert] B.
In dwarf land and cannibal country; a record of travel and discovery in Central Africa. By A. B. Lloyd; with introduction by Sir J. H. Kennaway. New York: E. P. Dutton and Co., 1907. 318 p., 1 l., 3 maps, 31 pl., 1 port. 8°.

1. Africa (Central).—Description, tc., 1894. 2. Kennaway, Sir John H., bart.
N. Y. P. L. January 27, 1914.

NL 0426688 NN PPD PPL

Lloyd, Albert Bushnell.
A life's thrills; brief records of my life, 1894–1946. With a foreword by the Bishop of Worcester. London, Lutterworth Press [1948]
142 p. port., map. 19 cm.

1. Missions—Uganda.

BV3625.U4L5 [266.3] 276.761 49–22988*

NL 0426689 DLC CtY-D

BV 3625 U4K6 V28
Lloyd, Albert Bushnell.
More about Apolo. Lond., Church Missionary Society, 1929, c1928.
63 p. port. illus.

NL 0426690 MBU

DT 434 .U2L79
Lloyd, Albert B.
Uganda to Khartoum; life and adventure on the upper Nile, ...With a preface by Victor Buxton ... With 33 illustrations. London, Collins' Clear-Type Press [1906?]
350 p. front., plates, ports., fold. map.

1. Uganda--Descr. & trav. 2. Africa, British East--Descr. & trav. I. Title.

NL 0426691 ICU KU GU

Lloyd, Albert B.
Uganda to Khartoum; life and adventure on the upper Nile, by Albert B. Lloyd ... With a preface by Victor Buxton ... With 80 illustrations. London, T. F. Unwin, 1906.
xii, 312 p. front., plates, ports., fold. map. 22½cm.

NL 0426692 NIC NBuC CU NSyU

Lloyd, Albert Bushnell.
Uganda to Khartoum; life and adventure on the Upper Nile. With a pref. by Victor Buxton. New York, E. P. Dutton, 1906.
xii, 312 p. plates, ports., map. 23 cm.

1. Uganda—Descr. & trav. 2. Africa, British East—Descr. & trav. I. Title.

DT434.U2L7 7–35191 rev*

NL 0426693 DLC OCl OO PRosC CtY MB PPA

Eff 901Lc
Lloyd, Albert B
Uganda to Khartoum; life and adventure on the upper Nile, by Albert B.Lloyd ... with a preface by Victor Buxton. Second impression ... London,T.F.Unwin,1907.
xii,312p. front.,plates,ports.,fold.map. 22½cm.

NL 0426694 CtY NBuU PPFr OCl ICN NN

Eff 901Ld
Lloyd, Albert B
Uganda to Khartoum; life and adventure on the upper Nile, by Albert B.Lloyd ... with a preface by Victor Buxton ... New York, C.Scribner's sons,London,T.F.Unwin[1911]
319,[1]p. front.,plates,ports. 21cm.
"First edition, 1906 ... third impression, 1911."

NL 0426695 CtY NcD

DT434 U2L62
Lloyd, Albert Bushnell
Van Oeganda naar Khartoem; leven en avonturen aan den Boven-Nyl ... [Amsterdam, Mij. voor Goede en goedkoope lectuur, 1913]
208 p. plates. (Van reizen en trekken, onder leiding van ... N. van Suchtelen)

1. Uganda - Descr. & trav. 2. Africa, British East - Descr. & trav.

NL 0426696 CU IEN

Lloyd, Albert Hugh.
The early history of Christ's college, Cambridge, derived from contemporary documents, by A. H. Lloyd ... Cambridge [Eng.] The University press, 1934.
xvii, [1], 477 p. front. (port.) illus., plates, fold. plans, facsims. 23½cm.
"History of the college before 1505."—p. [v]

1. Cambridge. University. Christ's college. 2. Cambridge. University—Biog. I. Title.

Library of Congress LF143.L5 35–6799
378.42

NL 0426697 DLC CtY OCl PPPD ICU NN

Lloyd, Albert Hugh.
... The Lloyd collection. London, Pub. for the British academy by H. Milford, Oxford university press, 1933–
v. plates. 40cm. (Sylloge nummorum graecorum. vol. II)
Each plate accompanied by leaf with descriptive letterpress.
Text by E. S. G. Robinson.

1. Coins, Greek. I. Lloyd, Miss M. E. H. II. Robinson, Edward Stanley Gotch. III. British academy, London.

Library of Congress CJ314.S9 vol. 2 33–38351
[3] (737.0938) 737.0938

NL 0426698 DLC ViU

Lloyd, Albert Hugh.
Two monumental brasses in the chapel of Christ's College. (*In* Cambridge Antiquarian Society. Proceedings. Vol. 33, pp. 61–82. Plates. Genealogical charts. Cambridge. 1933.)

D9452 — Monumental brasses. — University of Cambridge. Christ's College.

NL 0426699 MB

Lloyd, Albert Lancaster, 1908– *comp.*
Coaldust ballads. London, Workers' Music Association, c1952.
score (38 p.) 25 cm.
Cover title.
For 1-4 voices and piano, with tonic sol-fa notation.

1. Miners—Songs and music. I. Title.

M1977.M5L5 M 53–1332

NL 0426700 DLC IU ScU

Lloyd, Albert Lancaster, 1908– *comp.*
Come all ye bold miners; ballads and songs of the coalfields. London, Lawrence & Wishart, 1952.
143 p. 23 cm.
Includes unacc. melodies.
Bibliographical references included in "Notes" (p. 133–139)

1. Miners—Songs and music. 2. Coal mines and mining—Poetry. 3. English ballads and songs. I. Title.

PR1195.M5L55 821.04 53–25390

IaU
NL 0426701 DLC WaS WaU NcD MiU KU TU IU CoU IEN FU

VOLUME 337

Lloyd, Albert Lancaster, 1908–
Corn on the cob; popular and traditional poetry of the U. S. A. London, Fore Publications, 1945.
66 p. 22 cm.

1. Folk-songs, American. I. Title.

PS593.L8L55 811.04 46–2955 rev*

NL 0426702 DLC MiU RPB NN TxU PU NNJef

GV1635 L58 Lloyd, Albert Lancaster, 1908–
Dances of Argentina. London, Parish [1954]
40p. col. illus. 19cm. (The Traditional dances of Latin America [2])

Includes arrangements for piano of the dances.

1. Dancing - Argentina. I. Title.

NL 0426703 IaU NN PP MiD Wa

Lloyd, Albert Lancaster, tr.

García Lorca, Federico, 1899–1936.
... Lament for the death of a bullfighter, and other poems in the original Spanish, with English translation by A. L. Lloyd. New York, Oxford university press [1937]

Lloyd, Albert Lancaster, 1908–
Shadow of the swastika; a radio-drama in six parts of the story of the German National Socialistic Party, produced for broadcasting by Laurence Gilliam for the British Broadcasting Corporation. By A. L. Lloyd and Igor Vinogradoff. London, J. Lane [1940]
194 p. plates. 22 cm.
Bibliography: p. 194.
1. Nationalsozialistische Deutsche Arbeiter-Partei—Drama. I. Vinogradoff, Igor, joint author. II. British Broadcasting Corporation. III. Title.
PR6023.L48S5 1940 792 41–6982 rev*

NL 0426705 DLC CLU NN OCl MiU TxU

Lloyd, Albert Lancaster, 1908–
The singing Englishman, an introduction to folksong. London, Workers' Music Association [1944]
70 p. music. 19 cm. (Keynote series [of music books] Book 4)
Bibliography: p. 69.

1. Folk-songs, English—Hist. & crit. I. Title. (Series)

ML3650.L53 784.4942 44–44653 rev

NL 0426706 DLC CoU TU MiD WaTC

ML3652 L5 **Lloyd, Albert Lancaster, 1908–**
The singing Englishman; a festival year re-issue of An introduction to folk song. London, Workers' Music Association [1951]
70 p. 19cm.
Includes music (principally unacc. melodies)
Bibliography: p. 69.

1. Folk-songs, English—Hist. & crit. 2. Ballads, English—Hist. & crit. I. Title.

NL 0426707 MB

Lloyd, Alfred Henry, 1864-1927, ed.

Michigan. University.
... Bibliography of publications by members of the several faculties from July 1, 1909, to June 30, 1918. Alfred H. Lloyd ... editor. Ann Arbor, The University, 1920.

Lloyd, Alfred Henry, 1864–
Citizenship and salvation; or, Greek and Jew; a study in the philosophy of history, by Alfred H. Lloyd ... Boston, Little, Brown, and company, 1897.
3 p. l., 142 p. 20cm.
CONTENTS.—The death of Socrates.—The death of Christ.—Resurrection.

1. History—Philosophy. 2. Civilization. 3. Socrates. 4. Jesus Christ. I. Title.

Library of Congress D16.9.L6 12–36281

NL 0426709 DLC OrU NcRS MiU OCl NN

Lloyd, Alfred Henry, 1864–1927.
Dynamic idealism: an elementary course in the metaphysics f psychology, first entered upon in lectures before students in philosophy at the University of Michigan, by Alfred H. Lloyd ... Chicago, A. C. McClurg and company, 1898.
x, [11]–248 p. 19cm.
Appendix (p. [225]–241): A study of immortality in outline.

1. Idealism. 2. Psychology. 3. Immortality. I. Title.

Library of Congress BF41.L6 11—22228

NL 0426710 DLC OrU ICRL TU KEmT MiU OO ODW NjP ICJ MH PPL PU PHC

LLOYD, Alfred Henry.
Epistemology and physical science. n.p., [1898?]

NL 0426711 MH

LLOYD, Alfred Henry.
Freedom. Professor of Philosophy, University of Michigan, Ann Arbor, Mich.

Official copy of a thesis presented for the doctor's degree at Harvard University. 1893.

NL 0426712 MH

LLOYD, Alfred Henry.
History and materialism. n.p., 1905.

Reprinted from the American Historical Review.

NL 0426713 MH

LLOYD, Alfred Henry, 1864–
...Incarnation; an essay in three parts. [by], A.H.Lloyd.

Reprinted from the American journal of theology, Vol. XX, No.1. Jan,1916. p. 45-80.

NL 0426714 MH

Lloyd, Alfred Henry, 1864–
Leadership and progress, and other essays of progress, The newspaper conscience, Ages of leisure, by Alfred H. Lloyd. Boston, Mass., The Stratford company, 1922.
6 p. l., 171 p. 19½cm.
"Of the two essays on Leadership and progress the first has already been published in the International journal of ethics, vol. XXXII, no. 2. Also, the essay on the Newspaper conscience was published in the American journal of sociology, vol. XXVII, no. 2, and that on the Ages of leisure in the same journal, vol. XXVIII, no. 2."—Pref.

1. Leadership. 2. Newspapers. I. Title: Progress, Leadership and.

Library of Congress HM141.L7 22–19696

NL 0426715 DLC CU NIC KEmT NcRA OU ODW MiU PSC PV ME

Lloyd, Alfred Henry, 1864-1927.
Phi Beta Kappa at Michigan, by Alfred H. Lloyd. ... Ann Arbor, The Ann Arbor press, 1908.
cover-title, [4] p. 24 cm.
"Reprinted from Michigan alumnus, December, 1907."
1. Phi Beta Kappa. Alpha chapter, University of Michigan.

NL 0426716 MiU-H

Lloyd, Alfred Henry,1864-1927.
Philosophy in the service of science... 1920.

NL 0426717 MiU

Lloyd, Alfred Henry, 1864–1927.
Philosophy of history; an introduction to the philosophical study of politics, by Alfred H. Lloyd ... Ann Arbor, G. Wahr, 1899.
250 p., 1 l., iv p. 18½cm.

1. History—Philosophy. 2. Social sciences. I. Title.

Library of Congress D16.8.L6 0—158

NL 0426718 DLC OrU OOxM MiU OCl

LLOYD, Alfred Henry.
Physical psychology. n.p., [190o?]

NL 0426719 MH

LLOYD, Alfred Henry.
Professor Fullerton on the doctrine of space and time. New York,1902.

"Reprinted from the Psychological Review, vol. ix, no. 2. March,1902".

NL 0426720 MH

LLOYD, Alfred Henry.
Radical empiricism and agnosticism. [Aberdeen], n. d.

NL 0426721 MH

LLOYD, Alfred Henry.
The social will. [Boston,1902].

NL 0426722 MH

LLOYD, Alfred Henry.
The stages of knowledge. NewYork, etc., [1897].

NL 0426723 MH

Lloyd, Alfred H
Time in its relation to history. n.p. n.d. pp. [40]-48

Reprinted from the Philosophical Review, vol.8, no.1., Jan.1899.

NL 0426724 OClWHi

VOLUME 337

Lloyd Alfred Henry, 1864-1927.
... The will to doubt; an essay in philosophy for the general thinker, by Alfred H. Lloyd ... London, S. Sonnenschein & co., lim., 1907.
2 p. l., [vii]-x p., 1 l., 285, [1] p. 19½cm. (The ethical library)
"Except for some revision chapters V. and VII. have already been published—Science, July 5, 1902, and the Journal of philosophy, psychology and scientific methods, June, 1905."—Pref.
8-13674
NjP ICJ MB NN P PBm PSC
NL 0426725 DLC WaWW NIC ICRL OrPS OU ODW MiU ICN

Lloyd, Alfred Manby, 1868-
Notes on American shrines in England [by] A. Manby Lloyd. London, Talbot & co. [1930]
3 p. l., iii-vii, 168 p. illus. (incl. maps) plates. 17½cm.
Maps on lining-papers.
1. England—Descr. & trav. 2. England—Historic houses, etc. I. Title. II. Title: American shrines in England.
Library of Congress DA630.L55 30-10951
Copyright A ad int. 13582 [3] 914.2
NL 0426726 DLC NN

Lloyd, Alice Marie
see Lloyd, Marie, 1916-

Lloyd, Lady Alicia (Eustace) d. 1860, plaintiff.

Lloyd, *Sir* Evan, *d.* 1846, *plaintiff.*
Report of the trial of an issue, directed by the lord high chancellor of Ireland, wherein Major General Evan Lloyd, and Alicia, baroness Trimlestown, his wife, Peter, count Dalton, and Rosalie [!] countess Dalton, his wife, were the plaintiffs, and the Right Hon. Thomas, lord baron Trimlestown, was the defendant. Had before the Right Hon. William Downes, lord chief justice, and the Hon. Judge Mayne, and a special jury of the county of Dublin, in the Court of King's bench, Ireland, on the 11th, 15th, 16th, 17th, 18th, 19th, 20th, 22d, 23d, 24th, 25th, 26th, 27th, 29th days of June, and 1st day of July, 1818. By John Hatchell ... Dublin, Printed by Thomas Courtney, 1819.

Lloyd, Alma Estelle, 1899-
This was their land [by] A. E. Lloyd. New York and London, Harper & brothers [1943]
4 p. l., 263, [1] p. 21cm.
"First edition."
I. Title.
Library of Congress PZ3.L7718Th 43-13078
NL 0426730 DLC WaS OLak PP

LLOYD, Alma ESTELLE, 1899-
c The war and our nerves/[by] A. Estelle Lloyd, Helen Hiett, David Seabury [and] Gregory Zilboorg. Columbia univ. press c1942.
31 p. (America's town meeting of the air, v.7, no.20)
Also contains Morale - the front within, by Abraham Myerson.
Bibliography: p.22.
NL 0426731 Or

Lloyd, Andrew J & co.
Photographic encyclopedia. Boston, Lloyd, n.d.
416p. illus. P.
NL 0426732 OO

Lloyd, Andrew J., and Company.
Photographic encyclopedia. 1901.
= Boston. [1901.] (4), 404 pp. Illus. 8°.
A catalogue of photographic goods for sale by the firm, with formulas, notes, etc.
Jan. 9, 1902
E2557 — Photography. Catalogues
NL 0426733 MB

Lloyd, Angharad
see Llwyd, Angharad, of Caerwys.

LLOYD, ANGLESEA.
Mary Clarkson; or, The Kirkstall abbey murder. Leeds, F. R. Spark & co., 1864. 32 p. 19cm.
Film reproduction. Master negative. Positive in *Z-1773.
"Re-printed from the 'Leeds Express'."
NL 0426735 NN

Lloyd, Ann, joint author.
DA630 .L56
Lloyd, Montague.
Through England's waterways, by Montague & Ann Lloyd. London, Imray, Laurie, Norie & Wilson [1948]

[Lloyd, Anne Gladys] 1889-
A. B. C. capers; a playlet in one scene for twenty-eight children, fourteen boys and fourteen girls. By Soemple [sic, pseud.] Franklin, O. [etc.] Eldridge, c1921. 11 p. 19cm. (Eldridge juvenile plays.)
1. Juvenile literature—Drama, American. I. Title.
N. Y. P. L. May 12, 1948
NL 0426737 NN RPB

Lloyd, Anne Gladys, 1889-
Bonnie Highlanders. A Scotch drill. Lebanon, Ohio [c1930]
6 p. 18 cm.
By Someple, pseud.
NL 0426738 RPB

Lloyd, Anne Gladys, 1889-
The children's Armistice day book of recitations songs, drills, exercises and playlets. Lebanon, Ohio, [1926]
51 p. music 19 cm.
By Someple, pseud.
NL 0426739 RPB

Lloyd, Anne Gladys, 1889-
The children's closing day book, by Ann Gladys Lloyd. Lebanon, O., March brothers [°1929]
118 p. illus., diagrs. 18½cm.
Contains music.
1. Schools—Exercises and recreations. I. Title.
Library of Congress PN4305.S4L6 CA 29-224 Unrev'd
NL 0426740 DLC Or

Lloyd, Anne Gladys, 1889-
The children's Hallowe'en book of recitations, songs, drills, exercises and stories. Lebanon, Ohio, [c1926]
63 p. 19 cm.
By Someple, pseud.
NL 0426741 RPB

PN4305 .I6L6 Lloyd, Anne Gladys, 1889-
The children's Indian book of verse, Songs and adaptations, by Ann Gladys Lloyd. Lebanon, O., March brothers [1926]
96 p. 18½cm.
Includes music.
1. Indians of North America--Drama. 2. Indians of North America--Music. 3. Indians of North America--Poetry. I. Title.
NL 0426742 DLC Or

Lloyd, Anne Gladys, 1889-
The Christmas book; a collection of songs, drills and short plays for Christmas entertainments, by Gladys Lloyd. Chicago, The Dramatic publishing company [°1931]
107 p. diagrs. 18½cm.
1. Christmas. 2. Christmas plays. I. Title.
Library of Congress PN4305.H7L48 31-23157
——— Copy 2.
Copyright A 41369 [3] [818.5] 394.268
NL 0426743 DLC IdB Or OO OCl

Lloyd, Anne Gladys, 1889-
Commencement specialities, by Gladys Lloyd; a valuable collection for eighth grade and junior high. Franklin, O., Eldridge entertainment house [c1926]
84p.
NL 0426744 NcC

[Lloyd, Anne Gladys] 1889-
The complete Christmas book, by Someple [pseud.] Lebanon, O., March brothers [°1923]
104 p. illus., diagrs. 18½cm.
Contains music.
1. Christmas. I. Title.
Library of Congress PN4305.H7L5 23-16809 Revised 2
NL 0426745 DLC Or OrCS

Lloyd, Anne Gladys, 1889-
The complete social book, by Ann Gladys Lloyd. Lebanon, O., March brothers [°1930]
106 p. 18½cm.
I. Title.
Library of Congress PN6120.Z9L6 CA 30-1499 Unrev'd
Copyright A 27894 818.5
NL 0426746 DLC RPB

Lloyd, Anne Gladys, 1889-
Easy parodies for popular singing, by Gladys Lloyd. Boston, Mass. and Los Angeles, Cal. [Walter H. Baker co., °1939]
80 p. 19cm. (*On cover: Baker's specialties*)
Without music; tunes indicated by title.
1. Songs, English. 2. Parodies. I. Title.
Library of Congress M1985.L45E2 40-14688
Copyright AA 300646 [2] 784.7
NL 0426747 DLC Or Wa WaSp

Lloyd, Anne Gladys, 1889-
Easy recitations and dialogs, by Gladys Lloyd. Lebanon, Ohio, March brothers [c1932]
NL 0426748 RPB

VOLUME 337

Lloyd, Anne Gladys, 1889-
Economical Abbie. A comedy ...
Lebanon, Ohio [c1924]
17 p. 19 cm.
By Someple, pseud.

NL 0426749 RPB

Lloyd, Anne Gladys, 1889-
The favorite closing day collection, by Ann Gladys Lloyd. Lebanon, O., March brothers [c1929]
96 p. diagrs. 18½cm.
Contains music.

1. Schools—Exercises and recreations. I. Title.
CA 29-223 Unrev'd
Library of Congress PN4305.S4L63

NL 0426750 DLC Or

Lloyd, Anne Gladys, 1889-
The favorite Hallowe'en collection. Lebanon, Ohio, [c1928]
79 p. music. 18 cm.
By Someple, pseud.

NL 0426751 RPB

Lloyd, Anne Gladys, 1889-
The favorite Hallowe'en collection. (A rev. ed.) By Ann Gladys Lloyd and Laura Rountree Smith. Dayton, O., Paine publishing company [c1938]
140 p. 18cm.

1. Halloween. I. Smith, Laura Rountree, 1876-1924, joint author. II. Title.
Library of Congress PN4305.H3L55 1938 39-2555
——— Copy 2.
Copyright AA 281262 [3] 394.268

NL 0426752 DLC

Lloyd, Anne Gladys, 1889-
Graduation days, written and arranged by Ann Gladys Lloyd; illustrated by George Gustin. Lebanon, O., March brothers [c1926]
367, [1] p. incl. front., illus. 20½cm.

1. Schools—Exercises and recreations. I. Title.
26-5726 Revised
Library of Congress LB3020.L5

NL 0426753 DLC OrP WaS Or ViU

Lloyd, Anne Gladys, 1889-
Hallowe'en frolics for little folks by Gladys Lloyd. Franklin, O., Denver, Colo., Eldridge entertainment house, inc.; Boston, Mass., Walter H. Baker co. [c1927]
81 p. 19cm.

1. Halloween. I. Title.
CA 28-773 Unrev'd
Library of Congress PN6120.H3L5

NL 0426754 DLC NN Or

Lloyd, Anne Gladys, 1889-
Hallowe'en pranks and parties, by Gladys Lloyd. Franklin, O., Denver, Col., Eldridge entertainment house, inc., c1927.
73 p. 19cm.

1. Halloween. I. Title.
28-11556
Library of Congress GT4965.L5

NL 0426755 DLC Or Wa

[Lloyd, Anne Gladys] 1889
The happy Christmas book, by Someple [pseud.] Willis N. Bugbee, Lillian H. Vandeveer, Harriette Wilbur. Syracuse, N. Y., The Willis N. Bugbee company [c1924]
87 p. 18½cm.

1. Christmas. I. Bugbee, Willis Newton, 1870- joint author II. Vandeveer, Lillian H., joint author. III. Wilbur, Harriette, joint author IV. Title.
Library of Congress PN4305.H7L53 24-25559 Revised

NL 0426756 DLC NN

Lloyd, Anne Gladys, 1889-
Here comes the groom! A farce in one act, by Gladys Lloyd. Philadelphia, Penn publishing co., 1924.
14 p. 19 cm.

NL 0426757 RPB

Lloyd, Anne Gladys, 1889-
The house that Jack built by Someple, pseud. Lebanon, Ohio, 1922.
8 p. 18 cm.

NL 0426758 RPB

Lloyd, Anne Gladys, 1889-
Jack-in the-box. A Christmas dialog. Lebanon, Ohio, [1924]
5 p. 19 cm.
By Someple, pseud.

NL 0426759 RPB

Lloyd, Anne Gladys, 1889-
Jingle bells. [A singing-musical piece for any number of children divided into groups) Lebanon, Ohio, [c1930]
5 p. 18 cm.
By Someple, pseud.

NL 0426760 RPB

Lloyd, Anne Gladys, 1889-
Johnny and his pa. Lebanon, Ohio, c1930.
3 p. 23 cm.
At head of title: March's famous funny farces.
Cover title.
By Someple, pseud.

NL 0426761 RPB

Lloyd, Anne Gladys, 1889- joint author.
Freeman, Carolyn R.
The kiddies' Christmas book, by Carolyn R. Freeman, Ann Gladys Lloyd, and others ... Syracuse, N. Y., The Willis N. Bugbee co., c1925.

Lloyd, Anne Gladys, 1889-
Lest we forget
see under title

Lloyd, Anne Gladys, 1889-
Merry Christmas for young folks; a book of recitations, songs, exercises, dialogues and plays, by Gladys Lloyd. Philadelphia, The Penn publishing company [c1938]
192 p. 19cm.

1. Christmas. I. Title.
Library of Congress PN4305.C5L67 39-168
——— Copy 2.
Copyright A 123917 [3] 394.268

NL 0426764 DLC Or OClh

LLOYD, ANNE GLADYS
Merry Christmas in the primary grades. Paine c1932.
75 p.

NL 0426765 Or

Lloyd, Anne Gladys, 1889-
Mr. Massy makes a fourth at bridge. A farce in one act ... Lebanon, Ohio, [c1930]
12 p. 18 cm.
By Someple, pseud.

NL 0426766 RPB

Lloyd, Anne Gladys, 1889-
More stunts, by Ann Gladys Lloyd. Lebanon, O., March brothers publishing co. [c1931]
90 p. diagr. 18½cm.

1. Amusements. I. Title.
Library of Congress GV1471.L815 32-113
Copyright A 44173 [2] 793

NL 0426767 DLC OU

[Lloyd, Anne Gladys] 1889-
Mother Goose dramatized, by Someple [pseud.] Lebanon, O., March brothers [c1923]
25 p. illus. 18½cm.

I. Mother Goose. II. Title.
Library of Congress PN6120.A5L5 23-6918 Revised

NL 0426768 DLC NN

Lloyd, Anne Gladys, 1889-
Of course! Lebanon, Ohio, c1930.
4 p. 23 cm.
At head of title: March's famous funny farces.
Cover title.
By Someple, pseud.

NL 0426769 RPB

Lloyd, Anne Gladys, 1889-
One maddening day and knight. A comedy in five scenes, by Someple, pseud. Lebanon, Ohio, [c1924
20 p. 18 cm.

NL 0426770 RPB

Lloyd, Anne Gladys, 1889-
Pad and pencil puzzles, by Gladys Lloyd ... New York, Thomas Y. Crowell company [c1934]
ix, 85 p. 21cm.
Blank pages for "Notes" (80-85)

1. Puzzles. I. Title.
Library of Congress GV1493.L55 34-7171
——— Copy 2.
Copyright A 69857 [3] 793.73

NL 0426771 DLC WaSp

Lloyd, Anne Gladys, 1889-
Puzzles for parties, by Gladys Lloyd ... New York, Thomas Y. Crowell company [c1935]
viii p., 1 l., 11-95 p. 21cm.
Blank pages for notes (86-95)

1. Puzzles. 2. Games. I. Title.
Library of Congress GV1493.L56 35-19657
——— Copy 2.
Copyright A 86665 [3] 793.7

NL 0426772 DLC MB Or WaS IdB WaE

VOLUME 337

Lloyd, Anne Gladys, 1889–
The Santa Claus package, a one-act play for Christmas, by Ann Gladys Lloyd. Lebanon, O., March brothers [°1928]
14 p. 18½cm.

1. Christmas plays. I. Title.
CA 36-1286 Unrev'd
Library of Congress PN6120.C5L55
Copyright D 85128 [2] 812.5

NL 0426773 DLC

Lloyd, Anne Gladys, 1889–
Sleighbell capers. A drill ... Lebanon, Ohio, [c1930]
5 p. 18 cm.
By Someple, pseud.

NL 0426774 RPB

[LLOYD, Anne GLADYS,]
Spring victorious, by Someple [pseud.]... New York: E.S. Werner & Co., cop. 1928. 18 p. 12°

Cover-title.

581915A. 1. Juvenile literature—Drama, American. I. Title.

NL 0426775 NN RPB

Lloyd, Anne Gladys, 1889–
Stunts for everybody, by Ann Gladys Lloyd. Lebanon, O., March brothers [°1930]
96 p. 18½cm.
Advertising matter: p. 96.

1. Amusements. I. Title.
Library of Congress GV1471.L82 CA 30-1464 Unrev'd
Copyright A 27892 798

NL 0426776 DLC RP RPB OU

Lloyd, Anne Gladys, 1889–
10 one-act humorous plays for high schools and adults, by Gladys Lloyd. Lebanon, O., March brothers publishing company [°1932]
94 p. 18½cm.

1. College and school drama. 2. Amateur theatricals. I. Title.
CA 36-1596 Unrev'd
Library of Congress PN6120.A5L52
Copyright AA 105502 [2] 812.5

NL 0426777 DLC

Lloyd, Anne Gladys, 1889–
The Thanksgiving program book, by Gladys Lloyd. Dayton, O., Paine publishing company [°1931]
118 p. diagrs. 18cm.
Contains music.

1. Thanksgiving day.
CA 31-1090 Unrev'd
Library of Congress PN4305.H7L45
Copyright A 41681 394.268

NL 0426778 DLC

Lloyd, Anne Gladys, 1889–
Thanksgiving school programs, by Gladys Lloyd. Franklin, O., Denver, Col., Eldridge entertainment house, inc.; Boston, Walter H. Baker company, °1927.
78 p. 19cm.

1. Thanksgiving day. I. Title.
28-11343
Library of Congress PN4305.H7L55

NL 0426779 DLC CaBVa Or

Lloyd, Anne Gladys, 1889–
Tip-top Halloween book
see under title

Lloyd, Anne Gladys, 1889–
Up on the housetop and other plays for Christmas, by Ann Gladys Lloyd. Lebanon, O., March brothers publishing co. [°1931]
115 p. 18½cm.

1. Christmas plays. I. Title.
CA 36-1287 Unrev'd
Library of Congress PN6120.C5L57
Copyright A 44172 [2] 812.5

NL 0426781 DLC

Lloyd, Anne Gladys, 1889–
Vacation, a closing day play ... Lebanon, Ohio, [c1923]
18 p. 18 cm.
By Someple, pseud.

NL 0426782 RPB

Lloyd, Anne Gladys, 1889–
Wanted: a private secretary; a pantomime, by Ann Gladys Lloyd. Lebanon, O., March brothers publishing co. [°1931]
8 p. 18½cm.

1. Pantomimes. I. Title.
37-31806
Library of Congress PN6120.P3L3
Copyright A 43613 [3] 792.3

NL 0426783 DLC RPB

Lloyd, Anne Gladys, 1889–
The wedding of Rudy and Nanette, a pantomime, by Ann Gladys Lloyd. Lebanon, O., March brothers publishing co. [°1931]
8 p. 18½cm.

1. Pantomimes. I. Title.
37-31807
Library of Congress PN6120.P3L62
Copyright A 43612 [3] 792.3

NL 0426784 DLC

LLOYD, ANNE PORTER (LYNES), 1874-1948.
Antique shop. Cover design by Cateau DeLeeuw. Plainfield, N.J., Printed by the Recorder press, 1941 [c1928] 30 p. 18cm.

Poems.

NL 0426785 NN

Lloyd, Anne Porter (Lynes) 1874–
Antiques and amber, by Anne Lloyd. New York, The Derrydale press, 1928.
7 p. l., 103 p., 1 l. 24cm.
Poems.
"Four hundred copies of Antiques and amber have been printed ... of which 150 are on Ingres paper, autographed and numbered, and 250 are on Louvain paper."

I. Title.
29-3204 Revised
Library of Congress PS3523.L53A7 1928

NL 0426786 DLC PU PP

[Lloyd, Anne Porter (Lynes) 1874-1948.
Banked fires. [A poem by Anne P. L. Field. New York, E. P. Dutton, c1915]
[4] p. 18 cm.
Caption title

NL 0426787 RPB

Lloyd, Anne Porter (Lynes) 1874–
Brief procession, by Anne Lloyd ... New York, London, G. P. Putnam's sons, 1934.
xii, 13–106 p. 21cm.
Poems.

I. Title.
35-51 Revised
Library of Congress PS3523.L53B7 1934
[r44d2] 811.5

NL 0426788 DLC MB

Lloyd, Anne Porter (Lynes) 1874–
Sight and sound; poems by Anne Lloyd. New York, The Fine editions press [1944]
56 p. 19cm.

I. Title.
45-167
Library of Congress • PS3523.L53S5
[3] 811.5

NL 0426789 DLC FU

[Lloyd, Anne Porter (Lynes)] 1874-1948.
Singing mothers. Philadelphia: Amer. Institute of Child Life [1912]. 4 l. 8°.
Repr.: Craftsman. Nov., 1912.
By Anne P.L. Field.

1. Mothers. 2. American Institute of Child life. 3. Title.
N. Y. P. L. January 5, 1914.

NL 0426790 NN

Lloyd, Anne Porter (Lynes) 1874–
The story of Canada Blackie, by Anne P. L. Field; with an introduction by Thomas Mott Osborne ... New York, E. P. Dutton & company [°1915]
vii p., 1 l., 157 p. 18½cm.

1. Sing Sing prison, Ossining, N. Y. I. Title: Canada Blackie.
15-16245 Revised 2
Library of Congress HV9475.N78L55
[r44j2] 365.9747

OSC PPFr OrU OrP OrPR WaS PU ViU OCl OClU
NL 0426791 DLC NIC NcU MB NN NjP PPL PP PPGi PHC

Lloyd, Anne Porter (Lynes) 1874-1948.
365.9747 L793S The story of Canada Blackie, by Anne P. L. Field; with an introduction by Thomas Mott Osborne. Toronto, T. Allen, 1916 [c1915]
vii, 157 p. 18 cm.

1. Sing Sing Prison, Ossining, N. Y. I. Title. II. Title: Canada Blackie.

NL 0426792 NcD

Lloyd, Arnold.
Creative learning; an application to education of Jean Piaget's theory of knowledge; an inaugural lecture delivered in the Great Hall on 25th August, 1953. Natal, University Press, 1953.
13 p. 22 cm.

1. Piaget, Jean, 1896– 2. Learning, psychology of. I. Title.
LB775.P49L6 54-41694 ‡

NL 0426793 DLC

Lloyd, Arnold.
Quaker social history, 1669–1738. With an introd. by Herbert G. Wood. London, New York, Longmans, Green [1950]
xv, 207 p. illus., facsims. 23 cm.
Bibliography: p. 185–194.

1. Friends, Society of—Hist. 2. Friends, Society of—Charities. 3. Friends, Society of. England. I. Title.
BX7676.L6 289.642 50-7502

WaSpG
MdPB PPFr PPL OrCS Or AU AAP CaBVaU CaBViP OrU WaS
NL 0426794 DLC NcGU OO PHi NcD TxU MB ICU DFo MH PP

VOLUME 337

Lloyd, Arthur.
Arthur & Martha; comic song. Figure 3.5 in oval surrounded by 8 stars. Boston, Oliver Ditson & Co.; New Orleans, L. Grunewald; Savannah, Ludden & Bates [not after 1889]
5 p. 35 cm. [Sheet music collection, v. 8, no. 16]
1. Songs with piano. I. Title.

NL 0426795 ViU

Lloyd, Arthur.
The foreign count. New York, B. W. Hitchcock, °1869.
[3] p. 27 cm. (Hitchcock's half dime series of music for the million, no. 62)
1. Songs (Medium voice) with piano. I. Title.
M1621.L M 54-78

NL 0426796 DLC

MF784.3 L7931 Music lib. Lloyd, Arthur.
I'll strike you with a feather, or (I'll stab you with a rose) Great song sung by G. H. Macdermott. London, A. D'Alcorn [n.d.] Pl. no. H.D. 1228.
5p. 37cm. (New Popular and standard comic songs)
Cover title.
I. Title. II. Title: I'll stab you with a rose.

NL 0426797 NcU

Lloyd, Arthur.
Immenseikoff. [Song with pianoforte accomp.]
Boston. Cundy. 1869. (3) pp. [Cundy's Five cent series of popular music. No. 43.] 8°.
F5883 — T.r. — Songs. With music.

NL 0426798 MB

---

* M1640 .L56M4 1864 Lloyd, Arthur
Medley; or, Song of many songs. Arr. for the piano. Figure 3 in 7 pointed star. Boston, Oliver Ditson & Co., 277 Washington St. ... °1864. Pl. no. 22272.
5 p. 36cm.
Stamped on cover: R. B. Butland, Importer of music, No. 37 King St., West, Toronto.
1. Potpourris (Piano). 2. Songs with piano. I. Title.

NL 0426799 ViU

Lloyd, Arthur.
Not for Joseph. [Song with pianoforte accomp.]
Boston. Cundy. 1869. (3) pp. [Cundy's Five cent series of popular music. No. 51.] 8°.
F5884 — T.r. — Songs. With music.

NL 0426800 MB

Lloyd, Arthur.
Not for Joseph. For voice and piano. New York, B. W. Hitchcock, °1869.
[3] p. 27 cm. (Hitchcock's half dime series of music for the million, no. 5)
1. Songs (Medium voice) with piano. I. Title.
M1621.L M 54-124

NL 0426801 DLC MH

Lloyd, Arthur
Repertoire of the legitimate, veritable, and popular comic songs, sung by Arthur Lloyd ... 3d edition.
London. D'Alcorn. [186-?] 48 pp. 8°.
Oct. 5, 1903
E6496 — Songs. Without music.

NL 0426802 MB

Lloyd, Arthur, 1852-1911
Admiral Togo, by Arthur Lloyd, M. A. Tokyo, Japan, The Kinkodo publishing co.; London, The Probsthain & co., agents, 1903.
2 p. l., ii, 160 p., 1 l. front., ports. (partly col.) 18½cm.
Added t.-p., in Japanese, at end.
1. Tōgō, Heihachirō, 1847- 2. Russo-Japanese war, 1904-1905—Naval operations.
Library of Congress DS884.T6L5 9-19051

NL 0426803 DLC

Lloyd, Arthur, 1852-1911.
Admiral Togo, by Arthur Lloyd, M. A. Tokyo, Japan, The Kinkodo publishing co.; London, The Probsthain & co., agents, 1905.
2 p. l., ii, 160 p., 1 l. front., ports. (part col.) 18½cm.
Added t.-p., in Japanese, at end.
1. Tōgō, Heihachirō, 1847- 2. Russo-Japanese war, 1904-1905—Naval operations.
Library of Congress DS884.T6L5 9-19051 Revised

NL 0426804 DLC IaU CU NcD NbU MU CtY PPL DW ICJ NN MB DN

Lloyd, Arthur, 1852-1911, tr.
Mayet, Paul, 1846-
Agricultural insurance in organic connection with savings-banks, land-credit, and the commutation of debts, by P. Mayet ... Tr. from the German by the Rev. Arthur Lloyd ... London, S. Sonnenschein & co., 1893.

Lloyd, Arthur, 1852-
A birth-day book of Japanese verse, old and new, by many authors, tr. by A. Lloyd. [111]p. col.il. Tokyo, The Shimbi shoin, 1910.
Arranged in calendar form, with blanks left under each date for memoranda.
"The great majority of the poems... are taken from the works of the late Madame Saisho Atsuko."-Preface.

NL 0426806 OCl

Lloyd, Arthur. 1852-
A brand from the burning.
= [N. p. 1908.] 29 pp. 8°.
The title is on the cover. The sub-title, p. 1, reads: Formative elements of Japanese Buddhism. Introductory essay.
G9548 — T.r. — Buddha and Buddhism. — Japan. Hist. Relig.

NL 0426807 MB

Lloyd, Arthur, 1852-1911.
Buddhist meditations from the Japanese with an introductory chapter on modern Japanese Buddhism. Tokyo, Rikkyo Gakuin Press, 1905.
130 p.
1. Buddha and Buddhism - Japan. I. Title.

NL 0426808 MoSCS CtY

[Lloyd, Arthur] 1852-1911.
Catalogue of Japanese books published January-June 1902.
(In Asiatic society of Japan. Transactions. [Yokohama, etc., 1902] 23cm. v. 29, pt. 2. 16 p.)
Compiled by Rev. A. Lloyd, librarian of the society.
1. Japanese literature—Bibliography.
Chicago. Univ. Library for Library of Congress AS552.A83 vol. 29 [AS552.Y8 vol. 29, pt. 2] A C 39-1430
[4] (068.52)

NL 0426809 ICU DLC NcD

Lloyd, Arthur, 1852-1911.
Catalogue of recently published Japanese books.
(In Asiatic society of Japan. Transactions. Tokyo, 1902. 23cm. v. 30, pt. 3, p. [463]-572)
Preliminary statement signed: Arthur Lloyd.
1. Japanese literature—Bibliography.
Chicago. Univ. Library for Library of Congress AS552.A83 vol. 30 [AS552.Y8 vol. 30] A C 39-1436
[4] (068.52)

NL 0426810 ICU DLC NcD

Lloyd, Arthur. 1852-1911.
The creed of half Japan. Historical sketches of Japanese Buddhism.
— London. Smith, Elder & Co. 1911. x, 393, (1) pp. 20 cm., in 8s.
H8093 — T.r. — Buddha and Buddhism. — Japan. Hist. Relig.

NL 0426811 MB NNC NjNbS NjP CU ICJ PHC OO MiU ICN OCl CU OrP OrU

BL 1440 .L793 1911a Lloyd, Arthur, 1852-1911.
The creed of half Japan; historical sketches of Japanese Buddhism. London, Smith, Elder, 1911.
393 p.
Photocopy. Ann Arbor, Mich., University Microfilms, 1972. 393 p. (on double leaves)
1. Buddha and Buddhism--Japan. I. Title.

NL 0426812 MiU

Lloyd, Arthur, 1852-1911.
The creed of half Japan; historical sketches of Japanese Buddhism, by Arthur Lloyd ... New York, E. P. Dutton & company, 1912.
x, 393, [1] p. 20½cm.
Printed in Great Britain.
1. Buddha and Buddhism—Japan. 2. Japan—Religion. 3. Buddha and Buddhism—Hist. I. Title.
Library of Congress BL1440.L5 12-40672
[a35b1] 294.32

NL 0426813 DLC CaBVaU Or WaS NcD ViU OCl ODW PPL PPM PPPD NN

Lloyd, Arthur, 1852-1911.
Developments of Japanese Buddhism. By Rev. A. Lloyd ...
(In Asiatic society of Japan. Transactions. Yokohama, 1894. 23cm. v. 22, pt. 3, p. 337-506. illus.)
1. Buddha and Buddhism—Japan.
Chicago. Univ. Library for Library of Congress AS552.A83 vol. 22 [AS552.Y8 vol. 22] A C 38-3576
[4] (068.52)

NL 0426814 ICU MH DLC

VOLUME 337

Lloyd, Arthur, 1852–1911.
Every-day Japan, written after twenty-five years' residence and work in the country, by Arthur Lloyd ... introduction by Count Hayashi ... with eight plates in colour and ninety-six reproductions from photographs. London, New York ₍etc.₎ Cassell and company, limited, 1909.
xvi, 381, ₍1₎ p. 8 col. pl. (incl. front.) plates, ports. 23½ᶜᵐ.

1. Japan—Soc. life & cust. I. Title.

Library of Congress DS810.L5 9—15392

NN NjP PPL PP PPFr
NL 0426815 DLC CU IaU NBuU OCl MiU OOxM PPA PU MB

915.2 L775e 1911 Lloyd, Arthur, 1852-1911.
Every-day Japan: written after twenty-five years' residence and work in the country. Introduction by Count Hayashi, with eight plates in colour and ninety-six reproductions from photographs. Popular ed. London, New York, Cassell, 1911.
381p. illus.(part.col.) 22cm.

1. Japan. 2. Japan. Social life and customs. I. Title.

NL 0426816 KU NjNbS ICJ

Lloyd, Arthur, 1852-
Formative elements of Japanese Buddhism. [Lectures.] Plate.
(In Asiatic Society of Japan. Transactions. Vol. 35, part 2, pp. 191-244. Yokohama. 1908.)
Contents. — Manichaeism and Kobo. — Daruma and the Buddhist canon. Tendai and Shinshiu. — Nichiren and Hokekyo.

H2143 — Buddha and Buddhism. — Japan. Myth.

NL 0426817 MB

Lloyd, Arthur, 1852–1911.
The gold demon, by Ozaki Kōyō; re-written in English by A. and M. Lloyd. Tokyo, Seibundo, 1917.
xvii, 562 p. 19 cm.
With an introd. by A. Lloyd dated 1905.

I. Lloyd, Mary von Fallot, joint author. II. Ozaki, Kōyō, 1868–1903. Konjiki yasha. III. Title.
PZ3.L7719Go 56-54180
[PR4890.L75]

NL 0426818 DLC OkU

Lloyd, Arthur, 1852–1911.
The higher Buddhism in the light of the Nicene creed, by the Rev. A. Lloyd ... ₍Tokyo₎ Printed at the Tokyo Tsukiji type foundry, 1893. 39 p. 19cm.

1. Buddhism and Christianity.
N. Y. P. L. April 3, 1912

NL 0426819 NN

Lloyd, Arthur, 1852-
Historical development of the Shushi philosophy in Japan.
(In Asiatic Society of Japan. Transactions. Vol. 34, part 4, pp. 1-80. Yokohama. 1907.)
One of the three schools of Confucian thought.

H1983 — Japan. Phil. — Confucius.

NL 0426820 MB

Lloyd, Arthur, 1852-1911, comp. and tr.
Imperial songs; poems by T.M. the Emperor and Empress of Japan, and other imperial and distinguished personages. Tokyo, Rikkyo Gakuin Press, 1905.
159p.

Japanese text and English translation on opposite pages.

NL 0426821 OCl NjR MdBP UU CtY PPrHi PP MH WaS

Pvb35 L77 Lloyd, Arthur, 1852-
Japanese colloquial texts with translations and notes. London,K.Paul,Trench,Trübner[c1890]
95p. 19cm.
Printed in Japan.

NL 0426822 CtY OCl

LLOYD, Arthur, 1852-
Kenshin's vision. A poem of Japan.
= Tokyo. Maruya & co. 1894. (1), 27 pp. Pls. 24°.

NL 0426823 MB

Lloyd, Arthur, 1852-
Kenshin's vision; a poem of Japan. [Tokyo] Printed at the Rikkyō Gakuin Press, 1903
iii, 32 p.

NL 0426824 MH

Gest 2098 .592 Lloyd, Arthur, 1852-1911.
Model translations and dialogues, with the author's autograph letter and letters from Prof.Baron N.Kanda, and Mrs.M.Rodwell. The English Speaking Department, Tokyo Higher Commercial School. Tokyo, Eigo-Kenkyu-Sha, 1913.
327 p. illus. 20 cm.

Contents.- Translations: Dopposhu ₍by, Doppo Kunikida, Association song of the Hitotsubashi Kwai.- Dialogues.

NL 0426825 NjP MiU UU HU

Lloyd, Arthur, 1852–1911.
Nasu no Yumoto. An old Japanese inn. By Rev. Arthur Lloyd ...
(*In* Asiatic society of Japan. Transactions. Yokohama, 1896. 23ᶜᵐ. v. 24, p. 176–187)

1. Yumoto, Japan. I. Title.
A C 39-1411
Chicago. Univ. Library for Library of Congress AS552.A83 vol. 24 [AS552.Y8 vol. 24]
₍4₎ (068.52)

NL 0426826 ICU NcD DLC

PL898 .T57N3 Lloyd, Arthur, 1852-1911, tr.

₍Tokutomi, Kenjiro₎ 1868–1927.
Nature and man, by Tokutomi Roka ₍*pseud.*₎ Translated by Arthur Lloyd, M. von Fallot, and H. Ono. Tokyo, Kogakukwan ₍1913₎

Lloyd, Arthur, 1852-
Notes on Japanese village life. Read 8. November, 1905.
(In Asiatic Society of Japan. Transactions. Vol. 33, pp. 133-158. Yokohama. 1905.)

H1982 — Japan. Manners. — Villages and village life.

NL 0426828 MB OCl OC

Lloyd, Arthur, 1852-
Notes on the Japanese drama.
(In Asiatic Society of Japan. Transactions. Vol. 35, part 2, pp. 97-112. Yokohama. 1907.)

H2145 — Japan. Drama.

NL 0426829 MB

Lloyd, Arthur, 1852-1911, tr.

Florenz, Karl Adolf, 1865–
Poetical greetings from the Far East. Japanese poems. From the German adaptation of Dr. Karl Florenz, by A. Lloyd. M. A. Tokyo, Japan, T. Hasegawa ₍1897₎

Lloyd, Arthur, 1852–1911.
The Remmon kyō. By Rev. A. Lloyd ...
(*In* Asiatic society of Japan. Transactions. Tokyo, 1901. 23ᶜᵐ. v. 29, pt. 1, p. ₍1₎–16)

1. Remmon (Sect) 2. Faith-cure.
A C 39-1427
Chicago. Univ. Library for Library of Congress AS552.A83 vol. 29 [AS552.Y8 vol. 29, pt. 1]
₍4₎ (068.52)

NL 0426831 ICU DLC NcD

Lloyd, Arthur, 1852-
Shinran and his work. Studies in Shinshu theology.
= Tokyo. Kyobunkwan. 1910. (5), 182, 15, (1) pp. 18 cm.

H4261 — Shinran Shōnin. 1173-1262. — Shinshu theology. — T.r. — Buddha and Buddhism. — Japan. Hist. Relig.

OCl MH ODW OClW ViU CtY OrU-Or
NL 0426832 MB CtY-D NcU CSt NNC NRCR MH NBC PU NcD

Lloyd, Arthur, 1852-
A sutra in Greek.
(In Asiatic Society of Japan. Transactions. Vol. 38, part 3, pp. 75-89. Yokohama. 1910.)
The author finds the sutra in the Gnostic Pistis-Sophia, written during the early portion of the 3d century. The paper is a study of the early connection between Christianity and Buddhism.

H6477 — Pistis Sophia. — Christianity. — Buddha and Buddhism.

NL 0426833 MB

Lloyd, Arthur, 1852–1911.
The wheat among the tares; studies of Buddhism in Japan. A collection of essays and lectures, giving an unsystematic exposition of certain missionary problems of the Far East, with a plea for more systematic research, by the Rev. A. Lloyd, M. A. ... London, Macmillan & co., ltd., 1908.
xv, 145, ₍1₎ p. 20 cm.
Cover-title: "Studies of Buddhism in Japan."

1. Buddha and Buddhism. 2. Missions—East (Far East)
A 10—2441
Enoch Pratt Free Libr. for Library of Congress ₍a63b1₎

NL 0426834 WaU CoU PPL PCC CtY WU OU OrP OrU MdBE

Lloyd, Arthur Edward, 1876–
The law of carriers of passengers and goods; master and servant, ₍i₎nterpretation of statutes, Interstate commerce act, the Employers' liability and Safety appliance act, Workmens compensation, the Hours of service and the Twenty-eight hour stock law. The law of drains, ditches, right of way, fires, fences and miscellaneous laws relating to the construction, maintenance and operation of railroads. With citations, by Arthur E. Lloyd ... Niagara Falls, N. Y., Brown Delaney publishing co., inc., 1915.
1 p. l., xix, 252 p. 20ᶜᵐ.
1. Railroad law—U. S. 2. Carriers. ₍3. Master and servant₎ I. Title.
Library of Congress 16-380

NL 0426835 DLC

Lloyd, Arthur Henry.
Engineering for forest rangers in tropical countries, with special reference to Burma, by A. H. Lloyd... Oxford: Clarendon Press, 1929. xvi, 228 p. incl. tables. front., illus. (plans), plates. 8°.

Some plates printed on both sides.
Bibliography, p. ₍222₎

430474A. 1. Lumbering—Handbooks. manuals, etc., 1929. 2. Forestry—Tropics.
N. Y. P. L. September 21, 1929

NL 0426836 NN

VOLUME 337

JN1413
1879
.L6
Lloyd, Arthur R.
Ireland for the Irish: or, A word to home-rulers. 2d ed. Dublin, Hodges, Foster and Figgis, 1879.
14, (2) p. 20 cm.

1. Home rule-Ireland. I. Title.

NL 0426837 MB

Lloyd, Arthur Selden, *bp.*, 1857-1936.
The bishop, extracts from the correspondence of Arthur Selden Lloyd ... [New York, Friebele press, 1938]
61, [2] p. front. (port.) 20½cm.
"First printing, April, 1938."

I. Title.
38-12105
Library of Congress BX5995.L6A42
——— Copy 2.
Copyright A 116555 [2] 922.373

NL 0426838 DLC ViU

Lloyd, Arthur Selden, *bp.*, 1857-1936.
Christianity and the religions; being three lectures delivered at the summer school of Harvard university in July, 1908, by the Rev. Arthur Selden Lloyd ... New York, E. P. Dutton & company [c1909]
3 p. l., 127 p. 19½cm.

1. Christianity and other religions. I. Title.
9-10259
Library of Congress BR127.L6

NL 0426839 DLC NRCR MB ViU

Z
940.9196
L775j
Lloyd, Arthur Wynell
"Jambo", or; With Jannie in the jungle; thirty East African sketches by A.W. Lloyd. With an introd. by Sir Percy Fitzpatrick. Cape Town, Published by the Central News Agency [1917]
1v. (unpaged) illus. 26cm.
Cartoons.
1. European War, 1914-1918 - Campaigns - Africa - German East. 2. European War, 1914-1918 - Humor, caricatures, etc. I. Title.

NL 0426840 TxU

Lloyd, Arthur Wynell.
Jambo; or, With Jannie in the jungle, thirty East Africa sketches. London, African Publications [192-]
66 p. illus.
1. South African War, 1899-1902.
2. Cariacatures and cartoons, British.
I. Title.
II. Title: With Jannie in the jungle.

NL 0426841 CaOTP IEN

Lloyd, Arthur Young, 1908-
The slavery controversy, 1831-1860, by Arthur Young Lloyd, PH. D. Chapel Hill, The University of North Carolina press, 1939.
xi, 337 p. 22 cm.
"Selected bibliography": p. [287]-322.

1. Slavery in the U. S. 2. Slavery in the U. S.—Anti-slavery movements. 3. Slavery—Justification. I. Title.
E449.L76 326.973 39—19293

CaBVaU MtU OrU WaSpG
NcRA MiU NIC KyHi AU WaU PHC PU CSmH ViU OrP WaS
NL 0426842 DLC KyBgW KMK IU MH PRosC OCl OClW OO

Lloyd, Augustus Parlett, *pub.*
The Chesapeake illustrated. Baltimore, A. P. Lloyd [c1879]
23 p. illus. 23½cm.

1. Chesapeake bay.
Rc-3436 Revised
Library of Congress F187.C5L7

NL 0426843 DLC

Lloyd, Augustus Parlett.
Cranks' retreat. A comedy-drama, in four acts. By A. Parlett Lloyd ... Baltimore, O. W. Clay & co. (limited) 1885.
85 p. 22½cm.
"This drama is printed, not published. The author reserves the exclusive right of its production."

I. Title.
13-21433
Library of Congress PS2249.L46

NL 0426844 DLC

Lloyd, Augustus Parlett.
Cranks' retreat. A comedy-drama, in four acts. Baltimore, O.W. Clay, 1885.
85 p. 23 cm.
"This drama is printed, not published. The author reserves the exclusive right of its production."
Micro-opaque.

NL 0426845 CSt CaBVaU

Lloyd, Augustus Parlett.
The law of divorce. Containing the causes for which divorce will be granted in all the States and many of the territories. Baltimore, Clay & co. 1886.
70 p.

NL 0426846 PPB

Lloyd, Augustus Parlett.
A treatise on the law of building and buildings; especially referring to building contracts, leases, easements, and liens, containing also various forms useful in building operations, a glossary of words and terms commonly used by builders and artisans, and a digest of the leading decisions on building contracts and leases in the United States. By A. Parlett Lloyd ... Boston, New York, Houghton, Mifflin and company, 1888.
li, 618 p. 23½cm.
1. Building laws — U. S. 2. Real property — U. S. 3. Mechanics' liens—U. S. 4. Forms (Law)—U. S.
33-13249

ICJ MB IaAS
NL 0426847 DLC CaBVaU WaU-L NcD CtY NjP PPB MH IU

Lloyd, Augustus Parlett.
A treatise on the law of building and buildings; especially referring to building contracts, leases, easements, and liens, containing also various forms useful in building operations, a glossary of words and terms commonly used by builders and artisans, and a digest of the leading decisions on building contracts and leases in the United States. By A. Parlett Lloyd ... 2d ed., rev. and enl. Boston and New York, Houghton, Mifflin and company, 1894.
I, 537 p. 24cm.
1. Building laws — U. S. 2. Real property — U. S. 3. Mechanics' liens—U. S. 4. Forms (Law)—U. S.
12-36233

NL 0426848 DLC PV PPB MoU MB InI

Lloyd, Augustus Parlett.
A treatise on the law of divorce, with the causes for which divorces will be granted in all the states and territories: the time of residence required in each: and a brief digest of the leading decisions by the appellate courts. containing also a careful compilation of the latest divorce statistics. by A. Parlett Lloyd ... Boston and New York. Houghton, Mifflin and company. 1887.
xxiv, 323 p. 20cm.

1. Divorce—U. S.
33-13250

NL 0426849 DLC MH ICU CtY PPB

496.39
L77k
19--
Lloyd, B G
Kitchen-Kafir; grammar & vocabulary. 2d ed. Transvaal, Central News Agency [19--]
48p. 19cm.

NL 0426850 IU

Lloyd, B G
... Kitchen-Kafir grammar & vocabulary. By B. G. Lloyd. [3d ed.] Johannesburg [etc.] Central news agency, ltd. [19—]
48 p. 18cm.

1. Kafir language (Bantu)—Glossaries, vocabularies, etc. 2. Kafir language (Bantu)—Grammar. I. Title.
43-50174
Library of Congress PL8322.L6

NL 0426851 DLC

Lloyd, B G
... Kitchen-Kafir grammar & vocabulary. By B. G. Lloyd ... [4th ed.] [Johannesburg] Central news agency, ltd. [19-?]
48 p. 16½cm.

NL 0426852 NcD

Lloyd, B G
... Kitchen-Kafir grammar & vocabulary. By B. G. Lloyd ... [7th ed.] [Johannesburg] Central news agency, ltd. [19—]
48 p. 16½cm.

1. Kafir language (Bantu)—Glossaries, vocabularies, etc. 2. Kafir language (Bantu)—Grammar. I. Title.
44-49608
Library of Congress PL8322.L6

NL 0426853 DLC

Lloyd, B G
... Kitchen-Kafir grammar & vocabulary. By B. G. Lloyd ... [8th ed.] [Johannesburg] Central news agency, ltd. [1944]
48 p. 16½cm.

1. Kafir language (Bantu)—Glossaries, vocabularies, etc. 2. Kafir language (Bantu)—Grammar. I. Title.
45-18448
Library of Congress PL8322.L6 1944
[2] 496.3

NL 0426854 DLC NN

Lloyd, B G
Kitchen-Kafir grammar & vocabulary. 11th ed. [Cape Town] Central News Agency [19--?]
32 p.
Cover title.

NL 0426855 CLU MiEM

916.7
L78m
Lloyd, B W
Men of Livingstone; a brief account of their part in his major expeditions, 1852-1873. London, C. J. Sawyer, 1955.
23p. illus., ports. 23cm.

1. Livingstone, David, 1813-1873. I. Title.

NL 0426856 IEN CLU NcD NIC

550.5
R89
G342j
v.6
Lloyd, Bartholomew, 1772-1837.
An address delivered at the first annual meeting of the Geological society of Dublin, on the 8th February, 1832. By the Rev. Bartholomew Lloyd... Dublin, P.D. Hardy, 1832.
vi p., 1 ℓ., 35 p. 22½ cm.
Bound with Royal geological society of Ireland. Journal...v.6...1856.

NL 0426857 MiU PPAN CtY MH

VOLUME 337

Lloyd, Bartholomew, 1772-1837
An elementary treatise of mechanical philosophy, written for the use of the undergraduate students of the university of Dublin. Dublin, Printed for R. Milliken, 1826.
2v. illus.

NL 0426858 ScU

Lloyd, Bartholomew, 1772-1837.
An elementary treatise of mechanical philosophy, written for the use of the undergraduate students of the University of Dublin. Vol. I. Second edition. Dublin, Printed at the University Press for Milliken and son, 1835.
xxxv, 395 p. fold. plates. 22cm.

No more published?

NL 0426859 NNC RPB CU

Lloyd, Bartholomew Clifford, 1808-1872, reporter.
Gt. Brit. *Court of chancery.*
Condensed reports of cases decided in the High court of chancery in England [1807-1839] ... Philadelphia, J. Grigg, 1831-42.

Lloyd, Bartholomew Clifford, 1808-1872, ed.
FOR OTHER EDITIONS SEE MAIN ENTRY
Ireland. *Court of chancery.*
Reports of cases argued and determined in the High court of chancery, in Ireland, during the time of Lord Chancellor Sugden, from the commencement of Hilary term, 1835, to the commencement of Easter term, 1835, by Bartholomew Clifford Lloyd and Francis Goold ... New York, Albany, Banks & brothers, 1865.

Lloyd, Bartholomew Clifford, 1808-1872.
A selection of cases argued and determined in the High court of chancery in Ireland
see under Ireland. Court of chancery.

Lloyd, Beatrix Demarest.
The house in St. Cloud, by Beatrix Demarest Lloyd. New York, R. M. McBride & company [c1935]
4 p. l., 3-313 p. 20cm.
"First edition."

I. Title.
Library of Congress PZ3.L772Ho 35-5700

NL 0426863 DLC MB

Lloyd, Beatrix Demarest.
The pastime of eternity, by Beatrix Demarest Lloyd. New York, C. Scribner's sons, 1904.
3 p. l., 364 p. 19 cm.

I. Title.
Library of Congress PZ3.L772P 4—9633

NL 0426864 DLC NN IU

BV380 .L6 1845
Lloyd, Benjamin, 1804-1860, comp.
The primitive hymns, spiritual songs, and sacred poems, regularly selected, classified and set in order, and adapted to social singing and all occasions of divine worship. 3d ed. Wetumpka, Ala., 1845.
290p. 13cm.
Without music.

1. Baptists—Hymns.

NL 0426865 T NNUT

245.2 L772p 1872 Rare Books Col
Lloyd, Benjamin, 1804-1860, comp.
The primitive hymns, spiritual songs, and sacred poems, regularly selected, classified and set in order, and adapted to social singing and all occasions of divine worship. By Benjamin Lloyd ... Stereotype ed. Greenville, Ala., Published for the proprietor, 1872.
xxii, 558p. front.(port.) 14½cm.

Without music.

1. Hymns, English. I. Title.

NL 0426866 TxU

Lloyd, Benjamin, 1804-1860. comp.
The primitive hymns, spiritual songs, and sacred poems, regularly selected, classified and set in order, and adapted to social singing and all occasions of divine worship. Stereotype ed. Greenville, Ala., Pub. for the proprietors, 1882.
xxii, 558p.

NL 0426867 OCU

Lloyd, Benjamin, 1804-1860.
The primitive hymns, spiritual songs, and sacred poems, regularly selected, classified and set in order, and adapted to social singing and all occasions of divine worship. By Benjamin Lloyd ... Stereotype ed. Temple, Tex., Pub. for the proprietress, Mrs. M. E. Atkins [c1906]
xxii, 554 p. 15cm.
Preface dated 1854.

6-41053

NL 0426868 DLC

Lloyd, Benjamin, 1804-1860, *comp.*
The primitive hymns, spiritual songs, and sacred poems, regularly selected, classified and set in order, and adapted to social singing and all occasions of divine worship. By Benjamin Lloyd ... Stereotype ed. La Mesa, Calif., Pub. for the proprietors, O. L. Terry and La V. L. Smith, 1921.
xxii, 558 p. front. (port.) 14½cm.
Without music.

I. Title.
Library of Congress BV380.L6 1921 22-5824

NL 0426869 DLC

Lloyd, Benjamin E.
Lights and shades in San Francisco. By B. E. Lloyd. With appropriate illustrations... San Francisco, Printed by A. L. Bancroft & company, 1876.
4 p. l., [7]-523 p. plates. 23½cm.
Added half-title, illus.

1. San Francisco. I. Title.
Library of Congress F869.S3L7 1-Rc-677

NL 0426870 DLC CaBViP MWA NN PPL WaT MB

Lloyd, Bertram, *ed.*
The great kinship; an anthology of humanitarian poetry, ed. by Bertram Lloyd. London, G. Allen & Unwin ltd. [1921]
xviii p., 1 l., 271, [1] p. front. 20 cm.
Bibliography: p. 259-261.

1. Animals—Poetry. 2. Birds in literature. 3. English poetry (Collections) I. Title.
PN6110.A7L6 1921 21—12587

NL 0426871 DLC NcU MB OCl NN CaBVaU CLSU

Lloyd, Bertram, *ed.*
The paths of glory; a collection of poems written during the war, 1914-1919, ed. by Bertram Lloyd. London, G. Allen & Unwin ltd. [1919]
119, [1] p. 17½cm.
Poems which emphasize the horrors of war.
Bibliography: p. 117-118.

1. European war, 1914- —Poetry. 2. War. I. Title.
Library of Congress PR1225.L7 20-6154

NL 0426872 DLC MH

Lloyd, Bertram, *ed.*
Poems written during the great war, 1914-1918; an anthology ed. by Bertram Lloyd. London, G. Allen & Unwin ltd. [1918]
111, [1] p. 17½cm.
"First published July 1918; reprinted December 1918."
Bibliography: p. 110-111.

1. European war, 1914- —Poetry.
Library of Congress D526.L5 19-2840

NL 0426873 DLC MiU CaBVaU ViU NN

[Lloyd, Mrs Bitha (Fox)] 1811-
[Pictures of heroes, and lessons from their lives. Philadelphia, Lippincott [1859]
247p.

NL 0426874 OClW CU

920 L77p
[Lloyd, Mrs Bitha (Fox)], 1811-
Pictures of heroes and lessons from their lives. Philadelphia [1860]
247p. front., plates.

Illus. t.-p.

NL 0426875 IU MH

Lloyd, *Mrs.* Bitha (Fox) 1811-
Studies of Christian character, by Bitha Fox ... with illustrations by James Godwin ... London, J. Hogg & sons [1860]
xiii, 337, [1] p. front., plates. 19½cm.
Illustrated t.-p.

1. Christian biography. I. Title.
37-17404
Library of Congress BR1700.L6
[2] 922

NL 0426876 DLC ICMcC IdU PPPrHi ODW NN CtW

Lloyd, *Mrs.* Bitha (Fox) 1811-
Watchers for the dawn, and other studies of Christian character. By Mrs. W. R. Lloyd. With illustrations by James Godwin. New York, Virtue and Yorston [187-?]
3 p. l., [iii]-viii, [9]-272 p. plates. 17½cm.
Added t.-p. (illustrated): Watchers for the dawn ... 2d ed. London, J. Hogg and son.
First published, 1860, under title: Studies of Christian character.

1. Christian biography. I. Title. II. Title: Studies of Christian character.
Library of Congress BR1700.L62 38-24327

NL 0426877 DLC ODW

Lloyd, Blodwen.
A dictionary of botanical terms. London, University of London Press [c1950]
64 p. illus. 19 cm.

1. Botany—Dictionaries.
QK9.L74 580.3 63-2090

WaTC OrP OrCS OrU WaE
WaWW IdB IdPI WaPS IdU MtBC WaSp MtU Wa WaSpG
MiEM DSI NNC LU KU MsU NN NIC DNAL CaBVa CaBVaU
NL 0426878 DLC MtBuM OrU-M Or OrSaW OrStbM Or

VOLUME 337

Sci QK 51 L57 1949 Lloyd, Blodwen.
Handbook of botanical diagrams. [2d ed. London, University of London Press [1949] 108p. (chiefly illus.)

1. Botany - Study and teaching. 2. Botany - Anatomy. 3. Botany - Terminology.

NL 0426879 FTaSU IaU DNAL WaU NBuC InU MiU IU

Lloyd, Blodwen, *ed.*
Science in films; a world review and reference book. London, S. Low, Marston [1948-
v. illus. 23 cm.
Includes bibliographies.

1. Photography—Scientific applications. 2. Moving-pictures, Documentary—Catalogs. 3. Science—Study and teaching.

Q186.L55 507 49-54149*

NL 0426880 DLC ScU DNLM NcD CaBVaU OrCS OrP MiD CLSU

Lloyd, Bolivar Jones, 1872-
Código telegráfico, para uso de la Oficina sanitaria panamericana, los departamentos nacionales de sanidad de las repúblicas americanas y organismos cooperadores, compuesto por el Dr. Bolívar J. Lloyd ... espagñol—portuguez—français—English. Washington, D. C., Unión panamericana, 1928.
cover-title, ii, 93 p. 23cm. (Publicacion no. 2, Oficina sanitaria panamericana)

1. Cipher and telegraph codes—Contagion and contagious diseases. I. Title.

28-24712

Library of Congress HE7677.C68L6

NL 0426881 DLC

RA 10 .A6 P97 1926-40 Lloyd, Bolivar Jones, 1872
Cooperación panamericana en sanidad, las conferencias sanitarias y la Oficina Sanitaria Panamericana. Washington, Unión Panamericana, 1932.
13 p. illus. maps. ([Pan American Union] Serie sobre salubridad pública y previsión social, no. 68)
Portuguese ed. has series no. 39, and English ed. is no. 10.
"Del Boletín de la Unión Panamericana, abril 1932".

1. Pan American Sanitary Bureau. 2. Public health- America. I. Title. II. Series.

NL 0426883 DPAHO

G980.6 P191c no.10 [LLOYD, BOLIVAR JONES] 1872-
... Pan American cooperation in public health work ... Washington, D.C. [1932]
1p.l.,14p. incl. maps. 23½cm. (Congress and conference series. no.10)
"By Bolivar J. Lloyd, M.D." - cf. p.l.
"Reprinted from the April, 1932, issue of the Bulletin of the Pan American union."

1. Hygiene, Public. 2. Spanish America - Sanit. affairs. 3. Pan American sanitary bureau. I. Title. II. Series (contents)

NL 0426884 TxU

Lloyd, Bolivar Jones, 1872-
... A plan to establish in the United States a morbidity registration area; that is, an area for the more complete collection of data relating to the diseases of man, by B. J. Lloyd, assistant surgeon general, United States Public health service ... Washington, Govt. print. off., 1925.
12 p. incl. tables, diagr. 23cm.
Reprint no. 1032 from the Public health reports, v. 40, no. 30, July 24, 1925 (p. 1549-1559)
Running title: Morbidity registration area.
"Read as a part of the proceedings of the Annual conference of state and territorial health officers with the surgeon general, Washington, D. C., June 1, 1925."—p. 2.
1. Diseases—Registration. I. U. S. Public health service. Public health reports. Reprint 1032. II. Title. III. Title: Morbidity registration area.

25-26972

Library of Congress RA404.A3A4 1925

NL 0426885 DLC WaWW

RA 10 .A6 P97 1926-40 Lloyd, Bolivar Jones, 1872-
Public health significance of our newer knowledge of yellow fever. 1936.
9 p.
"Reprinted from the Southern Medical Journal... vol. 29, no. 5, May 1936, pp. 533-536."

1. Yellow fever- Prevention.

NL 0426886 DPAHO

RA 10 .A6 P97 1926-40 Lloyd, Bolivar Jones, 1872-
Yellow fever- yesterday, today, and tomorrow. 1937.
81-88 p.
"Reprinted from The Military Surgeon, vol. 81, no. 2, August, 1937."

1. Yellow fever- Prevention.

NL 0426887 DPAHO

323.4 L775c Lloyd, Brian.
The censorship and public morality; an Australian conspectus, by Brian Lloyd and George Gilbert. Sydney, Angus & Robertson, 1930.
56p. 17cm.

1. Censorship. 2. Literature and morals. I. Gilbert, George, joint author. II. Title.

NL 0426888 TxU

Lloyd, C., of Melbourne
see Lloyd, Clifford.

Lloyd, C B
Reports of Messrs. Lloyd and Vanderplank on outbreak of rinderpest
see under Natal. Dept. of agriculture.

Lloyd, C. Francis
see Lloyd, Charles Francis, 1852-1917.

---

808 L77o Lloyd, C T
On the teaching of English composition. Boston, Mass. [1930]
13p.

NL 0426892 IU

Lloyd, C V.
From Hongkong to Canton by the Pearl River. By Captain C. V. Lloyd ... Hongkong [1902]
xi, 80 p. plates, fold. maps. 21cm.

1. China—Descr. & trav.

5-30498

Library of Congress DS793.K7L7

NL 0426893 DLC CtY PP MSaE

Lloyd, Carl.

Martin, Paul Sidney, 1899-
Archaeological work in the Ackmen-Lowry area, southwestern Colorado, 1937, by Paul S. Martin ... With reports by Carl Lloyd and Alexander Spoehr. [Chicago, 1938]

Lloyd, Caro
see
Lloyd, Caroline Augusta, 1859-

[**Lloyd, Caroline**]
A memorial of Lt. Daniel Perkins Dewey, of the Twenty-fifth regiment, Connecticut volunteers. Hartford, Press of Case, Lockwood & company, 1864.
126 p. front. (port.) 18cm.
Published anonymously.

1. Dewey, Daniel Perkins, 1843-1863. I. Title.

7-21670

Library of Congress E601.D51

NL 0426896 TxU DLC CtY OClWHi Nh CtY MH NjP OClW NNC

Lloyd, Caroline Augusta, 1859-
Henry Demarest Lloyd, 1847-1903, a biography by Caro Lloyd, with an introduction by Charles Edward Russell ... New York and London, G. P. Putnam's sons, 1912.
2 v. fronts., plates, ports., facsims. 23½cm.
A list of the writings of Henry Demarest Lloyd: v. 2, p. 351-364.

1. Lloyd, Henry Demarest, 1847-1903.

12-10840

Library of Congress HB119.L7L7

NL 0426897 LU NjNbS MeB NcRS NIC KyLx CU TU PHC PSC PP MtU OrP NN MB ICJ NjP ViU OCl OO OFH DLC IdB WaTC OrCS WaS WaT NcD PBm PU

Lloyd, Cecil Francis, 1884-1928.
Landfall; the collected poems of Cecil Francis Lloyd. Toronto, Ryerson press [1935] xi, 47 p. 19cm.

NL 0426898 NN TxU CaBVaU ICU RPB CaOTU

Lloyd, Cecil Francis.
Leaves of the sybil, by Cecil Francis Lloyd ... [n. p.] 1927.
45 p. 16½cm.
Poems.

I. Title.

31-19151

Library of Congress PS3523.L54L4 1927

NL 0426899 DLC

Lloyd, Cecil Francis.
Leaves of the sibyl, by Cecil Francis Lloyd. Toronto, The Hunter-Rose co., ltd., 1928.
47 p. 19½cm.

1. Canadian poetry. I. Title.

Queen's Univ. Library. 1928-21

NL 0426900 CaOKQ CaOTU

Z 819.1 L775m Lloyd, Cecil Francis, 1884-1928.
Malvern essays. Toronto, Ryerson Press [c1930]
51p. 28cm.

Reprinted from the Canadian bookman.
"Of this edition ... two hundred and fifty copies have been printed."

NL 0426901 TxU CaOTU CaBVaU

VOLUME 337

Lloyd, Cecil Francis.
Rosemary and rue, by Cecil Francis Lloyd. Winnipeg, Stovel co., 1929.
16 p. 19½cm.

1. Canadian poetry. I. Title.

Queen's Univ. Library. 1931-29

NL 0426902 CaOKQ CaBViP

Lloyd, Cecil Francis.
Sunlight and shadow, by Cecil Francis Lloyd. . . Toronto, The Hunter-Rose co., ltd., 1928.
ix, 83 p. 19½cm.

1. Canadian essays. I. Title.

Queen's Univ. Library 1928-20

NL 0426903 CaOKQ

Lloyd, Cecil Francis, 1884-1938.
Vesper bells, by Cecil Francis Lloyd ... Toronto, The Hunter-Rose company, limited, 1929.
3 p.l., 19 p. 20cm.

NL 0426904 CaBVaU MH

Lloyd, Charles, barrister-at-law.
A calm inquiry into all the objections made to the educational provisions of the factory bill, exhibiting the nature, tendency, and object of the new principles by which the dissenting bodies stand opposed thereto. By Charles Lloyd ... London, J. Hatchard & son, 1843.
25 p. 20cm.

1. Religious education—Gt. Brit. 2. Church and state [in] Gt. Brit.

E 15—1441

U. S. Off. of educ. Library for Library of Congress LC116.G7L7 [a41b1]

NL 0426905 DHEW MH-BA CtY NN

Lloyd, Charles, of Slough.
Principles for the conduct of life. By Charles Lloyd ... London, Printed by J. Masters, 1848.
2 v. 21cm.
A compilation of quotations arranged alphabetically.

1. Conduct of life.

10-33814

Library of Congress BJ1571.L65

NL 0426906 DLC ICRL CtY

Lloyd, Charles, 1735-1773.
Works by this author printed in America before 1801 are available in this library in the Readex Microprint edition of Early American Imprints published by the American Antiquarian Society.
This collection is arranged according to the numbers in Charles Evans' American Bibliography.

NL 0426907 DLC

Lloyd, Charles, 1735-1773, supposed author.
The anatomy of a late negociation
see under title

[Lloyd, Charles] 1735-1773.
The conduct of the late administration examined. With an appendix, containing original and authentic documents ... London, Printed for J. Almon, 1767.
160, [2], liv p. 21 cm.
Charles Lloyd was secretary to George Grenville, and the authorship is attributed to him by Halkett and Laing (Dict.), Cushing (Anonyms), Winsor (Narr. & crit. hist.), British museum Catalogue, and Dictionary of national biography which adds that "much of this pamphlet ... was dictated by Grenville himself." W. J. Smith, editor of "The Grenville papers," maintains that Lord Temple was the author, while the Earl of Liverpool is mentioned by others.
1. Stamp act, 1765. 2. Gt. Brit. — Pol. & govt. — 1760-1820. I. Grenville, George, 1712-1770. II. Title.

E215.2.L78 8-9196

MH MnU CaBVaU CtY ViU NjP MB MiU-C MWiW-C
NL 0426909 DLC MdBJ-G NIC MnU PPL PHi RPJCB MHi ICN

Micro 3 [Lloyd, Charles] 1735-1773.
The conduct of the late administration examined. With an appendix, containing original and authentic documents . . . London, Printed for J. Almon, 1767.
Microcard edition (4 cards). (Jeffersonian Americana)
Charles Lloyd was secretary to George Grenville, and the authorship is attributed to him by Halkett and Laing (Dict.), Cushing (Anonyms), Winsor (Narr. & crit. hist.), British Museum Catalogue, and Dictionary of national biography which adds that "much of this pamphlet . . . was dictated by Grenville himself." W. J. Smith, editor of "The Grenville papers," maintains that Lord Temple was the author, while the Earl of Liverpool is mentioned by others.
cf. Evans 10663. Sabin 15202.

NL 0426910 ViU CaBVaU

[Lloyd, Charles] 1735-1773.
The conduct of the late administration examined, relative to the American stamp-act. With an appendix containing original and authentic documents ... 2d ed. London, Printed for J. Almon, 1767.
1 p. l., [5]-160, [2], liv p. 21cm.
Charles Lloyd was secretary to George Grenville, and the authorship is attributed to him by Halkett and Laing (Dict.), Cushing (Anonyms), Winsor (Narr. & crit. hist.), British museum Catalogue, and Dictionary of national biography which adds that "much of this pamphlet ... was dictated by Grenville himself." On the other hand W. J. Smith, editor of "The Grenville papers," maintains that Lord Temple was the author, and by others the Earl of Liverpool is mentioned.

1. Stamp act, 1765. 2. Gt. Brit.—Pol. & govt.—1760-1789. I. Grenville, George, 1712-1770. II. Title.

8—9198

Library of Congress E215.2.L79
——— Copy 2. [Almon, John. A collection of the most interesting tracts ... London, 1766-67. v. 3 (A third volume of interesting tracts, 1767) no. 1]

LNHT ViW ViU PSt PHi PPL MiU-C
NL 0426912 DLC PPAmP MoU CtY NN MH ICRL MiU-C NIC

[Lloyd, Charles] 1735-1773.
The conduct of the late administration examined. With an appendix, containing original and authentic documents ... London: printed. 1767. Boston, Reprinted and sold by Edes and Gill, 1767.
107 p. 18½cm.
Charles Lloyd was secretary to George Grenville, and the authorship is attributed to him by Halkett and Laing (Dict.), Cushing (Anonyms), Winsor (Narr. & crit. hist.), British museum Catalogue, and Dictionary of national biography, which adds that "much of this pamphlet ... was dictated by Grenville himself." On the other hand, W. J. Smith, editor of "The Grenville papers," maintains that Lord Temple was the author, and by others the Earl of Liverpool is mentioned.
1. Stamp act, 1765. 2. Gt. Brit.—Pol. & givt.—1760-1820. I. Grenville, George, 1712-1770. II. Title.
Library of Congress E215.2.L8 8—9197
——— Copy 2. [Miscellaneous pamphlets, v. 682, no. 1] AC901.M5 vol. 682

MBAt
NL 0426913 DLC PMA NIC MWA MB NjP NNC PHi PPL CtY

[Lloyd, Charles] 1735-1773, attributed author.
A critical review of the new administration. London, J. Wilkie, 1765.
48p. 20cm.

NL 0426914 CtY MH PPL RPJCB NN

[Lloyd, Charles] 1735-1773.
A defence of the majority in the House of commons, on the question relating to general warrants. In answer to The defence of the minority. London, Printed for J. Wilkie, 1764.
2 p. l., 52 p. 21cm.
A reply to Charles Townshend's A defence of the minority.

1. Warrants (Law)—Gt. Brit. 2. Gt. Brit.—Pol. & govt.—1760-1789. 3. Townshend, Charles, 1725-1767. A defence of the minority. I. Title.

38-34020 Revised

Library of Congress JN215.1764 f

NL 0426915 DLC RPJCB NIC ICRL CLU OKentU NNC MsU NN

[Lloyd, Charles] 1735-1773.
A defence of the majority in the House of commons, on the question relating to general warrants. In answer to The defence of the minority. 2. ed., to which is added, a postscript, in answer to The enquiry into the doctrine of libels, &c. and The reply to the defence of the majority. London: Printed for J. Wilkie, 1765. 66 p. 20cm.

NL 0426916 NN IaU CSmH MH MiU OClW CtY InU

J 54555 .19 v.1 Lloyd, Charles, 1735-1773.
A defence of the majority in the House of commons, on the question relating to general warrants. In answer to the defence of the minority... (in A collection of scarce and interesting tracts... 1787-88. v.1, p.73-92)

Caption title.
Maintains that a general warrant for apprehending and seizing the authors, printers and publishers of a seditious libel, is warranted by law.
For the speech to which this is a reply see Townshend, Charles. A defence of the minority... (J 54555.19, v.1)

NL 0426918 ICN CtY

[Lloyd, Charles] 1735-1773.
An examination of the principles and boasted disinterestedness of a late Right Honourable gentleman. In a letter from an old man of business, to a noble lord ... London, Printed for J. Almon, 1766.
34 p. 22½cm.
"A late Right Honourable gentleman" [i. e. William Pitt, earl of Chatham]
"A noble lord" [i. e. Lord North]

1. Pitt, William, 1st earl of Chatham, 1708-1778. I. Title.

4—22117

Library of Congress DA483.P62L7
——— Copy 2. [Miscellaneous pamphlets, v. 208, no. 3]

RPJCB
NL 0426919 DLC PHi CtY MiU-C NN MH MnU PPL MWA

[Lloyd, Charles,] 1735-1773.
An honest man's reasons for declining to take any part in the new administration, in a letter to the Marquis of ——. London: J. Wilkie, 1765. 23 p. 8°.

1. Great Britain—Hist.—George III, 1760-1820—Pamphlets. 2. Rockingham, Charles Watson-Wentworth, marquis of, 1730-1782. 3. Title.
N. Y. P. L. November 20, 1929

NL 0426920 NN RPJCB CSmH InU PU CtY TxU

DA510 .C66 v.2 [LLOYD, CHARLES] 1735-1773.
An honest man's reasons for declining to take part in the new administration.
(In A collection of scarce and interesting tracts. London, 1787. 22cm. v.II, p.[3]-6)

1. Gt. Brit.--Pol.& govt.--1765-1789--Pamphlets.

NL 0426921 ICU ICN

Lloyd, Charles, 1735-1773, supposed author
Principles for the conduct of life
see under Lloyd, Charles, of Slough.

[Lloyd, Charles] 1735-1773.
A true history of a late short administration. London, Printed for J. Almon, 1766.
22 p. 21 cm.

1. Gt. Brit.—Pol. & govt.—1760-1789. I. Title.

DA507.1766.L5 8—10770

MBAt MH
NL 0426923 DLC MH CaBVaU MiHM ViU ICN NN MiU RPJCB

VOLUME 337

[Lloyd, Charles] 1735-1773.
A true history of a late short administration.
London, Printed for J. Almon, 1766.
22p.

Microcard edition.

NL 0426924 ICRL TxU OU ViU PSt

J 54555 .19 v.2 Lloyd, Charles, 1735-1773.
A true history of a late short administration... (in A collection of scarce and interesting tracts... 1787-88. v.2, p.57-69)

Caption title.
"An answer to a pamphlet of Burke's written in praise of the Rockingham ministry and entitled: A short account of a late short administration."-Dict. of nat. biog.
The text of Burke's pamphlet is given in parallel columns with Lloyd's reply.

NL 0426926 ICN

[Lloyd, Charles] 1735-1773.
A true history of a late short administration. London: J. Stockdale, 1807. 23 p. 8°.
An answer to "A short account of a late short administration," written in imitation of an article with the same title published by Charles Lloyd in 1766. — *cf. Introd.*

FORD COLLECTION.
158625. 1. Great Britain—Hist.—George III, 1760-1820—Pamphlets. 2. A short history of a late short administration.
N. Y. P. L. January 20, 1930

NL 0426927 NN RPB CSt CSmH

Lloyd, Charles, 1748-1828, tr.

Horatius Flaccus, Quintus.
The epistles of Horace; tr. into English verse. Birmingham, Orton and Hawkes Smith, 1812.

PZ163 .L79T7 1815 [Lloyd, Charles] 1766-1829.
Travels at home, and voyages by the fire-side; for the instruction and entertainment of young persons. London, Longman, Hurst, Rees, Orme & Brown, 1815.
5 v.

NL 0426929 ICU

[Lloyd, Charles] 1766-1829.
Travels at home and voyages by the fireside, for the instruction and entertainment of young persons. v. 1- Philadelphia: E. Earle, 1816- v. 24°.
v. 1 incomplete, lacks pages following 292.
Contents: v. 1. Europe and Asia.

1. Geography.—Elementary and popular works. 2. Title.
N. Y. P. L. October 9, 1923.

NL 0426930 NN PPL IU NBu

MSS E7008++ Lloyd, Charles, 1775-1839.
[Autograph manuscript in the form of a long letter to Talfourd, dated March 6th, 1822]
ms. [7] p. 40cm.

This is a letter giving Talfourd a detailed account of his quarrel with Wordsworth.
In envelope, 37 x 30 cm.

NL 0426931 NIC

Lloyd, Charles, 1775-1839.
Blank verse, by Charles Lloyd and Charles Lamb. London Printed by T. Bensley for J. and A. Arch, 1798.
95, [1] p. 16cm.

I. Lamb, Charles, 1775-1834. II. Title.
44-12959
Library of Congress PR4890.L8A63

NL 0426932 DLC MWiW-C ICN MH CtY TxU CLU-C PPL ViU PPRF NcD MB NcU CU

Lloyd, Charles, 1775-1839.
Desultory thoughts in London, Titus and Gisippus, with other poems. By Charles Lloyd ... London, C. and H. Baldwyn, 1821.
viii, 251, [1] p. 19½cm.

I. Title: Desultory thoughts in London. II. Title: Titus and Gisippus.
1-13226
Library of Congress PR4890.L8A65

NL 0426933 DLC TxU NjP PHC PPL MiU CSmH MB CtY IU MWiW-C NIC RPB NN OOxM

Lloyd, Charles, 1775-1839.
The Duke d'Ormond, a tragedy; and Beritola, a tale ... London, Longman, Hurst, Rees, Orme & Brown [etc.] 1822.
xii p., 1 l., 285 p. 16°.

1-13225

NL 0426934 DLC OClW MWiW-C CtY OrU TxU CSmH

Lloyd, Charles, 1775-1839.
Edmund Oliver. By Charles Lloyd ... Bristol, J. Cottle, 1798.
2 v. 18½ cm.
Presentation copy to Thomas Manning from the author, with his autograph.

I. Title.
PR4890.L8A68 7—19399

NL 0426935 DLC CtY NIC FU MH NcD CSmH OClW

Lloyd, Charles, 1775-1839.
Isabel; a tale. London, 1810.
2 v. Microfilm.

NL 0426936 OClW

EC8 L7753 799l Lloyd, Charles, 1775-1839.
A letter to the anti-Jacobin reviewers. By Charles Lloyd ...
Birmingham, Printed by James Belcher; sold by J. and A. Arch, Grace-church street, London. 1799.
38p. 22.5cm., in folder 23.5cm.
A defence of himself and Charles Lamb against the strictures of reviewers.
Original purple wrappers; in cloth folder.

NL 0426937 MH CSmH CtY

Lloyd, Charles, 1775-1839. Nor 2107
Lines suggested by the fast appointed on Feb. 27, 1799. Birmingham, printed and sold by E. Piercy, etc. etc. 1799.
pp. (3), 11.
From the library of Charles Lamb.

NL 0426938 MH OClW CSmH

[Lloyd, Charles] 1775-1839.
Memoirs of the life and writings of Vittorio Alfieri ... London, C. and H. Baldwyn, 1821.
iv, 220 p. 19cm.

I. Alfieri, Vittorio, 1749-1803. II. Title.
16-3063
Library of Congress PQ4681.L6

NL 0426339 DLC TxU MB PPG MWA PU

Lloyd, Charles, 1775-1839.
Nugae canorae. Poems by Charles Lloyd ... 3d ed., with additions ... London, J. and A. Arch, 1819.
xxiv, 332 p. 16½cm.
Translations of tales selected from Ovid's Metamorphoses: p. [257]-332.

I. Ovidius Naso, Publius. Metamorphoses. II. Title.
25-25715
Library of Congress PR4890.L8A7

NL 0426940 DLC NcD OO NIC PHC CtY TxU ICU

Lloyd, Charles, poet. 1775-1839.
Poems. 2d edition.
(In Coleridge, Samuel Taylor. 1772-1834. Poems. 2d edition. Pp. 151-213. Bristol. 1797.)

NL 0426941 MB MH

Lloyd, Charles, 1775-1839.
Poems. By Charles Lloyd ... London, Longman, Hurst, Rees, Orme, and Brown; [etc., etc.] 1823.
2 p. l., 96 p. 18cm.

Library of Congress PR4890.L8A73 1-23228

NL 0426942 DLC NIC InU OClW MWiW-C MiU MB NN TxU NN CSmH NjP

Lloyd, Charles, 1775-1839.
Poems on the death of Priscilla Farmer by her grandson Char Lloyd. Bristol, N. Biggs, etc. etc. 1796.
f°. pp. 27. Port. of Charles Lamb inserted.
On fly-leaf: James Lloyd with tenderest regard from the author. MS. autograph letter of author to his brother James inserted.
This book may be consulted in the room of the Widener Collection.

NL 0426943 MH CSmH CtY ICN InU MH NjP PPRF ICN

Lloyd, Charles, 1775-1839. Nor 2107
Poems on various subjects. Carlisle; Penrith, printed by F. Jollie for J. Richardson, etc. etc. 1795.
pp. 104.
From the library of Charles Lamb, with corrections and table of contents in manuscript.

NL 0426944 MH CtY TxU NIC PPL MdBP OO MiU OrU CSmH

Lloyd, Charles, 1775-1839.
Poetical essays on the character of Pope, as a poet and moralist; and on the language and objects most fit for poetry. By Charles Lloyd. London, C. and H. Baldwyn, 1821.
2 p. l., 70 p. 18½cm.

1. Pope, Alexander, 1688-1744. I. Title.
22-151
Library of Congress PR4890.L8A75

NL 0426945 DLC NIC CSmH TxU

VOLUME 337

Lloyd, Charles, 1775-1839.
Poetical essays on the character of Pope, as a poet and moralist; and on the language and objects most fit for poetry. London, Baldwyn, 1821.
70 p. Microfilm.

NL 0426946 OClW

Lloyd, Charles, bp. of Oxford, 1784-1829.
Catalogue of the very valuable classical, theological, & miscellaneous library of the late Right Rev. Charles Lloyd. [Sold at auction by Sotheby, 7 July & 4 following days, 1829.] [London, 1829]
41p.
Priced, with buyers' names.

NL 0426947 MH NNC

Lloyd, Charles, Bp. of Oxford, 1784-1829, ed
Formularies of faith...
see under Church of England. Articles of Religion.

Lloyd, Charles, bp. of Oxford, 1784-1829, ed.
The King's book; or, A necessary doctrine and erudition for any Christian man, 1543, with an introduction by T. A. Lacey. Published for the Church historical society. London, Society for promoting Christian knowledge, 1932.

Lloyd, Charles, 1824-1862, supposed author.
A calm inquiry into all the objections ...
see under Lloyd, Charles, barrister-at-law.

Lloyd, Charles, 1824-1862.
Catalogue of the Aldine collection, formed by the late Rev. Charles Lloyd, senior student of Christ church, Oxford ... genealogical and historical papers of the late Joseph Hunter, F. S. A., and the remaining library of Joseph Gwilt, esq., F. S. A. Which will be sold by auction by Messrs. S. Leigh Sotheby & John Wilkinson, auctioneers ... 18th June, 1862, and two following days ... London, Printed by J. Davy & sons ⌊1862⌋
1 p. l., 88 p. 22cm.
No. 1 in a vol. of pamphlets lettered: Sale catalogues. v. 1.
1,107 lots.
Some of the prices noted in ms.
1. Manuzio, family of printers, Venice. I. Hunter, Joseph, 1783-1861. II. Gwilt, Joseph, 1784-1863.
13-6869
Library of Congress Z997.L793 vol. 1, no. 1

NL 0426951 DLC MH NN

Lloyd, Charles Allen.
We who speak English and our ignorance of our mother tongue, by Charles Allen Lloyd. New York, Thomas Y. Crowell company ⌊c1938⌋
3 p. l., 308 p. 22½cm.

1. English language — Idioms, corrections, errors. 2. English language—Pronunciation. I. Title.
38-27941
Library of Congress PE1460.L5
——— Copy 2.
Copyright A 120886 ⌊5⌋ 428.3

OO ViU PU PWcS NN WaS NcRA OrSaW OrMonO OrAshS OrCS
NL 0426952 DLC IEN OrP PPPL PPT PP PPD OEac OClW

Lloyd, Charles Allen
We who speak English and our ignorance of our mother tongue, ... N.Y,Crowell,[1941]

NL 0426953 OU NcD

Lloyd, Charles B.
Maryland. *State roads commission.*
First, second, third, and fourth annual reports of the State roads commission for the years 1908, 1909, 1910 and 1911 to the General assembly of Maryland. Baltimore, 1912.

Lloyd, Charles Christopher
see Lloyd, Christopher, 1906-

Lloyd, Charles Dalton Clifford. Br 12075.10
Ireland under the land league; a narrative of personal experiences. Edinburgh, etc., W. Blackwood and Sons, 1892.
pp. xv, 243.

Land-Ireland||

NL 0426956 MH IU NN MB PPL CtY

Lloyd, Charles Edward, *pseud.*
see Harris, Carrie (Jenkins) *d.* 1903.

Lloyd, Charles Francis, 1852-1917.
God be merciful unto us. Anthem for solo [S. A. T. B.] and chorus. [Accomp. for organ.]
(In Novello's Collection of Anthems. Vol. 12, pp. 26-38. London. [1881?])

E3570 — T.r. — Church music. Anthems, &c.

NL 0426958 MB

M1619 Lloyd, Charles Francis, 1852-1917.
S69 ⌊Woodland voices; acc. piano⌋
v.278 Woodland voices; words by Augusta Hancock. New York, Luckhardt & Belder ⌊18--?⌋ Pl. no. L. & B. 2767-21/2.
5 p. 28cm. (no.183-10)
Caption title.
Vol. 278 in a set lettered:Songs.

1.Part-songs, Secular - Trios. I.Title.

NL 0426959 CSt

Lloyd, Charles Frederick. FOR OTHER EDITIONS SEE MAIN ENTRY
Gt. Brit. *Laws, statutes, etc.*
The factory and truck acts, by Alexander Redgrave. 11th ed. by Charles F. Lloyd. Statutory orders, regulations, special rules and forms revised by W. Peacock. London, Shaw, 1909.

Lloyd, Charles Frederick, ed.
Gt. Brit. Laws, statutes, etc.
The Factory, Truck and Shops acts, by the late Alexander Redgrave ... 12th ed. By Charles F. Lloyd ... Statutory orders, regulations, special rules and forms, rev. by W. Peacock ... London, Shaw & sons ⌊etc.⌋ 1916.

Lloyd, Charles Frederick. FOR OTHER EDITIONS SEE MAIN ENTRY
Gt. Brit. Laws, statutes, etc.
The sale of food & drugs acts, and forms, regulations, orders and notices issued thereunder, with notes and cases by the late Sir William J. Bell ... 7th ed., by Charles F. Lloyd ... The chemical notes rev. and enl. by R. A. Robinson ... London, Butterworth & co.; ⌊etc., etc.⌋ 1923.

Lloyd, Charles Harford, 1849-1919.
Allegro agitato for the organ.
= *Autograph manuscript.* [189-?] 4 pp. 34½ cm.

K8010 — Organ. Music. — Manuscripts in this Library. Music.

NL 0426963 MB

Lloyd, Charles Harford, 1849-
Allen-a-Dale. For chorus and orchestra. [Piano score.]
(In Novello's Part-Song Book. 2d series. Vol. 17, pp. 63-74. London. [188-?])

E3576 — T.r. — Part songs.

NL 0426964 MB

Lloyd, Charles Harford,1849-1919.
...Andromeda; a dramatic cantata for solo voices, chorus and orchestra. The libretto written by Frederic E.Weatherly... London, Novello, Ewer & co., n.d.

Piano arrangement of orchestra part.
Written by request for ... the Gloucester triennial musical festival in September 1886.

NL 0426965 OCl

A784.24 LLOYD, CHARLES HARFORD, 1849-1919.
L774A ⌊Andromeda. Vocal score⌋
...Andromeda. a dramatic cantata for solo voices, chorus, and orchestra, the libretto written by Frederic E.Weatherly, the music composed by Charles Harford Lloyd... London & New York,Novello,Ewer and co.⌊ ⌋
vii,⌊1⌋,162p. 25½cm. (Novello's original octavo edition)

English text.
Publ.plate no. not given.

NL 0426966 PU

Lloyd, Charles Harford.
Art thou weary? Anthem (unaccompanied) for an eight-part choir.
(In Novello's Collection of Anthems. Vol. 11, pp. 177-192. London. [1880?])

E3576 — T.r. — Church music. Anthems, &c.

NL 0426967 MB

VM LLOYD, CHARLES HARFORD, 1849-1919.
1533 The ballad of Sir Ogie and the
L 79a Ladie Elsie. Englished from the 16th century Danish ballad "Aage og Else" by Frederick York Powell and set to music for mezzo-soprano and barytone soli, chorus, and orchestra by Charles Harford Lloyd. London & New York,Novello,Ewer & co.,c1894.
iv,27p. 26cm. (Novello's original octavo edition)
Vocal score with piano accompaniment.
English words.
Cover-title: Sir Ogie and the Ladie Elsie.

NL 0426968 ICN

Lloyd, Charles Harford.
Blessed is he that considereth the poor. Anthem, for S. or T. solo, chorus and organ.
(In Novello's Collection of Anthems. Vol. 13, pp. 61-83. London. [1884?])

E3577 — T.r. — Church music. Anthems, &c.

NL 0426969 MB

LLOYD, Charles Harford.
Christ was delivered for our offences; anthem for Easter on Sunday. [London 1905]

NL 0426970 MH

VOLUME 337

Lloyd, Charles Harford, 1849-1919, ed.
Church hymns. With tunes....
see under Society for promoting Christian knowledge, London. Church hymn-book committe.

Lloyd, Charles Harford, 1849-1919.
Fly to my mistress. Glee [A. T. B. B.]
(In The Orpheus. New series. Vol. 7, p. 10-14. London, [188-?])

NL 0426972 MB

Lloyd, Charles Harford, 1849–1919.
Free accompaniment of unison hymn singing, by Charles Harford Lloyd... London: H. F. W. Deane & Sons[, 1928]. 43 p. f°.

English words; music for 1 voice with organ acc.
Edited by Martin Akerman.

JUILLIARD FOUNDATION FUND.
469031A. 1. Hymns. 2. Musical accompaniment. I. Akerman, Martin, editor. II. Title.
N. Y. P. L. May 10, 1930

NL 0426973 NN MB OO

Lloyd, Charles Harford. No. 12 in **M.195.1.15
Give the Lord the honour. Anthem for 3 solo voices [S. S. T.] and chorus. [Accomp. for organ.]
(In Novello's Collection of Anthems. Vol. 15, pp. 90-111. London. [1888?])

E3577 — T.r. — Church music. Anthems, &c.

NL 0426974 MB

Lloyd, Charles Harford.
The gleaners' harvest. Cantata for female voices. The poetry written by Jetty Vogel. The music composed by Charles Harford Lloyd. [Accomp. for pianoforte.]
London. Novello, Ewer & Co. [189-?] vi, 32 pp. L. 8°.

E3577 — Vogel, Jetty. — Cantatas. Female voices

NL 0426975 MB

Lloyd, Charles Harford, 1849-
Hero and Leander; a dramatic cantata for soprano and barytone solos, chorus, and orchestra, the libretto written by Frederic E. Weatherly, the music composed by Charles Harford Lloyd. This cantata was written... for performance at the Worcester Triennial Musical Festival, in September, 1884... London: Novello, Ewer and Co. [1884.] viii, 57 p. 4°.

At head of title: Novello's original octavo edition.
English words accompany score, and also precede it.
Vocal score.

1. Cantatas. 2. Weatherly, Frederic Edward, 1848-

NL 0426976 NN CaBVaU

A784.24
H676S.E
LLOYD, CHARLES HARFORD, 1849-1919.
[Hero and Leander. Vocal score]
...Hero and Leander, a dramatic cantata for soprano and barytone solos, chorus and orchestra. The libretto written by Frederic E. Weatherly. The music composed by Charles Harford Lloyd... 2d ed. London & New York, Novello, Ewer and co. [1884]
viii, 55p. 26cm. (Novello's original octavo edition)

English text.
Publ. plate no. not given.

Bound with Hofmann, Heinrich Karl Johann. [Die schöne Melusine. Op.30. Vocal score] The legend of the fair Melusina. [ ]

NL 0426978 PU FU OCl

A784.25
L774L
LLOYD, CHARLES HARFORD, 1849-1919.
[The longbeards' saga]
...The longbeards' saga, chorus for male voices, with pianoforte obbligato. Words from Charles Kingsley's "Hypatia", music by Charles H. Lloyd. London & New York, Novello, Ewer and co. [ ]
1l., 40p. 27½cm.

English text with piano acc.
Publ. plate no. 7388.

NL 0426979 PU MB OCl

Lloyd, Charles Harford, 1849-1919.
The music to the Alcestis of Euripides. 2d ed. London & New York, Novello, Ewer [1887?]
64 p. (Novello's original octavo edition)
For chorus of tenor and bass; accompaniment of flute, clarinet and harp.

NL 0426980 OCl

WW
-Y
LL9233o
1918
Lloyd. Charles Harford, 1849-1919
O captain. My captain! unison song. Music by Charles H. Lloyd; poem by Walt Whitman. London, H.F. W. Deane & sons, The Year book press, ltd., 1918.
6 p. 26 cm.

"Composed for the Liverpool Children's Musical Festival, 1918."

NL 0426981 RPB

Lloyd, Charles Harford.
Pack, clouds, away. A four-part song.
(In Novello's Part-Song Book. 2d series. Vol. 17, pp. 88-95. London. [188-?])

NL 0426982 MB

Lloyd, Charles Harford.
The patriot. A four-part song [T. T. B. B.].
(In The Orpheus. New series. Vol. 6, pp. 172-175. London. [188-?])

NL 0426983 MB

Lloyd, Charles Harford. No. 3 in 8040.572
Postlude in E flat. For the organ. By C. H. Lloyd.
= London. Novello & Co., Ltd. 1905. 7 pp. 26½ × 36½ cm.

N7780 — Organ music.

NL 0426984 MB

Lloyd, Charles Harford, 1849-
Sonata for the organ in D minor. [By] Charles H. Lloyd. [London: Novello, Ewer & Co., 1886.] Publ. pl. no. 7088. 1 p.l., 17 p. ob. 4°.

Caption-title.
Dedication at head of caption-title.
t.-p. reads: Original compositions for the organ... no. 48.

1. Organ.—Sonatas.

NL 0426985 NN

VM
1533
L 79s
LLOYD, CHARLES HARFORD.
The song of Balder, for soprano solo, chorus and orchestra. The words written by Frederic E. Weatherly. The music composed by Charles Harford Lloyd. London, Novello [1885]
44p. 26cm. (Novello's original octavo edition)

Vocal score with piano accompaniment.
"Written by request for performance at the Hereford Triennial Musical Festival in September, 1885."

NL 0426986 ICN PU

VM
2023
L 79s
LLOYD, CHARLES HARFORD.
A song of judgment, a sacred cantata. The words selected from the books of the prophets Ezekiel and Habakkuk by the Rev. J. Powell Metcalfe. The music composed by Charles Harford Lloyd. London, Novello, Ewer and co., c1891.
iv, 89p. 26cm. (Novello's original octavo edition)

Vocal score with piano accompaniment.
English words also printed on p.[iii]-iv.
Plate no.: 8150.

NL 0426987 ICN MB

Lloyd, Charles Harford.
Tantum. [For 4 voices and organ.]
Manuscript hektograph copy. [1890?] 3 pp. F°.

E3578 — T.r. — Church music. Anthems, &c.

NL 0426988 MB

Lloyd, Charles Harford.
To a skylark. Trio [S. S. A. Accomp. for pianoforte ad lib.].
(In Novello's Collections of Trios, etc. Vol. 7, pp. 99-106. London. [188-?])

NL 0426989 MB

Lloyd, Charles Harford, *1849-* **M.140.37
[Trios for female voices.] The words written by Harold Boulton. The music composed by Charles H. Lloyd. [With accompaniment for the pianoforte.]
= London. Novello, Ewer & Co. 1893. 2 parts in 1 v. [Octavo edition of trios ... for female voices. No. 273, 285.] 26½ cm.
Contents. — 1. Little thoughts that grow. 2. Honey-bees love heath'ry heights.

D3613—Double main card.—Lloyd, Charles Harford, 1849-. (M1) — Boulton, Sir Harold Edwin, Baronet, 1859-. (M2) — T.r. (2 in contents.) (1)— Part songs. Female voices. Colls. (1)

NL 0426990 MB

Lloyd, Charles Harford. No. 1, 2 in 8040.572
Two scherzos for the organ. By C. H. Lloyd.
= London. Novello & Co., Ltd. 1905. 2 v. in 1. 26 × 36½ cm.
Contents. — No. 1 in C minor. — No. 2 in E major.

N7780 — Scherzos. Organ.

NL 0426991 MB

Lloyd, Charles Harford, 1849-1919. No. 14 in **M.205.10.7
A wet sheet and a flowing sea. A four-part song [T. T. B. B.].
(In The Orpheus. New series. Vol. 7, pp. 53-58. London. [188-?])

F3578 — T.r. — Part songs.

NL 0426992 MB

Lloyd, Mrs. Charles L.
see
Mapes, Ella (Stryker) "Mrs. C. L. Lloyd," 1870-

Lloyd, Charles Mostyn, 1878-
The abolition of the Poor law. London, Standing joint committee of the Independent labour party and the Fabian society, 1912. 18 p. 21cm. (War against poverty.)

1. Poor laws--Gt. Br., 1912. I. Independent labour party (Gt. Br.) II. Fabian society, London.

NL 0426994 NN

VOLUME 337

Lma92 C55 1903
Lloyd, Charles Mostyn, 1878-
Carminis bucolici quaenam fuerit ars et ratio ... Oxford,B.H.Blackwell[etc.,etc.]1903.
19p. 22cm. ([Oxford. University.] Chancellor's[prize] Latin essay, 1903)

NL 0426995 CtY MH MiU PU

HD7333 A3L97
Lloyd, Charles Mostyn, 1878-
Housing. London, Fabian Society, 1920.
24 p. 22cm. (Fabian tract, 193)
Cover title.

1. Housing - Gt. Brit. I. Title

NL 0426996 CSt-H NN ICN MH

Lloyd, Charles Mostyn, 1878–
The new children's charter. London, Standing joint committee of the Independent labour party and the Fabian society. 1912. 19 p. 21cm. (War against poverty)

1. Children—Charities—Gt. Br. 2. Children—Jurisp.—Gt. Br., 1912. I. Independent labour party (Gt. Br.) II. Fabain society, London.

NL 0426997 NN

LLOYD, Charles Mostyn, 1878-
The present state of the poor law,with foreword by George Lansbury. London, [Leicester Co-operative Printing Society, ltd., 1920]

Pamphet.
Cover serves as title-page.
At head of title: The Labour Party.

NL 0426998 MH DL

Lloyd, Charles Mostyn, 1878–
The reorganisation of local government: being a series of essays prepared by Captain C. M. Lloyd for a conference of the Labour research department, together with an introduction by Sidney Webb, with an appendix giving a report of the Labour research department conference on 15th, 16th and 17th May, 1919. Chairman: Rt. Hon. J. R. Clynes, M. P. ... Westminster, The Labour research department; ₍London₎ G. Allen & Unwin ltd. ₍1919₎
cover-title, 45, ₍1₎ p. 21½cm. (Local government series, no. 1)

CONTENTS.—The coming revolution in local government. By S. Webb.—The reorganisation of local government. By Captain C. M. Lloyd. Public health and housing. The sick and infirm and mentally deficient. Education (boarding and nursery schools, etc.) Unemployment. Constitutional problems.—Appendix.

1. Local government—Gt. Brit. 2. Gt. Brit.—Sanit. affairs. I. Labour research department. II. Title.
22-3423 Revised
Library of Congress JS3020.L6 no. 1

NL 0427000 DLC NBuU-L IU NN

Lloyd, Charles Mostyn, 1878–
Russian notes ₍by₎ C. M. Lloyd. London, L. and Virginia Woolf at the Hogarth press, 1932.
40 p. 18½cm. (On cover: Day to day pamphlets, no. 7)
"Appeared in the autumn of 1931 as a series of articles in the New statesman and Nation."—Pref.

1. Russia—Economic policy—Five-year plan (1928–1932) I. Title.
33-4427
Library of Congress HC335.L6
₍3₎ 330.947

NL 0427001 DLC CU NN

---

*EP85 F1127t v.195
Lloyd, Charles Mostyn, 1878-
... The scandal of the Poor law, by C. M. Lloyd, M.A.
Published and sold by the Fabian society,25, Tothill street,Westminster,London,S.W.1 ... July,1920.
19p. 21.5cm.,in case 26.5cm. (Fabian tract no.195.)

NL 0427002 MH CSt-H ICN NN

Lloyd, Charles Mostyn, 1878–
Trade unionism, by C. M. Lloyd. London, Adam & Charles Black ltd., 1915.
vii, 244 p. diagrs. 19cm. (Half-title: The social workers series ...)
"Select bibliography": p. 237-240.

1. Trade-unions—Gt. Brit. 2. Trade-unions. I. Title.
Library of Congress HD6664.L66 16-1724 Revised

MdBJ NN
NL 0427003 DLC NjP CU IdU CaBVaU PU-W OO PBm ICJ

Lloyd, Charles Mostyn, 1878–
Trade unionism, by C. M. Lloyd. London, Adam & Charles Black ltd., 1919₍1915₎
vii, 244 p. diagrs. 19cm. (Half-title: The social workers series ...)
"Select bibliography": p. 237-240.

NL 0427004 OrU DL

Lloyd, Charles Mostyn, 1878-
Trade unionism, by C. M. Lloyd. 2d ed., rev. and enl. London, A. & C. Black ltd., 1921.
viii, 291 p. diagrs. 19½cm.
"Select bibliography": p. 283-286.

1. Trade-unions—Gt. Brit. 2. Trade-unions. I. Title.
L 22-208
Library, U. S. Dept. of Labor HD6664.L71

NL 0427005 DL MiU NjP ICJ NN DAU MU

Lloyd, Charles Mostyn, 1878-
Trade unionism, by C. M. Lloyd. 3d ed., rev. and enl. London, A. & C. Black ltd., 1928.
vii,194 p. diagrs. 19½cm.
"Select bibliography": 187-189
"Third edition published in 1928."

NL 0427006 ViU CU NcD CSt-H OClU NN

Lloyd, Charles Mostyn, 1878–
... Urban district councils: their constitution, powers and duties. By C. M. Lloyd, M. A. Westminster, London, The Fabian society, 1920.
15, ₍1₎ p. 21½cm. (Fabian tract no. 189)
"Some useful books": p. 15.

1. Municipal government—Gt. Brit. I. Title.
36-3043
Library of Congress HX11.F25 no. 189
(335.106242) 352.042

NL 0427007 DLC INS CaBVaU NcD NN MH

---

*EP85 F1127t v.189c
Lloyd, Charles Mostyn, 1878-
Urban district councils, their constitution, powers and duties, by C. M. Lloyd, M.A. Revised by A. E. Lauder.
London:Fabian publication ltd.,11,Dartmouth street,S.W.1.[1946]
15,[1]p. 21cm.,in case 26.5cm. (Fabian tract no.189)
At head of cover: Local government series.
"Printed 1920. Revised, February, 1946."
Original orange printed wrappers.

NL 0427008 MH

Lloyd, Charlotte (Rees), 1782-1818.
An address to the poor. York, 1811.

NL 0427009 PHC

Lloyd, Charlotte (Rees), 1782-1818.
Address to the poor. Stockport. 1812.

NL 0427010 PSC-Hi

₍Lloyd, Mrs. Charlotte (Rees)₎ 1782-1818.
Parental instruction, in familiar dialogues: intended principally for children of the Society of Friends. Bristol₍Eng.₎ Printed by T. Lane ₍1811₎
55 p.

NL 0427011 PSC-Hi PHC PPFr

Lloyd, Charlotte (Rees) 1783-1818.
The school-boys, or Truth and industry recommended. Bristol, Printed by T.Lane,1811.

24 p. 15 cm.

NL 0427012 MH

Mhm69 1796 L7
Lloyd, Charlotte (Rees), 1783-1818.
Sermons, from the following texts, viz. 2 Cor. iv. 8,9,10; Isaiah lxv. 13, 14; Exodus xiii, 21,22; Psalm xxxvi. 7,8; Micah vi. 8. By Charlotte Rees, written before she was twelve years of age, and published for her benefit. Bristol,W.Pine and son,1796.
viii,84p. 20½cm.
Preface signed: Shurmer Bath.

NL 0427013 CtY

Lloyd, Christopher, 1906–
Captain Cook. London, Faber and Faber ₍1952₎
172 p. illus. 21 cm.

1. Cook, James, 1728–1779.
Full name: Charles Christopher Lloyd.
G246.C7L75 1952 923.942 53-15760 ‡

IEN NNC Wa
NL 0427014 DLC MiU PBL PU MB TxU FTaSU WaU NIC

Lloyd, Christopher, 1906–
Captain Cook. New York, Roy Publishers ₍1955?₎
172 p. illus. 21 cm.

1. Cook, James, 1728–1779.
Full name: Charles Christopher Lloyd.
[G246] 923.942 55-9185 ‡
Printed for U. S. Q. B. R. by Library of Congress ₍5₎

NL 0427015 NcD KEmT CaBVa NcU PP

Lloyd, Christopher, 1906–
Captain Marryat and the old navy, by Christopher Lloyd ... London, New York ₍etc.₎ Longmans, Green and co. ₍1939₎
xiii, 286 p. front. (port.) illus. (map) plates. 22½cm.
"First published 1939."
"References": p. 277-281.

1. Marryat, Frederick, 1792–1848. I. Title.
39-18606
Library of Congress PR4978.L6
₍10₎ 928.2

ICN NN CSmH ICU CaBVaU
NL 0427016 DLC MB NIC DSI WaS OU OClRC OCU PPL PU

VOLUME 337

Lloyd, Christopher, 1906–
Democracy and its rivals; an introduction to modern political theories, by Christopher Lloyd ... London, New York [etc.] Longmans, Green and co. [1938]
vii, [1], 226 p. 19½cm.
"First published 1938."
"Suggested reading" at end of each chapter.

1. Democracy. 2. Political science. I. Title.
38-18337
Library of Congress JC257.L5
[5] 321

NL 0427017 DLC NIC IEN FU OrP NcD NN OCl OCU OrPR ViU

LLOYD, Christopher, 1906–
Democracy and its rivals; an introduction to modern political theories. London, etc., Longmans, Green and Co., [1939].
19 cm.

NL 0427018 MH MtU NcRS

Lloyd, Christopher, 1906–
Democracy and its rivals; an introduction to modern political theories, by Christopher Lloyd ... London, New York [etc.] Longmans, Green and co. [1946]
vii, [1], 199 p. 19cm.
"First published 1938 ... Second edition 1946."
"Suggested reading" at end of each chapter.

1. Democracy. 2. Political science. I. Title.
JC257.L5 1946 321 47-1489

NL 0427019 DLC CaBVaU

Lloyd, Christopher, 1906– ed.
PR3316 .A4Z56
Arblay, Frances (Burney) d', 1752–1840.
The diary of Fanny Burney. Selected and ed. by Christopher Lloyd. London, R. Ingram [1948]

Lloyd, Christopher, ed, 1906–
The Englishman and the sea, an anthology, edited by Christopher Lloyd. London, G. Allen & Unwin ltd. [1946]
162 p. 20cm. (Library of English thought and life)
"First published in 1946."

1. Sea in literature. 2. Seamen. I. Title.
46-17869
Library of Congress PR1111.S4L6
[3] 820.82

NL 0427021 DLC CtY FMU

Lloyd, Christopher, 1906–
Fanny Burney, by Christopher Lloyd ... London, New York [etc.] Longmans, Green and company, 1936.
viii, 319, [1] p. front., pl., ports. 22½ cm.
"References": p. 311-317.

1. Arblay, Mme. Frances (Burney) d', 1752-1840.
Full name: Charles Christopher Lloyd.
PR3316.A4Z665 928.2 37-11964

NL 0427022 DLC MiU TU MsU NcU CaBVaU IdU PPT OrU NN

Lloyd, Christopher, 1906–
Fanny Burney, by Christopher Lloyd ... London, New York [etc.] Longmans, Green and company [1937]
viii, 319, [1] p. front., pl., ports. 22½ cm.
"References": p. 311-317.

NL 0427023 WaU

Lloyd, Christopher, 1906– ed.
DA536 .G8A425
Greville, Charles Cavendish Fulke, 1794–1865.
The Greville memoirs, selected and ed. by Christopher Lloyd. London, R. Ingram [1948]

Lloyd, Christopher, 1906–
Lord Cochrane: seaman, radical, liberator; a life of Thomas, Lord Cochrane, 10th earl of Dundonald. London, New York, Longmans, Green [1947]
viii, 222 p. illus., ports. 22 cm.
Bibliography: p. 212-216.

1. Dundonald, Thomas Cochrane, 10th earl of, 1775-1860.
Full name: Charles Christopher Lloyd.
DA88.1.D9L6 923.542 A 47-34*
Harvard Univ. Library for Library of Congress [a61e½]†

NL 0427025 MH MiU MH TxU MB ViU PBm DLC GU OCU CaBVaU MtU OrSaW OrU WaSpG WaTC

Lloyd, Christopher, 1906–
The nation and the navy; a history of naval life and policy. London, Cresset Press, 1954.
287 p. illus. 23 cm.
Includes bibliography.

1. Gt. Brit. Navy—Hist. 2. Gt. Brit.—History, Naval. I. Title.
Full name: Charles Christopher Lloyds.
DA85.L55 942 54—9570 ‡

NL 0427026 DLC OU CaBVaU CaBVa OU NN MB TxU IaU ViU PP NcU NcD MiU

Lloyd, Christopher, 1906–
The navy and the slave trade; the suppression of the African slave trade in the nineteenth century. London, New York, Longmans, Green [1949]
xiii, 314 p. plates, maps. 23 cm.
Bibliography: p. 292-307.

1. Slave-trade—Gt. Brit. 2. Gt. Brit. Navy—Hist. I. Title.
HT1162.L58 326.1 50-916

NL 0427027 DLC CU MiU DAU CaBViP CaBVaU OrU WaS NcD MB MH ICU NcU TxU TU

Lloyd, Christopher, 1906–
Pacific horizons, the exploration of the Pacific before Captain Cook, by Christopher Lloyd ... London, G. Allen and Unwin ltd. [1946]
188 p. incl. front. pl., port., maps (1 double) 22 cm.
"First published in 1946."
"List of books": p. [181]-184.

1. Oceanica—Disc. & explor. 2. Pacific ocean. I. Title.
DU20.L72 990 46-8139

NL 0427028 DLC LU TxU NIC NcU NBC MiU TU CaBViP NcD CtY PU MB OO NNC PU PBm CoU CU CaBVa Or OrP OrHi OrPS OrU Wa WaS WaSpG

Lloyd, Christopher, 1906–
A short history of the Royal navy, 1805 to 1918, by Christopher Lloyd ... London, Methuen & co. ltd. [1942]
vii, 134 p., 1 l. illus. (plans) 19cm.
"First published in 1942."

1. Gt. Brit.—History, Naval—19th cent. 2. European war, 1914-1918—Naval operations. 3. Gt. Brit.—Navy—Hist.
A 42-5309
Harvard univ. Library for Library of Congress DA88.L55
[4]† 359

NL 0427029 MH ICN DLC

Lloyd, Christopher, 1906–
A short history of the Royal navy, 1805 to 1918, by Christopher Lloyd ... 2d ed. London, Methuen & co. ltd. [1943]
vii, 134 p., 1 l. illus. (plans) 19cm.
"First published May 7th, 1942."

1. Gt. Brit.—History, Naval—19th cent. 2. European war, 1914-1918—Naval operations. 3. Gt. Brit.—Navy—Hist.
A 43-1655
New York. Public library for Library of Congress [DA88.L]
[2] 359

NL 0427030 NN NcD

Lloyd, Clara E H ed.
Levi Hancock
see under Hancock, Levi Ward, 1803-1882.

Lloyd, Claude.
Edmund Waller as a member of the Royal Society.
(*In* Modern Language Association of America. Publications. Vol. 43, pp. 162-165. Menasha, Wis. 1928.)

D6047 — Waller, Edmund, 1605-1687. — Royal Society, London.

NL 0427032 MB

Lloyd, Claude.
An obscure analogue of The compleat angler.
(*In* Modern Language Association in America. Publications. Vol. 42, pp. 400-403. Menasha, Wis. 1927.)
Refers to Robert Boyle's Occasional reflections.

D6047 — Boyle, Robert. 1626-1691. — Walton, Izaak, 1593-1683.

NL 0427033 MB

Lloyd, Clement Elphinstone, 1851- ed.
The County courts act, 1888
see under Gt. Brit. Laws, statutes, etc., 1837-1901 (Victoria)

Lloyd, Clement Elphinstone, 1851- ed.
Oliphant, George Henry Hewit.
The law of horses, including the law of innkeepers, veterinary surgeons, &c., by George Henry Hewitt Oliphant ... 6th ed. By Clement Elphinstone Lloyd ... and the veterinary portion revised by F. T. Barton ... with Canadian notes by Charles Morse ... London, Sweet & Maxwell, limited; Toronto, The Carswell co., limited, 1908.

VOLUME 337

Lloyd, Clifford.
The Australian carpenter. Melbourne, Macmillan, 1948.
xii, 206 p. illus. 25 cm.

1. Carpentry. I. Title

TH5604.L5 694 48-22828*

NL 0427036 DLC CaBViP

Lloyd, Clifford.
The Australian carpenter. [1st ed.] Melbourne, Macmillan, 1950.
xii, 212 p. illus. 25 cm.
"Reprinted ... with slight additions."

1. Carpentry. I. Title.

TH5604.L5 1950 694 50-55460

NL 0427037 DLC

Lloyd, Clifford.
Building construction for craftsmen and builders. [1st ed.] Melbourne, Macmillan, 1953.
168 p. illus. 25 cm.

1. Building. I. Title.

TH146.L55 690 55-1849 ‡

NL 0427038 DLC MB NN IU

Lloyd, Clifford, Special Resident Magistrate in Ireland
see Lloyd, Charles Dalton Clifford.

Lloyd, Clinton.
The great lesson of the war. Lecture delivered before the Soldiers' and sailors' national union league, Washington city, D. C., November 14, 1865, by Clinton Lloyd ... Washington, D. C., Chronicle print [1865]
18 p. 23½cm.

1. U. S.—Hist.—Civil war—Addresses, sermons, etc. I. Soldiers' and sailors' national union league of Washington, D. C.

18-2378

Library of Congress E649.L79

NL 0427040 DLC MB MnHi PHi OClWHi NIC MB

Lloyd, Clio L
Santa Barbara. [Santa Barbara, Calif., Daily Press Print, 1892?]
36 p.
Cover title.
Signed on p. 4: Clio L. Lloyd.
1. Santa Barbara County, Calif. - Descr. & trav.

NL 0427041 CLU

Lloyd, C[urtis] G[ates], 1859-
Berberidaceae. The botanical description, commercial history, medical properties and pharmaceutical preparations. By C.G. and J.U.Lloyd. Cincinnati, Tidball, 1878.
16p.

NL 0427042 MiU

Lloyd, Curtis Gates.
Catalogue of books relating to the flora of Europe, contained in the botanical library of C. G. Lloyd, Cincinnati
see under Lloyd Library and Museum, Cincinnati.

Lloyd, Curtis Gates, 1859-1926, comp.
Catalogue of periodical literature in the botanical department of Lloyd library, Jan., 1899
see under Lloyd Library and Museum, Cincinnati.

Lloyd, Curtis Gates, 1859-1926.
A compilation of the *Volvæ* of the United States. [By] C. G. Lloyd. Cincinnati, 1898.
1 p. l., 21, [1] p. illus. 23cm. (*In his* Mycological writings. vol. I)

1. Agaricaceae. 2. Fungi—U. S.

4-6397 Revised

Library of Congress QK603.L6 vol. 1

NL 0427045 DLC NcD CtY DNLM NN

Lloyd, Curtis Gates, 1859-1926, ed.
Drugs and medicines of North America
see under title

Lloyd, Curtis Gates, 1859-1926.
... Flora of Samoa, by C. G. Lloyd and Walter H. Aiken. [Cincinnati, 1934]
4 p. l., 113, [3] p. illus., pl. 26½cm. (Bulletin of the Lloyd library and museum of botany, pharmacy and materia medica ... [no. 33] Botany series, no. 4)
Bibliography included in preface.

1. Botany—Samoan islands. I. Aiken, Walter Harris, 1856-1935, joint author. II. Title.

35-20495 Revised

Library of Congress QK473.S3L6

581.9961

CaBViP WaS
NL 0427047 DLC NNBG NcD PU OO OU OCU MBH ViU

Lloyd, Curtis Gates, 1859-1926.
... The *Geastrae* ... By C. G. Lloyd. Cincinnati, O., J. U. & C. G. Lloyd, 1902.
43, [1] p. illus. 23cm. (Bulletin of the Lloyd library of botany, pharmacy and materia medica, no. 5. Mycological series, no. 2)

1. [Geastrae]

Agr 10-1022

U. S. Dept. of agr. Library for Library of Congress 396.8L77 no.5 [a41r27f1]

NL 0427048 DNAL DLC ICJ PU PPAN NNBG MBH CU NcD

Lloyd, Curtis Gates, 1859-
... The genera of *Gasteromycetes* ... By C. G. Lloyd. Cincinnati, O., J. U. & C. G. Lloyd, 1902.
24 p. incl. illus., 11 pl. on 6 l. 23cm. (Bulletin of the Lloyd library of botany, pharmacy and materia medica, no. 3. Mycological series, no. 1)

1. Gasteromycetes.

Agr 10-1023

Library, U. S. Dept. of Agriculture 396.8L77 no. 3

NL 0427049 DNAL DNLM PPAN PU NN MBH ICJ DLC

Lloyd, Curtis Gates, 1859-1926.
The genus Radulum. Cincinnati, 1917.
12 p. illus. 23 cm.

1. Radulum. 2. Hydnaceae. 3. Basidiomycetes.

NL 0427050 NNBG OO DLC MBH

B589.233
L77 LLOYD, Curtis Gates, 1859-1926.
The Geoglossaceae (Viz., The genus Geoglossum and related genera.)... Cincinnati, Ohio, 1916.
24 p. illus. (incl. port.) 23cm.
Manuscript notes in margins.
"Mycological notes and other publications issued by C.G. Lloyd": p. 23.
1.Geoglossaceae.

NL 0427051 MnU DLC MBH

Lloyd, Curtis Gates, 1859-1926, joint author.

Lloyd, John Uri, 1849-1936.
... *Hydrastis canadensis.* Facsimile, reprint and illustrations of the article in Drugs and medicines of North America. 1884. By J. U. & C. G. Lloyd. Cincinnati, J. U. & C. G. Lloyd, 1908.

QK603
.L6 **Lloyd, Curtis Gates, 1859-1926.**
The large Pyrenomycetes. Second paper, by C.G. Lloyd. Cincinnati, O., 1919.
p. 17-32. illus. 23 cm. (In his Mycological writings. vol. V) S.

NL 0427053 DLC

W
6
P3 **LLOYD, Curtis Gates, 1859-1926**
The large Pyrenomycetes, 2d paper. Cincinnati, 1919.
17-32 p. illus.
Also issued in v. 5 of the author's Mycological writings.

NL 0427054 DNLM MBH

Lloyd, Curtis Gates, 1859-1926.
Letters, no. 1-69
see under Lloyd Library and Museum, Cincinnati.

QK
180
.L79 **Lloyd, Curtis Gates, 1859-1926.**
List of plants observed growing wild in the vicinity of Cincinnati, O. [Cincinnati, 1891]
7 p. 22½ cm.
Caption title.
"Prof.L.H.Bailey has ... gone over the carices ... Professor F.L.Scribner has revised the grasses ... Professor M.S.Bebb has named the willows."

1.Botany--Ohio --Cincinnati.

NL 0427056 MiU OO

VOLUME 337

Lloyd, Curtis Gates, 1859-1926.
The *Lycoperdaceae* of Australia, New Zealand and neighboring islands ... By C. G. Lloyd. Cincinnati, O., J. U. & C. G. Lloyd, 1905.
42, [2] p. illus., pl. 25-39. 23 cm. (Bulletin of the Lloyd library of botany, pharmacy and materia medica, no. 8. Mycological series, no. 3)

1. Lycoperdaceae. 2. Botany—Australasia.
AS36.L592 no. 8 Agr 5-662
U. S. Dept. of Agr. Libr. 396.8L77 no. 8
for Library of Congress [a58r28g½]†

NL 0427057 DNAL DLC ICJ DNLM OCU MiU OU CtY NNBG NcD MBH CU

Lloyd, Curtis Gates, 1859-1926.
The *Lycoperdaceae* of Australia, New Zealand and neighboring islands. Illustrated with 15 plates and 49 figures. By C. G. Lloyd. Cincinnati, O., Issued at the Lloyd library, 1905.
42, [2] p. illus., pl. 25-39. 23cm. (*In his* Mycological writings, vol. I)

1. Lycoperdaceae. 2. Botany—Australasia. [2. Australasia—Botany]
Agr 5-661 Revised
Library, U. S. Dept. of Agriculture 462L77L
Library of Congress QK603.L6 vol. 1

NL 0427058 DNAL

Lloyd, Curtis Gates, 1859-1926.
Mycological notes
see under Lloyd Library and Museum, Cincinnati.

Lloyd, Curtis Gates, 1859-1926.
... Mycological writings of C. G. Lloyd. Cincinnati, O. [1898]-1929.
7 v. illus., plates, ports. 23-29½cm.
The parts composing these volumes were originally issued independently, and were later grouped in volumes, with general title-page (reading "Index of the mycological writings of C. G. Lloyd") table of contents and index for each volume.

CONTENTS.

vol. I, 1898-1905. Mycological notes. no. 1-18, Nov. 1898-July, 1904.—A compilation of the *Volvae* of the United States. 1898.—The genera of *Gastromycetes*. Illustrated with 49 figures. Jan. 1902.—The *Geastrae*. Illustrated with 80 figures. June, 1902.—The *Lycoperdaceae* of Australia, New Zealand and neighboring islands. Illustrated with 15 plates and 49 figures. Apr. 1905.—Notes on the amanitas of the southern Appalachians. pt. 1. Sub-genus *Amanitopsis*. Illustrated with three plates. By H. C. Beardslee, Sept. 1902.—Puff ball letter no. 1-3.—Plates 1-39.

vol. II. 1905-08. Mycological notes. no. 19-31, May, 1905-Aug. 1908.—The *Tylostomeae*. Illustrated with twelve plates and six figures. Feb. 1906.—The *Nidulariaceae* or "Bird's nest *Fungi*". Illustrated with ten plates and twenty figures. Dec. 1906.—The phalloids of Australasia. July, 1907.—Puff ball letter (*later*, Letter) no. 4-24.—Plates 40-123.
vol. III, 1909-12. Mycological notes. no. 32-37, Feb. 1909-Apr. 1911.—Mycological notes. Old species series, no. 1. June, 1908.—Mycological notes. Polyporoid issue, no. 1-3. Feb. 1908-Aug. 1910.—Synopsis of the known phalloids. With an illustration of each species. Sept. 1909.—Synopsis of the genus *Hexagona*. June, 1910.—Synopsis of the sections *Microporus*, *Tabacinus* and *Funales* of the genus *Polystictus*. Aug. 1910.—Synopsis of the section *Ovinus* of *Polyporus*. Oct. 1911.—Synopsis of the stipitate polyporoids. Mar. 1912.—Letter no. 25-38.

vol. IV, 1913-16. Mycological notes. no. 38-41, Nov. 1912-Mar. 1916.—Synopsis of the genus *Cladoderris*. July, 1913.—Synopsis of the stipitate stereums. Dec. 1913.—Synopsis of the genus *Fomes*. Jan. 1915.—Synopsis of the Cordyceps of Australasia. Mar. 1915.—Synopsis of the section *Apus* of the genus *Polyporus*. June, 1915.—Letter no. 39-61 (including no. 39bis: *Fungi* of Madagascar)
vol. V, 1916-19. Mycological notes. no. 42-60, June, 1916-Aug. 1919.—The genus *Radulum*. May, 1917.—The *Geoglossaceae* (*viz.*, the genus *Geoglossum* and related genera) May 1916.—Synopsis of some genera of the large Pyrenomycetes: *Camillea*, *Thamnomyces*, *Engleromyces*. Jan. 1917.—The large Pyrenomycetes. Second paper. July, 1919.—Xylaria notes. no. 1, Sept. 1918.—Xylaria notes. no. 2, Dec. 1918.—Myths of mycology. Dec. 1917.—Letter no. 62-69.

vol. VI, 1920-21. Mycological notes. no. 61-65, Oct. 1919-Nov. 1920. (Mimeographed) Plates 124-185.
vol. VII, 1922-25. Mycological notes. no. 66-75, Feb. 1922-July, 1925. Plates [186]-344.

—— General index to the Mycological writings of C. G. Lloyd. 1898-1925. Cincinnati, O., 1933.
64 p. 29cm. (*On cover:* Bulletin of the Lloyd library of botany, pharmacy and materia medica. no. 32, 1933. Mycological series no. 7)
By John A. Stevenson.

1. Fungi. I. Stevenson, John Albert, 1890- comp. II. Title.
15-24801 Revised
Library of Congress QK603.L6
[2] 589.2081

NL 0427063 DLC TU NcD MiU OU PU OCU OU PPAN ICJ NN MsSM CU NNBG NcRS AAP MiU NcS OrU OrCS CaBVaU

QK604
.L55
Lloyd, Curtis Gates, 1859-1926.
The myths of mycology, as noted by C. G. Lloyd. Part 1. Cincinnati, 1917.
16 p. 23 cm.

Caption title.

1. Mycology. i.t.

NL 0427064 NNBG DLC OrCS IdU MBH PPAN OO

Lloyd, Curtis Gates, 1859-1926.

QK600
.L7
no. 8
Stevenson, John Albert, 1890-
... The new fungus names proposed by C. G. Lloyd, by John A. Stevenson and Edith K. Cash. [Cincinnati, The Lloyd library and museum, 1936]

Lloyd, Curtis Gates, 1859-
The *Nidulariaceae*, or "Bird's-nest fungi" ... by C. G. Lloyd. Cincinnati, O., 1906.
32 p. illus., 102-111 pl. 23cm.
Plates printed on both sides, 10 pl. on 10 l.
Advertising matter included in paging.

1. Nidulariaceae.
7-1724
Library, U. S. Dept. of Agriculture 462L77N

NL 0427066 DNAL MBH IdU PPAN NN DLC

Lloyd, Curtis Gates, 1859-1926.
Opuscula. [1895-1925]
15 v. in 1. illus., ports. 26 cm.
Binder's title.
1. Fungi.

NL 0427067 CU

Lloyd, Curtis Gates, 1859-
The phalloids of Australasia; an account of what is known, or rather what little is known, of the subject, and illustrations (more or less accurate) of the species that have been figured, by C. G. Lloyd. Cincinnati, O., 1907.
24 p. illus. 23cm.

1. Phalloideae. 2. Australasia. Botany.
Agr 7-2203
Library, U. S. Dept. of Agriculture 462L77Ph

NL 0427068 DNAL MBH NNBG PPAN NN OU OO

QK623
.P9
L55
Lloyd, Curtis Gates, 1859-1926.
Synopsis of some genera of the large Pyrenomycetes: Camillea, Thamnomyces, Engleromyces. Cincinnati, 1917.
15 p. illus. 23 cm.

Cover title.

1. Pyrenomycetes. i. t.

NL 0427069 NNBG DLC MBH OO

Lloyd, Curtis Gates, 1859-
Synopsis of the genus *Cladoderris*, by C. G. Lloyd. Cincinnati, O., 1913.
12 p. illus 23cm.

1. Cladoderris.
14-6072
Library of Congress QK629.H9L7

NL 0427070 DLC MBH NNBG PPAN IU OO

QK629
.P7
L595
Lloyd, Curtis Gates, 1859-1926.
Synopsis of the genus Fomes. Cincinnati, 1915.
211-288 p. illus., port. 23 cm.

Cover title.
Copy 1 inscribed: G. Clyde Fisher.

1. Fomes. 2. Polyporaceae. 3. Bourdot, Hubert, 1861-1937, Portraits. i. t. a. Fisher, George Clyde, 1878-1949.

NL 0427071 NNBG DLC

Lloyd, Curtis Gates, 1859-
Synopsis of the genus *Hexagona*, by C. G. Lloyd. Cincinnati, O., 1910.
1 p. l., 46 p. illus. (incl. port.) 23cm. (*In his* Mycological writings. vol. III)

1. Hexagona.
11-8017 Revised
Library of Congress QK603.L6 vol. 3
—— —— Copy 2. QK629.H5L6

NL 0427072 DLC DNAL ICJ

Lloyd, Curtis Gates, 1859-1926.
... Synopsis of the genus *Hexagona*, by C. G. Lloyd. Cincinnati, J. U. & C. G. Lloyd, 1910.
1 p. l., 46 p. illus. (incl. port.) 23 cm. (Bulletin of the Lloyd library of botany, pharmacy and materia medica, no. 14. Mycological series, no. 5)

1. Hexagona.
AS36.L592 no. 14 Agr 12-595
U. S. Dept. of Agr. Libr. 396.8L77 no. 14
for Library of Congress [a58c½]†

NL 0427073 DNAL DLC MBH OO MiU OU ICJ OCU NcU CU

Lloyd, Curtis Gates, 1859-
Synopsis of the known phalloids, by C. G. Lloyd. With an illustration of each species. Cincinnati, O., 1909.
96 p. illus. (incl. port.) 23cm.

1. Phalloideae.
10-2959
Library of Congress QK629.P6L6

NL 0427074 DLC PPAN PU MBH OO

Lloyd, Curtis Gates, 1859-1926.
... Synopsis of the known phalloids, with an illustration of each species, by C. G. Lloyd. Cincinnati, O., J. U. & C. G. Lloyd, 1909.
96 p. illus. (incl. port.) 23 cm. (Bulletin of the Lloyd library of botany, pharmacy and materia medica, no. 13. Mycological series, no. 4)

1. Phalloideae.
AS36.L592 no. 13 Agr 10-1066
U. S. Dept. of Agr. Libr. 396.8L77 no. 13
for Library of Congress [a58c½]†

NL 0427075 DNAL DLC MiU ICJ OU OCU NNBG NcD CU

VOLUME 337

Lloyd, Curtis Gates, 1859–
Synopsis of the section *Apus* of the genus *Polyporus*. By C. G. Lloyd. Cincinnati, Ohio, 1915.
[2] p., p. 291–392. illus. (incl. port.) 23½cm.

NL 0427076 ICJ DLC MBH MiU IaU OO NNBG PPAN

Lloyd, Curtis Gates, 1859–
Synopsis of the section *Ovinus* of *Polyporus*, by C. G. Lloyd. Cincinnati, O., 1911.
1 p. l., p. 73–94. illus. (incl. port.) 23cm.

1. Polyporus.

12–2924

Library of Congress QK629.P7L6

NL 0427077 DLC NNBG PPAN OO MBH

Lloyd, Curtis Gates, 1859–
Synopsis of the sections *Microporus, Tabacinus* and *Funales* of the genus *Polystictus*. By C. G. Lloyd. Cincinnati, Ohio, 1910.
1 p. l., p. 49–70. illus. 23½cm.

1. Polystictus.

10–26277

Library of Congress QK629.P8L7

NL 0427078 DLC MBH PPAN

Lloyd, Curtis Gates, 1859–
Synopsis of the stipitate polyporoids, by C. G. Lloyd. Cincinnati, O., 1912.
1 p. l., 95–208 p. illus. 23cm.

1. Polyporiaceae.

12–11233

Library of Congress QK629.P7L7

NL 0427079 DLC OO

Lloyd, Curtis Gates, 1859–1926.
... Synopsis of the stipitate polyporoids, by C. G. Lloyd. Cincinnati, O., J. U. & C. G. Lloyd, 1912.
1 p. l., 95–208 p. illus. (incl. port.) 23 cm. (Bulletin of the Lloyd library of botany, pharmacy and materia medica. no. 20. Mycological series, no. 6)

1. Polyporaceae.

AS36.L592 no. 20 12—13686

NL 0427080 DLC MBH NcU NNBG PPAN PU OU MiU OCU CU

Lloyd, Curtis Gates, 1859–
Synopsis of the stipitate stereums, by C. G. Lloyd. Cincinnati, O., 1913.
1 p. l., p. 15–44 incl. illus., port. 23cm.

1. [Stereum]

Agr 14–333

Library, U. S. Dept. of Agriculture 462L77 vol. 3

NL 0427081 DNAL MBH NNBG PPAN MiU OO

Lloyd, Curtis Gates, 1859–1926.
The *Tylostomeae*, illustrated with twelve plates and six figures, by C. G. Lloyd. Cincinnati, O., 1906.
28 p. illus., 74–85 pl. 24cm. (*In his* Mycological writings. vol. II)
Plates printed on both sides.

1. Tylostomeae.

7–40982 Revised

Library of Congress QK603.L6 vol. 2

NL 0427082 DLC OO MBH

Lloyd, Curtis Gates, 1859–1926.
The use of kava by the Samoan islanders. n.p. [1900]
6 p.

NL 0427083 OU

589.235 Lloyd, Curtis Gates, 1859-1926.
L77x Xylaria notes ... no.1-2; Sept.-Dec.1918. Cincinnati, O. [1918]
32p. incl.illus.

Caption title.
No more published.

1. Xylaria. I. Title.

NL 0427084 IU DLC MBH IdU

Lloyd, Cyril.

Gt. Brit. *United kingdom sugar industry inquiry committee.*
Report of the United kingdom sugar industry inquiry committee ... London, H. M. Stationery off., 1935.

Lloyd, Cyril, 1906–
British services education. London, New York, Published for the British Council by Longmans, Green [1950]
95 p. illus. 22 cm.

1. Soldiers—Education, Non-military—Gt. Brit. I. Title.

U717.G7L5 355.07 50–12439

NL 0427086 DLC

Lloyd, D. Tecwyn
see Lloyd, David Tecwyn.

Lloyd, D Willson.
Cardiff, a commercial and industrial centre, 1919
see under Cardiff, Wales. City Council. Development Committee.

Lloyd, D. Willson.
...The coal export trade of the United Kingdom, 1910–1921 (with special reference to South Wales). By D. Willson Lloyd... [Cardiff, 1922.] 107 f. incl. diagrs., tables. f°.
"References and bibliography," f. 107.

1. Coal.—Trade and statistics, Gt. Br.
N. Y. P. L. December 1, 1924

NL 0427089 NN

Lloyd, D Willson.
English village; the story of Trumpington. [Cambridge, Eng. 195–?] 32 p. illus. 22cm.

1. Trumpington, Eng. 2. Architecture—Gt. Br.—Eng.—Trumpington.

NL 0427090 NN RPB

Lloyd, Daniel Boone, 1901– , joint author.
Tool, Arthur Quincy, 1877–
... Dimensional changes caused in glass by heating cycles, by A. Q. Tool, D. B. Lloyd, and G. E. Merritt ...
(R P 219, *in* U. S. Bureau of standards. Bureau of standards journal of research. Washington, U. S. Govt. print. off., 1930. 23½cm. September. 1930. v. 5, no. 3, p. 627–646. diagrs.)

Lloyd, Daniel Boone, 1901–
... Some properties of rational quintic equations ... by Daniel Boone Lloyd ... Washington, D. C., The Catholic university of America press, 1940.
3 p. l., 35 p. incl. tables. 23cm.
Thesis (PH. D.)—Catholic university of America, 1940.
Bibliography: p. 35.

1. Equations, Quintic. I. Title.

A 41–80

Catholic univ. of America. Library for Library of Congress QA215.L5
——— Copy 2. [2] 512.82

NL 0427092 DCU NcD CU NIC DLC OU

Lloyd, David.
Economy of agriculture: being a series of compendious essays on different branches of farming. By David Lloyd. Germantown, Pa., P. R. Freas & co., printers, 1832.
120 p. 17cm.

1. Agriculture—Addresses, essays, lectures.

Agr 23–987

Library, U. S. Dept. of Agriculture 30.4L77

NL 0427093 DNAL GU MiU-C FHi PPL PU PLF NjR

Lloyd, David.
Modern miscellany; consisting of poetry, history, philosophy, moral essays, and promiscuous pieces ... Philadelphia, Leary's book store, 1848.
vii, 216 p. 19 cm.
Imperfect: covers wanting.

NL 0427094 RPB

TF Lloyd, David, writer on architecture.
300 Railway station architecture. David
L55 Lloyd and Donald Insall. [n.p.]David and Charles[n.d.]
60p. illus. 21cm.

Reprinted from Industrial Archaeology.

1. Railroads - Stations. I. Insall, Donald.

NL 0427095 MU

AW
1 [Lloyd,David] 1597-1663.
R475: The legend of Captaine Iones ... London, Printed
1246 for I.M[arriott] 1631.
In verse.
Pt.1 only; complete work,in 2 pts.,first appeared in 1648. Cf.Hazlitt. Bibl.of early Engl.lit.,v.1, p.338.
"A copious commendation of a redde nose": 1 p.at end,printed in double columns.
Microfilm of original in the British Museum. Ann Arbor,Mich., University Microfilms, 1971. (Early English books,1475-1640,reel 1245)
Micro/ STC no.16614. Microfilm.

NL 0427096 MiU CaBVaU

VOLUME 337

STC 16615 ⌜Lloyd, David⌝ 1597-1663.
The legend of Captaine Iones: relating his adventure to sea ... his furious battell ... against the army of eleven kings ... his relieving of Kemper Castle. His strange and admirable sea-fight ... his taking prisoner ... lastly, his setting at liberty ... London, Printed for I. M., 1636.

A-C^4. (A1, probably blank, lacking; C3-4 torn and repaired affecting text.) 4to. front. lacking.
Grolier club, Catalogue (1905) v. 2, no. 524.

NL 0427097 DFo CtY

Ayer *110 L795 1648 ⌜LLOYD, DAVID⌝ 1597-1663.
The legend of Captaine Iones... London, Printed by M.F.for R.Marriot,1648.
2v.in 1. front. 19cm.

STC II L 2630.

NL 0427098 ICN NN CSmH CtY WU

⌜Lloyd, David⌝ 1597-1663.
The legend of Captain Jones. Relating his adventure to sea: his first landing, and strange combat with a mighty beare. His furious battell with his six and thirty men, against the army of eleven kings, with their overthtow ⌜sic⌝ and deaths. His relieving of Kemper castle. His strange and admirable sea-fight with six huge gallies of Spain, and nine thousand soldiers. His taking prisoner, and hard usage. Lastly, his setting at liberty by the kings command, and returne for England. London: Printed for R. Marriot, 1656. 13 p.l., 71(1) p. 14½cm. (8°.)

See: Sabin 41684. Hazlitt: Handbook, 338. See: Grolier Club, New York. Catalogve of ... English writers from Wither to Prior, v. 2, p. 138.
Part 2 (p. ⌜21⌝-71⟨1⟩) has special t.-p.: The legend of Captaine Jones: continved from his first part to his end: wherein is delivered his incredible adventures and atchievements by sea and land. Particularly, his miraculous deliverance from a wrack at sea by the support of a dolphin. His severall desperate duels. His combate with Bahader Cham a gyant of the race of Og. His loves. His deep imployments and happy successe in businesse of state. All which, and more, is but the tithe of his owne relation which he continued untill he grew speechlesse, and died.
In verse.

Imperfect: first leaf (engraved t.-p.?) wanting, some edges cropped.

NL 0427101 NN DFo CSmH CLU-C

Case Y 185 .L 773 ⌜LLOYD, DAVID⌝ 1597-1663.
The legend of Captain Jones, relating his adventure to sea... London,Printed for H.Moseley, 1659.
⌜23⌝,71,⌜1⌝p. front.

A 2d t.-p. is inserted at p.⌜21⌝: The legend of Captaine Jones continued from his first part to his end... London, Printed for R.Marriot, 1656.
Imperfect: front. wanting.
In verse.

NL 0427102 ICN NjP RPJCB CtY MH

Case 5A 1321 ⌜LLOYD, DAVID⌝ 1597-1663.
The legend of Captain Jones: relating his adventure to sea ... His furious battel, with his six and thirty men ... His relieving of Kemper Castle. His strange and admirable sea-fight with six huge gallies of Spain ... His being taken prisoner, and hard usage. Lastly, his being set at liberty by the kings command, and return for England. London, Printed for E. Okes, and F. Haley, 1671.
⌜12⌝ℓ.,70+p. 15cm.

In 2 pts., the 2d with special t.-p.: The legend of Captain Jones: continued from his first part to his end: wherein is delivered his incredible adventures and atchievements by sea and land ... London, Printed by E. O. for Francis Haley, 1670.
Sometimes attributed to Martin Lluelyn.
Imperfect: 4th prelim. leaf, p.11-12.

and all after p.70 wanting.
STC II L 2633.

NL 0427105 ICN DFo MB N ICU PSt MiU ViU CSmH RPJCB

⌜Lloyd, David⌝ 1597-1663.
The wonderful, surprizing and uncommon voyages and adventures of Captain Jones, to Patagonia ... With his elegy and epitaph. The 2d ed. London, J. Lever, 1766.
74 p. front. 19½cm.

"The legend of Captain Jones," 1631, by David Lloyd, 1631, with "the supplemental rodomontade of successive editors." *cf.* Dict. nat. biog.

I. Title.

12-37058

Library of Congress PR3541.L55A77 1766

NL 0427106 DLC RPJCB

Lloyd, David, 1635-1692, supposed author.
Cabala, or An impartial account of the non-conformists private designs, actings and wayes.

See under

⌜Birkenhead, Sir John⌝ 1616-1679.

Mhc8 1664 L77 [Lloyd, David] 1635-1692.
Cabala: or, The mystery of conventicles unvail'd: in an historical account of the principles and practices of the nonconformists, against church and state: from the first reformation under King Edward the VI. anno 1558. to this present year, 1664. With an appendix of an CXX. plots against the present government, that have been defeated. By Oliver Foulis[pseud. London,T.Holmwood,1664.
1p.ℓ.,95p. front. 17½cm.

NL 0427108 CtY NN DFo CSmH CLU-C

Lloyd, David, 1635-1692.
Dying and dead men's living words. Published by Da. Lloyd ... London, Printed for John Amery ... 1668.
3 p.l.,212 p. 14½cm.
Signatures: ⌜A⌝^{4}, B-I^{12}, K^{10} (A1 blank; H3 incorrectly signed H5)
Pages 61, 63, 90-91, 120, 142-143 incorrectly numberod 19, 93, 91, 90, 102, 140-141, respectively.
Caption title: Fair warnings to a careless world.
Bound in old calf.

NL 0427109 CLU-C

Lloyd, David, 1635-1692.
Dying and dead mens living words. Or, Fair warnings to a careless world ... London, Printed for John Amery, 1673.
3 p.ℓ., 181 (i.e. 171) p. 15cm.

Caption and running title: Fair warnings to a careless world.
A few errors in paging, including 150-171 numbered 160-181.
Wing L-2638.

NL 0427110 CU CLU-C NcD

L2639 Lloyd, David, 1635-1692.
Dying and dead mens living words: or, Fair warnings to a careless world ... London, Printed for John Amery, 1682.

⌜6⌝ 171 ⌜3⌝ p. A-G^{12}, H^6. (H3 misbound after H4) 12mo.
"Books printed for, and sold by John Amery," sig. H5v-H6v.
Religious tract society, London-Clark library duplicate copy.

NL 0427111 DFo CLU-C NNUT-Mc

By47b 660ℓ [Lloyd, David] 1635-1692.
Εἰκων βασιλικὴ or, The true pourtraiture of His Sacred Majestie Charls the II. In three books. Beginning from his birth 1630. unto this present year, 1660 ... By R.F. esq; an eye-witness ... London,Printed for H.Brome,and H.Marsh,at the Gun in Ivy-lane, and the Princes Arms in Chancery near Fleetstreet,1660.
3pts.in 1v. front.(group port.) 17cm.
Collation: 4p.ℓ.,93,79p.,1ℓ.,56[i.e.70]p.; signatures: A^{4}A-F^8(F$_8$ blank)A-E^{8}A-C^{8}d^{8}D^4.

Part 2, "printed by John Brudenell"; part 3, "printed by Peter Lillicrap".
Original calf binding, with CR (i.e., Charles II) under coronet stamped in gilt on sides.

NL 0427113 CtY NIC MH NNUT CLU-C MH ICU MnU DFo CSmH MH ICN

⌜Lloyd, David⌝ 1635-1692.
Fair warnings to a careless world: in the pious letter written by the Right Honourable James Earl of Marleburgh, a little before his death; to the Right Honourable Sir Hvgh Pollard ... with the last words of CXL. and upwards, of the most learned and honourable persons of England, and other parts of the world. London, Printed for Samuel Speed at the Rainbow in Fleet-street, 1665.
⌜4⌝, 42 p. 19cm.

By David Lloyd.--cf. Watt, Bibl. Britannica.

NL 0427115 NNC

BV 4500 .L68 Office Lloyd, David, 1635-1692.
Fair warnings to a careless world. York, Printed by Stephen Buckley, 1666.
1 v. 24°.

NL 0427116 DLC

Lloyd, David, 1635-1692.
The history of the statesmen and favorites of England, during the reigns of Henry VIII, Edward VI, Mary, Elizabeth, James and Charles I. By ... London, 1665.

NL 0427117 PPL

⌜Lloyd, David⌝ 1635-1692.
The kingdome saved. By a seasonable discourse of the Right Honorable the Countess of Bridgwaters ghost: to the present court. ⌜One line English quotation⌝ London, Printed in the year, 1663.
1 p. l., 70 p. 16½cm.

NL 0427118 ViU CtY

DA 445 L6 D7 1661 Cage ⌜Lloyd, David⌝ 1635-1692.
Koninclijcke beeltenis, ofte waerachtige historie van Karel de II. koninck van Groot Britannien ... En door-wrocht met een volkomen historie van de hertogen van Iorck en Glocester. Uyt het engels van een oogh-getuyge vertaelt... door L.v. Bos. Hier is noch by-gevoeght, Herstelde zeeg-triomf van Karel de tweede. Te Dordrecht, Voor Abraham Andriesz, 1660-1661.
Colophon to pt.1:... Ter druckerije van Gillis Neering.

2 pts. in 1 v. Pt.1: ⌜16⌝, 555 ⌜1⌝ p. *^{8}, A-Z^{12}, 2A^2; pt.2: ⌜2⌝ 70 p. a-c^{12}. 12mo. plates, some folded.

NL 0427120 DFo CLU-C ICU

VOLUME 337

Lloyd, David, 1635-1692.
Memoires of the lives, actions, sufferings & deaths of those noble, reverend, and excellent personages, that suffered by death, sequestration, decimation, or otherwise, for the Protestant religion, and the great principle thereof, allegiance to their soveraigne, in our late intestine wars, from the year 1637, to the year 1660, and from thence continued to 1666. With the life and martyrdom of King Charles I. London, Printed for Samuel Speed, and sold by him, by John Wright, John Symmes, and James Collins 1668.
7 p. ℓ., 708 (i.e. 710) p. front. (ports.) 31cm.

Title in red and black within double line border; text within line borders, double at top and outside to enclose headlines, paging and side notes.
Head pieces; initials.
Numerous errors in paging; including 501-502 repeated in numbering.
Wing L-2642.

1. Gt. Brit. - Hist. - 1625-1649 (Charles I) 2. Gt. Brit. - Hist. 1642-1660 (Puritan revolution) 3. Gt. Brit. - Biog.

TxU DFo MiU NNUT-Mc OU
DFo NjPS NN IEN CtY ICN TU NjPT NcGU MnU NjP MdBP
NL 0427122 CU ICU NN CtY DLC MH NcD CLU-C CSmH

Case J 5454 .517
LLOYD, DAVID, 1635-1692.
Modern policy compleated, or, The publick actions and councels both civill and military of His Excellency the Lord Generall Monck under the generall revolutions since 1639, to 1660. London, Printed by J.B. for H.Marsh, 1660.
2 pt. in 1v. 14cm.

Head-line of both parts reads "the second part".
STC II L 2644.

NL 0427123 ICN ICU NNUT-Mc CSmH MiU CtY

---

*EC C3804E 133
[Lloyd, David, 1635-1692]
The restavration of his Sacred Majesty Charles the II. Hopefully begun upon the death of Oliver Cromwell, and happily perfected upon that incomparable expedition of the renouned Lord General Monck. With the several mysteries of state tending thereunto discovered. The third book.
London, Printed by Peter Lillicrap, for Henry Broom, and Henry Marsh, and are to be sold at their shops, at the Gun in Ivie-lane, and at the Princes Arms in Chancery-lane. 1660.

1p.ℓ., 56(i.e.70)p. 17cm. (Pt.3 of his Εἰκων[!] βασιλικὴ ... 1660)
Madan 133.
Page 7 misnumbered 6; 33-46 repeated in the numbering.

NL 0427125 MH

Case E 445 .509
[LLOYD, DAVID] 1635-1692.
State-worthies. Or, The states-men and favourites of England since the reformation, their prudence and policies, successes and miscarriages, advancements and falls; during the reigns of King Henry viii, King Edward vi, Queen Mary, Queen Elizabeth, King James, King Charles I. The 2d edition with additions. London, Printed by T. Milbourn for S.Speed, 1670.
[17], 225, 369-680, 721-1051, [1]p. front. (ports.

Bookplate of Charles Bill.

Title in red and black.
"Epistle to the reader" signed: David Lloyd.
"Books printed for Samuel Speed" inserted between p.225 and 369, and at end.
First published in 1665 with title: The statesmen and favourites of England since the reformation.

Vi FU
MH CtY OCl MnU NjP OrU CSt-H CaOLU ICN MnU ViU ICU
NL 0427127 ICN PPL MdBP DFo IU MB MH CLU-C OrU OU

BC L793s Ed.2
Lloyd, David, 1635-1692
State-worthies, or, The states-men and favourites of England since the reformation... 2d ed. with additions. London, Printed for P. Parker, 1679.
1051p. front. (ports.) S.
"To the reader" signed David Lloyd.
First ed. published 1665 with title: The statesmen and favourites of England since the reformation.

NL 0427128 IaU NN CSmH MH-L OU

Lloyd, David, 1635-1692.
State-worthies: or, The statesmen and favourites of England from the reformation to the revolution ... By David Lloyd. To this edition is added the characters of the kings and queens of England, during the above period; with a translation of the Latin passages and other additions ... By Charles Whitworth ... London, Printed for J. Robson, 1766.
2 v. $18\frac{1}{2}$cm.
First edition published 1665 with title: The statesmen and favourites of England since the reformation.
1. Statesmen, British. 2. Favorites, Royal. 3. Gt. Brit.—Kings and rulers. I. Whitworth, Sir Charles, 1714?-1778, ed.

Library of Congress DA317.2.L8 4—35469

MdBP MiU NjP CaBVaU
NL 0427129 DLC ViU MH-L MdBP PPT KyLx CtY CLU-C

DA 317 .2 .L8
Lloyd, David, 1635-1692.
State-worthies: or, The statesmen and favourites of England from the reformation to the revolution... By David Lloyd. To this edition is added the characters of the kings and queens of England, during the above period; with a translation of the Latin passages and other additions... By Charles Whitworth... London, Printed for J. Robson, 1768.

2 v.

First edition published 1665 with title: The statesmen and favourites of England since the reformation.

NL 0427131 MoU

[Lloyd, David] 1635-1692.
The states-men and favourites of England since the reformation ... During the reigns of King Henry VIII. King Edward VI. Queen Mary. Queen Elizabeth. King James. King Charles I. London, Printed by J. C. for S. Speed, 1665.
7 p. l., 828 p. $17\frac{1}{2}$cm.
"Epistle to the reader" signed David Lloyd.

1. Statesmen, British. 2. Favorites, Royal. I. Title.

Library of Congress DA317.2.L78 4—34681

NL 0427132 DLC MnU CtY MdBP NcD IU CU MH CSmH MdBP

[Lloyd, David] 1635-1692.
Wonders no miracles; or, Mr. Valentine Greatrates gift of healing examined, upon occasion of a sad effect of his stroaking, March the 7. 1665. at one Mr. Cressets house in Charter-house-yard. In a letter to a reverend divine, living near that place. London, Printed for S. Speed, 1666.
1 p. l., 46 p. $18\frac{1}{2}$cm.

1. Greatrakes, Valentine, 1629-1683. I. Title.

18-6625

Library of Congress R133.L7

NL 0427133 DLC NNUT-Mc DNLM MH CSmH

Lloyd, David, 1656-1731.
Works by this author printed in America before 1801 are available in this library in the Readex Microprint edition of Early American Imprints published by the American Antiquarian Society.
This collection is arranged according to the numbers in Charles Evans' American Bibliography.

NL 0427134 DLC

Lloyd, David, 1656-1731.
A Defence of the Legislative Constitution of the Province of Pennsylvania. As it now stands confirmed and established, by Law and Charter. With some observations, on the proceedings published by sixteen members of Assembly, in a paper, entitled, The Votes and proceedings of the House of Representatives: recommended to the consideration of all the freemen of the Province. [Philadelphia, Printed by Andrew Bradford, 1728.)
11 p. fol.
Evans 3050

NL 0427135 PHi PPAmP

Lloyd, David, 1656-1731.
Memoires of the lives, actions ...
see under Lloyd, David, 1635-1692.

Lloyd, David, 1656-1731.
A Vindication of the legislative power, submitted to the Representatives of all the free-men of the Province of Pennsylvania, now sitting in Assembly. (Philadelphia, Printed by Andrew Bradford, 1725)
4 p. fol.
Evans 2649

NL 0427137 PHi

Tm L776 792b
Lloyd, David, 1752-1838.
Characteristics of men, manners, and sentiments: or, The voyage of life, 2d. ed. rev., and other poems. London, Cadell and Davies, 1812.
340p. 17cm.
First pub. under title: Voyage of life.
Half title: Poems characteristic of human life.
Binder's title: Voyage of life.

NL 0427138 CtY CLSU

LLOYD, David, 1752-1838.
The voyage of life; a poem in nine books. London, Printed for C.Dilly, 1792.
nar.12°. front. 221 p. 18433.48

NL 0427139 MH OCU CtY

Lloyd, David, 1867–
Which is right? Souvenir book, two letters written on Arizona's prohibition amendment, by David Lloyd. Clifton, Ariz., Copper era printing & publishing co. [°1915]
150 p. incl. front. (port.) $18\frac{1}{2}$cm. $0.40

1. Prohibition—Arizona.

Library of Congress HV5090.A6L7 15-3898

NL 0427140 DLC ICJ

Lloyd, David Demarest, 1851-1889.
Poor Ogla Moga.
(In Stories by American authors. Vol. 3, pp. 99-134. New York, 1896.)

NL 0427141 MB MdBP NBuG OU NN

Lloyd, David Demarest, 1851-1889
Poor Ogla-Moga.
(In Stories by American authors. Vol. 3, pp. 99-134. New York. 1912.)

NL 0427142 MB

VOLUME 337

LLOYD, DAVID DEMAREST, 1851-1889.
"The senator," by [David Demarest] Lloyd & [Sydney] Rosenfeld. [New York? 188-?] 1 v. (various pagings) 30cm.

Typescript; includes ground plans.
Produced at the Star theatre, New York, in Jan. 1880.

1. Drama, American. I. Rosenfeld, Sydney, 1855-1931, joint author. II. Title.

NL 0427143 NN

LLOYD, DAVID DEMAREST, 1851-1889.
The senator; an original comedy in four acts, by David D. Lloyd and Sydney Rosenfeld. [New York? 1889?] 1 v. (various pagings) 27cm.

Typescript.
Prompt-book.
On cover in ms.: Original acting copy, De Vere 1889 production.
Produced at the Star theatre, New York, 13 Jan., 1890.
1. Drama, American. I. Rosenfeld, Sydney, 1885-1931, joint author. II. Title.

NL 0427144 NN

[Lloyd, David Demarest] 1851-1889.
"The senator"... [New York, 1890] 60 f. 32½cm.

Caption-title.
Typewritten.
By D. D. Lloyd and S. Rosenfeld.
First New York production at the Star theatre, Jan. 13, 1890.

——— Another version. 14 parts in 2 v. 31, 16cm.

Prompt-book, typewritten, with ms. corrections and notes; original cast, floor plans, and sides for 13 characters, included.

Imperfect: side for the part of Josie Armstrong wanting.
Vol. 1 bound with the above.

151920-21B. 1. Drama, American. 2. Prompt-books. I. Rosenfeld, Sydney, 1855-1931, jt. au. II. Title.
N. Y. P. L. March 31, 1942

NL 0427146 NN

Lloyd, David Demarest, 1851-1889.
The woman-hater; a farcical comedy in four acts, by David Demarest Lloyd... London: S. French, Ltd., cop. 1907. 106 p. 12°. (French's internat. copyrighted... ed. of the works of the best authors. no. 131.)

1. Drama, American. 2. Title.
N. Y. P. L. June 29, 1925

NL 0427147 NN IaU IU NNC CLSU RPB OCl MH

LLOYD, David Demarest, 1911-1962.
Fabian socialism in the new deal. American liberty league, 1935.
22 p. (American liberty league. Document no.50)

NL 0427148 Or

Lloyd, David Demarest, 1911-
Son and stranger. Boston, Houghton Mifflin, 1950.
209 p. 22 cm.

I. Title.
PZ3.L7735So 50-7620

NL 0427149 DLC TxU ViU NcRS PPL PP OCl TU

4PS
5444
Lloyd, David Demarest, 1911-
Unverstandener Sohn; Roman. Zürich, Humanitas Verlag [1951]
262 p.

NL 0427150 DLC-P4

LLOYD, David Demarest, 1911-1962.
A year of the automobile labor board.

(1)+23 fol. 4°. Typewritten.
Thesis --- Law School of Harvard University, 1934/35.

NL 0427151 MH-L

Lloyd, David John de
see De Lloyd, David John, d. 1948.

Lloyd, David Myrddin
Astudiaeth feirniadol o farddoniaeth Cynddelw Brydydd Mawr, o ran iaith a gwerth llenyddol

298 p.
Thesis - Swansea, 1931
Microfilm, negative, of copy in University College of Swansea Library

1. Cynddelw Brydydd Mawr, 12th cent.

NL 0427153 MH

Lloyd, David Myrddin, *ed.*
A book of Wales, edited by D. M. and E. M. Lloyd. [General ed.: G. F. Maine] London, Collins [1953]
384 p. illus. 19 cm.

1. Wales. 2. English literature (Selections: Extracts, etc.) 3. Welsh literature (Selections: Extracts, etc.) I. Lloyd, Elizabeth Mary, joint ed. II. Title.
PR1111.W3L5 914.29 56-18667 ‡

CtY KyU TNJ WaS WaSp
NL 0427154 DLC ViU CU MH NN N KU IEN CaBViP TxU

010.6
W466
v.6
Lloyd, David Myrddin.
Four centuries of Welsh printed literature: an exhibition. Carmarthen, Printed by W. Spurrell & son [1947]
p. [177]-200. facsims. 22cm. (The Journal of the Welsh bibliographical society, v. 6, no. 4)

Exhibition at the National library of Wales, 1947.
Bibliography: p. 186-200.

NL 0427155 NNC

Lloyd, David Price, called Bardd y Glynn.
Y ddwy bryddest wobrwyol, er coffadwriaeth am y diweddar Barch.H.Rowlands,G.C.,Plasgwyn, Mon. A gyhoeddwyd yn fuddugol mewn Eisteddfod a Gynaliwyd yn Niwbwrch, ar Ddydd Mawrth,yr 20fed o Fedi, 1842. Caernarfon, James Rees, 1842.

16°. pp.28.
By David Price Lloyd, called Bardd y Glynn, and R.M.Williamson called Bardd Du Mon.

NL 0427156 MH

Lloyd, David Tecwyn
Erthyglau beirniadol. [Llandysul] Y Clwb Llyfrau Cymreig, 1946.

88 p.

NL 0427157 MH NN

Lloyd, Demarest
see Lloyd, David Demarest, 1911-1962.

Lloyd, Dennis, 1915-
see Lloyd of Hampstead, Dennis Lloyd, Baron, 1915-

Lloyd, Dorothy Gwendolyn.
Official publications of Florida, 1821-1941. Urbana, Ill., 1943.

Microfilm copy of typewritten ms. Made by the University of Illinois Library. Negative.
Collation of the original, as determined from the film: iii, 537 l.
Thesis (M. A.)—University of Illinois.
Bibliography: leaves 522-529.

1. Florida—Government publications—Bibl.

Microfilm Z-24 Mic 51-222

NL 0427160 DLC IU

Lloyd, Dorothy Jordan, 1889-1946.
Chemistry of the proteins and its economic applications, by Dorothy Jordan Lloyd ... introduction by Sir Frederick Gowland Hopkins ... with 50 illustrations. London, J. & A. Churchill, 1926.
xii, 279 p. diagrs. 21cm.
Bibliography at end of each chapter.

1. Proteins.
Library of Congress QD431.L65 27-2462

PPD PP PPHa NcRS OCU MiU OO
NL 0427161 DLC ICRL OrCS NcD NN PPT ICJ OCl CU

Lloyd, Dorothy Jordan, 1889-
Chemistry of the proteins and its economic applications, by Dorothy Jordan Lloyd ... introduction by Sir Frederick Gowland Hopkins ... with 50 illustrations. Philadelphia, P. Blakiston's Son, 1926.
xii, 279 p. diagrs. 21cm.
Bibliography at end of each chapter.

NL 0427162 NIC

Lloyd, Dorothy Jordan, 1889-
Chemistry of the proteins, by Dorothy Jordan Lloyd .. and Agnes Shore ... 2d ed. Introduction by Sir Frederick Gowland Hopkins ... With 101 illustrations. London, J. & A. Churchill ltd., 1938.
xi, 532 p. plates, diagrs. 21 cm.

Errata slip inserted preceding p. 1.
First edition (1926) by Dorothy Jordan Lloyd was published under title: Chemistry of the proteins and its economic applications.
Bibliography at end of each chapter.

1. Proteins. I. Shore, Agnes, joint author.

Library of Congress QD431.L65 1938 38—34074
[a51g½] 547.8

CaBVaU TxU IdPI WaS NIC CU MH
NL 0427163 DLC CtY PPC PPT PBm ICJ NNC CU DNLM

VOLUME 337

Lloyd, Dorothy Jordan, 1889-1946
... Lecture on leather, by Dorothy Jordan-Lloyd ... London, 1943.
31 p. illus., diagrs. 22cm.
At head of title: The Royal Institute of Chemistry of Great Britain and Ireland.
References: p. 31.

NL 0427164 ICJ NN IU NIC

Lloyd, E
A visit to the antipodes, with some reminiscences of a sojourn in Australia, by a squatter. London, Smith, Elder, 1846.
viii, 188 p. illus.
Pref. signed: E. L.
On spine: Antipodes—Lloyd.
Photocopy. Adelaide, Public Library of South Australia, 1962. 17 cm. (South Australian facsimile editions, no. 22)

1. South Australia—Description and travel. I. A squatter. II. E. L. III. L., E. IV. Title. V. Title: Antipodes. (Series)
DU310.L55 1846a 919.4'2 71-17213 MARC

NL 0427165 DLC NN ICN MH KU NN

LLOYD(E.) and SON .
Catalogue of Lloyd and Son's British and foreign public subscription library Harley Street, London, [London, J.F.Dove, 1824].

NL 0427166 MH

Lloyd, E J.
Entrance scholarship questions for the chief public schools and H. M. S. Britannia with solutions and hints, by E. J. Lloyd ... London, S. Sonnenschein and co., ltd., 1903.
vii, 568 p. diagrs. 19cm.

1. Examinations—Questions—England. 2. Public schools (Endowed)—England—Entrance examinations. 3. Gt. Brit.—Navy—Entrance examinations.
E 10-1557
Library, U. S. Bur. of Education LB3056.G7L7

NL 0427167 DHEW CtY

Lloyd, E. L., of Winterbourne.
Yr eglwys yn gartref y Cristion, gan y Parch. E. L. Lloyd, B.A., rheithor, Winterbourne, Gunner, Salisbyr (Gynt Beriglor Carnor, a Dylife, Sir Drefaldwyn). Gremadog, Argraffwyd gan R. Isaac Jones, n.d.
54 p. 12°.

NL 0427168 MH

Lloyd, E. R., agriculturalist
see Lloyd, Edward Read, 1867-

LLOYD, E. W.
Field and methods of securing new business.
1.8°. ff.(25). Type -written.

NL 0427170 MH-BA

Lloyd, E. Walford-
see Walford-Lloyd, Edward, 1887-

Lloyd, Edith
Quaint spots in Chicago: number 6, St. Mark's church.

NL 0427172 ICHi

Lloyd, Edmund, tr.
Chardin, *Sir* John, 1643-1713.
Sir John Chardin's Travels in Persia, with an introduction by Brigadier-General Sir Percy Sykes ... London, The Argonaut press. 1927.

Lloyd, Edward, of Aberystwyth
Marwnad i'r diweddar barch.Richard Owen, y Diwygiwr. Tremadog, Jones [1887?]
8 p.

NL 0427174 MH

Lloyd, Edward, *of Drenewydd.*
Antiquities of Shropshire, from an old manuscript of Edward Lloyd ... rev. and enl. from private and other manuscripts, with illustrations, by Thomas Farmer Dukes ... Shrewsbury, Printed for the author, by J. Eddowes, 1844.
1 p. l., xviii, 321, lxxxiv, [58] p. illus. 32cm.
Title vignette.
An account of the principal books, mss., maps, views and portraits relating to Shropshire: 31 p. at end.
Subject entries: Shropshire—Antiq.
2-29501
Library of Congress, no. DA670.S4L7.

NL 0427175 DLC ICN MdBP OCl NN

Lloyd, Edward, of Ramsgate.
Bank charter act cannot be maintained without a relaxing clause... London, Wilson, 1858.
19 p.

NL 0427176 PU

[LLOYD, Edward] scientific writer.
Mathematical geography. [2d ed.] Treatise I. London, 1827.
Diagrs.
(Library of useful knowledge)

NL 0427177 MH MdBP

[LLOYD, Edward] scientific writer.
Mathematical Geography, pp. 32.
(NATURAL Philosophy, etc., 1829, etc., 8°. III, [iii]. Diagrams.

NL 0427178 MH

Lloyd, Edward, silk-thrower.
A description of the city of Dublin. Published, to give some idea of a country and people; may be render'd of the utmost service to the trading interest of England. To which is perfix'd[!], a scheme leading to ways, how to restore the trade of England; especially, the woollen manufacturing to the flourishing state it was in Charles II reign, with the assistance of the people of Ireland ... London, Printed and disposed of at William's coffee house [etc., 1732?]
3 p.l., 3-28 p. 19 cm.

NL 0427180 MH-BA

Lloyd, Edward, silk-thrower.
Thoughts on trade: intended to have been first publish'd in Ireland, with an account of the present state of the silken manufacturers, and the calamituous circumstances of a numerous poor in that kingdom. A pamphlet proper to be read and consider'd by such as are for farther restraining trade in Ireland ... To which thoughts are prefix'd, an humble application in favour of the British distillery ... London, 1736.
16 p. 18.5 cm.

NL 0427181 MH-BA NNC CtY

Lloyd, Edward, 1660-1709.
see
Lhuyd, Edward, 1660-1709.

Kress Room
Lloyd, Edward, fl. 1688-1726.
Ships arrived at, and departed from several ports of England, as I have account of them in London; from December 15. to December 22. 1696. Numb. 257 ... London, E.Lloyd [1696]
broadside. 26.5 x 16.5 cm.
Negative photostat. Source unknown.
Possibly one sheet from Lloyd's news.

NL 0427183 MH-BA

LLOYD, Edward, 1815-1890, pub.
Lloyd's reciter. London, [1846]-47.
2 series Illustr.
2d series has the title " Lloyd's illustrated Reciter".

NL 0427184 MH

LLOYD, Edward, 1815-1890, pub.
Lloyd's song book. London, [1846-47].
3 series. Illustr.
2d and 3d sries are "Illustrated ed."
"Forms a companion to the illustrated editions of the 'Songs of Dibdin and Lloyd's comic and sentimental reciter".

NL 0427185 MH

VOLUME 337

Lloyd, Edward, *d.* 1870.
The law of trade marks, with some account of its history and development in the decisions of the courts of law and equity. By Edward Lloyd ... 2d ed. London ₍Printed by Yates and Alexander₎ 1865.
xii, 83 p. 19ᶜᵐ.

1. Trade-marks—Gt. Brit.
34-34880

NL 0427186 DLC PPB PPT-L

Lloyd, Edward Archibald.
The co-operative movement in Italy, with special reference to agriculture, labour and production: a short study, by E. A. Lloyd, B. A. Westminster. The Fabian society; ₍London₎ G. Allen and Unwin, limited, 1925.
xii, 136 p. 22½ᶜᵐ.

1. Cooperation—Italy. 2. Agriculture, Cooperative—Italy. 3. Cooperative societies. I. Title.

Library of Congress HD3503.L6 26—2010

NL 0427187 DLC DL CSt-H NN CU CaBViP CtY NcD NcRS OCl ViU

HD3503 .L6 1926
Lloyd, Edward Archibald.
The co-operative movement in Italy.
New York, International Publishers, 1926.
xii, 136 p. 23 cm.

1. Cooperation--Italy. 2. Agriculture, Cooperative--Italy. 3. Cooperation--Societies. I. Title.

NL 0427188 TU MH OO PU

Lloyd, Edward John Denis.
... Stabilisation of rates, by E. J. D. Lloyd ... Westminster, London, Institute of public administration, 1935.
cover-title, 35, ₍1₎ p. 24ᶜᵐ. (Spelman research studies)
Bibliography: p. 30-31.

1. Taxation—Gt. Brit. 2. Municipal finance—Gt. Brit. I. Title.

Library of Congress HJ9427.L6 42-16673

NL 0427189 DLC CtY IU CtW

Lloyd, Edward John Denis
...A survey of London local government (with particular reference to finance) by E. J. D. Lloyd and J. H. Humphries. ₍Lond.₎ 1944.
67 ₍12₎ p., illus.

At head of title: Institute of municipal treasurers and accountants.

I. Humphries, J. H. II. Institute of municipal treasurers and accountants, London, pub.

NL 0427190 MiD MH

Lloyd, Edward L.

HF3506 .T8
Turner, S C
Co-operation for export selling ₍by S. C. Turner₎ Distribution costs ₍by Edward L. Lloyd₎ London, British Institute of Management, 1950.

Lloyd, Edward Mayow Hastings, 1889–
Experiments in state control at the War office and the Ministry of food, by E. M. H. Lloyd ... Oxford, The Clarendon press; London, New York ₍etc.₎ H. Milford, 1924.
xxiv, 460 p. diagrs. 25 cm. (*Added t.-p.:* ₍Carnegie endowment for international peace. Division of economics and history₎ Economic and social history of the world war. British series)
Half-title: Publications of the Carnegie endowment for international peace. Division of economics and history.

1. European war, 1914-1918—Economic aspects—Gt. Brit. 2. Price regulation—Gt. Brit. 3. Industry and state—Gt. Brit. I. Title. II. Title: State control.
HC56.C35 25—8703
——— Copy 2. HC256.8.L5
Library of Congress ₍a52v1₎

NL 0427192 DLC DAU KEmT DNW OrP IdU ODW Ok OU OCU ICJ NN MB CaBVa CaBVaU WaWW Wa IdU-SB WaS MtU OO OCl MiU WaTC ViU NcD PPAmP PBm PSC PHC PU PPT NjP

Lloyd, Edward Mayow Hastings, 1889–
Stabilisation; an economic policy for producers & consumers, by E. M. H. Lloyd ... London, G. Allen & Unwin ltd. ₍1923₎
128 p. 19ᶜᵐ.

1. Money. 2. Prices. I. Title.

Library of Congress HG229.L6 23-9209 Revised

NL 0427193 DLC CU Or OCl DL MiU NN

Lloyd, Edward Mayow Hastings, 1889–
Stabilisation; an economic policy for producers & consumers, by E. M. H. Lloyd. New York, A. A. Knopf, 1923.
140, ₍1₎ p. 19½ᶜᵐ.

1. Money. 2. Prices. I. Title.

Library of Congress HG229.L6 1923 a 23-16056 Revised

NL 0427194 DLC MB NIC OKentU PRosC PSC PU ScU LU

Lloyd, Edward Mostyn.
Tom Anderson, dare-devil; a Young Virginian in the revolution, by Edward Mostyn Lloyd ... Boston and New York, Houghton Mifflin company, 1916.
viii p., 1 l., 415, ₍1₎ p. col. front., col. plates. 21ᶜᵐ. $1.50

1. U. S.—Hist.—Revolution—Fiction. I. Title.

Library of Congress PZ3.L774T 16—22901

NL 0427195 DLC FU Or PP NN

Lloyd, Edward Read, 1867–
... Agricultural possibilities of the Florida everglades ... Letter from the secretary of war, transmitting a report made to the division engineer at New Orleans, by Mr. E. R. Lloyd on the agricultural possibilities of the Florida everglades ... ₍Washington, U. S. Govt. print. off.₎ 1930₎
21 p. incl. tables. fold. map. 23ᶜᵐ. (₍U. S.₎ 71st Cong., 2d sess. Senate. Doc. 85)
Presented by Mr. Fletcher. Ordered printed, with an illustration, January 6 (calendar day, February 13), 1930.

1. Agriculture—Florida—Everglades. I. Fletcher, Duncan Upshaw, 1859– II. U. S. Engineer dept. III. Title.

Library of Congress S451.F6L6 30-26442
——— Copy 2. ₍3₎ 630.9759

NL 0427196 DLC OO MiU

Lloyd, Edward Read, 1867– joint author.

Ward, William Francis.
... A comparison of concentrates for fattening steers in the South. By W. F. Ward and S. S. Jerdan ... and E. R. Lloyd ... Washington ₍Govt. print. off.₎ 1919.

Lloyd, Edward Read, 1867– joint author.

Ward, William Francis.
... A comparison of roughages for fattening steers in the South. By W. F. Ward ... Dan T. Gray ... and E. R. Lloyd ... Washington ₍Govt. print. off.₎ 1919.

Lloyd, Edward Read, 1867–
Corn silage compared with hulls for fattening steers. Jackson: Tucker Prtg. House, 1914. 8 p. 8°. (Mississippi. Agricultural Experiment Station. Bull. 167.)

1. Ensilage. 2. Cattle.—Feeding. U. S.: Miss.
N. Y. P. L. July 28, 1916.

NL 0427199 NN

Lloyd, Edward Read.
The cow pea
see under Tracy, Samuel Mills.

Lloyd, Edward Read, 1867– joint author.

Ward, William Francis.
... Fattening steers on summer pasture in the South. By W. F. Ward ... Dan T. Gray ... and E. R. Lloyd ... Washington, ₍Govt. print. off.₎ 1919.

Lloyd, Edward Read, 1867–
Feeding for beef. Agric. College, 1896.
155-166 p. 8° (Miss. Agric. Exp. St., Bull. no. 39)
By E. R. Lloyd and J. S. Moore.

NL 0427202 NN

Lloyd, Edward Read, 1867–
Varieties of cotton. n. p., 1892. 2 l. 8°. (Mississippi. Agricultural Experiment Station. Bulletin 18.)

1. Cotton plant, etc.—Varieties. U. S.: Mississippi.
N. Y. P. L. June 7, 1912.

NL 0427203 NN

Lloyd, Edward Walford
see Walford-Lloyd, Edward, 1887–

Lloyd, Edward William.
Artillery: its progress and present position. In two parts, with appendix. By E. W. Lloyd ... and A. G. Hadcock ... Portsmouth, J. Griffin & co.; New York, Van Nostrand; ₍etc., etc.₎ 1893.
xi, 463 p. col. front., illus., plates (1 col.) tables (1 fold.) diagrs. 25½ᶜᵐ.

1. Artillery. I. Hadcock, Albert George, 1861– joint author.

Library of Congress UF145.L7 11—34310

NL 0427205 DLC DNW KMK DN DSI NIC PP MB

VOLUME 337

PC4121
.L58
1940
Lloyd, Edward Windsor.

Explanatory notes on the Spanish conversational course. [London] Linguaphone Institute [194-?]
143 p. 21cm. (Linguaphone conversational courses. Span[ish] 407)

1. Spanish language—Conversational and phrase books. I. Linguaphone Institute, London.

NL 0427206 ViU OCl

Lloyd, Edwin.
Three great African chiefs (Khâmé, Sebelé and Bathoeng) by the Rev. Edwin Lloyd ... with portraits. A second ed., rev. and enl. and brought up to date. London, T. F. Unwin, 1895.
ix p., 2 l., 271 p. front. (ports.) 19½cm.

1. Khâmé. 2. Sebelé. 3. Bathoeng. I. Title.

A 14-790

Title from St. Paul Pub. Libr. Printed by L. C.

NL 0427207 MNS IEN CtY-D CSt-H CtY MB NcU

Lloyd, Edwin Russell, 1882- ed.

Woolsey, Lester Hood, 1877-
... The Bull mountain coal field, Musselshell and Yellowstone counties, Montana, by L. H. Woolsey, R. W. Richards and C. T. Lupton, comp. and ed. by E. Russell Lloyd. Washington, Govt. print. off., 1917.

QE75
.B9
no. 627
Lloyd, Edwin Russell, 1882- joint author.

Winchester, Dean Eddy, 1883-1936.
... The lignite field of northwestern South Dakota, by Dean E. Winchester, C. J. Hares, E. Russell Lloyd, and E. M. Parks. Washington, Govt. print. off., 1916.

Lloyd, Edwin Russell, 1882-
Pre-San Andres stratigraphy and oil-producing zones in southeastern New Mexico; a progress report. Socorro, 1949.
87 p. illus., map. 23 cm. (New Mexico. Bureau of Mines and Mineral Resources. Bulletin 29)
Part of the illustrative matter folded in pocket.
"Selected bibliography": p. 73-75.

1. Geology—New Mexico. 2. Petroleum—New Mexico. 3. Geology, Stratigraphic—Paleozoic. I. Title. (Series)
TN24.N6A232 no. 29 551.7 G S 50-50

U. S. Geol. Survey. Libr. for Library of Congress [3,†]

NL 0427210 DI-GS OU TxU MoU ViU DLC

Lloyd, Edwin Russell, 1882- ed.
West Texas-New Mexico symposium.
see under American association of petroleum geologists.

Lloyd, Eileen Wandin.
Songs of a southern land, by Eileen Wandin Lloyd. Boston, The Four seas company [c1928]
156 p. 19½cm.

I. Title.

Library of Congress PS3523.L56S6 1928 29-11046

NL 0427212 DLC

Lloyd, Eleanor, ed.

Gatty, Margaret (Scott) *"Mrs. Alfred Gatty,"* 1809-1873.
The book of sun-dials; originally comp. by the late Mrs. Alfred Gatty; now enl. and re-edited by H. K. F. Eden and Eleanor Lloyd. [4th ed.] London, G. Bell and sons, 1900.

[LLOYD, Eleanor.]
The Langdales of Langdale End; a tale. By the author of "Valeria." London, M. Ward & Co., etc., etc., 1879.

NL 0427214 MH NNU-W

Wor
PR
5875
P19
Lloyd, Eleanor.
Notes on a sun-dial at Patrington ... And a note by the Rev. Canon Maddock ... Hull, William Andrews & Co., 1897.
13 p. illus. 24cm.

"Reprinted from Vol. 5 of the Transactions of the East Riding Antiquarian Society."
No. 14 in vol. lettered: Pamphlets on the English Lake country.

NL 0427215 NIC

Lloyd, Elizabeth, 1848-1917.
An appeal for the Bondwoman...
see under Howell, Elizabeth (Lloyd) 1811-1896.

Lloyd, Elizabeth, 1848-1917.
The belief of Friends, as one of them interprets it ... 2d ed. Phil., Friends' general conference advancement committee, n.d.
[8] p. 18cm.

NL 0427217 PHC PHi PSC-Hi MH

Lloyd, Elizabeth, 1848-1917.
Literature for little folks. Selections from standard authors, and easy lessons in composition. By Elizabeth Lloyd. Philadelphia, Sower, Potts & co., 1876.
1 p. l., 7-143 p. front., illus. 17½cm.
Illustrated t.-p.

1. Readers and speakers—1800-1870.

Library of Congress PE1119.A1L73 12-6773

NL 0427218 DLC CSmH MH PHatU OO

Lloyd, Elizabeth, 1848-1917.
The old red school-house. A temperance story for teachers and pupils. By Elizabeth Lloyd. [Philadelphia] Friends' book association of Philadelphia, 1895.
127 p. front., illus. 18cm.

I. Title.

Library of Congress PZ7.L775O 7-19395

NL 0427219 DLC MH PSC-Hi PHC PU PHatU

Lloyd, Elizabeth, 1848-1917, attributed author.
Treasures of darkness
see under title

Lloyd, Elizabeth Maria.
Thirza
see under Ball, Hermann, novelist.

YA
.S875
Lloyd, Elizabeth Maria.
We are seven; or, The little mourner comforted New York [n.d.].
51p.

(Sunday school books; arr. numerically.)

NL 0427222 DLC DAU

PR1111
.W3L5
Lloyd, Elizabeth Mary, joint ed.

Lloyd, David Myrddin, *ed.*
A book of Wales, edited by D. M. and E. M. Lloyd. [General ed.: G. F. Maine] London, Collins [1953]

Lloyd, *Mrs.* **Ella Bentley.**
Grandma's cook book; a collection of tried recipes, by Mrs. Ella Bentley Lloyd ... Cincinnati, Printed for the author by Jennings & Graham, 1910.
2 p. l., 3-228 p. 19½cm. $1.25
Blank leaves interspersed.

1. Cookery, American.

Library of Congress TX715.L77 10-5049

NL 0427224 DLC NN

Lloyd, Mrs. Ella (Stryker) Mapes.
see
Mapes, Ella (Stryker) "Mrs. C. L. Lloyd," 1870-

VOLUME 337

Lloyd, Elwood.
Arizonology (knowledge of Arizona): a compilation of more than two thousand names found on the maps of Arizona, together with information concerning their meaning, history, and many other interesting facts about this wonderful state. By Elwood Lloyd IV. Flagstaff, Ariz., Done into print and covers by the Coconino sun, °1933.
92 p. 22½cm.
1. Names, Geographical—Arizona. 2. Arizona—Descr. & trav.—Gazetteers. I. Title.
Library of Congress F809.L56 34-17031

NL 0427226 DLC NjP

Lloyd, Elwood.
Enchanted sands. LA, Steake [c1939]
58, [3] p. illus. 21 cm.
1. Palm Springs, Calif. I. T.

NL 0427227 NjP

Lloyd, Elwood.
How to finance home life, by Elwood Lloyd, IV ... New York, The B. C. Forbes publishing co. [°1927]
ix, 238 p. 19½cm.
1. Domestic economy. I. Title.
Library of Congress TX326.L5 27-18352

NL 0427228 DLC WaT PP PPT MB ViU OClW OCl OCU

Lloyd, Elwood.
Meandering in the woods of words with the wise old codger. Pasadena, San Pasqual press, 1938.
67p. 18cm.

NL 0427229 MoU

Lloyd, Elwood.
Successful financing of the home, by Elwood Lloyd IV... [Los Angeles, 1925.] 439 p. 12°.
"A compilation of 154 editorials which appeared daily on the financial pages of The Evening Herald, January 1 to June 30, 1925."
268469A. 1. Budget, Family. 2. Property, Real. 3. Domestic economy. 4. Investments.
N. Y. P. L. November 24, 1926

NL 0427230 NN MiD

Lloyd, Elwood.
Where does your money go? New angles on family spending, by Elwood Lloyd, IV ... [Los Angeles] Los Angeles down town shopping news, 1937.
1 p. l., 34, [26] p. incl. forms. 28 x 21½cm.
1. Domestic economy—Accounting. I. Title.
Library of Congress TX326.L53 39-13570
——— Copy 2. [2] 647.1

NL 0427231 DLC

Lloyd, Emily, *pseud.*
see
Maurer, *Mrs.* **Ruth D Johnson,** 1870–

Lloyd, *Mrs.* **Emma (Rouse)** 1858–
Clasping hands with generations past, by Emma Rouse Lloyd. [Cincinnati] Priv. print. [Wiesen-Hart press] 1932.
6 p. l., 3-228, [7] p. front., illus. (incl. ports., facsims.) 23½cm.
"Five hundred copies printed for Emma Rouse Lloyd."
Blank pages for "Notes" ([230-235])
Bibliography: p. 207-210.
CONTENTS.—Rouse family.—Zimmerman family.—Tanner family.—Henderson family.—McClure family.—Porter family.—Allied families.—Our colored folk.—Appendix.
1. Rouse family. 2. Zimmerman family (Christopher Zimmerman, d. 1748) 3. Tanner family. 4. Henderson family (John Henderson, d. 1774) 5. McClure family. 6. Porter family. I. Title.
Library of Congress CS71.R864 1932 32-25410

OClWHi MB Vi
NL 0427233 DLC KyHi KyLx KyLxT NcD PHi OFH ViU

Lloyd, Ernest.
Animal heroes ... by Ernest Lloyd. Mountain View, Calif., Portland, Or. [etc.] Pacific press publishing assn. [1946]
160 p. illus. 20½cm.
1. Animals, Legends and stories of. I. Title.
Library of Congress PZ10.3.L77An 46-22075

NL 0427234 DLC WaSp

Lloyd, Ernest.
Lincoln's faith. Mountain View, Calif., Pacific Press Pub. Association [°1954]
26 p. 18 cm.
1. Lincoln, Abraham, Pres. U. S.—Religion. I. Title.
E457.2.L85 923.173 56-32595

NL 0427235 DLC IU RPB

Lloyd, Ernest, *comp.*
Our dog friends. Mountain View, Calif., Pacific Press Pub. Association [1950]
132 p. illus. 21 cm.
1. Dogs—Legends and stories. I. Title.
QL795.D6L6 636.78 50-2566

NL 0427236 DLC

Lloyd, Ernest, *ed.*
Prayer stories for boys and girls, retold and comp. by Ernest Lloyd; illus. by Luis Chavarria. Mountain View, Calif., Pacific Press Pub. Assn. [1948]
96 p. illus. 23 cm.
1. Prayer—Juvenile literature. I. Title.
BV212.L5 264.1 48-6238*

NL 0427237 DLC

Lloyd, Ernest, *ed.*
Scrapbook stories from Ellen G. White's scrapbooks; illustrated by Frank McMillan. Mountain View, Calif., Pacific Press Pub. Association [1949]
96 p. illus. 23 cm.
1. Children's stories. I. White, Ellen Gould (Harmon) 1827-1915. II. Title.
PZ5.L75Sc 52-35371

NL 0427238 DLC

Lloyd, Ernest.
Stories of clever dogs; old stories and new, retold by Ernest Lloyd. Washington, D. C., South Bend, Ind. [etc.] Review and herald publishing assn. [°1924]
92 p. incl. front., illus. 20cm.
1. Dogs—Legends and stories. I. Title.
Library of Congress PZ10.3.L77St 24-4559

NL 0427239 DLC

Lloyd, Ernest Barton, 1893-
Steam power generating stations; their operation and equipment... 1917.
Thesis. Ohio stateuniversity.

NL 0427240 OU

Lloyd, Ernest Frederick, 1866–
... The closed union shop versus the open shop: their social and economic value compared, by Ernest F. Lloyd ... Boston, Mass., National industrial conference board, °1920.
vi, 27 p. 23cm. (National industrial conference board. Special report, no. 11)
At head of title: National industrial conference board. Prize essays, 1919-1920.
1. Open and closed shop. I. Title.
Library of Congress HD6488.L5 20-15563 Revised

OO PBm PU PPT NcRS CU OrP IdU WaS OrPR OrU
NL 0427241 DLC IaU MiU OCl OClW OCU OU ViU DL MB

Lloyd, Ernest Frederick, 1866-
Educating the public...
[Grand Rapids, c1913]

HD2766
.L6

NL 0427242 DLC

331.86
L79s Lloyd,Ernest Frederick, 1866-
The social & economic significance of the automatic tool [by] Ernest F. Lloyd.
[No imprint]
[29]-36 p. 23 cm.
Caption title.
Reprinted from Michigan academy of science. Report no.21,1919.

NL 0427243 Mi

Lloyd, Ernest Guy Richard
see
Lloyd, Guy, 1890–

Lloyd, Ernest Marsh, 1840–
Canning and Spanish America, by Colonel E. M. Lloyd ...
(*In* Royal historical society, London. Transactions. London [1904] 22cm. n. s., v. 18, p. [77]-105)
1. Gt. Brit.—Foreign relations. 2. Canning, George, 1770-1827. 3. Spanish America—History—Wars of independence, 1806-1830.
A C 36-606
Newberry library for Library of Congress [DA20.R9 n. s., vol. 18] [a38c1] (942.0062)

NL 0427245 ICN RPB CLSU MB DLC

VOLUME 337

Lloyd, Ernest Marsh, 1840–
A review of the history of infantry, by E. M. Lloyd ... New York [etc.] Longmans, Green, and co., 1908.
xi, 308 p. 23cm.
Bibliography: p. 291–296.

1. Infantry—History.
War 9–4
U. S. Army war coll. Libr. for Library of Congress [a37c1]

OC1W OC1
NL 0427246 PCarlD CaBViP CLSU MB ICJ PU PP MiU

U 26 .515 LLOYD, ERNEST MARSH, 1840–
Vauban, Montalembert, Carnot: engineer studies. London, Chapman and Hall, 1887.
239p. ports. 21cm.

NL 0427247 ICN WaS CU CtY ICJ MiU MdBP MiD MB

Lloyd, Ernest T.
When Ulster stood alone. By Ernest T. Lloyd... Shrewsbury, 1914. 12 p. 12°.
Repr.: Shrewsbury chronicle.
Cover-title.

1. Ulster.—History, 1689.
N. Y. P. L. November 6, 1915.

NL 0427248 NN

Lloyd, Eunice A., b. 1823.

Coe, David Benton, 1814–1895.
Record of the Coe family and descendants from 1596 to 1856 (compiled by Daniel [!] B. Coe) from 1856 to 1885 (compiled by Eunice A. Lloyd) Cincinnati, Standard publishing company, 1885.

Lloyd, Eusebius Arthur, 1795–1862.
A treatise on the nature and treatment of scrophula; describing its connection with diseases of the spine, joints, eyes, glands, &c. &c. &c., founded on an essay to which the Jacksonian prize, for the year 1818, was adjudged by the Royal college of surgeons. To which is added, a brief account of the ophthalmia, so long prevalent in Christ's hospital. By Eusebius Arthur Lloyd ... London, J. Anderson; [etc., etc.] 1821.
xii, 330 p. 21½cm.

1. Scrofula. 2. Eye—Inflammation.
35-36253
Library of Congress RC295.L6

NL 0427250 DLC DNLM KyU MnU ICJ PPGenH PPPH

Lloyd, Evan.
Total abstinence the only true temperance. Substance of a lecture delivered...January 27, 1873. By Evan Lloyd... London: Published for the Clerkenwell Parochial Temperance Assoc., by W. Tweedie [1873?]. 16 p. 16°.
In: VTZ p. v. 97, no. 13.

1. Alcohol.—Physiological effect of. 2. Clerkenwell Parochial Temperance Association. 3. Title.
N. Y. P. L. July 1, 1918.

NL 0427251 NN

PR 3541 +L54 C6 [Lloyd, Evan] 1734–1776
Conversation; a poem. London, 1767.
50p. 27cm.

NL 0427252 WU CtY PU DFo ICN

---

*EC75 L7757 B766p [Lloyd, Evan, 1734-1776]
The curate. A poem. Inscribed to all the curates in England and Wales. By [E. Lloyd], author of The powers of the pen.
London:Printed for the author;and sold by Richardson and Urquhart,under the Royal-Exchange. M DCC LXVI.
2p.ℓ.,48(i.e.44)p. 23.5cm.
Error in paging: 37-40 omitted in numbering.
Author's name on t.-p. is in his autograph.
No.2 in a volume labelled: Lloyd's Poems.

NL 0427253 MH CtY WU DFo PU ICN CSmH TxU MH

Lloyd, Evan, 1734–1776.
An epistle to David Garrick, esq. By E. Lloyd ... London, Printed for the author, and sold by Richardson and Urquhart, 1773.
1 p. l., 5–24 p. 27cm. [With Sanitas, daughter of Aesculapius. London, 1772]

1. Garrick, David, 1717–1779.
19–1850
Library of Congress PN2598.G3S3

NL 0427254 DLC KU CU PP PU MH MB NjP

Lloyd, Evan. 1734–1776. No. 12 in **G.3822.1
[The jealous wife.] Prologue. Written by Mr. Lloyd. Spoken by Mr. Garrick.
[London. 1761.] (2) pp. 20½ cm.
The title-page is missing.
The jealous wife, a comedy, by George Colman, the Elder, may be found on shelf-numbers No. 2 in *6558.6.16; No. 5 in **T.37.1.1; etc.

K4981 — Garrick, David. 1717–1779. — Colman, George, the Elder. 1732–1794.

NL 0427255 MB

Lloyd, Evan, 1734-1776.
The Methodist, a poem ... London, 1766.

NL 0427256 TxU

PR 3541 L56P8+ [Lloyd, Evan] 1734-1776.
The powers of the pen. A poem addressed to John Curre, esqr. London, Printed for the author; sold by Richardson and Urquhart, 1766.
43 p. 26cm.

Contains an attack on Dr. Johnson and Dr. Warburton.

1. Johnson, Samuel, 1709-1784. 2. Warburton, William, Bp. of Gloucester, 1658-1779. I. Title.

NL 0427257 NIC PU DFo TxU ICN MH CSmH WU CtY MnU

Lloyd, Evan, 1734-1776.
The powers of the pen. A poem. Addressed to John Curre, Esq. By E. Lloyd, M. A. The 2d. ed., with large additions...London, Printed for the author, sold by Richardson and Urquhart, 1768.

NL 0427258 DFo

347.6 L77c Lloyd, Sir Evan, d.1846 and Lloyd, Lady Alicia (Eustace) plaintiffs vs. Trimlestown, John Thomas Barnewall, baron, defendant.
Counsel's statement of the defendant, Lord Trimlestown's case. [Dublin? 1819?]
92p.

Caption title.
Interleaved.

NL 0427259 IU

Lloyd, *Sir* **Evan,** *d.* 1846, *plaintiff.*
Report of the trial of an issue, directed by the lord high chancellor of Ireland, wherein Major General Evan Lloyd, and Alicia, baroness Trimlestown, his wife, Peter, count Dalton, and Rosalic [!] countess Dalton, his wife, were the plaintiffs, and the Right Hon. Thomas, lord baron Trimlestown, was the defendant. Had before the Right Hon. William Downes, lord chief justice, and the Hon. Judge Mayne, and a special jury of the county of Dublin, in the Court of King's bench, Ireland, on the 11th, 15th, 16th, 17th, 18th, 19th, 20th, 22d, 23d, 24th, 25th, 26th, 27th, 29th days of June, and 1st day of July, 1818. By John Hatchell ... Dublin, Printed by Thomas Courtney, 1819.
267 p. 21cm.
"The question ... is, 'whether a certain paper, dated the 8th of December, 1812, be or be not the last will and testament of Nicholas, lord baron Trimlestown, deceased'."—p. 6.

1. Trimlestown, Nicholas Barnewall, baron, 1726–1813. I. Lloyd, Lady Alicia (Eustace) d. 1860, plaintiff. II. D'Alton, Peter, count, plaintiff. III. D'Alton, Rosalie (Barnewall) countess, d. 1864, plaintiff. IV. Trimlestown, John Thomas Barnewall, baron, 1773–1839, defendant. V. Ireland. Court of King's bench. VI. Hatchell, John.
24-19408

NL 0427261 DLC

Lloyd, Evans.
All that I want is in Ireland... Words by Jeff Branen. Music by Evans Lloyd. New York, J. Branen [c1917]
First line: I'm over here and they're over there.
Chorus: Shamrocks, the Shannon.
Introduced by Harry Ellis.
Portrait of Harry Ellis on t.-p.

1. Ireland. 2. Ellis, Harry—Port. I. Branen, Jeff. II. Song index (3).
N. Y. P. L. December 23, 1949

NL 0427262 NN

Lloyd, Evans.
Valley rose. Words by Jeff Branen. Music by Evans Lloyd. New York, J. Branen [c1917]
First line: Yonder in the valley.

Printed for the Music Division
1. Separation. I. Branen, Jeff T., 1872-1927. II. Song index (2).
N. Y. P. L. December 5, 1949

NL 0427263 NN

---

qT636.2 L331Bℓ Lloyd, Everett.
Ed. C. Lasater, the world's Jersey king, and his 300,000-acre kingdom. [n.p., 1920?]
5p. illus.,port. 34cm.

"Reprint of a story appearing in the National magazine, issue of February, 1920."

1. Lasater, Edward Cunningham, 1860-1930.

NL 0427264 TxU

VOLUME 337

Lloyd, Everett.
Law west of the Pecos, the story of Roy Bean, by Everett Lloyd. San Antonio, Tex., The University press, inc. [°1931]
168 p. illus. (incl. ports.) 19cm.

1. Bean, Roy, d. 1903. I. Title.
Library of Congress F391.B32 31-19959
——— Copy 2.
Copyright A 38504 [3] 923.473

NL 0427265 DLC TxH

F391 B323 1935
Lloyd, Everett.
Law west of the Pecos, the story of Roy Bean. Sketches by Ben Carlton Mead. [Centennial or 2d ed.] San Antonio, Tex., Naylor Co., 1935.
124 p. illus., ports. 22cm.
Author's autograph presentation copy.

1. Bean, Roy, d. 1903. I. Title.

NL 0427266 CoU TxU

Lloyd, Everett.
Law west of the Pecos, the story of Roy Bean, by Everett Lloyd; sketches by Ben Carlton Mead. San Antonio, Tex., The Naylor company, 1936.
4 p. l., 124 p. front., illus., plates, ports. 21½cm.
"This is the Centennial edition (or third edition)"

1. Bean, Roy, d. 1903. I. Title. 37-25289
Library of Congress F391.B323
——— Copy 2. [3] 923.473

NL 0427267 DLC NBuU-L OrU KEmT WaU TxU

LD3907 .G7 1946 .L5
Lloyd, Everett Thomas, 1915-
The evolution of the attitude in the United States toward Emile Zola, 1870-1914... New York, 1946.
2p.l.,414 typewritten leaves. 29cm.
Thesis (Ph.D.) - New York university, Graduate school, 1946.
Bibliography: p.[377]-414p.
1.Zola, Émile, 1840-1902. 2.Literature, Comparative - American and French. 3.Literature, Comparative - French and American. I.Title: The attitude in the United States toward Emile Zola, 1870-1914.

NL 0427268 NNU

Lloyd, Everett Thomas, 1915-
The evolution of the attitude in the United States toward Émile Zola. New York, New York University, 1949.
18 p. 23 cm.
Abridgment of thesis—New York University.
"Footnotes" (bibliographical) : p. 17-18.

1. Zola, Émile, 1840-1902. 2. Literature, Comparative—American and French. 3. Literature, Comparative—French and American. I. Title: The attitude in the United States toward Émile Zola.
PQ2538.L5 A 50-1311
New York Univ. Wash. Sq. Library for Library of Congress [2†]

NL 0427269 NNU-W OrU NN NcD MH DLC

Z 636.5 L775b Thesis
Lloyd, Everton Alexander, 1887-
The business of commercial egg-farming in Western Washington. 1926. 95l.

NL 0427270 WaPS

Lloyd, Everton Alexander, 1887-
... Feeding for egg production. With records of results obtained with S. C. white leghorn, white Wyandotte, barred Plymouth Rock, and S. C. Rhode Island red pullets ... By E. A. Lloyd ... [and] V. S. Asmundson ... Victoria, B. C., Printed by W. H. Cullin, printer to the King's most excellent Majesty, 1923.
19 p. pl., diagrs. 26cm. (British Columbia. Dept. of agriculture. Bulletin no. 93)
British Columbia. University. College of agriculture. Bulletin no. 6.
1. Eggs—Production. 2. Poultry. 3. Feeding and feeding stuffs. [2, 3. Poultry—Feeding] I. Asmundson, V. S., joint author.
Agr 23-1144
Library, U. S. Dept. of Agriculture 7B77 no. 93

NL 0427271 DNAL CaBVaU

Lloyd, Everton Alexander, 1887-
Poultry Keeping (Agriculture 39) by E. A. Lloyd and Jacob Biely. [Vancouver, B. C., University of British Columbia] 1955.
20 papers in 1 v. illus. 29 cm. ([British Columbia] Dept. of Education. Vocational correspondence course)

NL 0427272 CaBVaU

S141 A4 no.107
Lloyd, Everton Alexander, 1887-
Practical poultry-feeding, by E. A. Lloyd and Jacob Biely. Victoria, B.C., 1938.
59 p. illus. (British Columbia. Dept. of Agriculture. Bulletin no. 107)
British Columbia University College of Agriculture. Bulletin no. 14)

1. Poultry - Feeding and feeds. I. Biely, Jacob, joint author.

NL 0427273 CU CaBVaU

Lloyd, Everton Alexander, 1887-

Masui, Kiyoshi.
Sexing baby chicks, by Kiyoshi Masui ... and Juro Hashimoto ... Translations by Hachiro Okumura. With an introduction by Everton A. Lloyd ... and Tokuzo Yamaguch ... Vancouver, B. C., Journal printing company, limited [1933]

Lloyd, Everton Alexander, 1887- joint author.

Riley, W J.
... A survey of poultry-farms in British Columbia, 1921-25, by W. J. Riley, E. A. Lloyd, and V. S. Asmundson ... Victoria, B. C., Printed by C. F. Banfield, printer to the King's most excellent Majesty, 1927.

Lloyd, Eyre.
Lieut. Beatrice Raymond, v. c.; a frontier novel, by Eyre Lloyd ... London, A. Melrose, ltd. [1920?]
213 p. 18½cm.

I. Title.
Library of Congress PZ3.L7743Li 20-10370

NL 0427276 DLC

LLOYD, Eyre, 1831-1895.
Law of Compensation under the Lands Clauses, Railways Clauses Consolidation, and Metropolitan Acts, & c., with forms and precedents. London,1867.

xxix+(1). 273 p.

NL 0427277 MH-L

Lloyd, Eyre, 1831-1895.
The law of compensation under the Lands clauses and Railways clauses consolidation acts, the Metropolis local management and other acts, &c., with a full collection of forms and precedents. By Eyre Lloyd ... 2d ed. London, Stevens & Haynes, 1870.
xxiv, 408 p. 22cm.
"The Lands clauses consolidation act, 1845" : p. [317]-357.

1. Compensation (Law) [1. Compensation—Gt. Brit.] 2. Forms (Law)—Gt. Brit. I. Gt. Brit. Laws, statutes, etc. II. Title.
29-15530

NL 0427278 DLC OU

Lloyd, Eyre, 1831-1895.
The law of compensation under the Lands clauses and Railways clauses consolidation acts, the Artizans and laborers dwellings improvement act, 1875, the Metropolis local management, and other acts, &c., with a full collection of forms and precedents. By Eyre Lloyd ... 3d ed. London, Stevens & Haynes, 1875.
xxvi, 469 p. 22½cm.
Appendix of statutes (p. [351]-411) : The Lands clauses consolidation act, 1845. The Artizans and laborers dwellings improvement act, 1875.
1. Compensation (Law) [1. Compensation—Gt. Brit.] 2. Forms (Law)—Gt. Brit. I. Gt. Brit. Laws, statutes, etc. II. Title.
29-15529

NL 0427279 DLC

Lloyd, Eyre, 1831-1895.
The law of compensation under the Lands clauses and Railways clauses consolidation acts, the Artizans and labourers dwellings improvement act, 1875, the Metropolis local management, and other acts, etc. With a full collection of forms and precedents. By Eyre Lloyd ... 4th ed. with additional forms ... London, Stevens & Haynes, 1877.
xxxii, 514 p.

NL 0427280 WaU-L MH-L

Lloyd, Eyre, 1831-95.
The law of compensation under the land clauses, railways clauses consolidation acts, the public health act, 1875, the artizans and labourers dwellings improvement act, 1875, and other acts. 5th ed. London, 1882.
8°

NL 0427281 MH-L

Lloyd, Eyre, 1831-1895.
The law of compensation under the lands clauses consolidation acts, the railways clauses consolidation acts, the Public health act, 1875, the Housing of the working classes act, 1890, the Metropolis local management act, and other acts. With a full collection of forms and precedents. By Eyre Lloyd ... 6th ed. By W. J. Brooks ... London, Stevens and Haynes, 1895.
xlv p., 1 l., 496 p. 22cm.

I. Brooks, William James, 1846- ed.
4-31991

NL 0427282 DLC OU CaBVaU MH

Lloyd, Eyre, 1831-1895.
The succession laws of Christian countries, with special reference to the law of primogeniture as it exists in England. By Eyre Lloyd ... London, Stevens and Haynes, 1877.
xl, 108 p. 21½cm.

1. Inheritance and succession. [1. Succession and descent] 2. Inheritance and succession—Gt. Brit. [2. Succession and descent—Gt. Brit.] I. Title. II. Title: Primogeniture, The law of.
29-15528

NL 0427283 DLC GU CtY PU-L NcD OU NN MH

Lloyd, Eyre, d. 1901
see Lloyd, T H Eyre, d. 1901.

VOLUME 337

Lloyd, Frances.
Educating the sub-normal child; aspects of the work of a junior school for educationally sub-normal children. With a foreword by M. F. Cleugh. London, Methuen [1953]
vii, 148 p. illus. 19 cm. (Contributions to modern education)

1. Handicapped children—Education. I. Title. (Series)

LC4036.G6L6 371.922 54—245

WaU KU OrLgE WaS NcGU CaBVaU CaBViP OrU CaBVa
NL 0427285 DLC Or IaU PPT TxU OCl OOxM PPPL CtY

LC 4015 L793e 1953
LLOYD, Frances
Educating the sub-normal child; aspects of the work of a junior school for educationally sub-normal children. New York, Philosophical Library [1953]
vii, 148 p. illus.

1. Mental deficiency - Education

NL 0427286 DNLM MB TU OU IEN Wa PP WaT OrMonO OrCS

BO 218 L79
Lloyd, Frances, writer on religion.
Joyways in doctrine. London, Sands [1941]
77p. illus. 19cm.

1. Apologetics - 20th cent.

NL 0427287 IMunS

Lloyd, Francis.
A vindication of the Athanasian Creed . . . in respect to the three distinct persons in the Godhead . . .
London. Bladon. 1769. (1), 62 pp. 12°.

E8006 — Athanasian creed. — Trinity.

NL 0427288 MB CLU-C

Lloyd, Francis, geographer.
The physiography of the Upper Engadine. With map and diagrams. London, 1881.
4 p.l., 62 p. front. (fold. map) diagrs. 14 x 11 cm.
1. Engadine, Upper. 2. Physical geography - Engadine, Upper.

NL 0427289 CtY

DA 16 .L56x
Lloyd, Francis, prof. at Halle & Athens.
Extension of empire, weakness? deficits, ruin? With a practicable scheme for the reconstitution of Asiatic Turkey, By Francis Lloyd and Charles Tebbitt. London, C. K. Paul, 1880.
110 p. 18 cm.

1. Great Britain--Colonies--History. 2. Imperialism. I. Title

NL 0427290 OKentU

PT 2379 L79
Lloyd, Francis, prof. at Halle & Athens.
Prussia's representative man by Francis Lloyd and William Newton. London, Trübner, 1875.
vi, 466 p. 19cm.

1. Kleist, Heinrich von, 1777-1811. I. Newton, William, F. R. G. S., joint auth.

NL 0427291 NIC NcD DNW PPL OClW IU

Lloyd, Francis, prof. at Halle & Athens.
... A scientific view of Mr. Francis Galton's theories of heredity. By Francis Lloyd. London, Trübner & co. [1876]
vii, [1], 48 p. 18.5 cm. (His Modern "science", no. 1)
Introduction signed W. Newton.

NL 0427292 CtY

Lloyd, Francis, writer on ventilation.
Practical remarks on the warming, ventilation, and humidity of rooms. By Francis Lloyd. London: G. Cox, 1854. 52 p. illus. 21cm.

1. Heating. 2. Ventilation.
N. Y. P. L. December 31, 1942

NL 0427293 NN DNLM

Lloyd, Francis, fl. 1640, joint author.

[Boothby, Richard] fl. 1640.
A briefe discovery or description of the most famous island of Madagascar or St Laurence in Asia neare unto East-India ... By R. B. and Francis Lloyd, merchants. The second edition corrected and amended. London, Printed for Iohn Hardesty, at the signe of the Black-spread Eagle in Duck-lane. 1647.

Lloyd, Francis Bartow, 1861–1897.
Sketches of country life; humor, wisdom and pathos from the "Sage of Rocky Creek." The homely life of the Alabama Back country has its sunny side: rough but wise and kindly talk. Selections from the writings of Francis Bartow Lloyd ("Rufus Sanders") Birmingham, Ala., Press of Roberts & son, 1898.
120, 127–300 p. front., pl., ports. 24^cm.
Pages 121–136 omitted in numbering.
Dedication signed by the author's widow, Lily C. Lloyd.
Preface signed by Chappell Cory.

I. Lloyd, Mrs. Lily C., ed.

Library of Congress PN6161.L58 10—4336

NL 0427295 DLC NcD ViU AU KEmT

Lloyd, Francis Bartow, 1861-1897.

PE2926 .F5
Figh, Margaret Gillis.
A word-list from "Bill Arp" [pseud.] and "Rufus Sanders" [pseud.] by Margaret Gillis Figh. Comments on word-lists in PADS, by James Nathan Tidwell. A word-list from southern Kentucky, by A. P. Dalton. The secretary's report. Greensboro, N. C., American Dialect Society, 1950.

Lloyd, Francis Ernest, 1868–
... Abscission in general and with special reference to the curtailment of fruitage in *Gossypium*, by Francis E. Lloyd ... Montreal, 1927.
cover-title, p. 195–207. pl. 13. 24½^cm. (McGill university publications. Series II (Botany) no. 51)
"Reprinted from memoirs of the Horticultural society of New York, 3, July, 1927."
"Literature cited": p. 206–207.

1. Abscission (Botany) 2. Cotton—Diseases and pests.

Library of Congress QK1.M14 no. 51 28-20890

NL 0427297 DLC CaBVaU OrU PU MiU OU

Lloyd, Francis Ernest, 1868–
... The abscission of flower-buds and fruits in *Gossypium*, and its relation to environmental changes. By Francis E. Lloyd ... Montreal, 1916.
cover-title, p. 55–61. 25^cm. (McGill university. Papers from the Dept. of botany. New ser., no. 1)
"Reprinted from the Transactions of the Royal society of Canada, section IV, May, 1916."

1. Cotton—Diseases and pests.

Library of Congress QK1.M14 no. 1 18—13012
——— Copy 2. SB608.C8L5

NL 0427298 DLC CaBVaU OrU OU MiU

Lloyd, Francis Ernest, 1868–
... Abscission of fruits in *Juglans californica quercina*, by Francis E. Lloyd ... Montreal, 1921.
cover-title, p. 17–22. illus., diagrs. 24½^cm. (McGill university publications. Series II (Botany) no. 8)
"Reprinted from Transactions of the Royal society of Canada, section V, 1920."

1. Abscission (Botany) 2. Walnut.

Library of Congress QK1.M14 no. 8 24-4162
——— Copy 2. QK763.L6

NL 0427299 DLC OrU OU MiU CaBVaU

Lloyd, Francis Ernest, 1868-
[Algae and related subjects - collected works] [1912-27]
12 no. in 1 v. 27 cm.

1. Algae - Collected works.

NL 0427300 CU

Lloyd, Francis Ernest, 1868-
The artificial induction of leaf formation in the ocotillo. 1905.
Reprinted from Torreya, v. 5, Oct. 1905.

NL 0427301 OU

Lloyd, Francis Ernest, 1868-1947.
The behaviour of vampyrella lateritia with special reference to the work of Professor Chr. Gobi. 1930.
(McGill university. Publications. Series II: Botany. no. 64)

NL 0427302 OrU

Lloyd, Francis Ernest, 1868-
The behaviour of Vampyrella lateritia with special reference to the work of Professor Chr. Gobi, ... Montreal, 1930.
Reprinted from Archiv fuer protistenkunde. band 67, heft 23, 1929.

NL 0427303 OU

VOLUME 337

Lloyd, Francis Ernest, 1868–
... The bog-forests of Lake Memphremagog: their destruction and consequent successions in relation to water levels, by F. E. Lloyd ... and G. W. Scarth, M. A. Ottawa [etc.] The Royal society of Canada, 1922.
cover-title, p. 45–48. 25cm. (McGill university publications. Series II (Botany) no. 15)
"From the Transactions of the Royal society of Canada. Third series—1922. volume XVI."
"References": p. 48.
1. Forests and forestry—Quebec (Province) 2. Memphremagog, Lake. I. Scarth, George W., joint author. II. Title.
Library of Congress QK1.M14 no. 15 24-16695

NL 0427304 DLC OrU CaBVaU MiU OU

Lloyd, Francis Ernest, 1868-1947.
The carnivorous plants - a review with contributions. Ottawa, Printed for the Royal society of Canada, 1933.
67 p.

NL 0427305 OCl

Lloyd, Francis Ernest, 1868–1947.
The carnivorous plants, by Francis Ernest Lloyd ... Waltham, Mass., Chronica botanica company, 1942.
2 p. l., [vii]–xv, [1], 352 p. incl. illus., plates, diagrs. 27 cm. (*Half-title:* A New series of plant science books, ed. by Frans Verdoorn, vol. IX)
"Literature cited" at end of most of the chapters.
1. Insectivorous plants
A 43—2743
Chicago. Univ. Libr. for Library of Congress QK917.L6
581.53332

MtBC
Wa WaS WaT WaTC WaWW CaBViP CaBVa CaBVaU IdPI OrU PPAN PPT PWcS CtY-M DLC ICJ MtU Or OrCS OrPR OrSaW CSt OCl OCU WaU OO ICJ MnU PSC NIC PCM NBuC PHC PU CtY NIC NBuU TxU AAP IU LU PSt OClW OU ViU RPB MiHM
NL 0427306 ICU ICF CLU-M MB KEmT NNBG OU CaOTP NcU

Lloyd, Francis E., and **C. S. Ridgway.**
Cedar-apples and apples. Montgomery: Brown Prtg. Co. [1911.] 19 p. 8°. (Alabama. Agriculture Department. Bulletin 39.)
1. Apples, U. S.: Ala. 2. Ridgway, C. S.
N. Y. P. L. November 20, 1912.

NL 0427308 NN

Lloyd, Francis Ernest, 1868–
... Cell disjunction in *Spirogyra*, by Francis E. Lloyd ... Montreal, 1927.
cover-title, p. 275–287. 1 illus., pl. XIX. 23cm. (McGill university publications. Series II (Botany) no. 46)
"Reprinted from Papers of the Michigan academy of science, arts and letters, vol. VI, 1926."
"References": p. 286.
1. Spirogyra. 2. Plant cells and tissues. I. Title.
Library of Congress QK1.M14 no. 46 28-20881

NL 0427309 DLC OrU CaBVaU MiU OU

Lloyd, Francis Ernest, 1868–
... The cobalt sodium hexanitrite reaction for potassium in plant cells, by F. E. Lloyd ... Montreal, 1925.
cover-title, p. [369]–385. pl. V. 23cm. (McGill university publications. Series II (Botany) no. 32)
"Presented originally before Sect. V. Royal society of Canada, May 1923."
"Reprinted from Flora oder Allgemeine botanische zeitung, n. f., 18 und 19 band. 1925."
"Citations": p. 384.
1. Microchemistry. 2. Cobalt sodium hexanitrite. 3. Plant cells and tissues. 4. Potassium.
Library of Congress QK1.M14 no. 32 28-28207
——— Copy 2. QK673.L6

NL 0427310 DLC OrU OU MiU CaBVaU

Lloyd, Francis Ernest, 1868–
... The colloidal properties of protoplasm: imbibition in relation to growth, by Francis E. Lloyd ... Montreal, 1918.
cover-title, p. 133–139. diagr. 25cm. (McGill university. Papers from the Dept. of botany. new ser., no. 3)
"Reprinted from Transactions of the Royal society of Canada, section IV, 1917."
1. Protoplasm.
Library of Congress QK1.M14 no. 3 19-16848
——— Copy 2. QH591.L5

NL 0427311 DLC CaBVaU OrU PU MiU OU OO

QK
1
T62
v.8
no.1
Lloyd, Francis Ernest, 1868-
The comparative embryology of the Rubiaceae. [New York?] 1899.
2 pts. in 1. illus. (Memoirs of the Torrey Botanical Club, vol.8, no.1, pt.1-2)
UU copy imperfect: wanting t.p. of pt.1.
1. Rubiaceae. I. Title.

NL 0427312 UU MB OU LU

Lloyd, Francis Ernest, 1868–
... Conjugation in *Spirogyra* (preliminary summary) by Francis E. Lloyd ... Montreal, 1925.
cover-title, p. 129–134. pl. X. 25cm. (McGill university publications. Series II (Botany) no. 30)
"Reprinted from the Transactions of the Royal Canadian institute, Toronto, vol. XV., part I ... 1924."
1. Spirogyra. 2. Plants—Reproduction. I. Title.
Library of Congress QK1.M14 no. 30 28-28208

NL 0427313 DLC CaBVaU OrU OU MiU NN

Lloyd, Francis Ernest, 1868-1947.
The contractile vacuole. 1928.
(McGill university. Publications. Series II. Botany. no. 58)

NL 0427314 OrU

Lloyd, Francis Ernest, 1868-
The contractile vacuole, ... Cambridge Engl. University press, 1928.

NL 0427315 OU

[**Lloyd, Francis Ernest**] 1868–
... Course in biology in the Horace Mann school. New York, Columbia university press, 1901.
cover-title, 68 p. 23½cm. (Teachers college record ... vol. II, no. 1)
p. 61–68, advertising matter.
"By Francis E. Lloyd and Maurice A. Bigelow."
1. Biology—Teaching. 2. Columbia university. Teachers college. Horace Mann school. I. Bigelow, Maurice Alpheus, 1872– joint author.
E 10-578
Library, U. S. Bur. of Education L11.T4

NL 0427316 DHEW CU PBm MiU ICJ

Lloyd, Francis Ernest, 1868–
... The cytology of vegetable crystals, by Francis E. Lloyd ... Montreal, 1923.
cover-title, 5 p. 24cm. (McGill university publications. Series II (Botany) no. 18)
"Reprinted from Science, vol. 57, no. 1470, March 2, 1923."
1. Plant cells and tissues. I. Title.
24-16693
Library of Congress QK1.M14 no. 18

NL 0427317 DLC CaBVaU OrU MiU OU

Lloyd, Francis Ernest, 1868-1947, joint author.

Scarth, George William, 1881–
An elementary course in general physiology: part I—Principles and theory, by G. W. Scarth ... part II—Laboratory exercises, by F. E. Lloyd ... and G. W. Scarth ... New York, J. Wiley & sons, inc.; London, Chapman & Hall, limited, 1930.

632.3
L77e
Lloyd, Francis Ernest, 1868-
Environmental changes and their effect upon boll-shedding in cotton (Gossypium herbaceum). New York, 1920.
cover-title, 131p. illus., diagrs. (Annals of the New York academy of sciences. v.XXIX, p.1-131)

NL 0427319 IU DAS

Lloyd, Francis Ernest, 1868–
... Environmental changes and their effect upon boll-shedding in cotton. (*Gossypium herbaceum*) by Francis E. Lloyd ... Montreal, 1921.
cover-title, 131 p. illus., diagrs. (1 fold.) 24cm. (McGill university publications. Series II (Botany) no. 6)
"Reprinted from Annals of New York academy of science, vol. XXXIX."
"Literature": p. 129–131.
1. Cotton. 2. Abscission (Botany) I. Title: Boll-shedding in cotton.
24—4161
Library of Congress QK1.M14 no. 6
——— Copy 2. SB249.L6

NL 0427320 DLC CaBVaU ICJ OrU MiU OU TxU

Lloyd, Francis Ernest, 1868-1947.
The extra-nuptial nectaries in the common brake, Pteridium aguilinum. n.p. [1901?]
6 p. 4°.
Repr.: Science, N.S., Vol. XIII., No. 336 ... 1901.

NL 0427321 NN

Lloyd, Francis Ernest. 1868–
... Fluorescence in the *Cyanophyceae*, by F. E. Lloyd ... Montreal, 1923.
cover-title, p. 129–136. 25cm. (McGill university publications. Series II. (Botany) no. 20)
"From the Transactions of the Royal society of Canada. Third series—1923. volume XVII."
Bibliography: p. 136.
1. Color of plants. 2. Fluorescence. 3. Cyanophyceae.
28-28209
Library of Congress QK1.M14 no. 20

NL 0427322 DLC CaBVaU OrU OU MiU

VOLUME 337

Lloyd, Francis Ernest, 1868-
... The fluorescence of certain lower plants, by Francis E. Lloyd ... Montreal, 1923.
cover-title, 4 p. 17cm. (McGill university publications. Series II (Botany). no. 21)
"Reprinted from Nature, July 28, 1923."

1. Color of plants. 2. Fluorescence.
Library of Congress QK1.M14 no. 21 28-28210

NL 0427323 DLC OrU OU MiU CaBVaU

Lloyd, Francis Ernest, 1868-
... The fluorescent colors of plants [by] Francis E. Lloyd ... Montreal, 1924.
cover-title, 21 p. 23½cm. (McGill university publications. Series II. (Botany) no. 24)
"Address of the vice-president and chairman of Section G—Botany—American association for the advancement of science, Cincinnati, Ohio, December, 1923."
"Reprinted from Science, March 14, 1924, vol. LIX, no. 1524."
"Citations": p. 20-21.

1. Color of plants. 2. Fluorescence.
Library of Congress QK1.M14 no. 24 28-28211

NL 0427324 DLC OrU CaBVaU OU MiU

Lloyd, Francis Ernest, 1868-
... Futher observations on the behavior of gametes during maturation and conjugation in spirogyra. Montreal, 1928.
cover-title, [45]-66 plate. 24.5 cm. (McGill university publications. Series ii (Botany) no. 56)
"References": p. 64-65.

NL 0427325 OrU CaBVaU

Lloyd, Francis Ernest, 1868-
Further observations on the behavior of gametes during maturation and conjugation in Spirogyra. Montreal, 1928.
Repr. from Protoplasma 1928, vol. IV, no. 1.

NL 0427326 OU

Lloyd, Francis Ernest, 1868-1947.
Futher studies in periodic precipitation. 1932. (McGill university. Publications. Series II. Botany. no. 71)

NL 0427327 OrCS

Lloyd, Francis Ernest, 1868-
Further studies in periodic precipitation, ... Montreal, 1932.
Reprinted from the Journal of physical chemistry vol. XXXV, 1512-1564 p. June, 1931.

NL 0427328 OU

Lloyd, Francis Ernest, 1868-
... Growth in *Eriogonum nudum* in relation to environmental factors, by Francis E. Lloyd ... Montreal, 1921.
cover-title, p. 211-244. illus., diagrs. 25cm. (McGill university publications. Series II (Botany) no. 7)
"Reprinted from the Transactions of the Royal Canadian institute, Toronto, vol. XIII, no. I."
"Literature references": p. 243-244.

1. Growth (Plants) 2. Eriogonum nudum.
Library of Congress QK1.M14 no. 7 24-4160
——— Copy 2. QK731.L8

NL 0427329 DLC OrU CaBVaU MiU OU

Lloyd, Francis Ernest, 1868-
Guayule (*Parthenium argentatum Gray*), a rubber-plant of the Chihuahuan desert, by Francis Ernest Lloyd ... Washington, D. C., Carnegie institution of Washington, 1911.
viii, 213 p. illus., 46 pl. incl. front., diagrs. 25½cm. (*On verso of t.-p.:* Carnegie institution of Washington. Publication no. 139)
Plates partly included in paging.
Bibliography: p. 211-213.

1. Guayule. 2. Rubber—Mexico.
Library of Congress SB291.G8L6 11-20873

PP PPAN DI IdPI WaSp CaBVaU WaWW
NcD MH-A ViU ICJ NN MB OO OCl PSC PPAmP PU PBm PHC
NL 0427330 DLC TU OrU CoU OrCS IdU OrP OAkU DPU CU

Lloyd, Francis Ernest, 1868-1947.
——— and Tracy, Samuel Mills. The insular flora of Mississippi and Louisiana. [New York. 1901.] 8°. Plates and diagrs.
"Reprinted from the *Bulletin of the Torrey botanical club,*" 1901, xxviii, 61-101.

NL 0427331 MH-A OU

Lloyd, Francis Ernest, 1868-
An introductory course in general physiology, by Francis E. Lloyd ... and George W. Scarth ... [Montreal, 1921]
16 p. 23cm. (*On cover:* McGill university publications. Series II (Botany) no. 10)

1. Physiology—Outlines, syllabi, etc. I. Scarth, George W., joint author.
Library of Congress QK1.M14 no. 10 24-3387
——— Copy 2. QP41.L6

NL 0427332 DLC CtY-M CaBVaU MiU OU

Lloyd, Francis Ernest, 1868-
... Maturation and conjugation in *Spirogyra longata*, by Francis E. Lloyd ... Montreal, 1926.
cover-title, 151-193, [4] p. illus., IV pl. 25cm. (McGill university publications. Series II (Botany) no. 38)
"Reprinted from the Transactions of the Royal Canadian institute, vol. XV, 1926."
"Citations": p. 191-193.

1. Spirogyra longata. 2. Plants—Reproduction.
Library of Congress QK1.M14 no. 38 28-20880

NL 0427333 DLC CaBVaU OrU MiU

Lloyd, Francis Ernest, 1868-1947.
The mechanism of the water tight door of the ultricularia trap. 1929. (McGill university. Publications. Series II: Botany. no. 62)

NL 0427334 OrU

Lloyd, Francis Ernest, 1868-
... A method of ultramicroscopy whereby fluorescence in the *Cyanophyceæ* and *Diatomaceæ* may be demonstrated ... Ultramicroscopically observable fluorescence, by Francis E. Lloyd ... Montreal, 1923.
cover-title, 3 p., 1 l. 24 x 19½cm. (McGill university publications. Series II (Botany) no. 22-23)
Reprinted from Science, August 3, 1923, vol. LVIII, no. 1492 and September 21, 1923, vol. LVIII, no. 1499.

1. Color of plants. 2. Fluorescence. 3. Cyanophyceae. 4. Diatomaceae.
Library of Congress QK1.M14 no. 22-23 28-28212

NL 0427335 DLC CaBVaU OrU MiU OU

Lloyd, Francis Ernest, 1868-1947
Mode of occurrence of caoutchouc in the gueyule, parthenium argentatum Gray and its function. 1932 (McGill university. Publications. Series II. Botany. #73)

NL 0427336 OrU

Lloyd, Francis Ernest, 1868-
... The mode of occurrence of tannin in the living cell, by Francis E. Lloyd ... Montreal, 1922.
cover-title, p. [430]-450. illus. 23cm. (McGill university publications. Series II (Botany) no. 12)
"Reprinted from the Journal of the American leather chemists association, September, 1922."
Bibliography: p. 448-450.

1. Tannins. 2. Botany—Physiology.
Library of Congress QK1.M14 no. 12 24-16694

NL 0427337 DLC OrU MiU OU CaBVaU

581.1
L773

Lloyd, Francis Ernest, 1868-
... A new and cheap form of auxanometer, by F. E. Lloyd. New York, 1903.
cover-title, 97-100 p. diagrs. (Contributions from the Department of botany of Columbia university, no 205)
"Reprinted from Torreya, 7 ... July, 1903.
I. Title: Auxanometer.

NL 0427338 NNC OU

Lloyd, Francis Ernest, 1868-
... The occurrence and functions of tannin in the living cell, by Francis E. Lloyd ... Ottawa [etc.] The Royal society of Canada, 1922.
cover-title, 13, [1] p. III pl. 24½cm. (McGill university publications. Series II (Botany) no 14)
"From the Transactions of the Royal society of Canada. Third series—1922. Volume XVI."
"Literature cited": p. 11-13.

1. Tannins. 2. Botany—Physiology.
Library of Congress QK1.M14 no. 14 24-15173

NL 0427339 DLC CaBVaU OrU OU

Lloyd, Francis Ernest, 1868-
On a abnormal cone in the Douglas spruce, ... 1898.
Repr. from Bulletin of the Torrey botanical club v. 25, no. 2, Feb., 1898.

NL 0427340 OU NjP

Lloyd, Francis Ernest, 1868-
On hypertrophied scale-leaves in Pinus ponderosa. 1898.
Repr. from Annals New York academy of science, v. 11, no. 4, March, 1898.

NL 0427341 OU OO

Lloyd, Francis Ernest, 1868-
... On the mutual precipitation of dyes and plant mucilages, by Francis E. Lloyd ... Montreal, 1921.
cover-title, p. 23-31. 24½cm. (McGill university publications. Series II (Botany) no. 9)
"Reprinted from Transactions of the Royal society of Canada, section v, 1920."

1. Dyes and dyeing. 2. Mucilage. 3. Botany—Physiology.
Library of Congress QK1.M14 no. 9 24-4163
——— Copy 2. QK899.L7

NL 0427342 DLC CaBVaU DNAL OrU MiU OU

VOLUME 337

Lloyd, Francis Ernest, 1868–
... The origin of *Ascidia* under quasi-experimental conditions, by Francis E. Lloyd ... Montreal, 1917.
cover-title, p. 71–80. illus. 25½cm. (McGill university. Papers from the Dept. of botany. new ser., no. 2)
"Reprinted from Transactions of the Royal society of Canada, section IV, 1917."

1. Ascidia (Botany)
Library of Congress QK1.M14 no. 2 19-16847
——— Copy 2. QK649.L6

NL 0427343 DLC CaBVaU PU MiU OU OO OrU

Lloyd, Francis Ernest, 1868-1947
Origin of vacuoles. 1926. (McGill university. Publications, Ser. II: Botany #37)

NL 0427344 OrU

Lloyd, Francis Ernest, 1868–1947.
The physiology of stomata, by Francis Ernest Lloyd. Washington, D. C., Carnegie institution of Washington, 1908.
142 p. illus., 14 pl. (incl. front.) diagrs. (1 fold.) 25½ cm. (*On verso of t.-p.:* Carnegie institution of Washington. Publication. no. 82)
Bibliography: p. 141–142.

1. Stomata.
QK873.L79 8—9545

OrPR OrU
IdPI CoU MU CU OrP IdU WaSp WaWW CLSU CaBVaU OrCS OCl ViU PP PU PPAmP TU MdPB PBm PHC ICJ NN MB Wa
NL 0427345 DLC DNLM I NcD MiU OU OCU OO OClW MH-A

Lloyd, Francis Ernest, 1868- ed.

The Plant world; a monthly journal of general botany ... v. 1–22; Oct. 1897–Dec. 1919. Binghamton, N. Y., W. N. Clute & co.; [etc., etc.] 1897–1919.

Lloyd, Francis Ernest, 1868–
... Plantation rubber: its source and acquisition [by] Professor Francis E. Lloyd ... Montreal, 1926.
cover-title, 11 p. illus. 20cm. (McGill university publications. Series II (Botany) no. 44)
"Reprinted from the Scientific monthly, September, 1926, vol. XXIII."

1. India-rubber.
Library of Congress QK1.M14 no. 44 28-20888

NL 0427347 DLC OrU CaBVaU OU MiU

Lloyd, Francis Ernest, 1868- ed.
Andrews, Eliza Frances, 1840–
A practical course in botany, with especial reference to its bearings on agriculture, economics, and sanitation, by E. F. Andrews ... with editorial revision by Francis E. Lloyd ... New York, Cincinnati [etc.] American book company [°1911]

Lloyd, Francis Ernest, 1868-
The problem of excretion with especial reference to the contractile vacuole. Montreal, 1930.
1163-1168 p. 25 cm. (McGill University publications. Series 2 (Botany) no. 69)

NL 0427349 OU OrU

Lloyd, Francis Ernest, 1868-

Torrey botanical club, *New York.*
Proceedings of the semi-centennial anniversary of the Torrey botanical club, October 18, 19 and 20, 1917. [New York, 1918]

Lloyd, Francis Ernest 1868-1947.
The pulsatory rhythm of the contractile vesicle in paramecium. 1929.
(McGill university. Publications. Series II: Botany. no. 60)
By F.E. Lloyd and J. Beattie.

NL 0427351 OrU

Lloyd, Francis Ernest, 1868–1947.
The range of structural and functional variation in the trap of *Utricularia.* Montreal, 1931.
[260]–276 p. illus. 23 cm. (McGill University publications, series 2 (Botany) no. 70)
"Reprinted from Flora, or, Allgemeine botanische Zeitung, n. F., 25. Band."
Includes bibliography.

1. Utricularia. 2. Botany—Morphology. I. Title.
QK1.M14 no. 70 583.825 52-54522 ‡
——— Copy 2. QK495.U8L6

NL 0427352 DLC OrU OU

Lloyd, Francis Ernest, 1868–
... River-bank and beach vegetation of the St. Lawrence river below Montreal in relation to water-levels, by Francis E. Lloyd ... and George W. Scarth, M. A. Ottawa [etc.] The Royal society of Canada, 1922.
cover-title, p. 49–50. 24½cm. (McGill university publications. Series II (Botany) no. 16)
"From the Transactions of the Royal society of Canada. Third series—1922. volume XVI."

1. Botany—St. Lawrence river. I. Scarth, George William, 1881– joint author.
Library of Congress QK1.M14 no. 16 24—16696

NL 0427353 DLC OrU MiU OU CaBVaU

Lloyd, Francis Ernest
Role of kinoplasm in the genesis of vacuoles. 1927.
(McGill university. Publications, Ser. II: Botany no. 49)
By F.E. Lloyd and G.W. Scarth.

NL 0427354 OrU

Lloyd, Francis Ernest, 1868-
...The role of the wall in the living cell as studied by the auxographic method...
Montreal, 1926

QK1
.M14
no. 40

NL 0427355 DLC OrU CaBVaU OU

Lloyd, F. ~~E.~~ Francis Ernest **and L. N. Duncan.**
School gardening. [Auburn, 1911.] 27 p. illus. 8°. (Alabama. Agricultural Experiment Station at Auburn. Circular 13.)

1. School grounds and gardens. 2. Duncan, L. N.
N. Y. P. L. June 17, 1913.

NL 0427356 NN

Lloyd, Francis Ernest, 1868–
... Sexual reproduction in water silk, by Francis E. Lloyd ... Montreal, 1926.
cover-title, 11 p. illus. 24½cm. (McGill university publications. Series II (Botany) no. 35)
"Reprinted from the Science monthly, April, 1926. vol. XXII."

1. Spirogyra. 2. Plants—Reproduction.
Library of Congress QK1.M14 no. 35 28-28213

NL 0427357 DLC CaBVaU OrU MiU OU

Lloyd, Francis E., and others.
Some Alabama plant diseases. By Francis E. Lloyd, C. S. Ridgway and H. J. Chatterton. I. An important pecan disease. II. Fire blight of pears, apples, etc. III. The black rot of grapes. March 15, 1910. [Montgomery: Brown Printing Co., 1910.] 22 p. illus. pap. 8°. (Alabama. Agriculture and industries commissioner. Bulletin of State agricultural department. 32.)

1. Pecan (tree and nut).—Diseases, etc. 2. Pear.—Diseases, etc. 3. Apple.—Diseases, etc. 4. Grape.—Diseases, etc. 5. C. S. Ridgway. 6. H. J. Chatterton.
N. Y. P. L. October 26, 1911

NL 0427358 NN

Lloyd, Francis Ernest, 1868–
... Some behaviors of *Vampyrella lateritia* and the response of *Spirogyra* to its attack. By Francis E. Lloyd ... Montreal, 1927.
cover-title, p. 395–416. illus., pl. XXV–XXVII. 23cm. (McGill university publications. Series II (Botany) no. 47)
"Reprinted from Papers of the Michigan academy of science, arts and letters, vol. VII, 1926."
"Citations": p. 414.

1. Vampyrella lateritia. 2. Spirogyra. 3. Plant cells and tissues.
Library of Congress QK1.M14 no. 47 28-20883

NL 0427359 DLC OrU MiU OU CaBVaU

Lloyd, Francis Ernest, 1868–
Some effects of narcotics on *Spirogyra,* by Prof. Francis E. Lloyd ... [Montreal, 1924]
12 p. illus. 21½cm. (*On cover:* McGill university publications. Series II. (Botany) no. 25)
"Read during the Third annual meeting of the Canadian society of anesthetists, with the Canadian medical association, Mount Royal Hotel, Montreal, June 12–14, 1923."
"Reprinted from Anesthesia and analgesia, February, 1924."

1. Spirogyra. 2. Anesthetics.
Library of Congress QK1.M14 no. 25 28-28214

NL 0427360 DLC OrU CaBVaU MiU OU

Lloyd, Francis Ernest, 1868–
... Some features of structure and behaviour in *Vampyrella lateritia,* by Francis E. Lloyd ... The origin of vacuoles, by Francis E. Lloyd ... Montreal, 1926.
cover-title, 5, 4 p. 22cm. (McGill university publications. Series II (Botany) no. 36–37)
The second paper signed: F. E. Lloyd, G. W. Scarth.
"Reprinted from Science, April 2 and 30, 1926. vol. LXIII."

1. Vampyrella lateritia. 2. Plant cells and tissues. 3. Spirogyra. I. Scarth, George William, 1881– II. Title: Vacuoles, The origin of.
Library of Congress QK1.M14 no. 36-37 28-20884

NL 0427361 DLC CaBVaU OrU OU MiU

VOLUME 337

Lloyd, Francis Ernest, 1868- joint author.
Lowe, Charles William, 1885-
... Some observations on *Hydrodictyon reticulatum* (L.) Lagerh., with special reference to the chloroplasts and organization, by Charles W. Lowe and Francis E. Lloyd ... Montreal, 1928.

Lloyd, Francis Ernest, 1868-
The structure of cereal straws, by Francis E. Lloyd ... Montreal, 1922.
cover-title, [16] p. illus. 29½ x 23cm. (McGill university publications. Series II (Botany) no. 11)
Rearranged and reprinted from the Pulp and paper magazine, vol. XIX ... 1921.
"Literature": p. [16]

1. Straw. 2. Grain. 3. Botany—Morphology. 4. Paper.
28-28215
Library of Congress QK1.M14 no. 11
——— Copy 2. TS1109.L785

NL 0427363 DLC OrU OU MiU CaBVaU

Lloyd, Francis Ernest, 1868-
... The structure of hailstones of exceptional form and size. By Francis E. Lloyd ... Montreal, 1916.
cover-title, p. [47]-50. illus. 25cm. (McGill university. Papers from the Dept. of meteorology. new ser. no. 1)
"Reprinted from the Transactions of the Royal society of Canada, section III, September 1916."

1. Hail.
18-11523
Library of Congress QC851.M12 no. 1

NL 0427364 DLC CaBVaU PU MiU DAS OU

Lloyd, Francis Ernest, 1868-
... Studies in periodic precipitation, by F.E.Lloyd ... and V.Moravek ... Montreal, 1928.
cover-title, p.101-130, plates. 25.5 cm. (McGill university publications. Series ii (Botany) no.55)
Reprinted from Plant physiology, v.3. "Literature cited:" p.124-125.

NL 0427365 OrU CaBVaU

Lloyd, Francis Ernest, 1868-
... Studies on *Spirogyra* ... by Francis E. Lloyd ... Montreal, 1926.
cover-title, p. 75-110, 1 l. 2 pl. 24½cm. (McGill university publications. Series II (Botany) no. 39)
"Reprinted from the Transactions of the Royal society of Canada, Section V, 1926."
The substance of the first paper was presented at the joint session of the American society of plant physiologists and the Physiological section of the Botanical society of America, Kansas City, Dec. 31, 1925. cf. p. 75.
"References": p. 109-110.
CONTENTS.—I. Additional studies on conjugation.—II. Adhesions and geniculations.
1. Spirogyra longata. 2. Plants—Reproduction.
28-20882
Library of Congress QK1.M14 no. 39

NL 0427366 DLC OrU MiU OU CaBVaU

Lloyd, Francis Ernest, 1868-
... A surface tensiometer and an osmometer for class work and ... The role of kinoplasm in the genesis of vacuoles, by Francis E. Lloyd ... and G. W. Scarth ... Montreal, 1927.
cover-title, 1 p. l., 2 p. 26cm. (McGill university publications. Series II (Botany) no. 48-49)
"Reprinted from Science, Sept. 10, 1926, vol. LXIV, no. 1654 ... and Science, June 17, 1927, vol. LXV, no. 1694."

1. Botanical apparatus. 2. Cells. I. Scarth, George William, 1881- joint author.
28-20889
Library of Congress QK1.M14 no. 48-49

NL 0427367 DLC OrU NcU MiU OU CaBVaU

Lloyd, Francis Ernest, 1868- 580.7 Q302
... . Syllabus of a course of six lectures on the vegetation of the earth. I. Plant life: large groups and characteristics. 2. Plants in their environment. 3. The vegetation of the Arctic regions and of mountain tops. 4. The vegetation of the temperate regions: the forests. 5. The vegetation of the temperate regions: the deserts. 6. The vegetation of the tropics. By Francis Ernest Lloyd, ... New York City, Teachers College, Columbia University, ©1903.
8 p. 24cm. (Extension syllabi, series B, no. 3. Columbia University in the city of New York.)

NL 0427368 ICJ

Lloyd, Francis Ernest, 1868-
... The teaching of biology in the secondary school, by Francis E. Lloyd, A. M. and Maurice A. Bigelow, PH. D. ... New York [etc.] Longmans, Green, and co., 1904.
viii, 491 p. 20½cm. (American teachers' series)
Contains bibliographies.

1. Biology—Study and teaching. I. Bigelow, Maurice Alpheus, 1872- joint author.
Library of Congress QH315.L79 4-22995

NL 0427369 DNLM WaWW MiU OCU ViU OO ICJ NN DLC FMU NNBG ICRL MB PBm PPGi PPM NjP

Lloyd, Francis Ernest, 1868-
... The teaching of biology in the secondary school, by Francis E. Lloyd ... and Maurice A. Bigelow ... New York [etc.] Longmans, Green, and co., 1907.
viii, 491 p. 20½cm. (*Half-title:* American teachers' series)
Series title also at head of t.-p.
Contains bibliographies.

1. Biology—[Study and] teaching—[Secondary schools] I. Bigelow, Maurice Alpheus, 1872- joint author.
E 8-253
U. S. Off. of educ. Library for Library of Congress QH315.L8 [a40g1]

NL 0427370 DHEW NN WaS Or PU PBa PU

Lloyd, Francis E[rnest], and M. A. Bigelow.
The teaching of biology in the secondary school. New York: Longmans, Green, and Co., 1909. viii, 491 p. 8°. (American teachers series.)
Bibliographies at the beginning of most of the chapters. Includes: The teaching of zoölogy in the secondary school.

CENTRAL CIRCULATION.
1. Bigelow, Maurice Alpheus, jt. au. 2. Biology. 3. Botany. 4. Zoölogy. 5. Physiology. 6. Series. 7. Two title cards.
N. Y. P. L. June 15, 1911.

NL 0427371 NN ViU MiU

Lloyd, Francis Ernest, 1868-
... The teaching of biology in the secondary school, by Francis E. Lloyd ... Maurice A. Bigelow ... New ed. New York [etc.] Longmans, Green, and co., 1914.
viii, 491 p. 20½cm. (*Half-title:* American teachers series, ed. by J. E. Russell) $1.50
Series title also at head of t.-p.
Contains bibliographies.

1. Biology—Study and teaching I. Bigelow, Maurice Alpheus, 1872- joint author.
Library of Congress QH315.L79 1914 14-18896

NL 0427372 DLC NcD MB DNLM PV PU-BZ ODW OClh

Lloyd, Francis E[rnest], and M. A. Bigelow.
The teaching of biology in the secondary school. London: Longmans Green and Co., 1919. 491 p. New ed. 8°. (American teachers series.)
Bibliography at beginning of some chapters.
Botanical literature, p. 229-236.
Zoological books, p. 417-447.

CENTRAL CIRCULATION.
1. Botany.—Teaching. 2. Bigelow, Maurice Alpheus, jt. au. 3. Biology.—Teaching. 4. Zoology.—Teaching. 5. Physiology.—Teaching. 6. Series.
N. Y. P. L. July 13, 1921.

NL 0427373 NN

Lloyd, Francis Ernest, 1868-
... University extension. New York, Columbia university press, 1903.

Lloyd, Francis Ernest, 1868-
... The vegetation of Canada [by] Francis E. Lloyd ... Montreal, 1924.
cover-title, p. 207-228. illus. 20½cm. (McGill university publications. Series II (Botany) no. 29)
"From the Handbook of the British association for the advancement of science, Toronto, 1924."

1. Botany—Canada.
28-28216
Library of Congress QK1.M14 no. 29

NL 0427375 DLC CaBVaU OrU

Lloyd, Francis Thomas, 1838-1912.
First or Grenadier guards in South Africa 1899-1902
see under Gt. Brit. Army. Grenadier guards.

PS2386 .L66 1942
Lloyd, Francis V
Melville's first lectures [by] Francis V. Lloyd, Jr.
(In American literature. Durham, N. C. 26cm. v. 13, no. 4 (Jan., 1942) p. [391]-395)

1. Melville, Herman, 1819-1891—Addresses, essays, lectures. I. American literature.

NL 0427377 ViU

792.94 L793d
Lloyd, Frank.
The dramatic and undramatic in the photoplay. Los Angeles, Palmer Photoplay Corporation [c1920]
[15]p. port. 21cm. (On cover: Palmer plan of photoplay writing)

1. Moving-pictures. I. Title.

NL 0427378 CLSU

Lloyd, Mrs. Frank.
British museum. *Dept. of ceramics and ethnography.*
Catalogue of the Frank Lloyd collection of Worcester porcelain of the Wall period, presented by Mr. and Mrs. Frank Lloyd in 1921 to the Department of ceramics and ethnography in the British museum, by R. L. Hobson ... [London] Printed by order of the Trustees, 1923.

Lloyd, Frank Sidney, 1897-
Health as a total concept [by] Frank S. Lloyd.
(*In* National education association of the United States. Addresses and proceedings, 1932. p. 457)

1. Hygiene. I. Title.
E 33-913
Library, U. S. Office of Education L13.N212 1932
Library of Congress L13.N4 1932

NL 0427380 DHEW

VOLUME 337

Lloyd, Frank Sidney, 1897-
Notes on the history of physical education, prepared by Professor Frank S. Lloyd ... [New York] New York university press book store, 1935.
cover-title, 63 numb. l. 27.5 cm.

NL 0427381 OrCS

Lloyd, Frank Sidney, 1897-
Safety in athletics; the prevention and treatment of athletic injuries, by Frank S. Lloyd ... George G. Deaver ... [and] Floyd R. Eastwood ... Philadelphia and London, W. B. Saunders company, 1936.
1 p. l., 11-432 p. illus., diagr. 20cm.
"Selected bibliography": p. 391-394.
1. Athletics. 2. Sports—Accidents and injuries. 3. Accidents—Prevention. 4. Physical education and training. I. Deaver, George Gilbert, 1890- joint author. II. Eastwood, Floyd Reed, 1900- joint author. III. Title.
36-37506
Library of Congress GV344.L54
——— Copy 2.
Copyright A 101125 [5] 796

OU OCU OCl ODW OO KEmT OrLgE OrAshS
NL 0427382 DLC TxU OrU NcD PPGi PU-Penn PWcS PPD

GV 344 L54
Lloyd, Frank Sidney, 1897-
Safety in athletics; the prevention and treatment of athletic injuries, by Frank S. Lloyd ... George G. Deaver ... [and] Floyd R. Eastwood ... Philadelphia and London, W. B. Saunders Co. 1937.
432p. illus. 20cm.
Includes bibliography.
1. Athletics 2. Sports - Accidents and injuries 3. Accidents - Prevention 4. Physical education and training I. Deaver, George Gilbert, 1890- joint author II. Eastwood, Floyd Reed, 1900- joint author III. Title

NL 0427383 WU OrP TU

GV 344 .L54 1939
Lloyd, Frank Sidney, 1897-
Safety in athletics; the prevention and treatment of athletic injuries, by Frank S. Lloyd ... George G. Deaver ... [and] Floyd R. Eastwood ... Philadelphia and London, W. B. Saunders company 1939.
1 p. l., 11-432 p. illus., diagr. 20cm.
"Selected bibliography": p. 391-394.

NL 0427384 MoU

Lloyd, Frank Sidney, 1897-
Safety in physical education in secondary schools. New York, National Bureau of Casualty and Surety Underwriters, 1933.
x, 167 p. diagrs., forms. 23 cm. (Publications of the National Bureau of Casualty and Surety Underwriters. Educational series, v. 9)
Bibliography: p. 141-143.
1. Physical education and training—Safety measures. 2. Accidents—Prevention. 3. School sports. I. Title. (Series: National Bureau of Casualty Underwriters. Publications. Educational series, v. 9)
GV344.L55 371.73 33-12567 rev*

TxU KEmT OrU
NL 0427385 DLC OrCS NcD PU-Penn PWcS OCl OU OCU WU

Lloyd, Frederic Ebenezer John, 1859-1933, pub.
The American church clergy and parish directory for 1903 ... Cleveland, Frederic E. J. Lloyd, 1903.
363 p.

NL 0427386 ICRL

Lloyd, Frederic Ebenezer John, 1859-1933, pub.
The American Church, clergy and parish directory for 1905. Uniontown, Pa., Lloyd, 1905.
422 p.

NL 0427387 PPPrHi PHi

Lloyd, Frederic Ebenezer John, 1859- , joint editor.
The church school hymnal, with tunes
see under Attwood, William Rix, d. 1910.

BX5830 .S8
Lloyd, Frederic Ebenezer John, 1859-1933, ed.
The Clerical directory of the Protestant Episcopal Church in the United States of America.
New York [etc.] Published by the Church Hymnal Corporation for the Church Pension Fund [etc.]

Lloyd, Frederic Ebenezer John, 1859- comp.
Lloyd's church musicians' directory (1910) The blue book of church musicians in America, comp. by Rev. Frederic E. J. Lloyd ... [vol. 1] ... Chicago, Ritzmann, Brookes & co. [c1910]

BX5943 .A1 1910
Lloyd, Frederic Ebenezer John, 1859- comp.
Protestant Episcopal church in the U. S. A. *Book of common prayer.*
The prayer book of the Protestant Episcopal church simplified and arranged. Chicago, Ritzmann, Brookes & co. [c1910]

Lloyd, Frederic Ebenezer John, 1859-1933.
Two years in the region of icebergs, and what I saw there. By the Rev. F. E. J. Lloyd... London, Society for promoting Christian knowledge [etc., etc., 188-] 127 p. front. 17cm.
274077B. 1. Newfoundland. I. Society for promoting Christian knowledge, London.
N. Y. P. L. June 19, 1944

NL 0427392 NN OCl CtY

Lloyd, Frederic Lindsay. *4013.282.29
Oil engines, heavy & light oils, for tracton work & motor vehicles: comparison between them and electrically-driven vehicles from economic points of view. Plates. Plans.
(In Professional Papers of the Royal Engineers. Vol. 29, pp. 81-97. Chatham. 1903.)
K4321 — Automobiles. — Petroleum motors.

NL 0427393 MB

LLOYD, Frederick.
Brief biographical sketch of Theodore S. Parvin. n.p., [1877]
By Frederick Lloyd and W.B.Langridge.

NL 0427394 MH Ia-HA

Lloyd, Frederick.
Special report on Indians at San Carlos agency, Arizona. [San Carlos, Ariz., 1883.] 10 p. 8°.
Title from cover.
1. Indians, North America.
N. Y. P. L. August 22, 1912.

NL 0427395 NN DNLM ICN NSchU

Lloyd, Frederick, esq.
An accurate and impartial life of the late Lord Viscount Nelson ... comprehending authentic and circumstantial details of his glorious achievements ... by Frederick Lloyd ... Ormskirk, Printed by J. Fowler, 1806.
2 p. l., 303 p. front., plates, ports. 20½cm.
1. Nelson, Horatio Nelson, viscount, 1758-1805.
4-25898†
Library of Congress DA87.1.N4L7

NL 0427396 DLC NN

Lloyd, Frederick, of Iowa, ed.
Annals of Iowa. A historical quarterly. v. [1]-12, 1863-74; new ser., v. 1-3, 1882-84; 3d ser., v. 1- Apr. 1893-
Iowa City [etc.] 1863-19

Lloyd, Frederick, of Iowa, ed.
Iowa historical record, published by the State historical society at Iowa City. v. 1-18; 1885-1902. Iowa City, Ia., 1887-1902.

Lloyd, Frederick Charles.
The art and technique of wine, by F. C. Lloyd ... edited by Stephen Gwynn ... London, Constable & co., ltd. [1936]
xvi, 253, [1] p. front. (port.) illus., plates (1 double) 22½cm.
1. Wine and wine making. I. Gwynn, Stephen Lucius, 1864- ed. II. Title.
37-1504
Library of Congress TP548.L6 1936
Copyright A ad int. 22346 [3] 663.2

NL 0427399 DLC NN

WI L793d 1904
LLOYD, Frederick George
Diseases of the appendix vermiformis and their treatment. London, Bale & Danielsson, 1904.
37 p.
Reprint and enlargement of articles which appeared in the Lancet and in the West London medical journal, 1904.

NL 0427400 DNLM

Lloyd, Frederick James, 1852-
... Cidermaking. By F. J. Lloyd ... Adelaide, Hussey & Gillingham, general printers, 1905.
cover-title, 84 p. illus. 24cm. (South Australia. Dept. of agriculture. Bulletin no. 3)
Reprinted from Bulletin of Board of agriculture, England.
1. Cider.
Agr 13-1429
Library, U. S. Dept. of Agriculture 23So84B no. 3

NL 0427401 DNAL

Lloyd, Frederick James, 1852-
Gt. Brit. *Board of agriculture and fisheries.*
... Report on the results of investigations into cidermaking, carried out on behalf of the Bath and west and southern counties society in the years 1893-1902, by F. J. Lloyd ... Presented to both houses of Parliament by command of His Majesty. London, Printed for H. M. Stationery off., by Darling & son, ltd., 1903.

VOLUME 337

Lloyd, Frederick James, 1852-
... Report on the results of investigations into Cheddar cheese-making, carried out on behalf of the Bath and West and Southern countries society in the years 1891-98 ... London, Printed for Her Majesty's Stationery office by Darling & son, 1899.
251⌈1⌉p. 25cm. (At head of title: Board of agriculture)

NL 0427403 PSt CaBVaU IdU

Lloyd, Frederick James, 1852-
The science of agriculture, by Frederick James Lloyd ... London, Longmans, Green, and co., 1884.
vi p., 1 l., 365 p. illus. 23cm.
"Mainly a reproduction of lectures delivered at King's college, London."

1. Agriculture.
15-16153
Library of Congress S513.L7

NL 0427404 DLC CtY NcSal

Lloyd, Freeman.
A B C of dogs, illustrations by Diana Thorne, verses by Freeman Lloyd. Chicago, New York ⌈etc.⌉ Rand McNally & company, ©1938.
⌈44⌉ p. illus. (part col.) 19½cm.

I. Thorne, Diana, illus. II. Title.
38-18281
Library of Congress PZ8.3.L829A

NL 0427405 DLC

Lloyd, Freeman.
All setters, their histories, rearing and training, bench show points and characteristics, by Freeman Lloyd ... New York, F. Lloyd ⌈©1931⌉
1 p. l., 124, ⌈1⌉ p. illus. 22½cm.
Illustrated t.-p.

1. Setters (Dogs) I. Title.
31-8085
Library of Congress SF429.S5L5
Copyright A 36128 ⌈2⌉ 636.71

NL 0427406 DLC OrP ViW DNAL

Lloyd, Freeman.
All spaniels; their rearing and training, bench show points and characteristics, by Freeman Lloyd ... New York, F. Lloyd ⌈1930⌉
cover-title, 72 p. illus. 21½cm.

1. Spaniels. I. Title.
30-25043
Library of Congress SF429.S7L5
——— Copy 2.
Copyright A 28658 ⌈a35c1⌉ 636.75

NL 0427407 DLC MB ViW OrP

Lloyd, Freeman.
Field dogs in action. By Freeman Lloyd. ⌈Washington, 1937⌉
84-108 p. illus. (part col.) 25½cm.
(In National geographic, v. 71, no. 1, Jan. 1937)
Caption title.

1. Hunting dogs. I. Title.
SF427.L714

NL 0427408 ViW

Lloyd, Freeman.

Cobb, Bert.
Hunting dogs, by Bert Cobb; with an article by Freeman Lloyd. New York, The Crafton collection, inc. ⌈©1931⌉

Lloyd, Freeman.
Man's oldest ally, the dog; since cave-dweller days this faithful friend has shared the work, exploration, and sport of humankind. By Freeman Lloyd. ⌈Washington, 1936⌉
246-274 p. illus. (part col.) 25½cm.
(In National geographic, v. 69, no. 2, Feb. 1936)
Caption title.

1. Dogs. I. Title.
SF427.L715

NL 0427410 ViW

Lloyd, Freeman.
The whippet and race-dog: how to breed, rear, train, race, and exhibit the whippet . . .
= London. Gill. 1894. vi, (1), 204 pp. Illus. Plates. Plans. 18.5 cm., in 8s.

NL 0427411 MB ICJ OKentU ViW

Lloyd, Freeman.
The whippet or race-dog: its breeding, rearing and training for races and for exhibition. With illustrations of typical dogs and diagrams of tracks. By Freeman Lloyd ... Second edition. London: L. Upcott Gill ⌈19-?⌉
2 p. ℓ., 88 p. front., illus. (incl. plans) plates. 18½cm.

1. Whippets. I. Title.

NL 0427412 ViW

Lloyd, Freeman.
The whippet or race-dog; its breeding, ...
2d ed. Lond., The Bazaar, ... 1922.
90 p.

NL 0427413 OU

Lloyd, Freeman.
The whippet or race-dog: its breeding, rearing, and training for races and for exhibition. With illustrations of typical dogs and diagrams of tracks, by Freeman Lloyd, with an entirely new chapter on the whippet as a show-dog by B. S. Fitter. 3d ed. Philadelphia, David McKay co. ⌈1928⌉
vii, 90 p. front., illus. (incl. plans) plates. 18cm.
"Printed in Great Britain."

1. Whippets. I. Fitter, B. S.
29-13999
Library of Congress SF429.W5L6 1928

NL 0427414 DLC MdBE NN OCl

Lloyd, F supposed author.

A letter to the Right Hon. the Viscount Althorp, chancellor of the exchequer, &c., on his proposed interference with the present system of country banking. By a country banker. London, J. Ridgway, 1833.

Lloyd, F C
The rex rabbit. Vancouver, B.C., Mitchell printing & pub. co., 1931.
53 p. front.
1. Rabbits.

NL 0427416 CaBVa

Lloyd, F H M
Hurricane, the story of a great fighter, by F. H. M. Lloyd. Leicester, Published with the co-operation of Hawker aircraft, limited, by the Harborough publishing company ltd., 1945.
3 p. l., 9-136 p. incl. plates (3 double) ports. 22½cm.

1. World war, 1939-1945—Aerial operations. I. Title.
A 47-3665
New York. Public library for Library of Congress ⌈3⌉

NL 0427417 NN NcD

Lloyd, F K.
... Studies in nineteenth-century literature: Antonio Alcalá Galiano, by F. K. Lloyd. Liverpool, "Bulletin of Spanish studies", 1933.
cover-title, 12 p. 23½cm. (Publications of the "Bulletin of Spanish studies". Monograph series: Literature, no. 1)
Includes the text of the most important part of the inaugural lecture delivered by Alcalá Galiano in the University of London, 1828.

1. Alcalá Galiano, Antonio, 1789-1865. I. Title.
40-4578
Library of Congress PQ6020.A5L5
⌈2⌉ 860.9

NL 0427418 DLC CtY CU

WF 140 qL793e 1945
LLOYD, F P
The effect of sulphadiazine prophylaxis on respiratory infection of serving soldiers. Report to Associate Committee on Army Medical Research, National Research Council of Canada. ⌈Camp Borden, 1945?⌉
6, ⌈8⌉ ℓ.
1. Respiratory system - Diseases
2. Sulfadiazine I. National Research Council, Canada. Associate Committee on Army Medical Research

NL 0427419 DNLM

Lloyd, G. The improved art of riding, exemplified in the following rules . . . by G. Lloyd and R. Symes, riding masters. London [1810]. 12mo. Illus. 146349

NL 0427420 CSmH NjP

Lloyd, G. Owen
see Lloyd, Geraint Owen.

Lloyd, G.W., Rev.
see Lloyd, George William, d. 1906.

VOLUME 337

Lloyd, George, ed.

Gerard, Alexander, 1792–1839.
Account of Koonawur, in the Himalaya, etc. ... By the late Capt. Alexander Gerard. Ed. by George Lloyd. London, J. Madden & co., 1841.

Lloyd, George, ed.

FOR OTHER EDITIONS SEE MAIN ENTRY

Lloyd, *Sir* William.
Narrative of a journey from Caunpoor to the Boorendo pass, in the Himalaya Mountains, viâ Gwalior, Agra, Delhi, and Sirhind: by Major Sir William Lloyd. And Captain Alexander Gerard's account of an attempt to penetrate by Bekhur to Garoo, and the Lake Manasarowara: for the purpose of determining the line of perpetual snow on the southern face of the Himalaya ... London, J. Madden & co., 1846.

Lloyd, George.
Soldanella and other poems. Wuxham, 1839.

NL 0427425 PSC-Hi

Lloyd, George, of Seattle.
With the tide: original, tested, proven plans on salesmanship, by George Lloyd. [Seattle, Pigott-Washington printing co., °1937]
94 p. 18½cm.

1. Salesmen and salesmanship. I. Title.
37-10437
Library of Congress HF5438.L66
——— Copy 2.
Copyright A 104378 [3] 658.8

NL 0427426 DLC

Lloyd, George, 1913–
[John Socman. Piano-vocal score. English]
John Socman, opera in three acts and five scenes. Libretto by William Lloyd. [n. p., 1951]
302 p. 28 cm.
Reproduced from ms.

1. Operas—Vocal scores with piano. I. Lloyd, William Alexander Charles, 1885– John Socman. II. Title.
M1503.L785J6 1951 52-28784

NL 0427427 DLC

Lloyd, George, 1913–
The serf, opera in three acts. Libretto by William Lloyd, music by George Lloyd. London, W. and G. Lloyd, °1938.
2 p. l., 252 p. 31 x 24cm.
Music reproduced from manuscript.

1. Operas—Vocal scores—Pianoforte accompaniment. I. Lloyd, William. The serf. II. Title.
42-12843
Library of Congress M1503.L785S4

NL 0427428 DLC MH

Lloyd, George, 1913–
[Symphony, no. 3, F]
Symphony no. 3, in F. [n. p., 1948]
score (115 p.) 36 cm.
Reproduced from ms.

1. Symphonies—Scores.
M1001.L79 no. 3 49-27852*

NL 0427429 DLC

Lloyd, George Ambrose Lloyd, *baron*, 1879–1941.
Британска теза. Уводна реч од лорда Халифакса. Београд, Штампарија Д. Грагорића, 1940.
54 p. 20 cm.

1. World War, 1939–1945—Causes. 2. World War, 1939–1945—Gt. Brit. I. Title. *Title transliterated:* Britanska teza.
D742.G7L617 53-48049

NL 0427430 DLC

Lloyd, George Ambrose Lloyd, *baron*, 1879–
The British case, by the Right Honourable Lord Lloyd of Dolobran ... with an introduction by the Right Honourable Viscount Halifax ... [London] Eyre & Spottiswoode limited, 1939.
61 p., 1 l. 19cm.
"First impression, December, 1939."

1. European war, 1939– —Causes. 2. European war, 1939– Gt. Brit. I. Title.
40-4274
Library of Congress D742.G7L6 1939
Copyright A ad int. 25723 [3] 940.53112

NL 0427431 DLC CtY PHi MH NNC

Lloyd, George Ambrose Lloyd, *baron*, 1879–
The British case, by the Right Honourable Lord Lloyd of Dolobran ... with an introduction by the Right Honourable Viscount Halifax ... New York, The Macmillan company, 1940.
4 p. l., 7–93 p. 17cm.

1. European war, 1939– —Causes. 2. European war, 1939– Gt. Brit. I. Title.
40-4275
Library of Congress D742.G7L6 1940
——— Copy 2.
Copyright A 137452 [15] 940.53112

NL 0427432 DLC OrU CaOTP IdU Or PU OO OCl OU ViU

D742 G7L7636

Lloyd, George Ambrose Lloyd, baron, 1879–
La causa de Inglaterra, por lord Lloyd; con una introducción del vizconde de Halifax. Madrid, Sociedad general española de librería [1939]
50,[1] p. 18cm.
"Printed in England."
Translation of the author's "The British case."

1.World war, 1939– - Causes. 2.World war, 1939– - Gt. Brit. I.Title.

NL 0427433 CSt-H

Lloyd, George Ambrose Lloyd, *baron*, 1879–
Egypt since Cromer, by Lord Lloyd ... London, Macmillan and co., limited, 1933–34.
2 v. fold. maps. 23cm.
"Intended as a sequel to [Lord Cromer's] Modern Egypt."—p. vi.

1. Egypt—Hist.—British occupation, 1882– 2. Egypt—Hist.—1919– 3. Egypt—Pol. & govt.—1882– 4. Egypt—Pol. & govt.—1919– I. Title.
33-11253 Revised
Library of Congress DT107.C882

PPDrop CU CaBVa MiEM OrPS OrU
CtY NcD PU PBm PHC WaS OU MB WaTC OrP OrPR CaBVaU
NL 0427434 DLC NN WaSpG MiEM WaU CtY-D ScU OrPS

Lloyd, George Ambrose Lloyd, *baron*, 1879–
The great opportunity, by Sir George Lloyd and Major the Hon. Edward Wood, M. P. London, J. Murray, 1918.
ix, 101 p. 17cm.
CONTENTS.—Introduction.—Healthy nationalism: on what it depends.—Before the war.—The machinery of government.—Reconstruction: 1. Economics. 2. Agriculture. 3. Housing. Drink. Education.

1. Reconstruction (1914–)—Gt. Brit. 2. Gt. Brit.—Pol. & govt.—1910– I. Wood, Hon. Edward Frederick Lindley, 1881– joint author. II. Title.
19-3065 Revised
Library of Congress D659.G7L7
[r33e2] 942.083

NL 0427435 DLC ICJ MiU

Lloyd, George Ambrose Lloyd, *baron*, 1879–
... Leadership in democracy, by the Right Honourable Lord Lloyd of Dolobran ... delivered before the University of St. Andrews, 14 November, 1938. London, Oxford university press, H. Milford, 1939.
21, [1] p. 21½cm. (Walker trust lectures on leadership, no. VII)

1. Leadership. 2. Democracy. I. Title.
39-25983
Library of Congress HM141.L72

NL 0427436 DLC NN NjP MH ODW OU CtY

Lloyd, George Ambrose Lloyd, baron, 1879–1941.
Lord Lloyd salutes the colonial empire at war... [London? 1941] 11 p. 22cm.

1. World war, 1939–1945—Gt. Br. —Colonies.
N. Y. P. L. July 8, 1946

NL 0427437 NN

Lloyd, George Christopher, ed.

Iron and steel institute.
... Carnegie scholarship memoirs. v. 1–
London [and] New York, 1909–

Lloyd, George Christopher, ed.

Institution of electrical engineers, *London.*
Journal of the Institution of electrical engineers, including original communications on telegraphy and electrical science ... v. 1– 1872/73–
London, New York [1873,–19

Lloyd, George Christopher, ed.

Iron and steel institute.
The Journal of the Iron and steel institute. 1871–
London [1871]–19

Lloyd, George Christopher.

Gt. Brit. *Dept. of scientific and industrial research.*
... Report on the sources and production of iron and other metalliferous ores used in the iron and steel industry. London, H. M. Stationery off. [Darling and son, limited, printers] 1918.

Lloyd, George Exton, *bp.*, 1861–1940.
The building of the nation; natural increase and immigration [by] Right Rev. Dr. G. E. Lloyd, bishop of Saskatchewan. [Edmonton? Alberta, 1928?]
29 p., 1 l. 17½cm.
On cover: A paper read before the Grand Orange lodge of British America ... at Edmonton, Alberta, July 26th, 1928.

1. Canada—Emig. & immig. I. Title.
43-27375
Library of Congress JV7225.L56
[2]

NL 0427442 DLC

VOLUME 337

Lloyd, George Henry, 1833–1915. **M.421.31
[Collection of church music. With accompaniment for organ.]
= *Autograph manuscript*. 1867–1913. 39 v. 33½ cm., and 27 × 34½ cm.
These pieces were written between 1859 and 1912. Many of the earlier ones were revised later.
Contents. — 1. Crudelis Herodes. (2 settings.) — Jesu dulcis memoria. (2 settings.) — Jesu corona. (7 settings.) — Quodcunque in orbe. — Egregie. Doctor Paule. — Audi benigne. — Ave maris stella. (13 settings.) — Maerentes oculi. (2 settings.) — Pange lingua. (10 settings.) — Lauream certaminis. — Exite Sion. (2 settings.) — Festivis resonent. — O quot undis. — Exultet orbis. — Iste confessor. (15 settings.) — Vexilla regis. (7 settings.) — Te Joseph celebrent. (6 settings.) — Deo gratias. — Ad regias. (2 settings.) — Christe sanctorum. — Tantum ergo. — Deus tuorum. (4 settings.) — Tristes errant. (2 settings.) — Rex gloriose. — Salutis humanae. — Veni creator. — Jam sol recedit. — Saepe dum Christi. — Auctor beate. (2 settings.) — Fortem virili. — Ut queant laxis. — Placare Christe. (3 settings.) — O salutaris hostia. — Jesu redemptor. — Salvete flores. — Gentis polonae. — Audiat miras. — Creator alme. — Regis superni. — Jesu magister. — Custodes hominum. — Saepe dum Christi. — Coelestis urbs. 2–4. Alma redemptoris. (3 settings.) 5. Alma redemptoris. — Ave regina. (2 settings.) — Regina coeli. (2 settings.) — Tantum ergo. — Ave maris stella. — Ad regias. — My God, my life, my love. 6. Regina coeli. (2 settings.) — Salve regina. — Ave maris stella. 7. Regina coeli. — Alma redemptoris. 8. Regina coeli. (3 settings.) 9. Regina coeli. — Coelestis urbs. — Ave maris stella. (2 settings.) — O quot undis. — Ave verum. — Deus tuorum. — Salutis humanae. — Auctor beate. 10. Salve regina. — Tantum ergo. — Ave maris stella. 11. Salve regina. (2 settings.) 12. Hymns, English and Latin, for the months of May or October. 13. Pange lingua. (6 settings.) — Vexilla regis. (2 settings.) — Christus factus est. — Regina coeli.— Ad regias. (3 settings.)— How pure, how frail.— O salutaris hostia. — Rock of Ages. — Five primrose springs. — Jesus, Jesus come to me. — Hail Jesus. — Hail Queen of Heaven. — Holy Ghost. — O Jesus Christ remember. — Iste confessor. — Come Holy Ghost. — Salve regina. (3 settings.) — Ecce panis. (2 settings.) — Te Deum (short). — Viva Pio Nono. — Lauda Sion. — Te Joseph celebrent — Ave maris stella. (11 settings.) — Exultet orbis. — Tantum ergo. (2 settings.) — Tristes errant. 14. Lauda Sion. 15. Puer nobis. 16. Alma redemptoris. (2 settings.) — Ave maris stella. (5 settings.) — I am a faithful Catholic. — O salutaris hostia. — Ave regina. (2 settings.) — Regina coeli. 17. Ave maris stella. (4 settings.) — Ave verum. — Sacred heart of Jesus. — Tantum ergo. (14 settings.) — We adore Thee Oh Christ and we bless Thee. (Lent stations.) — Regina coeli. — Placare Christe. — O salutaris. — Crudelis Herodes. (2 settings.) — Alma redemptoris. — Mass No. 13 (Requiem). — Dixit, in B flat. — O sanctissima. — Crudelis Herodes. — Salvete flores. — Vexilla regis. — Jam sol recedit. 18. Domine, in C. — Dixit, in F. — Regina coeli. — Salvete flores. — Crudelis Herodes. — Ave maris stella. — Tantum ergo. (2 settings.) — Salve regina. (Festival.) — Crudelis Herodes. 19. Alma redemptoris. — Regina coeli. — Ad regias. — Ave maris stella. — Holy name of Mary. — O quot undis. — Creator alme. — The snow lay on the ground. (Christmas carol.) — Ego propter te. — Popule meus. (Improperia.) — Ad regias. — Ave maris stella. — Ad regias. 20. Ave maris stella. (10 settings.) — Tantum ergo. (2 settings.) — Placare Christe. — Jam sol recedit. — Stabat Mater. — Iste confessor. — Ad regias. (2 settings.) — Jesus my Lord. — The loving heart of Jesus. — O quot undis. 21. Verbum supernum. — Ave Maria. (11 settings.) — Salve regina. — Magnificat. — Laudate pueri. — Ave maris stella. (6 settings.) — Pange lingua. (2 settings.) — Regina coeli. (2 settings.) — Vexilla regis. — Alma redemptoris. — Salve regina. — Jesu redemptoris. — Crudelis Herodes. — Te Joseph celebrent. — Bone pastor. — Tantum ergo. (12 settings.) — Jesu dulcis. (2 settings.) — O salutaris hostia. (4 settings.) — Yes dear Jesus. — Salvete flores. — Improperium. — Jesu redemptor. — Salvete flores. — Iste confessor. (2 settings.) — Te Joseph celebrent. — Ad regias. (2 settings.) — Vexilla regis. — Gentle star of ocean. — Guide me Oh Thou Great Jehovah. 22. Regina coeli. (2 settings.) — Lucis creator. — Ave maris stella. (2 settings.) — Auctor beate. — Dearest Mother Mary. — Sweet and low. — From Thy bright throne. — Pange lingua. — Tibi Christe. — Dixit, in F. — Magnificat. — Domine. — Alma redemptoris. — A pleasant invitation. 23. Ave verum. (4 voices.) — Ave maris stella. (36 settings.) — Veni creator. (2 settings.) — Auctor beate. — Quodcunque in orbe. — Iste confessor. (2 settings.)— Ad regias. (2 settings.) — Adoro te. — Te lucis. — Vexilla regis. (2 settings.) — Lucis creator. (3 settings.) — Sanctorum meritis. — Placare Christe. — O quot undis. (2 settings.) — Jesu corona virginum. — Tantum ergo. (2 settings.) — Te Joseph celebrent. — O salutaris hostia. — Litany of B. V. M. — Jesu dulcis. — Pange lingua. — Jesu redemptor. (2 settings.) — O quot undis. — Ad regias. — Crudelis Herodes. — Tristes errant. — Exultet orbis. 24. O salutaris hostia. — Jam hiems transit. — Ave maris stella. (2 settings.) — Regina coeli. — Salve regina. — Spiritus Domine. — Confirma hoc. — Te Deum. — Veni creator. 25. Rock of Ages. — Beatus vir. — Softly now the light. — Ave Maria. (2 settings.) — Audi benigne. — O salutaris hostia. (2 settings, one by V. Bellini.) — Regina coeli. — Exultet orbis. — Tantum ergo. — Ad regias. 26. Alma redemptoris. (2 settings.) — Ad regias. (3 settings.) — Tantum ergo. (4 settings.) — Ave maris stella. (2 settings.) — Ad regias. 27. Alma redemptoris. — O sanctissima. — Tantum ergo. (2 settings.) — Regina coeli. — Ad regias. 28. Lauda Sion. (Festival setting, complete.) — Ad regias. (4 settings.) — Ave maris stella. (3 settings.) 29. Adoro te. — Alma redemptoris. — Jack and Jill. — The man in the moon. — Pie Jesu. — Ad regias. (5 settings.) — Regina coeli. (4 settings.) — Marcia Moresco. (4 hands.) — Vexilla regis. (2 settings.) — O salutaris hostia. (6 set-

Continued in next column

Continued from preceding column

tings.) — Salutis humanae. — Jesu redemptor. — Tantum ergo. (3 settings.) — Ave maris stella. (10 settings.) — Crudelis Herodes. (2 settings.) — Te Joseph celebrent. — Lucis creator. — Qui cunque Christum quaesitis. — Pange lingua. (3 settings.) — Veni creator. — Jam sol recedit. (2 settings.) — Stabat Mater. — O quot undis. (2 settings.) — Exultet orbis. — Tristes errant. — Deus tuorem. — Rex gloriose. — Jesu corona. — Fortem virili. — Salutis humanae. — Coelestis agui. — Iste confessor. (2 settings.) — Coelestis urbs. — Rocco's song from "The vampire." — Magnificat. — Illumina faciem. 30. Victimae paschali. — Tantum ergo. (4 settings.) — Te Deum. — Christus factus est. — Alma redemptoris. — Ave regina. — Regina coeli. — Salve regina. — Stabat Mater. — Ave maris stella. — Iste confessor. — O sacrum convivium. 31. Veni creator. — Tantum ergo. — Asperges me. — Regina coeli. — Basque ballad. (2 versions.) — Sacred heart. — Introito ad altare. — Et glorificabo. — Virgines post eam. — Quinque prudentes. — Bonum est. — Perfice gressus. — Ave maris stella. — Benedictus es. — There is an hour of hallowed peace. — Dixit, in F. — Ave verum. — Tantum ergo. — Alma redemptoris. — Salve regina. 32. Ave maris stella. (2 settings.) — Ad regias. — Mass. (Requiem.) — Sacred heart. — Alma redemptoris. 33. Pange lingua. (2 settings.) — Jam sol recedit. — Veni sancte. — Ave verum. — Pastores loquebantur. — Jesu redemptor. — Tantum ergo. (2 settings.) — Crudelis Herodes. — Vidi aquam. — Confitemini Domino. — Look down Oh Mother Mary. — Dixit, in G. — Alma redemptoris. (2 settings.) — Amarit eum. — Tantum ergo. — O salutaris hostia. — Domine ad adjurandum. — Oh Mary blest. 34. Jam sol recedit. (2 settings.) — Iste confessor. — Ad regias. (2 settings.) — Veni creator. — Salve regina. — Hymn for communion. — Missa brevis, no. 7. 35. Crudelis Herodes. — O quot undis. — Speciosa Facta es. — Ave maris stella. — Duo, Solve vincla reis. — Monstrate esse. — Virgo singularis. — Nos culpis. — Vitam praesta. — Sit laus deo. — Gloria in excelsis Deo. 36. Regina coeli. (3 settings.) — O salutaris hostia. — Alma redemptoris. (2 settings.) 37. Alma redemptoris. — Salve regina. — Tantum ergo. (5 settings.) — Pange lingua. — O salutaris hostia. (3 settings.) — Ave maris stella. (5 settings.) — Quicunque Christum. — Creator alme. — Salutaris humana. — Veni creator. — Pater superni. — Jesus lover of my soul. — Iste confessor. — Pange lingua. 38. [Mise] rere peccatorum. — Ad regias. — Resurrexi. — Haec dies. (Gradual.) — Terra tremuit. — Haec dies. (Hymn.) — Alma redemptoris. — Tantum ergo. (3 settings.) — Regina coeli. (3 settings.) — Ave regina. — O salutaris hostia. — Ave verum. (2 settings.) — Hail Oh Queen of Heaven. — Pange lingua. — Te Joseph celebrent. — Cradle song. (Words by Bayard Taylor.) — Pascha nostrum. 39. Pange lingua. (2 settings.) — My God, my life, my love. — Tantum ergo. (10 settings.) — Alma redemptoris. (2 settings.) — Sacred heart. — Ad regias. (2 settings.) — Regina coeli. (3 settings.) — Ave regina. — Ave maris stella. — Gentle star of ocean. — Jesu corona. — Iste confessor. (3 settings.) — O salutaris hostia.

NL 0427457 MB

Lloyd, George Henry, 1833–1915.
Masses. Nos. 1, 2, 4, 5, 8–12, 14–16. [With accompaniment for organ.]
Autograph manuscript. 12 v. 33½ cm., and 26½ × 33½ cm.
**M.421.26
These masses were composed 1862–1910.
The volume containing no. 8 includes a Christmas canticle (Adeste fideles) and a Tantum ergo in B♭.
Same. No. 13. No. 26 in **M.421.31.2

K8197 — Masses. Colls. — Manuscripts in this Library. Music.

NL 0427458 MB

Lloyd, George Henry, 1833–1915. **M.421.28
"Messa" de Immaculata Conceptione "1864." Rescensio. 1898. [With accompaniment for organ.]
Autograph manuscript. [1898.] (113) pp. 34 cm.

K8197 — Masses. — Manuscripts in this Library. Music.

NL 0427459 MB

Lloyd, George Henry, 1833–1915.
Requiem in D min. [With accompaniment for organ.]
Autograph manuscript. [1913.] (58) pp. 34½ cm.

K8107 — Masses. Requiem. — Manuscripts in this Library. Music.

NL 0427460 MB

Lloyd, George Henry, 1833–1915. **M.421.29
Stabat mater. [Anthem with accompaniment for organ.]
Autograph manuscript. [1900.] (71) pp. 33½ cm.

K8197 — T.r. — Manuscripts in this Library. Music.

NL 0427461 MB

Lloyd, George Henry, 1833–1915. **M.421.30
Vespers for the Immaculate Conception. [With accompaniment for organ.]
Autograph manuscript. [1898.] (163) pp. 34 cm.
These vespers were finished in 1860 and revised 1898.

K8197 — Manuscripts in this Libr... Music. — Vespers. — Immaculate Conception, Feast of the.

NL 0427462 MB

Lloyd, George N d.1843.
Botanical terminology, or dictionary explaining the terms most generally employed in systematic botany. By G.N.Lloyd ... Edinburgh, Printed for Bell & Bradfute; London, Longman, Rees, Orme, Brown, & Green [etc.] 1826.
3 p.l.,[v]-vii,228 p. 18½cm.
Interleaved: manuscript additions throughout.
Intended as an appendix to Sir J.E.Smith's Compendium florae britannicae. cf.p.vi.

1.Botany—Dictionaries.

QK9.L79

NL 0427463 MiU OkU PPC

Lloyd, George Thomas.
Thirty-three years in Tasmania and Victoria; being the actual experience of the author, interspersed with historic jottings, narratives, and counsel to emigrants: by George Thomas Lloyd. London, Houlston and Wright, 1862.
xii, 515 p. 20½cm.

1. Tasmania—Hist. 2. Tasmania—Descr. & trav. 3. Victoria, Australia—Hist. 4. Victoria, Australia—Descr. & trav. I. Title.
4—2212
Library of Congress DU460.L8

NL 0427464 DLC CtY CSt PHC PPL MB

4K Gt. Brit. 151
Lloyd, George William
The practice in enfranchisements under the Copyhold act, 1894, and in redemptions of quit rents and other perpetual charges under the Conveyancing and law of property act, 1881. London, Stevens, 1913.
144 p.

NL 0427465 DLC-P4

[Lloyd, George William] d.1906.
The devil in Dixie: a tale of the times. Serio-comical, semi-historical, and quasi-diabolical ... New-York, American news company, 1865.
76 p. 19cm.

1. Slavery in the U. S.—Poetry. 2. U. S.—Hist.—Civil war—Poetry. I. Title.
30-112
Library of Congress PS2248.L67

NL 0427466 DLC NjP NN OClWHi

VOLUME 337

Lloyd, George William, d. 1906
76
LL7891
Lyrics of lake and stream, by G.W. Lloyd. Branchville, N. J. c1899
38 p. illus. 21 cm.

NL 0427467 RPB

Lloyd, George William, *d.* 1906.
The patriot's death—its bloody lessons. A funeral discourse on the death of Corp'l James S. Gustin, who fell in the advanced guard before Williamsburg, Va. Preached in the Presbyterian church of Branchville, N. J., by Rev. G. W. Lloyd. New York, J. F. Trow, printer, 1862.
24 p. 23½cm.
Text on third page of cover.
Gustin was a corporal in the 7th regiment, New Jersey infantry volunteers.
1. Gustin, James S., d. 1862. 2. New Jersey infantry. 7th regt., 1861–1865. I. Title.
Library of Congress E521.5.7thL 19—12945

NL 0427468 DLC NjR

Lloyd, Georgia, 1913- joint author.
JX1944
.W8
1949
FOR OTHER EDITIONS SEE MAIN ENTRY
Wynner, Edith.
Searchlight on peace plans; choose your road to world government by Edith Wynner and Georgia Lloyd. New and enl. ed. New York, E. P. Dutton, 1949.

Lloyd (Georgius). *De cute ejusque functionibus. 1 p. l., 22 pp. 8°. *Edinburgi, P. Neill* 1825. [P., v. 1871.]

NL 0427470 DNLM

LLOYD, Geraint Owen.
Amazwi AsiXhenxe; isiva esilandelelanayo samanqaku eentsumayelo. [n.p.] Lovedale press, 1954. 30 p. front. 19cm.
In Xhosa.
1. African languages--Kafir--Texts and translations.

NL 0427471 NN

Lloyd, Geraint Owen.
A study of some Xhosa words of Afrikaans origin. [Lovedale, S. A., South African Outlook, 1955]
11 p. 19 cm.
Cover title.
"Reprinted from the South African Outlook, June, 1955"
1. Kaffir language (Bantu)—Etymology.

NL 0427472 MB

Lloyd, Gladys.
An Englishwoman's adventures in the German lines, by Gladys Lloyd. London, C. A. Pearson ltd., 1914.
128 p. incl. front. (plan) 18½cm. 1/-
1. European war, 1914- —Personal narratives.
Library of Congress D640.L6 14-21605

NL 0427473 DLC CtY NN NjP

Lloyd, Gladys, *actress*
see her real name
Robinson, Gladys Lloyd (Cassell)

Lloyd, Gladys, 1889–
see
Lloyd, Anne Gladys, 1889–

Lloyd, Godfrey Isaac Howard.
The cutlery trades; an historical essay in the economics of small-scale production, by G. I. H. Lloyd ... with 16 illustrations and 3 maps. London, New York [etc.] Longmans, Green, and co., 1913.
3 p. l., ix–xvi, 493, [1] p. incl. front., plates, tables. 23½cm.
1. Cutlery—Hist. I. Title.
Library of Congress HD9529.C8L6 14—2037

PP MiU OCU OClW NN NjP
NL 0427476 DLC WaSpG ICJ CU IaU NcU CLSU Vi NcD

Lloyd, Godfrey Isaac Howard.
The cutlery trades, an historical essay in the economics of small-scale production, by G. I. H. Lloyd, ... With 16 illustrations and 3 maps. New York, Bombay and Calcutta, Longmans, Green, and Co., 1913.
xvi, 493, [1] p. incl. front., plates, tables. 23½cm.

NL 0427477 ICJ MB

PR4935
.L52E3
1883
Lloyd, Grant.
Ebb and flow; or, He did his best. A story of five years ago. London, Smith, Elder, 1883.
2 v.

NL 0427478 ICU IU

Lloyd, Grant.
Thornwell Abbas... London, Low, 1876.
2 v. 19½ cm.

NL 0427479 NjP

Lloyd, Guillermo
see
Lloyd, William, engineer.

Lloyd, Gulielmus, fl.1814
see Lloyd, William, M.D., of Edinburgh.

Lloyd, Guy, 1890–
Commentaries on European affairs; an M. P. speaks out, by Major Guy Lloyd... Glasgow, W. Maclellan [1944] 59 p. 21cm.
1. World war, 1939-1945—Addresses, sermons, etc.
N. Y. P. L. July 8, 1946

NL 0427482 NN

Lloyd, Guy, 1890–
Never again! Thoughts on our post-war European policy, by Major Guy Lloyd ... [Edinburgh, Printed by T. Nelson and sons ltd., 1944]
cover-title, 15, [1] p. 18cm.
1. World war, 1939–1945—Peace. I. Title.
[Full name: Ernest Guy Richard Lloyd]
Library of Congress D816.5.L58 46-13634
[2] 940.531

NL 0427483 DLC

Z7914
.A2 I 53
Lloyd, Gwendolyn, ed.
Industrial relations theses and dissertations accepted at universities.
Berkeley, Institute of Industrial Relations, University of California.

Lloyd, H., writer on safety measures in mining
see Lloyd, Harry

Lloyd, H. Alan
see Lloyd, Herbert Alan.

Lloyd, H. H.
Study of conductivity of certain organic acids in ... ethyl alcohol. Gettysburg, 1915.

NL 0427487 NjP

Lloyd (H. H.) & Co., publishers
see Lloyd (Henry H.) & Co., publishers.

[Lloyd, H J]
... Physical geography ... Published under the superintendence of the Society for the diffusion of useful knowledge ... London, Baldwin and Cradock; New York, G. & C. Carvill [etc., etc.] 1828-1829.
2 v. in 1. tables, diagrs. 23½cm. (Library of useful knowledge [Treatises; 23, 47]
Cover-title.
Paged continuously.
Part 1 2d ed., published April 1, 1828; pt.II published April 1, 1829.
1. Physical geography I. Society for the diffusion of useful knowledge. London. II. Ser.

NL 0427489 ViU MdBP MH RPB

Lloyd, H[annibal] **E**[vans] 1771–1847.
Alexander I., emperor of Russia; or, a sketch of his life, and of the most important events of his reign. By H. E. Lloyd ... London, Treuttel & Würtz [etc.] 1826.
1 p. l., [v]–xxxv, 315 p. front. (port.) plan. 22cm.
1. Alexander I, czar of Russia, 1777–1825. 2. Russia—Hist.—Alexander I, 1801–1825.
Library of Congress DK191.L7 5-7022

NL 0427490 DLC WaU CSt ICU PPL

VOLUME 337

Lloyd, Hannibal Evans, 1771-1847, tr.

Bjørnstjerna, [Magnus Fredrik Ferdinand] *grefve*, 1779–1847.
The British empire in the East. By Count Björnstjerna. London, J. Murray, 1840.

DA533 .R245 Lloyd, Hannibal Evans, 1771-1847, joint tr.

Raumer, Friedrich Ludwig Georg von, 1781–1873.
England in 1835: being a series of letters written to friends in Germany, during a residence in London and excursions into the provinces: by Frederick von Raumer ... Translated from the German, by Sarah Austin and H. E. Lloyd. Philadelphia, Carey, Lea, and Blanchard, 1836.

Lloyd, Hannibal Evans, 1771-1847, tr.

Raumer, Friedrich [Ludwig Georg] von, 1781–1873.
England in 1841: being a series of letters written to friends in Germany, during a residence in London and excursions into the provinces: by Frederick von Raumer ... Translated from the German by H. Evans Lloyd ... London, J. Lee, 1842.

Lloyd, Hannibal Evans, 1771-1847.
...Englische Sprachlehre für Deutsche. Nach vieljährig gegebenem Unterricht ausgearbeitet und mit fasslichen Uebungen nach den Regeln der Sprache versehen. Hamburg: Hoffmann und Campe, 1816. xiv, 328 p. 16°.

65142A. 1. English language.—Text-books for foreigners (German). N. Y. P. L. December 6, 1922.

NL 0427494 NN

---

435 L776 Lloyd, Hannibal Evans, 1771-1847.
Englische und deutsche Gespräche; ein Erleichterungsmittel für Anfänger, nach J. Perrin. Nebst einer Sammlung besonderer Redensarten. 6.verb.Aufl. Hamburg, A. Campe, 1827.
vii,312p. 19cm.

Text in English and German; added title page in English: English and German dialogues; a guide to conversation in both languages, on the plan of John Perrin.

NL 0427495 OrU NjP

Lloyd, Hannibal Evans, 1771-1847, ed.
European commerce ...
see under Rordansz, C W

Lloyd, H[annibal] E[vans] 1771–1847.
George IV.; memoirs of his life and reign, interspersed with numerous personal anecdotes; to which is prefixed, an historical account of the house of Brunswick, from the earliest period. By H. E. Lloyd, esq. With a portrait and autograph of His Majesty. London, Treuttel and Würtz, Treuttel jun. and Richter, 1830.

6 p., 1 l., [ix]–cviii, 284 (*i. e.* 484) p. incl. front. (port.) 22cm.

p. 484 numbered 284.

Subject entries: 1. George IV, king of Great Britain, 1762–1830. 2. Brunswick, House of.

3-26703

Library of Congress, no. DA538.A1L7.

NL 0427497 DLC CtY PPL MdBP MB

Lloyd, Hannibal Evans, 1771-1847, tr.

Wolff, Oskar Ludwig Bernhard, 1799–1851, *ed.*
The German tourist. for MDCCCXXXVII. Edited by Prof. O. L. B. Wolff, and Dr. H. Doering, translated by H. E. Lloyd, esq. Illustrated with seventeen engravings from drawings, by A. G. Vickers, esq. London and Berlin, A. Asher; Philadelphia, De Silver, Thomas and co. [1836]

Lloyd, Hannibal Evans, 1771-1847, tr.

Saabye, Hans Egede, 1746–1817.
Greenland: being extracts from a journal kept in that country in the years 1770 to 1778. By Hans Egede Saabye ... To which is prefixed, an introduction; containing some accounts of the manners of the Greenlanders, and of the mission in Greenland ... By G. Fries. 2d ed. Tr. from the German. London, Boosey and sons, 1818.

Lloyd, Hannibal Evans, 1771-1847.
*XH .814 .L77H Hamburgh; or, A particular account of the transactions which took place in that city, during the first six months of the year 1813; with a view of its previous state, and of the conduct of the French, during their six years possession, both before and after its being annexed to the French empire. By Hannibal Evans Lloyd ...
Philadelphia: Published by Bradford and Inskeep, and Abraham H.Inskeep,New-York. 1814.
124p. 20cm.(8vo)
Shaw/Shoemaker 31945.
Imperfect: half-title wanting.

NL 0427500 MB ScU CtY MdBP PPL

Lloyd, Hannibal Evans, 1771-1847, tr.
The history of the English revolution
see under Dahlmann, F[riedrich Christoph]

Lloyd, Hannibal Evans, 1771-1847, tr.

Wied-Neuwied, Maximilian Alexander Philipp, *prinz* von, 1782–1867.
... Maximilian, prince of Wied's Travels in the interior of North America, 1832–1834. Cleveland, O., The A. H. Clark company, 1906.

Lloyd, Hannibal Evans, 1771-1847, tr.

Iffland, August Wilhelm, 1759–1814.
The nephews: a play, in five acts. Freely tr. from the German of William Augustus Iffland, by Hannibal Evans Lloyd, esq. London, Printed by W. and C. Spilsbury 1799.

Lloyd, Hannibal Evans. 1771–1847.
Nieuwe Engelsche spraakkunst. Naar den negenden druk voor Nederlanders bewerkt door D. Bomhoff, Hzn. Herzien door M. P. Lindo. 5. druk.
— Arnhem. Thieme. 1855. (3), 413, vi pp. 20 cm., in 8s.

H6054 — Lindo, Mark Prager, ed. — English language. Gram. For Dutchmen.— Bomhoff, Dirk, ed. 1792–1860.

NL 0427504 MB ICN

Lloyd, Hannibal Evans, 1771-1847.

Turner, Joseph Mallord William, 1775–1851.
Picturesque views in England and Wales, from drawings by J. M. W. Turner ... engraved under the superintendence of Mr. Charles Heath. With descriptive and historic illustrations by H. E. Lloyd ... London, Longman, Orme, Brown, Green, and Longmans, 1838.

Lloyd, Hannibal Evans, 1771-1847, tr.
Raumer, Friedrich [Ludwig Georg] von, 1781–1873.
The political history of England, during the 16th, 17th and 18th centuries. By Frederick von Raumer ... v. 1–2. London, A. Richter & co.; [etc., etc.] 1837.

Lloyd, Hannibal Evans, 1771-1847, tr.

Feuchtersleben, Ernst, *freiherr* von, 1806–1849.
The principles of medical psychology: being the outlines of a course of lectures by Baron Ernst von Feuchtersleben, M. D. (Vienna, 1845) tr. from the German by the late H. Evans Lloyd, esq., rev. and ed. by B. G. Babington ... London, Printed for the Sydenham society, 1847.

Lloyd, Hannibal Evans, 1771-1847.
Theoretisch-praktische englische Sprachlehre für deutsche. Hamburg, 1823.

NL 0427508 PWW PBa

Lloyd, Hannibal Evans, 1771-1847.
H. G. Lloyd's theoretisch-praktische englische Sprachlehre für Deutsche. 3. verb. Ausgabe. Hamburg, August Campe, 1828.
365p.

NL 0427509 ICRL ViU

Lloyd, Hannibal Evans, 1771-1847.
Theoretisch-praktische englische Sprachlehre. Baltimore, 1833.

NL 0427510 PPG

Lloyd, Hannibal Evans, 1771-1847.
Theoretisch-praktische Englische Sprachlehre für Deutsche. Mit fasslichen Uebungen nach den Regeln der Sprache versehen. 8.verb. Ausg. Leipzig, Brockhaus, 1848.

NL 0427511 MH NNC

Lloyd, Hannibal Evans, 1771-1847, tr.

F2511 .S76 Rare Bk. Coll. **Spix, Johann Baptist von, 1781–1826.**
Travels in Brazil, in the years 1817–1820. Undertaken by command of His Majesty the King of Bavaria. By Dr. Joh. Bapt. von Spix and Dr. C. F. Phil. von Martius ... London, Longman, Hurst, Rees, Orme, Brown, and Green, 1824.

Lloyd, Hannibal Evans, 1771-1847, tr.

Wied-Neuwied, Maximilian Alexander Philipp, *prinz* von, 1782–1867.
Travels in the interior of North America. By Maximilian, prince of Wied ... Tr. from the German, by H. Evans Lloyd. To accompany the original series of eighty-one elaborately-coloured plates ... London, Ackermann and co., 1843.

Lloyd, Hannibal Evans, 1771-1847, tr.

Timkovskiĭ, Egor Fedorovich, 1790–1875.
Travels of the Russian mission through Mongolia to China, and residence in Pekin, in the years 1820–1821. By George Timkowski. With corrections and notes by Julius von Klaproth ... London, Longman, Rees, Orme, Brown, and Green, 1827.

VOLUME 337

Lloyd, Hannibal Evans, 1771-1847, tr.

Tams, Georg.
Visit to the Portuguese possessions in south-western Africa. By G. Tams, M. D. Tr. from the German, with an introduction and annotations, by H. Evans Lloyd ... London, T. C. Newby [1845]

Lloyd, Hannibal Evans, 1771-1847, tr.

Kotzebue, Otto von, 1787-1846.
A voyage of discovery, into the South sea and Beering's straits, for the purpose of exploring a north-east passage, undertaken in the years 1815-1818, at the expense of His Highness ... Count Romanzoff, in the ship Rurick, under the command of the lieutenant in the Russian imperial navy, Otto von Kotzebue ... London, Longman, Hurst, Rees, Orme, and Brown, 1821.

Lloyd, Harold Clayton, 1894–
An American comedy, acted by Harold Lloyd, directed by Wesley W. Stout. New York [etc.] Longmans, Green and co., 1928.
vii p., 1 l., 204 p. front., plates, ports. 21cm.

I. Stout, Wesley Winans. II. Title. 28-25756
Library of Congress PN2287.L5A3

NL 0427517 DLC CaBViP WaS LU IU WU TxU NcGU PP WaT MB NN OCl

Lloyd, Harold Clayton, 1894-

Paillot, Fortuné.
... Et puis ça va; ou, Le docteur Jack, roman-film adapté par Fortuné Paillot. Paris, E. Flammarion [°1925]

Lloyd, Harold Clayton, 1894-

Paillot, Fortuné.
... Monte là-dessus, roman-film, adapté par Fortuné Paillot. Paris, E. Flammarion [°1925]

Lloyd, Mrs. Harriet (Raymond) ed.

Raymond, John Howard, 1814-1878.
Life and letters of John Howard Raymond, ed. by his eldest daughter. New York, Fords, Howard, & Hulbert, 1881.

[Lloyd, Harriette]
Hindu women: with glimpses into their life and zenanas. By H. Ll ... London, J. Nisbet & co., 1882.
3 p. l., 143 p. 17½cm.

1. Women in India. I. Title.
A 12-1498
Title from Univ. of Chicago DS422.W8L9 Printed by L. C.

NL 0427521 ICU

[Lloyd, Harriette]
Hindu women: with glimpses into their life and zenanas. By H. Ll ... London, J. Nisbet & co., 1883.
3 p. l., 143 p. 17½cm.
Second edition.

NL 0427522 CSaT OClStM

TN295
G603
no.37
Lloyd, Harry
An angle comparator for laboratory use, by H. Lloyd, A. T. F. Simmons and G. E. Winder. [Sheffield] 1952.
12 p. illus., diagrs. 24 cm. (Gt.Brit. Safety in Mines Research Establishment. Research report no. 37)
Cover title.
Bibliography, p. 12.

1. Optical instruments. 2. Explosives.

NL 0427523 DI

TN295
G603
no.29
Lloyd, Harry
An automatic dust sampler, by H. Lloyd, G. E. Winder & D. A. Gillard. [Sheffield] 1951.
18 [1] p. illus., diagrs. 24 cm. (Gt. Brit. Safety in Mines Research Establishment. Research report no. 29)
Cover title.
Bibliography, p. 17.

1. Dust. I. Title. (Series)

NL 0427524 DI

Lloyd, Harry
... An automatic firedamp recorder, by H. Lloyd. London, H. M. Stationery off., 1934.
16 p. illus., 3 pl. on 2 l., diagrs. 28cm. ([Gt. Brit.] Safety in mines research board. Paper no. 86)
At head of title: Mines department.

1. Fire-damp. 2. Coal mines and mining—Safety measures. I. Title.
C D 37-7
Library of Congress Card Div. TN295.G65 no. 86

NL 0427525 DLC

TN295
G603
no.14
Lloyd, Harry
Flame safety-lamp design; a review of locking and re-lighting mechanisms, with some new suggestions. [London] 1950.
26 p. illus., diagrs. 24 cm. (Gt. Brit. Safety in Mines Research Establishment. Research report no. 14)
Cover title.
"References," p. 25-26.

1. Safety-lamp. I. Title. (Series)

NL 0427526 DI

TN295
G603
no.112
Lloyd, Harry
Internal re-lighters for gas-testing flame safety-lamps. [Sheffield] 1955.
12 p. illus. 24 cm. (Gt. Brit. Safety in Mines Research Establishment. Research report no. 112)
Cover title.
Bibliography: p. 12.

1. Safety-lamp. I. Title: Gas-testing flame safety-lamps. (Series)

NL 0427527 DI

Lloyd, Harry, joint author.

Allsop, George, 1898–
... A recording manometer having low inertia, by G. Allsop and H. Lloyd. London, H. M. Stationery off., 1935.

TK152
.G73
1944
Lloyd, Harry.

Gt. Brit. *Ministry of fuel and power.*
... A review of electrical research and testing with regard to flame-proof enclosure and intrinsic safety of electrical apparatus and circuits ... London, H. M. Stationery off., 1944.

TN295
G603
no.26
Lloyd, Harry
The S.M.R.E. convergence recorder. [Sheffield] 1951.
14 p. illus., diagrs. 24 cm. (Gt. Brit. Safety in Mines Research Establishment. Research report no. 26)
Cover title.
Bibliography, p. 14.

1. Roofs (in mines). I. Title: Convergence recorder. (Series)

NL 0427530 DI

TN295
G603
no. 6
Lloyd, Harry
The S.M.R.T.B. cap-lamp densitometer. [n.p.] 1950.
6 p. plate, diagrs. 24 cm. (Gt. Brit. Safety in Mines Research & Testing Branch. Research report no. 6)
Cover title.
On "A portable instrument for estimating the concentration of air-borne dust in coal mines."

1. Dust.

NL 0427531 DI

TN295
G603
no.74
Lloyd, Harry
Two testing sets for determining the inductance and effective resistance of coils with iron cores. [Sheffield] 1953.
22 p. plates, diagrs. 24 cm. (Gt. Brit. Safety in Mines Research Establishment. Research report no. 74)
Cover title.
Bibliography, p. 22.

1. Electricity in mining - Safety measures. 2. Induction coils - Testing.

NL 0427532 DI

TN295
G603
no.33
Lloyd, Harry
The use of break-flash apparatus no. 3 for intrinsic safety testing, by H. Lloyd & E. M. Guénault. [Sheffield] 1951.
23 p. illus., diagrs. 24 cm. (Gt. Brit. Safety in Mines Research Establishment. Research report no. 33)
Cover title.
Bibliography, p. 23.

1. Electricity in mining - Safety measures. I. Guénault, E.M., jt. auth. (Series)

NL 0427533 DI

VOLUME 337

Lloyd, Harvey Dale.
Care and repair of automobiles, by Prof. H. D. Lloyd ... [Kansas City, Mo., Printed by the Punton bros., °1915]
93 p. front. (port.) plates (part col., 1 fold.) 24cm. $3.00

1. Automobiles, Gasoline. I. Title. 15-21586

Library of Congress TL208.L6

NL 0427534 DLC

Lloyd, Hazel Pearl, 1891-

CS71 .C69 1931 **Coles, William Bedford,** 1865-
The Coles family of Virginia: its numerous connections, from the emigration to America to the year 1915. New York, 1931.

LLOYD, HAZEL PEARL, 1891-
An index to Coles family of Virginia by W. M. Coles. Author c1949.
unpaged.

NL 0427536 Or

Lloyd, Helen, joint author.

Wilson, Jacobine Menzies.
Amelia, the tale of a plain Friend, by Jacobine Menzies-Wilson and Helen Lloyd. London, New York [etc.] Oxford university press, 1937.

Lloyd, Helen.

Smithers, *Mrs.* Elsa (Dietrich) 1862-
March hare: the autobiography of Elsa Smithers. London, Oxford university press, H. Milford, 1935.

Lloyd, Helen A
Songs of the child-world
see under Gaynor, Jessie Lovel (Smith) 1863-1921.

Lloyd, Helen Alice, 1922-
I. Solvent effects in reactions of alkyl durene-carboxylates with N-methylpiperidine. II. Diene reactions of 2-methoxybutadiene ... 1951.
71 numb. l.
Thesis (PH.D.) - Ohio state university, 1951.

NL 0427540 OU

PS635 .Z99L8 Lloyd, Helen J.
The road to broadway...
Rock Island, Ill., c1935.
1 pam. 4°

NL 0427541 DLC RPB

Lloyd, Henry.
The smoking concert reciter. By Henry Lloyd (Didimus Goggs) ... London, Hutchinson and co. [1890]
160 p. 18½cm. (*On cover:* Platform series)
Prose and verse.

1. Smoking. I. Title. 41-39621

Library of Congress GT3020.L54

NL 0427542 DLC OCl

Lloyd, Henry, called Ab Hevin or Ap Hefin
see Lloyd, Henry, 1870-

LLOYD, H[enry], "Castellydd".
History of Caerphilly, from the earliest period to the present time. Pontypridd, F.J.Harries, 1900.

pp.86. Ports., plates and plan.

NL 0427544 MH

[**Lloyd, Henry**] of Gloucestershire.
The cry of oppression and cruelty inflicted upon divers innocent people called Quakers, in the county of Glocester, for peaceable meeting together to worship God; being a copy of a paper directed to the judges of the late assizes at Glocester; presented to the tender consideration of such, who are in power to relieve the oppressed. [n. p., 1677]
8 p. 18cm.
Caption title.
Signed: Henry Lloyd, Jenkin Hopkin, William Hibbs, John Hibbs, William Howel, John Gwyn.
"A postscript", signed William Gibson: p. 7-8.
I. Hopkin, Jenkin. II. Hibbs, William. III. Hibbs, John. IV. Howel, William. V. Gwyn, John. VI. Gibson, William, 1629-1684. VII. Title. 22-6483

Library of Congress BX7677.G5L5

NL 0427545 DLC DFo MH CtY PHC PHi PSC-Hi DFo ICN

Lloyd, Henry, 1685-1763.

[**Barck, Dorothy C**] *ed.*
Papers of the Lloyd family of the manor of Queens Village, Lloyd's Neck, Long island, New York. 1654-1826. New York, Printed for the Society, 1927

U 2 .515 LLOYD, HENRY, 1720?-1783.
Abhandlung über die allgemeinen Grundsätze der Kriegskunst. Aus dem Englischen. Frankfurt, P.H.Perrenon, 1783.
xxii, 159p. fold.maps, fold.diagrs. 25cm.

Translated by Hermann Flensberg.-- cf. Brit. Mus. Cat.

NL 0427547 ICN CSt

HG221 .E75 [Lloyd, Henry] 1720?-1783
An essay on the theory of money. London, Printed for J.Almon, 1771.
viii, x, 161 p. 19½cm.
"By Henry Lloyd" in manuscript on t.-p.

1.Money.

NL 0427548 ICU MH MH-BA CtY InU NNC IEN CtY PU

F 4797305 .5165 [LLOYD, HENRY] 1720?-1783.
Geschichte des letzten Krieges in Teutschland zwischen dem Könige von Preussen und der Kayserin Königin und ihren Alliirten in den Jahren 1756 und 1757. Von einem Generale der verschiedene Feldzüge hindurch bey der Oestreichischen Armee gedienet hat. Aus dem Englischen übersetzt [von Julius August Remer] 2. verbesserte und von neuen durchgesehene Aufl. Braunschweig, Im Verlage der Fürstl. Waysenhaus-Buchhandlung, 1779.
227p. fold. maps, fold. tables. 22cm.

NL 0427549 ICN

Lloyd, Henry, 1720?-1783.
Geschichte des siebenjährigen krieges in Deutschland zwischen dem könige von Preussen und der kaiserin königin mit ihren alliirten, vom General Lloyd. Aus dem Englischen aufs neue übersetzt, mit verbesserten planen und anmerkungen, von G. F. Tempelhof ... Berlin, J. F. Unger, 1783-1801.
6 v. fold. maps, fold. tables. 26cm.
Vol. 2-6 have title: "Geschichte des siebenjährigen krieges in Deutschland zwischen dem könige von Preussen und der kaiserin königin mit ihren alliirten als eine fortsetzung der geschichte des General Lloyd, von G. F. v. Tempelhof."

1. Seven years' war, 1756-1763. I. Tempelhof, Georg Friedrich von, 1737-1807.

NL 0427551 MiU MH OCl NIC ICN NjP CSdS CSt CtY

LLOYD, [Henry] 1720?-1783.
Guerre de sept ans. Atlas.
Bruxelles, J.B.Petit, 1841.

f°. pp.(4). 9 maps.

NL 0427552 MH

(Lloyd, Henry) 1720-1783.
...Guerre de sept ans. Atlas.
Bruxelles, J. B. Petit, 1842.
33x52cm. fold. to 33 x 26cm.

NL 0427553 DNW

Lloyd, Henry, 1720?-1783.
Histoire de la guerre d'Allemagne, pendant les années 1756 et suivantes, entre le Roi de Prusse et l'Impératrice d'Allemagne et ses alliés; traduite en partie de l'anglais de Lloyd, et en partie rédigée sur la correspondance originale de plusieurs officiers français, et principalement sur celle de M. de Montazet... Par le C. Roux Fazillac... Paris: Magimel, an XI — 1803. 3 v. in 2. fold. maps, fold. plans. 12°.
Paging continuous; t.-p. of v. 3 wanting.
Binder's title: Guerre de sept ans.
With book-plate of Winfield Scott.

Contents: Tome 1. Campagnes de 1756-1757. Tome 2. Campagnes de 1758-62. Journal du siége de la ville de Schweidnitz, par Simon L. Lefebvre. Tome 3. Relation de la campagne du Roi de Prusse en 1744, écrite par lui-même.

1. Seven Years' war. 2. Roux-Fazillac, Pierre, 1750-1833, translator and editor. 3. Montazet, de, Lieutenant General. 4. Lefebvre, Simon, 1712-71. 5. Frederick II, the Great, king of Prussia, 1712-86.
N. Y. P. L. November 20, 1915.

NL 0427555 NN MH NWM

Lloyd, Henry, 1720?-1783.
The history of the late war in Germany, between the king of Prussia and the empress of Germany and her allies; with a map of the seat of the war, plans of bettle, &c. By a general officer (Lloyd) London, 1763.

NL 0427556 PPL

VOLUME 337

[Lloyd, Henry] 1720?-1783.
The history of the late war in Germany; between the king of Prussia, and the empress of Germany and her allies ... By a general officer, who served several campaigns in the Austrian army ... London, Printed for the author, 1766-81.
2 v. fold. plates, fold. maps, fold. tables. 27½ x 21½cm.
Vol. 2 has title: Continuation of The history of the late war ... Part II ... By Major-General Lloyd.

1. Seven years' war, 1756-1763. I. Title.

Library of Congress DD411.L79 4—28032

FU NN
NL 0427557 DLC MBAt MH ICN OCl MoU NjP MdBP OCl

Lloyd, [Henry,] 1720?-83.
The history of the late war in Germany, between the king of Prussia, and the empress of Germany and her allies... Part 1 and v. 2. London: S. Hooper. 1781-90. 2 v. maps, pl. 4°.
v. 2 has slightly different title-page, reading: The history of the late war in Germany... Published from the general's manuscripts, under the inspection of an English officer, and illustrated with notes critical, historical, and explanatory. London: printed for T. and J. Egerton, 1790.

NL 0427558 NN MdBP CtY NIC MB MH

F 4797305 .516 LLOYD, HENRY, 1720?-1783.
The history of the late war in Germany, between the king of Prussia, and the empress of Germany and her allies... London, T.and J.Egerton, 1790.
v2 27½cm.

Vol.2: Published from the General's manuscripts, under the inspection of an English officer, and illustrated with notes critical, historical and explanatory.
Bookplate of Edward Wilberforce Unwin.

NL 0427559 ICN

Lloyd, Henry, 1720?-1783.
The history of the seven years' war in Germany, by Generals Lloyd and Tempelhoff, with observations and maxims extracted from the treatise of great military operations of General Jomini...London, R. G. Clarke (n.d.)
v. front. (fold.map) maps, plans. 23 cm.

NL 0427560 DAS

DD 411 .L 79 1784 QC Lloyd, Henry, 1720?-1783.
Introduction a l'histoire de la guerre en Allemagne, en M. DCC. LVI. Entre le roi de Prusse, et l'impératrice-reine avec ses alliés. Ou, Mémoires militaires et politiques du général Lloyd. Traduit & augmenté de notes, & d'un précis sur la vie & le caractere de ce général. Par un officier françois... Londres, 1784.
2 p.l., iij, xxij (i.e. lxxij), 216, [2], v. p. fold. maps, fold. plans. 28½cm.

Edited and translated by Germain Hyacinthe de Romance de Mesmon.
Half-title: Mémoires militaires et politiques.

NL 0427561 MdBJ

Lloyd, Henry, 1720-1783.
Introduction of the late war in Germany.

NL 0427562 NWM

Lloyd, [Henry], 1720?-1783. Carl 233*
Mémoires militaires et politiques servant d'introduction à l'Histoire de la guerre en Allemagne en 1756. Traduits par un officier français [M. de Romance, marquis de Mesmon]. Paris, Magimel, 1801.
pp. xlviij, 354.
Formerly owned by Thomas Carlyle; with his book-plate, autograph, and manuscript marginal notes.

Seven years' war, 1756-1763||

NL 0427563 MH NWM NN DNW

Lloyd, Henry, 1720?-1783.
Memoria politica e militare sopra l'invasione e la difesa della Gran-Brettagna, e riflessioni su l'invasione di Francia, del generale Lloyd ... Tr. sulla 6. ed., ed accresciuta di note politico-statistiche da Lorenzo Manini ... Milano, Presso Pirotta e Maspero, 1804.
149 p. fold. maps. 20 cm.
1. Gt. Brit. - History, Military - 1789-1820.
2. France - History, Military - 1715-1789.
I. Manini, Lorenzo, tr.

NL 0427564 CU

Lloyd, Henry, 1720?-1783.
Militairisch-praktisches Handbuch für Officiere. Nach seiner im siebenjährigen Kriege gemachten Erfahrung entworfen. Mit Anmerkungen. Neue Aufl. Leipzig, J.C. Hinrichs, 1802.
viii, 160 p. 16.5 cm.

NL 0427565 CtY

---

fU O .514 LLOYD, HENRY, 1720?-1783.
Notes inédites de l'empereur Napoléon Ier sur les Mémoires militaires du général Lloyd Publiées par Ariste Ducaunnès-Duval... Bordeaux, G.Gounouilhou,1901.
22p. II fold.facsims. 30cm.

"Extrait du tome XXV des 'Archives historiques de la Gironde'."

NL 0427566 ICN

C901 .D8 Lloyd, Henry, 1720?-1783
A political and military rhapsody on the invasion and defence of Great Britain and Ireland ... London, Egerton, 1790.
xxxv, 104 p. map, plates, plans. (Duane pamphlets, 34:1)

NL 0427567 DLC

Lloyd, Henry, 1720?-1783.
A political and military rhapsody on the invasion and defence of Great Britain and Ireland. To which is annexed a short account of the author, and a supplement by the editor. 2d ed., with additions and improvements. London, Sold by Debret, etc., 1792.

xix, 226 p. fold plate, 2 fold. maps. 22 cm.

NL 0427568 MH CtY DLC

Beinecke Library NZ 793pf Lloyd, Henry, 1720?-1783
A political and military rhapsody, on the invasion and defence of Great Britain and Ireland. By the late General Lloyd ... To which is annexed, a short account of the author, and a supplement by the editor. ... The 4th ed. with additions and improvements. London, Sold by Debrett [etc.] 1795.
(In Playfair, William. Thoughts on the present state of French politics. London, 1793. 1 p.l., v, xix, 286 p. 4 fold.pl. 22 cm.)

NL 0427569 CtY ViU ICN

DA 50 .L55 Lloyd, Henry, 1720?-1783
A political and military rhapsody on the invasion and defence of Great Britain and Ireland, by the late General Lloyd. To which is annexed a short account of the author, and a supplement by the editor. 5th ed., with additions and improvements. London, Egerton, 1798.
297 p. illus. 23 cm.

1. Gt. Brit. - Hist. - Invasions.

NL 0427570 WU MnU

Lloyd, Henry, 1720?-1783
A political and military rhapsody on the invasion and defence of Great Britain and Ireland ... By the late General Lloyd. To which is added a supplement by the editor; and in this edition, the sketch of an original plan for the fortification and defence of London. 6th ed., with impr. & cor. London, Printed by W. Bulmer and co., 1803.
xxiv,288p. 3 fold. pls.

NL 0427571 ScU NWM NcD

Lloyd, [Henry], 1720?-1783.
A rhapsody on the present system of French politics; on the projected invasion, and the means to defeat it. Illustrated with a chart of the opposite coasts of England and France. [London,] 1779. 1 p.l., (i)vi-viii, (1)108-187 p., 1 map. 8°.
Preface, and Essay on the present state of French politics, wanting. Bound with: Opinions delivered by the Earl of Essex...London, 1794. 8°.

1. Great Britain.—History, 1779. 2. Defence, Great Britain, 1779. 3. France.—History, 1779.
N. Y. P. L. February 6, 1911.

NL 0427572 NN CtY WU IU

FILM 5981 HF Lloyd, Henry, fl.1765-1767.
Foreign marketing, 1765-1767. Boston, Mass., 1765-67.
553 p. On film.

Microfilm copy of original manuscript in Baker library, Harvard university Graduate school of business administration.
"Letters relate to export and import trading, largely with West Indies ..."

NL 0427573 CU

Lloyd, Henry, 1870- , comp.
Cofiant a gweithiau y parchedig David Silyn Evans, gweinidog Eglwys Siloa, Aberdar, gan ddeugain o sgrifenwyr, yn cynnwys llith gan R. Ifor Parry. Casglwyd gan Ap Hefin [pseud.] Aberdar, Hy. Lloyd, 1937. 296 p. illus.,ports. 19cm.

1. Evans, David Silyn, 1850-1930. 2. Welsh language—Texts and translations. I. Title.

NL 0427574 NN

LLOYD, HENRY, 1870-
Cywyddau [gan] Ap Hefin [pseud.] Aberdar, H. Lloyd (Ap Hefin) [1946] 56 p. ports. 19cm.

On cover: Llyfr 17.

1. Welsh language--Texts and translations.

NL 0427575 NN MH

Lloyd, Henry, 1870-
Dringo'r Bannau, ac awdlau eraill. Gan Ap Hefin. Aberdar, The author, 1934

80 p. ports.

NL 0427576 MH

VOLUME 337

LLOYD, Henry, 1870–
Mafon Duon y Deau. Pant yr onen, ac odlau ereill. Gan Ab Hevin. Merthyr Tydfil, Joseph Williams, 1899.

12°. Port.

NL 0427577 MH

Lloyd, Henry, 1870–
Y twyni grug a'r Goeden Las, a chathlau ereill. Aberdar, 1910

51 p. illus.

NL 0427578 MH

Lloyd, Henry Demarest, 1847–1903.
Address, delivered by Henry D. Lloyd, June 19, 1897, at Ruskin, Tennessee, on the occasion of laying the corner stone of the College of the New Economy, an institution now being built by voluntary contributions from the people and the labor of cooperators. .... Ruskin, Tenn., The Coming Nation Press, 1898.

28 p. illus. (port.), 2 pl. 24cm.

"The address ... has been incorporated as chapter IX in 'Man, the social creator'. ... But in this pamphlet alone is the address to be found as originally written."—Ms. letter from Mrs. Lloyd.

NL 0427579 ICJ MB OC1WHi

Lloyd, Henry Demarest, 1847-1903.
Chicago traction question. Chicago, Western newspaper union, 1901?
96 p.

NL 0427580 ICHi

Lloyd, Henry Demarest, 1847–1903.
The Chicago traction question. By Henry Demarest Lloyd. [Chicago, 1903?]

[8], 92, [4] p. front. (port.) 24½cm.

NL 0427581 ICJ NN RPB NjP MiU ICN MB

Lloyd, Henry Demarest, 1847–1903.
A country without strikes; a visit to the compulsory arbitration court of New Zealand, by Henry Demarest Lloyd, with introduction by William Pember Reeves ... New York, Doubleday, Page & co., 1900.

xiv p., 1 l., 183 p. 19cm.

1. Strikes and lockouts—New Zealand. 2. Labor and laboring classes—New Zealand. 3. Arbitration, Industrial—New Zealand. I. Title.

0—2844

Library of Congress HD5630.N6L8

Copyright 1900 A 10653 [a33g1]

·331.09931

NIC WaTC IdU OrU WaWW
MiU NjNbS NcD PSC NjP PHC PPL PPM PV PBm PPA DAU Or
NL 0427582 DLC NjNbS TU WaU NN MB ICJ OU OO I OC1

Lloyd, Henry Demarest, 1847-1903.
A country without strikes; a visit to the compulsory arbitration court of New Zealand; with introduction by William Pember Reeves, ex-minister of labor in New Zealand. New York: Doubleday, Page & Co., 1902. xiv(i), 183 p. 12°.

1. Strikes and lockouts. 2. Arbitration, Industrial. 3. New Zealand. 4. Title.

CENTRAL CIRCULATION.

N. Y. P. L. March 28, 1911.

NL 0427583 NN CU OCU ODW NcRS OrP

Lloyd, Henry Demarest.
Emerson's wit and humor.
From- The Forum, Nov., 1896. 24 cm.
p. [346]-357.

NL 0427584 RPB

Lloyd, Henry Demarest, 1847–1903.
In der organisation der arbeiter liegt das heil der zukunft. Vortrag, gehalten in Chicago in der dreizehnten jährlichen convention der American federation of labor, von Henry D. Lloyd. Im auftrage der convention publicirt. New York, A. F. of L. office, 1894.

10 p. 23½cm.

Translated from the English.

1. Trade-unions.

Library of Congress HD6511.L53 10-2725

NL 0427585 DLC

Lloyd, Henry Demarest, 1847-1903.
In memoriam. Henry Demarest Lloyd
see under title

Lloyd, Henry Demarest, 1847–1903.
Labor copartnership: notes of a visit to co-operative workshops, factories and farms in Great Britain and Ireland, in which employer, employé, and consumer share in ownership, management and results. By Henry Demarest Lloyd ... New York and London, Harper & brothers, 1898.

3 p. l., 351 p. incl. tables. front., plates. 19cm.

1. Cooperation—Gt. Brit. I. Title.

Library of Congress HD3486.L5

PPL OrP WaTC
NcD OCU OO MiU OU OC1 WaU MB PPFr NjP MdBJ PPD PP
NL 0427587 DLC WaSpG CU MtU NIC KEmT CoU DAU FU

Lloyd, Henry Demarest, 1847-1903.
Labor copartnership: notes of a visit to co-operative workshops, factories and farms in Great Britain and Ireland, in which employer, employé, and consumer share in ownership, management and results. New York: Harper & Brothers, 1899. 3 p.l., 351 p., 13 pl. 12°.

NL 0427588 NN WaS PHC PPT PU N ICJ

Lloyd, Henry Demarest, 1847–1903.
Lords of industry, by Henry Demarest Lloyd ... New York and London, G. P. Putnam's sons, 1910.

v, 355 p. 20½cm.

Partly reprinted from various periodicals.

CONTENTS.—The story of a great monopoly. 1881.—The political economy of seventy-three million dollars. 1882.—Making bread dear. 1883.—Lords of industry. 1884.—Servitudes not contracts. 1889.—What Washington would do to-day, February 22, 1890.—Uses and abuses of corporations. 1894.—The sugar trust and the tariff. 1897.—The national ownership of anthracite coal mines. 1903.—The failure of railroad regulation. 1903.—Index.

1. Trusts, Industrial—U. S. 2. U. S.—Econ. condit. I. Title.

10—27032

Library of Congress HD2795.L7

CaBViP WaTC Or MtU OrP WaS
PPM PP MB OC1W OCU OU OO OC1 MiU ICJ NjNbS NjP PPFr
NL 0427589 DLC ViU WaE NIC CoU OrPS CU PBm PHC PU

Lloyd, Henry Demarest, 1847–1903.
Man, the social creator, by Henry Demarest Lloyd ... New York, Doubleday, Page & company, 1906.

5 p. l., 3-279 p. front. (port.) 21½cm.

CONTENTS.—The discovery of social love.—Social progress always religious.—Mere contact making for spiritual union.—Social love creating new forms of social life.—The new conscience.—New conscience in industry.—New conscience transforming politics—killing the party spirit.—The new conscience manifesting itself in educational methods and aims.—A new political economy predicting a new wealth.—The church of the deed.—The religion of labour.

1. Social problems. 2. Social ethics. I. Title.

6—16757

Library of Congress HN64.L8

OU CU OrP PPA PP PU P NcD OOxM OC1 ICJ OCU MiU NN MB
NL 0427590 DLC GU KEmT ICRL OKentU OrU PSt CaBVa

Lloyd, Henry Demarest, 1847–1903, *comp.*
A manual for the guidance of voters in the general state election to be held in New York city, Nov. 7, 1871. Comp. by Henry D. Lloyd ... [New York, Atherton & Coles, printers, 1871]

12 p. 16½cm.

Caption title.

1. Elections—New York.

9-32962†

Library of Congress JK2023.N7L6

NL 0427591 DLC

Lloyd, Henry Demarest, 1847–1903.
Mazzini, and other essays, by Henry Demarest Lloyd ... New York and London, G. P. Putnam's sons, 1910.

v, 239 p. 20½cm. $1.50

The essay entitled "Emerson's wit and humor" was first published in the Forum. *cf.* Prefatory note.

CONTENTS.—Mazzini; prophet of action.—A day with William Morris.—Emerson's wit and humor.—Sir Harry Vane.—Some Dutch notions.—Free speech and assemblage.—The scholar in contemporary practical questions.—Is personal development the best social policy?—No mean city.—Index.

1. Social problems. I. Title.

10—27887

Library of Congress HN64.L82

PBm PSC PHC PU PP WaE TU OO OU OC1 ICJ NN MB
NL 0427592 DLC Or WaS WaT IdB MtU OrP NIC CU NjNbS

Lloyd, Henry Demarest, 1847–1903.
Men, the workers, by Henry Demarest Lloyd ... New York, Doubleday, Page & company, 1909.

viii, 280 p. front. (port.) 21½cm. $1.50

A collection of articles and addresses edited by Anne Withington and Caroline Stallbohm.

CONTENTS.—The labour movement. July 4, 1889.—The union forever.—The safety of the future lies in organized labour. December, 1893.—Arbitration.—Illinois factory law speech. 1894.—The new independence.—Strikes and injunctions. 1894.—Boomerang law. 1895.—Speech at the reception to Eugene V. Debs. 1895.—Lessons of the Debs case. 1895.—Argument before the Anthracite coal strike commission. 1903.—Speech at the Mitchell, Darrow, Lloyd reception. 1903.—Addenda: A. The political economy of child labour. 1887. B. Civilization as heralded by Labour day. 1898.

1. Labor and laboring classes. 2. Labor and laboring classes—U. S. I. Withington, Anne, ed. II. Stallbohm, Caroline, joint ed.

Library of Congress HD8072.L65 9—35791

OrP WaS MiU OC1 MB ICJ NN
NL 0427593 DLC CU WHi KEmT DAU IaU FU PU PHi WaE

Lloyd, Henry Demarest, 1847-1903.
The new conscience, or religion of labour.
Lond., Reeves, 1889.
22 p. [Fellowship ser. 3] Sm. 8°.

NL 0427594 MB

Lloyd, Henry Demarest, 1847–1903.
Newest England; notes of a democratic traveller in New Zealand, with some Australian comparisons, by Henry Demarest Lloyd. New York, Doubleday, Page & co., 1900.

4 p. l., 387 p. front., plates, ports. 23cm.

1. Socialism in New Zealand. 2. New Zealand—Pol. & govt. 3. New Zealand—Descr. & trav. 4. Government ownership. 5. Labor and laboring classes—New Zealand. I. Title.

0—6424

Library of Congress HC622.L5, 1900.

ICJ OU NIC TxU TU Nj NjP PPFr PPL
NL 0427595 DLC ICRL DN NN PPD PU MB OrP Or WaS OkU

Lloyd, Henry Demarest, 1847–1903.
Newest England; notes of a democratic traveller in New Zealand, with some Australian comparisons. New York: Doubleday, Page & Co., 1901. 4 p.l., 287 p., 16 pl. 8°.

NL 0427596 NN

VOLUME 337

Lloyd, Henry Demarest, 1847-1903.
Newest England, notes of a democratic traveller in New Zealand, with some Australian comparisons; by Henry Demarest Lloyd. New York, Doubleday, Page & co., 1903.
4 p. l., 387 p. 16 pl. (incl. front., 3 port.) 21½cm.

1. New Zealand. 2. Government ownership. I. Title.
4-16764
Library of Congress HC622.L5 1903
[a36j1] 330.9931

NL 0427597 DLC KMK PBm PIm ODW OCl

Lloyd, Henry Demarest, 1847-1903.
Problems in modern democracy ... [Philadelphia, The Booklovers library [1901]

NL 0427598

Lloyd, Henry Demarest, *1847-1903.*
Problems of the Pacific — New Zealand.
(*In* National Geographic Magazine. Vol. 13, pp. 342-352. Washington. 1902.)
An economic study.

M2814 — New Zealand. Pol. econ.

NL 0427599 MB

Lloyd, Henry Demarest, 1847-1903.
The safety of the future lies in organized labor. By Henry D. Lloyd ... A paper read before the thirteenth annual convention of the American federation of labor, Chicago, December, 1893. Pub. by authority of the convention. Chicago, The Eight-hour herald [1893]
8 p. 23cm.

1. Trade-unions.
8-5558
Library of Congress HD6511.L5

NL 0427600 DLC MB Nh DL WHi CU MiU OO ICJ NN

Lloyd, Henry Demarest, 1847-1903.
A sovereign people; a study of Swiss democracy, by Henry Demarest Lloyd; ed. by John A. Hobson. New York, Doubleday, Page & company, 1907.
xvi, 273 p. front. 21cm.
"References": p. 261.

1. Switzerland—Pol. & govt. 2. Referendum. 3. Government ownership—Switzerland. I. Hobson, John Atkinson, 1858-1940, ed. II. Title.
7-38223
Library of Congress JN8766.1907.L6

NL 0427601 DLC NcU OrPR OrP NjP PHi PPT PSC PU PP OCl OClW ICJ NN MB OO OU ODW NIC WaTC PPL PRosC NcD WaSpG WaS

Lloyd, Henry Demarest, 1847-1903.
Story of a great monopoly. [Boston, 1881]
317-334 p. 8°.
n.t.-p.
Fragment of The Atlantic Monthly. v. 47.
In: * C p.v. 1285.

NL 0427602 NN

Lloyd, Henry Demarest, 1847-1903.
... A strike of millionaires against miners; or, The story of Spring Valley. An open letter to the millionaires, by Henry D. Lloyd. Chicago, Belford-Clarke co., 1890.
264 p. 19cm. ("Our bad wealth" series, no. 1)

1. Spring Valley, Ill.—Strike and lockout, 1889.
7-29952
Library of Congress HD5325.M63.1889.L5

NL 0427603 DLC CLU CU CtY KU OCl MiU ODW ICJ NN MB WaU OrP

Lloyd, Henry Demarest, 1847-1903.
The Swiss democracy; the study of a sovereign people, by Henry Demarest Lloyd, ed. by John A. Hobson. London [etc.] T. F. Unwin, 1908.
xvi, 273 p. front. 21cm.
"Printed in New York, U. S. A."
American edition published in 1907 under the title A sovereign people; a study of Swiss democracy.
"References": p. 261.

1. Switzerland—Pol. & govt. 2. Referendum. 3. Government ownership. I. Hobson, John Atkinson, 1858- ed.
8-12217
Library of Congress JN8766.1908.L6

NL 0427604 DLC ViU

Lloyd, Henry Demarest, 1847-1903.
Wealth against commonwealth, by Henry Demarest Lloyd. New York, Harper & brothers, 1894.
iv, 563 p. 22cm.
A study of trusts, particularly of the Standard oil company.

1. Trusts, Industrial. 2. Standard oil company. I. Title.
4-3852
Library of Congress HD2769.O4L8
338 [s26m1]

NL 0427605 DLC MsU OU MiU OClW ODW DL NcD ViU DN OU OO WaTC ViU MB I ICJ MH NN PBm PCC PWcS PPL PPPD Or PSC MH WaSpG OrStbM OrPS OrP IdU OrCS IdPI MtHi MtU PBa CU CoU KMK ICU GU OKentU NIC NjNbS FTaSU OClW

Lloyd, Henry Demarest, 1847-1903.
Wealth against commonwealth. N.Y., 1896.
563 p.

NL 0427606 OCU

Lloyd, Henry Demarest, 1847-1903.
Wealth against commonwealth, by Henry Demarest Lloyd. New York, Harper & brothers, 1898.
iv, 563 p. 22 cm.
A study of trusts, particularly of the Standard oil company.

NL 0427607 ViU PHC TU Wa OrPR

Lloyd, Henry Demarest, 1847-1903.
Wealth against commonwealth, by Henry Demarest Lloyd. New York and London, Harper & brothers, 1899.
iv, 563 p. 19 1/2cm.

NL 0427608 MB OClWHi MH CaBVaU PU

Lloyd, Henry Demarest, 1847-1903.
Wealth against commonwealth. New York and London, Harper & brothers, 1902.

NL 0427609 MH

Lloyd, Henry Demarest, 1847-1903. Econ 3872.1.4
Wealth against commonwealth. New York, etc., Harper & Brothers, 1903 [cop. 1894].
pp. (1), iv, 563, x.

NL 0427610 MH PPT NjP

Lloyd, Henry Demarest, 1847-1903.
Wealth against commonwealth, by Henry D. Lloyd; edited by Charles C. Baldwin; foreword by John Chamberlain. Washington, D. C., National home library foundation, 1936.
3 p. l., 366 p. 17cm. (National home library, 29)

1. Trusts, Industrial—U. S. 2. Standard oil company. I. Baldwin, Charles C., ed. II. Title.
38-9374
Library of Congress HD2769.O4L8 1936
[5] 338.80973

NL 0427611 DLC PPLas PPCC CaBVaU OrStbM OrSaW OCl OrU-M MtBuM Wa WaE IdB WaPS NN MtU OrCS OrPR OrP OrU WaSp WaS WaT WaTC WaWW DLC Or IdPI IdU MtBC NNC ViU

Lloyd, Henry E.
I've got a passion for pistachio nuts. Words by Wm. S. Kearns. Music by Henry E. Lloyd... New York, Shapiro, Bernstein & co. inc. [c1933]
First line: Once I dreamed of Spanish moonlight.
Portrait of the Sizzlers on t.-p.

Printed for the Music Division
1. Nuts. 2. Sizzlers—Port. I. Kearns, William S. II. Song index (2).
N. Y. P. L. September 2, 1948

NL 0427612 NN

Lloyd, Henry Evans.
See
Lloyd, Hannibal Evans.

E470 .L79
Lloyd, Henry H.) & Co., publishers.
Lloyd's battle history of the great rebellion, complete, from the capture of Fort Sumter, April 14, 1861, to the capture of Jefferson Davis, May 10, 1865, embracing General Howard's tribute to the volunteer ... and a general review of the war for the union. New York, H. H. Lloyd & co.; Boston, B. B. Russell & co.; [etc., etc.] 1865.

NL 0427614

Lloyd, Henry H.) & Co., pub.
Lloyd's Dollar map
see under title

Lloyd, Henry H.) & Co., pub.
Lloyd's handy atlas
see under title

Lloyd, Henry H., & Company, publishers. No. 3 in *Map 19.3
Map showing the telegraph lines in operation, under contract, and contemplated, to complete the circuit of the globe.
New York. [187-?] Size, 12⅛ × 19¾ inches. Scale, Mercator's.

H1775 — Telegraph. Maps.

NL 0427617 MB

Lloyd, Henry H., & co., publishers. *Map 118.
H. H. Lloyd & co.'s military campaign charts compiled from official data by Egbert L. Viele and Charles Haskins; showing the principal strategic places of interest, etc. Published under the auspices of the American geographical society. Fifteen maps on one sheet.
N. Y. Lloyd & co. 1861. Size, 33¾ x 26½ inches.
Contents. — Annapolis harbor. — Cairo. — Charlestown harbor. — Chesapeake and Delaware bays. — Potomac and James rivers. — District of Columbia. — Galveston bay — Hampton Roads. — Key West. — Mobile bay. — New Orleans. — New York City & vicinity. — Norfolk harbor. — Pensacola bay. — Savannah. — United States.

Feb. 17, 1898

NL 0427618 MB

UA993 .L548 1865
Lloyd (Henry H) and Co., publishers.
Military map refering [!] to the campaigns of the Army of the Potomac in Virginia, Maryland and Pennsylvania. New York, 1865.
map. 125 x 95cm. fold. to 27 x 18cm.
Scale 1:330,000.
On cover: Campaign map of the Army of the Potomac.

1. U. S. Army. Army of the Potomac. 2. U. S.—Hist.—Civil War—Maps. 3. Maps, Military. 4. Va.—Maps. 5. Md.—Maps. 6. Pa.—Maps.

NL 0427619 ViU

VOLUME 337

Lloyd (Henry H.) & Co., publishers.
Lloyd's new country map of the United States
see under title

Lloyd (Henry H.) & Co. pub.
Lloyd's new map of the Mississippi River
see under title

Lloyd (Henry H.) & Co., publishers.
Lloyd's new military map of the border & Southern states
see under title

Lloyd, Henry H., & Co., *publishers.* No. 10 in *Map.19.3
Telegraph chart. Chart showing the track of the great submarine Atlantic telegraph, with the principal land & submarine telegraph lines in Europe & America. Also tracks of steamships, and the depth of the ocean.
— *Broadside.* New York. 1858. Illus. Portraits. Map. Size, 33¾ × 26¾ inches. Size of map, 10½ × 23¾ inches. Scale, none.
The text consists of two articles entitled: Account of the invention and operation of the magnetic telegraph; Description of making and laying submarine telegraph cables.

N6380 — Telegraph. — Submarine telegraph. — Atlantic telegraph.

NL 0427623 MB

Lloyd (Henry H.) & Co., publishers.
12,000 square miles around New York City, New York, 1866.
2 sheets. 16°

NL 0427624 NN

Lloyd, Henry Humphrey Evans, 1720?-1783.
See
Lloyd, Henry, 1720?-1783.

Lloyd, Herbert.
Vaudeville trails thru the West, "by one who knows," copyrighted ... by Herbert Lloyd. [Chicago] °1919.
4 p. l., 3-220 p. illus., diagrs. 20cm.
Contains advertising matter.

1. Vaudeville—U. S.

Library of Congress PN2289.L7 19-17491

NL 0427626 DLC NN WaU OrU OrHi Wa

Lloyd, Herbert, of Philadelphia.
... Early American and English antiques ... from the estates ...
see under Freeman (Samuel T.) & Co., auctioneers, Philadelphia. [supplement]

Lloyd, Herbert Alan.
Chats on old clocks. London, E. Benn [1951]
186 p. [75] p. of plates. [The Chats series; practical handbooks for collectors]

"This title by Arthur Hayden originally published 1917." Rewritten, with new illustrations. Cf. p. 5.

NL 0427628 MiD

NK7486 Lloyd, Herbert Alan
.L55 Chats on old clocks. [3d ed. new and revised] New York, A.A. Wyn, 1952.
186p. illus. 23cm. (Practical handbook for collectors)

First two ed. were written by Arthur Hayden.

1. Clocks and watches - Collectors and collecting. 2. Clocks and watches - History. I. Hayden, Arthur, 1868-1946. II. Title.

NL 0427629 PSt LU NN OClW MB OrP WaT

Lloyd, Herbert Alan.
The English domestic clock, its evolution and history; a brief guide to the essential details for dating a clock, by H. Alan Lloyd; with fifty-seven illustrations ... [London and Birmingham, Priv. print. for the author by Silk & Terry, ltd., 1938]
3 p. l., 5-28, [2] p. illus. (incl. ports.) 24½ x 19½ cm.

1. Clock and watch making—England. I. Title.
NK7495.G7L6 1938a 681.1130942 39-4274 rev

NL 0427630 DLC CSmH PU

q681.11
L776g
Lloyd, Herbert Alan.
Giovanni de Dondi's horological masterpiece, 1364. [n.p., 1955]
22,[1]p. illus. 30cm.
Caption title.

1. Dondi dall'Orologio, Giovanni de, 1318-1389.

NL 0427631 TxU CSdS NN

Lloyd, Herbert Marshall, 1862- ed.

FOR OTHER EDITIONS SEE MAIN ENTRY
Morgan, Lewis Henry, 1818-1881.
League of the Ho-de-no-sau-nee or Iroquois, by Lewis H. Morgan ... A new ed., with additional matter. Ed. and annotated by Herbert M. Lloyd ... New York, Dodd, Mead and company, 1901.

Lloyd, Herbert Summers.
The popular cocker spaniel; its history...and elementary training for sport and field trials, with a list of winning dogs. By H. S. Lloyd... With an introduction by C. A. Phillips...illustrated by Mr. Hay Hutchinson... London, Popular dogs pub. co. [1924?]
103 p. illus. 19cm.

312372B. 1. Dog—Spaniel.
N. Y. P. L. January 31, 1946

NL 0427633 NN ViW

SF429
.C55L5
1929
Lloyd, Herbert Summers
The popular cocker spaniel; its history, strains, pedigrees, breeding kennel management, ailments, exhibition, show points, and elementary training for sport and field trials, with a list of winning dogs, by H.S. Lloyd "of Ware"; with an introduction to this edition by Mrs. Hester Higgens; illustrated by Mr. Hay Hutchinson. London, Popular Dogs Publishing Co. [1929]
ix, 113 p. illus. 19 cm.
"2nd ed."

NL 0427634 AAP CaBVa

Lilly
PR 4890
.L 77 R9
LLOYD, HORACE AMELIUS
Rummio and Judy; or, Oh, this love!! This love! This love! A serio-comic-parodi-tragedi-farcical burlesque. In two acts. By Horace Amelius Lloyd ... Edinburgh, J. Menzies etc., etc., 1841.
44 p. 21.5 cm.

First edition.
In the Stock catalogue, this work is ascribed to William Hugh Logan, writing under the pseudonym of H. A. Lloyd; not ascribed thus in British Museum Catalogue.
Bound in quarter red morocco; uncut.

I. Logan, William Hugh, d. 1883--Supposed author II. Title

NL 0427636 InU CSmH

LLOYD, H[oratio] F[rederick], 1806-1889.
AUTOBIOGRAPHY of H.F.Lloyd, comedian, late of the Theatres Royal, Edinburgh & Glasgow compiled from the columns of the Glasgow Evening times, in which newspaper it appeared bi-weekly from 19 May to 17 July 1886. Glasgow, 1886.

Mounted with portraits, in scrapbook, sm.4°. Playbills and autograph letters, inserted at end. TS 158.50

NL 0427637 MH

Lloyd, Howard Huntley, 1892-
A study of the conductivity of certain organic acids in absolute ethyl alcohol at 15°, 25°, and 35°. By Howard Huntley Lloyd ... [Gettysburg] Gettysburg compiler print [1915]
58 p. diagrs. 23cm.
Thesis (PH. D.)—Johns Hopkins university, 1915.
Biography.

1. Electrolytes, Conductivity of. 2. Acids, Organic.

Library of Congress QD565.L8 16-10056
Johns Hopkins Univ. Libr.

NL 0427638 MdBJ DLC NIC PU

Lloyd, Howard William?.
Codiogan of Nannau.
[Phila., ? 1894?]

CS71
.L675
.1894

NL 0427639 DLC

Lloyd, Howard Williams. Inscriptions on gravestones in St. Peter's Episcopal church-yard, East Whiteland, Pa. 9 pp. (*Pa. Mag. Hist.* v. 15. 1891, p. 440.)

NL 0427640 MdBP

VOLUME 337

Lloyd, Howard Williams.
Lloyd manuscripts. Genealogies of the families of Awbrey-Vaughan, Blunston, Burbeck, Garrett, Gibbons, Heacock, Hodge, Houlston, Howard, Hunt, Jarman, Jenkin-Griffith, Jones, Knight, Knowles, Lloyd, Newman, Paschall, Paul, Pearson, Pennell, Pott, Pyle, Reed, Sellers, Smith, Thomas, Till, Williams, Wood. Welsh records from the collection of the late Howard Williams Lloyd. Lancaster, Pa., Press of the New era printing company, 1912.
vii p., 2 l., 3-437 p. fold. geneal. tab. 25½cm.
Preface signed: Thomas Allen Glenn.
1. Lloyd family. I. Glenn, Thomas Allen, 1864- ed.
13-4158
Library of Congress CS71.L792 1912

NL 0427641 DLC OrHi CU Or WaS PPAmP PSC-Hi PU PV PP PHi PPL ViU MB NN PHC

WB 33984 Lloyd, Howel William
Anglicanism in the diocese of St. Asaph in the year of Our Lord 1880, in a series of letters in the Oswestry Advertizer. Oswestry, Woodall and Venables, 1881.
60 p.

POOR CONDITION

1. Church of England - Doctrinal and controversial works - 19th cent.

NL 0427642 CtY

LLOYD, Howel W[illiam], compiler.
Emynau Catholig. Llundain, 1894.
pp.31.

NL 0427643 MH

Lloyd, Hoyes.
Canada's feathered friends. [Ottawa, Department of the interior, n.d.].
6p.D.

NL 0427644 CaBViP

Lloyd, Hugh.
... Among the river pirates, by Hugh Lloyd ... illustrated by Seymour Fogel. New York, Grosset & Dunlap [c1934]
vi, 7-197 p. front. 19½cm. (*His* Skippy Dare mystery stories)

I. Title.
Library of Congress PZ7.L778Sk no. 1 34-6276

NL 0427645 DLC

Lloyd, Hugh.
... The clue at Skeleton rocks, by Hugh Lloyd ... illustrated by Bert Salg. New York, Grosset & Dunlap [c1931]
vi, 276 p. front., plates. 19½cm. [*His* Hal Keen mystery stories]

I. Title.
Library of Congress PZ7.L777Hal no. 7 32-13241

NL 0427646 DLC

Lloyd, Hugh.
... The Copperhead trail mystery, by Hugh Lloyd ... illustrated by Bert Salg. New York, Grosset & Dunlap [c1931]
vi, 218 p. front., plates. 19½cm. [*His* Hal Keen mystery stories]

I. Title.
Library of Congress PZ7.L777Hal no. 1 31-12243

NL 0427647 DLC

Lloyd, Hugh.
... The doom of Stark house, by Hugh Lloyd ... illustrated by Bert Salg. New York, Grosset & Dunlap [c1933]
vi, 238 p. front., plates. 19½cm. (*His* Hal Keen mystery stories)

I. Title.
Library of Congress PZ7.L777Hal no. 8 33-3288

NL 0427648 DLC

Lloyd, Hugh.
... Held for ransom, by Hugh Lloyd ... illustrated by Seymour Fogel. New York, Grosset & Dunlap [c1934]
vi, 7-221 p. front. 19½cm. (*His* Skippy Dare mystery stories)

I. Title.
Library of Congress PZ7.L778Sk no. 3 34-6278

NL 0427649 DLC CtY

Lloyd, Hugh.
... The hermit of Gordon's creek, by Hugh Lloyd ... illustrated by Bert Salg. New York, Grosset & Dunlap [c1931]
vi, 237 p. front., plates. 19½cm. [*His* Hal Keen mystery stories]

I. Title.
Library of Congress PZ7.L777Hal no. 2 31-12242

NL 0427650 DLC MH

Lloyd, Hugh.
... Kidnapped in the jungle, by Hugh Lloyd ... illustrated by Bert Salg. New York, Grosset & Dunlap [c1931]
vi, 244 p. front., pl. 19½cm. [*His* Hal Keen mystery stories]

I. Title.
Library of Congress PZ7.L777Hal no. 3 31-12241

NL 0427651 DLC ViU

Lloyd, Hugh.
... The Lonesome swamp mystery, by Hugh Lloyd ... illustrated by Bert Salg. New York, Grosset & Dunlap [c1932]
vi, 264 p. front., plates. 19½cm. (*His* Hal Keen mystery stories)
At head of title: A Hal Keen mystery story.

I. Title.
Library of Congress PZ7.L777Hal no. 6 32-2021

NL 0427652 DLC

Lloyd, Hugh.
... The lost mine of the Amazon, by Hugh Lloyd ... illustrated by Bert Salg. New York, Grosset & Dunlap [c1933]
vi, 212 p. front., plates. 19½cm. (*His* Hal Keen mystery stories)

I. Title.
Library of Congress PZ7.L777Hal no. 9 33-24531

NL 0427653 DLC

Lloyd, Hugh.
... The mysterious Arab, by Hugh Lloyd ... illustrated by Bert Salg. New York, Grosset & Dunlap [c1931]
vi, 237 p. front., plates. 19½cm. [*His* Hal Keen mystery stories]

I. Title.
Library of Congress PZ7.L777Hal no. 5 31-22802

NL 0427654 DLC

Lloyd, Hugh.
... The mystery at Dark star ranch, by Hugh Lloyd ... illustrated by Bert Salg. New York, Grosset & Dunlap [c1934]
vi, 240 p. front., plates. 19½cm. (*His* Hal Keene mystery stories)

I. Title.
Library of Congress PZ7.L777Hal no. 10 34-32208

NL 0427655 DLC

Lloyd, Hugh.
... Prisoners in Devil's bog, by Hugh Lloyd ... illustrated by Seymour Fogel. New York, Grosset & Dunlap [c1934]
vi, 212 p. front. 19½cm. (*His* Skippy Dare mystery stories)

I. Title.
Library of Congress PZ7.L778Sk no. 2 34-6277

NL 0427656 DLC

Lloyd, Hugh.
... The smugglers' secret, by Hugh Lloyd ... illustrated by Bert Salg. New York, Grosset & Dunlap [c1931]
vi, 249 p. front., plates. 19½cm. (*His* Hal Keen mystery stories)

I. Title.
Library of Congress PZ7.L777Hal no. 4 31-21183

NL 0427657 DLC

Lloyd, Hugh.
The story of a fight from Concord bridge to a field at Yorktown, by Hugh Lloyd ... New York, McLoughlin brothers [c1907]
245 p. col. front., illus. 20½cm.

1. U. S.—Hist.—Revolution.
Library of Congress E208.L79 7-32382
(Copyright 1907 A 189170)

NL 0427658 DLC

Lloyd, *Sir* Hugh Pughe, 1895-
Briefed to attack; Malta's part in African victory. With a foreword by Lord Tedder. London, Hodder & Stoughton [1949]
230 p. illus., ports., maps. 23 cm.

1. World War, 1939-1945—Malta. 2. World War, 1939-1945—Campaigns—Africa, North. 3. World War, 1939-1945—Personal narratives, English. I. Title.
D763.M3L6 940.53458 49-6184*

NL 0427659 DLC CaBVa CaBVaU CaBViPA PP

VOLUME 337

QC355 .L8 Lloyd, Humphrey, 1800-1881.
Abriss einer geschichte der fortschritte und des gegenwärtigen zustandes der physischen optik. Von Humphrey Lloyd... Aus dem Report of the fourth meeting of the British association for the advancement of science. London, 1835. Übers. und mit ergänzenden anmerkungen versehen von G. A. Kloeden. Berlin, C.G. Lüderitz, 1836.
[1], 195 p. 20cm.

1. Optics, Physical.

NL 0427660 ICU

Lloyd, Humphrey, 1800-1881.
Account of the Magnetical observatory of Dublin, and of the instruments and methods of observation employed there. Dublin, Printed at the University Press by Graisberry and Gill, 1842.

NL 0427661 MH MiU DAS PPAmP

F 4293 .185 LLOYD, HUMPHREY, 1800-1881.
Address delivered at the opening meeting of the British Association for the Advancement of Science, held at Dublin on August 26, 1857. Dublin, University Press, 1857.
24p. 22cm.

Binder's title: Collection of pamphlets on Dublin.

NL 0427662 ICN

Lloyd, Humphrey, 1800-1881.
Circular for the information of the directors of the British colonial magnetical observatories. London, 1848.
7 p. 19cm.

NL 0427663 DN-Ob CtY

551.56 L77c Lloyd, Humphrey, 1800-1881.
The climate of Ireland, and the currents of the Atlantic. A lecture delivered before the Dublin young men's Christian association in connexion with the United church of England and Ireland, October 25th, 1865. Dublin, 1865.
55p.

NL 0427664 IU DAS

[LLOYD, HUMPHREY] 1800-1881.
The doctrine of absolution ... By a member of the Revision Committee of the Church of Ireland. Dublin, Hodges, Foster and Co., 1871.
41p. 21cm.

NL 0427665 ICN

QC 357 .L79 Lloyd, Humphrey, 1800-1881.
Elementary treatise on the wave-theory of light. By Humphrey Lloyd. 2d ed. with additions. London, Longman, Brown, Green, Longmans, and Roberts, 1857.
xii, 208 p. illus. 22 cm.

NL 0427666 OKentU

Lloyd, Humphrey, 1800-1881.
Elementary treatise on the wave-theory of light. By Humphrey Lloyd ... 2d ed. with additions. London, Longman, Brown, Green, Longmans, and Roberts, 1857.
xii, 208 p. illus., diagrs. 22cm.

1. Optics, Physical. 2. Light, Wave theory of.

Library of Congress QC357.L79 5—5352

NL 0427667 DLC CU CtY PPF PU ViU OU MiU NN

Lloyd, Humphrey, 1800-1881.
Elementary treatise on the wave-theory of light. 3d ed rev. and enl. London, Longmans, Green, 1873.
xi, 247 p. illus. 24 cm.

1. Optics, Physical. 2. Light, Wave theory of.

QC357.L79 1873 49-57050*

NL 0427668 MiU CtY DBS ICJ MiHM CU NIC WU CSt WaS DLC DNLM MB ViU NNC OU PU PHC NNCoCi

---

Lloyd, Humphrey, 1800-1881.
Elements of optics. By Humphrey Lloyd ... Dublin, Hodges and Smith, 1849.
vi, 115 p. 22½cm.

1. Optics.

12-31682

Library of Congress QC355.L6

NL 0427669 DLC DNLM CtY NjP DI-GS

LC 116 .G8 L79 Lloyd, Humphrey, 1800-1881.
"Is it a sin?" An inquiry into the lawfulness of complying with the rule of the National board, relative to religious instruction. Dublin, Hodges, Smith & co., 1860.
iv, [5]-42 p. 21cm.
Author's presentation copy.

1. Religious education—Ireland. 2. Education—Ireland. 3. Church and education in Ireland. I. Title.

NL 0427670 MiU

Lloyd, Humphrey, 1800-1881. 535.1 K100
Lectures on the wave-theory of light. By the Rev. H. Lloyd, ... Printed by order of the Board of Erasmus Smith [University of Dublin]. Dublin, A. Milliken, 1841.
iv, [5]-83 p. II fold. pl. 23cm.

NL 0427671 MA RPB ViLxW CtY ICJ WU ScU OkU NRU CU PPAmP PU NWM MH

Re4.075 Lloyd, Humphrey, 1800-1881.
[Miscellaneous pamphlets on magnetism, terrestrial magnetism and electricity] 33cm.

NL 0427672 CtY

Lloyd, Humphrey, F.R.S., 1800-1881. 530.4 L77
Miscellaneous papers connected with physical science. ... iv, [2], 509, [2] p. 2 maps, 5 tables. O. London: Longmans, Green, & Co., 1877.
Reprinted from the *Transactions of the Royal Irish Academy*, the *Reports of the British Association for the Advancement of Science*, etc.

NL 0427673 DN ViU NjP ICJ PPF PBm PPAmP PU ICJ NBuU MdBP DSI NN DBS IU DP NRU PSt

---

Lloyd, Humphrey, 1800-1881.
Notes on the meteorology of Ireland deduced from observations made in the year 1851, under the direction of the Royal Irish academy. By Humphrey Lloyd ... Dublin, Printed by M. H. Gill, 1854.
1 p. l., p. [411]-498. pl. VII-X, tables. 27½ x 22½cm.
"From the Transactions of the Royal Irish academy, vol. XXII.—Science."

1. Meteorology—Ireland. I. Royal Irish academy, Dublin.

16-24005

Library of Congress QC989.G8L7

NL 0427674 DLC DAS

QC802 .D8 Lloyd, Humphrey, 1800-1881.

Dublin. University. *Magnetical and meteorological observatory.*
Observations made at the Magnetical and meteorological observatory at Trinity college, Dublin: under the direction of Humphrey Lloyd ... Printed by order of the Board of Trinity college. v. 1-2; 1840-50. Dublin, Hodges, Smith and co.; [etc., etc.] 1865-69.

Lloyd, Humphrey, 1800-1881.
Observations on the direction and intensity of the terrestrial magnetic force in Ireland, made by the Rev. Humphrey Lloyd ... Captain Edward Sabine ... and Captain James Clarke Ross ... London, Printed by R. Taylor, 1836.
1 p. l., p. 117-162 incl. tables, diagr. 23½cm.
"From the Report of the British association for the advancement of science for 1835."

1. Magnetism, Terrestrial—Ireland. I. Sabine, Sir Edward, 1788-1883. II. Ross, Sir James Clark, 1800-1862.

30-14700

Library of Congress QC825.4.I.6 538.7

NL 0427676 DLC

Lloyd, Humphrey, 1800-1881.
On the determination of the intensity of the earth's magnetic force in absolute measure. Dublin, Printed at the Univ. Press, 1843.

"From the Transactions of the Royal Irish Academy, vol.21, pt.1."

NL 0427677 MH DN-Ob

Lloyd, Humphrey, 1800-1881.
... On the direct magnetic influence of a distant luminary upon the diurnal variations of the magnetic force at the earth's surface. By the Rev. H. Lloyd ... [London, 1858]
5 p. 21½cm.
Caption title.
"From the Philosophical magazine for March 1858."

1. Magnetism, Terrestrial.

11-23541

Library of Congress QC831.L79

NL 0427678 DLC

Lloyd, Humphrey, 1800-1881.
On the direction and intensity of the terrestial magnetic force in Ireland. London, 1836.
8°

NL 0427679 NN

VOLUME 337

Q311
.L65
v.18,
no.14

Lloyd, Humphrey, 1800-1881.
On the light reflected and transmitted by thin plates. Read April 11, 1859. [Dublin, 1859]
15 p. 33cm. [Lomb miscellaneous pamphlets, v. 18, no. 14]
Caption title.
Detached from Transactions of the Royal Irish Academy. [Vol. XXIV, 1859]
Original paper wrappers.

1. Optics, Physical. I. Title.

NL 0427680 ViU

Lloyd, Humphrey, 1800-1881.
On the mutual action of permanent magnets, considered chiefly in reference to their best relative position in an observatory. Dublin, Graisberry, 1840.
20 p.

NL 0427681 PPAmP

Lloyd, Humphrey, 1800-1881.
Praelection on the studies connected with the School of Engineering. Dublin, 1841.
32 p. 8°. [In India Tracks, v. 22]

NL 0427682 CtY

Lloyd, Humphrey, 1800-1881.
Report on the magnetic isoclinal and isodynamic lines in the British islands
see under Sabine, Edward, 1788-1883.

Lloyd, Humphrey, 1800-1881.
Supplement to a paper on the mutual action of permanent magnets, considered chiefly in reference to their best relative position in an observatory.
Dublin, 1841
1 pl. 10 p. 25½cm.

Dublin, R. I. Acad. Trans., 19, 1843, p. 249-256.

NL 0427684 DN-Ob

Lloyd, Humphrey, 1800-1881.
A treatise on light and vision. By the Rev. Humphrey Lloyd ... London, Printed for Longman, Rees, Orme, Brown, and Green, 1831.
xxx, (2), 402 p. tables, diagrs. 22cm.
With Miller, W. H. The elements of hydrostatics and hydrodynamics. 1843.

1. Optics.

MWelC PPL PU PPM WU DNLM CU NNC
NL 0427685 MiU NjP CtY ViU NWM DBS NNCoCi RPB ViU

Lloyd, Humphrey, 1800-1881.
A treatise on magnetism, general and terrestrial. By Humphrey Lloyd ... London, Longmans, Green, and co., 1874.
xv p., 1 l., 239 p. 3 pl. (incl. fold. map) tables, diagrs. 23cm.

1. Magnetism.

5-5326

Library of Congress QC753.L79

CtY MdBP CU CSt
NL 0427686 DLC NjP ICJ NN OU OCl DAS OClW PPF PPFr

Lloyd, Humphrey, 1800-1881.
Two introductory lectures on physical & mechanical science delivered in Hilary term.1834. Dublin, Milliken, 1834.
77 p.

NL 0427687 PU

[Lloyd, Humphrey] 1800-1881.
The University of Dublin in its relation to the several religious communions. Dublin, Hodges, Smith, & Foster, 1868.
32 p. 21 cm.
No. 4 of a collection of pamphlets lettered: University education, Ireland, v. 1.

1. Dublin. University. 2. Universities and colleges—Ireland. I. Title.

2-14791

Library of Congress LA647.U5

NL 0427688 DLC

PB
2297
O8245
Rare
Book
(Va.)

[Lloyd, Isaac]
Goronwy'r alltud, gan Glan Rhyddalt [pseud.] ... Lerpwl, Gwasg y Brython Hugh Evans a'i Feibion, Cyf. [1947]
64 p. front., plates. 19cm.

1. Owen, Goronwy, 1722-1769? I. Lloyd, David, ed. II. Title. x: Glan Rhyddalt, pseud x: Rhyddalt, Glan, pseud.

NL 0427689 ViW MH

Lloyd, J. A., of Dixon, Ill.
see Lloyd, Julius Anderson, 1849-

Lloyd, J. A. T.
see
Lloyd, John Arthur Thomas. 1870-1956.

Lloyd, J. C.
Discourses on the Lord's Prayer. Dublin, Times, 1831.
197 p.

NL 0427692 PPLT

Lloyd (J. H.) On improving the sanitary condition of towns by purifying them from sewage by means of dry closets (or closets), [etc.] 39 pp. 8°. Manchester & London, 1861. [P., v. 524.]

NL 0427693 DNLM

Lloyd, J H
Rational principles and practice of public cleanliness, in town and country, being a collection of the original papers, letters and correspondence on the subject, since 1857. [4th] ed. [n.p., n.d.]
v[9]40,37p. 22cm.

"Proof copy."
Letter of 3 Sept. 1876, from J.H. Lloyd, tipped in.
Vol. 6, no. 2 of a collection with binder's title: Pamphlets, sewage & sanitary, &c.

NL 0427694 KU-M

PB2298
L56T7

Lloyd, J H. novelist.
Trevor of Nant Gwynant, by J. H. Lloyd. London, Heath Cranton, 1927.
298 p.

NL 0427695 CU

Lloyd, J. Henry, writer on gild socialism
see Lloyd, James Henry, 1885-

Lloyd, Mrs. J. J.
see Lloyd, Marietta.

Lloyd, J Morgan.
Caneuon gwion bach. Wrecsam a Chaerdydd, Hughes a'i fab [192-?]
11 p. 25 cm.
Welsh songs for children. Words by T.Gwynn Jones. Music by J.M.Lloyd.

NL 0427698 MH

285.8
B391ZL

Lloyd, J T
Henry Ward Beecher, his life and work. London, W. Scott, 1887.
343 p. illus. 19 cm.

1. Beecher, Henry Ward, 1813-1887.

NL 0427699 LU CoU

BX 7260
B3
L56
1881

Lloyd, J T
Life of Henry Ward Beecher. Glasgow, J. McGready [1881]
320 p. port. (Memorable men of the nineteenth century, 3)

1. Beecher, Henry Ward, 1813-1887.

NL 0427700 CaBVaU

Lloyd, J. T., freethinker
see Lloyd, John T., 1850-

Lloyd, J. William
see Lloyd, John William, 1857-

Lloyd, Jacob Youde William, 1816-1887.
The history of the princes, the lords marcher, and the ancient nobility of Powys Fadog, and the ancient lords of Arwystli, Cedewen, and Meirionydd. By J. Y. W. Lloyd ... London, T. Richards [etc.] 1881-87.
6 v. fronts., illus., plates, plans. 23cm.

1. Wales—Geneal. 2. Wales—Antiq. 3. Powys—Geneal.

10-7185

Library of Congress CS454.L6

NL 0427703 DLC MiU MdBP CtY PHi MB MdBP OCl

VOLUME 337

Lloyd, *Gen.* James.
Works by this author printed in America before 1801 are available in this library in the Readex Microprint edition of Early American Imprints published by the American Antiquarian Society.
This collection is arranged according to the numbers in Charles Evans' American Bibliography.

NL 0427704 DLC

Lloyd, James, *Gen. James.*
Address of General James Lloyd, To the Citizens of Kent and Queen Anne's Counties, in Answer to the late Calumniuos Charge made against him by Robert Wright,.........
Annapolis: Printed by Frederick Green, Printer to the State.(1794.)
Pp. 38.

NL 0427705 PPL PHi MBAt

E13 .U5 v. 2, no. 40
Lloyd, James, 1769-1831.
Amendment. April 11th, 1810. Printed by order of the Senate of the U. S. States. Washington City: Printed by R. C. Weightman, 1810.
[2] 1. 22cm. [U. S. Congress. Senate. Library. Senate. State papers, v. 2, no. 40]

1. Citizenship—U. S.

NL 0427706 ViU

Lloyd, James, 1769-1831.
Massachusetts.
Considerations and documents relating to the claim of Massachusetts for expenditures during the late war. Washington, January, 1818. Washington, Printed by E. De Krafft, 1818.

Cb4 90 1
Lloyd, James, 1769-1831.
Discours de M. Lloyd, du Massachusets en faveur de l'abolition des droits d'importation et de tonnage sur la navigation étrangère. Traduit de l'anglais par A.C. Paris, Sautelet, 1826.
22 p. 21 cm.

NL 0427708 CtY

---

*Ch.D .6.63
Lloyd, James, 1769-1831.
Embargo by express. Boston, Friday evening, April 3, 1812—6 o'clock. The following letter is this moment handed me by express. Harrison G. Otis. "Mr. Calhoun ... has this moment informed Mr. Quincy, that the Committee of Foreign Relations have decided to lay a proposition for an embargo on the table ... tomorrow ... James Lloyd, Josiah Quincy, James Emott. Washington, Tuesday March 31, 1812 ... [Boston, 1812]

broadside. 14 x 14cm.

1. U. S.--Pol. & govt.—1809-1813. 2. U. S.—Hist.—1809-1813. 3. Broadsides—U. S. I. Otis, Harrison Gray, 1765-1848. II. Title.

NL 0427710 MB

Lloyd, James, 1769-1831.
Hon. Mr. Lloyd's letter, on impressments. [Boston? 1813]
4 p. 22½cm.
Caption title.
On the impressment of American seamen by the British.

1. Impressment.

A 31-1165

Title from H. E. Huntington Libr. Printed by L. C.

NL 0427711 CSmH CtY MWA MH CSt MWA MiU-C RPB

E13 .U5 v.2, no.33
Lloyd, James, 1769-1831.
Motion. April 5th, 1810. Printed by order of the Senate of the U. States. Washington City: Printed by R. C. Weightman, 1810.
[2] 1. 22cm. [U. S. Congress. Senate. Library. State papers, v. 2, no. 33]

1. U. S.—Militia.

NL 0427712 ViU

HF3028 .L75
[Lloyd, James], 1769-1831.
Remarks on the report of the Committee of commerce of the Senate of the United States, thirty-first of March, 1826, on the British colonial intercourse. [n.p., 1826?]
[1], 51 p. 23½cm.

1. U.S.--Comm.--Gt.Brit. 2. Gt.Brit.--Comm.--U.S 3. U.S. Senate. Committee on commerce. Report on the memorial of Baltimore merchants.

NL 0427713 [illegible] NNC

Lloyd, James, 1769-1831.
Mr. Lloyd's speech in the Senate, Monday, Dec. 19. On the bill making further provisions for enforcing the embargo. [1808?]
7p. 22cm.
Caption title.

NL 0427714 NNU-W KyU

LLOYD, JAMES, 1769-1831.
Mr. Lloyd's speech in the Senate of the U. States, February 21, on the bill interdicting an intercourse with Great-Britain and France. [Washington? 1809?] 11 p. 23cm.

Caption-title.

712219A. 1. Embargo—U.S., 1807-1809.

NL 0427715 NN MH NBu

Lloyd, James, 1769-1831.
Mr. Lloyd's speech in the Senate of the U. States, February 21, on the Bill interdicting an intercourse with Great-Britain and France. [n.p., 180-?]
11p.

Microcard edition.

NL 0427716 ICRL TxU OU ViU PSt ViU CaBVaU

Lloyd, James, 1769-1831. *4413.187
Mr. Lloyd's speech, in the Senate of the United States, on the bill "concerning the naval establishment." February 28, 1812. [Washington? 1812.] 24 pp. 22 cm., in 4s.
There is no title-page.

K8206 — United States. A. & n. Navy.

NL 0427717 MB MH CtY MiD-B MWA

Lloyd, James, 1769-1831.
Mr. Lloyd's speeches in the Senate of the United States, on Mr. Hillhouse's resolution to repeal the embargo laws; November 21 [and 28] 1808. [n. p., 1808]
16 p. 23cm.
Caption title.
Speech of Nov. 28 has separate caption title.

1. Embargo, 1807-1809.

Library of Congress HF3027.1.L79 6-36223
——— Copy 2. [Pamphlets addresses, v. 29, no. 1]

NL 0427718 DLC NNU-W KyU CtY CSt NBu CSmH NIC NNU-W MH CtY MH-BA

Lloyd, James, 1769-1831.
[Two speeches in the U. S. Senate on the embargo, November 21 and 26, 1808] n. p., n. d.
16 p.

NL 0427719 KyU

Lloyd, James, 1810-1896.
Flore de l'ouest de la France, ou Description des plantes qui croissent spontanément dans les départements de: Charente-Inférieure, Deux-Sèvres, Vendée, Loire-Inférieure, Morbihan, Finistère, Côtes-du-Nord, Ille-et-Vilaine, par M. James Lloyd. Nantes, J. Forest ainé, 1854.
3 p. l., 198 p., 1 l., 576 p. 15cm.

1. France. Botany.

Agr 10-1532

Library, U. S. Dept. of Agriculture 459L77

NL 0427720 DNAL NNBG MH-AH

QK313 .L55 1868
Lloyd, James, 1810-1896.
Flore de l'ouest de la France; ou Description des plantes qui croissent spontanément dans les départements de: Charente-Inférieure, Deux-Sèvres, Vendée, Loire-Inférieure, Morbihan, Finistère, Côtes-du-Nord, Ille-et-Vilaine. 2. éd. Nantes, Th. Veloppé, 1868.
ccxv, 644 p. 15 cm.

5547 Pritzel.

1. Botany - France. i.t.

NL 0427721 NNBG MH

QK313 .L55 1876
Lloyd, James, 1810-1896.
Flore de l'ouest de la France; ou, Description des plantes qui croissent spontanément dans les départements de: Charente-Inférieure, Deux-Sèvres, Vendée, Loire-Inférieure, Morbihan, Finistère, Côtes-du-Nord, Ille-et-Vilaine. 3. éd. Nantes, Veloppé, 1876.
cxxiii, 407 p. 19 cm.

"Herborisations de 1876, 1877"(15 p.) bound with copy 1.
1. Botany - France. i.t.

NL 0427722 NNBG MH

VOLUME 337

Lloyd, James, 1810-1896.
Flore de l'ouest de la France; ou, Description des plantes qui croissent spontanément dans les départements de: Charente-Inférieure, Deux-Sèvres, Vendée, Loire-Inférieure, Morbihan, Finistère, Côtes-du-Nord, Ille-et-Vilaine, par m. James Lloyd. 4. éd. augm. des plantes de la Gironde, des Landes et du littoral des Basses-Pyrénées, par m. J. Foucaud. Nantes, Mme T. Veloppé; ;etc., etc.; 1886.
4 p. l., ;iii;-lxxi, ;1;, 454, ;2; p. 22cm. (Added t.-p.: Académie de la Rochelle. Société des sciences naturelles de la Charente-Inférieure. Annales de 1885. No 22 (t. II))
1. Botany—France. I. Foucaud, Julien, 1847-1904. II. Title.
6-36330 Revised
Library of Congress Q46.C45 no. 22, t. 2

NL 0427723 DLC GU MH PPAN NNBG

LLOYD, James, 1810-1896.
Flore de l'ouest de la France: Herborisat. de 1887 à 1890. [Nantes], O. Weigel, [1890].
sm. 8°.

NL 0427724 MH

Lloyd, James, 1810-1896.
Flore de l'Ouest de la France, ou, Description des plantes qui croissent spontanément dans les départements de: Charente-Inférieure, Deux-Sèvres, Vendée, Loire-Inférieure, Morbihan, Finistère, Côtes-du-Nord, Ille-et-Vilaine, par James Lloyd. 5. éd., pub. par les soins de M. Émile Gadeceau. Nantes, R. Guist'hau, 1897.
5 p. l., cxxiv p., 1 l., 458 p. port. 20cm.
1. Botany—France.
S 18-28
Library, U. S. National Museum

NL 0427725 DSI MH ICJ

QK313 .L55 1898a
Lloyd, James, 1810-1896.
Flore de l'ouest de la France; ou, Description des plantes qui croissent spontanément dans les départements de: Charente-Inférieure, Deux-Sèvres, Vendée, Loire-Inférieure, Morbihan, Finistère, Côtes-du-Nord, Ille-et-Vilaine. 5. éd. Publiée par les soins de M. Emile Gadeceau. Nantes, R. Guist'hau, 1897 [cover: Paris, Librairie des sciences naturelles, 1898] cxxiv, 458 p. front. (port.) 20 cm.
1. Botany - France. 2. Lloyd, James, 1810-1896 - Portraits. i.t.

NL 0427726 NNBG MH

Lloyd, James, 1810-1896.
Flore de la Loire-Inférieure, par M. James Lloyd. Nantes, P. Sebire, 1844.
3 p. l., 38, (2), xxxii, 335 p. 14½cm.
1. Botany—France—Loire-Inférieure. [1. France. Département de la Loire-Inférieure—Botany]
Agr 26-160
Library, U. S. Dept. of Agriculture 459.5L77F

NL 0427727 DNAL PPAN MH-AH

Lloyd, James, 1846-
My circus life; being the life and adventures, and the world travels and experiences of an artist and circus proprietor, now aged 79 years. The last of the Mohicans emanated from "The cradle of the circus world", Astley's amphitheatre, Westminster Bridge road, London, James Lloyd. Introduction by G. K. Chesterton. London, N. Douglas, 1925.
x, 11-101, ;1; p. front., plates, ports. 19½cm.
1. Circus. I. Title.
Library of Congress GV1815.L6 26-3171

NL 0427728 DLC CtY NN WHi IU TxD OClh OCl

Lloyd, James Hendrie, 1853-
Alcohol and insanity. Detroit, 1915.

NL 0427729 NjP

Lloyd, James Hendrie, 1853 -
Benjamin Rush and his critics.
= New York. 1930. (1), 470-475 pp. 28 cm.
Reprinted from Annals of medical history, published by Paul B. Hoeber, Inc., new series, vol. 2, no. 5.
References, p. 475.
D6338 — Rush, Benjamin, M.D., 1745-1813.

NL 0427730 MB MH PPAmP

Lloyd, James Hendrie, 1853-
Case of dislocation of the atlas. n.p., [1904]

NL 0427731 NjP

Lloyd, James Hendrie, 1853-
Case of hematomyelia. n.p. [1900]

NL 0427732 NjP

Lloyd, James Hendrie, 1853 -
A case of tumor of the mid-brain and left optic thalamus. n. t.-p. [Philadelphia, 1892.] 6 p. 12°.
Title from cover.
Repr.: Medical news. January 30, 1892.
1. Brain.—Tumors.
N. Y. P. L. December 18, 1912.

NL 0427733 NN OClW

Lloyd, James Hendrie, 1853-
The case of William Cowper, the English poet.
= Chicago. American Medical Association. [1930.] 8 pp. 25½ cm.
Reprinted from the Archives of Neurology and Psychiatry, October 1930, vol. 24, pp. 682-689.
D6660 — Cowper, William, 1731-1800. — American Medical Association. Pubs.

NL 0427734 MB OO MH ICarbS PPL PHC MB

Lloyd, James Hendrie, 1853 -
The claim of moral insanity in its medico-legal aspects. n. t.-p. New York: Trow's Printing and Bookbinding Co., 1887. 16 p. 12°.
Title from cover.
Repr.: Medical record. May 14, 1887.
1. Insane.—Jurisprudence.
N. Y. P. L. December 18, 1912

NL 0427735 NN

LLOYD, James Hendrie, 1853 -
The diseases of occupations. Philadelphia, 1880.
pp.311-496. Illus. 23 1/2 cm.
(Extracted from the 20th Century Practice of Medicine.)
Med. School

NL 0427736 MH

Lloyd, James Hendrie, 1853-
Diseases of the cerebrospinal and sympathetic nerves. [n.p., 1897]

NL 0427737 NjP

Lloyd, James Hendrie, 1853 -
Diseases of the cerebrospinal and sympathetic nerves. Illus.
(In Stedman. Twentieth Century practice. Vol. 11, pp. 1-476. New York, 1897.)
Bibliographical references, pp. 467-476.
E9912 — Nervous system.

NL 0427738 MB

Lloyd, James Hendrie, 1853-
Diseases of the peripheral nervous system. [n.p., 1903]

NL 0427739 NjP

Lloyd, James Hendrie, 1853 -
Diseases of the peripheral nervous system. Illus.
(In Stedman. Twentieth Century practice. Vol. 21, pp. 494-525. New York, 1903.)
E9903 — Nerves. Peripheral.

NL 0427740 MB

LLOYD, James Hendrie, 1853 -
Diseases of the spinal cord.
(In Wilson and Eshner. An American text-book of applied therapeutics. Pp. 1027-1064. Phila., 1896.)

NL 0427741 MB

Lloyd, James Hendrie, 1853-
Faith-cures. N.Y., 1886.

NL 0427742 NjP

Lloyd (James Hendrie), 1853 - Hysteria; a study in psychology. 21 pp. 8°. [New York, G. P. Putnam's Sons, 1883.]
Repr. from: J. Nerv. & Ment. Dis., Chicago, 1883, x.

NL 0427743 DNLM

Lloyd, James Hendrie, 1853-
Hysteria; diseases of the spinal cord. [n.p., 1895]

NL 0427744 NjP

Lloyd, James Hendrie, 1853-
Insanity and diseases of...nervous system in child bearing-woman. [n.p., 1889]

NL 0427745 NjP

VOLUME 337

Lloyd, James Hendrie, 1853-
Insanity: forms and medico-legal relations.
Wharton, Francis, 1820-1889.
Wharton and Stillé's medical jurisprudence ... 5th ed. Rochester, N. Y., The Lawyers' co-operative publishing company, 1905.

Lloyd, J[ames] Hendrie, 1853-
The insanity of Oscar Hugo Webber. Read before the Medical Jurisprudence Society of Philadelphia, November 13th, 1888. n. t.-p. [Philadelphia, 1888.] 5 p. 8°.

Repr.: Medical Jurisprudence Soc. of Philadelphia. Proc. November, 1888
Title from cover.

1. Webber, Oscar Hugo.
N. Y. P. L. December 18, 1912.

NL 0427747 NN

Lloyd (James Hendrie). Moral insanity; a plea for a more exact cerebral pathology. A thesis for admission into the American Neurological Association. 17 pp. 8°. [New York, 1886.]
Repr. from: J. Nerv. & Ment. Dis., N. Y., 1886, xi.

NL 0427748 DNLM OC1W PHi

Lloyd, James Hendrie, 1853-
Morphology and functions of the corpus striatum. n.p., [1915]

NL 0427749 NjP

Lloyd, James Hendrie, 1853-
Nuclear ophthalmoplegia. [Philadelphia, 1899]

NL 0427750 NjP

Lloyd, James Hendrie, 1853-
Paralysis of the peroneal nerve following childbirth. n.p., c1906.

NL 0427751 NjP

Lloyd, James Hendrie, 1853- ed.

R11
.P5
The Philadelphia medical journal. v. 1-11, no. 24; Jan. 1, 1898-June 13, 1903. Philadelphia, The Philadelphia medical publishing company, 1898-1903.

Lloyd, James Hendrie, 1853-
Purulent cerebro-spinal meningitis. n.p., [1898]

NL 0427753 NjP

Lloyd, James Hendrie, 1853-
Report of a case of syringomyelia. n.p., [1893]

NL 0427754 NjP

Lloyd, James Hendrie, 1853-
Rhythmical hysteria. n.p., 1900.

NL 0427755 NjP

Lloyd, James Hendrie, 1853-
The so-called Oedipus-complex in Hamlet. [Chicago, 1911]
7 p. 21.5 cm.
"Reprinted from the journal of the American medical association, May 13, 1911, vol. 1 vi, p. 1377-1379."

NL 0427756 PU NjP

Lloyd, James Hendrie, 1853-
Study of the lesions in a case of trauma of the cervical region of the spinal cord. n.p. [1894]

NL 0427757 NjP

Lloyd, James Hendrie, 1853-
Total transverse lesions of the spinal cord. n.p., c1915.

NL 0427758 NjP

Lloyd, James Hendrie, 1853-
Trauma of the spinal cord. n.p., [1900]

NL 0427759 NjP

Lloyd, James Hendrie, 1853-
Trial of the insane for crime; historical retrospect. n.p., [1907]

NL 0427760 NjP

Lloyd, James Hendrie, 1853-
Tumors of the brain and its envelopes
see under Mills, Charles Karner, 1845-1931.

Lloyd, James Hendrie, 1853-
Tumors of the spinal cord and its envelopes
see under Mills, Charles Karsner, 1845-1931.

Lloyd, James Henry, 1885-
Domestic servants and the insurance acts; a guide for mistresses and servants. London: Sir I. Pitman & Sons, Ltd., 1914. v, 30 p. 16°.

At head of cover title: National health insurance acts.

1. Insurance (Workmen's), Gt. Br. 2. Servants (Domestic), Gt. Br. 3. Title.
N. Y. P. L. September 30, 1914.

NL 0427763 NN DL

Lloyd, James Henry, 1885-
... Guilds and the salary earner, by J. Henry Lloyd. London, Published for the National guilds league by the Labour publishing company, limited, 1921.
cover-title, 15 p. 21½cm.

1. Gild socialism. I. National guilds league, London. II. Title. III. Title: The salary earner.

Library of Congress HD6479.L6 22-3109

NL 0427764 DLC CaBVaU CtY MiU NN

Lloyd, James Henry, 1885- ed.
National insurance acts, 1911 and 1913 ...
see under Gt. Brit. Laws, statutes, etc., 1910-1936 (George V)

Lloyd, James Henry, 1885-
Trade unionism for clerks. By J. Henry Lloyd and R. E. Scouller. With introductions by the Rt. Hon. J. R. Clynes and G. Bernard Shaw. London: C. Palmer and Hayward[, 1912]. 31 p. incl. diagr. 21cm.

First edition.
Covers included in paging.

629341A. 1. Trades unions, Clerks'. I. Scouller, R. E., jt. au. II. Shaw, Bernard, 1856-
N. Y. P. L. September 11, 1933

NL 0427766 NN CSmH DL NSyU NNG

Lloyd, James Henry, 1885-
Trade unionism for clerks. By J. Henry Lloyd and R. E. Scouller, with introductions by the Rt. Hon. J. R. Clynes and G. Bernard Shaw. London, C. Palmer and Hayward [1919]
31 p. diagr. 21½cm.

1. Clerks—Gt. Brit. 2. Trade-unions—Gt. Brit. I. Scouller, R. E., joint author. II. Title.

Library of Congress HD6668.M4L5 45-29637

NL 0427767 DLC CSt ICN WU MH NcU InU MiU

Lloyd, James Henry, 1885-
Trade unionism for clerks. By J. Henry Lloyd and R. E. Scouller, with introductions by the Rt. Hon. J. R. Clynes and G. Bernard Shaw. London, Cecil Palmer and Hayward [192-?]
31 p. (incl. covers) diagr. 22cm.

629341A. 1. Trade unions, Clerks'—Gt. Br. I. Scouller, R. E., jt. au. II. Shaw. Bernard. 1856-1950. i. subs for *KF. 1912.

NL 0427768 NN NIC

Lloyd, James T.
Lloyd's American guide
see under title

Lloyd, James T.
Lloyd's American railroad map. New York, 1860.
col. 94 x 119 cm.
Inset: Lloyd's Map of the eastern states.

NL 0427770 RPB

VOLUME 337

Lloyd, James T.
Lloyd's American railroad map.
= New York. [1861.] Size, 37 × 46⅞ inches. Scale, 30 miles to 1 inch. Folded.
Submaps. — 1. Map of Escambia & Santa Rosa Cos. Fl. showing, Pensacola Harbor and channel, Ft. Pickens, Ft. McRae, Bragg's Batteries and the position of the U. S. fleet now before the harbor. 2. Time dial.

Covers the United States west to Louisiana.

H9581 — United States. Geog. Maps. — United States. R.Rs. — Pickens, Fort.

NL 0427771 MB

Lloyd, James T.
Lloyd's list of post offices in the United States and the Canadas. Alphabetically arranged. Also containing the postal laws and regulations, classified by subjects, omitting such as are not of importance to the public generally. New York, Lloyd, 1863.
xxiv, 3-352 p. 21 cm., in 16s.
1. Post offices. Directories. 2. United States. Post offices. 3. Canada. Post offices.

NL 0427772 MB

Lloyd, James T.
Lloyd's map of the eastern states. [New York, 1860]
col. 53 x 41 cm.
Inset in Lloyd's American railroad map, 1860.

NL 0427773 RPB ICU

Case G 10875 .495
LLOYD, JAMES T.
Lloyd's map of the lower Mississippi river from St. Louis to the gulf of Mexico. Compiled from government surveys in the Topographical bureau, Washington, D.C. Revised and corrected to the present time, by Captains Bart. and William Bowen... Exhibiting the sugar and cotton plantations, cities, towns, landings, railroads, &c. along the river... New York, J.T.Lloyd, 1862.
map. 93x128cm.fold.to 25cm.
Scale: 5 miles to an inch.

NL 0427774 ICN IGK MB OC

F207 L6
Lloyd, James T
Lloyd's map of the southern states showing all the railroads, their stations & distances, also the counties, towns, villages, harbors, rivers and forts. Compiled from the latest government and other reliable sources. New York, J. T. Lloyd, 1861.
col.map. 134½x99½cm. folded to 24cm.

NL 0427775 NBuG NcD

Lloyd, James T.
Lloyd's map of the southern states, showing all the railroads, their stations and distances, also the counties, towns ... and forts.
New York, 1863 Size, 36¼ × 47⅛ inches. Scale (computed), 1.4 miles to 1 inch. No. 2 in *Map 118.1

NL 0427776 MB

Lloyd, James T.
Lloyd's military map and gazetteer of the southern states. New York [Published by J. T. Lloyd] c1861.
sheet. 99 1|2 x 138 1|2 cm. fold. to 69 1|2 x 50 1|2 cm.
Text (4 p.) on one side of sheet, col. map on the other.
Caption-title.
Text in newspaper form; part of text lacking on p. [1] in lower right corner, because of folding of paper at time of printing.
Map has title: Lloyd's map of the southern states, showing all the railroads, their stations & distances, also the counties, towns, villages, harbors, rivers and forts. Compiled from the latest government and other reliable sources. 1863. New York, J. T. Lloyd, publisher, c1862. ("Scale of statute miles, 69.1 to a degree"; 100 to 7.9 cm.)
1. Maps—U. S. (Southern states) c1862. 2. Maps—U. S. (Southwest, Old) c1862. 3. Southern states—Descr. & trav.—Gazetteers. I. Title.

NL 0427778 CSmH

G1405 1863
LLOYD, JAMES T.
Lloyd's new map of the United States, the Canadas and New Brunswick from the latest surveys showing every railroad and station finished to June 1862 and the Atlantic and Gulf coasts, from the United States Superintendent's official reports of the coast survey by order of Congress. New York, J.T.Lloyd, 1863.
sheet. 97x129cm.fold.to 25cm.
Label pasted on verso of map reads: Lloyd's Railway and military map of the United States and Canada. London, Bacon and co.

NL 0427779 ICU MiU-C

Lloyd, James T
Lloyd's numerical and alphabetical index to the railways in actual operation in the British Isles
see under title

Lloyd, James T.
Lloyd's Official map of Missouri.
New York. 1861. Size, 21 × 26¼ inches. Scale, 12 miles to 1 inch.

H4852 — Missouri. Geog. Maps.

NL 0427781 MB

Lloyd, James T.
Lloyd's Official map of the State of Kentucky.
New-York. 1862. Size, 30 × 40 inches. Scale (computed), 8 miles to 1 inch.

H5183 — Kentucky. Geog. Maps.

NL 0427782 MB

Lloyd, J.T.
Lloyd's official map of the state of Tenessee. Comp. from actual surveys and official documents, showing every railroad and railroad station with the distances between each station. Also the counties and county seats, cities, towns, villages, post offices, wagon roads, canals, forts, fortifications, &c. N.Y., J.T. Lloyd,

NL 0427783 TKL

Lloyd, James T.
Lloyd's Official map of the State of Virginia.
New York. 1861. Size, 29⅜ × 46⅜ inches. Scale (computed), 10 miles to 1 inch. Folded. *Map 1020.32

F0578 — Virginia. Geog. Maps.

NL 0427784 MB

918.79 L79
Lloyd, James T.
Lloyd's official map of the state of Virginia, from actual surveys by order of the executive 1828 & 1859. Cor.& rev.by J. T.Lloyd to 1862, from surveys made by Capt. W.Angelo Powell...New York, J.T.Lloyd, 1862.
map. 81 x 125 cm.fold.to 18½ cm.
Caption title.

NL 0427785 Mi NN NBuG ViU NcD NjP ICU

Lloyd, James T.
Lloyd's Railroad, telegraph & express map of the Eastern States.
= New York. 1868. Size, 37 × 25½ inches. Scale (computed), 13½ miles to 1 inch.
Submaps. — 1. Rivière du Loup Branch, or northern terminus of Grand Trunk R. R. 2. [Boston and vicinity.] 3. Railways leading out of Philadelphia.

F7864 — New England. Geog. Maps. — New England. R.Rs.

NL 0427786 MB

Lloyd, James T
Lloyd's steamboat directory, and disasters on the western waters, containing the history of the first application of steam, as a motive power; the lives of John Fitch and Robert Fulton ... History of the early steamboat navigation on western waters ... Full accounts of all the steamboat disasters ... A complete list of steamboats and all other vessels now afloat on the western rivers and lakes ... maps of the Ohio and Mississippi rivers ... List of plantations on the Mississippi river ... One hundred ... engravings, and forty-six maps ... By James T. Lloyd. Cincinnati, O., J. T. Lloyd & co., 1856.
vi, 7-326 p. illus. (incl. ports., maps, facsim.) 23½ cm.

1. Steamboat disasters. 2. Steam-navigation — Mississippi valley. 3. Mississippi valley—Descr. & trav. 4. Mississippi river—Descr. & trav. 5. Ohio river—Descr. & trav. 6. Railroads—U. S.—Hist. 7. Fitch, John, 1743-1798. 8. Fulton, Robert, 1765-1815. I. Title.

F353.L79 1—8710

NL 0427788 DLC MoSW NBu LU InU NN NcD NcU MdBP

Lloyd, James T.
Lloyd's steamboat directory, and disasters on the western waters, containing the history of the first application of steam, as a motive power; the lives of John Fitch and Robert Fulton ... history of the early steamboat navigation on western waters ... a complete list of steamboats and all other vessels now afloat on the western rivers and lakes ... maps of the Ohio and Mississippi rivers ... History of all the rail roads in the United States ... One hundred fine engravings, and sixty maps ... By James T. Lloyd. Cincinnati, O., J. T. Lloyd & co., 1856.

vi, 7-331 p. illus. (incl. maps) 22½cm.

1. Steamboat disasters. 2. Steam navigation—Mississippi Valley. 3. Mississippi Valley—Descr. & trav. 4. Mississippi River—Descr. & trav. 5. Ohio River—Descr. & trav. 6. Railroads—U. S.—Hist. 7. Fitch, John, 1743-1793. 8. Fulton, Robert, 1765-1815. I. Title.

6—1693

Library of Congress F353.L81

NL 0427790 DLC IGK WaS MoU OC MdBP Ia-HA IaHi OFH OClWHi KyBgW ICJ NjP MB

VOLUME 337

Lloyd, James T.
Lloyd's steamboat directory, and disasters on the western waters, containing the history of the first application of steam, as a motive power; the lives of John Fitch and Robert Fulton ... History of the early steamboat navigation on western waters ... Full accounts of all the steamboat disasters ... A complete list of steamboats and all other vessels now afloat on the western rivers and lakes ... maps of the Ohio and Mississippi rivers ... History of all the rail roads in the United States ... One hundred ... engravings ... and sixty maps ...

By James T. Lloyd. Cincinnati, O., J. T. Lloyd & co.; Chicago, Ill., D. B. Cooke & co., 1856.
vi, 7-331 p. illus. (incl. ports., maps, facsim.) 22½cm.

1. Steamboat disasters. 2. Steam-navigation—Mississippi valley. 3. Mississippi valley—Descr. & trav. 4. Mississippi river—Descr. & trav. 5. Ohio river—Descr. & trav. 6. Railroads—U. S.—Hist. 7. Fitch, John, 1743-1798. 8. Fulton, Robert, 1765-1815. I. Title.
1—8711
Library of Congress F353.L80

NL 0427792 DLC ViW NjP ViU

Micro Film D50 reel 379 no.13
Lloyd, James T
Lloyd's steamboat directory, and disasters on the western waters, containing the history of the first application of steam, as a motive power; the lives of John Fitch and Robert Fulton ... History of the early steamboat navigation on western waters ... Full accounts of all the steamboat disasters ... A complete list of steamboats and all other vessels now afloat on the western rivers and lakes ... maps of the Ohio and Mississippi rivers ... History of all the rail roads in the United States ... One

hundred ... engravings ... and sixty maps ... By James T. Lloyd. Cincinnati, O., J.T. Lloyd & co.; Chicago, Ill., D.B. Cooke & co., 1856.
(On American culture series, reel 379, no.13)
Microfilm (positive). 35mm. Ann Arbor, Mich., University Microfilms, 1968.
Collation of the original: vi,7-331p. illus. (incl.ports.,maps, facsim.) 23cm.

1. Steamboat disasters. 2. Steam-navigation - Mississippi river. 3. Mississippi valley - Descr. & trav. 4. Mississippi river - Descr. & trav. 5. Ohio river - Descr. & trav. 6. Railroads - U.S. - Hist. 7. Fitch, John, 1743-1798. 8. Fulton, Robert, 1765-1815. ~~I. Title.~~ I. Title: Steamboat directory, and disasters on the western waters.

NL 0427795 PSt

Case G 875 515
LLOYD, JAMES T.
Lloyd's steamboat directory, and disasters on the western waters, containing the history of the first application of steam, as a motive power; the lives of John Fitch and Robert Fulton... History of the early steamboat navigation on western waters... History of all the rail roads in the United States... Philadelphia,Penn'a,J.T.Lloyd & co. ₍c1856₎
vi,7-331p. illus.,ports.,maps,facsim. 22½cm.
In case.
Bookplate of Neva and Guy Littell. Kenilworth, Illinois

NL 0427796 ICN OC

G 1080 .51
Lloyd, James T.
Lloyd's topographical and railway map of America, 1877. Projected by J.T.Lloyd. Philadelphia,E.Lloyd [1877] 93x119½cm.
Scale: 83 miles to one inch.

NL 0427797 ICN

912.758 L793
Lloyd, James T.
Lloyd's topographical map of Georgia from state surveys before the war showing railways, stations, villages, mills &c ... New York, J.T. Lloyd, 1864.
fold.col.map. (90x77cm.fold.to 18cm.)
Scale: 10 miles = 1 inch.

1. Georgia – Descr. & tr. – Maps.

NL 0427798 LNHT NN IU

Mann G 3802 H8 C 1 1864 L79 Map
Lloyd, James T
Lloyd's topographical map of the Hudson River from the head of navigation at Troy to its confluence with the ocean at Sandy Hook embracing an area of 4 miles on either side from trigonometrical surveys and personal reconnaisance. Exhibiting minutely all the topographical data of cities, towns, villages, mountains and hills, with their altitudes in feet; lakes, roads, buildings, with the owners' nam[illegible]s. Railroads with their

stations and distances, and the river channe and mileage. New York, 1864.
col. map. 127x94 cm.
Scale 1:70,000 (not 1/2 mile to 1 inch.)
Map divided into 4 sections lengthwise.
Wall map.

1. Hudson River - Maps.

NL 0427800 NIC

Lloyd, James Tilgh man₎ 1857-1944.
Bankruptcy bill. Speech ... in the House ... February 18, 1898. Washington ₍Gov't print. off.₎ 1898.
8 pp. 8°.

HG 3766. Z9 1-4641

NL 0427801 DLC

Lloyd, James Tilghman, 1857-
... Constitutional amendment with relation to national prohibition. Memorandum on the nature and method of amendment of the Constitution of the United States with relationship to national constitutional prohibition, by Mr. James T. Lloyd ... Washington, Govt. print. off., 1917.
8 p. 23cm. (₍U. S.₎ 65th Cong., 1st sess. Senate. Doc. 67)
Presented by Mr. Stone. Ordered printed July 30, 1917.

1. Prohibition—U. S. I. Title.
17-26691 Revised
Library of Congress HV5089.L7

NL 0427802 DLC MiU OO MB

Lloyd, James Tilgh man₎ 1857-1944.
The Loud postal bill. Speech ... in the House ... March 3, 1898. Washington ₍Gov't print. off.₎ 1898.
7 pp. 8°.

HE 6341. L79 1-4642

NL 0427803 DLC

627.5 L77n
Lloyd, James Tighlman, 1857-
National drainage congress. Remarks in the House of Representatives, Friday, November 14, 1913. [Washington] 1913. 8p.

NL 0427804 IU

Lloyd, James Tilghman, 1857-
The Puerto Rico tariff. Speech of Hon. James T. Lloyd, of Missouri, in the House of representatives, Friday, February 23, 1900. Washington ₍Govt. print. off.₎ 1900.
8 p. 23cm.

1. Porto Rico tariff bill of 1900.
1-4964 Revised
Library of Congress HF1896.L79

NL 0427805 DLC

Lloyd, James Tilgh man₎ 1857-1944.
Remarks ... in the House ... on the civil service and other subjects, January 6, 12, and 27, 1898 Washington ₍Gov't print. off.₎ 1898. 7 pp. 8°.
CONTENTS:—Civil service.—New York dry dock.—Free-delivery system.
1-4651

NL 0427806 DLC

Lloyd, James Tilghman, 1857-

U. S. *Congress. House. Committee on agriculture.*
Transportation and marketing of farm products. Hearings before the Committee on agriculture, House of representatives, Sixty-sixth Congress, third session. Statements of James T. Lloyd and Martin Dodge. February 8, 1921. Washington, Govt. print. off., 1921.

Lloyd, James Tilghman, 1857-
War revenue and bond issue. Speech of Hon. James T. Lloyd, of Missouri, in the House of representatives, Thursday, April 28, 1898. Washington ₍Govt. print. off.₎ 1898.
7 p. 24cm.

1. War revenue law of 1898.
1-4643 Revised
Library of Congress HJ2375.L7

NL 0427808 DLC

Lloyd, Jane G.
The fountain and the rose. By M. G. B. ₍Philadelphia, Becktold & co., 1883₎

Lloyd, Jessie.
Gastonia; a graphic chapter in southern organization. New York, 1930.
30 p. 19 cm.

NL 0427810 MH-PA

F865G2 .L1
Lloyd, Jessie
Gastonia, a graphic chapter in southern organization. New York [Conference for Progressive Labor Action, National executive committee] 1930.
31 p. 19 cm. (Progressive labor library pamphlet, no. 4)

NL 0427811 WHi CtY

VOLUME 337

Lloyd, Jessie.
It's hard. Words and tune by Jessie Lloyd. Harmony by Gertrude P. Smith. Chicago, Campaign for world government [c1945]
First line: Our land holds many states.
Chorus: Oh yes it's hard.
I. No subject. I. Smith, Gertrude P. II. Song index (3).
N. Y. P. L. December 5, 1947
NL 0427812 NN

Lloyd, Mrs. Jessie (Bross), 1844-1904.
In memoriam, Jessie Bross Lloyd
see under title

Lloyd, Jessie C.
U. S. *Immigration commission*, 1907-1910.
... Immigrants as charity seekers (in two volumes) Washington, Govt. print. off., 1911.

823 L777h Lloyd, Jessie Sale (Hopkins) 1846-
The Hazelhurst mystery. A novel. London, Tinsley Bros., 1877.
2v. 20cm.
NL 0427815 IU MH

Lloyd, Jessie Sale (Hopkins) 1846-
Ragamuffins; or, the Arabs of Love Lane. A tale. London. Shaw. [1879.] Illus. Sm. 8°.
NL 0427816 MB

823 L777s Lloyd, Jessie Sale (Hopkins) 1846-
Scamp, a novel. London, F. V. White, 1887.
3v. 19cm.
NL 0427817 IU

Lloyd, Jessie Sale (Hopkins) 1846-
Shadows of the past
see under Kenyon, Charles, 1809-

823 L777w Lloyd, Jessie Sale (Hopkins) 1846-
We Costelions, a novel. London, Tinsley Bros., 1882.
3v. 20cm.
NL 0427819 IU

Lloyd, John, comp.
The story of E. R. A.; comp. by John Lloyd, with an introd. by Earl Howe and a technical supplement by A. F. Rivers Fletcher. Abingdon-on-Thames [Eng.] Motor Racing Publications [1949]
46 p. illus. (Motor racing scrapbook, no. 3)
NL 0427820 MiD

Lloyd, John, freethinker
see Lloyd, John T 1850-

LLOYD, John, M.A., of Dolgelly.
Llyfr darllen ac ysgrifennu. Gwrecsam, Hughes a'i fab, 1913.
Plates.
At head of title-page:-Buddugol yn eisteddfod frenhinol genedlaethol Gwrecsam, medi, 1912.
NL 0427822 MH

Lloyd, John, M.A., of Dolgelly.
Mabinogion.
The Mabinogion, a new translation, by T. P. Ellis, M. A. & John Lloyd ... Oxford, The Clarendon press, 1929.

Lloyd, John, novelist.
The captain's wife, by John Lloyd. New York, M. Kennerley [1908]
319 p. incl. col. front. 19cm.
Library of Congress PZ3.L7748C 8-15725
NL 0427824 DLC

Lloyd, John, of Gilden Sutton.
The blanket. A poem, in imitation of Milton. By John Lloyd, M. A. and rector of Gilden Sutton, in Cheshire. London, Printed for J. Batley, at the Dove in Pater-Noster-Row, 1733.
9, [1] p. 34 cm.
NL 0427825 TxU

PR3541 .L553P7 1730 LLOYD, JOHN, of Gilden Sutton.
The play, a satire: upon our late dramatick pieces, The beggars opera, Timoleon, The humours of Oxford, &c. By John Lloyd... [London?] 1730.
12 p. 19½cm.
In verse.
NL 0427826 ICU DFo

Ak L777 730sa LLOYD, JOHN, of Gilden Sutton.
A satyr on the times: and some of the modern plays, viz. Beggar's opera, Timoleon, Humours of Oxford, Cheshire comicks, &c. By John Loyd, M.A., minister of Gilden Sutton in Cheshire, and author of The art of politicks ...
[London] Printed in the Year 1730. 15p. 23½cm.
In verse.
Negative photostatic reproduction of the copy in the Harvard college library.
NL 0427827 TxU

Lloyd, John, of Jesus College, Oxford.
Thesaurus Ecclesiasticus. 1790
see under Ecton, John, d. 1730.

Lloyd, John, of Merthyr Tydfil.
... Llyfr darllen cyntaf i Ysgolion elfennol. Cardiff, Educational pub.co., (Cyfres y modd uniongyrchol) [1927]
NL 0427829 CaBVa

Lloyd, John, *of Tenterden, Eng.*
A sermon on the ministration of angels. Delivered at Folkstone, in Kent, June 7, 1786; to an association of the ministers and messengers of several Baptist churches, in Kent and Sussex. By John Lloyd. The 2d ed. London, Printed by L. Wayland, 1788.
32 p. 18cm. [*With* Scott, Thomas. A vindication of the divine inspiration of the Holy Scriptures. London, 1796] 4-12276
NL 0427830 DLC

Edsc C54 780b Lloyd, John, of Tureen.
... A short tour in the county Clare 1780; an exact reprint, edited by Henry Henn ... Cambridge [J. Palmer] 1893.
5p.l., [iii]-iv, 59, [1]p. 18cm.
Includes reprint of original t.-p.: A short tour; or, An impartial and accurate description of the county of Clare ... Ennis, Printed by J. Busteed and G. Trinder, 1780.
NL 0427831 CtY

Lloyd, John, *of Vienna.*
Austria at random. Drawings by Traute von Kaschnitz. Salzburg, K. Gordon, 1949.
102 p. illus. 19 cm.
1. Austria—Soc. life & cust. I. Title.
DB30.L6 914.36 51-29537
NL 0427832 DLC NN

Lloyd, John, *pseud.*
see
Morgan, Jacque Lloyd, 1873-

Lloyd, John, Rector of Llanvapley.
An analysis of the Book of Ecclesiastes... London, Bagster, 1874
see under Bible. O.T. Ecclesiastes. Hebrew. 1874.

Lloyd, John, rector of Llanvapley.
An analysis of the first eleven chapters of the book of Genesis: with reference to the Hebrew grammar of Gesenius, and with notes critical and explanatory.
London. Bagster. 1869. iv, 157, (3) pp. 22 cm., in 8s.
Attributed to Julius Lloyd by B.M., but not included among his works in D.N.B.
K3810 — Bible. O.T. Genesis. Crit., interp., etc.
NL 0427835 MB NN CtW TxDaM

VOLUME 337

Lloyd, John, rector of Llanvapley.
The book of Joshua. A critical and expository commentary of the Hebrew text. By the Rev. John Lloyd... London: Hodder and Stoughton, 1886. vii, 368 p. 8°.

140976A. 1. Bible.—Old Testament: Joshua. Commentaries. N. Y. P. L. October 7, 1924

NL 0427836 NN

B 1827
528.5* Lloyd, John, rector of North Mimms.
Bibliotheca Lloydiana, sive Catalogus variorum librorum selectissimae bibliothecae rev. doct. viri d. Joan. Lloydii, B.D., quondam de North-mimmes in comitatu de Hertfordshire. Accessit bibliotheca historica, & philologica honorab. Thomae Raymondi equitis nuperrimè de banco-regio justiciarii; cum plurimis aliis latinis, anglicis, gallicisq; libris. Quorum auctio habebitur Londini apud domum auctionariam ex adverso Nigri Cygni, in vico vulgò dicto Ave-Mary-lane, propè Ludgate-street, tertio die decembris, 1683. Per Edvardum Millingtonum ...
[London] 1683.
4°. 2p.ℓ.,28,24,32,25-32p. 26cm.

NL 0427838 MH

Lloyd, John, rector of North Mimms.
A treatise of the episcopacy, liturgies, and ecclesiastical ceremonies of the primitive times, and of the mutations which happened to them in the succeeding ages: gathered out of the works of the ancient fathers and doctors of the church ... London, Printed by W.G. for J. Sherley and R. Littlebury, 1660.
[18],81 p. 19cm.
From the Isaac Foot collection.
Wing L-2659

NL 0427839 CLU-C CtY ICU DFo CSmH NNUT-Mc ICN

Lloyd, John, 1485 (ca.)-1523.
Missa "O quam suavis"
see under title

FILM
Lloyd, John, 1558-1603, ed.
Peplvs. Illvstrissimi viri D.Philippi Sidnaei svpremis honoribvs dicatvs ... Oxonii, excudebat Iosephus Barnesius ... 1587.
Edited by John Lloyd. cf.Dedication.
University microfilms no.15499 (case 59, carton 353)
Short-title catalogue no.22552.

1.Sidney, Sir Philip, 1554-1586. I. Title.

NL 0427841 MiU

B 1827
528* Lloyd, John, bp. of St. David's, 1638-1687.
The library of the Right Reverend Father in God, John Lloyd ... which will be sold by auction at Tom's coffee-house, adjoyning to Ludgate, on Monday the sixth of February next, and the following days, at three in the afternoon. By John Bullord ...
[London] 1699.
8°. 1p.ℓ.,60p. 19.5cm.

NL 0427842 MH NN

Lloyd, John, 1644-1682.
Shir ha-shirim: or, Solomon's song paraphras'd ... London, 1681
see under Bible. O.T. Song of Solomon. English. Paraphrases. 1681. Lloyd. Also with date 1682 (title: Shir ha-shirim; or, the Song of songs; being a paraphrase...)

Lloyd, John, 1644-1682.
The six days work. London, Printed by H.H. for H. Faithorne and John Kersey, 1681
see in (with, as issued?)
Bible. O.T. Song of Solomon. English. Paraphrases. 1682. Lloyd.
Shir ha-shirim, or, the Song of songs ... London, ... 1682.

Lloyd, John, fl. 1713.
The egregious folly and sinfulness of the most detestable crime of scoffing and derision, exposed and laid open: in a sermon preached...August the 30th, 1713. By...John Lloyd, of Brazen-Nose College.... London, H. Clements, 1713.
p. [2] 1-20 [21-22]. orn.
Last two pages blank.
Running title: The folly and sinfulness of scoffing and derision.
Text: Proverbs XIX:29.
s/cI. Sermons. English. 18th cent. II. Title. III. The folly and sinfulness of scoffing and derision.

NL 0427845 KU

Lloyd, John, 1745-1792.

Barck, Dorothy C , *ed.*
Papers of the Lloyd family of the manor of Queens Village, Lloyd's Neck, Long island, New York, 1654-1826. New York, Printed for the Society, 1927.

921
L777 Lloyd, John, fl. 1782.
Anecdotes of John Lloyd, a pretended clergyman, who was committed to prison on Friday, September 6th, 1782, charged with several highway robberies. To which is added, the remarkable sermon he preached at Gravesend the Sunday before his commitment. London, A. Milne, 1782.
20 p. 21cm.
1. Brigands and robbers. I. Title.

NL 0427847 MnU

Lloyd, John, d. 1790.
Romp
see under Bickerstaffe, Isaac, d. 1812?

Lloyd, John, 1797-1875.
The ballad of Edge Hill fight and other poems, by John Lloyd, esq. London, Longmans, Green and co., 1867.
viii, 83 p. 18 cm.

NL 0427849 CtY

Lloyd, John, 1797-1875.
The English country gentleman, his sports and pastimes. London, Longman; Llandovery, W. Rees, 1849.
51 p. 21 cm.
Inscribed by the author.
Errata-slip inserted.

NL 0427850 CU-S CtY MH

Ip
L777
849b **Lloyd, John, 1797-1875**
The English country gentlemen: his sports and pastimes. 2d ed. London, Longman, 1854.
51p. 20cm.
In verse.

NL 0427851 CtY

Lloyd, John, 1797-1875.
The English country gentleman and other poems. By John Lloyd, esquire. A new ed. London, Longman, Green, Longman, Roberts, & Green, 1865.
viii, 117 p. front. 19½cm.

1. Title.

25-25716

Library of Congress PR4890.L82E6 1865

NL 0427852 DLC

Ip
L777
847 Lloyd, John, 1797-1875
Poems. London, Longman, 1847.
247p. 20cm.

NL 0427853 CtY CtU NjP

Lloyd, John, 1833-
London municipal government. History of a great reform, 1880-1888. By John Lloyd ... London, P. S. King & son, 1910.
x, 72 p. front., plates, ports. 27½cm.

1. London—Pol. & govt. 2. London municipal reform league.

10-26756

Library of Congress JS3585.L6

NL 0427854 DLC WaSpG NcD IaU ICJ MiU

---

*A
1850-97 **Lloyd, John, fl. 1869, complainant.**
.V59
no.24 John Lloyd vs. Jos. Smith. [Alexandria? Va., 1869?]
32, [2] p. 21½cm. ([Virginia legal pamphlets. no. 24])
Caption title.
At head of title: District Court of Appeals. District IV.
I. Smith, Joseph, respondent. II. Virginia. Court of Appeals (4th Judicial District, Fredericksburg)

NL 0427855 ViU

Lloyd, John Alexander, 1878-
Nitraniline und nitrosoaniline als pseudobasen.
Inaug. diss. Wuerzburg, 1903.

NL 0427856 ICRL MH PU

M2132
.W3H8 Lloyd, John Ambrose, 1815-1874.

Hughes, Hugh J *d.* 1872.
Y drysorfa gerddorol; sef, Casgliad newydd o donau, anthemau, a darnau gosodedig; yn cynnwys, tonau cynnulleidfaol, priodol i addoliad y gwir Dduw, yn nghydag amrywiaeth o donau ac anthemau cyfaddas at wahanol achosion crefyddol: yn wreiddiol a detholedig o waith yr awduron goreu hen a diweddar, gan Hugh J. Hughes ... Rome, N. Y., R. R. Meredith. 1857.

VOLUME 337

Lloyd, John Arthur Thomas, 1870-1956.
Edgar Allan Poe.
From- Fortnighly Review. June, 1928.
24 cm. [828]-840 p.

NL 0427858 RPB

Lloyd, John Arthur Thomas, 1870-
Eros, by J. A. T. Lloyd ... London, S. Paul & co., ltd. [1926]
383 p. 19½cm.

I. Title.

Library of Congress PZ3.L7749Er 26-16913

NL 0427859 DLC

PG3328 L7
Lloyd, John Arthur Thomas, 1870-
Feodor Dostoieffsky, a great Russian realist. London, S. Paul [1914]
296 p. port. 21cm.

Originally published under title: A great Russian realist.

1. Dostoevskii, Fedor Mikhailovich, 1821-1881. I. Title: A great Russian realist.

NL 0427860 GU NN Or IEdS WaSp

Lloyd, John Arthur Thomas, 1870-
Feodor Dostoieffsky: A great Russian realist, by J. A. T. Lloyd ... With a photogravure frontispiece. New York, John Lane company, 1914.
296 p. incl. front. (port.) 21cm. (On cover: The Essex library) $1.50
"Printed in Great Britain."

1. Dostoevskii, Fedor Mikhailovich, 1821-1881. I. Title.

A 15-820

Title from A.L.A Booklist. Printed by L. C.

NL 0427861 IU PPL PP PU PPFr

Lloyd, John Arthur Thomas, 1870-
Fyodor Dostoevsky. London, Eyre & Spottiswoode [1946]
206 p., [1] l. 22 cm.
Bibliography: p. [207]

1. Dostoevskii, Fedor Mikhailovich, 1821-1881.

PG3328.L5 1946 48-17835*

NL 0427862 DLC WaWW OrU OrPR OrP OCU TxU OrCS MtU WaSpG WaT WaE WaPS WaTC MtBC NcU NBC AU ScU CSt CaBVaU WaS WaSp IdB IdU Wa

Lloyd, John Arthur Thomas, 1870-
Fyodor Dostoevsky. New York, C. Scribner's Sons, 1947.
324 p. 22 cm.
"Author's note" (bibliographical): p. 316-317.

1. Dostoevskii, Fedor Mikhailovich, 1821-1881.

PG3328.L5 1947 928.917 47-4243*

NL 0427863 DLC PPT OKentU CoU TU KyLx OrPS OOxM NNC ICU ViU MH TxU NcGU NcD PJB CU ScU CaBVa WaTC OrCS OrU WaS WaSpG PPCCH

Lloyd, John Arthur Thomas, 1870-
"Good-Better-Best" by ... London, R. Holden & co., ltd., 1926.
320 p.

NL 0427864 PU

Lloyd, John Arthur Thomas, 1870-
A great Russian realist (Feodor Dostoieffsky) by J.A.T.Lloyd. London, S.Paul [n.d.]
296p. port. 23cm.
Also issued (Essex library, 1914) under title: Feodor Dostoieffsky; a great Russian realist.

1.Dostoevskii. Feodor Mikhailovich, 1821-1881.

NL 0427865 CLSU ICU FU LU CU NN ODW

Lloyd, John Arthur Thomas, 1870-
A great Russian realist (Feodor Dostoieffsky) by J. A. T. Lloyd ... With a photogravure frontispiece. New York, John Lane company, 1912.
296 p. incl. front. (port.) 23½cm.
"Printed in Great Britain."
Issued in the Essex library 1914 under title: Feodor Dostoieffsky: a great Russian realist.

1. Dostoevskii, Fedor Mikhailovich, 1821-1881. I. Title.

12—11124

NL 0427866 DLC OrP WaS TxU NN OCl OClW PPM PPL ViU CtY

LLOYD, JOHN ARTHUR THOMAS, 1870-
A great Russian realist (Feodor Dostoieffsky) New York, J. Lane, 1912. 296 p. 23cm.

Film reproduction. Positive.
Published also with title: Fyodor Dostoevsky.

1. Dostoyevski, Fiodor Mikhaĭlovich, 1821-1881.

NL 0427867 NN

Lloyd, John Arthur Thomas, 1870-
Ivan Turgenev, by J. A. T. Lloyd ... London, R. Ha limited, 1942.
227 p. front., plates, ports. 22cm.
"Author's note" (bibliography): p. 224.

1. Turgenev, Ivan Sergeevich, 1818-1883.

A 43-2425

Harvard univ. Library for Library of Congress PG3435.L5

928.9

NL 0427868 MH OrU LU TU ICU CU NIC TNJ CSt ScU NcD CtY DLC OCU OCl PPD PP PRosC

PS2631 L6 1928
Lloyd, John Arthur Thomas, 1870-
The murder of Edgar Allan Poe. London, S. Paul, 1928.
288 p. plates, ports. 24cm.
"The illustrations in this volume are reproduced from 'Edgar Allan Poe - the man', by Mary E. Phillips (The John C. Winston Co., Philadelphia)" - Publishers' note.

1. Poe, Edgar Allan, 1809-1849.
2. Griswold, Rufus Wilmot, 1815-1857.
I. Title.

NL 0427869 CoU MB

Lloyd, John Arthur Thomas, 1870-
The murder of Edgar Allan Poe, by J. A. T. Lloyd ... with 12 half-tone illustrations. London, S. Paul & co., ltd. [1931]
288 p. incl. front. (port.) plates, ports. 24cm.
"The illustrations in this volume are reproduced from 'Edgar Allan Poe—the man', by Mary E. Phillips (The John C. Winston co., Philadelphia)"—Publishers' note.

1. Poe, Edgar Allan, 1809-1849. 2. Griswold, Rufus Wilmot, 1815-1857.

Library of Congress PS2631.L6 1931 32-540

Copyright A ad int. 15881 [3] 928.1

NL 0427870 DLC ICU FTaSU OrU TxU NN NcD PU PPL MiU ViU

Lloyd, John Arthur Thomas, 1870-
Prestige, by J. A. T. Lloyd ... London, S. Paul & co. [1920]
2 p. l., [7]-334 p. 19½cm.

I. Title.

Library of Congress PZ3.L7749Pr 20-15388

NL 0427871 DLC PU

Lloyd, John Arthur Thomas, 1870-
Proximity, by ... ... London, E. Nash & Grayson, ltd., 1928.
320 p.

NL 0427872 PU

Lloyd, John Arthur Thomas, 1870-
The real Canadian, by J. A. T. Lloyd ... London, Everett & co., ltd., 1913.
3 p. l., 249 p. 23cm.

1. Canada—Hist. I. Title.

14-3215 Revised

Library of Congress F1027.L79

NL 0427873 DLC CaBVaU TxU CU PU OCl ICJ NN TAW

F 5054 L46
Lloyd, John Arthur Thomas, 1870-
The real Canadian, by J.A.T. Lloyd. Toronto, McClelland & Goodchild [1913?]
249 p.

1. Canada - History I. Title

NL 0427874 CaOTU MH

Gfs20 y910l
[Lloyd, John Arthur Thomas] 1870-
Sappho, life and work. London, A.L. Humphreys, 1910.
253p. 17cm. (The Royal library. Belles lettres series)

NL 0427875 CtY

Lloyd, John Arthur Thomas, 1870-
The skein, by J. A. T. Lloyd ... London, S. Paul & co., ltd. [1925]
287 p. 19½cm.

I. Title.

Library of Congress PZ3.L7747Sk 25-8214

NL 0427876 DLC

VOLUME 337

Lloyd, John Arthur Thomas, *1870–*
The staircase. [Fiction.]
London. Robert Holden & Co., Ltd. [1927.] 318 pp. 18½ cm.

NL 0427877 MB

891.73
T844Bll

LLOYD, JOHN ARTHUR THOMAS, 1870-
Two Russian reformers, Ivan Turgenev, Leo Tolstoy; by J.A.T. Lloyd. London, Stanley Paul & co. [1910]
335p. incl. front.,plates, ports. 23cm.

1. Turgenev, Ivan Sergeevich, 1818-1883. 2. Tolstoi, Lev Nikolaevich, graf, 1828-1910. I. Title.

NL 0427878 MtU ICU CU PPL PPA CtY OU IaU TxU RPB ICarbS NNC NBC OC1W OC1 OO MB

Lloyd, John Arthur Thomas, 1870–
Two Russian reformers, Ivan Turgenev, Leo Tolstoy; by J. A. T. Lloyd. New York, John Lane company, 1911.
335 p. incl. front., plates, ports. 23cm. $3.50

I. Title.

11—4137

NL 0427879 DLC CSt Or IdB WaS OrCS NN

Lloyd, John Arthur Thomas, 1870–
Who wrote "English notes"?
(*In* The Colophon. New York, 1930–40. 24 cm. new ser., v. 1, no. 1 (1935) p. 107–118)

1. Quickens, Quarles, pseud. English notes.
[Z1007.C71 new ser., vol. 1, no. 1] A 52–2940

Grosvenor Library
for Library of Congress [2]

NL 0427880 NBuG

Lloyd, John Augustus, 1800-1856.
Account of levellings carried across the Isthmus of Panama, to ascertain the difference in the level of the Pacific and Atlantic Oceans.
London, 1829.
4to.

NL 0427881 NN

Lloyd, John Augustus, 1800-1856
An account of levellings across the isthmus of Panama.
London, 1830
[Miscellaneous pamphlets, v. 325]

NL 0427882 DLC PU

Lloyd, John Augustus, 1800-1856.
Account of perations carried on for ascertaining the difference of level between the River Thames at London Bridge and the Sea.
London, 1831.
4to.

NL 0427883 NN

AC901
.M5

Lloyd, John Augustus, 1800-1856.
Notes respecting the Isthmus of Panama. Communicated by J.A. Lloyd. Extracts from them read 28th of February and 14th of March, 1831.
75-101 p. (Miscellaneous pamphlets, 325:21)

NL 0427884 DLC OOC

Lloyd, John Augustus, 1800–1856.
On the facilities for a ship canal communication, between the Atlantic and Pacific oceans, through the isthmus of Panamá. By Lieut.-Col. John Augustus Lloyd ... with an abstract of the discussion upon the paper. Excerpt minutes of Proceedings, vol. IX. of the Institution of civil engineers. By permission of the council. London, Printed by W. Clowes and sons, 1850.
34 p., 1 l. illus., fold. pl., fold. map. 21cm.

1. Canals, Interoceanic.

6—16033

Library of Congress TC773.L79
[a35b1]

NL 0427885 DLC DN

Kress
Room

Lloyd, John Augustus, 1800-1856.
Papers relating to proposals for establishing colleges of arts and manufactures for the better instruction of the industrial classes ... London, Printed by W.Clowes and sons, 1851.
40 p.incl. tables. 22.5 cm.

"For private circulation."

1.Technical education. 2.Education - Gt.Brit. 3.Paris. Conservatoire national des arts et métiers.

NL 0427886 MH-BA IEN NjP

LLOYD, John Augustus, 1800-1856.
The typhodeictor, or storm indicator invented by Lieut.-Col. J.A. Lloyd. London, Printed by W. Clowes & sons, 1851. 12 p. illus. 22cm.

Reprinted from the Great exhibition illustrated catalogue, part II, p. 431.

1. Cyclones. 2. Nautical instruments. t.1851

NL 0427887 NN

Lloyd, *Rev.* John Augustus, 1849–. Discovery of 2 graves cut in the solid chalk rock at Broad Hinton. 8 pp. (*Wiltshire Archaeol. and Nat. Hist. Mag.* v. 19, 1881, p. 109.)

NL 0427888 MdBP

968.2
L793o

Lloyd, John Barclay, 1864 –
One thousand miles with the C. I. V.
London, Methuen, 1901.
xii,288p. port., fold. map. 20cm.

1. Gt. Brit. Army. City Imperial Volunteers. 2. South African War, 1899-1902. Regimental histories. I. Title.

NL 0427889 IEN NN MH

Lloyd, John Barclay, 1864-
Report of the Commission appointed to enquire into the law relating to mining and prospecting for diamonds ...
see under Orange Free State (Orange River Colony, 1900-1910) Diamond laws commission.

Lloyd, John Calvin.
Fluctuations in gold, fair to good refining and white "A" sugar, from 1861 to 1868;; also stock of raw sugars at the port of New York...New York, 1868.
f°

NL 0427891 NN

Lloyd, John Davies Knatchbull, 1900-
Powers and duties of local authorities in connection with rural amenities
see under Council for the Preservation of Rural Wales.

Lloyd, Sir John Edward, 1861-1947.
Lewis, Hubert, 1825–1884.
The ancient laws of Wales, viewed especially in regard to the light they throw upon the origin of some English institutions. By the late Hubert Lewis ... Ed. by J. E. Lloyd ... London, E. Stock, 1889.

[**Lloyd,** *Sir* **John Edward**] 1861–
... A brief bibliography of Welsh history for the use of teachers. [London, The Historical association, 1921]
8 p. 20½cm. (The Historical association. Leaflet no. 49. March, 1921)

Caption title.
Signed: J. E. Lloyd.

1. Wales—History—Bibliography. I. Historical association, London.

A 35-282

Title from Stanford Univ.
Library of Congress [D1.H25 no. 49]

NL 0427894 CSt CaOTP CtY NN

Lloyd, John Edward, 1861-1947.
... Carnarvonshire, by J. E. Lloyd ... With maps, diagrams and illustrations. Cambridge, University press, 1911.
xi, 171, [1] p. illus., map, diagrs. 19cm. (*Added t.-p.: Cambridge County geographies ...*)
Series title also at head of t.-p.
Physical and geological maps on end-papers.

1. Carnarvonshire, Wales.

A 12-894

Title from Enoch Pratt Free Libr. Printed by L. C.

NL 0427895 MdBE PP PWcS OO MiU MB NN

PB2344
.C9

Lloyd, Sir John Edward, 1861-1947.

Cymru a'i phobl. The Cymry of '76, by Alexander Jones. Brief history of Wales and its literature, by J. Morris Jones, and others. Hanes yr hen Gymry, gan J. E. Lloyd. Cymru a'i gwroniaid, gan O. M. Edwards. Traddodiadau dyddorol a barddoniaeth wladgarol, gan wahanol awduron. Utica, N. Y., Swyddfa y Drych, 1894.

Usb75
ol2
906

Lloyd, John Edward, 1861-
The early history of the Old South Wales iron works (1760 to 1840). From original documents ... London,Bedford press,1906.
viii,218p. 29½cm.

1.Old South Wales iron works. 2.Iron industry and trade - Wales.

NL 0427897 CtY MnU OkU NcD ICU MH

VOLUME 337

Lloyd, Sir John Edward, 1861-
Golwg ar hanes Cymru. Cyfieithiad Cymraeg gan R.T. Jenkins. [Aberystwyth] Gwasg Aberystwyth, 1943
87 p. port.

NL 0427898 MH

942.9 L77g
Lloyd, John Edward, 1861-
The great forest of Brecknock; history of the forest from the conquest of England to the present time (from original documents) London, Bedford Press, 1905.
144, lxv p. illus. 29cm.

1. Brecknockshire, Wales--Hist. I. Title.

NL 0427899 IU MH

Lloyd, John Edward, 1861-1947.
History.
(In Spencer, editor. Chapters on the aims and practice of teaching. p. 141-156 Cambridge, 1897)

NL 0427900 MB

Lloyd, *Sir* John Edward, 1861- *ed.*
A history of Carmarthenshire, edited for the London Carmarthenshire society by Sir John E. Lloyd ... Cardiff, Printed for the Society by W. Lewis limited, 1935-
v. front., illus. (incl. plans) plates, maps (part fold.) facsim. 31cm.
Includes bibliographies.

1. Carmarthenshire, Wales—Hist. I. London Carmarthenshire society.

36-20713
Library of Congress DA740.C34L6
942.98

NL 0427901 DLC CaBVa MB NN CtY OCl

DA714 L58
Lloyd, John Edward, 1861-
A history of Wales. London, Benn [1930]
80 p. 18cm. (Benn's sixpenny library, no.119)
Bibliography: p.79-80.

NL 0427902 C

Lloyd, John Edward, 1861-
A history of Wales. London, E. Benn, ltd. [1933].
80 p.

NL 0427903 OCl

Lloyd, *Sir* John Edward, 1861-
A history of Wales from the earliest times to the Edwardian conquest, by John Edward Lloyd ... London, New York [etc.] Longmans, Green, and co., 1911.
2 v. fold. map, geneal. tables. 23½cm.
"Index of authors, works, mss., etc., cited": v. 1, p. xiii-xxiv.

1. Wales—Hist.—To 1536.

11-9062
Library of Congress DA715.L8

MiU OCU ViU NN MB WaSpG CrStbM WaT WaTC OrSaW WaWW IdU OrP OrCS IdPI CaBVaU IdB C IEN NjP PP OKentU PBm
NL 0427904 DLC WaSp WaE WaPS MtU Wa OrU MtBC OrPR Or

DA715 L8 1912
Lloyd, Sir John Edward, 1861-1947
A history of Wales from the earliest times to the Edwardian conquest. 2d ed. London, New York, Longmans, Green, 1912.
2 v. (xxiv, 815 p.) fold. map, geneal. tables. 24 cm.
Bibliography: v. 1, p. xiii-xxiv.

1. Wales - Hist. - To 1536.

NL 0427905 MeB OrP MdBP OClW OCl OU PU PHC CaBVaU

Lloyd, *Sir* John Edward, 1861-
A history of Wales from the earliest times to the Edwardian conquest, by Sir John Edward Lloyd ... London, New York [etc.] Longmans, Green and co. [1939]
2 v. fold. map, geneal. tables. 22½cm.
"First published ... 1911; Second edition ... 1912; Third edition ... 1939."
"Index of authors, works, mss., etc., cited": v. 1, p. xv-xxviii.

1. Wales—History—To 1536.

A 40-3123
Newberry library for Library of Congress [DA715.L]

NL 0427906 ICN NNCU-G NIC OrPR PSC ScU GU

Lloyd, Sir John Edward, 1861-1947.
A history of Wales from the earliest times to the Edwardian conquest, by Sir John Edward Lloyd... London [etc.] Longmans, Green and co. [1948] 2 v. map. 23cm.
Bibliography, v. 1, p. xv-xxviii.

521956-7B. 1. Wales—Hist., to 1536.
N. Y. P. L. May 26, 1950

NL 0427907 NN NcGU CaBViP

DA715 L3
Lloyd, John Edward, 1861-
A history of Wales from the earliest times to the Edwardian conquest. Third ed. London, Longmans, Green [1948]
lv,356p. 22cm.

NL 0427908 NBuG

Lloyd, Sir John Edward, 1861-
A history of Wales, from the earliest times to the Edwardian conquest. [3d ed.] L, Longmans [1954]
2 v. geneal. tables, map

NL 0427909 MH

[Lloyd, Sir John Edward] 1861- , ed.
Hywel dda, penn a molyant yr holl vrytanyeit [Brut y tywysogion] 928-1928. Caerdydd: Gwasg Prifysgol Cymru, 1928. 44 p. illus. (incl. facsims.) 21½cm.
Welsh and English on opposite pages.
"Paratowyd y llyfryn hwn gan yr Athro J. E. Lloyd...ar gais Bwrdd Gwybodau Celtaidd Prifysgol Cymru."
"Bibliography," p. 44.

1. Howel, the Good, Welsh king, d. 950. I. Wales. University. Board of Celtic studies. II. Title.
N. Y. P. L. September 19, 1939

NL 0427910 NN NNC MH

Lloyd, John Edward, 1861-
Llyfr cyntaf [ail,] hanes. Gan John Edward Lloyd. Caernarfon, Cwmni'r Wasg Genedlaethol Gymreig (cyf) 1893-1896.
2 v. 1 illustr., maps, tables.
"Llyfrau Ysgol Cymru Fydd".

NL 0427911 MH

Lloyd, Sir John Edward, 1861-1947
Outlines of the history of Wales for the use of schools and colleges. Carnarvon, Welsh Pub. Co., 1906
248 p. illus.

1. Wales - Hist. - Outlines, syllabi, etc.

NL 0427912 MH CaBVaU

Lloyd, John Edward, 1861-
... Owain Glyn Dŵr (Owen Glendower) by Professor J. E. Lloyd ... London, Pub. for the Historical association by G. Bell and sons, ltd., 1932.
16 p. 21½cm. (Historical association leaflet, no. 87)
"Notes on authorities": p. 16.

1. Glendower, Owen, 1359?-1416? 2. Wales—History—To 1536. I. Historical association, London.

A 33-158
Title from Yale Univ. Library of Congress [D1.H25 no. 87]

NL 0427913 CtY CaBVaU PU CaOTP MiU

Lloyd, John Edward, 1861-
Owen Glendower; Owen Glyn Dŵr, by J. E. Lloyd. Oxford, The Clarendon press, 1931.
xiv, 161, [1] p. 23cm.
"Index of abbreviations and short titles": p. [xi]-xiv; "Welsh sources for the history of the Glyn Dŵr movement": p. [147]-158.

1. Glendower, Owen, 1359?-1416? 2. Wales—Hist.—To 1536.

32-10618
Library of Congress DA716.G5L6

TU CaBVaU OrP OrPR IdB OrU IdPI Wa IdU WaE MtBC WaPS OCl ODW CtY WaWW WaTC WaT WaSpG WaSp OKentU LU DAU
NL 0427914 DLC MtBuM OrU-M OrSaW OrStbM MH NN MB Or

Lloyd, Sir John Edward, 1861- ed.
Sir Harry Reichel, 1856-1931; a memorial volume with two photographs, edited by Emeritus Professor Sir J. E. Lloyd ... Cardiff, The University of Wales press board. 1934.

Lloyd, *Sir* John Edward, 1861-
... The story of Ceredigion (400-1277) by John Edward Lloyd ... Cardiff, University of Wales press board, 1937.
viii, 105, [1] p. plates, fold. map. 22cm. (Gregynog lectures, 1937)
Bibliographical foot-notes.

1. Cardiganshire—Hist. 2. Wales—Hist.—To 1536. I. Title.

39-11780
Library of Congress DA740.C3L5
[2] 942.95

NL 0427916 DLC FU CtY CU-I LU NN

Lloyd, John Edward, 1861-
The University college of North Wales
Davies, William Cadwaladr, *d.* 1905.
... The University of Wales and its constituent colleges, by W. Cadwaladr Davies ... and W. Lewis Jones ... London, F. E. Robinson & co., 1905.

Lloyd, John Edward, 1861-
..."Wales and the past — two voices," by Professor John Edward Lloyd. The inaugural lecture delivered in the Reardon Smith lecture theatre on the 2nd November, 1932. Cardiff: Published by the National Museum of Wales, and the Press Board of he Univ. of Wales, 1932. 16 p. front. (port.), pl. 21½cm.
At head of title: Amgueddfa Genedlaethol Cymru, National Museum of Wales.

735335A. 1. Wales—Archaeology. 2. Wales—Hist. I. Cardiff, Wales. National Museum of Wales.
N. Y. P. L. November 9, 1934

NL 0427918 NN DSI CaBViP

VOLUME 337

Lloyd, John Edward, 1861-

Map, Walter, *fl.* 1200.
... Walter Map's "De nugis curialium" translated by Montague R. James ... with historical notes by John Edward Lloyd ... edited by E. Sidney Hartland ... London, Issued by the Honourable society of Cymmrodorion, 1923.

Lloyd, John Edward, 1861- 1947.
The Welsh chronicles, by John Edward Lloyd ... London, H. Milford [1929]
25, [1] p. 25½cm. (The Sir John Rhys memorial lecture. British academy, 1928)
"From the Proceedings of the British academy. Volume xiv."
"The mss. of 'Brut y tywysogion'": p. 21-25.

1. Brut y tywysogion. I. Title.

Library of Congress DA700.B85L6 34-18439

NL 0427920 DLC IU MB NN CtY CU DDO MH IU

Lloyd, John Edward, 1861- 1947.
... The Welsh chronicles, by John Edward Lloyd ...
(*In* British academy, London. Proceedings, 1928. London [1930] 26cm. [v. 14] p. [369]-391)
At head of title: The Sir John Rhys memorial inaugural lecture.
"Read December 12, 1928."

1. Brut y tywysogion. I. Title.

Title from Wisconsin Univ. A 34-2680
Library of Congress [AS122.L5 vol. 14]

NL 0427921 WU OrU MiU

Lloyd, John Edwin, 1900- *comp.*
I went to Noke; an anthology of rustic rhymes. Illus. by Sancho Panza. London, Allenson [1946]
55 p. illus. 16 cm.

1. Poetry of places—England. 2. England—Descr. & trav.—Poetry. I. Title.

PN6110.P7E556 821.91 48-17544*

NL 0427922 DLC MH

Lloyd, John F
Wine as a beverage: the teaching of the Scriptures on the use of fermented drinks; with supplement giving statistics of the liquor-traffic. Cincinnati, Chicago [etc.] Hitchcock and Walden; New York, Nelson and Phillips, 1874.
iv,52p. tables.

NL 0427923 GEU-T

Lloyd, John Finden.
The boy in business; how to choose a career and ensure success, by John Finden Lloyd. With a preface by F. G. L. Spain ... London, J. Long, limited [1916?]
xxii, 23-112 p. 19cm.
p. i-xii, xvi, advertisements.

1. Success. 2. Profession, Choice of. I. Title.

E 16-570

Library, U. S. Bur. of Education HF5386.L77

NL 0427924 DHEW ICJ NN

Lfa63+
G7
2
Lloyd, John Frederick.
Brief remarks upon the principles of the national system of education, occasioned by Dr. Elrington's suggestions to the clergy ... Dublin,Hodges and Smith,1847.
40p. 21½cm. [Binder's title: Church education]

NL 0427925 CtY

283
L777
Lloyd, John Griffiths.
A plain pamphlet, on real and rational reform in the established Church of England and both our universities, &c. ... London, J. Ridgway, 1835.

48 p. 21cm.

1. Church of England. Clergy.

NL 0427926 MnU

Lloyd, John H *of Highgate.*
The history, topography, and antiquities of Highgate, in the county of Middlesex; with notes on the surrounding neighbourhood of Hornsey, Crouch End, Muswell Hill, etc. By John H. Lloyd ... Highgate [Middlesex, Eng.] Printed by subscription on behalf of the Library fund, 1888.
xiv p., 1 l., 519 p. front. (port.) illus., fold. map, facsim. 26 x 20cm.
Title in red and black.

1. Highgate, Eng. (Middlesex) 2. Hornsey, Eng. (Middlesex)

Library of Congress DA690.H7L7 2—28961

NL 0427927 DLC CLSU NcD CtY OCl NN

Lloyd, John Hall Seymour.
Elections and how to fight them. By J. Seymour Lloyd ... With an introduction by A. E. Southall ... London, Vacher & sons, 1905.
xii, 183, [xiii]-xxi p. 18½cm.

1. Politics, Practical. 2. Gt. Brit.—Pol. & govt. 3. Election law—Gt. Brit. I. Title.

Library of Congress JF2051.L5 44-38407

NL 0427928 DLC NIC

[Lloyd, John Hall Seymour]
Elections and how to fight them. New and revised ed. London,Vacher & Sons,1909.

19 cm.
"Devoted to the practical work of parliamentary elections."- Preface to new ed.

NL 0427929 MH

Lloyd, John Hall Seymour.
Land taxes and the budget. An analysis and criticism of part I. of the Finance bill, 1909. By J. Seymour Lloyd ... Westminster, The National union of conservative & constitutional associations [1909]
152 p. 21 cm. (*On cover:* The Campaign guide against the budget, 1909. Pt. I)

1. Land — Taxation — Gt. Brit. 2. Finance, Public — Gt. Brit. — 1815-1918. I. Titl

HJ1023.C2 pt. I 10—8211

NL 0427930 DLC

Lloyd, J[ohn] Hall Seymour.
Municipal elections and how to fight them; a practical handbook for candidates and workers at elections. London, Vacher & Sons, 1906.
pp. xiv, 137.

Elections-Gt. Brit.||

NL 0427931 MH

Lloyd, John Hall Seymour.
Municipal elections and how to fight them. By J. Seymour Lloyd ... A practical handbook for candidates and workers at elections ... New ed. (rev.) London, Vacher & sons, 1909.
xi, 159 p. 19cm.

1. Elections—Gt. Brit.

A 14-1545

Title from Univ. of Calif. JS3693.L6 Printed by L. C.

NL 0427932 CU ICJ

974.8
Zp447
Lloyd, John Henry.
[Letter requesting aid, "to carry out the project inaugurated by Horace J. Smith, Esq., of Philadelphia, to commemorate the courage and endurance of the jurymen engaged in the trial of William Penn and William Mead in 1670, by a mural tablet on the Old Bailey." Birmingham [Eng.] 1905.
[3] p. 26 cm.

1. Penn, William, 1644-1718. 2. Mead, William, 1628- 1713. I. Smith, Horace J.

NL 0427933 N

Lloyd, John Horatio, 1798 - 1884.
... Mercantile cases
see under Gt. Brit. Courts.

Lloyd, John Horatio, 1798-1884. ed.

Paley, William, *barrister-at-law.*
FOR OTHER EDITIONS SEE MAIN ENTRY
A treatise on the law of principal and agent, chiefly with reference to mercantile transactions. By William Paley ... with extensive additions, by Messrs. J. H. Lloyd ... and John A. Dunlap ... 4th American ed., with further extensive additions, by Thomas W. Waterman ... New York, Banks, Gould & co.; Albany, Gould, Banks & co.. 1856.

Lloyd, John Ivester.
Beagling. The photos. specially taken to illustrate this book are by K. H. Purkiss. London, Jenkins [1954]
148 p. illus. 23 cm.

1. Beagling.

SK291.L55 799.25 55-20096 ‡

NL 0427936 DLC CaBVa PP

VOLUME 337

Lloyd, John Ivester.
Come hunting! Illustrated by reproductions of oil paintings and sketches by T. Ivester Lloyd, sketches by the author and photos. by K. H. Purkiss. London, Vinton, 1952.
244 p. illus. 22 cm.

1. Hunting—Gt. Brit. 2. Coursing. I. Title.

SK31.L68 799.2942 53-27206 ‡

NL 0427937 DLC

Lloyd, John Ivester.
Flash; the Gipsy dog, by J. Ivester Lloyd. Illustrated by T. Ivester Lloyd. London, J. Murray [1939]
vii, 209 p. 19.5 cm.

NL 0427938 ViW

Lloyd, John Ivester.
Ginger. Illustrated by Geoffrey Whittam. London, Country Life [1951]
111 p. illus. 22 cm.

I. Title.

PZ7.L778Gi 51-14787 rev ‡

NL 0427939 DLC

Lloyd, John Ivester.
The people of the valley. Illustrated by T. Ivester Lloyd & Stanley Lloyd. London, Country Life, ltd. [1943]
vi, 73 p. plates. 22 cm.

I. Title.

PZ7.L778Pe 45-10703 rev*

NL 0427940 DLC

W.C.L. J823.91 L793P **Lloyd, John Ivester.**
The people of the valley. Illustrated by T. Ivester Lloyd & Stanley Lloyd. London, Country Life, ltd. [1948]
vi, 73 p. plates. 22 cm.
First published 1943.

NL 0427941 NcD

F L772s Chapin Lloyd, John Ivester.
Scrap: the terrier dog, by J. Ivester Lloyd ... London, John Murray [1938]
v, 228 p. illus. 19½cm.

NL 0427942 ViW

Lloyd, John Morgan.
Cerddi'r Pergam wedi'r gad [by] Hedydd Milwyn [pseud.] Glynnedd, Lewis [19-]
40 p.

NL 0427943 MH

Lloyd, John Seymour
see Lloyd, John Hall Seymour.

Lloyd, John T., 1850–
From Christian pulpit to secular platform, by John Lloyd.. London: Pioneer Press, 1903. 59 p. 12°.
Repr.: The Freethinker.

1. Atheism. 2. Christianity (Anti). 3. Christianity (Personal).
N. Y. P. L. June 27, 1921.

NL 0427945 NN WU MH

BV 827 L46 Lloyd, John T 1850-
God-eating; a study in Christianity and cannibalism. London, Pioneer Press, [188-?]
45 p.

1. Lord's supper - Real presence. I. Title.

NL 0427946 CaBVaU

Lloyd, John T., 1850-
God-eating; a study in Christianity and cannibalism. London, Pioneer Press [1898]

NL 0427947 MH

Lloyd, John T., 1850–
God-eating. A study in Christianity and cannibalism. By J. T. Lloyd. London: The Pioneer Press, 1921. 45 p. 12°.

1. Lord's supper. 2. Cannibals. 3. Christianity (Anti).
N. Y. P. L. February 15, 1923.

NL 0427948 NN

Lloyd, John T., 1850-
Prayer: its origin, history, and futility. By J. T. Lloyd... London: Pioneer Press, 1916. 32 p. 12°.
Cover-title.

1. Prayer.
N. Y. P. L. September 26, 1918.

NL 0427949 NN

T1921 L 793 **Lloyd, John Thomas, 1884–**
The biology of North American caddis fly larvae. Ithaca, N. Y., 1920.
200 l. plates. 27cm.

Thesis (Ph.D.)—Cornell Univ., 1920.
Typewritten.
Bibliography: leaves 198-200.

1. Caddis-flies.

NL 0427950 NIC

Lloyd, John Thomas, 1884–
The biology of North American caddis fly larvae ... by John Thomas Lloyd ... Cincinnati, O., 1921.
124 p. illus. 26½cm.
Thesis (PH. D.)—Cornell university, 1921.
"Reprinted from Bulletin of the Lloyd library, no. 21, Entomological series no. 1."
Bibliography: p. 120–124.

1. Caddis-flies.

Library of Congress QL517.1.L6 1921 21-18272

NL 0427951 DLC CU MiU OU OCU

Lloyd, John Thomas, 1884–
... The biology of the North American caddis fly larvae. By John Thomas Lloyd. [Cincinnati, O., J. U. & C. G. Lloyd, 1921]
124 p. illus. 26½cm. (Bulletin of the Lloyd library of botany, pharmacy and materia medica, no. 21. Entomological series, no. 1)
Published also as thesis (PH. D.) Cornell university, 1921.
Bibliography: p. 120–124.

1. Caddis-flies. [1. Trichoptera]

Agr 21-501

U. S. Dept. of agr. Library for Library of Congress 396.81.77 no. 21 QL517.1.L6 1921 a

NL 0427952 DNAL CU NcD ViU DLC ICJ

Lloyd, John Thomas, 1884- joint author.
FOR OTHER EDITIONS SEE MAIN ENTRY
Needham, James George, 1868–
The life of inland waters; an elementary textbook of freshwater biology for students, by James G. Needham ... and J. T. Lloyd ... 3d ed. Ithaca, N. Y., Comstock publishing company, inc., 1937.

Lloyd, John Uri, 1849–1936.
FOR OTHER EDITIONS SEE MAIN ENTRY
Ellingwood, Finley, 1852–
American materia medica, therapeutics and pharmacognosy, developing the latest acquired knowledge of drugs, and especially of the direct action of single drugs upon exact conditions of disease, with especial reference to the therapeutics of the plant drugs of the Americas, by Finley Ellingwood ... with a practical consideration of the principles of pharmacy and pharmacognosy, by Prof. John Uri Lloyd ... Chicago, Evanston, Ill., "Ellingwood's therapeutist" [1919]

Lloyd, John Uri, 1849–1936.
Areca catechu, L. By John Uri Lloyd ... [Chicago? 1897?]
cover-title, 8 p. 18cm.
Reprinted from the Western druggist, Chicago, May, 1897.
"Literature on *Areca catechu*": p. 8.

1. Areca catechu.

Library of Congress RS165.A8L6 10—30609

NL 0428002 DLC

Lloyd, John Uri, 1849-1936.
The assay of alkaloidal preparations exemplified by that of fluid extract of nux vomica... Phil., 1892.
17 p.

Repr. from the American journal of pharmacy, July, 1892.

NL 0428003 OU

VOLUME 337

Lloyd, John Uri, 1849–1936.
The chemistry of medicines, practical. A text and reference book for the use of students, physicians, and pharmacists, embodying the principles of chemical philosophy and their application to those chemicals that are used in medicine and in pharmacy, including all those that are officinal in the pharmacopœia of the United States ... By J. U. Lloyd ... Cincinnati, The author, 1881.
451 p. illus. 20½cm.

1. Chemistry, Medical and pharmaceutical.
7—33004
Library of Congress RS403.L8

NL 0428004 DLC CtY-M OU DSI

RS403 L4 1881 Lloyd, John Uri, 1849-1936
The chemistry of medicines, practical. A text and reference book for the use of students, physicians, and pharmacists, embodying the principles of chemical philosophy and their application to those chemicals that are used in medicine and in pharmacy, including all those that are officinal in the pharmacopoeia of the United States. With fifty original cuts. 2d ed. Cincinnati, Clarke, 1881.
451p. illus. 21cm.

NL 0428005 IaU ICRL ViU DNLM OC1W MiU ICJ

---

540 L793c4 Lloyd, John Uri, 1849-1936.
The chemistry of medicines, practical. A text and reference book for the use of students, physicians, and pharmacists, embodying the principles of chemical philosophy and their application to those chemicals that are used in medicine and in pharmacy, including all those that are officinal in the Pharmacopoeia of the United States ... 4th ed. Cincinnati, R. Clarke & co., 1883.
451p. illus.

NL 0428006 IU-M ICRL

Lloyd, John Uri, 1849-1936.
The chemistry of medicines, practical. A text and reference book for the use of students, physicians, and pharmacists, embodying the principles of chemical philosophy and their application to those chemicals that are used in medicine and in pharmacy, including all those that are officinal in the pharmacopoeia of the United States. With fifty original cuts. Cincinnati, Robert Clarke, 1885.
451p. ⁄13p.(advertisements) illus. 21cm.

NL 0428007 KU-M

---

540 L793c5 Lloyd, John Uri, 1849-1936.
The chemistry of medicines, practical. A text and reference book for the use of students, physicians, and pharmacists, embodying the principles of chemical philosophy and their applications to those chemicals that are used in medicine and in pharmacy, including all those that are officinal in the Pharmacopoeia of the United States ... 5th ed. Cincinnati, R. Clarke & co., 1885.
451p. illus.

NL 0428008 IU-M ICRL OCU NcRS

---

540 L793c8 Lloyd, John Uri, 1849-1936.
The chemistry of medicines, practical. A text and reference book for the use of students, physicians, and pharmacists, embodying the principles of chemical philosophy and their application to those chemicals that are used in medicine and in pharmacy, including all those that are officinal in the Pharmacopoeia of the United States ... 8th ed. Cincinnati, The R. Clarke company, 1897.
451p. illus.

1. Drugs. 2. Chemistry. 3. Chemistry, Medical and pharmaceutical.

NL 0428009 IU-M OU

615.336 L77ci Lloyd, John Uri, 1849-1936
Citrullus colocynthis. [Chicago, 1898]
cover-title, 11p.

"Literature on Citrullus colocynthis": p.11.
Reprinted from the Western druggist, Chicago, June, 1898.

NL 0428010 IU

Lloyd, John Uri, 1849-1936.
Collected papers of John Uri Lloyd. n.p., 1878-1936.
1 v.

NL 0428011 OU

Lloyd, John Uri, 1849–1936.
Croton tiglium. By John Uri Lloyd ... [Chicago, 1898]
cover-title, 8 p. 18cm.
"Literature": p. 7-8.
Reprinted from the Western druggist, Chicago, April, 1898.

1. Croton tiglium.
7—18058
Library of Congress RM666.C9L7

NL 0428012 DLC

Lloyd, John Uri, 1849–
Do physicians and pharmacists live on the misfortunes of humanity? An essay by Prof. John Uri Lloyd. Reprinted from the Coming age, Boston, April, 1899. [Boston? 1899]
1 p. l., (9) p. port. 19½cm.

5–163†
Library of Congress R708.L79

NL 0428013 DLC

Lloyd, John Uri, 1849-1936, ed FOR OTHER EDITIONS SEE MAIN ENTRY
Drugs and medicines of North America; a publication devoted to the historical and scientific discussion of botany, pharmacy, chemistry and therapeutics of the medical plants of North America, their constituents, products and sophistications ... v. 1–2; [Apr. 1884–June 1887] Cincinnati, J. U. & C. G. Lloyd, 1884–87. [Cincinnati, Lloyd library, 1930–31]

Lloyd, John Uri, 1849- FOR OTHER EDITIONS SEE MAIN ENTRY
Webster, Herbert Tracy, 1836–
Dynamical therapeutics; a work devoted to the theory and practice of specific medication, with special reference to the newer remedies, with a clinical index, adapting it to the needs of the busy practitioner, by Herbert T. Webster ... with notes on practical pharmacy by Prof. J. U. Lloyd and therapeutics of the eye and ear by Prof. Kent O. Foltz, M. D. 2d ed., rev. and enl. ... San Francisco, Cal., Webster medical publishing company [°1898]

Lloyd, John Uri, 1849–
Echinacea angustifolia [by] John Uri Lloyd. [Cincinnati, Lloyd brothers, °1923]
80 p. illus. 23cm.
Caption title.

1. Echinacea.
23–12827
Library of Congress RS165.E4L6

NL 0428016 DLC

[**Lloyd, John Uri**] 1849–
... The eclectic alkaloids, resins, resinoids, oleo-resins and concentrated principles. Including portraits and biographies of John King, William Stanley Merrell, Alexander Wilder, William Tully, Grover Coe, Robert Stafford [!] Newton, Edward S. Wayne, Calvin Newton and John Coakley Lettsom. Cincinnati, O., J. U. & C. G. Lloyd [°1910]
vii, 54 p. 9 port. (incl. front.) 26½cm. (Bulletin of the Lloyd library of botany, pharmacy and materia medica, no. 12. Pharmacy series, no. 2)

"For the biographies, the footnotes, and all uncredited material of this bulletin the author is responsible. John Uri Lloyd."—Pref.
Each plate accompanied by guard sheet with descriptive letterpress.

1. Materia medica. 2. Medicine, Eclectic. 3. King, John, 1813–1893. 4. Merrell, William Stanley, 1798–1880. 5. Wilder, Alexander, 1823–1908. 6. Tully, William, 1785–1859. 7. Coe, Grover, 1825–1860. 8. Newton, Robert Safford, 1818–1881. 9. Wayne, Edward S., 1818–1885. 10. Newton, Calvin, 1800–1853. 11. Lettsom, John Coakley, 1744–1815. I. Title.
10—13136
Library of Congress RV401.L7

NL 0428018 MBH DLC OC1W MiU OU OCU OO NcD ICJ PU NNBG

Lloyd, John Uri, 1849–
Elixirs and flavoring extracts, their history, formulæ, and methods of preparation; by J. U. Lloyd ... New York, W. Woods & company, 1892.
v, 191 p. 24½cm.

1. Elixirs. I. Title.
7—32998
Library of Congress RS201.E4L79

NL 0428019 DLC OCU OU

Lloyd, John Uri, 1849-1936.
Elixirs, their history, formulae, and methods of preparation ....
see his Pharmaceutical preparations.

Lloyd, John Uri, 1849–
Etidorhpa; or, The end of earth. The strange history of a mysterious being and the account of a remarkable journey as communicated in manuscript to Llewellyn Drury who promised to print the same, but finally evaded the responsibility, which was assumed by John Uri Lloyd; with many illustrations by J. Augustus Knapp. Author's ed., limited. Cincinnati, J. U. Lloyd, °1895.
xiii, 376 p. incl. illus., plates. front. (port.) facsims. 27cm.

9–2488†
Library of Congress

NL 0428021 OC1WHi OCU PPPCPh DLC OkU CtY NIC T PSt NcD KyLxT PPL

FILM 4274 PR v.3 reel L22 **Lloyd, John Uri,** 1849-1936.
Etidorhpa; or, The end of earth. The strange history of a mysterious being and the account of a remarkable journey as communicated in manuscript to Llewellyn Drury who promised to print the same, but finally evaded the responsibility, which was assumed by John Uri Lloyd; with many illustrations by J. Augustus Knapp. Author's ed., limited. Cincinnati, J. U. Lloyd, °1895.
(Wright American Fiction, v. III, 1876-1900, no. 3368, Research Publications, Inc. Microfilm, Reel L-22)

NL 0428022 CU

Lloyd, John Uri, 1849–1936.
Etidorhpa; or, The end of earth. The strange history of a mysterious being and the account of a remarkable journey as communicated in manuscript to Llewellyn Drury who promised to print the same, but finally evaded the responsibility which was assumed by John Uri Lloyd; with many illustrations by J. Augustus Knapp. 2d ed. Cincinnati, The Robert Clarke company [°1896]
xvi, 386 p. incl. illus. (incl. map, facsims.) plates. front. 23½ cm.
1. Title.
(✱ PZ3.L775E 2) 7—19398

NL 0428023 OC1W PSt WaS

VOLUME 337

4A
9910 LLOYD, JOHN URI, 1849-1936.
Etidorhpa; or, The end of earth. The strange history of a mysterious being and the account of a remarkable journey as communicated in manuscript to Llewellyn Drury who promised to print the same, but finally evaded the responsibility which was assumed by John Uri Lloyd... Illustrations by J. Augustu Knapp. 3d ed. Cincinnati, The Robert Clarke company ,1896.
xvi,386p. illus.,plates 24cm.

NL 0428024 OCl

PS3523 .L64 E8 1896d Lloyd. John Uri, 1849-1936.
Etidorhpa; or, The end of earth. The strange history of a mysterious being and the account of a remarkable journey as communicated in manuscript to Llewellyn Drury who promised to print the same, but finally evaded the responsibility which was assumed by John Uri Lloyd; with many illustrations by J. Augustus Knapp. 6th ed. Cincinnati, The Robert Clarke company [c1896]
xvi,386p. incl.illus.(incl.map,facsims.)plates. front. 24cm.
First ed. 1895.

Facsim. of author's ms. note "to the recipients of the Author's editon of Etidorhpa", p.[364-365]
"Story of the life of Prof. Daniel Vaughn. By Prof. Richard Nelson."- p.[367]-380.
Reviews reprinted: p.368-386.
1. Vaughan, Daniel, 1821-1879. I. Title.
II. Title: The end of the earth. III. Au/t for II.

NL 0428026 PSt ViU MH-AH NNC NN P

Lloyd, John Uri, 1849-1936.
Etidorhpa; or, The end of the earth. The strange history of a mysterious being, and the account of a remarkable journey, as communicated in manuscript to Llewellyn Drury, who promised to print the same, but finally evaded the responsibility, which was assumed by John Uri Lloyd. With many illustrations by J. A. Knapp. Cincinnati: R. Clarke Co., 1897. xvi, 386 p., 1 pl. illus. 7. ed. 8°.

1. Fiction (American). 2. Occultism, etc.—Fiction. 3. Knapp, J. A., illustrator. 4. Title.
N. Y. P. L. May 3, 1913.

NL 0428027 NN PP

818
L777e Lloyd, John Uri, 1849-1936.
Etidorhpa; or, The end of earth. The strange history of a mysterious being and the account of a remarkable journey, as communicated in manuscript to Llewellyn Drury who promised to print the same but finally evaded the responsibility which was as sumed by John Uri Lloyd. With many illustrations by J. Augustus Knapp. 8th edition. Cincinnati, The Robert Clarke company, c1896.
xvi, 386p. front., illus. 24cm.

NL 0428028 LU

Lilly
PS 2248
.L 7 E7 LLOYD,JOHN URI,1849-1936
Etidorpha; or, The end of earth. The strange history of a mysterious being and the account of a remarkable journey as communicated in manuscript to Llewellyn Drury ... with many illustrations by J. Augustus Knapp. 9th ed. Cincinnati, The Robert Clarke Company, 1898.
xvi,386,[1] p.incl.illus.(incl.facsims., map)front.,plates. 8vo(23 cm.)

Integral publisher's ads at end. [1] p.

Inscribed by John W. Harper to Gral. Lew Wallace, dated Jan. 18, 1899.
From the library of J.K. Lilly.
Bound in original brown marble cloth; in blue cloth slipcase.

I. Title. II. Title: The end of earth.
III. Association: Wallace,Lewis,1827-1905.
IV. Provenance: Lilly,J.K.

NL 0428030 InU

Lloyd, John Uri, 1849-1936.
Etidorhpa; or, The end of earth. The strange history of a mysterious being and the account of a remarkable journey as communicated in manuscript to Llewellyn Drury who promised to print the same, but finally evaded the responsibility which was assumed by John Uri Lloyd; with many illustrations by J. Augustus Knapp. 10th ed. Cincinnati, Robert Clarke Co., 1900.
386 p. illus.

NL 0428031 CaOTP

Lloyd, John Uri, 1849-1936.
Etidorhpa; or, The end of earth; the strange history of a mysterious being and the account of a remarkable journey, by John Uri Lloyd ... with many illustrations by J. Augustus Knapp. 11th ed., rev. and enl. New York, Dodd, Mead & company, 1901.
vii p., 1 l., 375 p. front., illus., plates. 19cm.

I. Title. 1—31751

Library of Congress PZ3.L775E 6

NL 0428032 DLC KyHi Or OrU

FOR OTHER EDITIONS SEE MAIN ENTRY

PS3523 .L64 E8 1901a Lloyd, John Uri, 1849-1936.
Etidorpha;or,The end of earth...
11th ed. Toronto, W.J. Gage, 1901.
375p. illus.

NL 0428033 NcU

Lloyd, John Uri, 1849-1936.
Etidorhpa; or, The end of earth; the strange history of a mysterious being and the account of a remarkable journey; with many illustrations by J. Augustus Knapp. New York: Dodd, Mead, & Co., 1907. vii(i), 375 p., 15 pl., 1 port. diagr., fac., illus., map. 11. ed. rev. and enl. 12°.

NL 0428034 NN

Lloyd, John Uri, 1849-
Felix Moses, the beloved Jew of Stringtown on the pike; pages from the life experiences of a unique character—a man whose romantic record challenges imagination, by John Uri Lloyd ... illustrated by J. Augustus Knapp. Cincinnati, O., Printed for the author by the Caxton press [1930]
xxix, 354 p. front., illus. (incl. map, music) plates, ports., facsim., diagr. 25cm.
Map on lining-paper.
"Second printing, one thousand copies, November, 1930."
1. Moses, Felix, 1827-1886. I. Title. 31-13353
Library of Congress E184.J5M85
——— Copy 2.
Copyright A 38137 [3] [922.96] 920

OC NcD OCU OCl PPPCPh
NL 0428035 DLC KyLE KyHi CBM TxU PPRF KyLxT KyU

Lloyd, John Uri, 1849-1936.
... History of the vegetable drugs of the Pharmacopeia of the United States, by John Uri Lloyd ... with portraits of Charles Rice ... and Joseph P. Remington ... Cincinnati, O., J. U. & C. G. Lloyd, 1911.
1 p. l., v, 135 p. 2 port. (incl. front.) 26cm. (Bulletin of the Lloyd library of botany, pharmacy and materia medica, no. 18. Pharmacy series, no. 4)
Bibliography: p. 94-135.
1. Materia medica—Vegetable. [1. Drugs] Agr 12—632
U. S. Dept. of agr. Library for Library of Congress 396.8L77 no. 18 RS164.L7

PU DLC NNBG CaBVaU
NL 0428036 DNAL OO MBH MiU OCU OU CU NcD ICJ DNLM

Lloyd, John Uri, 1849-1936.
"Husa." By John Uri Lloyd ... [Cincinnati? 1899]
10 p. 23 cm.
Caption title: An investigation into "Husa," an asserted plant preparation to cure the opium habit.
Reprinted from the Eclectic medical gleaner, April, 1899.

1. Opium habit. I. Title. 7—33139

Library of Congress RC371.O6L8

NL 0428037 DLC

615.336 L77h Lloyd, John Uri, 1849-1936.
Hydrastis canadensis. [Chicago, 1897]
5p.
"List of references made to Hydrastis canadensis": p.5.
Reprinted from the Western druggist, Chicago, February, 1897.

NL 0428038 IU

Lloyd, John Uri, 1849-1936.
... *Hydrastis canadensis*. Facsimile, reprint and illustrations of the article in Drugs and medicines of North America. 1884. By J. U. & C. G. Lloyd. Cincinnati, J. U. & C. G. Lloyd, 1908.
1 p. l., p. [75]-184 incl. illus., plates, map. 26½cm. (Bulletin of the Lloyd library of botany, pharmacy and materia medica, no. 10. Reproduction series, no. 6)
"Pharmaceutical and medical references to *Hydrastis*": p. 181-183.
"Botanical references to *Hydrastis canadensis* Linneus": p. 183-184.
1. Hydrastis canadensis. I. Lloyd, Curtis Gates, 1859-1926, joint author.
Agr 10—1065
U. S. Dept. of agr. Library for Library of Congress 396.8L77 no. 10 RS82.H8L5

DLC OCU
NL 0428039 DNAL NcD CU NNBG PU ICJ MiU MBH OU OO

615.336 L77j Lloyd, John Uri, 1849-1936
Jateorhiza columba. [Chicago, 1898]
cover-title, 10p.
"Literature on Jateorhiza columba": p.9-10.
Reprinted from the Western druggist, Chicago. January, 1898.

NL 0428040 IU

Lloyd, John Uri, 1849- joint ed.

King, John, 1813-1893.
King's American dispensatory, by Harvey Wickes Felter ... and John Uri Lloyd ... Entirely rewritten and enl. 18th ed 3d revision ... Cincinnati, The Ohio Valley company, 1898-1900.

[Lloyd, John Uri] 1849-1936.
... Life and medical discoveries of Samuel Thomson, and a history of the Thomsonian materia medica, as shown in "The new guide to health," (1835), and the literature of that day. Including portraits of Samuel Thomson; fac-simile of Thomson's "patent" to the practice of medicine; the famous letters of Professor Benjamin Waterhouse, M. D.; the celebrated "Trial of Dr. Frost," and other features of a remarkable epoch in American medical history. Cincinnati, O., J. U. & C. G. Lloyd [1909]
1 p. l., iv, 91, [1], 63-106, 137-140 p. illus., 2 port. (incl. front.) facsim. 26½cm. (Bulletin of the Lloyd library of botany, pharmacy and materia medica, no. 11. Reproduction series, no. 7)

Editor's introduction signed: John Uri Lloyd.

1. Medicine, Botanic. 2. Thomson, Samuel, 1769-1843. 3. Frost, Richard K. I. Waterhouse, Benjamin, 1754-1846.
9—19576
Library of Congress RV8.T5L6

NL 0428043 DLC DNLM ICJ OO OU OCU NcD NN NNBG MBH

VOLUME 337

632.59 Lloyd, John Uri, 1849-
L793L Loco, or crazy weed. n.p.,n.p.,n.d.
8p. 23cm.

Caption title.

Read before the Cincinnati medical society, Sept. 8, 1893, and reprinted from the Eclectic medical journal.

1. Loco plant.

NL 0428044 LNHT

QK 73 .L6 L6 1911 Lloyd, John Uri, 1849-1936.
The Lloyd library Botanical park and arboretum by John Uri Lloyd. [Boston? 1911?]
14 p., 1 l. incl. 1 illus., ports. 23½cm.

"Contributed to the Historical section of the American pharmaceutical association, Boston, 1911."

NL 0428045 MdBJ

Lloyd, John Uri, 1849-

American drug manufacturers' association.
Origin and history of all the pharmacopeial vegetable drugs, chemicals and preparations, with bibliography ... Prepared under the auspices of and published by the American drug manufacturers' association, Washington, D. C. Cincinnati, The Caxton press ₍°1921₎

Lloyd, John Uri, 1849-
Our Willie; a folklore story of the Gunpowder creek and hills, Boone county, Kentucky, by John Uri Lloyd ... Cincinnati, J. G. Kidd & son, inc. ₍°1934₎
xix p., 1 l., 375 p. incl. front., illus. 19½cm.

I. Title.
Library of Congress PZ3.L775Ou 34-37241

NL 0428047 DLC NIC WU CoU InU KyBgW OCU

Lloyd, John Uri, 1849-
Pharmaceutical preparations. Elixirs: their history, formulæ, and methods of preparation ... with a résumé of unofficinal elixirs from the days of Paracelsus; by J. U. Lloyd ... Cincinnati, R. Clarke & company, 1883.
187 p. 20½cm.

1. Elixirs.
Library of Congress RS201.E4L8 7-33000†

NL 0428048 DLC DSI InU MiU OClW

Lloyd, John Uri, 1849-1936.
Pharmaceutical preparations. Elixirs, their history, formulae and methods of preparation, ... together with a resume of unofficinal elixirs from the days of Paracelsus ... 2nd. ed. Cincinnati, Clarke, 1883.
187 p.

NL 0428049 PPPCPh

Lloyd, John Uri, 1849-1936.
Pharmaceutical preparations. Elixirs, their history, formulae, and methods of preparation.... 3d ed. Cincinnati, Robert Clarke, 1885 ₍c1883₎
187 p.+₍2₎p. (advertisements) 21 cm.

1. Elixirs. I. Title. II. Title: Elixirs ...

NL 0428050 KU-M OCl

Lloyd, John Uri, 1849-1936.
Punica granatum. By John Uri Lloyd ... ₍Chicago? 1897₎
cover-title, 3-10 p. 19½cm.
Reprinted from the Western druggist, Chicago, May, 1897.
"Literature of *Punica granatum*": p. 9-10.

1. Pomegranate.
Library of Congress RS165.P8L6 10-30864

NL 0428051 DLC

515.336 Lloyd, John Uri, 1849-1936.
L77q Quassia amara. [Chicago, 1897]
5p
"List of references to Quassia amara, p.5.
Reprinted from the Western druggist, Chicago, January, 1897.

NL 0428052 IU

Lloyd, John Uri, 1849-1936.
... References to capillarity to the end of the year 1900; being chapter VII of "A study in pharmacy", by John Uri Lloyd, PHR. M. The references collected and abstracted under the auspices of John Uri Lloyd by Sigmund Waldbott ... ₍Cincinnati, J. U. & C. G. Lloyd, 1902₎
1 p. l., 2, ₍101₎-212 p. 26½cm. (Bulletin of the Lloyd library of botany, pharmacy and materia merica, no. 4. Pharmacy series, no. 1)

1. Capillarity—Bibl. I. Waldbott, Sigmund, 1865- 6-10958
Library of Congress Z7144.C25L5

NL 0428053 DLC NNBG DNLM NcD MiU OCU OU ICJ DNAL O

Lloyd, John Uri, 1849-
Red Head, by John Uri Lloyd ... illustrations and decorations by Reginald B. Birch. New York, Dodd, Mead and company, 1903.
xii p., 1 l., 208 p. front., 9 pl. 22cm.
Ornamental borders.
3-27219

NL 0428054 DLC NSyU IaU OU InU CoU NIC CLSU NNC NcD OC ICU OClW OCl OOxM NN CSmH

Lloyd, John Uri, 1849-
The right side of the car, by the author of Etidorhpa (John Uri Lloyd) Boston, R. G. Badger & company, 1897.
4 p. l., 21-59 p., 1 l. incl. plates. front., facsim. 21cm.

Library of Congress PZ3.L775Ri 7-19397†

NL 0428055 DLC IaU NcD MH InU OC MiU OrP WaS

813 L793sc Lloyd, John Uri, 1849-1936.
Scroggins. Illus. Reginald B. Birch. N. Y. Dodd. c1900.
119 p. illus.

NL 0428056 KyHi

Lloyd, John Uri, 1849-
Scroggins, by John Uri Lloyd ... illustrations and decorations by Reginald B. Birch. New York, Dodd, Mead & company, 1904.
1 p. l., vii, 119 p. front., illus., 3 pl. 20cm.
4-33121

NL 0428057 DLC ViU ScU GU KyU OKentU CoU OOxM NjP NN CSmH

Lloyd, John Uri, 1849-1936.
Stringtown on the pike; a tale of northernmost Kentucky, by John Uri Lloyd ... New York, Dodd, Mead and company, 1900.
v p., 1 l., 414 p. front., plates. 19cm.

I. Title. 0-6663
Library of Congress PZ3.L775St

NL 0428058 DLC WaS KyLx KyU DNLM NcD PP PPL MiU OCl OClW OO Or Wa WaSpG InU MH OU WaTC OrU NjP KyLxT OC TNJ InU MB KyU-A WaU ViU CoU

PS2248 .L788 Lloyd, John Uri, 1849-
Stringtown on the pike; a tale of northernmost Kentucky, by John Uri Lloyd ... With illustrations. New York, Grosset & Dunlap ₍c1900₎
v,414p. front.,plates. 20cm.

NL 0428059 NBuG MH

Lloyd, John Uri, 1849-1936.
Stringtown on the pike; a tale of northernmost Kentucky. New York: Dodd, Mead and Co., 1903. 414 p. pl. 12°.

1. Kentucky—Fiction. 2. Title.
N. Y. P. L. April 17, 1925

NL 0428060 NN

Lloyd, John Uri, 1849-1936.
Stringtown on the pike; a tale of northernmost Kentucky. New York: Dodd, Mead and Co., 1905. 414 p. pl. 12°.

1. Kentucky.—Fiction. 2. Title.
N. Y. P. L. October 24, 1916.

NL 0428061 NN

PS2248 .L788 1927 Lloyd, John Uri, 1849-1936.
Stringtown on the pike; a tale of northernmost Kentucky, by John Uri Lloyd. New York, Dodd, Mead and Company, 1927.
v, 414 p. front.,plates. 20 cm.

NL 0428062 T KyHi OCU NIC PPPCPh

Lloyd, John Uri, 1849-
Stringtown on the pike; a folk-lore tale of northernmost Kentucky, by John Uri Lloyd ... Cincinnati, The Ruter press, 1934.
v p., 1 l., 414 p. front., plates. 19½cm.

I. Title. 34-40678
Library of Congress PZ3.L775St 34

NL 0428063 DLC

Lloyd, John Uri, 1849-1936.
Strophanthus hispidus, D. C. By John Uri Lloyd ... ₍Chicago? 1897?₎
cover-title, 3-11 p. 19½cm.
Reprinted from the Western druggist, Chicago, September, 1897.
"Literature on *Strophanthus*": p. 10-11.

1. Strophanthus hispidus. 10-31128
Library of Congress RS165.S8L6

NL 0428064 DLC

VOLUME 337

615.336 Lloyd, John Uri, 1849-1936.
L77st Strychnos nux vomica. [Chicago, 1897]
5p.

"Literature on Nux vomica": p.4-5.
Reprinted from the Western druggist, Chicago, March, 1897.

NL 0428065 IU

[Lloyd, John Uri] 1849-1936.
A study in pharmacy ... [Cincinnati, O.] °1894.
1 p. l., 19 p. 23cm.
Signed: J. U. Lloyd.
Preliminary to a book which if completed is to form [vol. 2] of a contemplated series.

1. Pharmacy—Addresses, essays, lectures.
7—20174
Library of Congress RS99.L8

NL 0428066 DLC

Lloyd, John Uri, 1849-1936.
Study in pharmacy. Nature's percolation processes in connection with the formation and excretion of dew, versus artificial percolation. 1924.
p. 407-519. illus. 26 cm.

NL 0428067 DAS

Lloyd, John Uri, 1849- joint author.
King, John, 1813-1893.
Supplement to the American dispensatory. By John King ... and John U. Lloyd ... Cincinnati, Wilstach, Baldwin & co., 1880.

Lloyd, John Uri, 1849- FOR OTHER EDITIONS SEE MAIN ENTRY
Locke, Frederick John, 1829-1903.
... Syllabus of eclectic materia medica and therapeutics. Comp. from notes taken from the lectures of Frederick J. Locke ... ed., with pharmacological additions, by Harvey W. Felter ... with notes on specific medicines by John Uri Lloyd. Cincinnati, J. M. Scudders' sons, 1895.

Lloyd, John Uri, 1849-
Ellingwood, Finley, 1852-
A systematic treatise on materia medica and therapeutics with reference to the most direct action of drugs. By Finley Ellingwood ... With a condensed consideration of pharmacy and pharmacognosy. By Prof. John Uri Lloyd ... Chicago, Chicago medical press co. [°1898]

Lloyd, John Uri, 1849-1936.
Theodore Lund August Greve, by John Uri Lloyd. Cincinnati, 1900.
8 p. illus. (port.) 23cm.
Reprinted from the Eclectic medical journal, Cincinnati, February, 1900.

1. Greve, Theodore Lund August, 1830-1898.
15—21248
Library of Congress RS73.G7L7

NL 0428071 DLC

Lloyd, John Uri, 1849-
—— A treatise on apis (the bee), tela araneæ (cobweb), spongia and cantharis. 48 pp. 8°. Cincinnati, Lloyd Bros., 1911.

NL 0428072 DNLM

Lloyd, John Uri, 1849-1936.
Treatise on the development of the pharmaceutical stidl. Cin., Lloyd.1905.
25 p.

NL 0428073 PU-S

Lloyd, John Uri, 1849-1936
Ellingwood, Finley.
A treatise on therapeutics and materia medica; with reference to the most direct action of drugs, as developed by the eclectic physicians of the United States. By Finley Ellingwood ... With a condensed consideration of pharmacy and pharmacognosy. By Prof. John Uri Lloyd ... Chicago, The author [1898

615.336 Lloyd, John Uri, 1849-1936.
L77va Vanilla planifolia. [Chicago, 1897
cover-title, 13p.

"Literature on Vanilla planifolia": p.13.
Reprinted from the Western druggist. Chicago, December, 1897.

NL 0428075 IU DLC

Lloyd, John Uri, 1849-1936.
Vegetable drugs. 8th and 9th decennial revisions [of the Pharmacopeia of the United States of America]. (Botanical descriptions omitted.)
Cincinnati. The Caxton Press. [1921.] (1), xiv, 449 pp. Plates. [American Drug Manufacturers' Association. Origin and history of all the pharmacopeial vegetable drugs, chemicals, and preparations. Vol. 1.] 19½ cm., in 8s.
Bibliography, pp. 357-424.

M6582 — T.r. — S.r.c. — Van Guelpen. Edna, indexer. — Drugs. — Pharmacy.

NL 0428076 MB PU-V PU-Z

Lloyd, John Uri, 1849-1936.
Veratrum viride, by John Uri Lloyd ... [Chicago? 1897]
cover-title, 3-8 p. 19cm.
Reprinted from the Western druggist, Chicago, October, 1897.
"Literature on *Veratrum viride*": p. 7-8.

1. Veratrum viride.
10—30866
Library of Congress RS165.V5L6

NL 0428077 DLC

Lloyd, John Uri, 1849-1936.
The war tax. Its objects, defects, and wrongs—the changes which should be made in order to render the act less burdensome and more equitable. By Prof. John Uri Lloyd. Reprinted from Bulletin of pharmacy, March, 1899. Detroit, Mich., W. M. Warren, 1899.
cover-title, 6 p. 17cm.

1. War revenue law of 1898. 2. Medicines, Patent, proprietary, etc.
CA 9—4654 Unrev'd
Library of Congress HD9665.8.U5L5

NL 0428078 DLC

Lloyd, John Uri, 1849-1936.
Warwick of the Knobs; a story of Stringtown county, Kentucky, by John Uri Lloyd ... with photographic illustrations of Knob county. New York, Dodd, Mead & company, 1901.
1 p. l., xv p., 1 l., 305 p. incl. plates. front. 19cm.

I. Title.
1—25456
Library of Congress PZ3.L775W

KyLxT KyU-A KyLE CLSU PPAp
MB OCl OCU PP PHatU PPL FTaSU KyLx KyHi NjP CoI
NL 0428079 DLC KyU TNJ CaOTP InU OU NcD ViU MnU NN

Lloyd, John Uri, 1849-1936.
Warwick of the Knobs; a story of Stringtown county, Kentucky, by John Uri Lloyd ... with photographic illustrations of Knob county. New York, Dodd, Mead & company, 1901.

Microfiche (negative) [Louisville, Ky.] Lost Cause Press [1973] 9 cards. 7.5x12.5cm. ([Kentucky culture series])
I.Title. (Series: Kentucky culture series)

NL 0428080 CLSU

LLOYD, John Vaughan.
Glyndwr, a poem. Ruthin, 1826.

NL 0428081 MH

Lloyd, John William, 1857-
Aw-aw-tam Indian nights; being the myths and legends of the Pimas of Arizona, as received by J. William Lloyd from Comalk-Hawk-Kih (Thin Buckskin) thru the interpretation of Edward Hubert Wood. Westfield, N. J., The Lloyd group [°1911]
2 p. l., 241 p. port. 19½cm.

1. Pima Indians—Legends. 2. Folk-lore, Indian. I. Comalk-Hawk-Kih. II. Wood, Edward Hubert. III. Title.
11-15554 rev.
Library of Congress E99.P6L7

NL 0428082 DLC FU OU NjP OCl NN

Lloyd, John William, 1857-
Dawn-thought on the reconciliation; a volume of pantheistic impressions and glimpses of larger religion. Wellesley Hills, Mass., Maugus press [1900]
xi, 197 p. front. (port.) sq. 16°.

Feb. 21, 1901-119

NL 0428083 DLC CoU

Lloyd, J[ohn] William, 1857-
Dawn thought on the reconciliation; a volume of pantheistic impressions and glimpses of larger religion, by J. Wm. Lloyd ... 2d ed., rev., with appendix. Westfield, N. J., The Lloyd group [1904]
xi, 197 p. front. (port.) 18 x 15½cm.
4-13662

NL 0428084 DLC IU NN

BL Lloyd, John William, 1857-
220 Dawn thought on the reconcilation; a volume
L777d of pantheistic impressions and glimpses of
1928 larger religion. 2d ed.,rev. with appendix.
San Pedro [1938]
xi,197 p.

1. Pantheism. I. Title.

NL 0428085 CLU

VOLUME 337

Lloyd, J[ohn] William, 1857–
The dwellers in Vale Sunrise, how they got together and lived happy ever after; a sequel to "The natural man," being an account of the tribes of him, by J. Wm. Lloyd. Westwood, Mass., The Ariel press, 1904.
195 p. 17cm.
5-19416

NL 0428086 DLC CaBVaU ICJ

Lloyd, John William, 1857–
Eneres; or, The questions of Reksa, by J. William Lloyd, with an introduction by Havelock Ellis ... London, Allen & Unwin [1929]
191, [1] p. 20.5 cm.

NL 0428087 FU ICU NN

Lloyd, John William, 1857–
Eneres; or, The questions of Reksa, by J. William Lloyd, with an introduction by Havelock Ellis ... Boston and New York, Houghton Mifflin company [1930]
191, [1] p. 20½cm.
Printed in Great Britain.
"This little work is personal-impersonal as it were, autobiographical. It represents, expresses, sums up, the spiritual and moral conclusions of my life, to the present time."—Foreword.

I. Title. II. Title: The questions of Reksa.
30—28472
Library of Congress BD431.L5
[a36c1] 170

NL 0428088 DLC PSt OKentU MB NN OU

Lloyd, John William, 1857–
Fantasies of the strange, by J. William Lloyd ... Berkeley Heights, N. J., The Oriole press, 1940.
3 p. l., 9–47 p. 23½cm.
Verse.

I. Title.
40-30798
Library of Congress PS3523.L65F3 1940
——— Copy 2.
Copyright A 143137 [2] 811.5

NL 0428089 DLC OU MiU

Lloyd, John William, ed.
The Free comrade ... new ser. v. 1– Jan. 1900– new ser. v. 1, v. 2, no. 1– July 1910– 3d ser. v. 1, no. 1, May 1912. Wellesley, Mass., C. L. Swartz [etc.] 1900–12.

Lloyd, John William, 1857–
From hill-terrace outlooking; poems of perception, intuition and prophecy, by J. William Lloyd ... Los Angeles, Printed by S. Stebb [c1939]
1 p. l., 5–48 p. 23 cm.

I. Title.
PS3523.L65F7 1939 811.5 40—31000

NL 0428091 DLC MiU IU

Lloyd, John William, 1857–
Honorable war.
From– The Forum. September 1915.
Bd. with– The scripture of the serene life.

NL 0428092 RPB

Lloyd, John William.
Iris-heart. Some strange songs about what no man may say, a guesswork for artists in love, by J. William Lloyd ... Stelton, N. J., J. Ishill, 1917.
51 p. 23½ x 11cm.

I. Title.
17-16748
Library of Congress PS3523.L65I7 1917

NL 0428093 DLC NN MiU IU CaBVaU

---

201 Lloyd, John William, 1857–
L793L8 Der Lichtgedanke; ein Ausgleich der Religionen und ein Ausblick in eine schöne Zukunft. Einzig berechtigte Übersetzung aus dem Englischen von Helene Scheu-Riess. Leipzig, Theosophisches Verlagshaus [n.d.]
xvi,200p. 15x22cm.

1.Religion - Philosophy. I.Title.

NL 0428094 CLSU

Lloyd, John William, 1857–
Life's beautiful battle; or, The human soul before pain; a study in the reconciliation, by J. William Lloyd ... Westfield, N. J., The Lloyd group [c1910]
2 p. l., iii–viii, 296, [3] p. 18 x 16cm. $1.25

1. Life. 2. Good and evil.
10-13749
Library of Congress

NL 0428095 DLC NN

Lloyd, J[ohn] William, 1857–
The natvral man; a romance of the golden age, by J. William Lloyd. Newark, N. J., B. Prieth [1902]
140 p. 16½ x 12½cm.
2-19080

NL 0428096 TxU OKentU IU MB DLC

Lloyd, John William, 1857–
Oriole Emerson Lloyd
see under Lloyd, Oriole Emerson, 1884–1907.

Lloyd, John William, 1857–
Pain [a poem] [Christmas greeting 1913]
Los Angeles, 1913.
2 l. 21 cm.
Bd. with– The scripture of the serene life.

NL 0428098 RPB

[Lloyd, John William] 1857–
Ix Psalms of the race roots and songs by the
L7774 side of the great river. A scripture of the
900 larger love given to the world by one who loves it ... [n.p.,n.d.]
2p.l.,52p. 17½cm.
"Author's private edition. A gift-book for his friends."

NL 0428099 CtY RPB

---

335 Lloyd, John William, 1857–
L793 The red heart in a white world. A suggestive manual of free society; containing a method and a hope ... [N. Y., Holland pub. co., 1897]
49p. 19cm. [Holland library, no.6]

1.Socialism. I.Title.

NL 0428100 N MB RPB

Lloyd, John William, 1857–
The red heart in a white world: a suggestive manual of free society, containing a method and a hope... 2 ed. Westfield, N.J., 1898.
56 p. D.
Unbound.
Contains poems.

NL 0428101 RPB

LLOYD, JOHN WILLIAM, 1857–
The red heart in a white world. A suggestive manual of free society, containing a method and a hope. 2d ed. Westfield, N.J., The author, 1898.
56 p. 20cm.

Microfiche (neg.) 2 sheets. 11 x 15cm. (NYPL FSN-02256)

1. Anarchism.

NL 0428102 NN

Lloyd, John William, 1857–
The scripture of the serene life. Westwood, Mass. [1911?]
14 p. 22 cm.

NL 0428103 RPB

Lloyd, John William, 1857–
The scripture of the serene life, by J. Wm. Lloyd ... Roscoe, California [1939?]
17 p. 17.7cm.

NL 0428104 CSmH

Lloyd, John William, 1857–
Songs of the desert, by J. William Lloyd... Westfield, N. J.: The Lloyd group [1905] 26 p., 1 l. 18cm.
No. 48 of 500 copies printed.
With autograph of author.

989511A. 1. Poetry, American. I. Lloyd group, Westfield, N. J. II. Title.
N. Y. P. L. August 17, 1939

NL 0428105 NN RPB NBuG

Lloyd, John William, 1857–
76-01
L793so Songs of the desert, by J. William Lloyd.
1911 [Westfield, N.J.?] The Berryhill Co., 1911.
23 p. 18 cm.

NL 0428106 RPB

VOLUME 337

Lloyd, John William, 1857-
Songs of the desert, by J. William Lloyd ... Third edition. Hollywood, California, John C. Farley, publisher, 1932.
23 p., 1 l. 17.7cm.
Poems.
"... a reprint from the edition published for her father by Oriole Emerson Lloyd ... at ... Westfield, New Jersey."

NL 0428107 CSmH

Lloyd, John William, 1857-
Songs of the unblind cupid, by J. Wm. Lloyd ... [Wellesley, Mass., A. E. Wight, 1899]
12 p. 18½cm.
650 copies printed and the type distributed.

I. Title.
99-2809 Revised
Library of Congress PS3523.L6586 1899

NL 0428108 DLC NcD NN

Lloyd, John William, 1857-
Songs overseas: pictures and memories in verse of a vacation voyage to Great Britain and Switzerland in the spring and summer of 1913, by J. William Lloyd ... Westfield, New Jersey, The Lloyd publishing group [c1914]
1 p.l., 5-40 p. 9.2cm. Green paper cover, tied

NL 0428109 CSmH RPB

Lloyd, John William, 1857-
Wind-harp songs, by J. William Lloyd ... Author's ed. Buffalo, The Peter Paul book company, 1895.
x, [11]-132 p. 17½cm.

I. Title.
Library of Congress PS3523.L65W5 1895 33-31981
Copyright 1895: 63377 811.5

NL 0428110 DLC OkU NBuG NBuU NjP FU ViU IU CtY NN PP MH

Lloyd, John William, 1876- joint author.
Newell, Horace Mead, 1902-
... Air circulation and temperature conditions in refrigerated carloads of fruit, by H. M. Newell and J. W. Lloyd ... [Urbana, Ill.] University of Illinois [1932]

Lloyd, John William, 1876-
... Bush lima beans as a market garden crop, by J. W. Lloyd ... Urbana [University of Illinois] 1928.
1 p. l., p. 391-399. illus., tables. 23cm. (University of Illinois. Agricultural experiment station. Bulletin no. 307)

1. [Lima bean] I. Title.
A 28-476
Title from Illinois Univ. Printed by L. C.

NL 0428112 IU

Lloyd, John William, 1876-
... Care of the garden in hot weather, by J. W. Lloyd ... [Urbana, University of Illinois, 1918]
4 p. 23cm. (University of Illinois. Agricultural experiment station ... Circular no. 224)
Caption title.

1. Vegetable gardening. I. Title.
A 18-939
Title from Illinois Univ. Printed by L. C.

NL 0428113 IU

Lloyd, John William, 1876-
Carrot culture, by J. W. Lloyd ... [Urbana, Ill.] University of Illinois [1932]
8 p. illus. 23cm. (University of Illinois. College of agriculture and Agricultural experiment station. Circular 386)

1. Carrots. I. Illinois. University. College of agriculture. II. Illinois. Agricultural experiment station, Urbana. III. Title.
A 32-442
Title from Illinois Univ.
Library of Congress [S55.E3 no. 386]
[2]

NL 0428114 IU

Lloyd, John William, 1876-
Cauliflower for corn-belt gardens, by J. W. Lloyd ... [Urbana, Ill.] University of Illinois [1932]
11 p. illus. 23cm. (University of Illinois. College of agriculture and Agricultural experiment station. Circular 385)

1. Cauliflower. I. Illinois. University. College of agriculture. II. Illinois. Agricultural experiment station, Urbana. III. Title.
A 32-441
Title from Illinois Univ.
Library of Congress [S55.E3 no. 385]

NL 0428115 IU

Lloyd, John William, 1876-
Causes of damage to fruits and vegetables during shipment, by J. W. Lloyd and H. M. Newell ... [Urbana, Ill.] University of Illinois [1932]
1 p. l., p. 83-119 incl. illus., tables. 23cm. (University of Illinois. Agricultural experiment station. Bulletin 379)

1. Fruit—Marketing. 2. Farm produce—Marketing. I. Newell, Horace Mead, 1902- joint author. II. Title.
A 32-2353
Title from Illinois Univ.
Library of Congress [S55.E2 no. 379]

NL 0428116 IU

Lloyd, John William, 1876-
Co-operative and other organized methods of marketing California horticultural products ... by John William Lloyd ... [Urbana, 1919]
cover-title, 142 p. 24½ cm.
Thesis (PH. D.)—University of California, 1917.
University of Illinois studies in the social sciences vol. VIII, no. 1, March, 1919, with special thesis t.-p. dated 1917, attached to the cover-title.
Bibliography: p. 133-137.

1. Fruit—Cooperative marketing. 2. Fruit trade—California. I. Title.
HD1484.L6 20—5070

NL 0428117 DLC

Lloyd, John William, 1876-
... Co-operative and other organized methods of marketing California horticultural products, by John William Lloyd ... Urbana, University of Illinois [c1919]
cover-title, 142 p. 25cm. (University of Illinois studies in the social sciences. vol. VIII, no. 1)
Issued also as thesis (PH. D.) University of California.
Bibliography: p. 133-137.

1. Agriculture, Cooperative. 2. Fruit trade—California. 3. Fruit—Marketing. I. Title.
19—19261
Library of Congress H31.I 4 vol. VIII, no. 1

NL 0428118 DLC CoU NbU ViU WaS PBm PU NcD MiU OU OCU ICJ

Lloyd, John William, 1876-
... Cooperative marketing of horticultural products, by J. W. Lloyd. Urbana [University of Illinois] 1920.
cover-title, 15 p. 23cm. (University of Illinois. Agricultural experiment station. Circular no. 244)

1. Agriculture, Cooperative. 2. Fruit trade. 3. Fruit—Marketing. I. Title.
A 21-45
Title from Illinois Univ. Printed by L. C.

NL 0428119 IU

Lloyd, John William, 1876- joint author.
Stubenrauch, Arnold Valentine, 1871-
... Directions and formulas for spraying. Urbana, Ill., 1902.

Lloyd, John William, 1876-
... Directions for grading and packing Illinois peaches, by J. W. Lloyd ... Urbana, Ill. [University of Illinois, 1926]
8 p. illus. 23cm. (University of Illinois. Agricultural college and Experiment station. Circular no. 310)

1. Fruit—Marketing. 2. Peach. I. Illinois. University. College of agriculture. II. Illinois. Agricultural experiment station, Urbana. III. Title.
A 26-399
Title from Illinois Univ. Printed by L. C.

NL 0428121 IU

Lloyd, John William, 1876-
Directions for grading and packing Illinois peaches, by J. W. Lloyd ... [Urbana] University of Illinois [1929]
8 p. illus. 23cm. (University of Illinois. College of agriculture and Agricultural experiment station. Circular 343)
"This circular is a revision of Circular 310, bearing the same title, published in June, 1926."

1. Peach. 2. Fruit—Marketing. I. Illinois. University. College of agriculture. II. Illinois. Agricultural experiment station, Urbana. III. Title.
A 29-765
[S55.E3 no. 343]
Title from Illinois Univ. Printed by L. C.

NL 0428122 IU

Lloyd, John William, 1876-
Eighteen varieties of edible soybeans, by J. W. Lloyd and W. L. Burlison ... [Urbana, Ill., 1939]
cover-title, 1 p. l., p. 385-438. illus., col. pl., maps, tables, diagrs. 23cm. (University of Illinois. Agricultural experiment station. Bulletin 453)

1. Soy-bean. I. Burlison, William Leonidas, 1882- joint author. II. Title.
A 39-456
Illinois. Univ. Library for Library of Congress [S55.E2 no. 453]
[2] (630.72)

NL 0428123 IU DLC OrP

Lloyd, John William, 1876-
... Experiments in onion culture, by John W. Lloyd. Urbana, Ill., 1914.
1 p. l., p. 337-362. illus. 23cm. (University of Illinois. Agricultural experiment station. Bulletin no. 175)

1. Onion.
A 14-2885
Title from Illinois Univ. Printed by L. C.

NL 0428124 IU NN

VOLUME 337

Lloyd, John William, 1876-
Factors influencing the refrigeration of packages of apples, by J. W. Lloyd and S. W. Decker ... [Urbana, Ill.] University of Illinois [1934]
1 p. l., p. [15]-50 incl. illus., tables, diagrs. 23cm. (University of Illinois. Agricultural experiment station. Bulletin 410)
"Literature cited": p. 50.
1. Apple. 2. Fruit—Marketing. I. Decker, Samuel Wesley, 1900- joint author.
A 35-278
Title from Illinois Univ. Library of Congress [S55.E2 no. 410]

NL 0428125 IU

Lloyd, John William, 1876-
Factors influencing the refrigeration of packages of peaches ... By J. W. Lloyd and S. W. Decker. [Urbana, Ill.] University of Illinois [1935]
1 p. l., p. 439-464 incl. illus., tables, diagrs. 23cm. (University of Illinois. Agricultural experiment station. Bulletin 418)
"Literature cited": p. 464.
1. Peach. 2. Fruit—Marketing. I. Decker, Samuel Wesley, 1900- joint author.
A 35-1862
Title from Illinois Univ. Library of Congress [S55.E2 no. 418]

NL 0428126 IU

Lloyd, John William, 1876-
... Fall preparations for spring gardening, by J. W. Lloyd ... Urbana [University of Illinois] 1918.
4 p. incl. illus. 23cm. (University of Illinois. Agricultural experiment station. Circular no. 232)
Caption title.
1. Vegetable gardening. I. Title.
A 18-2149
Title from Illinois Univ. Printed by L. C.

NL 0428127 IU

Lloyd, John William, 1876-
... The farmer's vegetable garden. By John W. Lloyd ... Urbana, 1901.
16 p. illus. 23½cm. (University of Illinois. Agricultural experiment station. Bulletin no. 61)
1. Vegetables.
A 11-916
Title from Illinois Univ. Printed by L. C.

NL 0428128 IU

Lloyd, John William, 1876-
... The farmer's vegetable garden, by John W. Lloyd. Urbana, Ill., 1906.
1 p. l., p. 153-205. illus., 4 pl. 23½cm. (University of Illinois. Agricultural experiment station. Bulletin no. 105)
Plates printed on both sides of leaf.
1. Vegetables. 2. Gardening.
A 11-666
Title from Illinois Univ. Printed by L. C.

NL 0428129 IU MBH NN

Lloyd, John William, 1876-
... Fertilizer experiments with greenhouse lettuce and tomatoes, by J. W. Lloyd ... Urbana, Ill. [University of Illinois] 1927.
1 p. l., p. 311-336. illus., tables. 23cm. (University of Illinois. Agricultural experiment station. Bulletin no. 286)
1. Fertilizers and manures. 2. Lettuce. 3. Tomatoes. I. Title.
A 27-189
Title from Illinois Univ. Printed by L. C.

NL 0428130 IU

[**Lloyd, John William**] 1876-
Fertilizer experiments with greenhouse tomatoes, by J. W. Lloyd and B. L. Weaver ... [Urbana, Ill., 1937]
1 p. l., 275-287, [1] p. illus., tables. 23cm. (University of Illinois. Agricultural experiment station. Bulletin 438)
"By J. W. Lloyd ... and B. L. Weaver."—p. 275.
"Literature cited": p. 287.
1. Tomatoes. 2. Fertilizers and manures. I. Weaver, Brayton Ladd, 1888- joint author. II. Title.
A 38-430
Illinois. Univ. Library for Library of Congress [S55.E2 no. 438]
[2] (630.72)

NL 0428131 IU

Lloyd, John William, 1876-
... Fertilizer experiments with muskmelons, by John W. Lloyd. Urbana, Ill., 1912.
cover-title, 25-64 p. illus. 23½cm. (University of Illinois. Agricultural experiment station. Bulletin no. 155)
1. Muskmelons. 2. Fertilizers.
A 12-1452
Title from Illinois Univ. Printed by L. C.

NL 0428132 IU Or NN MB

Lloyd, John William, 1876-
Fertilizer experiments with ten market-garden crops in Cook county, Illinois; spinach, lettuce, beets, peas, beans, tomatoes, peppers, carrots, potatoes, and cauliflower. By J. W. Lloyd and E. P. Lewis ... [Urbana, Ill.] University of Illinois [1932]
36 p. incl. illus., tables, diagrs. 23cm. (University of Illinois. Agricultural experiment station. Bulletin 377)
1. Fertilizers and manures. 2. Vegetable gardening—Illinois—Cook county. I. Lewis, Ernest Paul, 1897- joint author. II. Title.
A 32-670
Title from Illinois Univ. Library of Congress [S55.E2 no 377]

NL 0428133 IU

Lloyd, John William, 1876-
... Fertilizer experiments with truck crops in southern Illinois, by J. W. Lloyd ... Urbana [University of Illinois] 1929.
1 p. l., p. 285-298. illus., tables. 23cm. (University of Illinois. Agricultural experiment station. Bulletin no. 319)
1. Vegetable gardening—Illinois. 2. Fertilizers and manures. I. Title.
A 29-275
Illinois. Univ. Library for Library of Congress [S55.E2 no. 319]
[a37b1] (630.72)

NL 0428134 IU

Lloyd, John William, 1876-
Fertilizing onion sets, sweet corn, cabbage, and cucumbers in a four-year rotation, by J. W. Lloyd and J. P. McCollum ... [Urbana, Ill., 1940]
1 p. l., 21-236 p. incl. illus., tables. 23cm. (University of Illinois. Agricultural experiment station. Bulletin 464)
Vi ICJ ViU OrCa
1. Fertilizers and manures. 2. Cabbage. 3. Cucumbers. 4. Maize. 5. Onions. I. McCollum, John Paschal, 1906- joint author. II. Title.
A 40-912
Illinois. Univ. Library for Library of Congress [S55.E2 no. 464]
[3] (630.72)

NL 0428135 IU Vi ICJ ViU OrCS

Lloyd, John William, 1876-
Fertilizing tomatoes, sweet corn, and muskmelons in a three-year rotation, by J. W. Lloyd. [Urbana] University of Illinois [1931]
18, [1] p. incl. illus., tables. 23cm. (University of Illinois. Agricultural experiment station. Bulletin 364)
1. Fertilizers and manures. 2. Tomatoes. 3. Maize. 4. Melons. I. Title.
A 31-378
Title from Illinois Univ. Library of Congress [S55.E2 no. 364]

NL 0428136 IU

Lloyd, John William, 1876-
Fertilizing twenty-five kinds of vegetables, by J. W. Lloyd and L. H. Strubinger ... [Urbana] University of Illinois [1930]
1 p. l., p. 303-320. illus., tables. 23cm. (University of Illinois. Agricultural experiment station. Bulletin 346)
1. Vegetable gardening—Illinois. 2. Fertilizers and manures. I. Strubinger, Lucian Hart, joint author. II. Title.
A 30-1133
[S55.E2 no. 346]
Title from Illinois Univ. Printed by L. C.

NL 0428137 IU

Lloyd, John William, 1876-
Green peas for Illinois markets, by J. W. Lloyd ... [Urbana, Ill., 1938]
8 p. illus., tab. 23cm. (University of Illinois. College of agriculture. Agricultural experiment station and Extension service in agriculture and home economics. Circular 483)
Bibliographical foot-notes.
1. Peas. I. Title.
A 38-434
Illinois. Univ. Library for Library of Congress [S55.E3 no. 483]
[2] (630.72)

NL 0428138 IU

Lloyd, John William, 1876-
Growing and marketing muskmelons, by J. W. Lloyd ... [Urbana, Ill.] University of Illinois [1933]
20 p. illus. 23cm. (University of Illinois. College of agriculture and Agricultural experiment station. Circular 405)
1. Melons.
A 33-1036
Title from Illinois Univ. Library of Congress [S55.E3 no. 405]

NL 0428139 IU

Lloyd, John William, 1876-
Growing and marketing small fruits and vegetables. (In: Illinois. Farmers' Institute. 18. annual report, 1913. p. 349-361. [Springfield, 1914.] 8°.)
1. Fruit.—Culture, U. S.: Ill. 2. Vegetables.—Culture, U. S.: Ill.
N. Y. P. L. April 3, 1916.

NL 0428140 NN

Lloyd, John William, 1876-
... Growing tomatoes for early market, by John W. Lloyd and I. S. Brooks. Urbana, Ill., 1910.
1 p. l., p. 47-88. illus. 23½cm. (University of Illinois. Agricultural experiment station. Bulletin no. 144)
1. Tomato. I. Brooks, Ira Sandford, joint author.
A 11-638
Title from Illinois Univ. Printed by L. C.

NL 0428141 IU OrP MBH NN

Lloyd, John William, 1876-
... The home vegetable garden, by John W. Lloyd. Urbana, Ill., 1911.
32 p. illus. 23½cm. (University of Illinois. Agricultural experiment station. Circular no. 154)
1. Gardening. 2. Vegetables.
A 12-176
Title from Illinois Univ. Printed by L. C.

NL 0428142 IU Or NN MB

VOLUME 337

Lloyd, John William, 1876–
... How to grow muskmelons, by John W. Lloyd. Urbana, Ill., 1910.
19 p. 7 illus. 24½cm. (University of Illinois. Agricultural experiment station. Circular no. 139)

1. Muskmelon.

A 11-1744

Title from Illinois Univ. Printed by L. C.

NL 0428143 IU NN

Lloyd, John William, 1876–
... How to grow muskmelons, by John W. Lloyd. Urbana, Ill., 1915.
18 p. illus. 23cm. (University of Illinois. Agricultural experiment station. Circular no. 139 (2d ed., revised, February, 1915))

1. Melons.

A 15-785

Title from Illinois Univ. Printed by L. C.

NL 0428144 IU Or

Lloyd, John William, 1876–
... Large peach crop calls for organized marketing, b J. W. Lloyd ... Urbana, Ill. [University of Illinois, 192
4 p. 23cm. (University of Illinois. Agricultural college and Experiment station. Circular no. 307)
Caption title.

1. Fruit—Marketing. 2. Peach. I. Illinois. University. College of agriculture. II. Illinois. Agricultural experiment station, Urbana. III. Title.

A 26-308

Title from Illinois Univ. Printed by L. C.

NL 0428145 IU

Lloyd, John William, 1876- joint author.

Decker, Samuel Wesley, 1900–
The market for fresh fruits and vegetables in Peoria, by S. W. Decker and J. W. Lloyd ... [Urbana, Ill., 1937]

Lloyd, John William, 1876–
... Marketing Calhoun County apples, by J. W. Lloyd and H. M. Newell ... Urbana, Ill. [University of Illinois, 1928.
1 p. l., p. 563-612. illus., tables, diagrs. 23cm. (University of Illinois. Agricultural experiment station. Bulletin no. 312)

1. Fruit—Marketing. 2. Apple. I. Newell, Horace Mead, joint author. II. Title.

A 28-581

Title from Illinois Univ. Printed by L. C.

NL 0428147 IU

Lloyd, John William, 1876–
Marketing the Illinois apple crop; present practices and historical review. By J.W.Lloyd and V.A.Ekstrom ... [Urbana, Ill., 1943]
cover-title, 1 p.l., p.497-547, [1] p.incl. tables. illus., chart. (University of Illinois. Agricultural experiment station. Bulletin 497)

NL 0428148 MH

Lloyd, John William, 1876–
... Marketing the muskmelon, by John W. Lloyd. Urbana, Ill., 1908.
1 p. l., p. 295-322. illus. 23½cm. (University of Illinois. Agricultural experiment station. Bulletin no. 124)

1. Muskmelon.

A 11-667

Title from Illinois Univ. Printed by L. C.

NL 0428149 IU MBH NN

Lloyd, John William, 1876–
Muskmelon production, by John William Lloyd ... New York, Orange Judd publishing company, inc.; London, K. Paul, Trench, Trübner & co., ltd., 1928.
126 p. front., plates. 19cm. (*Lettered on cover: Farm and garden library*)
"Literature on muskmelons": p. 118-122.

1. Melons. I. Title.
ICJ

Library of Congress SB339.L6 28-5903

NL 0428150 TU ICJ DLC OrP WaSp Or CaBViP NcRS MBH PP CU

Lloyd, John William, 1876–
... Observations on the refrigeration of some Illinois fruits in transit, by J. W. Lloyd and H. M. Newell ... Urbana, Ill. [University of Illinois] 1929.
1 p. l., p. 511-544. illus., tables. 23cm. (University of Illinois. Agricultural experiment station. Bulletin no. 334)
"Literature cited": p. 543-544.

1. Fruit—Marketing. 2. Refrigerator-cars. I. Newell, Horace Mead, 1902– joint author. II. Title.

[S55.E2 no. 334]

A 29-829

Title from Illinois Univ. Printed by L. C.

NL 0428151 IU

Lloyd, John William, 1876–
... Onion culture [by] John W. Lloyd. Urbana, Ill., 1914.
16 p. 23cm. (University of Illinois. Agricultural experiment station ... Circular no. 173)

1. Onion.

A 14-2354

Title from Illinois Univ. Printed by L. C.

NL 0428152 IU

Lloyd, John William, 1876–
Onion culture, by J. W. Lloyd ... [Urbana, Ill.] University of Illinois [1933]
16 p. illus. 23cm. (University of Illinois. College of agriculture and Agricultural experiment station. Circular 410)

1. Onions.

A 33-2825

Title from Illinois Univ.
Library of Congress [S55.E3 no.410]

NL 0428153 IU

Lloyd, John William, 1876–
Pan American trade, with special reference to fruits and vegetables, by John William Lloyd ... [Danville, Ill., The Interstate] 1942.
345 p. incl. illus., tables. front. 22cm.
"Sources of information": p. 336-338.

1. Fruit trade—Spanish America. 2. Vegetables. 3. U. S.—Comm.—Spanish America. 4. Spanish America—Comm.—U. S. I. Title.

42-12625

Library of Congress HD9254.A2L6
[3] 338.1

NL 0428154 OCl OU OrCS IdU DLC IU DAU FMU CU NIC TU P PPD NcD ICJ

Lloyd, John William, 1876–
Precooling rail shipments of Illinois peaches with special reference to the use of ventilated packages, by J. W. Lloyd ... [Urbana, Ill., 1939]
1 p. l., p. 511-544 incl. illus., tables, diagrs. 23cm. (University of Illinois. Agricultural experiment station. Bulletin 455)
"Literature cited": p. 544.

1. Peach. 2. Fruit—Marketing. I. Title.

A 39-638

Illinois. Univ. Library for Library of Congress [S55.E2 no. 455]
[2] (630.72)

NL 0428155 IU WaPS Vi ICJ ViU InLPU I OrCS MU

Lloyd, John William, 1876–
... Productive vegetable growing, by John W. Lloyd ... 193 illustrations in the text ... Philadelphia & London, J. B. Lippincott company [c1914]
xiii, 339 p. col. front., illus. (incl. map) 21½cm. (Lippincott's farm manuals) $1.50

1. Vegetable gardening. I. Title.

Library of Congress SB321.L7 14—20685

NL 0428156 NN ICJ PU DLC WaS CaBVaU TU CU PWcS MBH OCl OU MB

Lloyd, John William, 1876–
... Productive vegetable growing, by John W. Lloyd ... 194 illustrations in the text ... 3d ed., rev. Philadelphia & London, J. B. Lippincott company [c1918]
3 p. l., v-xiii, 339 p. col. front., illus. (incl. map) 21½cm. (Lippincott's farm manuals, ed. by K. C. Davis)

1. Vegetable gardening. I. Title.

18—11111

Library of Congress SB321.L7 1918

NL 0428157 IU IdU-SB OU OO NcRS DLC

Lloyd, John William, 1876–
... Productive vegetable growing, by John W. Lloyd ... 194 illustrations in the text ... 4th ed., rev. Philadelphia & London, J. B. Lippincott company [c1923]
4 p. l., v-xiii, 343 p. col. front., illus. (incl. map) diagrs. 21½cm. (Lippincott's farm manuals, ed. by K. C. Davis)

NL 0428158 OU NcRS

Lloyd, John William, 1876–
... Productive vegetable growing, by John W. Lloyd ... 194 illustrations in the text ... 5th ed., rev. Philadelphia & London, J. B. Lippincott company [c1925]
4 p. l., v-xiii, 343 p. col. front., illus. (incl. map) diagrs. 21½cm. (Lippincott's farm manuals, ed. by K. C. Davis)

1. Vegetable gardening. I. Title.

Library of Congress SB321.L7 1925 25-21699

NL 0428159 DLC WaS ICRL ViU

Lloyd, John William, 1876–
... Productive vegetable growing, by John W. Lloyd ... 194 illustrations in the text ... 6th ed., rev. Philadelphia & London, J. B. Lippincott company [c1930]
4 p. l., v-viii, ixxiia, 343 p. col. front., illus. (incl. map) diagrs. 21½cm. (Lippincott's farm manuals, ed. by K. C. Davis)

1. Vegetable gardening. I. Title.

30-10236

Library of Congress SB321.L7 1930
Copyright A 20809 [5] 635

NL 0428160 DLC MBH PPHor

VOLUME 337

Lloyd, John William, 1876–
... Productive vegetable growing, by John W. Lloyd ... 193 illustrations in the text ... 7th ed. rev. Chicago, Philadelphia, J. B. Lippincott company [°1935]
4 p. l., v–viii, lxxii a, 343 p. col. front., illus. (incl. map) diagrs. 21½cm. (Lippincott's farm manuals, ed. by K. C. Davis)

1. Vegetable gardening. I. Title.
Library of Congress SB321.L7 1935 35-8565
——— Copy 2.
Copyright A 83151 [5] 635

NL 0428161 DLC OrP IdB WaS TU NcRS PP OEac

634 Lloyd, John William, 1876-
L77p Publications of John William Lloyd, University of Illinois, 1901-1940. Bulletins and circulars [of the Agricultural experiment station] ... [Urbana, Ill., 1940?]
2v. illus., maps, tables, diagrs.

Each volume has a typewritten t.-p. and table of contents.

1. Vegetable gardening. 2. Fruit-culture.

NL 0428162 IU

Lloyd, John William, 1876–
Range of adaptation of certain varieties of vegetable-type soybeans [by] J. W. Lloyd ... [Urbana, Ill., 1940]
1 p. l., p. 79–100 incl. illus., maps, tables. 23cm. (University of Illinois. Agricultural experiment station. Bulletin 471)

1. Soy-bean. I. Title.
A 41-743
Illinois. Univ. Library for Library of Congress [S55.E2 no. 471]
[2] (630.72)

NL 0428163 IU

Lloyd, John William, 1876–
... The right time to plant vegetables, by J. W. Lloyd ... [Urbana, University of Illinois, 1918]
4 p. 23cm. (University of Illinois. Agricultural experiment station ... Circular no. 217)
Caption title.

1. Vegetable gardening. I. Title.
A 18-564
Title from Illinois Univ. Printed by L. C.

NL 0428164 IU

Lloyd, John William, 1876–
... Shall I plant a garden this year? By J. W. Lloyd ... [Urbana, University of Illinois, 1918]
4 p. 2 diagr. 23cm. (University of Illinois. Agricultural experiment station. Circular no. 209)
Caption title.

1. Vegetable gardening. I. Title.
A 18-178
Title from Illinois Univ. Printed by L. C.

NL 0428165 IU

Lloyd, John William, 1876–
... Some economic aspects of fruit and vegetable storage, by J. W. Lloyd ... Urbana [University of Illinois] 1919.
8 p. 23cm. (University of Illinois. Agricultural experiment station. Circular no. 237)
Caption title.

1. Fruit. 2. Vegetables. 3. Farm produce—Storage. I. Title.
A 19-1368
Title from Illinois Univ. Printed by L. C.

NL 0428166 IU

Lloyd, John William, 1876–
Some factors influencing the keeping quality of fruit in transit, by J. W. Lloyd and H. M. Newell ... [Urbana, Ill.] University of Illinois [1930]
1 p. l., p. 461–484. illus., tables, diagrs. 23cm. (University of Illinois. Agricultural experiment station. Bulletin 350)
"Literature cited": p. 484.

1. Fruit—Marketing. I. Newell, Horace Mead, 1902– joint author. II. Title.
A 30-1275
[S55.E2 no. 350]
Title from Illinois Univ. Printed by L. C.

NL 0428167 IU

Lloyd, John William, 1876–
Some tests in the culture of peppers, by J. W. Lloyd Urbana, Ill. [University of Illinois] 1926.
[4], 331–336 p. illus., tables. 23cm. (University of Illinois. Agricultural experiment station. Bulletin no. 274)

1. Pepper. I. Title.
A 26-233
Title from Illinois Univ. Printed by L. C.

NL 0428168 IU

Lloyd, John William, 1876–
Spinach early and late, by J. W. Lloyd ... [Urbana] University of Illinois [1933]
8 p. illus. 23cm. (University of Illinois. College of agriculture and Agricultural experiment station. Circular 404)

1. Spinach.
A 33-591
Title from Illinois Univ. Library of Congress [S55.E3 no. 404]

NL 0428169 IU

Lloyd, John William, 1876–
... Spraying for the codling moth, by John W. Lloyd. Urbana, Ill., 1907.
1 p. l., p. 377–429. 5 illus. 23½ cm. (University of Illinois. Agricultural experiment station. Bulletin no. 114)

1. Codling-moth.
A 11—668
Illinois Univ. Library for Library of Congress [a51b½]

NL 0428170 IU NN MBH

Lloyd, John William, 1876–
... Storage of vegetables for winter use, by J. W. Lloyd ... [Urbana, University of Illinois, 1918]
4 p. 23cm. (University of Illinois. Agricultural experiment station ... Circular no. 231)
Caption title.

1. Vegetables. 2. Farm produce—Storage. I. Title.
A 18-2082
Title from Illinois Univ. Printed by L. C.

NL 0428171 IU

Lloyd, John William, 1876–
Studies in horticulture, by John William Lloyd ... edited by Eugene Davenport ... Chicago, New York, Rand McNally & company [°1924]
viii, 421 p. incl. front., illus. 20cm.
"List of books": p. 404–406.

1. Fruit-culture. 2. Vegetable gardening. I. Davenport, Eugene, 1856– ed.
24—5367
Library of Congress SB355.L6

NL 0428172 DLC CaBVaU NNBG CU LU TU

Lloyd, John William, 1876–
Substitution of commercial fertilizers for manure in vegetable production, by J. W. Lloyd and E. P. Lewis ... [Urbana, Ill.] University of Illinois [1935]
1 p. l., p. 579–610 incl. tables, diagrs. 23cm. (University of Illinois. Agricultural experiment station. Bulletin 421)
"The material reported in this bulletin is the result of eight years of experimental work. (1925–1932) ... The results of the first five years' work were published in bulletin 377."

1. Fertilizers and manures. 2. Vegetable gardening—Illinois—Cook co. I. Lewis, Ernest Paul, 1897– joint author. II. Title.
A 36-153
Title from Illinois Univ. Library of Congress [S55.E2 no. 421]
[3]

NL 0428173 IU

Lloyd, John William, 1876–
... Tests with nitrate of soda in the production of early vegetables, by John W. Lloyd. Urbana, Ill., 1915.
1 p. l., p. 29–46. illus. 23cm. (University of Illinois. Agricultural experiment station. Bulletin no. 184)

1. Fertilizers. 2. Vegetables.
A 16-36
Title from Illinois Univ. Printed by L. C.

NL 0428174 IU MBH ICJ

Lloyd, John William, 1876–
... The war garden, by J. W. Lloyd ... Urbana, Pub. by the University of Illinois, under the direction of the War committee, 1918.
cover-title, [4] p. 22½cm. (University of Illinois bulletin. vol. XV, no. 25)

1. Vegetable gardening. I. Title.
A 18-371
Title from Illinois Univ. Printed by L. C.

NL 0428175 IU

Lloyd, John William, 1876–
Yields of asparagus as affected by severe cutting of young plantation, by J. W. Lloyd and J. P. McCollum ... [Urbana, Ill., 1938]
1 p. l., 159–171, [1] p. incl. tables, diagrs. 23cm. (University of Illinois. Agricultural experiment station. Bulletin 448)

1. Asparagus. I. McCollum, John Paschal, 1906– joint author. II. Title.
A 39-12
Illinois. Univ. Library for Library of Congress [S55.E2 no. 448]
[2] (630.72)

NL 0428176 IU DLC

Lloyd, Jonathan.
"The Quakers in Wales" by Jonathan Lloyd, clerk - General meeting for Wales of the Religious society of Friends (Quakers) n.p., 1947.
8 p. 20.5 cm.

NL 0428177 PSC-Hi

VOLUME 337

Lloyd, Jonathan.
Y Crynwyr yng Nghymru. Darllediad o'r Gorfforaeth Ddarlledu Brydeinig, Stesión Radio Cymru, 1947. Troswyd gan E.Lewis Evans. n.p. [1947?]
8 p.

NL 0428178 MH

Lloyd, Joseph, comp.
Alasdair Mac Colla; sain-eolus ar a gníomarṫaib gaisge. Seosaṁ Laoiḋe do ċuir le ċéile; déantúsaí ó Eoin Mac Néill agus ó Niall Mac Muireadaiġ sa leabhar so. Baile Áta Cliat, Clóḋanna do Ċonnrad na Gaedilge, 1914.
xx, 76 p. 18 cm.

1. MacDonald, Alaster, d. 1647. I. MacNeill, John. II. Mac Vurich, Niall.

NL 0428179 MB MH

LLOYD, Joseph, ed.
Breaga Eireann. Michéal Mhag Ruaidhrí d'innis. Baile átha cliath, Chonnradh na gaedhilge, 1906.
pp.16. (LEABHAIRINI gaedhilge le haghaidh an tsluaigh, 23.)

NL 0428180 MH

Lloyd, Joseph.
Brisleach mohr Mháighe Muirtheimhne
see under Cuchulain.

LLOYD, Joseph.
Cruaċ Ċonaill tiomsuġad spíontóg de sgéalaiḋeacht an Foċla. Seosam Laoide do rinne díosgán díoḃ. [Baile Áta Cliat], Connrad na Gaedilge, 1909.
18 cm.

NL 0428182 MH

Y 82882 .52 LLOYD, JOSEPH.
Cruaċ Ċonaill; tiomsuġad spiontóg de sgéalaiḋeaċt an foċla. Át cliat Cualann [i.e. Baile Áta Cliat], Connrad na gaedilge, 1913.
180p. 18cm.

Title-page and text in Irish character.

NL 0428183 ICN CU

Lloyd, Joseph, comp.
An cúigeadh leabhar. Baile Átha Cliath, Clódhanna teo. ar n-a chur amach do Chonnradh na Gaedhilge, 1914
v, 241 p.

NL 0428184 MH

Y 82885 .52 LLOYD, JOSEPH, comp.
Duanaire na Miḋe. Baile áta Cliat, Ċonnrad na gaedilge, 1914.
148p. 18cm.

Title-page and text in Irish character.
"The songs and poems contained in this book were all composed by natives of Meath."

NL 0428185 ICN CU MH

PB1395 .M4L5 Lloyd, Joseph, ed.
Duanaire na Mide. Baile Átha Cliath, Clódhanna, teo., ar n-a chur amach do Chonnradh na Gaedhilge, 1941.
148 p. 19 cm.
Title page (transliterated) and text in Irish.

1. Irish poetry (Collections) 2. Irish language—Texts. I. Gaelic League, Dublin. II. Title. Title transliterated: Duanaire na Midhe.

NL 0428186 MB

Y 8284 .517 LLOYD, JOSEPH, ed.
Fian-laoiṫe. Tiomargaḋ laoiteaḋ bfiannaiġeaċta as dá ṫir móra an tre-foid .i. hÉirinn is a hAlbain. Seoram Laoide de ṫiomairg- Baile áta cliaṫ, Ċonnraḋ na gaedilge, 1916.
122p. 19cm.

Title-page and text in Irish character.
Dated on cover, 1917; date on t.-p. covered by publisher's label.
Contains music.
"Priom ḃona (.i. Sources)": p.87-93.

NL 0428187 ICN IU

Lloyd, Joseph.
An léigteoir Gaedealoz
see under MacFionnlaoic, Pedar.

LLOYD, Joseph.
Mac Mic Iasgaire Ḃuide Luimnige. Sean-sgéal as Tír Amalgaid. Seosaṁ Laoide do ċuir i n-eagar. I mBaile Áta Cliat, Ċonnrad na Gaedilge, 1909.
18.5 cm. pp.60,(2).

NL 0428189 MH

Lloyd, Joseph.

891.623 Ir4 Mac mic iargaire Ḃuidhe luimniġhe. Sean-sgéal as tir amhalghaidh. Clódhanna Teo, 1911.
60p.

no.2 in a volume of four pamphlets lettered Irish folk tales, no.1 being; Ruaidhré, Micheal Mhag ("Mearthog Gnoill") and Laoide, Seosamh. Lùb na Cailllighe.

NL 0428190 IU

Lloyd, Joseph, ed.
... Madra na noct gcos 7 sgéalta eile ... "Sgríob Liat an Earraig" do cnuasuig. Seosam Laoide do cuir i n-eagar. Baile Átha Cliath, Connrad na Gaedilge, 1907.
vii, 130 p. 21 cm. (Imteacta an oireactais, 1901. Leabar III. Comórtas XIV. Sean-sgéalaideact. Cuid II)

NL 0428191 CU

LLOYD, Joseph.
Measgán Músgraiġe, cnuasaċ beag sgéalaideacta Seosam Laoide do ċuir do ċuir i n-eagar. I mBaile Áta Cliat, Connrad na Gaedilge, 1907.
16 cm.

NL 0428192 MH CU MB IU

Lloyd, Joseph.
Post-sheanchas i n-a bhfruil cúigí, dúithchí, conntaethe, & bailte puist na h Eireann. Cuid I. Sacsbhearla-Gaedhilge, i mBaile Átha Cliath, Chonnradh na Gaedhilge [Dublin, The Gaelic League] 1905.
124 p. 18 cm.
By Seosamh Laoide.

NL 0428193 PV CU

Lloyd, Joseph.
Post-sheanchas i n-a bhfuil cúigí, dúithchí, conntaethe, agus bailte puist na hÉireann. Seosamh Laoide do chuir i n-eagar. Baile Átha Cliath, Clodhanna teo., ar n-a chur amach do Chonnradh na Gaedilge, 1911
pt. 2

NL 0428194 MH CU

Lloyd, Joseph
Réalta de'n spéir; leabhar léightheoireachta iolsgol agus árdsgol. Seosamh Laoide do chuir i n-eagar. Baile Atha Cliath, Clódhanna, teo., ar n-a chur amach do Chonnradh na Gaedhilge, 1915
v, 242 p.
Prose and poetry

NL 0428195 MH

---

829 L79s Lloyd, Joseph.
Scéalaide Óirġiall... Stories of Oriel. Dublin, 1905. 153p. 19cm.

NL 0428196 CU

Lloyd, Joseph.
Sgéal Cúculainn ag Cuan Carn, sean-sgéal conallac
see under Cuchulain.

LLOYD, Joseph.
Sgéalaide Óirġiall. i. Sgéalaide Fearnmuiġe agus Tuillead Leis: Seosaṁ Laoide do ċuir i n-eagar. I mBaile Áta Cliat, Ċonnrad na Gaedilge, 1905.
18 cm.

NL 0428198 MH IU ICN

Lloyd, Joseph.
...An t-éinín órúa... The little gold bird an other stories. Dublin, 1910. 106p. 22cm.

NL 0428199 CU

VOLUME 337

Y 828846 .5 LLOYD, JOSEPH, ed.
Tonn Tóime; tiomargad sean-pisreog, seanrócan, seán-sgéal, sean-ceist, sean-naiteann, sean-focal agus sean-rád Ó Ciarraige Luacra. Seoram Laoide do cnuasuig. Baile áta Cliat, Conrad na gaedilge, 1915.
x, 162p. 18cm.
Title-page and text in Irish character.

NL 0428200 ICN MH CU

Y 8285 .L 77 LLOYD, JOSEPH.
Trí torpáin; sgéalta side... Baile áta Cliat, Conrad na gaedilge [1918]
55p. 18cm.
Title-page and text in Irish character.

NL 0428201 ICN MH

Lloyd, Joseph Henry, fl. 1875.
Idioms of the German language, together with the proverbs. London. 1875. 12°. —2136

NL 0428202 MdBP

Lloyd, Joyce.
Dyes from plants. [Lower Hutt? N. Z., 1950]
30 p. 22 cm.
1. Dyes and dyeing. 2. Dye plants.
TP919.L6 667.2 51-24260

NL 0428203 DLC IEdS

Lloyd, Joyce.
Dyes from plants. [Lower Hutt? N. Z., 1950]
30 p. 22 cm.
Second edition.

NL 0428204 DSI

TP 919 L6 Lloyd, Joyce.
Dyes from plants. 4th ed, revised. [Wellington, N.Z., 1950?]
32 p. 22 cm.

NL 0428205 NBuC

Lloyd, Mrs. Julia Margaret Fuller.
The Negro and civilization
Goodale, Mrs. Frances Abigail (Rockwell) ed.
The literature of philanthropy, edited by Frances A. Goodale. New York, Harper & brothers, 1893.

Lloyd, Julius, 1830-1892, supposed author.
An analysis of the first eleven chapters of the Book of Genesis
see under Lloyd, John, rector of Llanvapley.

Lloyd, Julius, 1830-1892.
Duty and faith; an essay on the relation of moral philosophy to Christian doctrine. Manchester, etc., J. Heywood, 1884.
pp. 88.

NL 0428208 MH

LLOYD, JULIUS, 1830-1892.
The Gallican church. Sketches of church history in France. By Julius Lloyd... London: Soc. for Promoting Christian Knowledge [1879] 168 p. incl. front. 17½cm.

740340A. 1. Church history—France.

NL 0428209 NN NjP PPPD TxDaM-P

Lloyd, Julius, 1830-1892.
The life of Sir Philip Sidney. By Julius Lloyd ... London, Longman, Green, Longman, Roberts, and Green, 1862.
xvi, 244 p. 19cm.
1. Sidney, Sir Philip, 1554-1586.
Library of Congress DA358.S5L7 4-33701†

NL 0428210 DLC CtY MdBP PPL

Lloyd, Julius, 1830-1892.
Maintenance of the Church of England as an established church. pp. 489-581. (Peek Prize Essays, No. 3.)

NL 0428211 PPPD

Lloyd, Julius, 1830-1892.
... The North African church. By Julius Lloyd, M.A. Published under the direction of the Tract committee. London, Society for promoting Christian knowledge; New York, Pott, Young and co., 1880.
xii, 427 p. incl. plan. front. (map) 19cm. (The home library)
Bibliographical foot-notes.
1. Africa, North—Religion. I. Society for promoting Christian knowledge, London. Tract committee. II. Title. III. Ser.

NL 0428212 NjNbS InU NjPT MBU ViU GEU-T CtY KyWAT KyU ICU ODW MA

Lloyd, Julius, 1830-1892.
Sketches of church history in Scotland. By Julius Lloyd ... Published under the direction of the Tract committee. London, Society for promoting Christian knowledge; New York, Pott, Young, & co. [189-?]
144 p. incl. front., 2 plates. 17½cm.

NL 0428213 DNC

Coll LL9235c Lloyd, Julius Anderson, 1849- comp.
A collection of letters and poems, written by Hezekiah Davies, Harriet Anderson, Patrick Anderson [and others] Collected and printed by Julius A. Lloyd. Dixon, Ill., Star press, 1880.
4p.l., [5]-42p. front. (port.) illus. plates 22cm.

NL 0428214 RPB PHi NN

Lloyd, Julius Anderson, 1849-
Family history. Containing a brief account of the families of Anderson, Davies, Wersler, by J. A. Lloyd. Dixon, Ill., 1880.
8 p. l., 80 p. 20cm.
1. Anderson family. 2. Davis family. 3. Wersler family.
Library of Congress CS71.A55 1880 39-16923

NL 0428215 DLC PWcS PHi WHi

LLOYD, Julius Anderson, 1849-
Family history, containing a brief account of the families of Anderson, Davies, Wersler. Dixon, Ill., 1880. 80p.
1 card (GL 61: 1000)

NL 0428216 WaS

929.2 A5455 Lloyd, Julius Anderson, 1849-
Family history - Anderson, etc. Addenda and errata, memorandum from notes of the Anderson family history ... published in 1880 ... [Dixon? Ill., 1949?]
26 p. 23 cm.
Caption title.
1. Anderson family. 2. Genealogy. Anderson family.

NL 0428217 N

---

76 LL793h Lloyd, Julius Anderson, 1849-
History of little Johnny Brown, multum in parvo, by J. A. Lloyd. [Stonington, Conn.] 1878.
[28] p. illus. 17 cm.
In verse.

NL 0428218 RPB

Lloyd, Julius Anderson, 1849-
Home-made hash; or, Chips from old blocks. A menagerie of ideas, original, rare and exotic ... Dixon, Ill., 1883.
xvi, [6]-295 p. illus.

NL 0428219 NNC PWcS IU NN

Lloyd, Julius Anderson, 1849-
Home made hash; or, Scraps from old feasts; a menagerie of ideas, original, rare and exotic, by Julius A. Lloyd ... illustrated by E. H. Brotts, with a few done to death by the author. 2d ed., rev. and enl. Dixon, Ill., Rogers & Owen, printers, 1909.
8 p. l., [15]-320, [7] p. front. (port.) illus., 2 pl. 20cm.
"No. 449."
9-8588

NL 0428220 DLC

942.91K31 K31l Lloyd, Lady Katharine Helena.
An epitome of the twenty-five Lords of Kemes, A.D. 1087-1914. Carmarthen, Printed by W. Spurrell, 1930.
104 p. illus. 27cm.
Cover title: The Lords marchers of Kemes.
1. Kemes, Lords of. 2. Kemes district Wales.

NL 0428221 MnU

VOLUME 337

Lloyd, Katharine (Parker)
Christian work in Zulu Land. The seed and the sheaves. [Anon.] New York. Randolph. 1868. 76, 7 pp. 17½ cm., in 12s.

L9077 — Missions. Zulus. — Anon. ref.

NL 0428222 MB

[Lloyd, Katharine (Parker)]
Christian work in Zulu land. The seed and the sheaves. 2. ed., enl. New York, A. D. F. Randolph & co., 1870. v, 7–88, 7 p. 18cm.

Cover-title: The seed and the sheaves.

292944B. 1. Missions, Foreign—Zululand. I. Title. II. Title: The seed and the sheaves.
N. Y. P. L. January 4, 1945

NL 0428223 NN CtY MH

---

815 Box 7 [LLOYD, Katharine (Parker]
Christian work in Zulu Land. 3d. ed., enlarged. New York, Anson D.F. Randolph, 1879.
101p. map. 19cm.

Cover-title: The seed and the sheaves.

NL 0428224 MH-AH

815.743 L793ch 1880 [LLOYD, Katharine (Parker)]
Christian work in Zulu Land. Fourth edition, enlarged. New York, Anson D.F. Randolph [188-?]
v,120p. map,plates 19cm.

NL 0428225 MH-AH

Thesis 1954 PH D Lloyd, Kenneth Edward, 1925-
The retention of responses to classes of verbal stimuli compared with the retention of responses to specific verbal stimuli. 1954.
52 l.

Thesis - Ohio State University.

1. Learning, Psychology of. 2. Memory.

NL 0428226 OU

M 1495 .L6862 Lloyd, Kingsley Kendrick, comp.
Songs my brother loves; illus. by Mabel Kathryn Hatt. New York, Noble [c1915]
48 p. illus. 27 cm.

1. Songs (Medium voice) with piano. 2. Choruses (Mixed voices, 4 pts.), Unaccompanied. Title.

NL 0428227 OkU RPB ODaU

Lloyd, Lavender, 1924-
The verandah room. London, Eyre & Spottiswoode, 1955.
271 p. 20 cm.

I. Title.

PZ4.L793Ve 55-38606 ‡

NL 0428228 DLC CU MN

Lloyd, Lavender, 1924-
Your father and I. London, Eyre & Spottiswoode [1953]
254 p. 19 cm.

I. Title.

PZ4.L793Yo 54-19816 ‡

NL 0428229 DLC PU

Lloyd, Leonila M.

George, Edwin B.
The Philippine cotton-goods and hosiery markets, by Edwin B. George, American trade commissioner, Manila and the Philippine embroidery industry, by L. M. Lloyd, Textile division. United States Department of commerce. Bureau of foreign and domestic commerce. [Washington, Govt. print off., 1926]

PR1852 .L6 Lloyd, Leslie John, ed.

Chaucer, Geoffrey, d. 1400.
A Chaucer selection, edited by L. J. Lloyd. London, G. G. Harrap, 1952.

Lloyd, Leslie John.
The English traveller. Exeter, A. Wheaton [1953]
175 p. 19 cm. (English inheritance series)

1. Travelers, English. I. Title.

DA28.9.L55 55-23509 ‡

NL 0428232 DLC CtY CU TU

Lloyd, Leslie John.
John Skelton; a sketch of his life and writings, by L. J. Lloyd ... Oxford, B. Blackwell, 1938.
4 p. l., 152 p. front. (facsim.) 22cm.

1. Skelton, John, 1460?–1529. 39-16448
Library of Congress PR2348.L5
[3] 928.2

OrCS OrU
OCU OO OU CSmH ICN PBm PSt PV PU CaBVaU IdU MtU
NL 0428233 DLC WaU NIC DAU CoU NcD CtY OC1W OC1

Lloyd, Lewis
see
Lloyd, Lodowick, fl. 1573-1610

Lloyd, Lewis E 1907-
Alteration of adsorption properties of charcoal: activation of charcoal in different gases at different temperatures ... by Lewis E. Lloyd ... Easton, Pa., Mack printing company, 1938.
10 p. diagrs. 26½ x 20cm.

Thesis (sc. d.)—University of Michigan, 1938.
"Reprinted from the Journal of the American chemical society, 60 ... (1938)."
Bibliographical foot-notes.

1. Gases—Absorption and adsorption. 2. Carbon, Activated. 3. Benzene. 39-10776 Revised
Library of Congress QC182.L55 1938
[r43d2] 533.1

NL 0428235 DLC MH OCU

Lloyd, Lewis E 1907-
Tariffs: the case for protection. New York, Devin-Adair Co., 1955.
207 p. illus. 21 cm.

1. Tariff—U. S. 2. Free trade and protection—Protection.

HF1756.L55 337.3 55-7950 ‡

OCU OC1W PHC NcRS PU PV KyU NcGU
WaSpG WaTC WaWW PBm PU-W PSC AU PSt PLF PPT OC1
ViU MB NN PBL PP CaBVa CaBVaU Or OrP OrU WaS WaT
NL 0428236 DLC DI GU-L NBuC MiU OU TxU NcC NcD

Lloyd, mrs. Lily C., ed.

Lloyd, Francis Bartow, 1861-1897.
Sketches of country life; humor, wisdom and pathos from the "Sage of Rocky Creek." The homely life of the Alabama Back country has its sunny side: rough but wise and kindly talk. Selections from the writings of Francis Bartow Lloyd ("Rufus Sanders") Birmingham, Ala., Press of Roberts & son, 1898.

Lloyd, Ll.
Lice and their menace to man, by Lieut. Ll. Lloyd ... with a chapter on trench fever, by Major W. Byam ... London, H. Frowde; Hodder & Stoughton, 1919.
xii p., 1 l., 136 p. front., illus., diagrs. 22cm.

"References" at end of most of the chapters.

1. Lice. 2. (Lice as carriers of contagion) 3. Military hygiene. 4. (Trench fever) 5. European war, 1914- —Medical and sanitary affairs. I. Byam, William.

S G 19-163
Library, U. S. Surgeon-General's Office

NN ICJ
NL 0428238 DNLM MU NIC CU CtY PPHa PPJ PBm PU-Z

Lloyd, Ll., joint author.

Byam, William, 1882-
Trench fever, a louse-borne disease. By Major W. Byam ... Captains J. H. Carroll ... J. H. Churchill ... Lyn Dimond ... V. E. Sorapure ... R. M. Wilson ... and Ll Lloyd ... with an introduction by Lieut.-General Sir T. H Goodwin ... A foreword by Major-General Sir David Bruce ... and a summary of the report of the American trench fever commission, by Lieut. R. H. Vercoe ... London, H. Frowde [etc.] 1919.

---

293 L77 Lloyd, Ll., writer on sewage purification.
Animal life in sewage purification processes. Hampton-on-Thames, Institute of Sewage Purification [1945?]
23 p.

NL 0428240 DNAL

Lloyd, Llewelyn.
Correlative English; a textbook for the second year of high school, by Llewelyn Lloyd, M. A. St. Louis, Mo. and London, B. Herder book co., 1936.
xii, 303 p. 19½cm.
Bibliography: p. 295-297.

1. English language—Rhetoric. I. Title. 36-4434
Library of Congress PE1408.L585
——— Copy 2.
Copyright A 91663 [3] 808

NL 0428241 DLC

VOLUME 337

Lloyd, Llewelyn.
... La pittura dell' ottocento in Italia. Firenze [, cop. 1929]. 64 p. incl. front. illus. 23½cm. (Novissima enciclopedia monografica illustrata. [n.] 8.)

617156A. 1. Painting, Italian. 2. Paintings, Italian. I. Ser.
N. Y. P. L. December 28, 1932

NL 0428242 NN OO NNC

Lloyd, Llewellyn, of the Church Missionary Society.
Chinese pie, stories and articles ...
see under title

[LLOYD, Llewelyn, 1792-1876].
Credenze popolari svedesi sul matrimonio, la gravidansa e i bambini. Traduzione dallo svedese. Noto, F. Zammit, 1886.

1.8°. pp.15.
At head of title: Mattia di Martino [translator].
A chapter of his Peasant life in Sweden.

NL 0428244 MH

Lloyd, Llewelyn, 1792-1876.
Field sports of the north of Europe; comprised in a personal narrative of a residence in Sweden and Norway, in the years 1827-28. By L. Lloyd ... London, H. Colburn and R. Bentley, 1830.
2 v. fronts., illus., plates, maps, plans. 22cm.

1. Hunting—Scandinavia. 2. Scandinavia—Descr. & trav.

Library of Congress SK208.L79 5-2646

NL 0428245 DLC OU OC CtY MH ICU PPL NN

Lloyd, Llewelyn, 1792-1876.
Field sports of the North of Europe, comprised in a personal narrative of a residence in Sweden and Norway in the years 1827-28, by L. Lloyd. 2d ed., with additions. London, H. Colburn and R. Bentley, 1831.
2 v. illus., maps (1 fold.) plans, plates. 24 cm.
Notes in ms. in v. 1.

1. Hunting—Scandinavia. 2. Scandinavia—Descr. & trav. I. Title.

SK208.L79 1831 65-59799

NL 0428246 DLC NcU OU

SK 208 .L79 1842

Lloyd, Llewelyn, 1792-1876.
Field sports of the north of Europe; comprised in a personal narrative of a residence in Sweden and Norway. New ed. with additions. London, Colburn, 1842.

2 v. fronts., illus., plates, maps, plans. 22cm.

NL 0428247 MiEM MH

Uzn35 S1 885l

Lloyd, Llewelyn, 1792-1876.
The field sports of the north of Europe. A narrative of angling, hurting, and shooting in Sweden and Norway ... Enl. and rev. ed. London, Hamilton, Adams & co. [etc., etc.] 1885.
416p. 22½cm.
"The present edition is ... re-arranged and ... enlarged from the author's other and later writings ... Some ... matters are omitted." - p.6.

NL 0428248 CtY CU MH OCl IRA

Lloyd, Llewelyn, 1792-1876.
The game birds and wild fowl of Sweden and Norway; together with an account of the seals and salt-water fishes of those countries ... By L. Lloyd ... London, Day & son, limited, 1867.
xx, 599 p. illus., 52 pl. (48 col., incl. front.) 26cm.

1. Game and game birds—Scandinavia. 2. Marine fauna—Scandinavia.

5-40106

Library of Congress SK315.L79

NL 0428249 DLC CSmH PHC MdBP ICJ

Lloyd, Llewelyn, 1792-1876.
The game birds and wild fowl of Sweden and Norway, with an account of the seals and salt-water fishes of those countries, by L. Lloyd ... London, F. Warne and co., 1867.
xx, 599 p. col. front., illus., plates (part col.) 27cm.

1. Game and game-birds—Scandinavia. 2. Marine fauna—Scandinavia.

A 18-1509

Title from Harvard Univ.
Library of Congress [SK315.L]

NL 0428250 MH LU OClW OCl

Lloyd, Llewelyn, 1792-1876.
The game birds and wild fowl of Sweden and Norway; with an account of the seals and salt-water fishes of those countries. By L. Lloyd ... 2d ed., with map, woodcuts, and chromo illustrations. London, F. Warne and co., 1867.
xx, 599 p. col. front., illus., plates (part col.) fold. map (in pocket) 26½cm.

1. Game and game-birds—Scandinavia. 2. Marine fauna—Scandinavia.

17-15717

Library of Congress SK315.L8 1867 a

NL 0428251 DLC CtY NN

SK 208 .7917 1883

Lloyd, Llewelyn, 1792-1876.
Jagt-nöjen i Sverige och Norge. Öfversättning. 2. öfversedda och tillökade uppl. Landskrona, J. L. Törnqvist [1883]
vi, 186 p. illus.

Translation of Field sports of the North of Europe.

NL 0428252 WaU

Lloyd, Llewelyn, 1792-1876, ed.

Andersson, Karl Johan, 1827-1867.
The lion and the elephant. By Charles John Anderson ... Ed. by L. Lloyd ... London, Hurst and Blackett, 1873.

Lloyd, Llewelyn, 1792-1876, ed.

Andersson, Karl Johan, 1827-1867.
Notes of travel in South Africa. By Charles John Andersson ... Ed. by L. Lloyd ... London, Hurst and Blackett, 1875.

DT731 .A536 1875 a

Lloyd, Llewelyn, 1792-1876, ed.

FOR OTHER EDITIONS SEE MAIN ENTRY

Andersson, Karl Johan, 1827-1867.
Notes of travel in south-western Africa. By C. J. Andersson ... New York, G. P. Putnam's sons, 1875.

Lloyd, Llewelyn, 1792?-1876.
Peasant life in Sweden. By L. Lloyd ... London, Tinsley brothers, 1870.
1 p. l., x, 479, [1] p. front., plates. 22½cm.
Added t.-p., illus.

1. Sweden—Soc. life & cust. 2. Peasantry—Sweden.

5-11496

Library of Congress DL631.L7

NL 0428256 DLC TxU MnHi CtY MdBP PBa PP PPL OCl OCU MiU IRA

Film 2730 Reel 10

Lloyd, Llewelyn, 1792?-1876.
Peasant life in Sweden. By L. Lloyd ... London, Tinsley brothers, 1870.
1 p. l., x, 479, [1] p. front., plates. 22½cm.
Added t.-p., illustrated.
Microfilm. Cambridge, Mass., Filmed by General Microfilm Co. for Erasmus Press, Lexington, Ky. 35mm.
Title on microfilm box label: Literature of folklore.

NL 0428257 TxU

Lloyd, Llewelyn, 1792-1876.
Scandinavian adventures, during a residence of upwards of twenty years; representing sporting incidents, and subjects of natural history, and devices for entrapping wild animals. With some account of the northern fauna. By L. Lloyd ... London, R. Bentley, 1854.
2 v. fronts., illus., pl. 25½cm.

1. Hunting—Scandinavia. 2. Fishing—Scandinavia. 3. Zoology—Scandinavia. I. Title.

6-334

Library of Congress QL286.L8

NL 0428258 DLC NIC KyLoU OU CU CtY MdBP OCU NjP NjR PPWa PBa PPL MH ICJ NN AAP OrP

Lloyd, Llewelyn, 1792-1876.
Scandinavian adventures, during a residence of upwards of twenty years. Representing sporting incidents, and subjects of natural history, and devices for entrapping wild animals. With some account of the northern fauna. 2d ed. London, R. Bentley, 1854.
2 v. illus. (part col.) ports., col. map. 28 cm.

1. Hunting—Scandinavia. 2. Fishing—Scandinavia. 3. Game and game-birds—Scandinavia. I. Title.

SK208.L8 1854 64-58415

NL 0428259 DLC NN ICJ MH

DL 631 .L519

Lloyd, Llewelyn, 1792-1876.
Swenska allmogens plägseder. Öfversättning af O. Swederus. Stockholm, Tryckt hos P. G. Berg, 1871.
264 p. illus. 22 cm.
Added t.p., illustrated.
Translation of Peasant life in Sweden.

NL 0428260 MnHi InU

VOLUME 337

Lloyd, Llewelyn C.

DA670 S3S35 v. 48 The book-trade in Shropshire. Some account of the stationers, booksellers and printers at work in the county to about 1800. By Llewelyn C. Lloyd. [Shrewsbury, Brown & Brinnand, ltd., printers, 1935-36]

2 pts. illus. (incl. facsims.) 23 cm.
(In Shropshire archaeological and natural history society. Transactions ... v. 48, p. 65-142 [145]-200)
Caption title.
Bibliography: pt. 1. p. 66-69.

NL 0428261 CSmH

Z325 L5 Lloyd, Llewelyn C.
The book-trade in Shropshire, some account of the stationers booksellers and printers at work in the country to about 1800. Shropshire, Eng., 1936.

65-200 p. facsims. 22 cm.

Cover-title.
"Reprinted from the Transactions of the Shropshire Archaeological and Natural History Society vol. XLVIII (1935-6)
"Bibliography" p. 66-69.

NL 0428262 RPJCB

Lloyd, Llewelyn Southworth, 1876–
Decibels and phons, a musical analogy, by Ll. S. Lloyd ... London, New York ͺetc.ͺ Oxford university press, 1938.

18, ͺ2ͺ p. diagrs. 22cm.

"Part I ... is, in the main, taken from an article by the author which appeared in the 'Musical times' of December 1937."—Pref.

1. Music—Acoustics and physics. 2. Sound—Measurement. I. Title. II. Title: Phons.

39-13457

Library of Congress ML3807.L78D3

781.22

NL 0428263 DLC OrP PU-El NcD

ͺLloyd, Llewelyn Southworthͺ 1876–
... Finance of a county system of secondary schools. London, Printed for H. M. Stationery off., by Wyman & sons, limited ͺ1906ͺ

13 p. col. diagrs. (part fold.) 25cm. (ͺGt. Brit.ͺ Board of education. Educational pamphlets, no. 5)

At head of title: Board of education.
"Report ... of scheme ... established by the Cheshire county council" ...—Pref. note.
Signed: Ll. S. Lloyd.

1. Education, Secondary. ͺ1. Secondary education—Cheshire co., England—Financeͺ I. Gt. Brit. Board of education. II. Title.

E 21-721

Library, U. S. Office of Education LB2902.C4L7

NL 0428264 DHEW NN

Lloyd, Llewelyn Southworth.
Music and sound, by L. S. Lloyd; with a foreword by Sir William Bragg. London, New York ͺetc.ͺ Oxford Univ. Press ͺ19—?ͺ 181 p. diagrs., front., tables. 8°.

Music in text.

1. Sound. 2. Musical instruments. 3. Title.
N. Y. P. L. April 4, 1938

NL 0428265 NN

Lloyd, Llewelyn Southworth, 1876–
Music and sound, by Ll. S. Lloyd ... with a foreword by Sir William Bragg ... London, New York ͺetc.ͺ Oxford university press, 1937.

xiv, 181, ͺ1ͺ p. front. (port.) illus. (music) diagrs. 22½cm.

1. Music—Acoustics and physics. 2. Sound. I. Title.

38-11381 Revised

Library of Congress ML3805.L58M9

ͺr39m2ͺ 781.1

NL 0428266 OU NN WaS OrU OrCS CaBVaU DLC NIC DAU NcD CoU CU PV PSC PPT PP

Lloyd, Llewelyn Southworth, 1876–
Music and sound; with a foreword by Sir William Bragg. 2d ed. London, Oxford University Press, 1951.

xiv, 181 p. illus., port., music. 22 cm.

1. Music—Acoustics and physics. 2. Sound. I. Title.

[ML3805.L58M] 781.1 A 53—9950

Stanford Univ. Library for Library of Congress ͺ60r58h1ͺ

NL 0428267 CSt CaBVa OrP FU ICU MiU MiD N WaT

Lloyd, Llewelyn Southworth, 1876–
The musical ear, by Ll. S. Lloyd ... London, New York ͺetc.ͺ Oxford university press, 1940.

ix, 87, ͺ1ͺ p. illus. (incl. music) II pl. (diagrs.) 22cm.

1. Music—Acoustics and physics. I. Title.

40-33171

Library of Congress ML3830.L46M8

ͺ6ͺ 781.1

NL 0428268 OC1W OU OC1 CaBVa IdPI WU PSt DLC OrP WaS MiU NBuC FMU TU NcD PWcS PPT

Lloyd, Llewelyn Southworth, 1876–
A musical slide-rule, by Ll. S. Lloyd ... London, New York ͺetc.ͺ Oxford university press, 1938.

1 p. l., 25 p. illus. (music) 22cm.
Slide-rule in pocket at end.

1. Musical intervals and scales. 2. Musical temperament. I. Title.

39-18865

Library of Congress ML3812.L79M9

ͺ2ͺ 781.22

NL 0428269 DLC

Lloyd, Lodowick, *fl.* 1573–1610.
ͺA briefe conference of diuers lavves, diuided into certaine regiments. London, Printed by Thomas Creede, 1602ͺ

148, ͺ6ͺ p. 19cm. ͺ*With his* The stratagems of Jerusalem. London, 1602ͺ

A–V⁴ (A₁ and V₄ wanting)
Imperfect: 4 l. (t.-p. and introductory matter) wanting; title supplied from British museum catalogue.

1. Law—Hist. & crit. 2. Comparative law. 3. Religion and law.

42-6514

Library of Congress U101.L55

NL 0428270 DLC IU PU-L CtY CSmH CLL DFo MH

Lloyd, Lodowick, fl. 1573-1610.
A briefe conference of divers lawes: diuided into certaine regiments. London, Printed by T. Creede, 1602.
Short-title catalogue no.16616 (carton 809)

1. Law--Hist. & crit. 2. Comparative law. 3. Religion and law.

NL 0428271 MiU

Lloyd, Lodowick, fl. 1573 - 1610.
A catalogue of some books printed for Lodo. Lloyd, and are to be sold at his shop next to the Castle-Tavern in Cornhill.
(In Norton, John. Abel being dead yet speaketh; . . . 5 pp. at end. London. 1658.)

H8101 — Catalogues. Booksellers'.

NL 0428272 MB

ͺLloyd, Lodowick, fl. 1573-1610.
CERTAINE Englishe verses, presented unto the Queens most excellent maiestie, by a courtier. London, H. Haslop, 1586.

pp. (9).
(In HAZLITT, W.C., editor. Fugitive tracts, 1875, I.)

NL 0428273 MH

FILM 9362 PR ͺLloyd, Lodowickͺ fl. 1573-1610.
Certaine Englishe verses, presented unto the Queenes most excellent maiestie, by a courtier ... London, Printed by H. Haslop, 1586.
ͺ8ͺ p. On film (Positive) (Modern Language Association of America. Collection of photographic facsimiles, no. 464P)

Microfilm. Original in British Museum.

NL 0428274 CU OU

Case K 71 .514 LLOYD, LODOWICK, fl. 1573-1610.
The choice of ievvels... London, Printed by T. Purfoot, 1607.
ͺ8ͺ, 39p. illus. (coat of arms) 19cm.

Printer's device on t.-p.; initials, head and tail-pieces.
STC 16618.

NL 0428275 ICN CSmH DFo MH

Lloyd, Lodowick, fl. 1573-1610.
The choyce of ievvels. London, Printed by T. Purfoot, 1607.
Short-title catalogue no.16618 (carton 809)
Film

NL 0428276 MiU

Lloyd, Lodowick, *fl.* 1573–1610.
The consent of time, disciphering the errors of the Grecians in their olympiads, the vncertaine computation of the Romanes in their penteterydes and building of Rome, of the Persians in their accompt of Cyrus, and of the vanities of the Gentiles in fables of antiquities, disagreeing with the Hebrewes, and with the Sacred histories in consent of time. Wherein is also set downe the beginning, continuance, succession, and overthrowes of kings, kingdomes, states, and gouernments. By Ludovvik Lloid ... London, Imprinted by G. Bishop, and R. Nevvberie, 1590.

8 p. l., 722 p. 20½cm.
Initials; head and tail pieces.

Subject entries: History, Ancient.

3-7265

Library of Congress, no. D59.L79.

NL 0428278 DLC IU NN DFo CtY TxU

VOLUME 337

FILM Lloyd, Lodowick, fl. 1573-1610.
The consent of time, discipherinq the errors of the Grecians in their olympiads, the vncertaine computation of the Romanes in their penteterydes and building of Rome, of the Persians in their accompt of Cyrus, and of the vanities of the Gentiles in fables of antiquities, disagreeing with the Hebrewes, and with the Sacred Histories in consent of time. Wherein is also set downe the beginning, continuance, succession, and ouerthrowes of kings, kingdomes, states, and gouernments. By Lodovvik Lloid ... Imprinted at London by George Bishop, and Ralph Nevvberie ... 1590.
University microfilms no.15922 (case 68, carton 406)
Short-title catalogue no.16619.
1.History, Ancient. I.Title.

NL 0428279 MiU ViU

Lloyd, Lodowick, fl. 1573-1610.
An Epitaph vpon the death of the honorable, Syr Edward Saunders...who dyed the .19. of Nouember, 1576. London, by H.S. for Henry Disle, December .3, [1576]
Broadside.
Laid (51) in the same vol. with: Awdelay or Awdeley, John. ECCLESI. XX. 1569.

NL 0428280 CSmH DFo

FILM Lloyd, Lodowick, fl. 1573-1610.
An epitaph vpon the death of the honorable, Syr Edward Saunders ... who dyed the.19.of Nouember.1576 ... Jmprinted at London by H.S.ꞏingleton, for Henry Disle ... ꞏ1576ꞏ
Signed: Lodowick Lloyd.
Broadside.
University microfilms no.15923 (case 68, carton 406)
Short-title catalogue no.16620.

1.Saunders, Sir Edward, d.1576.

NL 0428281 MiU ViU

D11 .L8 Rare bk room DFo PBL Lloyd, Lodowick, fl. 1573-1610.
The first part of the diall of daies, containing 320. Romane triumphes, besides the triumphant obelisks and pyramydes of the Aegyptians, the pillers, arches, and trophies triumphant, of the Græcians, and the Persians ... of feastes and sacrifices both of the Iewes and of the Gentils ... with the birthes and funeral pomps of kinges and emperours ... By Lodowick Lloid ... London, Printed for R. Ward, 1590.
[6], 196 (i. e. 194), [1] p. 18½cm.
Numerous errors in paging.
Head and tail pieces; initials.
Closely trimmed.
1. Chronology, Historical.

NL 0428282 ICU CSmH DFo PBL

FILM Lloyd, Lodowick, fl. 1573-1610.
The first part of the diall of daies, containing 320.Romane triumphes, besides the triumphant obelisks and pyramydes of the Aegyptians, the pillers, arches, and trophies triumphant, of the Graecians, and the Persians ... of feastes and sacrifices both of the Iewes and of the Gentils ... with the birthes and funeral pomps of kinges and emperours ... By Lodowick Lloid ... London Printed for Roger Ward ... 1590.
University microfilms no.15924 (case 56, carton 335)
Short-title catalogue no.16621.
1.Chronology, Historical. I.Title: Diall of daies.

NL 0428283 MiU

[Lloyd, Lodowick, or Lewis] fl. 1573-1610.
Hilaria: Or The Trivmphant Feast for the fift of August. Imprinted at London by Simon Stafford, ... 1607.
sm. 4 to.
Unbound; in envelope.

NL 0428284 CSmH

Lloyd, Lodowick, fl. 1573-1610.
Hilaria: or The trivmphant feast for the fift of August. London, Imprinted by S. Stafford, 1607.
University microfilms no.21608 (carton 723)
Short-title catalogue no.16622.

NL 0428285 MiU

STC 16623 Lloyd, Lodowick, fl. 1573-1610.
The iubile of Britane ... London, Printed by Thomas Purfoot, 1607.

A^2, $B-F^4$, G^2. 4to.
Gordonstoun library-Richard Heber-Britwell Court-Harmsworth copy.

NL 0428286 DFo CtY CSmH

FILM Lloyd, Lodowick, fl. 1573-1610.
The ivbile of Britane. London, Printed by T. Purfoot, 1607.
Short-title catalogue no.16623 (carton 844)

NL 0428287 MiU

Ih L777 607 Lloyd, Lodowick, fl. 1573-1610.
Linceus spectacles ... written by Lodowicke Lloide esquire. London, Printed by Nicholas Okes, dwelling neere Holborne bridge. 1607.
4p.ℓ., 67p. 19cm.
Signatures: A-I⁴K².
Imperfect: 1st prelim. leaf (blank except for signature-mark?) wanting.

NL 0428288 CtY CSmH DFo

FILM Lloyd, Lodowick, fl. 1573-1610.
Linceus spectacles. London, Printed by N. Okes, 1607.
University microfilms no.20820 (carton 721)
Short-title catalogue no.16623a.

NL 0428289 MiU

LLOYD, LODOWICK, fl. 1573-1610
The marrow of history: or, The pilgrimage of kings and princes ... Collected by Lodowick Lloyd ... and corrected and revived ꞏIꞏ by R.C. ... London, Printed by E. Alsop, 1653.
3 p.ℓ., 311 p. 12mo

Wing L2660.
Bound in brown calf.

MiDW MH CLU-C PU NPV CSmH MH
NL 0428290 InU MiU NjP RPB ICN IEN MiU IU IaU

STC 16633 [Lloyd, Lodowick] fl. 1573-1610.
The order, solemnitie, and pompe, of the feastes, sacrifices, vowes, games, and triumphes: vsed vpon the natiuities of emperours, kinkes [!] princes, dukes, popes, and consuls ... Imprinted at London, 1610.

[A]^1, $B-I^4$. (I4, probably blank, lacking.) 4to.
Running titles read "The triplicitie of triumphes" which was the title under which this work was originally issued.

NL 0428291 DFo CSmH MH

Lloyd, Lodowick, fl. 1573-1610.
The order, solemnitie, and pompe, of the feastes, sacrifices, vowes, games, and triumphes: vsed vpon the natiuities of emperours, kinkes, princes, dukes, popes, and consuls: with the custome, order, and manner of their inaugurations, coronations, and annoynting. With a briefe rehearsall of the funerall solemnities at some emperours, kings, and princes burials. London, 1610.
Caption title: The triplicitie of triumphes.
Short-title catalogue no.16633 (carton 809)
1.Rites and ceremonies. I.Title.

NL 0428292 MiU

Case J 22 .515 LLOYD, LODOWICK, fl. 1573-1610.
The pilgrimage of princes, penned out of sundry Greeke and Latine aucthours... London, Printed by [J. Kingston? for] VV. Iones [1573]
[16] p., 218 numb. leaves, [4] p. 20½cm.

Title within woodcut border. Initials, tailpieces.
Date stamped on cover: 1597.
Issued in 1653 with title: The marrow of history; or, The pilgrimage of kings and princes.
STC 16624.

NL 0428293 ICN DFo IU MH WU ICN CSmH

FILM Lloyd, Lodowick, fl. 1573-1610.
The pilgrimage of princes, penned out of sundry Greeke and Latine aucthours, by Lodovvicke Lloid ... At London Printed by ꞏJ. Kingston? for. VVilliam Iones ... ꞏ1573ꞏ
University microfilms no.15925 (case 56, carton 335)
Short-title catalogue no.16624.

1.Kings and rulers. I.Title.

NL 0428294 MiU CtY

Case J 22 516 LLOYD, LODOWICK, fl. 1573-1610.
The pilgrimage of princes, newly published... London, I. Wolfe, 1586.
[15] p., 214 numb. leaves, [3] p. 18cm.
Black letter. Title within woodcut border. Initials, head and tail pieces. Side notes.
Imperfect: t.-p. and prelim. leaf 7 wanting; leaf following t.-p. mutilated, mended; last leaf mounted; upper margin closely trimmed. T.-p. and other missing leaf supplied in photostat (positive) from Huntington library copy.
STC 16625. Ms. notes in margins.
Bookplate of Frederic Ives Carpenter.

NL 0428295 ICN MiU DFo TxU CSmH ICN PU MB MdBJ-G

FILM Lloyd, Lodowick, fl. 1573-1610.
The pilgrimage of princes, newly published, Lodowicke Lloid ... Imprinted at London, by Iohn Wolfe. 1586.
University microfilms no.15926 (case 56, carton 336)
Short-title catalogue no.16625.

1.Kings and rulers. I.Title.

NL 0428296 MiU

STC 16626 Lloyd, Lodowick, fl. 1573-1610.
The pilgrimage of princes. Newly published ... London, Printed by W. White, 1607.

$A-3C^4$, $3D^2$. (Some upper margins trimmed affecting running titles.) 4to.

NL 0428297 DFo ICN IEN IU

VOLUME 337

STC 16627 Lloyd, Lodowick, fl.1573-1610.
The practice of policy. Written by Lodowike Lloyd ...
Imprinted at London by Simon Stafford, dwelling in Hosier lane, neere Smithfield, 1604.
2p.l., 84p. 20cm.
Printer's mark (McK. 281) on t.-p.

NL 0428298 MH CSmH

LLOYD, LODOWICK, fl. 1573-1610.
The practice of policy. S. Stafford, 1604.

NL 0428299 ICU

STC 16628 Lloyd, Lodowick, fl. 1573-1610.
Regum gemma e sacris Biblijs desumpta ...
Londini, Apud Iohannem Windet [1600?]
A^6, B-K^{12}, L^6. 12mo.
Newdigate family library copy.

NL 0428300 DFo

Lloyd, Lodowick, fl. 1573-1610.
The stratagems of Ierusalem: vvith the martiall lavves and militarie discipline, as vvell of the Iewes, as of the gentiles, by Lodowick Lloyd, esquier ... London, Printed by Thomas Creede, 1602.
4 p. l., 352, [13] p. 19cm.
Title vignette: Device of T. Creede.
Head-pieces, initials.
With this is bound the author's A briefe conference of diuers lavves diuided into certaine regiments. London, 1602.
Imperfect: p. 305-314 wanting; supplied in photostatic facsimile.
1. Military art and science—Early works to 1800. 2. Jews—Hist. 3. Military history, Ancient. I. Title.
42-6513
Library of Congress U101.L55

NL 0428301 DLC DFo MB CtY MH ICU CSmH NN

FILM
Lloyd, Lodowick, fl.1573-1610.
The stratagems of Ierusalem: with the martiall lawes and militarie discipline, as well of the Iewes, as of the Gentiles. London, Printed by T. Creede, 1602.
Short-title catalogue no.16630 (carton 809)

1. Military art and science--Early works to 1800. 2. Jews--Hist. 3. Military history, Ancient. I. Title.

NL 0428302 MiU

Case Y 145 .L 772 LLOYD, LODOWICK, fl.1573-1610.
The tragicocomedie of serpents... London, Printed by T. Purfoot, and are to be sold by A. Iohnson, 1607.
[8], 97, [3]p. illus. (coat of arms) 18cm.
"A curious collection, chiefly of classical and biblical fables."—Dict. of national biography.
STC 16631.
Bookplate of J. Brand.

NL 0428303 ICN CSmH

AW 1 R475: 1246 Lloyd, Lodowick, fl.1573-1610.
The tragicocomedie of serpents. By Lodowik Lloid ... London, Printed by T. Purfoot, 1607.
"A curious collection, chiefly of classical and biblical fables."--Dict.nat.biog.
CaBVaU Microfilm of original in the Huntington Library. Ann Arbor, Mich., University Microfilms, 1971. (Early English books, 1475-1640, reel 1246)
STC no.16631.
Microfilm.

NL 0428304 MiU CaBVaU

Case F 034 .51 Lloyd, Lodowick, fl.1573-1610.
The triplicitie of triumphes; containing the order, solempnitie and pompe of the feastes, sacrifices, vowes, games, and triumphes used vpon the natiuities of emperours, kinges, princes, dukes, popes, and consuls, with the custome, order and maners of their inaugurations, coronations, and annointing... With a briefe rehearsall of the funerall solempnities at some emperors, kings, and princes burials... London, Ihones, 1591.
[65]p.

NL 0428305 ICN CSmH MH

FILM
Lloyd, Lodowick, fl.1573-1610.
The triplicitie of triumphes. Containing, the order, solempnitie and pompe, of the feastes, sacrifices, vowes, games, and triumphes: vsed vpon the natiuities of emperours, kinges, princes, dukes, popes, and consuls, with the custome, order and maners of their inaugurations, coronations and annointing. Wherein is also mentioned, the three ... daies, in September, Nouember and Ianuary, by the name of, Triplicia festa. With a briefe rehearsall of the funerall solempnities at some emperors, kings, and princes burials. By Lodowike Lloyd ... Imprinted at London, by Richard Ihones ... 1591 ...
University microfilms no.12355 (case 64, carton 380)
Short-title catalogue no.16632.
1. Rites and ceremonies. I. Title.

NL 0428306 MiU DFo ViU

LLOYD, LOLA MAVERICK.
[Autograph letters and postal cards to her daughter Jessie Lloyd O'Connor, Feb. 4, 1908-Dec. 16, 1930. v.p., 1908-30] ca.235 p.

Film reproduction. Positive.
Includes a few letters from other members of the family.

NL 0428307 NN

3'8 Z Box 677 Lloyd, Lola Maverick.
Chaos, war, or a new world order, by Lola Maverick Lloyd and Rosika Schwimmer ... [Enlarged ed.] Chicago, Campaigns for world government, 1942.
8 p.

1. Reconstruction (1939-) I. Schwimmer Rosika, jt au.

NL 0428308 NNC

Oop37 1 1942 Lloyd, Lola Maverick.
Chaos, war, or a new world order. By Lola Maverick Lloyd and Rosika Schwimmer ...
Chicago, Campaign for world government, 1942.
"Enlarged edition, fourth printing, November, 1942."

NL 0428309 CtY InU

Lloyd, Lola Maverick.
Common questions about the future united states of the world ... [Rev. ed.] Chicago, Campaign for world government, 1943.
14 p.

1. World politics. I. Title: United states of of the world.

NL 0428310 NNC

Lloyd, Lorenzo L., joint author.

Fort, M.
The chemistry of dyestuffs; a manual for students of chemistry and dyeing, by M. Fort ... and L. L. Lloyd ... Cambridge [Eng.] University press, 1917.

QD406 .L7 Lloyd, Lorenzo L.
Studien ueber chromonderivate.
Bern, 1903.
27p.
Inaug diss. Bern.

NL 0428312 DLC DNLM NN PU

Lloyd, Lowell Clyde, d. 1936.
A new genus and species of Monorchidae ...
[Seattle?] 1932.
231-239 p.
Repr. from the Journal of parasitology, June, 1932, vol. 18....

NL 0428313 OU

Lloyd, Lowell Clyde, d.1936.
Some digenetic trematodes from Puget sound fish
N.p. Journal of parasitology, 1938.
pp.103-133, plates, O. (Washington (state) - University - Publications in oceanography; supplementary series. no.70)

NL 0428314 CaBViP

398.2 L7931a Lloyd, Lucy Catherine, d. 1914.
African folk-lore. [Cape Town, 1878]
v. 23cm.

Reprinted from Cape monthly magazine.

1. Folk-lore. Africa, South.

NL 0428315 IEN

Microfilm Lloyd, Lucy Catherine, d.1914, joint author.

Bleek, Wilhelm Heinrich Immanuel, 1827-1875.
The Mantis and his friends; Bushman folklore collected by the late Dr. W. H. I. Bleek and the late Dr. Lucy C. Lloyd, edited by D. F. Bleek; illustrated with many reproductions of Bushman drawings. Cape Town, T. M. Miller; London and Oxford, B. Blackwell ltd. [1924]

VOLUME 337

Lloyd, Lucy Catherine, *d.* 1914.
A short account of further Bushman material collected. By L. C. Lloyd ... London, D. Nutt, 1889.
3 p. l., [3]-28 p. 33½ x 21½ᶜᵐ.
"Third report concerning Bushman researches, presented to both houses of the Parliament of the Cape of Good Hope, by command of His Excellency the Governor."

1. Bushmen. 2. Folk-lore, Bushman.
43-44775
Library of Congress GR360.B9L6

NL 0428317 DLC NN MH OCl PU CtY NcD CU DSI

Lloyd, Lucy Catherine, d. 1914.
Bleek, Wilhelm Heinrich Immanuel, 1827-1875, *comp.*
Specimens of Bushman folklore, collected by the late W. H. I. Bleek, PH. D., and L. C. Lloyd; ed. by the latter; with an introduction by George McCall Theal ... Translation into English; illustrations; and appendix. London, G. Allen & company, ltd., 1911.

Lloyd, Lucy Catherine, d. 1914.

Bleek, Wilhelm Heinrich Immanuel, 1827-1875.
Das wahre gesicht des Buschmannes in seinen mythen und märchen, nach original-Buschmannerzählungen niedergeschrieben von dr. W. H. I. Bleek und Lucy C. Lloyd, übersetzt von Käthe Woldmann. Basel, Kommissionsverlag Zbinden & Hügin, 1938.

Lloyd, Ludovic
see
Lloyd, Lodowick, fl. 1573-1610

Lloyd, Mrs. M., supposed author.
"Sunny memories." Part I. Containing personal recollections of some celebrated characters. By M. L. 2d ed., with notes and additions ... Printed for private circulation ... London, Women's printing society limited, 1880.

PR3541 .L555K6 1646 Rare bk room
LLOYD, M., captain.
The king found at Southwell, and the Oxford gigg playd, and sung at Witney wakes: with the masque shewed before divers courtiers, and cavaliers, that went thither from Oxford, and severall ketches and songs at the said wakes. Presented to the Duke of Yorke. By Mr. Loyd, studient of Christ church in Oxford, and captaine of that garison. London, Printed for F.L., 1646. [London, 1922]
facsim.: 5 l. 27½x29cm.
Photostat copy (negative); original in British museum.

NL 0428322 ICU

Lloyd, M. B.
Explosion during repairs to the corning house at factory no. 34, Westmorland. Accident no. 318, 1901. Report...on the circumstances attending an explosion which occurred during repairs to the corning house, at the factory of the Elterwater Gunpowder Company, Limited, at Elterwater, near Ambleside, on the 23rd October, 1901. London: Darling & Son, Ltd., 1901. 9(1) p. f°. (Great Britain. Explosives, Inspectors of. Report 149.)

1. Explosions.—Gt. Br.: Eng.: Elterwater.
N. Y. P. L. August 24, 1911.

NL 0428323 NN

Lloyd, M. B.
Explosion during thawing of gelignite at Nether Walstead, near Haywards heath, Sussex. Accident no. 270, 1905. Report... on the circumstances attending an explosion which occurred at Nether Walstead, near Haywards heath, in the county of Sussex, on the 26th October, 1905. London: Darling & Son, Ltd., 1906. 8 p., 1 plan. f°. (Great Britain. Explosives, Inspectors of. Report 173.)

1. Explosions.—Gt. Br.: Eng.: Nether Walstead.
N. Y. P. L. August 24, 1911.

NL 0428324 NN

Lloyd, M. B.
Explosion in a fitters' shop at factory no. 188, Essex. Accident no. 179, 1905. Report...on the circumstances attending an explosion of nitro-glycerine which occurred in the fitters' shop of the factory of the "Explosives and Chemical Products, Limited," at Bramble island, in the county of Essex, on the 11th July, 1905. London: Darling & Son, Ltd., 1905. 17 p. f°. (Great Britain. Explosives, Inspectors of. Report 171.)

1. Explosions.—Gt. Br.: Eng.: Bramble island.
N. Y. P. L. August 24, 1911.

NL 0428325 NN

Lloyd, M. B.
Explosion in a mixing house at factory no. 38, Kent. Accident no. 11, 1904. Report...on the circumstances attending an explosion of gunpowder which occurred in the mixing house of the factory of Messrs. Curtis's and Harvey, Limited, at the Marsh, Faversham, on the 2nd February, 1904. London: Darling & Son, Ltd., 1904. 15 p., 2 plans. f°. (Great Britain. Explosives, Inspectors of. Report 165.)
In: ††VOG p. v. 2, no. 15.

1. Explosions.—Gt. Br.: Eng.: Faversham.
N. Y. P. L. August 24, 1911.

NL 0428326 NN

Lloyd, M. B.
Explosions in glazing and corning houses at factory no. 33, Westmorland. Accident no. 79, 1903. Report...on the circumstances attending explosions of gunpowder which occurred in the glazing and corning houses of the factory of the Sedgwick Gunpowder Company, Limited, at Sedgwick, near Kendal, in the county of Westmorland, on the 30th March, 1903. London: Darling & Son, Ltd., 1903. 12 p., 3 plans. f°. (Great Britain. Explosives, Inspectors of. Report 160.)

1. Explosions.—Gt. Br.: Eng.: Sedgwick.
N. Y. P. L. August 24, 1911.

NL 0428327 NN

Lloyd, M. B.
Explosion of a dynamite cartridge hut at factory no. 3, Ayr. Accident no. 15, 1901. Report...on the circumstances attending an explosion which occurred in one of the dynamite cartridge huts at the factory of Nobel's Explosives Company, Limited, at Ardeer, near Stevenston, in the county of Ayr, on the 29th January, 1901. London: Darling & Son, Ltd., 1901. 12 p. f°. (Great Britain. Explosives, Inspectors of. Report 145.)

1. Explosions.—Great Britain: Scotland: Ardeer.
N. Y. P. L. August 24, 1911.

NL 0428328 NN

Lloyd, M. B.
Explosion of cartridges on registered premises. Accident no. 1, 1908. Report...on the circumstances attending an explosion of cartridges which occurred on the registered premises of Messrs. F. Dyke and Company, at 5, St. George's avenue, Aldermanbury, London, E. C., on the 1st January, 1908. London: Darling & Son, Ltd., 1908. 25 p. f°. (Great Britain. Explosives, Inspectors of. Report 182.)

1. Explosions.—Gt. Br.: Eng.: London.
N. Y. P. L. August 23, 1911.

NL 0428329 NN

Lloyd, M. B.
Explosion of gelignite on the Fishguard Railway construction works. Accident no. 46, 1906. Report...on the circumstances attending an explosion which occurred during the operation of thawing gelignite in connection with the construction of the new Great Western Railway line from Clarbeston road to Fishguard, in the county of Pembroke, on the 26th February, 1906. London: Darling & Son, Ltd., 1907. 9 p. f°. (Great Britain. Explosives, Inspectors of. Report 175.)

1. Explosions.—Gt. Br.: Wales. Fishguard.
N. Y. P. L. August 23, 1911.

NL 0428330 NN

Lloyd, M. B.
Explosion of gunpowder at the new harbour works, East Cliff, Dover. Accident no. 12, 1900. Report...on the circumstances attending an explosion of gunpowder on the works of the new admiralty harbour, East Cliff, near Dover, on the 14th January, 1900. London: Darling & Son, Ltd., 1900. 18 p. f°. (Great Britain. Explosives, Inspectors of. Report 137.)

1. Explosions.—Great Britain: England: Dover.
N. Y. P. L. August 24, 1911.

NL 0428331 NN

Lloyd, M. B.
Explosion of gunpowder on registered premises, no. 3359, at Marple, near Stockport. Accident no. 123, 1902. Report...on the circumstances attending an explosion of gunpowder which took place on the registered premises of Messrs. James Lee and Sons, New road, Marple, on the 26th April, 1902. London: Darling & Son, Ltd., 1902. 13 p. f°. (Great Britain. Explosives, inspectors of. Report 153.)

1. Explosions.—Gt. Br.: Eng.: Marple.
N. Y. P. L. August 24, 1911.

NL 0428332 NN

Lloyd, M. B.
Explosion of gunpowder press house. Accident no. 120, 1900. Report...on the circumstances attending the destruction by explosion of a press house at the gunpowder factory of Messrs. F. C. Dickson & Co., at Blackbeck, Haverthwaite, Lancashire, on the 26th May, 1900. London: Darling & Son, Ltd., 1900. 11 p., 1 plan. f°. (Great Britain. Explosives, Inspectors of. Report 138.)

1. Explosions.—Great Britain: England: Blackbeck.
N. Y. P. L. August 24, 1911.

NL 0428333 NN

Lloyd, M. B.
Explosion of mixing house and stove at factory no. 149, Suffolk. Accident no. 239, 1900. Report...on the circumstances attending explosions which occurred in the mixing house and stove at the factory of Messrs. Curtis's and Harvey, Limited, at Trimley marsh, Suffolk, on the 28th November, 1900. London: Darling & Son, Ltd., 1901. 14 p. f°. (Great Britain. Explosives, Inspectors of. Report 144.)

1. Explosions.—Great Britain: England: Trimley marsh.
N. Y. P. L. August 24, 1911.

NL 0428334 NN

Lloyd, M. B.
Explosion of nitro-glycerine at factory no. 3, Ayr. Accident no. 272, 1902. Report...on the circumstances attending an explosion of nitro-glycerine which occurred in one of the final washing houses of the factory of Nobel's Explosives Company, Limited, at Ardeer, near Stevenston, Ayrshire, on the 7th October, 1902. London: Darling & Son, Ltd., 1903. 16 p., 3 plans. f°. (Great Britain. Explosives, Inspectors of. Report 156.)

1. Explosions.—Gt. Br.: Scotland: Ardeer.
N. Y. P. L. August 24, 1911

NL 0428335 NN

VOLUME 337

Lloyd, M. B.
Registered premises no. 2749, at Liskeard.—Explosion of detonators. Accident no. 3, 1899. Report...on the circumstances attending an explosion of detonators on the registered premises of Messrs. J. C. & C. Isaac at Liskeard, Cornwall, on the 5th January, 1899. London: Darling & Son, Ltd., 1899. 11 p. f°. (Great Britain. Explosives, Inspectors of. Report 131.)

1. Explosions.—Great Britain: England: Liskeard.
N. Y. P. L. August 24, 1911.

NL 0428336 NN

784.8 qL793 Lloyd, Mrs. M.B., fl.1842, arr.& ed.
Parlour melodies, comprising music, original and selected, for the pianoforte and organ, with several tunes for the harp and guitar. Adapted to a series of original songs, moral and religious; arr. and ed. by M.B. Lloyd and M.E. Bailey. New York, Harper, 1842.
112+ p. 30 cm.
1. Songs with piano. 2. Sacred songs. I. Bailey, Miss M E jt. arr. and ed.

NL 0428337 N IEN ViU NN

Lloyd, Miss M.E.H.

Lloyd, Albert Hugh.
... The Lloyd collection. London, Pub. for the British academy by H. Milford, Oxford university press, 1933–

Lloyd, Mabel Pearl, *comp.*
Modern short stories for oral interpretation; a compilation of stories chosen for the purpose of adaptation for oral interpretation, together with an introduction on the art of reading aloud, adapting a reading, and arranging a program, by M. Pearl Lloyd and John Tryon Marshman ... ₍Menasha, Wis. Print. by G. Banta publishing company, °1933₎
viii p., 1 l., 306 p. 24½ᶜᵐ.

1. Short stories, American. I. Marshman, John Tryon, 1874– joint comp. II. Title.
33–36719
Library of Congress

OrU-M MtBuM CaBVaU WaE WaS WaSpG WaTC Wa WaPS WaSp OrCS OrP OrPR ViU OU OO ODW OCl Or OrStbM OrSaW OrU
NL 0428339 DLC OrMonO OrLgE IdB IdPI IdU MtU MtBC

Lloyd, Mabel Pearl.
Our first speech book, by M. Pearl Lloyd ... with illustrations by Zhenya Gay. New York, Newson & company ₍1942₎
xxvi, 163 p. illus. 21ᶜᵐ. (*Half-title:* Newson language arts series; general editors: F. M. Garver, W. L. Uhl)
Includes songs with music.
"Suggested reading for the teacher": p. 161–163.
PJB
PU-Penn

1. English language—Phonetics. I. Title. 42–5751
Library of Congress PE1135.L5
₍4₎ 372.4

OCU ODW PJB PU-Penn OrMonO OrU MB
NL 0428340 DLC IdPI Or OrAshS WaS MB ViU P PPPL TxU

Lloyd, Mabel Pearl.
Our second speech book; with illus. by Mary Royt. New York, Newson, 1947.
xiv, 146 p. illus. 20 cm. (Newson language arts series)

1. Voice culture—Exercises. I. Title.
PN4197.L55 372.4 47–11953

MiU PJB
NL 0428341 DLC Or OrMonO PU-Penn MB MH PU ICU PSt

Lloyd, Malcolm.
A practical treatise on mapping and lettering, including the construction of the basic alphabets and the elements of map design, by Malcolm Lloyd; a text book for students, draftsmen & engineers. Philadelphia, P. Blakiston's son & co., inc. ₍°1930₎
viii, 58 p. illus., pl., diagrs. 20 x 28ᶜᵐ.

1. Map drawing. 2. Lettering. I. Title: Mapping and lettering.
30–25589
Library of Congress GA105.L6
——— Copy 2.
Copyright A 27554 ₍3₎ ₍744₎ 526.98

NL 0428342 DLC Wa WaS NcD MiU OCl OU

Lloyd, Malcolm, b. 1874.
Law as related to civilization.
Ms.

NL 0428343 NjP

Lloyd, Malcolm. b. 1874.

Philadelphia. Bourse.
The "Philadelphia plan" for unified federal regulation of railroads; a specific plan for the concentration of the control of the interstate carriers of the United States in the hands of the federal government, presented by the Philadelphia Bourse, and a program of basic regulatory legislation presented by the Philadelphia Joint committee on the reasonable regulation of railroads ... Philadelphia, Pa., 1917.

Lloyd, Malcolm, *b.* 1874.
The principles of the law relating to corporate liability for acts of promoters. Being the Sharswood prize thesis in the Law department of the University of Pennsylvania for the year eighteen hundred and ninety-seven. By Malcolm Lloyd, jr. ... Philadelphia, G. T. Bisel, 1897.
xiii, ₍1₎, 17–92 p. 24 cm.

1. Promoters—U. S. 2. Corporation law—U. S.
5–33007 rev

NL 0428345 DLC NjP RPB

Lloyd, Malcolm, b. 1874.

Joint committee on reasonable regulation of railroads.
Reasonable regulation of railroads. A report submitted by a sub-committee to the Joint committee on reasonable regulation of railroads. Composed of representatives of ... commercial organizations of Philadelphia ... Philadelphia, March 14, 1916. ₍Philadelphia, 1916₎

784 L777W Lloyd, Marc.
What you do about your song; the songwriter's handbook. Hollywood, Lloyds, c1951.
28 p. illus.

1. Composition (Music)
2. Copyright. I. Title
3. Music, Popular (Songs, etc.)

NL 0428347 WaT

Lloyd, Margaret.
The Borzoi book of modern dance. ₍1st ed.₎ New York, A. A. Knopf, 1949.
xxiii, 356, xxvi p. illus. 25 cm.
Bibliography: p. 355–356.

1. Dancers. 2. Dancing—Hist. I. Title.
GV1785.A1L6 1949 793.32 49–7736*

Or OrP OrU Wa WaE WaS WaT DAU ScU NN KEmT PU-Penn PSt PPT Mi PP PBm CaBVa CaBViP CaBVaU IdB IdPI LN
NL 0428348 DLC CoU NbU TU NNC MB OOxM ViU OU TxU

Lloyd, Margaret.
Late harvest: poems. ₍Privately published₎ 1951. 68p. 23cm.

NL 0428349 MWelC

Lloyd, Margaret S., ed.

The Investor; a financial guide to Southern California and a weekly journal of finance, insurance and trade. Los Angeles, Cal.,

Lloyd, Marie, 1916–
Tall grows the tree. Dallas, Story Book Press ₍1953₎
68 p. 20 cm.
Verse and prose.

I. Title. *Full name:* Alice Marie Lloyd
PS3523.L66T3 811.5 53–39891

NL 0428351 DLC

Lloyd, Marietta.
A trip to Ireland, giving an account of the voyage, scenes and incidents on landing. Sketch of the round towers of Ireland. Also a graphic description of travel and sightseeing in Ireland, interspersed with historical legends and stories of her remarkable antiquities, including a romantic tour on the lakes of Killarney. By Mrs. J. J. Lloyd... Chicago: Donohue & Henneberry ₍cop. 1893₎. 193 p. front. (port.), plates. 12°.

104862A. 1. Ireland.—Description and travel, 1800–1900.
N. Y. P. L. November 7, 1923.

NL 0428352 NN IMunS IU

Lloyd, Marion.
Penny and Peter of the island, by Marion Lloyd; pictures by Agnes Tait. New York, J. Messner, inc. ₍°1941₎
₍62₎ p. col. illus. 28ᶜᵐ.
Maps on lining-papers.

1. Dominican republic—Descr. & trav. I. Tait, Agnes, 1897– illus. II. Title.
41–18852
Library of Congress PZ9.L77Pe

NL 0428353 NN WaSp Or OCl DLC

PS 3523 L657 T4 1945 Lloyd, Marion.
Through a glass, a play in three acts. ₍Hollywood, Calif.₎ c1945.
1 v. (various pagings) 29 cm.

NL 0428354 OU

Lloyd, Marjorie Lewis.
Crowns and crosses; thoughts and poems about life's crosses. Washington, Review and Herald ₍1949₎
128 p. 20 cm.
Pub. in 1944 under title: His crown—or His cross.

1. Consolation. I. Title.
BV4905.L55 1949 242 49–23481*

NL 0428355 DLC

VOLUME 337

Lloyd, Marjorie Lewis.
Crucified and risen. Washington, Review and Herald [1949]
125 p. 20 cm.

1. Atonement. I. Title.

BT265.L5 232.3 49-4010*

NL 0428356 DLC

Lloyd, Marjorie Lewis.
Faith on tiptoe. Washington, Review and Herald [1949]
127 p. 20 cm.

1. Christian life. I. Title.

BV4501.L515 248 49-3531*

NL 0428357 DLC

Lloyd, Marjorie Lewis.
Flickering desire. Washington, Review and Herald [1953]
95 p. 21 cm.

1. Youth—Religious life. I. Title.

BV4531.L47 248 54-1210 ‡

NL 0428358 DLC

Lloyd, Marjorie Lewis.
His crown, or His cross; thoughts and poems about life's crosses, by Marjorie Lewis Lloyd. [Portland, Or.] ©1944.
104 p. illus. 20ᶜᵐ.

1. Consolation. I. Title.

Library of Congress BV4905.L55 44-51417
[3] 242

NL 0428359 DLC

Lloyd, Marjorie Lewis.
Love on fire. Decorations by Iris Johnson. Washington, Review and Herald Pub. Association [1952]
127 p. illus. 18 cm.
Prose and poems.

I. Title.

PS3523.L67L6 *269 243 52-32440 ‡

NL 0428360 DLC

1926 Lloyd, Marjorie Lewis.
LL7953t Tangled threads. [Portland, Ore.] 1942.
[16]p. 16 cm.

NL 0428361 RPB

Lloyd, Marjorie Lewis.
The way back. Washington, Review and Herald Pub. Assn. [1949]
128 p. 20 cm.
Verse and prose.

I. Title.

PS3523.L67W3 244 49-24270*

NL 0428362 DLC

[Lloyd, Mary] *comp.*
Ad lucem. New York, T. Y. Crowell & co. [1889]
1 p. l., 5-149 p. 15½ᶜᵐ.
Preface signed: Mary Lloyd.
Selections in verse from various authors.

1. Consolation. I. Title.

Library of Congress PN6110.R4L55 1889 16-9874

NL 0428363 DLC MH MB OCl

Lloyd, Mary, *ed.*
Elegies: ancient and modern. With an introductory study of the history of elegiac poetry from the earliest days down to the present time. By Mary Lloyd. Volume I. Trenton, N. J., A. Brandt, 1903.
308 p. 20ᶜᵐ.
No more published?
"History of the elegy": p. 15-107. Elegies: Rig Veda—Congreve.

1. Elegiac poetry. 2. Elegiac poetry—Hist. & crit. I. Title.

Library of Congress PN1389.L5 3-31977 Revised

PU PP OO ODW MB
NL 0428364 DLC OrStbM PJB PBm PPD PPL PPM PPPD

Lloyd, Marv. ladv, tr.

Mérimée, Prosper, 1803-1870.
Carmen, by Prosper Mérimée, with an introduction by Konrad Bercovici, illustrated with lithographs in color by Jean Charlot, the translation by Lady Mary Lloyd. New York, The Limited editions club, 1941.

*EC8 Lloyd, Mary, fl.1809.
L7777 Brighton. A poem. Descriptive of the place and
809b parts adjacent. And other poems. By Mary Lloyd.
London:Printed for the author.Sold by J. Harding,36,St.James's-street;and by all the booksellers at Brighton,Worthing and Eastborne. 1809.
2p.l.,iii,88,12p. front.,plate. 19cm.,in case 20cm.
Contemporary blue boards; in cloth case.
In BM copy the "List of subscribers" (here 12p. at end) is apparently bound at front.

NL 0428366 MH NjP CtY IU ViU

WB **Lloyd, Mary Anne.**
M559t Susanna Meredith: a record of a vigorous life. London, Hodder and Stoughton, 1903.
viii, 220 p. 19 cm..
Facsimile of the last letter written by Mrs. Meredith 3 pages at end of book.

NL 0428367 NcGU

Lloyd, Mary (Clarke) 1681-1749.
Works by this author printed in America before 1801 are available in this library in the Readex Microprint edition of Early American Imprints published by the American Antiquarian Society.
This collection is arranged according to the numbers in Charles Evans' American Bibliography.

NL 0428368 DLC

Lloyd, Mary (Clarke) 1681-1749.
Meditations on Divine Subjects... with an account of her life, and character, by E. Pemberton. Boston, 1745.
4 to.

NL 0428369 MHi

Lloyd, Mary (Clarke) 1681-1749.
Meditations on divine subjects, by Mrs. Mary Lloyd. To which is prefixed an account of her life and character by E. Pemberton. New York, Printed and sold by J. Parker, 1750.

NL 0428370 DLC PPL MB NN

Lloyd, Mary(Clarke) 1681-1749.
Meditations on divine subjects. To which is prefix'd an account of her life and character by Rev. Ebenezer Pemberton. New-York: Printed and sold by J. Parker ... 1750.
Microcard edition (3 cards).
Evans 6530.

1. Lloyd, Mary Clarke. I. Pemberton, Ebenezer, 1704-1777. II. Title.

NL 0428371 ViU

LLOYD,Mrs.Mary [(Clarke)] 1681-1749.
Meditations on divine subjects ; to which is prefixed An account of her life and character,by E.Pemberton. New York,printed; New-London,reprinted,by S.Green,1802.

NL 0428372 CtHi MWA NSm

PR Lloyd, Mary E
6023 Men I have proposed to. Sydney, Edwards,
L776me Dunlop, 1915.
159 p.

NL 0428373 CLU

PR Lloyd, Mary E
6023 A mock widow [by] M. E. Lloyd. Melbourne,
L776m Robertson & Mullens [1938]
324 p.
Author's autographed presentation copy to Mr. Judd.

NL 0428374 CLU IaU TxU

Lloyd, Mary Edna.
Jesus, the children's friend. Pictures by Grace Paull. New York, Abingdon Press, ©1955.
unpaged. illus. 21 cm.

1. Jesus Christ—Fiction. I. Title.

PZ7.L7783Je 55-14816 ‡

NL 0428375 DLC Or WaSp PPEB OO

VOLUME 337

Lloyd, Mary Edna.
Jesus, the little new baby. Pictures by Grace Paull. New York, Abingdon-Cokesbury Press, °1951.
unpaged. illus. 21 cm.

1. Jesus Christ—Nativity—Juvenile literature. I. Title.
BT315.L57 232.921 51-12137 ‡

NL 0428376 DLC Or OrU WaS WaSp IEG

Lloyd, Mary Edna
Nursery children in the church, by Mary Edna Lloyd ... Nashville, Dallas [etc., etc.] Methodist publishing house [1942]
88 p. illus. 20½cm.
"Library for workers with nursery children": p. 87-88.

NL 0428377 NcD OkEG

Lloyd, Mary Edna.
Nursery class teaching; religious guidance [by] Mary Edna Lloyd; edited by Lucius H. Bugbee. New York, Cincinnati [etc.] The Methodist book concern [°1934]
192 p. 21ᶜᵐ.
Music: p. 167-178.

1. Sunday-schools. I. Bugbee, Lucius Hatfield, 1874- ed. II. Title.
Library of Congress BV1540.L5 34-29171
——— Copy 2.
Copyright A 73847 [2] 268.432

NL 0428378 DLC

Lloyd, Mary Edna.

Methodist Episcopal church. *Board of education.*
Planning for the nursery child in the church school. Chicago, Ill., Dept. of religious education of children, Division of religious education in the local church, Board of education, Methodist Episcopal church [°1935]

BV1540 .L8 Lloyd, Mary Edna.
Religious nurture in nursery class and home, by Mary Edna Lloyd. Nashville, Tenn., Graded press [c1942]
236 p. 22cm.
Contains music.
Bibliography: p.234-236.

1. Sunday-schools. 2. Nursery schools.

NL 0428380 ICU CLamB N PJB NNUT NcD KyLxCB KyU IEG

Lloyd, Mary Hester.
The Celtic otherworld; its influence upon mediaeval literature... 1929.
Thesis - Ohio state university.

NL 0428381 OU

Lloyd, Mary Lou.
Pure water for Honolulu

see under Honolulu. Board of Water Supply.

Lloyd, Mary Tash.
Red lilies and other poems, by Mary Tash Lloyd. Philadelphia, Pa., Burns press [°1931]
5 p. l., 3-23 p. 18½ᶜᵐ.

I. Title.
Library of Congress PS3523.L7R4 1931 31-15664
——— Copy 2.
Copyright A 38918 [2] 811.5

NL 0428383 DLC

Lloyd, Mary von Fallot, joint author.

PZ3 .L7719 Go

Lloyd, Arthur, 1852-1911.
The gold demon, by Ozaki Kōyō; re-written in English by A. and M. Lloyd. Tokyo, Seibundo, 1917.

Lloyd, Mary von Fallot, tr.

PL898 .T57N3

[**Tokutomi, Kenjiro**] 1868-1927.
Nature and man, by Tokutomi Roka [*pseud.*] Translated by Arthur Lloyd, M. von Fallot, and H. Ono. Tokyo, Kogakukwan [1913]

Lloyd, Merle G
An objective method for forecasting radiation fog at Salt Lake City Airport

see under

U.S. Weather Bureau.

Lloyd, Michael, 1922-
Apulian summer, and other episodes. London, Heinemann [1953]
200 p. 21 cm.

1. Apulia—Descr. & trav. I. Title.
DG975.A65L7 914.575 53-34141 ‡

NL 0428387 DLC PSt MH

Lloyd, Minnie, joint author.

D21 .S63

Smith, Emma Peters.
World history, the struggle for civilization, by Emma Peters Smith, David Saville Muzzey and Minnie Lloyd. Boston, New York [etc.] Ginn and company [1946]

Lloyd, Morgan, *o Wynedd*
see
Llwyd, Morgan, 1619-1659.

Lloyd, Morgan, 1822-1893, joint author.

Cox, Edward William, 1809-1879.
The law and practice of the County courts in England and Wales; comprising the rules, instructions, forms, and all cases decided in the superior courts and in the County courts. 4th ed., containing the alterations made by the Extension act, the cases up to the present time, the new scale of fees, the new rules and orders, and the Absconding debtors act. By Edward W. Cox and Morgan Lloyd ... London, J. Crockford, 1851.

Lloyd, Morgan, 1822-1893.
A treatise on the law of prohibition, containing a concise view of the principles on which that writ is granted; and also the practice relating to the same. Together with an appendix, containing a collection of points decided on applications for prohibitions to the new County courts. By Morgan Lloyd ... London, W. Benning & co., 1849.
xv, 127 p. 19ᶜᵐ.
"Appendix (B.) Ancient precedents of pleadings, &c., in prohibition, extracted from Lilly's Entries": p. 105-120.
1. Prohibition (Writ)—Gt. Brit. 2. Gt. Brit. County courts. I. Lilly, John.
33-17842

NL 0428391 DLC PU-L

Lloyd, Morgan David Idwal.
... Studien zu Heinrich von Beringens schachgedicht, von M. D. I. Lloyd ... Berlin, E. Ebering, 1930.
48 p. 24ᶜᵐ. (Germanische studien ... hft. 83)

1. Heinrich von Beringen, 12th cent. 2. Chess.
Library of Congress PT1537.H3L6 30-29864
[2] 831.2

CtY CoU MU CLSU NcD OCl
NL 0428392 DLC CaBVaU MH KU CU OU GU NcU TxU MiU

Lloyd, Montague.
Through England's waterways, by Montague & Ann Lloyd. London, Imray, Laurie, Norie & Wilson [1948]
117 p. plates, col. map (inserted) 23 cm.

1. England—Descr. & trav. 2. Canals—England. 3. Rivers—England. I. Lloyd, Ann, joint author. II. Title.
DA630.L56 914.2 49-26510*

NL 0428393 DLC

Lloyd, Morris Van Voorhees, 1921-
A comparison of critical fusion frequencies for different areas in the fovea and periphery. 1951.
346-357 p. tables. 23cm.
Thesis, Columbia university.
"Reprinted from the American journal of psychology, LXV, 1952."
Bibliographical footnotes.

NL 0428394 NNC

Lloyd, Morton Githens, 1874-
... An apparatus for determination of the form of a wave of magnetic flux, by M. G. Lloyd ... and J. V. S. Fisher ... ⟨November 15, 1907⟩ ... Washington, Govt. print. off., 1908.
1 p. l., p. 467-476. pl., diagrs. 25½ᶜᵐ. (Reprint no. 87, from Bulletin of the Bureau of standards. v. 4, no. 4)
At head of title: Department of commerce and labor. Bureau of standards. S. W. Stratton, director.
Running title: Wave form of magnetic flux.
1. Electric apparatus and appliances. I. U. S. Bureau of standards. Scientific papers, no. 87. II. Fisher, James V. S., joint author. ...
Library of Congress QC543.L84 8-35654

NL 0428395 DLC OO OCl NN

Lloyd, Morton Githens, 1874-
... Dependence of magnetic hysteresis upon wave form, by Morton G. Lloyd ... ⟨October 10, 1908⟩ ... Washington, Govt. print. off., 1909.
1 p. l., 381-411 p. diagrs. (1 fold.) 25½ᶜᵐ. (Reprint no. 106 from Bulletin of the Bureau of standards, vol. 5, no. 3)
At head of title: Department of commerce and labor. Bureau of standards. S. W. Stratton, director.

1. Hysteresis. I. U. S. National bureau of standards. Scientific papers no. 106.
Library of Congress QC761.L72 9-35506

NL 0428396 DLC OrU OrCS NN OO OCl

VOLUME 337

Lloyd, Morton Githens, 1874- joint author.

Rosa, Edward Bennett, 1861–1921.
.. The determination of the ratio of transformation and of the phase relations in transformers, by E. B. Rosa ... and M. G. Lloyd ... <February 25, 1909> ... Washington, Govt. print. off., 1909.

Lloyd, Morton Githens, 1874–
... Effect of phase of harmonics upon acoustic quality. By M. G. Lloyd ... and P. G. Agnew ... <June 30, 1909> ... Washington, Govt. print. off., 1910.

1 p. l., p. 255–263. $25\frac{1}{2}^{cm}$. (Reprint no. 127, from Bulletin of the Bureau of standards, v. 6, no. 2)

At head of title: Department of commerce and labor. Bureau of standards. S. W. Stratton, director.

1. Sound. I. Agnew, Paul G., joint author. II. U. S. Bureau of standards. Scientific papers. no. 127. III. Title.

Library of Congress QC243.L7 10—35159

NL 0428398 DLC OrU MiU OO OCl NN

Lloyd, Morton Githens, 1874–
Effect of wave form upon the iron losses in transformers, by Morton G. Lloyd ... <October 31, 1907> ... Washington, Govt. print. off., 1908.

1 p. l., p. 477–510. tables, diagrs. $25\frac{1}{2}^{cm}$. (Reprint no. 88, from Bulletin of the Bureau of standards, v. 4, no. 4)

At head of title: Department of commerce and labor. Bureau of standards. S. W. Stratton, director.

1. Electric transformers. I. U. S. Bureau of standards. Scientific papers, no. 88.

Library of Congress TK2551.L6 8—35637

NL 0428399 DLC OrU OO OCl NN

Lloyd, Morton Githens, 1874–
... Errors in magnetic testing with ring specimens, by Morton G. Lloyd ... <August 19, 1908> ... Washington, Govt. print. off., 1909.

1 p. l., p. 435–452. diagrs. $25\frac{1}{2}^{cm}$. (Reprint no. 108, from Bulletin of the Bureau of standards, v. 5, no. 3)

At head of title: Department of commerce and labor. Bureau of standards. S. W. Stratton, director.

1. Magnetism. I. U. S. Bureau of standards. Scientific papers, no. 108.

Library of Congress QC761.L75 9—35477

NL 0428400 DLC NN OCl

Lloyd, Morton Githens, 1874-
...Errors in magnetic testing with ring specimens Washington, 1909 [i.e. 1914]

QC761
L75
1914

NL 0428401 DLC

Lloyd, Morton Githens, 1874–
.... Function of a periodic variable given by the steady reading of an instrument; with a note on the use of the capillary electrometer with alternating voltages, by Morton G. Lloyd ... <December 30, 1907> Washington, Govt. print. off., 1908.

1 p. l., p. 525–532. diagrs. $25\frac{1}{2}^{cm}$. (Reprint no. 90, from Bulletin of the Bureau of standards, v. 4, no. 4)

At head of title: Department of commerce and labor. Bureau of standards. S. W. Stratton, director.

1. Electric apparatus and appliances. 2. Electrometer. I. U. S. Bureau of standards. Reprint no. 90.

Library of Congress QC543.L88 8—35655

NL 0428402 DLC OO OCl NN

Lloyd, Morton Githens, 1874- joint author.

Rosa, Edward Bennett, 1861–1921.
... Influence of wave form on the rate of integrating induction wattmeters, by E. B. Rosa ... M. G. Lloyd ... and C. E. Reid ... Washington, Govt. print. off., 1905.

Lloyd, Morton Githens, 1874–1941.

QC100
.U565
no. 2

U. S. *National bureau of standards.*
... National safety code for the protection of the heads and eyes of industrial workers. 1st ed., December, 1920 ... Washington, Govt. print. off., 1921.

Lloyd, Morton Githens, 1874–
[Papers on physics, chiefly electricity and magnetism.] Washington, Gov't Print. Off., 1908–1910.

7 pamphlets in 1 vol. tables, diagrs. 26^{cm}.

Reprinted from the Bulletin of the Bureau of Standards, U. S. Department of Commerce and Labor.

Contents.—An apparatus for determination of the form of a wave of magnetic flux, by M. G. Lloyd and J. V. S. Fisher. [2], 467–476 p. 1 pl.—Function of a periodic variable given by the steady reading of an instrument; with a note on the use of the capillary electrometer with alternating voltages. 1908. [2], 525–532 p.—Dependence of magnetic hysteresis upon wave form. 1909. [2], 381–411 p. 1 fold. diagr.—Errors in magnetic testing with ring specimens 1909. [2], 435–452 p.—The testing of transformer steel, by M. G. Lloyd, and J. V. S. Fisher. 1909. [2], 453–482 p.—The determination of the ratio of transformation and of the phase relations in transformers, by E. B. Rosa, and M. G. Lloyd. 1909. [2], 30 p.—Effect of phase of harmonics upon acoustic quality, by M. G. Lloyd and P. G. Agnew. 1910. [2], 255–263 p.

NL 0428405 ICJ

Lloyd, Morton Githens, 1874–
... The regulation of potential transformers and magnetizing current. By M. G. Lloyd ... and P. G. Agnew ... <June 21, 1909> ... Washington, Govt. print. off., 1910.

1 p. l., p. 273–280. diagr. $25\frac{1}{2}^{cm}$. (Reprint no. 129, from Bulletin of the Bureau of standards, v. 6, no. 2)

At head of title: Department of commerce and labor. Bureau of standards. S. W. Stratton, director.

1. Electric transformers. I. Agnew, Paul G., joint author. II. U. S. Bureau of standards. Reprint no. 129. III. Title.

Library of Congress TK2551.L7 10—35162

NL 0428406 DLC OO OCl NN

Lloyd, Morton Githens, 1874–
... The testing of transformer steel, by M. G. Lloyd ... and J. V. S. Fisher ... <January 29, 1909> ... Washington, Govt. print. off., 1909.

1 p. l., p. 453–482. illus. $25\frac{1}{2}^{cm}$. (Reprint no. 109 from Bulletin of the Bureau of standards, v. 5, no. 4)

At head of title: Department of commerce and labor. Bureau of standards. S. W. Stratton, director.

1. Magnetism. I. Fisher, James V. S. II. U. S. Bureau of standards Reprint no. 109.

Library of Congress QC761.L77 9—35690

NL 0428407 DLC OrU OCl OO NN

Lloyd, Morton Githens, 1874-
The testing of transformer steel,... Washington, 1909 [i.e. 1914]

QC761
.D77
1914

NL 0428408 DLC

Lloyd, Morton Githens, 1874 -
The transversal thermomagnetic effect in bismuth ... Philadelphia, Avil printing co., 1900.

23 p. 8°.

Inaug.-diss.—University of Pennsylvania.

1-13221

NL 0428409 DLC NjP PPAmP PU MH ICJ

LLOYD, Nathaniel, 1867 - 1933.
Aspects of houses in relation to wind, rainfall and sunshine. [London, 1924.]

1.8°. Diagrs.
Journal of the Royal Institute of British Architects, vol. XXXI, 3d ser., no.19, 20 Sept. 1924, pp.633-[644].

NL 0428410 MH

Lloyd, Nathaniel, 1867–1933.
Building craftsmanship in brick and tile and in stone plates, by Nathaniel Lloyd ... Cambridge [Eng.] The University press, 1929.

5 p. l., 90, [1] p. illus. (incl. plans) 29 cm.

1. Building, Brick. 2. Tile construction. 3. Architecture, Domestic.

NA4120.L73 29—20802

NcGU
NL 0428411 DLC OCl WaS CtY PP ViU NN MB OU CU-S

Lloyd, Nathaniel, 1867–1933.
Garden craftsmanship in yew and box, by Nathaniel Lloyd ... London, E. Benn, limited, 1925.

36 p., 1 l. 54 p. $25\frac{1}{2}^{cm}$.

1. Box [(Shrub)] 2. Topiary work. 3. Yew. I. Title.

Agr 26—636

U. S. Dept. of agr. Library for Library of Congress 98L77 [a43e1]

NL 0428412 DNAL OrP CU PP MiU MB ViU MBH OCl

Lloyd, Nathaniel, 1867–1933.
A history of English brickwork with examples and notes of the architectural use and manipulation of brick from mediaeval times to the end of the Georgian period. By Nathaniel Lloyd ... with an introduction by Sir Edwin L. Lutyens, R. A. London, H. G. Montgomery; New York, W. Helburn, inc., 1925.

xv, 397 p., 398–440 numb. l., 441–449 p., 1 l. incl. plates (part fold.) $31\frac{1}{2}$ cm.

1. Bricks. 2. Building, Brick. 3. Architecture—Gt. Brit. I. Title: Brickwork, English.

NA4120.L75 26—10975

NcD OCIW IEN
NL 0428413 DLC OrP PP PU-FA NN MB MU NjP NIC ViU

1720.942
L777h
1928
Arch
Lib'y

Lloyd, Nathaniel, 1867-1933.
A history of English brickwork with examples and notes of the architectural use and manipulation of brick from mediaeval times to the end of the Georgian period. By Nathaniel Lloyd ... with an introduction by Sir Edwin L. Lutyens, R.A. London, H.G. Montgomery; New York, W. Helburn, inc., 1928.
xv,[1],397p.,398-440 numb.*l.*,441-449p.,1*l*. incl. plates (part fold.) $31\frac{1}{2}$cm.

1. Bricks. 2. Building, Brick. 3. Architecture - Gt. Brit.

NL 0428414 TxU WaS OrCS ViU NNC

Lloyd, Nathaniel, 1867–1933.
A history of English brickwork, with examples and notes of the architectural use and manipulation of brick from mediaeval times to the end of the Georgian period, by Nathaniel Lloyd ... with a foreword by Sir Edwin L. Lutyens, R. A. New and abridged ed., with preface, by Leslie Mansfield. London, H. G. Montgomery [1935]

xiv, 77 p. incl. front. (facsim.) CXL pl. on 70 l. 29 x 22cm.

1. Bricks. 2. Building, Brick. 3. Architecture—Gt. Brit. I. Mansfield, Leslie, ed. II. Title: Brickwork, English.

37-3319

Library of Congress NA4120.L76 [3] 691.3

NL 0428414-1 DLC PHC

VOLUME 337

NA 7328 L6 Lloyd, Nathaniel, 1867-1933.
A history of the English house from primitive times to the Victorian period. London, Architectural Press[1931]

487 p. illus.

1. Architecture, Domestic--England. 2. Architecture--Details.

NL 0428415 KMK KyLx NcU

Lloyd, Nathaniel, 1867–
A history of the English house from primitive times to the Victorian period, by Nathaniel Lloyd ... London, The Architectural press; New York, W. Helburn, inc., 1931.
xvii, 487 p. incl. illus., plates, plans, diagrs. 32½cm.

1. Architecture, Domestic—England. 2. Architecture—Details. I. Title.

Library of Congress NA7328.L6 32-5921 [5] 728.0942

OrP WaS CaBVaU OrCS OrU
MiU OU ViU PPT MB MH NN PBm PP PU-FA AAP WaU NcD
NL 0428416 DLC ScCleA FMU LU MiDA NIC NcRS OO OCl

Lloyd, Nathaniel, 1867-1933.
A history of the English house from primitive times to the Victorian period. [New ed.] London, Architectural Press [1949]
ix, 487 p. illus. 33 cm.

1. Architecture, Domestic—England. 2. Architecture—Details.

NA7328.L6 1949 728 49-48113*

NL 0428417 DLC Or WaT NcU MiEM

1728 L777h 1949r Arch Lib'y Lloyd, Nathaniel, 1867-1933.
A history of the English house from primitive times to the Victorian period. [New ed.] London, Architectural Press [1951]
ix, 487p. illus. 33cm.

"Second impression [New ed.] 1949. Third impression, 1951."

1. Architecture, Domestic - England. 2. Architecture - Details.

NL 0428418 TxU NBC CtY GU IU

Lloyd, Nelson McAllister, 1873–
The chronic loafer, by Nelson Lloyd. New York, J. F. Taylor & company, 1900.
254 p. 20cm.

I. Title.

Library of Congress PZ3.L777C 0-2110 Revised

NL 0428419 DLC ViU PPGi PPL

PZ3 .L777 C **Lloyd, Nelson McAllister,** 1873-
The chronic loafer. [2d ed.] New York, J. F. Taylor, 1900.
254 p. 21 cm.

NL 0428420 MB

Lloyd, Nelson McAllister, 1873–
David Malcolm, by Nelson Lloyd. New York, C. Scribner's sons, 1913.
3 p. l., 413 p. 19½cm. $1.35

I. Title.

Library of Congress PZ3.L777Da 13-18074

NL 0428421 DLC PPL OCl NN

Lloyd, Nelson McAllister, 1873–
A drone and a dreamer, by Nelson Lloyd ... New York, J. F. Taylor & company, 1901.
259 p. incl. front. plates. 20cm.

I. Title.

Library of Congress PZ3.L777D 1-18531 Revised

NL 0428422 DLC OrU ViU PPL PPM OCl

Lloyd, Nelson McAllister, 1873–1933.
... How we went to war, by Nelson Lloyd ... New York, C. Scribner's sons, 1918.
4 p. l., 253 p. front., plates. 19½cm. (America in the war. [III])

1. European war, 1914–1918—U. S. I. Title.

Library of Congress D570.A2A8 III 18—22355

OrStbM
NL 0428423 DLC NBuC MsU OKentU PP PV OCl WaWW

Lloyd, Nelson McAllister, 1873-
... How we went to war, by Nelson Lloyd ... New York, C. Scribner's sons, 1919.
4 p. l., 253 p. front., plates. 19½cm. (America in the war. [III])

1. European war, 1914-1918--U.S. I. Title. II. Ser.

NL 0428424 ViU MB ICarbS CoU NcRS

Lloyd, Nelson [McAllister] 1873–
Mrs. Radigan; her biography, with that of Miss Pearl Veal, and the memoirs of J. Madison Mudison, by Nelson Lloyd ... New York, C. Scribner's sons, 1905.
vii, 344 p. 18cm.

Library of Congress Copyright 5-29982

NL 0428425 DLC NN PPL NjP OCl

Lloyd, Nelson McAllister, 1873-
The retreat from Gettysburg, by Nelson Lloyd. (12) p. 23 cm.

NL 0428426 DNW

Lloyd, Nelson McAllister, 1873–
The Robberies company, ltd., by Nelson Lloyd. New York, C. Scribner's sons, 1906.
v, 404 p. front. 19½cm.

Library of Congress PZ3.L777R 6-34042

NL 0428427 DLC WaU-L ViU PPL PPYH NjP

Lloyd, Nelson McAllister, 1873–
Six stars [stories] by Nelson Lloyd ... New York, C. Scribner's sons, 1906.
4 p. l., 315 p. front., 7 pl. 19½cm.

Library of Congress PZ3.L777Si 6-11676

NL 0428428 DLC PPL MB

Lloyd, Nelson McAllister, 1873–
The soldier of the valley, by Nelson Lloyd; illustrated by A. B. Frost. New York, C. Scribner's sons, 1904.
vi p., 1 l., 335 p. incl. front., illus., plates. 19½cm.

Library of Congress PZ3.L777So 4-25389

NL 0428429 DLC WaS PPL PHatU PPGi NN

PR 6023 .L446D5x Lloyd, Nevil.
Dicing with death. Illus. by George Lane. London, Metchim & son [1936]
118 p. illus. 20 cm.

NL 0428430 OKentU

Lloyd, Nicolas, 1630–1680.
Catalogus librorum bibliothecæ Reverendi Nicolai Lloydii ... Horum auctio habebitur Londini, quarto die julii, in ædibus Joannis Dunmore ... [Londini] 1681.
2 p. l., 55 p. 23 x 18cm.

1. Bibliography—Rare books. I. Dunmore, John, auctioneer.

Library of Congress Z997.L798 6-18156

NL 0428431 DLC NNGr

Lloyd, Nicolas, 1630-1680.

DE5 .E7 1671 Rare Bk Coll **Estienne, Charles,** 1504-1564. FOR OTHER EDITIONS SEE MAIN ENTRY
Dictionarium historicum, geographicum, poeticum, authore Carolo Stephano, gentium, hominum, deorum gentilium, regionum, locorum ... antiqua recentioraque ad sacras, & profanas historias, poetarumque fabulas intelligendas necessaria nomina, quo decet ordine complectens. Ed. novissima ... Recensuit, supplevit, locisque penè infinitis emaculavit Nicolavs Lloydivs ... Oxonii, excudebat, G. H. & G. D. sumptibus Johan. Williams, Georg. VVest, Amos Curteyne & Johan. Crosley, 1671.

LLOYD, NORA.
The young May moon. London, New York, Nelson [1935] 310 p. 19cm. (Nelson novels)

Novel.

NL 0428433 NN

M1627 .B7F5 **Lloyd, Norman,** 1909– arr.
Boni, Margaret Bradford, 1893– *ed.*
Fireside book of folk songs, selected and ed. by Margaret Bradford Boni, arr. for the piano by Norman Lloyd; illus. by Alice and Martin Provensen. [New York] Simon and Schuster [1947]

VOLUME 337

Lloyd, Norman, 1909- *arr.*
The new golden song book; 74 nursery, cradle, folk and patriotic songs, hymns, carols, rounds, and singing games. Pictures by Mary Blair. New York, Simon and Schuster ⌊1955⌋
96 p. col. illus. 33 cm. (A Giant golden book, 708)
For piano, with interlinear words.

1. Nursery schools—Music. 2. Children's songs. 3. Games with music. I. Title.
M1990.L76N4 M 55-1006

NL 0428435 TxU CaBVa Or WaS CLSU OOxM MB PP DLC

Lloyd, *Mrs.* Olivia Moreland.
Around the world on an army transport, by Olivia Moreland Lloyd. ⌊Phoenix, Ariz., °1927⌋
66 p. 21cm.

1. Voyages around the world. I. Title.
Library of Congress G440.L8 28-5006

NL 0428436 DLC

Lloyd, Oriole Emerson, 1884-1907.
L7933p Harris Coll. Oriole Emerson Lloyd; her poems, prose-bits, and appreciations. Ed. by her father J. William Lloyd. Westwood, Mass., Ariel Press [1907?]
82p. plate, ports. 23cm.
Harris copy unbound.

NL 0428437 RPB

Lloyd, Orson Gunnell, 1884- joint author.
⌊Moore, Harry Elias⌋ 1902-
... The back-to-the-land movement in southern Indiana. Lafayette, Ind., Purdue university, Agricultural experiment station, 1936.

Lloyd, Orson Gunnell, 1884- joint author.
Gray, Lewis Cecil, 1881-
... Farm land values in Iowa. By L. C. Gray ... and O. G. Lloyd ... Washington, Govt. print. off., 1920.

Lloyd, Orson Gunnell, 1884 -
Farm leases in Iowa. Ames, 1915. 2 p.l., 157-206 p. illus. 8°. (Iowa. Agricultural Experiment Station. Bull. 159.)

1. Farms, U.S.: Ia.
N. Y. P. L. May 9, 1916.

NL 0428440 NN

Lloyd, Orson Gunnell, 1883 -
Farm leases in Iowa ⌊by O. G. Lloyd⌋. Ames ⌊1915⌋. 30 p. illus. 8°. (Iowa. Agricultural Experiment Station. Bull. no. 159 abridged.)

1. Farms, U. S.: Ia. 2. Leases, U. S.: Ia. 3. Series.
N. Y. P. L. July 7, 1917.

NL 0428441 NN

S59 .E3 no. 488
Lloyd, Orson Gunnell, 1884- joint author.
⌊Quackenbush, Gerald Glenn⌋ 1916-
... Farm tenure in Indiana by type-of-farming areas ... Lafayette, Ind., Purdue university, Agricultural experiment station, 1943.

⌊Lloyd, Orson Gunnell⌋ 1884-
... Feeding and marketing of early spring pigs on Indiana farms ... ⌊By O. G. Lloyd and G. E. Young⌋ Lafayette, Ind., 1927.
14 p. illus., tables, diagrs. 22½cm. (Indiana. Agricultural experiment station. Bulletin no. 310)
On cover: Purdue university.
Purdue university and Bureau of agricultural economics, U. S. Dept. of agriculture, cooperating.

1. Swine. I. Young, Gladwin Ellis, 1900- joint author. II. U. S. Dept. of agriculture. Bureau of agricultural economics. III. Title.
Title from Purdue Univ. Printed by L. C. A27-455

NL 0428443 InLP

Lloyd, Orson Gunnell, 1884- joint author.
⌊Wilcox, Walter William⌋ 1904-
... The human factor in the management of Indiana farms. ⌊By W. W. Wilcox and O. G. Lloyd⌋ Lafayette, Ind., Purdue university, Agricultural experiment station, 1932.

Lloyd, Orson Gunnell, 1884-
Laborer-operator relationships on Indiana farms ⌊by O. G. Lloyd and Jean C. Evans⌋ Lafayette ⌊1950⌋
38 p. illus. 23 cm. (Indiana. Agricultural Experiment Station ⌊Lafayette⌋ Station bulletin 546)

1. Agricultural laborers—Indiana. I. Evans, Jean C., joint author. II. Title. (Series: Indiana. Agricultural Experiment Station, Lafayette. Bulletin 546)
S59.E3 no. 546 331.183 A 50-9453
Purdue Univ. Library for Library of Congress ⌊3⌋†

NL 0428445 DLC InLP

Lloyd, Orson Gunnell, 1884- joint author.
⌊Smith, Fernel Van⌋ 1906-
... Part-time farming in Indiana. Lafayette, Ind., Purdue university, Agricultural experiment station, 1936.

⌊**Lloyd, Orson Gunnell**⌋ 1884-
... Relation of farm power and farm organization in central Indiana. ⌊By O. G. Lloyd and L. G. Hobson⌋ Lafayette, Ind., 1929.
37 p. illus. 22½cm. (Indiana. Agricultural experiment station. Bulletin no. 332)
On cover: Purdue university.

1. Traction-engines. 2. Agriculture—Indiana. I. Hobson, Leo Guy, 1897- joint author. II. Title. III. Title: Farm power. IV. Title: Farm organization in central Indiana.
A 30-577
[S59.E3 no. 332]
Title from Purdue Univ. Printed by L. C.

NL 0428447 InLP

⌊**Lloyd, Orson Gunnell**⌋ 1884-
... Principal methods of share renting and compensation for unexhausted improvements in four type-of-farming areas in Indiana. Lafayette, Ind., Purdue university, Agricultural experiment station, 1942.
24 p. incl. illus., tables, diagrs. 22½cm. (Indiana. Agricultural experiment station. Bulletin no. 464)
By O. G. Lloyd, H. S. Morine, jr., and J. R. Hays. *cf.* p. 3.

1. Landlord and tenant—Indiana. I. Morine, Harold S., 1918- joint author. II. Hays, John Robert, 1909- joint author. III. Title. IV. Title: Share renting and compensation for unexhausted improvements in four type-of-farming areas in Indiana.
A 42-2028
Purdue univ. Library for Library of Congress [S59.E3 no. 464]
⌊3⌋ (630.72)

NL 0428448 InLP

Lloyd, Oscar.
A poor man singing, by Oscar Lloyd ... ⌊London⌋ G. Gill and sons ⌊1943⌋
24 p. 19½cm.
Poems.

I. Title.
Library of Congress PR6023.L49P6 44-33217

NL 0428449 DLC

Lloyd, Owen, fl. 1662.
Het gezigt van den panther . . . , zo als het op den 28. van Wintermaand 1653 . . . vertoond wierdt aan O. L. . . . Zynde 't selve in Engeland gedrukt in 1662. Waar by nu gevoegd is zyne brief aan John Rogers, . . . Uyt het Engelsch vertaald. *n. p.*, 1688. 18 pp. 4°.

NL 0428450 NN

[Lloyd, Owen, fl.1662]
*fEC65 L7779 662p The panther-prophecy or, A premonition to all people of sad calamities and miseries like to befal these islands. To which is added, an astrological discourse concerning that strange apparition of an army of horse seen in Wales near Mongomry, December the 20th. 1661. ...
[London]Printed[!] in the year,1662.
f°. 2p.l.,7p. 29cm.,in folder 35.5cm.
A translation into Dutch is not anonymous.
Fifth-monarchy tract.

NL 0428451 MH DFo

Lloyd, P.
Gas turbine development, B.M.W., Junkers, Daimler Benz. Reported by S/Ldr. P.Lloyd ... Jet propulsion. ⌊London⌋ Combined intelligence objectives sub-committee, G-2 division, SHAEF (rear) ⌊1945?⌋
30 p.incl.plans (part fold.) (CIOS target nos. 5/13/, 5/57/, 5/64/, 5/180/, 26/79/)
On cover: Item no. 5 & 26; File no. XXIV-6.
Typewritten copy.

NL 0428452 MH-PA

Lloyd, Paul T., joint author.
Long, Frederick A.
The use of the Roentgen ray in the study of vertebral mechanics with special reference to its adaptability in osteopathic procedure ... by Frederick A. Long ... and Paul T. Lloyd ... ⌊Philadelphia, °1938⌋

Lloyd, Peirson, d. 1781.
A sermon preached in Lambeth-chapel, at the consecration of ... John, lord bishop of Lincoln; and Thomas, lord bishop of Bristol; on Monday, December 28,1761 ... London,Printed for B.Barker,1762.
24p. 22cm.
[Sermons and miscellaneous, 1758]

1. Newton, Thomas, bp.of Bristol,1704-1782.
2.Green,John,bp.of Lincoln,1706?-1779.

NL 0428454 CtY

VOLUME 337

Lloyd, Peirson, d.1781.
Sermons on several occasions, preached in Westminster-abbey, and St.Margaret's, Westminster. By Peirson Lloyd, M.A., second master of Westminster-school. London, Printed for the author, 1765.
x p., 2l., 379p. 23½cm.
Imperfect copy: p.[i]-ii wanting.

NL 0428455 MoU CtY MH IU

394 L79m Lloyd, Pemberton
The months of the year. London, Collingridge [1909]
307p. front.,plates. O.

NL 0428456 IaU InU CtY

Lloyd, Percy Robert, tr.

Pons, Amilda A.
The holocaust, Italy's struggle with the Hapsburg, by A. A. Pons; tr. by P. R. Lloyd ... London, J. Murray, 1919.

Lloyd, Percy Robert, tr.

Yongden, Albert Arthur.
Mipam, the lama of the five wisdoms, a Tibetan novel by lama Yongden. London, John Lane [1938]

Lloyd, Percy Thomas, 1881–
Research in the office, by P. T. Lloyd ... London, Gee & co. limited, 1935.
4 p. l., 132 p. illus., diagrs., forms. 25cm.

1. Office management. 2. Office supplies. I. Title.
A 37-130
Illinois. Univ. Library for Library of Congress [2]

NL 0428459 IU NcGU OCl NN

Lloyd, Percy Thomas, 1881–
The technique of efficient office methods, by P. T. Lloyd ... with a foreword by Sir Henry Bunbury ... London, Gee & co., ltd., 1930.
4 p. l., 163 p. incl. illus., diagrs., forms. 25cm.
"Notes on book publishers, suppliers of office equipment, &c.": p. 149-157.

1. Office management. 2. Office supplies. I. Title.
31-1026
Library of Congress HF5547.L6 [5] 651

NL 0428460 DLC CtY MiU

Lloyd, Peter.
Theory of industrial gas heating, by Peter Lloyd ... with a foreword by Stephen Lacey ... London, W. King, ltd. [1933]
x, 104 p. illus., diagrs. 22cm.
Bibliography: p. 101.

1. Gas as fuel. 2. Gas—Heating and cooking. I. Title: Industrial gas heating. II. Title: Gas heating.
34-23259
Library of Congress TP345.L5 [2] 662.6

NL 0428461 DLC MB NN NNC

Lloyd, Peter.
Theory of industrial gas heating, by Peter Lloyd ... With a foreword by Stephen Lacey ... New and rev. ed. London, W. King, ltd. [1938]
x, 171 p. tables, diagrs. 22cm.
Bibliography: p. 167-168.

1. Gas as fuel. 2. Gas—Heating and cooking. I. Title: Industrial gas heating. II. Title: Gas heating.
A 41-2164
Iowa. State coll. Library for Library of Congress [2]

NL 0428462 IaAS

Joyce Y440 Lloyd, Peter G
The development of motifs in James Joyce. London, 1949.
p.6-12. 22cm.
In Mandrake, v.1, no.6, 1949, p.6-12.

1. Joyce, James, 1882-1941. Crit. & interp. I. Mandrake, v.1, no.6.

NL 0428463 KU

Lloyd, Philena Ricker (Maxwell) Peabody-
See
Peabody-Lloyd, Philena Ricker (Maxwell), 1863–

*EC7 M1327 751sb Lloyd, Philip, 1729-1790.
The new style the true style: or, The reasons for altering the style laid down in a plain and easy manner; and the objections to the new style answered, so far as religion is concerned. A sermon. By P. Lloyd ...
London:Printed for C.Bathurst,at the Cross-Keys,over-against St.Dunstan's church,Fleet-street.M.DCC.LIII.
8°. 32p. 20.5cm.
Erroneously assigned by BM to Peirson Lloyd.
No.5 in a volume labeled on spine: Tracts on old and new stile.

NL 0428465 MH

Lloyd, R.
A new table of costs, in Parliament, Chancery, and the Exchequer: including conveyancing, bankruptcy, and lunacy. Also, appeals from the colonies, and the Court of chancery, with costs in error, from the King's bench to the House of lords, &c. &c. In two volumes. By R. Lloyd ... London, Printed for the author, and sold by R. Pheney, 1820.
xvi, 360 p. 22cm.
At foot of p. 360: End of vol. I.
No more published?

1. Costs (Law)—Gt. Brit. I. Title.
37-39154

NL 0428466 DLC

Lloyd, R Duppa
Historical chart and notes on the origin of the British Victorian monarchy. London, C. J. Clark, 1892.
8p. fold.chart.
Cover-title: Origin of the Guelphs.

NL 0428467 MdBP OCl

Lloyd, R. J. Some researches into the nature of vowel-sound ...
see under [Pipping, Hugo] 1864–

* T176 .T9 no.120 1949 Lloyd, R L
Preliminary results with a thrust plate for the determination of specific impulse [by] R. L. Lloyd, B. E. Cooper and J. B. Fenn. Richmond, 1949.
2 l. diagrs. 28cm. (Experiment inc., Richmond. TM-120)
Includes bibliography.

1. Aerodynamics. I. Cooper, B E joint author. II. Fenn, John B joint author. III. Se.

NL 0428469 ViU

621.33 L77f Lloyd, R McA
A few notes on electric railways. n.p. 1888.
p.14-21.

A paper read at the Proceedings of the Engineers' society of Western Pennsylvania, 1888.

NL 0428470 IU

Lloyd, R R
Pilot-plant production of electrolytic magnesium from magnesia, by R. R. Lloyd [and others]
(In Metals technology. New York, 1945. 23 cm. v. 12, no. 3, Apr. 1945. 25 p. illus.)
American Institute of Mining and Metallurgical Engineers. Technical publication no. 1848 (Class D, Nonferrous metallurgy, no. 89)
"References": p. 25.

1. Magnesium—Metallurgy. I. Title. II. Title: Electrolytic magnesium.
[TN1.A5255 vol. 12, no. 3] P O 49-163
U. S. Patent Office. Libr. for Library of Congress [1]

NL 0428471 DP

QD341 .A8L79 Lloyd, Rachel, PH. D.
On the conversion of some of the homologues of benzol-phenol into primary and secondary amines.
Zuerich, 1887.
26p.
Inaug. diss. Zuerich.

NL 0428472 DLC

Lloyd, Rachel, PH. D.
On the conversion of some of the homologues of benzol-phenol into primary and secondary amines.
(In Nebraska. University. University studies. Lincoln [1888, 23 cm. v. 1, no. 2, p. 97-118)

1. Amines. 2. Phenols. I. Title.
AS36.N2 vol. 1, no. 2 4-2315

NL 0428473 DLC ICJ MB PSt NIC MU OrU

Q311 .L65 v.18, no.15 Lloyd, Ralph Irving, 1875–
Blocking of macular arterioles as a cause of central and paracentral scotoma of the macular bundle type. [By] Ralph I. Lloyd. [New York? 1918?]
7 p. illus. 33cm. (Lomb miscellaneous pamphlets, v. 18, no. 15)
Caption title.
"Reprinted from the American Journal of ophthalmology, June, 1918."
Unbound.

1. Optics, Physiological. I. Title.

NL 0428474 ViU

VOLUME 337

Q311 .L65 v.18, no.16 Lloyd, Ralph Irving, 1875–
Hemianopsia, by Ralph I. Lloyd. [New York? 1917?]
25 p. illus. 33cm. [Lomb miscellaneous pamphlets, v. 18, no. 16]
Cover title.
"Reprinted from the Ophthalmic record, October, 1917."
Original paper wrappers.

1. Optics, Physiological. I. Title.

NL 0428475 ViU

Q311 .L65 v.18, no.17 Lloyd, Ralph Irving, 1875–
Measuring the deviation of a strabismic eye on the stereoscopic campimeter. [By] Ralph I. Lloyd. [New York? 1923?]
2 p., 1 l. illus. 33cm. [Lomb miscellaneous pamphlets, v. 18, no. 17]
Caption title.
"Reprinted from the American journal of ophthalmology, October, 1923, Vol. 6, No. 10."
Unbound.

1. Optics, Physiological. I. Title.

NL 0428476 ViU

Q311 .L65 v.18, no.18 Lloyd, Ralph Irving, 1875–
Methods of measuring strabismus, by Ralph I. Lloyd. [New York? 1922?]
[3] p. illus. 33cm. [Lomb miscellaneous pamphlets, v. 18, no. 18]
Caption title.
"Reprinted from the Eye, ear, nose and throat monthly, October, 1922."
Unbound.

1. Optics, Physiological. I. Title.

NL 0428477 ViU

Q311 .L65 v.18, no.19 Lloyd, Ralph Irving, 1875–
Perimetry and campimetry, by Ralph I. Lloyd. Rochester, N. Y., Bausch & Lomb Optical Co., ©1918.
27 p. illus. 33cm. [Lomb miscellaneous pamphlets, v. 18, no. 19]
Cover title.
"Scientific and technical publications."
"No. II, XI–18."
Original paper wrappers.

1. Optics, Physiological. I. Title.

NL 0428478 ViU NN

Q311 .L65 v.18, no.20 Lloyd, Ralph Irving, 1875–
Phantom intraocular tumor. Multilocular cyst of iris and ciliary body. By Ralph I. Lloyd. [New York, The Knickerbocker Press, 1919?]
489–491 p. plate. 33cm. [Lomb miscellaneous pamphlets, v. 18, no. 20]
Cover title.
"Reprinted from the Archives of ophthalmology, Vol. xlviii., No. 5, 1919."
Original paper wrappers.

1. Optics, Physiological. I. Title.

NL 0428479 ViU

---

* Q311 .L65 v.18, no.21 Lloyd, Ralph Irving, 1875–
The stereo-campimeter and its use; presentation of a new instrument for the study of central field defects. By Ralph I. Lloyd. [New York? 1921?]
5 p. 33cm. [Lomb miscellaneous pamphlets, v. 18, no. 21]
Caption title.
"Reprinted from The Journal of ophthalmology, otology and laryngolo[gy] October, 1921."
Unbound.

1. Optics, Physi[ological] ological. I. Title.

NL 0428480 ViU

Q311 .L65 v.18, no.22 Lloyd, Ralph Irving, 1875–
The stereoscopic campimeter slate. Demonstration at the New York Ophthalmic Hospital during the clinical congress. [New York] A. R. Elliott Pub. Co., ©1920.
13, [1] p. illus. 33cm. [Lomb miscellaneous pamphlets, v. 18, no. 22]
Caption title.
"Reprinted from the New York Medical Journal for December 11, 1920."
Unbound.

1. Optics, Physiol[ogical.] I. Title.

NL 0428481 ViU

Lloyd, Ralph Irving, 1875–
Visual field studies, by Ralph I. Lloyd ... 124 illustrations. New York, The Technical press, 1926.
3 p. l., 216 p. illus., diagrs. 24cm.

1. Ophthalmology. 2. Eye—Diseases and defects. 3. Eye—Examination. I. Title.

26-8246

Library of Congress RE48.L6
[3]

NL 0428482 DLC MnU-B ICRL DNLM ICJ MiU OU

Lloyd, Ralph S., 1908– joint author.
FOR OTHER EDITIONS SEE MAIN ENTRY

Clark, Taliaferro, 1867–
Children's teeth, a community responsibility. The need for adequate preventive, corrective and educational measures, by Taliaferro Clark and Harry B. Butler. Revised by Ralph S. Lloyd ... [Washington, U. S. Govt. print. off., 1940]

Lloyd, Ralph S., 1908–
Role of the dentist in oral cancer detection.
Pub. health repts. 63:805-12, June 18, 1942.

NL 0428484 PU-D

Lloyd, Randall Edward.
Response-frequency recorder... [Columbus] Ohio state university, 1939.
Thesis - Ohio state university.

NL 0428485 OU

LD3907 .E3 1946 .L5 Lloyd, Raymond Grann, 1918–
Techniques of political persuasion used by certain congressmen from selected states, 1921-1946... New York, 1946.
2p.ℓ.,iv,423 typewritten leaves. 29cm.
Thesis (Ph.D.) - New York University, School of Education, 1946.
Bibliography: p.414-423.
"Abstract": [5] typewritten leaves bound in following t.-p.

NL 0428486 NNU-W

Lloyd, Raymond Grann, 1918–
Techniques of political persuasion used by certain congressmen from selected states, 1921–1946. [New York] 1946.
Microfilm copy of typewritten ms. Made in 1947 by University Microfilms (Publication no. 833) Positive.
Collation of the original: iv, 423 l.
Thesis—New York Univ.
Abstracted in Microfilm abstracts, v. 7 (1947) no. 2, p. 121.
Bibliography: leaves 414–423.

1. Southern States—Pol. & govt.—1865– 2. Negroes—Politics and suffrage. 3. State rights.
Microfilm AC–1 no. 833 Mic A 47-41*

Michigan. Univ. Libr. for Library of Congress [1]†

NL 0428487 MiU DLC

Lloyd, Raymond Grann, 1918–
White supremacy in the United States, an analysis of its historical background, with especial reference to the poll tax. Washington, Public Affairs Press [1952]
23 p. 23 cm. (Annals of American research)

1. Negroes—Civil rights. 2. Negroes—Politics and suffrage. 3. Poll-tax—U. S. I. Title.
E185.61.L6 52—1917
*301.451 325.260973

NL 0428488 DLC OrPR OrU WaS Wa CU NcD ViHaI TxU OFH NN DHU MH

LLOYD,Rees,1759-1838.
Marwnad,neu dduwiol goffadwriaeth,am y parchedig Edmund Jones,[etc.,etc.] Ynghyd â phregeth o eiddo y Parch.E.Jones,yn dangos Mawr fudd duwioldeb. Trefecca,Argraphwyd yn y Flwyddyn,1794.
17 cm. pp.12.
Rowlands' Cambrian Bibliography,1794 § 26.

NL 0428489 RPB MH

[**Lloyd, Rees**] 1759–1838.
The Richmond alarm; a plain and familiar discourse in the form of a dialogue between a father and his son; in three parts: I. Containing introduction, with many instructive hints and observations upon many of the most remarkable occurrences, wonders and curiosities in history; with a short account of the four religions of the world, viz. Pagan, Jewish, Mahometan and Christian religion; and a brief account of the Greek church, Popish church, and Protestant church. II. An account of the burning of the theatre in Richmond, December 26, 1811; with observations upon the nature and effects of stage plays, masquerades, balls, puppet shows, horse races, and gambling. III. Reflections upon that conflagration; with a solemn application to people of every rank and character ... Written at the request of a number of pious persons, by an independent minister ... Philadelphia: Printed for the author. J. Bioren, printer, no. 38 Chesnut street. Price 50 cents. [1814]
v, [6]–144 p. 14½cm.
Imperfect; p. 53–56 wanting.
Preface dated April 10, 1813; entered for copyright, April 7, 1814.
1. Richmond—Theater disaster. 1811. I. Title.

7-16684 Revised

Library of Congress F234.R5L78

NL 0428491 DLC ViU

[**Lloyd, Rees**] 1759–1838.
The Richmond alarm; a plain and familiar discourse: written in the form of a dialogue, between a father and his son ... Written at the request of a number of pious persons by an independant minister ... 2d ed., cor. With an additional account of the conversion of an Indian, included in a letter written by himself and sent to his friend in America, from London, 2nd ed. in the year 1774. Pittsburgh, Printed for Rees Lloyd, (minister of the gospel at Ebensburgh) by Robert Ferguson & co. 1815.
iv, [5]–158 p. 13½cm.
"A letter from an Indian to his friend in Maryland. From the 2d edition printed in London in the year 1774" (signed: Laurence Harlow): p. 145–163.

1. Richmond—Theatre disaster, 1811. I. Harlow, Laurence. II. Tit[le]

18-882[2]

Library of Congress F234.R5L79

NL 0428493 DLC CSmH MWA

VOLUME 337

Lloyd, Reginald, *ed.*
Impresiones de la República Argentina en el siglo veinte; su historia, gente, comercio, industria y riqueza. Director-en-jefe, Reginald Lloyd, editores ingleses, W. Feldwick, Oliver T. Breakspear ₍y₎ L. T. Delaney, editores españoles, José Pla Carceles ₍y₎ Luis Baldasano López, historiador, Arnold Wright. Londres, Lloyd's Greater Britain Pub. Co., 1911.
897, vii p. illus. (part col.) ports., maps (part col.) 31 cm.

1. Argentine Republic. I. Title.

F2846.L75 48-30764*

NL 0428494 DLC

Lloyd, Reginald, ed.
Impressiones de la Republica de Chile en el siglo veinte, historia, gente, comercio, industria y riqueza. Director en jefe: Reginald Lloyd, editores ingleses: W. Feldwick, L.T. Delaney editor español: José Plá Cárceles. Londres [Impr. J. Truscott and son] 1915.
568 p. illus., ports., maps (part col.) 31 cm.

NL 0428495 PU

Lloyd, Reginald.
Impresiones de la república del Uruguay en el siglo veinte. Historia, gente, comercio, industria y riqueza. Director en jefe: Reginald Lloyd ... Editores ingleses: W. Feldwick ... L. T. Delaney ... Editor español: José Plá Cárceles ... Historiador: Arnold Wright ... Londres ₍etc.₎ Lloyds greater Britain publishing company, limited, 1912.
511 p. incl. illus., ports. map. 31½ᶜᵐ.

1. Uruguay. I. Feldwick, Walter. II. Delaney, L. T. III. Plá Cárceles, José, 1879- IV. Wright, Arnold. V. Title.

41-40473

Library of Congress F2726.L6
₍2₎ 918.9

NL 0428496 DLC MH

Lloyd, Reginald, *ed.*
Impresiones de las Repúblicas Sud-Americanas del Oeste en el siglo veinte. Historia, población, comercio, industria y riqueza. Director en jefe: Reginald Lloyd, editores ingleses: W. Feldwick, L. T. Delaney, editor español: Eugenio Xammar, historiador: José Plá Cárceles. London ₍Lloyd's Greater Britain Pub. Co.₎ 1915.
1019 p. illus., ports., maps (part col.) 31 cm.

1. South America—Descr. & trav. I. Xammar, Eugenio, 1888- ed. II. Title.

F2213.L55 47-40804*

NL 0428497 DLC ViU NN TxU

Lloyd, Reginald.
... Impressões do Brazil no seculo vinte. Sua historia, seo povo, commercio, industrias e recursos. Director principal: Reginald Lloyd ... Editores inglezes: W. Feldwick ... ₍e₎ L. T. Delaney ... Editor brazileiro: Joaquim Eulalio. Historiador: Arnold Wright ... Londres ₍etc.₎ Lloyd's greater Britain publishing company, ltd., 1913.
5 p. l., ₍13₎-1079 p. illus., ports., maps, diagrs. 31½ᶜᵐ.
Published also in English under title: Twentieth century impressions of Brazil.

1. Brazil. I. Feldwick, Walter. II. Delaney, L. T. III. Eulalio, Joaquim. IV. Wright, Arnold. V. Title.

44-29110

Library of Congress F2508.L788

NL 0428498 DLC LNHT

Lloyd, Reginald.
... Twentieth century impressions of Brazil. Its history, people, commerce, industries, and resources. Director-in-chief: Reginald Lloyd ... Editors: W. Feldwick ... L. T. Delaney ... Historian: Arnold Wright ... London ₍etc.₎ Lloyd's greater Britain publishing company, ltd., 1913.
5 p. l., ₍13₎-1064 p. illus., ports., maps. 31½ᶜᵐ.

1. Brazil. I. Feldwick, W. II. Delaney, L. T. III. Wright, Arnold. IV. Title.

14-3170

Library of Congress F2508.L79

NL 0428499 DLC MiU

Lloyd, Reginald, *ed.*
Twentieth century impressions of Chile: its history, people, commerce, industries, and resources. Director in chief: Reginald Lloyd; editors: W. Feldwick ₍and₎ L. T. Delaney; historian: José Plá Cárceles. London, 1915.
568 p. illus., ports., maps. 32 cm.

1. Chile. I. Title.

F3058.L57 60-5800

NL 0428500 DLC MiU NIC

Lloyd, Reginald.
Twentieth century impressions of Cuba. Its history, people, commerce, industries, and resources. Director-in-chief: Reginald Lloyd ... Editors: W. Feldwick ... L. T. Delaney ... Historian: José Plá Cárceles London ₍etc.₎ Lloyds Greater Britain publishing company, ltd., 1913.
4 p. l., 11-513 p., 3 l. illus., port., map. 31ᶜᵐ.

1. Cuba. I. Feldwick, W., ed. II. Delaney, L. T., ed. III. Plá Cárceles, José. IV. Title.

22-4161

Library of Congress F1787.L95

NL 0428501 DLC

Q
F
2726
L68
LAC
Lloyd, Reginald.
Twentieth century impressions of Uruguay; its history, people, commerce, industries, and resources. London, Lloyd's Greater Britain Pub. Co., Ltd., 1912.
524p. illus. 31cm.

1. Uruguay. I. Title. Sp.: Lucuix Collection.

NL 0428502 TxU DLC

Lloyd, Rhys Gerran,

Kerly, *Sir* Duncan Mackenzie, 1863-1938.
Law of trade marks and trade names, with chapters on trade secret, trade libel and the Merchandise marks acts, and a full collection of statutes and rules. 7th ed. by R. G. Lloyd and F. E. Bray. London, Sweet & Maxwell, 1951.

Lloyd, Rhys R.
Baptism as taught in the Scriptures, by Rhys R. Lloyd ... Boston and Chicago, Congregational Sunday-school and publishing society ₍1895₎
4 p. l., 7-101 p. 17½ᶜᵐ.

1. Baptism—Biblical teaching.

22-13814

Library of Congress BV806.L5

NL 0428504 DLC OO

226.47
L793
Lloyd, Rhys R.
The best address ever made; an exposition of the fifteenth chapter of Luke .. Chicago, H. S. Elliott, 1905.
47 p. 14cm.

1. Bible. N. T. - Criticism, interpretation, etc. I. Title.

NL 0428505 IEN

Lloyd, Rhys R.
Historic Christ in the letters of Paul. n.p. n.d.
Repr. fr. Bib. Soc. April, 1901.

NL 0428506 OO

Lloyd, Richard, ed. & tr.
Connection of the Ethics of Aristotle
see under Aristoteles. Ethica Nicomachea. English. 1840.

Lloyd, Richard, fl. 1584.
A briefe discourse of the most renowned actes and right valiant conquests of those puisant princes, called the nine worthies ... Compiled by Richard Lloyd ... Jmprinted at London by R. Warde ... 1584.

In verse.
University microfilms no.16374 (case 80, carton 475)
Short-title catalogue no.16634.

1. Nine worthies.

NL 0428508 MiU

LLOYD, Richard, d. 1834.
The harmony of religion and civil polity. A sermon, in London, March 20, 1811. 3d ed. London, 1811.

NL 0428509 MH

Lloyd, Richard, *d.* 1834.
Christian theology; or, An inquiry into the nature and general character of revelation. By the Rev. Richard Lloyd ... London, J. Hatchard, 1804.
3 p. l., ₍vii₎-xxx, 382p., 1 l. 22cm.

1. Christianity. Evidences. I. Title.

Printed by the Wesleyan University Library, 1936

NL 0428510 CtW CtY MH

Lloyd, Richard, d. 1834.
Letter to a Member of Parliament, shewing (in these days of infidelity & sedition) the serious & dangerous defects of the British & Foreign School, & of Mr. Brougham's Bill... London, 1821.
55 p. 8°. [In v. College Pamphlets]

NL 0428511 CtY NN

Lloyd, Richard, d. 1834.
An extensive inquiry into the important questions, what it is to preach Christ, etc. London, 1825.

NL 0428512 RP

VOLUME 337

Lloyd, Richard, d. 1834.
Memoir of the Rev. Thomas Lloyd. To which is annexed, An essay on the literary beauties of the Scriptures. By Richard Lloyd. London, 1830.
vi, 396 p. 23 cm.
"An essay on the literary beauties of the Scriptures. By Thomas Lloyd. 1784."
(p. [283]-396) has special half-title.
I. Lloyd, Thomas, 1762?-1828. An essay on the literary beauties of the Scriptures.

NL 0428513 CtY MiD

C 6526 .514 LLOYD, RICHARD, d. 1834.
A reply to letters illustrative of recent transactions in the town of Midhurst... and an interesting account of the recent conduct and present state of the Rev. Robert Taylor. London, J. Walker, 1819.
89p. 21cm.

NL 0428514 ICN CtY

Lloyd, Richard David Vivian Llewellyn
see
Llewellyn, Richard.

Lloyd, Richard Ernest, 1875–
The growth of groups in the animal kingdom. By R. E. Lloyd ... London, New York [etc.] Longmans, Green, and co., 1912.
vii, [1], 185 p. front., illus., map. 23½cm.

1. Evolution. I. Title.

A 13—513

Brown univ. Library for Library of Congress [a40f1]

PWcS PP PPAN
NL 0428516 RPB OrCS CU ICU MiU ViU NN MB ICJ PHC

Lloyd, Richard Ernest, 1875–
11462 The internal anatomy of *Bathynomus giganteus*, with a description of the sexually mature forms. By R. E. Lloyd, ...
(*In* Memoirs of the Indian Museum. Calcutta, 1908. 31½cm. Vol. I, p. [81]–102. 7 illus., pl. IX–XII. 31½ x 25cm.)
Each plate accompanied by leaf with descriptive letter-press.
"Literature," p. 101–102.

NL 0428517 ICJ NN

Lloyd, Richard Ernest, 1875–
Life and word, an essay in psychology, by R. E. Lloyd ... London, New York [etc.] Longmans, Green and co., 1924.
xvi, 139 p. 22cm. $2.50

1. Thought and thinking. 2. Evolution. I. Title.

24-24725

Library of Congress BF455.L5

NL 0428518 DLC MiU NN

Lloyd, Richard Ernest, 1875–
... The races of Indian rats. [By] Capt. R. E. Lloyd ... Calcutta, Trustees of the Indian museum, 1909.
cover-title, 100 p., 6 l. VII pl. (incl. 2 diagr. (1 fold.) fold. map) 27cm. (Records of the Indian museum ... vol. III, pt. I, May 1909)
"Literature": p. 99–100.

1. Rat.

Agr 10–497

Library, U. S. Dept. of Agriculture 410.9 In2R v. 3, pt. 1

NL 0428519 DNAL

Lloyd, Richard Ernest, 1875–
Two African plays, by R. E. Lloyd. London, New York [etc.] Longmans, Green and co., 1932.
v, 184 p., 1 l. 20½cm.
CONTENTS.—Beyond the road.—Up the road.

I. Title. II. Title: Beyond the road. III. Title: Up the road.

32-18846

Library of Congress PR6023.L5T8 1932
[2]

NL 0428520 DLC WaU TxU MB CaOTP NN

575 L79w Lloyd, Richard Ernest, 1875-
What is adaptation? by R.E.Lloyd...London. New York [etc.] Longmans, Green & co., 1914
xi, 110 p. 23 cm.

NL 0428521 MiU NjP CU NIC PU-Z ICJ NN

Lloyd, Mrs. Richard Harman.
The pedigree of the Lloyds of Dolobran. Kingston-on-Thames, G. Phillipson, prtr., 1877.
13 p., 1 pl. 8°.
Repr.: Burke's Landed Gentry, 1. ed. 1836.

NL 0428522 NN

3680 .6 .792 Lloyd, Richard John.
Arthur Hugh Clough; a paper read before the Literary and philosophical society of Liverpool, 3rd October, 1898. [Liverpool, 1898]
34 p. 22 cm.

Cover title.

1. Clough, Arthur Hugh, 1819-1861.

NL 0428523 NjP

811.37 L793J Lloyd, Richard John
James Russell Lowell; inaugural address delivered at the opening of the sixty-eighth session of the Liverpool Philomathic Society, September 28th, 1892. Liverpool, Printed by D. Marples, 1893.
42 p. 21 cm.

1. Lowell, James Russell, 1819-1891.

NL 0428524 NcD

LLOYD Richard John.
The landowner and the state. Thesis [at] the university of London, 1887. [Liverpool], 1887].

pp.(40).
Paged continuously with three other of his essays.

NL 0428525 MH

PE1171 .L8 Lloyd, Richard John.
.. Northern English, phonetics, grammar, texts, by Richd. J. Lloyd ... Leipzig, B. G. Teubner; New York, Lemcke & Buechner; [etc., etc.] 1899.
vi, 127 p. 18cm. (Skizzen lebender sprachen...)

NL 0428526 ICU CtY OClW MiU OCl MH

Lloyd, Richard John.
... Northern English; phonetics, grammar, texts. By Richd. J. Lloyd ... 2d ed. Leipzig und Berlin, B. G. Teubner; New-York, Lemcke & Buechner [etc., etc.] 1908.
vi, 127, [1] p. 17½cm. (Skizzen lebender sprachen, hrsg. von Wilhelm Viëtor. I)

1. English language—Phonetics. 2. English language—Grammar. I. Title. II. Ser.

NL 0428527 ViU MB RPB PSt NjP

ar W 18610 Lloyd, Richard John.
Phonetic attraction. [Liverpool] 1888.
[97]-152 p. 23cm.

Diss.--London, 1888.

1. Grammar, Comparative and general--Phonology. I. Title.

NL 0428528 NIC

LLOYD, Richard John.
Phonetic attraction; [an essay upon the influence of similarities in sound upon the growth of language and the meaning of words] Thesis [at] the university of London, 1888. [Liverpool, 1888].

pp.(58).
Paged continuously with three other of his essays.

NL 0428529 MH CU

LLOYD, R[ichard] J[ohn].
Pessimism; a study in contemporary sociology Liverpool, H. Young, 1880.

pp; 52. Phil 9430.8

NL 0428530 MH

Lloyd, Richard John
Sound-waves made visible by photography, also an improved method of measuring articulations; a paper read before the Literary and Philosophical Society of Liverpool, Apr. 20th, 1891. n.p. [1891?]

NL 0428531 MH

800.5 L79 Lloyd, Richard John.
Vowel-sound...[Liverpool, Turner & Dunnett 1890.]
1 p.l., [157]-202 p. 22cm.
Thesis-Univ. of London

NL 0428532 MiU MH

CS435 .Y4 vol. 120, etc. Lloyd, Richard Leslie Harris, ed.
Coxwold, Eng. (Parish)
The parish registers of Coxwold, 1583– Transcribed and edited by R. L. H. Lloyd. [Leeds, Priv. print. for the Yorkshire Parish Register Society, 1955–

Lloyd, Richard Louis, comp.
A record of the descendants of Robert Lloyd, who came from Wales and settled in the Welsh tract at Merion, Pennsylvania about 1684... Comp. by R. Louis Lloyd. [n. p., 1947] 119 p. 1 illus. 28cm.

On cover: Lloyd genealogy.

429490B. 1. Lloyd family. N. Y. P. L. February 1, 1948

NL 0428534 NN MnHi PHC

VOLUME 337

Lloyd, Richard W.
A practical treatise on agriculture...the improvement of arable land...the value of certain plants... London, Whittaker, Treacher & Co., 1833.
vi, 7-52 p. 8°.

NL 0428535 NN

CS71 .M28 1923 Lloyd, Richard Wingate.
The Man family; notes collected by Richard Wingate Lloyd. Haverford, Pa., 1923.
1 p.ℓ., 24 numb.ℓ. 25cm.

NL 0428536 MnHi

Lloyd, Rickard William, 1859–
The cult of old paintings and the Romney case, by Rickard W. Lloyd, with a foreword by Sir Edward J. Poynter, bart., P. R. A.; illustrated with sixteen plates. London, Skeffington & son, ltd. [1917]
195, [1] p. front., plates. 19½cm.

1. Paintings. 2. Romney, George, 1734–1802. I. Title. II. Title: Romney case.
Library of Congress ND1140.L6 18-20414

NL 0428537 DLC WaS ViU NN MB

Lloyd, Ridgway Robert Syers Christian Codner, 1842-1884, ed. and tr.
An account of the altars, monuments, & tombs existing A.D. 1428 in Saint Alban's Abbey
see under Amundesham, Johannes, fl. 1421-1440.

Lloyd, Ridgway Robert Syers Christian Codner, 1842–1884.
An architectural & historical account of the shrines of Saint Alban and Saint Amphibalus, in Saint Alban's abbey, by Ridgway Lloyd... Saint Alban's [Eng.]: Langley, 1873. 24 p. 8°.
"Some portions of the historical sections of this pamphlet formed part of a paper read at the anniversary meeting of the Architectural and Archæological Society of St. Alban's, held on June 27th, 1872."

1. Monasteries, Gt. Br.: England: St. Alban's abbey.
N. Y. P. L. July 3, 1922.

NL 0428539 NN CtY

[Lloyd, Ridgway Robert Syers Christian Codner] 1842-1884.
Verulam, and Saint Alban's; an account of the ancient city of Verulam, of St. Alban's abbey, the several churches of the town, and other public buildings, with historical records relating to the town and neighbourhood. St. Alban's, W. Langley, 1874.
4 p.l., [3]-42 p. front., illus., plates. 21.5 x 17.5 cm.
Half-title: A short history of Saint Alban's. An account of the altars, tombs, etc., in the abbey, together with a description of the shrines of St. Alban, and St. Amphibalus.

NL 0428541 CtY

Lloyd, Ridgway Robert Syers Christian Codner, 1842-1884.
Wall-paintings in St. Alban's Abbey.
7 p. (Archaeol. Journ. v. 39, 1882. p. 64)

NL 0428542 MdBP

Lloyd, Robert.
Good morning, Mr. Zip-Zip-Zip! [Song with accompaniment for the pianoforte.]
= New York. Leo. Feist, Inc. [1918.] 3 pp. Illustrated cover. [War edition.] 27 cm.

D1377 — T.r. — Songs. With mus.. — European War, 1914-1919. Music. Songs. With music.

NL 0428543 MB

Lloyd, Robert.
The Robert Lloyd tone system; the right way to use the voice in speech or song; the correction of stammering. San Francisco, Calif., Harr Wagner publishing company [°1929]
xv, 105 p. 16½cm.

1. Singing and voice culture. 2. Stammering. 3. Voice. I. Title.
29-17521
Library of Congress MT825.L7
——— Copy 2. PN4162.L6

NL 0428544 DLC CU

[Lloyd, Robert, called Llwyd o'r Bryn]
Y Pethe, gan Llwyd o'r Bryn [pseud.] Darluniau gan I. Owen. [Bala] Gwasg y Bala [1955]

170 p.

NL 0428545 MH NN

FILM 13498 QD Lloyd, Robert, chemist.
Potentiometric determination of the formation constants of the complexes of monamines with ions of silver, copper and nickel in aqueous solution. [Philadelphia, Pa., 1954]
80 ℓ. diagrs., tables. On film (positive)
Microfilm. Original in Temple Univ. Library.
Bibliography: ℓ. 79-80.
Thesis - Temple Univ.

1. Amines. 2. Complex ions. I. Title.

NL 0428546 CU PPT

[Lloyd, Robert] hatter.
Hints to the new school, or, Remarks, on the stile and general formation of Lloyd's new-invented hats, with a novel delineation of their characters, shewing the manner in which they should be worn, the sort of face and person best suited to each particular hat, and the many rare virtues that belong to them... London: Printed for the author, by T. Sorrell [1819] 16 l. 22cm
Signed: Jonathan Castor (pseud.)

1. Hats. I. Lloyd & company, London. II. Title.
N. Y. P. L. October 10, 1939

NL 0428547 NN

---

40 Lloyd, Robert, hatter.
Treatise on Hats. 4th ed. London, 1821
(Pol. Pam., v. 64)

NL 0428548 DLC

Lloyd, Robert, 1733–1764.
Works by this author printed in America before 1801 are available in this library in the Readex Microprint edition of Early American Imprints published by the American Antiquarian Society.
This collection is arranged according to the numbers in Charles Evans' American Bibliography.

NL 0428549 DLC

[Lloyd, Robert] 1733-1764.
The actor. A poetical epistle to Bonnell Thornton, esq. ... London, Printed for R. and J. Dodsley, in Pall-mall, 1760.
2p.ℓ., 20p. 24½cm. 2 copies (cop. in Miscel. poems, v.20, 23cm.)
Signatures: 2ℓ. unsigned, B-C⁴, D².

1. Thornton, Bonnell, 1724-1768. I. Title.

NL 0428550 CtY MiU DFo MH ICU IU NNC

[Lloyd, Robert] 1733-1764.
The actor. A poetical epistle to Bonnell Thornton, Esq. ... London, R. and J. Dodsley, 1759.
20 p. 29cm.

I. Thornton, Bonnell, 1724-1768. II. Title.

NL 0428551 NNC

Lloyd, Robert, 1733-1764.
The actor. A poetical epistle to Bonnell Thornton, esq; by the Rev. Mr. Loyd, one of the masters of Westminster school ... 3d ed. London, R. and J. Dodsley; Dublin, Reprinted for W. Whitestone, 1760.
20 p. 19½cm.

1. Thornton, Bonnell, 1724-1768. I. Title.
Library of Congress PR3541.L56A74 24-12464

NL 0428552 DLC UU NIC MiU MH

Im L778 +760d Lloyd, Robert, 1733-1764.
The actor. Addressed to Bonnell Thornton, esq. By R. Lloyd ... 4th ed. London, Printed for G. Kearsly, 1764.
2p.ℓ., 16p. 29½cm.
In verse.

1. Thornton, Bonnell, 1724-1768. I. Title.
stamp 1, I

NL 0428553 CtY NNC MB MH

Lloyd, Robert, 1733–1764.
The actor, a poem by Robert Lloyd, to which is prefix'd an essay by Edmund Blunden, the whole embellish'd with theatrical figures by Randolph Schwabe. London, C. W. Beaumont 1926.
3 p. l., v-xix, 1 l., 23-42, [4] p. incl. illus., plates. 24cm.
"Limited to 60 copies ... printed on Japanese vellum signed by the editor, artist and publisher and numbered 1 to 60 and 210 copies ... on hand-made paper numbered 61 to 270. This is number 59."

I. Blunden, Edmund Charles, 1896– ed. II. Schwabe, Randolph, 1885– illus. III. Title.
Library of Congress PR3541.L56A74 1926 46-42825

NL 0428554 DLC CaOTP ICU CoU GU CLU INS KMK NNC MH MnU NN PSC LU ICN

Lloyd, Robert, 1733-1764.
Arcadia [or, The Shepherd's wedding] London, 1761.
(In Three centuries of drama: English, 1751-1800)
Microprint.

NL 0428555 MoU

VOLUME 337

[Lloyd, Robert] 1733-1764.
Arcadia; or, The shepherd's wedding. A dramatic pastoral. As it is performed at the Theatre-Royal in Drury-Lane. The music composed by Mr. Stanley ... London, J. and R. Tonson, 1761.
20 p. 19½cm.
[Longe, F. Collection of plays. v. 52, no. 5]
Without the music.

I. Stanley, John, 1714-1786. II. Title. III. Title: Shepherd's wedding.

24-309

Library of Congress PR1241.L6 vol. 52

NL 0428556 DLC PBm PPL IU MiU CtY NcD MH NN TxU CSmH

Lloyd, Robert, 1733-1764.
Arcadia; or, The shepherd's wedding. A dramatic pastoral, as it is performed at the Theatre-Royal in Drury-Lane. By Mr. Lloyd. The music composed by Mr. Stanley ... London, Printed for J. and R. Tonson; Dublin, Re-printed for R. Watts [etc.] 1761
1 p. l., [5]-21 p. 17cm. [With Thomson, James. Edward and Eleonora. n. p., 17--]

I. Stanley, John, 1744-1786.

7-34483

NL 0428557 DLC CLU-C PPL

[Lloyd, Robert] 1733-1764.
Arcadia; or, The shepherd's wedding. A dramatic pastoral.. [London? 1778?] 3 p. 22cm. (Theatrical magazine. v. 2.
Caption-title.
Without the music by Stanley.

244646B. 1. Drama, English. I. Title. II. Ser.
N. Y. P. L. January 4, 194

NL 0428558 NN MiU CtY TxU DFo

Lloyd, Robert, 1733-1764.
The capricious lovers: a musical entertainment: taken from the opera of that name. Written by the late Mr. R. Lloyd. The music composed by Mr. Rush. London, R. Withy [etc.] 1765.
2 p. l., 27 p. 20cm.
[Longe, F. Collection of plays. v. 26, no. 4]
Founded on Favart's "Le caprice amoureux; ou, Ninette à la cour".
Without the music.

I. Favart, Charles Simon, 1710-1792. II. Rush, George, fl. 1760-1785. III. Title.

24-310

Library of Congress PR1241.L6 vol. 26

NL 0428559 DLC InU ViU MH CtY IU TxU NN CSmH

Lloyd, Robert, 1733-1764.
The complaint. And Appeal of authors to the court of Apollo
see under title

PR
3541
.L56
P7
1952

Lloyd, Robert, 1733-1764.
An edition of Robert Lloyd's "The Poetry Professors". Washington, 1951 [i.e. 1952]
xviii, 45 l. 28cm.
Sister Mary Edith Madden's thesis--CUA--English---8216.
Bibliography: l. 37-45.

, Madden, Mary Edith, Sister, R.S.M., ed.
II. Title: The Poetry professors.

NL 0428561 DCU

Lloyd, Robert, 1733-1764.
An epistle to C. Churchill, author of the Rosciad ... By R. Lloyd, M. A. London, W. Flexney, 1761.
1 p. l., iv, 14 p. 25cm.
In verse, an attack on the writers of the Anti-Rosciad and Critical review, in defence of Churchill.

1. Churchill, Charles, 1731-1764. I. Title.

26-20809

Library of Congress PR3541.L56E5

NL 0428562 DLC NcU PU CtY MiU TxU MH NN

Lloyd, Robert, 1733-1764, supposed author.
The minister of state...
see under title

Lloyd, Robert, 1733-1764, joint tr.

FOR OTHER EDITIONS SEE MAIN ENTRY

Marmontel, Jean François, 1723-1799.
Moral tales, by M. Marmontel. Translated from the French ... Cooke's ed. ... London, C. Cooke [1795?]

Lloyd, Robert, 1733-1764.
The New-river head. A tale. Attempted in the manner of Mr. C. Denis, and inscribed to John Wilkes, Esq. by Robert Lloyd ... London, Printed for G. Kearsly and W. Flexney, 1763.
19 p. 27cm.

In verse.

NL 0428565 NNC NcU TxU MH

Lloyd, Robert, 1733-1764.
New school for women. (In St. James Magazine. Vol. I) London, 1762-1763.
(In Three centuries of drama: English, 1751-1800)
Microprint.

NL 0428566 MoU

822.6
L793p

[Lloyd, Robert] 1733-1764.
Phillis at court; a comic opera. The music by Tomaso Giordani. Dublin, J.Mitchell, 1767.
55p. 17cm.

Altered from Lloyd's Capricious lovers, which in turn was founded on Favart's Le caprice amoureux; ou, Ninette à la cour.

NL 0428567 IEN NcD CLU-C CSt

[Lloyd, Robert] 1733-1764.
Phillis at court; a comic opera of three acts. As it is now performing, with great applause, at the Theatre-Royal in Crow-street, Dublin. The music by Signior Tomaso Giordani. London, J. Williams, 1767.
40 p. 20cm.
[Longe, F. Collection of plays. v. 36, no. 3]
Altered from Lloyd's Capricious lovers", which in turn was founded on Favart's "Le caprice amoureux; ou, Ninette à la cour".

I. Favart, Charles Simon, 1710-1792. II. Giordani, Tommaso, fl. 1769-1789. III. Title.

24-311

Library of Congress PR1241.L6 vol. 36
——— Copy 2. 21cm. [Dramatic pamphlets. v. 39, no. 2]
Imperfect: t.-p. mutilated, part of imprint wanting.
PR1241.D7

NL 0428568 DLC ICU CtY PBm MiU

Lloyd, Robert, 1733-1764.
Phillis at court. London, 1767.
(In Three centuries of drama: English, 1751-1800)

Microprint.
Altered from Lloyd's Capricious lovers which in turn was based on Favart's Le caprice amoureux ou, Ninette a la cour.

I. Favart, Charles Simon, 1710-1792. Le caprice amoureaux. II. Title. III. Title: Capricious lovers.

NL 0428570 MoU

Lloyd, Robert, 1733-1764, supposed author.
Phoebe at court
see under Arne, Thomas Augustine, 1710-1778, supposed author.

Lloyd, Robert, 1733-1764.
Poems. London, Printed for the author by D. Leach and sold by T. Davies, 1762.
xix, 277 p. 25 cm.

PR3541.L56 1762 48-40619*

NL 0428572 DLC NBuG CaBVaU NcU CtY IU DFo MiU MB MH NjR CU-A TxU ICN NcD OCU OU FTaSU FU ICU

Lloyd, Robert, 1733-1764.
The poems of Robert Lloyd.
(In Johnson, Samuel, ed. The works of the English poets. London, 1790. 16½cm. v. 68)

11-30542

Library of Congress PR1171.J6

NL 0428573 DLC MdBP

Lloyd, Robert, 1733-1764.
The poems of Robert Lloyd.
(In Chalmers, Alexander, ed. The works of the English poets ... London, 1810. 24cm. v. 15, p. [69]-153)

12-3885

Library of Congress PR1173.C5 vol. 15

NL 0428574 DLC WaS

Lloyd, Robert, 1733-1764.
Poetical works. To which is prefixed an account of the life and writings of the author by W. Kenrick. London, printed for T. Evans, 1774.
2 vol. Port.

NL 0428575 MH ICU MiU NcU MnU NjP ScU PPYH PPL CtY ViU CSmH OCl

---

Lloyd, Robert, 1733-1764.
Poetical works... To which is prefixed the life of the author. Edinburgh: Mundell and Son, 1794. 611-701 p. 8°. (In: R. Anderson, Works of the British poets... London: J. & A. Arch, 1795. v. 10.)

1. Poetry (English).
N. Y. P. L. June 26, 1914.

NL 0428576 NN OU MdBP

VOLUME 337

Im L778 751
[Lloyd, Robert] 1733-1764.
The progress of envy. A poem, in imitation of Spenser. Occasioned by Lauder's attack on the character of Milton. Dedicated to the Right Honourable the Earl of Bath ... London, Printed for J. Newbery, 1751.
xii, 16p. 26½cm.

1. Lauder, William, d.1771. 2. Milton, John, 1608-1674. 3. Bath, William Pulteney, earl of, 1684-1764. I. Title.

NL 0428577 CtY DFo MH RPB ICN IU

Lloyd, Robert, 1733-1764, supposed author.
The prophecy of genius...
see under title

Lloyd, Robert, 1733-1764, ed.
The St. James's magazine. v. 1-
Sept. 1762-
London, Printed for W. Flexney [etc.] 1762-

LLOYD, ROBERT, 1733-1764.
Select poems of Robert Lloyd. [London, J. Sharpe, 1807]
p.[129]-179. 13cm. (Cover-title: Select poems. Parnell, Harte, West, Cawthorn & Lloyd)

754437A. 1. Poetry, English.

NL 0428580 NN

Lloyd, Robert, 1733-1764.
Select poems of Robert Lloyd.
(In The works of the British poets, collated by T. Park. London, 1808-28. 13½cm. v. 43 (pt. 1) p. [128]-179)

12-2036

Library of Congress PR1173.B62

NL 0428581 DLC

Lloyd, Robert, 1733-1764.
[Select poems of] Robert Lloyd.
(In The works of the British poets ... Philadelphia, 1819-23. 15cm. v. 37, p. [189]-199)

11-27574

Library of Congress PR1173.B64

NL 0428582 DLC ViU DGU

PR 3112 .G2 L8
Lloyd, Robert, 1733-1764.
Shakespeare: an epistle to Mr. Garrick; with an Ode to genius ... London, T. Davies; [etc., etc., 1760]
2 p.ℓ., 11 p. 27cm.
Closely trimmed; foot-note, p.10, cut away.

1. Shakespeare in fiction, drama, poetry, etc. 2. Garrick, David, 1717-1779. I. Title. II. Title: Ode to genius.

NL 0428583 MiU MH DFo CtY MB

Im L778 760t
[Lloyd, Robert] 1733-1764.
The tears and triumph of Parnassus: an ode for musick, as it is perform'd at the Theatre-Royal in Drury-Lane. London, Printed for P. Vaillant, 1760.
1p.ℓ., 9, [1]p. 22cm.

NL 0428584 CtY MH

Lloyd, Robert, 1733-1764.
Tears and triumph of Parnassus. London, 1760.
(In Three centuries of drama: English, 1751-1800)

Microprint.

NL 0428585 MoU

Lloyd, Robert, 1733-1764.
The Triumph of Genius, A Dream Sacred to the Memory of the late Mr. Charles Churchill... London, for the author, 1764.

NL 0428586 PU

Lloyd, Robert, 1733-1764, joint author.
[Colman, George] 1732-1794.
Two odes ... London, H. Payne, 1760.

Lloyd, Robert, 1733-1764, supposed author.
Woman: an epistle...
see under title

Lloyd, Robert, 1864-
The treasure of Shag rock; an adventure story, by Robert Lloyd; illustrated by I. B. Hazelton. Boston, Lothrop publishing company [1902]
344 p. front., pl. 19½cm.

I. Title.

Library of Congress PZ3.L778T 2-19881

NL 0428589 DLC

Lloyd, Robert Alleyn, 1892-
A trooper in the 'Tins'; autobiography of a lifeguardsman, by R. A. Lloyd. Introduction by Major the Hon. J. J. Astor... London: Hurst & Blackett, ltd. [1938] 320 p. front. 22cm.

962845A. 1. European war, 1914-1918—Personal narratives, English. I. Title.
N. Y. P. L. September 30, 1938

NL 0428590 NN CU MH MBAt

Qk12 238f
Lloyd, Robert Evans.
An epitome of astronomy, with a concise history of its origin and Progress; being a companion to the lectures given on the diastrodoxon, or, new transparent orrery ... by R.E. Lloyd. To which is added, an essay on the nature and appearance of comets ... Exeter, Printed by R.Trewman and son[n.d.]
26p., 1ℓ. 21cm.

NL 0428591 CtY

Lloyd, Robert Evans.
An epitome of astronomy; a companion to a course of lectures, illustrated by the dioastrodoxon or transparent orrery. Sheffield, n.d.
16°

NL 0428592 NN

Lloyd, Robert Evans.
A syllabus of a course of lectures on astronomy; illustrated by ... the new dioastrodoxon; or, grand transparent orrery, twenty-one feet diameter ... With an epitome of that branch of science, its origin and progress ... Wrexham, from the press of J.Painter, [1801?]
24p. 17cm.

1. Astronomy. (stamped)

NL 0428593 CtY

Lloyd, Robert Evans.
A syllabus of a course of lectures on astronomy; illustrated by ... the new dioastrodoxon; or, grand transparent orrery, twenty-one feet diameter ... With an epitome of that branch of science, its origin and progress ... Oxford, printed by Munday and Slatter, 1812.
48p. front., plate. 17½cm.

1. Astronomy (stamp)

NL 0428594 CtY

CJ 1 C55 no.147
Lloyd, Robert H
National bank notes, Federal Reserve Bank notes, Federal Reserve notes, 1928-1950. New York, W. Raymond, 1953.
16 p. 28 cm. (The Coin collector's journal, v. 20, no. 1, whole no. 147)
Cover title.

1. National bank notes. 2. Paper money - U. S. I. Title: Federal Reserve Bank notes.

NL 0428595 Vi

Mhc8 1705 L77
Lloyd, Robert Lumley, 1666?-1730
Christian charity: a sermon preach'd at Great St. Maries, before the University of Cambridge, Oct.12.1701 ... London, Printed by E.P. for R.Wilkin, 1705.
1p.ℓ., 24p. 19cm.

NL 0428596 CtY DFo

BV 4253 L7 S15 Cage
Lloyd, Robert Lumley, 1666?-1730.
A sermon preached on Wednesday the 8th of March, 1703/4. Being the day of Her most sacred Majesty's inauguration, at the parish-church of Epsome in Surrey... London, Printed by E.P. for R. Wilkin, 1704.

[2] 50 p. A-F^4, G^2. 4to.

NL 0428597 DFo

Bd.in BV 4242 S22 Cage
Lloyd, Robert Lumley, 1666?-1730.
A sermon preached on Wednesday the 8th of March 1703/4. Being the day of Her Most Sacred Majesty's inauguration. At the parish-church of Epsome in Surrey. By Robert Lloyd of Cheame ... London, Printed by E. P. for R. Wilkin, 1704.

[2] 22 p. A-C^4. (A1 and A4 are disjunct) 4to.
Bound in Sermons, 1704-1716.

NL 0428598 DFo

VOLUME 337

Lloyd, Robert Lumley, 1666? - 1730.
A sermon [on Jer.xxiii.10] preach'd at the assizes, held at Guilford, July 19. 1705. Before ... Ld Chief Justice Holt, and Mr. Justice Gould ... London, J. Nutt, 1705.
[2],24 p. 22cm.

NL 0428599 CLU

Lloyd (Robert Lumley) 1666? - 1730.
A sermon preach'd at St. Paul's Covent Garden, on the thirtieth of Jan. 1709. Being the anniversary-fast for the martyrdom of King Charles the first. *London: J. Archer*, 1710. 16 pp. 12°.
ª: CL. p. v. 73.

NL 0428600 NN CLU NIC NjPT CSmH MH

---

ar W 9120 Lloyd, Robert Lumley, 1666? - 1730.
A sermon preach'd at St. Paul's, Covent-Garden, on the 30th of January, 1711, being the anniversary-fast for the martyrdom of King Charles the First. London, Printed for A. Baldwin, 1712.
16 p. 21cm.

No. 5 in vol. lettered: Charles I. 1711-9.

1. Charles I, King of Great Britain, 1600-1649.

NL 0428601 NIC

Lloyd, Robert Lumley, 1666? - 1730.
A sermon preach'd at St. Paul's Covent-Garden, on the 5th of November, 1711. Being the anniversary for the happy discovery of the powder-traitors; and our no less happy deliverance from the late attempts of popery and arbitrary power, by the blessed King William of immortal memory ... London, A. Baldwin, 1711.
16 p. 19cm. [Miscellaneous sermons. [London, 1710-45] no.3]

NL 0428602 CLU-C RPB

Bd.in BV 4242 S22 Cage Lloyd, Robert Lumley, 1666?-1730.
A sermon preach'd at St. Paul's Covent-Garden, on the 5th of November, 1711. Being the anniversary for the happy discovery of the powder-traitors; and our no less happy deliverance from the late attempts of popery and arbitrary power, by the blessed King William of immortal memory ... London, Printed for A. Baldwin, 1711.
27 [1] p. [A]^4, B-C^4, D^2. 8vo.
Bound in Sermons, 1704-1716.

NL 0428603 DFo

Lloyd, Robert Lumley, 1666? - 1730.
A sermon preach'd at St. Paul's Covent-Garden, on the 5th of November, 1711. Being the anniversary for the happy discovery of the powder-traitors; and our no less happy deliverance from the late attempts of popery and arbitrary power, by the blessed King William of immortal memory ... London, A. Baldwin, and reprinted by F. Dickson, 1711.
12 p. 20cm.

NL 0428604 CLU-C MiU

Lloyd, Robert Lumley, 1666? - 1730.
A sermon preach'd at St. Paul's, Covent-Garden, on the 5th of November 1712. Being the anniversary for the happy discovery of the powder-traitors; and our no less happy deliverance from the late attempts of popery and arbitrary power, by the blessed King William of immortal memory. By the Honourable Robert Lumley Lloyd... London: Printed for A. Baldwin, 1712. 23 p. 19cm.

866040A. N. Y. P. L. 1. Gunpowder plot, 1605 —Anniversary sermons.
January 21, 1937

NL 0428605 NN InU

---

ar W 9120 Lloyd, Robert Lumley.
A sermon preach'd at St. Paul's Covent-Garden, on the 30th of January, 1713-14. Being the anniversary-fast for the martyrdom of King Charles the First. London, Printed for J. Roberts, 1714.
23 p. 21cm.

Nos. 10 and 11 in vol. lettered: Charles I. 1711-9.

1. Charles I, King of Great Britain, 1600-1649.

NL 0428606 NIC DLC DFo

Augustan DA 501 .A2 L 7 LLOYD,ROBERT LUMLEY,1666-1730
A sermon preach'd at St. Pauls Covent-garden, on the first of August, 1716. Being the most happy inauguration of his sacred Majesty King George. By the Reverend and Honourable Robert Lumley Lloyd ... London, Printed by J. Darby,1724.
viii, 20 p. plate.

1. George I,king of Great Britain and Ireland, 1660-1727.

NL 0428607 InU CSmH

---

*pEB7 L7785 712t Lloyd, Robert Lumley, 1666?-1730.
To King William. Written in the year 1689. By the Honourable Mr. Lloyd, then batchelor of arts, and fellow of Pembroke-hall in Cambridge. [London] Printed for A.Baldwin.M.DCC.XII.

2p. 35x21.5cm.
Caption title; imprint on p.2.
In verse.

NL 0428608 MH

Lloyd, Roger Bradshaigh, 1901-
An adventure in discipleship; the Servants of Christ the King. With a pref. by the Bishop of Ely. London, New York, Longmans, Green [1953]
127 p. 17 cm.

1. Servants of Christ the King. I. Title.

BX5013.S4L5 267.183 53-13210 ‡

NL 0428609 DLC CtY-D NN NjPT NcD ICU MB

Lloyd, Roger Bradshaigh, 1901 -
The approach to the reformation, by Roger B. Lloyd; with an introduction by the Bishop of Manchester. London, L. Parsons [1925]
227 p. 19cm.

Library of Congress BR295.L5 26-3301

NL 0428610 DLC NcD NN

Lloyd, Roger Bradshaigh, 1901 -
The beloved community, by Roger Lloyd ... New York, The Macmillan company, 1937.
183 p. 22cm.
"Manufactured in Great Britain."

1. Sociology, Christian. 2. Church. I. Title

Library of Congress BR115.S6L53 38-9161
[5] 261

NL 0428611 DLC NcD PPPD

264.03 L793b Lloyd, Roger Bradshaigh, 1901-
The Book of common prayer and the pastoral ministry, by Roger Lloyd, with an introduction by the Bishop of Winchester. London, S.P.C.K., 1949.
15,[1]p. 21cm.

1. Church of England. Book of common prayer.

NL 0428612 TxDaM

Lloyd, Roger Bradshaigh, 1901 -
Christianity, history and civilization, by Roger B. Lloyd ... London, L. Dickson & Thompson, limited [1936]
3 p. l., 9-282, [1] p. 22½cm.

1. Civilization, Christian. 2. Christianity—Apologetic works—20th cent. I. Title.

36-8949

Library of Congress BR115.C5L6 1936
Copyright A ad int. 21225 [3] 261.6

NL 0428613 DLC ICU CtY NcD NN

Lloyd, Roger Bradshaigh, 1901-
The Church and the artisan today. London, New York, Longmans, Green [1952]
101 p. 19 cm.

1. Church and social problems—Church of England. I. Title.

HN37.A6L56 *261.8 53-7967 ‡

NL 0428614 DLC CLU PPPD NcD ICU

Lloyd, Roger Bradshaigh, 1901-
The Church of England in the twentieth century. London, New York, Longmans, Green [1946-50]
2 v. 23 cm.

1. Church of England—Hist.

BX5101.L6 283 48-4584 rev

NL 0428615 DLC KEmT OrU WaS CaBViP CSt PSC TU NcD ICU MiU PPEB PU PPPD PPWe

---

BX5175 .L79 1936 in: SWTS Lloyd, Roger Bradshaigh, 1901 -
Crown Him Lord of all. The story of a mission in a Lancashire town. London, Hodder & Stoughton [1936]
125p. 18cm.

1. Missions--Great Harwood, Eng. 2. Parish missions--Anglican Communion. I. Title.

NL 0428616 IEG

Lloyd, Roger Bradshaigh, 1901-
The fascination of railways. London, Allen & Unwin [1951]
160 p. illus., port. 23 cm.

1. Railroads—Gt. Brit. I. Title.

HE3015.L55 385 51-4572 rev

NL 0428617 DLC CaBVa NN OCl MH CtY

VOLUME 337

Lloyd, Roger Bradshaigh, 1901–
The glorious liberty, by Roger Lloyd ... With a foreword by the Bishop of London. London, New York [etc.] Longmans, Green and co. [1946]
3 p. l., 89, [1] p. 18½cm.
On cover: The Bishop of London's Lent book.
"First published 1946."

1. Christian life. I. Title. II. Title: Bishop of London's Lent book.
A 46-4451
Harvard univ. Library for Library of Congress [3]

NL 0428618 MH

Lloyd, Roger Bradshaigh, 1901–
The golden middle age, by Roger Lloyd ... London, New York [etc.] Longmans, Green and co. [1939]
xii, 255 p. 22½cm.
"This book rests so fully on John of Salisbury and so constantly calls his writings as evidence that it might almost bear the subtitle John of Salisbury and his circle."—Introd.
"First published 1939."

1. Civilization, Medieval. 2. Twelfth century. 3. Education, Medieval. 4. Universities and colleges—Europe—Hist. 5. Learning and scholarship—Hist. 6. John of Salisbury, bp. of Chartres, d. 1180. I. Title.
39-31322
Library of Congress CB351.L5
[15] 901

NL 0428619 DLC NBuU N ScU MU DAU OU TU PBm PSC CU MtU NcD OCU OClW OrPR WaS OrCS IEG NN

Lloyd, Roger Bradshaigh, 1901–
The mastery of evil, by Roger Lloyd ... London, The Centenary press, 1941.
156 p. 19cm. (*Half-title:* The Christian challenge series, ed. by Ashley Sampson)
Bibliographical foot-notes.

1. Good and evil. I. Title.
A 41-2545
Harvard univ. Library for Library of Congress [2]

NL 0428620 MH NjPT IEG

Lloyd, Roger Bradshaigh, 1901–
Peter Abelard: the orthodox rebel. [2d ed., rev. and reset] London, Latimer House [1947]
224 p. 20 cm.
"First published as 'The stricken lute' 1932."

1. Abailard, Pierre, 1079–1142.
BX4705.A2L55 1947 921.9 A 48-2213*
Rochester. Univ. Libr. for Library of Congress [2]†

NL 0428621 NRU MiU KyLxCB KyU TxU ICarbS CBGTU CBPac ICU NNC TU NcD PJB FTaSU DLC MtBC IdPI

Lloyd, Roger Bradshaigh, 1901–
Railwaymen's gallery. London, Allen & Unwin [1953]
186 p. illus. 23 cm.

1. Railroads—Gt. Brit.—Hist. I. Title.
HE3018.L55 *385.1 53-11929 rev ‡

NL 0428622 DLC IEG TxU NN WaS

Lloyd, Roger Bradshaigh, 1901–
The religious crisis, by Roger B. Lloyd ... London, L. Dickson, limited [1934]
291 p. 19cm.
"First published 1934."
A few paragraphs are reprinted from the author's "The undisciplined life". cf. Pref.

1. Apologetics—20th cent. 2. Humanism—20th cent. 3. Church of England—Apologetic works. I. Title.
34-39556
Library of Congress BT1101.L58
[2] 239

NL 0428623 DLC ICU NN

Lloyd, Roger Bradshaigh, 1901–
Revolutionary religion: Christianity, fascism and communism, by Roger Lloyd ... London, Student Christian movement press [1938]
191, [1] p. 19cm.

1. Sociology, Christian. 2. Fascism. 3. Communism. I. Title.
38-7900
Library of Congress BR115.P7L55 1938
Copyright A ad int. 23609 [3] 261

NL 0428624 DLC NBuU CoU OrU OCl

Lloyd, Roger Bradshaigh, 1901–
Revolutionary religion: Christianity, fascism, and communism, by Roger Lloyd ... New York and London, Harper & brothers [1938]
190 p. 19½cm.
"First edition."

1. Sociology, Christian. 2. Fascism. 3. Communism. I. Title.
38-8538
Library of Congress BR115.P7L55 1938 a
——— Copy 2.
261

NL 0428625 DLC Or NNC NcD PCC NN

Lloyd, Roger Bradshaigh, 1901–
The stricken lute; an account of the life of Peter Abelard, by Roger B. Lloyd ... London, L. Dickson, limited, 1932.
221 p. 22½cm.

1. Abailard, Pierre, 1079–1142. I. Title.
33-5724
Library of Congress BX4705.A5L55
[2] 921.9

NL 0428626 DLC CaBVaU MiU NcD CLSU IEG N NBuU OCU CtY PU NN NB MB

823
H98Y1
Lloyd, Roger Bradshaigh, 1901–
The undisciplined life; an examination of Mr. Aldous Huxley's recent works ... London, Society for promoting Christian knowledge [1931]
32p.

1. Huxley, Aldous Leonard, 1894– I. Title.

NL 0428627 IU NN

BX4700
.G8L45
Lloyd, Ronald, ed.
St. Louis-Marie de Montfort, 1673-1716. A small volume to commemorate the canonization of Blessed De Montfort and to propagate the reign of Jesus through Mary, edited by Ronald Lloyd, S. M. M. Colbury, Totton, Hants, The Montfort Fathers, 1947.
87 p. illus., ports., maps. 24cm.
1. Grignon de Montfort, Louis Marie, Saint, 1673-1716. 2. Company of Mary.

NL 0428628 MB

LLOYD, R[upert] A[lstyne], jr.
A Latin MS. of the New Testament in the Library of Harvard University. MS. Sum.53. Report submitted by R.A.Lloyd.
Typewritten. 4°. ff.(1),19.
Sum 53.2*

NL 0428629 MH

Film
BX
8695
S6
L56
Lloyd, Russell Sherman.
This is "that day" for the promised return of Joseph Smith "in the flesh" or the raising up of the man like Moses [n.p.] L. D. S. Researchers [n.d.]
1v.(various pagings)
Written by Russell J. (i.e.S.) Lloyd.
Microfilm (negative) Salt Lake City, Universal Microfilming Corp., n.d. 1 reel. 35mm.
UU copy 2 is positive.

NL 0428630 UU

Lloyd, Ruth Smith.
Adolescence of macaques (Macacus rhesus)...
Thesis - Western Reserve university, 1941.

NL 0428631 OClW

[**Lloyd, S O**]
For myself alone. A drama, in three acts. By "Marius" (*pseud.*) ... New York, De Witt, 1884.
20 p. 19½cm. (*On cover:* De Witt's acting plays, no. 322)

I. Title.
Library of Congress PS635.Z9L85 12-36512

NL 0428632 DLC CLSU

Lloyd, Sampson S
The fair-trade position explained; being a series of three letters addressed by Mr.Sampson S.Lloyd, as chairman of the Executive committee of The National fair-trade league, to the Times & other newspapers, with notes and tables illustrative of the fair-trade argument and replies to opponents by James Edgcome. Authorised ed. London, National fair-trade league, 1884.

NL 0428633 MH NcD NN

Lloyd, Sampson S., tr.
FOR OTHER EDITIONS SEE MAIN ENTRY
List, Friedrich, 1789–1846.
The national system of political economy, by Friedrich List, tr. by Sampson S. Lloyd, with an introduction by J. Shield Nicholson ... New impression. London, New York [etc.] Longmans, Green, and co., 1909.

Lloyd, Sampson Zachary, 1843-1914.
Gt. Brit. *Historical manuscripts commission.*
... The manuscripts of the Earl of Westmorland, Captain Stewart, Lord Stafford, Lord Muncaster, and others ... London, Printed by Eyre and Spottiswoode [for Her Majesty's stationery office] 1885.

DP38
L55
[Lloyd, Samuel]
Cruise of the "Red Rose". April and May, 1880. Birmingham, Hudson [1880]
65,viii p. illus.

1. Spain - Descr. & trav. 2. Portugal - Descr. & trav. 3. Red Rose (Yacht) I. Title.

NL 0428636 CU

Lloyd, Samuel, ed.
The Sanitary plumber, heating and ventilating engineer.
New York, Hydraulic and sanitary plumber publishing co., limited [etc.] 1885-99.

VOLUME 337

Lloyd, Samuel, of Bradford.
The government of Ireland, past, present, and prospective...by Rev. S. Lloyd...with short introductions by Alfred Illingworth [and others]... and an appendix on the "Present land war in Ireland," by Rev. J. Ellis...Bradford, T. Brear. London, Simpkin, Marshall & co. [1887]
4 p.l., [5]-452 p. 19 cm.
"List of authorities": 2 p.
1. Irish question. I. Ellis, Joseph.

NL 0428638 CU

Lloyd, Samuel, of New Jersey?

The New Jersey annual register, and general calendar for the year 1846, by Samuel Lloyd. Trenton, Printed by R. Gosman, 1845.

Lloyd, Samuel, 1827?- , tr.
The corrected English New Testament ... London, Bagster, 1905 (also N.Y., Putnam)
see under Bible. N.T. English. 1905. Lloyd.

Lloyd, Samuel, 1827?-
The Lloyds of Birmingham, with some account of the founding of Lloyds bank, by Samuel Lloyd. 2d ed. Birmingham, Cornish brothers, limited; [etc., etc.] 1907.
xvi, 246 p. 25 pl. (incl. front., ports., plan, facsims.) fold. geneal. tab. 23½cm.
Introduction signed: E. V. Lucas.

1. Lloyd family. 2. Banks and banking—Birmingham, Eng. 3. Lloyd banking company limited, Birmingham, Eng.
8—9082
Library of Congress CS439.L6 1907

NL 0428641 DLC CaBVaU PPFa ICU ICJ NN

LLOYD, Samuel, 1827?-
The Lloyds of Birmingham with some account of the founding of Lloyds bank. 3d ed. Birmingham, Cornish brothers, limited, etc., etc., 1908.

pp.xvi,271. Ports.,plates,facsimile plates, and geneal.table.

NL 0428642 MH ScU

Lloyd, Samuel, 1827?-
The Lloyds of Birmingham, with some account of the founding of Lloyds bank, by Samuel Lloyd. 3d. ed. With six appendices. Birmingham, Cornish brothers, limited; [etc., etc.] 1909.
xvi, 271 p. 28 pl. (incl. front., ports., plan, facsims.) fold. geneal. tab. 23.5 cm.
Introduction signed: E.V. Lucas.
1. Lloyd family. 2. Banks and banking. Birmingham, Eng. 3. Lloyds bank, Ltd. 4. Genealogy - Lloyd.

NL 0428643 CtY

HE435
L55

Lloyd, Samuel, b. 1827?
A national canal between the four rivers; a national necessity ... London, J. Hogg and sons [1888]
1 p.l., [5]-64 p. front. (map.) 21cm.

1. Canals--Great Britain. 2. Inland navigation--Gt. Brit.

NL 0428644 RPB

Lloyd, Samuel 1860-1926.
Bright's disease as a complication of surgical procedures. 11 pp. 12°. [New York, 1887.]
Repr. from: N. York M. J., 1887, xlvi.

NL 0428645 DNLM

Lloyd, Samuel, 1860-1926.
The surgical treatment of empyema. Reprinted from Annals of Surgery.
New York, 1907

NL 0428646 DCU-H

Lloyd, Samuel H.
Glimpses of the spirit-land. Addresses, sonnets, and other poems. By Samuel H. Lloyd. Printed for private distribution. New-York, J. A. Gray & Green, printers, 1867.
[3]-145 p. 17cm.

I. Title.
3—9668
Library of Congress PS2248.L75

NL 0428647 DLC TNJ MB MH NN MWA MiU OO OU

LLOYD, Samuel H.
Glimpses of the spirit-land; addresses, sonnets, and other poems. New York, J.A.Gray & Green, 1869.

NL 0428648 MH RPB

Lloyd, Samuel H.
Life insurance offering. By Samuel H. Lloyd ... New York, S. W. Green, printer, 1871.
70 p. 15cm.

1. Insurance, Life—Addresses, essays, lectures.
7-1107†
Library of Congress HG8773.L79

NL 0428649 DLC NN

Lloyd, Samuel H.
Wayside thoughts. New York: W. J. Widdleton, 1869.
3 p.l., (1)6-83 p. 8°.
With author's autograph.

1. Aphorisms (American). 2. Title.
N. Y. P. L. August 12, 1912.

NL 0428650 NN OO RPB

W 4A
qL793s
1939

LLOYD, Samuel Joseph, 1910-
A study of bile flow, bile acids and bilirubin in dogs with complete external biliary fistulae. [Minneapolis] 1939.
61 ℓ. illus.
Thesis (M. S. in Surgery) - Univ. of Minnesota.
Typewritten copy.

NL 0428651 DNLM

1901
LL9232b

Lloyd, Sarah Elizabeth.
Brain children. [Los Angeles, Commercial Printing House, 1910]
[40] p. illus. 24 cm.

Poems.
Author's autographed presentation copy.

NL 0428652 RPB

Lloyd, Seton.
Dwellers in Mesopotamia, by Seton Lloyd, F. S. A. [n. p., 1943?]
2 p. l., 44 p. plates, fold. map. 22cm.
Map attached to p. [3] of cover.
"These articles were first published in the early months of 1943. Ten of them formed a series in 'The Iraq times' under the title 'Historical spotlight' and the remaining six appeared in the Paiforce weekly 'Truck call'."—Foreword.

1. Mesopotamia—Hist.—Addresses, essays, lectures. I. Title.
44-24812
Library of Congress DS78.L5
[2] 935.8

NL 0428653 DLC

Lloyd, Seton.
Foundations in the dust; a story of Mesopotamian exploration. London, Oxford Univ. Press, 1947.
xii, 237 p. illus., ports., maps (part fold.) 22 cm.
Bibliography: p. 225-227.

1. Excavations (Archeology)—Iraq. 2. Iraq—Antiq. 3. Archaeologists, English. I. Title.
A 48-4763*
Harvard Univ. Library for Library of Congress [3]

NL 0428654 OClW ICU NNC WaS OrPR CaBViP MtBC MH PPEB MiU NcD PP PBm PPT MiU OCl CtY

Lloyd, Seton.
Foundations in the dust; a story of Mesopotamian exploration. London, New York, Oxford University Press [1949]
xii, 237 p. illus., ports, maps. (1 fold.) 22 cm.
Bibliography: p. 225-227.

1. Excavations (Archeology) — Mesopotamia. 2. Mesopotamia—Antiq. 3. Archaeologists, English. I. Title.
DS70.L48 1949 913.358 50-769

NL 0428655 DLC OrP CaBVa AU NcU CU PPWe TxU OCl

913.35
L778f1

Lloyd, Seton.
Foundations in the dust, a story of Mesopotamian exploration. Baltimore, Penguin Books [1955]
256 p. map. (Pelican Books, A336)

Includes bibliographies.

1. Excavations (Archeology) - Iraq. 2. Iraq - Antiquities. 3. Archeologists. I. Title.

NL 0428656 WaU ScU

VOLUME 337

935
L793p
1955
Lloyd, Seton.
Foundations in the dust; the story of exploration in Mesopotamia and the great archaeological discoveries made there. [Harmondsworth, Middlesex, England] Penguin Books [1955]
265p. 19cm. (Pelican books)

Bibliography: p.[241]-243.

1.Excavations (Archaeological) - Mesopotamia. 2.Mesopotamia - Antiquities. I.Title.

NL 0428657 CaBViP ICarbS MWelC GU MU CoU NcU NIC CU FU CaBVaU Or IdPS CLSU CSt MiU NN NNC N IU NcU CtY-M DAU

Lloyd, Seton, joint author.

Frankfort, Henri, 1897–
... The Gimilsin temple and the palace of the rulers at Tell Asmar, by Henri Frankfort, Seton Lloyd and Thorkild Jacobsen, with a chapter by Günter Martiny. Chicago, Ill., The University of Chicago press [°1940]

Lloyd, Seton.
... Iraq, by Seton Lloyd. [London, New York, Bombay, etc.] H. Milford, Oxford university press [1944]
31, [1] p. $18\frac{1}{2}$cm. (Oxford pamphlets on Indian affairs, no. 13)
"First published, June 1943. Second edition, August 1944."
Printed in India.
Map on p. [2] of cover.

1. Iraq.
45-9637
Library of Congress DS78.L52 1944
[3] 956.7

NL 0428659 DLC

Lloyd, Seton.
Mesopotamia; excavations on Sumerian sites, by Seton Lloyd. London, L. Dickson [1936]
xiii, 198 p., 1 l. illus. (map, plans) plates (1 fold.) fold. tab. 19cm.
Bibliography: p. [190]-192.

1. Excavations (Archaeology)—Mesopotamia. 2. Sumerians. 3. Mesopotamia—Antiq.
36-31514
Library of Congress DS70.L5
[3] 913.35

NL 0428660 OO OCU NN OCl OrP DLC NIC NcD CU InU CtY PBm MdBWA MiU

Lloyd, Seton.

Delougaz, Pinhas.
... Pre-Sargonid temples in the Diyala region, by Pinhas Delougaz and Seton Lloyd, with chapters by Henri Frankfort and Thorkild Jacobsen. Chicago, Ill., The University of Chicago press [1942]

Lloyd, Seton.
Ruined cities of Iraq, by Seton Lloyd, F. S. A. Issued for the Iraq government, Directorate-general of antiquities. [London, New York, Bombay, etc.] H. Milford, Oxford university press [1943]
3 p. l., 78 p., 2 l. 27 pl. (incl. maps, plans) on 14 l. 19cm.
Map on lining-papers.
"First published 1942 ; second edition 1943."
Bibliography: p. [75]-78.

1. Mesopotamia—Antiq. 2. Mesopotamia—Descr. & trav. 3. Excavations (Archaeology)—Mesopotamia. 4. Cities and towns, Ruined, extinct, etc. I. Iraq. Directorate-general of antiquities. II. Title.
A 44-2863
Harvard univ. Library for Library of Congress DS70.L53 1943
[15]† 913.358

NL 0428662 MH NIC CU WaS Or IdU DDO OO OCl OCU DLC

Lloyd, Seton.
Ruined cities of Iraq, by Seton Lloyd, F. S. A. Issued for the Iraq government Directorate-general of antiquities. [London, Bombay, etc.] Indian branch, H. Milford, Oxford university press [1945]
3 p. l., 70, [3] p. plates, maps, plans. 19cm.
"First published 1942 ... Third edition 1945."
Bibliography: p. [66]-70.

1. Iraq—Antiq. 2. Iraq—Descr. & trav. 3. Excavations (Archaeology)—Iraq. 4. Cities and towns, Ruined, extinct, etc. I. Iraq. Directorate general of antiquities. II. Title.
[DS70.L] 913.358 A 47-1238
Harvard univ. Library for Library of Congress [3]

NL 0428663 MH KyLoS OClW OO OU PBm PU ICU

Lloyd, Seton.
Ruined cities of Iraq. Issued for the Iraq Government, Directorate-General of Antiquities. [3d ed. Bombay, New York] Indian Branch, Oxford University Press [1945]
70 p. illus., maps. 19 cm.
Bibliography: p. [67]-70.

1. Iraq—Antiq. 2. Iraq—Descr. & trav. 3. Excavations (Archaeology)—Iraq. 4. Cities and towns, Ruined, extinct, etc. I. Iraq. Directorate-General of Antiquities. II. Title.
DS78.L527 1945 913.358 50-58141

NL 0428664 DLC PPDrop TxU

Lloyd, Seton.

Jacobsen, Thorkild, 1904–
... Sennacherib's aqueduct at Jerwan, by Thorkild Jacobsen and Seton Lloyd; with a preface by Henri Frankfort. Chicago, Ill., The University of Chicago press [1935]

Lloyd, Seton.
Twin rivers, a brief history of Iraq from the earliest times to the present day, by Seton Lloyd ... [London] H. Milford, Oxford university press [1943]
vi, [2], 230 p. incl. front. plates, maps (1 fold.) 22cm.
"Iraq museum, chart of historical periods in room 1 [and room 2]" on lining-papers.
"First published, September 1943."
"Serial list of works quoted or used": p. [215]-216.

1. Iraq—Hist. I. Title.
45-1534
Library of Congress ° DS78.L53
[3] 956.7

NL 0428666 DLC NSyU NNZI OCl

Lloyd, Seton.
Twin rivers, a brief history of Iraq from the earliest times to the present day. [2d ed.] [Bombay] Indian Branch, Oxford Univ. Press [1947]
vi, 244 p. plates, maps (part fold.) 22 cm.
"Serial list of works quoted or used": p. [227]-229.

1. Iraq—Hist. I. Title.
DS78.L53 1947 956.7 48-13960*

NL 0428667 PPC OCU ViU ICU OClU NNUN FMU WaS Or OrCS CaBVa CaBViP DLC CU PPDrop MiU OClCC MdBWA NcD OClW

955.1
L
Lloyd, Seton
Twin rivers; a brief history of Iraq from the earliest times to the present day. (London) Oxford university press, 1947.
244p. front., illus., maps, diagrs. 22cm.

Second edition.

NL 0428668 NNZI NNC CtY MB

LLOYD, Seton
Twin rivers; a brief history of Iraq from the earliest times to the present day. Oxford, Oxford University Press [1947]
vi,244p. illus.,maps. 23cm.

NL 0428669 MH-AH

220.94
L77a
Lloyd, Simon, 1756-1836.
Amseryddiaeth ysgrythyrol; yn cynnwys hanesyddiaeth yn Hen Destament a'r Newydd, mewn saith dosparth, o greadigaeth y byd hyd y flwyddyn 98ain o oed Crist ... 2. argraphiad. Bala, 1842.
501p.

NL 0428670 IU MH

Lloyd, Simon, 1756–1836.
Esponiad byr ar Lytr y Datquddiad... Bala, 1828.
see under Bible. N.T. Revelation. Welsh. 1828.

Lloyd, Mrs. Sophia Webster.
Poems. Cincinnati, Standard Publishing Co. 1887.
sm. 4°. pp. vi, 128.
"Printed only for distribution."

NL 0428672 MH ViU IEN CtY OClWHi OCU MB

Lloyd, Stewart Joseph, 1881–
Alkaline electrolytec iron. American Electrochemical Society, 1929.

NL 0428673 AU

Lloyd, Stewart J[oseph] 1881-
A chemical survey of the Birmingham district, prepared by Dr.Stewart J.Lloyd dean of School of chemistry, University of Alabama, for the Birmingham industrial board, Birmingham, Alabama. [Birmingham, Ala., Birmingham industrial board, 1932]
cover-title, 94p.incl.maps. 23cm.
1. Chemicals - Manufacture and industry - Birmingham, Ala. 2. Birmingham, Ala. - Industries. 3. Birmingham, Ala. - Surveys. I. Title.

NL 0428674 NRU

Lloyd, Stewart Joseph, 1881–
... The determination of phenol ... Tribromphenolbromide, its detection, estimation, rate of formation, and reaction with hydriodic acid, by S. J. Lloyd ... [Toronto] The University library, pub. by the librarian, 1905.
cover-title, [16]-24, [7]-15 p. illus. $23\frac{1}{2}$cm. (University of Toronto studies. Papers from the chemical laboratories, no. 51-52)
"Reprinted from the Journal of the American chemical society, vol. XXVII."

1. Phenols. 2. Hydriodic acid.
5-33580 Revised
Library of Congress QD1.T65

NL 0428675 DLC NN MiU OCU OU OO ICJ NN

VOLUME 337

Lloyd, Stewart Joseph, 1881-
The determination of phenol and the detection, estimation, and rate of formation of tribromphenolbrom; thesis submitted with application for the 1851 Exhibition Scholarship. [Toronto, 1904.
[2], 30 leaves. diagr.

Reproduced from typewritten copy. Manuscript additions and corrections throughout.

Bibliographical footnotes. In portfolio.

NL 0428677 CaOTU

Lloyd, Stewart Joseph, 1881-
Eugene Allen Smith, Alabama's great geologist. New York, Newcomen Society in North America, 1954.
22 p. plates, ports. 23cm. [Newcomen Society for the study of the History of Engineering and Technology. American Branch. Addresses. Alabama dinner, 1954]

1. Smith, Eugene Allen, 1841-1927. I. Ser.

NL 0428678 ViU OrCS NcRS MoU FTaSU NcU CU AAP WHi

Lloyd, Stewart Joseph, 1881-
... Oil prospecting in Alabama, by Stewart J. Lloyd ... University, Ala., 1920.
[3] p. incl. map. 22½cm. (Alabama. Geological survey. Leaflet no. 2)
"Originally published in the 'Birmingham news' of Feb. 1, 1920."

1. Petroleum—Alabama. I. Title.
——— Copy 2.
G S 24-197
Library, U. S. Geological Survey (235) Le no. 2

NL 0428679 DI-GS

Lloyd, Stewart Joseph, 1881-
... Studies in radio-activity ... by Stewart Joseph Lloyd. [Chicago] 1910.
1 p. l., p. [509]-527, [476]-481. 24 cm.
Thesis (PH. D.)—University of Chicago, 1910.
Bibliographical foot-notes.
CONTENTS.—The beta activity of uraninite.—The estimation of radium.

1. Radioactivity.
QC721.L74 A 11-1112
Chicago. Univ. Libr. for Library of Congress [a48b1]†

NL 0428680 ICU NjP NIC PPAmP PU MiU ICJ NN CU DLC

Lloyd, Strauss Leonidas, 1881-
Mining and manufacture of fertilizing materials and their relation to soils, by Strauss L. Lloyd ... New York, D. Van Nostrand company, 1918.
vi, 153 p. illus. 19½cm.

1. Fertilizers and manures.
Library of Congress S635.L5 19-1345

NL 0428681 NN DLC IdU WaS CU DNAL GU NcRS ViU MB ICJ

Lloyd, Stuart McGehee, 1878-
... Reading in a Texas city, diagnosis and remedy, by S. M. Lloyd ... and C. T. Gray ... Austin, Tex., The University [1920]
vii, 107 p. incl. tables, diagrs. 23½cm. (University of Texas bulletin, no. 1853: Sept. 20, 1918 ... Education series, no. 4)
Bibliography: p. 106-107.

1. Reading, Psychology of. 2. Eye—Movements. I. Gray, Clarence Truman, joint author. II. Title.
Library of Congress LB1573.L5 20-27356

NL 0428682 DLC P NN MB OrU ICJ

Lloyd, Stuart Phinney, 1923-
The angular correlation of successive nuclear radiations. Urbana [1951]
iv, 45l. 28cm.

Thesis--University of Illinois.
Typewritten (carbon copy)
Vita.

1. Nuclear physics. I. Title.

NL 0428683 IU

Lloyd, Susette Harriet.
Sketches of Bermuda. By Susette Harriet Lloyd ... London, J. Cochrane and co., 1835.
xv, 258 p. 3 pl. (incl. front.) map. 20cm.

1. Bermuda Islands—Descr. & trav. I. Title.
2-14201
Library of Congress F1631.L79

NL 0428684 DLC CtY PPL FU ICJ NN-Sc

Lloyd, T.
The relative values of our home and our foreign trade.
(In Co-operative wholesale societies limited, England and Scotland. Annual for 1895, p. 312-344. Manchester, 1895)

NL 0428685 MB

Lloyd, T., of Wanstrow, Somerset.
Instructions for using the carpenter's improved sliding rule ... Frome, sold by W. Sparks [etc., etc.] 1842.
11, [1] p. 18 cm.

NL 0428686 CtY

Lloyd, T., of Wanstrow, Somerset.
Instructions for using the carpenter's improved sliding rule ... Frome, sold by T. G. Coles [etc., etc.] 1844.
16 p. 16 cm.

NL 0428687 CtY

Lloyd, T. A.

FOR OTHER EDITIONS SEE MAIN ENTRY

Bickerstaffe, Isaac, *d.* 1812?
The romp: a musical entertainment, in two acts. Altered from Love in the city, by Mr. Bickerstaffe. (2d ed.) New-York: Published by D. Longworth, at the Dramatic repository, Shakspeare gallery. Dec.—1812.

Lloyd, T Alwyn
see Lloyd, Thomas Alwyn, 1881-

LLOYD, T.G.B
On the "Beothucs", a tribe of red Indians, supposed to be extinct, which formerly inhabited Newfoundland. In: Jl. Anthrop. Inst. Gt. Brit. & Ireland, vol.4 (1875) pp.37-39, Vocabulary of Mary March's language. Pilling 2298.

NL 0428690 ICN

Lloyd, T H Eyre, d.1901.
Boer War; diary of Captain Eyre Lloyd, 2nd Goldstream Guards. London, Printed by the Army and Navy Co-operative Society, 1905.
299 p. illus., port. 20 cm.

"Printed for private circulation amongst the family."
"Assistant Staff Officer, Colonel Benson's Column, killed at Brakenlaagte, 30th October, 1901."

NL 0428691 CtY NcD

Lloyd, T Ivester
Hounds. London, Hutchinson, 1934.
96 p. col. illus. 25cm.

1. Hounds.

NL 0428692 FU NjP

Lloyd, T. Ivester, illus.

Buchanan-Jardine, *Sir* **John**, *bart.*, 1900-
... Hounds of the world, foreword by the Duke of Beaufort ... eight coloured plates from paintings by Baron Karl Reille, twelve coloured plates from paintings by T. Ivester Lloyd and 24 collotype plates. New York, C. Scribner's sons, 1937.

Lloyd, T P , ed.

Swedenborg, Emanuel, 1688-1772.
Arcana cœlestia; the heavenly arcana contained in the Holy Scriptures, or Word of the Lord, unfolded, beginning with the book of Genesis: together with wonderful things seen in the world of spirits and in the heaven of angels. By Emanuel Swedenborg ... London, W. Newbery, 1819-48.

Lloyd, T. S
I've something sweet to tell you. Poetry by Frances S. Osgood. Music by T. S. Lloyd. [Price] 25¢ net. Boston, G. P. Reed & Co., 17 Tremont Row, ©1853. Pl. no. 1746.
5 p. 33 cm. [Sheet music collection, v. 128, no. 38]
To Jennie E. Clark.

1. Songs with piano. I. Osgood, Frances Sargent (Locke), 1811-1850. I've something good to tell you II. Title

NL 0428695 ViU

VOLUME 337

Lloyd, T W
Four new airs, composed & arr. for the piano forte or harp. London, J. Fentum ₍181-?₎ Pub. no. 34.
2 p. 32 cm.
Caption title.
Includes directions for the dances.
CONTENTS.—Vestris's waltz.—Madame Angiolina's pas seul.—The Scotch bustle.—The new Lord Mayors day.
1. Dance music.
M30.L 76-204422
NL 0428696 DLC

Lloyd, Ted.
Pulitzer prize winner, by Ted Lloyd. New York, Paris, Empire publishing company ₍©1934₎
2 p. l., ₍7₎-373 p. 22½cm.
"First printing."
I. Title.
Library of Congress PZ3.L7783Pu 34-15302
NL 0428697 DLC ViU

Lloyd, Temperance.
True and impartial relation of the informations against three witches
see under title

3A 4356 no. 11
LLOYD, TERESA.
A child's life of Blessed Thomas More. London, Catholic truth society ₍1930₎
16 p. 19 cm.
Bound in a collection of pamphlets published by the Catholic truth society.
NL 0428699 ICN

BX 3659 .F76 L79
Lloyd, Teresa.
Desert call; the story of Charles de Foucauld, explorer of Morocco and hermit of Sahara. London, D. Organ [1948]
121 p. illus. 19cm.
1. Foucauld, Charles Eugène, vicomte de, 1858-1916. I. Title.
NL 0428700 DCU WaSpG

232 L
Lloyd, Teresa.
Jesus: for little folk. St. Louis, B. Herder Book Co., 1934.
182 p. illus. 20 cm.
1. Jesus Christ - Biography - Juvenile literature. I. Title.
NL 0428701 DCU

225.92 L
Lloyd, Teresa.
The twelve apostles. Harrow, Middlesex, Paschal Press ₍1952₎
112 p. fronts. (maps) 20 cm. (The Vine Series, 1)
1. Apostles - Juvenile literature. I. Title.
NL 0428702 DCU

Lloyd, Theodore Cynric, 1901-
The extraction of tar acids from high temperature tar ... by Theodore C. Lloyd ... New York city, 1930.
56, ₍2₎ p. diagrs. 23cm.
Thesis (PH. D.)—Columbia university, 1931.
Vita.
"Literature cited": p. ₍57₎
1. Coal-tar products.
Library of Congress TP953.L55 1931 31-8923
Columbia Univ. Libr. ₍2₎ 668.7
NL 0428703 NNC DLC OU MiU

Lloyd, Thomas
The general history of England, from the earliest accounts to the summer of the year 1764 ... Lond., Ptd. for The Author, and sold by I. Pottinger, 1764.
5 v.
NL 0428704 MiD-B

Lloyd, Thomas.
General view of the agriculture of the county of Cardigan
see under Gt. Brit. Board of agriculture.

Lloyd, Thomas.
Lloyd's pocket companion and guide through New York city, for 1866-67. Published by Thomas Lloyd ... New York, Torrey brothers, printers, 1866.
v, 6-150 p. front., 1 illus., plates. 19cm.
1. New York (City)—Descr.—Guide-books. I. Title.
Library of Congress F128.47.L79 1-14694
NL 0428706 DLC MB NN

Lloyd (Thomas). The ventilation of churches, chapels, public buildings, hospitals, barracks, schools, offices, workrooms, stables, etc., with some remarks on the sanitary arrangements of our dwellings. 13 pp., 1 pl. 8°. *Warren, Wilton*, [1879].
NL 0428707 DNLM

Lloyd, Thomas, of Birmingham.
A letter to Lord Viscount Palmerston, containing a refutation of Mr. Turnbull's statements that British merchants are implicated in the slave-trade. ₍London₎ printed for private circulation. ₍1850₎
31 p.
NL 0428708 TNF

Lloyd, Thomas, of London.
Bimetallism examined. By T. Lloyd. Reprinted from the "Statist." London, "Statist" Press, 1894.
135 p. 22cm.
A collection of papers which appeared in the Statist, Nov. 11, 1893-Sept. 22, 1894.
NL 0428709 ICJ CU IEN OClWHi

Lloyd, Thomas, of London.
An inquiry into the causes of the growth and decay of civilisation, by Thomas Lloyd ... London, "The Statist", 1926.
xiv, 809 p. 25cm.
1. Civilization—History.
Library, U. S. Dept. of Agriculture 280L773 Agr 27-833
NL 0428710 DNAL WaSpG MtU ICJ NN

Lloyd, Thomas, of London.
The making of the Roman people, by Thomas Lloyd ... London, New York ₍etc.₎ Longmans, Green and co., 1914.
vii, 136 p. 22½cm.
1. Ethnology—Rome. 2. Latin language—Foreign words and phrases—Celtic. 3. Aryans. I. Title. II. Title: Roman people.
A 15-691
Title from Leland Stanford Jr. Univ. Printed by L. C.
NL 0428711 ICJ CSt IEG PU OClW MiU OO OU NjP NN MB MiU

Lloyd, Thomas, *of London.*
The silver crisis. By T. Lloyd. Reprinted from "The Statist." London, "The Statist" offices, 1892.
60 p. 22cm.
1. Bimetallism. I. Title.
Library of Congress HG941.L7 6-41987
NL 0428712 DLC CtY

Lloyd, Thomas, *of London.*
The theory of distribution and consumption, by T. Lloyd. London, J. Nisbet & co., limited, 1911.
xvi, 508 p. 23cm.
CONTENTS.—pt. I. The United Kingdom.—pt. II. India.—pt. III. The crown colonies and protectorates.—pt. IV. The self-governing dominions, commonwealths, and unions.
1. Economics. 2. Gt. Brit.—Econ. condit. 3. Gt. Brit.—Colonies. 4. Consumption (Economics) I. Title: Distribution and consumption.
Library of Congress HC246.L75 12-1145 Revised
NL 0428713 ICJ PPComm DLC CtY PU OOxM OU NjP ICU CaBVaU NN

LLOYD, Thomas, print collector.
A catalogue of a collection of prints, paintings, manuscripts, books, &c. of Thomas LLoyd comprising British portraits & topography; with the chef d'ouvres [sic], and rarest specimens of engraving, from the earliest period of chalcography. Auction, by Mr. Sotheby, 6th of Dec. 1820, and seven following days. [London, 1820].
f.(1), pp.65. FA 91.1
NL 0428714 MH

Lloyd, Thomas, *print collector.*
A catalogue of a collection of prints the property of Thomas Lloyd ... which will be sold by auction by Mr. Sotheby ... April 10, 1817 ... London, Wright and Murphy, printers ₍1817₎
viii, 51 p. 23cm.
Priced.
Library of Congress 6-24849
NL 0428715 DLC

LLOYD, Thomas, print collector.
Catalogue of the collection of prints, the property of Thomas Lloyd, containing numerous specimens of great rarity, in the Italian, German Flemish, French & English schools, from the earliest period of the art of engraving. Auction, by George Jones, 1st July, 1825, etc. [London, 1825].
4°. f.(1), pp.72. Priced.
NL 0428716 MH

VOLUME 337

Lloyd, Thomas, print collector.
... A catalogue of the extensive, valuable, and highly interesting collection of prints, the property of Thomas Lloyd ... Which will be sold by auction, by Mr. George Jones ... the 1st day of July, 1825 ... ₍London₎ J. Davy ₍1825₎
72 p. 22½ cm.

Marginal manuscript notes of buyers and prices.
Bound with: Catalogue of a curious and valuable library. ₍1799₎

1. Engravings - Pri collections.

NL 0428717 NNC

Lloyd, Thomas, print collector.
A catalogue of the rare and curious collection of books of Thomas Lloyd. [Sold at auction by Sotheby, 8 July & 5 following days, 1819.] [London, 1819]
70p.
Priced.

NL 0428718 MH NNC DLC

Lloyd, Thomas, traveller.
Across the Rhine, by T. Lloyd. London: A. H. Stockwell ₍1923₎. 48 p. 12°.

123495A. 1. Germany.—Description and travel, 1914- 2. Rhine valley.—History, 1918- . N. Y. P. L. May 19, 1924.

NL 0428719 NN

D640 L796 Lloyd, Thomas, traveller.
The blazing trail of Flanders. London, H. Cranton, 1933.
254 p. 16 plates. 23cm.

1. European War, 1914-1918 - Personal narratives, English. 2. European War, 1914-1918 - Campaigns - Belgium. I. Title.

NL 0428720 CSt-H

British Tracts 1784 L77 Lloyd, Thomas, 1750-1828
An essay on the literary beauties of the Scriptures ... Chester, Printed by J. Fletcher, and sold by J. & J. Merrill in Cambridge, 1784.
24p. 24cm.

NL 0428721 CtY ICN PPL

Lloyd, Thomas, 1750-1828.
Memoir and commercial journal of Colonel Lloyd, formerly of Leeds, merchant. Edited by a Lancashire vicar ... Warrington, Mackie, Brewtnall, and co., 1878.
63 p. 29 cm.

"Printed for private circulation only."
Colonel Lloyd's journal was kept during 1774-1776.

NL 0428722 MH-BA

Mhc8 1779 L77 [Lloyd, Thomas] fl. 1779.
An essay on the toleration of papists ... London, J. Dodsley, 1779.
31p. 20cm.

NL 0428723 CtY CLU-C InU

Lloyd, Thomas, *fl.* 1788-1819.

Works by this author printed in America before 1801 are available in this library in the Readex Microprint edition of Early American Imprints published by the American Antiquarian Society.
This collection is arranged according to the numbers in Charles Evans' American Bibliography.

NL 0428724 DLC

Lloyd, Thomas, fl. 1788-1819.
The Congressional register; or, History of the proceedings and debates of the first House of representatives of the United States of America
see under U.S. 1st Congress, 1789-1791. House.

Lloyd, Thomas, fl. 1788-1819.
Debates of the convention of the state of Pennsylvania
see under Pennsylvania. Convention, 1787.

Lloyd, Thomas, *fl.* 1788-1819.
Lloyd's stenography, publicly practised by him for nearly half a century, with his latest improvements patented ... Philadelphia, T. Lloyd, 1819.
3 p. l., 31 p. v pl. 14½ x 10½cm.
Engraved half-title.

1. Shorthand.

11-6605

Library of Congress Z56.L79

NL 0428727 DLC PHi DFo TU NN

Lloyd, Thomas, fl. 1788-1819.
Report of the case of trespass & assault and battery, wherein John Evans was plaintiff ...
see under Evans, John, of Philadelphia, plaintiff.

Lloyd, Thomas, fl. 1788-1819, reporter.
A report of the whole trial of Gen. Michael Bright
see under Bright, Michael, defendant.

Lloyd, Thomas, fl. 1788-1819, reporter.

Lyon, Patrick, *plaintiff.*
Robbery of the Bank of Pennsylvania in 1798. The trial in the Supreme court of the state of Pennsylvania. Reported from notes by T. Lloyd. Upon which the president of that bank, the cashier, one of the directors (who was an alderman) and another person who was the high constable of Philadelphia; were sentenced to pay Patrick Lyon, twelve thousand dollars damages, for a false and malicious prosecution against him, without either reasonable or probable cause. Philadelphia: Printed for the publishers. 1808.

Lloyd, Thomas, fl. 1788-1819.

The system of short-hand practised by Mr. Thomas Lloyd, in taking down the debates of Congress; and now (with his permission) published for general use, by J. C. ... Philadelphia, Sold by H. and P. Rice, no. 50. Market-street, 1793.

Lloyd, Thomas, fl. 1788-1819, reporter.

Addison, Alexander, 1759-1807.
The trial of Alexander Addison, esq., president of the Courts of common pleas, in the circuit consisting of the counties of Westmoreland, Fayette, Washington and Allegheny, on an impeachment, by the House of representatives, before the Senate of the commonwealth of Pennsylvania. Taken in short hand by Thomas Lloyd. 2d ed., with additions. Lancaster: Printed by George Helmbold, junior, for Lloyd and Helmbold, jun. 1803.

Lloyd, Thomas, fl. 1788-1819, defendant.

Duffin, Patrick William, *defendant.*
The trial of P. W. Duffin, late a captain of the Fourth company in the volunteer regiment of Irish brigade, Dublin. And Thomas Lloyd, a citizen of the United States of America, for a supposed libel. To which is annexed a letter to Thomas Pinckney, the American minister; wherein Thomas Lloyd claims the interference of the United States of America, to obtain him a satisfaction for the unparalleled tortures, and cruel oppressions which he has experienced under the British government ... The 2d ed. London, D. J. Eaton, 1793.

Lloyd, Thomas, fl. 1788-1819, reporter.

Chase, Samuel, 1741-1811, *defendant.*
Trial of Samuel Chase, an associate justice of the Supreme court of the United States, impeached by the House of representatives, for high crimes and misdemeanors, before the Senate of the United States. Taken in short-hand, by Samuel H. Smith and Thomas Lloyd ... Washington city: Printed for Samuel H. Smith. 1805.

Lloyd, Thomas, fl. 1788-1819, reporter.
The trial of the boot & shoemakers of Philadelphia
see under Federal society of journeymen cordwainers, defendants.

Lloyd, Thomas, fl. 1788-1918, reporter.

Selfridge, Thomas Oliver, *d.* 1816, *defendant.*
Trial of Thomas O. Selfridge ... before the Hon. Isaac Parker ... For killing Charles Austin, on the public exchange, in Boston, August 4th, 1806. Taken in short hand, by T. Lloyd ... and Geo. Caines ... And sanctioned by the court, and reporter to the state ... Boston, Published by Russell and Cutler, Belcher and Armstrong, and Oliver and Munroe. Sold by them, by Wm. Blagrove, no. 5, School-street, and by the principal booksellers throughout the union. <Retail price one dollar in boards.> ₍1807₎

Lloyd, Thomas, fl. 1788-1819, reporter.

Smith, William Stephens, 1755-1816, *defendant.*
The trials of William S. Smith, and Samuel G. Ogden, for misdemeanours, had in the Circuit court of the United States for the New-York district, in July, 1806. With a preliminary account of the proceedings of the same court against Messrs Smith & Ogden, in the preceding April term. By Thomas Lloyd ... New-York: Printed by and for I. Riley and co. 1807

Lloyd, Thomas Alwyn, 1881-
Planning in town and country, by T. Alwyn Lloyd ... London, G. Routledge and sons, ltd., 1935.
viii, 208 p. front., illus. (incl. maps, plans) plates. 19cm. (*Half-title; The new world series*)
Bibliography: p. 203-204.

1. Cities and towns—Planning. 2. Regional planning. I. Title.

Library of Congress NA9185.L56 35-32756
₍3₎ 711

NL 0428738 DLC NcU ViU NN

VOLUME 337

Lloyd, Thomas Alwyn, 1881–
South Wales outline plan for the South Wales and Monmouthshire development area (excluding the Borough of Pembroke) by T. Alwyn Lloyd [and] Herbert Jackson. Prepared for the Minister of Town and Country Planning. [London] H. M. Stationery Off., 1949.
106 p. illus., maps (part fold., part col.; 4 in pocket) 25 x 31 cm.

1. Regional planning—Wales, South. 2. Regional planning—Monmouthshire. I. Jackson, Herbert, joint author. II. Gt. Brit. Ministry of Town and Country Planning.

NA9193.L6 711.3 50-12673

NL 0428739 DLC IU NN CSt ICU

Lloyd, Thomas Alwyn, 1881–
Town planning and post-war development
see under Stourbridge, Eng. Borough Council.

Lloyd, Thomas Alwyn, 1881– comp.
Town planning and post-war reconstruction.
see under Dudley, Eng. (Worcestershire) Town council.

Lloyd, **Thomas Augustus.**
The history of England, from the peace in 1783. ... London, C. Cooke, 1796.
2 v.

NL 0428742 MiU

---

*
DA30
.L8
1800

Lloyd, **Thomas Augustus.**
The history of England, from the peace in 1783, to the present time. Designed as a supplement to Hume, Smollet, and Cormick. London: Printed for C. Cooke [1800?]
2 v. plates. ports. 15cm.
Added t. p., engr.

1. Gt. Brit.—Hist. 2. Hume, David, 1711-1776. History of England. I. Smollet, Tobias George, 1721-1771. III. McCormick C
M

NL 0428743 ViU

Lloyd, Thomas Blair, 1921–
A review of polarization and metal electrode-position.
95 l.
Thesis. May 13, 1946.

NL 0428744 OC1W

Lloyd, ***Rev.*** **Thomas Bucknall. Architectural history of S. Mary's church, Shrewsbury. 14 pp. 2 pl. (Shropshire Archaeol. and Nat. Hist. Soc. *Trans.* 2 s. v. 6, 1894. p. 258.)**

NL 0428745 MdBP

Lloyd, Thomas Bucknall.
Notes on St. Mary's church, Shrewsbury, by the late Ven. Archdeacon Lloyd... Shrewsbury, Adnitt and Naunton, 1900.
147 p. 22cm.

361821B. 1. Shrewsbury, Eng.— Churches—St. Mary's.
N. Y. P. L. March 26, 1948

NL 0428746 NN NcD MH

Lloyd, Thomas Cox, joint author.

FOR OTHER EDITIONS SEE MAIN ENTRY

Puchstein, Albert Frederick, 1886–
Alternating-current machines, by A. F. Puchstein ... and T. C. Lloyd ... 2d ed. New York, J. Wiley & sons, inc.; London, Chapman & Hall, limited, 1942.

Lloyd, Thomas Cox.
Electrical equipment, by T. C. Lloyd ... New York, J. Wiley & sons, inc.; London, Chapman & Hall, limited, 1930.
ix, 287 p. illus., diagrs. 24cm. $3.50

1. Electric engineering. I. Title.

30-31874
Library of Congress TK146.L6
Copyright A 30682 [5] 621.3

MiHM MB
NL 0428748 DLC IdU WaS CU NcD PU-E1 PHC PCM OC1W

D620.7
L77

Lloyd, Thomas Cox
The practice and teaching of electrical design, by T. C. Lloyd ... [193-]
9 numb. l. 28cm.

Caption title.
Reproduction of typewritten copy.

1. Electric engineering - Study and teaching.
I. Title: Electrical design.

NL 0428749 NNC

[**Lloyd,** ***Sir*** **Thomas Davies,** ***bart.***] **1820–1877,** ***ed.***
Baronia de Kemeys. From the original documents at Bronwydd. Printed for the Cambrian archaeological association. London, J. R. Smith; [etc., etc., 1862]
4 p. l., [3]–136 p. fold. map, fold. geneal. tab. 22cm.
The various documents referring to the Lordship of Kemeys are preserved in the muniment room at Bronwydd by the present owner of the manor, Thomas Davies Lloyd, and by him communicated to the Cambrian archaeological association. *cf.* Pref.
Pedigree of Thomas Davies Lloyd, based on the original pedigree of 1677, was prepared and brought down to 1861 by Sir Thomas Phillipps. fold. geneal. tab.
1. Kemeys, Barony of—Charters, grants, privileges. 2. Kemeys family. 3. Lloyd family. I. Cambrian archaeological association, London. II. Phillipps, Sir Thomas, bart., 1792–1872. III. Title.

22–24633
Library of Congress CS459.K3 1862

NL 0428750 DLC CtY MH ICU ViU

Lloyd, Thomas Ernest.
African harvest. London, Lutterworth Press [1953]
96 p. plates, ports. 19 cm.

1. Missions—Africa, East. 2. Missions—Africa, Central. I. Title.

BV3530.L6 [266] 276.76 A 54-7726
Rochester. Univ. Libr. for Library of Congress [a57b1]†

TxU
NL 0428751 NRU DLC KU KyWAT ICU NjPT NN NcD OO

Lloyd, Thomas Ifan, 1903–
"The Seine! The Seine!" A military bridging narrative. With pref. by Sir Donald Bailey. London, Sifton, Praed [1946]
42 p. 18 cm.

1. World War, 1939–1945—Engineering and construction. 2. World War, 1939–1945—Personal narratives, English. 3. Seine River. I. Title.

D795.G7L55 940.542 47-27671*

NL 0428752 DLC

Lloyd (T[homas] Mortimer). Some evidence relating to Asheville and the mountains of North Carolina in the climatic treatment of phthisis. 17 pp. 8°. [*New York*, 1887.]
Repr. from: N. York M. J., 1887, xlv.

NL 0428753 DNLM

Lloyd, Thomas Spencer.
Breathe low thou gentle wind; a requiem. Albany Published by Newcomb & Co 524 Broadway ... °1863.
5 p. 36 cm.
For voice and piano.

1. Songs (High voice) with piano. I. Title.

M1621.L 52-52683

NL 0428754 DLC

Lloyd, Thomas Spencer.
Christ the Lord is risen today. [S. solo and chorus. Accomp. for organ.]
Albany. Hidley. 1860. 7 pp. [Carmina sacra. No. 2.] F°.

E3578 — T.r. — Church music. Anthems, &c.

NL 0428755 MB

Lloyd, Thomas Spencer.
Come, said Jesus' sacred voice. Solo [S. or T.] & quartette, with accomp. for the organ or pianoforte.
Boston. Tolman & Co. 1864. 7 pp. F°.

E3578 — T.r. — Church music. Anthems, &c.

NL 0428756 MB

Lloyd, Thomas Spencer

Albany. First Lutheran church.
The manual of the First Lutheran church in the city of Albany. Albany, J. Munsell, 1871.

Lloyd, Thomas Spencer.
Pompir!
see under Sanford, Mary William.

Lloyd, Thomas Spencer.
"Softly now the light of day". Motet, for alto and soprano solo, duet and chorus [with piano acc.] by T.S. Lloyd. Albany, J.H. Hindley, cop. 1860.
5 p. f°. (Cantica sacra. Motets. No. 6)

NL 0428759 NN

32
10103

Lloyd, Thomas Spencer.
Te Deum Laudamus in C. For quartette and chorus. New York, W.A. Pond & co. [1882]
19 p. 8°.

NL 0428760 DLC

VOLUME 337

*
M1640
.L567T4 Lloyd, Thomas Spencer.
1863

Te Deum laudamus, in E flat. Figure 10 in 6 pointed star. New-York, Wm. A. Pond, & Co., 547 Broadway, ©1863. Pl. no. 5708.
14 p. 35cm.
Stackpole, Sc.
"To John Tweedie, esq., Albany, N. Y."

1. Te Deum laudamus (music). 2. Sacred songs with organ. I. Title.

NL 0428761 ViU MB

Lloyd, Thomas W 1855–
History of interesting places on the Susquehanna trail, "the scenic highway of America", by Thomas W. Lloyd ... Williamsport, Pa., Coleman distribution service [©1931]
5 p. l., [9]–78 p. incl. front., illus. 21½cm.

1. Susquehanna valley—Historic houses, etc. 2. Susquehanna valley—Descr. & trav.—Guide-books. I. Title.

Library of Congress F157.S8L58 31-17161
Copyright A 37459 [3] 917.48

NL 0428762 DLC PSt PHi OCl

Lloyd, Thomas W 1855–
History of Lycoming county, Pennsylvania, by Colonel Thomas W. Lloyd ... Topeka, Indianapolis, Historical publishing company, 1929.
2 v. front. (port.) plates. 27½cm.

1. Lycoming co., Pa.—Hist. 2. Lycoming co., Pa.—Biog.

A 41-2626

Grosvenor library for Library of Congress F157.L9L6 [2]

NL 0428763 NBuG ICU

Lloyd, Thomas W 1855 -
Ole Bull in Pennsylvania, by Thomas W. Lloyd... The pilgrimage to the Ole Bull castle, Potter county, Pennsylvania, July 29, 1920, by Charles T. Logue (David of Happy Valley). With preface by Henry W. Shoemaker... Altoona, Pa.: Tribune Press, 1921. 46 p. illus., ports. 8°.
Partly reprinted from various periodicals.

1. Bull, Ole Bornemann, 1810-80. 2. Logue, Charles T.
N. Y. P. L. December 2, 1921.

NL 0428764 NN

L616.15
V002

Lloyd, Thomas Wigram.
On the aetiology of acholuric family jaundice [by] T. W. Lloyd. [Smethwick, Eng., B. T. Hill] 1940.
51 p. tables, diagrs. 26cm.
Thesis—Oxford University, 1941.
References: p. 47-48.

NL 0428765 ICJ PPC MiD-W IaU NNC MiU MH PPJ

Lloyd, Trevor, 1906– joint author.

F1015
.T25

Taylor, Thomas Griffith, 1880–
Canada and her neighbours, by Griffith Taylor, Dorothy J. Seiveright and Trevor Lloyd. Toronto, Ginn [1947]

Lloyd, Trevor, 1906 –
Canada's last frontier, by Trevor Lloyd ... [Toronto, Canadian institute of international affairs and the Canadian association for adult education, 1943]
cover-title, 32 p. illus. (map) 20½cm. (Behind the headlines. Vol. 3, no. 4)
"Reading suggestions": p. 31.

1. Northwest, Canadian—Descr. & trav. I. Title.

43-17589

Library of Congress F1034.B4 vol. 3, no. 4
[3] (971.0082) 917.12

NL 0428767 DLC ViU

Lloyd, Trevor, 1906–
Frontier of destiny, the Canadian Arctic. [Toronto, Canadian Association for Adult Education, ©1946]
cover-title, 16 p. 21 cm. (Behind the headlines, vol. 6, no. 7)
Map on p. [3] of cover.
"Further reading": p. 16.

1. Northwest Territories, Can. I. Title. II. Series.
F1034.B4 vol. 6, no. 7 917.12 47-28194*

NL 0428768 DLC CaBViP ICN ViU MH

DL414
.L79 Lloyd, Trevor, 1906-
Hammerfest Meridian Momment. [New York, American Geographical Society] 1954.
[411]-414 p. illus., table. 25½cm.

Reprinted from Geographical Review, v. 44, no. 3, July 1954.
Includes typewritten supplement containing additional information secured following publication of the article in a Hammerfest newspaper.

NL 0428769 IaDL

553.3
L771 Lloyd, Trevor, 1906-
Iron ore production at Kirkenes, Norway. Maps drafted by Don C. Foote, Chiao-min Hsieh and J. T. Tangerman. [Hanover, N.H., Dept. of Geography, Dartmouth College, 1954]
vi, 39p. illus., maps. 28cm. (Technical report ONR[438]-03-02, June, 1954)

"Field work during July-August, 1949 and March-April, 1951, was made possible by a grant from the Arctic Institute of North America and the Carnegie Corporation. Preparation of the final report was aided by support from the U.S. Office of Naval Research."
Bibliography: p. [20]-22.

1. Iron ores--Norway. I. Title.

NL 0428771 IU IaDL IEN

Lloyd, Trevor, 1906-
The new North. [Ottawa, Cloutier], 194
19p. illus. D. (Canadian affairs, vol. 1, no. 3)

NL 0428772 CaBViP

DL458
.L78
(Ge) Lloyd, Trevor, 1906-
The Norwegian-Soviet boundary; a study in political geography. [Hanover, N. H., Department of Geography, Dartmouth College, 1954.
vi, 32 p. illus., maps. (U. S. Office of Naval Research. Technical report)
Bibliographic assistance by Edward P. Weir; maps drafted by Don C. Foote with the author's guidance.
Includes bibliography.

NL 0428773 ICU IEN IaDL IEdS

Lloyd, Trevor, 1906–
Sky highways; geography from the air, [by] Trevor Lloyd, illustrated by Armstrong Sperry. Boston, Houghton Mifflin company, 1945.
1 p. l., 61 p. incl. illus. (part col.; incl. maps) pl. 28½ x 23½cm.

1. Geography—Juvenile literature. 2. Aeronautics—Juvenile literature. 3. Voyages around the world. I. Sperry, Armstrong, 1897– illus. II. Title.

45-3901

Library of Congress ° G570.L5
[20] 910

OCl
NL 0428774 DLC WaSp PWcS PU-Penn PP IU PPT OEac

Lloyd, Trevor, 1906–
Sky highways; geography from the air, [by] Trevor Lloyd, illustrated by Armstrong Sperry. New York, Jr. Lit. Guild; Boston, Houghton Mifflin, 1945.
1 p. l., 61 p. incl. illus. (part col.; incl. maps) pl. 28½ x 23½ cm.

NL 0428775 IdPS Or

G 617
.L 79 LLOYD, TREVOR, 1906-
Some recent developments in Arctic research. Hanover, N. H. [Dartmouth College] 1952.
9 p.

" Introductory remarks as chairman of a symposium held during New Hampshire Academy of Science annual meetings, at Dartmouth College, April, 1952.

I. Title: Arctic research.

NL 0428776 InU

Lloyd, Victor.
Son of Peter, by Victor Lloyd. London, E. Nash & Grayson, limited [1930]
288 p. 19cm.

I. Title.

Library of Congress PZ3.L7785So 30-16011

NL 0428777 DLC

Lloyd, Virginia, ed.

Poor aeronaut's almanac; the year book, published by the students of South high school, Denver, Colorado.
[Denver, ©192

Lloyd, W A.
... Address of W. A. Lloyd, late of the Australian imperial forces in the near East. Delivered in the Central hall, Liverpool, January 8th, 1920 ... [London] The Anglo-Hellenic league, 1920.
cover-title, 16 p. 20cm. ([The Anglo-Hellenic league. Publications] no. 41)

1. Eastern question (Balkan)

20—17486

Library of Congress DF838.A2A3

NL 0428779 DLC OU OO NN OClWHi

HE2727
.L76 Lloyd, W Alvin.
... W. Alvin Lloyd's railroad guide ...

New York, W.A. Lloyd, 1867-
v. plates, tables. 18cm. monthly.

1. Railroads--U.S.--Time-tables. 2. Railroads--Canada--Time-tables. I. Title.

NL 0428780 DLC

VOLUME 337

HE 627 .L79 Lloyd, W Alvin.
W. Alvin Lloyd's Steamboat and railroad guide, containing the sinking, explosions and collisions of all the steamboats on the southern and western rivers--the number of human lives lost by these terrible accidents within the last forty four years; also, many of the principal railroads in the United States, and a portion of the Canadas. The tornado at Natchez in 1840, with a magnificent view of the city of New Orleans, a sketch of its population and commerce, its principle business houses, &c. &c. &c. Illustrated with engravings. New Orleans, 1857.
xii, 123 p. (p. [16] advertising matter) illus, plate, maps. 24 cm.
At head of title: southern book of great interest.
Advertising matter interspersed.

NL 0428781 MiU CSmH TxU MBAt IGK

Lloyd, W Alvin.
W. Alvin Lloyd's Steamboat & railroad guide. Illustrated with engravings. New York, 1860.
Library has vol. 7. 1 illus. (map), plates, ports. 23cm.

NL 0428782 ICJ

Lloyd, W Butler, tr.
Bills of exchange code
see under Germany. Laws, Statutes, etc.

Lloyd, W. E. G., ed.

Lecky, William Edward Hartpole, 1838-1903.
Clerical influences; an essay on Irish sectarianism and English government. By W. E. H. Lecky. Ed. with an introduction by W. E. G. Lloyd and F. Cruise O'Brien, M. A. Dublin. Pub. for the Irish self-government alliance by Maunsel and co., ltd., 1911.

Z997 L79 Lloyd, W H
Catalogue of a portion of the library of W. H. Lloyd, esq. ... which will be sold by auction, by Messrs. Sotheby, Wilkinson & Hodge, auctioneers ... the 30th of January, 1902 ... [London] Dryden press, J. Davy and sons [1902]
20 p. 22cm. Maroon cloth.
278 entries.
In library, Dec. 7, 1927.
1. Gt. Brit.--History, Local--Bibl. 2. English literature--Bibl.--First editions.
35-1027-6

NL 0428785 CSmH

Lloyd, Mrs. W. R.
see
Lloyd, Mrs. Bitha (Fox) 1811-

Lloyd, W S
When witches ride the countryside. Halloween, with its stories of goblins, is indelibly associated with the legends of evil hags roaming the skies on brooms. By W. S. Lloyd.
(In Cleveland plain dealer. Cleveland, Ohio, 1929. 41½-27½cm. October 20, 1929, p. 20-21. illus. (incl. port.))
Detached copy.

1. Witchcraft. 2. Mather, Cotton, 1663-1728. 3. Halloween. I. Title. II. Ser.

NL 0428787 ViU

Lloyd, Wallace.
Houses of glass. A philosophical romance. By Wallace Lloyd ... New York, G. W. Dillingham co., 1898.
398 p. 19½cm.

Dec. 14, 98-79

Library of Congress PZ3.L779H Copyright

NL 0428788 DLC

BS2421 .L77 Lloyd, Walter.
The Galilean: a portrait of Jesus of Nazareth. By Walter Lloyd. London and Edinburgh, Williams and Norgate, 1892.
[3], 80 p. 19cm.

1. Jesus Christ.

NL 0428789 ICU NjPT

Lloyd, Walter.
The story of Protestant dissent and English Unitarianism, by Walter Lloyd ... London, P. Green, 1899.
236 p. 19½cm.
"Principal authorities consulted": p. [11]-15.

1. Unitarianism—Hist. 2. Dissenters. I. Title.

1-25121

Library of Congress BX9834.L8

NL 0428790 DLC NcD MB

Lloyd, Warren Estelle, 1869-1922.
Psychology, normal and abnormal; a study of the processes of nature from the inner aspect, by Warren E. Lloyd ... assisted by Annie Elizabeth Cheney. Los Angeles, Cal., Baumgardt publishing co. [c1908]
2 p. l., vii-xii, 127 p. 20½cm.

1. Psychology. I. Cheney, Annie Elizabeth, joint author.

8-20998 Revised

Library of Congress BF131.L7

NL 0428791 OC1W OU NIC ICRL DLC NjP PSC PU NcD MiU ViU ICJ NN OCU

Lloyd, Warren Estelle, 1869-1922.
Psychology, normal and abnormal: a study of the processes of nature from the inner aspect.
= New York. Roger. 1910. vii-xii, 127 pp. 19 cm.

M6122 — T.r. — Jt. auth. — Psychology.

NL 0428792 MB NIC DNLM MH

Lloyd, Wesley, 1883-

U. S. *Congress. House. Committee on the judiciary.*
... Crime to advocate the overthrow of the government by force and violence ... Report. (To accompany H. R. 6427) ... [Washington, U. S. Govt. print. off., 1935]

Lloyd, Wesley Parkinson, 1904-
... The rise and development of lay leadership in the Latter-day saint movement ... by Wesley P. Lloyd ... [Chicago] 1939.
1 p. l., 17 p. 24cm.
Thesis (PH. D.)—University of Chicago, 1937.
Lithoprinted.
"Private edition, distributed by the University of Chicago libraries, Chicago, Illinois."

1. Mormons and Mormonism. I. Title: Lay leadership in the Latter-day saint movement.

40-4963

Library of Congress BX8635.L5 1937
Univ. of Chicago Libr.
——— Copy 2. [2] 289.3

NL 0428794 ICU OrU MH NcU NcD OCU DLC

LA1311 .8 .J3 1952 Lloyd, Wesley Parkinson, 1904-

Japanese Universities Institutes for Student Personnel Services, *1951-1952.*
Student counseling in Japan; a two-nation project in higher education, by Wesley P. Lloyd, director. Minneapolis, University of Minnesota Press [c1953]

Lloyd, Wesley Parkinson, 1904-
Student personnel services in Japan
see under Japanese Universities Institutes for Student Personnel Services, 1951-1952.

Lloyd, Wildon, 1893-
The Comic Elements in Shakespeare's Tragedies. A thesis for the degree of Master of Arts in English. Catholic University, Washington, D. C., 1933.

NL 0428797 DFo ViU

Lloyd, Wildon, 1893-
The Emperor of the Moon [a tale of the South Sea. Washington? 19—]
Microfilm copy of typescript. Negative.
Collation of the original, as determined from the film: 1 v. (various pagings) map.

I. Title.

Microfilm PZ-4 Mic 52-49

NL 0428798 DLC

Lloyd, Wildon, 1893-
... The European war debts and their settlement; foreword by Herbert Wright ... New York, Committee for the consideration of inter-governmental debts [c1934]
xii p., 1 l., 88, [2] p. tables (part fold.) 23 cm.
The folded tables are mounted on p. [3] of cover.
Blank pages for "Memoranda" ([2] at end)

1. Debts, Public. 2. European war, 1914-1918—Finance. 3. European war, 1914-1918—Reparations. I. Title.

HJ8011.L5 336.3 34-36267 rev

NL 0428799 IdU-SB OrCS WaTC CU TxU Or CaBViP FTaSU OrU FMU ScU CaBVaU OrLgE DLC NcD IdU PV PPT PBm OOxM OC1 ViU MB

Lloyd, Wildon, 1893-
The false archdukes. [Washington, Recordak Microfilming Service, Recordak Corp., 1950]
Microfilm copy of typescript. Negative.
Collation of the original, as determined from the film: 1 v. (various pagings) ports., facsims.
Includes bibliography.

1. Rudolf, Crown Prince of Austria, 1858-1889. 2. Johann Nepomuk, Archduke of Austria, 1852-1891. I. Title.

Microfilm DB-9 Mic 52-38

NL 0428800 DLC

Lloyd, Wildon, 1893-
The false archdukes. [Washington, Microfilming Service, Recordak Corp., 1952]
Microfilm copy of typescript. Positive.
Collation of the original, as determined from the film: 1 v. (various pagings)
Revision of the text of 1949.
Includes bibliography.

1. Rudolf, Crown Prince of Austria, 1858-1889. 2. Johann Nepomuk, Archduke of Austria, 1852-1891. I. Title.

Microfilm DB-14 Mic 53-139

NL 0428801 DLC

VOLUME 337

Lloyd, Wildon, 1893–
The false archdukes; an exposé of the fictitious tales about the love children of Crown Prince Rudolf of Austria and about the impersonators of Archduke Johann-Salvator of Tuscany. [Rev. ed. Washington, Microfilming Service, Recordak Corp., 1954]
Microfilm copy (positive) of typescript.
Collation of the original, as determined from the film: 1 v. (various pagings)
Film imperfect? Illus. listed but wanting.
Includes bibliography.
1. Rudolf, Crown Prince of Austria, 1858-1889. 2. Johann Nepomuk, Archduke of Austria, 1852-1891. I. Title.
Microfilm 4018 DB Mic 61-7405

NL 0428802 DLC

Lloyd, Wildon, 1893–
Mayerling Lloyd-Davis collection. A collection of documents and old newspaper clippings obtained by Mr. Edwin W. Davis of Avoca, Iowa, in 1901-1952, and by Mr. Wildon Lloyd of Washington, D.C., in 1949-1952
see under title

Lloyd, Wildon, 1893–
Microfilm DB-4
Mayerling Lloyd-Mitis collection; a collection of newspaper clippings from rare and old issues, letters and documents, photographs, all related to the mysterious death of Crown Prince Rudolf of Austria in January 1889, and to the disappearance of Archduke Johann-Salvator of Tuscany in July 1890; also related to the number of impostors claiming to be the sons or daughters of Rudolf or those impersonating the lost Archduke Johann-Salvator. Washington, W. Lloyd, 1950.

Lloyd, Wildon, 1893–
The Mayerling mystery. [Washington, Recordak Microfilming Service, Recordak Corp., 1950]
Microfilm copy of typescript. Negative.
Collation of the original, as determined from the film: 1 v. (various pagings) plates, ports., facsims.
Includes bibliography.
1. Rudolf, Crown Prince of Austria, 1858-1889. I. Title.
Microfilm DB-10 Mic 52-39

NL 0428805 DLC

Lloyd, Wildon, 1893–
The Mayerling mystery. [Washington, Microfilming Service, Recordak Corp., 1952]
Microfilm copy of typescript. Positive.
Collation of the original, as determined from the film: 1 v. (various pagings)
Revision of the text of 1949.
Includes bibliography.
1. Rudolf, Crown Prince of Austria, 1858-1889. I. Title.
Microfilm DB-15 Mic 53-140

NL 0428806 DLC

Lloyd, Wildon, 1893–
The Mayerling mystery; an exposé of the fictitious tales about the suicide, murder, and resurrection of Crown Prince Rudolf of Austria. [Rev. ed. Washington, Microfilming Service, Recordak Corp., 1954]
Microfilm copy of typescript. Positive.
Collation of the original, as determined from the film: 1 v. (various pagings)
Film imperfect? Illus. listed but wanting.
Includes bibliography.
1. Rudolf, Crown Prince of Austria, 1858-1889. I. Title.
Microfilm DB-4019 54-203

NL 0428807 DLC

Lloyd, Wilfred, 1894– joint author.
Tonks, Laurance Henry, 1895–
... The geology of Manchester and the southeast Lancashire coalfield, by L. H. Tonks ... R. C. B. Jones ... W. Lloyd ... and R. L. Sherlock ... with a chapter on the Palaeontology, by W. B. Wright ... London, Printed under the authority of H. M. Stationery off., 1931.

Lloyd, Wilfred, 1894–
Bromehead, Cyril Edward Nowill, 1885–
... The geology of the country around Holmfirth and Glossop, by C. E. N. Bromehead ... and Wilfrid Edwards ... D. A. Wray ... and J. V. Stephens ... With notes by G. V. Wilson ... and W. Lloyd ... London, Published by H. M. Stationery off., 1933.

Lloyd, Wilfred, 1894–
Wright, William Bourke, 1876–
... The geology of the Rossendale anticline. By W. B. Wright ... R. L. Sherlock ... D. A. Wray ... W. Lloyd ... & L. H. Tonks ... London, Printed under the authority of H. M. Stationery off., 1927.

HS 537 N56L79
Lloyd, Will L.
Address of right illustrious Will L. Lloyd, acting Grand Master, at the annual assembly of the Grand Council Royal and Select Masters of the State of New York, held August 23, 1910, at Albany, N. Y. [New York, N. Y., 1910]
32 p. 23cm.

NL 0428811 NIC

Lloyd, William, supposed author.
Letters from a Moor at London to his friend at Tunis ...
see under title

Lloyd, William, *catholic priest.*
Saints of 1881. Sketches of St. Clare of Montefalco, St. Laurence of Brindisi, St. Benedict Jos. Labre & St. John Baptist de Rossi. Lond., Burns & Oates, 1882.
iv, 122 p.

NL 0428813 PV

Lloyd, William, *engineer.* L656.0981 N500
Caminho de ferro de D. Isabel, da provincia do Paraná á de Matto-Grosso. Considerações geraes sobre á empreza pelo visconde de Manã. Relatorio por William Lloyd, ... Rio de Janeiro, typ. de G. Leuzinger & filhos, 1875.
xv, 152 p. 5 phot. (2 fold.), 1 fold. map, 1 fold. table, 1 fold. diagr. 28½ x 21cm.

NL 0428814 ICJ IU NIC LNHT TxU

Lloyd, *William, engineer.*
Informe sobre la via que ha de preferirse para una línea férrea desde Talcahuano a Concepcion i Chillan, pasado al gobierno por Don Guillermo Lloyd. Santiago de Chile, Imprenta nacional, 1864.
cover-title, 37 p. tables. 25cm.
1. Railroads—Chile.
CA 25-979 Unrev'd
Library of Congress HE2940.T3L6

NL 0428815 DLC

Pamphlet Chile 1855 +L77
Lloyd, William, engineer
Informe sobre varias propuestas hechas al gobierno para la construccion de un muelle de Valparaiso, por Guillermo Lloyd ... Traducido por D.R.Peña. Santiago,1855.

NL 0428816 TxU

Lloyd, William, *M. D.*
Letters from the West Indies, during a visit in the autumn of MDCCCXXXVI, and the spring of MDCCCXXXVII; by William Lloyd, M. D. ... London, Darton and Harvey; [etc., etc., 1839]
viii, 263 p. front. (fold. map) plates. 20cm.
1. West Indies, British—Descr. & trav. I. Title.
2-25699
Library of Congress F2131.L79

NL 0428817 RPJCB MBCo DLC CU NIC LU ICU TxU CtY OCl MdBP PPL

Lloyd, William, M.D. of Edinburgh.
De morbis genu humani symptomaticis. Edinburgi, Neill et soc., 1814.
1 p.l., 28 p. 8°.

NL 0428818 DNLM

Lloyd, *Sir* **William.**
Narrative of a journey from Caunpoor to the Boorendo pass, in the Himalaya Mountains, viâ Gwalior, Agra, Delhi, and Sirhind; by Major Sir William Lloyd. And Captain Alexander Gerard's account of an attempt to penetrate by Bekhur to Garoo, and the Lake Manasarowara: with a letter from the late J. G. Gerard, esq. detailing a visit to the Shatool and Boorendo passes, for the purpose of determining the line of perpetual snow on the southern face of the Himalaya ... Ed. by George Lloyd ... London, J. Madden & co., 1840.
2 v. front. (map) 2 fold. maps. 21½cm.
1. Himalaya Mountains—Descr. & trav. I. Gerard, Alexander, 1792-1839. II. Gerald, James Gilbert, 1795-1835. III. Lloyd, George, ed.
5—6850
DS485.H6L6

NL 0428819 OCl NN NjP DLC NcU GASC MdBP NSyU CtY PPL WaU WU

Lloyd, *Sir* **William.**
Narrative of a journey from Caunpoor to the Boorendo pass, in the Himalaya Mountains, viâ Gwalior, Agra, Delhi, and Sirhind: by Major Sir William Lloyd. And Captain Alexander Gerard's account of an attempt to penetrate by Bekhur to Garoo, and the Lake Manasarowara: for the purpose of determining the line of perpetual snow on the southern face of the Himalaya ... London, J. Madden & co., 1846.
2 v. in 1. front., map. 23cm.
First published 1840.
Ed. by George Lloyd.
A letter from the late Mr. J. G. Gerard detailing his visit to the Shatool and Boorendo passes, for determining the line of perpetual snow on the southern face of the Himalaya, v. 1, p. [281]-347.
1. Himalaya Mountains—Descr. & trav. 2. Snow-line. I. Gerard, Alexander, 1792-1839. II. Gerard, James Gilbert, 1795-1835. III. Lloyd, George, ed.
[29d1]
Library of Congress DS485.H6L7 5-6851 *

NL 0428821 DLC OrPR CU NSyU PPL PU NN MB

[Lloyd, William, bp. of Worcester] 1627-1717.
Against the doctrine of the Papal supremacy. [In a discourse, entituled; Considerations touching the true way to suppress popery in this kingdom, &c. By William Lloyd, late Bishop of Worcester] (In: A Preservation against popery ... London, Printed for H. Knaplock, J. Walthoe [and others] 1738. f°. v. 1. Tit. II. 5 p.)

NL 0428822 NN

VOLUME 337

CBA p.v.113

[Lloyd, William, bp. of Worcester] 1627-1717.
An answer to the Bishop of Oxford's reasons for abrogating the test, impos'd on all members of Parliament anno 1678. Octob. 30... By a person of quality. London: Printed in the year 1688. 46 p. 19cm.

Preface signed: Drawdereve Rofmada.
Signed, p. 46: Dra. Locnil.

1. Test acts—Gt. Br. 2. Parker, Samuel, bp. of Oxford, 1640-1688. I. A person of quality. II. Title.
N. Y. P. L. October 5, 1939

NL 0428823 NNC NN MnU ICN CSmH CtY MH Vi NjPT CLU CU

282.42 L793a Sutro
Lloyd, William, 1627-1717.
An Apology in behalf of the Papists, supposed to be writ by Roger Palmer...Reprinted and answered by William Lloyd, sometime Bishop of St. Asaph. London, reprinted and sold by M. Cooper, 1746.
72p. 20cm.

First printed 1667.

P. E. 1187.

NL 0428824 C-S

LLOYD, WILLIAM, bp. of Worcester, 1627-1717.
The Bishop of St. Asaph's charge to the clergy of that diocese, in 1710. And now made publick, by His Lordship's permission. London: Printed for S. Buckley, and sold by D. Midwinter, 1712. 72 p. 16cm.

1. Church of England—Govt. and discipline.

NL 0428825 NN CtY

Lloyd, William, Bp. of Worcester, 1627-1717.
The Bishop of Worcester's answer to Mr. Locke's Second letter; wherein his notion of ideas is prov'd to be inconsistent with itself, and with the Articles of the Christian faith. London, Printed by J.H. for Henry Mortlock, 1698.
178 p. 20 cm.
1. Locke, John, 1632-1704. A second letter concerning toleration. 2. Imprints - London, 1698. 3. Imprints - Mortlock, Henry, 1698. I. Title.

NL 0428826 MdBP

Lloyd, William, Bp. of Worcester, 1627-1717.
A chronological account of the life of Pythagoras, and of other famous men his contemporaries, with an epistle to the Rd. Dr. Bentley, about Porphyry's and Jamblichus's lives of Pythagoras, by William, Ld. Bp. of Coventry and Lichfield. London, Printed by J. H. for H. Mortlock, 1699.
lviii, 18 p. 20 cm.

1. Pythagoras and Pythagorean school. I. Title.

B243.L6 58-51485

NL 0428827 ICN NjP DLC WU IEN IU InU DFo PU FU CLU-C

[LLOYD, WILLIAM, Bp. of Worcester] 1627-1717.
A conference between two Protestants and a papist; occasion'd by the late Seasonable discourse. [London?] 1673.
[1], 33p. 19cm.

STC II L 2675.

NL 0428828 ICN CLU-C NNG

[Lloyd, William, bp. of Worcester] 1627-1717.
Considerations touching the true way to suppress popery in this kingdom ... On occasion whereof is inserted an historical account of the reformation here in England. London, Printed for H. Brome, 1677.
8 p. l., 164 p.

1. Catholic church in Great Britain. 2. Reformation—Gt. Brit. I. Title.
8—16648
Library of Congress DA432.1677.L5

NL 0428829 CtY ICN NNUT-Mc MnU CLU-C FU TxDAM CU DLC CU-A NcD IaU DFo PU NN IEG MH TxU

Lloyd, William, bp. of Worcester, 1627-1717.
A Confutation of the chief doctrines of popery... A sermon preached before the King, at White-Hall, the 24th of November, 1678. [By William Lloyd, late bishop of Worcester] (In: A Preservative against popery ... London, Printed for H. Knaplock, J. Walthoe [and others] 1738. f°. v. 2. p. 134-151)

NL 0428830 NN

Lloyd, William, Bp. of Worcester, 1627-1717.
The difference between the Church and Court of Rome, considered: in some reflections on a dialogue entituled, A conference between two Protestants and a Papist. 2d ed., corr. and augm. by the author of the late Seasonable discourse. London, Printed by A. Clark for H. Brome, 1674.
38 p. 20 cm.

1. Catholic Church—Doctrinal and controversial works—Protestant authors. I. Title.

BX1763.L7 1674a 50-49122

NL 0428831 CSmH NN CLU-C ICN C FU CU NNG PU DLC CU-A IaU NNUT-Mc MnU MH TxU RPB NjP

283.42 L793d
Lloyd, William, bp. of Worcester, 1627-1717.
A discourse of God's ways of disposing of kingdoms. Part I. [Six lines] Publish'd by authority. London, Printed by H. Hills for Thomas Jones at the White-Horse, without Temple-Bar, 1691.
[iv], 71, [1] p. 20cm.

Title within double line border.
Marginal notes.
Based on sermon on Psalm 75,6,7.

Disbound.
First edition; issued only in one part.
Wing L2679; described in DNB.

1. Sovereignty. 2. Justice. I. Title.

NL 0428832 CSt NNUT-Mc MH FU CtY ICN MB CLU-C CU-A PU NjPT InU

T.R. BX5087 .A1T75 no.4
[Lloyd, William] Bp. of Worcester, 1627-1717.
A discourse of God's ways of disposing of kingdoms. Part I. 2d ed. London, Printed by H. Hills for Thomas Jones, 1691.
[2]l., 71p. 21cm. (Tracts. no. 4)

1. Church and state in Great Britain. I. Title.

NL 0428833 IEG

Lloyd, William, bp. of Worcester, 1627-1717.

Gt. Brit. *Parliament, 1702. House of commons.*
The evidence given at the bar of the House of commons, upon the complaint of Sir John Pakington, against William lord bishop of Worcester and Mr. Lloyd, his son. Together with the proceedings of the House of commons thereupon. London, E. Jones, and T. Goodwin, 1702.

Lloyd, William, bp. of Worcester, 1627-1717.
Four sermons: I. On the death of Queen Mary, 1694. II. On the death of the Duke of Gloucester, 1700. III. On the death of King William, 1701. IV. On the Queen's accession to the throne, in 1703. By William, lord bishop of St. Asaph. London: Sold by A. Baldwin, 1712. vii, 8-96 p. 16cm.

1. Mary II, queen of Great Britain, 1662-1694. 2. William, duke of Gloucester, 1689-1700. 3. William III, king of Great Britain, 1650-1702. 4. Anne, queen of Great Britain, 1665-1714. 5. Great Britain—Govt., 1702-1832.
N. Y. P. L.

NL 0428835 NN

Rare Books Dept.
Lloyd, William, bp. of Worcester, 1627-1717.
An historical account of church-government as it was in Great Britain and Ireland, when they first received the Christian religion. 2d ed. London, Printed by M. Flesher for Charles Brome, 1684.
34 p.l., 182 p. 18cm.

"Authors cited in this book": 32d-34th prelim. leaves.
Wing L-2682.

1. Gt. Brit. - Church history. 2. Episcopacy - To 1800. 3. Celtic church - Government.

NL 0428836 RPB MiU-L PU PPL NNUT-Mc PBL N CtY TxDaM-P CU WaU TxU NcD CLU-C ICU MdBP ICN DFo IU

BR747 .L75
Lloyd, William, bp. of Worcester, 1627-1717.
The history of the government of the church, as it was in Great-Britain and Ireland, when they first received the Christian religion. By William Lloyd... 3d ed. London, C. Brome, 1703.
[66], 182 p. 18½cm.
"Authours cited": p. [61]-[66]

1. Gt. Brit.--Church history. 2. Celtic church--Discipline and government. 3. Episcopacy.

NL 0428837 ICU NNG

Lloyd, William, Bp. of Worcester, 1627-1717, supposed ed.
The Holy Bible... Oxford, University Printers, 1701. f°.
see under Bible. English. 1701. Authorized. Also with imprint London Printed by C. Bill and the executrix of T. Newcomb, 1701. f°.

[Lloyd, William, bp. of Worcester] 1627-1717.
The late apology in behalf of the papists re-printed and answered, in behalf of the royalists. London, Printed for M. N., 1667.
1 p. l., 46 p. 20cm.

1. Castlemaine, Roger Palmer, earl of, 1634-1705. The Catholique apology. 2. Catholics in England. 3. Gt. Brit.—Pol. & govt.—1660-1688—Pamphlets. I. Title.

40-18693
Library of Congress BX1492.L65 1667
[2] 282.42

NL 0428839 NNUT-Mc MdBP NN CLU PU CU-A CLU-C MoU NNG InU C-S DLC CLU PU MH WU TxDaM-P CtY MnU CSmH

Lloyd, William, bp. of Worcester, 1627-1717.
The late apology in behalf of the Papists. 1672.

NL 0428840 DFo

VOLUME 337

[Lloyd, William, *bp. of Worcester*] 1627–1717.
The late apology in behalf of the papists, reprinted and answered in behalf of the royalists. London, Printed for H. Brome, MDCLXXIII.
1 p. l., 46 p. 19cm.
Title vignette: publisher's device.

1. Castlemaine, Roger Palmer, earl of, 1634–1705. The Catholique apology. 2. Catholics in England. 3. Gt. Brit.—Pol. & govt.—1660–1688—Pamphlets. I. Title.

40-18694
Library of Congress BX1492.L65 1673
[2] 282.42

NL 0428841 DLC CLU-C

[Lloyd, William, bp. of Worcester,] 1627–1717.
The late Apology in behalf of the Papists, reprinted and answered in behalf of the Royalists... London: H. Brome, 1675. 46 p. 4. ed., rev. 12°.

428552A. 1. Great Britain—Hist.—Charles II, 1660–1685—Pamphlets. 2. Castlemaine, Roger Palmer, earl of, 1634–1705: The Catholique apology. I. Title.
N. Y. P. L. October 26, 1931

CU-A CLU-C NNG
NL 0428842 NN TxDaM-P TxU ViU MH NNUT-Mc CaOLU InU

DA463
1689
.T75

[LLOYD, WILLIAM] bp. of Worcester, 1627-1717.
A letter to Dr. Sherlock, in vindication of that part of Josephus's history, which gives an account of Iaddus the high-priest's submitting to Alexander the Great while Darius was living. Against the answer to the piece intituled, Obedience and submission to the present government. London, Printed for T. Jones, 1691.
[3], 33 p. 20½cm.
[Tracts. 1689-1700? no. 8]

NNUT-Mc IU TxDaM-P DFo CtY
NL 0428843 ICU MB ICN MH CU-A CLU-C InU CSmH

Lloyd, William, bp. of Worcester, 1627-1717, supposed author.
Lex talionis: or, The author of Naked truth stript naked
see under [Fell, Philip] 1633?-1682.

BR748
.S8

Lloyd, William, bp. of Worcester, 1627-1717.
Stillingfleet, Edward, *bp. of Worcester*, 1635–1699.
Origines britannicæ; or, The antiquities of the British churches. By Edw. Stillingfleet. To which is added, An historical account of church government as first received in Great Britain and Ireland. By W. Lloyd ... New ed., with additional notes by the Rev. Thomas Pinder Pantin ... Oxford, The University press, 1842.

BX1767
G35
v.3

Lloyd, William, bp. of Worcester, 1627-1717.
... The papal supremacy a novel doctrine, in a discourse, entitled, Considerations touching the true way to suppress popery in this kingdom, etc.
(In Gibson, E. a preservative against popery. London, 1848. 20½cm. v.III. p.[1]-7)
Running title: Against the doctrine of the papal supremacy.

NL 0428846 CtY

[Lloyd, William] bishop of Worcester, 1627-1717.
Papists No Catholicks: And Popery No Christianity. London, Printed for the Author, 1677.
2 p.l., 12 p., (A-B in fours) sm. 4to.
Upper margins cropped.
The Bridewater Library copy 4/C 17(4)
Bound with: A Letter To A Priest of the Roman Church... 1675.

NL 0428847 CSmH CtY WU

Case
J
5454
.2666

[LLOYD, WILLIAM, Bp. of Worcester] 1627-1717.
Papists no Catholicks: and popery no Christianity. The 2d ed. much enlarged. London, H. Brome, 1679.
[12], 55p. 20cm.

Binder's title: English tracts, 1678-89.
STC II L 2689.

NL 0428848 ICN CLU-C CtY NNUT-Mc NNG

Lloyd, William, bp. of Worcester, 1627-1717.
The pretences of the French invasion.

Les amours d'Anne d'Autriche, épouse de Louis XIII. avec Monsieur le C. D. R., le véritable père de Louis XIV. aujourd'hui roi de France. Ou l'on voit au long comment on s'y prit pour donner un heritier à la couronne, les resors qu'on fit jouer pour cela, & enfin tout le denouement de cette comedie. A Cologne, chez Pierre Marteau, 1693.

Lloyd, William, bp. of Worcester, 1627-1717, defendant.
Sancroft, William, *abp. of Canterbury*, 1617–1693, *defendant*.
The proceedings and tryal in the case of the Most Reverend Father in God William lord archbishop of Canterbury, and the Right Reverend Fathers in God, William lord bishop of St. Asaph, Francis lord bishop of Ely, John lord bishop of Chichester, Thomas lord bishop of Bath and Wells, Thomas lord bishop of Peterborough, and Jonathan lord bishop of Bristol. In the Court of Kings-bench at Westminster, in Trinity-term in the fourth year of the reign of King James the Second, annoque Dom. 1688 ... London, Printed for Thomas Basset, and Thomas Fox, 1689.

[Lloyd, William, *bp. of Worcester*] 1627–1717.
A reasonable defence of the Seasonable discourse: shewing the necessity of maintaining the established religion in opposition to popery. Or, A reply to a treatise, called, A full answer and confutation of a scandalous pamphlet, &c. London, Printed for H. Brome, 1674.
1 p. l., 46 p. 20cm.
Title vignette: publisher's device.
1. Castlemaine, Roger Palmer, earl of, 1634–1705. A full answer and confutation of a scandalous pamphlet called A seasonable discourse. 2. Lloyd, William, bp. of Worcester, 1627–1717. A seasonable discourse shewing the necessity of maintaining the established religion, in opposition to popery. 3. Catholics in England. 4. Gt. Brit.—Pol. & govt.—1660–1688—Pamphlets. I. Title.

40-20202
Library of Congress BX1492.L72

NNUT-Mc TxU MH IEN NIC NjP CtY MoU
NL 0428851 DLC CSaT CLU-C CU IaU CU-A NPV NN CSmH

---

*EC65
L7796
673sg

[Lloyd, William, bp. of Worcester, 1627-1717].
Seasonable advice to Protestants: shewing the necessity of maintaining the established religion, in opposition to popery. By Dr. Fell, late lord bishop of Oxford.
London, Printed for Charles Brome, at the Gun, at the vvest-end of St. Paul's church-yard. 1688.
4°. 1p.ℓ., 37p. 20cm.
The attribution to Fell is not now accepted (cf. Morison & Carter, John Fell, Oxford, 1967, p.215).

Originally published with title "A seasonable discourse shewing the necessity of maintaining the established religion"; also published with title Seasonable advice to all Protestant people.

NL 0428853 MH

BX1492
.L79
Rare BK

[Lloyd, William, Bp. of Worcester] 1627-1717.
A seasonable discourse shewing the necessity of maintaining the established religion, in opposition to popery. 2d ed., cor. London, Printed for H. Brome, 1673.
36 p. 20 cm.
Ascribed also to Dr. Fell. Cf. Halkett. Dict. of anon. and pseud.

1. Catholic Church in England. 2. Catholic Church--Doctrinal and controversial works--Protestant authors I. Title.

NL 0428854 ICU NNC CU-A NIC MiU MoU InU

282
L779s
1673b

[Lloyd, William] bp. of Worcester, 1627-1717.
A seasonable discourse shewing the necessity of maintaining the established religion, in opposition to popery. The third edition corrected. London, Printed for Henry Brome, at the Gun in S. Paul's church-yard, 1673.
1 p.l., 35(i.e.36)p. 21cm.

Device of bookseller on t.-p.
Error in paging: 36 numbered 35.
Ascribed also to Dr. Fell. cf. Halkett and Laing. Dict. of anon. and pseud. Engl. lit.

TxU NNUT-Mc DFo CtY MH ViU ICN TxDaM-P CLU-C CU-A
NL 0428855 IU PU CtY IEG CSmH NN MnU IEN PPL-R

[Lloyd, William, *bp. of Worcester*] 1627–1717.
A seasonable discourse shewing the necessity of maintaining the established religion, in opposition to popery. The 4th ed., cor. according to the mind of the author. London, Printed for H. Brome, MDCLXXIII.
1 p. l., 37 p. 20cm.
Title vignette: publisher's device.
Ascribed also to Dr. Fell. *cf.* Halkett and Laing. Dict. of anon. and pseud.
1. Catholic church in England. 2. Catholic church—Doctrinal and controversial works—Protestant authors. 3. Gt. Brit.—Pol. & govt.—1660–1688—Pamphlets. I. Title.

40-20200
Library of Congress BX1492.L7 1673

InU MnU CU NNUT-Mc CSmH NN MH
NL 0428856 DLC PLatS CLU-C CU-A DFo CtY NjP CU

[Lloyd, William, Bp. of Worcester] 1627-1717.
A seasonable discourse shewing the necessity of maintaining the establish'd religion, in opposition to popery, written by that most pious and learned prelate Dr. Fell, Lord Bishop of Oxford. 6th ed. London, J. Baker [1704]
35 p.

1. Catholic Church in Gt. Brit. 2. Catholic Church - Doctrinal and controversial works - Protestant authors. I Fell, John, Bp. of Oxford, 1625-1685, supposed author. II. Title.

NL 0428857 CU

Lloyd, William, *Bp. of Worcester*, 1627–1717.
A sermon at the funeral of Sir Edmund-Bury Godfrey, one of His Majesties justices of the peace, who was barbarously murthered. Preached on Thursday the last day of Octob. 1678, in the parish-church of St. Martin in the Fields. London, Printed by M. Clark for H. Brome, 1678.
43 p. 20 cm.

1. Godfrey, Sir Edmund Berry, 1621–1678.

49-41533*

NL 0428858 DLC DFo NNG CLU-C

Lloyd, William, *Bp. of Worcester*, 1627–1717.
A sermon at the funeral of Sr. Edmvnd-Bvry Godfrey, one of His Majesties justices of the peace, who was barbarously murthered. Preached on Thursday, Oct. 1678, in the parish church of St. Martin in the Fields. London, Printed by T. Newcomb for H. Brome, 1678.
42 p. 19 cm.

1. Godfrey, Sir Edmund Berry, 1621–1678.

49-34588*

CtY IU NNUT-Mc NN TxU CU WU LU CLU-C CU-A FU TxDaM-
NL 0428859 DLC DFo MH ViU MiU ICU ICN MnU CSmH RPB

VOLUME 337

AC911
W5
no.L2709

Lloyd, William, Bp. of Worcester, 1627-1717.
A sermon preached at St. Martins in the Fields on November the fifth, 1678. By William Lloyd, D.D. Dean of Bangor, and one of His Majesties Chaplains in Ordinary. London, Printed by T.N. for Henry Brome, 1679.
2 p.ℓ., 34 p. 20 cm.
In envelope.
Wing L-2709.

NL 0428860 CU-A DFo CtY IEN ICN CLU-C TxDaM-P MnU NNUT-Mc

252
L779s

Lloyd, William, bp. of Worcester, 1627-1717.
A sermon preached at the funeral of the right reverend father in God John late lord bishop of Chester. At the Guildhal chappel London, on Thursday the 12 of December, 1672. By William Lloyd D.D. dean of Bangor, and one of His Majesties chaplains in ordinary. London, Printed by A. C. for Henry Brome, at the Gun at the west-end of S. Pauls. 1672.
36p. 19½cm.
Title within mourning border.
1. Sermons.

NL 0428861 IU ICN PPL NjP DFo PU NNG MB NNUT Nh NNUT-Mc InNd

*H.97
.188

Lloyd, William, Bp. of Worcester, 1627-1717.
A sermon preached at the funeral of the Right Reverend father in God, John late Lord Bishop of Chester, at the Guildhall chappel London, on Thursday the 12. of December, 1672. London, Printed for H. Brome, 1678.
55 p. 18cm. (In Wilkins, John, Bp. of Chester. Of the principle and duties of natural religion. London, Printed for T. Basset, etc., 1678)
1. Wilkins, John, Bp. of Chester, 1614-1672.

NL 0428862 MB

Lloyd, William, bp. of Worcester, 1627–1717.
A sermon preached at the funeral of the Right Reverend Father in God, John, late lord bishop of Chester, at the Guildhall chappel, London, on Thursday the 12. of December, 1672. By William Lloyd... London, C. Brome, 1694. 55 p. 19cm.
1. Wilkins, John, bp. of Chester, 1614–1672.
N. Y. P. L. August 13, 1947

NL 0428863 NN PPiPT NNUT-Mc

rBX5199
W65
L5

Lloyd, William, Bp. of Worcester, 1627-1717.
A sermon preach'd at the funeral of the Right Reverend Father in God, John, late Lord Bishop of Chester, at the Guildhall Chappel, London, on Thursday the 12th of December, 1672. By William Lloyd ... London, Printed for Charles Brome, 1698.
55 p. front. (port.) 19 cm.

Wilkins, John, Bp. of Chester, 1614-1672

NL 0428864 CU-A MH

BL180
.W5

Lloyd, William, bp. of Worcester, 1627-1717.
A sermon preached at the funeral of John Wilkins
Wilkins, John, *bp. of Chester*, 1614–1672.
Of the principles and duties of natural religion ... By the Right Reverend Father in God, Dr. John Wilkins ... to which is added. A sermon preached at his funeral, by William Lloyd ... 7th ed. London, Printed for R. Bonwicke [etc.], 1715.

252
Se662
v.7

Lloyd, William, bp. of Worcester, 1627-1717.
A sermon preached before the House of lords, on November 5.1680. By the Right Reverend Father in God, William lord bishop of St. Asaph. London, Printed by M. C. for Henry Brome, at the Gun in St. Paul's church-yard, 1680.
4 p.l., 39p. 19½cm.
[Sermons on various subjects, 1637-1706. v.7, no.6]
1. Sermons. 2. Catholic church.

NL 0428866 IU MH ICN NjP CtY MB CLU-C NNUT-Mc CSmH

British Tracts 1690 L77

Lloyd, William, Bp. of Worcester, 1627-1717.
A sermon preached before the King & Queen at White-Hall, March the twelfth, 1689/90. Being the fast-day. By the Bishop of St. Asaph, Lord Almoner to Their Majesties. Published by Their Majesties command. London, Printed for Robert Clavell at the Peacock in St. Paul's Church-yard. 1690.
2 p.ℓ., 32 p. 20 cm.

NL 0428867 CtY ICN PU CLU-C NNUT-Mc TxU

252
L779sk

Lloyd, William, bp. of Worcester, 1627-1717
A sermon preached before the king at White-hall March 6.1673/4. By William Lloyd, D.D. dean of Bangor, and one of His Majesties chaplains in ordinary. Published by His Majesties command. London, Printed by Andrew Clark, for Henry Brome at the Gun at the west-end of St. Paul's, 1674.
1 p.l., 33, [1]p. 19½cm.
Caption title: A Lent-sermon.
Imperfect: lower margin of t.-p. closely trimmed; part of imprint removed.
1. Sermons.

NL 0428868 IU NjP NBU MnU MH CSmH RPB ICU

Lloyd, William, Bp. of Worcester, 1627-1717.
A sermon preached before the King at White-Hall, on Decemb. 1. M.DC.LXVII. Being the first Sunday in Advent ... London, Printed by E. Cotes, for H. Brome, 1668.
35 p. 20cm.
Imperfect copy: outer margins closely trimmed.
Wing L-2702
___ Another copy. 21cm. [Collection of miscellaneous English sermons. London [etc.] 1641-1795. v.5, no.1]

NL 0428869 CLU-C CSmH MH ICN CtY IU DFo PU NNUT-Mc

252
L779sb
1674

Lloyd, William, bp. of Worcester, 1627-1717.
A sermon preached before the king at White-hall, on Decemb.1.M.DC.LXVII. By William Lloyd D.D. dean of Bangor, and one of His Majesties chaplains in ordinary. Published by His Maiesties command. London, Printed by A. C. for Henry Brome at the Gun in St. Paul's church yard at the west end, 1674.
1 p.l., 35p. 19½cm.
1. Sermons.

NL 0428870 IU PPiPT NNC CLU-C CtY NjP

282
An46

Lloyd, William, bp. of Worcester, 1627-1717.
A sermon preached before the king at White-hall. The 24th of Novemb.1678. By William Lloyd, D.D. dean of Bangor, and chaplain in ordinary to His Majesty. Published by His Majesties command. London, Printed by M. C. for Henry Brome, at the Gun at the west-end of St. Pauls. 1679.
3 p.l., 3-72p. 20½cm.
[Anglican tracts attacking Roman catholicism. 12]
1. Sermons. 2. Catholic church--Doctrinal and controversial works --Protestant authors.

NL 0428871 IU MnU CU-A MnU ICN NjP InNd NcD PPiPT PU DFo NNUT-Mc IEN DFo CLU-C

Mhc7
G35
v.12

Lloyd, William, bp. of Worcester, 1627-1717.
... A sermon preached before the King, at Whitehall, the 24th of November, 1678.
(In Gibson, E. A preservative against popery. London,1848. 20½cm. v.XII p.[1]-43.
Running title: A confutation of the chief doctrines of popery.

NL 0428872 CtY

BX
5133
L4
Rare
Book

Lloyd, William, bp. of Worcester, 1627-1717.
A sermon preached before Their Majesties at Whitehall, on the fifth day of November, 1689. Being the anniversary-day of thanksgiving for that great deliverance from the gunpowder-treason, and also the day of His Majesties happy landing in England. By the Bishop of St. Asaph, Lord Almoner to Their Majesties. By Their Majesties command. London, Printed for Robert Clavell, 1689.
2 p. ℓ., 32 p. 20cm.
1. Gunpowder plot, 1605 - Anniversaries, etc. 2. Thanksgiving sermons. I. William III, king of Great Britain, 1650-1702. II. Mary II, queen of Great Britain, 1662-1694. III. Title

NL 0428874 ViW CU-A CLU-C ICN CtY DFo TxU

Lloyd, William, 1674-1719.

Gt. Brit. *Parliament, 1702. House of commons.*
The evidence given at the bar of the House of commons, upon the complaint of Sir John Pakington, against William lord bishop of Worcester and Mr. Lloyd, his son. Together with the proceedings of the House of commons thereupon. London, E. Jones, and T. Goodwin, 1702.

Lloyd, William, 1674–1719.
Series chronologica, olympiadum, pythiadum, isthmiadum, nemeadum, quibus veteres Græci tempora sua metiebantur ... Per Gulielmum Lloyd ... Oxoniæ, e theatro Sheldoniano, 1700.
4 p. l., xlii, 161 p. 31cm.
1. Chronology, Greek—Tables.
Library of Congress DF207.L7 4-35347

NL 0428876 DLC CtY PPL

Lloyd,William,d.1679,defendant.
The last speech of Mr.William Lloyd a clergyman,who was tryed and condemned at Brecknock in South-Wales. An.Dom.1679.and dyed in prison there a week before he was to be executed; and left this speech in writing. [London? 1679?]
2 p. 31cm.
No.12 in a volume lettered: Collection of tryals.
1.Popish plot, 1678.

NL 0428877 MiU-L

Lloyd, William, 1874-
Hay-fever, hay-asthma, its causes, diagnosis, and treatment. By William Lloyd, ... Chicago, W. T. Keener & Co., 1907.
[6], 95 p. 22cm.

NL 0428878 ICJ PPC IU-M MiD DNLM

VOLUME 337

Lloyd, William, 1874–
Hay-fever, hay asthma, its causes, diagnosis and treatment, by William Lloyd ... Third edition. London, Straker brothers limited, 1931.
vii, 124 p. 2 pl. 22cm.
Revised by Dr. Eldon Pratt. *cf.* Preface.
"First edition 1907."
Bibliographical foot-notes.

1. Hay-fever. I. Pratt, Eldon, ed.
A 32–41
Title from Univ. of Mich. 615.3L793 1931 Printed by L. C.

NL 0428879 MiU PPC DNLM MiD IU-M ICJ

Lloyd, William A C
The return from the masque, and other poems, by William A. C. Lloyd. London, Constable and co., 1911. viii, 101 p. 20cm.
"1st edition" in ms. on lining paper.
Author's autographed presentation copy to W. H. Powell.

362059B. 1. No subject. I. Title.
N. Y. P. L. March 21, 1947

NL 0428880 NN

Lloyd, William A C.
Vincenzo Bellini, a memoir by William A. C. Lloyd. London, Sisley's ltd. [1908]
4 p. l., 232 p. front. (port.) 22½cm.

1. Bellini, Vincenzo, 1801–1835.
9–28743
Library of Congress ML410.B44L7

NL 0428881 DLC PPCI MB

LLOYD, WILLIAM A. C.
Vincenzo Bellini; a memoir. London, Sisley's [1908] 232 p. 23cm.

Film reproduction. Negative.

JULIAN EDWARDS COLLECTION

1. Bellini, Vincenzo, 1801-1835.

NL 0428882 NN LU

Lloyd, William Alford.
A list,with descriptions,illustrations,and prices,of whatever relates to aquaria. [By] W.Alford Lloyd... London,[Hayman bros., printers],1858.

128 p. front. illus. 19 cm.
F 6248.58.40

NL 0428883 MH

Lloyd, William Alford.
Why the sea is salt. Illus.
(In Brown, Robert, editor. Science for all. Vol. 2, pp. 25-34. London. [1879.])

E5070 — Sea-water.

NL 0428884 MB

1.9
Ex892LL
Lloyd, William Allison, 1870-1946.
[Collected papers, 1913-1945]
[Washington, 1913-45]
3 v.

1. Agricultural extension. 2. County agricultural agents. I. Lloyd, William Allison, 1870-1946. Addresses, essays, lectures, etc.

NL 0428885 DNAL

275.2
L77B
Lloyd, William Allison, 1870-1946.
Boys' and girls' 4-H club work; what it is. [n.p.,] 1936.
6 l.

NL 0428886 DNAL

Lloyd, William Allison, 1870–
... County agricultural agent work in the northern and western states. Status and results in 1915– By W. A. Lloyd ... [Washington, Govt. print. off.] 1916–
v. illus. 23cm. (S. R. S. Doc. 32, 60. Circular no. 1, 5. Ext. N)
At head of title: Cooperative extension work in agriculture and home economics. U. S. Dept. of agriculture and state agricultural colleges cooperating. States relations service, Office of extension work, north and west.
1915 has title: Status and results of county agricultural agent work in the northern and western states, 1915.
1. Agricultural education. [1. Agricultural extension] 2. [County agricultural agents]
Agr 16–1354 Revised
Library, U. S. Dept. of Agriculture 1Ex89D no. 32

NL 0428887 DNAL

Lloyd, William Allison, 1870–
... County agricultural agent work under the Smith-Lever act, 1914 to 1924. [By William A. Lloyd] [Washington, Govt. print. off., 1926]
ii, 60 p. illus., maps, diagrs. 23cm. (U. S. Dept. of agriculture. Miscellaneous circular no. 59)
Contribution from Office of cooperative extension work.

1. [County agricultural agents] 2. [Smith-Lever act]
Agr 26–688
Library, U. S. Dept. of Agriculture 1Ag86Cm no. 59

NL 0428888 DNAL WaWW MB PPComm

Lloyd, William Allison, 1870–
... An extension program for range management and range livestock as adopted at a regional extension conference held at Spokane, Wash., May 24–27, 1937. By W. A. Lloyd ... [Washington, U. S. Govt. print. off., 1938]
11 p. 23cm. (U. S. Dept. of agriculture. Circular no. 468)
Contribution from Extension service.

1. Agriculture—Congresses. [1. Agricultural extension—Congresses] 2. Cattle—U. S. [2. Ranges, Cattle] 3. Stock-ranges. [3. Ranges—Management] I. Title.
Agr 38–175
U. S. Dept of agr. Library 1Ag84C no. 468
for Library of Congress [S21.A48 no. 468]
[5*] (630.6173)

NL 0428889 DNAL WaWW DLC

Lloyd, William Allison, 1870–
... An extension program in crop production to reenforce range livestock, dairying, and human nutrition for the western states. [By] W. A. Lloyd ... Washington [Govt. print. off.] 1924.
16 p. 23cm. (U. S. Dept. of agriculture. Department circular 335)
Contribution from Office of cooperative extension work.

1. [Agricultural extension] 2. Agriculture—Western states. 3. Dairying—Western states. 4. Nutrition. 5. [Stock]-ranges. I. Title.
Agr 25–11
Library, U. S. Dept. of Agriculture 1Ag84D no. 335
Library of Congress [S21.A47 no. 335]

NL 0428890 DNAL WaWW

Lloyd, William Allison, 1870–
... An extension program in home management and farm management for the western states, with reports of standing regional committees on range livestock, dairying, farm crops, and human nutrition. [By] W. A. Lloyd ... Washington [Govt. print. off.] 1925.
16 p. 23cm. (U. S. Dept. of agriculture. Department circular 375)
Contribution from Office of cooperative extension work.
1. Agricultural education—Congresses. [1. Agricultural extension—Congresses] 2. Agriculture—The West. [2. Agriculture—Western states] 3. Dairying—The West. [3. Dairying—Western states] 4. Nutrition. 5. [Stock] ranges. I. Title.
Agr 26–7
Library, U. S. Dept. of Agriculture 1Ag84D no. 375

NL 0428891 DNAL

Lloyd, William Allison, 1870–
... An extension program in range livestock, dairying, and human nutrition for the western states. [By] W. A. Lloyd ... Washington [Govt. print. off.] 1924.
14 p. illus. 23cm. (U. S. Dept. of agriculture. Department circular 308)
Contribution from Office of cooperative extension work.

1. Agricultural education—Congresses. [1. Agricultural extension—Congresses] 2. Dairying — The West. [2. Dairying — Western states] 3. Nutrition. 4. Stock-ranges—The West. [4. Ranges] I. Title.
Agr 24—108
U. S. Dept. of agr. Library 1Ag84D no. 308
for Library of Congress [a41e1]

NL 0428892 DNAL WaWW

S544
L55
Lloyd, William Allison, 1870-
The relation of age to extension work. Is extension service as at present organized reaching young men and women (age 16 to ∞) in sufficient numbers? [Logan, Utah, 1931]
4 v. in 1. diagrs.,tables.

Caption title.
"For presentation at the Western States Extension Conference, Logan, Utah, July 21-25, 1931."

NL 0428893 CU

Lloyd, William Allison, 1870–
... A review of five years of fact organization and state and regional program making in the western states, and a report of the 1927 extension conference. [By] W. A. Lloyd ... Washington [U. S. Govt. print. off.] 1927.
19 p. illus. 23½cm. (U. S. Dept. of agriculture. Miscellaneous publication no. 8)
Contribution from Office of cooperative extension work.
This review, in slightly different form, was presented ... at the Western states extension conference, Reno, Nev., July 11, 1927.
1. Agricultural education. [1. Agricultural extension] 2. Agricultural education—Congresses. [2. Agricultural extension—Congresses] I. Title.
Agr 27–644
Library, U. S. Dept. of Agriculture 1Ag84M no. 8

NL 0428894 DNAL WaWW OU

Lloyd, William Allison, 1870- 1946

U. S. *States relations service.*
... Status and results of county-agent work, northern and western states, 1915–1921. [Washington, Govt. print. off.] 1916–22.

Geneal.
Case
MS
E
7
.L 769
LLOYD, WILLIAM ARTEMUS, 1832-1910.
Lloyd genealogy... [n.p.,n.d.]
231p. 26cm.
Title from label on cover.
In manuscript.

NL 0428896 ICN

VOLUME 337

Lloyd, William Artemus, 1832-1910.

Milles, *Mrs.* **Bess Lucile (Lloyd) 1898–**
Lloyds of Blandford, Massachusetts, and some of their descendants, by Bess Lloyd Milles. Ann Arbor, Mich., Edwards brothers, inc., 1938.

Lloyd, William B *comp.*
... The hog and hog cholera, by fifteen specialists, comp. by William B. Lloyd ... Chicago, Ill., Rural press company ₍1900₎
53 p. illus. 19½cm. (The rural press series. no. 1)

1. Swine. 2. Hog cholera.

11-18832

Library of Congress SF973.L6

NL 0428898 DLC

Lloyd, William B.
Lloyd's modern poultry book guide and directory, by W. B. Lloyd ... Chicago, Howard & Wilson publishing co., 1894.
280, 20 p. illus. 19½cm. (*On cover:* Farmer's reading circle library. no. 4)

1. Poultry.

Library of Congress SF487.L79 12-27276

NL 0428899 DLC DNAL

Lloyd, William Bross, 1875- defendant.
The people of the state of Illinois vs. William Bross Lloyd ₍et al.₎ ₍Transcript of record, March term 1920, in the state of Illinois, County of Cook in the Criminal Court. Papers before the Supreme Court of Illinois, Oct. term 1922₎ Chicago, 1920-1922.
3 reels.
Microfilmed for the Fund for the Republic. Positive.

NL 0428900 ICRL

Lloyd, William Bross, 1875–
The Socialist party and its purposes, by William Bross Lloyd (assisted by Isaac Edw. Ferguson) Chicago, The Goodspeed press, 1918.
cover-title, 40 p. 19½cm.
Portrait of author on p. ₍2₎ of cover.

1. Socialist party (U. S.) I. Ferguson, Isaac Edward, joint author. II. Title.

24-17406

Library of Congress HX89.L5

NL 0428901 DLC NN

Lloyd, William Bross, 1909–
Constitutional action for peace. Hinsdale, Ill., H. Regnery Co., 1947.
25 p. 22 cm. (The Human events pamphlets, no. 24)

1. U. S.—For. rel. 2. U. S. Constitution—Amendments. I. Title. (Series)

H39.H8 no. 24 342.732 48—5032*

NL 0428902 DLC MB PPT

Lloyd, William Bross, 1908–
Town meeting for America; how citizens can set the course for United States world relations. New York, Island Press Cooperative ₍1951₎
84 p. 29 cm.
Bibliographical footnotes.

1. International organization. 2. U. S.—For. rel. 3. U. S.—Constitutional history. I. Title.

JX1954.L57 327.73 51-11213 rev

NL 0428903 DLC Or MB NN NcU

Lloyd, William Forster, 1794-1852.
An early exposition of "final utility." W.F.Lloyd's lecture on "The notion of value" (1833) reprinted. ₍London, Macmillan and co., limited; New York, The Macmillan company, 1927₎
₍168₎-183 p. 24cm.
Caption title.
On cover: Econ.hist.no.2 ₍i.e.v.2₎ ... Reprinted from "The Economic journal" (Supplement) May,1927.
Foreword signed: R.F.Harrod.
1.Value. I.Harrod,Roy Forbes,ed. II.Title: Final utility.

HB201.L79

NL 0428904 MiU

339.42 L779f 1834 **Lloyd, William Forster,** 1794-1852.
Four lectures on poor-laws, delivered before the University of Oxford, in Michaelmas term, 1834. London, Roake and Varty, 1835.
128p. 23cm.

1. Poor laws. Gt.Brit. I. Title.

NL 0428905 KU MH CtY MdBP

Lloyd, William Forster, 1794-1852.
A lecture on the notion of value, as distinguishable not only from utility, but also from value in exchange. Delivered before the University of Oxford, in Michaelmas term 1833, by the Rev. W. F. Lloyd ... London, Roake and Varty; Oxford, J. H. Parker, etc., 1834.
40 p. 20½cm.
1. Value. 2. Exchange.

NL 0428906 NNC MH PU InU MdBP

HB 31 .R4 no.1 Lloyd, William Forster, 1794-1852.
Lectures on population, value, poor-laws, and rent, delivered in the University of Oxford during the years, 1832-1836. London, Roake & Varty, 1837.
1 v. (various pagings) (Reprints of economic classics, no.1)
Library's copy is a reprint: New York, A.M. Kelley, 1968.
1. Poor laws-Gt. Brit. 2. Population. 3. Gt. Brit.-Econ. policy-1800-1837. I. Title. II. Series.

NL 0428907 DAU MH-BA MH ICJ NNC ICN

Lloyd, William Forster, 1794–1852.
Prices of corn in Oxford in the beginning of the fourteenth century: also from the year 1583 to the present time. To which are added some miscellaneous notices of prices in other places. Collected from manuscripts at Oxford. With a full account of the authorities on which the several prices are stated. By the Rev. W. F. Lloyd ... Oxford, The University press, 1830.
viii, 100 p. incl. tables. 23½cm.

1. Grain trade—Oxford. 2. Prices—Gt. Brit.—Hist.

5—16024

Library of Congress HD9041.4.L6

NL 0428908 DLC MH-BA FTaSU NIC CtY PU NcU MiU

LLOYD, WILLIAM FORSTER, 1794-1852.
Prices of corn in Oxford in the beginning of the fourteenth century. Also from the near 1583 to the present time... Oxford, University press, 1830.
viii, 100 p. 23cm.

Film reproduction. Negative.

1. Prices, Grain--Gt. Br.--Eng.--Oxford.

NL 0428909 NN

Lloyd, William Forster, 1794-1852.
Two lectures on poor-laws, delivered before the University of Oxford, in Hilary term, 1836. London, Roake and Varty, 1836.
71 p. 23 cm.
Bound with his Two lectures on the checks to population. Oxford, 1833.

NL 0428910 MdBP MH

Lloyd, William Forster, 1794-1852.
Two lectures on the checks to population, delivered before the University of Oxford, in Michaelmas term 1832 ... Oxford, Printed by S.Collingwood for the author, 1833.
1 p.l., ii, 75 p. 22.5 cm.

NL 0428911 MH-BA PU IU InU MH MdBP

Lloyd, William Forster, 1794-1852.
Two lectures on the justice of poor-laws, and one lecture on rent, delivered in the University of Oxford, in Michaelmas term, 1836. London, Roake and Varty, 1837.
106 p. 23 cm.
Bound with his Two lectures on the checks to population. Oxford, 1833.

NL 0428912 MdBP MH NcU

Lloyd, William Francis.
Capital for labour, by W. Francis Lloyd and Bertram Austin ... with forewords by W. L. Hichens ... and Arthur Pugh ... London, T. F. Unwin limited (E. Benn ltd.) 1927.
141, ₍1₎ p. 22cm.

1. Gt. Brit.—Indus. 2. Labor and laboring classes—Gt. Brit. I. Austin, Bertram Herbert, joint author. II. Title.

27-12543

Library of Congress HC256.3.L6 1927

NL 0428913 DLC KU MiU OCl NN

Lloyd, William Francis.
Capital for labor, by W. Francis Lloyd and Bertram Austin ... with forewords by W. L. Hichens and Arthur Pugh. New York, Dodd, Mead & company, 1927.
142 p. 19½cm.

1. Gt. Brit.—Indus. 2. Labor and laboring classes—Gt. Brit. I. Austin, Bertram Herbert, joint author. II. Title.

27-11626

Library of Congress HC256.3.L6 1927 a

NL 0428914 DLC OrP WaS ViU NcD PPF PPM CaBViP OrCS ICJ NN

HD4945 .A82 Lloyd, William Francis, joint author.

Austin, Bertram Herbert.
Het geheim van een hoogen loonstandaard, door Bertram Austin en W. Francis Lloyd, met een woord vooraf voor de Nederlandsche uitgave door P. J. C. Tetrode en voor de oorspronkelijke uitgave door Walter T. Layton. Amsterdam, Scheltema & Holkema ₍pref. 1926₎

VOLUME 337

Lloyd, William Francis, joint author.

HD4945 .A83 Austin, Bertram Herbert.
... Das rätsel hoher löhne, aus dem englischen übersetzt vo Carl Trapp. Braunschweig, F. Vieweg & sohn akt.-ges., 192

HD4945 .A8 1926 a Lloyd, William Francis, joint author.

Austin, Bertram Herbert.
The secret of high wages, by Bertram Austin ... and W. Francis Lloyd ... with a foreword by Walter T. Layton ... New York, Dodd, Mead and company, 1926.

Lloyd, William Franklin, 1855–
Two years in a growing prayer meeting, by Rev. W. F. Lloyd ... Nashville, Tenn., Dallas, Tex., Publishing house of the M. E. church, South, Smith & Lamar, agents, 1907.
122 p. 19cm.

1. Prayer-meetings. I. Title.

Library of Congress BV285.L6 7-34573

NL 0428918 DLC ViU

LLOYD, W[illiam] F[rederick].
Versions and perversions. Windsor, [Eng], Luff & sons, 1920.

NL 0428919 MH

Lloyd, William Frederick.
The Welsh fasting girl, and other plays. By W.F. Lloyd, &c. Swansea, Thomas & Parry Ltd., printers, 1923.
sq. 16°.
With Welsh translations of the Welsh fasting girl, and of Cum Farm.

NL 0428920 MH NN

Lloyd, William Freeman, 1791-1853.
The abridged Bible catechism, arranged in forty divisions: all the answers to the questions being in the exact words of Scripture: intended for the religious instruction of the young, both in families and schools. By W. F. Lloyd. Philadelphia, American Sunday school union, 1826.
iv, ₍5₎-96 p. 11cm.
(DLC: BT 1031. L5 (Rare bk. room)

NL 0428921 NNC DLC

Lloyd, William Freeman, 1791-1853.
The Bible catechism... By W. F. Lloyd. 2d ed. London, Printed by Weed and Rider, 1823.
2 p. l., 140 p.

NL 0428922 MiU

Lloyd, William Freeman, 1791-1853.
A catechism on the evidences of the Bible; in easy rhyme. Intended for the young to commit to memory. By W.F. Lloyd. London, published and sold at the Sunday-school union depôt, R. Davis, [etc.] no date.
iv, [5]-36 p. 13.5 cm.

NL 0428923 NNUT

Bonaparte Collection No.6879
LLOYD, WILLIAM FREEMAN, 1791-1853.
Hum curto catichismo da Biblia, disposado em quarento divisaõs; todas as repostas per as perguntas sendo ne as palavras de as Santas Escrituras. Traducido em indo-portugueza, de Robert Newstead. Londres, J.Rider₍n.d.₎
104p. 14cm.

NL 0428924 ICN

Office **Lloyd, William Freeman,** 1791–1853.
Sketch of the life of Robert Raikes, esq. and of the history of Sunday schools. By W. F. Lloyd. From the London edition. Revised by the editors. New-York, Lane & Scott, for the Sunday-school union of the Methodist Episcopal church, 1849.
1 p. l., ₍v₎–viii, ₍9₎–125 p. 15½cm.

1. Raikes, Robert, 1736–1811. 2. Sunday-schools—Hist.

Library of Congress BV1518.R3L5 7-34564

NL 0428925 DLC MB

---

268 R779
Lloyd, William Freeman, 1791-1853.
Sketch of the life of Robert Raikes, esq. and of the history of Sunday schools. By W. F. Lloyd. From the London edition. New York, Phillips, 1879.
125 p.

1. Raikes, Robert, 1736-1811.

NL 0428926 NNC

Lloyd, William Freeman, 1791-1853
The teacher's manual; or, Hints to a teacher on being appointed to the charge of a Sunday school class ... Philadelphia, 1825.
112p. 15cm.
Revised by the Committee of publication of the American Sunday school union.

1. Sunday schools--Teaching. I. American Sunday school union--Committee of publication.

NL 0428927 RPB

BV1534 .L75 LLOYD, WILLIAM FREEMAN, 1791-1853.
The teacher's manual; or, Hints to a teacher on being appointed to the charge of a Sunday school class. By W.F.Lloyd. Rev.by the Committee of publication. Philadelphia, American Sunday school union[1826?]
v, [7]-108 p. 15cm.

1.Sunday-school teaching.

NL 0428928 ICU PSt NBuG

Lloyd, William Freeman, 1791-1853.
Thoughts in rhyme. London, Hamilton, Adams, 1851.
106 p. 14.5 cm.

1. Religious poetry, English. I. Title.

NL 0428929 MBU-T

Lloyd, William Henry, 1870-1936.
Cases on certain equitable doctrines and remedies, selected and annotated by William H. Loyd ... Philadelphia, Pa., International printing company ₍°1917₎
cover-title, viii, 418 p. 25cm. $4.50

1. Equity—Cases. 2. Equitable remedies—Cases.

Library of Congress 17-25791 Revised

NL 0428930 DLC PU-L PU

Lloyd, William Henry, 1870-1936.
Cases on civil procedure. pt. 1– By William H. Loyd ... Philadelphia, International printing co., 1910–
v. 23cm.
Cover-title.

10-22420

NL 0428931 DLC PU

Lloyd, William Henry, 1870–1936, *ed.*
Cases on civil procedure, selected and annotated by William H. Loyd ... Indianapolis, The Bobbs-Merrill company ₍°1916₎
xiii, 962 p. 23½ cm.

1. Civil procedure—Cases.

17—9476

NL 0428932 DLC IdU IU FU NcD PPT-L PU PU-L PPB

Lloyd, William Henry, 1870–1936, *ed.*
Cases on pleading in actions at law, selected and annotated by William H. Lloyd ... Indianapolis, The Bobbs-Merrill company ₍°1927₎
x, 805 p. 26cm.

1. Pleading—Cases. I. Title.

27—25375

NL 0428933 DLC MtU PU NcD PU-L PPB NSyU FU WaU-L

Lloyd, William Henry, 1870–
The early courts of Pennsylvania, by William H. Loyd ... Boston, The Boston book company, 1910.
4 p. l., ₍v₎–vii, ₍1₎ p., 1 l., 287 p. 21cm. (*On cover:* Univ. of Penna. Law school series. II) $3.50

1. Courts—Pennsylvania. I. Title.

Library of Congress 10-29779 Revised
——— Copy 2. JK93.P4L8

PHi PPB PPL
NL 0428934 DLC WaU-L PMA CU-AL NcD MiU NN Ok PU

Lloyd, William Henry, 1870-1936.
The federal courts; brief outline of their organization and jurisdiction under the new "judicial code". Philadelphia, 1911.

NL 0428935 PU-L

VOLUME 337

Lloyd, William Huntley.

Presbyterian church in the U. S. A. *Presbytery of Long Island.*
Epher Whitaker of Southold, pub. as a memorial by the Presbytery of Long Island. [n. p., 1917?]

Lloyd, William L
An analysis of Temple commandery, no. 2 of Albany, N.Y.
see under Freemasons. Albany. Knights Templars. Temple Commandery, No. 2.

Lloyd, William L.
Hours of service law for railroad men, with official rulings and opinions of the Inter-state commerce commission, analyzed by Will L. Lloyd ... Albany, The Argus company, printers, 1908.
cover-title, 8 p. 24cm.

1. Railroads—U. S.—Employees. 2. Hours of labor.

A 13-2525

Title from Bureau of Railway Economics. Printed by L. C.

NL 0428938 DBRE

JK3430 .N5 **Lloyd, William L., ed.**

... The **New York** red book, containing latest information re lating to the state government ...
Albany, J. B. Lyon company, 18

Lloyd, William Penn, 1837-1911.
The Banker and the Lawyer; an address delivered before the Department of Law of the University of Pennsylvania, Nov. 16, 1900.
n.p., n.d.
28 p.

NL 0428940 MH-L

[Lloyd, William Penn] 1837-1911.
History of the First reg't. Pennsylvania reserve cavalry, from its organization, August, 1861, to September, 1864, with list of names of all officers and enlisted men who have ever belonged to the regiment ... Philadelphia, King & Baird, printers, 1864.
216 p. 19½cm.
Preface signed: Wm. P. Lloyd.

1. Pennsylvania cavalry. 1st regt., 1861-1865. 2. U. S.—Hist.—Civil war—Regimental histories—Pa. cav.—1st. I. Title.

Library of Congress E527.6.1st 2-15694 Revised

PPL PU OClWHi
NL 0428941 DLC IaU ViU PSt NIC NjP DNW NcD MiU PP

Micro 3 Lloyd, William Penn, 1837-1911
History of the First reg't. Pennsylvania reserve cavalry, from its organization, August, 1861, to September, 1864, with list of names of all officers and enlisted men who have ever belonged to the regiment ... Philadelphia, King & Baird, printers, 1864.
216p. 20cm.
Micro-opaque. Louisville, Ky., Lost Cause Press, 1957. 5 cards. 7.5x12.5cm. (Travels in the Confederate states)
1. Pennsylvania cavalry. 1st regt., 1861-1865.

NL 0428942 PSt OOxM OU TxU ICRL MsU

Lloyd, William Penn, 1837-1911
Women as lawyers. Argument for applicant in the Miss Ida G. Kast case. [Mechanicsburg, Pa., 1893] 13 p. 8°.

1. Woman.—Lawyers, U. S.: Penn. 2. Kast, Ida G.
N. Y. P. L. March 25, 1911.

NL 0428943 NN

Lloyd, William Reese, 1913–
A phytochemical study of *Leptotaenia multifida* (Nuttall) ... by William Reese Lloyd ... [n. p., 1942]
[33]-38 p. 23cm.
Abstract of thesis (PH. D.)—University of Minnesota, 1941.
Thesis t.-p. and Vita on p. [2] of cover.
A reprint (by W. R. Lloyd and G. L. Jenkins) from the Pharmaceutical archives, May, 1942.
"References": p. 38.

1. Leptotaenia multifida. I. Jenkins, Glenn Llewellyn, 1898– joint author.

Library of Congress QK866.L53L5 43-10198

NL 0428944 DLC

Lloyd, Mrs. William Reynolds
see
Lloyd, Mrs. Bitha (Fox) 1811-

Lloyd, William Supplee, 1860–
Catalogue of various editions of Robinson Crusoe and other books by and referring to Daniel Defoe. Library of William S. Lloyd, Germantown, Philadelphia ... [Philadelphia, Shaw printing co., 1915]
43 p. incl. facsim. 23cm.
Caption title.
Book-plate of collection (vignette) on cover.

1. Defoe, Daniel, 1661?-1731—Bibl. 2. Defoe, Daniel, 1661?-1731. Robinson Crusoe—Bibl.

16-15123

Library of Congress Z8821.L66

NL 0428946 DLC MB PHi PP ICN MWA PP MiU ICN

Lloyd, William Valentine, 1825-1896.
Description of the armorial insignia of the Vaughans of Llwydiarth, which once surrounded their family pew in Llanfihangel church, but are now in Wynnstay chapel; with memorials of the Lloyds of Dolobran and other cognate families. By the Rev. W. V. Lloyd ...
(*In* Powys-land club, Welshpool, Wales. Collections historical & archæological relating to Montgomeryshire and its borders. London, 1881. 22cm. vol. XIV, ii, 355-396 p. illus., coats of arms)

1. Vaughan family. 2. Lloyd family. 3. Heraldry—Wales.

16-25572

Library of Congress DA740.M7P8 vol. 14
——— Separate. CS459.V3
"A few copies of the paper on 'The armorial insignia of the Vaughans of Llwydiarth' have been reprinted in a separate form."

NL 0428947 DLC

Lloyd, William Valentine, 1825-1896.
The sheriffs of Montgomeryshire, with their armorial bearings, and notices, genealogical & biographical, of their families, from 1540 to 1639. By Rev. W. V. Lloyd ... London, T. Richards, 1876.
2 p. l., xxiv, 546 p. plates, geneal. tables (part fold.) coats of arms. 23cm.
"Two hundred copies ... printed."
"These memoirs originally appeared in the 'Collections, archæological and historical, relating to Montgomeryshire, and its borders,' issued by the Powys-land club."—Pref.

1. Sheriffs — Montgomeryshire, Wales. 2. Montgomeryshire, Wales — Geneal. 3. Montgomeryshire, Wales—Biog. I. Title.

13-12664

Library of Congress CS455.S5L6

NL 0428948 DLC CtY

Lloyd, William Watkiss, 1813-1893.
The age of Pericles: a history of the politics and arts of Greece from the Persian to the Peloponnesian war; by William Watkiss Lloyd ... London, Macmillan and co., 1875.
2 v. 22½cm.

1. Greece—Hist. 2. Greek literature—Hist. & crit. 3. Art, Greek.

Library of Congress DF227.L7 4-34999

OrStbM CaBVaU
ViU OCX OCU CtY MdBP DGU OrP MeB NIC MtU WaSp OrU
NL 0428949 DLC OU NjP PHC PSC PPL PPM NcD OO OCl

Lloyd, William Watkiss 1813-1893.
Christianity in the cartoons, referred to artistic treatment and historic fact. Lond., J. E. Taylor, 1863.
391 p. plates.

NL 0428950 MiD

Lloyd, William Watkiss, 1813-1893.
Critical essays on the plays of Shakespeare, by William Watkiss Lloyd. London, G. Bell and sons, 1875.
viii, 493, [1] p. 17½cm.
On cover: The Aldine edition.

1. Shakespeare, William—Criticism and interpretation.

Library of Congress PR2976.L6 3-11272

NN CaBVa
NL 0428951 DLC MdBP WaU NBC CtY PU-F MiU NjP NcU

Lloyd, William Watkiss, 1813-1893.

Critical essays on the plays of Shakespeare, b William Watkiss Lloyd. London and New York, G. Bell & sons, 1892.
viii, 493, [1] p. 17½cm.
On cover: The Aldine edition? p. i-iv, 157-180, 189-190 wanting (rebound)
"Reprinted from stereotype plates."

1. Shakespeare, William—Criticism and interpretation.

NL 0428952 ViU PU PPPL OCl OClW PPi

Lloyd, William Watkiss, 1813-1893.
Critical essays on the plays of Shakespeare, by William Watkiss Lloyd. London, Bell, 1894.
493 p.

NL 0428953 NcRS WaS PRosC

PR 2976 .L6 1904 Lloyd, William Watkiss, 1813-1893.
Critical essays on the plays of Shakespeare. London, G. Bell, 1904.
viii, 293p. 18cm.

On cover: Aldine edition.

1. Shakespeare, William. Criticism and interpretation.

NL 0428954 OrU

822.32 L77c **Lloyd, William Watkiss,** 1813-1893.
Critical essays on the plays of Shakespeare, by William Watkiss Lloyd. London, G. Bell and sons, 1909.
viii, 493, [1] p. 17½ cm.
On cover: The Aldine edition.

NL 0428955 LU OrU

VOLUME 337

PR 3446 .Z5 L8 Lloyd, William Watkiss, 1813-1893.
Elijah Fenton: his poetry and friends. A monograph by William Watkiss Lloyd M.R.S.L. Edited by the Rev. George Livingstone Fenton ... Preceded by a new life of the poet, by Robert Fenton ... With a brief sketch of the author (W.W.L.) by Sophia Beale. Hanley [England] Allbut and Daniel, 1894.
4 p.l., [7]-190, [12] p. front. (port.), plates, facsim. 22½cm.
"Of this book only 250 copies have been printed."
"Erratum" slip inserted.
1. Fenton, Elijah, 1683-1730. I. Fenton, Robert. II. Beale, S. Sophia. III. Fenton, George Livingstone, ed.

NL 0428956 MiU PSt IU CtY MnU ICN OC1W CU OrU

PR 2976 .L79 Lloyd, William Watkiss, 1813-1893.
Essays on the life and plays of Shakespeare, by William Watkiss Lloyd; contributed to the edition of the poet by S.W. Singer, 1856. London Printed by C. Whittingham, 1858.
[592] p. 20cm.
Published later without the Life, under title: Critical essays on the plays of Shakespeare.
Author's presentation copy.
1. Shakespeare, William--Biog. 2. Shakespeare, William--Criticism and interpretation.

00xM
NL 0428957 MiU KU IU MWelC NNU-W CtW PU-F ICN OC1

Lloyd, William Watkiss, 1813-1893.
The history of Sicily to the Athenian war; with elucidations of the Sicilian odes of Pindar. By W. Watkiss Lloyd ... London, J. Murray, 1872.
x p., 1 l., 396 p. map. 23cm.
1. Sicily—Hist. 2. Pindarus.
4-30490
Library of Congress DG55.S5L7

MiU MB NjP
NL 0428958 DLC NIC MsU CtY PU MdBP PPFr PSC PPM

LLOYD William Watkiss, 1813-1893.
Homer, his Art and his Age. (The Classical Museum, etc., 1849 [1848?]. 6.387-431.)
The same. [London, 1848]. pp. 47.

NL 0428959 MH

Lloyd, William Watkiss, 1813-1893.
The life of William Shakespeare.
(In Shakespeare, William. Works. The dramatic works . . . Vol. 1, pp. ix-xci. London. 1884.)
H400 — Shakespeare, William. Biog. and crit.

NL 0428960 MB

Lloyd, William Watkiss, 1813-1893.
Memoir on the systems of proportion employed in the design of the Doric temples at Phigaleia and Aegina. Addressed to C. R. Cockerell.
(In Cockerell, Charles Robert. The temples of Jupiter Panhellenius at Aegina and of Apollo Epicurius at Bassae. Pp. 61-94. Plate. London. 1860.)
L1081 — Proportion. Architectural.

NL 0428961 MB

LLOYD, WILLIAM WATKISS, 1813-1893.
The Moses of Michelangelo. London, 1863.

NL 0428962 MdBP

Lloyd, William Watkiss, 1813-1893.
On the central groups of the eastern frieze of the Parthenon. By W. Watkiss Lloyd ...
(In Royal society of literature of the United Kingdom, London. Essays by divers hands, being the transactions. London [1893] 23cm. 2d ser., vol. XVI, p. 73-98. fold. pl.)
"Read November 23rd, 1892."
Bibliographical foot-notes.
1. Athens. Parthenon.
A C 39-2846
Illinois. Univ. Library for Library of Congress [PN22.R6 ser. 2, vol. 16] [2] (806.242)

NL 0428963 IU MH DLC

LLOYD, W[illiam] Watkiss, 1813-1893.
On the general theory of proportion in architectural design and its exemplification in detail in the Parthenon. Read at the Royal Institute of British Architects, June 13th, 1859. London, John Weale, 1863.
1.8°. pp. 20. 10 plates.
Arc 712.22

NL 0428964 MH

Lloyd, William Watkiss, 1813-1893.
On the Homeric design of the shield of Achilles ... London, Williams and Norgate, 1854.
45 [1] p. 2 front. (1 fold. diagr. & 1 col.) 24.5 cm.

NL 0428965 CtY PBL

Lloyd, W[illiam] Watkiss, 1813-1893.
Panics and their panaceas. The theory of money, metallic or paper in relation to healthy and disturbed interchange, by W. Watkiss Lloyd. London, Harrison, 1869.
2 p. l., [3]-57 p. 22½cm.
1. Panics. 2. Money.
6-32280†
Library of Congress HB3723.L8

NL 0428966 DLC NcD MdBP NN

Lloyd, William Watkiss, 1813-1893.
Philosophy, theology, and poetry, in the age and the art of Rafael. By William Watkiss Lloyd. London and Edinburgh, Williams and Norgate, 1867.
4 p. l., 194 p. 3 pl. 28½cm.
Contents.—The school of Athens.—The dispute of the sacrament.—The Mount Parnassus.
1. Raffaele Sanzio, 1483-1520. 2. Renaissance—Italy.
11-26734
Library of Congress ND623.R3L7

NL 0428967 DLC OC1W

Lloyd, William Watkiss, 1813-1893, tr.
Pindarus.
Pindar and Themistocles: Ægina and Athens. By William Watkiss Lloyd ... London, Williams and Norgate, 1862.

LLOYD, William Watkiss, 1813-1893.
The Portland Vase. (The Classical Museum, etc. 1849 [1848?], 6.253-278.)
The same. [London, 1848]. pp. 28.

NL 0428969 MH

Lloyd, William Watkiss, 1813-1893.
NA275 .C6 Folio Cockerell, Charles Robert, 1788-1863.
The temples of Jupiter Panhellenius at Ægina, and of Apollo Epicurius at Bassæ near Phigaleia in Arcadia. By C. R. Cockerell ... To which is added a memoir of the systems of proportion employed in the original design of these structures. By William Watkiss Lloyd. London, J. Weale, 1860.

Lloyd, William Watkiss, 1813-1893.
Xanthian marbles: the Nereid monuments; an historical and mythological essay. London, W. Pickering, 1845.
pp. (7), 109 +. Plates and other illus.
Nereids|Xanthus||

NL 0428971 MH NN NcD OCU

Lloyd, William Whitelocke.
On active service, by W. W. Lloyd... London: Chapman & Hall, ltd., 1890. 20 col'd pl. (incl. t.-p.) 22 x 31½cm.
94171B. 1. Military life—Africa, South. I. Title.
N. Y. P. L. March 10, 1941

NL 0428972 NN MoKU DN MiD

LLOYD, WILLIAM WHITELOCKE.
Lloyd's sketches of Indian life. London: Chapman & Hall, Ltd., 1890. 18 col'd pl. f°.
557033A. 1. India—Views. I. Title.

NL 0428973 NN CaOTP IEN NjP CU ICN

Lloyd, William Whitelock
Union jottings, from original design.
Lond, 1899.

NL 0428974 PPI

Lloyd, W[oodrow] S[tanley], 1913-
The archives and the public records program in Saskatchewan. [N.p.n.pub.] 1955.
6p. Nar. F.

NL 0428975 CaBViP

LE 3 T52 PhD 1930 L643 Lloyd, Wray
Contributions to cardiology, from the laboratories of pathology and bacteriology, University of Toronto. [Toronto 1930?]
156, 23 leaves. illus, plates., 2 fold. tables.
Thesis - University of Toronto.
Thesis accepted 1930.
Includes bibliography.
Contents: The myocardium in yellow fever.- Experimental heart block in the rabbit.

NL 0428976 CaOTU

VOLUME 337

Lloyd, Wray.
... The myocardium in yellow fever, by Wray Lloyd ... [Toronto] The University of Toronto press, 1931.
172 p. incl. plates, tables, diagrs. 23cm. (University of Toronto studies. Pathological series. [no. 8])
"This monograph, together with other papers, has been included in a thesis submitted ... for a degree of doctor of philosophy in the University of Toronto."—Pref.
Bibliography: p. 125–172.
1. Yellow fever. 2. Heart—Diseases. I. Title.
34-14214
Library of Congress RB6.T65 no. 8
[3] (616.082) 616.928

NL 0428977 DLC DNLM MiU OCU OU MH-M

Lloyd, Wylie Everette, 1881- joint author.
Butterfield, Harry Morton, 1887- FOR OTHER EDITIONS SEE MAIN ENTRY
... Rabbit raising [by] H. M. Butterfield and W. E. Lloyd ... [Berkeley, Calif., University of California press, 1935]

Lloyd, Wylie Everette, 1881- joint author.
McFarlane, Neville Lewis, 1901-
... Turkey raising in California [by] N. L. McFarlane, W. E. Lloyd, and Grant Merrill ... [Berkeley, Calif., University of California print. off., 1931]

Lloyd, Wylie Everette, 1881- joint author.
Hinshaw, William Russell, 1896-
... Vitamin-A deficiency in turkeys [by] W. R. Hinshaw and W. E. Lloyd.

Lloyd, Wyndham Edward Buckley, joint ed.
British health resorts association.
... British health resorts, spa, seaside, inland, including those of the British dominions and colonies with chapters on the science of waters and baths, the climates of the coast and the "invalids' winter"; also maps, charts and many illustrations. Edited for the association by R. Fortescue Fox ... assisted by Wyndham E. B. Lloyd ... With a foreword by the Rt. Hon. Walter Elliot ... London, British health resorts association, 1939.

Lloyd, Wyndham Edward Buckley.
A hundred years of medicine, by Wyndham E. B. Lloyd ... London, Duckworth [1936]
344 p. 22cm.
"Chronological table of events of medical importance": p. 325–329.
"Short bibliography": p. 331–335.
1. Medicine—History. I. Title.
S G 38-34
U. S. Surg.-gen. off. Library for Library of Congress R149 [2]

DNLM
NL 0428982 DI-GS CaBVaU ICJ CtY PPC PPJ PV NN OCl

Lloyd, Wyndham Edward Buckley, joint author.
Haagensen, Cushman Davis, 1900-
A hundred years of medicine, by C. D. Haagensen and Wyndham E. B. Lloyd. New York, Sheridan house [1943]

Lloyd, Wynne Llewelyn.
Trade and transport; an account of the trade of the port of Swansea and the transport facilities and industry in the district. [Cardiff] Published by the University of Wales Press Board on behalf of the college, 1940.
108 p. maps, diagrs. 23 cm. (Social and economic survey of Swansea and district. Pamphlet no. 6)
Bibliography: p. [107]–108.
1. Swansea, Wales—Comm. 2. Transportation—Wales—Swansea. I. Title. (Series: Wales. University. University College, Swansea. Social and economic survey of Swansea and district. Pamphlet no. 6)
HF3510.S9L55 382 51-48904

NL 0428984 DLC NN

W 6 P3 **LLOYD-BAKER, Olive**
The celibate woman. London, Provisional National Council for Mental Health, 1945.
15 p.
Cover title.
Lecture given in a series on The psychology of frustration and fulfilment in adult life.
1. Celibacy 2. Mental hygiene

NL 0428985 DNLM

LLOYD BROWNE, FANNY.
L'art chorégraphique chez les Javanais; par Mlle. Lloyd Browne. [Paris, Maisonneuve, 1872?]
18-142 p. plate. 30cm.
Caption title.
Detached from Mémoires de l'Athénée oriental. Session de 1872.
1. Dancing--Java.

NL 0428986 NN

Lloyd-Davies, D.E., 1875-
Alexandria, *Egypt.*
... Rapport sur l'assainissement de la ville d'Alexandrie, par D. E. Lloyd-Davies ... ingénieur en chef de la municipalité. Alexandrie, Société de publications égyptiennes, 1909.

Lloyd Davies, Trevor Arthur.
The practice of industrial medicine, with a chapter on The hazards of coal mining, by G. F. Keatinge. London, J. & A. Churchill, 1948.
vii, 244 p. diagrs. 23 cm.
Includes bibliographies.
1. Medicine, Industrial. 2. Coal-miners—Diseases and hygiene.
RC963.L55 331.82 49-4298*

NL 0428988 DLC CaBVaU DNLM ICU NNC WaU PPC

Lloyd-Dodd, Frederic Thomas, 1879-
Organization and administration of industry, by F. T. Lloyd-Dodd ... and B. J. Lynch ... with a foreword by the Right Hon. J. Milne Barbour ... London, Sir I. Pitman & sons, ltd., 1935.
xiv, 501 p. diagrs. 22cm.
Bibliography: p. 492–494.
1. Industry. 2. Industry—Organization, control, etc. 3. Efficiency, Industrial. I. Lynch, B. J., joint author. II. Title.
37-23953
Library of Congress HD2326.L6
[5] 331

NL 0428989 DLC CU CtY PU-W OCl NN

Lloyd George, David Lloyd George, 1st earl, 1863-1945.
Modigliani, Ettore, 1873-
... A Londra durante la guerra; in appendice: il discorso pronunciato dall'onorevole David Lloyd George ... ai 19 settembre 1914; con 20 fototopie fuori testo e 6 pagine di musica nel testo. Milano, Fratelli Treves, 1915.

Lloyd George, David Lloyd George, *1st earl*, 1863–1945.
Abraham Lincoln; an address before the Midday luncheon club, Leland hotel, Springfield, Illinois, Thursday, October 18, 1923, by David Lloyd George. Cleveland, Priv. print. for S. W. Tener, 1924.
13 p. 24½ cm.
"Three hundred copies printed ... number 33."
1. Lincoln, Abraham, pres. U. S.—Addresses, sermons, etc.
E457.8.L79 24-9698 rev

NL 0428991 DLC MWA NIC MiU-C PHi OCl OU NN MB NcD

Lloyd George, David Lloyd George, 1st earl, 1863-194
... Addresses on German reparation, by the Rt. Hon. David Lloyd George and Dr. Walter Simons, London, March 3rd and 7th, 1921 ... New York city, Greenwich, Conn., American association for international conciliation [1921]
36 p. 19½cm. (International conciliation, pub. monthly by the American association for international conciliation ... May, 1921, no. 162)
"Addresses ... reprinted from the London Times of March 4 and 8 ... given during the meetings of the Reparations conference in London, March 1 to 7, 1921."—p. 5.
1. Indemnity. 2. European war, 1914–1918—Claims. I. Simons, Walther, 1861–1937. II. Title: German reparation.
21—10353
Library of Congress JX1907.A8 no. 162

MB OCl OO CaBVaU
NL 0428992 DLC OrPR WaS WaU-L PCC PHC PPT MiU OU

Lloyd-George, D[avid] Lloyd George, 1863-1945.
Benefits of the Insurance Act; a speech delivered at Sutton-in-Ashfield, on August 9th, 1913. London: Liberal Publ. Dept., 1913. 14 p., 1 l. 8°. (Liberal Publ. Dept. Pamphlets and leaflets for 1913. no. 11.)
Authorised ed.
1. Insurance (Workmen's), Gt. Br.
N. Y. P. L.

NL 0428993 NN

JN234 1911 L415 **LLOYD GEORGE, David Lloyd George, 1st earl, 1863-1945.**
Bessere Zeiten. [Autorisierte Übersetzung von Helene Simon] 1. bis 4. Tausend. Jena, Diederichs, 1911.
255p.
Translation of 'Better times'... speeches by Lloyd George, incl. two budget addresses.
1. Taxation--Gt. Brit. 2. Finance--Gt. Brit. 3. Gt. Brit.-Pol. & govt.--1901-1910. I. Title.

NL 0428994 CU-Riv GU FMU ICJ

Lloyd George, David Lloyd George, *1st earl*, 1863–1945.
Better times; speeches by the Right Hon. D. Lloyd George ... London, Hodder & Stoughton, 1910.
vi p., 1 l., 326 p., 1 l. 19 cm.
1. Gt. Brit.—Pol. & govt.—1901–1910. 2. Taxation—Gt. Brit. 3. Finance—Gt. Brit. I. Title.
JN234 1910.L4 11-2523 rev

ICU PHC OCl MiU IdU OrPR WaS MH
NL 0428995 DLC NNC ViU OO MB CtY NN ICJ PBm PPFr

VOLUME 337

Lloyd George, David Lloyd George, *1st earl*, 1863-1945.
British war aims; statement by the prime minister, the Right Honourable David Lloyd George, on January 5, 1918. Pub. by authority of the British government. London, H. M. Stationery off., Hazell, Watson & Viney, ld. [printers, 1918]
12 p. 21½ cm.

1. European war, 1914-1918—Peace.
D613.L6 1918a 19-10143 rev

NL 0428996 DLC NN NjP

Lloyd George, David Lloyd George, *1st earl*, 1863-1945.
British war aims; statement by the Right Honourable David Lloyd George, January fifth, nineteen hundred and eighteen. Authorized version as pub. by the British government. New York, George H. Doran company [1918]
cover-title, 15 p. 18½ cm.

1. European war, 1914-1918—Peace.
D613.L6 18-6056 rev

NL 0428997 MB MiU OO OU PCC PHi PPL PU NjP MH DLC NcD NcU PLatS CaBViP DNAL KU

Lloyd George, David Lloyd George, *1st earl*, 1863-1945.
... The budget of 1909. A speech delivered by the Right Hon. D. Lloyd-George, M. P. (chancellor of the Exchequer) in the House of commons on April 29th, 1909. [Authorised ed.] London, The Liberal publication department, 1909.
cover-title, 72 p. 21 cm.
Index on p. [3] of cover.

1. Budget—Gt. Brit. 2. Finance—Gt. Brit. 3. Gt. Brit.—Pol. & govt.—1901-1910.
HJ1023.L68 10-33483 rev

NL 0428998 DLC CtY ICJ

Lloyd George, David Lloyd George, *1st earl*, 1863-1945.
Ce que dit Lloyd George après 4 ans de guerre. [Londres, Imprimé par R. Clay and sons, ltd., 1918]
cover-title, 27 p. illus. 18½ cm.
Portrait on cover.
"Discours prononcé à la Chambre des communes le 7 août 1918."

1. European war, 1914-1918—Addresses, sermons, etc. I. Title.
D525.L53 25-21220 rev
Library of Congress

NL 0428999 DLC

Lloyd George, David Lloyd George, *1st earl*, 1863-1945.
Coal and power; the report of an inquiry presided over by the Right Hon. D. Lloyd George ... London, Hodder and Stoughton limited [1924]
xiv, 285 p., 1 l. illus. (plans) plates, diagr. 19 cm.

1. Coal trade—Gt. Brit. 2. Coal-miners—Gt. Brit. 3. Mines and mineral resources—Government ownership. 4. Electric utilities—Gt. Brit. I. Title.
HD9551.6.L55 25-3640

NL 0429000 DLC CaBVaU OrU CSt NN CtY ICU CU

Lloyd George, David Lloyd George, 1st earl, 1863-1945.
American association for international conciliation.
... I. Correspondence between Mr. Lloyd George and Sir James Craig on the position of Ulster. II. Articles of agreement establishing the Irish Free State. III. Irish Free State (agreement) bill ... New York city, Greenwich, Conn., American association for international conciliation [1922]

D617 L7926
Lloyd George, David Lloyd George, 1st earl, 1863-
...Discorsi per la guerra. Con prefazione di Orazio Raimondo... Roma, Biblioteca della rivista "L'Eloquenza", 1919.

xiv, 195, [1] p. 18cm.
Portrait on cover.

1. European war, 1914-1918. I. Title.

NL 0429002 CSt-H CSt

Lloyd George, David Lloyd George, *1st earl*, 1863-1945.
England og Tyskland. Hvad Lloyd George mente i 1908. Forord af Louis v. Kohl. Med et faksimile af Lloyd George's tale af 28. juli 1908. København, Nordiske forfatteres forlag, 1917.
12 p. facsim. 21½ cm.
Facsimile (7 p. inserted between p. 6 and 7): England & Germany. Speech by the Rt. Hon. D. Lloyd George ... July 28th, 1908. Published by the National peace council ...

1. Gt. Brit.—For. rel.—Germany. 2. Germany—For. rel.—Gt. Brit. I. *Kohl, Louis von, 1882- II. Title.
DA47.2.L5 21-16123 rev

NL 0429003 DLC NN

Lloyd George, David Lloyd George, *1st earl*, 1863-1945.
Fact v. fiction ... Mr. Lloyd George's statement on shipping and food supplies. (House of commons, Thursday, 16th August, 1917.) London, New York [etc.] Hodder & Stoughton [1917]
8 p. illus. 22 cm.

1. European war, 1914-1918—Food question. 2. European war, 1914-1918—Gt. Brit. I. Title.
HD9011.5.L5 29-30060 rev

NL 0429004 DLC MH NN OU

Lloyd George, David Lloyd George, 1st earl, 1863-1945.

Fête nationale belge, Belgian independence day, Belgisch nationaal feest: discours prononcés au Queen's hall, addresses delivered at the Queen's hall, redevoeringen uitgesproken in den Queen's hall, by the Right Hon. D. Lloyd George, par M. Hymans, door M. Standaert, 21 juillet, 1917 ... [London, The Menpes printing and engraving co., ltd., 1917]

Lloyd George, David Lloyd George, *1st earl*, 1863-1945.
Das gewappnete Deutschland, ein englisches lob; reden des munitionsministers Lloyd George. München und Berlin, G. Müller, 1916.
127 p. 20 cm.
"Einleitung" signed: Dr. Rudolf Friedmann.

1. European war, 1914-1918—Addresses, sermons, etc. I. Friedmann, Rudolf, comp. and tr. II. Title.
D523.L58 21-7682 rev

NL 0429006 DLC

Lloyd George, David Lloyd George, 1st earl, 1863-1945.
Government of Ireland. [n.p., 1920?]
see under title

Rare Books and Special Collections
Lloyd George, David Lloyd George, 1st earl, 1863-1945
The great war; speech delivered ... at the Queen's Hall, London, on September 19th, 1914. Toronto, Hodder and Stoughton [1914?]
16 p.

At head of title: Authorised edition.

1. European War, 1914-1918 - Addresses, sermons, etc. I. Title

NL 0429008 CaOTU

Lloyd George, David Lloyd George, *1st earl*, 1863-1945.
... Great Britain's war aims; speech delivered by the Rt. Hon. David Lloyd George at the Trade union conference on man power, January 5, 1918.
(*In* Association for international conciliation. American branch. International conciliation. New York, 1918. 19½ cm. no. 123, p. 35-47)
Caption title.
Published also under title: British war aims.

1. European war, 1914-1918—Peace.
JX1907.A8 no. 123 18-8792 rev

NL 0429009 OU NjP DLC CaBVaU WaS OrPR WaU-L OO OCl MiU

Lloyd George, David Lloyd George, 1st earl, 1863-1945.
The great crusade; extract from speeches delivered during the war, by the Rt. Hon. David Lloyd George... Arranged by F. L. Stevenson... London: Hodder and Stoughton, 1918. viii, 215(1) p. 12°.

1. European war, 1914- .—Addresses, sermons, etc. 2. Stevenson, F. L., compiler. 3. Title.
N. Y. P. L. September 10, 1918.

NL 0429010 NN CaBVa

Lloyd George, David Lloyd George, *1st earl*, 1863-1945.
The great crusade; extracts from speeches delivered during the war, by the Rt. Hon. David Lloyd George, M. P. Arranged by F. L. Stevenson ... New York, George H. Doran company [1918]
viii p., 1 l., 11-307 p. 21 cm.

1. European war, 1914-1918—Addresses, sermons, etc. 2. European war, 1914-1918—Gt. Brit. I. Stevenson, F. L., comp. II. Title.
D523.L57 18-14198 rev

NL 0429011 PU PP ODW OU ICJ OCl NN MB KyLoU DLC WaS MtU OrP NcRS PPM PPFr PPT PSC

Lloyd George, David Lloyd George, *1st earl*, 1863-1945.
... The great war. Speech delivered by the Rt. Hon. David Lloyd George, M. P. (chancellor of the Exchequer) at the Queen's hall, London, on September 19th, 1914. [London, Printed by the Clerkenwell press, ltd., 1914]
12 p. 20½ cm.
On cover: Authorised ed.

1. European war, 1914-1918—Addresses, sermons, etc. I. Title.
D525.L55 19-18193 rev

NL 0429012 DLC MH MB

Lloyd George, David Lloyd George, 1st earl, 1863-1945.
The great war; speech delivered by the Rt. Hon. David Lloyd George...at the Queen's Hall, London, on September 19th, 1914. Toronto: Hodder and Stoughton, Ltd. [1914?] 16 p. 12°.
Cover-title.

1. European war, 1914- .—Addresses, sermons, etc.
N. Y. P. L. October 24, 1921.

NL 0429013 NN MH CtY CaBViP

Lloyd George, David Lloyd George, 1st earl, 1863-1945.
La guerra europea, discurso pronunciado en el Queen's Hall de Londres, el 19 de Septiembre de 1914. n.p., [1914].

pp.11.

NL 0429014 MH CtY

Lloyd George, David Lloyd George, 1st earl, 1863-1945.
La guerre européenne. Discours prononcé par M. David Lloyd George (Chancelier de l'echiquier) au Queen's hall de Londres, le 19 septembre, 1914. Lausanne, Payot et cie. [1914]
15 p. 15.5 cm.
Published under various titles: Honour and dishonour; "Through terrors to triumph!". London, 1914; Honneur et dishonneur, Genève, 1914.

NL 0429015 CSt-H CtY

VOLUME 337

Lloyd George, David Lloyd George, *1st earl*, 1863–1945.
Honour and dishonour. A speech by the Right Hon. D. Lloyd George ... at the Queen's hall, London, Sept. 19, 1914. London, Methuen & co., ltd. ⌈1914⌉
cover-title, 11 p. 21½ cm.

1. European war, 1914–1918—Causes. I. Title.
War 15–11 rev
U. S. Army war coll. Libr. for Library of Congress ⌈r47b1⌉

NL 0429016 PCarlA NjP NN

Lloyd George, David Lloyd George, *1st earl*, 1863–1945.
Honour and dishonour, a speech, by the Right Hon. D. Lloyd George ... at the Queen's hall, London, Sept. 19, 1914. ⌈2d ed.⌉ London, Methuen & co., ltd. ⌈1914⌉
11 p. 22 cm.

1. European war, 1914–1918—Addresses, sermons, etc. I. Title.
D511.L5 1914 15–5050 rev

NL 0429017 DLC CtY

Lloyd George, David Lloyd George, *1st earl*, 1863–1945.
How to tackle unemployment; the Liberal plans as laid before the government and the nation, by the Rt. Hon. D. Lloyd George ... the Marquess of Lothian ... and B. Seebohm Rowntree. London ⌈The Press printers⌉ 1930.
104 p. 20½ cm.

1. Unemployed—Gt. Brit. 2. Gt. Brit.—Economic policy. 3. Gt. Brit.—Public works. 4. Liberal party (Gt. Brit.) I. Lothian, Philip Henry Kerr, 11th marquis of, 1882–1940, joint author. II. Rowntree, Benjamin Seebohm, 1871– joint author. III. Title.
HD5767.L5 331.137942 31–964 rev 2

NL 0429018 DLC CLU DS OCl NN PU-W IU CtY

Lloyd George, David Lloyd George, *1st earl*, 1863–1945.
Is it peace? By the Right Hon. David Lloyd George ... London, Hodder and Stoughton limited ⌈1923⌉
xii, 291 p. 22½ cm.
American edition (New York, George H. Doran company) with a different arrangement of the articles and addresses, has title: Where are we going?

1. European war, 1914–1918—Influence and results. 2. World politics. 3. Peace. 4. European war, 1914–1918—Reparations. 5. Germany—Econ. condit.—1918– I. Title.
D653.L6 1923a 23–16552 rev

NL 0429019 DLC CtY CaBVaU OrPR OKentU CtY DN NIC MeB MB DAU

Lloyd George, David Lloyd George, *1st earl*, 1863–1945.
Ist wirklich Friede? Ins Deutsche übertragen und eingeleitet von W. Simons. Leipzig, P. List ⌈1924⌉
xiv, 191 p. 25 cm.

1. European War, 1914–1918—Influence and results. 2. World politics. 3. Peace. 4. European War, 1914–1918—Reparations. 5. Germany—Econ. condit.—1918– I. Title.
D653.L614 52–51044

NL 0429020 DLC CSt-H GU MH

Lloyd George, David Lloyd George, *1st earl*, 1863–1945.
... Der kampf um den englischen boden; autorisierte uebersetzung von Paul Helbeck, mit einem geleitwort von dr. iur. Albert v. Schwerin ... Berlin, Verlag "Bodenreform" g. m. b. h., 1914.
viii, 64 p. 22½ cm. (Soziale zeitfragen ... Hrsg. von A. Damaschke. hft. 54/55)
On cover: 3. tausend.
"Einige der neuesten der hervorragenden reden des englischen schatzkanzlers Lloyd George."—Geleitwort.
CONTENTS.—Das ländliche bodenproblem: worin besteht es? Bedford, 11. oktober 1913.—Das ländliche bodenproblem: die lösung. Swindon, 22. oktober 1913.—Die städtische bodenfrage. London, 30. oktober, und Middlesbrough, 8. november 1913.
1. Land tenure—Gt. Brit. I. Helbeck, Paul, tr.
HD655.S6 hft. 54/55 15–7185 rev

NL 0429021 DLC ICJ

Lloyd George, David Lloyd George, *1st earl*, 1863–1945.
... Liberal finance: a reply to Mr. Bonar Law. A speech delivered at the City Liberal Club, London, on February 3rd, 1912. ⌈Authorised ed.⌉ London, Liberal Pub. Dept., 1912.
19 p. 21½ cm.

1. Law, Andrew Bonar, 1858–1923. 2. Finance—Gt. Brit. I. Title.
HJ1023.L682 47–41613*

NL 0429022 DLC

H 5045 .598 LLOYD GEORGE, DAVID LLOYD GEORGE, 1st Earl, 1863, 1945.
The liberal pledge to conquer unemployment. A speech delivered to liberal candidates on March 1st, 1929. London, Liberal Publication Department ⌈1929⌉
30p. 21cm.

Binder's title: Pamphlets on labor.

NL 0429023 ICN TNJ CtY

Lloyd George, David Lloyd George, 1st earl, 1863–1945.
Lloyd George and labour's future London: W. H. Smith & Son ⌈1919⌉. 8 p. 8°.
"Extracted from a speech by the Prime Minister in the House of Commons on February 11th, 1919."

1. Labor.—History and conditions, Gt. Br., 1919.
N. Y. P. L. November 7, 1919.

NL 0429024 NN

Lloyd George, David Lloyd George, 1st earl, 1863–1945.
...Lloyd George's message: Looking forward. Substance of a speech delivered by the prime minister at Manchester, September 12, 1918... London: National War Aims Committee ⌈1918⌉. 8 l. 16°. (Message series. no. 6.)

1. European war, 1914– .—Addresses, sermons, etc. 2. National War Aims Committee. 3. Title: Looking forward.
N. Y. P. L. May 16, 1919.

NL 0429025 NN

Lloyd George, David Lloyd George, 1st earl, 1863–1945.
The lords, the land, and the people. London: Hodder & Stoughton ⌈1909⌉. xii, 13-96 p. illus. 8°.

1. Great Britain.—Politics, 1909. 2. Finance (Public), Gt. Br., 1909.
N. Y. P. L. June 10, 1913.

NL 0429026 NN

Lloyd George, David Lloyd George, 1st earl, 1863–1945.
The lords, the land, and the people, by the Right Hon. David Lloyd George ... London, Hodder & Stoughton, [1910].
xii, 13–96 p. incl. front., illus. 22cm.

NL 0429027 ICJ MH CtY

Lloyd George, David Lloyd George, *1st earl*, 1863–1945.
... Mein anteil am weltkrieg; kriegsmemoiren (War memoirs) ... Berlin, S. Fischer, 1933–36.
3 v. 23 cm.
"Erste bis dritte auflage."
Vols. 1–2, "übertragen von Peter Wit"; v. 3, "übertragen von Dagobert von Mikusch."

1. European war, 1914–1918. I. Wit, Peter, tr. II. *Mikusch, Dagobert von, 1874– tr. III. Title.
D546.L53 1933 940.342 34–7766 rev

NL 0429028 DLC NN WaU

Lloyd George, David Lloyd George, *1st earl*, 1863–1945.
... Mémoires de guerre; traduction de Charles Bonnefon. Paris, A. Fayard & cie ⌈1934–
v. 23 cm.
At head of title: Lloyd George.

1. European war, 1914–1918. I. Bonnefon, Charles, 1871–1935, tr. II. Title.
D546.L52 940.342 34–28611 rev

NL 0429029 DLC

Lloyd George, David Lloyd George, *1st earl*, 1863–1945.
Memoirs of the Peace conference, by David Lloyd George ... New Haven, Yale university press, 1939.
2 v. fronts., ports., maps, facsims. 24½ cm.
Paged continuously.
London edition (V. Gollancz ltd.) has title: The truth about the peace treaties.

1. European war, 1914–1918—Peace. 2. Paris. Peace conference, 1919. I. Title.
D644.L55 1939 940.314 39–4896 rev

NL 0429030 DLC NcD OU ViU NN OCU MiHM OClW OO OCl WaWW Or OrSaW WaS PHC PP PSC PPA PPT PBm ICJ OrP MB NIC CaBVa CU-I

Lloyd George, David Lloyd George, 1st earl, 1863–1945.

Guedalla, Philip, 1889–
Napoleon and Palestine, by Philip Guedalla. With a foreword by Israel Zangwill, and an afterword by the Rt. Hon. David Lloyd George ... London, G. Allen & Unwin, ltd. ⌈1925⌉

Lloyd George, David Lloyd George, 1st earl, 1863–1945.

Gt. Brit. *Chancellor of the Exchequer.*
National health insurance. Statements as to the administration of medical benefit and correspondence thereon between the chancellor of the Exchequer and the British medical association ... London, H. M. Stationery off., printed by Darling and son, limited, 1912.

Lloyd George, David Lloyd George, *1st earl*, 1863–1945.
The National insurance bill; its proposals, summarised and explained ⌈by⌉ Mr. Lloyd George; speech in introducing the bill, House of commons, May 4th, 1911. London, The Liberal publication department, 1911.
cover-title, 23 p. 21 cm.

1. Insurance, Health—Gt. Brit.
HD7102.G7L6 11–20889 rev

NL 0429033 DLC WaS

HD7166 .A5 1911 d Lloyd George, David Lloyd George, 1st earl, 1863–1945.

Gt. Brit. *Laws, statutes, etc.*
The National insurance bill; together with official explanatory memoranda on its provisions. Report of Mr. Lloyd George's speech on the introduction of the measure, and notes, by the editors of the "Poor-law officers' journal." London, Poor-law publications company, 1911.

Lloyd George, David Lloyd George, *1st earl*, 1863–1945.
Organizing prosperity; a scheme of national reconstruction, being the memorandum on unemployment and reconstruction submitted to the government by Mr. Lloyd George, by Rt. Hon. David Lloyd George ... London, I. Nicholson and Watson limited, 1935.
vii, 107 p. 21½ cm.
"First edition."

1. Gt. Brit.—Econ. condit.—1918– 2. Gt. Brit.—Economic policy. 3. Unemployed—Gt. Brit. I. Title.
HC256.3.L63 1935 330.942 35–34852 rev

NL 0429035 DLC CaBViP ICU NN

VOLUME 337

Lloyd George, David Lloyd George, *1st earl*, 1863-1945.
Peace proposals and the attitude of the allies; speech by the prime minister, the Right Hon. D. Lloyd George, on December 19th, 1916. London, Hayman, Christy & Lilly, ltd., 1916.
22 p. illus. (port.) 21½ cm.

1. European war, 1914-1918—Peace. 2. Gt. Brit—Pol. & govt.—1910-1936. I. Title.
D613.L7 17-7536 rev

NL 0429036 DLC MB OrU NcD CtY NjP PHi PPL PU OC1W MiU OU OO NN

Lloyd George, David Lloyd George, 1st earl, 1863-1945.
... Peace through conferences: I. Text of an address delivered by Mr. Lloyd George at Central hall, Westminster, London, on January 21, 1922. II. Text of the resolution of the Supreme council calling the Genoa conference ... New York city, Greenwich, Conn., American association for international conciliation [1922]

Lloyd George, David Lloyd George, *1st earl*, 1863-1945.
The people's budget, explained by the chancellor of the Exchequer, the Right Hon. David Lloyd George ... London, Hodder & Stoughton [1909]
xi, [1], 196 p. incl. front., plates, ports. pl. 22½ cm.
"Consists of extracts from [the author's] ... House of commons speeches explaining and defending the provisions of the budget [which he] ... introduced on April 29th, 1909."—Pref.

1. Taxation—Gt. Brit. 2. Finance—Gt. Brit. 3. Gt. Brit.—Pol. & govt.—1901-1910. I. Title.
HJ1023.L7 10-7315 rev

NL 0429038 DLC CaBViP CaBVa CtY PU NN ICJ MiU

HD7166 .L6 1911
Lloyd-George, David Lloyd George 1st Earl 1863-
The people's insurance. New ed., containing the text of the Insurance Bill as amended in the House of Commons. London, New York, Hodder and Stoughton, 1911.
vii,236 p.

1. Insurance, Industrial - Gt. Brit. 2. Insurance, Social - Gt. Brit. 3. Insurance, Health - Gt. Brit. 4. Insurance, Unemployment - Gt. Brit. Laws, statutes, etc., 1910-1936 (George V)

NL 0429039 CU CaBVaU ICN OC1W PPComm

Lloyd George, David Lloyd George, *1st earl*, 1863-1945.
The people's insurance, explained by the chancellor of the Exchequer, the Right Hon. David Lloyd George ... 3d ed., containing the text of the National insurance act (1911), together with explanations of the insurance commissioners. London, New York [etc.] Hodder and Stoughton, 1912.
3 p. l., 306, [1] p. 21½ cm.

1. Insurance, Social—Gt. Brit. I. Gt. Brit. Laws, statutes, etc. II. Title.
HD7166.L6 1912 12-35688 rev

NL 0429040 DLC MtU WaS RPB CU NN

Lloyd George, David Lloyd George, 1st earl, 1863-
Miller, James Martin, 1859-
The people's war book; history, cyclopaedia and chronology of the great world war, by James Martin Miller ... and H. S. Canfield ... and Canada's part in the war, by W. R. Plewman ... containing official war reports and authentic articles by Marshal Foch ... Lloyd George ... [and others] with many war maps, charts and diagrams, and nearly five hundred illustrations and colored plates, including the official photographs of the American, British, Canadian, French and Italian governments. Cleveland, O., The R.C. Barnum co.; Detroit, Mich., The F.B. Dickerson co.; [etc., etc.] 1919.

Lloyd George, David Lloyd George, 1st earl, 1863-1945.
Pour la democratie et la paix du monde. Les declarations de Lloyd George et du president Wilson, Janvier, 1918. Genève, Imprimerie"Atar" 1918.
61p. illustrated cover(ports) 21cm.

NL 0429042 DNW

Lloyd George, David Lloyd George, 1st earl, 1863-1945.
...The prime minister on the peace treaty... London: W. H. Smith & Son [1919]. 16 p. 8°.
"Speech...in the House of Commons on July 3, 1919."

1. Versailles (Treaty of), 1919. 2. Title.
N. Y. P. L. March 18, 1920.

NL 0429043 NN

Lloyd George, David Lloyd George, 1st earl, 1863-1945.
The problem of unemployment. A speech delivered by the Right Hon. D. Lloyd-George...in the Queen's Hall on December 31st, 1909. London: The Liberal Publ. Dept., 1910. 16 p. 8°.

1. Labor (Unemployed), Gt. Br. 2. Liberal Publication Department.
N. Y. P. L. February 17, 1922.

NL 0429044 NN

Lloyd George, David Lloyd George, *1st earl*, 1863-1945.
Las proposiciones de paz, y la actitud de los aliados. Discurso pronunciado por el primer ministro de la Gran Bretaña el muy hon. D. Lloyd George, el 19 de diciembre de 1916. Londres, Hayman, Christy & Lilly, ltd., 1917.
40 p. 21½ cm.

1. European war, 1914-1918—Peace. 2. Gt. Brit.—Pol. & govt.—1910-1936. I. Title.
D613.L75 25-21219 rev

NL 0429045 DLC

Lloyd George, David Lloyd George, *1st earl*, 1863-1945.
Les propositions de paix et l'attitude des alliés. Discours prononcé par le très honorable D. Lloyd George, premier ministre de Grande Bretagne, le 19 décembre 1916. Londres, Hayman, Christy & Lilly, ltd., 1917.
32 p. 21½ cm.

1. European war, 1914-1918—Peace. 2. Gt. Brit.—Pol. & govt.—1910-1936.
D613.L73 24-21217 rev

NL 0429046 DLC NN

Lloyd George, David Lloyd George, *1st earl*, 1863-1945.
Los propósitos británicos en la guerra, declaración del primer ministro, el excmo. sr. don David Lloyd George, hecha el 5 de enero de 1918. Londres, R. Clay & sons, ltd., 1918.
16 p. 21½ cm.

1. European war, 1914-1918—Peace. I. Title.
D613.L65 25-21218 rev

NL 0429047 DLC

Lloyd George, David Lloyd George, 1st earl, 1863-
Quand la guerre finira ... (London, Hayman, Christy & Lilly, ltd., 1917)
cover-title, 16 p. 21½ cm.

NL 0429048 DNW

Lloyd George, David Lloyd George, *1st earl*, 1863-1945.
Quelques discours par David Lloyd George, avec une salutation personelle aux enfants de la France de la part du premier ministre de la Grande-Bretagne. [London, The Field and queen ltd] 1917.
3 p. l., 45 p., 1 l. port. 21½ cm.

1. European war, 1914-1918—Addresses, sermons, etc.
D523.L59 24-11752 rev

NL 0429049 DLC

Lloyd George, David Lloyd George, 1st earl, 1863-
Le proposte di pace e l'atteggiamento degli alleati; discorsi pronunciati il 19 dicembre 1916, alla Camera dei communi, e il 12 gennaio 1917 al Guidhall [!] di Londra, dall' Onor. D. Lloyd George ... Versione italiana di Pietro Santamaria. Roma, 1917.

NL 0429050 CtY

Lloyd George, David Lloyd George, 1st earl, 1863-
Great Britain.
... Relations between Great Britain and Ireland; proposals of British government, July 20, 1921, and correspondence between Mr. Lloyd George and Mr. De Valera ... New York city, Greenwich, Conn., American association for international conciliation [1921]

DA566 .9.L5 A2
Lloyd George, David Lloyd George, 1st earl, 1863-1945.
Slings and arrows; sayings chosen from the speeches of the Rt. Hon. David Lloyd George, ed. with introduction by Philip Guedalla. New York, Harper [n.d.]
xvii, 324 p. port. 20cm.

1. Gt. Brit. - Pol. & govt. - 1910- 2. Finance - Gt. Brit. 3. European war, 1914-1918 - Addresses, sermons, etc. I. Guedalla, Philip, 1889- ed. II. Title.

NL 0429052 OrCS WaWW MWelC PPT PPL PP NN

Lloyd George, David Lloyd George, *1st earl*, 1863-1945.
Slings and arrows; sayings chosen from the speeches of the Rt. Hon. David Lloyd George ... edited with introduction by Philip Guedalla. London [etc.] Cassell and company, ltd. [1929]
xvii p., 1 l., 324 p. front. (port.) 19 cm.

1. Gt. Brit.—Pol. & govt.—1910-1936. 2. Finance—Gt. Brit. 3. European war, 1914-1918—Addresses, sermons, etc. I. Guedalla, Philip, 1889-1944, ed. II. Title.
DA566.9.L5A4 29-18443 rev.

NL 0429053 DLC WaS CaBVaU Or OrP FMU Or CtY PPT OCU OC1 NN IU

Lloyd George, David Lloyd George, *1st earl*, 1863-1945.
Spain and Britain ... London [Friends of Spain] 1937.
18 p. 21 cm.
"Speech ... in the House of commons ... October 28th, 1937."
No. [26] in a volume with binder's title: Pamphlets on the Spanish civil war.

DP269.P25 no. 26 43-26414 rev
Brief cataloging

NL 0429054 DLC LU NcD TxU GU

Lloyd George, David Lloyd George, *1st earl*, 1863-1945.
Spain and Britain ... New York [American friends of Spanish democracy] 1937.
15 p. 21 cm.
"Speech ... in the House of commons ... October 28, 1937."
No. [27] in a volume with binder's title: Pamphlets on the Spanish civil war.

DP269.P25 no. 27 43-26415 rev
Brief cataloging

NL 0429055 DLC OrU CtY MH IU

VOLUME 337

Lloyd George, David Lloyd George, 1st Earl, 1863-1945.
Speech of the Prime Minister of Great Britain [David Lloyd George] before the House of Commons, December 19, 1916.
(In Official documents looking toward peace. Ser. 1, pp. 22-26. New York. 1917.)
Occasioned by the proposal of the Central Powers of Dec. 12, 1916, printed in this volume.

L2365 — Double main card. — Great Britain. Prime Minister. (M1) — George, David Lloyd, 1863 (A2) — European War, 1914- . Peace. (1) — Central Powers. (1)

NL 0429056 MB

Lloyd George, David Lloyd George, *1st earl*, 1863–1945.
The task before us, by the Rt. Hon. David Lloyd George, M. P., chancellor of the Exchequer. London, Jarrold & sons [1915]
29 p. 18 cm.
Address delivered at Bangor, Wales, Feb. 28, 1915. "Reprinted by permission from 'The Times.'"

1. European war, 1914–1918—Addresses, sermons, etc.

D525.L58 15–12858 rev

NL 0429057 DLC CtY NjP DN NN

Lloyd George, David Lloyd George, *1st earl*, 1863–1945.
... "Through terror to triumph!" An appeal to the nation by the Chancellor of the Exchequer ... [Authorised ed.] London, Parliamentary recruiting committee, 1914.
15 p. 19½ cm. [Gt. Brit. Parliamentary recruiting committee. Publications. 9]
"A speech delivered at the Queen's hall, London, on September 19th, 1914."

1. European war, 1914–1918. I. Title.

D525.L6 15–3751 rev

NL 0429058 DLC NN CtY ICJ

Lloyd George, David Lloyd George, *1st earl*, 1863–1945.
Through terror to triumph; speeches and pronouncements of the Right Hon. David Lloyd George, M. P., since the beginning of the war, arranged by F. L. Stevenson, B. A. (Lond.) London, New York [etc.] Hodder and Stoughton, 1915.
xii, 187, [1] p. 18½ cm.

1. European war, 1914–1918. I. Stevenson, F. L., ed. II. Title.

D517.L55 15–23055 rev

ICJ MB MH NN OC1W OU
NL 0429059 DLC CaBVaU CaBViP IdU WaWW PU PPL OCU

Lloyd George, David Lloyd George, 1st earl, 1863-
Through terror to triumph. La victoire en marche, par David Lloyd George; traduit d'après l'arrangement de F. L. Stevenson par Charles M. Garnier et Mme. M. Mantoux. Paris: H. Didier, 1916. 2 p.l., (i)x-xiv, 263 p., 1 l. 12°.

1. European war, 1914- .—Addresses, sermons, etc. 2. Stevenson, F. L., editor. 3. Garnier, Charles Marie, translator. 4. Mantoux, Mme. M., jt. translator. 5. Title. 6. Title: La victoire en marche.
N. Y. P. L. November 28, 1916.

NL 0429060 NN

Lloyd George, David Lloyd George, *1st earl*, 1863–1945.
The truth about reparations and war-debts, by the Right Hon. David Lloyd George. Garden City, N. Y., Doubleday, Doran & company, inc., 1932.
4 p. l., 150 p. 20 cm.
"First edition."

1. European war, 1914–1918—Reparations. 2. Debts, Public–Europe. 3. Debts, Public—U. S. 4. Economic conditions—1918– I. Title.

D648.L6 1932 940.31422 32–10655 rev

Or WaS
KU PU-W NN DN MB NcRS MeB MH-L OU MU FU IdPI OrP
NL 0429061 DLC OKentU ICU OC1 OOxM MiU PP ViU WaU

Lloyd George, David Lloyd George, *1st earl*, 1863–1945.
The truth about reparations and war-debts, by the Right Hon. David Lloyd George. London, W. Heinemann, ltd., 1932.
4 p. l., 150 p. 20½ cm.

1. European war, 1914–1918—Reparations. 2. Debts, Public—Europe. 3. Debts, Public—U. S. 4. Economic conditions—1918– I. Title.

D648.L6 1932a 940.31422 32–12099 rev

MH NcD ViU ICJ PBm NN
NL 0429062 DLC CaBVaU WaSp DAU IdU NBuU OrSaW WaSpG

Lloyd George, David Lloyd George, *1st earl*, 1863–1945.
The truth about the peace treaties, by David Lloyd George ... London, V. Gollancz ltd., 1938.
2 v. fronts., illus. (maps) pl., ports., facsims. 23 cm.
Paged continuously.
American edition (New Haven, Yale university press) has title: Memoirs of the Peace conference.

1. European war, 1914–1918—Peace. 2. Paris. Peace conference, 1919. I. Title.

D644.L55 1938 940.314 39–50 rev

OU ICN CtY CU NBuU
CaBViP ScU OrU OC1WHi NNC PPD PBm PPL PU OC1W OCU
NL 0429063 DLC IdU CaBVaU CaBVa WaTC OrP WaE WaS

Lloyd George, David Lloyd George, *1st earl*, 1863–1945.
... The urban land problem: leaseholds — housing. A speech delivered by the Right Hon. D. Lloyd George, M. P., at Holloway, on November 29th, 1913. [Authorised ed.] London, The Liberal publication department, 1913.
15, [1] p. 21½ cm.

1. Housing—Gt. Brit. 2. Landlord and tenant—Gt. Brit. I. Title.

HD7333.A3L7 14–5193 rev

NL 0429064 DLC NN CtY

Lloyd George, David Lloyd George, *1st earl*, 1863–1945.
... Victory or defeat: no half-way house; speech delivered by the Rt. Hon. David Lloyd George at Gray's Inn, December 14, 1917.
(*In* Association for international conciliation. American branch. International conciliation. New York, 1918. 19½ cm. no. 123, p. 5–22)
Caption title.

1. European war, 1914–1918—Addresses, sermons, etc. 2. European war, 1914–1918—Peace.

JX1907.A8 no. 123 18–8794 rev

NL 0429065 DLC OU MiU OC1 OO WaS OrPR CaBVaU WaU-L

Lloyd George, David Lloyd George, *1st earl*, 1863–1945.
Die wahrheit über reparationen und kriegsschulden, von Right Hon. David Lloyd George; deutsch von Edgar von Schmidt-Pauli. Berlin, Verlag für kulturpolitik, 1932.
196 p., 1 l. 22 cm.

1. European war, 1914–1918—Reparations. 2. Debts, Public—Europe. 3. Debts, Public—U. S. 4. Economic conditions—1918– I. Schmidt-Pauli, Edgar von, 1881– tr. II. Title.

D648.L63 940.31422 32–23302 rev

NL 0429066 DLC CaBVaU NcD NN

[Lloyd George, David] Lloyd George, 1st earl, 1863-
The war; its causes and its message ... 5th ed. ... London [1941]
39 p.

NL 0429067 NNC

Lloyd George, David Lloyd George, *1st earl*, 1863–1945.
War memoirs of David Lloyd George ... London, I. Nicholson & Watson [1933–36]
6 v. fronts., plates, ports., maps, facsims. (1 fold.) 23 cm.
Paged continuously.

1. European war, 1914–1918. I. Title.

D546.L5 1933 940.342 33–28755 rev 3

OrPS CtY OKentU MH ScU NN CU-I
NL 0429068 DLC WaSpG CaBVaU CaBVa MiU OC1W ViU-L

Lloyd George, David Lloyd George, *1st earl*, 1863–1945.
War memoirs of David Lloyd George ... Boston, Little, Brown, and company, 1933–37.
6 v. fronts., plates, ports., maps, facsims. 24 cm.

1. European war, 1914–1918. I. Title.

D546.L5 1933a 940.342 33–28754 rev 2

MdBP CaBViP MiU OKentU NmU OU OC1 OrSaW OrStbM OOxM OCU OU ViU MB NN MeB WaWW GASC MdBP OrCS DNW CoU Or WaT NN WaSp DN WaS PPT PSC PPD PHC PU
NL 0429069 DLC IdB OO IdU MtU OrP NIC NcD OrU

Lloyd George, David Lloyd George, *1st earl*, 1863–1945.
War memoirs of David Lloyd George ... London, Odhams press limited [1938]
2 v. front., illus. (incl. maps, facsims.) plates, ports. 22 cm.
Paged continuously.
"New edition."

NL 0429070 CU InU CaBVa

Lloyd George, David Lloyd George, *1st earl*, 1863–1945.
War memoirs of David Lloyd George ... London, Odhams press limited [1942]
2 v. front., illus. (incl. maps, facsims.) plates, ports. 22 cm.
Paged continuously.

1. European war, 1914–1918. I. Title.

D546.L5 1942 940.342 43–18058 rev

NL 0429071 DLC IEdS

Lloyd George, David Lloyd George, 1st earl, 1863-

We can conquer unemployment; Mr. Lloyd George's pledge. London, Cassell and company, ltd., 1929.

Lloyd George, David Lloyd George, *1st earl*, 1863–1945.
When the war will end [Mr. Lloyd George's speech at Glasgow, 29 June, 1917. London, Printed by Alabaster, Passmore & sons, ltd., 1917]
1 p. l., 15, [1] p. 21½ cm.

1. European war, 1914–1918—Addresses, sermons, etc. I. Title.

D525.L62 17–23037 rev

NL 0429073 DLC NN PHi KU CtY PU PPL OU OO MB MiU MH

Pam. Coll. 35619
Lloyd George, David Lloyd George, *1st earl*, 1863–1945.
When the war will end [Mr. Lloyd George's speech at Glasgow, 29 June, 1917. London, Printed by Hayman, Christy, & Lilly, 1917?]
15, [1] p. 22 cm.
Cover title.

NL 0429074 NcD

Lloyd George, David Lloyd George, *1st earl*, 1863–1945.
Where are we going? By the Right Honourable David Lloyd George ... New York, George H. Doran company [1923]
xxiv p., 1 l., 25–371 p. 22½ cm.
London edition (Hodder and Stoughton limited) with a different arrangement of the articles and addresses, has title: Is it peace?

1. European war, 1914–1918—Influence and results. 2. World politics. 3. Peace. 4. European war, 1914–1918—Reparations. 5. Germany—Econ. condit.—1918–1945. I. Title.

D653.L6 23—16478

PV PPA NIC PP PPFr PHC NjN ViU OC1W OO OC1 OCU NN
NL 0429075 DLC OkU WaT WaS OrSaW CaBVa UU MB TxU TNJ

VOLUME 337

Lloyd George, David Lloyd George, *1st earl*, **1863-1945.**
Why the allies will win. An interview with the Rt. Hon. D. Lloyd George ... by the editor of the Secolo of Milan. London, "The Daily chronicle" [1916?]
12 p. 16½ cm.

1. European war, 1914-1918.

D525.L63 16-17189 rev

MiU OC1W OO IaU NjP
NL 0429076 DLC CaBViP PU PHi NjP NN MB NcD CtY PPT

Lloyd George, David Lloyd George, *1st earl*, **1863-1945.**
The wit & wisdom of Lloyd George, compiled and edited by Dan Rider. London, G. Richards, limited, 1917.
94 p. 19 cm.

I. Rider, Dan, ed. II. Title.

DA566.9.L5A5 17-31663 rev

NL 0429077 DLC

Lloyd George, Frances Louise (Stevenson) Lloyd George, countess, 1888- joint author.

DA566 .9 .L5T53 **Thomson, Malcolm.**
David Lloyd George; the official biography by Malcolm Thomson with the collaboration of Frances, countess Lloyd-George of Dwyfor. London, New York, Hutchinson [1948]

Lloyd George, Richard Lloyd George, *2d earl*, **1889-**
Dame Margaret; the life story of his mother, by Viscount Gwynedd (now Earl Lloyd George of Dwyfor) London, G. Allen & Unwin [1947]
viii, 239 p. illus., ports., map (on lining-papers) 22 cm.

1. Lloyd George, Dame Margaret (Owen) d. 1941.

A 48-8197*

Harvard Univ. Library for Library of Congress [1]

NL 0429079 MH ICU RPB

Lloyd George of Dwyfor, Richard Lloyd George, *2d earl*
see **Lloyd George, Richard Lloyd George,** *2d earl*, **1889-**

Lloyd-Greame, Sir Philip, 1884- joint ed.

MacSwinney, Robert Forster, 1848- *ed.*
The Coal mines act, 1911, and other acts affecting mines and quarries, with a commentary by Robert Forster MacSwinney ... and P. Lloyd-Greame ... London, Sweet and Maxwell, limited, 1912.

Lloyd-Greame, Sir **Philip,** 1884-
The Imperial Economic Conference, by the Rt. Hon. Sir Philip Lloyd-Greame... Westminster: National Unionist Assoc.[, 1924.] 14 p. 8°. (National Unionist Assoc. Unionist workers' handbooks. no. 4.)

1. Colonies and colonization, British—Congresses. 2. Tariff, Preferential—Gt. Br., 1923. 3. Economic history—Gt. Br.—Colonies. 4. Commerce, Colonial—Gt. Br. 5. Ser.
N. Y. P. L. October 23, 1925

NL 0429082 NN

Lloyd-Greame, Sir Philip, 1884 -

MacSwinney, Robert Forster, 1848-
The law of mines, quarries, and minerals, by Robert Forster MacSwinney ... 4th ed. by the author, assisted by Philip Lloyd-Greame ... London, Sweet and Maxwell, limited, 1912.

Lloyd-Hughes, J.R.

see Hughes, J.R. Lloyd.

Lloyd-Jacob, George Harold.
Nationality and domicile; with special reference to early notions on the subject. By G. H. Lloyd Jacob ...
(*In* Grotius society, London. Problems of peace and war. London, 1925. 22cm. v. 10, p. 89-114)

1. Nationalism and nationality. 2. Domicile.

A 25-673 Revised

Carnegie endow. int. peace. for Library of Congress Library JX31.G7 vol. 10

NL 0429085 DGW-C WaU-L MiU DLC

Lloyd James, Arthur, 1884-1943.

British broadcasting corporation.
... The B. B. C.'s recommendations for pronouncing doubtful words, reissued with criticisms, edited by Robert Bridges. [Oxford] The Clarendon press, 1929.

Lloyd James, Arthur, 1884-
A Basic phonetic reader, by A. Lloyd James ... London, New York [etc.] T. Nelson and sons, ltd. [1938]
vi, 198 p., 1 l. 17½cm.
Table on lining-paper and fly-leaf.
"First published 1937; reprinted, 1938."
Selections in Basic English and transcriptions in international phonetic script on opposite pages.

1. Basic English. 2. English language—Pronunciation. I. Title.

39-5736

Library of Congress PE1073.5.L5
[3] [421.5] 408.9

NL 0429087 DLC WaU IaU CaOTP NN OU

Lloyd James, Arthur, 1884-1943.

British broadcasting corporation.
Broadcast English ... Recommendations to announcers ... With an introduction by A. Lloyd James ... London, The British broadcasting corporation, 1932-

---

Lloyd James, Arthur, 1884-
The broadcast word, by A. Lloyd James ... London, K. Paul, Trench, Trubner & co., ltd., 1935.
xii, 207 p. 22cm.
"Some books on linguistic phonetics": p. 201-202.

1. English language—Pronunciation. 2. Radio broadcasting. 3. Language and languages. I. Title.

35-11180

Library of Congress PE1137.L55
[3] 421.5

OC1W OC1 OU MB NN CtW
NL 0429089 DLC OC1U CaBVaU OrU NcU WaU LU NIC MiD

PN4162 L655 Lloyd-James, Arthur, 1884-1943.
General exercises to Our spoken language. London, T.Nelson and Sons [c1938]
xii, 76p. 19cm.

1. English language - Phonetics. I. Lloyd-James, Arthur, 1884-1943. Our spoken language.

NL 0429090 IaU MU

Lloyd James, Arthur, 1884-1943.
Historical introduction to French phonetics, by A. Lloyd James ... London, University of London press, ltd., 1929.
3 p. l., 171 p. illus., diagrs. 22½cm.

1. French language—Phonetics. 2. Phonetics. I. Title.

30-13280

Library of Congress PC2135.L6
[3] 441.5

NL 0429091 DLC NN PPT CU MiU OCU

Lloyd James, Arthur, 1884-
Our spoken language, by A. Lloyd James ... London, New York [etc.] T. Nelson and sons, ltd. [1938]
vi, 7-176 p. illus. 19 cm.

NL 0429092 OrU MB IU FU

Lloyd James, Arthur, 1884-
Our spoken language, by A. Lloyd James ... London, New York [etc.] T. Nelson and sons, ltd. [1939]
vi, 7-176 p. illus. 19cm. (*Half-title:* Discussion books. General editors: Richard Wilson ... and A. J. J. Ratcliff ... no. 9)
"First published in this series, September 1938; reprinted, January 1939."

1. Speech. 2. Voice. 3. English language—Phonetics. I. Title.

39-22150

Library of Congress PN4162.L65 1939
——— Copy 2. [3] 808.5

NL 0429093 DLC WaTC IaU CoU PPT NcRS OC1W OO OU

PN4162 L65 1946 Lloyd James, Arthur, 1884-
Our spoken language. London, New York, T. Nelson [1946]
176 p. illus. 19cm. (Discussion books, no. 9)

"First published in this series, September, 1938; reprinted ... 1946"

1. Speech. 2. Voice. 3. English language - Phonetics. I. Title.

NL 0429094 GU

---

*PE1137 .L56 **Lloyd James, Arthur, 1884-**
Recommendations to announcers regarding the pronunciation of some British family names and titles. Collected and transcribed for the BBC advisory committee on spoken English. 1st ed. London, British Broadcasting Corporation, 1939.
102 p. 22cm. (Broadcast English, VII)

1. English language--Pronunciation. 2. Radio broadcasting. I. Title.

NL 0429095 MB

Lloyd James, Arthur, 1884-
Speech signals in telephony, by A. Lloyd James ... London, Sir I. Pitman & sons, ltd., 1940.
vii, 49 p. 19cm.

1. Telephone. 2. Signals and signaling. 3. Speech. I. Title.

42-31409

Library of Congress TK6188.L55
[2] 621.385

NL 0429096 DLC CaBVa OC1

421.5 L793t Lloyd James, Arthur, 1884-
Talks on English speech; a short gramophone course of English pronunciation, prepared and recorded by A. Lloyd James ... London, Linguaphone Language Institute [n.d.]
31p.
"Published with five double-sided ten-inch records."

1. English language - Pronunciation.

NL 0429097 FTaSU

VOLUME 337

Barnard
D629.15
L773
Lloyd James, Arthur, 1884-1943.
Talks on English speech; a short gramophone course of English pronunciation prepared and recorded by A. Lloyd James. ⌈London⌉ Linguaphone Institute ⌈193-?⌉
30 p.

"A brief epitome of the series of Wireless talks on English speech broadcast to schools in Great Britain from September 1930 to June 1931."

NL 0429098 NNC

Lloyd-Johnes, Herbert Johnes, joint author.

NK2540
.D3
Davies, *Sir* Leonard Twiston, 1894–
Welsh furniture; an introduction ⌈by⌉ L. Twiston-Davies and H. J. Lloyd-Johnes. Cardiff, University of Wales Press, 1950.

Lloyd-Jones, Charles, 1897–
A comedy of Eros, by Charles Lloyd-Jones. London, L. Dickson limited ⌈1938⌉
277 p. 19cm.
"First published 1938."

I. Title.
38-18533
Library of Congress PZ3.L7792Co

NL 0429100 DLC

Lloyd-Jones, Charles, 1897–
Gemini , by Charles Lloyd-Jones.
London, Duckworth, 1927.
287 [1] p. 19 1/2 cm.

NL 0429101 DSI

220.88
L77
Lloyd-Jones, Charles, 1897- comp.
Great dramas and poems from the Bible, illus. with reproductions of sixteen celebrated paintings. London, Macgibbon & Kee, 1953.
199p. 21cm.

1. Bible stories, English. I. Title.

NL 0429102 KU

Lloyd-Jones, Charles, 1897-
Her name was Tokio, by Charles Lloyd-Jones. New York, Farrar & Rinehart, incorporated ⌈°1934⌉
5 p. l., 3-311 p. 19½cm.
London edition (L. Dickson, limited) has title: Sea change.

I. Title.
34-28968
Library of Congress PZ3.L7792He

NL 0429103 DLC IU

Lloyd-Jones, Charles, 1897-
The house of the goat, by Charles Lloyd-Jones. London, Duckworth ⌈1926⌉
317 p. 19cm.

I. Title.
26-17243
Library of Congress PZ3.L7792Ho

NL 0429104 DLC

Lloyd-Jones, Charles, 1897-
"Irene says..." By Charles Lloyd-Jones. London, Jarrolds limited ⌈1930⌉
288 p. 19½cm.

I. Title.
30-11731
Library of Congress PZ3.L7792 Ir

NL 0429105 DLC

Lloyd-Jones, Charles, 1897-
Laughter in heaven, by C. Lloyd-Jones. London, W. Heinemann, ltd. ⌈1933⌉
4 p. l., 3-310 p. 19cm.

I. Title.
33-16247
Library of Congress PZ3.L7792Lau

NL 0429106 DLC

Lloyd-Jones, Charles, 1897-
The matriarch ⌈by⌉ Charles Lloyd-Jones. London, E. Benn limited ⌈1928⌉
277 p., 1 l. 19cm.

I. Title.
28-24958
Library of Congress PZ3.L7792Ma

NL 0429107 DLC

Lloyd-Jones, Charles, 1897-
Sea change, by Charles Lloyd-Jones ... London, L. Dickson, limited ⌈1934⌉
315 p. 19cm.

I. Title.
34-22039
Library of Congress PZ3.L7792Se

NL 0429108 DLC

Lloyd-Jones, Charles, 1897–
Village wooing ⌈by⌉ Charles Lloyd-Jones. London, L. Dickson & Thompson, limited ⌈1935⌉
3 p. l., 297 p. 19cm.

I. Title.
35-29221
Library of Congress PZ3.L7792 Vi

NL 0429109 DLC

Lloyd Jones, Chester
see Jones, Chester Lloyd, 1881-1941.

Lloyd Jones, Cyril Walter
see Jones, Cyril Walter Lloyd.

Lloyd-Jones, David Martyn.

Perry, Charles Bruce, 1903–
Bacterial endocarditis, by C. Bruce Perry ... With an appendix on an experimental study of malignant endocarditis by D. M. Lloyd-Jones ... Bristol, J. Wright and sons ltd.; ⌈etc., etc.⌉ 1936.

224.95
L777f
Lloyd-Jones, David Martyn.
From fear to faith; studies in the book of Habakkuk. London, Inter-Varsity Fellowship ⌈1953⌉
72p.

"First published ... 1953."

1. Bible. O.T Habakkuk--Criticism, interpretation, etc.

NL 0429113 TxFTC CLamB

DQ50
L779f
Lloyd-Jones, David Martyn
From fear to faith; studies in the book of Habakkuk. London, Inter-Varsity fellowship ⌈1955⌉
76 p. 19 cm.

First published in 1953.

NL 0429114 CtY-D PPWe NcD

Lloyd-Jones, David Martyn.
The plight of man and the power of God... London, Hodder and Stoughton ⌈1942⌉
96 p., 19cm.

NL 0429115 NjPT

Lloyd-Jones, David Martyn.
The plight of man and the power of God ⌈by⌉ D. Martyn Lloyd-Jones ... New York, Nashville, Abingdon-Cokesbury press ⌈1943⌉
120 p. 19½cm.

1. Salvation. I. Title.
43-3145
Library of Congress BT751.L55
⌈8⌉ 234

NL 0429116 DLC WaS OrU ICU PPT PPWe OCl

Lloyd-Jones, David Martyn.
Truth unchanged, unchanging. New York, Revell ⌈1950⌉
96 p. 20 cm. (Jonathan Blanchard lectures, 1st ser.)

1. Man (Theology) I. Title. (Series)
BT701.L7 233 50-6961

NL 0429117 DLC PPWe

Lloyd-Jones, David Martyn.
Why does God allow war? A general justification of the ways of God ⌈by⌉ D. Martyn Lloyd-Jones ... London: Hodder and Stoughton ⌈1940⌉ 125 p. 19cm.
"Sermons ... delivered ... at Westminster chapel."

145767B. 1. War and Christianity. I. Title.
N. Y. P. L. November 25, 1941

NL 0429118 NN MH-AH PPWe

Lloyd Jones, E
Standard of medical care for tea plantations in India
see under India (Dominion) Director General of Health Services.

Lloyd-Jones, Mrs. Esther Leona (McDonald)
see
Lloyd-Jones, Mrs. Esther (McDonald) 1901-

VOLUME 337

Lloyd-Jones, Mrs. Esther (McDonald) 1901-
Annotated bibliography for Social competence and college students. ₍n.p., 1940?₎
2 p.l., 2-29 numb. l. 29cm.
Caption title.
Processed.

NL 0429121 OrU

Lloyd-Jones, Esther (McDonald) 1901–
Coming of age, by Esther Lloyd-Jones ... and Ruth Fedder ... New York, London, Whittlesey house, McGraw-Hill book company, inc. ₍°1941₎
x, 280 p. 23½ᶜᵐ.
Bibliography: p. 273-280.

1. Youth. 2. Success. I. Fedder, Ruth, 1907– joint author. II. Title.
₍Full name: Esther Leona (McDonald) Lloyd-Jones₎
41—13814
Library of Congress HQ796.L6
₍a45k2₎ 301.1584

OrPS
WaS WaWW WaSp OrCS Or Wa WaOB OrU-M OrSaW MtU PPPL WU NcC PBm PSC MiDP CtY-M OrP IdU IdB OrU OOxM OCl ODW OCU OO OU ViU PPGi PU-Penn PPT PP
NL 0429122 DLC CaBVa MtBC KEmT IU WaU CU CaBVaU

Lloyd-Jones, Mrs. Esther (McDonald) 1901-
joint author.
Watson, Goodwin Barbour, 1899–
Redirecting teacher education, by Goodwin Watson, Donald P. Cottrell ₍and₎ Esther M. Lloyd-Jones ... New York city, Teachers college, Columbia university, 1938.

Lloyd-Jones, Esther (McDonald) 1901–
... Social competence and college students, by Esther Lloyd-Jones ... ₍Washington₎ 1940.
cover-title, xiii, 89, ₍2₎ p. 23 cm. (American council on education. Studies. Ser. VI. Student personnel work. Vol. IV, no. 3)
Bibliography: p. 79-89.

1. Personnel service in education. 2. Students. I. Title.
E 41—161
U. S. Office of Education. Library
for Library of Congress [LB2343.A45 vol. 4, no. 3]
₍a48i1₎ (378.113)

ViU OU OCU NBuC MiU WaWW IdPI MtBC KEmT
NL 0429125 DHEW MiDP OrU MiU NcD PPPL PPT PU PWcT

Lloyd-Jones, Esther (McDonald) 1901–
A student personnel program for higher education, by Esther McD. Lloyd-Jones ... and Margaret Ruth Smith ... 1st ed. New York and London, McGraw-Hill book company, inc., 1938.
x, 322 p. diagrs. 23½ᶜᵐ.
Bibliography at end of each chapter; "A selected list of tests for college students and adults": p. 291-311.
*2d impression.
1. Personnel service in education. I. Smith, Margaret Ruth, 1902– joint author. II. Title.
₍Full name: Mrs. Esther Leona (McDonald) Lloyd-Jones₎
38—20603

PBm PPT ViU MtU IdU WaS OrU OrPS CaBVaU
NL 0429126 ViU MiHM NcD NcRS PWcS P PP PU-Penn PBm

Lloyd-Jones, Esther (McDonald) 1901– ed.
Student personnel work as deeper teaching, edited by Esther Lloyd-Jones and Margaret Ruth Smith. ₍1st ed.₎ New York, Harper ₍1954₎
361 p. 22 cm.

1. Personnel service in education. I. Smith, Margaret Ruth, 1902– joint ed. II. Title.
Full name: Esther Leona (McDonald) Lloyd-Jones.
LB2343.L49 371.422 53—11851 ‡

WaWW
OClU OCl OOxM OCU PWcS IdPI PSt PPLas IdU WaTC NcD MB TU PPPTe OrU OrSaW PIm ScCleA CaBVaU IdPI NN AU OrPS OClW PPPL PU-Penn PPT OU OO ViU TxU
NL 0429127 DLC OrMonO OrLgE Or OrAshS MtBuM KEmT

Lloyd-Jones, Esther (McDonald) 1901–
Student personnel work at Northwestern university, by Esther McD. Lloyd-Jones, PH. D., with a foreword by Walter Dill Scott ... New York and London, Harper & brothers, 1929.
xx, 253, ₍1₎ p. incl. tables, diagrs. forms (1 fold.) 21½ cm.
Thesis (PH. D.)—Columbia university, 1929.
Without thesis note.
"Supplemental readings in mental hygiene for colleges": p. 135-136. An abbreviated list of students' general reading: p. 243.
1. Northwestern university, Evanston, Ill. Personnel office. 2. Personnel service in higher education. I. Title.
Full name: Esther Leona (McDonald) Lloyd-Jones.
LB2343.L5 29—18271
——— Copy 3. Thesis note on label mounted on t.-p. and vita on p. ₍254₎

PP ICJ MiHM OrU OrPR FMU Or
NL 0429128 DLC OrSaW CaBVaU OrLgE NcU NcD PPT PSC PV

Lloyd-Jones, John, 1885, ed.
Hughes, John Ceiriog, 1832–1887.
Caneuon Ceiriog detholiad. ₍Printer's mark₎ ₍Drenewydd yn sir Drefaldwyn₎ Gwasg Gregynog, 1925.

Lloyd-Jones, John, 1885–
The court poets of the Welsh princes.
(In British Academy, London. (Founded 1901) Proceedings, 1948. London ₍1952₎ 26 cm. v. 34, p. ₍167₎-197)
The Sir John Rhys memorial lecture, read 24 Nov., 1948.
"Notes and references": p. 193-197.

1. Bards and bardism. 2. Welsh poetry—Hist. & crit. I. Title. (Series: British Academy, London (Founded 1901) The Sir John Rhys memorial lecture, 1948)
AS122.L5 vol. 34 A 52-7225
Wisconsin. Univ. Libr.
for Library of Congress ₍1₎†

NL 0429130 WU NNC DLC

Lloyd-Jones, John, 1885–
The court poets of the Welsh princes. London, G. Cumberlege ₍1948₎
31 p. 25 cm. (The Sir John Rhys memorial lecture)
Cover title.
"From the Proceedings of the British Academy, vol. XXXIV."

1. Bards and bardism. 2. Welsh poetry—Hist. & crit. I. Title. (Series: British Academy, London (Founded 1901) The Sir John Rhys memorial lecture, 1948)
A 51-6453
Grosvenor Library PB2231-L6
for Library of Congress ₍2₎

NL 0429131 NBuG CaBVaU NN MB MH

Lloyd-Jones, John, 1885–
Enwau lleoedd sir Gaernarfon (traethawd arobryn yn Eisteddfod Caernarfon, 1921) gan J. Lloyd-Jones ... Caerdydd, Gwasg Prifysgol Cymru, 1928.
xv, 151, ₍1₎ p. 19ᶜᵐ.

1. Names, Geographical—Wales—Carnarvonshire. I. Eisteddfod, Carnarvon, Wales, 1921.
32-33136
Library of Congress DA740.C35L63 929.4094292

NL 0429132 DLC PBm ICU MH ICN

PB2188
.L8
LLOYD-JONES, JOHN, 1885–
Geirfa barddoniaeth gynnar Gymraeg, gan J. Lloyd-Jones... Caerdydd, Gwasg Prifysgol Cymru; ₍etc., etc.₎ 1931–
v. 29½cm.

1. Welsh language—Glossaries, vocabularies, etc. 2. Welsh poetry—Dictionaries, indexes, etc.

NL 0429133 ICU MH CtY ICN NN FU MiU OU

Lloyd-Jones, John, 1885–
Y drws agored; drama mewn tair act. Llandysul, J. D. Lewis ₍1935₎ 63 p. 14cm.

1. Welsh language—Texts and translations.

NL 0429134 NN

Lloyd Jones, John, 1885–
...Yr hen deiliwr; darlun ar fywyd gwledig er ys tua phedwar ugain mlynedd yn ol... Gan J. Lloyd Jones... London, S. French; Cardiff, Educational pub. co. ₍etc., etc., 193–?₎ 46 p. 16cm. (Welsh drama ser. no. 16.)

1. Welsh language—Texts and translations. I. Title. II. Ser.
N. Y. P. L. May 12, 1948

NL 0429135 NN

Lloyd Jones, John, 1885–
...Yr hen grydd; drama fer mewn un act, yn darlunio bywyd Cymreig yn y wlad, gan J. Lloyd Jones. London, S. French; Cardiff, Educational pub. co. ₍etc., etc., 193–?₎ 34 p. 16cm. (Welsh drama ser. no. 2.)

1. Welsh language—Texts and translations. I. Title. II. Ser.
N. Y. P. L. May 12, 1948

NL 0429136 NN

Lloyd-Jones, John, 1885–
Yr Hen Scwlin; drama mewn tair act yn darlunio hen ysgol ddyddiol yng Nghymru. Cardiff, Educational pub. co. ₍1920₎ 27 p. 16cm. (E. P. C. Welsh drama series. no. 22)

1. Welsh language—Texts and translations.

NL 0429137 NN

Lloyd-Jones, Orren, 1885-
Hays, Frank A.
The influence of excessive sexual activity of male rabbits ... by Frank A. Hays ... ₍Philadelphia, 1918₎

Lloyd-Jones, Orren.
Studies on inheritance in pigeons II. A microscopical and chemical study of the feather pigments ₍by₎ Orren Lloyd-Jones ... ₍Baltimore, The Waverly press, 1915₎
cover-title, p. 453-509 incl. illus., 7 pl. 26½ᶜᵐ.
The author's thesis (PH. D.)—University of Wisconsin, 1913.
"Reprinted from the Journal of experimental zoölogy, vol. 18, no. 3, April, 1915."
Bibliography: p. 494-495.

1. Heredity. 2. Pigeons.
15-27307
Library of Congress QH431.L5
Univ. of Wisconsin Libr.

NL 0429139 WU DLC

T1956
L793
Lloyd-Jones, Richard, 1927-
Common speech - a poetic effect for Hopkins, Browning and Arnold.

Thesis (Ph.D.) - Iowa.

1. Speech. 2. Hopkins, Gerard Manley, 1844-1889. 3. Browning, Robert, 1812-1889. 4. Arnold, Matthew, 1822-1888.

NL 0429140 IaU

Lloyd-Jones, William, 1886–
Havash! Frontier adventures in Kenya by Brevet-Major W. Lloyd-Jones ... with 28 photographs and a map. London, Arrowsmith ₍1925₎
317, ₍1₎ p., 1 l. front., plates, ports., map. 22½ᶜᵐ.

1. Africa, British East. 2. Hunting—Africa, British East. 3. Gt. Brit. Army. King's African rifles. I. Title.
DT425.L5 25-25029

NL 0429141 DLC CaBVaU CU NcD NSyU CtY PP MH NN

VOLUME 337

Lloyd-Jones, William, 1886-
K. A. R.; being an unofficial account of the origin and activities of the King's African rifles, by W. Lloyd-Jones. With a foreword by Major-General Sir Cecil Pereira ... With 43 photographs and a map. London, Arrowsmith [1926]
296 p. front., plates, ports., fold. map. 23cm.
"First published in 1926."
Bibliography: p. 283-284.

1. Gt. Brit.—Army—Infantry—King's African rifles. 42-40814
Library of Congress UA652.K48L6

NL 0429142 DLC CU IU CtY MH CSt-H NN NcD

Lloyd-Mostyn, Llewelyn Nevill Vaughan, ed baron Mostyn
see Mostyn, Llewelyn Nevill Vaughan Lloyd-Mostyn, baron, 1856-1929.

Lloyd of Doloran, George Ambrose Lloyd, 1st baron, 1879-
see Lloyd, George Ambrose Lloyd, baron, 1879-1941.

Lloyd of Hampstead, Dennis Lloyd, *Baron*, 1915-
The law relating to unincorporate associations, being the Yorke prize essay for the year 1937, by Dennis Lloyd. London, Sweet & Maxwell, 1938.
xvi, 248 p. 23 cm.

1. Unincorporated societies—Gt. Brit. 2. Unincorporated societies. I. Yorke prize essay, 1937.
39-30406

NL 0429145 DLC IU CaBVaU NcD CtY ViU-L MH PU-L

Lloyd of Hampstead, Dennis Lloyd, *Baron*, 1915-
Public policy; a comparative study in English and French law, by Dennis Lloyd. [London] University of London, Athlone Press, 1953.
xxii, 166 p. 23 cm. (University of London legal series, 1)
Bibliographical footnotes.

1. Public policy (Law) — Gt. Brit. 2. Public policy (Law) — France. (Series: London. University. Institute of Advanced Legal Studies. Legal series, 1)
55-22154

PPT-L MoU CaBVaU TU CNoS OrU-L WaU-L ViU-L
NL 0429146 DLC MB CSt N NcU NN CU NNC OU ICU TxU NcD

Lloyd of Hampstead, Dennis Lloyd, *Baron*, 1915-
Rent control, by Dennis Lloyd and John Montgomerie. London, Butterworth, 1949.
L, 454 p. 22 cm.
"Statutes": p. [283]-417.
——— Supplement. London, Butterworth, 1951.
xvi, A 60 p. 22 cm.
Includes legislation.
1. Rent control—Gt. Brit. I. Montgomerie, John, joint author. II. Gt. Brit. Laws, statutes, etc.
333.63 50-19650

NL 0429148 DLC CU CaBVaU WaU-L OU CSt

Lloyd of Hampstead, Dennis Lloyd, *Baron*, 1915-
Rent control, by Dennis Lloyd and John Montgomerie. 2d ed. London, Butterworth, 1955.
lxviii, 617 p. 23 cm.
"Statutes": p. [303]-482.

1. Rent control—Gt. Brit. I. Montgomerie, John, joint author. II. Gt. Brit. Laws, statutes, etc.
333.63 56-47501

NL 0429149 DLC CaBVaU OU CU

Lloyd-Oswell, William Henry, 1844-
Pedigrees and genealogical memoranda relating to the family of Oswell of Shrewsbury, etc. London: Mitchell Hughes and Clarke, 1905. 26 p. 4°.
Repr.: Miscellanea genealogica et heraldica.

1. Oswell family.
N. Y. P. L. February 4, 1911.

NL 0429150 NN

Lloyd-Oswell, William Henry, 1844-
Pedigrees and genealogical memoranda relating to the family of Oswell of Shrewsbury, etc. By the Rev. W. H. Oswell ... London, Mitchell, Hughes and Clarke, 1906.
16 p. 28cm.
Reprinted from Miscellanea genealogica et heraldica. 4th ser., vol. II, 1906.
"Royal descent of Oswell": p. 8-9.
"Pedigree of Lloyd of Leaton, co. Salop": p. 10-11.

1. Oswell family. 2. Lloyd family. 3. Royal descent, Families of. I. Title.
23-14539
Library of Congress CS439.O67

NL 0429151 DLC

Lloyd-Owen, Frances.
The gnome's kitchen: a story of woodland animals; illus.by Ernest Aris. Lond.,Harrap[1937] [254]p.

NL 0429152 CaBVa CaBVaU

Lloyd-Owen, Frances.
Gold Nugget Charlie; a narrative compiled from the notes of Charles E. Masson, by Frances Lloyd-Owen. London [etc.] G. G. Harrap & co., ltd. [1939]
259, [1] p. front., plates, ports. 22cm.
Maps on lining-papers.
"First published, 1939."

1. Masson, Charles E., 1862?- 2. Klondike gold-fields. I. Title.
40-10831
Library of Congress F931.M36
——— Copy 2. [2] 923.973

NL 0429153 DLC OrU CaBVa CaBVaU

Lloyd-Owen, Frances.
Joe and Pinto; illus.by Ernest Aris. London,Harrap[c1937] 250p. illus.(part col.)

NL 0429154 CaBVa

Lloyd Renshaw, T., pseud.
see
Renshaw, Joseph Theodore.

Lloyd-Smith, P.
Aboriginal legends and poems of to-day, by P. Lloyd-Smith ... [Melbourne, S. John Bacon, 1941?]
59, [1] p. 19cm.

I. Title.
A 42-2532

NL 0429156 NN

Lloyd-Smith, Parker, 1902- joint ed.

White, David McKelvy, 1901- *ed.*
A book of Hill verse, 1913-1920, ed. by David McK. White, 20, and Parker Lloyd-Smith, 20. Philadelphia, The John C. Winston company, 1920.

Lloyd Still, Barbara (Biro) 1896-
Dr Barbara; an autobiography. Translated from the Hungarian by Lawrence Wolfe. [London] P. Elek [1950]
205 p. 22 cm.

I. Title.
RK43.L5A3 926.1 51-22696

NL 0429158 DLC DNLM

Lloyd-Taylor, A
Catalogue of the collection of pictures
see under
The Yorker, London.

Lloyd Thomas, Joseph Morgan
see
Thomas, Joseph Morgan Lloyd, 1868-

Lloyd Thomas, Mary Gwyneth, joint author.

Bradbrook, Muriel Clara.
Andrew Marvell, by M. C. Bradbrook ... and M. G. Lloyd Thomas ... Cambridge [Eng.] The University press, 1940.

Lloyd Thomas, Mary Gwyneth.
Hopkins as critic.
(*In* English Association, London. Essays and studies. Oxford, 1947. 22 cm. v. 32, p. [61]-73)

1. Hopkins, Gerard Manley, 1844-1889.
PR13.E4 vol. 32 A 48-4908*
Cleveland. Public Libr. for Library of Congress [3]†

NL 0429162 OCl CaBVaU PPT DLC

Lloyd Thomas, Mary Gwyneth, ed.

Philips, John, 1676-1709.
The poems of John Phillips, ed. by M. G. Lloyd Thomas. Oxford, B. Blackwell, 1927.

Lloyd Thomas, Mary Gwyneth, *comp.*
... Travellers' verse, chosen by M. G. Lloyd Thomas, with original lithographs by Edward Bawden ... London, F. Muller ltd [1946]
viii, 120 p. col. plates. 21 cm. (New excursions into English poetry; editors: W. J. Turner and Sheila Shannon)
"First published ... in 1946."

1. English poetry (Selections: Extracts, etc.) 2. Voyages and travels—Poetry. I. Bawden, Edward, 1903- illus. II. Title.
PR1195.T7L6 821.082 47-5339

NL 0429164 DLC CtY PSt GU FMU NBC

Lloyd-Verney, George Hope.
The Desert rats; the history of the 7th armoured division, 1938-1945
see under
Verney, Gerald Lloyd, 1900-

VOLUME 337

Lloyd-Williams, Bronwen, joint comp.

RJ101 .L5

Ling physical education association.

The use of exercise in the post-war rehabilitation of children in occupied countries, compiled by Olive Rendel ... Ursula Shelley ... Mary V. Lace ... ₍and₎ Bronwen Lloyd-Williams ... London, The Ling physical education association ₍1944?₎

NL 0429167 (see below)

WU 500 L793d 1931

LLOYD-WILLIAMS, E
Dental mechanics; a manual for students and junior practitioners. London, Bale & Danielsson, 1931.
v, 252 p.
1. Dentistry - Mechanical

NL 0429167 DNLM IU PU-D

Lloyd-Williams, Grace.

Trois légendes: La légende de saint Christophe, L'amant fidèle, Le chevalier au baril, par Grace Lloyd-Williams ... Illustré par M. Sankey. Oxford, The Clarendon press, 1920.

79, ₍1₎ p. illus. 19cm.

"La légende de saint Christophe" first appeared in English in the Treasury.

1. French language—Chrestomathies and readers. I. Title. II. Title: La légende de saint Christophe. III. Title: L'amant fidèle. IV. Title: Le chevalier au baril.

Library of Congress PC2127.F3L6 21-16355

NL 0429168 DLC

Lloyd-Williams, John

see

Williams, John Lloyd.

Lloyd-Williams, Katharine Georgina.

Anaesthesia and analgesia in labour, by Katharine G. Lloyd-Williams ... With a foreword by Dame Louise McIlroy ... Baltimore, W. Wood & company, 1934.

96 p. illus. 19cm.

"Printed in Great Britain."
"List of principal references in the text": p. 93-94.

1. Anesthetics in obstetrics. 2. Labor (Obstetrics) Title Analgesia in labour.

Library of Congress RG732.L55 36-20400
₍3₎ 618.4

PPJ
NL 0429170 DLC CaBVaU OrU-M IParkA IaU CtY-M NcD

Lloyd-Williams, Richard.

The village churches, of Denbighshire, illustrated by perspective, geometrical and detail drawings, by Lloyd-Williams & Underwood ... Denbigh, The authors ₍1872₎

cover-title, 2 p. l., 51 (*i. e.* 60) pl. (incl. plans) 35 x 39cm.

1. Churches—Wales—Denbighshire. I. Underwood, M., joint author. II. Title.

Library of Congress NA5493.D4L5 11—28248

NL 0429171 DLC CtY

₍Lloyd-Williams, Trefor₎ 1891-

... World trade alliance, a practical solution of the problem of unemployment after the war. ₍London₎ World trade alliance association ₍1943₎

12 p. 20cm.

At head of title: E. P. No. 6.
"Written by Trefor Lloyd-Williams."

1. Commercial policy. 2. Unemployed. I. World trade alliance association, London. II. Title.

Library of Congress HF1411.L55 45-18013
₍3₎ 382

NL 0429172 DLC CtY PSC NNC

Lloyd-Williams, Trevor, joint author.

Nicholson, Ivor.

Wales: its part in the war, ed. by Ivor Nicholson ... and Trevor Lloyd-Williams ... with a preface by Sir E. Vincent Evans ... London, New York ₍etc.₎ Hodder and Stoughton ₍1919₎

TL720 .9 .L5A4

Lloyd Aéreo Boliviano.

Cielos de Bolivia.

₍La Paz₎

Lloyd aéreo boliviano.

Memoria anual. 1.- 1926-
Cochabamba, Bolivia, 1927-

v. 24½cm.

Library of Congress TL720.9.L5A3 43-19103

NL 0429175 DLC MiU

Lloyd Aéreo Boliviano.

Veinticinco años al servicio de Bolivia, 1925-1950. ₍La Paz, Editorial e Impr. Artística, 1950₎

134 p. illus., facsims., ports. 20 cm.

I. Title.

HE9832.L55A5 72-217636

NL 0429176 DLC PPiU

Lloyd & Baumann, firm, Joplin, Mo.

The mineral wealth of Southwest Missouri. The lead and zinc mines of Granby, Minersville, Joplin, Grove creek, Stevens mines, Thurman, Cornwall, Conley, and others. Joplin, Mo., Published by Lloyd & Baumann, 1874.

64 p. incl. adv. fold. map. 21 1/2 cm.
Limp purple cloth.
Ms. on fly-leaf.

1. Lead mines and mining—Missouri. 2. Zinc mines and mining—Missouri. I. Title.

54-2027-9

NL 0429177 CSmH NNC

Law

Lloyd anversois.
Annuaire maritime.
Anvers.

v. illus., maps (part col., part fold.) 24 cm. annual.

Title varies: -1960, Annuaire maritime et agenda.

1. Antwerp—Harbor—Regulations. 2. Maritime law—Belgium. 3. Inland water transportation—Law and legislation—Belgium. I. Title.

64-29207

NL 0429178 DLC

Lloyd austriaco, Trieste
see Lloyd triestino.

Lloyd Austriaco sotto il patronato di S. A. S. il principe di Metternich
see Lloyd triestino.

F2501 .B798

Lloyd brasileiro.

Brazil, the land of opportunity. v. 1-
July 1921-
₍New York, 1921-

Lloyd brasileiro.

Relatório.

Rio de Janeiro

v. plates, maps, tables, diagrs. 28cm. annual.

Part of the illustrative matter is colored, part folded.
Publication suspended 1927?-41 (except 1932)

HE945.L57A33 46-44963

NL 0429182 DLC DS FU

Lloyd brasileiro

see also

Companhia commercial e maritima, *New York.*

QV 772 qL793

LLOYD Brothers, Cincinnati, O.
₍Collection of publications₎

The library has a collection of miscellaneous publications of this organization kept as received. These publications are not listed nor bound separately.
1. Drugs

NL 0429184 DNLM

615.14 L775d

Lloyd brothers, Cincinnati, O.
Dose book; a concise presentation of the principal uses and usual doses of all specific strength medicines and leading specialties. Cincinnati, O. ₍n.d.₎
1 v. (unpaged)

1. Medicines, Specific. 2. Drugs - Dosage.

NL 0429185 WaU

QV 772 L793d 1932

LLOYD Brothers, Cincinnati
Dose book; a concise presentation of the principal uses and doses of all specific medicines. Cincinnati, c1932.
247 p.
1. Drugs - Catalogs

NL 0429186 DNLM WaPS

Lloyd brothers, *Cincinnati, O.*

Dose book of specific medicines. Their history, characteristics, qualities, strengths, prices, and connected features of general interest to physicians. Together with fac-similes of labels giving their doses, uses, and therapeutic qualities, and a glossary of indicated remedies and disease names and definitions, by V. L. Bell, M. D. Cincinnati, O., Lloyd brothers, ©1907.

256 p. 17½cm.

1. Medicines, Specific. 2. Dosiology. I. Bell, V. L.

Library of Congress RS356.L68 7—39418

NL 0429187 DLC ICJ

Lloyd Brothers, Cincinnati, O.
₍Drug treatises, no. 1-32₎ Cincinnati, c1904-1918.
32v. in 1. illus.

NL 0429188 ICRL ICJ NIC

VOLUME 337

616.1
L793p Lloyd Brothers, Cincinnati, O.
Pharmacology & therapeutics of cobalt, with reference to Roncovite and its use in anemia. Cincinnati, O. [1954?]
47, [5] p. illus. 28 cm.
Bibliography: p. [48]-[52]

1. Anemia. 2. Cobalt. I. Title. II. Title: Roncovite and its use in anemia.

NL 0429189 MiU NBuG IU ICJ PPSKF DNLM

L916.75
L793c Le Lloyd commercial.
Le Congo belge. Bruxelles, 1928.
146p. illus. 32cm.

1. Congo, Belgian.

NL 0429190 IEN

Lloyd Committee
see
Philadelphia Committee for Unemployment Relief.

Lloyd George and the war; a personal history of his part in Armageddon, by an independent Liberal. London, Hutchinson and co. [1917]
2 p. l., 7-159 p. 19cm.

1. Lloyd George, David, 1863– 2. European war, 1914– —Gt. Brit. I. An independent Liberal.

18-1529

Library of Congress DA566.9.L5L5

NL 0429192 DLC CtY NjP PP MB DW ICJ NN

The **Lloyd George** liberal magazine. v. 1-3, v. 4, no. 1-2; **Oct.** 1920-Nov. 1923. [London, L. J. Gooding, 1920-23]
4 v. in 5. illus. (incl. ports.) plates. 21½-24cm. monthly.
Includes supplement "The Irish peace settlement", Dec. 1921 (16 p.)
No more published.

1. Liberal party (Gt. Brit.) 2. Gt. Brit.—Pol. & govt.—Period. 3. Gt. Brit.—Pol. & govt.—1910– 4. Lloyd George, David, 1863–

27-7553

Library of Congress JN1129.L4L6

NL 0429193 DLC

Lloyd, Lee; a story of Yale
see under Blair, Edward Tyler, 1857-1939.

Lloyd library and museum, *Cincinnati.*
Bibliographical contributions from the Lloyd library, Cincinnati, Ohio. vol. I-III, no. 7. 1911/14-Oct. 1918. Cincinnati, O., The Lloyd library [1911-18]
3 v. illus. 23cm. quarterly.
Vol. 1, nos. 7-8 and v. 3, nos. 4-5 (whole series no. 29-30) each issued in 1 number.
Edith Wycoff, librarian (no. 1-6, William Holden, librarian)
No more published.

CONTENTS.

Vol. I (1911-14) Bibliography relating to the floras: no. 1. Catalogue of the periodical literature in the Lloyd library, by Edith Wycoff. Jan. 1911.—no. 2. Bibliography relating to the floras of Europe in general and the floras of Great Britain. April, 1911.—**no. 3. Bibliography relating to** the floras of Austria, Bohemia, Poland, Hungary, Belgium, Luxemburg, Netherlands, and Switzerland. July, 1911.—**no. 4. Bibliography relating** to the flora of France. Oct. 1911.—**no. 5.** Bibliography relating to the flora of Germany. Jan. 1912.—**no. 6.** Bibliography relating to the floras of Italy, Spain, Portugal, Greece, European Turkey, Bulgaria, Montenegro, Moldavia, Roumania and Servia. April, 1912.—**no. 7-8.** Bibliography relating to the floras of Arctic regions, Iceland, Scandinavia, Denmark, Norway, Sweden, Russia, Finland, Lapland, Russian Poland, and Caucasia. Oct. 1912.—**no. 9.** Bibliography relating to the floras of North America and the West Indies. Jan. 1913.—**no. 10.** Bibliography relating to the floras of South America and the Antarctic regions. April, 1913.—**no. 11.** Bibliography relating to the flora of Asia. July, 1913.—**no. 12.**

Continued in next column

Continued from preceding column

Bibliography relating to the flora of Oceanica. Oct. 1913.—**no. 13.** Bibliography relating to the flora of Africa. Jan. 1914.
Vol. II (1914-17) Bibliography relating to botany, exclusive of floras: no. 1 (whole ser. no. 14) Catalogue of the periodical literature in the Lloyd library. April, 1914.—**no. 2** (whole ser. no. 15) Catalogue of the books and pamphlets of the Lloyd library. Botany—Authors, A. July, 1914.—**no. 3-12** (whole ser. no. 16-25) Bibliography relating to botany, exclusive of floras. Authors, B-M. Oct. 1914-Jan. 1917.
Vol. III (1917-18) Bibliography relating to botany, exclusive of floras: no. 1-7 (whole ser. no. 26-32) Authors, N-Z. April 1917-Oct. 1918.

1. Botany—Bibl. I. Wycoff, Edith. II. Holden, William. III. Title.

11-4646 Revised

Library of Congress Z5353.L69

NcRA ICJ MiU OCl OU NIC CU NNBG PSt
NL 0429197 DLC CaBVaU ICU OrU KMK KyU CU Or NcU TU

Z
5351
.L56 Lloyd Library and Museum, Cincinnati.
Bibliography of botany. Compiled by the Lloyd Library. Cincinnati, Printed privately by the Lloyd Library, 1918-
v. 24 cm.

"Supposed to be a practically complete bibliography of the subject, taken from many sources and arranged alphabetically by authors."
Blank pages interleaved.

1. Botany--Bibl.

NL 0429198 OkU NNBG

Lloyd library and museum, *Cincinnati.*
... Bibliography relating to botany, exclusive of floras, [embracing botanical sections A-J, W of the Lloyd library] Authors ... Edith Wycoff, librarian. Cincinnati, O., **The Lloyd** library [1914-18]
18 pts. in 17. illus. 23cm. (Bibliographical contributions from the Lloyd library, Cincinnati, O. Vol. II, no. 2-12; vol. III, no. 1-7 (whole series, no. 15-32) July 1914-October 1918)
Part I has title: Catalogue of the books and pamphlets of the Lloyd library. Botany ...

1. Botany—Bibl.—Catalogs. I. Wycoff, Edith.

Agr 14-1283 Revised 2

U. S. Dept. of agr. Library 241.75L77 no. 15-32
for Library of Congress Z5353.L69 vol. 2-3
——— Copy 2. Z5360.L78
[r43d2]†

NL 0429199 DNAL DLC OU

Lloyd library and museum, *Cincinnati.*
... Bibliography relating to the flora of Africa. **Embracing** botanical section V of the Lloyd library. Edith Wycoff, librarian. Cincinnati, O., The Lloyd library [1914]
1 p. l., 493-513, [2] p. 1 illus. 23cm. (Bibliographical contributions from the Lloyd library, Cincinnati, O. No. 13, January, 1914)

1. Botany—Africa—Bibl. [1. Africa—Botany—Bibl.] I. Wycoff, Edith.

Agr 14-1313 Revised

U. S. Dept. of agr. Library 241.75L77 no. 13
for Library of Congress Z5353.L69 no. 13
——— Copy 2. Z5358.A18L6

NL 0429200 DNAL DLC OCl OU

Lloyd library and museum, *Cincinnati.*
... Bibliography relating to the flora of Asia. Embracing botanical section T of the Lloyd library. Edith Wycoff, librarian. Cincinnati, O., The Lloyd library [1913]
1 p. l., 439-468, [2] p. 1 illus. 23cm. (Bibliographical contributions from the Lloyd library, Cincinnati, O. No. 11, July, 1913)

1. Botany—Asia—Bibl. [1. Asia—Botany—Bibl.] I. Wycoff, Edith.

Agr 13-1783 Revised

U. S. Dept. of agr. Library 241.75L77 no. 11
for Library of Congress Z5353.L69 no. 11
——— Copy 2. Z5358.A82L6

NL 0429201 DNAL DLC OU OCl

Lloyd library and museum, *Cincinnati.*
... Bibliography relating to the flora of France. Embracing botanical section N of the Lloyd library. William Holden, librarian. Cincinnati, O., Lloyd library [1911]
1 p. l., 133-186 p., 2 l. illus. 23cm. (Bibliographical contributions from the Lloyd library, Cincinnati, O. No. 4, Oct. 1911)
Interleaved.

1. Botany—France—Bibl. [1. France—Botany—Bibl.] I. Holden, William.

Agr 11-2259 Revised

U. S. Dept. of agr. Library 241.75L77 no. 4
for Library of Congress Z5353.L69 no. 4
——— Copy 2. Z5358.F8L6
[r43e2]†

NL 0429202 DNAL DLC DNLM OCl OU

Lloyd library and museum, *Cincinnati.*
... Bibliography relating to the flora of Germany. Embracing botanical section O of the Lloyd library. William Holden, librarian. Cincinnati, O., Lloyd library [1912]
1 p. l., 187-262, [2] p. illus. 23cm. (Bibliographical contributions from the Lloyd library, Cincinnati, O. No. 5, Jan. 1912)

1. Botany—Germany—Bibl. [1. Germany—Botany—Bibl.] I. Holden, William.

Agr 12-205 Revised

U. S. Dept. of agr. Library 241.75L77 no. 5
for Library of Congress Z5353.L69 no. 5
——— Copy 2. Z5358.G3L7

NL 0429203 DNAL DLC OCl OU

Lloyd library and museum, *Cincinnati.*
... Bibliography relating to the flora of Oceanica. Embracing botanical section U of the Lloyd library. Edith Wycoff, librarian. Cincinnati, Lloyd library [1913]
1 p. l., 469-492, [2] p. 1 illus. 23cm. (Bibliographical contributions from the Lloyd library, Cincinnati, O. No. 12, October, 1913)

1. Botany—Oceanica—Bibl. [1. Oceanica—Botany—Bibl.] I. Wycoff, Edith.

Agr 13-1996 Revised

U. S. Dept. of agr. Library 241.75L77 no. 12
for Library of Congress Z5353.L69 no. 12
——— Copy 2. Z5358.O3L6

NL 0429204 DNAL DLC

Lloyd library and museum, *Cincinnati.*
... Bibliography relating to the floras of Arctic regions, Iceland, Scandinavia, Denmark, Norway, Sweden, Russia, Finland, Lapland, Russian Poland, and Caucasia. Embracing botanical section Q of the Lloyd library. Edith Wycoff, librarian. Cincinnati, O., The Lloyd library [1912]
1 p. l., 311-354, [2] p. 1 illus. 23cm. (Bibliographical contributions from the Lloyd library, Cincinnati, Ohio. Nos. 7-8, October, 1912)

1. Botany—Arctic regions—Bibl. [1. Arctic regions—Botany—Bibl.] 2. Botany—Europe—Bibl. [2. Europe—Botany—Bibl.] I. Wycoff, Edith.

Agr 12-2043 Revised

U. S. Dept. of agr. Library 241.75L77 no. 7-8
for Library of Congress Z5353.L69 no. 7-8
——— Copy 2. Z5358.A7L6

NL 0429205 DNAL DNLM DLC OCl OU

Lloyd library and museum, *Cincinnati.*
... Bibliography relating to the floras of Austria, Bohemia, Poland, Hungary, Belgium, Luxemburg, Netherlands, and Switzerland. Embracing section M of the Lloyd library. William Holden, librarian. Cincinnati, O., Lloyd library [1911]
1 p. l., 71-132, [2] p. illus. 23cm. (Bibliographical contributions from the Lloyd library, Cincinnati, O. No. 3, July, 1911)

1. Botany—Europe—Bibl. [1. Europe—Botany—Bibl.] I. Holden, William.

Agr 11-2261 Revised

U. S. Dept. of agr. Library 241.75L77 no. 3
for Library of Congress Z5353.L69 no. 3
——— Copy 2. Z5358.E8L72

NL 0429206 DNAL DLC

Lloyd library and museum, *Cincinnati.*
... Bibliography relating to the floras of Europe in general and the floras of Great Britain. Embracing botanical sections K and L of the Lloyd library. William Holden, librarian. Cincinnati, O., Lloyd library [1911]
1 p. l., 70 p., 2 l. illus. 23cm. (Bibliographical contributions from the Lloyd library, Cincinnati, O. No. 2, April 1911)

1. Botany—Europe—Bibl. [1. Europe—Botany—Bibl.] 2. Botany—Gt. Brit.—Bibl. [2. Gt. Brit.—Botany—Bibl.] I. Holden, William.

Agr 11-2260 Revised

U. S. Dept. of agr. Library 241.75L77 no. 2
for Library of Congress Z5353.L69 no. 2
——— Copy 2. Z5358.E8L7 1911

NL 0429207 DNAL Or OCl OU DLC

Lloyd library and museum, *Cincinnati.*
... Bibliography relating to the floras of Italy, Spain, Portugal, Greece, European Turkey, Bulgaria, Montenegro, Moldavia, Roumania and Servia. Embracing botanical section P of the Lloyd library. William Holden, librarian. Cincinnati, O., Lloyd library [1912]
2 p. l., 265-306, [4] p. illus. 23cm. (Bibliographical contributions from the Lloyd library, Cincinnati, O. No. 6, April, 1912)

1. Botany—Europe—Bibl. [1. Europe—Botany—Bibl.] I. Holden, William.

Agr 12-841 Revised

U. S. Dept. of agr. Library 241.75L77 no. 6
for Library of Congress Z5353.L69 no. 6
——— Copy 2. Z5358.I8L6

NL 0429208 DNAL DNLM OCl OU DLC

VOLUME 337

Lloyd library and museum, *Cincinnati.*
... Bibliography relating to the floras of North America and the West Indies. Embracing botanical section R of the Lloyd library. Edith Wycoff, librarian. Cincinnati, O., The Lloyd library [1913]
1 p. l., 355-417, [2] p. 1 illus. 23cm. (Bibliographical contributions from the Lloyd library, Cincinnati, Ohio. No. 9, Jan., 1913)
1. Botany—North America—Bibl. [1. North America—Botany—Bibl.] 2. Botany—West Indies—Bibl. [2. West Indies—Botany—Bibl.] I. Wycoff, Edith.
Agr 13-285 Revised
U. S. Dept. of agr. Library for Library of Congress 241.75L77 no. 9 Z5353.L69 no. 9
——— Copy 2. Z5358.N86L6

NL 0429209 DNAL OC1 OU DLC

Lloyd library and museum, *Cincinnati.*
... Bibliography relating to the floras of South America and the Antarctic regions. Embracing botanical sections of the Lloyd library. Edith Wycoff, librarian. Cincinnati, The Lloyd library [1913]
1 p. l., 419-437, [2] p. 1 illus. 23cm. (Bibliographical contributions from the Lloyd library, Cincinnati, O. No. 10, April, 1913)
1. Botany—South America—Bibl. [1. South America—Botany—Bibl.] 2. Botany—Antarctic regions—Bibl. [2. Antarctic regions—Botany—Bibl.] I. Wycoff, Edith.
Agr 13-1784 Revised
U. S. Dept. of agr. Library for Library of Congress 241.75L77 no. 10 Z5353.L69 no. 10
——— Copy 2. Z5358.S5L6

NL 0429210 DNAL OC1 OU DLC

Lloyd Library and Museum, *Cincinnati.*
Bulletin. no. 1-35; 1900-36. Cincinnati.
35 no. illus., ports., maps. 23-30 cm. irregular.
No. 1-33, 35 numbered also in subseries: Reproduction series, Mycological series, Pharmacy series, Botany series, Entomological series and Historical series.
Issued by the Library under variant names: no. 1-32, Lloyd Library of Botany, Pharmacy and Materia Medica; no. 33-35, Lloyd Library and Museum of Botany, Pharmacy and Materia Medica.
Superseded by Lloydia.
L. C. set incomplete: no. 28 wanting.
1. Botany—Collected works. 2. Pharmacy—Collected works. 3. Entomology—Collected works.
AS36.L592 58-52447

AAP NcU
IU-M DNLM MdBJ NjR AzU ICU ICJ KMK ScCleU NcD GU CU
NL 0429211 DLC KyU NcD ICRL CU OrU OrCS CaBVaU IdU

Lloyd Library and Museum, *Cincinnati.*
Bulletin. Botany series
see its
Bulletin.

Lloyd Library and Museum, *Cincinnati.*
Bulletin. Entomological series
see its
Bulletin.

Lloyd Library and Museum, *Cincinnati.*
Bulletin. Historical series
see its
Bulletin.

Lloyd Library and Museum, *Cincinnati.*
Bulletin. Mycological series
see its
Bulletin.

Lloyd Library and Museum, *Cincinnati.*
Bulletin. Pharmacy series
see its
Bulletin.

Lloyd Library and Museum, *Cincinnati.*
Bulletin. Reproduction series
see its
Bulletin.

Lloyd library and museum, *Cincinnati.*
Catalogue of books relating to the flora of Europe, contained in the botanical library of C. G. Lloyd, Cincinnati ... embracing the sections K (part,) L, M, N, O, P, and Q (part,) of the library. Cincinnati, 1894.
cover-title, 32 p. 23cm.
"The library is systematically arranged in sections (numbered by letters of the alphabet) ... The 'flora of Europe' embraces five of these sections, viz: L, M, N, O, P and parts of two other sections, viz: K and Q. Many works relating to the medical flora of Europe are not placed in these sections and hence not found in this catalogue, being included in a separate section, relating to medical botany."—Pref.
1. Botany—Europe—Bibl.
10-3463 Revised
Library of Congress Z5358.E8L7

NL 0429218 DLC MH MH-A

Lloyd library and museum, *Cincinnati.*
Catalogue of periodical literature in the botanical department of Lloyd library, January 1899. [Cincinnati, 1899]
8 p. 22cm.
Caption title.
1. Botany—Period.—Bibl.
7-862 Revised
Library of Congress Z5353.L7 1899

NL 0429219 DLC CtY PPAN PPAmP

Lloyd library and museum, *Cincinnati.*
Catalogue of periodical literature in the Lloyd library. January, 1900. [Cincinnati, 1900]
16 p. 23cm.
Caption title.
1. Botany—Period.—Bibl.
43-40604
Library of Congress Z5353.L7 1900

NL 0429220 DLC MH

Lloyd library and museum, *Cincinnati.*
... Catalogue of the periodical literature in the Lloyd library. By Miss Edith Wycoff. Cincinnati, O., Lloyd library [1911]
1 p. l., 80, [2] p. illus. 23cm. (Bibliographical contributions from the Lloyd library, Cincinnati, O. No. 1, Jan. 1911)
1. [Botany—Period.—Bibl.] 2. [Pharmacy—Period.—Bibl.] 3. Periodicals—Bibl.—[Catalogs] I. Wycoff, Edith.
Agr 11-2286 Revised 2
U. S. Dept. of agr. Library for Library of Congress 241.75L77 no. 1 Z5353.L69 no. 1
——— Copy 2. Z5353.L7 1911

NL 0429221 DNAL DLC OU OC1

Lloyd library and museum, *Cincinnati.*
... Catalogue of the periodical literature in the Lloyd library. Edith Wycoff, librarian. Cincinnati, O., The Lloyd library [1914]
1 p. l., 123 p. 1 illus. 23cm. (Bibliographical contributions from the Lloyd library, Cincinnati, O. Vol. II, no. 1 (whole ser., no. 14) April, 1914)
1. [Botany—Period.—Bibl.] 2. [Pharmacy—Period.—Bibl.] 3. Periodicals—Bibl.—[Catalogs] I. Wycoff, Edith.
Agr 14-1314 Revised
U. S. Dept. of agr. Library for Library of Congress 241.75L77 no. 14 Z5353.L69 no. 14
——— Copy 2. Z5353.L7 1914

NL 0429222 DNAL DLC OU OC1

Lloyd library and museum, *Cincinnati.*
... Catalogue of the periodical literature in the Lloyd library, by Walter H. Aiken and Sigmund Waldbott. Cincinnati, O., 1936.
2 p. l., 108 p. port. 27 cm. (Bulletin of the Lloyd library and museum of botany, pharmacy and materia medica ... No. 34)
1. Botany—Period.—Bibl. 2. Pharmacy—Period.—Bibl. 3. Periodicals—Bibl.—Catalogs. I. Aiken, Walter Harris, 1856-1965. II. Waldbott, Sigmund, 1865-
Z5353.L7 1936 016.05 36-4974

TU OrU OrCS CaBVaU CU
NL 0429223 DLC NcRS OCU MiU LU NcD MBH NNBG OU PU

Lloyd library and museum, Cincinnati
Letters. no. 1- 1904- Cincinnati
1-5, title reads: Puff ball letters

NL 0429224 WvU MBH CU PPAmP CCC

Lloyd Library and Museum, Cincinnati.
Lloydia; a quarterly journal of biological science
see under title

QK Lloyd Library and Museum, Cincinnati.
600 Mycological notes. no.1-75. 1898-1925.
L55 Cincinnati.
nos. illus.,plates. 29cm.
Editor: C.G. Lloyd. DLC: QK 600.M93.
1. Mycology - Period. I. Title. II. Lloyd, Curtis Gates, 1859-1926.

NL 0429226 IdU IaU DNLM MH-A DLC

Lloyd library and museum, *Cincinnati.*
... Report on the Lloyd mycological museum ... [1st]- 1895- [Cincinnati, 1896-
v. illus. 23-24½cm.
Caption title.
First report has title: Additions to Mycological museum ... during 1895.
Includes catalogs of specimens.
1. Fungi.
42-29218
Library of Congress QK600.L8

NL 0429227 DLC OU DNLM MBH

Lloyd Library and Museum, Cincinnati.
Xylaria notes
see under Lloyd, Curtis Gates, 1859-1926.

Lloyd Library and Museum of Botany, Pharmacy and Materia Medica
see
Lloyd Library and Museum, Cincinnati.

Lloyd Library of Botany, Pharmacy and Materia Medica
see
Lloyd Library and Museum, Cincinnati.

Lloyd, Newlands & Wood.
Mining stock
see under Fromm, A plaintiff-respondent.

Lloyd Royal, Compagnie Maritime Belge
see Compagnie Maritime Belge (Lloyd Royal)

VOLUME 337

Lloyd savings and loan association, *of New Brighton, Pa.*
By-laws of the Lloyd savings and loan association, of New Brighton, Pa. ... Rochester, Pa., Printed by H. A. Sutherland, 1889.
11 p. 17½cm.
Blank pages at end ruled for account.

CA 7-7447 Unrev'd

Library of Congress HG2626.N32L7

NL 0429233 DLC

Lloyd-Thomas Company, *Chicago.*
What the business man should know about fire insurance. New ed. Chicago ₍1952₎
99 p. 22 cm.
1928 ed. by J. J. Thomas.

1. Insurance, Fire. I. Thomas, John Jerome, 1876- What the business man should know about fire insurance. II. Title.

HG9665.L55 368.1 52-66334 ‡

NL 0429234 DLC NBuU OU

LLOYD-THOMAS COMPANY, Chicago.
What the business man should know about fire insurance. New ed., based on the original book by John J. Thomas. Chicago [c1953] 99 p. 22cm.

1. Insurance, Fire--U.S. I. Thomas, John Jerome, 1876- . What the business man should know about fire insurance. II. Thomas, John Jerome, 1876-

NL 0429235 NN

HE945 L6A49
Lloyd triestino.
Fünfundsiebzig Jahre Osterreichischer Lloyd, 1836-1911, hrsg. vom Publizistischen Bureau des Osterreichischen Lloyd. Triest, 1911.
147 p. illus.(part fold.,part col.) 29cm.

NL 0429236 CSt

Lloyd triestino.
Il Lloyd triestino, contributo alla storia italiana della navigazione marittima. ₍Verona₎ Officine grafiche A. Mondadori, 1938.
3 p. l., ix-₍xii₎, 582, ₍2₎ p. plates (part col.) ports., maps (part fold.) fold. plan, facsims. (1 fold.) diagr. 29½cm.
Half-title: Il Lloyd triestino (1836-1936)
"I primi otto capitoli sulla antica storia del Lloyd triestino furono scritti da Giuseppe Stefani; gli altri tre e l'epilogo, riguardanti i moderni sviluppi, da Bruno Astori."
Bibliography included in "Note" at end of each chapter.

I. Stefani, Giuseppe, 1887- II. Astori, Bruno, 1893-

42-42974

Library of Congress HE945.L6A5

NL 0429237 DLC CSt CtY NN PHC

Lloyd triestino.
Illustrirtes Familienbuch zur Unterhaltung & Belehrung häuslicher Kreise. Herausgegeben vom Oesterreichischen Lloyd. Triest, Oesterreichischer Lloyd, 1855.
v. illus.

NL 0429238 ICRL

Kress Room
Lloyd triestino.
Lloyd Austriaco sotto il patronato di S.A.S. il principe di Metternich. Trieste, I.Papsch & c., 1846.
2 p.ℓ., 30 p.incl.tables. 21.5 cm.

Half-title: Regolamento per le agenzie della prima sezione del Lloyd Austriaco.
Folded map bound in front.
With this is bound its l'organizzazione del Lloyd Austriaco, 1847.

NL 0429239 MH-BA

Lloyd triestino.
L'organizzazione del Lloyd Austriaco sotto il protettorato di sua altezza il principe Metternich nell' anno 1847. Trieste, I.Papsch & c., 1847.
31 p. 20.5 cm.

Added t.-p.: Die verfassung des Oesterreichischen Lloyd ...
Text in Italian and German on opposite pages.
Bound with its Lloyd Austriaco. 1846.

NL 0429240 MH-BA

Lloyd triestino.
... Overland route via Triest. Handbook of information for passengers proceeding from England to India, China and Australia and viceversa by the above route. Austrian Lloyd's steam packet company, Trieste. ₍Trieste₎ Printed at the Austrian Lloyd's ₍1861₎
38 p. fold. map. 18½ cm.

1. Voyages and travels—Guide-books.

G153.L63 5-23719 rev

NL 0429241 DLC

Lloyd triestino.
...Relazione e bilancio...
Esercizio 19

Trieste, 19 31cm.
no.

1 19 title adds: Assemblea generale ordinaria... 19 ... assemblea della società.

1. No subject.
N. Y. P. L. May 12, 1937

NL 0429242 NN

Lloyd triestino.
Venedig. Historisch-topographisch-artistisches reisehandbuch für die besucher der lagunenstadt. Hrsg. vom Oesterreichischen Lloyd in Triest. Mit zwölf ansichten und einem plane der stadt in stahlstich. 2. wesentlich verb. und verm. aufl. Triest, Literarisch artistische abtheilung des Oesterr. Lloyd, 1857.
viii, 206 p. 12 pl., fold. map. 17 cm. (*Added t.-p.: Lloyd's illustrirte reisebibliothek 1*)
With additions by Friedrich Pecht.

1. Venice—Descr.—Guide-books. I. Pecht, Friedrich, 1814-1903. II. Title.

DG672.L6 1857 18-22703 rev

NL 0429243 DLC

Lloyd, triestino.
Venise; guide historique-topographique et artistique. 2e éd.,augmentée et corrigée. Trieste,section littéraire-artistique du Lloyd autrichien,1861.

sq.16o. Plates,and plans. Ital 4871.16

NL 0429244 MH

Lloydia; a quarterly journal of biological science. v. 1-
1938-
Cincinnati, Lloyd Library and Museum.
v. in illus. 25 cm.
Supersedes the Bulletin of Lloyd Library and Museum.
Issues for 1938 published in combined form.
Editor: 1938- T. Just.

1. Biology—Period. I. Just, Theodor, 1904- ed. II. Lloyd Library and Museum, Cincinnati.

QH1.L94 574.05 41-7175 rev*

FTaSU
OC1W OrCS TNJ CoD ICJ CU-A NIC TU OCU OU PPC DNLM
NL 0429245 DLC IU CSt KyU PPPC ICJ OrU OO MiU CaBVaU

Microfilm
78 Lloydminster times. Ap. 25, 1905-
Lloydminster, Saskatchewan.
Microfilm.

NL 0429246 GEU

Lloydminster times.
Saskatchewan golden jubilee, 1905-1955. ₍Lloydminster, 1955₎
₍52₎ p. illus., facsims., ports. 58 cm.

Its issue of Wed. July 20, 1955.
Includes facsims. of early issues of the paper.

NL 0429247 CaBViPA

Lloyds, F
Practical guide to scene painting and painting distemper. By F.Lloyds ... New York, J.Haney & company, n.d.
vi,₍7₎-90p. illus. 25cm.

1. Scene-painting.

NL 0429248 DP DSI MH WaU

Lloyds, F.
Practical guide to scene painting and painting in distemper. With illustrations drawn by the author. London: G. Rowney & Co. ₍1875.₎ vi, 97 p., 12 pl. illus. 4°.

1. Stage scenery. 2. Painting (Distemper).
N. Y. P. L. June 20, 1912.

NL 0429249 NN MH RPB MiDA ICU

Lloyd's.

HJ6190 .L6
Lloyd's import duties list. no. 1-
Feb. 1, 1932-
₍London₎

QA95 .G65
Lloyd's.
Gooda, W G *comp.*
Lloyd's log problem book, compiled by W. G. Gooda; illustrations by Mary Pearce; cover design by E. F. Phillips. London, Lloyd's ₍1944₎

E-11
529

LLOYD'S.
Lloyd's under fire; a tribute to the Civil defence services of Lloyd's, 1938-1945. London [1946?]
128 p. illus.,ports.,col. map. 24cm.

1. Civilian defense--Gt. Br.--Eng.--London. 2. World war, 1939-1945--War work--Gt. Br.--Eng.--London.

NL 0429252 NN

Lloyd's.

Dawson, Warren Royal, 1888- *ed.*
The Nelson collection at Lloyd's; a description of the Nelson relics and a transcript of the autograph letters and documents of Nelson and his circle and of other naval papers of Nelson's period, edited by Warren R. Dawson ... with twenty-one plates. London, Printed at Lloyd's for the corporation of Lloyd's and pub. by Macmillan & co., limited, 1932.

VOLUME 337

Lloyd's.
Rules and regulations of Lloyd's. [London? 1811]
11 p. 21½cm.

Caption title.

NL 0429254 MdBJ

Lloyd's.
The rules and regulations of Lloyd's; with a copy of the trust deed, and copies of the instructions to the agents. London, W. Hughes, 1813.
2 p.l., 37-46, [29]-36, 51-61 p. 20·5 cm.

NL 0429255 MH-BA

Lloyd's.
Survey handbook, compiled and edited by ⌐A. W. Cooper¬ the controller of agencies, Lloyd's. ⌐1st ed.¬ London ⌐1952¬
111 p. 22 cm.

1. Ships—Cargo. 2. Commercial products—Dictionaries. I. Cooper, A. W. II. Title.

VK235.L55 *387.51 656 52-43643 ‡

NL 0429256 DLC NN

Lloyd's.
The treasures of Lloyd's; a descriptive account...
see under Dawson, Warren Royal, 1888-

Lloyd's. List of emergency customs duties
see Lloyd's import duties list.

Lloyd's American guide: containing new arranged time tables ... population, states, and distances to every place on all the railroad routes in the United States and Canadas.
Philadelphia, J. T. Lloyd & co.,
v. ports. 18 x 15½cm. monthly.

1. Railroads—U. S.—Time tables. 2. Railroads—Canada—Time tables.

CA 9-4097 Unrev'd

Library of Congress HE2727.L79

NL 0429259 DLC OOC NN

Lloyd's American railroad map
see under Lloyd, James T.

LLOYD'S Australian and New Zealand trade register.
Sydney, Australia. v. illus.
25-28cm.

Annual.
Published by Lloyd's Australian register of trade and commerce.
Title varies: 1948/49, The Australian and New Zealand trade register.

1. Commerce--Direct.--Australia. 2. Commerce--Direct.--New Zealand. I. Lloyd's Australian register of trade and commerce. II. Title: The Australian and New Zealand trade register.

NL 0429261 NN NIC MiU MB

Lloyds Bank Limited.
Annual meeting of shareholders.

⌐London¬
v. 25 cm.

HG3000.L74L6 50-48342 ‡

NL 0429262 DLC NN

Lloyd's Bank, Ltd.
A book of numbers. A calendar for 1931.
= [London. 1931.] 1 v. Illus. Decorated cover. 19 cm.

N9143 — T.r. — Calendars.

NL 0429263 MB

Lloyds Bank, Ltd.
The Dark horse. Supplement
see also Gilbert, T.R.
The Lloyds of Lloyds bank.

Lloyds bank limited.
How to use a bank; with a preface by Hartley Withers ... [London, Printed by W.H. Smith & son, 1926?]
48 p. illus. (forms) 22 cm.
1. Banks and banking - Gt. Brit.

NL 0429265 CtY

Lloyds Bank Limited.

List of members of the staff serving with His Majesty's forces, with bodies affiliated to the Central Association of Volunteer Training Corps, as special constables, &c.: up to the 31st May, 1915. [London, 1915?]

33 p. 33 cm.

1. European War, 1914-1918 - Registers, lists, etc.

NL 0429266 CaBVaU

HG3000
.L84L68 Lloyds Bank Limited.
1914
Lloyds Bank Limited, its history and progress. London ⌐G. Putnam¬ 1914.
55, ⌐1¬ l. incl. plates, ports. 36cm.

1. Banks and banking—Gt. Brit.

NL 0429267 ViU IEN CaBVaU

Lloyds Bank Limited.
Lloyds bank review

see under title.

Lloyds bank limited.

League of nations. *Secretary-general, 1919-1933 (Earl of Perth)*
... Loan for the construction of the new building of the International labour office. Memorandum by the Secretary-general. Geneva, 1923.

Lloyds Bank Limited.
Monthly review
see
Lloyds Bank review.

Lloyds Bank Limited.
Permanent staff training and foreign scholarships. London, 1919.
8p. 21cm.

NL 0429271 IEN

338.1 Lloyds bank, limited.
L779p The planning of British agriculture. ⌐London¬ Author ⌐1935¬
31 ⌐1¬ p.

NL 0429272 WaPS

HG3000
.L84
L653 Lloyds Bank Limited.
Report of directors and balance sheet.

London.
v. 26 cm. annual.

HG3000.L84L653 50-33000 ‡

NL 0429273 DLC IU NN

Lloyds Bank, Ltd.
...Report of directors, and statement of liabilities and assets ... ⌐London, ¬ v. 4°.

1. Banks and banking, Gt. Br.
N. Y. P. L. September 8, 1922.

NL 0429274 NN

Lloyds Bank Limited.
Statement by the chairman ⌐of the Board of Directors¬

⌐London¬
v. 26 cm. annual.

"Accompanying the Report of directors and balance sheet."

HG3000.L84L654 50-35299 ‡

NL 0429275 DLC

Lloyds bank limited.
'Twixt Lombard street and Cornhill; designed, written & illustrated by the staff of Lloyds bank limited. ⌐London, Printed by Sir J. Causton & sons, ltd., 1930¬
⌐72¬ p. illus. (part col.; incl. plans) 28½cm.
Ornamental borders and illustrated lining-papers in colors.
Brief description of the new building in Lombard street and Cornhill, which has been erected for the head and city offices of the bank, together with a short history of the site between the two famous thoroughfares. cf. Foreword.

1. London—Descr. 2. London—Hist. 3. London—Streets. I. Title.

32-8661

Library of Congress DA678.L55
⌐4¬ 942.12

NL 0429276 DLC OrU OrP MB TU NN

Lloyds banks, ltd.
'Twixt Lombard street and Cornhill. ⌐London, etc.: Printed by the Mercury press, 193-¬ 37 l. illus. (part col'd, incl. plan.) 19cm.

Title and text with col'd type ornament border.
"The original...issue of this souvenir was designed, written and illustrated by members of the staff of Lloyds bank ltd. in the year of 1930." — *Foreword.*

1. London—Hist. I. Title.
N. Y. P. L. August 23, 1940

NL 0429277 NN

Lloyds bank limited monthly review
see
Lloyds bank review.

Lloyds bank monthly
see
Lloyds bank review.

VOLUME 337

Lloyds bank monthly financial report
see
Lloyds bank review.

Lloyds Bank review.
[London]
v. diagrs. 25 cm.
Monthly, quarterly, July 1946-
Publication suspended during World War II.
Issues for called new ser. July 1946- called new ser. no. 1-
Title varies: Monthly review.
Separately paged supplements accompany some volumes.

I. Lloyds Bank Limited.

HC10.L55 330.904 43-29531 rev

CU-Riv NcD NN MiU MiD NCH OkS NGrUN
NL 0429281 DLC CaBVaU OrU NIC ICU NcU NN DS TxU NNC

Lloyd's battle history of the great rebellion, complete, from the capture of Fort Sumter, April 14, 1861, to the capture of Jefferson Davis, May 10, 1865, embracing General Howard's tribute to the volunteer ... and a general review of the war for the union. New York, H. H. Lloyd & co.; Boston, B. B. Russell & co.; [etc., etc.] 1865.
1 p. l., viii, [3]-506 p. front., plates, ports., maps (part fold.) 24cm.
Title and text enclosed in ornamental border.

1. U. S.—Hist.—Civil war—Campaigns and battles. I. Lloyd, H. H. & co., pub. II. Title: Battle history of the great rebellion.

2-10098

Library of Congress E470.L79

OrU
NL 0429282 DLC ICN NjP MB OClWHi DNW NcU NcA MiD

Lloyds battle history of the great Rebellion. Portraits, maps and woodcuts. New York, 1866.

NL 0429283 PPL

Lloyd's book of house flags & funnels of the principal steamship lines of the world and the house flags of various lines of sailing vessels. London, Pub. for the Committee of Lloyd's, Spottiswoode & co., ltd [1904]
3 p. l., xviii p., 3 l., iii, 28 p. 82 pl. (74 fold.) 25cm.

1. Flags. 2. Signals and signaling.

5-10480

Library of Congress VK385.L8

NL 0429284 DLC

Lloyd's book of house flags & funnels of the principal steamship lines of the world and the house flags of various lines of sailing vessels. London, Lloyd's [1912?]
1 v. (chiefly col. illus.) 26 cm.
Cover title.

1. Flags. 2. Signals and signaling.

VK385.L8 1912 52-55085

NL 0429285 DLC CaBViP MH DN-Ob DN PP NN

Lloyd's book of ports and shipping places; a list, arranged geographically, of ports and shipping places of the world with complete index: compiled from Lloyd's records and edited by the shipping editor at Lloyd's ... London. The Corporation of Lloyd's, 1937.
2 p. l., 84 col., [17] p. 25½cm.
In double columns.

1. Harbors.

38-23001

Library of Congress HE551.L53

NL 0429286 DLC CoU Or NIC PPT PP NN ICU ICN OU

Lloyd's calendar,
London, Lloyd's
v. illus., col. pl., maps, diagrs. 21 cm.

1. Navigation—Year-books. 2. Calendars.

VK8.L6 CA 9—1354 Unrev'd

NL 0429287 DLC P OrPS

Lloyd's Canadian chemical directory.
[Scarborough, etc., Ont., Lloyd Publications of Canada, etc.]
v. 31 cm. annual.
"Established 1947."
Vols. for 1962/63-1963/64 called 39th-40th ed.; 1965- called 18th- ed.
Title varies: -1963/64, Willson's Canadian chemical directory.

1. Chemical industries — Canada — Direct. I. Title: Willson's Canadian chemical directory. II. Title: Canadian chemical directory.

HD9655.C2W5 338.4766002571 59-26563 rev

NL 0429288 DLC

Lloyd's Canadian chemical, pharmaceutical, and product directory.
West Hill, Ont., Lloyd Publications of Canada.
v. 29 cm. annual.
Continues Lloyd's Canadian chemical directory.

1. Chemical industries—Canada—Directories. I. Title: Canadian chemical, pharmaceutical, and product directory.

HD9655.C2W5 338.4'766002571 72-626360

NL 0429289 DLC

691
L779
Arch
Lib'y

Lloyd's Canadian hardware, electrical and building supply directory.
Scarborough, Ont., Lloyd Publications of Canada.
v. 28cm.

1. Building materials - Catalogs. 2. Hardware Canada - Direct. 3. Electric apparatus and appliances - Direct. 4. Canada - Manuf. - Direct.

NL 0429290 TxU

HD
9864
C2L5

Lloyd's Canadian textile directory.
Scarborough, Ont. [etc.] Lloyd Publications of Canada [etc.]
v. illus.

Running title: Canadian textile directory
Title varies: -1963, Willson's Canadian textile directory.
Vols. for include, as a separately paged section, Lloyd's Canadian toy, notion, and stationery directory.

Issued also, with sections in reverse order, as Lloyd's Canadian toy, notion, and stationery directory.

NL 0429292 CaOTU

HD
9999
T7C35

Lloyd's Canadian toy, notion and stationery directory.
Scarborough, Ont. [etc.] Lloyd Publications of Canada [etc.]
v. illus.

Running title: Canadian toy, notion & stationery directory.
Title varies: -1963, Willson's Canadian toy, notion and stationery directory.

Vols. for include, as a separately paged section, Lloyd's Canadian textile directory.
Issued also, with sections in reverse order, as Lloyd's Canadian textile directory.

NL 0429294 CaOTU

Hymn Society Library
VA20
L79

Lloyd's church musicians' directory (1910) The blue book of church musicians in America, comp. by Rev. Frederic E. J. Lloyd ... [vol. 1] ... Chicago, Ritzmann, Brookes & co. [c1910]
167 p. 23½cm.
No more published.

1. Musicians, American—Direct. I. Lloyd, Frederic Ebenezer John, 1859- comp.

10-26385 Revised

Library of Congress ML17.L5

NL 0429295 DLC NIC NNUT

Lloyd's clerical directory
see
The **Clerical** directory of the Protestant Episcopal Church in the United States of America.

HE565
.A3L68

Lloyd's confidential index of foreign steam and motor vessels.
London, Lloyd's.
v. 25 cm.

1. Ship registers.

HE565.A3L68 387.2 57-24350

NL 0429297 DLC

TL500
.L53

Lloyd's confidential record of civil aviation.
London, Lloyd's.
v. 25 cm. annual.

1. Aeronautics—Yearbooks. 2. Aeronautics, Commercial—Direct.

TL500.L53 387.7058 60-40721 ‡

NL 0429298 DLC

Lloyds directory of manufacturers, merchants, and shipping trades in all parts of the world. ... London [etc.] Lloyds Publishing Co., Ltd. [1923-]
Library has 1923; and from 1928/29 to date. 28cm.

NL 0429299 ICJ ICRL MiD

Lloyds directory of manufacturers, merchants, shippers, and professional, for Great Britain and Ireland, Canada, South Africa, Australia and New Zealand, Egypt, India, China, Japan, United States of America, South America, and the Continent of Europe, etc., etc.
19
London: Lloyds Pub. Co. Ltd. [19 4°.
v.

1. Commerce.—Directories. 2. Manufacturers.—Directories.
N. Y. P. L. April 4, 1921.

NL 0429300 NN MB ICJ OCl PP

Lloyd's Dollar map of the north-eastern states.
New York. 1876. Size, 26⅛ × 37 inches. Scale, 32 miles to 1 inch. Folded.
Includes the country west to Wisconsin and Illinois, south to Kentucky and Virginia.

L7000 — United States. Geog. Maps.

NL 0429301 MB

Lloyd's encyclopædic dictionary: a new and original work of reference to the words in the English language. With a full account of their origin, meaning, pronunciation, and use ... London: E. Lloyd, Ltd., 1895-96. 7 v. illus. 4°.
v. 5 and 7 published by Greig & Co., with title: The encyclopædic dictionary.

1. English language—Dictionaries. 2. Encyclopedias, English.
N. Y. P. L. September 26, 1928

NL 0429302 NN CtY OC ICU

VOLUME 337

070
L85 Lloyd's evening post,& British chronicle
L79 ... London, [1757]-
29 cm. 3 times a week.

NL 0429303 MiU IU KU ICRL DFo

D525 Lloyd's family album of the great war...
L795 [London? 1914]

cover-title, [20] p. illus. (incl. ports.) 34cm

"The family record of the great war": p. [9-12]

1. European war , 1914-1918 - Miscellania.

NL 0429304 CSt-H

Lloyds Greater Britain Publishing Company, Ltd., London.
Impresiones de la republica de Cuba en el siglo veinte. Historia, gente, comercio, industria y riqueza... Londres: Lloyds Greater Britain Publ. Co., Ltd., 1913. 520 p. incl. ports. illus. (incl. facsims., plans), maps. 31½ × 26cm.

556029A. 1. Cuba. 2. Economic history—Cuba. I. Title.
N. Y. P. L. August 29, 1932

NL 0429305 NN

L968.4
L793t Lloyd's Greater Britain Publishing Company.
Twentieth century impressions of Natal; its people, commerce, industries, and resources. [Durban?] 1906.
667p. illus.(incl.maps) 32cm.

1. Natal. I. Title.

NL 0429306 IEN DAU

Lloyd's handy atlas, containing maps of the world, and its grand divisions, the United States, and the different states and territories of the Union, etc. etc. Letter-press matter embracing the census of 1870, and a list of all the post offices in the United States. 91 pp. incl. 25 col. maps, 1 col. pl. fol. Concord, N. H. and Boston, D. L. Guernsey, 1872. 864

NL 0429307 DLC

Lloyd's import duties list. no. 1-
Feb. 1, 1932-
[London]
no. in v. 23 cm.

Frequency varies.
Title varies: Feb. 1, 1932, List of emergency customs duties.
Supplements accompany some numbers.

1. Tariff—Gt. Brit. 2. Customs administration—Gt. Brit.
I. Lloyd's.
HJ6190.L6 336.265 50-17353

NL 0429308 DLC MB

Lloyd's list
see Lloyd's list and shipping gazette.

Lloyd's list annual review.
[London]
v. 37 cm.

Supplement to Lloyd's list and shipping gazette.

1. Shipping—Yearbooks. I. Lloyd's list and shipping gazette.

HE561.L633 55-32639 ‡

NL 0429310 DLC DS

Lloyd's list and shipping gazette.
London [Corporation of Lloyds] 191
v. 51cm. daily (except Sunday)

Title varies: -Feb. 3, 1916, Lloyd's list.
Feb. 4, 1916-Feb. 1922, Lloyd's list, with which is incorporated the Shipping & mercantile gazette.
Mar. 1922- Lloyd's list and shipping gazette.
Lloyd's list, in this form, was apparently begun by the Corporation of Lloyds in July 1914, though the Shipping & mercantile gazette was not acquired until Feb. 1916.
The numbering of the individual issues evidently includes the earlier publications, Lloyd's list (1726?-1884) and Shipping & mercantile gazette.

1. Shipping—Period.

Library of Congress HE561.L63 CA 27-168 Unrev'd

NL 0429311 DLC MH-BA InU ICRL

Lloyd's list and shipping gazette.
A book of port plans. London, Lloyd's list and shipping gazette, 1930.
35, [1] p. incl. 55 maps. 29cm.

1. Harbors—Europe—Maps. I. Title.
Map 42-76

Library of Congress. Div. of maps

NL 0429312 DLC

Lloyd's list and shipping gazette.
HE561
.L633
Lloyd's list annual review.
[London]

Lloyd's list law reports, reprinted from "Lloyd's list".
Michaelmas sittings [Oct. 14] 1919-
v. 1-
London, Lloyd's, 1919-
v. 25½cm.

"Maritime and commercial reports."—Lloyd's list.

1. Maritime law—Gt. Brit. 2. Commercial law—Gt. Brit. 3. Law reports, digests, etc.—Gt. Brit. 4. Law—Period.

Library of Congress 22-4401

NL 0429314 DLC NcD-L TxU NcU CaBVaU WaU-L

Lloyd's list law reports.
Law
Henley, Henry Patten, ed.
Digest no. [1]- of Lloyd's list law reports. 1919/22-
London, Lloyd's.

Lloyd's list of post offices in the United States and the Canadas
see under Lloyd, James T.

Lloyd's loading list.
[London, Corporation of Lloyd's]

Lloyd's map of the eastern states
see under Lloyd, James T.

Lloyd's map of the lower Mississippi river from St. Louis to the gulf of Mexico
see under Lloyd, James T.

Lloyd's map of the southern states
see under Lloyd, James T

Lloyd's maritime atlas. 1st- ed.; 1951-
London, Lloyd's.
v. col. maps (part fold.) 25 cm.

1. Shipping—Maps. I. Title: Maritime atlas.

G1060.L6 Map 52-874 rev

NL 0429321 DLC CoU MiU NbU MiD PPT CU LU MdBP OrPS TU TxU

F158 Lloyd's mercantile port folio and business man's
.24 guide, designed to be a book of reference, for
.L8 western & southern merchants trading with Philadelphia. v.1- Philadelphia, 1855-
v.

1. Philadelphia--Direct.

NL 0429322 ICU

Lloyd's military map and gazetteer of the southern states
see under Lloyd, James T.

M1977.S2 Lloyd's Naval songster. An extensive
L55 collection of the most favourite sea songs.
[No imprint, 1840?]

[8]p. 18cm.

Without music.

I. Title: Naval songster.
1. Sea songs.
2. Sailors' songs.

NL 0429324 NBuG

Lloyd's New county map of the United States and Canadas showing battle fields, railroads, &c., compiled from the latest government surveys & other reliable & official sources.
New York. 1863. Size, 36⅝ × 50¼ inches. Scale (computed), 40 miles to 1 inch.
Submaps. — Part of Florida. — California, Oregon and the territories of the United States.

K88,1 — United States. Geog. Maps. — Canada. Geog. Maps.

NL 0429325 MB

Lloyd's New map of the Mississippi River from Cairo to its mouth.
New York. [1861.] Size, 31¼ × 8⅜ inches. Scale, 11 miles to 1 inch.

H6762 — Mississippi River. Maps.

NL 0429326 MB

Lloyd's new map of the United States, the Canadas and New Brunswick
see under Lloyd, James T.

Map
G
10834 Lloyd's new military map of the border &
.497 Southern states. New-York,H.H.Lloyd & co., 1862.
map. 75x104cm.

At head of map: H.H.Lloyd & co's new military map of the Southern and border states.
Scale: about 32 miles to 1 inch.
Drawn by Edward S.Hall.
Inset: southern part of Florida.

NL 0429328 ICN

VOLUME 337

Lloyd's new military map of the border and southern states ... New York, 1864.
75 x 105 cm.
Scale of 30 miles to 1 inch.

NL 0429329 RPB MB

Dawes
+G
10834
.5
Lloyd's new military map of the border & Southern states... New-York, H.H. Lloyd & co., 1865.
map. 74½x104cm. fold. to 41cm.

At head of map: The rebellion as it was and as it is.
Scale: 30 miles to 1 inch.

NL 0429330 ICN MB NIC

"Lloyd's News" ABC of the War
see under Lloyd's Weekly news.

Lloyd's numerical and alphabetical index to the railways in actual operation in the British Isles up to June, 1865, with the number and official name of each railway ... to accompany Lloyd's topographical county and railway map of the British Isles. Comp. from official information ... New York [etc.] J. T. Lloyd, 1865.
24, [1] p. facsim. 18 x 14½cm.

1. Railroads—Gt. Brit.—Direct.

Library of Congress HE3014.L79 7-10106†

NL 0429332 DLC

HE3014
L79
Lloyd's numerical and alphabetical index to the railways in actual operation in the British Isles, up to January, 1867, with the number and official name of each railway, and its total length... to accompany Lloyd's topographical county and railway map of the British Isles. Compiled from official information. New York, J. T. Lloyd, 1866.
Transportation
25 p. 19cm.

1. Railroads - Gt. Brit. - Direct. I. Title.

NL 0429333 CSt

Lloyd's of London (Motion Picture)
Lloyd's of London [screen play]
see under Kenyon, Curtis.

Lloyd's Official map of Missouri
see under Lloyd, James T.

Lloyd's Official map of the State of Kentucky
see under Lloyd, James T.

Lloyd's official map of the state of Tenessee
see under Lloyd, J. T.

Lloyd's Official map of the State of Virginia
see under Lloyd, James T.

HF
5770
.L79
Lloyd's Packing Warehouses, ltd.
The story of the bale. Manchester [Eng.] 1926.
27 p. illus.

1. Lloyd's Packing Warehouses, ltd.
2. Packing for shipment.

NL 0429339 MiU

Lloyd's Pickwickian Twelfth night characters!!! [London] E. Lloyd [184-?] broadside. illus. 50 x 38cm.

Cuts of twenty-eight named "characters," each accompanied by a conundrum, with "Key to the conundrums" printed in lower center of sheet.
Illustrations colored by hand.

612103B. 1. Riddles, English. 2. Caricature and comic art, British. 3. Dickens, Charles, 1812-1870. Pickwick papers. I. Title: Pickwickian Twelfth night characters!!!

NL 0429340 NN

Lloyd's pocket companion and guide through New York city, for 1866-67
see under Lloyd, Thomas.

Lloyd's Railroad, telegraph & express map of the Eastern States
see under Lloyd, James T.

Lloyd's reciter
see under Lloyd, Edward, 1815-1890, pub.

Lloyd's register of American yachts; a list of the power and sailing yachts, yacht clubs and yachtsmen of the United States, the Dominion of Canada, and the West Indies; and the American yachting trade directory.

New York, Lloyd's register of shipping [19
v. col. plates. 14½ x 24-18½ x 24cm.
Subtitle varies.

1. Yachts and yachting—Period.

Library of Congress GV825.L7 3-14412 Additions

MB MiU
NL 0429344 DLC WaS DN CU-I TxU NIC PHi PP NNC ICJ

Lloyd's register of British and foreign shipping
see
Lloyd's register of shipping.

Lloyd's register of shipping.

London, Wyman and sons [etc.] 18 -19
v. 26-30cm. annual.

"Founded 1760. Re-constituted 1834. United with the Underwriters' registry for iron vessels in 1885."
Title varies: 18 -1913, Lloyd's register of British and foreign shipping.
1914- Lloyd's register of shipping.
Includes appendix which is issued with special t.-p. and paging from 18 to 19 No appendix was issued for 1917/18-1918/19.

1. Shipping—Period. 2. Insurance, Marine—Period. 3. Shipping—Gt. Brit.

Library of Congress HE565.A3L7 CA 8—1387 Unrev'd

WaT NIC MoU MiU IU DNW NBuU CSdS ICRL NbU
CLU NNC MH MdBJ PU-W PPComm CtY WaS CaBVaU CaBVa
CU CSt NN ICU CSt KU DN ICRL GU ICJ MB Wa P GU
NL 0429346 DLC WaS CaOTU InU NcU FTaSU DSI ICJ

Lloyd's register of shipping.
Annals of Lloyd's register; being a sketch of the origin, constitution, and progress of Lloyd's register of British and foreign shipping. London, 1884.
1 p. l., x, 166 p. 2 port. (incl. front.) facsim. 25cm.

Library of Congress HE565.A3L8 4-20212 Revised

NL 0429348 DLC CaBViP KMK PHi

Lloyd's register of shipping.
Annals of Lloyd's register: being a sketch of the origin, constitution, and progress of Lloyd's register of British & foreign shipping. London [Wyman and sons, printers] 1884.
x, 165 p., 1 l. front., plates, facsims. (1 fold.) 25cm.
Added t.-p., engr.
Frontispiece and plates are mounted illustrations clipped from a periodical.

I. Title.

Library of Congress HE565.A3L8 1884 a 17-11719

NL 0429349 DLC WaTC CtY NcD

Lloyd's register of shipping.
Annals of Lloyd's register. Centenary edition, 1934. [London, Lloyd's register, 1934]
6 p. l., 3-251, [22] p., 1 l. front., illus., plates, ports. 25 x 19½cm.

I. Title.

Library of Congress HE565.A3L8 1934 35-9684
[3]

NL 0429350 DLC CaBViP MB NcRS CtY NN ViU NcU AU

Lloyd's register of shipping.
Annual report
see its
Report of the society's operations.

Lloyd's Register of Shipping
Annual summary of the mercantile shipbuilding of the world. London

1. Shipping 2. Periodicals - U.K.

NL 0429352 NNUN OrU NN NNC MH-BA

HE565
.A3L83
Lloyd's register of shipping.
Centenary celebration of the reconstitution of Lloyd's register of shipping. October, 1934. [London, Printed by Lloyd's register of shipping, at the Society's printing house, 1934]
cover-title, 48 p. 1 illus., fold. pl. 24½cm.

NL 0429353 DLC CtY ICU MB NN

VM
147
.L79
Lloyd's Register of Shipping.
Electric arc welding; electrodes approved for ship construction. London, 1954.
30 p. 26 cm.

VM
147
.L79
Suppl.
-- ---Supplement to list of approved electrodes; alterations and additions ... since February. [London, 1954.
11 l. 26 cm.
1. Ships--Welding.

NL 0429354 MiU

VOLUME 337

HE 565 .A3 L8 E9 1942
Lloyd's register of shipping.
... Extracts from the rules. London ⌈Printed by Lloyd's register of shipping⌉ 1942.
xi,403 p.incl.tables,diagrs. 19cm.

1.Ship-building—Contracts and specifications. 2. Ship-building—Gt.Brit.

NL 0429355 MiU

HE 565 .A3 L8 G3 1925
Lloyd's register of shipping.
Geometrical properties of ship girders and sections giving,for a wide range of thickness,the sectional area,centre of gravity of area,moment of inertia and modulus of resistance of the various sections and girders,with and without plating,which are commonly used in shipbuilding and engineering. From the use of naval architects, shipbuilders,and structural engineers. Compiled by Lloyd's register of shipping ... 2d ed.(enl.) ... London ⌈Printed by Lloyd's register of shipping, 1925⌉
117 p.,1 l.incl.tables,diagrs. 24 x 19cm.
"First published in 1920."
1.Ships,Iron and steel. 2.Girders. I.Title II.Title: Ship girders and sections.

NL 0429356 MiU NN

HE 565 .A3 L8 G3 1947
Lloyd's register of shipping.
Geometrical properties of ship sections and girders,compiled by Lloyd's register of shipping. For the use of naval architects, shipbuilders,and structural engineers. London, 1947.
156 p.incl.tables,diagrs. 24 x 19cm.
"Third edition (enlarged)"
"First printed 1920."

1.Ships,Iron and steel. 2.Girders. I.Title. II. Title: Ship sections and girders.

NL 0429357 MiU NN OrP

Lloyd's register of shipping.

Jordan, Charles H.
Jordan's tabulated weights of iron and steel **sections,** and other information, for the use of **naval architects,** shipbuilders and manufacturers, edited by **Lloyd's register of shipping.** 8th ed. Rev. London, **Pub.** for Lloyd's register of shipping, by E. & F. N. Spon, **ltd.,** 1923.

Lloyd's register of shipping.
Lloyd's register of shipping. The register book. A lecture ...
see under Mayne, Frederick Arthur.

VM 1 .L792
Lloyd's register of shipping.
⌊Papers and discussions⌋
London.

NL 0429360 MiU

Lloyd's register of shipping.
... Particulars of the war ships of the world, extracted from the Universal register for the year commenced 1st April, 1887. London, Printed by W. Clowes and sons, limited, 1887.
4 p. l., ⌊102⌋ p. 28 x 22½cm.
Partly in French.
Includes Statistics of merchant shipping.

1. War-ships. 2. Navies. 3. Merchant marine.

26-1246

Library of Congress VA40.L79 1887

NL 0429361 DLC

Lloyd's register of shipping.
... Particulars of the war ships of the world, extracted from the Universal register for the year commenced 1st April, 1888. London, Printed by W. Clowes and sons, limited, 1888.
4 p. l., ⌊117⌋, 56 p. 28 x 22½cm.
Partly in French.
Includes Statistics of merchant shipping; lists of merchant steamers capable of maintaining a speed of 12 knots an hour and above; Particulars of dry and wet docks, pontoons, patent slipways, tidal harbours, quays, etc., in all parts of the world.

1. War-ships. 2. Navies. 3. Merchant marine. 4. Docks. 5. Harbors.

26-1245

Library of Congress VA40.L79 1888

NL 0429362 DLC

Lloyd's register of shipping.
Particulars of the war ships of the world. 8th revised issue. London, 1890.

At head of title: Lloyd's register of British and foreign shipping.
"Extracted from Lloyd's register book, 1890-91."
"Particulars of dry and wet docks, etc." has separate pagination.

NL 0429363 MH

Lloyd's register of shipping.
Particulars of the war ships of the world. **10th rev.** issue. (Extracted from Lloyd's register book, 1892–93) London ⌊Lloyd's register⌋ 1892.
ii p., 3 l., 119, 17, ⌊6⌋, 101 p. 29 x 25cm.
Partly in English and French.
"Particulars of dry and wet docks, pontoons, patent **shipways, harbours,** quays, etc.," 101 p. at end.

1. Navies. 2. Docks. 3. Harbors.

13-3380

Library of Congress VA40.L79

NL 0429364 DLC

Lloyd's register of shipping.
... Particulars of the war ships of the world. (Extracted from Lloyd's register book, 1893–94) London ⌊Lloyd's register⌋ 1893.
5 p. l., ⌊3⌋–119, 24, 101 p. 29 x 25cm.
Partly in English and French.
Includes Lists of merchant steamers capable of maintaining, at sea, a speed of 12 knots an hour and above; Statistical tables of merchant shipping; Particulars of dry and wet docks, pontoons, patent slipways, harbours, quays, etc.

1. War-ships. 2. Navies. 3. Merchant marine. 4. Docks. 5. Harbors.

15-24448

Library of Congress VA40.L79 1893

NL 0429365 DLC

Lloyd's register of shipping.
... Particulars of the war ships of the world. (Extracted from Lloyd's register book, 1894–95.) London ⌊Lloyd's register⌋ 1894.
5 p. l., ⌊3⌋–104, 24, 114 p. 29 x 25cm.
Partly in French.
Includes statistics of merchant shipping, a list of fast merchant steamers and a list of dry and wet docks, &c., in all parts of the world.

1. War-ships. 2. Navies. 3. Merchant marine. 4. Docks. 5. Harbors.

26-1244

Library of Congress VA40.L79 1894

NL 0429366 DLC

Lloyd's Register of Shipping
Press releases. London

1. Shipping 2. Periodicals - U.K.

NL 0429367 NNUN

GV825 .R4
Lloyd's register of shipping.
Register of yachts.
London, Lloyd's register of shipping.

Lloyd's register of shipping.
Report made to the committee of Lloyd's register of British and foreign shipping, by the society's chief surveyor and his assistants, concerning the dismasting of large iron sailing ships. London ⌊Printed by T. Scott, 1886⌋
xii, 185 p., 1 l. illus., XIX pl. (incl. diagrs.) fold. tables. 25cm.
Drawn up by Mr. W. John, late assistant to the chief surveyor. *cf.* Prefatory note, signed: B. Martell, chief surveyor.
Lettered on cover: Report on masting.
1. Masts and rigging. I. John, William, 1845–1890. II. Title: Dismasting of large iron sailing ships.

26-1243

Library of Congress VM531.L6

NL 0429369 DLC NIC

Lloyd's register of shipping.
Report of the society's operations.
London
v. 25½cm.
Report year ends June 30.
Issues for –1912/13 published under an earlier name of the society: Lloyd's register of British and foreign shipping.
Half-title, : Annual report (1918/19, Report)

45-52400

Library of Congress HE565.A3L74

NL 0429370 DLC OClW

HE 565 .A3 L8 R4
Lloyd's register of shipping.
... Requirements for welded pressure vessels intended for land purposes. London ⌈Printed by Lloyd's register of shipping, 1937⌉
39,⌊1⌋ p. illus. 19cm.

1.Pressure vessels. 2.Welding.

NL 0429371 MiU

Lloyd's register of shipping.
Rules and regulations for the construction and classification of steel ships. 1890/91- London.

Crerar has 1906/07, 1958-
For beginning date cf.British union catalogue of periodicals.
Title varies slightly.
Vol.for 1906/07 published by the periodical under an earlier name: Lloyd's register of British and foreign shipping.

Additions and amendments, issued separately, accompany some vols.

I. Title. 623.80942005 623.84052

NL 0429373 ICJ KMK

HE 565 .A3 L8 R8
Lloyd's register of shipping.
... Rules & regulations for the construction and classification of steel trawlers. London ⌈Printed by Lloyd's register of shipping, 1939⌉
2 p.l.,vii-xxiv,195 p.incl.tables,diagr. 22cm.

1.Ship-building—Gt.Brit. 2.Ships,Iron and steel.

NL 0429374 MiU

VOLUME 337

Lloyd's register of shipping.
... Rules & regulations for the construction and classification of steel vessels.
London,
v. plates, tables, diagrs. 24cm. annual.

1. Shipping—Year-books. 2. Ship-building—Year-books.
7—17765
Library of Congress HE565.A3L75

NL 0429375 DLC WaS CU NIC FU IU MB MH ICJ NN

Lloyd's register of shipping.
... Rules & regulations for the construction and classification of wood vessels.
London,
v. fold. pl., tables (part fold.) 24cm. annual.

1. Shipping—Year-books. 2. Ship-building—Year-books.
Library of Congress HE565.A3L76 CA 21-396 Unrev'd [2]

NL 0429376 DLC

Lloyd's Register of Shipping.
Rules & regulations for the construction and classification of yachts.
19
London, 19 8°.
On cover, 1913- : Rules for the building & classification of yachts.

1. Yachts.
N. Y. P. L. October 19, 1914.

NL 0429377 NN MB IU

HE 565 .A3 L8 R9 1941
Lloyd's register of shipping.
... Rules for electric propelling machinery and electrical equipment. London [Printed by Lloyd's register of shipping] 1939 (Reprinted 1941)
xiii,172 p.incl.tables,diagr. 18½cm.

1.Ship propulsion,Electric. 2.Electricity on ships.

NL 0429378 MiD MiU

Lloyd's register of shipping.
...Rules for welded pressure vessels. London [1943] 39 p. 19cm.

348652B. 1. Welding. 2. Pressure vessels.
N. Y. P. L. December 24, 1946

NL 0429379 NN

Lloyd's Register of Shipping
Statistical notes on the appendix to Lloyd's register book. London

For a record of the Library's holdings consult the Reference Staff or the serial checklist

1. Shipping 2. Periodicals - U.K.

NL 0429380 NNUN

Lloyd's Register of Shipping.
Statistical summary of merchant ships totally lost, broken up, etc. (excluding ships of less than 100 tons gross)
London.
v. 34 cm.

1. Ship registers. 2. Marine accidents. 3. Shipwrecks. I. Title.
HE565.A3L87 72-622468

NL 0429381 DLC DS NN

Lloyd's register of shipping.
Statistical tables.
London.
v. 29 cm.

1. Merchant marine—Stat.
HE563.A3L5 59-39152

NL 0429382 DLC MiU

VM162 L6 Engin. Lib.
Lloyd's register of shipping.
... Tests of materials. London.Lloyd's register of shipping, 1924.
121 p. illus.,tables,diagrs. 19cm.

1. Strength of materials.

NL 0429383 CU

HE 565 .A3 L8 T3
Lloyd's register of shipping.
... Tests of materials. London [Printed by Lloyd's register of shipping] 1939.
xvi,131 p. illus.,tables. 18½cm.

1.Metals--Testing. I.Title.

NL 0429384 MiU

LLOYD'S REGISTER OF SHIPPING.
The treasures of Lloyd's;a descriptive catalogue of the monuments,pictures,drawings,plate medals,manuscripts,and other objects of historic interest preserved at Lloyd's,London, preceded by a sketch of the history of Lloyd's. 3d ed.,revised and enlarged. London,Lloyd's, 1930.
22 plates (incl.ports.)

NL 0429385 MH

Lloyd's register of shipping.
Universal register. [1st]- 1st Apr. 1886-
London, Printed by W. Clowes & sons, limited, 1886-
v. 27cm. annual.
English and French.

1. Shipping—Year-books. 2. Insurance, Marine—Year-books. I. Title.
16-22487
Library of Congress HE565.A3L77

NL 0429386 DLC

LLOYD'S register shipbuilding returns. 19
London. v. tables. 35cm.

Quarterly.
"Merchant ships of 100 tons gross and upwards."
Issued by Lloyd's register of shipping.

1. Shipbuilding--Stat.--Gt. Br. I. Lloyd's register of shipping.

NL 0429387 NN NNUN

Lloyd's reports of prize cases ... during the European war, which began in August, 1914. Reprinted from "Lloyd's list" by direction of the Committee of Lloyd's ... London, Lloyd's, 1915–24.
10 v. 24 cm.
Vols. 1–5, cases decided by Sir Samuel Evans, president of the Probate, divorce and admiralty division [v. 2–5 "and on appeal by the Judicial committee of the Privy council"]; v. 6–10, cases decided by Sir Samuel Evans, Lord Sterndale and Sir Henry Duke, presidents of the Probate, divorce and admiralty division "and on appeal by the Judicial committee of the Privy council" (v. 8–10, "and by the Naval prize tribunal")

Editors: v. 1, J. B. Aspinall.—v. 2–10, E. L. De Hart.

Continued in next column

Continued from preceding column

1. Prize law—Cases. 2. Prize-courts—Gt. Brit. 3. European war, 1914–1918—Prizes, etc. I. Gt. Brit. High court of justice. Probate, divorce and admiralty division. II. Gt. Brit. Privy council. Judicial committee. III. Gt. Brit. Naval prize tribunal. IV. Evans, Sir Samuel Thomas, 1859–1918. V. Sterndale, William Pickford, baron, 1848–1923. VI. Merrivale, Sir Henry Edward, Duke, baron, 1855–1939. VII. Aspinall, John Bridge, ed. VIII. De Hart, Edward Louis, 1858–1927, ed.
JX5245.L6 16—10713

NL 0429389 DLC WaU-L CtY MiU ViU-L NcD-L MB

...Lloyd's reports of prize cases (Second series) ... v.1- ;Jan.1940-
London,Printed by the Corporation of Lloyd's [1940-
v. 24cm. irregular.
Editors:1940- H.P.Henley.

1.Prize law--Cases. 2.Prize-courts--Gt.Brit. I.Henley,H P ed.

NL 0429390 ICU MiU-L CtY MH CU

Lloyd savings and loan association, *of New Brighton, Pa.*
By-laws of the Lloyd savings and loan association, of New Brighton, Pa. ... Rochester, Pa., Printed by H. A. Sutherland, 1889.
11 p. 17½cm.
Blank pages at end ruled for account.

CA 7-7447 Unrev'd
Library of Congress HG2626.N32L7

NL 0429391 DLC

Lloyd's song book
see under Lloyd, Edward, 1815-1890, pub.

385.975 L77
Lloyd's southern railroad guide. v.1- 18 -18 ; n.s.,v.1- 18 -
Mobile,18 -
v. 19cm. tables. monthly.
v. - also numbered old series, v. -

1. Railroads--Southern states. I. Lloyd, Alvin, ed.

NL 0429393 LU NcD

Lloyd's stenography, publicly practised by him for nearly half a century ...
see under Lloyd, Thomas, fl. 1788-1819.

LM L793
Lloyd's Students' Society.
A series of lectures on the principles and practices of insurance. London, Printed by the Corporation of Lloyd's, 1924.
218 p.

1.Insurance, Marine. 2.Insurance, Fire.

NL 0429395 MH-BA

Lloyd's topographical and railway map of America, 1877
see under Lloyd, James T.

Lloyd's topographical map of Georgia
see under Lloyd, James T.

VOLUME 337

Lloyd's topographical map of the Hudson River
see under Lloyd, James T

Lloyd's typographical and railway map of the seat of war in Europe 1870. New York, London, E. Lloyd, 1870.

col.map. 126mx196cm.folded to 26cm.

Millard Fillmore's copy, with his signature.

NL 0429399 NBu

Lloyd's underwriters' fire and non-marine association.
...Copies of standard policies, approved clauses proposal forms and renewal receipts...

London, Lloyd's
v. 25½cm.
1. Insurance - Gt. Brit.

NL 0429400 NNC

Lloyd's Underwriters' Fire and Non-Marine Association.
Non-marine policy forms and wordings, clauses, riders, proposal forms, etc. ...

London, Lloyd's [19
v. 26cm.

Vols. for issued in looseleaf form.
Vols. for 19 have title: Copies of standard policies, approved clauses, proposal forms and renewal receipts.

NL 0429402 NNC

Lloyd's universal American register of shipping
see American Lloyd's registry of American and foreign shipping.

Lloyd's Weekly News.
"Lloyd's News" A B C of the war; a complete reference book of facts and figures which all should know. London: Issued for "Lloyd's Weekly News" by Hodder & Stoughton. 1914. 128 p. illus., maps, tables. 8°. (Lloyd's News war library. no. 1.)

1. European war, 1914-
N. Y. P. L. November 5, 1914.

NL 0429404 NN NjP CtY ICJ CSt-H

Lloyd's weekly volume of amusing and instructive literature.

London, E. Lloyd [18
v. illus. 18½cm.
Published 1845-47. cf. Brit. mus. Catalogue.

Library of Congress AP4.L445 44-52907

NL 0429405 DLC NcU

Lloyd's who's who in the great war. London, Issued for Lloyd's weekly news by Hodder and Stoughton, 1914.
128 p. 21½cm. (On cover: Lloyd's news' war library, no. 2)

1. European war, 1914- —Biog.

Library of Congress D523.L63 15-7023

NL 0429406 DLC NN NjP

Lloydverney, George Hope
see Verney, George Hope Lloyd.

Lloyvyr du Kaer Vyrddin
see
Black book of Carmarthen

Llozer, Valentín Almirall y
see
Almirall y Llozer, Valentín, 1810-1904.

Llubera, Ignacio González
see
González Llubera, Ignacio, 1893-

Lluberes, Alcides García
see
García Lluberes, Alcides.

Lluberes, Leonidas García
see
García Lluberes, Leonidas, 1882-1962.

Lluberes, Pedro A
... Ensayo jurídico sobre el artículo 911 del Código civil ... Santo Domingo, Imp.La Cuna de America, 1909.
46,[1] p. 25cm.
Errata leaf inserted.
Tesis - Instituto profesional de Santo Domingo. Facultad de derecho civil.
Año académico de 1908 á 1909,núm.2.
"Autores consultados": p.[47]

NL 0429413 MiU-L

Llubià i Munné, Lluís María
see
Llubiá Munné, Luis María.

Llubiá Munné, Luis María, joint author.

NK4123
.B3

Batllori Munné, Andrés.
Ceràmica catalana decorada, per Andreu Batllori i Munné i Lluís Mª Llubià i Munné. Pròleg per Joan Ainaud de Lasarte. Barcelona, Llibreria Tuebols, 1949.

Llubiá Munné, Luis María, joint author.

NK4123
.B318

Batllori Munné, Andrés.
Cerámica catalana decorada, por Andrés Batllori Munné y Luis Mª Llubià Munné. Prólogo de Juan Ainaud de Lasarte. Barcelona, Librería Tuebols, 1949.

Llubiá Munné, Luis María.
La cerámica murciana decorada, por Luis Mª Llubiá Munné y Miguel López Guzmán. Murcia, Sucesores de Nogués, 1951.
51 p. illus. 27 cm.

1. Pottery—Murcia, Spain (Province) I. López Guzmán, Miguel, joint author. II. Title.
NK4123.L5 738 53-29558 rev ‡

NL 0429417 DLC MH MdBWA

Llubiá Munné, Luis María.
Terminología tipológica de la cerámica española y etimología de la palabra mayólica, por Luis Mª Llubiá Munné y Andrés Batllori Munné. Barcelona, 1955.
x, 63 p. 23 cm.

1. Pottery—Terminology. 2. Mayólica (The word) I. Batllori Munné, Andrés, joint author. II. Title.
NK3770.L55 59-48079 ‡

NL 0429418 DLC

Lluch, Antonio Rubió y
see
Rubió y Lluch, Antonio, 1856-1937.

Lluch, Emilio.
... Carburantes substitutos y gasógenos para automóviles. Barcelona, Bosch [1941]
203 p. illus., diagrs. 19½ cm.

1. Automobiles—Gas-producers. 2. Motor fuels.
TL229.G3L55 629.2538 A 43-2392

NL 0429420 NN DLC

G368
L779s

LLUCH, EMILIO
... Sugestiones [por] Emilio Lluch. Colaboración a favor de quien se interese por el corretaje de seguros de vida. [Montevideo? Tall. graf. Bouzout] 1945.
164p. incl. tables. 19½cm.

At head of title: Banco de seguros del estado.

1. Insurance, Life. 2. Insurance, Life - Uruguay. I. Banco de seguros del estado, Montevideo.

NL 0429421 TxU

Lluch, Luis Carlos Viada y.
See
Viada y Lluch, Luis Carlos.

Lluch, Pedro Gomis
see Gomis Lluch, Pedro.

Lluch, Rafael Gayano
see Gayano Lluch, Rafael.

Lluch, Ramón Robres
see
Robres Lluch, Ramón.

Lluch, Salvador Soler
See
Soler Lluch, Salvador.

Lluch, Vicente Rojo
see
Rojo Lluch, Vicente, 1894-1966.

VOLUME 337

DP269 L58 Lluch Fabado Valls, Francisco
Mi diario entre los mártires, cárcel de Málaga, año 1937. [n.p.] Editorial Dardo, 1937.
206 p.

1. Spain - Hist. - 1936-1939 (Civil war) - Prisoners and prisons. I. Title.

NL 0429428 CU IEN

Lluch Fabado Valls, Francisco.
... Mi diario entre los mártires, cárcel de Málaga, año 1937. (2. ed.) Granada, Imprenta H.° de Paulino Ventura, 1937.
209, [1] p. 20½cm.
At head of title: F.co Lluch F. Valls.

1. Spain—Hist.—Civil war, 1936-1939—Prisoners and prisons. I. Title.

Library of Congress DP269.L62 1937 a 38-34296 [2] 946.08

NL 0429429 DLC TxU MH

946.85 L77s Lluch Fabado Valls, Francisco.
Semilla azul, por Francisco Lluch F. Valls. [Granada, Impr. H. de Paulino Ventura] 1939.
228p. 23cm.

1. Malaga, Spain--Hist. 2. Spain--Hist.--Civil War, 1936-1939. I. Title.

NL 0429430 IU IEN MH MiU

Lluch Mora, Francisco.
Canto desesperado a la ceniza, elegía. Yauco, P. R. [1955]
21 p. 20 cm. ("Colección Rodadero"; poesía puertorriqueña, 1)
"Este poema forma parte del libro inédito: Poemas de la ceniza."

I. Title.

PQ7439.L63C3 57-31914

NL 0429431 DLC OrU MiU NN

Lluch Mora, Francisco.
Cuaderno de sonetos, 1947. [Yauco?] Puerto Rico, 1953.
15 p. 14 cm. (Colección Pegaso; poesía mínima, 1)
"Edición de 250 ejemplares numerados. No. 146."

I. Title.

PQ7439.L63C8 56-38648

NL 0429432 DLC

Lluch Mora, Francisco.
Del asedio y la clausura. San Juan, P. R., Editorial Yaurel, 1950.
55 p. 23 cm. (Colección Yaurel)

I. Title.

PQ7439.L63D4 A 52-1704

New York. Public Libr. for Library of Congress [1]†

NL 0429433 NN NjR DPU NN CtY DLC

Lluch Mora, Francisco.
Del barro a Dios (1949-1950) San Juan, Puerto Rico, Editorial Yaurel, 1954.
50 p. 16 cm.
Poems.

I. Title.

PQ7439.L63D43 55-23760 ‡

NL 0429434 DLC MiU

330.109 L779h 1935 Lluch y Capdevila, Pedro.
Historia de las doctrinas económicas. Barcelona [Artes Gráficas] 1935.
343p. 22cm.

"(XII Conferencias en la Associació de Comptables de Catalunya)"
Bibliography: p. 334-336.

1. Economics. History. I. Title.

NL 0429435 KU

Lluch y Capdevila, Pedro.
Historia de las doctrinas económicas, por Pedro Lluch y Capdevila ... 2. ed. Barcelona, Bosch [1941]
290 p. 22cm.
"Bibliografía": p. [283]-284.

1. Economics—Hist.

New York. Public library for Library of Congress [2] A 44-199

NL 0429436 NN KU

330.9 L779h 1947 LLUCH Y CAPDEVILA, PEDRO
Historia de las doctrinas económicas, por Pedro Lluch y Capdevila ... 3. ed. Barcelona, Bosch [1947]
290p. 22cm.

"Bibliografía": p.[283]-284.

1. Economics - Hist.

NL 0429437 TxU

330.109 L779h 1954 Lluch y Capdevila, Pedro.
Historia de la doctrinas económicas. 5. ed. Barcelona, Editorial Lux, 1954.
290p. 23cm.

"Bibliografía": p.[283]-284.

1. Economics. History. I. Title.

NL 0429438 KU

Lluch y Capdevila, Pedro
Legislación financiera por Pedro Lluch y Capdevila ... Barcelona, Lux, 1948.
528 p. forms. 22½cm.

NL 0429439 MH-L

Lluch y Capdevila, Pedro.
Legislación financiera. 2. ed. Barcelona, Editorial Lux, 1952.
496 p. 23 cm.

1. Finance, Public—Spain—Law. 2. Taxation—Spain—Law. I. Title.

54-26461

NL 0429440 DLC

Lluch y Garriga, Joaquin, Cardinal.
Corona fúnebre á la buena memoria del emmo. y rmo. señor Dr. D. Fr. Joaquin de la S. R. I. Cardenal Lluch y Garriga ...
see under title

HD 8372 L5 Lluch y Garriga, Joaquin
La international. Salamanca, Impr. de Oliva y Hermano, 1872.
68p. 22cm.
Bibliographical footnotes.

1. The International 2. Labor and laboring classes - Spain I. Title

NL 0429442 WU

Lluchmayor, Majorca. Archivo Municipal.

CD1877 .L54L54 Llado y Ferragut, Jaime, ed.
Catálogo de la sección histórica del Archivo Municipal de la ciudad de Lluchmayor (Baleares) Documentos y noticias por Jaime Lladó y Ferragut. Prólogo por Jaime Sastre Vidal. Palma de Mallorca, Imp. SS. Corazones, 1955.

Llucia, Hervé, 1906-
... Les typhlites appendiculaires à retardement ... Lyon, 1935.
Thèse - Univ. de Marseille.
"Bibliographie consultée": p. [81]-83.

NL 0429444 CtY

La Llucia dels cabells de plata...
see under Arus y Arderiú, Rosendo.

Llueca, Federico Gomez
see
Gomez Llueca, Federico

Lluelles, Enric.
Bon amor no vol cadenes; comedia original en tres acts de Enric Lluelles ... [Barcelona, Ráfols, 1920]
52 p. port. on cover. 19 cm. (La Novel-la teatral catalana. Any III, núm. 33)

NL 0429447 NcU

Lluelles, Enric.
La festa del carrer; sainet en un acte ... Barcelona, Bonavía, 1935.
28 p. 18 cm. (La Escena catalana. Any XVIII [2. época] núm. 414)
At head of title: Enric Lluelles.
With this is bound: Es rifa un home! Roas Mª. Arquimbau; Antonieta [de] Tristan Bernard.

NL 0429448 NcU

Lluelles, Enric.
Les indecises; obra en tres actes... Barcelona, Millà, 1934.
64 p. 20 cm. (Catalunya teatral. Any III, núm. 56)

NL 0429449 NcU

Lluelles, Enric.
Marionetes; llegenda d'amor i de vilesa ... 2. ed. [Barcelona, Bonavía, 1927]
25 p. 28 cm. (La Escena catalana. Any X [2. época] núm. 228)
"Obres d'Enric Lluelles": p. [27]

NL 0429450 NcU

VOLUME 337

Lluelles, Enric.
El neguit de les ombres; tres actes ...
Barcelona, Millà [1932]
51 p. 20 cm. (Catalunya teatral. Any I, no. 10)

NL 0429451 NcU

Lluelles, Enric.
La nova llum; obra en tres actes ...
Barcelona, Millà, 1933.
47 p. 20 cm. (Catalunya teatral. Any II, núm. 32)

NL 0429452 NcU

Lluelles, Enric.
Parelles al vel; comèdia frívola en 3 actes ...
[Barcelona, Bonavía, 1926]
20 p. port. on cover. 28 cm. (La Escena catalana. Any IX [2. época] núm. 211)
At head of title: Enric Lluelles.
"Obres del mateix autor": p. 20.

NL 0429453 NcU

Lluelles, Enric.
L'obstacle; drama en tres actes ...
[Barcelona, Bonavía, 1926]
17 p. 28 cm. (La Escena catalana. Any IX [2. época] núm. 217)
At head of title: Enric Lluelles.
"Obres del mateix autor": p. [18]
"Teatre Català": p. [19]

NL 0429454 NcU

Lluelles, Enric.
...Una pedra al pas; comèdia en un acte, original d'Enric Lluelles. [Barcelona, 1934] 21 p. 18½cm. (El nostre teatre; [Any 1, no. 14] Supplement.)
"Aquesta comèdia fou estrenada al teatre Novetats...el dia 3 de juny del 1934." — p. [2].

955901A. 1. Drama, Catalan. I. Title. II. Ser.
N. Y. P. L. January 5, 1939

NL 0429455 NN NcU

Lluelles, Enric.
La pols del camí; tres actes ... [Barcelona, Bonavía, 1926]
18 p. 28 cm. (La Escena catalana. Any IX [2. época] núm. 198)

NL 0429456 NcU

Lluelles, Enric.
Tres milions busquen hereu; farsa melodramàtica en tres actes... [Barcelona, Bonavía, 1932]
26 p. 28 cm. (La Escena catalana. Any XV [2. época] núm. 362)

NL 0429457 NcU

Ex
3829 Lluellyn, Eliza Augusta
.94 Poems. [n.p., 18--?]
.1800 126 p. 22 cm.

NL 0429458 NjP

Lluelyn, Martin, 1616-1682.
An elegie on the death of the prince Henry duke of Glocester.
Oxford, printed by H. Hall for R. Davis, 1660.
f°. pp. 8.

NL 0429459 MH CSmH IU PPL CtY

*EC65 Lluelyn, Martin, 1616-1682.
L7797 The marrow of the muses: express'd in that
646mbaa excellent facetious poem stiled Men-miracles; with other choice pieces. By the most highly ingenious Dr. M. Lluellen. The second edition.
London,Printed for William Sheares at the Bible in Bedford street in Covent-Garden,1661.
8p.ℓ.,112p. 14.5cm.
First published in 1646 with title "Men-miracles. With other poemes"; a second ed., with same title, appeared in 1656; this is a reissue of the sheets of the 1656 ed. with cancel t.-p.
In this copy prelim. leaf 8 (with Table) is bound at end.

NL 0429460 MH

Lluelyn, Martin, 1616-1682.
Men-miracles. With other poems, on several subjects. By M. Lluellin... London, Printed, and are to be sold by Peter Parker, 1679. 8 p.l., 112 p. 14cm. (8°.)
Hazlitt, I, 260. Wing L2627.
Imperfect: a few upper and lower edges cropped.
With autographs of John Underhill.

J. S. BILLINGS MEM. COLL.
502385B. I. Title.
N. Y. P. L. October 3, 1949

NL 0429461 NN MB MH

Case
Y [LLUELYN, MARTIN] 1616-1682.
185 Men, miracles and poems. By M.L.L. [London,1644[i.e.1646]
.L 799 [14],112(i.e.110)p.

Error in paging: no.78-79 omitted.
Imperfect: pages 9-10, 41-42, 75-76 wanting.
Bookplate of Thos. Folley.
Published 1679 under title: Lluellin's Marrow of the muses.

NL 0429462 ICN

PR2659 Lluellyn, Martin, 1616-1682.
.L55 Men-miracles, with other poemes. [Oxford,
M4 H. Hall] 1646.
1646a 150p. (on double leaves)

Xeroxed copy by Univ. Microfilms.

I. Title.

NL 0429463 NcU

PR3541 [Lluelyn,Martin]1616-1682.
f.L58T6 To the Kings most excellent Majesty. [London,
1660 Printed for J.Martin,J.Allestry,T.Dicas,1660]
Rare bk 12 p. 30½cm.
room Head-pieces; initials.
Contains also congratulatory poems to the Duke of York,later King James II,and to Henry,duke of Gloucester; all three poems signed:Martin Lluelyn.

1.Charles II,king of Great Britain,1630-1685--Poetry.

NL 0429464 ICU CSmH CtY MH TxU

[Lluelyn, Martin] 1616-1682.
Wickham wakened, or, The Quakers Madrigall in rime dogrell. [London]Printed in the yeare
v.346 1672.
8p. 19½cm.
Page 3 misnumbered 1.
Title vignette; head-piece.

NL 0429465 CtY CSmH MH PHC

LLUELLYN, Raymond Maude, 1842-1886.
Occasional contributions to "The Globe" ... [London, 1887?]
8, 370p. front. (port.) 23cm.
"Printed for private circulation."

NL 0429466 MnU

Lluesma, Baltasar Bonet
see Bonet Lluesma, Baltasar.

Lluesma, Eusebio Gimenez.
see Gimenez Lluesma, Eusebio.

WD Lluesma-Uranga, Estanislao
1251 Afecciones quirúrgicas del peritoneo.
L793a Buenos Aires, "La Prensa Médica argentina",
1945 1945.
157 p. illus.

1. Peritoneum - Surgery 2. Peritonitis

NL 0429469 DNLM

WI LLUESMA URANGA, Estanislao
535 Apendicitis infantil. Madrid, Ferreira,
L793a 1932.
1932 184 p.
1. Appendicitis - Children

NL 0429470 DNLM

Lluesma-Uranga, Estanislao.
Los fundamentos de la cirugía estética. [Buenos Aires] Editorial Americalee [1943]
147, [7] p. illus. 21 cm.
Bibliography: p. [150]-[153]

1. Surgery, Plastic.

RD118.L6 51-47616

NL 0429471 DLC DNLM DPU

WG LLUESMA URANGA, Estanislao
510 Heridas de guerra de las arterias;
qL793h secuelas de estas lesiones; concepto
1941 clínico y terapéutico de los aneurismas arteriovenosos. Buenos Aires, "El Ateneo," 1941.
42 p. illus.
1. Arteries - Wounds & injuries

NL 0429472 DNLM

WL LLUESMA-URANGA, Estanislao
600 Neurovegetativo. Buenos Aires, Ló-
qL793n pez & Etchegoyen, 1948.
1948 xvi, 595 p. illus.

1. Autonomic nervous system

NL 0429473 DNLM ICJ

...¡Llueven palos!... Serie 1- Manila: Imp. de e [sic] Grito del pueblo, 1905 v. 17cm. (Biblioteca sensacional de el Grito del pueblo.)
Introduction signed Isabelo de los Reyes.
A series of articles appearing in: El Grito del pueblo.

1. Philippine Islands—Politics. I. Reyes y Florentino, Isabelo de los, 1865– , ed. II. El Grito del pueblo.
N. Y. P. L. March 23, 1939

NL 0429474 NN NcD

VOLUME 337

[Llúfriu, José Juan] Manifestacion del prefecto del distrito de Puebla, sobre la conducta que ha observado en la exaccion de la contribucion personal, y las imposturas con que ha informado sobre esto al supremo gobierno D. Paulino Garcia. Puebla, Imprenta antigua, 1844. 26p. 19cm. (Papeles varios. 39:12)

NL 0429475 CU-B

Llugain, Francisco Barredo
see
Barredo Llugain, Francisco.

Llugdar, E
Sinopsis del curso de obligaciones [por] E. Llugdar y R. A. Feraud. Buenos Aires, P. M. Aquino, 1927.
127 p. 16 x 24 cm.

1. Contracts—Argentine Republic. I. Feraud, R. A., joint author. II. Title.
54-45063

NL 0429477 DLC

Lluis y Navas, Jaime
see
Lluis y Navas-Brusi, Jaime.

DP302 P2L5 Lluis, Juan
El meu Pallars. Barcelona, Barcino, 19
v. illus. (Col·lecció Tramuntana, v.

Contents.-
v. 2 El Pallars sobirà.

1. Pallars, Spain - Descr. & trav. I. Title.

NL 0429479 CU

Lluis, Juan.
Records de la meva vida de pastor. Pròleg de R. Violant i Simorra. Barcelona [Editorial Barcino, 1955.
98 p. illus. 19 cm. (Biblioteca folklòrica Barcino, v. 12)

1. Shepherds—Spain—Pallars. I. Title.

GT5895.S5L5 60-23208 ‡

NL 0429480 DLC NN

Lluis, L'Avi, pseud.
See
Barrière, Louis.

Lluís, Pedro Pagés
see Pagés Lluís, Pedro.

Lluis y Navas-Brusi, Jaime.
Consideraciones en torno al perpetuo problema de la divinidad. Barcelona, 1950

NL 0429483 MH

Lluis y Navas-Brusi, Jaime.
Criticismo y catolocismo. Barcelona, 1951

NL 0429484 MH

Lluis y Navas-Brusi, Jaime.
Las cuestiones legales sobre la amonedación peninsular en la edad antigua. Madrid, 1953.
98 p. 22 cm. (Fábrica Nacional de Moneda y Timbre. Numismática, publicación no. 1)
"Primera parte de nuestra tesis doctoral sobre la Historia de la legislación sobre fabricación de moneda en España, que fué sostenida en la Facultad de Filosofía y Letras, de Madrid."
Bibliographical footnotes.

1. Coinage—Spain—Hist. 2. Spain—Hist.—Roman period, 218 B. C.-414 A. D. I. Title. (Series)

65-86931 rev

NL 0429485 DLC

Lluis y Navas-Brusi, Jaime.
El sujeto de la historia y los problemas de su estudio. Barcelona, 1951

NL 0429486 MH

Llull, Francisco Ferrer
see
Ferrer Llull, Francisco.

Llull, Ramón
see
Lull, Ramón, d. 1315.

PC 3941 .L58 R4 Llunas, J
La revolució; poema en tres cants. Ilus. d' en M. Moliné. [Barcelona, Tip. La Academia, 1886]
32 p. illus. 20 cm.

NL 0429489 WU IEN

Llurba, Rossend, ed.
El cuplet català (primera serie)
see under title

Llurba, Rossend.
La darrera disbauxa; impresió trágica, guanyadora del premi d'honor en el Concurs de diàlecs organissát per la revista teatral. [Barcelona: B. Baxarías, 1912.] 23(1) p. 12°. (Biblioteca "De tots colors.")
Author's name at head of title.

1. Drama (Catalan). 2. Title.
N. Y. P. L. September 18, 1918.

NL 0429491 NN OO

Lluria, Enrique, 1863-
Evolución super-orgánica... Por Enrique Lluria. Editada por la Asociación cooperativa de obreros constructora de casas. Parte Habana: "El Score," 19 v. diagrs. 8°.
Contents: Parte 2. La humanidad del porvenir y la solución del problema social.

1. Sociology and evolution. 2. Sociology.—Essays and misc. 3. Asociación cooperativa de obreros constructora de casas, Havana.
N. Y. P. L. September 6, 1922.

NL 0429492 NN MH

Lluria, Enrique, 1863-
...Evolución super-orgánica, (la naturaleza y el problema social); prólogo del Dr. D. Santiago Ramón y Cajal. Barcelona: Administración, 1905. xii, 222, lii, 13 p. incl. tables. front. (port.), illus. [2. ed.] nar. 12°.
Bibliographical footnotes.

1. Sociology and evolution. 2. Ramón y Cajal, Santiago, 1852-
N. Y. P. L. November 30, 1921.

NL 0429493 NN

Lluria, Enrique, 1863-
... La máquina contra el obrero en el régimen capitalista. Madrid, Gráfica socialista [1930]
32 p. 19cm.

1. Machinery in industry. I. Title.
[Full name: Enrique Lluria y Despau]
32-14220

Library of Congress HD6331.L6 338.4

NL 0429494 DLC

Lluria, Enrique, 1863-
El medio social y la perfectibilidad de la salud, por Enrique Lluria y Despau. [Parte 1- Madrid: Fortanet, 1898-
v. 12°.

1. Hygiene (Personal). 2. Hygiene (Sexual).
N. Y. P. L. September 7, 1923.

NL 0429495 NN DNLM

Lluria, Enrique, 1863-
Super-organic evolution; nature and the social problem, by Dr. Enrique Lluria, with a preface by Dr. D. Santiago Ramon y Cajal; tr. by Rachel Challice and D. H. Lambert ... London, Williams & Norgate, 1910.
xix, 233 p. illus. 20½cm.

1. Evolution. I. Challice, Rachel, tr. II. Lambert, Daniel Henry, 1852- tr.
11-32482

Library of Congress QH366.L7

NL 0429496 DLC CU NIC OCl MiU ICJ MB

Lluria, María de.
Conferencia leída en la velada necrologica celebrada en homenaje á la memoria de la ilustre escritora Condesa de Pardo Bazán. Habana, 12 de mayo de 1922. Habana, Seoane y Fernández [1922].
16 p.
At head of title: Centro gallego.

NL 0429497 MH

Lluria y Despau, Enrique, 1863-
SEE
Lluria, Enrique, 1863-

Lluscia, Marcellin.
De la decheance du terme dans la faillite et la liquidation judiciaire. Toulouse, 1907.
In. Diss. Bibl.

NL 0429499 ICRL

Llusiá, José Botella
see Botella Llusiá, José.

VOLUME 337

Lluveres, José Llampayas
see
Llampayas, José.

Lluy, Nicolás
see
Lluy y Hernández, Nicolás, d. 1911.

Lluy y Hernández, Nicolás, d. 1911, ed.

Law
Círculo de abogados de la Habana.
Memorias de la Seccion de procedimientos del Circulo de abogados de la Habana ...
Habana, Imprenta del Gobierno y capitanía general por S. M., 18

Lluzar Rodrigo, José.
Los buques submarinos actuales, su construcción, armamento, maniobras, táctica y empleo en la defensa de las costas y en la guerra naval, por J. Lluzar Rodrigo ... Madrid, Bailly-Bailliere, 1916.
440 p. illus., plates, diagrs. 22cm.
"Indice bibliográfico": p. [435]-436.

1. Submarine boats.
Library of Congress VM365.L5 43-41011

NL 0429504 DLC

Llwyd, Angharad, of Caerwys.
Wynn, Sir John, bart., 1553-1626.
The history of the Gwydir family, by Sir John Wynn ... First pub. by the Honorable Daines Barrington, with an introduction and notes; now re-edited, with additional notes, by a native of the principality: to which is added, an original work, containing memoirs of celebrated and distinguished cotemporary Welshmen, bishops, &c. by the same author. Ruthin, Printed by R. Jones, 1827.

Llwyd, Angharad, of Caerwys.
942.91
qL793H
A history of the island of Mona, or Anglesey ... being the prise essay to which was adjudged the first premium at the Royal Beaumaris Eisteddfod, held in the month of August, 1832. Ruthin, R. Jones, 1833.
iv, 413, 61 p. 28 cm.
"A brief sketch of the Royal Eisteddfod, held at Beaumaris, on Tuesday 28th, Wednesday 29th, Thursday 30th, and Friday 31st of August, 1832. Selected from the Bangor and Chester papers": p. [1]-61 (3d group)
1. Anglesey, Wales. History.

NL 0429506 NcD PU ICU MH

Llwyd, Edward, fl. 1328-1405
see Iolo Goch, fl. 1328-1405.

Llwyd, Edward, 1660-1709
See
Lhuyd, Edward, 1660-1709.

FILM
Llwyd, Humphrey, 1527-1568.
Angliae regni florentissimi nova descriptio avctore Hvmfredo Lhvyd ... [n.p.] 1573.
Map and text (1 p.) with caption: Angleterre.
University microfilms no.16375 (case 80, carton 475)
Short-title catalogue no.16635.

1. Gt. Brit.—Maps.

NL 0429509 MiU

Llwyd, Humphrey, 1527-1568.
The breuiary of Britayne. As this moſt noble, and renowmed iland, was of auncient time deuided into three kingdomes, England, Scotland, and Wales. Contaynyng a learned diſcourſe of the variable ſtate, & alteration therof, vnder diuers, as wel natural: as forren princes, & conquerours. Together with the geographicall deſcription of the ſame, ſuch as nether by elder, nor later vvriters, the like hath been ſet foorth before. Writen in Latin by Humfrey Lhuyd of Denbigh, a Cambre Britayne, and lately Engliſhed by Thomas Tvvyne, gentleman. [London, Imprinted by R. Iohnes] 1573.
22 p. l., 96 numb. l. 14½cm.
Title within ornamental black border.
Gothic type; marginal notes; initials; tailpieces.

Subject entries: Gt. Brit.—Descr. & trav.
2-30286
Library of Congress, no. DA610.L692.

NL 0429511 DLC CU-S PPRF InU DFo CtY MH ICN CSmH

Lhwyd, Humfrey
see Llwyd, Humphrey, 1527-1568.

FILM
Llwyd, Humphrey, 1527-1568.
The breuiary of Britayne. As this ... iland, was of auncient time deuided into three kingdomes, England, Scotland and Wales. Contaynyng a learned discourse of the variable state, & alteration therof ... Together with the geographicall description of the same ... Writen in Latin by Humfrey Lhuyd ... and lately Englished by Thomas Twyne ... [London, 1573.
Colophon: Imprinted at London, by Richard Iohnes ...
"Authours, whose names, and woorkes, are cited in this booke": 17th prelim. leaf.
University microfilms no.15927 (case 56, carton 336)
Short-title catalogue no.16636.
1. Gt. Brit.—Descr. & trav. I. Twyne, Thomas, 1543-1616, tr. II. Title.

NL 0429513 MiU

Llwyd, Humphrey, M. D. 1527-68.
Breviary of Britayne ... Lately Englished by Thos. Twyne. London, 1573; repr. 1729. fo. (With Lewis, J., Hist. of Gt. Britain.) 5.26

NL 0429514 MdBP

LLWYD, Humphrey, 1527-1568.
Britannicae descriptionis commentariolum, necnon De Mona insula, et Britannica Arce, sive Armamentario Romano disceptatio epistolaris. Accedunt AErae Cambrobritannicae. Accurante Mose Gulielmio. Londini, G. Bowyer, 1731.

4°. Map. Br 3615.72.5

NL 0429515 MH CSmH IU

Llwyd, Humphrey,
Cambriæ typus.
— [Amsterdam, 1633.] Size, 13 × 18¾ inches. Scale (computed), 10.8 miles to 1 inch.
Descriptive text in French on the back.
Cut from Mercator and Hondius: Atlas ou représentation du monde universel.

STC 16637? Oct. 4, 1900
*D6749 — Wales. Geog. Maps.

NL 0429516 MB

Llwyd, Humphrey, 1527-1568.
Commentarioli britan | nicae descri | ptionis fragmen | tvm. Avctore | Humfredo Lhuyd, Denbyghiense, | Cambro Britanno ... Coloniae Agrippinae, apud I. Birckmannum, 1572.
8 p. l., 78 numb. l. 16½cm.
Title vignette; marginal notes.

Subject entries: Gt. Brit.—Descr. & trav.
2-30285
Library of Congress, no. DA610.L69.

CSmH
NL 0429517 DLC CU-S DFo MnU CtY MH ICN CLU MiU OU

Llwyd, Humphrey, 1527-1568.
De Mona Drvidvm insvla, antiqvitati suæ restituta... Epistola... Humfredi Lhuyd: In qua etiam de armamentario romano...non inelegans disceptatio. (in Price, Sir John. Historiæ brytannicæ defensio. 1573. 19p. at end)

Caption title.
Colophon: Denbighiæ...quinto Aprilis, 1568.

NL 0429518 ICN NNC

Llwyd, Himphrey, 1527-1568.
L'histoire des Provinces-Unies, des Pais-Bas
see under Wicquefort, [Abraham] de.

Llwyd, Humphrey, 1527-1568.
DA130
.V5P7
Rare bk.
Coll.
Price, Sir John, d. 1573?
Historiae brytannicae defensio, Ioanne Priseo ... avthore. Londini, impressum in ædibus H. Binneman typographi, impensis Humfredi Toy, 1573.

Llwyd, Humphrey, 1527-1568, tr.
DA715
.C254
Rare Bk
Coll
FOR OTHER EDITIONS SEE MAIN ENTRY
Caradog, of Llancarvan.
The historie of Cambria, now called Wales, a part of the most famous yland of Brytaine, written in the Brytish language aboue two hundreth yeares past. Translated into English by H. Lhoyd. Cor., augm., and continued out of records and best approued authors, by Dauid Powel. London, Reprinted for J. Harding, 1811.

Llwyd, Humphrey, 1527-1568.
Ortelius, Abraham, 1527-1598.
Theatro del mondo di Abrahamo Ortelio: da lui poco inanzi la sua morte riueduto, & di tauole nuoue, et commenti adorno, & arricchito, con la vita dell' autore. Traslato in lingua toscana dal sigr. Filippo Pigafetta. In Anversa, Si vende nella libraria Plantiniana, M.DC.XII.

Llwyd, Humphrey, 1527-1568.
G1006
.T5
1592
Map Div.
Cage
FOR OTHER EDITIONS SEE MAIN ENTRY
[Ortelius, Abraham, 1527-1598.
Theatrvm orbis terrarvm. Opus nunc denuo ab ipso auctore recognitum, multisquè locis castigatum, & quamplurimis nouis tabulis atquè commentarijs auctum. [Colophon: Antverpiæ, in officina Plantiniana, auctoris ære & cura. M.D.XCII]

Llwyd, Humphrey, 1527-1568.
The treasury of healthe
see under Johannes XXI, pope, d. 1277.

Llwyd, Huw Cae
see Huw Cae Llwyd, fl. 1431-1504.

VOLUME 337

Llwyd, Ieuan ap Huw Cae
see Ieuan ap Huw Cae Llwyd, fl. 1477-1500.

Llwyd, John, 1808-31
Llofion o faes y trancedig, neu Gasgliad o ysgrifenadau y diweddar Mr. John Llwyd, Beaumaris. Caerlleon, Parry, 1832
48 p.

NL 0429527 MH

Llwyd, John Plummer Derwent, 1861-
The message of an Indian relic, by Rev. Dr. J. P. D. Llwyd. Seattle: Lowman & Hanford Co., cop. 1909. 21 p. illus., plates. 8°.

394537A. 1. Totems, Indian-American—U. S.—Wash.—Seattle.
N. Y. P. L. January 14, 1929

NL 0429528 NN CaBViPA Wa WaS WaT WaU N NBuG

Llwyd, John Plummer Derwent, 1861-
Mysticism and other essays, by the Very Reverend J. P. D. Llwyd... Toronto, The Macmillan company of Canada limited, 1926.
vii, 108 p. 19 cm.

NL 0429529 NNG TxU KyWAT CaBVa

Llwyd, John Plummer Derwent, 1861-1933
1901
LL979p Poems of nature, childhood, and religion, by J. P. D. Llwyd. Toronto, Macmillan, 1928.
5 p.l., 64 p. 20 cm.

1. Canadian poetry. I. Title.

NL 0429530 RPB TxU Wa CtY

Llwyd, John Plummer Derwent, 1861-
Son of thunder; a study of the life and work of John of Bethsaida, fisher of men, by J. P. D. Llwyd. New York, R. Long & R. R. Smith, inc., 1932.
xii p., 1 l., 170 p. 19cm.

1. John, Saint, apostle. I. Title.
Library of Congress BS2455.L6 32-3729
—— Copy 2.
Copyright A 47383 [3] 225.92

NL 0429531 DLC CaBVa NcD NN PCC WaWW

Llwyd, John Plummer Dervent, 1861-1933
1901
LL979s The song of the breakers, and other poems, by Rev. J. P. D. Llwyd. Seattle, Wash. [192-?]
[19] p. 18 cm.

1. Canadian poetry. I. Title.

NL 0429532 RPB WaS

Llwyd, John Plummer Derwent, 1861-
The vestal virgin; a dramatic poem, by J. P. D. Llwyd. Halifax, N. S., 1920.
58 p. 17½cm.

I. Title.
Library of Congress PR6023.L7V4 1920 22-1078

NL 0429533 DLC TxU

Llwyd, Justus. Satires. [Welsh.] 3 pp.
(Myvyrian archaiol. of Wales, v. 1, p. 557.)

NL 0429534 MdBP

Llwyd, Morgan, o Wynedd
see
Llwyd, Morgan, 1619-1659.

Llwyd, Morgan, 1619-1659.
Chwech ar hugain o bregethau, ar destynau pwysig. Gan y Parchedig Morgan Lloyd ... Gwyndod-Wryf, Llanrwst, Argraffwyd gan J. Jones, dros yr awdwr, 1830.
iv, [5]-284 p. 18½cm.

1. Sermons, Welsh. I. Title.

NL 0429536 NCH

[LLWYD, Morgan, 1619-1659].
Dirgelwch i rhai iw Ddeall ac i eraill iw Watwar sef Tri aderyn yn ymddiddan yr Eryr, a'r Golomen, a'r Gigfran. Neu Arwydd i Annerch y Cymru. Yn y flwyddyn 1653, cyn dyfod 666. [Y Mwythig], gan J.S. tros Nicholas Thomas, a Lewis Thomas, 1714.
nar. 24°. pp.191 (1).
Rowlands Cambrian Bibliog., 1714, 7.

NL 0429537 MH

PB2298
.L56D5
1828 Llwyd, Morgan, 1619-1659.
Dirgelwch i rai i'w ddeall, ac i eraill i'w wator, sef, tri aderyn, yn ymddiddan. Llanrwst, J. Jones [1828?]
107 p. 17 cm.

NL 0429538 MB IU

PB2298
.L56G3 Llwyd, Morgan, 1619-1659.
Gair o'r gair, neu son am swn, y lleferydd anfarwol. 3. argraffiad. Merthyr Tydfil, B. Morgan, 1829.
56 p. 19 cm.

NL 0429539 MB

Bonaparte
Collection [LLWYD, MORGAN] 1619-1659.
No.7530 Gwaedd ynghymru yn wyneb pob cydwybod euog Yr 2. argraphiad. Mwythig[Shrewsbury]T.Durston, 1750.
36p. 15cm.

By Morgan Llwyd.—cf. Cambrian bibliography, 1869, p.419.
"Llythyr at y darllennydd" signed: Dafydd Jones, Trefriw.

NL 0429540 ICN MB NN

Llwyd, Morgan, 1619-1659.
Gweithiau Morgan Llwyd, o Wynedd. Danolygiaeth Thomas E. Ellis. Bangor, Jarvis & Foster; [etc., etc.] 1899-1908.
2 v. 2 pl., facsims. 19½cm. (Half-title: Prifysgol cymru: University of Wales. [Reprints of Welsh prose works of the 16th, 17th, and 18th centuries. no. 1])
Title within ornamental border.
Vol. 2, edited by John H. Davies.
Some of the works are here published for the first time. The majority, however, are reprints of the original editions (with reproduction of the original title-pages) and include translations from Welsh into English. Vol. 2, p. 1-80, contains Welsh translations of two works of Jacob Boehme.
Bibliography: v. 2, p. 316-321.
I. Ellis, Thomas Edward, 1859-1899. ed. II. Davies, John Humphreys, 1871- ed. III. Böhme, Jakob, 1575-1624.
17-6169
Library of Congress PB2297.L6 1899

NL 0429541 DLC CU MH NN

891.66 Llwyd, Morgan, 1619-1659.
L77g Gweithiau ... Bangor, 1908-09.
2v.

v.1 edited by Thomas E. Ellis. v.2 edited by John H. Davies.

NL 0429542 IU

Bonaparte
Collection LLWYD, MORGAN, 1619-1659.
No.7886 Llyfr y tri aderyn. Dirgelwch i rai i'w ddeall, ac i eraill i'w watwor; sef, Tri aderyn yn ymddiddan... Caernarfon, L.E.Jones, 1826.
96p. 19cm.

NL 0429543 ICN MB

Llwyd, Morgan, 1619-59.
Llyfr y Tri Aderyn. Gyda rhagarweiniad gan y parch. O.Jones. Argraphiad newydd. Liverpool, Foulkes, 1893
xxi, 93 p.

NL 0429544 MH

LLWYD, Morgan, 1619-1659.
Llyfr y Tri Aderyn: gan Morgan Llwyd o Wynedd. Dirgelwch i rai i'w Ddeall, ac i eraill i'w Watwor; sef, Tri Aderyn yn Ymddiddan, - yr Eryr, a'r Golomen, a'r Gigfran; neu, Arwydd i Annerch y Cymry. Argraffiad y Bobl. Bala, Humphrey Evans, etc., etc., 1894.

NL 0429545 MH

LLWYD, Morgan, 1619-1659.
Llyfr y tri aderyn, neu Arwydd i annerch y Cymru. Llundain, J.M.Dent & Co., etc., etc., 1900.

NL 0429546 MH

PB2297
.L6T7
1910 Llwyd, Morgan, 1619-1659.
Llyfr y tri aderyn, gyda rhagdraeth a mynegai gan Anthropos. Caernarfon, Y Cyhoeddwyr Cymreig [1910]
118 p. 19 cm.

I. Rowlands, Robert Daniel. II. Title.

NL 0429547 MB MH

Y
835
.L 756 Llwyd, Morgan, 1619-1659.
Llyfr y tri aderyn (allan o argraffiad urdd y graddedigion o weithiau Morgan Llwyd) Caerdydd, Gwasg Prifysgol Cymru, 1928. 116p.

Cover-title.
With reproduction of t.-p. of 1653 edition: Dirgelwch i rai iw ddeall ac i eraill iw watwar, sef Tri aderyn yn ymddiddan yr eryr, a'r golomen, a'r gigfran...

NL 0429548 ICN

Llwyd, Morgan, 1619-1659.
Llythyr i'r Cymry cariadus a barddoniaeth. Wrecsam, Hughes [1932] 32 p. 17cm. (Llyfrau'r Ford Gron. Rhif 11)
Bibliography, p. vii.

1. Welsh language—Texts and translations.

NL 0429549 NN

VOLUME 337

LLWYD, Morgan, 1619-1659.
Morgan Llwyd, ymchwil i rai o'r prif ddylanwadau a fu arno. Gan E. Lewis Evans. Lerpwl, Hugh Evans a'r Feibion, 1930.

NL 0429550 MH ICN

Llwyd, Morgan, 1619-1659.
Yr YMRODDIAD: neu, Bapuryn a gyfieutnwyd i helpu'r Cymru allan o'r hunan a'r drygioni. At ba un y chwanegwyd, yn gyntaf y disgybl a'i athraw, o newydd. Yn ail, Cyfarwyddyd i'r Cymru. Ac yn drydydd, Gwyddor uchod, &c. 2. argraphiad. Wedi ei ddiwigio yn oflaus gan Ifan Tomas, argraphydd. Muythic, W. Williams, 1765.

By Morgan Llwyd.

NL 0429551 MH

---

953 L794 bea [Llwyd, Richard] 1752-1835.
Beaumaris Bay, a poem. With notes, descriptive and explanatory ... With an appendix containing an account of the Battle Beaumaris in 1648, and the taking of the castle. London, Printed by J. Fletcher [1800]
58 p.

First edition.

NL 0429552 CU MWelC

---

*EC8 L7798 804g Llwyd, Richard, 1752-1835.
Gayton wake, or Mary Dod; and her list of merits. A poem in four parts. By Richard Llwyd ...
Chester: Printed by J. Fletcher; and sold in London by E. Williams, no. 11, Strand, bookseller to the Duke and Duchess of York, and bookseller of Wales. 1804.
xxiii, [1], 62p. 17cm., in case 18cm.
Original half rose paper (backstrip wanting) & blue boards; advt. (1l.) at end; in cloth case.

Inscribed: from the author with best respects to his friend J. Dovaston Junr. Esqr.
Also contains Dovaston's own inscription.

NL 0429554 MH CtY

DA715 .C3 Llwyd, Richard, 1752-1835, ed.
Caradog, *of Llancarvan.*
The history of Wales. Written originally in British by Caradoc of Llancarvan; tr. into English by Dr. Powell; augm. by W. Wynne ... rev. and cor., and a collection of topographical notices attached thereto, by Richard Llwyd ... Shrewsbury, Printed by J. Eddowes, 1832.

Llwyd, Richard, 1752-1835.
Poems. Tales, odes, sonnets, translations from the British &c. &c. In two volumes. By Richard Llwyd ... Chester, Printed by J. Fletcher; and sold in London by E. Williams, 1804.
viii, 210 p., 1 l. 18½cm.
"Volume II", p. [103]-210, has no t.-p.

25-25717

Library of Congress PR4890.L88P6 1804

NL 0429556 DLC MH WU PHi NjP

PR4935 .L54 1837 **Llwyd, Richard**, 1752-1835.
The poetical works of Richard Llwyd, the bard of Snowdon; comprising Beaumaris Bay and other poems: with a portrait and memoir of the author ... London, Whittaker [etc., 1837]
cxv, 300 p. front., port. 20cm.

NL 0429557 ICU MH ICN CtY NcU

Llwyfo, *pseud.*
see **Lewis, Lewis William**, 1831-1901.

Llwyfo, Llew
Gemau Llwyfo; sef, Detholion o brif gyfansoddiadau a chaneuon Llew Llwyfo. Utica, N.Y., T. J. Griffiths, 1868.
300p.

NL 0429559 OClW

Llwyfo, Llwynog
see Jones, Hugh, called Llwynog Llwyfo.

Llwyn onn. The ash grove. [Welsh air.] Arr. [for 1 voice, also] harmonized for 4 voices.
(In Thomas. Welsh Melodies. Vol. 1, pp. 1-9. London. [1862.])

April 11, 1902.
E3686 — T.r. (2d title) — Part songs. — Songs. With music.

NL 0429561 MB

Y LLWYNOG, pseud.

See EVANS, J. E. called Y Llwynog.

Llwynog Llwyfo
see Jones, Hugh, called Llwynog Llwyfo.

Llwynrhudol, bardic name

see

Roberts, Thomas, fl. 1840

Llyfnwy, Glan, pseud.
see Davies, W J

Llyfr ancr Llanddewifrefi

see

Book of the anchorite of Llandewivrevi.

Llyfr Blegywryd
see
Dimetian code.

Llyfr canu myfyrwyr Prifysgol Cymru. The University of Wales students' song book
see under Evans, David, 1874-1948, ed.

Bonaparte Collection No.7887 Y LLYFR ceiniog, i ddysgu silladu a darllen cymraeg.. Caernarvon [H. Humphreys, n.d.]
12p. 16cm.

Caption title.

NL 0429569 ICN

LLYFR COCH HERGEST.

See RED BOOK OF HERGEST.

Y llyfr cyntaf i blentyn
see The child's first book, in English & Welsh.

Llyfr dadleuon, at wasanaeth cyfarfodydd ysgolion, llenyddol, a dirwestol. Wrexham, Hughes [18-]
iv, 128 p.

NL 0429572 MH

Llyfr du o Caerfyrddin

see

Black book of Carmarthen

Llyfr gwasanaeth i ysgolion
see under [Gwynn Williams, William Sidney] 1896- comp.

Llyfr gweddi y Catholig...
see under [Challoner, Richard] bp. 1691-1781.

Llyfr gweddi, yn cynnwys yr offeren yn lladin a chymraeg
see under Catholic Church. Liturgy and ritual. Welsh.

Llyfr gwyn Rhydderch

see

White book of Roderick

Llyfr hymnau a thônau y Methodistiaid. Carnarvon, Llyfrfa y Cyfundeb, 1897.
512p.

NL 0429578 ICRL

Bonaparte Collection No.7889 LLYFR i ddechreu dysgu darllen. Caerfyrddin, W. Spurrell [ca. 1850]
31p. 10½cm.

NL 0429579 ICN

Llyfr Iorwerth
see
Venedotian code.

Llyfr nest. Gan awdwr Llyfr del.

see under

[Edwards, Sir Owen Morgan] 1858 - 1920

VOLUME 337

Llyfr Taliesin
see
Book of Taliesin.

Llyfr Teilo
see
Liber landavensis

Llyfr tonau cynnulleidfaol
see under [Roberts, John] 1822-1877, comp.

Llyfr y ddau dwyll
see under Williams, David Rhys.

Bonaparte Collection No.7890
LLYFR y dosparth cyntaf... Llundain,Gymdeithas undeb yr ysgolion Sabbothol[ca.1850]
cover-title,16p. 16cm.

Bonaparte Collection No.7891
—— —— Llundain,Gymdeithas unol yr ysgolion Sabbothol[n.d.]
cover-title,16p. 15cm.

NL 0429586 ICN

Llyfr y pedair dameg. [189-]
see under Williams, David Rhys.

Bonaparte Collection No.7893
LLYFR y trydydd dosparth. At ddarllen, sillebu, ac egwyddori. Llundain,Gymdeithas undeb yr ysgolion Sabbothol[ca.1850]
cover-title,32p. 16cm.

NL 0429588 ICN

Llyfr ymddiddanion a geir-lechres gyflawn Saesneg a Chymraeg ...
see How to learn Welsh.

Bonaparte Collection No.7892
LLYFR yr ail ddosparth. At darllen, sillebu, ac egwyddori. Llundain,Gymdeithas undeb yr ysgolion Sabbothol[ca.1850]
cover-title,16p. 16cm.

NL 0429590 ICN

Bonaparte Collection No.7894
LLYFR ysgol dwy geiniog, sef Arweinydd i'r anllythyrenog i ddysgu darllen gair Duw yn yr iaith gymreig Caernafron,H.Humphreys[n.d.]
24p. 16cm.

NL 0429591 ICN

Llyfrbryf, properly Isaac Foulkes
see Foulkes, Isaac, 1836-1904.

Llyfrgell Genedlaethol Cymru
see **Wales. National Library,** *Aberystwyth.*

Llŷn, William, 1534?-1580.
Barddoniaeth Wiliam Llŷn, a'i eirlyfr, gyda nodiadau gan y parch J. C. Morrice... Bangor: Jarvis & Foster, 1908. 5 p.l., ix-xlii p., 1 l., 331(1) p. 12°. (Wales. University. — Guild of Graduates. Reprints of Welsh prose works. Supplementary volume.)

1. Poetry (Welsh). 2. Morrice, James Cornelius, 1874- , editor. 3. Series.
N. Y. P. L. February 5, 1919.

NL 0429594 NN CU MH

891.661 L77b
Llyn, William, 1534-1580.
Barddoniaeth William Llyn a'i eirlyfr gyda nodiadau gan y Parch. J. C. Morrice. Bangor, 1908.
329p.

NL 0429595 IU

Llythyr... at y cymry...
see under [Davies, Richard] bp. of St. David's, 1501-1581.

Llythr oddiwrth Dafydd ab Ioan y pererin at Ioan ab Gwilim y prydydd ...
see under [Jones, David] 1735-1810.

Llythyr oddiwrth Gymmanfa Weinidogion yr Independiaid ...
see under Independent Methodist Churches.

Llythyr ynghylch y ddyledswydd o gateceisio plant a phobl anwybodus
see under [Jones, Griffith] 1683-1761.

Llyvyr coch o Hergest.
see
Red book of Hergest

Llyvyr du or Weun
see
Wales. National Library, *Aberystwyth. Mss. (Peniarth 29)*

Llyvyr gwyn Rhydderch
see
White book of Roderick

Llyvyr Teilo
see Liber landavensis.

Y 835 .L 805
LLYWARCH HEN, 496?-646?
Canu Llywarch Hen, gyda rhagymadrodd a nodiadau gan Ifor Williams. Caerdydd,Gwasg Prifysgol Cymru,1935.
xcii,266p.

"Byrfoddau": p.245-247.

NL 0429604 ICN IU MB PBm MH

PB 2273 .L6 C2 1953
Llywarch Hen, 542?-646?
Canu. Gyda rhagymadrodd a nodiadau gan Ifor Williams. 2. argraffiad. Caerdydd, Gwasg Prifysgol Cymru, 1953.
xcii, 266 p. 19 cm.
Bibliographical footnotes.

I. Williams, Ifor, 1881- ed.

NL 0429605 DCU CSt ICU MH

---

*EC8 So888 Zz792l
Llywarch Hen, 496?-646?
The heroic elegies and other pieces of Llywarç Hen, prince of the Cumbrian Britons: with a literal translation, by William Owen ...
London:Printed for J.Owen,no.168,Piccadilly, and E.Williams,Strand.MDCCXCII.
8°. lxxx,149p. 21.5cm.
This state differs from another in the setting of the t.-p.; in this state the bars above & below the epigraph are 27mm. apart.
Welsh & English on opposite pages.
Robert Southey's copy, with his autograph & bookplate.

NjP MdBP
NL 0429606 MH PPA NNC IU ICU CU OCl RPB MdBP CtY

Llywarch-Hen. 550-640.
—— Poésies. Paris, 1860. 8°. (La Villemarqué, T. C. H. H., *Vicomte* de, *Les bardes bretons.*) 2375

NL 0429607 MdBP

Llywarch Hen, 486?-646?
the time of Prince Cynddylan. Powys-land in A tr. of ... the Elegy of Llywarch Hen. 81 pp. (Powys-land Club, *Coll.* v. 1, p. 433; v. 2, p. 1.)

NL 0429608 MdBP

Llywarch Hen, 496?-646?
The saga of Llywarch the old; a reconstruction by Glyn Jones with the verse interludes translated by T. J. Morgan, and an introd. by Sir Ifor Williams. Colour engravings by D. Braby. [London] Golden Cockerel Press, 1955.
38 p. illus. 24 cm.
"Limited to 200 numbered copies ... copy number: 117."

I. Jones, Glyn, ed. II. Title.

PB2273.L6 1955 891.661 56-3858

NL 0429609 DLC WU MH ICN CU NN

Llywelyn, *pseud.*
On wings [poems] Brisbane, Victory Press [1944]
[16] p. 18 cm.
"Errata": p. [3] of cover.

I. Title.

A 49-2804*

New York. Public Libr. for Library of Congress [1]

NL 0429610 NN

LLYWELYN,Wilym.
Gweledydd y glyn,alegori yn ffurf nofel. Wyddgrug,argraphwyd gan yr Armonic,1909.

NL 0429611 MH

VOLUME 337

Llywelyn-Williams, Alun.
Cerddi, 1934–1942. Llundain, Gwasg Gymraeg Foyle, 1944.
39 p. 19 cm.

PB2298.L6C4 49-40641

NL 0429612 DLC

Llywythlan, Evan David.
Natural observations on a wonderful pamphlet. The subject inoculation: the author Dr. Watts. In a letter to that learned gentleman ... London,Printed for S.Bladon,1768.
2p.l.,35p. 21cm.

1. Watts, Giles. A vindication of the new method of inoculating for the small-pox. 2. Smallpox, Inoculation of.

NL 0429613 CtY-M

Lo, Arthur Wu-nien, 1916–
Stagger-tuned constant envelope-delay video I. F. amplifiers. Urbana, 1949.
3 p. 23 cm.
Abstract of thesis—University of Illinois.
Vita.
Bibliography: p. 3.

1. Amplifiers, Vacuum-tube. I. Title. II. Title: Video I. F. amplifiers.

TK6655.A5L6 A 53-3289 rev

Illinois. Univ. Library for Library of Congress [r67b2]†

NL 0429614 IU DLC NIC

Lo, Arthur Wu-nien, 1916–
Transistor electronics [by] Arthur W. Lo [and others] Englewood Cliffs [N. J.] Prentice-Hall, 1955.
521 p. illus. 22 cm. (Prentice-Hall electrical engineering series)

1. Transistors. I. Title.

TK7872.T73L6 *621.343 621.38 55—10875 ‡

OCU NcC MB TxU PHC
MtBC Or OrU OOxM OCl ICJ OClU PSt PPT OClW PV
PPF NcD PPD TxU CaBVaU CaBVa ICJ OrCS IdU OrSaW
CU-I MsU MiU KemT PCM PSC PBL NN IU ViU TU CU
NL 0429615 DLC MiHM WaTC WaSpG WaT WaS OKentU

Lo, Ch'ang-p'ei, 1899–1958.
廈門音系 羅常培著 北平 國立中央研究院歷史語言研究所 [ ] 民國19 [1930]
xiv, 278 p. 26 cm. (國立中央研究院歷史語言研究所單刊甲種之4 Academia Sinica. National Research Institute of History and Philology. Monograph A, no. 4)
Introduction in English, with added cover title: Phonetics and phonology of the Amoy dialect.
Includes bibliographical footnotes.
1. Chinese language — Dialects — Amoy. I. Title. (Series: Chung yang yen chiu yüan. Li shih yü yen yen chiu so. Nan-kang, Formosa. Chung yang yen chiu yüan li shih yü yen yen chiu so tan k'an, chia chung chih 4)
Title romanized: Hsia-mên yin hsi.

PL1701.L6 1930 C 67-2942

NL 0429616 DLC

Lo, Ch'ang-p'ei, 1899–1958.
Kuo nei shao shu min tsu yü yen wên tzŭ kai k'uang
see under Chung-kuo yü wên tsa chi shê, Peking.

Lo, Ch'ang-p'ei, 1899–1958.
國音字母演進史 羅常培著 [上海] 商務印書館 [1934]
5, 4, 80 p. 20 cm.

1. Chinese language—Phonetics. I. Title.
Title romanized: Kuo yin tzŭ mu yen chin shih.

PL1205.L6 1934 C 67-1954

NL 0429618 DLC CaBVaU

Lo, Ch'ang-p'ei, 1899–
臨川音系 羅常培著 何繼曾校 長沙 商務印書館 民國 29 [1940]
viii, 237 p. illus., tables. 27 cm. (國立中央研究院歷史語言研究所單刊甲種之 17. Academia Sinica, The Institute of History and Philology monographs, series A, no. 17)
Summary in English, with added t. p.: The phonetics and phonology of Lin-Ch'uan dialect.
1. Chinese language—Phonology. 2. Chinese language—Dialects—Lin-ch'uan. I. Title. (Series: Chung yang yen chiu yüan. Li shih yü yen yen chiu so, T'ai-pei. Chung yang yen chiu yüan Li shih yü yen yen chiu so tan k'an, chia chung chih 17)
Title romanized: Lin-ch'uan yin hsi.

PL1201.L65 1940 C64-139

NL 0429619 DLC

Lo, Ch'ang-p'ei, 1899–
北京俗曲百種摘韻 羅常培[編著 北京] 來薰閣書店 [1950]
2, 2, 4, 4, 73 p. (古今民間文藝叢書專刊之1)
Photo-offset. 1969. 18 cm.

1. Chinese language—Phonology. I. Title.
Title romanized: Pei-ching su ch'ü pai chung chai yün.

PL1201.L66 71-838115

NL 0429620 DLC CaBVaU WU

Lo, Ch'ang-p'ei, 1899–1958.

PL1281 .T25 1932 Orien China

Tai, Chên, 1724–1777.
(Tai Tung-yüan hsü fang yen shou kao)
戴東原續方言手稿 [2卷 戴震手寫 羅常培序 北平] 國立中央研究院歷史語言研究所景印 民國 21 [1932]

Lo, Ch'ang-p'ei, 1899–1958.
唐五代西北方音 羅常培著 上海 [國立中央研究院歷史語言研究所] 民國22 [1933]
xxiii, 224 p. 8 facsims. 28 cm. (國立中央研究院歷史語言研究所單刊甲種之12. Academia Sinica. National Research Institute of History and Philology. Monographs. Series A, no. 12)
Added cover title: The Northwestern dialeacts [sic] of Tarng and five dynasties, by Luo Charngpeir.
Bibliographical footnotes.
1. Chinese language—Dialects. 2. Chinese language—Hist. I. Title. (Series: Chung yang yen chiu yüan. Li shih yü yen yen chiu so, Nan-kang, Formosa. Chung yang yen chiu yüan li shih yü yen yen chiu so tan k'an. Chia chung chih 12)
Title romanized: T'ang Wu-tai hsi-pei fang yin.

PL1510.L6 C 67-3423

NL 0429622 DLC OrU OU KU CLU-C WaU

Lo, Ch'ang-p'ei, 1899-1958.
Tung hsi wên hua chi ch'i chê hsüeh
see under Liang, Shu-ming, 1893-

Lo, Ch'ao-p'ing, *ed.*
廣東地方名人錄 駱超平[等]主編 廣州 廣東新聞出版社 民國 37 [1948]
244 p. illus. 26 cm.

1. Kwangtung, China (Province)—Biog. I. Title.
Title romanized: Kuang-tung ti fang ming jên lu.

DS734.L6 C 60-2641 ‡

NL 0429624 DLC PU

Lo, Che Pei, 1906-
Experimentelle untersuchungen des laufreibungswiderstandes am infanteriegewehr. ... Jena, 1936.
20 p.
Inaug. Diss. - Berlin, 1936.
Lebenslauf.

NL 0429625 ICRL MiU CtY

Lo Che Tsi.
... La succession "ab intestat" dans le code civil chinois ... Toul, Impr. Touloise, 1932.
2 p.l., [7]-115, [1] p. 25 cm.
Thèse - Faculté de droit de Nancy.
"Bibliographie": p. [109]-111.
Errata slip mounted on inside front cover.

NL 0429626 CtY

Lo, Chên-ch'ang.
論孔教會書 [羅振常著 上海? 乙卯(1915)記]
9 double l. 21 cm.
Caption title.

1. Confucianism. I. Title.
Title romanized: Lun K'ung chiao hui shu.

BL1840.L6 C 67-2921

NL 0429627 DLC

Lo, Chen-chuan
Tung oil and international market, by Lo Chen-chuan and Kao Ping-shu. Pub. by Sino-international economic research center. New York, Orientalia [c1948]
63 p. map, tables. 23cm. (Sino-international economic publications, no. 6)

"Selected bibliography": p. 61-63.

1. Tung-oil. I. Kao, Ping-shu, jt. au. II. Title. III. Sino-international economic research center.

NL 0429628 NNC NRU

Lo, Chên-ying.
... Les formes et les méthodes historiques en Chine. Une famille d'historiens et son œuvre, par ... m^lle Lo Tchen-ying ... Paris, P. Geuthner, 1931.
3 p. l., 116 p., 2 l. 25½cm. (Université de Lyon. Bibliotheca franco-sinica lugdunensis. Études et documents publiés par l'Institut franco-chinois de Lyon, t. IX)
"Le Tshyen han chou est attribué généralement à Pan Kou, bien qu'en réalité ce monument historique ait été rédigé successivement par trois membres de la famille Pan [c'est-à-dire Pan Pyeou, Pan Kou et Pan Tchao]"—p. [27]
"Notice bibliographique": p. [103]–104.
1. Pan Ku, 32–92. Ch'ien Han shu. 2. Pan Chao, 1st cent. 3. Pan Piao, 3–54. 4. China—Hist.—Historiography. 5. Historians, Chinese. I. Title. II. Title: Une famille d'historiens et son œuvre.

36-2050
Library of Congress DS734.8.L6
[3] 951.007

NL 0429629 DLC CU NIC PU NN NjP

Lo, Chên-yü, 1866–1940.
經義考目錄 [8卷] 羅振玉錄 [長春? 1933]
8 v. (double leaves) in case. 21 cm.
Caption title.
Vol. 8: 經義考校記
Lithoprinted.

I. Chu, I-tsun, 1629–1709. Ching i k'ao. II. Title.
Title romanized: Ching i k'ao mu lu.

Z3102.C483 1933 C 68-3152

NL 0429630 DLC

Lo, Chên-yü, 1866–1940, *ed.*
高昌壁畫菁華 [羅振玉選編 羅福萇譯述 n. p. 丙辰 (1916) 序]
4 p., 22 plates (on double leaves) 42 cm.
Cover title.

1. Painting—Asia, Central. 2. Paintings, Asiatic. I. Lo, Fu-ch'ang. II. Title.
Title romanized: Kao-ch'ang pi hua ching hua.

ND991.L6 C 65-270

NL 0429631 DLC CtY NjP NIC

VOLUME 337

Lo, Chên-yü, 1866–1940.
本朝學術源流概略 羅振玉述 大連 中日文化協會 [1930]
4, 27 p. 26 cm.
Cover title.
CONTENTS.—古今學術之遞變—本朝學術源流概略

1. Learning and scholarship—China. I. Title.
Title romanized: Pên ch'ao hsüeh shu yüan liu kai lüeh.

AZ791.L6 C 68–1089

NL 0429632 DLC

Lo, Chên-yü, 1866–1940.
三代吉金文存 [20卷 羅振玉類次 n.p. 上虞羅氏百爵齋印 丙子(1936)序]
20 v. (double leaves) in 4 cases. 37 cm. (集古遺文第2)

1. Inscriptions, Chinese. I. Title.
Title romanized: San tai chi chin wên ts'un.

PL2448.L59 C 68–1993

NL 0429633 DLC NIC MoSW

Lo, Chên-yü, 1866–1940, *ed.*
增訂殷虛書契考釋 3卷 [羅振玉類釋 北京] 東方學會 丁卯 [1927]
2, 2, 24, 79, 66, 2 double l. 32 cm.
Lithoprinted.

1. Oracle bones. I. Title.
Title romanized: Tsêng ting Yin hsü shu ch'i k'ao shih.

PL2448.L62 C 64–873

NL 0429634 DLC

PL2457
.C5L6
Orien
China

Lo, Chên-yü, 1866–1940, *ed.*
增訂殷虛書契考釋 3卷 [羅振玉類釋 臺北 藝文印書館 195–]
350 p. 19 cm.
Caption and cover title: 殷虛書契考釋
Photo-offset from 東方學會丁卯(1927)版

1. Inscriptions, Chinese. I. Title. II. Title. Yin hsü shu ch'i k'ao shih.
Title romanized: Tsêng ting Yin hsü shu ch'i k'ao shih.

PL2457.C5L6 C 67–1094

NL 0429635 DLC

Lo, Chên-yü, 1866–1940, *ed.*
殷虛書契 [羅振玉類次 n.p. 壬子(1912)序]
4 v. (double leaves) in case. 34 cm. (集古遺文第1)
——— 後編 [n.p.] 丙辰 [1916]
2 v. (double leaves) in case. 35 cm. (集古遺文第1)
PL2448.L6 Suppl. 1
——— 續編 [n.p.] 癸酉 [1933]
6 v. (double leaves) in case. 34 cm. (集古遺文第1)
PL2448.L6 Suppl. 2
1. Inscriptions, Chinese. I. Title.
Title romanized: Yin hsü shu ch'i.

PL2448.L6 C62-852

NL 0429636 DLC

Lo, Chên-yü, 1866–1940, *ed.*
殷虛書契續編校記六卷 [羅振玉輯 曾毅公校 濟南] 齊魯大學國學研究所 [1936]
1 v. (various double leaves) illus. 28 cm. (齊魯大學國學研究所國學彙編之)
Includes bibliographies.

1. Inscriptions, Chinese. I. Tsêng, I-kung, ed. II. Title. (Series: Ch'i Lu ta hsüeh, Tsinan, China. Kuo hsüeh yen chiu so. Ch' Lu ta hsüeh kuo hsüeh yen chiu so kuo hsüeh hui pien)
Title romanized: Yin hsü shu ch'i hsü pien chiao chi.

PL2448.L615 C 65–566

NL 0429637 DLC

Lo, Chên-yü, 1866–1940, *ed.*
殷虛書契待問編 羅振玉錄 [n.p. 丙辰 (1916) 序]
2, 50 double l. 27 cm.
Caption title.
Running title: 殷問
Facsimile reproduction of ms. copy.

1. Oracle bones. I. Title.
Title romanized: Yin hsü shu ch'i tai wên pien.

PL2448.L63 C 64–651

NL 0429638 DLC NIC

Lo, Chêng-lieh.
Hsin min pao shê lun
see under title

Lo, Chêng-yao, joint author.
T'iao chien fan shê chi yao li
see under Wei, Lien-chi.

Lo, Chi-kang.
鋼筋混凝土設計圖解 (附公式) 駱繼綱編 上海 龍門聯合書局 1950.
261 p. illus. 22 cm.

1. Reinforced concrete. I. Title.
Title romanized: Kang chin hun ning t'u shê chi t'u chieh.

TA444.L57 C 62–1328 ‡

NL 0429641 DLC

Lo, Chia-lun, 1896- ed.
Ko ming wên hsien
see under title

Lo, Chia-lun, 1896- ed.
Kuo fu p'i tu mo chi
see under Sun, Yat-sen, 1866-1925.

Lo, Chia-lun, 1897–1969.
(Liu shih nien lai chih Chung-kuo kuo min tang yü Chung-kuo)
六十年來之中國國民黨與中國 羅家倫著 [台北] 中國國民黨中央委員會第四組黨史史料編纂委員會 民國 43 [1954]
66 p. illus. 21 cm.

1. Chung-kuo kuo min tang. I. Title.

JQ1519.A52L6 1954 C 59–1309

NL 0429644 DLC CaBVaU IaU WU

DS777
L795

Lo, Chia- Lun, 1897-
The pictorial biography of Dr. Sun Yat-sen [Taipei, Taiwan, Historical Archives Commission of the Kuomintang, 1955]
128 p. illus., ports. 26cm.

1. Sun, Yat-sen, 1866-1925. 2. China - Hist. - 1912-1937. I. Kuo min tang. Chung-yang tang-shih shih-liao pien-tsuan wei-yüan hui. II. Title.

NL 0429645 CSt-H InU MiU MH NNC WU WaU CU CtY

Lo, Chia-lun, 1897–1969.
(Su O ti chi pên kuo ts'ê)
蘇俄的基本國策 羅家倫著 [臺北 中央文物供應社 民國 42 i. e. 1953]
2, 32 p. 19 cm. (國際問題叢書)

1. Russia—Politics and government—1945– I. Title.

DK273.L58 C 60–2582

NL 0429646 DLC MiU

Lo, Ch'ieh.
中國革命中的武裝鬥爭 羅伽編寫 上海 華東人民出版社 1954.
76 p. 18 cm.

1. China—Hist.—1912–1949. I. Title.
Title romanized: Chung-kuo ko ming chung ti wu chuang tou chêng.

DS774.L59 C 64–192 ‡

NL 0429647 DLC KMK NIC

Lo, Chieh-ch'iu, ed.
Shan-tung hsien hsing ts'ai chêng fa kuei
see under Shantung, China. Laws, statutes etc.

Lo, Chih-ju.
(Chiao yü t'ung chi hsüeh kang yao)
教育統計學綱要 羅志儒[著] 北平 文化學社 1931.
4, 253, 8 p. illus. 21 cm.

1. Education—Statistics. I. Title.

LB2846.L6 76–841829

NL 0429649 DLC

Lo, Chih-ju.
生命表編製法 羅志如著 上海 商務印書館 民國 23 [1934]
ii, 128 p. 24 cm. (國立中央研究院社會科學研究所叢刊第2種)

1. Mortality. I. Title. (Series: Chung yang yen chiu yüan. Shê hui k'o hsüeh yen chiu so, Nanking. Kuo li chung yang yen chiu yüan shê hui k'o hsüeh yen chiu so ts'ung k'an, ti 2 chung)
Title romanized: Shêng ming piao pien chih fa.

HG8783.L6 C 66–1312

NL 0429650 DLC

Lo, Chih-yüan.
中國縣政制度 羅志淵著 上海 群衆雜誌公司 民國 26 [1937]
2, 2, 104 p. tables. 22 cm.

1. Local government—China. I. Title.
Title romanized: Chung-kuo hsien chêng chih tu.

C 58–7407

Hoover Institution for Library of Congress 4742 [2]

NL 0429651 CSt-H

Lo, Chih-yüan, ed.
Chung-kuo hsien fa shih lun
see under China. Constitution.

VOLUME 337

Lo, Chih-yüan.
中國憲法的理論體系 羅孟浩[志淵]著 臺北 中華文化出版事業委員會 民國44 [1955]
2 v. 19 cm. (現代國民基本知識叢書第1輯)

1. China—Constitutional law. I. Title.
Title romanized: Chung-kuo hsien fa ti li lun t'i hsi.

C 66-2095

NL 0429653 DLC OO CLU-C MiEM

Law

Lo, Chih-yüan.
憲法講義 羅志淵編 [臺北?] 東方科學函授學校 [195-]
82 p. 18 cm.

1. China—Constitutional law. 2. Constitutional law. I. Title.
Title romanized: Hsien fa chiang i.

C 61-2629 ‡

NL 0429654 DLC

Lo, Chih-yüan.
地方自治原理 羅孟浩[志淵]著 台北 中央文物供應社 民國43 [1954]
2, 4, 96 p. 19 cm. (三民主義叢書)

1. Local government. 2. Local government—China. I. Title.
Title romanized: Ti fang tzŭ chih yüan li.

C 58-7305 rev

Hoover Institution
for Library of Congress [r65b2]

NL 0429655 CSt-H CtY

Lo, Chin-ch'un.
大衆滑翔學 羅錦春著 [重慶] 正中書局 民國32 [1943]
5, 154 p. illus. 21 cm. (應用科學叢書)

1. Gliders (Aeronautics) I. Title.
Title romanized: Ta chung hua hsiang hsüeh.

TL760.L6 C 66-1416

NL 0429656 DLC

Lo, Ching, *fl.* 1712.
臥龍岡志 [2卷 羅景輯 羅鈉校 n. p. 康熙壬辰 (1712) 跋]
2 v. (double leaves) illus. 28 cm.
In case, as issued, with 張鵬翮 忠武誌 [n. p., 1712]
Block print.

1. Chu-ko, Liang, 181-234. I. Title.
Title romanized: Wo-lung-kang chih.

DS748.2.C52C35 1712 C 67-2879

NL 0429657 DLC

Lo, Ching Chang
see Chang, Lu-ching.

Lo, Ching-hua.
長夏的南洋 羅靖華著 上海 中華書局 民國23 [1934]
4, 2, 248 p. illus. 19 cm.
Colophon title.

I. Title.
Title romanized: Ch'ang hsia ti Nan-yang.

PL2783.O2C45 C 66-897

NL 0429659 DLC

Lo, Ch'ing-shêng.
Shou i hsüeh ta i
see under title

Lo, Ch'iung, *comp.*
婦女運動文献 羅瓊編 [佳木斯] 東北書店 1948.
2, 115 p. 19 cm.

1. Women in China (People's Republic of China, 1949-)
I. Title.
Title romanized: Fu nü yün tung wên hsien.

HQ1738.L6 C 67-1462

NL 0429661 DLC

Lo, Chi-yuan
see
Lo, Chih-yüan.

Lo, Chü-fen.

Arndt, Paul, 1870-
Der arbeitslohn in China, von prof. dr. Paul Arndt, dr. rer. pol. Djini Shen und dr. rer. pol. Chü-fen Lo. Leipzig, Hans Buske verlag, 1937.

Lo, Ch'uan-fang, 1903-
... The affective values of color combinations ... by Ch'uan-fang Lo ... [Ithaca, N. Y., 1936]
1 p. l., p. 617-624. 23cm.
Part of thesis (PH. D.)—University of Chicago, 1935.
"Private edition, distributed by the University of Chicago libraries, Chicago, Illinois."
"Reprinted from the American journal of psychology, October 1936, vol. XLVIII."

1. Color—Psychology. I. Title.

Library of Congress BF241.L6 1935 37-5131
Univ. of Chicago Libr.

NL 0429664 ICU NcD OCU DLC

Lo, Ch uan-hua
see
Lowe, Chuan-hua, 1902-

Lo, Chün, 1874-1932.
諸子學述 羅焌著 上海 商務 民國36 [1947]
5, 4, 348 p. tables. 18 cm.

1. Philosophy, Chinese. 2. Philosophers, Chinese. I. Title.
Title romanized: Chu tzŭ hsüeh shu.

C 58-7009

NL 0429666 CSt-H

Lo, Chün, 1902-
see
Shên, Ts'ung-wên, 1902-

Lo, Chung-ta.
入集中營始末記 羅仲達著 Batavia 民國34 [1945]
150 p. 19 cm.

1. World War, 1939-1945—Prisoners and prisons, Japanese. 2. World War, 1939-1945—Personal narratives, Chinese. 3. Chinese in Indonesia. I. Title.
Title romanized: Ju chi chung ying shih mo chi.

C 58-7487

Hoover Institution 2343
for Library of Congress [2]

NL 0429668 CSt-H NIC

Lo, Chung-yen.
中國國民經濟史 羅仲言著 [上海] 商務印書館 [民國36-37 i. e. 1947-48]
2 v. 21 cm. (大學叢書)
Vol. 2: 發行者 長沙 經濟新潮社

1. China—Economic conditions. I. Title.
Title romanized: Chung-kuo kuo min ching chi shih.

HC427.L58 72-839383

NL 0429669 DLC

Lo, Êrh-kang, 1903-
(Chung-wang Li Hsiu-ch'êng tzŭ chuan yüan kao chien chêng)
忠王李秀成自傳原稿箋證 羅爾綱著 [北京] 開明書店 [1951]
xv, 188 p. illus. 18 cm.
At head of title: 湘鄉曾氏藏
Includes bibliographical references.

1. Taiping Rebellion, 1850-1864. 2. Li, Hsiu-ch'êng, 1823-1864. Li Hsiu-ch'êng kung. I. Li, Hsiu-ch'êng, 1823-1864. Li Hsiu-ch'êng kung. 1951. II. Title.

DS759.L786 1951 71-841691

NL 0429670 DLC

Lo, Êrh-kang, 1903-
(Chung-wang Li Hsiu-ch'êng tzŭ chuan yüan kao chien chêng)
忠王李秀成自傳原稿箋證 羅爾綱著 [修正版 北京] 中華書局 [1954]
210 p. illus. 18 cm.
Includes bibliographical references.

1. Taiping Rebellion, 1850-1864. 2. Li, Hsiu-ch'êng, 1823-1864. Li Hsiu-ch'êng kung. I. Li, Hsiu-ch'êng, 1823-1864. Li Hsiu-ch'êng kung. 1954. II. Title.

DS759.L786 1954 C 62-1842

NL 0429671 DLC CaBVaU

Lo, Êrh-kang, 1903-
綠營兵志 羅爾綱著 重慶 商務印書館 民國34 [1945]
5, 326 p. 21 cm. (國立中央研究院社會[科學]研究所叢刊第16種)
Includes bibliographical references.

1. China—History, Military. I. Title. (Series: Chung yang yen chiu yüan. Shê hui k'o hsüeh yen chiu so, Nanking. Kuo li chung yang yen chiu yüan shê hui k'o hsüeh yen chiu so ts'ung k'an, ti 16 chung)
Title romanized: Lu ying ping chih.

DS754.L6 C 66-873

NL 0429672 DLC NjP NIC

Lo, Êrh-kang, 1903-
捻軍的運動戰 羅爾綱著 長沙 商務 民國28 [1939]
2, 2, 59 p. 19 cm.
Bibliographical footnotes.

1. Nien Rebellion, 1853-1868. I. Title.
Title romanized: Nien chün ti yün tung chan.

DS759.5.L6 C 59-5261

Washington. Univ., Seattle. Far Eastern Library
for Library of Congress [2]†

NL 0429673 WaU DLC CaBVaU WaU-FE

Lo, Êrh-kang, 1903-
太平天国史記載訂謬集 羅爾綱著 北京 生活讀書·新知三聯書店 1955.
170 p. tables. 21 cm. (太平天国史論文集第1集)

1. Taiping Rebellion, 1850-1864. I. Title.
Title romanized: T'ai p'ing t'ien kuo shih chi tsai ting miu chi.

DS759.L797 C 59-5233

Cornell Univ. Library
for Library of Congress [2]†

NL 0429674 NIC DLC IaU CaBVaU

VOLUME 337

Lo, Êrh-kang, 1903–
太平天国史綱 羅爾綱著 上海 商務印書館 民國 26 [1937]
134 p. illus. 23 cm.

1. Taiping Rebellion, 1850–1864. I. Title.
Title romanized: T'ai p'ing t'ien kuo shih kang.

DS759.L7977 C 62–844 ‡

NL 0429675 DLC

Lo, Êrh-kang, 1903–
太平天国史稿 羅爾綱著 [修改] 北京 中華書局 1955.
5, 1, 6, 393 p. illus., tables. 21 cm.
Includes bibliographical references.

1. Taiping Rebellion, 1850–1864. I. Title.
Title romanized: T'ai p'ing t'ien kuo shih kao.

DS759.L8 1955 C 60–5277
Cornell Univ. Library for Library of Congress [3]†

NL 0429676 NIC CaBVaU DLC IaU

Lo, Êrh-kang, 1903–
太平天国史料辨偽集 羅爾綱著 北京 生活讀書新知三聯書店 1955.
138 p. illus., facsims., tables. 21 cm. (太平天国史論文集第3集)
Bibliographical footnotes.

1. Taiping Rebellion, 1850–1864.
Title romanized: T'ai p'ing t'ien kuo shih liao pien wei chi.

DS759.L812 C 59–5381
Cornell Univ. Library for Library of Congress [3]†

NL 0429677 NIC DLC MiU CaBVaU

DS759
L812
Orien
China

Lo, Êrh-kang, 1903–
太平天国史論文集 羅爾綱著 北京 生活讀書新知三聯書店 1955–58.
7 v. illus., facsims., tables. 21 cm.
Bibliographical footnotes.
CONTENTS.—第1集 太平天国史記載訂謬集—第2集 太平天国史事考—第3集 太平天国史料辨僞集—第4集 天曆考及天曆與陰陽曆日對照表—第5集 太平天国史料考釋集—第6集 太平天国文物圖釋—第7集 太平天国史蹟調查集 (L. C. set incomplete: v. 5 wanting.)
1. Taiping Rebellion, 1850–1864. I. Title.
Title romanized: T'ai p'ing t'ien kuo shih lun wên chi.

DS759.L812 C 63–1613 rev
Harvard Univ. Chinese-Japanese Library 2875 for Library of Congress [r63b3]†

NL 0429678 MH-HY DLC

Lo, Êrh-kang, 1903–
太平天國史辨偽集 羅爾綱著 上海 商務印書館 1950.
3, 2, 264 p. tables. 21 cm.

1. Taiping Rebellion, 1850–1864. I. Title.
Title romanized: T'ai p'ing t'ien kuo shih pien wei chi.

C 59–5276
Cornell Univ. Library for Library of Congress [3]

NL 0429679 NIC CaBVaU

Lo, Êrh-kang, 1903–
太平天国史事考 羅爾綱著 北京 生活讀書新知三聯書店 1955.
359 p. 21 cm. (太平天国史論文集第2集)
Bibliographical footnotes.

1. Taiping Rebellion, 1850–1864. I. Title.
Title romanized: T'ai p'ing t'ien kuo shih shih k'ao.

DS759.L813 C 59–5372
Cornell Univ. Library for Library of Congress [3]†

NL 0429680 NIC DLC IaU CaBVaU

Lo, Êrh-kang, 1903–
天曆考及天曆與陰陽曆日對照表 羅爾綱著 北京 生活·讀書·新知三聯書店 1955.
207 p. facsims. 21 cm. (太平天国史論文集第4集)
Includes bibliographical references.

1. Taiping Rebellion, 1850–1864—Chronology. 2. Calendar, Taiping. I. Title.
Title romanized: T'ien li k'ao chi t'ien li yü yin yang li jih tui chao piao.

DS759.L82 C 58–5595

NL 0429681 DLC CLU-C IaU CaBVaU

Lo, Êrh-kang, 1903– *ed.*
天地會文獻錄 羅爾綱編著 九龍 實用書局 [1942 序]
2, 1, 98 p. illus. 21 cm.

1. Hung mên. I. Title.
Title romanized: T'ien ti hui wên hsien lu.

HS295.H8L6 1942 76–836307

NL 0429682 DLC RPB

Lo, Êrh-kang, 1903– *ed.*
天地會文獻錄 羅爾綱編著 灤泉校對 [重慶] 正中書局 民國 32 [1943]
2, 1, 98 p. illus. 21 cm. (史地叢刊)
Colophon title.

1. Secret societies—China. I. Title.
Title romanized: T'ien ti hui wên hsien lu.

HS294.L6 1943 C63-1159

NL 0429683 DLC CtY

Lo, Êrh-kang, 1903– *ed.*
天地會文獻錄 羅爾綱編著 灤泉校對 [上海] 正中書局 民國36 [1947]
2, 1, 98 p. illus. 21 cm.
Colophon title.

1. Hung mên. I. Title.
Title romanized: T'ien ti hui wên hsien lu.

HS295.H8L6 1947 C 63–1180
Harvard Univ. Chinese-Japanese Library 4181 for Library of Congress [r39b1]† rev

NL 0429684 MH-HY DLC WaU-FE MiU

Lo, Fang-chou, *ed.*
現代中國小品散文選 羅芳洲選註 上海 中國文化服務社 民國 26 [1937]
10, 7, 334 p. 19 cm. (文學基本叢書之 7)

1. Chinese essays—20th cent. (Selections, Extracts, etc.) I. Title.
Title romanized: Hsien tai Chung-kuo hsiao p'in san wên hsüan.

C 62–4346
Harvard Univ. Chinese-Japanese Library 5238.9 for Library of Congress [2]

NL 0429685 MH-HY

Lo, Fang-shêng.
宋瑛事件 駱芳盛著 香港 南風出版社 1952.
38 p. 18 cm.

1. Chung-kuo kung ch'an tang—Discipline. I. Title.
Title romanized: Sung Ying shih chien.

JQ1519.A5L59 C 62–1802 ‡

NL 0429686 DLC MH-HY WaU-FE

Lo, Fêng-ho.
實用統計數學 駱風和編 上海 商務 1953.
2 v. illus. 21 cm.

1. Mathematical statistics. I. Title.
Title romanized: Shih yung t'ung chi shu hsüeh.

QA276.L58 C 59–642 ‡

NL 0429687 DLC

Lo, Fu, 1909–1931
see
Hsü, Yin-fu, 1909–1931.

Lo, Fu-ch'ang.
Kao-ch'ang pi hua ching hua
see under Lo, Chen-yü, 1866-1940, ed.

Lo, Fu-i, 1905– *comp.*
遼文續拾二卷補遺彙目各一卷 [羅福頤錄 大連] 墨緣堂印 乙亥 [1935]
1 v. (various pagings; on double leaves) in case. 20 cm.
Lithoprinted.

1. China—Hist.—Liao dynasty, 907–1125—Sources. 2. Inscriptions, Chinese. I. Title.
Title romanized: Liao wên hsü shih.

DS749.5.L6 C 63-561
California. Univ. East Asiatic Library for Library of Congress [3]†

NL 0429690 CU-E DLC

Lo, Fu-kên.
獸醫昆蟲學 羅伏根編著 瀋陽 東北醫學圖書出版社 1952.
8, 524 p. illus., tables. 18 cm.

1. Entomology. 2. Insects, Injurious and beneficial. I. Title.
Title romanized: Shou i k'un ch'ung hsüeh.

QL463.L6 C 62–2504

NL 0429691 DLC

Lo, Guan-Tsai, 1906-
... Ueber akute Magenlähmung ... Berlin [1934]
Inaug.-Diss. - Berlin.
Lebenslauf.
"Literatur-Verzeichnis": p. 29-33.

NL 0429692 CtY

Lo, Hai-po, joint author.
Lin ch'uang hsi chün hsüeh chien yen fa
see under Kuo, Mao-fu.

Lo, Hai-po.
内科病細菌學診斷手册 羅海波 江德果 郭茂福合編 上海 上海文通書局 1953.
117 p. 15 cm.

1. Bacteriology. I. Title.
Title romanized: Nei k'o ping hsi chün hsüeh chên tuan shou ts'ê.

QR41.L63 C 58–5697 ‡

NL 0429694 DLC

VOLUME 337

Lo, Ho.
圖算原理 羅河著 上海 中國科學圖書儀器公司 1953.
170 p. illus. 26 cm.

1. Nomography (Mathematics) I. Title.
Title romanized: T'u suan yüan li.

QA90.L58 C 59-2615 ‡

NL 0429695 DLC

Lo, Hsiang-lin, 1905–
中國民族史 羅香林著 臺北 中華文化出版事業委員會 民國 42 [1953]
3, 7, 223 p. 19 cm. (現代國民基本知識叢書, 第1輯)
Bibliography: p. 222–223.

1. China—Civilization. I. Title.
Title romanized: Chung-kuo min tsu shih.

DS721.L68 C 66-2659

NL 0429696 DLC CLU-C MH-HY NRU

Lo, Hsiang-lin, 1905–
An introduction to the study of the Hakkas in its ethnic, historical, and cultural aspects. Hsingning, China, Shi-shan Library, 1933.
1, 4 p.: [316] p. 27 cm.
Added t. p. in Chinese.
Chinese text paged with Chinese numerals.

1. Hakas (Tribe)

DS432.H3L6 56-55835

NL 0429697 DLC

Lo, Hsiang-lin, 1905–
客家研究導論 羅香林著 興寧 希山書藏 1933.
12, 2, 4, 2, 292, 2, 4, 1 p. 2 fold. col. maps, tables. 27 cm. (客家研究叢書之一)
Preface in French, foreword and table of contents in English, with added t. p.: An introduction to the study of the Hakkas in its ethnic, historical, and cultural aspects.
Includes bibliographical references.
1. Hakkas.
Title romanized: K'o chia yen chiu tao lun.

DS731.H3L6 C 62-1887 rev

NL 0429698 DLC WaU-FE

Lo, Hsiang-lin, 1905–
(Kuo fu chia shih yüan liu k'ao)
國父家世源流考 [羅香林著 重慶 商務印書館 民國 32 i. e. 1943]
10, 5, 57 p. maps. 21 cm.
Bibliography: p. 53–55.

1. Sun, Yat-sen, 1866–1925—Family. I. Title.

DS777.L593 1943 72-835741

NL 0429699 DLC

Lo, Hsiang-lin, 1905–
(Kuo fu chia shih yüan liu k'ao)
國父家世源流考 [羅香林著 上海初版 重慶 商務印書館 民國 34 i. e. 1945]
9, 6, 57 p. maps. 21 cm.
Bibliography: p. 53–55.

1. Sun, Yat-sen, 1866–1925—Family. I. Title.

DS777.L593 1945 72-835742

NL 0429700 DLC

Lo, Hsiang-lin, 1905–
(Kuo fu chia shih yüan liu k'ao)
國父家世源流考 羅香林著 修訂臺灣一版 臺北 臺灣商務印書館 民國 43 [1954]
5, 9, 62 p. illus. 21 cm.
Colophon title.
Bibliography: p. 54–56.

1. Sun, Yat-sen, 1866–1925—Family. I. Title.

DS777.L593 1954 72-835634

NL 0429701 DLC

Lo, Hsiang-lin, 1905–
國父之大學時代 羅香林著 增訂版 [臺北] 臺灣商務印書館 民國 43 [1954]
4, 9, 124 p. illus., facsims. 21 cm.
Bibliography: p. 120–124.

1. Sun, Yat-sen, 1866–1925. I. Title.
Title romanized: Kuo fu chih ta hsüeh shih tai.

DS777.L595 C 66-183

NL 0429702 DLC OrU MeU MoSW CaBVaU

Lo, Hsiang-lin, 1905–
歷史之認識 羅香林著 [重慶] 獨立出版社 [1944]
2 v. 18 cm.
L. C. set incomplete: v. 2 wanting.

1. China—Hist—Addresses, essays, lectures. I. Title.
Title romanized: Li shih chih jên shih.

DS735.L7 1944 C 68-333

NL 0429703 DLC

Lo, Hsiang-lin, 1905–
歷史之認識 羅香林著 香港 亞洲出版社 民國 44 [1955]
231 p. 21 cm.

1. China—Hist.—Addresses, essays, lectures. I. Title.
Title romanized: Li shih chih jên shih.

DS735.L7 C 58-5295 ‡

NL 0429704 DLC

Lo, Hsiang-lin, 1905- ed.
Liu Yung-fu li shih ts'ao
see under Liu, Yung-fu, 1837-1917.

Lo, Hsiang-lin, 1905–
百越源流與文化 羅香林著 臺北 中華叢書委員會 民國 44 [1955]
312 p. 19 cm. (中華叢書)
CONTENTS.—越族源出於夏民族考—古代越族分佈考—古代越族文化考—古代越族方言考—海南島黎人源出越族考—蜑民源流考—南詔種屬考—狼兵狼田考—僰夷種屬考—附錄：馬來人與古代越族之關係
1. Ethnology—China—Kwangtung. I. Title.
Title romanized: Pai-yüeh yüan liu yü wên hua.

DS731.K85L6 C58-5186 ‡

NL 0429706 DLC CLSU CaBVaU ViU NhD MdU

Lo, Hsiang-lin, 1905–
蒲壽庚傳 羅香林著 臺北 中華文化出版事業委員會 民國 44 [1955]
[10], 162, 16, 6 p. illus., geneal. tables. 19 cm. (現代國民基本知識叢書第 3 輯)
Appendix (p. 1–16 (3d group)): 1. 元初出自西域系統之福州蒲氏考—2. 廣州蒲氏宋元二代祖墳發現記
Bibliography: p. 1–6 (4th group)
1. P'u, Shou-kêng, fl. 1245–1284.
Title romanized: P'u Shou-kêng chuan.

DS751.L6 C 59-5027

Indiana. Univ. Libr.
for Library of Congress [2]†

NL 0429707 InU DLC OrU CaBVaU IaU MdU WU CLU-O

Lo, Hsiang-lin, 1905–
唐代文化史 羅香林著 [台北] 商務 民國 44 [1955]
255 p. 22 cm.

1. China—Hist.—T'ang dynasty, 618–905. I. Title.
Title romanized: T'ang tai wên hua shih.

DS749.3.L6 C 58-5200 ‡

NL 0429708 DLC CaBVaU NIC ViU NhD

Lo, Hsiang-lin, 1905–
唐代文化史研究 羅香林著 [重慶 商務印書館 1944]
1, 166 p. 18 cm.
Includes bibliographical references.

1. China—Civilization—Hist. 2. China—Hist.—T'ang dynasty, 618–907. 3. East and West. I. Title.
Title romanized: T'ang tai wên hua shih yen chiu.

DS721.L695 1944 C 68-1978

NL 0429709 DLC

Lo, Hsiang-lin, 1905–
顏師古年譜 羅香林著 [上海] 商務印書館 [民國 30 i. e. 1941]
1, 69 p. 18 cm. (中國史學叢書)

1. Yen, Shih-ku, 581–645.
Title romanized: Yen Shih-ku nien p'u.

PL2677.Y4Z77 70-840029

NL 0429710 DLC CaBVaU

Lo, Hsiao-chien.
Cooking the Chinese way, by Kenneth Lo. New York, Arco Pub. Co. [1955]
154 p. illus. 19 cm.

1. Cookery, Chinese. I. Title.

TX725.L52 641.5951 55-12661 ‡

NL 0429711 DLC Or KMK WaS WaT

Lo, Hsin, *comp.*
民青兩黨內幕 羅欣編 大連 大衆書店 1948.
34 p. 18 cm.

1. Chung-kuo ch'ing nien tang. 2. Min shê tang. I. Title.
Title romanized: Min Ch'ing liang tang nei mu.

JQ1519.A55L6 C 68-362

NL 0429712 DLC

Lo, Hsü.
Buckling of thin-walled cylinder under axial compression and internal pressure, by Hsu Lo, Harold Crate and Edward B. Schwartz. Washington, U. S. Govt. Print. Off., 1951 [i. e. 1952]
ii, 9 p. illus. 30 cm. ([U. S.] National Advisory Committee for Aeronautics. Report 1027)
Cover title.
Bibliography: p. 9.
1. Buckling (Mechanics) 2. Cylinders. I. Title. (Series)
TL521.A33 no. 1027 620.11283 52-60811
——— Copy 2. TA492.C9L6

NL 0429713 DLC PP

Lo, Huai.
... La nouvelle législation chinoise; ses fondements—ses tendances. Préface de m. le baron Silvercruys ... Paris, A. Pedone, 1932.
2 p. l., iii, 189 p. 25½cm.
At head of title: Lo-Hoai ...
"Annexes" (p. [159]–185): Texte de la Constitution provisoire de la République chinoise du 1er juin 1931.—Texte de la Loi révisée sur l'organisation du gouvernement national de la République chinoise (26 décembre 1931)—Aperçu historique du droit pénal chinois.
"Bibliographie": p. [186]–187.
1. Law—China. I. China. Constitution. II. Title.

33-24757

Library of Congress [2] [347.0951] 349.51

NL 0429714 DLC CU-L CU CtY DS MH NNC MH-L NN

VOLUME 337

Lo, Huang, 1897–
The civil service system of China, by Korch Huang Lo. Taipei, China Cultural Service [1954?]
35 p. 22 cm.

1. Civil service—China. I. Title.

JQ1512.L6 55-41849 ‡

NL 0429715 DLC CU IEN IU ICU MH NIC NNC MH-L NcD CtY

Lo, Hung-chao.
唯物辯証法述評 羅鴻詔著 臺北 華國出版社 民國 41 [1952]
1, 62 p. 19 cm. (通俗哲學小叢書之 3)

1. Dialectical materialism. I. Title.
Title romanized: Wei wu pien chêng fa shu p'ing.

B809.8.L6 C 59-568

NL 0429716 DLC

GA1124
1555
.F8

Lo, Hung-hsien, 1504–1564. Kuang-yü-t'u.

Fuchs, Walter, 1902–
The "Mongol atlas" of China, by Chu Ssu-pen, and the Kuang-yü-t'u. With 48 facsimile maps dating from about 1555. Peiping, Fu Jen Univ., 1946.

Lo, Hung-k'ai, 1900–
文選學 駱鴻凱著 上海 中華書局 民國 26 [1937]
4, 2, 486 p. 23 cm. (大學用書)
附編 (p. 377–478) : 1. 文選分體研究舉例 論–2. 文選專家研究舉例 陸士衡
選學書箸錄: p. 479–486.

1. Hsiao, T'ung, 501–531 ed. Wên hsüan. 2. Lu, Chi, 261–303. I. Title.
Title romanized: Wên hsüan hsüeh.

PL2668.H7W46 1937 C 61-1826

NL 0429718 DLC

Lo, I-chün.
婚姻法新話 羅怡君著 修訂本 上海 勞動出版社 1951.
4, 61 p. 23 cm.
1950年5月1日中央人民政府頒佈

1. Marriage law—China (People's Republic of China, 1949–) I. China (People's Republic of China, 1949–) Laws, statutes, etc. Hun yin fa. II. Title.
Title romanized: Hun yin fa hsin hua.

C 67-970

NL 0429719 DLC ICU

HC427
L6

Lo, IUan'-tszėn.
Экономические преобразования в Китайской Народной Республике. [Ленинград] 1955.
225 p. illus. 22 cm.
At head of title: Ленинградский государственный университет имени А. А. Жданова.
Errata slip inserted.

1. China—Econ. condit. 1949– I. Title.
Title transliterated: Ėkonomicheskie preobrazovaniia v Kitaiskoi Narodnoi Respublike.

HC427.L6 56-18243

NL 0429720 DLC

Lo, Jui-ch'ing, 1906–
[K'ang Jih chün tui chung ti cheng chih kung tso]
抗日軍隊中的政治工作 羅瑞卿著 [n. p.] 中國出版社 1939.
3, 4, 217 p. 19 cm.

1. Sino-Japanese Conflict, 1937–1945. 2. China. Lu chün. Ti 8 lu chün—Political activity. I. Title.

DS777.53.L582 72-836551

NL 0429721 DLC

Lo, Jui-ch'ing, 1906–
Shan pei ti ch'ing nien hsüeh shêng shêng huo
see under title

Lo, Jui-ch'ing, 1906– joint author.
Yu chi tui chung ti chêng chih kung tso
see under T'ieh-jên, pseud.

V743
C5L79

Lo, K H C
Forgotten wave; stories and sketches from the Chinese seamen during the second World War, including the epic of Poo Lim, who sat alone on a raft and survived 133 days of the open Atlantic. Padiham, Eng., Padiham Advertiser, 1947.
116 p. illus. 18cm.

1. Seamen - China - Anecdotes, facetiae, satire, etc. I. Title.

NL 0429724 CSt-H NIC

Lo, K'ai-fu.
Climatic atlas of China proper, by David Kai-foo Loa. [n. p.] 1944.
[2] l., 3, 92 maps. 36 x 49 cm.
Scale of maps ca. 1: 14,400,000.
"Supplement to R–109."
Issued also as thesis, Clark University.

1. China—Climate—Maps.

G2306.C8L6 1944 Map 52-684

NL 0429725 DLC DNAL OCU OrU

Lo, Kang.
(San min chu i ti t'i hsi yü yüan li)
三民主義的體系與原理 羅剛著 [重慶] 東方出版社 [民國 32 i. e. 1943]
8, 6, 446 p. illus. 22 cm.
Includes bibliographical references.

1. Sun, Yat-sen, 1866–1925. San min chu i. I. Title.

DS777.A567L59 70-841724

NL 0429726 DLC

Lo, Kên-tsê, 1903–
中國古典文學論集 羅根澤編著 北京 五十年代出版社 1955.
119 p. 18 cm.

1. Chinese literature—Hist. & crit. I. Title.
Title romanized: Chung-kuo ku tien wên hsüeh lun chi.

PL2921.L6 C 58-6089 ‡

NL 0429727 DLC

Lo, Kên-tsê, 1903–
中國文學批評史 羅根澤著 北平 人文書店 [1934]
4, 12, 350 p. 19 cm.
CONTENTS.—周秦的文學批評—兩漢的文學批評—魏晉六朝的文學批評

1. Chinese literature—Hist. & crit. I. Title.
Title romanized: Chung-kuo wên hsüeh p'i p'ing shih.

PL2262.L58 C 68-567

NL 0429728 DLC

Lo, Kên-tsê, 1903–
中國文學批評史 羅根澤編著 [重慶] 商務印書館 [1943–45 (v. 1, 1944)]
4 v. in 1. 21 cm. (中央大學文學叢書)
CONTENTS.—第1分册 周秦兩漢文學批評史—第2分册 魏晉六朝文學批評史 第3分册 隋唐文學批評史—第4分册 晚唐五代文學批評史
——— Another issue. [上海 1947]
PL2262.L612

1. Chinese literature—Hist. & crit. I. Title. (Series: Chung yang ta hsüeh, Nanking. Chung yang ta hsüeh wên hsüeh ts'ung shu)
Title romanized: Chung-kuo wên hsüeh p'i p'ing shih.

PL2262.L6 C 68-1401

NL 0429729 DLC

Lo, Kên-tsê, 1903– ed.
Ku shih pien
see under title

Lo, Kên-tsê, 1903–
墨子 羅根澤 康光鑑編著 重慶 勝利出版社 文信書局總經售 民國 34 [1945]
4, 4, 202 p. 19 cm. (中國歷代名賢故事集 第3輯 學術先進)

1. Mo, Ti, fl. 400 B. C. I. K'ang, Kuang-chien, joint author. II. Title.
Title romanized: Mo-tzŭ.

B128.M8L59 C 67-1630

NL 0429731 DLC NIC

Lo, Kêng-mo.
中日經濟提攜 駱耕漠著 上海 黑白叢書社 民國 26 [1937]
2, 65 p. 17 cm. (黑白叢書之 2)

1. China—Foreign economic relations—Japan. 2. Japan—Foreign economic relations—China. I. Title.
Title romanized: Chung Jih ching chi t'i hsi.

HF3778.J3L6 C 66-1458

NL 0429732 DLC

Lo, Kêng-mo.
我國過渡時期商品生產的特點和價值法則的作用 駱耕漠著 北京 財政經濟出版社 1954.
56 p. 19 cm.

1. Price regulation—China (People's Republic of China, 1949–) I. Title.
Title romanized: Wo kuo kuo tu shih ch'i shang p'in shêng ch'an ti t'ê tien ho chia chih fa tsê ti tso yung.

HB236.C55L6 C 59-2049 ‡

NL 0429733 DLC

Lo, Kenneth H C
Cooking the Chinese way, by Kenneth Lo. New York, Arco Pub. Co. [1955]
154 p. illus. 19 cm.

1. Cookery, Chinese. I. Title.

TX724.5.C5L597 641.5951 55-12661 ‡

NL 0429734 DLC NcC PPD MB MiD WU PP OCl

Lo, K'o-tien.
中國農村經濟概論 羅克典著 上海 民智書局 民國23 [1934]
6, 8, 390 p. 19 cm. (中國農村問題叢書)

1. Agriculture—Economic aspects—China. I. Title.
Title romanized: Chung-kuo nung ts'un ching chi.

HD2067.L6 C 67-945

NL 0429735 DLC

VOLUME 337

Lo, K'o-t'ing, joint author.
Hsin chê hsüeh chiao ch'êng
see under Hou, Wai-lu.

Lo, K'o-t'ing.
思想起源與思想方法 羅克汀著 廣州 正大書店 1950.
63 p. 18 cm.

1. Thought and thinking. I. Title.
Title romanized: Ssŭ hsiang ch'i yüan yü ssŭ hsiang fang fa.

BF455.L6 C63-505 ‡

NL 0429737 DLC

Lo, Koangting, 1901-
... La peste au sud du Kouang-Toung ...
Paris, 1929.
Thèse - Univ. de Paris.
"Bibliographie": p. [79]-82.

NL 0429738 CtY

Lo, Korch Huang
see
Lo, Huang, 1897-

DS777 .53 .L583 Orien China

Lo, Ku.
印緬之征戰 羅古著 南京 讀者之友社 民國 34 [1945]
2, 6, 134 p. illus., fold. col. map. 18 cm.
Colophon title.

1. Sino-Japanese Conflict, 1937-1945—Campaigns—Burma. 2. World War, 1939-1945—Campaigns—Burma. I. Title.
Title romanized: Yin Mien chih chêng chan.

DS777.53.L583 77-836413

NL 0429740 DLC

PL 2690 .S3171 1926

«Lo, Kuan-chung» ca. 1330-ca. 1400, supposed author.
The Battle of Red Cliff; an episode of the Story of the Three Kingdoms, retold in English by Z. Q. Parker. Shanghai, Commercial Press, 1926.
xi, 87 p. 19 cm.

Translation of an extract from San-kuo chih yen i.

NL 0429741 OU

Lo, Kuan-chung, *ca.* 1330–*ca.* 1400, *supposed author.*
諸葛亮 羅貫中原著 王永生改寫 上海 少年兒童出版社 1954.
3 v. illus., fold. map. 19 cm.
L. C. set incomplete: v. 2 wanting.

1. Chu-ko, Liang, 181–234. I. Wang, Yung-shêng.
Title romanized: Chu-ko Liang.

DS748.2.L6 1954 C 64-250

NL 0429742 DLC

[**Lo, Kuan-chung**] *ca.* 1330–*ca.* 1400, *supposed author.*
Die drei reiche (San kwo tschi) Roman aus dem alten China. Übertragen und mit einem nachwort versehen von dr. Franz Kuhn. Berlin, G. Kiepenheuer verlag [°1940]
4 p. l., 546 p. illus. 19½ cm.
Title in Chinese on verso of half-title.

I. *Kuhn, Franz, 1889– tr. II. Title. III. Title: San kwo tschi.

A 43-928 rev

Harvard Univ. Library for Library of Congress [r59c2]

NL 0429743 MH

Lo, Kuan-chung, *ca.* 1330–*ca.* 1400, *supposed author.*
... De eed in de perzikgaarde; of, Hoe een sandalenmaker het tot keizer bracht, roman uit het oude China. Naar de duitsche versie van dr. Franz Kuhn voor Nederland bewerkt door C. C. S. Crone. Utrecht, A. W. Bruna & zoon, 1943.
394 p. illus. 23½ cm.
At head of title: Loh Kwan Tsjoeng.
"Oorspronkelijke titel: San Kwo Tsji (Die drei reiche-Gustav Kiepenheuer verlag, Berlin)"

I. Kuhn, Franz, 1889– II. Crone, C. C. S., 1914– tr. III. Title. IV. Title: Hoe een sandalenmaker het tot keizer bracht.

PL2997.L6S28 895.13 46-43355 rev

NL 0429744 DLC

[**Lo, Kuan-chung**] *ca.* 1330–*ca.* 1400, *supposed author.*
... The 43rd chapter of the three kingdom novel "The logomachy." With map, introduction, biographical index, vocabulary, etc. By John Steele, B. A. Shanghai, Printed at the Presbyterian mission press, 1905.
vi, 62 p. map. 25 cm.
Title also in Chinese; map and "radical index" on inside of front and back cover.
Text in Chinese with English notes.

I. Steele, John Clendinning, 1868– ed. II. Title: Three kingdom novel.

PL2690.S315 1905 6-15729 rev 2

NL 0429745 DLC CU

Asia Library
PL 2694 .L793 S111 K94

Lo, Kuan-chung, ca.1330-ca.1400.
空城計--三國演義裏的一個故事 .羅貫中原著 陳剛改寫 北京 通俗讀物出版社 1954.
16 p. illus. 18 cm. (語文補充讀物)
Cover title.
I.Ch'en, Kang. II.Title: San kuo yen i.
Title romanized: K'ung ch'êng chi.

NL 0429746 MiU

Lo, Kuan-chung, ca. 1330-ca. 1400, supposed author.
Lin Ch'ung
see under Shui hu chuan. Selections.

PL2692 .S5G45

Lo, Kuan-chung, ca. 1330-ca. 1400, supposed author.
[**Shui hu chuan**]
Die räuber vom Liang schan moor. Mit sechzig holzschnitten einer alten chinesischen ausgabe. Aus dem chinesischen übertragen von Franz Kuhn. Leipzig, Insel-verlag [1934]

PZ3 .S56255 Ro 2

Lo, Kuan-chung, ca. 1330-ca. 1400, supposed author.
FOR OTHER EDITIONS SEE MAIN ENTRY
Shui hu chuan.
Robbers and soldiers, by Albert Ehrenstein, translated from the German by Geoffrey Dunlop. New York, Knopf, 1929.

PL 2690 .S512

«Lo, Kuan-chung» ca. 1330-ca. 1400, supposed author.
San-Koué-Tchy; Ilan koureun-i pithé. Histoire des Trois Royaumes. Roman historique, traduit sur les textes chinois et mandchou de la Bibliothèque royale, par Théodore Pavie. Paris, B. Duprat, 1845-51.
2 v. 24 cm.

"Cette traduction n'a pas été terminée; elle comprend: vol. 1 ... les trois premiers livres; vol. 2 ... les Livres 4-7 du San kouo tche." - Bibliotheca sinica.

NL 0429751 OU

Lo, Kuan-chung, *ca.* 1330–*ca.* 1400, *supposed author.*
三顧茅廬 三國演義新編 羅貫中原著 柳湘吟改編 [香港] 崇文書社 1955.
107 p. illus. 19 cm.
Fiction.

I. Liu, Hsiang-yin, ed. II. Title.
Title romanized: San ku mao lu.

PL2690.S3155 1955 C 62-2693 ‡

NL 0429752 DLC

PL2658 .E8Y8

Lo Kuan-chung, ca. 1330-ca. 1400, supposed author. San kuo chih yen-i.
Yüan, Chia-hua, 1904– *ed.*
... Romance of the three kingdoms and A mission to heaven (selections) selected and annotated by Yuan & Shih. Shanghai, China, The Peisin book co., ltd., 1931.

[**Lo, Kuan-chung**] *13th cent., supposed author.*
San kuo, or Romance of the three kingdoms, by C. H. Brewitt-Taylor ... An English version ... Shanghai [etc.] Kelly & Walsh, limited, 1925.
2 v. front. (fold. map) 24½ cm.

I. Brewitt-Taylor, Charles Henry, 1857– tr. II. Title. III. Title: The three kingdoms, Romance of.

29-4470 Revised

Library of Congress PL2997.L6S3
——— Copy 2. [r40e2] 895.13

NN MB MnU ViU NcD CtY CU MiU OrPR WaWW OrP
NL 0429754 DLC MiU CSt-H GASU PU OU OO OCl WaU NjP

---

*
PL2997 .L6S3 1929

[Lo, Kuan-chung] 13th cent., supposed author.
San Kuo, or Romance of the three kingdoms. By C. H. Brewitt-Taylor ... Popular ed. Shanghai, Kelly & Walsh, 1929.
2 v. 24cm.

I. Brewitt-Taylor, Charles Henry, 1857– tr. II. Title. III. Title: The three kingdoms, Romance of. IV. Title: Romance of the three kingdoms.

NL 0429755 ViU CU NIC NNC CaBVaU NcU

Lo, Kuan-chung, *ca.* 1330–*ca.* 1400, *supposed author.*
三國演義 節本 [羅貫中著] 周振甫節編 北京 通俗文藝出版社 1955.
2 v. (1, 22, 4, 523 p.) 19 cm.

I. Chou, Chên-fu, ed. II. Title.
Title romanized: San-kuo yen i.

PL2690.S3 1955 C 59-5214 rev

Michigan. Univ. Libr. for Library of Congress [r62b2]†

NL 0429756 MiU DLC

Lo, Kuan-chung, *ca.* 1330–*ca.* 1400, *supposed author.*
三國演義 [120回] 羅貫中著 北京 作家出版社 1955.
7, 8, 990 p. fold. map. 21 cm.
Fiction.

I. Title.
Title romanized: San kuo yen i.

PL2690.S3 1955a C 62-2273

NL 0429757 DLC

PL2694 .S5J37 Orien Japan

Lo, Kuan-chung, ca. 1330-ca. 1400.
Shui hu chuan. *Japanese.*
(Shin'yaku Suikoden) 新譯水滸傳 佐藤春夫 [譯 東京] 中央公論社 [昭和 27- i. e. 1952-

VOLUME 337

Lo, Kuan-chung, ca. 1330-ca. 1400, supposed author.
Shui hu
see under Shui hu chuan.

Lo, Kuan-chung, ca. 1330-ca. 1400, supposed author.
Shui hu chuan
see under Shui hu chuan.

Lo, Kuan-chung, ca. 1330-ca. 1400.
Sin'gyo Syuhoji
see under Shui hu chuan.

D899.6L78
W1

[Lo Kuan-chung, 13th cent.]
Translation into English of "The logomachy"; being the 43rd chapter of the Three kingdom novel. With the Chinese commentator's introduction and notes, by John Steele. Shanghai, Presbyterian mission press, 1907.
20 p.

"The authorship of the Three kingdom novel is assigned to Lo Kuan-chung, of the Sung Dynasty, by Lin San-shan ..."

NL 0429762 NNC-EA CU CtY IU

PZ3
.S56255
Wat

Lo, Kuan-chung, ca. 1330-ca. 1400, supposed author.
[Shui hu chuan]
Water margin, written by Shih Nai-an; translated by J. H. Jackson, edited by Fang Lo-tien ... Shanghai, The Commercial press, limited, 1937.

Lo, Kuan-chung, *ca.* 1330–*ca.* 1400.
五代殘唐演義 [羅貫中編輯] 胡協寅校勘 上海 廣益書局 民國 36 [1947]
100 p. illus. 18 cm.
At head of title: 繡像仿宋完整本
Fiction.

I. Title.
Title romanized: Wu-tai ts'an T'ang yen i.

PL2690.T8 1947 C 62–2785 ‡

NL 0429764 DLC

Lo, Kuan-yün.
合作社經濟基本知識 駱冠雲 彭伊洛編著 廣州 華南人民出版社 1952.
76 p. 18 cm.

1. Cooperative societies—China (People's Republic of China, 1949-) I. P'êng, I-lo, joint author. II. Title.
Title romanized: Ho tso shê ching chi chi pên chih shih.

HD3534.L6 C 60–2678 ‡

NL 0429765 DLC MiU

Lo, Kuang
see
Lokuang, Stanislao.

Lo Kwai Kwok
see Kwok, Lo Kwai.

Lo, Kwan-chung
see
Lo, Kuan-chung, *ca.* 1330–*ca.* 1400.

Lo, Liang-nêng.
Kuo min ching chi shih yung tz'ŭ tien
see under title

Lo, Lo.
人與生活 羅洛著 上海 泥土社 1953.
168 p. 18 cm.

I. Title. *Title romanized:* Jên yü shêng huo.

PL3000.L6J4 C 58–5020 ‡

NL 0429770 DLC

Lo, Lung-chi, 1896–1965.
The conduct of parliamentary elections in England. New York, J. Lewin, 1928.
186 p. 23 cm.
Thesis—Columbia.
Vita.
Includes bibliographical references.

1. Gt. Brit. Parliament — Elections. 2. Election law — Gt. Brit. I. Title.

JN955.L6 29–4791
rev
Columbia Univ. Libr. for Library of Congress [r71c2]

NL 0429771 NNC GU-L DLC NIC PU PBm NcU MiU

Lo, *Sir* Man Kam.
Comments on the Report of the Committee on Chinese Law & Custom in Hong Kong. [Hong Kong, Govt. Printer, 1953]
18 p. 23 cm.

1. Hongkong. Committee on Chinese Law and Custom. Chinese law and custom in Hong Kong.

57–45672

NL 0429772 DLC NNC NIC IU MH-L NN NNC CU HU

Lo, Mêng-hao
see
Lo, Chih-yüan.

Lo, Mêng-ts'ê, 1907–
福利宣言 Declaration of the welfares of man. 羅夢册著 [香港?] 主流社 [九龍] 時代思潮研究所發行 1950.
1, 130 p. 21 cm.
In Chinese.

1. Welfare economics. 2. State, The. I. Title.
Title romanized: Fu li hsüan yen.

HB99.3.L6 C 67–3288

NL 0429774 DLC WaU-FE NIC

Lo, Meng-tze, 1907–
Declaration on human welfare. [Hongkong] Chu Lieu (Main Current) Society [1951]
156 p. 23 cm.

1. Social problems. I. Title.

HN18.L62 301.153 52–66289 rev ‡

NL 0429775 DLC PU CtY ICU NN MH

Lo, Meng-tze, 1907-
Hsien shih tai chih ssŭ hsiang lun chan
see under title

Lo, Ming, *fl.* 1949–
革命人生觀 羅明編 天津 知識書店 1949.
46 p. 17 cm.

1. Communist ethics. I. Title.
Title romanized: Ko ming jên shêng kuan.

C 58–7076

Hoover Institution for Library of Congress [r70b1½] rev

NL 0429777 CSt-H

Lo, Ming, *fl.* 1949–
共產主義人生觀 羅明編 天津 知識書店 1949.
78 p. 17 cm.

1. Communist ethics. I. Title.
Title romanized: Kung ch'an chu i jên shêng kuan.

C 58–7037

Hoover Library for Library of Congress [r70b1½] rev

NL 0429778 CSt-H

Lo, Mu-t'ao, *ed.*
國史大事表 羅慕陶 陳大經合編 香港 捷成印務局 民國 26 [1937]
28 p. 19 cm.
In colophon: Principal events in the history of China.

1. China—Hist.—Chronology. I. Ch'ên Ta-ching, joint ed. II. Title.
Title romanized: Kuo shih ta shih piao.

C 61–4338

Harvard Univ. Chinese-Japanese Library 2458 for Library of Congress [⅔]

NL 0429779 MH-HY IaU

Lo, Nien-an
see
Lo, Hung-hsien, 1504–1564.

Lo, Pên
see
Lo, Kuan-chung, *ca.* 1330–*ca.* 1400.

Lo, Pin-chi, 1917–
蕭紅小傳 駱賓基著 上海 建文書店 民國 36 [1947]
162 p. 19 cm.

1. Chang, Nai-ying, 1911-1942—Fiction.
Title romanized: Hsiao Hung hsiao chuan.
Name originally: Chang, P'u-chün.

PL2880.O3H8 C 62–181 ‡

NL 0429782 DLC NIC WU HU WaU-FE

Lo, Ren Yen
see
Lo, Yün-yen, 1890–

VOLUME 337

3781 Lo, Robert Kaitze.
S78L Development of a transient technique for determining the convective heat transfer characteristics for flow of a gas normal to circular tube banks. [Stanford, Calif.] 1951.
114, [3] l. illus., tables, diagrs.
Thesis (Engineer) - Dept. of Mechanical Engineering, Stanford University, 1951.
"References": l. [1-3] at end.
3.3 ___ ___ Another copy.
1. Heat - Transmission. 2. Heat exchangers.

NL 0429784 CSt

Lô, Roger.
... Contribution clinique et expérimentale à l'étude du labyrintho-traumatisme électrique ... Toulouse, 1935.
Thèse - Univ. de Toulouse.
"Bibliographie": p. [83]-86.

NL 0429785 CtY

Lo, Shan-chih, fl. 1897.
Hsing hsüeh chü yü
see under Martin, William Alexander Parsons, 1827-1916.

Lo, Shih.
農工小資產階級革命同盟論的分析和糾正 羅什著 [n. p.] 再造社 民國17 [1928]
40 p. 19 cm. (再造社叢書之1)
Cover title.

1. Dictatorship of the proletariat. I. Title.
Title romanized: Nung kung hsiao tzŭ ch'an chieh chi ko ming t'ung mêng lun.

HX389.L6 76-835500

NL 0429787 DLC

Lo, Shih-chun.
Oscillating airfoil in parallel streams separated by an interface. Pasadena, 1951.
96 l. diagrs. 29 cm.
Thesis—California Institute of Technology.
On cover: Guggenheim Aeronautical Laboratory, California Institute of Technology.
Bibliography: leaves 95–96.

1. Flutter (Aerodynamics) 2. Aerofoils. 3. Aeroplanes—Tail surfaces.
TL574.F6L57 629.13236 51-40322

NL 0429788 DLC

Lo, Shih-lin, 1774-1853.
Ch'ou jên chuan
see under Juan, Yüan, 1764-1849.

Lo, Shih-p'u.
中國青年與世界青年 羅石圃著 幼獅通信社編 臺北 民國44 [1955]
41 p. illus. 19 cm. (幼獅通訊叢書第9種)

1. Youth—China. I. Title.
Title romanized: Chung-kuo ch'ing nien yü shih chieh ch'ing nien.

HQ799.C55L6 C 59-5073

Hoover Institution for Library of Congress [2]†

NL 0429790 CSt-H DLC

Lo, Shih-shih, 1902–
現代資本主義透視 羅時實著 臺北 中華文化出版事業委員會 民國41 [1952]
1, 5, 144 p. 19 cm. (現代國民基本知識叢書[第1輯])
Bibliography: p. 143–144.

1. Capitalism. I. Title.
Title romanized: Hsien tai tzŭ pên chu i t'ou shih.

HB501.L8 C 66-2627

NL 0429791 DLC CLU-O InU

Lo, Shih-shih, 1902–
馬克斯主義之批判 羅時實著 台北 中央改造委員會文物供應社 民國40 [1951]
42 p. 19 cm.

1. Communism. 2. Dialectical materialism. I. Title.
Title romanized: Ma-k'o-ssŭ chu i chih p'i p'an

C 58-7285

Hoover Institution for Library of Congress [2]

NL 0429792 CSt-H

Lo, Shih-shih, 1902–
馬克斯主義及其批判 羅時實著 臺北 中華文化出版事業委員會 民國41 [1952]
2, 6, 178 p. 19 cm. (現代國民基本知識叢書[第1輯])
Bibliography: p. 177–178.

1. Marx, Karl, 1818–1883. I. Title.
Title romanized: Ma-k'o-ssŭ chu i chi ch'i p'i p'an.

HX39.5.L58 C 66-2531

NL 0429793 DLC CLU-O MnU WU

Lo, Shih-shih.
民生主義與現代經濟趨向 羅時實著 台北 中央文物供應社 民國43 [1954]
2, 2, 42 p. 19 cm. (三民主義叢書)

1. Sun, Yat-sen, 1866–1925. San min chu i. I. Title.
Title romanized: Min shêng chu i yü hsien tai ching chi ch'ü hsiang.

C 58-7482

Hoover Institution for Library of Congress 4738.185 [2]

NL 0429794 CSt-H HU

Lo, Shih-wei.
橡膠草 羅士葦 馮午 吳相鈺編著 北京 中國科學院 1951.
iv, 147 p. illus., col. plate. 22 cm.
Bibliography: p. 86–146.

1. Latex. I. Title.
Title romanised: Hsiang chiao ts'ao.

TS1890.L6 C 62-1676

NL 0429795 DLC

MANN
QK Lo, Shih-wei.
753 Studies on the development of root system
N7 of cultivated plants. I. The effects of
L79 different kinds of water and of nitrogen content in culture medium, by Shih-Wei Loo. [Peiping] 1936.
31 p. diagrs., tables. 25 cm.
Caption title.
Reprinted from the Chinese journal of experimental biology, 1936, v. 1, no. 1.
Bibliography: p. 30-31.

NL 0429796 NIC

Lo, Shih-yang, *comp.*
活躍的青年軍 羅時暘編著 [重慶] 青年出版社 [1945]
4, 2, 189 p. 19 cm. (乙種青年叢書第4輯)

1. China. Lu chün. Ch'ing nien chün. I. Title.
Title romanized: Huo yüeh ti ch'ing nien chün.

UA837.L6 73-838090

NL 0429797 DLC

Lo, Shih-yang.
遠征軍在前線 羅時暘編 南京 青年出版社 民國35 [1946]
314 p. 18 cm. (青年模範叢書第4輯)

1. World War, 1939–1945—Campaigns—Burma. I. Title.
Title romanized: Yüan chêng chün tsai ch'ien hsien.

D767.6.L6 C 63-2216

NL 0429798 DLC

Lo, Shu-tzŭ.
北朝石窟藝術 羅未子著 上海 上海出版公司 1955.
238 p. illus. 21 cm.

1. Sculpture—China. 2. Art, Buddhist. I. Title.
Title romanized: Pei-ch'ao shih k'u i shu.

NB1043.L58 C 58-5049 ‡

NL 0429799 DLC CaBVaU WaU-FE

Lo, T.Y.
see Leo, T.Y.

Lo, Ta-kang, comp.
Antología de cuentistas chinos, selección y prólogo de Lo Ta Kang. [Traducción directa del chino por Ma Cé Hwang (Marcela de Juan)] Buenos Aires, Espasa-Calpe Argentina, [1947]
147 p. 18 cm. (Colección austral, no. 787)

NL 0429801 OU

Lo, Ta-kang, tr.
Cent quatrains des T'ang. Tr. du chinois par Lo Ta-kang. Préf. de Stanislas Fumet. Avec dix reproductions de peinture ancienne du palais impérial de Pékin et en fac-similé une lettre de Louis Laloy. 2. éd. [Neuchâtel] Éditions de la Baconnière [1947] 236 p. facsim., plates. 21cm.

603683B. 1. Chinese literature—Poetry. 2. Quatrains, Chinese. 3. Paintings, Chinese. I. Title.

NL 0429802 NN ICU NIC NNC

Lo, Ta-kang.
... La double inspiration du poète Po Kiu-yi (772–846) ... par Lo Ta-kang ... Paris, P. Bossuet, 1939.
2 p. l., [7]–156, [4] p. 22cm.
Thèse—Univ. de Paris.
"Bibliographie": p. [149]–151.

1. Po, Chü-i, 772–846. I. Title. 42-40952

Library of Congress PL2997.P7L6

NL 0429803 DLC MH CtY

VOLUME 337

PL 2827 .L78 Lo,Ta-kang.
Homme d'abord,poète ensuite; présentation de sept poètes chinois. Avec sept ports.anciens. Neuchâtel, La Baconnière ⌊1948,^c1949⌋
283 p. mounted ports. 22 cm.
Includes selections from the poets,in French translation.

1.Poets,Chinese. 2.Chinese poetry--Hist.& crit. I.Title.

NL 0429804 MiU ICU CU DLC-P4 NIC

Lo, Ta-kang, *comp.*
Der magische Spiegel; chinesische Märchen und Novellen aus den Zeiten der Blüte. Deutsche Fassung nach der französischen Übertragung durch Lo Ta-kang von Richard B. Matzig. Bern, A. Francke ⌊1944⌋
254 p. illus. 20 cm.
Added t. p. in Chinese.
French version has title: Le miroir antique.

1. Tales, Chinese. 2. Fairy tales. I. Matzig, Richard Blasius, 1904– tr. II. Title.

A 49-4792*

Harvard Univ. Library for Library of Congress ⌊1⌋

NL 0429805 MH OCl

398.2 L795mXF Lo,Ta-Kang comp.
Le miroir antique; contes et nouvelles chinois des hautes epoques. Traduction de Lo Ta-kang. Neuchatel, La Baconniere ⌊1943⌋
281p. illus. 22cm.

1. Tales, Chinese. 2. Fairy tales. I. Title.

NL 0429806 IEN NIC OrU

Lo, Tchen-ying
see
Lo, Chên-ying.

LO,Tek Hing.
A compilation of zoological and botanical terminologies,including a list of terminologies used in minerology. Shanghai,1935.
pp.ii,370. 8°.

NL 0429808 MH-A

Lo, Têng-i.
穀類化學 羅登義著 上海 中華書局 1951.
75 p. illus. 19 cm. (農業生物化學叢書)

1. Food—Analysis. 2. Cereals. I. Title.
Title romanized: Ku lei hua hsüeh.

TX545.L6 C 59-1 ‡
⌊2⌋

NL 0429809 DLC

Lo, Ting.
繼承法要論 羅鼎著 上海 大東書局 1946.
196 p. 22 cm. (法學叢書)

1. Inheritance and succession—China. I. Title.
Title romanized: Chi ch'êng fa yao lun.

C 61-2547 ‡

NL 0429810 DLC

Lo, Ting.
民法繼承論 羅鼎著 上海 上海法學編譯社 民國 22 ⌊1933⌋
10, 278 p. 21 cm. (法學叢書)
附錄 民法繼承編施行法 : p. 275-277.

1. Inheritance and succession—China. I. Title.
Title romanized: Min fa chi ch'êng lun.

C 62-80

NL 0429811 DLC CaBVaU

Lo, Ting, ed.
Min fa chi ch'êng shih yung.
FOR OTHER EDITIONS SEE MAIN ENTRY
China. *Laws, statutes, etc.*
民法繼承實用 羅鼎編著 謝冠生 王建今主編 上海 大東書局 民國 36 ⌊1947⌋

Lo, T'ing-kuang.
(Chiao hsüeh t'ung lun)
教學通論 羅廷光著 ⌊上海⌋ 中華書局 ⌊民國 29 i. e. 1940⌋
2, 6, 414 p. 23 cm. (大學用書)
Includes bibliographies.

1. Teaching. I. Title.

LB775.L6154 70-842164

NL 0429813 DLC

Lo, T'ing-kuang.
各國青年訓練述要 羅廷光著 重慶 商務印書館 民國 32 ⌊1943⌋
2, 209 p. 18 cm.

1. Youth movement. I. Title.
Title romanized: Ko kuo ch'ing nien hsün lien shu yao.

HQ799.C55L63 C 64-1717

NL 0429814 DLC

Lo, T'ing-kuang.
師範教育 羅廷光編著 ⌊上海⌋ 正中書局 民國 36 ⌊1947⌋
2, 267, 38, 10 p. 21 cm. (大學用書)
Colophon title.
Bibliography: p. 1-10 (4th group)

1. Teachers, Training of. I. Title.
Title romanized: Shih fan chiao yü.

LB1715.L57 C 67-436

NL 0429815 DLC

Lo, Ts'un.
(Fêng shui hsin t'an) 風水新談 羅邨著 ⌊北京⌋ 生活·讀書·新知三聯書店 ⌊1950⌋
2, 89 p. illus. 16 cm. (新中國百科小叢書)

1. Feng-shui. 2. Geology. I. Title.

BF1779.F4L6 74-840160

NL 0429816 DLC WU

Lo, Ts'un.
石油 羅邨著 北京 生活·讀書·新知三聯書店 1950.
88 p. illus. 16 cm. (新中國百科小叢書)

1. Petroleum. I. Title. *Title romanized:* Shih yu.

TN870.L6 C 61-2022 ‡

NL 0429817 DLC

Lo, Tun-wei, 1897-1964, joint author.
Chung-kuo chia t'ing wên t'i.
I, Chün-tso, 1898–
中國家庭問題 易家鉞 ⌊君左⌋ 羅敦偉合著 上海 泰東圖書局 民國 18 ⌊1929⌋

Lo, Tun-wei, 1897-1964.
中國金融改造問題 羅敦偉著 臺北 中央文物供應社 民國 41 ⌊1952⌋
72 p. 18 cm.

1. Currency question—China. I. Title.
Title romanized: Chung-kuo chin yung kai tsao wên t'i.

HG1224.L6 C 63-79 ‡

NL 0429819 DLC CtY

Lo, Tun-wei, 1897–1964.
中國統制經濟論 羅敦偉著 上海 新生命書局 民國 24 ⌊1935⌋
3, 12, 12, 468 p. 22 cm. (中國社會問題研究會叢書第1種)

1. China — Economic policy. I. Title. (Series: Chung-kuo shê hui wên t'i yen chiu hui. Chung-kuo shê hui wên t'i yen chiu hui ts'ung shu, ti 1 chung)
Title romanized: Chung-kuo t'ung chih ching chi lun.

HC427.8.L6 C 67-1925

NL 0429820 DLC WaU-FE

Lo, Tun-wei, 1897–
三民主義與中國及世界 羅敦偉著述 上海 三民公司 民國16 ⌊1927⌋
47 p. 19 cm.
Cover title.

1. Sun, Yat-sen, 1866-1925. San min chu i. I. Title.
Title romanized: San min chu i yü Chung-kuo.

DS777.A567L6 C 67-1286

NL 0429821 DLC

Lo, Tun-wei, 1897–1964.
我們的社會 羅敦偉編著 ⌊上海⌋ 正中書局 ⌊1937⌋
6, 3, 4, 178 p. 19 cm. (中國青年叢書)

1. China—Soc. condit. I. Title.
Title romanized: Wo mên ti shê hui.

HN673.L6 C 68-2918

NL 0429822 DLC

Lo, Wan-sen.
Probleme der agrarkreditpolitik in China, von dr. rer. pol. Lo Wan-sen. Würzburg-Aumühle, K. Triltsch, 1941.
4 p. l., 142 p. incl. illus. (2 maps) tables. 2 diagr. 23^cm.
Issued also as inaugural dissertation, Berlin.
"Literaturverzeichnis": p. 138–140.

1. Agricultural credit—China. I. Title.

A 41-4772

Harvard univ. Library for Library of Congress HG2051.C6L6
⌊2⌋ 332.710951

NL 0429823 MH WU NIC NjP CtY NNC CaBVaU DLC

Lo, Wan-sên.
Problems of agricultural credit policy in China (Probleme der Agrarkreditpolitik in China) Translated from German into English by Francis J. Weiss. Wuerzburg, K. Triltsch, 1941.
3, v, 151 l. 27 cm.

1. Agricultural credit—China. I. Title.

HG2051.C6L613 57-57273

NL 0429824 DLC

VOLUME 337

Lo, Mme. Wei-djen (Djang)
Economic reconstruction in China under the national government, 1927-1934. [Nanking, 1935] 10p. 0.

Cover-title.

NL 0429825 NcU

Lo, Wên.
一顆紅心爲革命 駱文著 馬三和插圖 武漢 湖北人民出版社 1955.

76 p. illus. 19 cm.

Poems and songs.

I. Title.
Title romanized: I k'o hung hsin wei ko ming.

PL2880.O365I2 C 62-2410 ‡

NL 0429826 DLC HU

Lo, Wên-chin
see
Lo, *Sir* Man Kam.

AG17 .C58 Orien China

Lo, Wên-han.
Chung-hua pai k'o tz'ŭ tien.
中華百科辭典 舒新城主編 羅文漢[等]編輯 民國24年增訂 上海 中華書局 民國25 [1936]

Lo, Wên-hung.
湖上曲 駱文宏著 [重慶] 獨立出版社 [1941]

1, 134 p. 18 cm.

Play.

I. Title.
Title romanised: Hu shang ch'ü.

PL2783.O27H8 C 68-629

NL 0429829 DLC

Lo, Wên-kan, 1888–
Appeal from the Chinese Government. Communication from the Chinese Delegation. [Text of a speech on August 29th] Geneva, 1932.

7 l. 33 cm.

Caption title.
At head of title: League of Nations.
Official no.: A.(Extr.)139.1932.VII.
Concerning Japanese aggression in Manchuria and principles of Chinese policy.

1. China—Hist.—1912-1937. [1. China—Hist.—1931-1945] 2. Manchuria—Hist.[—1931-1945] 3. China—For. rel.—Japan. 4. Japan—For. rel.—China. I. League of Nations.

A 49-3494*

Woodrow Wilson Memorial Library
for Library of Congress [2]

NL 0429830 NNUN-W

Lo, Wên-kan, 1888-

China. *Wai chiao pu.*
Appeal from the Chinese Government. Communication from the Chinese Government ... Nanking, 1st February. Geneva, 1932.

Lo Wen Kan, 1888-
China's case, by Lo Wen Kan ... V.K. Ting ... Hu Shih ... K.L. Yen ... [London, Caledonian press.ltd., 1925]
7, [1] p. 24.5 cm.
Published by the Union of Chinese associations (in Great Britain).

NL 0429832 CtY NN

Lo, Wen Kang
see **Lo, Wên-kan,** 1888–

Lo, Wu-nien
see
Lo, Arthur Wu-nien, 1916–

Lo, Yiu Ming, 1909-
... Zur Frage der Beeinflussbarkeit der Insulinwirkung durch andere Inkrete ... Charlottenburg [1937]
Inaug.-Diss. - Berlin.
Lebenslauf.
"Literatur": p. [27]-30.

NL 0429835 CtY

DS748 .P22H8 Orien China

Lo, Yü, 1924- joint author.
Pan Ch'ao.
Huang, Wên-pi, 1894–
班超 黃文弼 羅郁編著 [重慶] 勝利出版社 [文信書局總經售 1945]

Lo, Yü-tung.
中國釐金史 羅玉東著 上海 商務印書館 民國25 [1936]

2 v. (15, 649 p.) 23 cm. (國立中央研究院社會科學研究所叢刊第6種)

1. Taxation—China—Hist. I. Title. (Series: Chung yang yen chiu yüan. Shê hui k'o hsüeh yen chiu so, Nanking. Kuo li chung yang yen chiu yüan shê hui k'o hsüeh yen chiu so ts'ung k'an, ti 6 chung)
Title romanized: Chung-kuo li chin shih.

HJ2975.L6 C 65-1552

NL 0429837 DLC

Lo, Yüan-chih, 1920–
Electromagnetic field of a dipole source above a grounded dielectric slab by Yuen Tze Lo. Urbana, 1952.

2 p. 23 cm.

Abstract of thesis—University of Illinois.
Vita.

1. Electric waves. 2. Dielectrics.

QC661.L8 A 53-3084 rev

Illinois. Univ. Library
for Library of Congress [r62b½]†

NL 0429838 IU DLC NIC

Lo, Yüan-k'un.
中國近百年史 羅元鯤著 上海 商務 民國23 [1934]

2 v. port., maps, tables. 19 cm.

1. China—Hist.—19th cent. 2. China—Hist.—1900– I. Title.
Title romanised: Chung-kuo chin pai nien shih.

DS757.L6 C 59-5087

Indiana. Univ. Libr.
for Library of Congress [½]†

NL 0429839 InU DLC CaBVaU

Lo, Yuen-tze
see
Lo, Yüan-chih, 1920–

Lo, Yün-p'ing.
城塞工程 羅雲平著 中華自然科學社主編 上海 商務印書館 民國35 [1946]

158 p. illus. 19 cm. (國防科學叢書)

1. Walls. I. Title. *Title romanized:* Ch'êng sai kung ch'êng.

TH2221.L6 C 61-741 ‡

NL 0429841 DLC

Lo, Yün-yen, 1890–
China's revolution from the inside, by R. Y. Lo. New York, Abingdon Press [1930]

307 p. 20 cm.

1. China—Soc. condit. 2. China—Hist.—1912-1937. I. Title.

DS774.L6 30-3784 rev*

IdPI WaT OrU OrP NIC
NL 0429842 DLC OU OCl NN MB PU NcD CU NcRS CoU

Lo, Yün-yen, 1890–
中國勞工立法 羅運炎著 昆明 中華書局 民國28 [1939]

238 p. illus. 19 cm.

1. Labor laws and legislation—China. I. Title.
Title romanized: Chung-kuo lao kung li fa.

C 62-1220 ‡

NL 0429843 DLC CaBVaU WU

Lo, Yün-yen, 1890–
羅運炎論道文選 上海 廣學會 民國20 [1931]

270 p. 18 cm.

Colophon title: 羅運炎論道集 Selected Christian essays.

1. Christianity—Addresses, essays, lectures.
Title romanized: Lo Yün-yen lun tao wên hsüan.

C 62-4300

Harvard Univ. Chinese-Japanese Library
for Library of Congress 1975 2

NL 0429844 MH-HY

Lo, Yün-yen, 1890–
The opium problem in the Far East (遠東鴉片問題) by R. Y. Lo. Shanghai, Commercial Press, 1933.

iv, 146 p. 23 cm.

Colophon in Chinese.

1. Opium trade—China. 2. Opium. I. Title. II. Title: Yüan-tung ya p'ien wên t'i.

HV5816.L6 178.8 A 34-750 rev*

Yale Univ. Library
for Library of Congress [r60c2]†

NL 0429845 CtY DLC NcU MB NN CU NBC WaU-L NIC

Lo, Yün-yen, 1890–
毒品問題 羅運炎著 上海 商務 民國25 [1936]

8, 248 p. 20 cm. (現代問題叢書)

1. Narcotics. 2. Narcotic laws—China. I. Title.
Title romanised: Tu p'in wên t'i.

C 58-7414

Hoover Institution 4231
for Library of Congress [2]

NL 0429846 CSt-H

Lo, Yung.
鴨池十講 羅庸著 [桂林] 開明書店 [1943]

2, 1, 114 p. 17 cm.

I. Title.
Title romanized: Ya ch'ih shih chiang.

PL2783.O28Y2 C 68-614

NL 0429847 DLC

VOLUME 337

Lo, Yung-p'ei.
喜馬拉雅山上雪 (劇本) 羅永培著 長沙 商務印書館 民國29 [1940]
6, 99 p. 17 cm.

I. Title. *Title romanized:* Hsi-ma-la-ya shan shang hsüeh.
C 60-5346
Harvard Univ. Chinese-Japanese Library 5719 for Library of Congress [1]

NL 0429848 MH-HY InU HU MiU

Lo Jacono, Jean, 1921-
Filed as Lojacono, Jean, 1921-

Lo-Johansson, Ivar, 1901-
Ålderdom. Bild: Sven **Järlås. Utg. av Veckotidningen, Vi.** [Stockholm, KF:s bokförlag [1949]
80 p. (chiefly illus.) 29 cm.

1. Old age homes—Sweden. 2. Old age. I. Järlås, Sven.
Full name: Karl Ivar Lo-Johansson.
HV1441.S85L6 50-26471

NL 0429850 DLC NN IU

Lo-Johansson, Ivar, 1901-
Ålderdoms-Sverige, en stridsskrift. Stockholm, Bonnier [1952]
181 p. 20 cm. (Bonniers folkbibliotek)
"Denna bok utgörs inledningsvis av texten i den 1949 publicerade 'Alderdom' ... samt i huvudsak av essäer i frågen skrivna 1950 och 1951."

1. Old age homes—Sweden. 2. Old age. I. Title.
Full name: Karl Ivar Lo-Johansson.
HV1441.S85L62 52-32620 ‡

NL 0429851 DLC CU ICU MnU NN

Lo-Johansson, Ivar, 1901-
Analfabeten; en berättelse från min ungdom. Stockholm, Bonnier [1951]
385 p. 20 cm.

I. Title.
Full name: Karl Ivar Lo-Johansson.
PT9875.L67A76 52-16985 ‡

NL 0429852 DLC WaS PU NcD MnU NN MH CoU

PT 9875 L83A53D 1952
Lo-Johansson, Ivar, 1901-
Analfabeten; en beretning fra min ungdom. [Oversat fra svensk af Hagmund Hansen. 2. opl.] København, Fremad, 1952.
281 p.

NL 0429853 CLU

Lo-Johansson, Ivar, 1901-
Bara em mor, roman av Ivar Lo-Johansson. Stockholm, A. Bonnier [1939]
615 p. 19½ᶜᵐ.

I. Title. 40-6973
Library of Congress PT9875.L67B3 1939
Copyright A—Foreign 44861 [2] 839.736

NL 0429854 DLC WaS NN MnU TxU

PT9875 .L7B2 1944
Lo-Johansson, Ivar, 1901-
Bara en mor (Rya-Rya) roman ... Stockholm, A. Bonnier [1944]
2 v.

NL 0429855 ICU

PT9875 L67B3 1948
Lo-Johansson, Ivar, 1901-
Bara en mor (Rya-Rya). Roman. Stockholm, A. Bonnier [1948]
2 v.

NL 0429856 CU MH

839.7374 L835B
Lo-Johansson, Ivar, 1901-
... Bara en mor (Rya-Rya); roman ... Stockholm, Bonniers [1950]
2 v. 19 cm. (His Romaner och noveller i folkupplaga)

NL 0429857 NcD KU NNC

PT 9875 .L67 B3
Lo-Johansson, Ivar, 1901-
Bara en mor. Stockholm, Folket i bilds förlag, 1954.
511 p. 20 cm.

NL 0429858 WU

PT 9875 L83G11D
Lo-Johansson, Ivar, 1901-
Bisekraemmeren; en selvbiografisk beretning. [Oversat fra svensk af Hagmund Hansen] København, Fremad, 1953.
244 p.

Translation of Gårdfarihandlaren.

NL 0429859 CLU

Lo-Johansson, Ivar, 1901-
Gårdfarihandlaren; självbiografisk berättelse. Stockholm, Bonnier [1953]
329 p. 20 cm.
A continuation of the author's Analfabeten.

I. Title.
Full name: Karl Ivar Lo-Johansson.
PT9875.L67G3 53-39261 ‡

NL 0429860 DLC MH NN OCl CU MnU

Lo-Johansson, Ivar, 1901-
Geniet, en roman om pubertet. Stockholm, A. Bonnier [1947]
668 p. 20 cm.

I. Title.
Full name: Karl Ivar Lo-Johansson.
PT9875.L67G4 48-23204*

NL 0429861 DLC NcU MnU NN

PT9875 .L67G4 1949
Lo-Johansson, Ivar, 1901-
Geniet, en roman om pubertet. [Stockholm] A. Bonnier [c1949]
510 p. 20cm.

NL 0429862 ViU PU ICU

PT 9875 L83G3
Lo-Johansson, Ivar, 1901-
Geniet; ein roman om pubertet. Stockholm, A. Bonniers förlag [1951-
v. 20cm. (His Romaner och noveller i folkupplaga)

NL 0429863 NIC KU NcD

LO-JOHANSSON, IVAR.
Godnatt, jord; roman av Ivar Lo-Jahansson. Femte upplagan. Stockholm: A. Bonnier[, 1934]. 587 p. 20cm.

712564A. 1. Fiction, Swedish. I. Title.

NL 0429864 NN MnU

PT9875 L67G6 1944
Lo-Johansson, Ivar, 1901-
Godnatt, jord; roman. Stockholm, A. Bonnier [1944]
2 v. in 1.

NL 0429865 CU NNC ICU WaS

839.7374 L835G0
Lo-Johansson, Ivar, 1901-
... Godnatt, jord; roman ... Stockholm, Bonniers [1950]
2 v. 19 cm. (His Romaner och noveller i folkupplaga)

NL 0429866 NcD KU

PT 9875 L83G5 1953
Lo-Johansson, Ivar, 1901-
Godnatt, Jord; roman. Stockholm, A. Bonnier, [1953]
2 v. (586 p.) 20cm. (Bonniers folkbibliotek)

De Bästa arbetarskildrarna, en BFB-serie.
"Denna upplaga av Ivar Lo-Johanssons "Godnatt, Jord" återger originalets text utan förkortningar och sammandrag."

NL 0429867 NIC ViU

Lo-Johansson, Ivar, 1901-
Jordproletärerna; berättelser av Ivar Lo-Johansson. Stockholm, A. Bonnier [1941] 340 p. 20cm.

NL 0429868 NN WaS MnU WaE

839.7374 L835J
Lo-Johansson, Ivar, 1901-
... Jord-proletärerna; berättelser. Stockholm, Bonniers [1950]
340 p. 19 cm. (His Romaner och noveller i folkupplaga)

NL 0429869 NcD MH

914.2 L83k
Lo-Johansson, Ivar, 1901-
Kolet i våld; skisser från de Engelska gruvarbetarnas värld. Stockholm, Wahlström & Widstrand [1928]
224 p.

1. England - Description and travel. I. Title.

NL 0429870 WaU MH NN

LO-JOHANSSON, IVAR, 1901-
Kungsgatan; roman av Ivar Lo-Johansson. Tredje upplagan Stockholm: A.Bonnier [1935] 636 p. 19½cm.

819744A. 1. Fiction, Swedish. I. Title.

NL 0429871 NN

Lo-Johansson, Ivar.
Kungsgatan, roman. Stockholm, Albert Bonniers forlag, [c1936].

NL 0429872 OCl

VOLUME 337

Lo-Johansson, Ivar, 1901-
Kungsgatan; roman. Stockholm, Bonnier [1943]
2 v. in 1. 19cm.

NL 0429873 WU MH MiU NNC PU CU NIC ICU

839.78
L835ku
tK78
Lo-Johansson, Ivar, 1901-
Kungsgatan; Roman einer Strasse. [Aus dem Schwedischen übertragen von Egon Kütting. 1.bis 10.Tausend] Hamburg, E.Tessloff [c1949]
533 p. 20 cm.

I.Kütting, Egon, tr. II.Title.

NL 0429874 MiU

839.7369
L83kl
1950
Lo-Johansson, Ivar, 1901-
Kungsgatan, roman. Stockholm, A. Bonnier [1950]
2v. in 1. 20cm. (His Romaner och noveller i folkupplaga)

NL 0429875 KU

839.7374
L835K
Lo-Johansson, Ivar, 1901-
... Kungsgatan. Stockholm, Bonnier [1955]
350 p. illus. 25 cm. (Bestsellers genom tiderna)

NL 0429876 NcD

Lo-Johansson, Ivar, 1901-
Måna är död; roman... Stockholm, A. Bonnier [1932]
320 p. 19cm.

NL 0429877 MnU

Lo-Johansson, Ivar, 1901-
Måna är död; roman. Stockholm, Bonnier [1942]
320 p. (Bokklubben Svalen)

NL 0429878 MH

PT
9875
L83M3
Lo-Johansson, Ivar
Måna är död, roman. 3. uppl. Stockholm, Folket i bild, 1944.
239 p. port. 19cm.

1st ed., 1932.

NL 0429879 CLU CU NNC

839.7374
L835M
Lo-Johansson, Ivar, 1901-
... Måna är död; roman. Stockholm, Bonniers [1950]
286 p. 19 cm. (His Romaner och noveller i folkupplaga)

NL 0429880 NcD MH

914
L836
Lo-Johansson, Ivar, 1901-
Mina städers ansikten. Stockholm, Wahlström & Widstrand [1930]
268 p. 20cm.

1. Europe. Description and travel. I. Title.

NL 0429881 MnU

Lo-Johansson, Ivar, 1901-
Monism, en sexualteori i "Geniet." Stockholm, A. Bonnier [1948]
150 p. 20 cm. (Idé och debatt)

1. Lo-Johansson, Ivar, 1901- Geniet. 2. Sex in literature. (Series)
Full name: Karl Ivar Lo-Johansson.

PT9875.L67G46 48-25495

NL 0429882 DLC MH MnU

Lo-Johansson, Ivar, 1901-
Nederstigen i dödsriket; fem veckor i Londons fattigvärld, av Ivar Lo-Johansson. Stockholm: Wahlström & Widstrand [, 1929]. 223 p. 12°.

444029A. 1. London—Descr., 1900-
N. Y. P. L. December 26, 1929

NL 0429883 NN MnU

PT9875
L67A15
1955
Scandinavian
Dept.
Lo-Johansson, Ivar, 1901-
Noveller, med inledning och stilistisk kommentar av Arne Häggqvist. Stockholm, Svenska bokforlaget [1955]
117 p. port. (Skönlitteratur i skolan)

NL 0429884 CU NNC

Lo-Johansson, Ivar, 1901-
Okänt Paris. Text: Ivar Lo-Johansson, bild: Tore Johnson. [Stockholm?] Rabén & Sjögren [1954]
95 p. illus. 26cm.

1. Paris—Soc. condit. I. Johnson, Tore.

NL 0429885 NN

Lo-Johansson, Ivar, 1901-
Stad och land; en statarnovell av Ivar Lo-Johansson, med träsnitt av Sven Erixson. [Stockholm, Are förlag, 1945]
80 p. illus. 37cm.

NL 0429886 MnU

Lo-Johansson, Ivar, 1901-
Statarklassen i Sverige. Stockholm, Bonnier [1939]
64 p.

NL 0429887 MH

PT9875
.L67
S82
Lo-Johansson, Ivar, 1901-
Statarklassen i Sverige. Stockholm, A. Bonnier [1941]
64p. (Studentföreningen verdandis småskrifter, nr. 412)

NL 0429888 NcU

Lo-Johansson, Ivar, 1901-
Statarliv, av Ivar Lo-Johansson. Stockholm, Folket i bilds förlag [1941]
252, [2] p. illus. (port.) 19½cm. [Folket i bilds folkböcker. 6]
"Andra upplagan. 41:a-69:e tusendet."
"Den föreliggande boken, Statarliv, är hämtad ur Statarna I-II."—p. [6]

I. Title.

Library of Congress PT9875.L67S78 48-19623
[2] 839.736

NL 0429889 DLC MnU

LO-JOHANSSON, IVAR, 1901-
Statarna, av Ivar Lo-Johansson. [Volym 1- Stockholm: A.Bonnier [1936- v. 19cm.

Collection of short stories.

1. Fiction, Swedish. I. Title.

NL 0429890 NN NcD KU OCl ICU CU DLC

Lo-Johansson, Ivar, 1901-
Statarna i bild. Text: Ivar Lo-Johansson; bild: Gunnar Lundh. Stockholm, KF:s bokförlag, 1948.
64 p. illus. 28 cm.

1. Agricultural laborers—Sweden. 2. Sweden—Descr. & trav.—Views. I. Lundh, Gunnar, illus. II. Title.
Full name: Karl Ivar Lo-Johansson.
A 49-4354*

New York Univ. Wash. Sq. Library HD1536.S5L6
for Library of Congress [1]

NL 0429891 NNU-W

Lo-Johansson, Ivar, 1901-
Statarnoveller: Statarna I-II och Jordproletärerna. Stockholm, A. Bonnier [1945]
592 p. 23 cm. (*His* Samtliga noveller, 1)

I. Title. II. Title: Statarna. III. Title: Jordproletärerna.
Full name: Karl Ivar Lo-Johansson.
A 48-4214*

Harvard Univ. Library
for Library of Congress [1]

NL 0429892 MH MnU NNC

PT
9875
L6
S85
MAIN
Lo-Johansson, Ivar, 1901-
Stidsskrifter. Stockholm, A. Bonnier [1946]
302p. 20cm.

NL 0429893 TxU

Lo-Johansson, Ivar, 1901-
Stockholmaren; självbiografisk berättelse. Stockholm, Bonnier [1954]
326 p. 20 cm.
A continuation of the author's Gårdfarihandlaren.

I. Title.
Full name: Karl Ivar Lo-Johansson.

PT9875.L67S83 55-17452 ‡

NL 0429894 DLC TxU NIC NcU NcD MnU NN ICU CU OCl MH

PT
9875
L83S86D
Lo-Johansson, Ivar, 1901-
Stockholmeren; en selvbiografisk beretning. [Oversat fra svensk af Hagmund Hansen] København, Fremad, 1954.
250 p.

NL 0429895 CLU

Lo-Johansson, Ivar, 1901-
Stridsskrifter. Stockholm, A. Bonnier [1946]
302 p. 20 cm.

I. Title.
PT9875.L6S85 47-7849*

NL 0429896 DLC MnU ICJ PU KU

PT
9875
L83T68D
Lo-Johansson, Ivar, 1901-
Traktoren. [Oversat af Hagmund Hansen] København, Fremad, 1944.
2 v.

Translation of Traktorn.

NL 0429897 CLU NcU

VOLUME 337

Lo-Johansson, Ivar, 1901–
Traktorn, roman av Ivar Lo-Johansson. Stockholm, A. Bonnier [1943]
574, [1] p. 19½cm.
"Femte tusendet."

I. Title.

46-12762
Library of Congress PT9875.L67T7
[2] 839.736

NL 0429898 DLC MnU WU

Lo-Johansson, Ivar, 1901–
Traktorn, roman. Stockholm, Lantbruksförbundets tidskriftsaktiebolag [1946]
592p. 18cm.

NL 0429899 KU

Lo-Johansson, Ivar, 1901–
839.7374
L835TR
... Traktorn; Roman ... Stockholm, Bonniers [1951]
2 v. 19 cm. (His Romaner och noveller i folkupplaga)

NL 0429900 NcD ICU KU

Lo-Johansson, Ivar, 1901–
Ungdomsnoveller: Ett lag historier—Tidiga noveller. Stockholm, A. Bonnier [1948]
259 p. 20 cm.

I. Title.
Full name: Karl Ivar Lo-Johansson.
PT9875.L67U5 839.736 A 49-6425*
Minnesota. Univ. Libr for Library of Congress [1]†

NL 0429901 MnU NN DLC

Lo-Johansson, Ivar, *1901–*
Ur klyvnadens tid; dikter, av Ivar Lo-Johansson. Stockholm: Wahlström & Widstrand[, 1931]. 99 p. 8°.

576339A. 1. Poetry, Swedish. I. Title.
N. Y. P. L. March 29, 1932

NL 0429902 NN MH WU

Lo-Johansson, Ivar, 1901–
Vagabondliv. Stockholm, Bonnier [1949]
500 p. 23 cm.
CONTENTS.—Vagabondliv i Frankrike.—Kolet i våld.—Nederstigen i dödsriket.—Zigenare.—Mina städers ansikten.

I. Title.
Full name: Karl Ivar Lo-Johansson
PT9875.L67V3 49-51759'

NL 0429903 DLC

Lo-Johansson, Ivar, *1901–*
Vagabondliv i Frankrike, av Ivar Lo-Johansson. Stockholm: Wahlström & Widstrand[, 1927]. 168 p. 12°.

1. France—Social life, 1927. 2. Labor—France, 1927. 3. Title.
N. Y. P. L. April 7, 1928

NL 0429904 NN MH

Lo-Johansson, Ivar, 1901–
Vagabondliv i Frankrike. Stockholm, Folket i bilds förlag [1950]
233 p. 20 cm. (FIB:s folkböcker, 82)

I. Title.
Full name: Karl Ivar Lo-Johansson.
PT9875.U67V32 52-15378

NL 0429905 DLC NN

Lo-Johansson, Ivar, 1901–
Zigenar-väg; text, Ivar Lo-Johansson; bild, Anna Riwkin-Brick. Stockholm, Rabén & Sjögren, 1955.
86 p. illus. 26 cm.

1. Gipsies. I. Brick, Anna Riwkin. II. Title.
A 55-6063
Newberry Library for Library of Congress [1]

NL 0429906 ICN MH NN

Lo-Johansson, Ivar, 1901–
Zigenare; en sommar på det hemlösa folkets vandringsstigar, av Ivar Lo-Johannsson. Stockholm: Wahlström & Widstrand [1929] 235 p. plates. 22½cm.

820052A. 1. Gipsies. I. Title.
N. Y. P. L. June 19, 1936

NL 0429907 NN

Lo-Johansson, Karl Ivar
see **Lo-Johansson, Ivar, 1901–**

Lo-Looz, Robert de, 1730–1786.
Les militaires au-delà du Gange, par m. de Lo-Looz ... Paris, Bailly, 1770.
2 v. fronts., fold. plans. 20cm.

1. Military art and science—Early works to 1800. 2. Siam—Hist. 3. Cochin China—Hist.
1-24292
Library of Congress U101.L6

NL 0429909 DLC ICU CLSU

Lo-Looz, Robert de, 1730-1786.
Les militaires au-dela du Gange. Paris, 1821.
2 vols.

NL 0429910 NWM

Lo-Looz, Robert de, *1730–1786.*
Recherches d'antiquités militaires, avec la défense du chevalier Follard, contre les allégations inserées dans les Memoires militaires sur les Grecs & sur les Romains, par M. de Lo-Looz, chevalier de l'ordre royal & militaire de Saint Louis. Avec figures ... Paris, Charles-Antoine Jombert, 1770.
xxiv, 226, [2] p. 8 fold. plans. 25cm.
"Avec approbation et privilege du roi."
1. Military art and science—History. 2. Fortification—History. [2. Fortification, Field—History] 3. Sieges. [3. Siege warfare—History] 4. Battles. 5. Caesar, C. Julius. [5. Caesar, Cajus Julius, B. C. 100-44] 6. Guischardt, Karl Gottlieb, called Quintus Icilius, 1724-1775. Mémoires militaires sur les Grecs & les Romains. [6. Mémoires militaires ... (by Guischardt)] 7. Folard, Jean Charles, 1669-1752. Commentaires sur Polybe. [7. Commentaires sur Polybe (by Folard)] 8. [Means and methods of war—History] I. Title.
War 18-44
Library, War College Div. General Staff U29.L83 (1770)

NL 0429911 DNW NIC MiU

U
012
.519
[LO-LOOZ, ROBERT DE] *1730–1786.*
Recherches sur l'art militaire; ou, Essai d'application de la fortification a la tactique. Paris, Chez Desaint, 1766.
232p. 20cm.
DLC: YA 1510

NL 0429912 ICN DLC

Lo-Looz, Robert de, *1730–1786.*
Recherches sur les influences solaires et lunaires, pour prouver le magnétisme universel, &c. Londres, Paris, chez Couturier, 1788.
4v. in 1. 7 plates.
pt.1. Recherches sur le systême du monde.- pt.2. Recherches physiques et métaphysiques sur les influences celestes, sur le magnétisme universel, et sur le magnétisme animal.- pt.3. Methode simple et facile de determiner les longitudes en mer, inventée par M. de Sornay.- pt.4. Deux spéculations fondées sur des anecdotes historiques.

NL 0429913 NNE MdAN

Lo-chieh-ssŭ, Fu-lan-hsi M.
see **Rogers, Francis Millet.**

Lo-ching-t'ai-êrh
see **Rozental', Mark Moiseevich.**

Lo-fêng.
(Jên cha) 人渣 洛風著 [九龍] 求實出版社 [1953]
2, 4, 162 p. 19 cm.
Fiction.
[人渣]在香港新晚報副刊…連載…原名[某公館散記] 又名[本宅管事]

I. Title.
PL2880.O375J4 77-840682

NL 0429916 DLC

Lo-fu, *pseud.*
see **Hsü, Yin-fu, 1909–1931.**

Lo-i, pseud., joint author.
DS778
.W38P3
Orien
China
Wei Li-huang yü Ch'en Ming-jên.
P'an, Chi-chiung.
衛立煌與陳明仁 潘際坰 洛翼著 香港 大公報 1955.

Lo-lan, Lo-man
see **Rolland, Romain, 1866–1944.**

Lo-sên-t'a-êrh
see **Rozental', Mark Moiseevich.**

Lo-ssŭ-chin
see **Roskin, Aleksandr Iosifovich.**

Lo-ssŭ-fu
see **Roosevelt, Franklin Delano,** *Pres. U. S.,* **1882–1945.**

Lo-ssŭ-fu, Hsi-ao-t'ê
see **Roosevelt, Theodore,** *Pres. U. S.,* **1858–1919.**

VOLUME 337

Lo-su
see
Russell, Bertrand Russell, *3d earl*, 1872-

DS753 .L6 Orien China
Lo-t'ien-chü-shih, *pseud.*, comp.
痛史 ［樂天居士編］ 商務印書館校訂 上海
商務印書館 辛亥－民國6 ［1911-17］
22 v. (double leaves) in 33. 20 cm.
Colophon title.
In 2 cases.
L. C. set incomplete: v. 21 wanting.
CONTENTS.—第1種 福王登極實錄 附過江七事金陵紀略—第2種 哭廟記略—第3種 丁酉北闈大獄記略—第4種 莊氏史案 附秋思草堂遺集—第5種 研堂見聞雜記—第6種 思文大紀 1-4.—第7種 弘光實錄鈔 1-2.—第8種 淮城紀事 附揚州變略京口變略—第9種 烈皇小識 1-2.—第10種 浙東紀略—第11種 嘉定縣乙酉紀事 第12種 江上孤忠錄—第13種 啓禎記聞錄 1-4.—第14種 海上見聞錄. 1-2.—第15種 蜀記—第16種 鹿樵紀聞 1-8.—第17種 隆武遺事—第18種 客滇述—第19種守鄖紀略 附大梁守城記—第20種 國變難臣鈔 附錄 8種—
第22種 湖西遺事 附虔臺逸史
1. China—Hist.—Ming dynasty, 1368-1644—Sources. I. Shang wu yin shu kuan. II. Title.
Title romanized: T'ung shih.
DS753.L6 C 67-1421

NL 0429926 DLC WaU-FE

Lo del 28 de abril
see under El Imparcial, San José, Costa Rica.

Lo dicho, dicho. Comprobación al Manifiesto sobre la inutilidad de los provinciales
see under [Rosillo de Mier Quatemoczin, Juan]

Pamphlet Mexico 1821 L781
Lo dicho, dicho; tambien los de peluca las toman. [Mexico?1821?]
Imperfect: All after p.8 wanting.
Relates to a pamphlet entitled: Respuesta á la Carta confidencial contra el papel titulado, No paga Iturbide con condenarse.

NL 0429929 CtY

Lo here and lo there! or, The grave of the heart ...
see under [Mendon, Dan]

Lo! here my love and Love in her eyes sits playing
see under [Händel, Georg Friedrich] 1685-1759.

Lo Hua t'u shu kung ssŭ. Pien chi pu.

PL2277 .T34 Orien China
(Tang tai Chung-kuo tso chia lun) 當代中國作家論
［編者 樂華編輯部］ 上海 樂華圖書公司 1933.

Lo-lang, a report on the excavation of Wang Hsü's tomb in the "Lo-lang" province, ...
see under Harada, Yoshita.

Lo-ma-ni-ya
see Romania.

Pamphlet Mexico 1821 L78
Lo muy necesario. [Puebla,1821]
Asks for the restoration of the Jesuits to their religious posts in Mexico.

NL 0429935 CtY

Lo que aporta la ciencia a las industrias manufactureras ...
see under [Little, Arthur Dehon] 1863-1935.

914.7 L795
Lo que cuatro obreros argentinos hemos visto y comprobado en la Unión Soviética [por] Vicente Marischi [et al. Buenos Aires] Edición del Movimiento Pro Democratización e Independencia de los Sindicatos [1952]
78 p. illus. 18 cm.

1. Russia--Descr. & trav.--1945- 2. Communism--Russia. 3. Communism--Argentine Republic.
I. Marischi, Vicente.

NL 0429937 ICarbS

Pamphlet Mexico 1831 L88
Lo que debe pensarse del actual gobierno. [Mexico, Imprenta de Galvan á cargo de Mariano Arévalo, 1831]
24 p.

NL 0429938 CtY

PQ7751 .L62
Lo que dicen las horas; composiciones premiadas en el concurso de colaboraciones celebrado por El Diario Español en ocasión del Día de la Raza, 12 octubre 1921. Con prólogo de Martín Dedeu. [Buenos Aires?, Talleres Peuser] 1921.
94p. 19cm.
On cover: Poesías 1921.
"Premios Casa Escasany."
1. Argentine poetry (Collections). I. Dedeu, Martín II. El Diario Español

NL 0429939 PSt

Lo Que Dios Hizo Conmigo.
Reimpresa ... Murguia y Comp., 1853, Mexico.
62 p.
Backer-Sommervogel IX, 1158.

NL 0429940 RPJCB

Lo que el franquismo quisiera que se olvide
see under Euzkadi (Government in exile) Delegación en Chile.

Lo que el pueblo debe exigir a sus candidatos a la presidencia de la República, a senadores y a diputados al Congreso de la Unión
see under [Rojas, Ambrosio]

[Lo que es la republica federal y organización política que conviene a España, según un español independiente. Madrid, Imp. de la viuda de Martinez, 1869.
32°. pp.48. Folded map.

NL 0429943 MH

Lo que es "Movimiento de conciliacion nacionalista", contenido: discurso del dr. Jose Capote Diaz, ... [Habana, "La Habanera", 1939.
32 p.

NL 0429944 OCl

D 639 P7 M63 LAC-Z
Lo que es preciso saber; la galantería alemana. México, Alianza Francesa, 1918.
8p. 18cm.

1. European War, 1914-1918 - Propaganda.

NL 0429945 TxU

DT619 G84
Lo que es y lo que podrá ser la Guinea Española. Barcelona, Tip. Claret [1931?]
xx, 124 p. illus., ports., maps. 22 cm.

1. Guinea, Spanish. 2. Missions - Guinea, Spanish.

NL 0429946 CtY

Lo que ha de ser
see under [Vega Carpio, Lope Félix de] 1562-1635.

LO que han hecho en Galicia; episodios del terror blanco en las provincias gallegas contados por quienes los han vivido. [La Habana, Cuba, Ed. Facetas, s.a., 1937?]
20 cm. Illustr.
The illustrations are by Alfonso Rodríguez Castelao, and were published in his "Galicia Mártir."

NL 0429948 MH CtY

Lo que han hecho en Galicia; episodios del terror blanco en las provincias gallegas contados por quienes los han vivido. [París: Editorial españa, 1938] 214 p. 19cm.
"Este libro se ha escrito con los relatos verbales, tomados taquigráficamente, seleccionados, confrontados y depurados, de varias personas solventes, conocidas y bien reputadas en Galicia, que han permanecido allí durante la dominación fascista."—*Prefatory note.*

994452A. 1. Spain—Hist.—Civil war, 1936-1939. 2. Galicia—Hist. 3. Fascism—Spain—Galicia.
N. Y. P. L. August 3, 1939

NL 0429949 NN MH IU CSt-H

Lo que he comido, por un gourmet. Prólogo de Benjamín Subercaseaux. [Santiago de Chile] 1946.
250 p. 19 cm.

1. Cookery, Chilean. I. Un gourmet.
TX725.L6 641.5 49-22601*

NL 0429950 DLC

Gxx 972.04 L78
Lo que nos importa a todos, que lo remedie el gobierno. [México, Imprenta americana de d. José María Betancourt, 1822]
8p. 19½cm.
Caption title.
Signed at end: P.V.

1. Mexico - Pol. & govt. - 1821-1861. I. P.V. II. V., P.

NL 0429951 TxU

VOLUME 337

Lo que nunca se habia visto en esta America. Dialogo. Pedro y Francisca. [Mexico, Impr. americana de D. J. M. Betancourt, 1822]
[4] p. 23.5 cm.
Caption title.

NL 0429952 CtY

... Lo que passa en un torno de monjas. [Madrid, A. Sanz, n. d.]
[24] p. 21cm.
Caption title.
No. 7 in a volume of plays with binder's title: Comedias españolas.
At head of title: Num. 1.
Attributed to the Count of Lemos and to King Philip IV. cf. Barrera y Leirado.

1. Felipe IV, king of Spain, 1605-1665, supposed author. II. Lemos, Pedro Fernández de Castro, conde de, 1576-1622, supposed author.

NL 0429953 MiU NIC

... Lo que passa en un torno de monjas. [Sevilla, 1731?] 23 p. 21cm.
Caption-title.
At head of title: Plieg. 3. Num. 45. Comedia famosa.
Has been attributed to Count Lemos, and to Philip IV of Spain.

233578B. 1. Drama, Spanish. I. Lemos, Pedro Fernández de Castro, marqués de Sarriá, conde de, ca. 1576 – ca. 1634, supposed au. II. Philip IV, king of Spain, 1605–1665, supposed au.
N. Y. P. L. March 10, 1944

NL 0429954 NN

Lo que puede el hambre, Saynete.
En Madrid: Quiroga. Año de 1792. 12 pp. 21½ cm.
No. 25 in **D.177.12.2

NL 0429955 MB CtY NN

... Lo que puede el hambre. Para quince personas. [In one act and in verse] Valencia, J. Ferrer de Orga, 1815.
11, (1) p. 8°.
Headline reads: Saynete nuevo.

NL 0429956 NN MB

Lo que puede la aprehension
See under
Moreto y Cavaña, Agustin, 1618-1669.

¡¡¡¡¡¡ Lo que puede un empleo!!!!!! Ya te conozco maula; pero a mi no me la pegas. Diálogo muy interesante, entre dos oajaqueños llamados Joaquin y Manuel, el uno residente en este ciudad, y el otro recien llegado de aquel estado. [Mexico, Impr. del Aguila, dirigida por J. Ximeno, 1828]
12 p. 20.5 cm.
Caption-title.

NL 0429958 CtY

... Lo que se canta en Costa Rica
see under [Segura Méndez, Manuel] 1895- ed.

...Lo que sé por mi, confesiones del siglo. Prologo de Don Benito Pérez Galdos, portada de Echea... Madrid, 1915-
v. 19cm.

NL 0429960 MdBJ

Lo que se sigue es vn pedaco de vna carta y relacion que escriuio cierto hombre
see under [Casas, Bartolomé de las, bp. of Chiapa] 1474-1566.

...Lo que se tiene y lo que se pierde. Comedia en un acto, traducida de el francés por D. Luis Olona... [Madrid: V. de Lalama, 1849.] 11 p. 4°. (Biblioteca dramática.)
Caption-title.

1. Drama (French). 2. Olona, Luis de, 1823-63, translator.
N. Y. P. L. December 13, 1920.

NL 0429962 NN CtY

fF1223 .33 C6 no.25 x
Lo que son los españoles. Mexico, Impreso por el ciudadano Ignacio Cumplido, 1832.
broadside. 21x30 cm. [Colección de papeles políticos de Iturbide, Santa Anna y otros, no. 25]

1. Spaniards in Mexico.

NL 0429963 CU-B

Lo que son mujeres
See under
Rojas Zorrilla, Francisco de, 1607-1648.

Lo que tú debes saber. Breve enciclopedia de cultura general. Barcelona, Editorial Labor [1952]
xv, 545 p. illus., ports., maps, diagrs. 22 cm. (Colección Libros de hoy)

1. Encyclopedias and dictionaries, Spanish.
AG61.L6 53-23832

NL 0429965 DLC

... Lo que vale ser devotos de San Antonio de Padua. De un ingenio de este corte. [In three acts and in verse] [Madrid, A. Sanz, 1751]
32 p. 4°.
n.t.-p.
Headline reads: Comedia famosa.

NL 0429966 NN

Lo que vimos y oimos en estos dias los mexicanos
see under [Bustamante, Carlos María de] 1774-1848, attributed author.

1888 "Lo! the cranes of Ibycus." [A poem, in eight stanzas. anon.] Albany, Dec. 20, 1869. [Albany, 1869]
1 l. 12°.
By L.
Note: - Relates to the last illness of Dr. Alden March.

NL 0429968 DLC

Lo! the gladsome day is breaking. (Air, March of the men of Harlech.) Harmonised for 4 voices.
(In The Chorallst. Vol. 1, series 4. London. [186-?])

NL 0429969 MB

"Lo-Vol" spraying
see under [Watkins, Ivon, ltd.]

Loa, David Kai-foo
see Lo, K'ai-fu.

Loa, Kai-foo
see Lo, K'ai-fu.

Loa y Camacho, Rafael Rojas
see
Rojas Loa y Camacho, Rafael.

Loa y Medina (Carlos). *Patogenia de la albuminuria. 52 pp. 16°. México, J. A. Bonilla, [n. d.].

NL 0429974 DNLM

Una loa colonial en honor de Carlos III (1761) ... Buenos Aires, "Coni", 1923.
cover-title, 19 p. illus. (facsim.) 23cm. [Buenos Aires. Instituto de literatura argentina. Sección de documentos. Publicaciones. t. I, nº 1]
At head of title: Facultad de filosofia y letras de la Universidad de Buenos Aires. Instituto de literatura argentina. Director: Ricardo Rojas.
Caption title: Loa que hizo en esta ciud de San Juan deVera delas Siete. Corrientes en las fiestas dela feliz exaltazon al trono del mui augusto y mui poderoso Señor Dn Carlos Terzero, rey delas Españas é Indias.
"Breve noticia" signed: R. R. [i. e. Ricardo Rojas]

I. Rojas, Ricardo, 1882- ed.
25-16066
Library of Congress PQ7797.A1L6

NL 0429975 DLC NcU CtY CU

Loa critica, y sucinta, en que se elogia muger, de qualquier estado, nombre, ó otra circunstancia, porque es comun para todas espheras de mugeres. Cordoba, n.d.

NL 0429976 NNH

*D.174 .28
Loa de la comedia de Monivych. [Barcelona? 1641?]
[7] p. 20cm.
Caption title.
Signatures: [ ]4.

1. Monjuich, Spain--Hist.--Drama. [2. Spanish drama--Classical period, 1500-1700--Examples.] I. Title: Monivych, Loa de la comedia de.

NL 0429977 MB

Loa de representacion, y musica, que de orden de la Imperial Ciudad de Toledo en su celebridad de la possession de su arzobispado por el Serenissimo Infante Cardenal D. Luis Antonio Jayme de Borbon... Se executo por su Compania de Farsantes... 13. de Febrero de 1736... [Toledo?]
[16]p. 19cm.

NL 0429978 IEN

Loa enque la heroyca y noble ciudad de Cadiz manifesta a S. M. el Rey por los felices esponsales. Cadiz, 1816.

NL 0429979 PPL

VOLUME 337

Loa entretenida, breve, y deleytable, con la metaphora de la Fabula de Leandro, y Ero, y con dicho affumpto fe alaba, y obfeguia à qualquier perfona que fe quiere. Cordoba, n.d.

NL 0429980 NNH

Loa famosa, que se le recito al Excellentisimo Señor marques de Villena, Duque de Efcalona, à la entrada del Arco Triunfal de la Cathedral de Mexico. n.p., n.d.

NL 0429981 NNH

B5130 Loa novissima para celebrar a noite, e dia do precursor de Jezu Christo o senhor S. Joaõ Baptista. Lisboa, Francisco Sabino dos Santos, 1773.
16p. 19cm.

1. John the Baptist. s/cI.pri: Sabino dos Santos, Francisco.

NL 0429982 KU

863L78
I
LOA para la comedia del Sueño del perro, tercera parte de Hazer quenta sin la huespeda, y al freir de los huevos, que representaron los trufaldines de las cobachuelas. Compuesta por vn ciego de la estafeta. Traducida en castellano, y portuguès, por vn armenio de la Puerta del Sol. Conferencia bolatil, y terrestre, para fin de este año de 1710. y principios del de 1711... ⌊Zaragoza? 1711?⌋
22 p. 19cm.

Paging irregular.
Caption title.
"Comedia nveva, El sveno del perro. Competencia de animales terrestres, y bolatiles.": p.9-22.
"Pieza satirica, escrita contra los partidarios del archiduque en la guerra de sucesion."- Barrera y Leirado. p.584.

I. Un ciego de la estafeta. II. Un armenio de la Puerta del Sol. III. Title: El sueño del perro. IV. Title: Hacer la qventa sin la huespeda ⌊tercera parte⌋

NL 0429985 MnU

Loa que al recebimiento del exmo. Senor Don Ambrosio o Higgins de Ballenar.
[Lima, 1796]
Bd with Valdivieso y Torrejon, Miguel de, Oracion panegirica...[1762] pam. 4.

NL 0429986 RPJCB

Loa, que debe representarse el martes 23. de febrero de 1802. En el drama intitulado: La mayor piedad de Leopoldo el Grande. Tercera funcion con que el teatro de esta M.N. y L. ciudad de Lima celebra el recebimiento del Exmo. Señor Don Gabriel de Avilés y del Fierro, marqués de Avilés ... Lima, Imprenta real Calle de Concha [1802?]
[8] p. 20 cm. [Coleccion de folletos. Tom. XXXVIII. Poesias americanas. Segunda parte. 1737 á 1844]

NL 0429987 CtY

Loa, qve dixo vn cabo de esquadra en aplauso de D. Ygnacio de la Portilla, capitán del Batallon de infantería del comercio, el dia 23. de mayo de 1763, en presencia del noble auditorio que asistió en casa de dicho señor. [n.p., 1763?]
[8] p. 20 cm.
Caption title.
"Demonstracion afectvosa qve haze un apacionado de D. Ygnacio de la Portilla en aplauso del lucimiento con que presentó su compañía el día 23. de mayo de 1763. años en estas": p. [5]-[8]

NL 0429988 CtY

Loa que se ha de representar, en obsequio del muy ilustre Señor, Don Joseph de Amat ... [Lima, 176-?]
[10] p. 20 cm. [Coleccion de folletos. Tom. XXXVIII. Poesias americanas. Segunda parte. 1737 á 1844]
Caption title.
In verse.

NL 0429989 CtY

Loa que se representa en el Real colicèo, el dia I. de enero de [1]778 en celebridad del cumplimiento de años del Exmo Señor Don Manuel Guirior, dignisimo virrey del Perù. [n.p., 1778?]
[4] p. 20 cm. [Coleccion de folletos. Tom. XXXVIII. Poesias americanas. Segunda parte. 1737 á 1844]
Caption title.
In verse.

NL 0429990 CtY

Loa que segun estilo se dixo al exc^{mo}. señor virrey al llegar al arco. ⌊*Colophon:* ⌊Mexico⌋ Con licencia en la imprenta de la Biblioteca mexicana, año de 1761⌋

Film copy, made in 1941, of the original in the Medina collection, Biblioteca nacional de Santiago de Chile. Positive.
Negative film in Brown university library.
Collation of the original, as determined from the film: ⌊4⌋ p.
Caption title.
Poem.
Medina, La imprenta en México, 4684.

1. Cruillas, Joaquín de Monserrat, marqués de, viceroy of Mexico, 1700–1771—Poetry.
A 44-5619
Brown univ. Library for Library of Congress Film AC-2 reel 37, no. 6

NL 0429991 RPB DLC

Loa, representada en el Teatro de Lima, la noche del 9 de diciembre, con motivo de inaugurarse la estatua ecuestre del Libertador en la Plazuela de la Inquisición. Lima, Tipografia de A. Alfaro y ca., 1859.
1 p.l., [5]-16 p. 20 cm.
In verse.

NL 0429992 CtY

Loa, representada...en la fiesta... a S. Diego.
n.p.n.d. 4to.

Huth copy

NL 0429993 MWiW-C

La loa restituida a su primitivo ser. Carta de un literato sevillano a un amigo suyo de otro pueblo, en que se demuestra el verdadero espiritu en esta ciudad contra las interpretaciones del literato no sevillano; se impugna sólidamente el teatro; y se descubren los errores que en su indicación ha esparcido el apologista. Sevilla, Impr. de los señores Hijos de Hidalgo, y Gonzalez de la Bonilla, 1796.
52p. 20½cm.
Signed at end: L.J.A.C.
1. Spanish drama - 18th cent. - Hist. & crit. I. L.J.A.C. II. C., L.J.A.

NL 0429994 TxU

Loaces, Fernando de, 1497-1568.
Perutilis e singularis questio, seu tractatus super noua paganorū vel a nova paganorum regni Valentie cōuersione ... Valentie, Janfredus, 1525.

NL 0430001 PU

Loaces, Fernando de, 1497–1568.
Solennis atq; elegans Tractatus Jn causa matrimonij...Henrici et Catherine Anglie Regum Editus per Reuerendum... Ferdinandum de loazes...Jn principatu Cathalonie...Jnquisitorem apostolicum. ⌊Barchine: In officina Caroli Amorosii typis excussus, 1531⌋ lxxix f., 17 l. 29½cm. (f°.)

Brunet, III, 1133. Lowndes, p. 1378. Gallardo 2703.
Title within historiated border; coat of arms at head of title.
With colophon.

Dedicated to Charles V.
"Index," l. 2-16 at end.
Last leaf (blank?) wanting.

370808. 1. Henry VIII, king of England, 1491-1547. 2. Catharine of Aragon, queen consort of Henry VIII, 1485-1536.
N. Y. P. L. *Card revised* October 15, 1941

NL 0430003 NN

Loach, R J H de
see De Loach, Robert John Henderson, 1873-

Load; ideas and information for power sales engineers. v. 1- Apr. 1945-
⌊Schenectady, N. Y., General Electric⌋
v. in illus., ports. 29 cm. bimonthly.

1. Electric utilities—U. S.—Period. I. General Electric Company.
HD9685.U4L6 56-17590

NL 0430005 DLC InLP

Load lines-convention and final protocol between the U.S. of America and other powers
see under International load line conference, London, 1930.

A load of fun. [1884]
see under Tousey, Sinclair, comp.

Loader, Catharine M
Cairngorm adventure at Glenmore Lodge, Scottish Centre of Outdoor Training, written and illus. by Catharine M. Loader. Edinburgh, W. Brown, 1952.
53 p. illus. 25 cm.

1. Scottish Centre of Outdoor Training. 2. Outdoor life. I. Title.
GV563.S37L6 796.5 53-25589 ‡

NL 0430008 DLC OU

VOLUME 337

Loader, George
Plan of the city of Chichester, from an actual survey taken April 1812, George Loader, surveyor. 38cm. in 52 x 73½cm.

Binder's title: Maps and plans of Great Britain.

1. Chichester, Eng. - Description - Maps.

NL 0430009 NNC

Loader, James Henry
A cosmographical review of the universal law of the affinities of atoms. Chapman, 1896.
93 p.

NL 0430010 MiD

Loader, Lura J
Simplified English grammar with diagrams, a diagram method for sentence mastery, by Lura J. Loader ... Boston, D. C. Heath and company [1944]
vi, 41 p. 24cm.
PE1375.L6
—— Diagram patterns for exercises in Simplified English grammar ... Boston, D. C. Heath and company [1944]
1 p. l., 22 p. 24cm.

1. English language—Grammar—1870- 2. English language—Sentences.
Library of Congress PE1375.L6 Patterns 44-31442
[2] 425.2

NL 0430011 DLC

Loader, T B.
The illustrated atlas of ancient and modern geography, science, commerce, and statistics
see under title

Loader, T. B.
T. B. Loader's scientific and commercial map of England and Wales; in which are delineated the canals, rail-roads, & navigable rivers ... together with the geology and principal situations of the mineral productions. [London] W. Day, lith., 1831.
map. 135 x 108 cm. fold. to 23.5 x 14 cm.
Scale: 10 miles to the inch.

NL 0430013 MH-BA

Loader, T. B.
... T. B. Loader's scientific and commercial map of England and Wales in which are delineated the canals, rail-roads, & navigable rivers ... together with the geology, and principal situations of the mineral productions. [London, 1834].
map. 128 x 102 cm. fold. to 23 x 14 cm.

NL 0430014 MH-BA

LOADER, THOMAS.
Family immigration for Victoria; or, Every man his own immigration agent. By Thomas Loader... Melbourne: G. Robertson, 1861. 16 p. incl. tables. 21cm.

1. Emigration and immigration—Australia—Victoria.

NL 0430015 NN CSt

Loader, William Reginald.
No joy of Africa, a novel. London, Cape [1955]
220 p. 20 cm.

I. Title.
A 58-296
Rochester. Univ. Libr PZ4
for Library of Congress [8]

NL 0430016 NRU TxU NcD PU MB NjR IEN NN

Loades, H. Redfern.
Binet tests on South African natives - Zulus, by H. Redfern Loades... and S. G. Rich... [Worcester, Mass., 1917.
cover-title, p.373-383, 8 fold. leaves. illus. 23cm.
Reprinted from the Pedagogical seminary, Sept., 1917, v.24.

1. Binet-Simon tests. 2. Zulus. I. Rich, S. G., jt. author.

NL 0430017 NNU-W

NNdy71
U2
H4le
The Loading line; employee publication of the New River ordnance plant. v.1-
June 3,1941-
Dublin, Virginia[1941-
illus.,ports. 30-41cm. weekly.

Caption title.
Title varies: v.1,no.1-5, June 3-July 1,1941, Loading plant news; v.1,no.6- July 10,1941 - The Loading line.
Vol.1,no.1-35, June 3,1941-June 30,1942, published by Mason and Hanger co. with the cooperation of Hercules powder co. and the contracting quartermaster; v.1,no.37- Feb.13,1942- by Hercules powder company with the cooperation of the Army Ordnance department.

NL 0430019 CtY

635.93355
L795c
Loads, Frederick Walter
Chrysanthemums for everyone. London, G. Foyle; label: New York, Dover Publications [1955]
86p. illus. (Foyles handbooks)

1. Chrysanthemums.

NL 0430020 ICarbS

SB
349
L79
Loads, Frederick Walter.
Tomato culture by modern methods.
London, C. Arthur Pearson [c1952]
174 p. illus. 19 cm.

1. Tomatoes. I. Title.

NL 0430021 NIC DNAL ScCleU ICarbS NN

91.15
L78
Loads, Frederick Walter.
Vegetables in the small garden. London, Pitman [1949]
183 p.

1. Vegetable gardening. Gt.Brit.

NL 0430022 DNAL

Loads in structures, properties of sections, materials of structural engineering, beams and girders, columns and struts, details of construction, graphical analysis of stresses. Scranton: Internat. Textbook Co. [cop. 1905.] v. p. 8°. (Internat. library of technology. v. 51.)

1. Engineering.—Systematic works, 1904. 2. Materials.—Testing. 3. Materials.—Strength of. 4. Beams and girders. 5. Columns.
N. Y. P. L. August 29, 1913.

NL 0430023 NN

Loads on highway bridges; report of Joint committee
see under Institution of structural engineers, London.

968
L795l
Loadsman, Isobel Alice.
Little roads of Africa [by] I.A. Loadsman. Johannesburg, APB, 1950.
175p. illus., map.

1. Africa, South--Description and travel. I. Title.

NL 0430025 IEN

Loadsman, Isobel Alice.
The mystery of Dragon's Den [by] I. A. Loadsman... Johannesburg, A. P. B. bookstore, 1948. 370 p. 20cm.

NL 0430026 NN

Loaëc (René) [1886-]. *Des injections de sérum artificiel dans les gastro-entérites du premier âge. [Lyon.] 115 pp. 8°. Trévoux, 1914. No. 122.

NL 0430027 DNLM CtY

W 4
L99
1954/55
no.125
LOAËC, Yvec, 1926-
Les troubles métaboliques, dans les formes graves des "vomissements périodiques avec cétosémie." Lyon, 1955.
127 p. (Lyons. [Université] Faculté de médecine et de pharmacie. Thèse, 1954/55, no. 125)
1. Acidosis 2. Vomiting

NL 0430028 DNLM

Loaeus, Joannes
Correspondance inédite de Loaeus, abbé d'Eversham. Publiée avec une introd.et des notes par Alphonse Roersch. Gand, Impr.A.Siffer, 1898
171 p.

NL 0430029 MH

Loaeza, Antonio Arturo.
... Breve resumen de los estudios acerca del paludismo en los Estados unidos mexicanos. Resultados prácticos que de ellos se infieren y los cuales puede utilizar el supremo gobierno lo mismo que los particulares. Trabajo leído por el sr. dr. d. Antonio A. Loaeza en representación de la Sociedad de medicina interna. México, Tip. de la viuda de F. Díaz de León, sucs., 1911.
58 p. front. 23cm.
At head of title: Concurso científico y artístico del centenario promovido por la Academia mexicana de jurisprudencia y legislación.

Continued in next column

VOLUME 337

Continued from preceding column

"'Gaceta médica de México.' Notas relativas al paludismo": p. [15]–53.

1. Malarial fever—Mexico. I. Mexico (City) Concurso científico y artístico del centenario. II. Academia mexicana de jurisprudencia y legislación. III. Gaceta médica de México.

Library of Congress RC162.M6L6 41-35944
[2] 614.530972

NL 0430031 DLC CU-B

Loaeza (Antonio Arturo). *Contribución al estudio del catarro gastro-intestinal; casos observados en el consultorio particular del señor doctor Eduardo Licéaga. 71 pp. 8°. *México*, 1894.

NL 0430032 DNLM

Loaeza, Francisco
Comunicaciones oficiales dirigidas al c.general 2.° en gefe de la linea de oriente: la primera por el coronel Francisco Loaeza, informando en contra de la administracion del estado, y la segunda del gobierno y comandancia militar del mismo en justa vindicacion de aquella. Tuxtla-Gutierrez. Imprenta del gobierno, a cargo de J. M. Espinosa. 1866.
29p. 25.1cm.
Cover title.
1. Mex.-Hist.-Eur.interv. 2. Tabasco(State)-Hist. I. Title. II. Pantaleon Dominguez, José.

NL 0430033 MiU-C

Loaeza, Manuel Cardenas
see Cardenas Loaeza, Manuel.

Loaeza y Contreras, Ricardo.
Las verdaderas causas del suicidio del Gral. Gonzalez Salas. Batalla de "El Rellano" precediendo un relato sobre el asalto y toma de "Mapimi". Con interesantes y veridicos datos recopilados por Ricardo Loaeza y Contreras, teniente del 9° batallon. Monterrey, Imp. J. Cantu Leal, 1912.

cover-title, 76 p. $20\frac{1}{2}$ cm.

1. González Salas, José, d. 1912. I. Title.

25-2325

Library of Congress F1234.G67

NL 0430035 DLC CU-B TxU NN

Loaf, T.
...Der Kampf der Kohlenarbeiter in den Vereinigten Staaten von Nordamerika. Hamburg: Verlag der Kommunistischen Internationale, 1922. 67 p. incl. illus., tables. 8°.

1. Strikes and lockouts (Coal miners'), U. S., 1922.
N. Y. P. L. March 24, 1924.

NL 0430036 NN DLC-P4

LOAF, T.
Der Kampf der Kohlenarbeiter in den Vereinigten Staaten von Nordamerika. Hamburg, Verlag der Kommunistischen Internationale, 1922. 67 p. illus., tables. 23cm.

Film reproduction. Negative.

1. Strikes and lockouts, Coal miners'--U.S.. 1922.

NL 0430037 NN

A Loaf-bread baker.
Bread laws examined
see under title

The loaf of bread
see under American Sunday-School Union.

Loag, J.

Bücher, Hermann, 1882-
... Die heuschreckenplage und ihre bekämpfung. Auf grund der in Anatolien und Syrien während der jahre 1916 und 1917 gesammelten erfahrungen dargestellt, und im auftrage des Kaiserlich osmanischen landwirtschaftsministeriums unter mitwirkung von dr. V. Bauer, dr. G. Bredemann, dr. E. Fickendey, dr. W. La Baume und J. Loag, hrsg. von dr. H. Bücher ... Berlin, P. Parey, 1918.

1.913
S2P94
Loagans, Paul.
Proposal for setting up an extension studios and training program at North Carolina state college. [Washington?] 1946.
11 p.

Issued June 1946.

NL 0430041 DNAL

Loaisa, Bartolomé de
see **Loaysa, Bartolomé de.**

DD
180
.6
L79
1848
Loaísa, García de, cardinal, 1479?-1546.
Briefe an Kaiser Karl V., geschrieben von seinem Beichtvater in den Jahren 1530-32; in dem spanischen Reichsarchiv zu Simancas aufgefunden und mitgetheilt von G. Heine. Berlin, W. Besser, 1848.
viii, 562 p. 22cm.

I. Karl V., Emperor of Germany, 1500-1558. II. Heine, Go tthilf, ed. and tr.

NL 0430043 NIC MB MH NN KU

946
L78c
[Loaísa, García de, cardinal] 1479?-1546.
Cartas al emperador Carlos V, escritas en los años de 1530-32, por su confesor. Copiadas con real autorizacion de las autógrafas conservadas en el archivo de Simancas y publicadas por G. Heine. Berlin, W. Besser, 1848.
226p. 21cm.

Bound with Alba, Fernando Alvarez de Toledo. Correspondance sur l'invasion du comte Louis de Nassau en Frise, en 1568. Bruxelles, 1850.

NL 0430044 IU

Loaísa, García de, *cardinal*, 1479?-1546.
Correspondencia del cardenal de Osma con Carlos v y con su secretario, don Francisco de los Cobos, comendador mayor de Leon.

(*In* Colección de documentos inéditos para la historia de España ... Madrid, 1842-95. $21\frac{1}{2}$ cm. t. xiv (1849) p. [5]-284)

"Sacada del Archivo de Simancas."
All the letters are by the cardinal, written from Rome, and with dates ranging from 13 May 1530 to 23 Dec. 1531.

1. Europe—Hist.—1517-1648—Sources. 2. Reformation. 3. Catholic church—Relations (diplomatic) 4. Augsburg, Diet of, 1530. 5. Clemens VII, pope, 1478-1534. I. Karl v, emperor of Germany, 1500-1558. II. Cobos y Molina, Francisco de los, d. 1547.

A 41-4189

Illinois. Univ. Library
for Library of Congress [DP3.C69 vol. 14]
[3] (946.0082)

NL 0430045 IU MdBP MB MiU

Loaisa, García Jofre de, fl. 16th cent.
Expedition of García de Loaisa. 1525-26
see under title

Loaisa, García Jofre de, fl. 16th cent.
Viages al Maluco.
(In Fernández de Navarrete, Martin, editor. 1765-1844. Colección de los viages y descubrimientos, que hicieron por mar los Españoles desde fines del siglo XV. Tome 5, pp. 1-439. Madrid. 1837.)

K3121 — Moluccas. Hist. Disc. and col. — Spaniards in the Moluccas

NL 0430047 MB

Loaisa, Jofre de
see Loaysa, Jofre de, 13th cent.

BT660
O 32L6
in
RareBooks
Room
Loaisaga, Manuel de.
Historia de la milagrosissima imagen de Nuestra Señora de Occotlan, que se venera extramuros de la Ciudad de Tlaxcala. Sacala a luz el bachiller D. Manuel de Loaisaga. [Mexico] Imprenta de la viuda de Miguel de Ortega, 1745.
[44], 180, [2] p. plate. 16cm.

1. Ocotlán, Nuestra Señora de. 2. Tlaxcala, Mexico (City) Nuestra Señora de Ocotlán (Shrine) I. Title. II. Title: La milagrosissima imagen de Nuestra Señora de Occotlan.

NL 0430050 CoU

Loaisaga, Manuel de.
Historia de la milagrosissima imagen de nuestra señora de Occotlan, que se venera extramuros de la ciudad de Tlaxcala. Sacala a lvz el bachiller d. Manvel de Loaisaga ... Ponelo reverente a la proteccion de la muy illustre noble, y leal villa de Cordova, en sus benemeritos capitulares. Con licencia de los superiores: En la Puebla, En la imprenta de la viuda de Miguel de Ortega. En el portal de las Flores. Año de 1745.

Microfilm copy, made in 1943, of the original in the Medina collection, Biblioteca nacional de Santiago de Chile. Positive.
Negative film in Brown university library.

Collation of the original, as determined from the film: 22 p. l., 180 (i. e. 178), [2] p. pl.
Pages 176-178 incorrectly numbered 178-180.
Privileges signed: Dr. d. Antonio Joachin de Vrizar, y Bernal; Miguel Joseph de Ortega; Exmo. señor d. Pedro Cebrian y Augustin, conde de Fuenclara; Señor doctor d. Joseph de Mercado.
"Soneto" on 19th prelim. leaf.
"Primera edición."—Medina, La imprenta en la Puebla de los Angeles, 457.

1. Ocotlán, Nuestra Señora de.
Microfilm AC-2 reel 203, no. 11 Mic A 49-65

Brown Univ. Library
for Library of Congress [2]†

NL 0430052 RPB UU DLC

BA685
F632m
[R]
Loaisaga, Manuel de.
Historia De La Milagrosissima Imagen De Nra. Sra. De Occotlan, Que Se Venera Extramuros De La Ciudad De Tlaxcala. Dala A Nueva Luz Reimpressa, y añadida el Br. D. Manuel Loayzaga, Presbytero Domiciliario del Obispado de la Puebla de los Angeles, Capellan del Santuario de la Señora treinta, y quatro años hà, y humilde Siervo de la Amabilissima Reyna. ...
Con Licencia De Los Superiores: Reimpresso en Mexico por la Viuda de D. Joseph Hogal. Año de 1750.

14 p.ℓ., 146, [2] p. 20cm. 4°
First pub. Puebla, 1745.
License dated (10th p.ℓ.r) 1 Dec. 1750.
Preliminary matter includes poetry.
Bound in contemporary vellum with: Florencia, Francisco de. La Milagrosa Invencion De Vn Tesoro. [Mexico] 1685.
Palau(2)139385; Medina(Mexico)4001.

NL 0430054 RPJCB CU-B PPL NNH NN NNC CtY

VOLUME 337

x282 Loaisaga, Manuel de.
B685 Tesoro escondido para muchos. Salutaciones á
v.19 Jesucristo Nuestro Señor y Su Santísima Madre, que por conclusion á la historia de Nuestra Señora de Ocotlán, dió á la luz el lic. d. Manuel de Loaysaga, clérigo del obispado de Puebla, y capellan del santuario de la misma Senora, sita á estramuros de la ciudad de Tlaxcala. Guadalajara, Impreso en la oficina del c. M. Brambila, 1835.
[6]p.
[A collection of religious pamphlets in the Spanish language. 19]

NL 0430055 IU

Loaisel de Saulnays (Stanislas-Louis-Joseph). *Étude des complications pulmonaires et laryngées de la variole. 84 pp. 4°. *Paris*, 1870. No. 229.

NL 0430056 DNLM

Loaisel de Tréogate, Joseph Marie, 1752-1812.
Adelaide van Beijeren. Tooneelspel in vier bedrijven. Naar het Fransche. (In: Spectatoriaale Schouwburg... Amsterdam, 1775-1801. 16°. Deel 28, p. 145-210.)

1. Drama (French). 2. Title.
N. Y. P. L. May 1, 1911.

NL 0430057 NN CtY IaU

Loaisel de Tréogate, Joseph Marie, 1752-1812.
Ainsi finissent les grandes passions, ou Les dernières amours du chevalier de... Paris, Poinçot, 1788
2 v. in 1
Microfilm, negative, of copy in Bibliothèque nationale

NL 0430058 MH NNC

Loaisel de Tréogate, Joseph Marie, 1752-1812.
Aux ames sensibles, élégie par m. de Treogate. Paris, L. Jorry, 1780.
30p. 20cm.
No. 8 in a volume with binder's title Pièces diverses.

NL 0430059 IEN MH

Loaisel ~~de~~ Tréogate, Joseph Marie, 1752-1812
La bisarrerie de la fortune, ou Le jeune philosophe, comédie en cinq actes et en prose, représentée pour la premiére fois au théatre du Marais, a Paris, le 16 avril 1793 Par le C. Loaisel Treogate...Paris, Toubon, 1793.
112 p. 22 cm.
Bound with this are his La foret périleuse & his Le chateau du diable.

NL 0430060 MiU MH

Loaisel de Tréogate, Joseph Marie, 1752-1812.
La bisarrerie de la fortune; ou, Le jeune philosophe, comédie en cinq actes, en prose, représentée pour la première fois au théâtre du Marais, à Paris, le 16 avril 1793... Par J. M. Loaisel Tréogate. Seconde édition, revue et corrigée par l'auteur, avec un nouveau dénouement. Troyes: Chez Gobelet, an VII [1798]. 72 p. 21cm.

689918A. 1. Drama, French. I. Title.
N. Y. P. L. March 6, 1934

NL 0430061 NN

Loaisel de Tréogate, Joseph Marie, 1752-1812.
La bisarrerie de la fortune;....le 16 avril 1793...2d ed. avec un nouveau denouement. Troyes, Gobelet, 1799

NL 0430062 PU CtY

PQ1221 Loaisel de Tréogate, Joseph Marie, 1752-1812.
T53 Le château du diable, comédie héroïque,
v.10 en quatre actes et en prose. Paris, Toubon, 1793.
60p. 20cm. (Théâtre; opéras, comédies, drames et mélodrames, vaudevilles, v.10, no.6)

NL 0430063 IaU MH LNHT

Loaisel ~~de~~ Tréogate, Joseph Marie, 1752-1812.
Le chateau du diable, comédie héroique en quatre actes et en prose par J.M.Loaisel Tréogate. Représentée, pour la première fois sur le théatre de Molière, le 5 décembre 1792. Nouvelle ed., revue et cor. Paris, Barba, 1802.
47 p. 22 cm.
848 Bound with his Bisarrerie de la fortune.
L795b

NL 0430064 MiU

Lilly
PQ 1999 LOAISEL DE TRÉOGATE, JOSEPH MARIE, 1752-1812
.L 5 C72 Le combat des Thermopyles; ou, L'école des guerriers; fait historique en trois actes et en prose; par Loaisel ... Représenté pour la première fois, à Paris, sur le Théâtre de la Cité-Varietés, le cinq Thermidor, l'An Second de la République Française ... Paris, Toubon. [1794]
58 p. 8vo
First edition.

NL 0430065 InU IaU

PQ1999 LOAISEL DE TREOGATE, JOSEPH MARIE, 1752-1812.
.L6C7 La comtesse d'Alibre; ou, Le cri du sentiment; anec-
1779 dote françoise. Par m. Loaisel de Treogate ... La Haye, et se trouve à Paris, chez Belin, 1779.
xii, 146 p. 20½cm.

NL 0430066 ICU MH

LOAISEL DE TRÉOGATE, JOSEPH MARIE, 1752-1812.
Dolbreuse, ou, L'homme du siecle, ramené à la vérité par le sentiment & par la raison. Histoire philosophique. Amsterdam, 1783.
2v. in 1. fronts. 20cm.

NL 0430067 ICN

Loaisel de Tréogate, Joseph Marie, 1752-1812
Dolbreuse, ou L'homme du siècle ramené à la vérité par le sentiment & par la raison; histoire philosophique. Amsterdam, Bélin, 1783
2 v. in 1 illus.
Microfilm, negative, of copy in Bibliothèque nationale

NL 0430068 MH FU

PQ Loaisel de Tréogate, Joseph Marie, 1752-1812.
1999 Dolbreuse; ou, L'homme du siecle, ramené à
L78D6 la vérité par le sentiment & par la raison. Histoire philosophique. Par m. Loaisel de Tréogate ... A Paris, Chez Bélin. 1785.
2 v. in 1. fronts. 20cm.

I. Title. II. Title: L'homme du siecle.

NL 0430069 CLU OClW NPV

Loaisel de Tréogate, Joseph Marie, 1752-1812.
La forêt périlleuse; ou, Les brigands de la Calabre, drame en trois actes, en prose. Représenté pour la première fois, sur le Théâtre de la Cité, à Paris, le 18 floréal de l'an v, (17 mai 1797) Paris, Toubon, 1797.
72 p. 21 cm.
L. C. copy imperfect: p. 1-2 wanting.

I. Title. II. Title: Les brigands de la Calabre.

PQ1999.L485F6 53-53785

NL 0430070 DLC PU

Loaisel de Tréogate, Joseph Marie, 1752-1812.
La foret perilleuse; ou, Les brigands de la Calabre, drame en trois actes, en prose...represente pour la premiere fois... le 18 Floreal de l'an V. . Marseille, Mossy, 1798.
40 p.

NL 0430071 PU

PQ1221 Loaisel de Tréogate, Joseph Marie, 1752-1812.
A5 La forêt périlleuse, ou les brigands de
v.5 la calabre, drame, en trois actes, en prose par J.M.Loaisel-Tréogate. Nouvelle édition, revue et corrigée par l'auteur. Paris, Fages, An X (1802)
40p. 20cm. (Collection de piéce française; drames, v.5)

NL 0430072 IaU MH CtY

Loaisel ~~de~~ Tréogate, Joseph Marie, 1752-1812
La foret périlleuse, ou Les brigands de la Calabre, drame, en trois actes, en prose, par J.M.Loaisel-Tréogate. Presenté, pour la première fois, a Paris, sur le théatre de la cité, le 18 floréal, an V(17 Mai 1797); et repris sur le théatre de l'Ambigu-comique, le 3 pluviose an IX(23 Janvier 1800.) Nouvelle ed., revue et cor. par l'auteur. Paris, Roullet, 1802.
40 p. 22 cm.
Bound with his Bisarrerie de la fortune.

NL 0430073 MiU

Rare
PQ Loaisel de Tréogate, Joseph Marie, 1752-1812.
2338 La forêt périlleuse; ou, Les brigands de
L65 la Calabre. Mélodrame en trois actes et en
F7 prose. Representé pour la première fois, à
1816 Paris, sur le Théâtre de l'Ambigu-Comique, le 23 janvier 1800. Paris, Fages, 1816.
32 p. 21cm.

I. Title. II. Title: Les brigands de la Calabre.

NL 0430074 NIC

VOLUME 337

Loaisel de Tréogate, Joseph Marie, 1752–1812.
Le grand chasseur, ou, L'isle des Palmiers, mélodrame en trois actes, en prose, et à grand spectacle. Par mm. Loaisel-Tréogate, et ***. Représenté, pour la première fois, à Paris, sur le théâtre de l'Ambigu-comique, le 15 brumaire, an XIII. (6 novembre 1804). Paris, Fages, an XIII. (1804.)
48 p. 20½cm.
[Pièces de théâtre, v. 86, no. 13]
I. Pixérécourt, René Charles Guilbert de, 1773–1844, joint author. II. Title.
34-15146
Library of Congress PQ1213.P55 vol. 86, no. 13
(842.082) 842.61

NL 0430075 DLC MH PU OO

Loaisel de Tréogate, Joseph Marie, 1752-1812.
Lucile et Milcourt, ou Le cri du sentiment; anecdote Paris, Leprieur, L'an second de la Republique [1793]
214 p. front.
Microfilm, negative, of copy in Bibliothèque nationale

NL 0430076 MH

Loaisel de Tréogate, Joseph Marie, 1752-1812.
Lucile et Milcourt, ou, Le cri du sentiment; par Loaisel de Tréogate. 4. éd. ... Paris, Chez Le Prieur, an x [1802]
198 p. front. 14cm.

NL 0430077 MiU

Loaisel de Tréogate, Joseph Marie, 1752-1812.
Roland de Monglave, drame en quatre actes, en prose, à spectacle. Représenté, pour la première fois, à Paris, sur le théâtre de l'Ambigu-Comique, le 9 pluviôse, l'an 7 de la République. Par J. M. Loaisel-Tréogate... Paris, Barba [1799] 50 p. 20cm.
255535B. 1. Drama, French. 2. Roland—Drama.
N. Y. P. L. August 4, 1944

NL 0430078 NN

Loaisel de Tréogate, Joseph Marie, 1752-1812.
Roland de Monglave, drame en quatre actes, en prose, à spectacle ... Paris, Barba, an XI (1803)
44 p. 22cm.
No. 7 in volume lettered Drames et mélodrames [v. 45]

NL 0430079 MiU

Loaisel de Treogate, Joseph Marie, 1752-1812.
Turnbull, John D.
Rudolph, or The robbers of Calabria; a melo drame, in three acts. With marches, combats and chorusses, as performed at the Boston theatre. By John D. Turnbull ... Printed by B. True, 75 State-street, Boston. 1807.

[Loaisel de Tréogate, Joseph Marie] 1752-1812.
Soirées de mélancolie. Nouv. ed., avec gravures ... Paris, Louis, L'an III [1795]
2 v. 14 cm.
Short stories, sketches and poems.

NL 0430081 CtY

PQ1999 .L6V2 1776
LOAISEL DE TREOGATE, JOSEPH MARIE, 1752-1812.
Valmore, anecdote françoise. Par M. Loaisel de Treogate... Paris, Moutard, 1776.
96 p. front. 20cm.

NL 0430082 ICU

Loaisel de Tréogate, Joseph Marie, 1752-1812.
Valmore et Florello, nouvelles. Paris, Leprieur, L'an troisième de la République francaise [1794]
248 p. front.
Microfilm, negative, of copy in Bibliothèque nationale
Pages [241]-248 advertising

NL 0430083 MH

Loaisel-Tréogate, Joseph Marie
see
Loaisel de Tréogate, Joseph Marie, 1752–1812.

Loaiza, Antonio de Vega
see Vega, Antonio de, d. 1620.

Loaiza, Arturo Ramírez
see
Ramírez Loaiza, Arturo, 1909–

Loaiza, Carlos Zavala
see
Zavala Loaiza, Carlos, 1882–

Loaiza, Guillermo C
Boliviada, poema épico. Sucre [Bolivia] Impr. y Librería M. Pizarro, 1911.
481 p. port. 22 cm.
1. Bolívar, Simón, 1783–1830—Poetry. I. Title.
PQ7819.L57B6 53-49748

NL 0430088 DLC FU NjP MH NN

[Loaiza, Ignacio]
Al severo tribunal del publico, las victimas de Xuchitepec, por la inquisicion de Chalco
see under title

Loaiza, Joaquín Fernández
see
Fernández Loaiza, Joaquín.

Loaiza, Jose Ramon Lanao
see Lanao Loaiza, Jose Ramon.

Loaiza, Lautaro V
... Interpretación lógica del protocolo de Río de Janeiro, penetraciones peruanas que la contrarían. Quito, Imprenta del Ministerio de gobierno, 1942.
12 p., 1 l. fold. map. 21½cm.
"Edición del Departamento de prensa y publicaciones del Ministerio de relaciones exteriores del Ecuador."—Leaf at end.
1. Ecuador—Bound.—Peru. 2. Peru—Bound.—Ecuador. I. Ecuador. Ministerio de relaciones exteriores.
46-28110
Library of Congress F3451.B75L6

NL 0430092 DLC NN

Loaiza, Melquiades.
Breves anotaciones á la legislacion boliviana por Melquiades Loaiza ... Contiene en especial las resoluciones de la Corte suprema; algunas opiniones de los mejores tratadistas del derecho civil ... y una lijera ojeada á la lejislacion boliviana ... La Paz, Impr. de E. Arzadum, 1871.
3 p. l., xi, 149, [1] p. 21cm.
16-20081

NL 0430093 DLC TxU

LOAIZA, Melquiades.
Estudios para una reforma del código civil boliviano. Edicion oficial. La Paz, 1891.
(2)+56 p.

NL 0430094 MH-L

Loaiza, Melquiades
Generalización del derecho canónico para los alumnos de la Facultad de derecho de La Paz (Bolivia) por M. Loaiza. Santiago de Chile, Imprenta Cervantes, 1888.
cover-title, 17 p. 25cm.

NL 0430095 MH-L

Loaiza, Melquiades.
Indice alfabético de los casos de jurisprudencia que rejistra la "Gaceta judicial," por M. Loaiza. 2. ed., rev. y aumentada. (Publicacion particular) La Paz, Imp. de "El Ciudadano," 1878.
1 p. l., lxiii p. 21cm. [With Bolivia. Laws, statutes, etc. Compilacion de las leyes del procedimiento civil. La Paz, 1878]
"Ley promulgada ... 24 de noviembre de 1919": newspaper clipping mounted on verso of p. lxiii.
1. Law reports, digests, etc.—Bolivia—Indexes. I. La Gaceta judicial de Bolivia.
44-14553

NL 0430096 DLC CU

Loaiza, Melquiades, ed.
Bolivia. *Laws, statutes, etc.*
Ley del procedimiento criminal. Edicion con notas, comentarios, concordancias, referencias; un apéndice y suplemento, arreglada por Melquiades Loaiza. Seguida de un Indice alfabético y metódico de la "Gaceta judicial," que contiene los casos de jurisprudencia práctica en materia civil, criminal, mercantil, de minería, etc.—por el mismo. La Paz, Impr. de "La Libertad," 1875.

Loaiza, Melquiades.
Nociones de derecho civil boliviano... La Paz, Impr. de "El Comercio"1887.

NL 0430098 MH

VOLUME 337

LOAIZA, Melquíades.
La nueva legislación de minas de la República de Bolivia. La Paz, [Imp. Cervantes, Santiago de Chile], 1885.

NL 0430099 MH

Z 661 B6 L66 1889 LAC
Loaiza, Melquiades.
Reglamento de imprenta con anotaciones y comentarios. Ed. oficial. La Paz, Impr. de El Comercio, 1889.
xxii, 37p. 22cm.

1. Press law - Bolivia. Bolivia. Laws, statutes, etc. Reglamento de imprenta.

NL 0430100 TxU DLC MH-L

Loaiza (Rafael). *Estudio sobre higiene alimenticia. 118 pp. 8°. Tlaxcala, 189

NL 0430101 DNLM

Loaiza, Robert.
Duo fresh fruit and produce code (including general merchandise) ... compiled by Robert Loaiza ... This code is a supplement to the Duo (banking and commercial) code. The combination of the Duo fresh fruit and produce code renders approximately 220,000 translations ... San Francisco., Calif. Duo code directory, °1934.
155 numb. l. 30cm.
"The Duo five-letter figure code" on lining-paper.
1. Cipher and telegraph codes—Fruit. 2. Cipher and telegraph codes—Produce and provisions.
Library of Congress HE7677.F9L7 CA 34-1933 Unrev'd
——— Copy 2.
Copyright AA 157657 652

NL 0430102 DLC OrP

Loaiza, Rodolfo Zamalloa
see Zamalloa Loaiza, Rodolfo.

Loaiza, Viria Chavarria
see Chavarria, Loaiza, Viria.

[Loaiza Beltrán, Carlos]
... [Biografía sintética del general Simón Bolivar, descrita por C. L. B. 1830–1932 ... La Paz, Escuela tipográfica salesiana [1932] 34 p. illus. 27cm.
At head of title: Bibliografía nacional.
Dedication signed: El autor, Carlos Loaiza Beltrán.

1. Bolivar, Simón, 1783-1830. I. L. B., C. II. B., C. L. III. Title.
N. Y. P. L. June 30, 1947

NL 0430105 NN TxU

Loaiza Beltrán, Fernando.
... De Peñas, 4,000 metros, oteando el altiplano; impresiones del paisaje andino. La Paz, Bolivia, Arnó hermanos, 1935.
8 p. l., iv p., 1 l., 269 p. 21½cm.
At head of title: F. Loaiza Beltrán.

1. Peñas, Bolivia—Descr. 2. Oruro, Bolivia (Dept.)—Descr. & trav. I. Title.
36-13644
Library of Congress F3351.P4L63
[2] 918.4

NL 0430106 DLC LU FU CtY

Loaiza del Arco, Fernando Dávila Madrid
see Dávila Madrid Loaiza del Arco, Fernando, 1721-1762.

Loaizaga, Manuel
see Loaisaga, Manuel de.

Loam, Arthur S.

Lethbridge, H O.
... Australian aboriginal songs; melodies, rhythm and words truly and authentically aboriginal, collected and translated by Dr. H. O. Lethbridge. Accompaniments arranged by Arthur S. Loam ... Melbourne [etc.] Allan & co., pty., ltd. [°1937]

Loam, Arthur S arr.
... British folk songs and dances for piano, arranged by Arthur S. Loam ... Melbourne [etc.] Allan & co., pty., ltd. [°1940]
cover-title, 32 p. 31cm.
At head of title: Imperial edition no. 483.
Illustrated cover in color.
Publisher's plate no.: B. 3887.
Without the words of the songs.

1. Folk-songs, English. 2. Folk-songs, Scottish. 3. Folk-songs, Irish. 4. Folk-songs, Welsh. 5. Dance music—Folk and national dances. I. Title.
42-42278
Library of Congress M1738.L78B8
[2] 786.4

NL 0430110 DLC

Loan, Benjamin Franklin, 1819-1881.
Speech...delivered in the House of representatives of the United States on the 10th of May 1864...
Washington D. C. 1864? 8p

YA5000 J 17 (Congressional speeches, by author)

NL 0430111 DLC

Loan, Benjamin Franklin, 1819–1881.
Speech of Hon. B. F. Loan, of Missouri, on the relation of the rebel states to the government, and the duty of the government in re-establishing the union; delivered in the House of representatives, March 3, 1866. Washington, Printed at the Congressional globe office, 1866.
8 p. 23½cm.

1. Reconstruction.
Library of Congress E668.L79 34-25069

NL 0430112 DLC CSmH

Loan, Nguyen Kim
see
Nguyen Kim Loan.

A Loan collection of pictures by Nathaniel Hone...and John Butler Yeats... will be on view at 6 St.Stephen's Green, October 21st to November 3rd... [London, 1901]
15 p. 21cm.
"Modern landscape painters, apropos of Mr.Hone", by George Moore: p. [4]-7.
1.Hone, Nathaniel, 1718-1784. 2.Yeats, John Butler, 1839-1922. I.Moore, George, 1852-1933.

NL 0430114 NjP

Loan collection of portraits, views, and other objects of interest connected with ... Eton
see under Eton College.

A loan exhibition depicting Marlborough and the reign of Queen Anne, Chesterfield house ... 29th January-March, 1934. In aid of the Young women's Christian association ... [London, Printed by Battley brothers, limited, 1934]
109, [1] p., 2 l. 28 pl. on 14 l. (incl. ports.) 24 cm.
Ms. notes in margin.
1. Art, British - Exhibitions. 2. Marlborough, John Churchill, 1st duke of, 1650-1722. 3. Gt. Brit. - History - Anne, 1702-1714.

NL 0430116 CSmH

A loan exhibition depicting the history of the Scots guards, 39 Grosvenor square ... Dec. 1st-23rd, 1934
see under London. Scots guards exhibition, 1934.

N5055 .L78 A loan exhibition depicting the reign of Queen Elizabeth. 22 & 23 Grosvenor Place, S.W.1, 26th January--March, 1933. In aid of the Young Women's Christian Association. [Clapham Park, 1933]
76 p.

1. Art--Exhibitions. 2. Elizabeth, Queen of England, 1533-1603.

NL 0430117 ICU MWelC DFo

Loan exhibition, February, 1893. Catalogue [of] bronzes [by] Antoine Louis Barye. New York, Fine Arts society building [1893]
16 p. 23cm.
"Antoine Louis Barye, a note by M. Léon Bonnat (from the 'Gazette des beaux arts')": p.9-16.
Bound with [La Farge, John] Hokusai. 1897.
1. Barye, Antoine Louis, 1795-1875. I. Bonnat, Léon, 1833-1922.

NL 0430118 NNC

Loan exhibition; French and English art treasures of the eighteenth century. Madame Jacques Balsan, chairman, December 20 to 30, 1942. [New York, 1943]
82 p. 31 phot. 21½ x 28½cm.
Title from cover.
On spine: Photographs of eighteenth century French and English art exhibition.
Catalogue and 31 photographs. The catalogue (82 p. 20½cm) has title: French and English art treasures of the XVIII century; loan exhibition in aid of the American women's voluntary services. Catalogue compiled by the Selection committee from data furnished by the lenders. December 20 to 30, inclusive ... at the Parke-Bernet galleries, inc. ... New York 1942.

Continued in next column

VOLUME 337

Continued from preceding column

1. Art, French—Exhibitions. 2. Art, English—Exhibitions. 3. Art objects, French—Exhibitions. 4. Art objects, English—Exhibitions. I. Balsan, Consuelo (Vanderbilt) II. Parke-Bernet galleries, inc., New York. III. Title: French and English art treasures of the eighteenth century.

Library of Congress .N6846.L6 43-11859
[3] 709.4

NL 0430120 DLC

A loan exhibition of Degas for the benefit of the New York infirmary
see under Wildenstein and Company, inc., New York,

Loan exhibition of early American furniture and the decorative crafts for the benefit of Free hospital for Women, Brookline, Mass.,...
see under Brookline, Mass. Free Hospital for Women.

Loan exhibition of 18th century English conversation pieces. [London,] 1930. 18 l. 8°.

Foreword signed: Philip Sassoon.
Exhibition in aid of the Royal Northern Hospital, March 4th to April 6th, 1930.

1. Paintings, British—Exhibitions— Gt. Br.—Eng.—London. I. Sassoon, Sir Philip Albert Gustave David, 3d bart., 1868– .
N. Y. P. L. November 11, 1930

NL 0430123 NN

---

*8185.01-199

Loan exhibition of heirlooms and many other old-fashioned things from the homes on Nantucket Island at the Charles G. Coffin Mansion, Main Street. August 7th to 18th, 1935.
= [Nantucket, Mass. 1935.] 79 pp. Illus. Portraits. Plates. 23 cm.
The title is on the cover.

E1698 — Collection of bric-à-brac, paintings, etc. — Nantucket, Mass. F.a.— Nantucket, Mass. Exhibs. — Colonial furniture.

NL 0430124 MB CtY

Loan Exhibition of Japanese Works of Art and Handicraft, London, 1915
see London. Loan Exhibition of Japanese Art and Handicraft, 1915.

Loan exhibition of miniature period models
see under Young Women's Christian Association, London.

Loan exhibition of paintings by Elliott Daingerfield
see under [Sherman, Frederic Fairchild]

Loan exhibition of thirty-nine masterpieces of Venetian painting, in honour of the Coronation
see under Agnew, Thomas & Sons, ltd., London.

Loan exhibition of work of five contemporary English artists...
see under Harvard University. William Hayes Fogg Art Museum.

Loan fund life assurance society of London.
(Prospectus) New York, 1845.
28p.

YA 17386

NL 0430130 DLC

The Loan gazette
see
Consumer finance news.

LOAN INSURANCE COMPANIES.
[Explanation of the method.]
[1870?] 8 pp. 8°.

NL 0430132 MB

The loan of a lover
see under Planche, James Robinson, 1796-1880.

Loan Play Library, *University of Minnesota*
see Minnesota. University. *Loan Play Library*

The Loan shark problem today. [Durham, N. C.] School of Law, Duke University, 1954.

138 p. 27 cm. (Law and contemporary problems, v. 19, no. 1)

Cover title.
Bibliographical footnotes.

CONTENTS.—Foreword. Progress and problems in regulation of consumer credit, by F. B. Hubachek. A regulatory small loan law solves loan shark problem, by J. A. A. Burnquist. Nebraska has no loan shark problem today, by H. Johnson. Progress in consumer credit in Kentucky, by B. J. Lenihan. The loan shark problem in the Southeastern States, by W. H. Simpson. A bird's-eye view of the loan shark problem from the offices of the Legal Aid Society in Atlanta, Georgia, by C. M. Pennisi. Organized labor views the loan shark problem, by J. A. Woll. The responsibility of all consumer lending agencies to help eliminate the loan shark evil, by J. M. Redfield. Banking's opportunity to service the small loan needs of the public, by C. K. Dellmuth. What lies ahead in the field of small loans, by R. H. Smith. The future of the loan shark and consumer credit agencies, by L. Henderson.

1. Consumer credit—U. S. 2. Loans, Personal—U. S. 3. Usury laws—U. S. I. Duke University, Durham, N. C. School of Law. (Series)

54-7591

NL 0430136 DLC OrCS Wa MoU CoU MiU MB NcD

Loan to the city of Cairo, western America, United States. Specially secured upon the whole allotment and improvements of the corporation. Interest, six per cent per annum, payable in London, and a valuable bonus in stock. London, Dean & co., printers [1841]
23p. fold. map. 22cm.

NL 0430137 IHi

PQ 9698.22 .03 E62 1953

LOANDA, FERNANDO FERREIRA de.
Equinócio; poemas, 1947-1948. [Rio de Janeiro] Orfeu [1953]
47 p.

NL 0430138 InU

Loanda, Fernando Ferreira de, *ed.*
Panorama da nova poesia brasileira. [Rio de Janeiro?] Orfeu [1951]
239 p. illus. 24 cm.

1. Brazilian poetry—20th cent. I. Title.

PQ9658.L6 54-20175 ‡

NL 0430139 DLC IEN NcD CU NN CSt DPU CtY MH

Loanda [place]
see Luanda.

Loane, A. E.
Shipmates.
— London. Arnold. 1912. vii, 311 pp. 18 cm., in 8s.
"Portraits from memory of naval officers who were born between 1805 and 1827 and served their country for many years in all quarters of the globe."

L806 — T.r. — Anecdotes. — Seamen. — Great Britain. Biog. and geneal.

NL 0430141 MB CtY NN

Loane, Clarence Morrison, 1910–
A study of the activity of finely divided metals and metallic oxides ... by Clarence M. Loane ... [Ithaca, N. Y., 1933]

1 p. l., p. 615-622, 1 l. 1 illus. 25½ cm.

Thesis (PH. D.)—Johns Hopkins university, 1932.
Biography.
Caption title: A new method for the preparation of oxide catalysts for the carbon monoxide oxidation.
"Reprinted from the Journal of physical chemistry, volume XXXVII ... (1933)"
"References": p. 622.

1. Catalysis. 2. Oxides. 3. Carbon monoxide. 4. Oxidation.

Library of Congress QD501.L813 1932 33-36979
Johns Hopkins Univ. Libr.
[2] 541.39

NL 0430142 MdBJ DLC PPT OU

Loane, George Green, 1865-1945.
Beginner's guide to Latin; being a first Latin translation book ... London, 1918.
17.5 cm.

NL 0430143 CtY

Loane, George Green, 1865–1945 *ed.*
A book of story poems, selected & ed. by George G. Loane, M. A. London & Toronto, J. M. Dent & sons ltd.; [New York, E. P. Dutton and company, 1921]

224 p. incl. front. (port.) 15½ cm. (*Half-title:* The Kings treasuries of literature. General editor: Sir A. T. Quiller Couch)

1. English ballads and songs. 2. English poetry (Collections) I. Title.

Library of Congress PR1175.L52 22-18115

NL 0430144 DLC Or CU

VOLUME 337

PA6237 .A6H6 1914 Loane, George Green, 1865-1945, ed.
[Caesar's Gallic war; a vocabulary compiled by George G. Loane ... Oxford, At the Clarendon press [1930]
[64] p. 18½cm. (Half-title: A new Clarendon press series of classical authors for the use of schools)
With Caesar, C. Julius. ... De bello gallico commentarius sextus ... Oxford, 1914.
1. Caesar, C. Julius. De bello gallico—Glossaries, vocabularies, etc. I. Ser.

NL 0430145 ViU

808 L8 Loane, George Green, 1865-1945.
Diaconus, exercises in the meaning of English, by George G. Loane... London, Macmillan & co., 1912.
x, 184 p. 19 cm.

NL 0430146 MiU

Loane, George Green, 1865-1945.
Echoes in Tennyson, and other essays, by George G. Loane. London: A. H. Stockwell, Ltd.[, 1928.] 24 p. 12°.
Contents: Echoes in Tennyson. Nose-shyness. Buttered eggs. Ability at a discount. The Arabian nights.

413339A. 1. Tennyson, Alfred Tennyson, 1st baron, 1809-1892. 2. Title.
N. Y. P. L. July 1, 1929

NL 0430147 NN IU

PR1363 L66 Loane, George Green, 1865- ed.
Selected English essays, edited by George G. Loane. [London, J.M. Dent & Sons, Ltd., 1921.
256 p. front. (port.) 16cm. (The Kings treasuries of literature)

1. English essays.

NL 0430148 GU WaU

PR1363 L58 Loane, George Green, 1865-1945, ed.
Selected English essays, edited by George G. Loane ... New York, E. P. Dutton and company; London & Toronto, J. M. Dent & sons, ltd. [1923]
256p. front.(port.) 15½cm. (Half-title The Kings treasuries of literature. General editor: Sir A. T. Quiller Couch)
Title within ornamental border.
"First edition 1921. Reprinted 1922, 1923"
1. English essays.

NL 0430149 NBuG

Loane, George Green, 1865- ed.
Selected English essays, edited by George G. Loane, M. A. London & Toronto, J. M. Dent & sons, ltd.; [New York, E. P. Dutton and company, 1924]
256 p. incl. front. (port.) 15½cm. (Half-title: The Kings treasuries of literature. General editor: Sir A. T. Quiller Couch)
"First edition, 1921; reprinted ... 1924."
"Short biographies": p. 227-249.

NL 0430150 NcD

Loane, George Green, *editor*, 1865-1945.
Selected English essays.
— New York. Dutton & Co. [1927.] 256 pp. Portrait. [The king's treasuries of literature.] 15 cm., in 16s.
Short biographies, pp. 227-249.

NL 0430151 MB NBuG

Loane, George Green, 1865-1945, ed.
Selected English essays. London, Dent [1930]
256p. front.(port.) S. (The kings treasuries of literature)
Title on two leaves.

NL 0430152 IaU

Loane, George Green, 1865- ed.
Selected English essays, edited by George G. Loane, M. A. London & Toronto, J. M. Dent & sons, ltd.; [New York, E. P. Dutton and company, 1934]
256 p. incl. front. (port.) 15½ cm. (Half-title: The Kings treasuries of literature. General editor: Sir A. T. Quiller Couch)
"First published in this edition 1921; last reprint 1934."
"Short biographies": p. 227-249.

1. English essays.

PR1363.L66 1934 824.0822 36—19058

NL 0430153 DLC OCl

824.08 L795s Loane, George Green, 1865- ed.
Selected English essays. [London, Dent, 1941]
256p. front.(port.) (The King's treasury of literature)
First published in this edition in 1921.
Includes short biographies.
1. English essays.

NL 0430154 FTaSU KMK

Loane, George Green, 1865-
A short handbook of literary terms, by George G. Loane. London, T. F. Unwin, ltd. [1923]
195, [1] p. 19 cm.

1. Literature—Terminology. I. Title.

PN44.5.L6 24—10630

NL 0430155 DLC TxU OCU CoU IU NN OCl OClW CU DNLM

Loane, George Green, 1865-1945.
A short handbook of literary terms, by George G. Loane. New York, The Macmillan company [1923]
195, [1] p. 19cm.
Printed in Great Britain.

1. Literature—Dictionaries, indexes, etc. 2. Rhetoric. 3. English language—Terms and phrases. I. Title. II. Title: Literary terms.

A 24-750

Springfield, Mass. City libr. for Library of Congress [a37j1]

NL 0430156 OO ICJ MS OClW WaS OrPR CtY PPD OrP OOxM ViU

*PN43 .L6 1924 Loane, George Green, 1865-1945.
A short handbook of literary terms. London, T. F. Unwin [1924]
195 p. 19cm.

1. Literature—Dictionaries, index, etc. 2. Rhetoric. 3. English language—Terms and phrases. I. Title. II. Title: Literary terms.

NL 0430157 MB

Loane, George Green, 1865-
A short handbook of literary terms, by George G. Loane. New York: The Macmillan Co. [1924.] 195 p. 12°.
Printed in Great Britain.

NL 0430158 NN MB

Loane, George Greene, 1865-1945.
A thousand and one notes on "A new English dictionary". By George G. Loane ... Surbiton, Philpott & co., ltd., printers, 1920.
2 p. l., 64 p. 21½cm.

1. English language—Dictionaries, Supplementary. 2. Murray, Sir James Augustus Henry, 1837-1915. A new English dictionary. I. Title

Library of Congress PE1630.L6 22-13228

NL 0430159 DLC MB NN MiU

Loane (Georgius). *Disp. med. quædam de tetano complectens. 4 p. l., 23 pp. 8°. *Edinburgi, F. Neill*, 182°

NL 0430160 DNLM

Loane, Helen (Jefferson) 1907-

Committee of Latin teachers in Baltimore.
Exploring Latin, by a Committee of Latin teachers in Baltimore, Mary T. Brennan, chairman ... Helen J. Loane ... and Margaret T. Englar ... New York, Cincinnati [etc.] American book company [°1933]

Loane, *Mrs.* Helen (Jefferson) 1907-
Industry and commerce of the city of Rome (50 B. C.-200 A. D.) by Helen Jefferson Loane ... Baltimore, The Johns Hopkins press, 1938.
158 p., 1 l. 24½cm.
Thesis (PH. D.)—Johns Hopkins university, 1937.
Vita.
Published also as Johns Hopkins university studies in historical and political science, ser. LVI, no. 2.
Bibliographical foot-notes.
1. Rome (City)—Indus. 2. Rome (City)—Comm. I. Title.
[Full name: Mrs. Helen Curtis (Jefferson) Loane]

Library of Congress DG107.L6 1937 38-23135
Johns Hopkins Univ. Libr.
[2] 330.9376

NL 0430162 MdBJ DLC OrP

Loane, Helen (Jefferson) 1907-
... Industry and commerce of the city of Rome (50 B. C.-200 A. D.) by Helen Jefferson Loane. Baltimore, The Johns Hopkins press, 1938.
158 p. 24½ cm. (The Johns Hopkins university studies in historical and political science ... ser. LVI, no. 2)
Issued also as thesis (PH. D.) Johns Hopkins university.
Bibliographical foot-notes.

1. Rome (City)—Indus. 2. Rome (City)—Comm. I. Title.

H31.J6 ser. 56, no. 2 330.9376 38—23134
——— Copy 2. DG107.L6 1938

NL 0430163 OO OU CoU GU DDO GU-L Or OrCS OrU WaTC DLC PSt NcU ViU PHC PSC PU PHi PBm OCU

VOLUME 337

Loane, Helen (Jefferson) 1907–
... Industry and commerce of the city of Rome (50 B. C.–200 A. D.) by Helen Jefferson Loane. Baltimore, The Johns Hopkins press, 1938.
158 p. 24½ cm. (The Johns Hopkins university studies in historical and political science ... ser. LVI, no. 2)
Issued also as thesis (PH. D.) Johns Hopkins university.
Bibliographical foot-notes.
Photocopy. Ann Arbor, Michigan. University Microfilms, 1971.
1. Rome (City)—Indus. 2. Rome (City)—Comm. I. Title.

NL 0430164 NcGU

Loane, Joseph
——— Annual reports on the sanitary condition of the [Whitechapel district, with vital and other statistics, by the medical officer of health. 29.–36., 1884–91; 40., 1895; 42., 1897; 43., 1898. 8°. London, 1885–99.

NL 0430165 DNLM

Loane (Joseph). Reports (quarterly) on the sanitary condition of the Whitechapel district, by the medical officer of health. 1.–4. qr., 1884. 8°. London, 1884–5.

NL 0430166 DNLM

Loane, *Miss M*
The common growth, by M. Loane ... New York, Longmans, Green & co.; London, E. Arnold, 1911.
vii, 304 p. 19½cm.
A 11—1679
Wisconsin. Free libr. com. for Library of Congress [a40b1]

NL 0430167 WHi ICJ MB NN

Loane, *Miss* **M.**
An Englishman's castle; by M. Loane ... London, E. Arnold, 1909.
4 p. l., 308 p. 19½cm.
CONTENTS.—I. An Englishman's castle.—II. The pleasures of the poor.—III. Put yourself in his place.—IV. The moral effect of domestic legislation.—V. A handful of prejudices.—VI. The standard of comfort.—VII. The position of the wife in the working-class home.—VIII. The service of the poor.—IX. The social services of the district nurse.—X. The laws of thought.—XI. How the poor treat the poor.—XII. The fatigued philanthropist.
1. Poor. 2. Charity.
W 9-152
Washington, D. C. Public Library

NL 0430168 DWP CaBVaU KU CU CtY PPFr OrP OCl ICJ NN MB

Loane, *Miss* **M.**
From their point of view, by M. Loane ... London, E. Arnold, 1908.
vii, 309, [1] p. 20cm.
CONTENTS.—I. The manufacture of the tramp.—II. Family life among the poor.—III. Some mental and moral characteristics of the poor.—IV. Our masters' rulers.—V. Some of the causes of infant mortality.—VI. The working-class father.—VII. The cost of food.—VIII. What is charity?—IX. The practical drawbacks of small farms.—X. The spending of the superfluous.—XI. Why the poor prefer town life.—XII. The art of repairing.—XIII. Wasted effort among the poor.—XIV. Remedies for existing evils.
1. Poor. 2. London—Poor. 3. Charity. I. Title.
Library of Congress HV4088.L8L7 8—35515

NL 0430169 DLC OrP CU NjP PPL OCl DL MiU ICJ NN MB

Loane, *Miss* **M.**
Neighbours and friends, by M. Loane ... London, E. Arnold, 1910.
4 p. l., 322 p. 19½cm.
1. Poor. 2. Charity.
W 10-235
Washington, D. C. Public Library

NL 0430170 DWP MH PPL OClW OCl OU ICJ NN

Loane, *Miss* **M.**
The next street but one, by M. Loane ... London, E. Arnold, 1907.
viii, 309 p. 19½cm.
The greater part of the chapter entitled "Culture among the poor" appeared first in the Contemporary review.
I. Title.
W 7—77
Washington, D. C. Public library for Library of Congress [a40b1]

NL 0430171 DWP OrP CU CtY PPFr OClW OCl OU MB

Loane, *Miss M.*
The Queen's poor, life as they find it in town and country; by M. Loane. London, Edward Arnold, 1905.
viii, 312 p. 19½cm.
1. Poor.
W 6-172
Washington, D. C. Public Library

NL 0430172 DWP PPFr FMU OO ICJ MB

Loane, *Miss M.*
The queen's poor; life as they find it in town and country. London, Arnold, 1909.
312 p.

NL 0430173 OClW-H CtY

Loane, *Miss M.*
The queen's poor, life as they find it in town and country; ... Lond., Arnold, 1910.
312 p.

NL 0430174 OU

Loane, Marcus L
Cambridge and the Evangelical succession. London, Lutterworth Press [1952]
276 p. illus. 21 cm.
1. Evangelical revival. 2. Cambridge. University—Biog. I. Title.
BR758.L6 283.42 52—64451 ‡

NL 0430175 DLC PPT IEG IaU PPPD PPLT CtY-D NcD TxU PPWe PPEB NRCR

Loane, Marcus L
A centenary history of Moore Theological College. Sydney, Angus and Robertson [1955]
228 p. illus. 23 cm.
1. Moore Theological College, Sydney. I. Title.
BV4160.M6L6 207.94 58-32987 ‡

NL 0430176 DLC NcD CtY-D NN

Loane, Marcus L
John Charles Ryle, 1816–1900; a short biography. London, J. Clarke [1953]
62 p. illus. 19 cm.
1. Ryle, John Charles, Bp. of Liverpool, 1816–1900.
BX5199.R9L6 54–31522 ‡

NL 0430177 DLC NN PPWe NIC

Loane, Marcus L
Masters of the English Reformation. London, Church Book Room Press [1954]
247 p. illus. 22 cm.
Includes bibliographies.
1. Reformation—Biog. 2. Reformation—England. I. Title.
BR378.L6 922.342 55–20519 ‡

NL 0430178 DLC CU NIC NcU MH TxU NjPT CtY-D NcD PPPD PPT TNJ-R ViU PU NN CU

Loane, Marcus L
Oxford and the evangelical succession. London, Lutterworth Press [label: Chicago, A. R. Allenson, 1950]
300 p illus. 20 cm.
Includes bibliography.
1. Evangelical Revival—Biog. I. Title.
BR758.L63 922 53–32870 ‡

NL 0430179 DLC TxU NjPT CtY-D MH PPT NNUT KyLxCB KyU

Les Loanges et recommandations de la paix, extraictes de l'Escritvre Saincte. Remonstrent que cest chose fort deshonneste que les Chrestiens ayent guerre ensemble. Avec ample suasion a iceux de se contenir en paix, pour le repos du corps & d'ame. Lyon, 1568.

NL 0430180 WU NNUT

4BX Cath. 1609
Loango (Vicariate apostolic)
Catechisme bembe; mission de Nkenge. Rome, Sodalité de saint Pierre Claver, 1930.
240 p.

NL 0430181 DLC-P4

PL8815 .Z71 1930
Loango (Vicariate apostolic)
... **Katesisu,** milongi mi Dzambi (Kimbenza) Kimbenza, Mission des pères du Saint-Esprit, 1930.

Die **Loango-expedition** ausgesandt von der Deutschen gesellschaft zur erforschung aequatorial-Africas, 1873–1876. Ein reisewerk in drei abtheilungen von Paul Güssfeldt, Julius Falkenstein, Eduard Pechuël-Loesche. Mit illustrationen gezeichnet von A. Göring, M. Laemmel, G. Mützel. Leipzig, P. Frohberg; [etc., etc.] 1879–1907.
3 v. in 4. fronts. (v. 1, col.) illus., plates (1 col.) fold. maps. 29cm.
3. abt., 2. hft. pub. Stuttgart, Strecher & Schröder.
"Verzeichnis erwähnter schriften": 3. abt., 2. hft., p. [473]–474.
Each part has special t.-p.
1. abt. by P. Güssfeldt; 2. abt. by J. Falkenstein; 3. abt. by E. Pechuël-Loesche.
1. Loango. 2. Scientific expeditions. I. Güssfeldt, Paul i. e. Richard Paul, 1840– II. Falkenstein, Julius August Ferdinand, 1842– III. Pechuël-Loesche, Eduard, 1840–
Library of Congress DT639.L7 8—11810

NL 0430183 DLC WU CU CLU InU NN MiEM CtY PPAN OCl NjP MH-A MH ICJ

VOLUME 337

Loans and discounts; proved methods that build business—tested time-saving systems and records for loans of every sort—lending profitably to farmers—how to increase earnings. Chicago, New York [etc.] A. W. Shaw company [c1918]
xvi p., 1 l., 264, xvii-xxi p. incl. front. forms. 21½cm. (*Half-title:* The Shaw banking series)

1. Banks and banking—U. S. 2. Loans.

Library of Congress HG1641.L5 18—17979

ICJ
NL 0430184 DLC Or WaS PPLas PPFRB PP PV CU OOxM NN

Loans and investments; contributors: O. M. W. Sprague ... E. W. Kemmerer ... H. Parker Willis ... Thomas B. Paton ... Harold J. Dreher ... C. W. Allendoerfer ... George E. Allen ... New York city, American institute of banking [c1916]
304 p. 21cm. $2.00
Lettered on cover: Study course.

1. Banks and banking. 2. Investments. I. Sprague, Oliver Mitchell Wentworth, 1873– II. Kemmerer, Edwin Walter, 1875–
Library of Congress HG1641.L6 16–25103

NL 0430185 DLC OCIFRB CU

LOANS and standing armaments. London, Waterlow and Sons, 1849. 24 p. 21cm.

Microfiche (neg.) 1 sheet. 11 x 15cm. (NYPL FSN 13,033)
Reprinted from the Westminster and Foreign quarterly review, Oct. 1849.

Gift of Dr. J. S. Billings.
1. Debt, Public.

NL 0430186 NN

Loanz, Elijah, 1555–1636.
מכלול יופי ... פירוש נפלא על קהלת ... ברלין, תקל״ה.
Berlin [1775]
27 l. 21 cm.

1. Bible. O. T. Ecclesiastes—Commentaries. I. Title.
Title transliterated: Mikhlol yofi
BS1475.L58 54–55645

NL 0430187 DLC

Loanz, Elijah, 1555–1636.
נדבות פי רצה נא יי ... ספר רנת דודים ... ביאור על ספר שיר השירים. שחבר [אליא בן משה לואנץ] ... באסיליאה. נדפס בבית קונראד וואלדקירך [1600]
30 l. 20 cm.
Includes text of Song of Solomon.

1. Bible. O. T. Song of Solomon—Commentaries. I. Bible. O. T. Song of Solomon. Hebrew. 1600. II. Title: Rinat dodim.
Title romanized: Nidvot pi retseh na Adonai.

BS1485.L56 1600 74–251696

NL 0430188 DLC

---

fLA357 **Loar, Byron Melville.**
W52 A memoir of Western Pennsylvania classical and scientific institute. By Byron Melville Loar. Mount Pleasant, Pa., 1932.

36 p. incl. front., illus., port. 30 cm.

NL 0430189 PPiHi PHi

MICROFILM
F378.7CZO
L78
Loar, Howard Hunt
The spin of the π^+ meson via the reactions $\pi^+ + D \rightleftarrows P + P$. 1952.
viii, 68 l. diagrs., tables. ([University microfilms, Ann Arbor, Mich.] Publication no. 4581)

Thesis, Columbia university.
Abstracted in Microfilm abstracts.
Bibliographical footnotes.

NL 0430190 NNC

Loar, Jacques.
Ersatz losse invallen, humoristische teekeningen van Marcel Antoine. Gent, Snoeck-Ducaju [1944]
184 p. illus. 19 cm.
"Oorspronkelijke titel: Ersatz—Pièces détachées. Nederlandsche vertaling van Pierre Muller."

1. World War, 1939–1945—Anecdotes. I. Title.
D745.3.L613 50–52434

NL 0430191 DLC NN ICU MiU ICRL

D745.3 Loar, Jacques,
B138 Ersatz, pièces détachées [par] Jacques Loar [pseud.] Dessins humoristiques de Marcel Antoine Gand, Snoeck-Ducaju [1944]
195 p. illus. 19cm.

1. World War, 1939-1945 - Humor, caricatures, etc. 2. Belgian wit and humor. I. Title.

NL 0430192 CSt-H

LOAR, James L.
Utah Index-Digest; Decisions, Supreme Court, Utah, vol.1-8, and Pacific Reporter, vol.1-30, [1871-93]. Ogden, 1893.

8vo. Interleaved copy.

NL 0430193 MH-L

Loar, Lloyd
The American violin system for violin. First year's course published in six volumes. [n.p., Nicomede Music Co., c1930]
6 v. illus. 31cm.

Cover title.

NL 0430194 OO

Loara, Alma de, *ed.*
Gotitas de rocío; selección de poemas para los niños. México, Editorial "Novedades de Libros," 1954.
186 p. 20 cm.

1. Spanish poetry — Translations from foreign literature. 2. Poetry—Collections. 3. Spanish-American poetry (Collections) I. Title.
PN6108.L56 56–44893 ‡

NL 0430195 DLC CU NN RPB

Loarca, Miguel de.
Relacion de las Yslas Filipinas.
(In Blair and Robertson. The Philippine Islands. 1493–1803. Vol. 5, pp. 34–187. Cleveland, 1903.)
Spanish text and English translation on opposite pages.
The original manuscript is in the Archivo general de Indias, at Seville.
The translation is by Alfonso de Salvio, and Emma Helen Blair.

F1661 — Salvio, Alfonso de, tr. — Blair, Emma Helen. tr.

NL 0430196 MB

Loarer, Édouard. L'Himalaya, ses productions naturelles. Culture du thé dans l'Inde. Paris. 1868. 8°. pp. 62.
"Extrait du *Bulletin de la Société impériale d'acclimatation,*" 1868, 2e sér., v. 74-102, 192-224.

NL 0430197 MH-A

Loarer, Édouard.
A philloxera, pulgão da vinha; origem-introducção em França—seus estragos; estudo dos meios ensaios para impedir os seus estragos; descripção d'um processo infallivel para a destruir; com gravuras [por] Eduardo Loarer ... tr. com auctorisação do auctor por André Meyrelles de Tavora do Canto e Castro. 2. ed. Lisboa, Typographia progressista, 1873.
cover-title, 24 p. pl. 22½cm.

1. Phylloxera. I. Meyrelles de Tavora do Canto e Castro, André, tr.
19-11914
Library of Congress SB608.G7L75

NL 0430198 DLC

A LOARING, HENRY JAMES.
15 Common sayings, words, and customs: their
52 origin and history... Philadelphia, Porter [187-]
230p.

NL 0430199 ICN ViU

Loaring, Henry James, comp.
Common sayings, words, and customs: their origin and history. Selected by Henry James Loaring ... Philadelphia, Porter & Coates [1873]
2 p.l., 230, [1] p. 17½cm.
Printed by "Butler & Tanner, The Selwood printing works, Frome, and London."
First published in 1870.

1. Aphorisms and apothegms. 2. Epigrams. 3. Maxims. I. Title.

NL 0430200 ViU MdBP

Loaring, Henry James, *comp.*
Epitaphs: quaint, curious, and elegant. With remarks on the obsequies of various nations. Compiled and collated by Henry James Loaring ... London, W. Tegg [1873?]
vi p., 1 l., 262 p. incl. front. 16½cm.

1. Epitaphs. I. Title.
Library of Congress PN6291.L6 37-36308
[2] 929.5

NL 0430201 DLC TxU WU IEN DSI MB NN

E LOARING, HENRY JAMES, comp.
9 Epitaphs: quaint, curious, and elegant.
.514 With remarks on the obsequies of various nations. Compiled and collated by Henry James Loaring... London, Tegg [1876]
262p.

NL 0430202 ICN

---

803 **Loaring, Henry James.**
L78s A selection of common sayings, words, and customs: their origin and history. London [1870?]
230p.

NL 0430203 IU OCl

VOLUME 337

Loaring-Clark, *Mrs.* **Ada,** *comp.*
A book of devotions for women and girls, compiled by Ada Loaring Clark, with a foreword by the Rt. Rev. Thomas Campbell Darst ... Milwaukee, Morehouse publishing co. [°1931]
xiv, 98 p. 18½cm.

1. Protestant Episcopal church in the U. S. A.—Prayer-books and devotions. I. Title.
Library of Congress BV4860.L6 31-9790
Copyright A 35487 248

NL 0430204 DLC

FILM
Loarte,Gaspar,d.1578.
The exercise of a Christian life. Written in Italian. Newely perused & corrected by the translatour. With certaine verie deuout exercises and praiers added therunto,more than were in the first edition. [Rheims? 1579?]
Translator's dedication signed: Iames Sancer [pseud.of Stephen Brinkley]
University microfilms no.16376 (carton 660)
Short-title catalogue no.16642.

1.Christian life. I.Brinkley,Stephen,tr.

NL 0430205 MiU

STC 16641.8
[Loarte, Gaspar] d. 1578.
The exercise of a Christian life. Written in Italian ... And newly translated into Englishe. by I. S. [London, William Carter, 1579]
2*8, A-2E8. (2*1, title-page, lacking.) 8vo. woodcuts.
Translator's preface is signed "Iames Sancer" [pseudonym for Stephen Brinkley]
Title and imprint taken from Allison and Rogers, v. 1, p. 217, no. 462.
Harmsworth copy.

NL 0430206 DFo

STC 16643
Loarte, Gaspar, d. 1578.
The exercise of a christian life. Writen in Italian ... Newly perused and corected by the translatour ... [Rouen] 1584.
*8, A-2F4 in alternating 8's and 4's, 2Q4. 12mo. woodcuts.
Translator's preface signed "Iames Sancer" [pseudonym of Stephen Brinkley]
Allison and Rogers, v. 1, p. 217, no. 463.
Harmsworth copy.

NL 0430207 DFo CtY IU

FILM
Loarte,Gaspar,d.1578.
The exercise of a Christian life. VVriten in Italian by ... Iaspar Loarte ... Nevvly perused and corected by the translatour. VVith certaine very deuout exercises and prayers added therunto ... [Rheims?] 1584.
Translator's dedication signed: Iames Sancer [pseud. of Stephen Brinkley]
University microfilms no.16377 (case 80,carton 475)
Short-title catalogue no.16643.

1.Christian life. I.Brinkley,Stephen,tr.

NL 0430208 MiU

STC 16643.2
[Loarte, Gaspar.]
The exercise of a christian life, written by G. L. Being the first ground and foundaion[!], whence the two treatises appertaining to resolution, were made and framed, by R. P. ...
[London] Printed [by P.Short] for W.Leake,and are to be sold in Pauls church yard at the signe of the Crane.1594.
4p.ℓ.,112 numb.ℓ.,2ℓ.,[3]p. 14.5cm.
Title within ornamental border (McK.& F.173)
Leaf 88 misnumbered 86.

Continued in next column

Continued from preceding column

"Faults escaped": leaf [114].
Colophon: Imprinted at London by Peter Short, for William Leake.
Translated by Stephen Brinkley.
No.1 in a volume of tracts.

NL 0430210 MH

STC 16642
Loarte, Gaspar, d. 1578.
The exercise of a christian life. Written in Italian ... Newely perused & corected by the translatour ... [Printed secretly in England. 1596 or 1597]
¶4, B-2F8. (2F6-8, probably blank, lacking.) 8vo.
Translator's preface signed "Iames Sancer" [pseudonym of Stephen Brinkley]
Dated [Rheims? 1579?] in STC but see Allison and Rogers, v. 1, p. 217, no. 464 and British Museum Catalogue (1962)
R. W. Sibthorp - Harmsworth copy.

NL 0430211 DFo

AW 1 R475: 1278
Loarte,Gaspar,d.1578.
The exercise of a Christian life ... translated into English by S.B. Newly perused,& set forth in a more perfect method ... With certaine very deuout exercises & praiers added thereunto ... [St.Omer, English College Press] 1610.
Dedicatory epistle by the translator,Stephen Brinkley.
Microfilm of original in the British Museum. Ann Arbor,Mich., University Microfilms, 1972. (Early English books,1475-1640,reel 1278)
STC no.16644. Microfilm
1.Christian life. I.Brinkley,Stephen,tr. II. Title.

NL 0430212 CaBVaU MiU

FILM
Loarte,Gaspar,d.1578.
[The exercise of a Christian life. n.p., 1634]
Title-page lacking; title from running title.
Translator's dedication signed: Iames Sancer [pseud.of Stephen Brinkley]
University microfilms no.17719 (carton 673)
Short-title catalogue no.16645a[i.e.Bishop Checklist no.16645.1]
1.Christian life. I.Brinkley,Stephen,tr.

NL 0430213 MiU

HH 11803a
[Loarte, Gaspar] d. 1578.
The godly garden of| GETHSEMANI, furnifhed with| holfome fruites of Meditation| and prayer, vpon the bleffed| paffion of Chrift our| Redeemer.| [printer's mark of John Windet, McKerrow 237]...[London, ca. 1580]
A-S8. 16mo. 9x6.5cm. Black letter.
A translation of his Instruttioni et avisi per meditare la passione di Christo.
Woodcut illustrations.

Some head margins shaved.
Brand-Heber-Britwell Court-Harmsworth copy.
18th century calf.

NL 0430215 DFo

FILM
Loarte, Gaspar, d. 1578.
The godly garden of Gethsemani,furnished with holsome fruites of meditation and prayer, vpon the blessed passion of Christ our Redeemer ... [n.p., ca.1590]
University microfilms no.16790 (carton 644)
Short-title catalogue no.11803a.

1.Meditation. 2.Jesus Christ—Passion—Meditations.

NL 0430216 MiU

Loarte, Gaspar, d. 1578.
Instructio confessariorum....Acces sit Institutio confessariorum...Martino Fornario... Mechliniae, Hanicq, 1822.
264 p.

NL 0430217 PU

Mxt55 I98
Loarte, Gaspar, d.1578.
Instrvctions and advertisements, how to meditate the misteries of the rosarie of the ... Virgin Mary. Written in Italian by ... Gaspar Loarte ... And newly translated into English [by John Fenn] ... [Rouen?1600?]
3p.ℓ.,125[i.e.123]numb.ℓ.,1ℓ. illus. 13cm.
Imprint as above taken from the Short-title catalogue. Typewritten note by J.P.R.Lyell (mounted in front of the volume) ascribes the book to a Paris press, ca.1580.

NL 0430218 CtY CSmH

FILM
Loarte,Gaspar,d.1578.
Instrvctions and advertisements,how to meditate the misteries of the rosarie of the ... Virgin Mary. Written in Italian by ... Gaspar Loarte ... And newly translated into English ... [Rouen? 1600?]
Half-title: The fifteene misteries of the rosarie of Ovr Ladie.
Translated by John Fenn. cf.Short-title catalogue.
"Litaniae Deiparae Virginis ... quae in alma domo Lauretana ... musicè decantari solent": sig.Pj-Q[iii]
University microfilms no.15928 (case 56,carton 336)
Short-title catalogue no.16646.
1.Rosary. I. Fenn,John,d.1615,tr.

NL 0430219 MiU

AW 1 R475: 1278
Loarte,Gaspar,d.1578.
Instructions and advertisements,how to meditate vpon the misteries of the rosarie ... newly translated into English. Whervnto is annexed briefe, meditations for the seuen euenings,and mornings of the weeke. Rouen, C.Hamillon, 1613.
Translated by John Fenn. Microfilm
Imperfect: p.201-208 lacking.
Microfilm of original in the British Museum. Ann Arbor,Mich., University Microfilms, 1972. (Early English books,1475-1640,reel 1278)
STC no.16647.
1.Rosary. I.Fenn,John,d.1615,tr. II. Title.

NL 0430220 CaBVaU MiU

LOARTE,Gaspar, d. 1578.
Instruttione et avisi,per meditare la passione di Christo Nostro Redentore,con alcune meditationi di essa. Roma,nel Collegio della Compagnia di Giesu,1570.
pp.(94). Engrs.

NL 0430221 MH

Loarte, Gaspar, d. 1578.
Libro del modo, de pigliare il givbileo ...
see under title

AW 1 R475: 1279
Loarte,Gaspar,d.1578.
Meditations,of the life and passion of our Lord and Sauior Iesus Christ. With the arte how to meditate. Written in the Italian,by ... Gaspar Loart ... [n.p., ca.1596?]
Printed secretly in England. Cf.A.F.Allison and D.M. Rogers,A catalogue of Catholic books in English.
Translation of Instruttioni e avisi per meditare la passione di Christo. Microfilm
Earlier ed.has title: The godly garden of Gethsemani.
Microfilm of original in the Bodleian Library. Ann Arbor,Mich., University Microfilms, 1972. (Early English books,1475-1640 —el 1279)
STC no.16648.
1.Jesus Christ-- Passion. I.Title.

NL 0430223 CaBVaU MiU

VOLUME 337

Loarte, Gaspar, d. 1578.
Opusculum de sacris peregrinationibus atque indulgentiis. Omnia nunc Latinitati donata per Ioannem Gelderman. Coloniæ Agrippinæ, sumptibus B. Gualteri, 1619.
nar. 24°. pp. (16), 128, (7), 128-407.
Richeome, Louis: Apologia pro sacris peregrinationibus, Tractatus de sanctis reliquiis, Tractatus de divitiis, pp. (7), 128-407. Each has individual title-page, 1619.

NL 0430224 MH

Loarte, Gaspar de, d. 1578.
Sehr fürtreffliche, heylsame, kurtze und klare Lehren oder Anleytungen, für die Priester vnd Beichvätter. Dillingen, 1596.

NL 0430225 WU

Z242
L781 Loarte, Gaspar, d. 1578.
Trattato della continva memoria che si debbe havere della sacra passione di Christo, redentore nostro... In Vinegia, Apresso Gabriel Giolito de' Ferrari, 1575.
48 p. illus. 14cm.

NL 0430226 MnU

Loarte, Lucas.
Historia de la vida, milagros, y virtvdes del glorioso san Lvis Bertran, del Orden de predicadores. Compvesta por el padre presentado fr. Lvcas Loartf [sic] ... Consagrala al glorioso patriarca santo Domingo de Guzman, padre, y fundador de la Orden de predicadores. Año de 1672. Con licencia. En Madrid, Por Francisco Sanz, en la Imprenta del reyno.
Microfilm copy, made in 1943, of the original in the Biblioteca nacional de Santiago de Chile. Positive.
Negative film in Brown university library.

Collation of the original, as determined from the film: 10 p. l., 370 (i. e. 360) p.
Errors in pagination: nos. 257-266 omitted; several other pages misnumbered.
Medina, Biblioteca hispano-americana, 1528.

1. Luis Bertrán, Saint, 1526-1581.
Microfilm AC-2 reel 244, no. 1 Mic A 49-850

Brown Univ. Library for Library of Congress [2]†

NL 0430228 RPB DLC

[Loase, John F]
Complete phonetic alphabet, by the use of which al words recognized as English, may be uniformly spelle as pronounced, etc. New York city, The author, °1895.
10 l. 21½cm.
Copyright by John F. Loase.

1. Phonetic alphabet.
11-16109
Library of Congress PE1151.L6

NL 0430229 DLC

[Loase, John F]
The phonetic structure of the English language, as it is in actual speech. [New York, °1895]
8 p. incl. tab. 17½ x 25½cm.

1. English language—Phonetics.
CA 11-2072 Unrev'd
Library of Congress PE1135.L7
——— Copy 2. 19½ x 28½cm.

NL 0430230 DLC CtY

Loat, Leonard
see
Loat, William Leonard Stevenson

Loat, Lily.
The Sydney smallpox outbreak in 1913, by Miss L. Loat... London: National Anti-Vaccination League, 1914. 7(1) p. 8°.
Read at the Rome congress of the Anti-Vaccination League.

1. Vaccination, Anti. 2. Smallpox, Australia: New South Wales: Sydney. 3. National Anti-Vaccination League.
N. Y. P. L. March 10, 1916.

NL 0430232 NN

Loat, Lily.
The truth about vaccination and immunization. London, Health for All Pub. Co. [1951]
64 p. 19 cm.

1. Vaccination. 2. Immunity. I. Title.
RA638.L6 55-37312 ‡
[1]

NL 0430233 DLC DNLM ICJ

Loat, William Leonard Stevenson.
The Cemeteries of Abydos
Pub. by order of the Committee. London and Boston, Mass., Sold at the offices of the Egypt exploration fund; [etc., etc.] 19 -

---

Loat, William Leonard Stevenson.
Boulenger, George Albert, 1858-
... The fishes of the Nile. By G. A. Boulenger ... London, Pub. for the Egyptian government by H. Rees, ltd., 1907.

Loat, William Leonard Stevenson.
Gurob.
— [London. Quaritch. 1905.] (3), 8 pp. 19 plates. [British School of Archaeology in Egypt and Egyptian Research Account. 10th year. 1904.] 31 cm., in 4s.

L6507 — S.r. — Gurob, Egypt. Antiq.

NL 0430236 MB PU

Loat, William Leonard Stevenson, joint author.
Ayrton, Edward Russell, 1882-1914.
Pre-dynastic cemetery at El Mahasna, by Edward R. Ayrton and W. L. S. Loat ... Pub. by order of the Committee. London and Boston, Mass., Sold at the offices of the Egypt exploration fund [etc., 1911]

Loat, William Leonard Stevenson.
Murray, Margaret Alice.
... Saqqara mastabas, part I. By Margaret A. Murray. London, B. Quaritch, 1905.

Loats, Henry Andrew, 1913-
A program of industrial arts for the preparation of elementary teachers, Ball state teachers college, Muncie, Indiana ... 1950.
238 numb. l.
Thesis (Ph.D.) - Ohio state university, 1950.

NL 0430239 OU

Loaysa, Balthasar de.
Arte de la lengua hegue.
164 p. 18 cm.
Contents. - Grammer. - Catechism. Vocabulary.
Photographic copy of ms. formerly owned by Father Fisher, Maximilian's confessor.
Pages 123-126.missing.

NL 0430240 LNHT ICN

Loaysa, Bartolomé de.
Microfilm AC-2 reel 237, no. 3
Valdivieso y Torrejón, Miguel de.
Alegacion juridica en defensa del derecho con que el coronèl d. Bartholomé de Loaysa litiga el senecimiento de la compañia que escrituró sobre sus minas de Guantajaya. Escribiala el doctor don Miguel Valdivieso y Torrejôn ... Con licencia del superior govierno. Impresso en Lima, Por Francisco Sobrino, en la calle del Tigre, año de 1757.

Loaysa, Bartolomé de.
Defensa en derecho por el conde de San Ysidro, d. Juan Baptista de Casabona, y d. Francisco Gonzales Valdèz
see under Silva y la Vanda, Manuel de.

Loaysa, Blas de Herrera
see
Herrera Loaysa, Blas de, *17th cent.*

Loaysa, Garcia de
see
Loaisa, García de *cardinal*, 1479?-1546.

Loaysa, Garcia Jofre de
see Loaisa, Garcia Jofre de, fl. 16th cent.

Loaysa, Jofre de, 13th cent.
Chronique des Rois de Castille (1248-1305) Publiée par Alfred Morel-Fatio. Paris, 1898.
p. 325-378.
Extrait de la Bibliotheque de l'École des chartes, t. LIX, 1898.

NL 0430246 NNH NN

Loaysa, Juan de, pseud.
see Aranda, Gabriel de, d. 1709.

VOLUME 336

Loaysa, Pedro
Oraciones que se pronunciaron el diez y el diez y seis de julio del presente año: la una en la iglesia catedral de Lima en la misa de accion de gracias por la victoria que reportaron las armas del Peru sobre insurgentes del Rio de la Plata. La otra en el santuario de nuestra patrona Santa Rosa con ocasion de colocarse en el una de las banderas del egercito derrotado ... Los₍!₎ dijo el R.P.lect.eray₍!₎ Pedro Laysa ... Las saca á luz el Excmo.Cabildo de esta ciudad de Lima. ₍Lima₎Imprenta de los huerfanos,1811.
1p.ℓ.,46,28,₍i.e.36₎p. 19cm ₍Lettered on binding: Papeles₎
Celebrates the victory of Huaqui.
Pages 29-36 of 2d pagination wrongly numbered 21-28.

NL 0430249 CtY

Loaysa Girón, Pedro García de, *abp.*
see
García de Loaysa Girón, Pedro, *abp.*, 1542-1599.

Loayza, Carlos Arenas y
see
Arenas y Loayza, Carlos.

Loayza, Fernando Lopez
see
Lopez Loayza, Fernando

Loayza, Florencio.
... Condición legal de las comunidades indígenas; tesis presentada á la Universidad de Arequipa para optar el grado de doctor en la Facultad de derecho y obtener el título de abogado. Arequipa, Tip. Caceres, 1911.
25 p. 20½cm.

1. Indians of South America—Peru. 2. Indians of South America—Law and legislation. 3. Village communities—Peru. 4. Land tenure—Peru.
Library of Congress F3430.L6 43-40644
₍3₎

NL 0430253 DLC TNJ

Loayza, Francisco A
... Cahuide no existió; ensayo crítico-histórico, basado en antiguos documentos irrefutables, por Francisco A. Loayza. Lima, Perú ₍D. Miranda₎ 1944.
155 p., 2 l. illus. (facsim.) fold. pl., fold. map. 18½cm. (Los Pequeños grandes libros de historia americana. Ser. I, t. VI)

1. Peru—Hist.—Conquest, 1522-1548. 2. Kullash, d. 1536. I. Title.
A 46-1325
New York. Public library for Library of Congress ₍3₎

NL 0430254 NN TxU CU PSt PPT NjP

G985
L782c
1948
LOAYZA, FRANCISCO A
... Cahuide no se llamó Cahuide; ensayo crítico-histórico, basado en antiguos documentos irrefutables, por Francisco A. Loayza. (2. ed.) Lima, Peru [D. Miranda] 1948.
1p.ℓ.,155p.,2ℓ. illus.(facsim.) fold. pl., fold. map. 19½cm. (Los Pequeños grandes libros de historia americana. Ser.I, t.VI)
First edition, Lima, 1944, was published under title: Cahuide no existió.
1. Peru - Hist. - Conquest, 1522-1548. 2. Kullash, d. 1536. I. Loayza, Francisco A. Cahuide no existió. II. Title. III. Title: Cahuide no existió. IV. Series.

NL 0430255 TxU

Loayza, Francisco A
Chinos llegaron antes que Colón; tesis arqueológica, trascendental, sustentada por 150 de los más famosos autores, antiguos y modernos ... Lima ₍D. Miranda₎ 1948.
227 p. illus., maps. 19 cm. (Los Pequeños grandes libros de historia americana, ser. I, t. 14)

1. America—Disc. & explor.—Chinese. 2. America—Antiq. I. Title. (Series)
E109.C5L6 973.12 49-18214*

NL 0430256 DLC DPU TxU MnU ICN CtY CU

868.33
L795C
Loayza, Francisco A
Ciudad trágica; novela histórica peruana [por] Francisco A. Loayza. Pintó la portada Julio Malaga Grenet. Ilustró el texto M. Benavides Garate. Barcelona, Editorial Maucci [1935?]
303 p. illus. 20 cm.
Bibliographical references included in "Matrices históricas de 'Ciudad trágica'": p. [289]-296.
1. Peru. History. Conquest, 1522-1548. Fiction. I. Title.

NL 0430257 NcD CU WU InU DLC-P4 IU

Loayza, Francisco A ed.
Las costumbres antiguas del Peru y "La historia de los Incas" (Siglo XVI)
see under Valera, Blas, 1551-1597.

F3429
.M69
Loayza, Francisco A., ed.
Molina, Cristóbal de, *of Santiago de Chile*, 1494?-1578.
... Las crónicas de los Molinas. "Destrucción del Perú," crónica escrita por el año de 1553 por Cristóbal de Molina, sochantre de la catedral de Santiago de Chile. "Fábulas y ritos de los Incas," crónica escrita allá por el año de 1574 por Cristóbal de Molina, párroco de Ntra. Sra. de los Remedios del hospital del Cuzco. Prólogo bio-bibliográfico por Carlos A. Romero. Epílogo crítico-bibliográfico por Raúl Porras Barrenechea. Anotaciones y brevísimos comentarios por Francisco A. Loayza. Lima, Perú ₍Lib. y imp. D. Miranda₎ 1943.

F3444
.T9
Loayza, Francisco A., ed.
Túpac-Amaru, Juan Bautista, 1742?-1827.
... Cuarenta años de cautiverio (memorias del inka Juan Bautista Túpac Amaru) Prólogo de Carlos A. Romero ... Notas, comentarios y adiciones de documentos inéditos por Francisco A. Loayza. Lima, Perú ₍Lib. e imp. D. Miranda₎ 1941.

G985
L782cu
Loayza, Francisco A
... Culto libre entre los inkas, por Francisco A. Loayza; tesis presentada por su autor al Congreso americanista realizado en Sevilla, en 1935. Religión en Huarochiri; crónica escrita por el presbítero Francisco de Avila, en el año de 1608. Religión en Huamachuco; informe escrito por varios frailes agustinos en el año de 1557, de trascendental importancia. Lima, Perú [Librería e imprenta "D. Miranda"] 1952.
xv, 117p.,1ℓ. plates. 18cm. (Los pequeños grandes libros de historia americana, serie I, tomo XVII)
The "Religión en Huamachuco" (p.[47]-103) appears in Kechua, Latin, and Spanish under title: Francisci de Avila De priscorum huaruchiriensium origine et institutis ...
The "Huesos de gigantes" (p.105-117) is signed and dated: Quito, 16 de abril de 1780.—José García de León y Pizarro.

NL 0430262 MnU CtY TxU NjP MH-P KU CU PU IEN ICN NNC IU

F3444
.S3
Loayza, Francisco A., ed.
Sahuaraura Titu Atauchi, Rafael José.
... Estado del Perú; códice escrito en 1780 y que contiene datos importantes sobre la revolución de José Gabriel Túpac Amaru por Raphael José Sahuaraura Titu Atauchi. Notas, comentarios y adiciones de documentos inéditos por Francisco A. Loayza. Lima, Perú ₍D. Miranda₎ 1944.

Loayza, Francisco A
Fray Calixto Túpak Inka, documentos originales y, en su mayoría, totalmente desconocidos, auténticos, de este apóstol indio, valiente defensor de su raza, desde el año de 1746 a 1760. Las doce dudas, códice del año de 1570, de autor anónimo. Bibliografía particular del indígena se escribió el año de 1828 por José Domingo Chokewanka. Coordinación, acotaciones, comentarios y notas breves, por Francisco A. Loayza. Lima ₍D. Miranda₎ 1948.
ix, 144 p. port. 20 cm. (Los Pequeños grandes libros de historia americana, ser. 1, t. 15)
1. Túpac Inca, Calixto de San José, Brother, b. 1710? 2. Peru—Hist.—1548-1820. I. Chokewanka, José Domingo. II. Title: Las doce dudas. III. Title: Bibliografía particular del indígena. (Series)
F3444.T895L8 980.2 49-27868*
₍4₎

NL 0430264 DLC TxU ICN CU

F3444
.T893
Loayza, Francisco A., ed.
Tupac-Amaru, José Gabriel, *originally* Condorcanqui, *d.* 1781.
Genealogía de Túpac Amaru, por José Gabriel Túpac Amaru (documento inédito del año de 1777) Causas de la sublevación indígena, por Antonio González Pavón (documento inédito del año de 1788) Daños que se hacen a los Indios, por Francisco Falcón (códice del siglo XVI) Arreglo, introducción, notas y comentarios de Francisco A. Loayza. Lima, 1946.

Loayza, Francisco A
... El inka piadoso y justiciero (cuentos reales y leyendas extrañas) Barcelona, Maucci ₍1934₎
158 p., 1 l. front. (port.) 20½cm.

I. Title.
Library of Congress PQ8496.L6 I 5 44-49000
₍2₎ 863.6

NL 0430266 DLC PSt ICU NSyU CU MH ViU

VOLUME 337

Loayza, Francisco A *ed.*
... Juan Santos, el invencible (manuscritos del año de 1742 al año de 1755) Prólogo de Carlos A. Romero ... Notas y brevísimos comentarios de Francisco A. Loayza. Lima, Perú ₍Editorial D. Miranda₎ 1942.
xv, 246, ₍2₎ p. illus. (port.) fold. maps, fold. facsim. 19 cm. (Los Pequeños grandes libros de historia americana, ser. I, t. II)
"Erratas advertidas": p. ₍3₎ of cover.
1. Atahualpa, Juan Santos, fl. 1742. 2. Peru—Hist.—1548-1820—Sources. I. Title.
Harvard Univ. Library for Library of Congress F3444.A8L6 A 44—636
₍a49d½₎† 980.2

NL 0430267 MH DLC PPT PSt CU NcU WU ICU TxU OCl

4AC 120 Loayza, Francisco A
Llamaradas. Lima, Imp. "La Libertad", 1912.
153 p.

NL 0430268 DLC-P4

Loayza, Francisco A
... Manko Kapa (el fundador del imperio de los inkas fué japonés)... Pará, 1926. 133 p. maps. 19cm.
"Notas bibliográficas," p. 125-130.
1. Manco-Capac I, emperor of Cuzco, fl. 1021-1062. 2. Indians, American—Origin. 3. American languages—Quechua. 4. American languages—Indian words in foreign languages, Japanese. 5. Japanese language—Foreign words and phrases, Indian-American.

NL 0430269 NN NcD TxU

Loayza, Francisco A *ed.*
... Mártires y heroínas (documentos inéditos del año de 1780 a 1782) Introducción, adiciones, notas y comentarios de Francisco A. Loayza. Lima, Perú ₍D. Miranda₎ 1945.
205 p., 1 l. 1 illus. 18cm. (Los Pequeños grandes libros de historia americana. Ser. I, t. IX)
CONTENTS.—Micaela Bastidas.—Tomasa Titu Condemayta.—Cecilia Túpac Amaru.
1. Peru—Hist.—Insurrection of Tupac-Amaru, 1780-1781. 2. Bastidas, Micaela, d. 1781. 3. Titu Condemayta, Tomasa, d. 1781. 4. Túpac Amaru, Cecilia, d. 1783.
F3444.L82 985 47-1548

NL 0430270 DLC TxU PSt LNHT WU MH

4PL28 Loayza, Francisco A
Perlas de Oriente, proverbios-poesias-mujeres. Yokohama, Impr. Kinkosha, 1919.
155 p.

NL 0430271 DLC-P4

Loayza, Francisco A.
... Plantas textiles. Este informe consular, resultado de estudios directos, se ha llevado a cabo por orden e, iniciativa del Señor Presidente de la República, Doctor don José Pardo. ₍Lima? 1917.₎ 38 p. 16°.
1. Textile plants, Peru.
N. Y. P. L. November 30, 1921.

NL 0430272 NN

Loayza, Francisco A *ed.*
Preliminares del incendio; documentos del año de 1776 a 1780, en su mayoría inéditos, anteriores y sobre la Revolución Libertadora que engendró y dió vida José Gabriel Túpak Amaru, en 1780. Coordinación, acotaciones, comentarios y notas breves por Francisco A. Loayza. Lima, 1947.
158 p. facsims. 19 cm. (Los Pequeños grandes libros de historia americana, ser. 1, t. 13)
1. Peru — Hist. — Insurrection of Tupac-Amaru, 1780-1781. 2. Tupac-Amaru, José Gabriel, originally Condorcanqui, d. 1781. I. Title. (Series)
F3444.L825 985 49-20928*
₍₄₎

IEN WU
NL 0430273 DLC CU CtY OU TxU MnU ICN CU-B NcD MH

Loayza, Francisco A.
Simiente japonesa (leyendas y cuentos antiquos del Japon) con ilustraciones de Bumpo Miwa. Yokohama, Lit. imp. Konkosha, 1913.
290 p.

NL 0430274 OCl

F3444 .V46 Loayza, Francisco A., ed.
... La verdad desnuda; o, Las dos faces de un obispo; escrita en 1780 por un imparcial religioso. Introducción, notas y brevísimos comentarios de Francisco A. Loayza. Lima, Perú ₍Editorial de D. Miranda₎ 1943.

Loayza, Geronimo de, Abp., d. 1575.
Constituciones y ordenamientos hechos por el arzobispo de los reyes ... y los obispos
see under Lima (Ecclesiastical province) Council, 1552.

Loayza, Gerónimo de, Abp., d. 1575.
Ereccion de la santa iglesia metropolitana de Lima, seguida de la regla consueta y ritual diurno
see under Lima (Archdiocese)

Loayza, Geronimo de, abp., d. 1575
Traslado de una carta quel arzobispo de los Reyes excribio a los del consejo de las Indias del asiento de Canas sobre la robelion de Francisco Hernandez ...
(In Colleccion de documentos ineditos. Madrid, 1865. 21 1/2 cm. v. 3. p. 233-246)
E123 .C69

NL 0430278 DLC

Loayza, Hiram, 1889–
Compendio de derecho procesal civil, concordado con el Código de procedimiento civil boliviano, la Ley de organización judicial y leyes reformatorias, por Hiram Loayza ... La Paz, Bolivia ₍Empresa El Universo, 1946₎
4 p. l., ₍5₎-280 p. 19cm.
"Edición financiada por la 'Fundación universitaria Simón I. Patiño'."
1. Civil procedure—Bolivia.
47-23413

NL 0430279 DLC

Loayza, Hiram, 1889–
... El espionaje en Bolivia; delito de deserción frustrada proceso militar contra suboficiales extranjeros y civiles extranjeros. La Paz, Imp. artística, 1928.
2 p. l., ₍3₎-58 p., 1 l. 18½cm.
1. Spies. I. Title.
Library of Congress F3324.L6 44-50775

NL 0430280 DLC

Loayza, Hiram, comp.
Bolivia. *Laws, statutes, etc.*
Juicios de hacienda, comprende juicio coactivo—juicio de cuentas fiscales—juicios de comiso y defraudación—juicio coactivo municipal, compilación concordada y anotada por Hiram Loayza, con suplemento derecho administrativo ... por el doctor Enrique Mallea Balboa. La Paz, Imp. Velarde, 1906.

Loayza, Hiram.
... La riqueza petrolífera de Caupolicán y norte de Bolivia. La Paz, González y Medina, 1920.
2 p. l., 70 p., 1 l. 21cm.
1. Petroleum—Bolivia.
Library of Congress TN873.B6L6 21-3087

NL 0430282 DLC TxU FU CU

Loayza, José Jorge, 1827-
Peru. *Laws, statutes, etc.*
Proyecto de Código civil para la república del Perú, formado por los d. d. Juan Luna—Simón Gregorio Paredes—José Jorge Loayza—Manuel Santos Pasapera—Francisco M. Fernández. Lima, Impr. de J. F. Solis, 1890.

LOAYZA, José Manuel de.
Lijera contestacion al folleto publicado por Anjel Telleria sobre la cuarta parte y ganado de la finca de Pariri. Paz de Ayacucho 1868.

NL 0430284 MH-L

PQ8497 .L568P43 Loayza, Luis Aurelio.
Una piel de serpiente. [Lima] Populibros peruanos [n.d.]
120 p. (Populibros peruanos, 8 ser. a, no. 37)

NL 0430285 NBuU KyU

4PQ Span Am-555 Loayza, Luis Aurelio.
Piltrafas; cosas de mi tierra. Lima, E. Rosay, 1910.
109 p. (His Romances)

NL 0430286 PSt CtY DLC-P4

₍Loayza, Mariano M de₎
Refutacion a las observaciones publicadas por el sr. Encargado de negocios de S.M.B., d. B.H. Wilson, el el Correo n. 47. Por M.M.L. Lima, Imp. de J.M. Masias, 1840.
17 p. 18½cm.
Signed: Mariano M. de Loayza.

NL 0430287 MH-L

VOLUME 337

Loayza Beltrán, Fernando
see
Loaiza Beltrán, Fernando.

F 1414 L6 Loayza Camargo, Hernando.
Las nuevas generaciones ante los actuales problemas latinoamericanos; radiografía de un continente cuyo futuro es tan halagador como incierto. [Bogotá?, n. d.]
53p. port. 21cm.

Cover title.

1. Latin America - Politics - 1948- 2. Latin America - Soc. condit. I. Title.

NL 0430289 MU

Loayza de Brito, Julia.
Pétalos. La Paz, Bolivia, 1947.
88 p. port. 19 cm.
Poems.

I. Title.

PQ7819.L6P4 861.6 47-28258*

NL 0430290 DLC

Loayza Guerra, H Isaías.
... La autonomía de las nacionalidades en el Perú (sugerencia para la autonomía de las nacionalidades en el Perú). Arequipa, Perú, 1940 [i. e. 1941]
100 p. 21 x 17ᶜᵐ.

At head of title: Tesis para optar el grado de bachiller en la Facultad de filosofía, historia y letras [de la Universidad di Arequipa]
Colophon dated 1941.
"Bibliografía": p. 96-97.

1. Indians of South America—Peru. I. Title.

46-30115

Library of Congress F3430.L63
[2] 980.4

NL 0430291 DLC DPU NcD NIC IU ICU

Loayza V , Wenceslao.
Apañaqui diósana arunacapa yatiñataqui ... Laja curaua, castellanota aymararu haccoquipi, hukkampi khanachásina ... 2. ed. corr. y augm. ... La Paz, Tip. "El Illimani" Calle Gral González, 1918.
72 p. 25 cm.
[No. 6] in a volume of pamphlets lettered: Quechua.

NL 0430292 NcD

Loayzaga, Manuel de
see Loaisaga, Manuel de.

Loazes, Ferdinandus de
see Loaces, Fernando de, 1497-1568.

Lob, Albert.
Zwei weltanschauungen! Von ingenieur Albert Lob ... Düsseldorf, A. Lob [1925-
v. 22ᶜᵐ.

1. Finance—Germany. 2. Germany—Econ. condit.—1918- I. Title.
26-6179

Library of Congress HC286.3.L6

NL 0430295 DLC

WO 11 L796c 1950 LOB, Alfons, 1900-
Die Chirurgie im Wandel der Zeiten. [Wilhelmshaven, 1950?]
54 p. illus., port. (Wilhelmshavener Vorträge, Heft 6)
1. Surgery - Hist. Series

NL 0430296 DNLM MH

RD11 V957 v.8 1936 Lob, Alfons, 1900-
Die Kurzwellenbehandlung in der Chirurgie. Stuttgart, F. Enke, 1936.
68 p. 26 cm. (Vorträge aus der praktischen Chirurgie, 8. Heft)

1. Short wave therapy. 2. Diathermy. I. Title.
242064 (Series)

NL 0430297 CU-M DNLM

Lob, Alfons, 1900-
Ueber karzinome des duodenums. (Auszug).
Inaug. diss. Bonn, 1923.

NL 0430298 ICRL

Lob, Alfons, 1900-
... Die wirbelsäulenverletzungen und ihre ausheilung; experimentelle, pathologisch-anatomische und röntgenologisch-klinische untersuchungen, von dozent dr. med. habil. Alfons Lob ... Mit einem geleitwort von professor dr. G. Magnus ... Mit 289 abbildungen. Leipzig, G. Thieme, 1941.
182 p. illus. 29ᶜᵐ. (Added t.-p.: Archiv und atlas der normalen und pathologischen anatomie in typischen röntgenbildern)
Fortschritte auf dem gebiete der röntgenstrahlen ... Ergänzungsbd. 61.

1. Spine—Diseases. I. Title.

45-34808

Library of Congress RD690.L6
[2] 616.73

NL 0430299 DLC ICU NNC

Lob, Alfons, 1900-
Die Wirbelsäulenverletzungen und ihre Ausheilung: pathologische Anatomie, Klinik, Röntgendiagnostik, Begutachtungs- und Zusammenhangsfragen. 2., verm. und neugestaltete Aufl. Stuttgart, G. Thieme, 1954.
272 p. illus. 29 cm. (Archiv und Atlas der normalen und pathologischen Anatomie in typischen Röntgenbildern)
Fortschritte auf dem Gebiete der Röntgenstrahlen vereinigt mit Röntgenpraxis, Ergänzungsband 61.

1. Spine—Diseases. I. Title.

RD768.L82 1954 55-28563 ‡

NL 0430300 DLC MBCo MiU DNLM NNC-M ICU

Lob, Antal.
A d-galactose uj methyles acetonszarmazekai.
Inaug. diss. Budapest, 1927.

NL 0430301 ICRL

Lob, Berthold.
Ueber Abortus arteficialis bei einem kyphotischquerverengtem Becken. Heidelberg, Horning, 1893.
37 p.
Inaug.-Diss.

NL 0430302 PPC

Lob, Chester Godfrey, 1926-
Radial beam velocity modulated microwave tube. Ann Arbor, University Microfilms, 1951.
([University Microfilms, Ann Arbor, Mich.] Publication no. 2735)
Microfilm copy of typescript. Positive.
Collation of the original: iv, 51 l. illus., diagrs.
Thesis—University of Illinois.
Abstracted in Microfilm abstracts, v. 11 (1951) no. 4, p. 978-979.
Vita.
Bibliography: leaf 50.

1. Klystrons. I. Title.
Microfilm AC-1 no. 2735 Mic A 51-476

Michigan. Univ. Libr. for Library of Congress [1]†

NL 0430303 MiU IU DLC

Lob, Eugène, 1909-
... Névrites optiques et conjonctivites arsenicales ... Paris, 1936.
Thèse - Univ. de Paris.
"Bibliographie": p. [66]-68.

NL 0430304 CtY

Lob, Georges.
N.N'-dibenzyl-aethyleendiamine ... Leiden, [1935?]
Proefschrift - Leiden.
Summary in English.

NL 0430305 CtY

Lob, Jean.
Les pouvoirs de l'exécuteur testamentaire en droit suisse. Fribourg, Librairie de l'Université [1952]
151 p. 24 cm.

1. Executors and administrators—Switzerland. I. Title.

53-36377 ‡

NL 0430306 DLC CU-L TxU MH-L NNC ICU

W 4 L38 1945 LOB, Marc
Les problèmes fonctionnels posés par la silicose pulmonaire. Bâle, Schwabe, 1945.
28 p. illus.
Thèse - Lausanne.
Also published in the Journal suisse de médecine, 1945, nos. 13 and 14.

NL 0430307 DNLM

Lob, Marcel, tr.
Discours
see Cicero, Marcus Tullius. Orationes. Latin and French.

VOLUME 337

PQ 2635 05 Z7524 Lob, Marcel
Un grand Bourguignon, un grand Européen: Romain Rolland. D'après la conférence prononcée à l'Hôtel de Ville de Sens le 30 mars 1927. Auxerre, Impr. Tridon-Gallot, 1927.
83p. 19cm.

1. Rolland, Romain, 1866-1944 I. Title

NL 0430309 WU

---

32 10061 Lob, Otto, 1837-1908.
Israelitische tempel-gesaenge. Hymnen fuer sabbath- und fest-tage mit deutschem und englischem text. Chicago, E. Rubovits, 1876.
56 p., 1 l. 12°.

NL 0430310 DLC OCH

---

q784.3 Sh37 v.14 no.33 Lob, Otto, 1837-1908.
Love's lament. Fuer einen. [By] Otto Lob. [Chicago, Molter & Wurlitzer; Root & Cady; etc., etc., c1868]
5p. (His Six songs with English and German words. Op.42,no.3)
[Sheet music printed in Chicago prior to 1871. v.14,no.33]
Caption title.
"English version by Martin Meyer."

I. Meyer, Martin. tr. II. Title.

NL 0430311 IU

---

q784.3 Sh37 v.15 no.43 Lob, Otto, 1837-1908.
... Picnic, waltz by Otto Lob. Chicago, Root & Cady, c1865.
7p.

[Sheet music printed in Chicago prior to 1871. v.15,no.43]
Piano solo.
Plate no.: 704 6.

1. Pianoforte music. I. Title.

NL 0430312 IU

VM 2062.3 L 79s LOB, OTTO, *1837-1908.*
Praise to the great creator. Trio. Soprano, mezzo soprano & contralto... [Boston, Ditson, c1875]
7p. (Otto Lob's sacred trios. 1st collection. no.6)

Caption title.
Vocal score with organ accompaniment.
Plate no.: 45040 (1875)

NL 0430313 ICN MB

---

q784.3 Sh37 v.14 no.32 Lob, Otto, 1837-1908.
Repose. Geh'zur ruh. Words by Marg. Pilgram Diehl. Music by Otto Lob. [Chicago, Molter & Wurlitzer; Root & Cady; etc., etc., c1868]
5p. (His Six songs with English and German words. Op.42,no.2)
[Sheet music printed in Chicago prior to 1871. v.14,no.32]
Caption title.
"English version by Martin Meyer."
I. Diehl, Margaret Pilgram. II. Meyer, Martin, tr. III. Title.

NL 0430314 IU

VM 2062.3 L 79s LOB, OTTO, *1837-1908, ed and comp.*
Otto Lob's sacred trios. 1st collection... Boston, Ditson, c1875.
8v.in 1.

Vocal score with organ accompaniment.
Contents.—no.1. C.M.V.Weber. Lord, thy glory.—no.2. E.Mehul. Praise thou the Lord.—no.3. L.Spohr. Loud proclaim.—no.4. R.Wagner. Bow down thine ear.—no.5. Otto Nicolai. Saviour, breathe.—no.6. Otto Lob. Praise to the great.—no.7. H. Marschner. Sweet peace—no.8. G.Rossini. O, Lord, dismiss us.

NL 0430315 ICN

VM 2062.4 L 79s LOB, OTTO, *1837-1908.*
Six sacred quartetts for public worship and social circle... Boston, O.Ditson & co., c1870.
7v.in 1.

Op.51-56.
Vocal score with organ accompaniment.
Includes 3 copies of no.2, one in manuscript, also a manuscript copy of the bass part of no.3.
Contents.—The earth is the Lord's.—Angels ever bright.—The Lord is in His holy temple.—In time of tribulation.—Thy will be done—Softly now the light.

NL 0430316 ICN

M1619 S69 v.557 Lob, Otto, 1837-1908.
[Du lichter Stern; unacc.]
Thou lovely star (Du lichter Stern) Quartett for female voices, op.73, no.1. Chicago, Chicago Music Co., c1879.
4 p. 30cm.
Caption title.
Text in English and German.
Vol. 557 in a set lettered: Songs.
Copies 2-4 in same folder.
1.Vocal quartets (Women's voices) I.Title. II.Title: Thou lovely star.

NL 0430317 CSt

Lob der deutschen Sprache, Ansprachen von sechs Schweizer Autoren, am 6. März 1941, im Zunfthaus zur Meise, Zürich, mit den einleitenden Worten des Verlegers. Zürich, Atlantis Verlag [°1941]
51 p. 19 cm.
CONTENTS.—Einleitende Worte des Verlegers, von M. Hürlimann.—Sprechen und Sprache, von T. Vogel.—Schweizer Art im alemannischen Gedicht, von G. Thürer.—Sprache und Wesen, von A. Zollinger.—Die Universalität der deutschen Sprache, von E. Jaeckle.—Johann Jacob Bodmers Beispiel, von F. Ernst.—Gottfried Kellers Meisterschaft, von E. Staiger.
1. German language—Addresses, essays, lectures.
PF3035.L6 50-53048

NL 0430318 DLC

Lilly Library Z 127 .A2 L7 LOB DER EDLEN KUNST BUCH-DRUCKEREY. [Prag, Für den Verlag Herbert Reichner gesetzt von der Privatpresse Jaroslav Picka, 1933.
1 p.l., [10] p., [1] l. illus. 16.8 cm.

With woodcuts of František Vik.
In blue cloth with imitation leather spine.

NL 0430319 InU

Lob der ehe worte bedeutender Denker. Bern, Verlag"Die Fähre"[1951?]
21p.

NL 0430320 CtY DLC-P4

Lob der torheit
see Erasmus, Desiderius, d. 1536. Moriae encomium. German.

Lob des buches, ein almanach für bücherfreunde, 1936. Unbekannte aussprüche über das buch und seine umwelt aus allen zeiten gesammelt. [Potsdam, Gedruckt bei E. Stichnote, 1936]
78 p., 1 l. 15cm.

1. Books. 2. Quotations, German.
42-84073
Library of Congress Z992.L8

NL 0430322 DLC CtY

Lob des Krieges. London, etc., Europa-Verlag 1940.
22,[2] p. 15 cm.
"Informations-Schriften,1."
Cover title.

NL 0430323 MH

Lob des Landlebens
see under [Gleim, Johann Wilhelm Ludwig] 1719-1803.

Das Lob des tugendsamen Weibes
see under Kramer, Ludwig von, illus.

---

sLob-dpon
see
Padma Sambhava, ca. 717-ca. 762.

Lob Gottes aus kindermund; lieberbuch für Sonntagsschulen und kindergottesdienste. Heilbronn, Haering, n.d.
136 p.
Issued by the Sonntagschule, Heilbronn.

NL 0430327 PPLT

Lob Gottes im deutschen Gedicht. [Die Auswahl der Gedichte besorgte Richard Hoyer; Geleitwort von Jacob Kneip. Köln, Greven Verlag [1953]
320 p. 20 cm.

1. Religious poetry, German. I. Hoyer, Richard, 1904- comp.
PT1229.L6 54-20662 ‡

NL 0430328 DLC CtY

Lob und anbetung des Gottmenschen, am tage der einweihung der neuen orgel in der Deutschen Evangelisch lutherischen Zions kirche in Philadelphia ...
see under [Helmuth, Justus Henry Christian 1745-1825.

VOLUME 337

Lob-und danck andacht; zu der Göttlichen dreyfaltigkeit so glorwürdig ist in denen heiligen: ist gerichtet auff die hohe ehren-täg eines jeden heiligen oder seeligen. Wienn, Wolffgang Schwendimann, 1716.
[32p]

Bound with Wunder-und inser-spiegel der seelige Joannes Franciscus Regis.

NL 0430330 MoSU-D

Lob- und ehrenrede auf die helige Inquisition. Wien, n.p., 1782.
87 p.

NL 0430331 PU

Lob- und Ehrenrede des heiligen Erzmarthrers Stephaus gehalten von einem Pater aus dem heiligen Francisci Orden. [n.p.] 1777.

64 p. 18 cm. [Pamphlets on Austrian history. 1777:1]

1. Stephen, Saint, martyr.

NL 0430332 MnU CSt

LOB- Und Freudengesang zur Ehre unsers ...Königs und Herrn Friedrich Wilhelms des Zweiten...Gesungen von der Jüdischen Gemeinde zu Warschau...im Jahre 1796.
f° 21p Printed on silk. Covers red silk.
1.History-Poland-Warsaw. 2.History-Germany-Warsaw. 3.Liturgy-Special.
4.Hebrew title:
שיר תודה ושמחה לכבוד...פריעדריך ווילהעלם
השני...ווארשוי,תקנ"ו

NL 0430333 NNJ

252
L796

Loba, Jean Frederic
Wanted: The man who can and will. A message to young men, by Jean Frederic Loba, pastor of the First Congregational church, Evanston, Illinois. Printed by his friends. [Chicago, Ill., R.R. Donnelley & sons company, 1899]
27p., 1l. 20cm.

NL 0430334 IEN

Pamph
v.608

LOBA oba keplokah-keh sa-ah Jesus Christ. The death and resurrection of Christ. The passion story in Yakurr. [Shomolu, Kajola Print. Works] [n.d.]
13p. 18.5cm.

Cover-title.
Issued by the Institute of Linguistics.

NL 0430335 MH-AH

Lobach (Fredericus Albertus Arminius) [1816-]. *Pericarditidis rheumaticæ cum morbo cardiaco veterum comparatio. 30 pp., 1 l. 8°. *Berolini, typ. Nietackianis*, [1840].

NL 0430336 DNLM

Lobach, Katherine S

The referee's wife takes time out; a woman looks sports in the eye. New York, Exposition Press [1951]

91 p. 23 cm.

1. Sports. I. Title.

GV707.L6 796 51-11855 ‡

NL 0430337 DLC NN

Lobach, Walter 1863-
Die anomale rotationsdispersion in eisen... Inaug. Diss. Berlin, 1890 (Leipzig)

NL 0430338 ICRL

TL752
.L6

Lobach-Zhuchenko, Boris Mikhaĭlovich.

Передвижная таблица "Расчет парашютного прыжка." Под ред. Я. Д. Мошковского. Одобрено и рекомендовано для парашютных станций Осоавиахима. [Москва, Союзоргучет, 1937]

[3] p., 2 tables (1 sliding) 12 x 22 cm.

Cover title.

1. Parachutes. I. Title.
Title transliterated: Peredvizhnaia tablitsa.

50-50909

NL 0430339 DLC

Lobach-Zhuchenko, Boris Mikhaĭlovich.

... Развитие авиационных двигателей и их современное состояние. Москва [Издательство "Военный вестник"] 1924.

189, [5] p. illus., diagrs. (1 fold.) 23cm.

At head of title: Проф. Б. Лобач-Жученко.
Illustrated t.-p.
On cover: Общество друзей воздушного флота.

1. Aeroplanes—Motors. I. Obshchestvo druzeĭ vozdushnogo flota, Moscow. II. Title.

Library of Congress TL701.L6 38-25758

NL 0430340 DLC

Lobach-Zhuchenko, Boris Mikhaĭlovich, tr.

Kühne, Karl G.
... Технология авио и автоматериалов. Перевод с немецкого с дополнениями проф. Б. М. Лобач-Жученко. Москва, Государственное техническое издательство, 1924.

Lobach-Zhuchenko, Borys Borysovych.

Парусный спорт; учебное пособие для начинающих яхтсменов Латвийской ССР. Рига, Латвийское гос. изд-во, 1954.

225 p. illus. 23 cm.

Bibliography: p. [224]

1. Yachts and yachting—Russia. I. Title.
Title transliterated: Parusnyĭ sport.

GV817.R8L6 56-24298

NL 0430342 DLC

Lobach-Zhuchenko, Borys Borysovych.

GV817
.R8G7

Grigor'ev, Nikolaĭ Vladimirovich.
Парусный спорт; учебное пособие для секций парного спорта. Москва, Физкультура и спорт, 1954.

Lobach-Zhuchenko, Borys Borysovych.

Техника и тактика парусных гонок. Москва, ДОСААФ, 1955.

130 p. illus. 22 cm.

1. Yacht racing. I. Title.
Title transliterated: Tekhnika i taktika parusnykh gonok.

GV827.L55 56-28320 ‡

rev

NL 0430344 DLC

Lobachev, Grigoriĭ Grigor'evich, 1888-

Двенадцать детских песен народов Мари, для голоса с фортепиано. Op. 18. Москва, Гос. изд-во, 1929.

21 p. 36 cm.

Title also in Cheremissian.
For voice and piano. Russian and Cheremissian words.

1. Children's songs, Russian. 2. Folk-songs, Russian. I. Title.
Title transliterated: Dvenadtsat' detskikh pesen narodov Mari.

M1767.C5L M 56-1363

NL 0430345 DLC

Lobachev, Grigoriĭ Grigor'evich, 1888-
[Melodii narodov, op. 23]

Мелодии народов, для голоса с фортепиано. [Op. 23] Пор общей ред. А. Доливо-Соботницкого. Обложка художника Павла Кузнецова. Москва, Гос. изд-во, 1928-

v. 36 cm.

For voice and piano. Russian, French, and German words.

1. Folk-songs, Russian. 2. Songs (Medium voice) with piano. I. Title.
Title transliterated: Melodii narodov.

M1756.L8 op. 23 M 56-1365

NL 0430346 DLC

Lobachev, Grigoriĭ Grigor'evich, 1888-
[Norvezhskie pesni]

Норвежские песни. Перевод с различных норвежских диалектов С. А. Полякова. Стихотворная обработка С. С. Заяицкого. Op. 22. Москва, Музыкальный сектор Гос. изд-ва, 1926.

25 p. 36 cm.

For voice and piano. Norwegian, Russian, and German words.

1. Songs (Medium voice) with piano. 2. Songs, Norwegian. I. Title.
Title transliterated: Norvezhskie pesni.

M1621.L M 56-1430

NL 0430347 DLC

Lobachev, Grigoriĭ Grigor'evich, 1888-

Песни народа Мари, для голоса с фортепиано. Гармонизация Гр. Лобачева. Запись мелодии и текста Я. Эшпай. Обработка русского текста А. Струве. Москва, Гос. изд-во, 1930.

41 p. 32 cm.

Title in Cheremissian precedes Russian title.
For voice and piano. Russian and Cheremissian words.

1. Folk-songs, Russian. I. Title.
Title transliterated: Pesni naroda Mari.

M1766.C9L6 M 56-1364

NL 0430348 DLC

VOLUME 337

Lobachev, Grigorii Grigor'evich, 1888–

...7 chansons de différents peuples pour piano à 4 mains. Op. 20. Moscou: Section musicale des Éditions d'état, 1926. Publ. pl. no. M. 6582 Г. 15 p. 36cm.

For piano, 4 hands.
Cover-title (in Russian and French); t.-p. in Russian.
Contains arrangements of Uzbek, Kirghiz, Don region, Bashkir, Ukrainian and Georgian folk songs.

1. Piano—4 hands—1800– 2. Folk songs—Collections.
N. Y. P. L. July 29, 1938

NL 0430349 NN

Lobachev, Petr Vladimirovich.
Современные водомеры для водопроводов; проектирование, установка и эксплоатация. Москва, Гос. изд-во лит-ры по строительству и архитектуре, 1952.
231, [1] p. illus. 23 cm.
At head of title: П. В. Лобачев, Ф. А. Шевелев.
Second-3d eds. published under title: Водомеры для водопроводов и канализации.
Bibliography: p. [232]
1. Water-meters. I. Shevelev, F. A., joint author. II. Title.
Title romanized: Sovremennye vodomery dlia vodoprovodov.
TD499.L6 54-18418

NL 0430350 DLC

TJ935 .M6
Lobachev, Petr Vladimirovich.
Moscow. Vsesoiuznyi nauchno-issledovatel'skii institut vodosnabzheniia, kanalizatsii, gidrotekhnicheskikh sooruzhenii i inzhenernoi gidrogeologii.
Указания по применению современных водомеров на водопроводных станциях. [Автор: Лобачев П. В.] Москва, 1950.

RC857 .L6
Lobachev, S V
Острые панкреатиты. Москва, Медгиз, 1953.
174 p. illus. 23 cm.
Includes bibliography.
1. Pancreas—Diseases. I. Title.
Title transliterated: Ostrye pankreatity.
54-24421 ‡

NL 0430352 DLC

TC160 .L35
Lobachev, Vladimir Grigor'evich, 1883– joint author.
Latyshenkov, Arsenii Mikhailovich.
Гидравлика ... Для инженерно-строительных вузов по специальности водоснабжения и канализации. Под ред. В. Н. Кузнецова. Москва, Гос. изд-во строит. лит-ры, 1945.

TC175 .L6
Lobachev, Vladimir Grigor'evich, 1883–
Обобщенный метод гидравлического расчета каналов различных форм и различной шероховатости. Москва, Гос. изд-во строит. лит-ры, 1939.
66 p. diagrs. 21 cm.
At head of title: Всесоюзный научно-исследовательский институт водоснабжения, канализации, гидротехнических сооружений и инженерной гидрогеологии.
Errata slip inserted.
1. Canals. 2. Hydrodynamics.
Title transliterated: Obobshchennyi metod gidravlicheskogo rascheta.
TC175.L6 50-40627
Library of Congress [2]

NL 0430354 DLC

MT930 .G35
Lobacheva-TSyganova, Elizaveta Alekseevna.
Gembitskaia, Elena IAkovlevna.
Хор Института художественного воспитания; содержание и методы работы. Под ред. В. Н. Шацкой. Москва, Изд-во Академии педагог. наук РСФСР, 1954.

Lobachevskii, A
[Pamiatnaia knizhka o noshenii ordenov]
Памятная книжка о ношенiи орденовъ, медалей и другихъ знаковъ отличiя, съ приложенiемъ рисунковъ ихъ ношенiя и описанiя иностранныхъ орденовъ. Изд. 2. Составлена А. Лобачевскимъ. С.-Петербургъ, Воен. тип., 1887.
197 p. fold. illus. 13 cm.
1. Medals. I. Title.
CJ5729.L6 1887 72-224409

NL 0430356 DLC

Lobachevskii, Nikolai Ivanovich, 1792–1856.
Collection complète des œuvres géométriques de N. I. Lobatcheffsky. Édition de l'Université Impériale de Kasan. Ouvrages en langues française et allemande. Avec le portrait de l'auteur. Tome Kazan: Imperatorski Universitet, front. (port.), diagr. f°.
Title begins: Полное собранiе сочиненiй по геометрiи.
Bibliography tome 2, p. i–xx.
1. Geometry (Non-Euclidean). 2. Parallels.
N. Y. P. L. August 17, 1915.

NL 0430357 NN DN-Ob

Lobachevskii, Nikolai Ivanovich, 1792–1856.
Полное собрание сочинений. Под общей ред. В. Ф. Кагана [и др.] Глав. редактор В. Ф. Каган. Москва, Гос. изд-во технико-теорет. лит-ры, 1946–
v. plates, ports., diagrs., facsims. 26 cm.
Contents.—т. 1. Сочинения по геометрии.—
т. 3. Воображаемая геометрия. Применение воображаемой геометрии к некоторым интегралам. Пангеометрия.—т. 4. Сочинения по алгебре.—т. 5. Сочинения по математическому анализу, теории вероятностей, механике и астрономии.
1. Mathematics—Collected works. 2. Geometry, Non-Euclidean. I. Kagan, Veniamin Fedorovich, 1869–1953, ed.
Title transliterated: Polnoe sobranie sochinenii.
QA3.L6 49-18250 rev*

NL 0430358 DLC CaBVaU

Lobachevskii, Nikolai Ivanovich, 1792–1856.
Études géométriques sur la théorie des parallèles. Traduit de l'allemand par J. Hoüel. Suivi d'un extrait de la correspondance de Gauss et de Schumacher. Paris, Gauthier-Villars, 1866.
iv, 42 p. diagrs. 25 cm.
Bound with Quetelet, L. A. J. Histoire des sciences mathématiques et physiques chez les Belges. Bruxelles, 1864. Copy 2.
1. Geometry, Non-Euclidean.
QA685.L785 35-22001 rev*

NL 0430359 DLC MH

QA685 L786
Lobachevskii, Nikolai Ivanovich, 1792–1856
Geometriai vizsgalatok a párhuzamosok elmeletenek köreből. V. F. Kagan bevezetésével, magyarazataival, függelékével. Budapest, Akademiai kiado, 1951.
185p. diagrs. 25cm.
Translation of his Geometricheskie issledovaniia po teorii parallel'nykh linii.
"Bibliografia": p.184–185.

NL 0430360 RPB

Lobachevskii, Nikolai Ivanovich, 1792–1856.
Geometrical researches on the theory of parallels. Translated from the original by George Bruce Halsted. Austin, University of Texas, 1891.
50 p. diagrs. 23 cm. (Bulletin of the University of Texas)
1. Geometry, Non-Euclidean. I. Title.
QA685.L78 1891 5-14479 rev*

NL 0430361 NcD PBm PU PV OO NjP MiU OOxM OCU TxU CU DLC DSI TU CaBVaU ViU UU MdBP MH WaU

QA 685 L78 1892
Lobachevskii, Nikolai Ivanovich, 1792–1856.
Geometrical researches on the theory of parallels. Tr. from the original by George Bruce Halsted. Austin [1892]
50p. diagrs.
1. Geometry, Non-Euclidean. I. Halsted, George Bruce, 1853–1922, tr. II. Title.

NL 0430362 UU OrU

T513 L789gT4
Lobachevskii, Nikolai Ivanovich, 1792–1856.
Geometrical researches on the theory of parallels. Translated from the original by George Bruce Halsted. [4th ed.] Austin [1892]
50p. diagrs. 23cm.
1. Geometry, Non-Euclidean. I. Halsted, George Bruce, 1853–1922, tr. II. Title.

NL 0430363 TxU CSt PSC ICJ NjP

Lobachevskii, Nikolai Ivanovich, 1792–1856.
Geometrical researches on the theory of parallels. Translated from the original by George Bruce Halsted. New ed. Chicago, Open Court Pub. Co., 1914.
50 p. port., diagrs. 25 cm.
Bibliography: p. 49–50.
1. Geometry, Non-Euclidean. I. Title.
QA685.L78 1914 L 14-13988 rev

NL 0430364 OCU MiU ViU NBuU DAU TxU OU MB IdU NBuC WaU MtU OrPR OU MiD CLU OrCS NcC PSC PHa PHC PBa PPI OCl OU ODW DLC OClW IdPI WaSpG WaWW WaTC WaS PPT

QA685 .L783
Lobachevskii, Nikolai Ivanovich, 1792–1856.
Geometrical researches on the theory of parallels ... Tr. from the original by George Bruce Halsted ... New ed. Chicago [etc.] Open court pub. co. [c1942]
50 p. front. (port.), diagrs.
1. Geometry, Non-Euclidean.

NL 0430365 ICU

513.8 B71 1955
Lobachevskii, Nikolai Ivanovich, 1792–1856.
Geometrical researches on the theory of parallels; tr. by George Bruce Halsted. New York, Dover Publications [1955]
50 p. illus., diagrs. 21 cm. (In Bonola, Roberto. Non-Euclidean geometry; a critical and historical study of its developments. New York, [1955])
1. Geometry. Non-Euclidean. I. Halsted, George Bruce, 1853– tr. II. Title.

NL 0430366 N

VOLUME 337

Lobachevskiĭ, Nikolaĭ Ivanovich, 1792-1856.
Геометрические исследования по теории параллельных линий. Перевод, комментарии, вступ. статьи и примечания В. Ф. Кагана. Москва, 1945.
175 p. port., diagrs. 23 cm.
At head of title: Академия наук Союза ССР.
"Важнейшие даты в жизни Н. И. Лобачевского": p. [173]-174.
"Библиография": p. 174-175.
1. Geometry, Non-Euclidean. I. Title.
Title transliterated: Geometricheskie issledovaniâ po teorii parallel'nykh liniĭ.
QA685.L788 A 48-8991 rev*
Harvard Univ. Library for Library of Congress [r62b½]†

NL 0430367 MH DLC CaBVaU

[Lobachevskii, Nikolai Ivanovich,] 1792-1856.
Géometrie imaginaire. [Kasan, 1886.] p. 579-680, 1 diagr. f°.
Excerpt from his: Sammlung der geometrischen Arbeiten. Kasan, 1886. Theil 2.
First published Berlin, 1837.
1. Geometry (Non-Euclidean). 2. Title.
N. Y. P. L. February 28, 1920.

NL 0430368 NN

Lobachevskiĭ, Nikolaĭ Ivanovich, 1792-1856.
Geometrische untersuchungen zur theorie der parallellinien, von Nicolaus Lobatschewsky... Berlin, G. Fincke, 1840. 61, [1]p. fold. diagr. 19cm.

NL 0430369 MWelC MH NN

Lobachevskii, Nikolai Ivanovich, 1792-1856.
Geometrische Untersuchungen zur Theorie der Parallellinien. [Kasan, 1886.] p. 551-578, 3 diagr. f°.
Excerpt from his: Sammlung der geometrischen Arbeiten. Kasan, 1886. Theil 2.
First published in Berlin, 1840.
1. Parallels. 2. Title.
N. Y. P. L. February 4, 1919.

NL 0430370 NN

QA685 L775 Lobachevskii, Nikolai Ivanovich, 1792-1856.
Geometrische Untersuchungen zur Theorie der Parallellinien, von Nicolaus Lobatschewsky. 2. unveränderte Aufl. Berlin, Mayer & Müller, 1887.
61 p. 19cm. (Wissenschaftliche Classiker in Facsimile-Drucken. Bd.1)
1. Geometry, Non-Euclidean. 2. Parallels (Geometry) I. Title.

NL 0430371 CSt PU-Math DN-Ob ICJ CtNowaB

QA685 L788 1951 Lobachevskiĭ, Nikolaĭ Ivanovich, 1792-1856
Geometriska ispitivanja iz teorije paralelnih linija. Izd. 2. prošireno. Preveo i napomene dodao Branislav Petronijević. Beograd, [Naucna knjiga] 1951.
83 p. diagrs. 23 cm. (Srpska akademija nauka, Belgrad. Klasicni naucni spisi, 3)

NL 0430372 RPB OrU

Lobachevskiĭ, Nikolaĭ Ivanovich, 1792-1856.
... N. J. Lobatschefskijs Imaginäre geometrie und Anwendung der imaginären geometrie auf einige integrale. Aus dem russischen übers. und mit anmerkungen hrsg. von Heinrich Liebmann. Mit 39 figuren im text und auf einer tafel. Leipzig, B. G. Teubner, 1904.
xi, 187, [1] p. pl., diagrs. 24 cm. (Abhandlungen zur geschichte der mathematischen wissenschaften mit einschluss ihrer anwendungen ... xix. hft.)
1. Geometry, Non-Euclidean. 2. Calculus, Integral.
QA21.A2 hft. 19 5-6426 rev

NL 0430373 DLC CU LU NjP MB ICJ NN MiU OCU

Lobachevskiĭ, Nikolaĭ Ivanovich, 1792-1856.
In memoriam N. I. Lobatschevskii
see under title

LOBACHEVSKII, Nikolaĭ Ivanovich, 1792-1856.
The Introduction to Lobachevski's New elements of Geometry. Translated from the Russian by George Bruce Halsted. n.p., [189-?]
pp.17.
"Extract from a paper presented to the Texas academy of science, Dec.22, 1897."

NL 0430375 MH

Lobachevskii, Nikolaĭ Ivanovich, 1792-1856.
New principles of geometry, with complete theory of parallels ... Tr. from the Russian by Dr. George Bruce Halsted. Volume fifth of the Neomonic series. Austin, Texas, The Neomon, 1897.
cover-title, 26p. diagrs. 23cm. in envelope, 30cm.

NL 0430376 CLSU RPB CtY

Lobachevskii, Nikolai Ivanovich, 1792-1856.
Nouveaux principes de la géométrie avec une théorie complète des parallèles par Lobatchévsky. Traduit du russe pour la première fois par F. Mallieux. 132 p. 9 pl. O. Bruxelles: Hayez, 1901.

NL 0430377 ICJ

513.8 L796n5 Lobachevskii, Nikolai Ivanovich, 1792-1856.
Nuovi principi della geometria, con una teoria completa delle parellele. Saggio introduttivo, traduzione e note di Lucio Lombardo-Radice. [Torino] Edizioni Scientifiche Einaudi, 1955.
286p. illus. 22cm. (Biblioteca di cultura scientifica, 42)
Bibliographical footnotes.
1. Geometry, Non-Euclidean.

NL 0430378 CLSU

Lobachevskiĭ, Nikolaĭ Ivanovich, 1792-1856.
Объ изчезаніи тригонометрическихъ строкъ. Казань, Въ Унив. тип., 1834.
62 p. 25 cm.
"Перепечатано изъ 'Ученыхъ записокъ.'"
1. Fourier series. I. Title.
Title transliterated: Ob izchezanii trigonometricheskikh strok.
QA404.L76 62-57552

NL 0430379 DLC

Lobachevskiĭ, Nikolaĭ Ivanovich, 1792-1856.
Pangéométrie; ou, Précis de géométrie fondée sur une théorie générale et rigoureuse des parallèles, par N. Lobatcheffsky.
(*In* Kazan. Universitet. Сборникъ ученыхъ статей. Казань, 1856. 25½cm. t. 1, p. [277]-340, 1 l.)
1. Geometry, Non-Euclidean. I. Title.
Library of Congress Q60.K3 t.1 CA 28-900 Unrev'd

NL 0430380 DLC

[Lobachevskii, Nikolaĭ Ivanovich,] 1792-1856.
Pangéométrie; ou, Précis de géométrie, fondée sur une théorie générale et rigoureuse des parallèles. [Kasan, 1886.] 615-680 p. 31 x 24½cm.
Excerpt from his: Sammlung der geometrischen Arbeiten. Kasan, 1886.
900835. 1. Geometry, Non-Euclidean. I. Title.
N. Y. P. L. *Revised* February 28, 1934

NL 0430381 NN

QA685 .L8 Lobachevskiĭ, Nikolaĭ Ivanovich, 1792-1856.
Pangéométrie; ou, Précis de géométrie, fondée sur une théorie générale et rigoureuse des parallèles, par N.-J. Lobatschewsky. Réimpression fac-similé conforme à l'édition originale. Paris, A. Hermann, 1905.
[1], [279]-340, [1] p. 25cm.
1. Geometry, Non-Euclidean.

NL 0430382 ICU IU PSC RPB

Lobachevskiĭ, Nikolaĭ Ivanovich, 1792-1856.
Pangeometrie, von N. J. Lobatschefskij. Kasan 1856. Uebers. und hrsg. von Heinrich Liebmann. Mit 30 figuren im text. Leipzig, W. Engelmann, 1902.
95, [1] p. diagr. 19½ cm. (*On cover:* Ostwald's Klassiker der exakten wissenschaften, nr. 130)
First published in French under the title, "Pangéométrie, ou Précis de géométrie fondée sur une théorie générale et rigoureuse des parallels," in a collection issued by the professors of the University of Kasan, 1856. A Russian edition also published 1856.
1. Geometry, Non-Euclidean.
QA685.L8 3-19242 rev

NL 0430383 DLC OC1W PHC CU-S MH ICJ NN DNLM OU OCU PU CU NcU

QA 685 L8 1912 Lobachevskiĭ, Nikolaĭ Ivanovich, 1792-1856.
Pangeometrie, von N. J. Lobatschefskij. Kasan 1856. Uebers. und hrsg. von, Heinrich Liebmann. Mit 30 figuren im text. 2. Aufl. Leipzig, W. Engelmann, 1912.
99 p. illus. 19 cm. (On cover: Ostwald's Klassiker der exakten Wissenschaften, nr. 130)
First published in French under title, "Pangéométrie, ou Précis de géométrie fondée sur une théorie générale et rigoureuse des parallels", in a collection issued by the professors of the University of Kasan, 1856. A Russian edition also was published 1856.
Reproduced by Micro Photo Division, Bell & Howell Co., Cleveland, Ohio.

NL 0430384 NSyU OU RPB OC1W

Lobachevskii, Nikolai Ivanovich, 1792-1856.
N. I. Lobatschewsky, traduction J. Houel, Recherches géométriques sur la théorie des parallèles, suivies d'un extrait de la correspondance entre Gauss et Schumacher. H. von Helmholtz, traduction Houel, Sur les faits qui servent de bases à la géometrie. Paris, Hermann, 1895.
iv, 42, [372]-378 p. diagrs. 29cm.
1. Geometry, Non-Euclidean. 2. Parallels (Geometr I. Hoüel, Jules, 1823-1886, tr.

NL 0430385 NNC NjP

VOLUME 337

513.8 L78gFh Lobachevskii, Nikolai Ivanovich, 1792-185[6]
Recherches géométriques sur la théorie des parallèles suivies d'extraits de la correspondance de Gauss et Schumacher ... tr. de J. Houel. Paris, 1900.
42p. diagrs.

Bound with Helmholtz, H. L. F. von. Sur les faits qui servent de base à la géométrie. 1900?

NL 0430386 IU

QA685 .B83 1955 Lobachevskii, Nikolai Ivanovich, 1792-1856.
The theory of parallels.

Bonola, Roberto, 1874-1911.
Non-Euclidean geometry; a critical and historical study of its developments. Authorized English translation with additional appendices by H. S. Carslaw. With an introd. by Federigo Enriques. With a suppl. containing the George Bruce Halsted translations of The science of absolute space, by John Bolyai ⁅and⁆ The theory of parallels, by Nicholas Lobachevski. ⁅New York⁆ Dover Publications ⁅1955⁆

Lobachevskiĭ, Nikolaĭ Ivanovich, 1792-1856.
... Zwei geometrische abhandlungen aus dem russischen uebersetzt, mit anmerkungen und mit einer biographie des verfassers, von Friedrich Engel ... Leipzig, B. G. Teubner, 1898-99.
2 pts. in 1 v. front. (port.) diagrs. 25 cm. (*Added t.-p.:* Urkunden zur geschichte der nichteuklidischen geometrie, hrsg. von F. Engel und P. Stäckel)
Paged continuously: 1. t.: xvi, 235, ⁅1⁆ p.; 2 t.: 3 p. l., 239-476 p.
"Verzeichniss der gedruckten werke Lobatschefskijs nach der zeitfolge ihres erscheinens": p. ⁅446⁆-449.
CONTENTS.—1. t. Die uebersetzung: I. Ueber die anfangsgründe der geometrie. II. Neue anfangsgründe der geometrie mit einer vollständigen theorie der parallellinien.—2. t. Anmerkungen. Lobatschefskijs leben und schriften. Register.
1. Geometry, Non-Euclidean.
QA685.L83 5-12788 rev

NL 0430388 DLC MB ICJ OU MiU OCU CU

Lobachik, A. P.

Moscow. Vsesoiuznaia sel'skokhoziaistvennaia vystavka, 1954-
Павильон "Овцеводство"; путеводитель. ⁅Авторы А. П. Кажичкин, А. П. Лобачик. Ответственный редактор В. Н. Тихомиров⁆ Москва, Гос. изд-во сельхоз. лит-ры, 1954.

ML410 B4L62 1955 Music Library **Łobaczewska, Stefania**
Beethoven. [Wyd. 2., uzup. Kraków] Polskie Wydawn. Muzyczne [1955]
301 p. illus., ports., facsims., music. (Małe monografie muzyczne, t. 1)

Bibliography: p. 299-[300]

1. Beethoven, Ludwig van, 1770-1827.

NL 0430390 CU

⁅Łobaczewska, Stefania⁆
Estetyka muzyczna ... ⁅Lwów, Nakł. Filomaty ⁅etc.⁆ 1938-
v. 24cm.
Cover of v. 1 dated 1937.
Vol. 1 has also special t.-p. with author's name at head of title.
Vol. 1: Z subwencją Ministerstwa WR i OP w Warszawie.
"Bibliografia": v. 1, p. ⁅x⁆-xx.
CONTENTS.—I. Ogólny zarys estetyki muzycznej.

1. Music—Philosophy and esthetics. I. Title. 40-21476

Library of Congress ML3845.L8204

NL 0430391 DLC

Łobaczewska, Stefania.
Karol Szymanowski; życie i twórczość, 1882-1937. Kraków, Polskie Wydawn. Muzyczne ⁅°1950⁆
667, ⁅30⁆ p. illus., ports., facsims., geneal. tables. 25 cm.
Includes thematic index.
"Spis kompozycji Karola Szymanowskiego": p. ⁅1⁆-⁅10⁆ 2d group.
Bibliography: p. ⁅11⁆-⁅21⁆ 2d group.

1. Szymanowski, Karol, 1883-1937. 2. Szymanowski, Karol, 1883-1937—Thematic catalogs.

ML410.S99L6 53-20298

NL 0430392 DLC WU NN PU MiU IU CU MiD MH

Łobaczewska, Stefania.
Zarys historii form muzycznych; próba ujęcia socjologicznego. Kraków, Polskie Wydawn. Muzyczne, 1950.
344 p. 21 cm.

1. Music—Hist. & crit. I. Title.

ML160.L69 54-19196 ‡

NL 0430393 DLC

TH7227 .L6 **Lobaev, Boris Nikitich,** *ed.*
Новое в отопительной технике. Киев, Гос. изд-во техн. лит-ры УССР, 1955.
140 p. diagrs. 21 cm.
Includes bibliographies.

1. Heating—Addresses, essays, lectures. I. Title.
Title transliterated: Novoe v otopitel'noĭ tekhnike.

TH7227.L6 56-37667

NL 0430394 DLC

TH7467 L7 **Lobaev, Boris Nikitich.**
Отопление жилых и общественных зданий перегретой водой и паром. Киев, 1955.
97, ⁅3⁆ p. illus. 22 cm.
At head of title: Академия архитектуры Украинской ССР. Б. Н. Лобаев, Н. Т. Ральчук.
Errata slip inserted.
Bibliography: p. ⁅100⁆

1. Hot-water heating. 2. Steam-heating. I. Ral'chuk, Nikolaĭ Trofimovich, joint author. II. Title.
Title transliterated: Otoplenie zhilykh i obshchestvennykh zdaniĭ.

TH7467.L7 56-17121
Library of Congress ⁅3⁆

NL 0430395 DLC

TH7222 .L6 **Lobaev, Boris Nikitich,** *ed.*
Теплоснабжение и вентиляция малоэтажных жилых зданий. Киев, Гос. изд-во техн. лит-ры УССР, 1954.
238 p. illus. 21 cm.
At head of title: А. В. Грачев ⁅и др.⁆
Bibliography: p. 236-⁅237⁆

1. Dwellings—Heating and ventilation. I. Grachev, A. V. II. Title.
Title transliterated: Teplosnabzhenie i ventiliatsiia maloėtazhnykh zhilykh zdaniĭ.

TH7222.L6 59-40784

NL 0430396 DLC

DT 515 .L 79 1931 LoBagola, Bata Kindai Amgoza ibn.
... Autobiografía de un salvaje africano; traducción directa del inglés por F. Menéndez y Arranz. Madrid, Cenit, 1931.
279, [7] p., 1 l. 19½cm. (Colección: razas, países, pueblos)

"Primera edición."

NL 0430397 MdBJ

LoBagola, Bata Kindai Amgoza ibn.
The folk tales of a savage, by Lobagola; illustrated by Erick Berry. New York, A. A. Knopf, 1930.
7 p. l., 199, ⁅1⁆ p. front., illus. 20½cm.
Illustrated lining-papers.

1. Tales, African. I. Title.
Library of Congress GR350.L6 30-21411
——— Copy 2.
Copyright A 25961 ⁅3⁆ 398.21

NL 0430398 DLC Or WaSp WaU CU MoU MB OClh OCl OLak NN MB PP PWcS

DT 515 .6 L6 A3 LoBagola, Bata Kindai Amgoza ibn.
LoBagola; an African savage's own story. Leipzig, B. Tauchnitz, 1930.
294 p. port.

1. Ethnology--Nigeria.

NL 0430399 NSyU

LoBagola, Bata Kindai Amgoza ibn.
LoBagola; an African savage's own story. New York, A. A. Knopf, 1930.
xxiii p., 1 l., 402 p., 1 l. 2 port. (incl. front.) facsims. 21cm.

1. Ethnology—Nigeria.
Library of Congress DT515.L6 30-12774
——— Copy 2.
Copyright A 22724 ⁅5-2⁆ [572.9662] 920.9

NL 0430400 DLC OCl MiU OCH OO PBm PPL PHC PU PPA Or Wa WaSp MtBC OrSaW NjPT InU MB OKentU ViHaI NcRS TxU CU KEmT WaT OCH WaTC NcU OrP GU WaU NN

LoBagola, Bata Kindai Amgoza ibn
LoBagola, an African savage's own story. New York, A. A. Knopf, 1933. xxiii, 402 p. ports., facsims. 21cm.

NL 0430401 NN CaBVaU

LoBagola, Bata Kindai Amgoza ibn.
Lobagola; en innfødt afrikaners egen historie, oversatt av Hans Krag. Oslo: H. Aschehoug & co., 1931. 279 p. facsims., ports. 23cm.
"Oversatt efter: Lo Bagola; an African savage's own story.

47350B. 1. Jews in Nigeria. 2. African tribes—Nigeria. I. Krag, Hans, tr.
N. Y. P. L. May 31, 1940

NL 0430402 NN

LoBagola, Bata Kindai Amgoza ibn.
LoBagola; histoire d'un sauvage africain, par lui-même. Traduite de l'anglais par G. M. Michel Drucker. Paris: A. Michel ⁅1932⁆ 312 p. 19cm. (On cover: Nouvelle série. Collection des maitres de la littérature étrangère.)

43687B. 1. Jews in Nigeria. 2. African tribes—Nigeria. I. Drucker, Michel, tr.
N. Y. P. L. March 20, 1940

NL 0430403 NN IEN CtY

VOLUME 337

Lobai, Danylo.
Непереможна Україна; факти з совітських видань про боротьбу Москви з українським націоналізмом на культурному фронті по Другій Світовій війні. Вінніпег, Вид. Ком-ту українців Канади, 1950.
238 p. 22 cm. (Політична бібліотека Комітету українців Канади)

1. Ukraine — Intellectual life. 2. Ukraine — Relations (general) with Russia. 3. Russia—Relations (general) with the Ukraine. I. Title. *Title transliterated: Neperemozhna Ukraïna.*

DK508.4.L63 56-39006 ‡

NL 0430404 DLC CaBVa CaBVaU KU

Lobaina Gell, Victor
El Russelismo y las escrituras. [Mexico] Junta Bautista de Publicaciones de Cuba Oriental [1948]

NL 0430405 MH

Loban, Earl M.
Money raising plans for churches ... written, compiled, revised by Earl M. Loban ... Cedar Falls, Ia., The Woolverton printing company, °1932.
48 p. 23cm.

1. Church finance. I. Title.

Library of Congress BV772.L57 33-16337
Copyright A 53392 [2] 254

NL 0430406 DLC

Loban, Ethel H.
... The calloused eye ... Garden City, N. Y., Pub. for the Crime club, inc., by Doubleday, Doran & company, inc. [°1931]
4 p. l., 307 p. 20cm.
At head of title: Ethel Loban.
"First edition."

I. Title.
Library of Congress PZ3.L7796Cal 31-21435

NL 0430407 DLC MH NcD

Loban, Ethel H.
Signed in yellow, by Ethel H. Loban ... Garden City, N. Y., Pub. for The Crime club, inc., by Doubleday, Doran & company, inc., 1930.
3 p. l., 308 p. 19½cm.
"First edition."

I. Title.
Library of Congress PZ3.L7796Si 30-10253

NL 0430408 DLC

Loban, G Taylor.
... A paper entitled Some principles in the valuation of land and buildings. By G. Taylor Loban ... With discussion ... London, The Institution, 1912.
cover-title, p. [417]-466. incl. diagrs. 21cm. (The Surveyors' institution ... Westminster. Transactions: session 1911-1912. vol. XLIV.—part X)

1. Real property.

A 13-1768

Title from Univ. of Calif. Printed by L. C.

NL 0430409 CU

Loban, Joy Maxwell, 1887- joint author.

Bunn, Charles R.
Diet and exercise, by Charles R. Bunn ... and Joy M. Loban ... 1st ed. Denver, Colo., Bunn-Loban publishing co., 1928.

Loban, Joy Maxwell, 1887-
Technic and practice of chiropractic, by Joy M. Loban ... Davenport, Ia., Universal chiropractic college, 1912.
2 p. l., 7-234 p. plates. 20cm.

1. Chiropractic.

Library of Congress RM730.L6 12-2730

NL 0430411 DLC DNLM ICJ

Loban, Joy Maxwell, 1887-
Technic and practice of chiropractic, by Joy M. Loban ... 2d ed., rev. and enl. Davenport, Ia., Universal chiropractic college, 1915.
2 p. l., 7-352 p. plates. 20cm. $4.00

1. Chiropractic.

Library of Congress RM730.L6 1915 15-3458

NL 0430412 DLC OrU-M DNLM ICJ

Loban, Joy Maxwell, 1887-
Technic and practice of chiropractic, by Joy M. Loban, ...
119351 Third edition, revised and enlarged. Pittsburgh, Pa., Loban Publishing Co., 1916.
438 p. incl. tables, 31 pl. 20cm.

NL 0430413 ICJ

RM730
L5
1918

LOBAN, Joy Maxwell, 1887-
Technic and practice of chiropractic, by Joy M. Loban. 3d ed., rev. and enl. Pittsburgh,Pa.,Loban,1918[c1916]
438p. illus. 20cm.

1. Chiropractic I. Title

NL 0430414 CtY-M

Loban, Joy Maxwell, 1887-
Technic and practice of chiropractic, by Joy M. Loban... Pittsburgh: Loban Pub. Co., 1920. 438 p. incl. plates. 3. ed. 8°.

55788A. 1. Chiropractic.
N. Y. P. September 15, 1922.

NL 0430415 NN

Loban, Joy Maxwell, 1887-
Technic and practice of chiropractic, by Joy M. Loban... 3d. ed. Pittsburgh, Loban publishing co., 1922.
2p. l.,7-438p. plates. 20cm.

NL 0430416 KAS

Loban, Joy Maxwell, 1887-
Technic and practice of chiropractic, by Joy M. Loban ... 4th ed., rev. and enl. Denver, Colo., Bunn-Loban publishing co., 1928.
2 p. l., 7-440 p. illus. 20cm.

1. Chiropractic. I. Title.

Library of Congress RM730.L6 1928 28-21125

NL 0430417 DLC DNLM

Loban, Joy Maxwell, 1887-
A textbook of neurology, arranged for the classroom and for ready reference by the practitioner. By Joy M. Loban ... with 117 illustrations by H. R. Springer. Denver, Colo., The Bunn-Loban publishing company [°1929]
xiii, 563 p. col. front., illus. 26½cm.
"Aids to study": p. [515]-551.

1. Nervous system. 2. Nervous system—Diseases.

Library of Congress QM451.L6 29-6328

NL 0430418 DLC

Loban, Walter, joint ed.

PR1109
.S34
1947

Cook, Luella Bussey, 1890- ed.
Adventures in appreciation [by] Luella B. Cook ... H. A. Miller, jr. ... [and] Walter Loban ... 3d ed. New York, Chicago, Harcourt, Brace and company, 1947.

Loban, Walter, joint ed.

PR1109
.C64
1941

Cook, Luella Bussey, 1890- ed.
Adventures in literature ... [edited by] Luella B. Cook ... Walter Loban ... George W. Norvell ... [and] William A. McCall ... New York, Chicago, Harcourt, Brace and company, 1941-42.

Loban, Walter.
Literature and social sensitivity. Champaign, Ill., National Council of Teachers of English, °1954.
36 p. 23 cm.

1. Adolescence. 2. Sympathy. 3. Literature—Study and teaching. I. Title.
HQ796.L63 807.12 54-4848 ‡

OrPS OrLgE MtU IdPI
NL 0430421 DLC KEmT PPPL FMU TxU WaU CoU CaBVaU

Loban, Walter, joint ed.

PS507
.C6
1948

Cook, Luella Bussey, 1890- ed.
People in literature [by] Luella B. Cook, Walter Loban [and] Ruth M. Stauffer. New York, Harcourt, Brace, 1948.

TJ390
.L58

Lobanchenko, N G
Обдувка поверхностей нагрева котельных агрегатов. Москва, Гос. энерг. изд-во, 1952.
155, [1] p. illus. 21 cm.
At head of title: Н. Г. Лобанченко, М. А. Гуляев, Б. А. Зудин.
Bibliography: p. 154-[156]

1. Steam-boilers—Incrustations. I. Gulīaev, M. A. II. Title. *Title transliterated: Obduvka poverkhnosteĭ nagreva kotel'nykh agregatov.*

TJ390.L58 54-35070

NL 0430423 DLC

VOLUME 337

Lobanoff (Anna). *Contribution à l'étude de la migration du rein pathologique. 30 pp. 8°. Lausanne. A. Petter. 1906.

NL 0430424 DNLM

Lobanov, Alekseĭ Nikolaevich.
Теория трансформирования пары снимков и создание карты по трансформированным изображениям. Москва, Изд-во геодезической лит-ры, 1954.
108 p. illus., map. 25 cm.
Bibliography: p. 102.

1. Aerial photogrammetry. 2. Photographic surveying. I. Title.
Title transliterated: Teorii͡a transformirovanii͡a pary snimkov.

TA593.L58 55-20669 rev

NL 0430425 DLC

Lobanov, Arkadiĭ Zakhar'evich.
Законы механического движения. Москва, Гос. учебно-педагог. изд-во, 1955.
59 p. illus. 20 cm. (Библиотека школьника)
——— Microfilm copy (negative)
Made in 1956 by the Library of Congress.
Microfilm Slavic 708 Q

1. Motion. I. Title.
Title transliterated: Zakony mekhanicheskogo dvizhenii͡a.

QA841.L77 57-31516 ‡

NL 0430426 DLC

Lobanov, Dmitriĭ Ivanovich.
Александръ Николаевичъ Сѣровъ и его современники; біографическій очеркъ. С.-Петербургъ, Тип. Департамента удѣловъ, 1889.
40 p. 23 cm.

1. Serov, Aleksandr Nikolaevich, 1820–1871.
Title transliterated: Aleksandr Nikolaevich Sierov.

56-51097

NL 0430427 DLC

BF575
.L8L62

Lobanov, Dmitriĭ Ivanovich.
Что такое любовь; опытъ изученія половыхъ отношеній. ₍С.-Петербургъ₎ Тип. Н. Н. Гамрекелова, 1902.
110 p. illus. 19 cm.
Part 1 of Философія любви (transliterated: Filosofii͡a li͡ubvi) published in 1886.

1. Love. I. Title. *Title transliterated:* Chto takoe li͡ubov'.

BF575.L8L62 61-55501

NL 0430428 DLC

BF575
.L8L6

Lobanov, Dmitriĭ Ivanovich.
Философія любви. С.-Петербургъ, Тип. В. В. Комарова, 1886.
189 p. 26 cm.

1. Love. I. Title. *Title transliterated:* Filosofii͡a li͡ubvi.

BF575.L8L6 61-55500

NL 0430429 DLC

Lobanov, Dmitriĭ Ivanovich.
Искушеніе. Траги-комедія, изъ поэмы А. С. Пушкина, въ трехъ дѣйствіяхъ Дм. Лобанова. С.-Петербургъ, Типографія Н. А. Лебедева, 1887.
32 p. 21½cm.

I. Pushkin, Aleksandr Sergeevich. Anzhelo. II. Title.
Title transliterated: Iskushenie.
87-31015

NL 0430430 DLC

Lobanov, Dmitriĭ Ivanovich.
Русскіе современные дѣятели; сборникъ портретовъ замѣчательныхъ лицъ настоящаго времени съ біографическими очерками. Составленъ Д. И. Лобановымъ. С.-Петербургъ, Изд. А. О. Баумана, 1876–78.
3 v. in 2. ports. 24 cm.

1. Portraits, Russian. 2. Russia—Biography—Portraits. I. Title.
Title romanized: Russkie sovremennye dieiateli.

N7608.L63 75-286605

NL 0430431 DLC

TX353
.L6
1951

Lobanov, Dmitriĭ Ivanovich, *writer on food processing.*
Технология приготовления пищи. Допущено в качестве учебника для технологических факультетов экон высших учеб. заведений. Изд. 2., перер. Москва, Гос торгиздат, 1951.
316 p. illus. 23 cm.
Bibliography: p. 312.

1. Food. 2. Cookery. I. Title.
Title transliterated: Tekhnologii͡a prigotovlenii͡a pishchi

TX353.L6 1951 54-23730 rev

NL 0430432 DLC

SB357
.L72

Lobanov, G A
Как да създаваме сортове плодови и ягодови растения. Под ред. П. А. Яковлев. София, Земиздат, 1951.
115 p. port. 22 cm.

1. Michurin, Ivan Vladimirovich, 1855–1935. 2. Fruit-culture. I. Title.
Title transliterated: Kak da sŭzdavame sortove plodovi i i͡agodovi rastenii͡a.

SB357.L72 51-37023 ‡
Library of Congress ₍2₎

NL 0430433 DLC

Lobanov, G A
Выведение новых сортов плодовых и ягодных растений. Изд. 2., испр. и доп. Москва, Гос. изд-во сельхоз. лит-ры, 1954.
181, ₍3₎ p. illus. 20 cm.
Bibliography: p. 181 ₍182₎

1. Fruit-culture—Russia. 2. Michurin, Ivan Vladimirovich, 1855–1935 I. Title.
Title transliterated: Vyvedenie novykh sortov plodovykh i i͡agodnykh rastenii.

SB357.L73 1954 54-43483

NL 0430434 DLC CU

JS6068
.L6

Lobanov, I
Опыт работы агитпункта на городском избирательном участке. ₍Москва₎ Права, 1947.
47 p. 17 cm.
At head of title: И. Лобанов, М. Иванова.

1. Elections—Russia. 2. Municipal government—Russia. I. Ivanova, M₍ariia Nikolaevna₎ joint author. II. Title.
Title transliterated: Opyt raboty agitpunkta.

JS6068.L6 49-12405*

NL 0430435 DLC

RC626
.L6

Lobanov, Khrisanf Nikolaevich, 1846?–
О молочномъ леченіи скорбутныхъ больныхъ. Изъ терапевтической клиники Д. И. Кошлакова. С.-Петербургъ, Тип. Е. Евдокимова, 1888.
71 p. 25 cm. (Серія диссертацій, 1887/88 г., № 77)
Diss.—Voenno-medit͡sinskai͡a akademii͡a, Leningrad.
Vita.

1. Scurvy. I. Title.
Title transliterated: O molochnom lechenii skorbutnykh bol'nykh

52-55472
Library of Congress ₍2₎

NL 0430436 DLC

PA4152
.R8Z5

Lobanov, Mikhail Evstaf'evich, 1787–1846. Zhizn' i sochinenii͡a Nikolai͡a Ivanovicha Gni͡edicha.
Жизнеописанія Гомера и переводчика его Иліады на русскій языкъ Гнѣдича. Санктпетербургъ, У издателя, книгопродавца Лисенкова, 1867.

Lobanov, Nikolaĭ Vasil'evich.
Микотрофность древесных растений. Москва, Советская наука, 1953.
231 p. illus., maps (1 fold.) 23 cm.
Bibliography: p. 218–₍227₎

1. Mycorhiza. 2. Afforestation. I. Title.
Title transliterated: Mikotrofnost' drevesnykh rastenii.

QK604.L8 54-21193

NL 0430438 DLC

HD1491
.R9K52

Lobanov, Pavel Pavlovich, 1902-
Klimenko, Fedor Nikitovich.
The kolkhoz <collective farm> by F. Klimenko, K. Borin, P. Lobanov ₍and₎ V. Molyakov. Allahabad, Kitabistan ₍1943₎

HD9045
.R9L6

Lobanov, Pavel Pavlovich, 1902–
СССР—страна мощного зернового производства. Москва, Сельхозгиз, 1947.
62 p. 20 cm.

1. Grain—Russia. I. Title.
Title transliterated: SSSR—strana moshchnogo zernovogo proizvodstva.

HD9045.R9L6 48-21874 rev*

NL 0430440 DLC

VOLUME 337

Lobanov, Pavel Pavlovich, 1902–
The state farms of the U. S. S. R. Moscow, Foreign Languages Publishing House, 1939.
31 p. plates. 15 cm.

1. State farms—Russia.
HD1992.L56 338.12 46-34336 rev*

NL 0430441 DLC NcU NIC CU-B CtY NN NBC

TK4018 .L6
Lobanov, Vasiliĭ Nikiforovich.
Электробезопасность в сельском хозяйстве. [Москва] Профиздат, 1955.
137 p. illus. 20 cm.
Bibliography: p. [136]

1. Electricity in agriculture. I. Title.
Title transliterated: Ėlektrobezopasnost' v sel'skom khozĭaĭstve.
TK4018.L6 56-39846

NL 0430442 DLC

ND699 .G46L6 **Lobanov, Viktor Mikhaĭlovich,** 1885–
... А. М. Герасимов. Москва, Ленинград, Государственное издательство "Искусство," 1943.
108, [4] p. front., illus., plates, ports. 28 x 22cm.
At head of title: В. М. Лобанов.
Most of the illustrative matter is colored and mounted.
Bibliography: p. 106–[109]

1. Gerasimov, Aleksandr Mikhaĭlovich, 1881– *Title transliterated:* A. M. Gerasimov.
Library of Congress ND699.G46L6 44-18738

NL 0430443 DLC

NC269 .L3L6
Lobanov, Viktor Mikhaĭlovich, 1885–
Книжная графика Е. Е. Лансере. Москва, Гизлегпром, 1948.
106 p. illus., plates, port. 23 cm.
"Перечень графических произведений Е. Е. Лансере": p. 97–[104]

1. Lansere, Evgeniĭ Evgen'evich, 1875–
Title transliterated: Knizhnaĭa grafika E. E. Lansere.
50-38744

NL 0430444 DLC

ND699 .S6L6
Lobanov, Viktor Mikhaĭlovich, 1885–
Павел Петрович Соколов-Скаля. Москва, Искусство, 1940.
77 p. illus., plates (part col.) port. 27 cm.

1. Sokolov-Skalĭa, Pavel Petrovich, 1899– 2. Realism in art.
Title transliterated: Pavel Petrovich Sokolov-Skalĭa.
ND699.S6L6 A 48-2232*
Harvard Univ. Library for Library of Congress [1]†

NL 0430445 MH DLC

ND699 .S35L6
Lobanov, Viktor Mikhaĭlovich, 1885–
Саврасов, Алексей Кондратьевич, 1830–1897. Москва "Искусство"; [etc.] 1943.
11, [1] p. front., plates. 17 cm. (*On cover:* Массовая библиотека)

1. Savrasov, Alekseĭ Kondrat'evich, 1830–1897.
Title transliterated: Savrasov, Alekseĭ Kondrat'evich.
ND699.S35L6 49-31650

NL 0430446 DLC

Lobanov-Rostovskiĭ, Aleksandr Ĭakovlevich, *kniâź,* 1788–1866.
... Catalog enthaltend die kupferstichsammlung des verstorbenen fürsten Alexander Lobanow Rostowsky, nebst gleichwerthigem beitrage eines wohlbekannten deutschen sammlers. Mit zwei abbildungen in lichtdruck ... Versteigerung zu Berlin ... den 26. april 1881 und folgende tage ... im kunst-auctionshause von Rudolph Lepke ... Berlin [Leipzig, W. Drugulin's buch- und kunstdr.] 1881.
3 p. l., [iii]–vi, 128 p. 2 fold. pl. 26cm.
At head of title: xxiii. Berliner kupferstich-auction von Amsler & Ruthardt.
Priced in manuscript.
L. C. copy imperfect: both plates torn.
1. Engravings—Private collections.
Library of Congress NE59.L6 44-30723

NL 0430447 DLC MH MB NIC

Lobanov-Rostovskiĭ, Aleksandr Iakovlevich, *kniâź',* 1788–1866.
Catalogue des cartes géographiques, topographiques & marines, de la bibliothèque du prince Alexandre Labanoff de Rostoff, à Saint Pétersbourg, suivi d'une notice de manuscrits. Paris, Typ. de Firmin Didot, 1823.
2 p. l., viii, 494 p., 1 l. 22cm.
An edition of 340 copies printed.

1. Maps—Bibl.—Catalogs. 2. Manuscripts. Russia—Catalogs.
16-16655
Library of Congress Z6028.L79

NL 0430448 DLC MdBP NN MiU-C MB

Lobanov-Rostovskiĭ, Aleksandr Ĭakovlevich, kniâź, 1788–1866.
Letters of Mary Stuart, Queen of Scots
see under Mary Stuart, queen of Scots. 1788–1866.

[Lobanov-Rostovskiĭ, Aleksandr Iakovlevich, kniaz, 1788–1866.]
Lettre à M. le rédacteur du Globe au sujet de la prétendue ambassade en Russie de Charles de Talleyrand. [Anon.] 2e édition, augmentée d'un post-scriptum contenant une lettre inédite de Louis XIII.
— Paris. Firmin Didot. 1828. 23 pp. 8°.

Dec. 4, 1901
E224 – France. For. rel. Russia. — Louis XIII., of France.

NL 0430450 MB

Lobanov-Rostovskii, Aleksandr IAkovlevich, kniaz, 1788-1866, ed.
Mary Stuart, *queen of the Scots,* 1542–1587.
Lettres, instructions et mémoires de Marie Stuart, reine d'Écosse; publiés sur les originaux et les manuscrits du State paper office de Londres et des principales archives et bibliothèques de l'Europe, et accompagnés d'un résumé chronologique par le prince Alexandre Labanoff. Londres, C. Dolman, 1844.

DA 787 .A3 L8
LOBANOV-ROSTOVSKII, ALEKSANDR IAKOVLEVICH, kniaz, 1788-1866
Notice sur la collection des portraits de Marie Stuart, appartenant au Prince Alexandre Labanoff. Précédée d'un résumé chronologique. St. Petersbourg, Impr. d'É. Pratz, 1856.
224 p. port.

1. Mary Stuart, queen of the Scots, 1542-1587--Iconography.

NL 0430452 InU

[**Lobanov-Rostovskiĭ, Aleksandr Ĭakovlevich,** *kniaz*] 1788–1866.
Notice sur la collection des portraits de Marie Stuart appartenant au prince Alexandre Labanoff, précédée d'un résumé chronologique. Nouv. éd., considérablement augm. St.-Pétersbourg, Impr. d'É. Pratz, 1860.
xxiii p., 1 l., 345 p., 1 l. 26cm.

1. Mary Stuart, queen of the Scots, 1542–1587—Iconography. I. Title.
19-4736
Library of Congress DA787.A3L8 1860

NL 0430453 DLC RPJCB MeB CtY MB

Lobanov-Rostovskiĭ, Aleksandr Ĭakovlevich, *kniâź',* 1788–1866.
Recueil de pièces historiques sur la reine Anne ou Agnès, épouse de Henri Ier, roi de France et fille de Iarosslaf Ier, grand duc de Russie; avec une notice et des remarques du prince Alexandre Labanoff de Rostoff ... Paris, Typ. de Firmin Didot, 1825.
xxii p., 1 l., 60 p. fold. facsim. 24½cm.
Bibliography: p. 54–57.
1. Anne, queen consort of Henry I, king of France, b. 1024. 2. Henri I, king of France, 1008?–1060. I. Title.
18-20818
Library of Congress DC85.6.L6

NL 0430454 DLC PU

[**Lobanov-Rostovskiĭ, Aleksandr Ĭakovlevich,** kniaz'] 1788–1866.
Tablettes gastronomiques de Saint-Pétersbourg, rédigées par un amateur, et précédées d'une liste des ouvrages à consulter. St.-Pétersbourg, Impr. É. Pratz, 1856–58.
2 v. in 1. 26 cm.
"Tiré à 100 exemplaires."

1. Menus. 2. Cookery, Russian. 3. Cookery, French. I. Un amateur. II. Title.
TX728.L56 73-214313

NL 0430455 DLC

Lobanov-Rostovskiĭ, Aleksĕi Borisovich, *kniaz',* 1824–1896, *comp.*
... Русская родословная книга ... Изд. 2. С.-Петербургъ, А. С. Суворинъ, 1895.
2 v. 26cm.

Title transliterated: Russkaîa rodoslovnaîa kniga.
1. Russia—Geneal. 2. Russia—Nobility.
12-15967

NL 0430456 DLC

Lobanov-Rostovskiĭ, Vera (Dolgorouky) *kniaginia, d.* 1919?
... Catalogue des joyaux, colliers de perles, joailleries, perles & brillants, rivières en brillants et pierres de couleurs ayant composé l'écrin de la princesse Lobanoff de Rostoff, née princesse Dolgorouky, dont la vente aux enchères publiques aura lieu ... à Lausanne (Suisse) ... [Paris, Impr. Georges Petit, 1919]
75 p., 1 l. 28 pl. (1 double) 33cm.
At head of title: Étude de mm. Eug. & Ad. Monod, notaires à Vevey (Suisse)
Preface signed: Georges Berg.
Dates of sale: 12-17 janvier 1920.
1. Jewelry—Private collections.
G S 34-631
Library, U. S. Geol. Surv., Geo. F. Kunz Collection K480.5 qL78j

NL 0430457 DI-GS

VOLUME 337

Lobanov-Rostovsky, Andrei, 1892–
The grinding mill; reminiscences of war and revolution in Russia, 1913–1920, by Prince A. Lobanov-Rostovsky ... New York, The Macmillan company, 1935.
viii p., 2 l., 3-387 p. 20½cm.

1. European war, 1914–1918—Personal narratives, Russian. 2. Russia—Hist.—Revolution, 1917– —Personal narratives. I. Title. II. Title: Reminiscences of war and revolution in Russia, 1913–1920.

35-5135
Library of Congress DK265.L523
——— Copy 2.
Copyright A 82354 [5] 940.48147

PSC OClW OCl OU MB OO
NL 0430458 DLC NcD ICRL NcU CU NIC MoU NN OrU PU

Lobanov-Rostovsky, Andrei, 1892–
Illusions and realities of international coöperation, by André Lobanov-Rostovsky. The first annual lecture on the John Adams foundation at the University of California at Los Angeles, delivered May 16, 1934. Berkeley, Calif., University of California press, 1935.
2 p. l., 16 p. 24cm.

1. International cooperation. I. Title.

35-28193
Library of Congress JC362.L6
——— Copy 2.
[2] 321.041

NL 0430459 DLC DNAL OU MB NN

327
L781p Lobanov-Rostovsky, Andrei, 1892-
The problem of strategic frontiers. [Los Angeles] Regents of the University of California, c1941.
91-107p. 20cm.
"Reprinted from Frontiers of the future, lectures delivered under the auspices of the Committee on International Relations on the Los Angeles Campus of the University of California, 1940."
1. International relations. 2. Boundaries. 3. Geopolitics. I. Title.

NL 0430460 TxU

Lobanov-Rostovsky, Andrei, 1892–
Russia and Asia, by Prince A. Lobanov-Rostovsky ... New York, The Macmillan company, 1933.
viii p., 2 l., 334 p. incl. maps. 22½ cm.
Bibliography: p. 315-318.

1. Russia—For. rel.—Asia.
DK68.L6 327.47 33-5718

OrP IdB IdU WaSp OrPR OrCS WaS OrU OrSaW
InU OU OCU OO ViU OCl NcD PP PBm PHC MeB WaE WaT InU
NL 0430461 DLC IdPI CaBVaU CaBVa CU NcU GU ScU NIC

Lobanov-Rostovsky, Andrei, 1892–
Russia and Asia. Ann Arbor, G. Wahr Pub. Co., 1951.
342 p. illus. 23 cm.

1. Russia—For. rel.—Asia.
DK68.L6 1951 327.47 51-5701 ‡

OrSaW OrPS
NL 0430462 DLC ViU TU NN NNC MiU DS WaWW MtU OrMo

Lobanov-Rostovsky, Andrei, 1892–
Russia and Europe, 1789–1825. Durham, N. C., 1947.
xviii, [3]-448 p. 24 cm. (Duke University publications)
Bibliography: p. [429]-433.

1. Russia—For. rel.—1801–1825. I. Title.
DK197.L6 947.07 47-30958*

OrU OrPR MtBC OrCS WaWW MB
OClJC OO TxU ICU ViU CU ODW CoU NIC OU WaSpG WaS
NL 0430463 DLC IdPI NcGU MsSM AAP NjR MiU PSC PPSJ

Lobanov-Rostovsky, Andrei, 1892–
Russia and Europe, 1825–1878. Ann Arbor, Mich., G. Wahr Pub. Co., 1954.
330 p. 24 cm.

1. Russia—For. rel.—19th cent. 2. Europe—Politics—1789–1900. I. Title.
DK67.L6 940.28 55-1181 ‡

KU NjP ViU ICU ScU NcRS MH NBuT WaU MtU CaBVaU MsSM
LU OO PP ViU IaU PSC PSt OU MiU IU NcD CU CoU NcU
NL 0430464 DLC IdPI NcGU OrCS OrMonO MtU WaS IEN

Lobanov-Sibiryak, Vladimir Isidorovich
see Sibiriak, V

Lobanova, IU. V.
ND699
.B53S6
Soiuz khudozhnikov SSSR.
Иван Яковлевич Билибин, 1876–1942. [Выставка, май-июнь 1952. Каталог составлен Ю. В. Лобановой и М. П. Соколовой] Москва [Советский художник] 1952,

---

Lobanova, IU. V.
N7370
M6
Moscow. Vystavka proizvedenii khudozhnikov Uzbekskoi, Kazakhskoi, Kirgizskoi i Turkmenskoi SSR, *1949.*
Каталог выставки. [Составлен: М. Н. Гриценко и Ю. В. Лобановой] Москва [Советский художник] 1949.

Lobanova, IU. V.
ND699
.U4S6
Soiuz khudozhnikov SSSR.
Николай Павлович Ульянов, заслуженный деятель искусств РСФСР, член-корреспондент Академии художеств СССР, лауреат Сталинской премии, 1875–1949. [Каталог составлен Ю. В. Лобановой] Москва, Советский художник, 1951.

Lobanova, IU. V.
ND699
.B52S6
Soiuz khudozhnikov SSSR.
Выставка произведений военных художников Студии им. М. Б. Грекова: Виктор Сергеевич Бибиков и Владимир Валерианович Богаткин [апрель 1951 г.] Каталог [составлен Ю. В. Лобановой] Москва, Советский художник, 1951.

Lobanova, Nadezhda Vladimirovna (Giliarovskaia)
see **Giliarovskaia, Nadezhda Vladimirovna, 1886–**

Lobanovskii, IA. I., comp.

White Russia (S. S. R.) *Laws, statutes, etc.*
... Земельный кодекс БССР, с изданными в его развитие до 1 июля 1927 г. узаконениями, правилами, инструкциями и циркулярами, а также раз'яснениями и тезисами из определений Особой коллегии Высшего контроля по земельным делам. Сборник составлен по официальным материалам работниками Особой коллегии Высшего контроля. Минск, Издание Особой коллегии Высшего контроля при Наркомземе БССР, 1927.

Lobão,
... Fructidor. (Illustrações de Correia Dias.) Maceió: Of. graph. da Casa Ramalho, 1927. 82 p. incl. plates, port. 20½cm.
With autograph of author.
By Lobão Filho.

1. Poetry, Brazilian. I. Title.
N. Y. P. L. June 28, 1940

NL 0430472 NN

Greenlee
4504
P855
LOBAÕ, BERNARDO ANTONIO DE.
Justas lagrimas de Lisboa na sentida morte do ill.mo e ex.mo S.nr d. Jozé Thomáz de Menezes... Lisboa, A. Gomes, 1790.
14p. 20cm.

Verse.

NL 0430473 ICN

Greenlee
4504
P855
LOBAÕ, BERNARDO ANTONIO DE
Na sentida morte do ill.mo e ex.mo senhor d. Jozé Thomáz de Menezes... Lisboa, A. Gomes, 1790.
[3] leaves. 20cm.

Verse.

NL 0430474 ICN

981.1 Lobão, Eduardo Léger.
(301.422) A medicina em Belém. O mesticismo na
L796m sociedade belemnense. Para, Typ. de Tavares Cardoso, 1901.
113p. 23 cm.
Includes bibliographies.
1. Medicine - Brazil - Pará (State) 2. Indians of South America - Mixed bloods. 3. Miscegenation. 4. Negroes in Brazil.

NL 0430475 LNHT

Lobao, Manuel de Almeida e Sousa de, 1745-1817
see Sousa Lobao, Manuel de Almeida, 1745-1817.

Lobarzewska, Alina.
TP691
.P6
Poland. *Polski Komitet Normalizacyjny.*
Przetwory naftowe. [Opracował zespół: Alina Lobarzewska, Julian Solik, Zdzisław Stepek. Wyd. 1.] Warszawa Wydawn. Normalizacyjne, 19

VOLUME 337

fQK544
.P6
L6
Łobarżewski, Hiacinth Stržemù von, 1816-1862.
Muscorum frondosorum species novas Halicienses, profert ... Hyacinthus Strżemie Łobarżewski. [Wien, 1847]
[47]-64 p. 35 cm.

Caption title.
"Conventui amicorum scientiae naturalis ... Viennae 12. Nov. 1846."
From Naturwissenschaftliche Abhandlungen. Wien. Bd. 1.
1. Musci - Galicia. i. t.

NL 0430478 NNBG

Lobarzewski, [Ignacy Lada].
Respect dû à la tête couronnée, ou Exposé historique, politique et moral des grands évènements relatifs à la Pologne, en réponse aux écrits calomniant la mémoire du feu Stanislas Auguste, dernier roi électif de Pologne. St. Pétersbourg, Pluchart, 1818.
pp. 228 +.

Poland-Hist. 1763-95 |Stanisław II August, king of Poland|

NL 0430479 MH

HV9824
.S3L6
Lobas, Nikolaĭ Stepanovich, 1858–
Каторга и поселеніе на о-вѣ Сахалинѣ. (Нѣсколько штриховъ изъ жизни русской штрафной колоніи) [Павлоградъ] Изд. В. С. Лобасъ [1903]
160 p. illus., fold. map. 22 cm.

1. Penal colonies, Russian. 2. Sakhalin—Exiles. 3. Prisons—Sakhalin. I. Title.
Title transliterated: Katorga i poselenie na o-vie Sakhalinie.

HV9824.S3L6 49-31645
Library of Congress [1]

NL 0430480 DLC

HV7013
.L6
Lobas, Nikolaĭ Stepanovich, 1858–
Убійцы; нѣкоторыя черты психофизики преступниковъ. Москва, Тип. Т-ва И. Д. Сытина, 1913.
168 p. illus. 26 cm.
Bibliography: p. [0]

1. Crime and criminals—Russia. I. Title.
Title transliterated: Ubiĭtsy.

HV7013.L6 55-5594
Library of Congress

NL 0430481 DLC

Lobashev, M E
Очерки по истории русского животноводства. Москва, Изд-во Академии наук СССР, 1954.
342 p. illus., ports., maps. 23 cm.
At head of title: Академия наук СССР. Институт физиологии имени И. П. Павлова.
Errata slip inserted.
Bibliography: p. [323]-340.
——— Microfilm copy (negative)
Made in 1955 by the Library of Congress.
Microfilm Slavic 387 AC
1. Stock and stock-breeding—Russia.
Title transliterated: Ocherki po istorii russkogo zhivotnovodstva.

SF55.R95L6 55-40915

NL 0430482 DLC

Lobasserus, Ambrosius
see
Lobwasser, Ambrosius, 1515-1585.

MT7
V57
Music
Library
Lo Basso, Giuseppe
Elementi di musica. Napoli, Poliorama, 1854.
38 p. fold. music. [Bound with: Vitale, R. G. Grammatica musicale teorico-pratica. 1850]

1. Music - Manuals, text-books, etc.

NL 0430484 CU

Lobastov, Vasiliĭ Dmitrievich.
Расчет и конструирование телеграфной аппаратуры. Допущено в качестве учебника для техникумов. Москва, Гос. энерг. изд-во, 1949.
199, [1] p. diagrs. 23 cm.
Bibliography: p. [200]

1. Telegraph—Apparatus and supplies. I. Title.
Title transliterated: Raschet i konstruirovanie telegrafnoĭ apparatury.

TK5501.L6 52-36968

NL 0430485 DLC

TK5381
.L6
Lobastov, Vasiliĭ Dmitrievich.
Центральные телеграфные станции. Москва, Гос. изд-во лит-ры по вопросам связи и радио, 1938.
293 p. diagrs. 23 cm.
Bibliography: p. 292.

1. Telegraph stations—Management.
Title transliterated: TSentral'nye telegrafnye stantsii.

TK5381.L6 50-54208

NL 0430486 DLC

Lobat (Léon). Choléra-morbus asiatique. 15 pp. 8°. Paris, Mlle. Delaunay, 1832.

NL 0430487 DNLM

Lobatcheffsky, N
see
Lobachevskiĭ, Nikolaĭ Ivanovich, 1792-1856.

QW
900
L796m
1945
LOBATO, Affonso Sayão
Manual de técnicas aplicadas á alergia.
Rio de Janeiro, Editora Científica [1945]
175 p. illus.
1. Allergy

NL 0430489 DNLM

Lobato, Alceu, *ed.*
... Isenções e reduções de direitos aduaneiros; produtos similares (legislação fiscal) Rio de Janeiro, Officinas graphicas da empreza Almanak Laemmert ltda. [pref. 1931]
262 p. 23cm.

1. Tariff—Brazil—Law. 2. Customs administration—Brazil. I. Brazil. Laws, statutes, etc. II. Title.

42-49734
Library of Congress HJ6145.L6

NL 0430490 DLC

Lobato, Alexandre.
Aspectos de Moçambique no antigo regime colonial. Lisboa, Livraria Portugal, 1953.
54 p. 23 cm. (Estudos moçambicanos)

1. Mozambique—Hist. I. Title.

DT459.L58 57-26304 ‡

NL 0430491 DLC MU ICN CSt-H CU-S CtY IEN

Lobato, Alexandre.
A expansão portuguesa em Moçambique de 1498 a 1530. [Lisboa] Agência Geral do Ultramar, Divisão de Publicações e Biblioteca, 1954.
2 v. 24 cm. (Estudos moçambicanos)
Bibliographical footnotes.
CONTENTS.—livro 1. Descobrimento e ocupação da costa, 1498-1508.—livro 2. Política da capitania de Sofala e Moçambique de 1508 a 1530.

1. Mozambique—Hist.

DT459.L6 57-22766

IEN CU MiU NN CtY InU CSt ICU
NL 0430492 DLC CSt FU MU NSyU MBU NcD NN NcU TxU

Lobato, Alexandre, ed.
Fundação do estado da India
see under
Portugal. Ministerio do Ultramar.

Lobato, Alexandre.
Fundamentos da presença de Portugal na India. Lisboa [Comissariado Nacional da Mocidade Portuguesa] 1954.
144 p. 23 cm. (Esmeraldo; política & humanismo, no. 3, 1954)

1. Portuguese in India—Hist. I. Title. (Series)

AC70.E8 no. 3 55-23775

NL 0430494 DLC CSt CU

Lobato, Alexandre.
História da fundação de Lourenço Marques. Lisboa, Edições da Revista "Lusitânia," 1948.
127 p. 22 cm. (Estudos moçambicanos)

1. Lourenço Marquez (City)—Hist.

DT465.L3L57 54-37235 ‡

IU NN
NL 0430495 DLC CSt MiEM ViU MH CU ICN CtY NSyU

Lobato, Alexandre.
História do presídio de Lourenço Marques. Com um pref. do Prof. Doutor Marcelo Caetano. Lisboa, 1949–
v. 23 cm. (*His* Estudos moçambicanos)
"Documentos": p. [175]-206.

1. Lourenço Marquez (City)—Hist. I. Title.

DT465.L3L58 967.99 51-17120

NNS MB CSt CaBVaU WU CLSU ICIU
NL 0430496 DLC CtY IU MnU NN LU ICU FU MiEM NN MH

VOLUME 337

LOBATO, ALEXANDRE.
História do presídio de Lourenço Marques. Com um pref. de Marcelo Caetano. Lisboa, 1949-60. 2 v. 23cm. (Estudos moçambicanos)

Film reproduction. Positive.
CONTENTS.--1. 1782-1786.--2. 1787-1799.

1. Lourenço Marques (City)--Hist.

NL 0430497 NN

Lobato, Alexandre.
A ilha de Moçambique (monografia) Moçambique, Impr. Nacional, 1945.
x, 156 p. illus., ports., maps, col. coat of arms. 28 cm.

1. Mozambique—Descr. & trav. I. Title.

DT465.M8L55 55-36559

NL 0430498 DLC NSyU

DT 465 M17 L62 Lobato, Alexandre.
Novos subsídios para a história da fundação de Sofala. Lisboa, 1950.
[135]-150 p.
Cover title.
"XIII Congresso Luso-Espanhol para o Progresso das Ciencias. Separata do tomo VIII, 7ª secção, Ciencias Históricas e Filológicas."

1. Sofala, Mozambique--Hist. I. Associação Portuguesa para o Progresso das Ciencias. II. Asociación Española para el Progresso de las Ciencias. III. Title.

NL 0430499 NSyU

Lobato, Alexandre.
Sobre "Cultura moçambicana." Reposição de um problema e resposta a um crítico. Lisboa, 1952.
129 p. 23 cm. (Estudos moçambicanos)

1. Mozambique—Intellectual life. I. Title.

DT465.M8L57 54-31211 ‡

NL 0430500 DLC AzU CSt ICU CtY NSyU MH NN

Lobato, Antonio José dos Reis

see

Reis Lobato, Antonio José dos, 18th cent.

---

*Lobato, Gervasio, 1850-1895.

Pina, Marianno, 1860-1899.
... O Armador, por Marianno Pina. Memorias de Paulina, por Theophilo Braga. O roubo, por Fialho d'Almeida. A vingança de Figaro, por Gervasio Lobato. Uma canção romantica, por Pinheiro Chagas. Noticias velhas, por Eduardo Coelho. Lisboa, Typographia universal de T. Q. Antunes, 1882.

LOBATO, Gervasio, 1850-1895.
A burgueza; comedia em 1 acto. Representada no theatro da Trindade na noite de 2 janeiro de 1882. Lisboa, 1912.

NL 0430503 MH

Lobato, Gervasio, 1850-1895.
... A comedia de Lisboa; com um prologo por Pinheiro Chagas. Porto, E. Chardron; [etc., etc.] 1878.
xxvi, 302 p. 18½cm.
First published as a series of sketches in the Diario da manhã. cf. p. viii-ix.

1. Lisbon—Soc. life & cust. I. Title.
[Full name: Gervasio Jorge Gonçalves Lobato]
34-20823

Library of Congress PQ9261.L536C5 869.4

NL 0430504 DLC

Lobato, Gervasio, 1850-1895.
... A comedia do theatro. Lisboa, A. M. Pereira [18—]
276 p. 19½cm.

I. Title.
[Full name: Gervasio Jorge Gonçalves Lobato]
34-8879

Library of Congress PQ9261.L536C6 869.3

NL 0430505 DLC PU

PQ9261 .L536 C6 1911 Lobato, Gervásio, 1850-1895.
A comedia do theatro. 2. ed. Lisboa, A. M. Pereira, 1911.
256p. illus.

NL 0430506 NcU MiU MH

PQ 9261 .L536 C6 Lobato, Gervasio, 1850-1895
A comedia do theatro. Illustrada com 60 desenhos de Pedro Guedas. 3. ed. Lisboa, A.M. Pereira, 1918.
256 p. illus. 19 cm.

NL 0430507 WU NNU

Lobato, Gervasio, 1850-1895.
El comisario de policía, caricatura en cuatro actos, original del celebre escritor portugués Gervasio Lobato, arreglada a la escena española por los señores Carlos y Enrique Arroyo y Gonzalo Jover. Madrid, R. Velasco, 1905.
92p.

In: Teatro español, v.39, no. 1.
Teatro Moderno, 13 de abril, 1905.

NL 0430508 NcU TxLT MH NN

Lobato, Gervasio, 1850-1895.
O commissario de policia. Comedia original em quatro actos. Lisboa, B. Dias, 1898.
xvii, 130 p. 1 port. 12°.

NL 0430509 NN

LOBATO, GERVASIO, 1850-1895.
O commissario de policia; comedia original em quatro actos. Lisboa, B. Dias, 1898. xvii, 130 p. port. 18cm.

Film reproduction. Positive.

1. Drama. Portuguese. I. Title.

NL 0430510 NN

869.8 L796cn 1919 Lobato, Gervasio, 1850-1895.
Commissario de policia, comedia original em 4 actos; representada pela primeira vez em Lisboa, no Theatro do Gymnasio. 2.ed. Lisboa, A.Bordalo, 1919.
92 p.

NL 0430511 MiU MH

LOBATO, Gervasio, 1850-1895.
A condessa Heloisa; comedia original em 1 acto. [Representada no theatro da Rua dos Condes, em 19 de abril de 1878]. Lisboa, 1892.

NL 0430512 MH NN

LOBATO, GERVASIO, 1850-1895.
A condessa Heloisa. Comedia original em um acto. Lisboa, Typ. da Empreza litteraria, 1892. 30 p. 18cm.

Film reproduction. Negative.

1. Drama, Portuguese. I. Title.

NL 0430513 NN

---

*Lobato, Gervasio, 1850-1895.

Gomes Leal, Antonio Duarte, 1849-1921.
... O espelho da marqueza, por Gomes Leal. O diabo, por Monteiro Ramalho. A sessão de espiritismo, por Gervasio Lobato. Uma historia singular, por Christovão Ayres. Scenas de drama moderno, por Eduardo Coelho. Uma tourada no seculo xvii, por Eduardo Coelho. Os cinco irmãos, de Andersen. Lisboa, Typographia universal de T. Q. Antunes, 1881.

LOBATO, GERVASIO, 1850-1895.
O festim de Balthazar: farça original em um acto. Lisboa, Typographia da Empreza Litteraria de Lisboa, 1892. 38 p. 19cm.

1. Drama, Portuguese. I. Title.

NL 0430515 NN

LOBATO, Gervasio, 1850-1895.
O festim de Balthazar; farça original em um acto. 2a ed. Lisboa, 1892.

NL 0430516 MH

Lobato, Gervasio, 1850-1895.
O grade circo, romance de actualidade.

NL 0430517 OCl

PQ 9261 .L538 G75 LOBATO, GERVASIO, 1850-1895
O grande circo; romance da actualidade. Lisboa, A. M. Pereira, 1893.
559 p.

NL 0430518 InU

VOLUME 337

Lobato, Gervasio, 1850-1895.
...O grande circo, romace de actualidade. 3rd. ed. illustrada com 200 desenhos de Henrique Cabral. Lisboa, A. M. Pereira, 1922.
616 p.

NL 0430519 PU CU

PQ 9261 L536 I5
Lobato, Gervasio, 1850-1895
Os invisiveis de Lisboa; grande romance em 6 volumes [por] Gervasio Lobato & Jayme Victor. Desenhos de Manuel de Macedo. Executados pelos processos Ignio Eberle e Gillot. Lisboa, D. Corazzi, 1886-87.
6v. 20cm. (Horas románticas. Bibliotheca selecta illustrada)
I. Victor, Jayme, joint author II. Title

NL 0430520 WU InU

Lobato, Gervasio, 1850-1895.
...A lenda do Perú
see under Almeida, Francisco de.

Lobato, Gervasio, 1850–1895.
... Lisboa em camisa. [Lisboa] Empreza litteraria de Lisboa [1882]
310 p., 1 l. 18½cm.
I. Title.
[*Full name:* Gervasio Jorge Gonçalves Lobato]
34-13380
Library of Congress PQ9261.L536L5 1882 869.3

NL 0430522 DLC OCl PU

Lobato, Gervasio, 1850–1895.
... Lisboa em camisa. 2. ed. Com illustrações de Celso Herminio. Lisboa, A. M. Pereira, 1897.
331 p., 1 l. illus. 16cm.
I. Title.
[*Full name:* Gervasio Jorge Gonçalves Lobato]
34-13381
Library of Congress PQ9261.L536L5 1897 869.3

NL 0430523 DLC

Lobato, Gervasio, 1850–1895.
... Lisboa em camisa. 5. ed. Com illustrações de Celso Herminio. Lisboa, A. M. Pereira, 1907.
296 p. illus. 19cm.
I. Title.
[*Full name:* Gervasio Jorge Gonçalves Lobato]
34-13382
Library of Congress PQ9261.L536L5 1907 869.3

NL 0430524 DLC

Lobato, Gervasio, 1850–1895.
...Lisboa em camisa. Decima edição. Illustrada com 104 desenhos de Pedro Guedes. Lisboa: A. M. Pereira, 1919. 310 p. front. (port.), illus. 19cm.
984861A. 1. Fiction, Portuguese. I. Title.
N. Y. P. L. December 29, 1939

NL 0430525 NN

PQ9261 .L536 L5 1919
Lobato, Gervasio, 1850-1895.
Lisboa em camisa. 10. ed. Lisboa, Parceria Antonio Maria Pereira, 1919.
310p. illus.

NL 0430526 NcU

Lobato, Gervasio, 1850–1895.
... Lisboa em camisa. 12. ed., illustrada com 104 desenhos de Pedro Guedes. Lisboa, A. M. Pereira, 1931.
256 p. front. (port.) illus. 19½cm.
First published 1882.
I. Title.
[*Full name:* Gervasio Jorge Gonçalves Lobato]
41-38833
Library of Congress PQ9261.L536L5 1931
[2] 869.3

NL 0430527 DLC CU

Lobato, Gervasio, 1850-1895.
Lisboa em camisa. 14. ed., illustrada com 104 desenhos de Pedro Guedes. Lisboa, A. M. Pereira, 1954.
312 p. illus., port. 20 cm.

NL 0430528 MB IaU

Lobato, Gervasio, 1850–1895.
...A primeira confessada; romance. 2. ed. ... Lisboa [etc.] Portugalia, 1918. 372 p. illus. 20cm.
577039B. 1. Fiction, Portuguese.
NN

NL 0430529 NN MH MiU WU NcU

LOBATO, Gervasio, 1850-1895.
O seguro de vida; comedia em 2 actos. Lisboa, 1915.

NL 0430530 MH

[Lobato, Gervasio] 1850-1895.
Um sólo de flauta. Monologo, traduzida do francez. [By] José da Camara Manoel. Lisboa, F. Franco [189-?]
7 p. 16°. (Collecção de peças theatraes. no. 31)
In: NQM p.v. 57, no. 25.

NL 0430531 NN

LOBATO, Gervasio, 1850-1895.
Sua excellencia; comedia original em tres actos. Representada no theatro do Gymnasio e 7 de maio de 1884. [Lisboa], 1893.

NL 0430532 MH NN

Lobato, Gulnara de Morais
see
Morais Lobato, Gulnara de.

281.340 L78
Lobato, Homero Taveira.
A situação atual da indústria pecuária no Pará. Belém, Livraria Brasil, 1942.
57 p.
1. Para, Brazil (State) Domestic animals. I. Lobato, Adalberto Taveira, joint author.

NL 0430534 DNAL

Lobato, J Manuel
El contragambito de Greco. [2],80,[3]p. Puebla, [A. Vazquez] 1914. (Cartillas de ajedrez)

NL 0430535 OCl

Lobato, João Bernardo, 1882–
... As duas batalhas de Guararapes, com una introdução de João Duarte, filho. [Rio de Janeiro] D. N. P., 1939.
33, [1] p. map, plans. 18½cm.
At head of title: General Lobato Filho.
"Publicado, em primeira mão, no número de abril de 'Fronteiras'."—p. 7.
"Autores consultados": p. 33.
1. Guararapes, Battle of, 1648. 2. Guararapes, Battle of, 1649. I. Brazil. Departamento nacional de propaganda. II. Title.
45-49250
Library of Congress F2532.L6

NL 0430536 DLC NNC NN DPU

F 2532 .L6 1955 LAL
Lobato, João Bernardo, 1882-
As duas batalhas de Guararapes. [Com una introdução de João Duarte, filho. 2a. ed.] Rio de Janeiro, Irmãos Pongetti, 1955.
85 [1] p. maps, plans. 19 cm.
At head of title: General de Exercito Lobato Filho.
"Publicado, em primeira mão, no número de abril de 'Fronteiras'."-p. 14.
Includes bibliography.
1. Guararapes. Battle of, 1648. 2. Guararapes, Battle of, 1649. I. Brazil. Departamento nacional de propaganda. II. Title.

NL 0430537 LNHT IU TxU

Lobato, João Bernardo, 1882–
A última noite da Escola Militar da Praia Vermelha (contribuição para a história) Rio de Janeiro, Irmãos Pongetti [1948]
127 p. 19 cm.
1. Rio de Janeiro. Escola Militar. I. Title.
U474.R5L1 1948 A 52-4344
New York. Public Libr. for Library of Congress [1]†

NL 0430538 NN DLC

338.47678 L79b
Lobato, João Bernardo, 1910-
A borracha da Amazônia; sugestões para a solução prática de seus problemas. Rio de Janeiro, Pongetti, 1951.
97p. fold.plan. 20cm.
1. Rubber indus. & trade - Amazon Valley. I. Title.

NL 0430539 TNJ

VOLUME 337

Lobato, João Bernardo, 1910 -
Fronteiras sudoeste. Rio de Janeiro, Irmãos Pongetti, 1953.
241 p. illus. 19 cm.

1. South America. I. Title.

F2217.L6 56-17668 ‡

NL 0430540 DLC NN TxU IU

Lobato, José Antonio Pérez
see
Pérez Lobato, José Antonio.

Lobato, José Bento Monteiro, 1882-1948.
Obras completas. S. Paulo, Editora Brasiliense. 1946-47.
30 v. illus., ports., maps. 22 cm.

CONTENTS.—1. sér. Literatura geral: v. 1. Urupês. v. 2. Cidades mortas. v. 3. Negrinha. v. 4. Idéias de Jéca Tatú. v. 5. A onda verde. O presidente negro. v. 6. Na antevespera. v. 7. O escandalo do petroleo. Ferro. v. 8. Mr. Slang e o Brasil. Problema vital. v. 9. America. v. 10. Mundo da lua. Miscelanea. v. 11-12. A barca de Gleyre; quarenta anos de correspondencia literaria entre Monteiro Lobato e Godofredo Rangel. v. 13. Prefacios e entrevistas.—2. sér. Literatura infantil: v. 1. Reinações de Narizinho. v. 2. Viagem ao céu. O saci. v. 3. Caçadas de Pedrinho. Hans Staden. v. 4. Historia do mundo para as crianças. v. 5. Memorias da Emilia. Peter Pan. v. 6. Emilia no país da gramatica. Aritmetica da Emilia. v. 7. Geografia de dona Benta. v. 8. Serões de dona Benta. Historia das invenções. v. 9. D. Quixote das crianças. v. 10. O poço do visconde. v. 11. Historias de tia Nastacia. v. 12. O picapau amarelo. A reforma da natureza. v. 13. O Minotauro. v. 14. A chave do tamanho. v. 15. Fabulas. Historias diversas. v. 16-17. Os doze trabalhos de Hercules.

PQ9697.L59 1946 869.081 48-23228

NL 0430543 DLC TNJ TxU CtY NcU WaU NcD

Lobato, José Bento Monteiro, 1882-1948.
Obras completas. S. Paulo, Editora Brasiliense, 1948-
v. illus., ports. 22 cm.
Vols. 1, 7: 3. ed.; v. 3-6, 8-13: 2. ed.; v. 14, 16-17: 1. ed.

CONTENTS.—1. sér. Literatura geral: v. 1. Urupês. v. 2. Cidades mortas. v. 3. Negrinha. v. 4. Idéias de Jéca Tatú. v. 5. A onda verde. O presidente negro. v. 6. Na antevespera. v. 7. O escandalo do petroleo. Ferro. v. 8. Mr. Slang e o Brasil. Problema vital. v. 9. America. v. 10. Mundo da lua. Miscelanea. v. 11-12. A barca de Gleyre; quarenta anos de correspondencia literaria entre Monteiro Lobato e Godofredo Rangel. v. 13. Prefacios e entrevistas. v. 14. Literatura do minarete. v. 15. Conferências, artigos e crônicas. v. 16-17. Cartas escolhidas.

PQ9697.L59 1948 869.081 50-23605

InU
NL 0430544 DLC CoU LU NBuU CLU CSt CaBVaU OrPS

Lobato, José Bento Monteiro, 1882-1948.

[Dodgson, Charles Lutwidge] 1832-1898.
... Alice no país do espelho, por Lewis Carroll [pseud.] tradução de Monteiro Lobato. São Paulo, Companhia editora nacional, 1933.

Lobato, José Bento Monteiro, 1882-1948.
America. S. Paulo, Companhia Editora Nacional, 1932.
254 p. plates, diagr. 20 cm.

1. U. S.—Descr. & trav.—1920-1940. 2. U. S.—Soc. life & cust.—1918-1945. I. Title.

E169.L79 1932 917.3 33-12837 rev*

NL 0430546 DLC NcD NN FU

Lobato, José Bento Monteiro, 1882-1948.
America. 2. ed. São Paulo, Companhia Editora Nacional, 1934.
280 p. illus., diagr. 19 cm. (Collecção "Viagens," v. 1)

1. U. S.—Descr. & trav.—1920-1940. 2. U. S.—Soc. life & cust.—1918-1945. I. Title.

E169.L79 1934 917.3 34-25031 rev*

NL 0430547 DLC

Lobato, José Bento Monteiro, 1882-1948.
America. 3. ed. São Paulo, Companhia Editora Nacional, 1937.
280 p. illus., diagr. 19 cm. (Collecção "Viagens," v. 1)

1. U. S.—Descr. & trav.—1920-1940. 2. U. S.—Soc. life & cust.—1918-1945. I. Title.

E169.L79 1937 917.3 42-5471 rev*

NL 0430548 DLC TxU

Lobato, José Bento Monteiro, 1882-1948.
America; os Estados Unidos de 1929. S.Paulo, Editora brasiliense ltda.,1948.
viii,311 p. (His Obras completas. 1.a série. Literatura geral. vol.9)

NL 0430549 CU

Lobato, José Bento Monteiro, 1882-1948.
Arimetica da Emilia. Ilustrações de Belmonte. S. Paulo, Companhia Editora Nacional, 1935.
164 p. illus. 22 cm. (Biblioteca pedagogica brasileira. sér. 1.: Literatura infantil, v. 21)

1. Arithmetic—1901- I. Title.

QA103.L8 372.7 36-16827 rev*

NL 0430550 DLC

Lobato, José Bento Monteiro, 1882-1948.
Aventuras de Hans Staden, o homem que naufragou nas costas do Brasil em 1549 e esteve oito mezes prisioneiro dos indios tupinambás; narradas por dona Benta aos seus netos Narizinho e Pedrinho e redigidas por Monteiro Lobato. São Paulo, Companhia Editora Nacional, 1927.
148 p. illus. 19 cm.

1. Staden, Hans, 16th cent.—Juvenile literature. 2. Tupinamba Indians—Juvenile literature. I. Staden, Hans, 16th cent. Warhaftige Historia. II. Title.

F2528.L6 981 34-35342 rev*

NL 0430551 DLC

Lobato, José Bento Monteiro, 1882-1948.
Aventuras de Hans Staden, o homem que naufragou nas costas do Brasil em 1549 e esteve oito mezes prisioneiro dos indios tupinambas; narradas por dona Benta aos seus netos Narizinho e Pedrinho. 3. ed. S. Paulo, Companhia Editora Nacional, 1934.
116 p. illus., col. plates. 22 cm. (Biblioteca pedagogica brasileira. Ser. 1.: Literatura infantil, 5)

1. Staden, Hans, 16th cent. — Juvenile literature. 2. Tupinamba Indians—Juvenile literature. I. Staden, Hans, 16th cent. Warhaftige Historia. II. Title.

F2528.S84 1934 869.3 35-13594

NL 0430552 DLC

809.99 Lobato, José Bento Monteiro, 1882-1948.
M763.3
...Aventuras de Hans Staden, o homem que naufragou nas costas do Brasil em 1549 e esteve oito meses prisioneiro do indios tupinambas; narradas por dona Benta aos seus netos Narizinho e Pedrinho. 5.a edição. S.Paulo,Rio[de Janeiro,etc.] Companhia editora nacional [1940?]
3l.,[1l]-116p. illus.(part col.mount.) 22cm. (Biblioteca pedagogica brasileira. serie 1.a. Literatura infantil. vol.5)
At head of title: Monteiro Lobato.
Illustrated lining-papers.

NL 0430553 PU

Lobato, José Bento Monteiro, 1882-1948.
Aventuras de Hans Staden, o homem que naufragou nas costas do Brasil em 1549 e esteve oito meses prisioneiro dos indios tupinambás; narradas por dona Benta aos seus netos Narizinho e Pedrinho. 6. ed. São Paulo, Companhia Editora Nacional, 1944.
114 p. illus. 22 cm. (Biblioteca pedagogica brasileira. Ser. 1.: Literatura infantil, v. 5)

1. Staden, Hans, 16th cent.—Juvenile literature. 2. Tupinamba Indians—Juvenile literature. I. Staden, Hans, 16th cent. Warhaftige Historia. II. Title.

F2528.S84 1944 57-53481

NL 0430554 DLC OCU MH

Bra
PZ85
.M6
1945
Lobato, José Bento Monteiro, 1882-1948.
... Aventuras de Hans Staden; traducción del portugués por M. J. de Sosa; ilustractiones de Arturo Travi. Buenos Aires, Editorial Americalee [1945]
141 p. illus., plates. 21 cm.
"Segunda edición."

NL 0430555 DPU

G869.8
M764b
Lobato, José Bento Monteiro, 1882-1948.
A barca de Gleyre; quarenta anos de correspondencia literaria entre Monteiro Lobato e Godofredo Rangel, com um pref. de Edgard Cavalheiro. São Paulo, Companhia Editôra Nacional, 1944.
xiii, 504p. 22cm.

540525 1. Authors - Correspondence, reminiscences, etc. I. Rangel, Godofredo, 1884-1951.

NL 0430556 TxU MU LU MH

Lobato, José Bento Monteiro, 1882-1948.
A barca de Gleyre; quarenta anos de correspondencia literaria entre Monteiro Lobato e Godofredo Rangel. 2.ed. S.Paulo,Editora Brasiliense,1948.
2v. plates. 23cm. (Obras completas de Monteiro Lobato. 1.sér. Literatura geral.v.12-13)

NL 0430557 PU

Lobato, José Bento Monteiro, 1882-1948
... Brazilian short stories [by] Monteiro Lobato, with an introduction by Isaac Goldberg. Girard, Kan., Haldeman-Julius company [c1925]
64 p. 12½cm. (Little blue book, no. 733, ed. by E. Haldeman-Julius)
"The translations are by a woman friend of Lobato's, resident in Brazil."
Advertising matter: p. 62-64.

CONTENTS.—Introduction.—Modern torture.—The penitent wag.—The plantation buyer.

I. Goldberg, Isaac, 1887- ed. II. Title.

Library of Congress PZ3.L7796Br CA 26-674 Unrev'd

NL 0430558 DLC MiU NN

VOLUME 337

Lobato, José Bento Monteiro, 1882–1948.
As caçadas de Pedrinho. Illustrações de Jean G. Villin. S. Paulo, Cia. Editora Nacional, 1933.
119 p. illus., col. plates. 22 cm. (Bibliotheca pedagogica brasileira. Ser. 1.: Literatura infantil, v. 9)

I. Title.

PZ83.L56 869.3 34–33905

NL 0430559 DLC

Lobato, José Bento Monteiro, 1882-1948.
...As caçadas de Pedrinho; ilus. de J. U. Campos. 7. ed. São Paulo [etc.] Companhia editora nacional, 1944. 101 p. illus. (part col.) 25cm. (Biblioteca pedagogica brasileira. sér. 1. Literatura infantil. v. 9.)

392423B. 1. Juvenile literature—Fiction, Brazilian. I. Title.
N. Y. P. L. June 29, 1949

NL 0430560 NN

G-JP
M764cTSs Lobato, José Bento Monteiro, 1882-1948.
Las cacerías de Perucho; traducción del portugués por M.J. de Sosa. Ilus. de Silvio Baldessari Buenos Aires, Editorial Americalee [1945]
120p. illus.(part col.) 22cm.

I. Sosa, M.J., de, tr. II. Title.

NL 0430561 TxU

Lobato, José Bento Monteiro, 1882–1948.
A chave do tamanho; historia da maior reinação do mundo, na qual Emilia, sem querer, destruiu temporariamente o tamanho das oriaturas humanas. 3. ed. São Paulo, Cia. Editora Nacional, 1945.
161 p. illus. 22 cm. (Biblioteca pedagogica brasileira. Serie 1.: Literatura infantil, v. 33)

I. Title.

PZ83.L58 1945 52–21260

NL 0430562 DLC

Lobato, José Bento Monteiro, 1882-1948.
A chave do tamanho; história da maior reinação do mundo onde Emília reduz temporariamente o tamanho das criaturas humanas. Ilustrações de André le Blanc. 4.ª ed. São Paulo,Ed.Brasiliense,1949.
197p. illus. 22cm. (His Livros infantis, v.20)

At head of title: Monteiro Lobato.

NL 0430563 PU-Penn

Lobato, José Bento Monteiro, 1882–1948.
O choque das raças; ou, O presidente negro; romance americano do anno de 2228. S. Paulo, Companhia Editora Nacional, 1926.
279 p. 19 cm.

I. Title. II. Title: O presidente negro.

PQ9697.L59C5 29–11327

NL 0430564 DLC NIC NN PU NcD

PQ
9697
L787
C55
Lobato, José Bento Monteiro, 1882-1948.
Cidades mortas (contos e impressões)
S. Paulo, Revista do Brasil, 1920.
231 p. 27cm.

NL 0430565 NIC DPU OOxM

Lobato, José Bento Monteiro, 1882-1948.
...Cidades mortas (contos e impressões). Terceira edição ... S. Paulo: Monteiro Lobato & cia., 1921. 98 p. 22cm. (Collecção Brasilia. no. 3.)

Printed in double columns.
CONTENTS.—Cidades mortas.—Coisas do meu diario.—Grammatica viva.—Noite de S. João.—Pedro Pichorra.—As seis decepções.—Cabellos compridos.—Um avô.—O resto de onça.—Porque Lopes se casou.—O caso do tombo.—"Gens ennuyeux."—O figado indiscreto.—O plagio.—O romance do Chopim.—O luzeiro agricola.—A "cruz de ouro."—De como quebrei a cabeça á mulher do Mello.—A poesia e poeta.—O espião allemão.

102132A. 1. Fiction, Brazilian. I. Title.
N. Y. P. L. Revised October 13, 1933

NL 0430566 NN

Lobato, José Bento Monteiro, 1882–1948.
Cidades mortas; contos e impressões. 4. ed. [São Paulo] Monteiro Lobato, 1923.
259 p. 16 cm.
CONTENTS.—Cidades mortas.—Literatura do "Minarete."

I. Title.

PQ9697.L59 1923 30–7164

NL 0430567 DLC OOxM

PQ9697
.L72C5
Lobato, José Bento Monteiro, 1882-194
...Cidades mortas. São Paulo,Editora brasiliense limitada,1946. 8+273p. (His Obras completas,1.ser.,v.2)

NL 0430568 InU

Lobato, José Bento Monteiro, 1882-1948.
Cidades mortas. 2.ed. [S.Paulo,Editora Brasiliense,1948]
272p. 23cm. (Obras completas de Monteiro Lobato. 1.sér. Literatura geral. v.2)

NL 0430569 PU

Lobato, José Bento Monteiro, 1882-1948.
El comprador de haciendas. Tr. de Benjamin de Garay. Barcelona, Cervantes [pref. 1923]
150 p. 14 cm.

NL 0430570 CU

Lobato, José Bento Monteiro, 1882-1948, tr.
Grimm, Jacob Ludwig Karl, 1785–1863.
... Contos; traducção de Monteiro Lobato. S. Paulo, Cia. editora nacional, 1932.

Lobato, José Bento Monteiro, 1882-1948, tr.
Andersen, Hans Christian, 1805–1875.
... Contos de Andersen; traducção de Monteiro Lobato. S. Paulo, Cia. editora nacional, 1932.

Lobato, José Bento Monteiro, 1882-1948, tr.
Perrault, Charles, 1628–1703.
... Contos de fadas; tradução de Monteiro Lobato. S. Paulo, Companhia editora nacional, 1934.

Lobato, José Bento Monteiro, 1882–1948.
Contos leves (Cidades mortas e outros) São Paulo, Companhia Editora Nacional, 1935.
247 p. 18 cm. (Collecção "Os Grandes livros brasileiros," vol. 5)

I. Title.

PQ9697.L59C6 869.3 40–1547

NL 0430574 DLC MShM OU NBC MiU PSt ICU IU CU TxU

G869.8
M764cl
1941
Lobato, José Bento Monteiro, 1882-1948.
Contos leves (Cidades mortas, Negrinha e Macaco que se fez homem) Ed. definitiva. São Paulo, Companhia Editôra Nacional, 1941.
308p. 19cm. (Coleção "Os grandes livros brasileiros", v.5)

NL 0430575 TxU MiU MU OU

PQ
9697
.L59A6
Lobato, José Bento Monteiro, 1882-1948.
Contos pesados: Urupês, Negrinha e O macaco que se fez homem. Ed. definitiva. S[ão] Paulo, Companhia Editora Nacional, 1940.
358p. 19cm. (Coleção Os grandes livros brasileiros, v.2)
At head of title: Monteiro Lobato.

I. Title. II. Title: Urupês. III. Title: Negrinha. IV. Title: O macaco que se fez homem.

NN NBC TxU
NL 0430576 DGW OU TxU CoU LU ViU MiU OO ICU OCl

Lobato, José Bento Monteiro, 1882–1948.
A correspondência entre Monteiro Lobato e Lima Barreto. [Por] Edgard Cavalheiro. [Rio de Janeiro] Ministério da Educação e Cultura, Serviço de Documentação [1955]
71 p. 20 cm. (Os Cadernos de cultura, 76)

I. Lima Barreto, Afonso Henrique de, 1881–1922. II. Cavalheiro, Edgard, ed.

PQ9697.L59Z54 56–15300 ‡

NL 0430577 DLC TxU WU CaBVaU

Lobato, José Bento Monteiro, 1882–1948.
D. Quixote das crianças, contado por dona Benta; ilustrações de Gustavo Doré, capa de J. U. Campos. São Paulo, Companhia Editora Nacional, 1936.
172 p. illus. 22 cm. (Bibliotheca pedagogica brasileira. Ser. 1.ª: Literatura infantil, v. 25)

I. Cervantes Saavedra, Miguel de. Don Quixote. II. Doré, Gustave, 1832–1883, illus. III. Title.

PQ6333.P6L6 1936 863.32 38–32453 rev*

NL 0430578 DLC PU MH

Lobato, José Bento Monteiro, 1882–1948.
D. Quixote das crianças, contado por dona Benta; ilustrações de Gustavo Doré. 3. ed. São Paulo, Editora Brasiliense, 1944.
168 p. illus. 22 cm.

I. Cervantes Saavedra, Miguel de. Don Quixote. II. Doré, Gustave, 1832–1883, illus. III. Title.

PQ6333.P6L6 1944 863.32 46–1993 rev*

NL 0430579 DLC

VOLUME 337

Lobato, José Bento Monteiro, 1882–1948.
Don Quijote de los niños; traducción del portugués, especial para la Editorial Claridad, por Benjamín de Garay. Buenos Aires, Editorial Claridad [1938]
284 p. 18 cm. (Biblioteca de textos para lectura libre)

I. Cervantes Saavedra, Miguel de. Don Quixote. II. Title.

PQ6333.P6L618 863.32 43-40442*

NL 0430580 DLC TxU

Pn869.1 M763D Lobato, José Bento Monteiro, 1882-1948.
Os doze trabalhos de Hercules. São Paulo, Editora brasiliense, 1944.
12v. illus. 20cm.

Contents. -1.O leão de Nemeia. -2.A Hidra de Lerna. -3.A corça de pés de bronze. -4.O javalí de Erimanto. -5.As cavalariças de Augias. -6.As aves do lago estinfale. -7.O touro de Creta. -8.Os cavalos de Diomedes. -9.O cinto de Hipolita. -10.Os bois de Gerião. -11.O pomo das Hesperides. -12. Hercules e Cerbero.

NL 0430581 PU-Penn

Lobato, José Bento Monteiro, 1882–1948.
Emilia no país da gramatica. Ilustrações de Belmonte. S. Paulo, Companhia Editora Nacional, 1934.
172 p. illus. 22 cm. (Biblioteca pedagogica brasileira. Sér. 1.: Literatura infantil, v. 14)

1. Portuguese language—Grammar—1870–1950. I. Title.

PZ83.L59 1934 469.5 35-13593

NL 0430582 DLC

Lobato, José Bento Monteiro, 1882–1948.
Emilia no país da gramatica. Ilustrações de Belmonte. 3. ed. São Paulo, Companhia Editora Nacional, 1937.
172 p. illus. 22 cm. (Biblioteca pedagogica brasileira. Ser. 1.: Literatura infantil, v. 14)

1. Portuguese language—Grammar—1870–1950. I. Title.

PZ83.L59 1937 43-1618

NL 0430583 DLC

G981.06 B471 Ser.1 v.14 1940
Lobato, José Bento Monteiro, 1882-1948.
Emilia no país da gramatica. Ilus. de Belmonte. 4. ed. S[ão] Paulo, Companhia Editôra Nacional, 1940.
172p. illus. 22cm. (Biblioteca pedagógica brasileira. Sér.1: Literatura infantil. v.14)

1. Portuguese language - Grammar - 1870- I. Title. II. Series (contents)

NL 0430584 TxU NcD

Pn869.1 M763E Lobato, José Bento Monteiro, 1882-1948.
Emilia no país da gramatica. Ilustrações de André le Blanc. 7.ª ed. São Paulo, Ed. Brasiliense, 1949.
170p. illus. 22cm. (His Livros infantís, v.9)

At head of title: Monteiro Lobato.

NL 0430585 PU-Penn

Lobato, José Bento Monteiro, 1882-1948, tr.

Adams, James Truslow, 1878–
... A epopeia americana, tradução de Monteiro Lobato. São Paulo [etc.] Companhia editora nacional, 1940.

HD9574 B82L6 Stack
Lobato, José Bento Monteiro, 1883-1948.
O escandalo do petroleo; depoimentos apresentados á Comissão de Inquerito sobre o Petroleo [por] Monteiro Lobato. S[ão] Paulo, Companhia Editora Nacional, 1936.
314 p. 19cm.

1.Petroleum industry and trade - Brazil. 2. Mining law - Brazil. I.Comissão de Inquerito sobre o Petroleo. II.Title.

NL 0430587 CSt

TN 873 .B8 M7
Lobato, José Bento Monteiro, 1882-1948.
O escandalo do petroleo; depoimentos apresentados á Comissão de Inquerito sobre o Petroleo. 4. ed., aumentado de notas e documentos. São Paulo, Companhia Editora Nacional, 1936.
320 p. front.

1. Petroleum industry and trade--Brazil. 2. Mining law-- Brazil. I. Title.

NL 0430588 InU

Lobato, José Bento Monteiro, 1882–1948.
O escandalo do petroleo; depoimentos apresentados à Comissão de Inquerito sobre o Petroleo. 5. ed. aumentada de notas e documentos. São Paulo, Companhia Editora Nacional, 1937.
249 p. illus., diagrs., facsim., tables. 19 cm.

1. Petroleum industry and trade—Brazil. 2. Mining law—Brazil. I. Comissão de Inquerito sobre o Petroleo. II. Title.

TN873.B8L6 1937 338.2 39-33098 rev*

NL 0430589 DLC

HD9574 B82M65 1947
Lobato, José Bento Monteiro, 1882-1948.
O escandalo do petroleo e ferro, prefacio de Caio Prado, jr. S. Paulo, Editora Brasiliense [1947]
xvi, 316 p. diagrs. (His Obras completas. 1. sér. Literatura geral. v. 7)

1. Petroleum industry and trade - Brazil. 2. Iron. 3. Mining law - Brazil.

NL 0430590 CU PU

Pn869.1 M763F Lobato, José Bento Monteiro, 1882-1948.
Fabulas. Ilustrações de André le Blanc. 13.ª ed. São Paulo, Ed. Brasiliense, 1949.
193p. illus. 22cm. (His Livros infantís, v.21)

At head of title: Monteiro Lobato.

NL 0430591 PU-Penn

Lobato, José Bento Monteiro, 1882-1948.
Fabulas ... 1.a. ed. Sao Paulo, Monteiro Lobato, 1922.
174 p. illus.

NL 0430592 OOxM

TN 747 .L78 LOBATO, JOSÉ BENTO MONTEIRO, 1882-1948.
Ferro; a solução do problema siderurgico do Brazil pelo processo Smith. São Paulo, Companhia Editôra Nacional, 1931.
130 p. illus.

Author's name at head of title: Monteiro Lobato.

1. Steel--Metallurgy--Oxygen processes. 2. Iron industry and trade--Brazil. 3. Iron--Metallurgy. I. Title.

NL 0430593 InU

Lobato, José Bento Monteiro, 1882–1948.
O garimpeiro do rio das Garças. Desenhos de K. Wiese. São Paulo, Companhia Editora Nacional, 1930.
[31] p. col. illus. 23 cm. (Bibliotheca de Narizinho)

I. Title.

PZ83.L594 31-17663

NL 0430594 DLC

Lobato, José Bento Monteiro, 1882–1948.
Geografia de dona Benta. Ilustrações de J. U. Campos e Belmonte. S. Paulo, Companhia Editora Nacional, 1935.
234 p. illus., maps. 22 cm. (Biblioteca pedagogica brasileira. Ser. 1.: Literatura infantil, v. 22)

1. Geography—Juvenile literature. I. Title.

G133.L78 1935 910 36-36254 rev*

NL 0430595 DLC

G981.06 B471 Ser.1 v.22 1942
Lobato, José Bento Monteiro, 1882-1948.
Geografia de dona Benta. 3. ed. rev. Ilus. de J.U. Campos e Belmonte. São Paulo, Companhia Editôra Nacional [1942]
236p. illus. 22cm. (Biblioteca pedagógica brasileira. Ser.1: Literatura infantil. v.22)

1. Geography - Juvenile literature. I. Title. II. Series (contents)

NL 0430596 TxU DLC

Lobato, José Bento Monteiro, 1882–1948.
Geografia de dona Benta. 5. ed. rev. Ilus. de J. U. Campos e Belmonte. São Paulo, Companhia Editora Nacional, 1944.
234 p. illus., maps. 22 cm. (Biblioteca pedagogica brasileira. Ser. 1.: Literatura infantil, v. 22)

1. Geography—Juvenile literature. I. Title.

G133.L78 1944 910 48-39456 rev*

NL 0430597 DLC

Pn869.1 M763G Lobato, José Bento Monteiro, 1882-1948.
Geografia de dona Benta. Ilustrações de André le Blanc. 6.ª ed. São Paulo, Ed. Brasiliense, 1949.
230p. illus., maps. 22cm. (His Livros infantís, v.11)

At head of title: Monteiro Lobato.

NL 0430598 PU-Penn PU

Lobato, José Bento Monteiro, 1882-
Georgismo ou comunismo?
see under title

VOLUME 337

BS557 V3 Lobato, José Bento Monteiro, 1882-1948, tr.

Van Loon, Hendrik Willem, 1882-1944.
... A historia da Biblia, narrada e ilustrada por Hendrik Willem Van Loon. Tradução de Monteiro Lobato. São Paulo [etc.] Companhia editora nacional, 1945.

Lobato, José Bento Monteiro, 1882-1948, tr.

Macy, John Albert, 1877-1932.
... Historia da literatura mundial; ilustrações de Onorio Ruotolo, tradução de Monteiro Lobato. São Paulo, Companhia editora nacional [19—]

Lobato, José Bento Monteiro, 1882-1948.
Historia das invenções. Ilustrações de J. U. Campos. São Paulo, Companhia Editora Nacional, 1935.
152 p. illus. 22 cm. (Biblioteca pedagogica brasileira. Ser. 1. Literatura infantil, v. 23)

1. Invention—Juvenile literature. 2. Civilization—Hist.—Juvenile literature.

PZ86.L6 1935 608 36-20913

NL 0430602 DLC

Lobato, José Bento Monteiro, 1882-1948.
Historia das invenções. Ilustrações de J. U. Campos. 3. ed. São Paulo, Companhia Editora Nacional, 1942.
151 p. illus. 22 cm. (Biblioteca pedagogica brasileira. Ser. 1.: Literatura infantil, v. 23)

1. Inventions—Juvenile literature. 2. Civilization—Hist.—Juvenile literature.

PZ86.L6 1942 608 45-14623

NL 0430603 DLC

Pn869.1 M763Hi Lobato, José Bento Monteiro, 1882-1948.
Historia das invenções. Ilustrações de André le Blanc. 6.ª ed. São Paulo, Ed. Brasiliense, 1949.
162p. illus. 22cm. (His Livros infantis, v.13)

At head of title: Monteiro Lobato.

NL 0430604 PU-Penn PU

CB53 .D86 Lobato, José Bento Monteiro, 1882-1948.

Durant, William James, 1885-
... Historia de civilização ... Tradução de Gulnara de Morais Lobato, revista por Monteiro Lobato ... São Paulo [etc.] Companhia editora nacional, 19

Lobato, José Bento Monteiro, 1882-1948, tr.

Léry, Jean de, 1534-1611.
... Historia de uma viagem feita á terra do Brasil; tradução ordenada literariamente por Monteiro Lobato. Rio de Janeiro, S. Paulo, Companhia editora nacional, 1926.

Lobato, José Bento Monteiro, 1882-1948.
Historia do mundo para as crianças. 2. ed. rev. Adaptado de V. M. Hillyer. São Paulo, Companhia Editora Nacional, 1934.
295 p. illus., ports., maps. 22 cm. (Biblioteca pedagogica brasileira. Ser. 1.: Literatura infantil, v. 10)

1. World history—Juvenile literature. I. Hillyer, Virgil Mores, 1875-1931. A child's history of the world. II. Title.

D21.L77 1934 909 34-39816 rev*

NL 0430607 DLC

Pn869.1 M763His Lobato, José Bento Monteiro, 1882-1948.
História do mundo para as crianças. Ilustrações de André le Blanc. 11.ª ed. São Paulo, Ed. Brasiliense, 1948.
276p. illus. 22cm. (His Livros infantis, v.6)

At head of title: Monteiro Lobato.

NL 0430608 PU-Penn PU

Lobato, José Bento Monteiro, 1882-1948.
Historias de tia Nastacia. Ilustrações de Raphael de Lamo. São Paulo, Companhia Editora Nacional, 1937.
186 p. illus. 22 cm. (Biblioteca pedagogica brasileira. Ser. 1: Literatura infantil, v. 29)

1. Fairy tales. I. Title.

PZ84.L58 38-33045

NL 0430609 DLC OOxM

Lobato, José Bento Monteiro, 1882-1948.
Historias de tia Nastacia. Ilustrações de Rafael de Lamo. 3. ed. São Paulo, Companhia Editora Nacional, 1941.
187 p. illus. 22 cm. (Biblioteca pedagogica brasileira. Ser. 1.: Literatura infantil, v. 29)

1. Fairy tales. I. Title.

PZ84.L58 1941 42-45202

NL 0430610 DLC

Lobato, José Bento Monteiro, 1882-1948.
Historias de Tia Nastacia. Ilustrações de Raphael de Lamo. 5.ed. São Paulo, etc., Companhia editora nacional, 1945.
189 p. illus. 22 cm. (Literatura infantil. Biblioteca pedagogica brasileira, series 1, vol. XXIX.)

NL 0430611 MH

Pn869.1 M763H Lobato, José Bento Monteiro, 1882-1948.
Historias de tia Nastacia. Ilustrações de André le Blanc. 6.ª ed. São Paulo, Ed. Brasiliense, 1949.
187p. illus. 22cm. (His Livros infantis, v.16)

At head of title: Monteiro Lobato.

NL 0430612 PU-Penn PU

Lobato, José Bento Monteiro, 1882-1948.
How Henry Ford is regarded in Brazil. Articles by Monteiro Lobato...published in the Brazilian newspaper "O jornal" and put into English by Aubrey Stuart. Rio de Janeiro, 1926. 25 p. 20½ x 15cm.

332690A. 1. Ford, Henry, 1863- I. Stuart, Aubrey, translator.
N. Y. P. L. *Revised* October 3, 1933

NL 0430613 NN CtY MH

Lobato, José Bento Monteiro, 1882-1948.
Ideas de Jeca Tatu. 2. ed. S. Paulo, "Revista do Brasil", 1920.
238 p.

NL 0430614 CU PLF OOxM DPU MH CaBVaU

PQ 9697 L5913 1922 Lobato, José Bento Monteiro, 1882-1948.
Ideas de Jéca Tatú. 3. ediçao. S. Paulo, Monteiro Lobato[1922]
238p. 17cm.

NL 0430615 MU NN DPU ICarbS

Lobato, José Bento Monteiro, 1882-1948.
... Idéias de Jéca Tatú. S. Paulo, Editora Brasiliense limitada, 1946.
12+277 p. (His Obras completas, 1. ser., v. 4)

NL 0430616 InU

Lobato, José Bento Monteiro, 1882-1948.
Idéias de Jéca Tatú. 2.ed. S.Paulo, Editora Brasiliense, 1949.
275p. 23cm. (Obras completas de Monteiro Lobato. 1.sér. Literatura geral. v.4)

NL 0430617 PU

Lobato, José Bento Monteiro, 1882-1948.
Jeca-Tatuzinho. Desenhos de K. Wiese. São Paulo, Campanhia Editora Nacional, 1930.
[31] p. col. illus. 28 cm. (Bibliotheca de Narizinho)

I. Title.

PZ83.L596 31-17661

NL 0430618 DLC

E457 .S834 Lobato, José Bento Monteiro, 1882-1948, tr.

Stephenson, Nathaniel Wright, 1867-1935.
... Lincoln; narração de sua vida pessoal, especialmente dos moveis de sua ação, como foram revelados e aprofundados no transe da guerra civil. Tradução de Monteiro Lobato. Sao Paulo, Rio de Janeiro [etc.] Companhia editora nacional, 1942.

Lobato, José Bento Monteiro, 1882-1948.
Livros infantis. São Paulo, Editora Brasiliense [1948- v. 1, 1949]
v. illus. 22 cm.

CONTENTS.—v. 1. Reinações de Nazarinho. 14. ed.—v. 2. Viagem ao céu. 9. ed.—v. 3. O saci. 12. ed.—v. 5. Aventuras de Hans Staden. 7. ed.—v. 6. História do mundo para as crianças. 11. ed.—v. 7. Memórias da Emília. 6. ed.—v. 8. Peter Pan. 7. ed.—v. 9. Emília no país da gramatica. 7. ed.—v. 11. Geografia de dona Benta. 6. ed.—v. 12. Serões de dona Benta (Fisica e astronomia) 4. ed.—v. 13. Historia das invenções. 6. ed.—v. 14. D. Quixote das crianças. 4. ed.—v. 15. O poço do visconde (geologia para as crianças) 4. ed.—v. 16. Historias de tia Nastacia. 6. ed.—v. 17. O picapau amarelo. 6. ed.—v. 18. A reforma da natureza. 2. ed.—v. 19. O minotauro. 4. ed.—v. 20. A chave do tamanho. 4. ed.—v. 21. Fabulas. 12 ed.

1. Children's literature, Portuguese. I. Title.

PZ81.L6 51-30545

NL 0430621 DLC

VOLUME 337

Lobato, José Bento Monteiro, 1882-1948.
La llave del tamaño; historia de la mayor travesura del mundo, en la cual Emilia, sin querer, modificó temporalmente el tamaño de las criaturas humanas. Traducción del portugués por Ramon Prieto. Ilustraciones de Arturo Travi. Buenos Aires, Editorial Americalee [1946]

NL 0430622 MH

Lobato, José Bento Monteiro, 1882-1948.
O macaco que se fez homem. S. Paulo, Monteiro Lobato, 1923.
205 p. 17 cm.
CONTENTS.—Era no paraizo.—A nuvem de gafanhotos.—Tragedia de um capão de pintos.—Duas cavalgaduras.—Um homem honesto.—O bom marido.—O rapto.—Marabá.—Fatia de vida.—A morte do camicêgo.
I. Title.
PQ9697.L59M3 30-7165

NL 0430623 DLC WU

Lobato, José Bento Monteiro, 1882-1948.
Memorias da Emilia. Ilus. de Belmonte. São Paulo, Companhia Editora Nacional, 1936.
139 p. illus. 22 cm. (Biblioteca pedagogica brasileira. Ser. 1: Literatura infantil, v. 26)
I. Title.
PZ83.L598 1936 38-33044

NL 0430624 DLC

Lobato, José Bento Monteiro, 1882-1948.
Memorias da Emilia. 4. ed. Ilus. de Belmonte. São Paulo, Companhia Editora Nacional, 1945.
144 p. 22 cm. (Biblioteca pedagogica brasileira. Sér. 1: Literatura infantil, v. 26)
I. Title.
PZ83.L598 1945 49-30829

NL 0430625 DLC

---

qG-JP L781m Lobato, José Bento Monteiro, 1882-1948.
A menina do narizinho arrebitado. Livro de figuras por Monteiro Lobato com desenhos de Voltolino. São Paulo, Cia. Gráphico-Editôra Monteiro Lobato, 1925.
48p. col. illus. 29cm.

NL 0430626 TxU

Lobato, José Bento Monteiro, 1882-1948, joint tr.
Spring, Howard, 1889-
... Meu filho, meu filho! Tradução de Ligia Junqueira Smith e Monteiro Lobato. 3. ed. São Paulo [etc.] Companhia editora nacional, 1941.

PQ 9697 .L59 M6 LOBATO,JOSÉ BENTO MONTEIRO,1883-1948
O minotauro; maravilhosas aventuras dos netos de dona Benta na Grecia antiga. Ilustrações de Belmonte e Rodolpho. São Paulo, Companhia Editora Nacional, 1939.
220 p. illus. (Biblioteca pedagogica brasileira. Ser. la. Literatura infantil, v. 32)
At head of title: Monteiro Lobato.

NL 0430628 InU

Lobato, José Bento Monteiro, 1882-1948.
Mister Slang e o Brasil; colloquios com o inglez da Tijuca. S. Paulo, Companhia Editora Nacional, 1927.
178 p. 19 cm.
1. Brazil. I. Title.
F2509.L6 918.1 33-9657 rev*

NL 0430629 DLC TNJ InU

F 2509 .L6 1946 LAL Lobato, Jose Bento Monteiro, 1882-1948.
Mr. Slang e o Brasil, e Problema vital. São Paulo, Ed. Brasiliense, 1946.
viii, 340 p. (Obras completas de Monteiro Lobato. 1ª Série: Literatura Geral, vol. 8)
1. Brazil. I. Title. II. Title: Problema vital.

NL 0430630 LNHT NcU

869.1 M763M Lobato, José Bento Monteiro, 1882-1948.
Mr. Slang e Brasil e Problema vital. 2.ed. S.Paulo,Editora Brasiliense,1948.
340p. 22cm. (Obras completas de Monteiro Lobato. 1.sér. Literatura geral.v.8)
Partial contents. -2.ptie. Opiniões.

NL 0430631 PU

Lobato, José Bento Monteiro, 1882-1948.
Mundo da lua. S. Paulo, Monteiro Lobato, 1923.
158 p. 17 cm.
I. Title.
PQ9697.L59M8 869.8 41-35362

NL 0430632 DLC OOxM InU CaBVaU

869.1 M763mu Lobato, José Bento Monteiro, 1882-1948.
Mundo da lua e Miscelanea. 2.ed. S.Paulo,Editora Brasiliense,1948.
338p. 22cm. (Obras completas de Monteiro Lobato. 1.sér. Literatura geral. v.10)
Partial contents. -2.ptie. Miscellanea.

NL 0430633 PU

Lobato, José Bento Monteiro, 1882-1948.
Na antevespera; reacções mentaes dum ingenuo. São Paulo, Companhia Editora Nacional, 1933.
218 p. 19 cm.
"O 'conto do petroleo'" ([213a]-219a p.) inserted after p. 218.
I. Title.
PQ9697.L59N3 869.3 40-20985

NL 0430634 DLC

Lobato. José Bento Monteiro, 1882-1948.
Na antevespera. S.Paulo,Editora Brasiliense,1946.
310p. port. 22cm. (Obras completas de Monteiro Lobato. 1.sér. Literatura geral. v.6)

NL 0430635 PU

Lobato, José Bento Monteiro, 1882-1948.
Negrinha; contos. 1°. milheiro. S. Paulo, Edição da Revista do Brasil, etc., 1920.

NL 0430636 MH OOxM

Lobato, José Bento Monteiro, 1882-1948.
...Negrinha (contos). Segunda edição... S. Paulo: Monteiro Lobato & cia., 1922. 82 p. 22cm. (Collecção Brasilia. no. 8.)
Printed in double columns.
CONTENTS.—Negrinha.—As fitas da vida.—O drama da geada.—O bugio moqueado.—O jardineiro Timotheo.—O imposto unico.—Os negros.—Barba-azul.—O collocador de pronomes.
102132A. 1. Fiction, Brazilian. I. Title. N. Y. P. L. Revised October 13, 1933

NL 0430637 NN

Lobato, José Bento Monteiro, 1882-1948.
Negrinha; contos. 3. ed. S. Paulo, Monteiro Lobato, 1923.
224 p. 17 cm.
CONTENTS.—Negrinha.—As fitas da vida.—O drama da geada.—O bugio moqueado.—O jardineiro Timotheo.—O imposto unico.—Os negros.—Barba azul.—O collocador de pronomes.—Uma historia de mil annos.—O desplque.
I. Title.
PQ9697.L59N4 1923 29-11328

NL 0430638 DLC MU

Lobato, José Bento Monteiro, 1882-1948
Negrinha. São Paulo, Editora Brasiliense, 1948.
[viii], 298 p. 21 1/2 cm. (His Obras completas. Sér. 1.: Literatura geral, v. 3)
Contos.
At head of title: Monteiro Lobato.

NL 0430639 MoSU

Lobato, José Bento Monteiro, 1882-1948.
Os negros; ou, "Elle" e o "outro"; novella cine-romantica, com pios de coruja, noite tempestuosa, mortes tragicas e outros ingredientes de tomo; leitura perigosa ás meninas hystericas e aos velhos cardiacos que creem em almas do outro mundo. São Paulo, Soc. Editora O. Ribeiro [1921]
58 p. illus., plates, port. 17 cm. (A Novella nacional, no. 2)
I. Title. II. Title: "Elle" e o "outro."
PQ9697.L59N45 30-7162
[r70b2] rev

NL 0430640 DLC

PS3537 .T3234 M64 Lobato, José Bento Monteiro, 1882-1948, tr.
Steinbeck, John, 1902-
... Noite sem lua, tradução de Monteiro Lobato. São Paulo [etc.] Companhia editora nacional, 1943.

Lobato, José Bento Monteiro, 1882-1948.
Novas reinações de Narizinho; (continuação de Reinações de Narizinho) contendo as travessuras de Narizinho, Pedrinho, Emilia, Rabicó, o visconde de Sabugosa e o burro falante no sitio de dona Benta e suas aventuras pelos mundos maravilhosos. S. Paulo, Cia. Editora Nacional, 1933.
146 p. plates (part col.) 22 cm. (Biblioteca pedagogica brasileira. Ser. 1.: Literatura infantil, vol. 11)
I. Title.
PZ83.L6 869.3 34-33907

NL 0430642 DLC OrU

VOLUME 337

Lobato, José Bento Monteiro, 1882-1948, tr.

Andersen, Hans Christian, 1805–1875.
... Novos contos de Andersen; tradução de Monteiro Lobato. S. Paulo, Companhia editora nacional, 1934.

PQ 9697 .L59 O455 LOBATO, JOSÉ BENTO MONTEIRO, 1882-1948.
Los ojos que sangran; cuentos. Traducción de B. Sánchez Saez. Buenos Aires, Editorial Tor, 1924.
60 p.

NL 0430644 InU

PQ 9697 M72 O6 1921 LAC
Lobato, José Bento Monteiro, 1882-1948.
A onda verde; jornalismo. São Paulo, Ed. da "Revista do Brasil", M. Lobato, 1921.
252, ivp. 17cm.

CONTENTS.—A onda verde.—O "Grillo".—A lua cornea.—O incomprehendido.—Veteranos do Paraguay.—"Gaffe" da justiça.—Os eucalyptos.—Os tangarás.—O pae da guerra.—"Homo sapiens".—Luvas!—Dramas da crueldade.—Dialecto caipira.—Os livros fundamentaes.—Condes.—Uruguayana.—O direito de secessão.—O diccionario brasileiro.—O grande problema.—A grande idéa.—O 22 da "Marajó".

NL 0430646 TxU

Lobato, José Bento Monteiro, 1882–1948.
A onda verde. [2. ed.] São Paulo, Monteiro Lobato, 1922 [cover 1923]
227, [1] p. 17 cm.

CONTENTS.—A onda verde.—O "grillo."—O "grillo" Ximenes.—A lua cornea.—O incomprehendido.—Veteranos do Paraguay.—Os eucalyptos.—Mais eucalyptos.—Os tangarás.—O pae da guerra.—"Homo sapiens."—Luvas!—Dramas da crueldade.—Dialecto caipira.—Os livros fundamentaes.—Condes.—Uruguayana.—O diccionario brasileiro.—O grande problema.—A grande idéa.—O 22 da "Marajó."

I. Title.

PQ9697.L59O6 1923 30–7163

NL 0430647 DLC NcD MU NN IU

869.1 M753 O
Lobato, José Bento Monteiro, 1882-1948.
A onda verde e O presidente negro. S. Paulo, Editora Brasiliense, 1946.
330p. port. 23cm. (Obras completas de Monteiro Lobato. 1.sér. Literatura geral. v.5)

Alternative title for "O presidente negro" is "O choque das raças."

NL 0430648 PU

Lobato, José Bento Monteiro, 1882–1948.
Peter Pan; a historia do menino que não queria crescer, contada por dona Benta. S. Paulo, Companhia Editora Nacional, 1935.
104 p. illus., col. plates. 22 cm. (Bibliotheca pedagogica brasileira. Ser. 1.: Literatura infantil, v. 20)

I. Barrie, Sir James Matthew, bart., 1860–1937. Peter Pan. II. Title.

PZ84.L6 823.91 36–22738

NL 0430649 DLC

Lobato, José Bento Monteiro, 1882–1948.
O picapau amarelo (o sitio de Dona Benta, um mundo de verdade e de mentira) Illustrações de Rodolpho. 4. ed. São Paulo, Companhia Editora Nacional, 1944.
176 p. illus. 22 cm. (Biblioteca pedagógica brasileira. Sér. 1.: Literatura infantil, v. 31)

I. Title.

PZ84.L63 1944 57–30330

NL 0430650 DLC

Pn869.1 M763P
Lobato, José Bento Monteiro, 1882-1948.
O picapau amarelo; o sitio de dona Benta, um mundo de verdade e de mentira. Ilustrações de André le Blanc. 6.ª ed. São Paulo, Ed. Brasiliense, 1949.
159p. illus. 22cm. (His Livros infantis, v.17)

At head of title: Monteiro Lobato.

NL 0430651 PU-Penn

Lobato, José Bento Monteiro, 1882-1948, tr.

[Lorenzini, Carlo] 1831–1890.
... Pinocchio; tradução revista por Monteiro Lobato. São Paulo, Companhia editora nacional, 1933.

Lobato, José Bento Monteiro, 1882–1948.
O poço do visconde, geologia para as crianças. Ilus. de Belmonte. São Paulo, Companhia Editora Nacional, 1937.
184 p. illus. 22 cm. (Bibliotheca pedagogica brasileira. Ser. 1.: Literatura infantil, v. 27)

1. Petroleum—Juvenile literature. I. Title.

PZ86.L63 1937 38–33046

NL 0430653 DLC

Lobato, José Bento Monteiro, 1882–1948.
O poço do visconde, geologia para as crianças. Ilus. de Belmonte. 3. ed. São Paulo, Companhia Editora Nacional, 1944.
180 p. illus. 22 cm. (Bibliotheca pedagogica brasileira. Ser. 1: Literatura infantil, v. 27)

1. Petroleum—Juvenile literature. I. Title.

PZ86.L63 1944 49–30833

NL 0430654 DLC

Lobato, José Bento Monteiro, 1882-1948.
O poço do visconde; geologia para as crianças. Ilustrações de André le Blanc. 4.ª ed. São Paulo, Ed. Brasiliense, 1949.
236p. illus. 22cm. (His Livros infantis, v.15)

At head of title: Monteiro Lobato.

NL 0430655 PU-Penn PU

Lobato, José Bento Monteiro, 1882–1948.
El presidente negro; novela norteamericana del año 2228; traducción de Benjamín de Garay. Buenos Aires, Editorial Claridad [1935?]
189 p. 18 cm. (Colección Claridad. "Biblioteca de escritores americanos")

Translation of O choque das raças; ou, O presidente negro.

I. Title.

PQ9697.L59C515 869.3 36–31384

NL 0430656 DLC NcD

PQ 9697 .L59 P7
Lobato, José Bento Monteiro, 1882-1948
O presidente negro; ou, O choque das raças. Romance americano do ano 2228. São Paulo, Editora Brasilense, 1945.
198 p. 19 cm. (Coleção ontem e hoje, 3)

Published in 1926 under title: O choque das raças; ou, O presidente negro.

I. Title II. Title: O choque das raças

NL 0430657 WU LU

Lobato, José Bento Monteiro, 1882-1948
El Quijote de los Niños; traducción del portugues por M.J. de Sosa; illustraciones de Gustavo Dore. Buenos Aires, Editorial Americalee [1945]
1 ℓ., 238 p. 1 ℓ. 21 cm.

NL 0430658 TU

Lobato, José Bento Monteiro, 1882–1948.
A reforma da natureza e O espanto das gentes. Desenhos de Belmonte e J. U. Campos. São Paulo, Editora Brasiliense, 1944.
116 p. illus. 22 cm.

I. Title. II. Title: O espanto das gentes.

A 49–5278 rev*

New York. Public Libr. for Library of Congress [r52b]

NL 0430659 NN

Lobato, José Bento Monteiro, 1882-1948.
A reforma da natureza. Ilustrações de André le Blanc. 2.ª ed. São Paulo, Ed. Brasiliense, 1949.
110p. illus. 22cm. (His Livros infantis, v.18)

At head of title: Monteiro Lobato.

NL 0430660 PU-Penn

Lobato, José Bento Monteiro, 1882–1948.
As reinações de Narizinho; contendo as travessuras de Narizinho, Pedrinho, Emilia, Rabicó, o visconde de Sabugosa e o burro falante no sitio de dona Benta e as mais aventuras pelos mundos maravilhosos. S. Paulo, Cia. Editora Nacional, 1933.
130 p. plates (part col.) 22 cm. (Bibliotheca pedagogica brasileira. Ser. 1.: Literatura infantil, v. 1)

I. Title.

PZ83.L62 1933 869.3 34–33906

NL 0430661 DLC

VOLUME 337

Lobato, José Bento Monteiro, 1882-1948.
Reinações de Narizinho; contendo todas as travessuras de Narizinho, Pedrinho, Emilia, Rabicó, o visconde de Sabugosa e o burro falante no sitio de dona Benta e as mais aventuras pelos mundos maravilhosos. 7. ed. São Paulo, Companhia Editora Nacional, 1937.
231 p. plates. 22 cm. (Biblioteca pedagogica brasileira. Ser. 1: Literatura infantil, v. 1 e 11)

I. Title.
PZ83.L62 1937 42-3202

NL 0430662 DLC

G981.06 B471 Ser.1 v.1 1941
Lobato, José Bento Monteiro, 1882-1948.
Reinações de Narizinho; contendo todas as travessuras de Narizinho, Pedrinho, Emilia, Rabicó, o visconde de Sabugosa e o burro falante no sitio de dona Benta e as mais aventuras pelos mundos maravilhosos. 8. ed. São Paulo, Companhia Editôra Nacional, 1941.
231p. illus. 22cm. (Biblioteca pedagógica brasileira. Ser.1: Literatura infantil. v.1)

NL 0430663 TxU

Lobato, José Bento Monteiro, 1882-1948.
Reinações de Narizinho. Contendo todas as travessuras de Narizinho, Pedrinho, Emilia, Rabicó, o visconde de Sabugosa e o burro falante no sitio de dona Benta e mais as aventuras pelos mundos maravilhosos. 11. ed. São Paulo, etc., Companhia editora nacional, 1945.
256 p. (Literatura infantil. Biblioteca pedagogica brasileira. Serie 1. Vol. 1 e 2)

NL 0430664 MH

Lobato, José Bento Monteiro, 1882-1948.
Reinações de Narizinho; contendo todas as travessuras de Narizinho, Pedrinho, Emilia, Rabicó, o visconde de Sabugosa e o burro falante no sitio de dona Benta e as mais aventuras pelos mundos maravilhosos. Ilustrações de André le Blanc. 13.ª ed. São Paulo, Ed.Brasiliense, 1949.
292p. illus. 22cm. (His Livros infantis, v.1)
At head of title: Monteiro Lobato.

NL 0430665 PU-Penn

Lobato, José Bento Monteiro, 1882-1948.
... Robinson Crusoe
see Defoe, Daniel, 1661?-1731.
Robinson Crusoe. Portuguese.

Lobato, José Bento Monteiro, 1882-1948.
O saci. 5. ed. S. Paulo, Companhia Editora Nacional, 1934.
121 p. illus. (part mounted col.) 22 cm. (Biblioteca pedagogica brasileira. Ser. 1.: Literatura infantil, v. 4)

I. Title.
PG83.L63 1934 869.3 35-13597

NL 0430667 DLC

Lobato, José Bento Monteiro, 1882-1948.
...O saci; ilus. de J. U. Campos. 8. ed. São Paulo [etc.] Companhia editora nacional, 1944. 109 p. illus. 25cm. (Biblioteca pedagogica brasileira. ser. 1. Literatura infantil. vol. 4.)

392424B. 1. Juvenile literature—Fiction, Brazilian. I. Title.
N. Y. P. L. June 13, 1949

NL 0430668 NN MH

Lobato, José Bento Monteiro, 1882-1948.
Serões de dona Benta. São Paulo, Companhia Editora Nacional, 1937.
161 p. illus. 22 cm. (Biblioteca pedagogica brasileira. Ser. 1.: Literatura infantil, v. 28)

1. Science—Juvenile literature. I. Title.
PZ86.L64 1937 38-33047

NL 0430669 DLC

Lobato, José Bento Monteiro, 1882-1948.
Serões de dona Benta (fisica e astronomia) 3. ed. São Paulo, Editora Brasiliense, 1944.
170 p. illus., diagrs. 22 cm.

1. Science—Juvenile literature. I. Title.
PZ86.L64 1944 46-1900

NL 0430670 DLC

Lobato, José Bento Monteiro, 1882-1948.
Serões do dona Benta, fisica ó astronomia. Ilustrações de André le Blanc. 4.ª ed. São Paulo, Ed.Brasiliense, 1949.
224p. illus. 22cm. (His Livros infantis, v.12)
At head of title: Monteiro Lobato.

NL 0430671 PU-Penn

PQ 9697 M72 U7 1918
Lobato, José Bento Monteiro, 1882-1948.
Urupês; contos. 2. ed. Sao Paulo, Edicao da "Revista do Brasil," 1918.
241p. 20cm.

NL 0430672 MU

Lobato, José Bento Monteiro, 1882-1948.
Urupês (contos). 5. ed. ... S. Paulo, 1919.
184 p.

NL 0430673 IU

Br869.3 L796u6
Lobato, José Bento Monteiro, 1882-1948.
Urupês; contos. 6. ed. São Paulo, Revista do Brasil, 1920.
227 p. 19cm.

NL 0430674 FU DPU MH

G869.8 M764uTSg
Lobato, José Bento Monteiro, 1882-1948.
Urupés. Traduucción [sic] de Benjamin de Garay. Buenos Aires, Editorial "Patria", 1921.
222p. 18cm. (Biblioteca de novelistas americanos, 4)

NL 0430675 TxU InU

Lobato, José Bento Monteiro, 1882-1948.
...Urupês (contos). Setima edição... S. Paulo: Monteiro Lobato & cia., 1922. 82 p. 22cm. (Collecção Brasilia. no. 1.)
Printed in double columns.
CONTENTS.—Os pharoleiros.—O engraçado arrependido.—A colcha de retalhos.—A vingança da peroba.—"Meu conto de Maupassant."—Pollice verso.—Bucolica.—O mata-pau.—Boccatorta.—O comprador de fazendas.—Supplicio moderno.—O estigma.—Urupês.

102132A. 1. Fiction, Brazilian. I. Title. Revised
N. Y. P. L. October 13, 1933

NL 0430676 NN

Lobato, José Bento Monteiro, 1882-1948.
Urupês; contos. 9. ed. S. Paulo, Monteiro Lobato, 1923.
xix, 257 p. 17 cm.
CONTENTS.—Os pharoleiros.—O engraçado arrependido.—A colcha de retalhos.—A vingança da peroba.—"Meu conto de Maupassant."—"Pollice verso."—Buccolica.—O mata-páu.—Boccatorta.—O comprador de fazendas.—Um supplicio moderno.—O estigma.—Urupês.

I. Title.
PQ9697.L59U7 1923 29-11329

NL 0430677 DLC MoU PV PP NN OOxM NcD

PQ9697 L59 U7 1937
Lobato, José Bento Monteiro, 1882-1948.
Urupês [por] Monteiro Lobato. 11. ed. São Paulo, Companhia Editora Nacional, 1937.
243 p. (Collecção "Os Grandes livros brasileiros," vol.10)

NL 0430678 CU-A TxU ViU MiU ICU WU

PQ 9697 L68 U7 1943
Lobato, José Bento Monteiro, 1882-1948.
... Urupês, outros contos e coisas [por] Monteiro Lobato. Organizada e prefaciada por Artur Novos. São Paulo, Companhia editora nacional, 1943.
L, 663 p. 22 cm. (Biblioteca do espirito moderno. Sér. 4.a: Literatura, v. 18)
"'Edição onibus,' comemorativa do 25.° aniversário da estréia do escritor."
Contents. - Notas biograficas e criticas, por Artur Neves. - Algumas fontes para o estudo de Monteiro Lobato (p. xlv-l) - Urupês. - Cidades mortas. - Negrinha. - O macaco que se fez homem. - Ultimos contos. - Excertos de outros livros. - Avulsos. - Literatura infantil.

I. Neves, Artur, ed. II. Title.

NL 0430680 OU MH

Lobato, José Bento Monteiro, 1882-1948.
Urupês. Introdução de Edgard Cavalheiro; ilustrações de Paim. S. Paulo, Martins [1944]
221 p. illus. 25 cm. (Biblioteca de literatura brasileira, 8)
CONTENTS.—Os faroleiros.—O engraçado arrependido.—A colcha de retalhos.—A vingança de peroba.—Meu conto de Maupassant.—"Pollice verso."—Bucolica.—O mata-páu.—Bocatorta.—O comprador de fazendas.—Um suplicio moderno.—O estigma.—Urupês.

I. Title.
PQ9697.L59U7 1944 A 46-461

New York. Public Libr. for Library of Congress [r70c2]† rev

NL 0430681 NN DLC NNC

VOLUME 337

Lobato, José Bento Monteiro, 1882–1948.
Urupês, outros contos e coisas. 2. ed., **organizada** e prefaciada por Artur Neves. São Paulo, **Companhia Editora** Nacional, 1945.
L, 663 p. port. 22 cm. (Biblioteca do espírito moderno. Sér. 4.: Literatura, v. 18)
" 'Edição onibus,' comemorativa do 25.° aniversário da estréia do escritor."
CONTENTS.—Notas biograficas e criticas, por Artur Neves.—Algumas fontes para o estudo de Monteiro Lobato (p. xlv–1)—Urupês.—Cidades mortas.—Negrinha.—O macaco que se fez homem.—Ultimos contos.—Excertos de outros livros.—Avulsos.—Literatura infantil.
I. Title.
PQ9697.L59U7 1945 47–28145

NL 0430682 DLC

4PQ Port. 5 Lobato, José Bento Monteiro, 1882-1948.
Urupés (cuentos brasileros) Versión española de Juan Ramón Prieto. [1. ed.] Buenos Aires "El Ateneo" [1947]
420 p.

NL 0430683 DLC-P4

PQ9697 L59U79 Lobato, José Bento Monteiro, 1882-1948.
Urupês. [3. ed.] S. Paulo, Editora Brasiliense, 1949.
264 p. illus., port. 22cm. (His Obras completas. 1. serie. Literatura geral. v. 1)
"Algumas fontes para o estudo de Monteiro Lobato": p. 45-51.
I. Title. (Series: Monteiro Lobato, José Bento, 1883-1948. Obras completas. 1. ser. Literatura geral. v. 1)

NL 0430684 CoU MB RPB

Lobato, José Bento Monteiro, 1882–1948.
Viagem ao céu. Ilustrações [sic] de Jean G. Villin. 2. ed. S. Paulo, Companhia Editora Nacional, 1934.
114 p. illus., col. plates. 22 cm. (Biblioteca pedagogica brasileira. Ser. 1.: Literatura infantil, v. 3)
I. Title.
PZ83.L64 1934 869.3 35–13596

NL 0430685 DLC

Lobato, José Bento Monteiro, 1882–1948.
Viagem ao ceu. Ilustrações de J. U. Campos. 6. ed. São Paulo, Companhia Editora Nacional, 1945.
151 p. illus. 22 cm. (Biblioteca pedagogica brasileira. Ser. 1.: Literatura infantil, v. 3)
I. Title.
PZ83.L64 1945 57–29474

NL 0430686 DLC

PZ72 .M5V5 Lobato, José Bento Monteiro, 1882-1948.
Viagem ao céu. 10. ed. São Paulo, Editora Brasiliense, 1951.
152 p. illus. 22 cm.

NL 0430687 DPU

Lobato, José Bento Monteiro, 1882–1948.
Zé Brasil. Ilus. de Candido Portinari. Rio de Janeiro, 1951.
23 p. illus. 24 x 26 cm.
1. Peasantry—Brazil. 2. Communism—Brazil. 3. Prestes, Luiz Carlos, 1898– I. Title.
HD498.L6 53–16479 rev ‡

NL 0430688 DLC

[Lobato, José G]
Consideraciones generales sobre la geografía, meteorología y climatología de la zona intertropical de la República Mexicana con relación á la aclimatación del hombre. Mexico, Impr. de J. M. A. Ortiz, 1874.
57 p. 22½cm.
Signed: José G. Lobato.
1. Mexico—Descr. & trav. 2. Mexico—Climate. I. Title.
Library of Congress F1215.L79 2–4849

NL 0430689 DLC UU NN DNLM

Lobato, Jose G.
——. Estudio higienico hecho sobre la trichina.
34 pp. 8°. *México*, 1881.

NL 0430690 DNLM

Lobato, José G
Estudio quimico-industrial de los varios productos del maguey mexicano y analisis quimico del aguamiel y el pulque. Trabajos hechos por el Dr. Jose G. Lobato ... para la Exposicion universal de Nueva Orleans. México, Oficina tip. de la Secretaría de fomento, 1884.
viii, [9]–191 p. 19½ cm.
1. Agave. 2. Pulque.
SB317.A2L7 13–26991

DNLM NjP Nh CU NN MiU TxU NcGU
NL 0430691 DLC LNHT KU WU CLU NcD-MC CU-B PPF PPL

Lobato, José G.
Estudio sobre las aguas medicinales de la Republica Mexicana, por el Dr. José G. Lobato. México, Oficina tip. de Secretaría de fomento, 1884.
xiv, [15]–213 p. fold. pl., fold. plan. 23cm.
1. Mineral waters—Mexico.
Library of Congress RA811.5.L8 8–13844

NL 0430692 DLC CtY NjP TxU Nh PPC CU-B ICJ MH

---

308 Z Box 804 Lobato, José G
Saneamiento de las aguas potables de la Ciudad de México; estudio higienico. México, Imp. poliglota, 1884.
40 p. fold. table.
1. Mexico (City) - Water-supply.

NL 0430693 NNC

Lobato, José M. Antonio Pérez
see
Pérez Lobato, José Antonio.

F1203 F16 v.36:112 x [Lobato, José María]
Nuevas ocurrencias de la revolucion de Veracruz. [Mexico, Oficina de J.M. Fernandez de Lara, 1822]
4 p. 30cm. [Papeles varios. v.36, no.112]
Caption title.
Proclamations addressed to Iturbide, to José Dominguez, to his division, etc., by brigadier general José María Lobato.

NL 0430695 CU-B

---

fF1232 L62 x Lobato, José María
Los sucesos de Veracruz son en el dia el objeto del mayor interes; ellos tienen al publico en espectacion, y el Gobierno que ha ofrecido darle conocimiento de cuanto sele vaya comunicando, se apresura ahora a hacerlo de los documentos insertos a continuacion ... [Saltillo, Reimpreso en el Saltillo á 21 de Diciembre de 1822, segundo de la Independencia; Impr. de la Comandansia General de Oriente, Jose Manuel Bangs, impresor, 1822]
sheet 31cm.
Originally issued in Cordova 6 de Diciembre de 1822.
Provenance: H. H. Bancroft.
1. Vera Cruz, Mexico (State) - Defenses. 2. Mexico - Hist. - 1821-1861. 3. Yturbide, Agustín, de, Emperor of Mexico, 1783-1824. I. Bangs, Samuel, ca.1794-ca.1853, printer. II. Title.

NL 0430697 CU-B

F1207 S42 v.5:3 x Lobato, Juan Antonio.
El Phenix de las Indias vnico por Inmaculado floreciendo en vna tilma de palma, Maria en Sv Concepcion Pvrissima aparecida en Gvadalvpe ... Sermon, que en la plausible fiesta de la Concepcion predicó ... en el real y militar Convento de Nuestra Señora de la Merced, redempcion de cautivos, el r. p. presentado fr. Ioan Antonio Lobatto, visitador general ... Mexico, Doña Maria de Benavides, viuda de I. de Ribera, 1700.
9 p.l., 16 p. 1 illus. 20cm. [Sermones varios. v. 5, no. 3]

NL 0430698 CU-B

Lobato, Juan Barona
see **Barona Lobato, Juan.**

Lobato, Juan G. N., ed.
González Holguín, Diego, *d.* 1552.
... Arte y Diccionario qquechua-español, cor. y aumentado por los RR. PP. Redentoristas al que en 1608 publicó el Rvdo. P. Diego González de Holguín s. J. en esta Ciudad de los Reyes. Lima, Imp. del estado, 1901.

Lobato, Juan G. N.
... **Compendio** de la doctrina cristiana en cuatro lenguas: dos dialectos principales del qquechua que constituyen la 9. y 10. ed., y el castellano y aymara 1. ed., por el padre Lobato, redentorista; con aprobación del ordinario. Lima, Gil, 1904.

Lobato, Juan G. N.
... **Compendio** de la doctrina cristiana en qquechua general ó imperial. Por el P. Lobato ... 12. ed. ... Lima, Impr. y libreria de San Pedro, 1905.

Lobato, Juan G N , ed.
Kichua shimichu Diosnínzicta nañánapac
see under title

Lobato, Juan Gallardo
see Gallardo Lobato, Juan.

VOLUME 337

Lobato, Luis Guimarães.
Contribution à l'étude du problème du logement à Lisbonne. Communication présentée ⌐au¬ IIᵉ Congrès des capitales, 7.ᵉ Section: Problèmes du logement. Lisbonne, 1950.
37 p. illus. 24 cm.
Cover title.
"Annexe" (p. ⌐23¬-37): Aperçu de la législation portugaise sur le problème de l'habitation, par l'ing. Vasco Marques Leite.
1. Housing—Lisbon. I. Leite, Vasco Marques. II. Title.
HD7352.L5L63 331.833 53-30324

NL 0430705 DLC

Lobato, Luis Guimarães.
The housing problem in Lisbon; data to assist in the examination of the problem. Communication submitted ⌐to the¬ II Congress of the Capitals, 7th Section: Housing problems. Lisbon, 1950.
36 p. illus. 24 cm.
Cover title.
"Appendix" (p. ⌐23¬-36): Summary of Portuguese legislation concerning the housing problem, by Eng. Vasco Marques Leite.
1. Housing—Lisbon. I. Leite, Vasco Marques. II. Title.
HD7352.L5L62 331.833 53-30268

NL 0430706 DLC

Lobato, Luis Guimarães.
Lisboa, urbanismo e habitação; subsídios para o seu estudo, relatório. ⌐Lisboa¬ Câmara Municipal de Lisboa, 1952.
21 p. illus., maps (1 fold. col.) 24 cm.
At head of title: XXI Congresso da Federação Internacional de Habitação e Urbanismo.
Cover title.
1. Cities and towns—Planning—Lisbon. 2. Housing—Lisbon. I. Title.
NA9226.L5L6 57-43084

NL 0430707 DLC

Lobato, Luis Guimarães.
Lisbon: housing and city development; a contribution to their study; ⌐report presented by Luis Guimarães Lobato; Grafique disposal by José Espinho. Pictures taken by Horácio Novais and Armando Serodio. ⌐Lisbon¬ Printed by C. M. L. ⌐1952¬
20 p. illus., maps (1 fold.) 24 cm.
On cover: XXIst Congress of the International Federation for Housing and Town Planning.
1. Housing—Lisbon.
HD7352.L5L54 56-46692

NL 0430708 DLC

Lobato, Luis Guimarães.
Lisbonne, urbanisme et habitation; éléments d'étude, rapport. ⌐Lisbonne¬ Câmara Municipal de Lisboa, 1952.
21 p. illus., maps (1 fold. col.) 24 cm.
At head of title: XXIᵉ Congrès de la Fédération internationale de l'habitation et de l'urbanisme.
Cover title.
1. Cities and towns—Planning—Lisbon. 2. Housing—Lisbon. I. Title.
NA9226.L5L614 57-43083

NL 0430709 DLC

Lobato, Luis Guimarães.
O problema da habitação de Lisboa; subsídios para o seu estudo. Comunicação apresentada ⌐ao¬ II Congresso das Capitais, 7.ª Secção: Problemas da habitação. Lisboa, 1950.
36 p. illus. 24 cm.
Cover title.
"Anexo" (p. ⌐23¬-36): Súmula da legislação portuguesa relativa ao problema da habitação, pelo eng. Vasco Marques Leite.
1. Housing—Lisbon. I. Leite, Vasco Marques. II. Title.
HD7352.L5L6 331.833 53-30270

NL 0430710 DLC CU

Lobato, Luis Guimarães.
El problema de la vivienda en Lisboa; subsidios para su estudio. Informe presentado ⌐al¬ II Congreso de las Capitales, 7.ª Sección: Problemas de la vivienda. Lisboa, 1950.
36 p. illus. 24 cm.
Cover title.
"Anexo" (p. ⌐23¬-36): Síntesis de la legislación portuguesa relativa al problema de la vivienda, por el Ing. Vasco Marques Leite.
1. Housing—Lisbon. I. Leite, Vasco Marques. II. Title.
HD7352.L5L68 331.833 53-30269

NL 0430711 DLC

Lobato, M Pereira
see Pereira Lobato, Manuel.

Lobato, Manoel, tr.

Lecointe, Paul.
... A cultura do cacau na Amazonia, pelo engenheiro Paul Lecointe. Belem, Imprensa oficial do estado, 1918.

Lobato, Manoel.
Industria manufactureira...
see under Congresso de defesa economica da Amazonia.

---

*
F2546
.L62
1912

Lobato, *Manoel.*
O valle do Amazonas e o problema da borracha. New York ⌐York Printing Co.¬ 1912.
67 p. illus. 21cm.
Inscribed by the author.
1. Amazon Valley—Descr. & trav. 2. Rubber industry and trade—Amazon Valley. I. Title.

NL 0430715 ViU CU

Lobato, María Concepción Casado
see **Casado Lobato, María Concepción.**

Lobato, Milton.
Médicos brasileiros na U. R. S. S.; impressões de viagem e aspectos da medicina soviética ⌐por¬ Milton Lobato ⌐e¬ Reinaldo Machado. Rio de Janeiro, Editorial Vitória, 1955.
118 p. illus., ports. 20 cm.
"Notas de viagem ⌐por¬ Reinaldo Machado": p. ⌐85¬-118.
1. Hygiene, Public—Russia. 2. Russia—Descr. & trav.—1945- I. Machado, Reinaldo. II. Title.
RA513.L6 64-36386

NL 0430717 DLC NIC DNLM

Lobato, Monteiro
see
Lobato, José Bento Monteiro, 1882-1948.

Lobato, Rehuel Cohen, tr.
Paraphrasis caldaica en los Cantares de Salomon con el texto, traducida ...
see under Bible. O. T. Song of Solomon. Spanish. 1644. Lobato.

Lobato de Bulhoes Carvalho, Jose Luiz Zayao
see
Bulhoes Carvalho, Jose Luiz Sayao Lobato de

Lobato de Castro, Marcello
see Castro, Marcello Lobato de.

Lobato Filho, João Bernardo, *1882-*
see
Lobato, João Bernardo, 1882-

Lobato Filho, João Bernardo, 1910-
see Lobato, João Bernardo, 1910-

W 4
M61
1949

LOBATO GUERRA, Imelda
Duración de la inmunidad antivariolosa en el pueblo de Paraíso, Tabasco. México, 1949.
47 p.
Tesis - Univ. de México.
1. Public health - Mexico - Paraíso
2. Vaccination - Mexico - Paraíso

NL 0430724 DNLM

Lobato Guimarães, Maria de Nazareth
see **Nazareth Lobato Guimarães, Maria de.**

Lobato López, Ernesto.
... El crédito en México, esbozo histórico hasta 1925. México, Fondo de cultura económica ⌐1945¬
2 p. l., 7-316 p., 1 l. 22ᶜᵐ. (*Half-title:* Sección de obras de economía ⌐del Fondo de cultura económica; dirigida por Daniel Cosío Villegas)
"Primera edición, 1945."
"Bibliografía": p. ⌐303¬-314.
1. Credit—Mexico. 2. Debts, Public—Mexico. 3. Banks and banking—Mexico.
Library of Congress HG3729.M42L6 45-20835
⌐3¬ 332.7

NL 0430726 DLC PU GU NBC ViU DPU TxU

Lobato Guimarães, João José
see Guimarães, João José Lobato.

VOLUME 337

Lobato Pires, J[orge] G[uilherme]
Amor de poeta. Drama em 1 acto. Imitação em verso. Lisboa, Typ. universal, 1859.
54 p. 16°.

NL 0430728 NN

Lobaton, Aurelio.
Apuntes presentados en las audiencias de alegatos, ante el c. juez de letras del ramo civil del distrito del centro del estado de Coahuila, por el c. lic. Aurelio Lobaton, como apoderado jurídico del sr. Leopoldo F. Martínez, Albace de la intestamentaría del finado sr. lic. Jesús María Martínez Ancira, en el juicio reivindicatorio de propiedad del "Cañón del Astillero" promovido por el sr. lic. José M. Múzquiz en representación de los sres. Evaristo Madero y Evaristo Madero y Hernández. Saltillo, Tip. lit, y Enc. de Simón de la Peña, 1899
66 p. 21 cm.
(No. 9 in a vol. le ..ed: Internacional privado y publico, v. 45)

NL 0430729 DLC

Lobatón, Aurelio.
Estudio hecho por el Señor Lic. Aurelio Lobatón para determinar la capacidad jurídica de la Mexican coal and coke company, con motivo de la excepción de falta de personería opuesta por su cliente el Señor Roberto H. Mc.Cracken contra dicha compañía, al oponerse ésta al embargo precautorio, ejecutcado [!] sobre los predios carboníferos, Mota del Cura y Carrizo ... Saltillo, Coahuila, Oficina impresora del gobierno del estado, 1900.
21 p. 23cm.

1. Mines and mineral resources—Mexico—Coahuila. I. MacCracken, Robert H., plaintiff. II. Mexican coal and coke company, defendant. III. Title.

28-15834

NL 0430730 DLC

Lobaton, Carlos Viesca y
see
Viesca y Lobaton, Carlos, 1874-

Lobatón, Francisco Viesca
See
Viesca Lobatón, Francisco.

Lobatón, José
see Lobatón Garza, José.

Lobatón, José de Santiago Concha Jiménez
see Santiago Concha Jiménez Lobatón, José de, b. 1761.

Lobatón Garza, José.
El Gringo. [1. ed.] Ciudad de Méjico, Marquez, 1950.
247 p. 21 cm.

I. Title.

PQ7297.L58G7 51-27467

NL 0430735 DLC CU-SB CU TxU AAP

Lobatscheff, Gr
see
Lobachev, Grigorii Grigor'evich, 1888-

Lobatschefskij, N J
see
Lobachevskiĭ, Nikolaĭ Ivanovich, 1792-1856.

Lobatschewsky, Nikolaus
see
Lobachevskiĭ, Nikolaĭ Ivanovich, 1792-1856.

Lobatto, Juan Antonio
see Lobato, Juan Antonio.

LOBATTO, REHUEL, 1797-1866.
Beschouwing van den aard, de voordeelen en de inrigting der maatschappijen van levensverzekering; bevattende tevens eene verklaring der ware gronden van berekening tot het ontwerpen van duurzame weduwen-fondsen, bijzonderlijk opgesteld ten dienste der ongeoefenden in de wiskunde. Amsterdam, G. Portielje, 1830.
xii,177 p. tables. 23cm.
1. Insurance, Life.

NL 0430740 NN

QA531 L59 1877 Lobatto, Rehuel, 1797-1866.
Leerboek der rechtlijnige en bolvormige dreihoeksmeting. 4. druk, bewerkt en vermeerderd door dr. P. van Geer ... Schoonhoven, S. & W.N. Van Nooten, 1877.
viii,180 p. plates,diagrs.

Interleaved; manuscript notes.

1. Trigonometry I. Geer, Peter van, 1841- ed.

NL 0430741 CU

---

517 L781 Lobatto, Rehuel, 1797-1866.
Lessen over de differentiaal- en integraal-rekening ... 's Gravenhage, 1851-52.
2v. fold.diagrs.

Bibliographical foot-notes.

NL 0430742 IU MiU

QA153 L6 1862 Lobatto, Rehuel, 1797-1866.
Lessen over de hoogere algebra, opgesteld ten gebruike bij het onderwijs aan de Koninklijke Akademie ... 2. verb. druk. Amsterdam, Gebr. Diederichs, 1862.
349 p.

1. Algebra - 1801-1900.

NL 0430743 CU MiU CaBVaU

Lobatto, Rehuel, 1797-1866.
Lobatto's Lessen over de hoogere algebra. Vierde op nieuw bewerkte druk door A. E. Rahusen, ... Sneek, J. F. van Druten, 1892.
viii, 445 p. 22½cm.

NL 0430744 ICJ

512.8 L7819 Lobatto, Rehuel, 1797-1866.
Lessen over de hoogere algebra door Dr. Fred. Schuh. Uitgegeven als 9. druk van Lobatto's Lessen over de hoogere algebra ... Groningen, 1921-24.
2v. diagrs.

NL 0430745 IU

Qc7 63 Lobatto, Rehuel, 1797-1866.
Mémoire sur l'intégration des équations linéaires aux différentielles et aux différences finies ... Amsterdam,C.G.Sulpke, 1837.
75p. 26x21cm. [Bound with his Mémoire sur la théorie des caractéristiques ... 1837]

NL 0430746 CtY MB

Qc7 63 Lobatto, Rehuel, 1797-1866.
Mémoire sur l'intégration des équations linéaires aux différentielles partielles à trois variables ... Amsterdam,C.G.Sulpke,1837.
1p.ℓ.,105p. 26x21cm. [Bound with his Mémoire sur la théorie des caractéristiques ... 1837]

1. Differential equations - Partial.

NL 0430747 CtY

Lobatto, Rehuel, 1797-1866.
Mémoire sur l'intégration des équations linéaires du premier ordre aux différentielles partielles, à quatre variables. Par R. Lobatto.
(In K. Akademie van wetenschappen, Amsterdam. [Afdeeling voor de wis- en natuurkundige wetenschappen] Verhandelingen. Amsterdam, 1854. 28cm. 1. deel [no. 6] 30 p.)

1. Differential equations, Linear. 2. Differential equations, Partial.

A C 38-2973

Illinois. Univ. Library for Library of Congress [Q57.A53 vol. 1, no. 6]
[4] (508)

NL 0430748 IU OCU

Qc7 63 Lobatto, Rehuel, 1797-1866.
Mémoire sur la théorie des caractéristiques employées dans l'analyse mathématique ... Amsterdam,C.G.Sulpke,1837.
1p.ℓ.,82p. 26x21cm.

1. Calculus of finite differences.

NL 0430749 CtY

Lobatto, Rehuel, 1797-1866.
Mémoire sur une méthode d'approximation pour le calcul des rentes viagères. Par R. Lobatto.
(In K. Akademie van wetenschappen, Amsterdam. [Afdeeling voor de wis- en natuurkundige wetenschappen] Verhandelingen. Amsterdam, 1864. 28cm. 10. deel [no. 4] 32 p. incl. tables)
Also published separately, 1864.

1. Annuities. 2. Annuities—Tables.

A C 40-2796

Illinois. Univ. Library for Library of Congress [Q57.A53 vol. 10, no. 4]
[2] (508)

NL 0430750 IU OCU

VOLUME 337

Lobatto, Rehuel, 1797-1866.
Recherches sur la distinction des racines réelles et imaginaires dans les équations numériques, Precédées d'une novelle démonstration du théorême de M. Sturm ... Paris, Bachelier[etc.,etc.]1842.
2p.ℓ.,50p. diagrs. on fold.Pl. 26x21cm. [Mathematical tracts. v.3]

1.Equations - Numerical solutions. 2.Sturm, Charles,1803-1855.

NL 0430751 CtY

Lobatto, Rehuel, 1797–1866.
Recherches sur la sommation de quelques séries trigonométriques, par R. Lobatto. Delft: P. de Groot, 1827. 41 p. 26½ x 22½cm.

647526A. 1. Summation. 2. Series, Trigonometric.
N. Y. P. L. July 13, 1933

NL 0430752 NN NNC

Lobatto, Rehuel, 1797-1866.
Recueil de problêmes d'algèbre, composé a l'usage des athénées et collèges dans les provinces méridionales; par Lobatto. Bruxelles, 1823.
16 cm.

NL 0430753 CtY

Lobatto, Rehuel, 1797-1866.
Tafels bevattende de quadraten en cubieken der getallen van 1 tot 10000; de quadraat-en cubuswortels der getallen van 1 tot 1000 ... 's Gravenhage, 1834.
19 cm.
Introduction signed: R. Lobatto.

NL 0430754 RPB

Lobau, Richard.
Spaziergänge mit Planitz, dessen ideen und ansichten über Faust und heve. Tagesbuchnotizen. Wittenburg und Berlin, A. Biehler & Co. [1925]

NL 0430755 NIC

Lobaugh, D.O.
Shakespeare's fools and clowns.
Thesis.

NL 0430756 WaPS

Lobaugh, Dean.
A guide to school district reorganization in the state of Oregon. 1949.
314 l.
Thesis, Ed. D., Oregon.
Bibliography: l. [255]-258.
1. Oregon. Schools. Centralization. I. Title. II. Series for Theses.

NL 0430757 OrU

Lobaugh, Elma K 1907–
The devil is loneliness, by Elma K. Lobaugh. New York, Current books, inc., A. A. Wyn [1946]
253 p. 19½ᶜᵐ.

I. Title.

Library of Congress PZ3.L77963De 46-4928

NL 0430758 DLC ViU

Lobaugh, Elma K 1907–
Haze of evil, by Kenneth Lowe [pseud. 1st ed.] Garden City, N. Y., Published for the Crime Club by Doubleday, 1953.
188 p. 21 cm.

I. Title.

PZ4.L796Haz 53-8348 rev ‡

NL 0430759 DLC WaE OCl

Lobaugh, Elma K 1907–
I am afraid. [1st ed.] Garden City, N. Y., Pub. for the Crime Club by Doubleday, 1949.
185 p. 21 cm.

I. Title.

PZ3.L77963 I 49-4525*

NL 0430760 DLC OEac PP

Lobaugh, Elma K 1907–
No tears for Shirley Minton, by Kenneth Lowe [pseud. 1st ed.] Garden City, N. Y., Published for the Crime Club by Doubleday, 1955.
185 p. 21 cm.

I. Title.

PZ3.L77963No 55-10513 ‡

NL 0430761 DLC OrU WaE WaT OEac

Lobaugh, Elma K 1907–
Shadows in succession, by Elma K. Lobaugh. Garden City, New York, Pub. for the Crime club by Doubleday & company, inc., 1946.
4 p. l., [7]–187 p. 19ᶜᵐ.

I. Title.

Library of Congress PZ3.L77963Se 46-5743

NL 0430762 DLC CaBVa WaE ViU

Lobaugh, Elma K 1907–
She never reached the top, by Elma K. Lobaugh. Garden City, New York, Pub. for the Crime club by Doubleday, Doran & co., inc., 1945.
192 p. 18½ᶜᵐ.
"First edition."

I. Title.

Library of Congress PZ3.L77963Sh 45-7800

NL 0430763 DLC ICU IdPI OEac

Lobaus, Adam
Labor fraternity or consumers co-operation? [New York, Goodman press, c1937.
cover-title, 46 p.
1. Cooperative societies. I. Title.

NL 0430764 NNC

Lobay, W
Directions and precautions for using coyote getters...
see under Alberta. Dept. of Agriculture. Field Crops Branch.

Lobb, Albert James

Minneapolis. *Board of education.*
Financing the Minneapolis schools; sources of revenue; expenditures; comparison of principal items of expenditure with corresponding items in twenty-four other cities ... Ordered pub. by the Board of education, City of Minneapolis, 1916.

Lobb, Albert James, joint author.

Anderson, William, 1888–
... A history of the constitution of Minnesota, with the first verified text, by William Anderson ... in collaboration with Albert J. Lobb ... Minneapolis, University of Minnesota, 1921.

Lobb, Emmanuel, afterwards Joseph Simeon, 1594-1671
see Simeon, Joseph, 1594-1671.

Lobb, Frances, tr.

PZ8 .B965 Be

Buzzati, Dino, 1906–
The bears' famous invasion of Sicily, written and illus. by Dino Buzzati. Tr. by Frances Lobb. [New York] Pantheon Books [1947]

Lobb, Frances.
Handsome Johnnie, by Frances Lobb. London, Faber and Faber limited [1941]
3 p. l., 9–261 p. 19½ᶜᵐ.
"First published in August Mcmxli."

I. Title.

Library of Congress PZ3.L77965Han 41-25665

NL 0430770 DLC

Lobb, Frances.
...The strangers. London [etc.] A & E publishers [1947]
261 p. 19cm.

NL 0430771 NN PU

VOLUME 337

Lobb, Harry William, 1829-1889.
Aërated bread; the new system of bread manufacture. Extracted from "The hygiene of bread," by Harry William Lobb ... and a paper read before the Society of arts by Dr. Dauglish, the inventor of "aërated bread" ... London, 1864.
30 p.
I. Dauglish, John, 1824-1866.

NL 0430772 NjP

RC552 N4 872l
Lobb, Harry William, 1829-1889.
Nervous exhaustion: dyspepsia and diabetes. - London, Simpkin, Marshall & Co., 1872.
60p. 16cm.

1. Neurasthenia. 2. Dyspepsia. 3. Diabetes. I. Title.

NL 0430773 CtY-M

RC 340 .L6
Lobb, Harry William, 1829-1889
On some of the more obscure forms of nervous affections: their pathology and treatment; with an introd. on the physiology of digestion and assimilation, and the generation, and distribution, of nerve force, based upon original microscopical observations. Illustrated with original drawings by the author. London, J. Churchill, 1858.
312 p. illus. 23cm.

NL 0430774 WU DNLM PU PPC

Film 1023 no. 5
LOBB, Harry William, 1829-1889
On some of the more obscure forms of nervous affections, their pathology and treatment. With an introduction on the physiology of digestion and assimilation, and the generation and distribution of nerve force, based upon original microscopical observation. London, Churchill, 1858.
iv, 312 p. illus.
Film copy.

NL 0430775 DNLM

Lobb, Harry William, 1829-1889.
On the curative treatment of paralysis and neuralgia, and other affections of the nervous system with the aid of galvanism. By Harry Wm. Lobb ... 2d ed. London ⌈R. Clay, printer⌉ 1859.
2 p. l., ⌈vii⌉-viii, 152 p. 19cm.

1. Nervous system—Diseases. 2. Electrotherapeutics. I. Title.

34-35075

Library of Congress RC359.L6 1859

NL 0430776 DLC DNLM PPC

Lobb, Harry William, 1829-1889.
On the curative treatment of paralysis and neuralgia, and other affections of the nervous system with the aid of galvanism. By Harry Wm. Lobb ... 2d ed. London, H. Bailliere; New York, Bailliere brothers; ⌈etc., etc.⌉ 1859.
2 p. l., ⌈vii⌉-viii, 152 p. illus. 18cm.

1. Nervous system—Diseases. 2. Electrotherapeutics.

7—26671

Library of Congress RC343.L8

NL 0430777 DLC CtY-M DNLM PP ICJ

WBE L796p 1867
LOBB, Harry William, 1829-1889
A popular treatise on curative electricity; especially addressed to sufferers from paralysis, rheumatism, neuralgia, and loss of nervous & physical power. London, Simpkin, Marshall ⌈1867⌉
75 p.

NL 0430778 DNLM NcD-MC DP

Lobb, Harry William, 1829-1889.
——. Practical hints upon the administration of galvanism for the treatment of disease. 32 pp. 8°. London, Simpkin, Marshall & Co., 1858.
[Also, in: P., v. 524.]

NL 0430779 DNLM

LOBB, Harry William, 1829-1889.
Successful oyster culture. London, W. Ridgway, 1867.

IV, [5]-78 p., 1 l. 18 1/2 cm.

NL 0430780 MH NN CtY

Lobb, Henry Brougham.
A short regional geography of China, by H. B. Lobb ... and Llewelyn Tipping ... Calcutta, London ⌈etc.⌉ Macmillan & co., limited, 1926.
2 p. l., 55 p. illus. (maps) 24 x 18½cm.

1. China—Descr. & trav. I. Tipping, Llewelyn, joint author.

39-6694

Library of Congress DS710.L8
⌈2⌉ 915.1

NL 0430781 DLC

Lobb, Henry W.
A treatise on the errors of youth and diseases of the sexes. By Dr. Henry W. Lobb ... Philadelphia, Pa., 1894.
191, ⌈1⌉ p. 16cm.

1. Generative organs—Diseases.

CA 11-1891 Unrev'd

Library of Congress RC881.L79
Copyright 1894: 37721

NL 0430782 DLC DNLM

Lobb, John, 1840-1921, *ed.*
The busy life beyond death, from the voice of the dead, illus. with spirit photos. London, 1909.
xii, 161 p. plates. 19 cm.

1. Spiritualism. I. Title.

BF1301.L82 48-34194*

NL 0430783 DLC RPB

LOBB, John, 1840-1921.
Extravagance and mismanagement of the London school board; three years' experience. London, 'Christian Age', [1885].

pp.16.

NL 0430784 MH

Lobb, John, 1840-1921, ed.
Hanes bywyd "Uncle Tom" ganddo ef ei hun
see under Henson, Josiah, 1789-1881.

Lobb, John, 1840-1921.
The life and death of Rev. T. DeWitt Talmage, D. D. By Rev. John Lobb ... New York, J. S. Ogilvie publishing company ⌈1902⌉
1 p. l., ⌈7⌉-222 p. 18½cm.

1. Talmage, Thomas DeWitt, 1832-1902.

36-22117

Library of Congress BX9225.T3L6
Copyright A 31260 922.573

NL 0430786 DLC

Lobb, John, 1840-1921.
The life and death of Rev. T. De Witt Talmage, D. D., by Rev. John Lobb ... New York, J. S. Ogilvie publishing company, 1902.
1 p. l., ⌈7⌉-222 p. 18½cm. (Sunnyside series, no. 20)

1. Talmage, Thomas De Witt, 1832-1902.

2—13114

Library of Congress
Copyright ⌈a41b1⌉ 922.573

NL 0430787 DLC

Lobb, John, 1840-1921, ed.

Douglass, Frederick, 1817-1895.
The life and times of Frederick Douglass, from 1817-1882, written by himself ... With an introduction by the Right Hon. John Bright, M. P. Ed. by John Lobb ... London, Christian age office, 1882.

---

253 T147zl2
Lobb, John, 1840-1921, ed.
The life of Rev. T. De Witt Talmage, D.D.; with a history of the Brooklyn Tabernacle and specimens of his oratory. Edited by John Lobb. 2d. ed. London, Christian Age Offices, 1879.
ix, 189 p.

1. Talmage, Thomas De Witt, 1832-1902.

NL 0430789 MsSM

Lobb, John, 1840-1921.
Talks with the dead; luminous rays from the unseen world, illustrated with spirit photographs. Ed. by John Lobb. ... New ed. revised and enlarged. London, J. Lobb, 1907.
xxxvi, 156 p. incl. front. (port.) illus., ports. 19cm.

1. Spiritualism. I. Title.

NL 0430790 MiU

Lobb, John, 1840-1921, *ed.*
⌈Talks with the dead; luminous rays from the unseen world, illustrated with spirit photographs, edited by John Lobb ... New ed. (3d), rev. and enl. London, J. Lobb, 1909.
xxxvi, 156 p. front., plates, ports. 19cm.

1. Spiritualism. I. Title.

46-37981

Library of Congress BF1281.L6 1909

NL 0430791 DLC

VOLUME 337

Lobb, John, 1840-1921.
The young people's illustrated edition of "Uncle Tom's" story of his life (from 1789 to 1877)
see under Henson, Joseph, 1789-1883.
[Supplement]

Lobb, John Simonds.
Frontier adjustment in South Africa, by John Lobb ... ₍New Haven, 1937₎
cover-title, p. ₍395₎-410. 22ᶜᵐ.
Based on thesis (PH. D.)—Yale university, 1934.
Title type-written on label mounted on cover.
"From Studies in the science of society, G. P. Murdock, editor, Yale university press, 1937."
Bibliographical foot-notes.

1. Africa, South—Soc. condit. 2. Frontier and pioneer life—Africa, South. I. Title.

Library of Congress HN800.S6L6 41-19704
₍2₎ 916.8

NL 0430793 DLC CtY

Lobb, Kenneth Martyn.
The drama in school and church, a short survey. London, Harrap ₍1955₎
144 p. 19 cm.
Includes bibliographies.

1. Drama in education. 2. Religious drama—Hist. & crit. I. Title.
PN3175.L6 371.895 55-3300 ‡
Library of Congress ₍2₎

NL 0430794 DLC FTaSU OO ViU PP TxU

Lobb, Kenneth Martyn
T. S. Eliot: Murder in the cathedral, by K. Martyn Lobb. London, J. Brodie ₍1950₎
32 p. 19 cm. (Notes on chosen English texts)

1. Eliot, Thomas Stearns, 1888- Murder in the cathedral.

NL 0430795 RPB

---

*AC9 B℔464 T954ℓ
Lobb, Kenneth Martyn.
... T.S. Eliot: Murder in the cathedral, by K. Martyn Lobb ...
London:James Brodie,ltd.,Denmark place, W.C.2 [1954]
32p. 19cm. (At head of title: Notes on chosen English texts ...)
Publisher's device on t.-p.
Pages 28-32 are blank except for heading "Students' notes".
Original printed tan wrappers preserved; bound in cloth.

NL 0430796 MH CU

₍Lobb, Richard₎
The contemplative philosopher: or, Short essays on the various objects of nature throughout the year; with poetical illustrations and moral reflections on each subject... London, Robinson, 1800.
2 v. fronts. 18 ᶜᵐ.

1.Nature study. I.Title.

NL 0430797 NjP MH

Lobb, Richard.
The contemplative philosopher: or, Short essays on the various objects of nature noticed throughout the year; with poetical illustrations, and moral reflections on each subject. By Richard Lobb. Fourth edition, corrected and improved... London: Sherwood, Neely, & Jones, 1817. 2 v. fronts. 12°.
"The essays...appeared originally in a well known periodical miscellany."

1. Science.—Essays and misc. 2. Title.
N. Y. P. L. December 19, 1919.

NL 0430798 NN IU

Lobb, Rodmond Kenneth, 1925-
The study of supersonic flows in a shock tube. ₍Toronto₎ 1950.
v, 148 leaves. illus., diagrs., tables.

Thesis - University of Toronto.
Bibliography: leaf 129.

1. Aerodynamics, Supersonic 2. Shock tubes
I. Toronto. University. Theses (Ph.D.)
II. Title

NL 0430799 CaOTU

819.1 L782p
Lobb, Roy.
Plain folks; a book of friendly verse. [Beatty? Sask., 1949?]
146p. port. 16cm.

NL 0430800 TxU RPB

---

*EC7 L7826 746b
Lobb, Samuel, d.1760.
The benevolence incumbent on us, as men and Christians, considered. In a sermon preached at the assizes held at Taunton, April 1. 1746. before the Honourable Sir Thomas Dennison, and Sir Michael Foster,} knights, justices of his Majesty's Court of King's bench. By Samuel Lobb ...
London:Printed for James Buckland,bookseller at the Buck in Pater-noster row;and James Leak bookseller in Bath.M.DCC.XLVI.
8°. 32p. 19.5cm.

NL 0430801 MH

Lobb, Stephen, d. 1699.
An answer to Dr. Stillingfleet's sermon
see under [Humfrey, John] 1621-1719.

L2721A
Lobb, Stephen, d. 1699.
An appeal to...Edward Lord Bishop of Worcester, and...Dr. Edwards, principal of Jesus Coll. Oxon; for an impartial decision of the controversie between Mr. W. and S. L. about the great doctrine of Christ's satisfaction. In order to the settlement of the brethren on both sides in the sound faith thereof, against Socinianism... London, printed for Nath. Hiller, 1698.

₍8₎ 62 ₍2₎ p. A^4, ₍2d₎A-C^8, E^8 (A1 and E8, probably blanks, lacking) 8vo

"Books printed and sold by Nath. Hiller," sig. A4v.
Lobb's controversy is with Daniel Williams.

NL 0430804 DFo NjPT MH MWA CLU-C CtY

Lobb, Stephen, d. 1699.
A dreadful oration. Delivered by that sorely afflicted saint, Stephen Lobb. Held forth to the brethren, since his last retirement, (at a private meeting by night, to escape persecution,) [sic] in his antient [sic] meeting-house, near Swallow-Street, not far from that famous Whigg-Square. [London?] printed by N.T. at the entrance into the Old Spring Garden near Charing-Cross, 1683.
1, 18p., 1. 20cm.

NL 0430805 IEG CSmH

[Lobb, Stephen] d.1699.
A further defence of the report. Vindicating it from Mr. Alsops cavils, and shewing the difference between Mr. W's and my self to be real, and the charge in my appeal to be true ... London, N. Hiller, 1698.
79 p. 17ᶜᵐ. [With The specimen of a reply ... London, 1699]

WILLIAM ANDREWS CLARK MEMORIAL LIBRARY

Wing L-2724

NL 0430806 CLU-C

---

*EC65 L7823 680g
Lobb, Stephen, d.1699.
The glory of free-grace display'd: or, The transcendent excellency of the love of God in Christ, unto believing, repenting sinners, in some measure describ'd. Wherein 1.The followers of Dr. Crispe are prov'd to be abusers of the true gospel-notion of free-grace: and 2.The congregational clear'd from the reproach of being asserters of such errors as are found in Dr. Crispes writings, as appears by the prefix'd epistle of Dr. Owen. By Stephen Lobb.
London,Printed for Benjamin Alsop,at the Angel and Bible in the Poultrey over against the Counter.1680.
10p.ℓ.,118,xxiip.,1ℓ. 15cm.
Errata: 1ℓ. at end.
"To the reader" signed: John Owen.

NL 0430808 MH

274.2 L78h
₍Lobb, Stephen₎ d.1699.
The harmony between the old and present non-conformists principles, in relation to the terms of conformity, with respect both to the clergie, and the people. Wherein a short history of the original of the English liturgy, and some reasons why several truly conscientious Christians cannot joyn with the church in it. Humbly presented to publick consideration in order to the obtaining some necessary relaxation and indulgence. To which are added some letters that pass'd between the Lord Cecil, and Arch-bishop Whitgift ...

London, Printed and are to be sold by Joseph Collier on London-bridge, 1682.
4 p.l., 96p. 20½cm.

Armorial book-plate, with date 1705, of Henry duke of Beaufort.
With this are bound: Owen, John. A brief vindication of the non-conformists from the charge of schisme. 2d ed. London, 1680; ₍Pearse, Edward₎ The conformist's second plea for the non conformists. London, 1682; ₍L'Estrange, Sir Roger₎ Remarks on the growth and progress of non-conformity. London, 1682; ₍Kettlewell, John₎ Of Christian communion, to be kept on in the unity of Christs church. London, 1693.
1. Dissenters--England. 2. Church of England --Liturgy and ritual. I. Title.

NL 0430811 IU MH ICN NNUT-Mc CtY CLU-C

[Lobb, Stephen] d. 1699.
Healing attempt; being a representation of the government of the Church of England
see under Humfrey, John, 1621-1719.

VOLUME 337

LOBB, Stephen, d. 1699. A | Letter | To | Doctor Bates: | Containing | A Vindication of the Doctor, | and my Self, | Necessitated by Mr. W's. His Answer to Mr. | Hvmfrey. | By S.L. | ... (3 lines).
London, | Printed for Nathaniel Hiller at the Prince's-Arms in Leaden- | Hall-Street, over against St. Mary-Axe, 1695. | Line border. 20x15.2cm. (8),28p.
To the Reader, signed.

NL 0430813 NNUT-Mc DFo

Lobb, Stephen, d. 1699.
A modest and peaceable inquiry into the design and nature of some of those historical mistakes that are found in Dr. Stillingfleet's preface to his Unreasonableness of separation
see under [Humfrey, John] 1621-1719.

Rare Book Room Mhc9 L782 P4
Lobb, Stephen, d. 1699.
A peaceable enquiry into the nature of the present controversie among our united brethren about justification. Part I. By Stephen Lobb ... London,Printed for John Dunton at the Raven in the Poultrey.1693.
4p.ℓ.,159p. 16cm.
Signatures: A^4-L^8.
Imperfect: leaves bled.
No more appears to have been published.

NL 0430815 CtY NcU MH-AH

[Lobb, Stephen, d.1699]
A report of the present state of the differences in doctrinals, between some dissenting ministers in London, in a letter to a friend in the country.
London:Printed for Nath.Hiller in Leaden-hall-street,at the Princes-Arms over against St. Mary-Ax,1697.
15p. 19.5cm.

NL 0430816 MH CSmH NNUT-Mc

Beinecke Library Mhc9 L782 T76
[Lobb, Stephen] d.1699
The true Dissenter, or, The cause of those that are for gathered churches. Being a right state thereof, proposed and settled upon its proper foundations ... in order to that obedience which is lawful, and conducive to the healing of the nation. Occasion'd by some late writings, and especially by a book entituled, The cause of their mix'd churches against (or The axe laid to the root of) separation ... [London?] Printed in the year 1685.
7 p.ℓ., 142 p. 17 cm.

Signatures: A-K^8 (A_1 , K_8 blank? wanting)
Wing: L 2729.

1. Dissenters. I. Title
Div.School

NL 0430818 CtY MH MWA NNUT-Mc IU

18th cent.
Lobb, Theophilus, 1678-1763.
Anleitung zur ausübenden Arzneykunst in einer Anzahl von Vorlesungen über die Ursachen und Entstehung der Krankheiten und die Mittel solche zu heilen... Aus dem Englischen. Leipzig, Weidmann und Reich, 1772.
3p.ℓ.,606p.,ℓℓ. 20cm.

1. Medicine - Practice. 2. Diseases - Causes and theories of causation.

NL 0430819 CtY-M

Lobb, Theophilus. 1678-1763.
An answer to that important question, whether it is lawful for the professors of the Christian religion to go to plays? With some soliloquies annexed. [Anon.]
London: Printed for J. Buckland ... MDCCLVII. (1), 32 pp. 18½ cm., in 4s.
In opposition to the theatre.

J362 — Anon. ret. — Theatre. In opposition to.

NL 0430820 MB LNHT CtY NIC MH

---

*EC7 L7827 726b (A)
Lobb, Theophilus, 1678-1763.
A brief defence of the Christian religion: or The testimony of God, to the truth of the Christian religion. Recommended to the serious thoughts of Christians of all denominations, for their establishment in the faith; and to the impartial consideration of those who are fallen off from Christianity into deism, for their conviction and recovery. By Theophilus Lobb, M.D. ...
London,Printed for J.Clark and R.Hett,at the Bible and Crown in the Poultrey, near Cheapside. M.DCC.XXVI. Price 1s. 6d.

8°. xxiv,114p. 21cm.
Another copy. 20cm.
This volume was in the Harvard college library before the fire of 1764; it is listed in the supplementary catalogue of 1735.

NL 0430822 MH MH-AH

18th Cent.
Lobb, Theophilus, 1678-1763.
A compendium of the practice of physick: or the heads of a system of practical physick contained in twenty-four lectures on the following plan ... Whereunto is added, A letter, shewing what is the proper preparation of persons for inoculation, and for having the small-pox favourably in the natural way ... London:Printed for James Buckland,1747.
xi,ix,103,[3]p. 21cm.
Publisher's catalogue at end.

1. Medicine - Practice. 2. Smallpox, Inoculation of.

NL 0430823 CtY-M DNLM

610.4 L796c 1749 RARE BOOK COLLECTION
Lobb, Theophilus, 1678-1763.
A compendium of the practice of physick: being a summary of a course of lectures. [Twenty-two lines] The second edition, contrived to be useful in families.] London, Printed for J. Buckland, at the Buck in Pater-noster-Row, MDCCXLIX.
viii, 80, [1] p. 16cm.

Author's list of publications on last page.
Binder's title: Lobbs physick. Bound in mottled calf. Sprinkled red edges.

Bound with the author's Medical principles and cautions... 1751.

1. Medicine - Addresses, essays, lectures.
2. Medicine - Study and teaching. 3. Medicine - Practice. I. Title: Lobb's physick. II. Title.

NL 0430825 FU

Lobb, Theophilus, 1678-1763.
... Doctoris Lobb tractatus
see in In hoc volumine continentur. I. Doctoris Lobb tractatus.

Lobb, Theophilus, 1678-1763
General medical principles and cautions; shewing when bleeding, vomiting, purging, sweating, blistering, etc. ought and ought not to be advised. London, 1753.

NL 0430827 PPL PPC

Lobb ([Theophilus]) 1678-1763.
The good Samaritan; or, Complete English physician: containing observations on the most frequent diseases... with directions for the management of the sick; and a collection of the most approved receipts for making and preparing... medicines... To which is added, a method of restoring to life persons thought drowned, or in any other manner suffocated... *London: J. Cooke*, [1750] 71 pp., 1 pl. 12°.
In: *C. p. v. 800.

NL 0430828 NN WaU

And.Rm. BV4904 L6 1762
Lobb, Theophilus, 1678-1763.
Letters on the sacred predictions...collected out of the Holy Scriptures...Whereunto is added, Dr. Lobb's reply to the remarks made upon his Letters on the sacred predictions...Intended for promoting piety and the consolation of...Christians...when under affliction...By Theophilus Lobb...London, Printed for J. Buckland, 1762.
1 v. (various pagings) 20 cm.

NL 0430829 PPiPT

B616.923 L782
LOBB, Theophilus, 1678-1763.
Letters relating to the plague, and other contagious distempers. Part. I. Letters to Martin Folkes... Part II. Letters to *****. Also letters containing an account of... the murrain, or plague, among cattle... Whereunto are added copper-plates of machines, which may be useful in an infectious season... London, Printed for J. Buckland, 1745.
xx, [2], 411, [16] p. II fold. pl. 20cm.
"Books published by Dr. Lobb": p.[xxi-xxii]

NL 0430830 MnU DNLM

Lobb, Theophilus, 1678-1763.
Medicinal letters. In two parts. Part I. Contains letters on miscellaneous subjects, for removing various disorders from human bodies, and for the preservation of health. Part II. Contains letters on the most frequent and dangerous diseases incident to infants and children, men and women: with directions for the management of the sick, and making medicines for the cure of the several diseases. Intended chiefly for the benefit of those poor families which can neither have the advice of a physician, nor the attendance of an apothecary. The 3d ed. By Dr. Lobb ... London, J. Buckland, MDCCLXV.
4 p. l., 92 p. 17½cm.
1. Medicine—15th-18th cent. I. Title.
34-40049
Library of Congress R128.7.L78 1765

NL 0430831 DLC

RC106 L782
Lobb, Theophilus, 1678-1763.
Medical practice in curing fevers: correspondent to rational methods, &c. and to those curative indications, which arise from the febrile symptoms of the patient: and exemplified in many cases of the most usual fevers, with the medicines by which they are cured ... London, Printed for John Oswald, 1735.
xxx, [2], 431, [23] p.
1. Fever. I. Title.

NL 0430832 NNC DNLM MBCo PPC NNNAM

VOLUME 337

610.4
L796c
1749 Lobb, Theophilus, 1678-1763.
Medical principles and cautions. [Five lines. Fleuron] London, Printed for J. Buckland [etc.], 1751.
iv, 59, [1] p. 16cm.

Author's list of publications on last page.
Errata at end of text.
Bound with the author's A compendium of the practice of physick ... 1749.
1. Medicine - Practice. I. Title.

NL 0430833 FU CtY

R
128.7
.L58 Lobb, Theophilus, 1678-1763
A practical treatise of painful distempers, with some effectual methods of curing them, exemplified in a great variety of suitable histories. London, Printed for James Buckland, 1739.
320 p. 21 cm.

1. Medicine - 15th-18th cent. 2. Medicine Practice.

NL 0430834 WU PPL PPC DNLM ICJ NNNAM NcD-MC

Lobb, Theophilus, 1678-1763.
Practice of physic in general, as delivered in a course of lectures on the theory of diseases, and the proper method of treating them, by Theophilus Lobb ... Published from the doctor's own MS. In two volumes. London, Buckland, 1771.
2 v. front. (port., v. 1) 21 cm.

NL 0430835 NcD

RC106
L78
Lobb, Theophilus, 1678-1763.
Rational methods of curing fevers: deduced from the structure, and oeconomy of human bodies, and the different states of the solids, and fluids, under the different classes of fevers. Together with a particular account of the effects of artificial evacuations by bleeding, vomiting, purging, sweating, and blistering, &c., with practical rules deduced from them, shewing in what cases they are proper, and may be beneficial; and in what, they are improper, and will be hurtful ... London, Printed for John Oswald, 1734.

xiv p., 1 l., xv-xxii, [2], 403, [3] p. 3 plates.

"An account of the editions of the few authors cited in this book": p. xxi-xxii.

1. Fever. I. Title.

NL 0430837 NNC DNLM PPL PPC PU

[Lobb, Theophilus] 1678-1763.
Sacred declarations: or, A letter to the inhabitants of London, Westminster, and all other parts of Great Britain: on the account of those sins, which provoked God to send, and continue, the mortal sickness among the cattle, and to signify, by the late awful earthquakes, that His anger is not turned away... London: Printed for J. Buckland, 1750. 2 p.l., (1)+37(1) p. 21cm. (8°.)

Publisher's advertisements, p. [38]

109044B. 1. Earthquakes. 2. Conduct of life. I. Title.
N. Y. P. L. May 13, 1942

NL 0430838 NN

BV
4253
L8
S12
Cage
Lobb, Theophilus, 1678-1763.
A sermon preach'd at the ordination of the reverend Mr. John Greene, at Winburn, in Dorsetshire, July the 20th, 1708. And since enlarged, with some brief reflections on...a book, intituled The rights of the Christian church... London, Printed by R. Tookey, for the author [etc.] 1708.

64 p. A-B^{4}, C-E^{8}. 8vo.

Matthew Tindal wrote The rights of the Christian church.

NL 0430839 DFo MWA

Lobb, Theophilus, 1678-1763.
18th
cent
Tractatus de dissolventibus calculos ac curatione claculi et podagrae ope alimentorum. . . Quibus tandem porro adduntur directiones diaetae convenientes iis, qui affliguntur catarrhis, febribus, angina [etc] Ex Anglico in Latium versum. . . Basileae, Excudebat Johannes Christ, 1742.
xx, 327p., 14ℓ. 19cm.
With this are bound Hartley: De lithontriptico... 1741; and Staehelin: Epistola Eucharistica, 1742.

NL 0430840 CtY-M CLU-M

Lobb, Theophilus, 1678-1763.
18th
cent.
Traité des moyens de dissoudre la pierre, et de guérir cette maladie & celle de la goute, par le choix des alimens, traduit de l'Anglois par M. T. A. Paris, Durand, 1744.
xxvii, 501., [2]ℓ. 18cm.

1. Calculi. 2. Gout. 3. Diet - Early works to 1800.

NL 0430841 CtY-M CtY

Lobb, Theophilus, 1678-1763.
A treatise of the small pox ... By Theophilus Lobb ... London, T. Woodward [etc.] MDCCXXXI.
2 p. l., xl, [8], 472, [17] p. 20cm.
Head and tail pieces; initials.
"The names of the authors and books cited in the treatise": [3] p. preceding p. 1.

1. Smallpox.
35-36255
Library of Congress RC183.L78

NL 0430842 DLC MH PPC PPAN PU DNLM

Lobb, Theophilus, 1678-1763.
136092 A treatise on dissolvents of the stone; and on curing the stone and gout by aliment. Shewing by reason ſupported with experiments, and cases, the probability of diſſolving the stone either in the kidneys, or bladder; and of preventing the returns of the gout by ſuitable aliment, with proper rules of diet, ... To which are added, directions of diet proper for persons afflicted with colds, fevers, quinſeys, coughs, aſthma's, cholicks and pains of the stomach, coſtiveneſs, nervous diſeaſes, cachexies, dropſies, tumours, or scurvey. The whole form'd for usefulness in families. By Theophilus Lobb, ... London, Printed for J. Buckland, 1739.
xxii, 450, [20] p. 20½cm.

NL 0430843 ICJ DNLM CLU-M WU-M PPL PPJ PPC CaBVaU

Lobban, Albert A.
The Y and I price calculator; contains over 13,000 calculations from 1 inch to 20 yards, at the most popular prices, from .05 to $10.00 per yard ... copyright ... by A. A. Lobban. Warrensburg, Mo., ©1924.
67 p. 16cm.

1. Dry-goods—Tables, etc. I. Title.
Library of Congress HF5716.D8L6 24-8494

NL 0430844 DLC

Lobban, Charles Henry.
... "Some deflection problems." By Charles Henry Lobban ... London, The Institution, 1929.
24 p. diagrs. 21½cm. (The Institution of civil engineers. Selected engineering papers ... no. 80)

1. Strains and stresses.
Library of Congress G265.L6 30-8962

NL 0430845 DLC CaBVaU PPF MiU

PR1363
L8
Lobban, John Hay, ed.
English essays. With an introduction by J.H. Lobban. London, Blackie, 1896.
lxi, 257 p. 20cm. (The Warwick library)

Selected essays, with critical introduction.

1. English essays. 2. English essays - Hist. & crit. I. Title.

NL 0430846 GU NN PPD PSC NjP MH MiU

Lobban, John Hay, comp and ed.
English essays, selected and with an introduction, by J. H. Lobban, M.A. London [etc.] Blackie & son ltd. [190-?] lxi, 286 p. 18cm. (On cover: Standard English classics.)

Contents.—Francis Bacon.—Abraham Cowley.—Daniel Defoe.—Sir Richard Steele.—Joseph Addison.—Jonathan Swift.—Henry Fielding.—Alexander Pope.—George Colman and Bonnel Thornton.—William Cowper.—Philip Stanhope.—Horace Walpole.—Samuel Johnson.—Oliver Goldsmith.—Leigh Hunt.—William Hazlitt.—Charles Lamb.

51559B. 1. Essays, English—Collections.
N. Y. P. L. May 20, 1940

NL 0430847 NN OCl PU

Lobban, John Hay, ed.
English essays, with an introduction by J. H. Lobban. London [etc.] Blackie & son, limited [1902]
lxi, 257 p. (The Warwick library [of English literature])

1. English essays. 2. English essays - History and criticism. I. Title.

NL 0430848 WaU MoU

PR
1363
.L7
1903
Lobban, John Hay, ed.
English essays, with an introduction. London, Blackie & son, 1903.
vi-lxi, 257p. 20cm. (The Warwick library)

Selected essays, with critical introduction.
Contents.- Introduction.- Francis Bacon.- Abraham Cowley.- Daniel Defoe.- Sir Richard Steele.- Joseph Addison.- Jonathan Swift.- Henry Fielding.- Alexander Pope.- George Colman and Bonnel Thornton.- William Cowper.-

Contents continued.
Philip Stanhope.- Horace Walpole.- Samuel Johnson.- Oliver Goldsmith.- Leigh Hunt.- William Hazlitt.- Charles Lamb.

1. English essays. 2. English essays. Hist. & crit. I. Title. II. Series.

NL 0430850 OrU

Lobban, John Hay.
English essays. London, Blackie, 1905.
257 p.

NL 0430851 OClW

VOLUME 337

Lobban, John Hay.
English essays... L. Blackie, 1906.
257 p.

NL 0430852 OCIW

Lobban, John Hay, *ed.*
English essays, with an introduction by J. H. Lobban. London [etc.] Blackie & son, limited, 1909.
2 p. l., xii-lxi, 257 p. 19½cm. (*Half-title:* The Warwick library, ed. by C. H. Herford ...)
Selected essays, with critical introduction.
CONTENTS.—Introduction.—Francis Bacon.—Abraham Cowley.—Daniel Defoe.—Sir Richard Steele.—Joseph Addison.—Jonathan Swift.—Henry Fielding.—Alexander Pope.—George Colman and Bonnel Thornton.—William Cowper.—Philip Stanhope.—Horace Walpole.—Samuel Johnson.—Oliver Goldsmith.—Leigh Hunt.—William Hazlitt.—Charles Lamb.
1. English essays. 2. English essays—Hist. & crit. I. Title.
Library of Congress PR1363.L3 10—13406

NL 0430853 DLC OrU PBa NcU LU OCl

Lobban, John Hay, *ed.*
Shakespeare, William, 1564–1616.
... Macbeth; ed. by J. H. Lobban, M. A. Cambridge, University press, 1911.

Lobban, John Hay.
Oliver Goldsmith. By J.H. Lobban.
(In The Bookman. London, 1906. 33.5cm., in folder 35cm. vol.XXX, no.175, p.9-14. illus.)
Laid in as "Supplement to the Bookman. April, 1906" is a mounted port. of Goldsmith reproduced from the painting by Sir Joshua Reynolds.

NL 0430855 MH

Lobban, John Hay, *ed.*
Hunt, Leigh, 1784–1859.
... Selections in prose and verse, ed. with introduction and notes by J. H. Lobban ... Cambridge, University press, 1909.

Lobban, John Hay, *ed.*
Shakespeare, William, 1564–1616.
... The winter's tale, ed. by J. H. Lobban, M. A. Cambridge, University press, 1910.

Lobban, William
Greek unseens, being one hundred passages for translation at sight in junior classes, selected and arranged with introduction by William Lobban ... Edinburgh and London, W. Blackwood and sons, 1910.
xv, 67, [1] p. 18.5cm.
1. Greek language - Chrestomathies and readers.

NL 0430858 NNC

E170 L63
Lobbé, Guillermo, d. 1883.
Cartas a mis hijos, durante un viaje a los Estados Unidos, Francia e Inglaterra, en los siete últimos meses de 1837. Nueva York, Impr. de J. de la Granja, 1839.
272 p. 20 cm.
1. Voyages and travels - 1800-1850.

NL 0430859 CtY

Bra SB 205 .C8L7
Lobbe, Henrique.
...Estudo sobre 12 variedades de cowpea, pelo Dr.Henrique Lobbe...Rio de Janeiro, Officinas typographicas do Serviço de informações do Ministerio da agricultura, 1925.
cover-title, 10 p. illus., tables. 23 cm.
At head of title: Ministerio da agricultura, industria e commercio (Serviço de informações)

NL 0430860 DPU

G633.15 L782m
Lobbe, Henrique.
Milho. [São Paulo?] 1928.
275p. illus., port. 24cm.
1101579
1. Maize - Brazil. 2. Maize - Field experiments. 3. Maize - Varieties. 4. Campo de Sementes de São Simão.

NL 0430861 TxU DNAL NN

D524 .L8
Lobbedey, Emile Louis Cornil, *bp.* 1856–1916, *ed.*
... La guerre en Artois. Paroles épiscopales. Documents. Récits. Paris, P. Téqui, 1916.
xxi, 513 p. plates, port., map. 18½cm.
At head of title: Sous la direction de Monseigneur Lobbedey ...

NL 0430862 ICU NjP MH

Lobbedey, Émile Louis Cornil, *bp.* 1856–1916, *ed.*
... La guerre en Artois. Paroles épiscopales. Documents. Récits. 3. éd. Paris, P. Téqui, 1917.
xxi, 551 p. plates, ports., map. 19 cm.
At head of title: Sous la direction de Monseigneur Lobbedey, évêque d'Arras, Boulogne et St-Omer.
1. European war, 1914–1918—Campaigns—France. 2. Artois—Hist. 3. European war, 1914–1918—Religious aspects.
D548.L6 1917 17—9491

NL 0430863 DLC

W 4 L72 1939/40
Lobbedez, Pierre, 1912–
Péritonite primitive a streptocoques. Lille, Douriez-Bataille, 1939.
50 p. (Lille. [Université, Faculté de médecine et de pharmacie. Thèse. 1939/40. no. 99)
Bibliography: p. [49]-50.

NL 0430864 DNLM

Lobben, Peder, 1858–
Haandbok i maskinarbeide, av Peder Lobben. Oslo, H. Aschehoug & co., 1936.
xiii, 896 p. incl. illus., tables, diagrs. 19cm.
1. Machine-shop practice. 2. Machinery—Handbooks, manuals, etc. I. Title.
36-21654
Library of Congress TJ1160.L55
Copyright A—Foreign 32160
[2] 621.75

NL 0430865 DLC

Lobben, Peder, 1858–
Håndbok i maskinarbeid. 3. utg. Oslo, Aschehoug, 1948–51.
2 v. illus. 18 cm.
1. Machine-shop practice. 2. Machinery—Handbooks, manuals, etc. I. Title.
TJ1160.L553 621.75 50–20046 rev

NL 0430866 DLC

Lobben, Peder, 1858–
Induktions-motorer og transformatorer, af Peder Lobben ... Kristiania og Kjøbenhavn, H. Aschehoug & co. (W. Nygaard) 1917.
2 p. l., vii–viii, 148 p. incl. illus., 15 tab. 21cm. kr. 3
1. Electric motors, Induction. 2. Electric transformers. I. Title.
Library of Congress TK2785.L6 18–3807

NL 0430867 DLC

Lobben, Peder, 1858–
Lobbens korrespondance-skoles lærebøger. Samlet udg. af undervisningsbrevene som benyttes ved Peder Lobbens tekniske korrespondance-skole ...
Kristiania og Kjøbenhavn, H. Aschehoug & co. (W. Nygaard) 1922
v. 21cm.
I. Peder Lobbens tekniske korrespondance-skole, Christiania.
Library of Congress LC6065.L6 23-2400

NL 0430868 DLC

Lobben, Peder, 1858–
Lobbens tekniske bibliotek, samlet udgave af haandbøkerne ved Peder Lobbens tekniske korrespondance-skole ... Kristiania og Kjøbenhavn, H. Aschehoug & co. (W. Nygaard) 1923–
v. 20½cm.
1. Technology. 2. Mathematics. I. Title.
Library of Congress T45.L6 24-8467

NL 0430869 DLC

Lobben, Peder, 1858–
Lommebog for mekanikere; en praktisk haandbog indeholdende principer, formler, tabeller, regler og data til brug for mekanikere, tegnere, maskinkonstruktører og andre mekaniske arbeidere, af Peder Lobben. 6. udg. med ca. 330 figurer og over 160 tabeller. Kristiania og Kjøbenhavn, H. Aschehoug & co., 1920.
xx, 968 p. incl. illus., tables, diagrs. 17cm.
1. Mechanical engineering—Handbooks, manuals, etc. I. Title.
Library of Congress TJ151.L7 1920 21-5933

NL 0430870 DLC

VOLUME 337

Lobben, Peder, 1858–
Lommebok for mekanikere; en praktisk haandbok, indeholdende principer, formler, tabeller, regler og data til bruk for mekanikere, tegnere, maskinkonstruktører og andre mekaniske arbeidere, av Peder Lobben. 8. forøkede utgave, med ca. 360 figurer og over 170 tabeller. Oslo, H. Aschehoug & co., 1938.
1 p. l., xxii, 1196 p. incl. illus., tables, diagrs. 18½cm.

1. Mechanical engineering—Handbooks, manuals, etc. I. Title.
38-38507
Library of Congress TJ151.L7 1938
Copyright A—Foreign 40340
[2] 621.02

NL 0430871 DLC

Lobben, Peder, 1858–
Machinists' and draftsmen's handbook; containing tables, rules, and formulas ... intended as a reference book for all interested in mechanical work. New York, D. Van Nostrand co., 1900.
2 p. l., 438 p. illus. 20cm.

1. Mechanical engineering—Handbooks, manuals, etc. I. Title.
0—2023
Library of Congress TJ151.L78

NL 0430872 DLC PPF CU MB ICJ

Lobben, Peder.
Machinists' and draftsmen's handbook: containing tables, rules and formulas, with numerous examples explaining the principles of mathematics and mechanics as applied to the mechanical trades. ...
New York. Van Nostrand Co. 1910. x, 487 pp. Diagrams. 20 cm.

H4031 — Mechanics. Applied. — T.r.

NL 0430873 MB

Lobben, Peder, 1858–
Machinists' and draftsmen's handbook, containing tables, rules and formulas, with numerous examples explaining the principles of mathematics and mechanics as applied to the mechanical trades; intended as a reference book for all interested in mechanical work. By Peder Lobben ... 2d and enl. ed. New York, D. Van Nostrand company, 1910.
2 p. l., x, 487 p. incl illus., tables, diagrs. 20½cm. $2.50

1. Mechanical engineering—Handbooks, manuals, etc.
10—16722
Library of Congress TJ151.L8

NL 0430874 DLC OU OCl ICJ

Lobben, Peder, 1858–
Machinists' and draftsmen's handbook: containing tables, rules and formulas, with numerous examples explaining the principles of mathematics and mechanics as applied to the mechanical trades; intended as a reference book for all interested in mechanical work. By Peder Lobben ... 3d ed., rev. New York, D. Van Nostrand company, 1922.
2 p. l., x p., 1 l., 487 p. incl. illus., tables, diagrs. 19½cm. $3.00

1. Mechanical engineering—Handbooks, manuals, etc.
22-22269
Library of Congress TJ151.L8 1922

NL 0430875 DLC NN

TJ151 .W3
Lobben, Peder, 1858– Machinists' and draftsmen's handbook.
Wagener, Albert M
The machinists' and draftsmen's handbook [by] Albert M. Wagener ... and Harlan R. Arthur ... New York, D. Van Nostrand company, inc., 1945.

Lobben, Peder, 1858–
see also
Peder Lobbens tekniske korrespondanseskole, *Oslo.*

Lobbenberg, Ernst, 1909–
... Über einen Fall von Makroglossie ... Hamburg, 1932.
Inaug.-Diss. - Hamburg.
"Literatur": p. 15.
Lebenslauf.

NL 0430878 CtY

Lobbes, Heinz.
... Die nordschwedische grubenindustrie; beiträge zu ihrer entwicklung, von dr. Heinz Lobbes ... Greifswald, L. Bamberg, 1932.
xv,151 p., 1 l. 23½ cm. (At head of t.-p.: Greifswalder staatswissenschaftliche abhandlungen begründet von prof. Biermann und prof. Kähler. Hrsg. von prof. Kähler und prof. Muhs. 49)

"Literatur": p. [vii]-xii.

1. Mines and mineral resources--Sweden.

NL 0430879 NIC

Lobbes, Heriger von, 990-1007
see Heriger, Abbot of Lobbes, ca. 900-1007.

Hin5 76d
Lobbes, Otto, 1887-
Nordbergische Dialektgeographie ... Marburg, R.Friedrich's Universitätsbuchdruckerei (Inhaber:K.Gleiser),1912.
2p.l.,80p.,1l. fold.map. 23½cm.
Inaug.-Diss. - Marburg.
Lebenslauf.
"Sonderabdruck aus Heft VIII der Deutschen Dialektgeographie."

NL 0430881 CtY MH PU ICRL

Lobbes, Otto, 1887-
Wenker, Georg, 1852–1911.
Das rheinische platt, von Georg Wenker <neudruck>. Nordbergische dialektgeographie, von Otto Lobbes. Studien zur niederrheinischen dialektgeographie in den kreisen Rees, Dinslaken, Hamborn, Mülheim, Duisburg, von Heinrich Neuse. Studien zur niederrheinischen dialektgeographie zwischen Nymegen und Ürdingen, von Albert Hanenberg; mit vier karten. Marburg, N. G. Elwert, 1915.

Lobbes, Belgium. Saint-Pierre (*Benedictine abbey*)
Catalogue des manuscrits de l'abbaye de Lobbes (1049)
(*In* Revue des bibliothèques ... Paris, 1891. 25cm. 1. année, p. [5]-14)
Preliminary statement signed: H. Omont.

1. Manuscripts. Belgium—Catalogs. I. Omont, Henri Auguste, 1857–
A C 34-4630
Title from Cleveland Pub. Libr. [Z671.R45 1891]
Library of Congress

NL 0430883 OCl MiU

Lobbet de Lanthin, Jacques, 1592-1672.
Gloria patriarcharum, sive Quaestiones morales in evangelia festorum D.Augustini, D.Benedicti, D. Brunonis, D.Bernardi, D.Norberti, D.Dominici, D.Francisci Assisii, D.Francisci de Paula, D. Ignatii de Loiola, D.Philippi Nerii, D.Ursulae, D.Teresiae, nunc primum in lucem editae. Leodii, Ex off. typogr. Hoviorum, 1657

627 p.

NL 0430884 MH

Lobbet de Lanthin, Jacques, 1592-1672.
... Opera omnia in sex tomos distributa. Hac secunda editione recognita, et aucta tomis duobus ... Opus maxima parte novum, & concionibus, pastoribus, ac spiritualis vitae magistris atque religiosis perutile. Leodii, ex officina Joan. Mathiae Hovii, 1668.

2 v. 36 cm.
Title vignette. Initials. Bound in pigskin over boards. Blind-pressed. Clasps missing.

NL 0430885 PLatS

Oversize GS5 L782 A 1653
Restricted Circulation
Lobbet de Lanthin, Jacques, 1592-1672.
Iacobi Lobbetii ... Qvaestiones theologicae, historicae, morales in evangelia dominicarvm et festorvm totius anni ... Leodii, Ex officina typ. H. et I.M. Hoviorum. M. DC. LIII.
4 v. in 2. illus. 36 cm.

Title vignettes.
Vol. 1 has half-title: Iacobi Lobbetii ... Opera omnia in qvatvor tomos distribvta.

Vol. 4 has title: Iacobi Lobbetii ... Opvs morale de peccato, eivsqve natvra, poenis, ac remediis ... Ed. novissima, aucta & recognita ... Half-title of v. 4 reads: Iacobi Lobbetii ... Opvscvla moralia avctiora, sive Opervm tomvs IV.

1. Theology - Collected works - 17th cent. I. Title. II. Lobbet de Lanthin, Jacques, 1592-1672. Opera omnia.

NL 0430888 CtY-D WU

Lobbetius, Jacques
see Lobbet de Lanthin, Jacques, 1592-1672.

Lobbia, Cristiano, 1832-1876.
Dibattimenti nella cause contro Cristiano Lobbia, Antonio Martinati, Cristiano Giusto Caregnato, Giuseppe Novelli e Carlo Benelli imputati di simulazione di delitto. Rendiconti raccolti dagli stenografi della Camera dei deputati. [Fasc. I.] Firenze, per gli Eredi Botta, 1869.
4°.

NL 0430890 MH

W 4 M96 1951
LOBBICHLER, Hans, 1921-
Wandlung im symptomatischen Bild der luetischen Initailsklerose; ein Beitrag zur aetiologischen Deutung. München, 1951.
40 l. illus.
Inaug.-Diss. - Munich.
Typewritten copy.
1. Syphilis

NL 0430891 DNLM

783 L782
The lobby: or, Out-door conversation on the meeting of Parliament ... Dedicated to Richard Tickell, esq. The 2d ed. London:Printed for the author,by J.Cattermoul[1783]
2p.l.,28p. 26x21cm.
Dedication dated Nov.11,1783.
A satire in verse on the principal political personages of the time, based on Tickell's famous pamphlet "Anticipation."

NL 0430892 CtY

VOLUME 337

FILM
6597 The Lobby; or, Out-door conversation on the meeting of Parliament. The 2d ed. London, Printed for the author by J. Cattermoul ⌊1783⌋
28 p.
Microfilm (negative) New Haven, Yale University Library, 1941. 1 reel.

1. Gt. Brit.--Pol. & govt.--1760-1789.

NL 0430893 MiU

Lobdell, Barton S.
The Atlas globe manual; a guide to the study of terrestrial globes, by B. S. Lobdell, M. S. Chicago, Atlas school supply company ⌊1904⌋
140 p. illus., diagrs. 19cm.

1. Globes. I. Title.

Library of Congress GA12.L79 4-36080 Revised

NL 0430894 DLC

Lobdell, Barton S.
The telluric manual, a guide to the study of Swigert's lunar tellurian. By B. S. Lobdell, M. S. Chicago, Pub. by Central school supply house ⌊©1894⌋
1 p. l., 173 p. illus. 19½cm.

1. Astronomical models. I. Title.

Library of Congress QB67.L78 5—2141

NL 0430895 DLC

Lobdell, Charles Elmer, 1861-
Federal farm loans, purchase of debentures. Hearing before the Committee on banking and currency
see under U.S. Congress. Senate. Committee on Banking and Currency.

Lobdell, Edith
see
Reed, Edith (Lobdell)

Lobdell, Edwin Lyman, 1857-
Chicago's transportation problem ... Chicago, [1925-].
Library has 1925 *to date.* 23cm.
Title varies: 1925, Chicago's transportation problem at the close of the year, 1925.
1927- , ... in January 1927-.
1928- published as "continuation of 'Chicago's transportation problem in 1927 ...'"

NL 0430898 ICJ

Lobdell, Edwin Lyman, 1857-
Chicago's transportation problem in January 1927; some interesting facts concerning Chicago's traction history, compiled by Edwin L. Lobdell. Chicago ⌊Press of Cameron, Amberg & co., ©1927⌋
2 p. l., 27, ⌊1⌋ p. 23cm.

1. Street-railroads—Chicago. 2. Street-railroads—Chicago—Finance. I. Title.

Library of Congress HE4491.C45L6 27-10812

NL 0430899 DLC MiU ICJ NN

Lobdell, Edwin Lyman, 1857-
Chicago's transportation problem in January 1930, compiled by Edwin L. Lobdell ... ⌊Chicago, Press of Cameron, Amberg & co., ©1930⌋
2 p. l., 15, ⌊1⌋ p. 23cm.
"A review of present conditions and continuation of 'Chicago's transportation problem in 1927, 1928 and 1929'."

1. Street-railroads—Chicago. 2. Street-railroads—Chicago—Finance. I. Title.

Library of Congress HE4491.C45L62 30-5549

NL 0430900 DLC

Lobdell, Edwin Lyman, 1857-
Chicago's transportation problem in January 1931, compiled by Edwin L. Lobdell... [Chicago, cop.1931.] 16 p. incl. table. 8°.

566201A. 1. Railways, Street--U.S.--Ill.--Chicago, 1931.
N. Y. P. L. January 16, 1932

NL 0430901 NN MiU

LOBDELL, EDWIN LYMAN, 1857-
Chicago's transportation problem in January 1932, compiled by Edwin L. Lobdell. Chicago[: Press of Cameron, Amberg & Co., cop. 1932]. 16 p. incl. tables. 22½cm.

694512A. 1. Railways, Street--U.S.--Ill.--Chicago, 1930.

NL 0430902 NN

Lobdell, Frederick D.
Around robin; eight years in the mission field in the mountain district of western North Carolina. Hartford, Church Missions Pub. Co. [1916]

22 p. (Church Missions Publishing Co. Publication, 105)

NL 0430903 MH

Lobdell, George Henry, 1922-
A biography of Frank Knox. Ann Arbor, University Microfilms ⌊1954⌋
(⌊University Microfilms, Ann Arbor, Mich.⌋ Publication no. 9101)
Microfilm copy of typescript. Positive.
Collation of the original: xii, 365 l. ports., maps.
Thesis—University of Illinois.
Abstracted in Dissertation abstracts, v. 14 (1954) no. 11, p. 2049-2050.
Vita.
Bibliography: leaves 357-364.
1. Knox, Franklin, 1874-1944.
Microfilm AC-1 no. 9101 Mic A 54-3049

Illinois. Univ. Library for Library of Congress ⌊1⌋†

NL 0430904 IU CU NNC MoU IaU MU DLC

Lobdell, Harold Edward, 1896-
The De La Rue Georgians of South Africa, by H. E. Lobdell. ⌊New York, The Collectors club, inc., 1944⌋
cover-title, 100 p. illus. (incl. maps, facsims., coats of arms) 25½cm.
Bibliography: p. 98-100.

1. Postage-stamps—Africa, South. I. De La Rue (Thomas) and company, ltd., London. II. Collectors club, New York. III. Title.

Library of Congress ° HE6185.A5L6 45-1110
⌊3⌋ 383.22

NL 0430905 DLC CaBVaU OCl OClWHi

Lobdell, Helen.
Golden conquest; illustrated by Seymour Fleishman. Boston, Houghton Mifflin, 1953.
277 p. illus. 22 cm.

1. Mexico—Hist.—Conquest, 1519-1540—Fiction. 2. Cortés, Hernando, 1485-1547—Fiction. I. Title.

PZ7.L779Go 53-6208 ‡

NL 0430906 DLC OrLgE OrP Or WaT WaE WaS PPGi PP OCl

Lobdell, Helen.
The King's snare. Illustrated by C. Walter Hodges. Boston, Houghton Mifflin, 1955.
218 p. illus. 22 cm.
Includes bibliography.

1. Raleigh, Sir Walter, 1552?-1618—Fiction. I. Title.

PZ7.L779Ki 55-5917 ‡

NL 0430907 DLC OrP WaS WaSp NcU OCl PP OOxM

Lobdell, Henry. Letter respecting some recent discoveries at Koyunjik. 9 pp. (Am. Orient. Soc. Journ. v. 4, 1854, p. 472.)

NL 0430908 MdBP

Lobdell, Henry.
The religious, moral, and political evils of the liquor traffic, and their remedy. "Prevention is better than cure." An appeal for present action in the cause of temperance. By Henry Lobdell ... New York: Printed by W. Osborn, 1848. 31 p. 8°.
In: VTZ p. v. 181, no. 2.

1. Temperance.—Addresses, essays, lectures.
N. Y. P. L. June 28, 1919.

NL 0430909 NN

La
340.8 Lobdell, James L , complainant.
K58b [...Jas. L. Lobdell vs. W.H. Bushnell, et
v.5 als. New Orleans, 187 ?]
no.39 caption-title, 16p. 21½cm. (In King, W.W. [Briefs. v.5, no.39])

At head of title: Before Supreme Court, state of Louisiana.

I. Budd & Grover. II. Bushnell, W. H. III. Colwell, T. W. IV. La. Supreme court.

NL 0430910 LU

Lobdell, John Henry.
Determination of temperature in a low pressure flame. Pasadena, 1951.
80 l. diagrs. 29 cm.
Thesis—California Institute of Technology.
On cover: Guggenheim Aeronautical Laboratory, California Institute of Technology.
Bibliography: leaf 28.

1. Flame. I. Title.

QD516.L64 64-50120

NL 0430911 DLC

VOLUME 337

Lobdell, *Mrs.* **Julia Ardelia (Harrison)** 1839–
Bentley gleanings, comp. and pub. by (Mrs.) Julia Harrison Lobdell ... Family of John Witherstine. Chicago, A. W. Fleming, printer, 1905]
128 p. fold. map. 20½cm.
"They fought in '76; hitsory [!] of the Witherstine family ... compiled by Wm. Witherstine": p. [120]–128.
1. Bentley family. 2. Witherstine family (John Witherstine, b. 1762)
Library of Congress CS71.B477 1905 6–27432

NL 0430912 DLC NN MWA

Lobdell, *Mrs.* **Julia Ardelia (Harrison)** 1839–
... Simon Lobdell—1646 of Milford, Conn. and his descendants. Comp. and pub. by Julia Harrison Lobdell. Nicholas Lobden (Lobdell)—1635 of Hingham, Mass. and some of his descendants. Chicago, The Windermere press [1907?]
2 p. l., vi p., 2 l., 9–374 p., 1 l., xlvii p. ports., map. 24cm.
At head of title: 1907.
1. Lobdell family (Simon Lobdell, d. 1717) 2. Lobdell family (Nicholas Lobden, d. 1646?)
Library of Congress CS71.L796 1907? 9–8069

NL 0430913 DLC MWA PHi NN

Lobdell, Lucy Ann, *b.* 1829.
Narrative of Lucy Ann Lobdell, the female hunter of Delaware and Sullivan counties, N. Y. New York, The authoress, 1855.
47 p. 18½cm.
I. Title.
28–10446
Library of Congress CT275.L58A3

NL 0430914 DLC

Lobdell, W. Wayne, tr.

Streyffert, Thorsten, 1892–
The forests of Sweden, by Th. Streyffert. Stockholm, Printed by A. Bonniers boktryckeri, 1938.

Lobdzan Dandzin
see **bLo-bzań bsTan-'jin,** *fl.* 1650–1735.

Lobe, *ed.*
... Die preussische jagdgesetzgebung, eingeleitet von dr. Lobe ... Halle/S., Berlin, Buchhandlung des Waisenhauses gmbh., 1933.
8, cii, 82 p. 16½cm. (Die preussische landesgesetzgebung ... 9)
1. Game-laws—Prussia. 2. Fishery law and legislation—Prussia. I. Prussia. Laws, statutes, etc. II. Title.
34–12215

NL 0430917 DLC

4K 1243 Lobe, Adolf, 1860–
Die allgemeinen strafrechtlichen Begriffe nach Carpzov. Leipzig, Veit, 1894.
64 p.
(Ausgewählte Doktordissertationen der Leipziger Juristenfakultät)

NL 0430918 DLC-P4 MH-L

LOBE Adolf.
Die bekämpfung des unlauteren wettbewerbs. Leipzig, 1897.
4 vols.
Contents:-L.Der unlautere wettbewerb als rechtsverletzung nach dem bürgerlichen gesetzbuch und den enbengesetzen. 2.not received. 3.Materialien des gesetzes vom 27 mai 1896. 4.Gesetze verordnungen und verträge des Deutschen Reichs und der [bun]destaaten zum schutze gewerblicher tätig- keit.

NL 0430919 MH-L

Lobe, Adolf, 1860–
Die bekämpfung des unlauteren wettbewerbs, von dr. Adolf Lobe ... Leipzig, Dieterich, 1907.
3 v. 24cm.
Vol. 2 not likely to be published.
CONTENTS.—I. bd. Der unlautere wettbewerb als rechtsverletzung nach dem Bürgerlichen gesetzbuch und den nebengesetzen.—III. bd. Materialien des gesetzes zur bekämpfung des unlauteren wettbewerbes vom 27. mai 1896.—IV. bd. Gesetze, verordnungen, und verträge des Deutschen Reichs und der bundesstaaten zum schutze gewerblicher tätigkeit.
1. Competition, Unfair. 2. Industrial laws and legislation—Germany. 3. Commercial law—Germany. I. Germany. Laws, statutes, etc. II. Title.
[Full name: Karl Adolf Lobe]
8–11449 Revised 2
Library of Congress HD3626.G3L7

NL 0430920 DLC ICU CtY ICJ

Lobe, Adolf, 1860–

Germany. *Laws, statutes, etc.*
Das Bürgerliche gesetzbuch mit besonderer berücksichtigung der rechtsprechung des Reichsgerichts, erläutert von dr. Bessau, dr. Hallamik, dr. Lobe, Michaelis, dr. Oegg, Sayn, Schliewen und Seyffarth, reichsgerichtsräten und senatspräsidenten am Reichsgericht. 8., wesentlich umgearb. aufl. ... Berlin und Leipzig, W. de Gruyter & co., 1934–

Lobe, Adolf, 1860– *ed.*
... Bundesratsverordnung gegen preistreiberei vom 8. mai 1918, erläutert von dr. Adolf Lobe ... Als anhang: Begründung, ausführungsvorschriften der wichtigsten bundesstaaten, einschlagende andere verordnungen des Bundesrats und des reichskanzlers. Berlin, J. Guttentag, 1918.
2 p. l., [7]–308 p. 15½cm. (Guttentagsche sammlung deutscher reichsgesetze. nr. 133)
"Schrifttum": p. [298]–301.
I. Germany. Bundesrat. II. Germany. Laws, statutes, etc., 1888–1918 (William II)
[Full name: Karl Adolf Lobe]
21–3141

NL 0430922 DLC

LOBE,Adolf.
Das deutsche recht. Leipzig,Wien,1898.
4°. Ill.

NL 0430923 MH-L

Lobe, Adolf, 1860–

Meyer, Hans Heinrich Joseph, 1858–1929, *ed.*
Das deutsche volkstum. Unter mitarbeit von dr. Hans Helmolt [u. a.] ... hrsg. von dr. Hans Meyer. Mit 30 tafeln in farbendruck, holzschnitt und kupferätzung. Leipzig und Wien, Bibliographisches institut, 1898.

LOBE,Adolf.
Entwurf eines wahlgesetzes für die zweite kammer des sächsischen landtags. [Leipzig], n.d.
4°. 11 p.

NL 0430925 MH-L

Lobe, Adolf, 1860–
Die form der rechtsgeschäfte nebst einem verzeichnis der formbedürftigen rechtsgeschäfte. Zu jedermanns unterrichtung dargestellt von dr. Adolf Lobe ... Leipzig, T. Weicher, 1901.
42 p. 21.5 cm.

NL 0430926 CtY-L

Lobe, Adolf, 1860–
Fünfzig jahre Reichsgericht am 1. oktober 1929, von dr. Adolf Lobe ... unter mitarbeit von mitgliedern und beamten des Reichsgerichts, der reichsanwaltschaft und der rechtsanwaltschaft am Reichsgericht, mit 14 bildnissen und 15 abbildungen. Berlin und Leipzig, W. de Gruyter & co., 1929.
2 p. l., [vii]–viii, 436 p. 15 pl., 14 port. 26½cm.
"Die vorliegende schrift ist eine privatarbeit und hat keinen irgendwie amtlichen charakter ..."—Vorwort.
1. Germany. Reichsgericht. 2. Judges—Germany. 3. Lawyers—Germany. I. Title.
[Full name: Karl Adolf Lobe]
32–35078

NL 0430927 DLC CtY

LOBE,Adolf,1860–
Die Gesetzgebung des Reiches und der Länder zum Schutze der Republik. Berlin,O.Liebmann, 1922.
20 cm.

NL 0430928 MH

Lobe, Adolf, 1860–
Neue deutsche rechtssprichwörter für jedermann aus dem volke, von Dr. Adolf Lobe. Leipzig, Dieterich'sche verlagsbuchhandlung (T. Weicher) 1902.
147 p. 18½cm.
"1.-5. tausend."
Pages 142-147, advertising matter.
1. Proverbs, German.

NL 0430929 MiU NcU OCl

4K 10433 Lobe, Adolf, 1860–
Plaudereien über das neue Recht. Leipzig, F. W. Grunow, 1900.
803 p.

NL 0430930 DLC-P4 MH-L

Lobe, Adolf, 1860– joint ed.

FOR OTHER EDITIONS SEE MAIN ENTRY

Germany. *Laws, statutes, etc.*
Reichs-strafgesetzbuch nach seinen abänderungen durch die neueste gesetzgebung; Leipziger kommentar von dr. dr. Ludwig Ebermayer ... dr. Adolf Lobe ... und dr. Werner Rosenberg ... 5., verm. und verb. aufl. ... Berlin und Leipzig, W. de Gruyter, 1933–

VOLUME 337

LOBE, Adolf.
Über den einfluss des bürgerlichen gesetzbuches auf das strafrecht, unter besonderer berücksichtigung des besitzes. Leipzig, 1898.

46 p.

NL 0430932 MH-L

Lobe, Adolf, 1860-
Übermässiger gewinn im sinne von §5 nr. 1 der bundesratsverordnung vom 23. juli 1915/23. märz 1916. Zur aufklärung für verbraucher, gewerbetreibende und behörden, von dr. Adolf Lobe ... Leipzig, T. Weicher, 1916.
32 p.l., 23.5 cm.

NL 0430933 CtY-L

Lobe, Adolf, 1860- *ed.*
Die untersuchungshaft; kommentar zum IX. abschnitt des 1. buches der Strafprozessordnung in der fassung vom 27. dezember 1926, von dr. Adolf Lobe ... ₍und₎ dr. Max Alsberg ... Berlin, C. Heymann, 1927.
vii, 95 p. 22½cm.
Bibliography: p. ₍vi₎-vii.

1. Arrest—Germany. 2. Criminal law—Germany. 3. Criminal procedure—Germany. I. Alsberg, Max, 1877- joint ed. II. Germany. Laws, statutes, etc. III. Title.

32-15283

NL 0430934 DLC MH-L PU-L

4K Ger. 1644 Lobe, Adolf, 1860-
Ursprung und Entwickelung der höchsten sächsischen Gerichte; ein Beitrag zur Geschichte der sächsischen Rechtspflege. Leipzig, Dieterich, 1905.
139 p.

NL 0430935 DLC-P4

Lobe, Adolf, 1860-
Was verlangen wir von einem bürgerlichen Gesetzbuch? Ein Wort an den Reichstag von Dr. Adolf Lobe ... Leipzig, F. W. Grunow, 1896.
48 p. 19cm.

NL 0430936 MH-L

Lobé, Charles.
Quelques mots aux habitants de Curaçao, sur leur agriculture, et sur la manière de l'améliorer. Par C. Lobé ... Amsterdam ₍Impr. de C. A. Spin₎ 1839.
16 p. 27cm.

1. Agriculture—Curaçao. I. Title.

29-875

Library of Congress S517.C98L6

NL 0430937 DLC

HJ1201 .K83 Lobé, Charles.
Quelques considérations sur la situation financiere, politique, commerciale de la Neerlande en mars de 1843. Amsterdam, F. Canongette, 1843.
32 p. ₍With Korte opmerkingen over de gebeurtenissen van den dag. 1848₎

NL 0430938 ICU

Lobe, Felicitas, 1906-
... Zur Pathologie der pigmentarmen "weissen" Melanome ... Breslau, 1935.
Inaug.-Diss. - Breslau.
Lebenslauf.
"Literaturverzeichnis": p. [19]

NL 0430939 CtY MiU

Lobé, Guillermo, d.1883.
Cartas á mis hijos, durante un viaje á los Estados Unidos, Francia é Inglaterra; en los siete últimos meses de 1837. Por G. Lobé ... Nueva-York, Imprenta de don Juan de la Granja, 1839.
272 p., 1 l. 19 x 11cm.

1. Voyages and travels.

NL 0430940 MiU ICU NN MH

Lobé, Guillermo, *d.* 1883.
Cuba et les grandes puissances occidentales de l'Europe; ou, Identité qui existe entre les intérêts et l'importance actuels et futurs de l'île de Cuba, à l'égard du Nouveau monde, et en particulier des États-Unis de l'Amérique Septentrionale, collection de brochures et de lettres adressées à Madrid sur ces objets vitaux, par M. le chevalier Guillaume Lobé ... Paris, E. Dentu, 1856.
2 p. l., 220 p. 22cm.

1. Cuban question—To 1895. 2. Cuba—Pol. & govt.—1810-1899.

Library of Congress F1783.L84 12—5620

NL 0430941 DLC NIC CtY NcD ICU

Lobé, Guillermo, d. 1883.
Divorce imminent de la confédération nord-américaine. Amsterdam, Lvan Bakkenes, 1850.
46 p. 8°.
In: *C.p. 1212.

NL 0430942 NN

Lobé, Guillermo, d.1883.
Guide aux droits civils et commerciaux des étrangers en Espagne, ou, Recueil chronologique des traités, pactes, conventions et autres actes royaux et des Cortès, emanés du cabinet de Madrid, depuis le commencement du XVIIe siècle jusqu'à la fin du mois octobre 1819, par m. Guillaume Lobé ... Paris, Rodriguez, 1821.
vi, 499 p. 20½cm.
Book-plate of Manuel Gonzalez Salmon.

NL 0430943 MiU-L MH CtY

LOBÉ, Guillermo, d. 1883.
Guide aux droits civils et commerciaux des étrangers en Espagne ou recueil chronologique des traités, pactes, conventions et autres actes royaux et des cortès. 2de éd. Paris, 1837.

NL 0430944 MH-L DLC

LOBE, H.
Die Werthschätzung von Bergwerks-Unternehmungen.
(In Hoefer, Hans. Taschenbuch für Bergmänner. Pp. 521-534. Leoben, 1897.)

NL 0430945 MB

W 4 L68 v. 52 no. 7 LOBÉ, Janus
Specimen medicum inaugurale de enteritide ... Lugduni Batavorum, Apud Joannem Bos, 1775.
61 p. 24 cm.
Diss. - Leyden.

NL 0430946 DNLM

Lobe, Joannes Petrus.
De diversa lapidum origine. Lugd Bat., S. Luchtmans et fil., 1742
see his Dissertatio philosophica inauguralis de diversa lapidum origine.

Lobé, Joannes Petrus.
De oculo humano
see also his Dissertatio medica inauguralis de oculo humano.

W 4 L68 1742 L.3 LOBÉ, Joannes Petrus
Dissertatio medica inauguralis, de oculo humano ... Lugduni Batavorum, Apud Samuelem Luchtmans & Filium, 1742.
53 p. 23 cm.
Diss. - Leyden.

NL 0430949 DNLM InU PPC

W 4 L68 v.20 no.2 LOBÉ, Joannes Petrus
Dissertatio philosophica inauguralis. de diversa lapidum origine ... Lugduni Batavorum, Apud Samuelem Luchtmans & Filium, 1742.
29 p. 24 cm.
Diss. - Leyden.

NL 0430950 DNLM

Lobe, Johann Christian, 1797-1881, ed.

Allgemeine musikalische zeitung ... 1.-50. jahrg., oct. 1798-1848; neue folge 1.-3. jahrg., 1863-65; ₍3. folge₎ 1.-17. jahrg 1866-82. Leipzig, Breitkopf und Härtel; ₍etc., etc., 1798₎-1882.

Lobe, Johann Christian, 1797-1881.
Aus dem leben eines musikers. Von J. C. Lobe. Leipzig J. J. Weber, 1859.
xvi, 262 p., 1 l. 17cm.
"Felix Mendelssohn Bartholdy. Eine biographische skizze": p. ₍200₎-237.

1. Musicians—Correspondence, reminiscences, etc. 2. *Mendelssohn-Bartholdy, Felix, 1809-1847.

6-5770

Library of Congress ML410.L79L7

NL 0430952 DLC WU ICN PPPL

Lobe, Johann Christian, 1797-1881.
Le bréviaire du musicien; manuel général de musique par demandes et par réponses à l'usage des professeurs, des élèves et des amateurs. Adaptation française du "Katechismus der musik" de J. Lobe par Gustave Sandré. 13. éd. Paris, Costallat, 1913.
160 p. illus. (music) 17½ cm.
1. Music-Manuals, text-books, etc. I. Sandré, Gustave, 1843-1916, tr. & ed.

NL 0430953 NjP

VOLUME 337

Lobe, Johann Christian, 1797–1881.
Catechism of composition, by J. C. Lobe. Tr. by Fanny Raymond Ritter ... New-York, J. Schuberth & co.; [etc., etc., °1868]
vii, 183 p. 17½cm.

1. Composition (Music) I. Ritter, Mrs. Frances Malone (Raymond) 1830–1890, tr.
7–40489†
Library of Congress MT40.L78

NL 0430954 DLC PU-FA OCl OO

Lobe, Johann Christian, 1797–1881.
... Catechism of composition, by J. C. Lobe. Tr. by Fanny Raymond Ritter. Rev. and ed. by Dr. Theod. Baker. [2d and rev. ed.] New York, G. Schirmer, °1891.
vii, 200 p. 18½ cm.

1. Composition (Music) I. Ritter, Frances Malone (Raymond) 1830–1890, tr. II. Baker, Theodore, 1851–1934, ed.
7—40490
Library of Congress MT40.L782

NL 0430955 DLC CaBVaU NcGU CLU IEN

Lobe, Johann Christian, 1797–1881.
Catechism of music, by J. C. Lobe. Tr. by Fanny Raymond Ritter. New York, J. Schuberth & co.; [etc., etc., °1867]
vii, 126 p. 16½cm.

1. Music—Manuals, text-books, etc. I. Ritter, Mrs. Frances Malone (Raymond) 1830–1890, tr.
Library of Congress MT7.L82R5
7—

NL 0430956 DLC CtHT-W MB

Lobe, Johann Christian, 1797–1881.
Catechism of music, by J. C. Lobe. Tr. by Fanny Raymond Ritter. Philadelphia, F. A. North & co. [1876?]
130 p. 16cm.

1. Music—Manuals, text-books, etc. I. Ritter, Mrs. Frances Malone (Raymond) 1830–1890, tr. II. Title.
16–24470
Library of Congress MT7.L83R6

NL 0430957 DLC NBuG ICRL CoU NcU OO ViU

Lobe, Johann Christian, 1797 - 1881.
Catechism of music, by J.C.Lobe. Translated by Fanny Raymond Ritter. Boston, O. Ditson company; New York, C.H.Ditson & co. [etc.1880.]
130p. illus.(music) 17cm.

1.Music - Manuals, textbooks. etc.
I. Ritter, Mrs. Frances Malone (Raymond) 1830 - 1890. tr.

NL 0430958 KAS

MT7 L7972 1881
Lobe, Johann Christian, 1797-1881.
Catechism of music. Translated by Fanny Raymond Ritter. New and improved ed. edited and rev from the 20th German ed. by Th.Baker. New York G.Schirmer [c1881]
xvi,137 p. illus.,music. 18cm.

1.Music - Manuals, text-books, etc. I.Title.

NL 0430959 CSt OCl

V 5 .517
LOBE, JOHANN CHRISTIAN, 1797-1881.
...Catechism of music... Translated and edited by Constance Bache. London,Augener[1886]
144p. (Augener & co.'s edition, no.9178)

NL 0430960 ICN

Lobe, Johann Christian, 1797 - 1881.
Catechism of music, by J.C.Lobe. Translated and edited by Constance Bache. London, Augener & Co. [1890.]
iv,144p. illus.(music) 18½cm.

1. Music - Manuals, Textbooks, etc.
I. Bache, Constance, tr.

NL 0430961 KAS

Lobe, Johann Christian, 1797–1881.
...Catechism of music, by J. C. Lobe. Translated by Fanny Raymond Ritter. Edited and revised from the 20th German ed. by J. H. Cornell. New York: G. Schirmer, 1896. xvi, 136 p. New and improved ed. 12°.

91542A. 1. Music.—Instruction and study. 2. Ritter, Frances Malone (Raymond), 1830–90, translator. 3. Cornell, John Henry, 1828–94, editor.
N. Y. P. L. June 26, 1923.

NL 0430962 NN

Lobe, Johann Christian, 1797 - 1881.
... Catechism of music, by J. C. Lobe. Translated by Fanny Raymond Ritter, Edited and rev. from the 20th German ed. by J.H. Cornell. New York, G.Schirmer, 1906.
xvi,136p. illus.(music) 18½cm.

" New and improved edition."
Copy 2, 1909

NL 0430963 KAS

MT40 L55 Music Library
Lobe, Johann Christian, 1797-1881.
Compositions-Lehre oder umfassende Theorie von der thematischen Arbeit und den modernen Instrumentalformen, aus den Werken der besten Meister entwickelt und durch die mannichfaltigsten Beispiele erklärt. Von J.C. Lobe. Weimar, B.F. Voigt, 1844.
2 v.in 1. music.

1. Composition (Music) I. Title.

NL 0430964 CU ICN MB

Lobe, Johann Christian, 1797–1881.
Consonanzen und dissonanzen. Gesammelte schriften aus älterer und neuerer zeit von J. C. Lobe ... Leipzig, Baumgärtner's buchhandlung, 1869.
vi, 463, [1] p. 21cm.

1. Music—Addresses, essays, lectures. I. Title.
5—10243
Library of Congress ML60.L79

NL 0430965 DLC CLU

VM 1503 L 805f
LOBE, JOHANN CHRISTIAN, 1797-1881.
[Die Flibustier, arr.] I filibustii, opera in tre atti. Die Flibustier, Oper in drey Aufzügen. Dichtung von E.Gehe. Musik von J.C. Lobe. Klavierauszug mit deutschem und ital. Texte. Leipzig, Breitkopf & Härtel[1830?]
score(139p.) 25x33cm.

Label of Riegel und Wiessner, Nürnberg, mounted on cover.

NL 0430966 ICN MB

[**Lobe, Johann Christian**] 1797–1881.
Fliegende blätter für musik. Wahrheit über tonkunst und tonkünstler. Von dem verfasser der "Musikalischen briefe" ... Leipzig, Baumgärtner's buchhandlung, 1855–57.
3 v. 23cm.
Issued in 18 pts., 1853–57, v. 1–2 in 8 pts. each, v. 3 in 2 pts.
No more published.

1. Music—Period. I. Title.
5—20217
Library of Congress ML5.F62

NL 0430967 DLC MH NN NcU

VM 1503 L 805für
LOBE, JOHANN CHRISTIAN, 1797-1881.
[Die Fürstin von Grenada. Piano-vocal score. German] Die Fürstin von Grenada oder Der Zauberblick. Grosse Zauberoper mit Tanz, Pantomime und Tableaux in fünf Aufzügen. Musik von J.C.Lobe. Vollständiger Clavier Auszug von Ch: Rummel. Paris,B.Schott[1833?]
score(190p.)

Text: 11p. preceding score.

NL 0430968 ICN MB

ML80 .G5E2
Lobe, Johann Christian, 1797-1881.

Bode, Wilhelm, 1862–1922, *ed.*
Goethes schauspieler und musiker; erinnerungen von Eberwein und Lobe, mit ergänzungen von dr. Wilhelm Bode. Mit acht bildnissen. Berlin, E. S. Mittler und sohn, 1912.

Lobe, Johann Christian, 1797–1881.
Handbuch der musik, von J. C. Lobe. 30. aufl., durchgesehen von Richard Hofmann. Leipzig, J. J. Weber, 1918.
viii, 184 p. illus. (music) 17½cm.
First published (1851) under title: Katechismus der musik.

1. Music—Manuals, text-books, etc. I. Hofmann, Richard, 1844–1918, ed. II. Title.
32-19100
Library of Congress MT6.L83
[2] 780.2

NL 0430970 DLC WaU

Lobe, Johann Christian, 1797–1881.
Katechismus der Compositionslehre. 2., durchgesehene Aufl. Leipzig, J. J. Weber, 1871.
x, 194 p. music. 18 cm. (Illustrirte Katechismen, Nr. 50)

1. Composition (Music) (Series)
MT40.L783 1871 49-40734*

NL 0430971 DLC NIC NN

LOBE, JOHANN CHRISTIAN, 1797-1881.
Katechismus der Compositionslehre. 2., durchgesehene Aufl. Leipzig, J. J. Weber, 1871.
x, 194 p. music. 17cm.
Microfiche (neg.) 5 sheets. 11 x 15cm. (NYPL FSN 10, 981)

1. Composition, 1800-1900. (In German). 2. Composition. (Music).

NL 0430972 NN

VOLUME 337

Lobe, Johann Christian, 1797-1881.
Katechismus der compositionslehre. Von J. C. Lobe. 3. verb. aufl. Leipzig, J. J. Weber, 1876.
x, 194 p. illus. (music) 18 cm.
1. (Composition) Music.

NL 0430973 CU

Lobe, Johann Christian, 1797-1881
Katechismus der Compositionslehre. 4., verb.Aufl. Leipzig, Weber, 1882
194 p. (Webers illustrierte Katechismen)

NL 0430974 MH

Lobe, Johann Christian, 1797-1881.
Katechismus der Kompositionslehre. 7. verm. und verb. Aufl. von Richard Hofmann. Leipzig, J. J. Weber, 1902.
310 p. illus. 18 cm.

1. Composition (Music)

MT40.L783 1902 62-55018 ‡

NL 0430975 DLC OC1

Lobe, Johann Christian, 1797-1881.
Katechismus der kompositionslehre, von J. C. Lobe; durchgesehen und neu bearb. von professor dr. Otto Klauwell. [7. aufl.] Leipzig, Breitkopf & Härtel, 1914.
vii, 204 p. 20cm. (On cover: Breitkopf & Härtels musikbücher)

1. Composition (Music) I. Klauwell, Otto, 1851- ed.

Library of Congress MT40.L783 14-12970

NL 0430976 DLC

Lobe, Johann Christian.
Katechismus der Musik. 7. Auflage.
= Leipzig. Weber. 1864. viii, 144 pp. Diagrams. [Illustrierte Katechismen. No. 4.] 16°.

E2419 — Music. Instruction books. — S.r.

NL 0430977 MB

Lobe, Johann Christian, 1797-1881.
Katechismus der Musik. 13. Aufl. Leipzig, J. J. Weber, 1871.
viii, 144 p. music. 18 cm. (Illustrirte Katechismen, Nr. 4)

1. Music—Manuals, text-books, etc. (Series)

MT7.L83 1871 49-40812*

NL 0430978 DLC MH

Lobe, J[ohann] C[hristian], 1797, 1881.
Katechismus der Musik. 14. ed. Leipzig, J.J. Weber, 1872.
viii, 144 p. 16°.

NL 0430979 NN MB

LOBE, JOHANN CHRISTIAN, 1797-1881.
Katechismus der Musik. 14. Aufl. Leipzig, J. J. Weber, 1872. viii, 144 p. music. 17cm.

Microfiche (neg.) 4 sheets. 11 x 15cm. (NYPL FSN 10, 979)

1. Theory, 1851-1900. 2. Questions and answers (In German) 3. Music--Theory, 1851-1900. 4. Music-- Examinations, questions, etc.

NL 0430980 NN

Lobe, Johann Christian, 1797-1881.
Katechismus der musik. Von J.C. Lobe. 16. aufl. Leipzig, J.J. Weber, 1875.
viii, 144 p. illus. (music) 18 cm.
1. Music - Manuals, text-books, etc.

NL 0430981 CU

Lobe, Johann Christian, 1797-1881.
Katechismus der musik. Von J. C. Lobe. 17. aufl. Leipzig, J. J. Weber, 1876.
viii, 144 p. illus. (music) 17½cm.

1. Music—Manuals, text-books, etc. I. Title.

33-29062

Library of Congress MT7.L83 1876 781.2

NL 0430982 DLC

Lobe, J[ohann] C[hristian].
Katechismus der Musik. Leipzig: J. J. Weber, 1878. viii, 144 p. 19. ed. 16°.

1. Music.—Methods.
N. Y. P. L. September 15, 1913.

NL 0430983 NN

Lobe, Johann Christian, 1797-1881.
Katechismus der musik. 24. aufl. Leipzig, J. J. Weber, 1889.
viii, 144 p. illus. (music)

1. Music - Manuals, text-books, etc.

NL 0430984 NNC

LOBE, J[ohann] C[hristian], 1797-1881.
Katechismus der musik. Neue, von Franz Eschweiler verbesserte aufl. Köln a.Rh., P.J.Toner, [191-].

p.viii, 134.
At head of cover-title:-Tonger's musikbücherei, 1.

NL 0430985 MH

Lobe, Johann Christian, 1797-1881.
Katechismus der Musik. Von J. C. Lobe. Neue, von Franz Eschweiler verbesserte Auflage. Köln a. Rh.: P. J. Tonger [1912]. 2 p.l., [vii-]viii, 134 p. diagrs., illus. (music.) 12°. (Tonger's Musikbücherei. Bd. 1.)

1. Music.—Instruction and study. 2. Eschweiler, Franz, editor. 3. Title.
N. Y. P. L November 3, 1920.

NL 0430986 NN

Lobe, Johann Christian, 1797-1881.
Katechismus der musik, von J. C. Lobe, durchgesehen und neu bearb. von dr. Hugo Leichtentritt. Leipzig, Breitkopf & Härtel, 1913.
viii, 156 p. 20cm. (On cover: Breitkopf & Härtels musikbücher)
p. [144]-156, advertising matter.
"Literaturverzeichnis": p. [vii]-viii.

1. Music—Manuals, text-books, etc. I. Leichtentritt, Hugo, 1874- ed.
Library of Congress MT7.L83L4 14-4761

NL 0430987 DLC

LOBE, JOHANN CHRISTIAN, 1797-1881.
Katechismus der Musik; als Neubearbeitung und Erweiterung des gleichnamigen Werkes von J.C. Lobe hrsg. von Werner Neumann. Leipzig, Breitkopf & Härtel, 1949. viii, 128 p. music. 19cm.

Bibliography, p. vii-viii.

1. Music--Examinations, questions, etc. 2. Questions and answers (In German). I. Neumann, Werner, ed. II. Title.

NL 0430988 NN

Lobe, Johann Christian, 1797-1881.
Katechismus der Musik, als Neubearbeitung und Erweiterung des gleichnamigen Werkes von J. C. Lobe, hrsg. von Werner Neumann. Leipzig, Breitkopf & Härtel, 1949 [i. e. 1950]
128 p. music. 19 cm.

1. Music—Manuals, text-books, etc. I. Neumann, Werner, ed.

MT7.L83 1950 781 51-17471

NL 0430989 DLC

Lobe, Johann Christian, 1797-1881.
Katechismus der Musik; als Neubearbeitung und Erweiterung des gleichnamigen Werkes von J. C. Lobe, hrsg. von Werner Neumann. 3. Aufl. Leipzig, Breitkopf & Härtel, 1953 [°1950]
128 p. illus. 19 cm.

1. Music—Manuals, text-books, etc. I. Neumann, Werner, ed.

MT7.L83 1953 54-27549 ‡

NL 0430990 DLC

MT 40 L79

Lobe, Johann Christian, 1797-1881.
Lehrbuch der musikalischen Komposition. Leipzig, Breitkopf und Härtel, 185/-
v. 23cm.

Contents.--

2. Bd. Die Lehre von der Instrumentation. 1855.--

4. Bd. Die Oper. 2. Aufl., neu bearb. von Hermann Kretzschmar. 1887.

NL 0430992 NIC MB

VOLUME 337

Lobe, Johann Christian, 1797–1881.
Lehrbuch der musikalischen komposition, von J. C. Lobe ... Leipzig, Breitkopf und Härtel, 1858–67.
4 v. illus. (music) 23cm.
CONTENTS.—1. bd. Von den ersten elementen der harmonielehre an bis zur vollständigen komposition des streichquartetts und aller arten von klavierwerken. 2. verb. aufl. 1858.—2. bd. Die lehre von der instrumentation. 2. verb. aufl. 1864.—3. bd. Lehre von der fuge, dem kanon und dem doppelten kontrapunkte, in neuer und einfacher darstellung mit besonderer rücksicht auf selbstunterricht. 1860.—4. bd. Die oper. 1867.
1. Composition (Music)
Library of Congress MT40.L786 8–27858

NL 0430993 DLC NcD NN

Lobe, Johann Christian, 1797–1881.
Lehrbuch der musikalischen komposition, von J. C. Lobe ... Leipzig, Breitkopf und Härtel, 1860–67
cv.1, 1866,
4v. music. 23cm.
CONTENTS.—1. bd. Von den ersten elementen der harmonielehre an bis zur vollständigen komposition des streichquartetts und aller arten von klavierwerken. 2 verb. aufl. 1866—2. bd. Die lehre von der instrumentation. 2. verb. aufl. 1864.—3. bd. Lehre von der fuge, dem kanon und dem doppelten kontrapunkte, in neuer und einfacher darstellung mit besonderer rücksicht auf selbstunterricht. 1860.—4. bd. Die oper. 1867.

NL 0430994 IU NjP CtY NN

MT 40 L79 1900
Lobe, Johann Christian, 1797–1881.
Lehrbuch der musikalischen Komposition. Leipzig, Breitkopf & Härtel ,1864–1900;
v.1, 1900,
4 v. music. 23cm.
Contents.-- 1. Bd. Von den ersten Elementen der Harmonielehre an bis zur vollständigen Komposition des Streichquartetts und aller Arten von Klavierwerken. 6. Aufl., neu bearb. von Hermann Kretzschmar.-- 2. Bd. Die Lehre von der Instrumentation. 2. verb. Aufl. 1864.-- 3. Bd. Lehre von der Fuge, dem Kanon und dem doppelten Kontrapunkte in neuer und einfacher Darstellung mit besonderer Rücksicht auf Selbstunterricht. 2. Aufl. 1875.-- 4. Bd. Die Oper. 2. Aufl., neu bearb. von Hermann Kretzschmarr. 1887.
1. Composition (Music) I. Kretzschmar, Hermann, 1848-1924.

NL 0430997 NIC NN MH PP

MT 40 L792 1866
Lobe, Johann Christian, 1797-1881
Lehrbuch der musikalischen Komposition. 3., verb. Aufl. Leipzig, Breitkopf und Härtel, 1866.
4v. illus. (music) 23cm.
1. Composition (Music) I. Title

NL 0430998 WU

Lobe, Johann Christian, 1897-1881.
Lehrbuch der musikalischen komposition, ... Leipzig, Breitkopf & Härtel, 1867-78.
4 v.

NL 0430999 MiU OCl

Lobe, Johann Christian, 1797–1881.
Lehrbuch der musikalischen komposition, von J. C. Lobe ... Leipzig, Breitkopf & Härtel, 1875–1900.
4 v. 22cm.
CONTENTS.- 1. bd. Von den ersten elementen der harmonielehre an bis zur vollständigen komposition des streichquartetts und aller arten von klavierwerken. 6. aufl. neu bearb. von Hermann Kretzschmar. 1900.— 2. bd. Die lehre von der instrumentation. 3. aufl. 1878.—3. bd. Lehre von der fuge, dem kanon und dem doppelten kontrapunkte, in neuer und einfacher darstellung mit besonderer rücksicht auf selbstunterricht. 2. aufl. 1875.—4. bd. Die oper. 2. aufl. neu bearb. von Hermann Kretzschmar. 1887.
1. Composition (Music) I. *Kretzschmar, Hermann, 1848–1924 ed.
Library of Congress MT40.L792 4—9018

NL 0431000 DLC MH OrU CLU FMU OO

LOBE, JOHANN CHRISTIAN, 1797-1881.
Manuel général de musique par demandes et par réponses à l'usage de professeurs, des élèves et des amateurs. Adaptation française du "Katechismus der Musik" (23.éd) par Gustave Sandré. 9.éd. Leipzig, Breitkopf & Härtel, 1910. vi, 160 p. music. 18cm.
1. Music--Instruction and study. 2. Music--Examinations, questions, etc. 3. Instruction and study. 4. Questions and answers (In French). I. Sandré, Gustave, 1843-1916, tr.

NL 0431001 NN

,Lobe, Johann Christian, 1797–1881.
Musikalische briefe. Wahrheit über tonkunst und tonkünstler. Von einem wohlbekannten ... Leipzig, Baumgärtner, 1852.
2 v. in 1. 16cm.
1. Music—Addresses, essays, lectures. I. Title.
Library of Congress ML60.L523 10—9361

NL 0431002 DLC WU CSt CtY

ML60 L6 1860
Lobe, Johann Christian, 1797-1881.
Musikalische briefe. Wahrheit über Tonkunst und Tonkünstler. 2. Aufl. Von einem Wohlbekannten. Leipzig, Baumgärtner, 1860.
283 p. 20cm.
1. Music - Addresses, essays, lectures. I. Title.

NL 0431003 GU MH CU PPL

Lobe, Johann Christian, 1797-1881, tr.
Berlioz, Hector, 1803–1869.
Musikalische reise in Deutschland. In briefen an seine freunde in Paris von Hector Berlioz. Aus dem französischen. Leipzig, Friedlein und Hirsch, 1843.

Lobe, J,ohann, C,hristian, 1797–1881.
A new catechism of music on the plan of J. C. Lobe; ed. and comp. by Oscar Coon. Newly improved and up-to-date ed. New York, C. Fischer ,1905,
vi, 137 p. 19cm.
1. Music—Manuals, text-books, etc. I. Coon, Oscar, ed.
Library of Congress MT7.L8 Copyright 5-12268

NL 0431005 DLC PP OCl

LOBE, JOHANN CHRISTIAN, 1797-1881.
[DIE FLIBUSTIER. OVERTURE. ARR. FOR PIANO]
Ouverture de l'opéra Les flibustiers, par J.C. Lobe. Pour le piano-forte. Leipsic, Breitkopf & Härtel [ca. 1881] Pl. no. 5056. 9 p. 33 x 24cm.
1. Overtures--Arr. for piano. I. Title: Die Flibustier.

NL 0431006 NN

Lobe, Johann Christian, 1797-1881.
Quatuor pour pianoforte, violon, viola et violoncelle, composé par J.C.Lobe. Leipsic, Breitkopf & Härtel, n.d. 4 parts in portfolio. 36cm.
Publ.no. 3599.

NL 0431007 CU

LOBE, JOHANN CHRISTIAN, 1797-1881.
Reiselust. Les charmes de voyage; cinquième ouverture à grand orchestre, composée par J.C. Lobe, op. 26. Leipzig, C.A. Klemm [185-?] 15 parts. 34cm.
1. Overtures (Parts) I. Title. II. Title: Les charmes de voyage.

NL 0431008 NN

Lobe, Johann Christian, 1797–1881.
Traité pratique de composition musicale depuis les premiers éléments de l'harmonie jusqu'à la composition raisonnée du quatuor et des principales formes de la musique pour piano, par J. C. Lobe. Traduit de l'allemand (d'après la 5me édition) par Gustave Sandré... Leipzig: Breitkopf & Härtel, 1889. viii, 378 p. illus. (music.) 21½cm.
JUILLIARD FOUNDATION FUND.
687610A. 1. Composition (music). I. Sandré, Gustave, musician, translator.
N. Y. P. L. March 9, 1934

NL 0431009 NN IEN CaBVaU

Lobe, Johann Christian, 1797–1881.
Vereinfachte harmonielehre, von J. C. Lobe. I. theil: für dilettanten. II. theil: für kenner. Leipzig, C. F. W. Siegel ,1861,
viii, 215, ,1, p. 21½cm.
1. Harmony.
Library of Congress MT50.L823 10-9362

NL 0431010 DLC NN NBuG

Lobé, Juan Fontán
see Fontán Lobé, Juan, d. 1944.

Lobe, Karl Adolf.
See
Lobe, Adolf, 1860–

Lobe, Karlis, ed.
Generālis Goppers; kara un laika biedru atmiņās. Rakstu un materialu krājums Kārļa Lobes un Miķeļa Goppera red. ,Stockholm, Zelta ābele, 1951.
68 p. illus. 23 cm.
1. Goppers, Kārlis, 1876–1941. I. Goppers, Miķelis, joint ed.
DK511.L168G6 56–37464 ‡

NL 0431013 DLC MH NN

Lobe (N.B.) & Co., auctioneers.
Catalogue of a ... collection of rare antique furniture, china, cut glass, ceramics, silver, etchings, engravings, colored prints, etc. ... To be sold at public auction ... on Monday, Tuesday and Wednesday, February 13th, 14th, & 15th, 1922 ... [Baltimore, 1933]?
45 p. illus. 26 cm.
1. Furniture - Private collections. 2. Art objects - Private collections.

NL 0431014 MdBP

VOLUME 337

Lobe, Nora, 1910-
... Ein Fall von geplatztem Hydrocephalus als Versuch einer Selbstheilung bei Hydrocephalus internus permagnus ... Düsseldorf, 1938.
Inaug.-Diss. - Berlin.
Lebenslauf.

NL 0431015 CtY

Lobe, Waldemar, ed.

Delius, Hans, 1859-1932, *ed.*
Das jagdrecht in der gerichtlichen praxis; entscheidungen der ordentlichen gerichte einschl. der strafgerichte und der verwaltungsgerichte in systematischer anordnung nebst erläuterungen von dr. Hans Delius ... Berlin, F. Vahlen [1930]-

Lobé, Wilhelmus, 1765-1794.
De ventriculo
see also his Dissertatio medica inauguralis de ventriculo.

Lobé, Wilhelmus, 1765-1794.
De vi corporum electrica
see his Dissertatio philosophica inauguralis, de vi corporum electrica.

W 4 L68 1788 L.2
LOBÉ, Wilhelmus, 1765-1794
Dissertatio medica inauguralis de ventriculo, plurimorum morborum fonte ... Lugduni Batavorum, S. et J. Luchtmans et P. Pluygers, 1788.
iii p. 25 cm.
Diss. - Leyden.

NL 0431019 DNLM

W 4 L68 v.20 no.5
LOBÉ, Wilhelmus, 1765-1794
Dissertatio philosophica inauguralis, de vi corporum electrica ... Lugduni Batavorum, Apud Samuelem Luchtmans & Filium, 1743.
29 p. 24 cm
Diss. - Leyden.

NL 0431020 DNLM

Lobe, William.
Die ziegen-und kaninchenzucht. 1875.

NL 0431021 DNAL

Lobe den Herrn, meine Seele; der hundertvierte Psalm mit Holzschnitten... Berlin, 1951
see under Bible. O.T. Psalms. CIV. German. 1951. Luther.

Tr.R. Lobechius, David, praeses.

Disputationes theologicae xxx articvlorum Augustanae Confessionis ἀνάλυσιν complectentes & orthodoxam Ecclesiarum Evangelicarum doctrinam ἀντιθέσει heterodoxae illustratam explicantes. Habitae in Academia Rostochiensi. Witebergae, Wolgangus Meisnerus, 1610.
680, [34] p. 19cm.

Dissertations by 29 respondents.
Title within ornamental borders. Head-pieces. Initials.

1. Augsberg Confession.

NL 0431024 NcD

Lobeck, ———, ed.
Archiv für stenographie; monatshefte für die wissenschaftliche pflege der kurzschrift aller zeiten und länder ...
Berlin, Commissionsverlag d. Enslin'schen buchhandlung, 1862-

Lobeck, Armin Kohl, 1886-1958
Airways of America; guidebook no. 1- ... by A. K. Lobeck ... with maps and illustrations ... New York, The Geographical press, Columbia university, 1933-
v. front., illus., maps (1 fold. in pocket) diagrs. 26½cm. (James Furman Kemp memorial series. Publication no. II)
Maps on lining-papers
No. 1 "published on the occasion of the sixteenth International geological congress at Washington".
1. Airways—U. S.—Guide-books. 2. U. S.—Descr. & trav.—Guide-books. 3. Physical geography—U. S. 4. Geology—U. S. 5. U. S.—Descr. & trav.—Maps. I. Title.
Library of Congress TL726.2.L6 33—29147
——— Copy 2.
Copyright A 65287 [a38m1] 387.70973

NL 0431026 MiU OC1W NN OrP Or DSI NBuU CoU NcD PBm PU PP PWcS OU OCU OC1 DLC MB OrCS OrU WaS CaBVaU IdU-SB OrMonO

Lobeck, Armin Kohl, 1886- *comp.*
Atlas of American geology, compiled and arranged by A. K. Lobeck. New York, The Geographical press, Columbia university, 1932.
100 l. incl. illus., maps, diagrs. 29cm.
Caption title.
Printed by offset process.
"Diagrams, maps, and other illustrations selected from a wide variety of sources ... [arranged] by physiographic provinces ... of the United States."
1. Geology—U. S.—Maps. 2. Atlases. I. Title. 33-11446
Library of Congress QE77.L6
——— Copy 2.
Copyright A 52892 [3] 557.3084

NL 0431027 NcD NcRS OCU OC1W OU DLC MtBC OrU MtU IaU TxU LU DI PBm PU-W

Xs35 U2 +920
Lobeck, Armin Kohl, 1886-
Bibliography of the physiography of the United States, by A.K.Lobeck.
[N.p.,1920?] 28cm.
Mimeographed, with typewritten half titles.
Various pagination.

1.Physical geography - U.S. - Bibl.
2.Geology - U.S. - Bibl.

NL 0431028 CtY

Lobeck, Armin Kohl, 1886-
Block diagrams and other graphic methods used in geology and geography, by Armin Kohl Lobeck ... New York, J. Wiley and sons, inc.; [etc., etc.] 1924.
xi, 206 p. incl. front., illus., diagrs. 21½ x 28cm. $4.50
"References": p. 199-201.

1. Relief-maps. I. Title. 25—778
Library of Congress GA140.L6

NL 0431029 OrU OrP OrCS MtBuM CaBVaU PHC PBm TxU NcRS NcD MiU ScU NIC WaTC OrAshS MtU DLC MiHM NN ICJ OC1 OO OU OOxM PU PWcS

Lobeck, Armin Kohl, 1886-
Block diagrams and other graphic methods used in geology and Geography, by Armin Kohl Lobeck ... New York, J. Wiley and sons, inc.; [etc., etc., 1943]
xi, 206 p. incl. front., illus., diagrs. 21½ x 28cm.
"References": p. 199-201.

NL 0431030 ViU

Lobeck, Armin Kohl, 1886-

Destructional [and constructional] forms, explanations and problems based on accompanying sheet of topographic maps showing representative examples. New York, Geographic Press, Columbia University, 1943.
[8] p. incl. maps on 2 sheets. 48 x 31cm. fold. to 24 x 31cm.
Caption title.

1. Geology—Maps. I. Title.

NL 0431031 ViU

Lobeck, Armin Kohl, 1886-

Savage, Thomas Edmund, 1866-
The Devonian rocks of Kentucky; a presentation of the areal extent, stratigraphic, structural and paleontologic relationship of all sediments between the Silurian and Mississippian systems in this commonwealth, by Thomas Edmund Savage ... assisted by Russell Spurgeon Poor, Charles Fernando Bassett, Harold Bowen Willman, Harry Charles Spoor, jr. And a separate report on the Geology of the Midland trail in Kentucky, by Armin Kohl Lobeck ... Frankfort, The Kentucky geological survey, 1930.

Lobeck, Armin Kohl, 1886-

The earth in space, by A. K. Lobeck. New York, The Geographical press, Columbia university, 1929 [i. e. 1942]
6 (i. e. 8) p. incl. illus.(incl. maps, diagrs.) table. 48½ x 30½cm.
"Reprinted ... 1942."
Caption title.

1. Astronomical geography. 2. Earth. I. Title.

NL 0431033 ViU

Lobeck, Armin Kohl, 1886-
Elementary exercises in topographic and structural geology, by A.K.Lobeck. New York, The Geographical press, Columbia university, 1934.

[8]p. maps. 48x31cm.,folded to 31x25cm.

NL 0431034 MoU OrP

Lobeck, Armin Kohl, 1886-

Elementary exercises in topographic and structural geology, by A. K. Lobeck. 1934. New York, The Geographical press, Columbia university [1941]
[8] p. illus., diagrs. 48½ x 30½cm.
Caption title.
"Reprinted 1941."

1. Geology. 2. Geology, Structural. I. Title: Topographic and structural geology.

NL 0431035 ViU

Lobeck, Armin Kohl, 1886-1958.
Fisiografía de Europa; versión y adaptación por Juan Carandell. Cabra (Córdoba) M. Cordón, 1927.
86 p. fold. map (in pocket)

1. Physical geography - Europe. I. Carandell, Juan tr.

NL 0431036 NNC

VOLUME 337

Lobeck, Armin Kohl, 1886-

Geologic map of Europe, by A. K. Lobeck ... New York, The Geographical press, Columbia university, 1942.
col. map 60½ x 97cm. fold. to 48½ x 30½cm.
"Scale 1:5,000,000 One eighth inch equals 10 miles."
Text ([4] p., illus.(maps, profiles)) on verso of map.

1. Geology—Europe—Maps.

NL 0431037 ViU DI IU

GDA-caq 1941 L6 Lobeck, Armin Kohl, 1886-1958.
Geologic map of the United States, by A. K. Lobeck. / Data by United States Geological survey. New York, The Geographical press, Columbia university, 1941.
col.map. 57½x93cm.
"Scale 1:5,000,000. One-eighth inch equals 10 miles."
Text and map of the domes and basins of the United States on verso.
Inset: [Physiographic regions of the United States]

NL 0431038 IU NNC DNAL ViU

Lobeck, Armin Kohl, 1886-
Geological diorama of the United States. New York, Geographical Press, 1948.
col. map on sheet 49 x 122 cm. fold. to 25 x 31 cm.
Horizontal scale ca. 1: 5,322,000.
Perspective map in 2 pts., with descriptive text, showing a geological cross-section from New York to San Francisco.

1. Geology—U. S. 2. U. S.—Maps, Physical. I. Title.
G3700.C5 1948.L6 Map 49-124*

NL 0431039 DLC

Lobeck, Armin Kohl, 1886-
The geology and physiography of the Mammoth Cave national park, by Armin Kohl Lobeck ... Illustrated with thirty-nine photographs, maps, and diagrams. Frankfort, Ky., The Kentucky Geological survey, 1928.
7 p. l., 69 p. incl. front., illus., maps, diagrs. 22½cm. (Kentucky. Geological survey. Ser. VI. Pamphlet XXI)

1. Geology — Kentucky — Mammoth Cave. 2. Mammoth Cave, Kentucky. 3. Physical geography—Kentucky—Mammoth Cave.
G S 28-376
—— Copy 2.
Library, U. S. Geological Survey (238) K92 no. 21

OU NN
NL 0431040 DI-GS MtBuM KyHi KyBgW PHi PP OCl OCU

Lobeck, Armin Kohl, 1886-1958.
The geology of the midland trail in Kentucky. 1930. (Kentucky. Geological survey. Report. ser. 6, #33)

NL 0431041 OrU

Lobeck, Armin Kohl, 1886-
Geomorphology, an introduction to the study of landscapes, by A. K. Lobeck ... 1st ed. New York and London, McGraw-Hill book company, inc., 1939.
xii, 731 p. incl. front., illus., diagrs. 24½ cm.
Bibliography at end of each chapter.

1. Geology, Structural. 2. Physical geography. 3. Landscape. I. Title.
39—17524
Library of Congress QE501.L6 1939
[a50w⁵2] 551

OrLgE OrMonO Wa OrPS OrSaW OrStbM WaTC
MB MiU NcD WU DAS MtU OrP OrPR WaS OrCS OrAshS
OrU MtBC CaBVa CaBViP OU NcD KEmT MCM NSyU CU
PU PPD TU MB MBH PHC ICJ OCl MtBuM CaBVaU IdPI
NL 0431042 DLC NcRS MiU-C ViU OO MiHM PWcS PBm

Lobeck, Armin Kohl, 1886-

Historical geology of the United States. New York, Geographical Press, Columbia University, 1932.
11 maps. 22 x 28cm.
Maps: 1. Pre-Cambrian archeozoic and proterozoic. 2. The Cambrian period. 3. The Ordovician period. 4. The Silurian period. 5. The Devonian period. 6. The Mississippian period. 7. The Pennsylvanian period. 8. The Permian period. 9. The Triassic and Jurassic periods. 10. Cretaceous time. 11. The Cenozoic era.

1. Geology—U. S.—Maps. 2. Geology, Stratigraphic. I. Title.

NL 0431044 ViU

Lobeck, Armin Kohl, 1886-
Historical geology of the United States. Map set, rev. 1947. New York, Geographical Press, Columbia Univ. [1947]
xi l. of maps. 30 cm.
Title from maps.

1. Geology—U. S.—Maps.
Map 49-506*

NL 0431045 DLC

D550 L78 Lobeck, Armin Kohl, 1886-
History of the earth and the advent of man; a syllabus for Science B1, the third semester of a two-year course in science in Columbia college [by] A. K. Lobeck [and] Ralph L. Miller. New York, Columbia university press, 1937.
viii, 65 p. front. 23cm.

"Bibliography": p. [61]-65.

1. Earth. 2. Geology. 3. Man - Origin. I. Miller, Ralph LeRoy, 1909- , jt. au.

NL 0431046 NNC

Geology D550 L781 Lobeck, Armin Kohl, 1886-
History of the earth and the advent of man; science B1, the third semester of a two-year course in science in Columbia College, by A. K. Lobeck, assisted by Ralph L. Miller [and others] New York, Dept. of Geology, Columbia University, 1941.
xvi, 240 p. illus., maps, diagrs.

Bibliography: p. v-viii.

NL 0431047 NNC

Lobeck, Armin Kohl, 1886-
Illustrations to accompany physiographic diagram of Australia. New York, Geographical press, 1952.
[4] p. 49cm.

Bound with Gentilli, Joseph. Physiographic diagram of Australia. 1951.

NL 0431048 NNC

Lobeck, Armin Kohl, 1886-
The Midland trail in Kentucky, a physiographic and geologic guide book to U. S. highway no. 60, by Armin Kohl Lobeck ... illustrated with thirty-nine photographs, maps, and diagrams. Frankfort, Ky., Kentucky Geological survey, 1930.
viii, 82 p. incl. front., illus., maps. 23cm. (Kentucky. Geological survey. Ser. VI, pamphlet XXII)

1. Kentucky—Descr. & trav. 2. Physical geography—Kentucky. 3. Geology—Kentucky. I. Title.
44-42981
Library of Congress QE115.A3 no. 22
[2] (557.69) 557.69

NL 0431049 DLC LU CU

Lobeck, Armin Kohl, 1886-
The Midland Trail in Kentucky; a physiographic and geologic guide book to U. S. highway no. 60. By Armin Kohl Lobeck ... Illustrated with thirty-nine photographs, maps, and diagrams. Frankfort, Ky., Geological survey, 1930.
[163]-252 p. incl. front., illus., maps. 23½cm.
Published as an appendix to "Devonian rocks of Kentucky", by T. E. Savage, and forms part of Kentucky geological survey. ser. 6. [Geologic reports] v. 33.

1. Geology—Kentucky. 2. Physical geography—Kentucky. I. Title. II. Title: U. S. highway no. 60, A physiographic and geologic guide book to.
G S 30-189
Library, U. S. Geological Survey (238) K61 ser. 6, vol. 33

NL 0431050 DI-GS MtBuM OU OClW

Lobeck, Armin Kohl, 1886-
Military maps and air photographs, their use and interpretation, by A. K. Lobeck ... and Wentworth J. Tellington ... with an introduction by John K. Wright. 1st ed. New York and London, McGraw-Hill book company, inc., 1944.
x, 256 p. illus. (incl. maps) plates, diagrs. 29 x 22½cm.
Two folded maps and ruler in pocket.

1. Maps. 2. Photographic surveying. 3. Photography, Aerial. I. Tellington, Wentworth Jordan, joint author.
44-3132
Library of Congress GA151.L6
[a44o²7] 623.71

OrCS CaBVaU MtBC MtBuM
PWcS PP PHC PU PSt TxU OrU MtU WaTC DNAL IdU OrP Or
NL 0431051 DLC NcD NcRS TU MiHM OCU OCl OU OOxM PPT

Lobeck, Armin Kohl, 1886-1958.
Miscellaneous publications. [1917-54] cover-title, 13 articles in 1 v. illus., port., maps (part fold.) diagrs. (part fold.) profiles.

Includes bibliography.

1. Geology - Collected works. 2. Physical geography - Collected works.

NL 0431052 NNC

Lobeck, Armin Kohl, 1886-

Berkey, Charles Peter, 1867-
... New York city and vicinity; prepared under the direction of Charles P. Berkey ... Washington, U. S. Govt. print. off., 1933.

Lobeck, Armin Kohl, 1886-
Panorama of physiographic types, by A. K. Lobeck ... Madison, Wis., Wisconsin geographical press, 1926.
[4] p. double maps. 48½cm.

1. Physical geography. I. Title. II. Title: Physiographic types.
26-9383
Library of Congress GB401.L6

NL 0431054 DLC OrCS PU ViU

GB 401 .L6 1926 Lobeck, Armin Kohl, 1886-
Panorama of physiographic types, by A. K. Lobeck. Madison, Wis., Wisconsin geographical press, 1926.
[7] p. illus. 29 cm.

1. Physical geography. I. Title II. Title: Physiographic types.

NL 0431055 OKentU

Lobeck, Armin Kohl, 1886-
Panorama of physiographic types, by A.K. Lobeck ... [New York, Geographical press, Columbia university press] 1934, c1926.
[4] p. double maps. 48½cm.

NL 0431056 OrU

VOLUME 337

Lobeck, Armin Kohl, 1886–
Physiographic diagram of Africa, by A. K. Lobeck. New York, The Geographical press, Columbia univ., 1946. diagram. fold. 24 x 31cm.
Caption-title from verso.
Folds into 6 pages with text (on verso and rectos of map).
1. Africa—Geography, Physical. 2. Geology—Africa. 3. Africa—Maps.
N. Y. P. L. March 28, 1951

NL 0431057 NN NNC OrU ViU

Map G 7401 C2 1945 L6
Lobeck, Armin Kohl, 1886–
Physiographic diagram of Asia. New York, Geographical Press, 1945.
map 57 x 61cm.
Scale 1:20,000,000.
Text.
On verso: Physiographic provinces of Asia.
1. Asia-- Maps.

NL 0431058 NIC

Lobeck, Armin Kohl, 1886–
Physiographic diagram of Asia. By A. K. Lobeck. 1945 small scale edition. New York, The Geographic press, Columbia university, °1945.
8 p. 2 maps on fold. l. 48 x 30½cm.
Maps accompanied by explanatory text.
1. Physical geography—Asia. 2. Asia—Descr. & trav.—Maps.
G S 46-30
U. S. Geol. survey. Library for Library of Congress [2]

NL 0431059 DI-GS FU ViU

Lobeck, Armin Kohl, 1886–
Physiographic diagram of Australia. New York, Geographical Press, 1951.
map 44 x 51 cm.
Scale ca. 1: 7,500,000; 120 miles to the inch.
Issued also with "text description and geological sections which were prepared by Joseph Gentilli and R. W. Fairbridge."
Includes 8 profile diagrs., and insets: [The physiographic regions of Australia]—[Tasmania and nearby islands]
1. Australia—Maps, Physical. I. Gentilli, Joseph. Physiographic diagram of Australia. II. Geographical Press, New York. III. Title.
G8961.C2 1951.L6 Map 52-118

NL 0431060 DLC OU

---

q551 L78p
Lobeck, Armin Kohl.
Physiographic diagram of Europe. 1923. [Madison?] 1923.
[8]p. incl. double map.
Caption title.
The map (physiographic diagram) is printed on p.[2] and [7]

NL 0431061 IU

Lobeck, Armin Kohl, 1886–
Physiographic diagram of Europe. By A. K. Lobeck, University of Wisconsin. 1923. Small scale ed. Madison, Wisconsin geographical press, 1923.
[8] p. incl. map. 48 x 30 cm.
1. Physical geography—Europe. I. Title.
G S 26—195
U. S. Geol. Survey. Libr. for Library of Congress 503(500)qL78 [a48c½]

NL 0431062 DI-GS OU FU NNC

---

f912.4 923ℓ
Lobeck, Armin Kohl, 1886-
Physiographic diagram of Europe, by A. K. Lobeck. New York, The Geographical press, Columbia university [c1923]
map. 44 x 56cm.
Scale: approximately 1:9,000,000.
1. Physical geography--Europe. 2. Europe--Maps.

NL 0431063 IU

Lobeck, Armin Kohl, 1886-
Physiographic diagram of Europe, ... 1923. Small scale ed. (reprinted 1925, 1927, 1930) N.Y., Columbia university, The geographical press [1930]
8 p. incl. map. 48.5cm. x 30.5cm.
Caption title.
Folded into envelope.

NL 0431064 OO

---

map case 331 L78P
Lobeck, Armin Kohl, 1886-
Physiographic diagram of Europe, by A. K. Lobeck, 1923. Small scale edition... New York, The Geographical press, Columbia university, 1935.
8 p. incl. double map. 48cm.

NL 0431065 DNAL OCl

CAA-cbad 1944 L6
Lobeck, Armin Kohl, 1886-
Physiographic diagram of Europe, by A. K. Lobeck, 1944. Large scale ed. ... New York, The Geographical press, Columbia university, 1944.
map on 2 sheets. 152½x173½cm.
"Scale 1:2,000,000. 32 miles to one inch."
1. Europe--1944. 2. Physical geography--Europe--1944. I. Title.

NL 0431066 IU

Lobeck, Armin Kohl, 1886–
Physiographic diagram of Europe, by A. K. Lobeck. 1923. Small scale ed. ... New York, The Geographical press, Columbia university [1944]
8 p. incl. double map. 48½ x 30½cm.
Caption title.
"Reprinted ... 1944."
1. Physical geography—Europe. I. Title.

NL 0431067 ViU IU

GGB-cbad 1932 L6
Lobeck, Armin Kohl, 1886-
Physiographic diagram of Kentucky, by A. K. Lobeck. New York, The Geographical press, Columbia university [1932?]
map. 13x20cm.
No scale.
Includes cross-section.
1. Kentucky--1932? 2. Physical geography--Kentucky--1932? I. Title.

NL 0431068 IU

Lobeck, Armin Kohl, 1886–
Physiographic diagram of North America. New York, Geographical Press, Columbia Univ., 1948.
map 81 x 58 cm.
Scale ca. 1: 12,000,000.
"Based partly upon the Geological map of North America, scale 1: 5,000,000, published in 1946 by the Geological Society of America."
Insets: [The Aleutian Islands]—[The Lesser Antilles and part of Venezuela]
In lower margin: Geological section[s] across Canada ... the United States ... [and] Mexico.
On verso: Physiographic provinces of North America [same scale]—[List of] the physiographic divisions of North America.
1. North America—Maps, Physical. 2. Physical geography—North America. I. Title. II. Title: Physiographic provinces of North America.
G3300.C2 1948.L6 Map 49-67*

NL 0431069 DLC FU N NBuU

Lobeck, Armin Kohl, 1886–
Physiographic diagram of Pennsylvania. Preliminary sketch ed. New York, Geographical Press, 1951.
map on sheet 61 x 97 cm.
Scale 1: 450,000.
Includes 2 profile diagrs.
1. Pennsylvania—Maps, Physical. I. Geographical Press, New York. II. Title.
G3821.C2 1951.L6 Map 51-793

NL 0431070 DLC

GB121 f.L8 (G1)
Lobeck,A[illegible] K.
A physiographic diagram of the United States, by A.K.Lobeck,University of Wisconsin(provisional ed.)... Chicago,A.J.Nystrom & co.,1921.
fold.map. 108x82cm.
Printed on both sides.

NL 0431071 ICU

GDA-cbad 1921 L6
Lobeck, Armin Kohl, 1886-
A physiographic diagram of the United States, by A. K. Lobeck ... (Provisional ed.) Chicago, A. J. Nystrom & co.[1921]
col.map. 101½x156cm.
"Scale 1:3,000,000, approximately 50 miles to 1 inch."
Text in lower left corner.
1. United States--1921. 2. Physical geography--U.S.--1921. I. Nystrom (A. J.) & co., Chicago. II. Title.

NL 0431072 IU

Map case 331 L78 Prov.ed.
Lobeck, Armin Kohl, 1886-
A physiographic diagram of the United States, by A.K. Lobeck... (Provisional edition) Chicago, A.J. Nystrom & co., 1921.
sheet. 98x132½cm.

NL 0431073 DNAL PU

Lobeck, Armin Kohl.
Physiographic diagram of the United States, by A. K. Lobeck. Small scale ed. [Madison?] 1922.
[8] p. incl. double map. 48 x 30½cm.
The map (physiographic diagram) is printed on p. [2] and [7]
1. Physical geography—U. S. 2. Geology—U. S. I. Title.
22-1215
Library of Congress GB121.L6

NL 0431074 DLC

Lobeck, Armin Kohl, 1886-
Physiographic diagram of the United States, ... Small sacle ed. [Madison?] 1923.
[8] p.

NL 0431075 CU

VOLUME 337

Lobeck, Armin Kohl, 1886-
Physiographic diagram of the United States. Small scale edition. N.Y., Columbia university, Geographical press, 1932.
8 p. incl. double map.

Scale; about 150 miles to one inch.
Size: 14 x 22 inches.

NL 0431076 OCl

GDA-cbad 1932 L6p
Lobeck, Armin Kohl, 1886-
Physiographic diagram of the United States, by A. K. Lobeck. New York, The Geographical press, Columbia university, c1932.
map. 18½x29cm.

Scale ca.1:17,000,000 (erroneously given as "approximately 1:9,000,000 or about 150 miles to one inch")

1. United States--1932. 2. Physical geography --U.S.--1932. 3. Geology--U.S.--1932. I. Title.

NL 0431077 IU

---

map case 331 L78 1922
Lobeck, Armin Kohl, 1886-
Physiographic diagram of the United States, by A. K. Lobeck, 1922. Small scale edition... New York, The Geographical press, Columbia university, 1937.
8 p. incl. double map. 48cm.

NL 0431078 DNAL

GDA-cbad 1932 L6
Lobeck, Armin Kohl, 1886-
Physiographic diagram of the United States, by A. D. Lobeck. 1922. Small scale ed. ... New York, The Geographical press, Columbia university, 1941.
8p. incl.double map. 48x30½cm.

"Reprinted ... 1941."
The map (physiographic diagram) dated 1932, is printed on p.2 and 7.
Scale of map "approximately 1:9,000,000 or about 150 miles to one inch."

NL 0431079 IU ViU

Lobeck, Armin Kohl, 1886-

Physiographic diagram of the United States, by A. K. Lobeck. 1922. Small scale ed. ... New York, The Geographical press, Columbia university ⌊1943⌋
8 p. incl. double map. 48 x 30½cm.
Caption title.
"Reprinted ... 1943."

1. Physical geography—U. S. I. Title.

NL 0431080 ViU

Lobeck, Armin Kohl, 1886-1958.
Physiographic diagram[s] New York, Geographical Press, Columbia Univ., 1923-52.
7 pts. in portfolio. 30 cm.

NL 0431081 PBm

Lobeck, Armin Kohl, 1886-
The physiography of Porto Rico, by Armin Kohl Lobeck ... New York, New York academy of sciences, 1922.
cover-title, 1 p. l., p. 301-379. illus., fold. maps 24 cm.
Thesis (PH. D.)—Columbia university, 1917.
Vita.
One map laid in.
Published also as New York Academy of sciences. Scientific survey of Porto Rico and the Virgin Islands, v. 1, part 4.
"Contributions from the Department of geology, Columbia university, vol. XXVIII, no. 6."
Bibliography: p. 376-379.

1. Physical geography—Porto Rico. 2. Geology—Porto Rico. I. Title.

24-14178

Library of Congress GB121.L63
Columbia Univ. Libr. ⌊2⌋

NL 0431082 NNC TxDaM NIC DLC

Lobeck, Armin Kohl, 1886-

The physiography of the New York region. Text by A. K. Lobeck, map by Erwin J. Raisz, sketches by Robert L. Dickinson. 1930. New York, The Geographical press, Columbia university ⌊1944⌋
⌊4⌋, 4 p. incl. illus.(incl. profiles) map. 30½cm.
Caption title.
"Reprinted 1944."

1. Physical geography—New York (State) I. Raisz, Erwin Josephus, 1893- II. Dickinson, Robert Latou, 1861- illus. III. Title.

NL 0431083 ViU

Lobeck, Armin Kohl, 1886-

Places of the world, by A. K. Lobeck and Guy-Harold Smith. New York, The Geographical press, Columbia university, 1927 ⌊i. e. 1943⌋
7, ⌊1⌋ p. incl. maps. 48½ x 30½cm.
Caption title.
"Reprinted ... 1943."

1. Geography. I. Smith, Guy Harold, 1895- joint author. II. Title.

NL 0431084 ViU

Lobeck, Armin Kohl, 1886-

Leverett, Frank, 1859-
The Pleistocene of northern Kentucky, a regional reconnaissance study of the physical effects of glaciation within the commonwealth. By Frank Leverett, assistant geologist. Preface, by T. C. Chamberlin. Presented with four separate geological papers, by Stephen Sargent Visher, Arle H. Sutton, James ⌊!⌋ K. Roberts and Armin Kohl Lobeck. Illustrated with sixteen photographs, maps, and diagrams. Frankfort, The Kentucky Geological survey, 1929.

Lobeck, Armin Kohl, 1886-
... A popular guide to the geology and physiography of Allegany state park, by A. K. Lobeck ... Albany, The University of the state of New York, 1927.
1 p. l., 5-288 p. illus., 3 fold. maps. 19cm. (New York state museum. Handbook 1)
Bibliography: p. 277-281.

1. Allegany state park, N. Y. 2. Geology—New York (State)—Allegany state park.

27-27406

Library of Congress QE146.A4L6

PU PPAmP PPAN PBm OU OCl MiU OCU ICJ NN MB
NL 0431086 DLC OrU WaS MtBC TxU NNBG FMU OrP MtBuM

GGJ-cbad 1932 L6
Lobeck, Armin Kohl, 1886-
State of Texas, from Physiographic diagram of United States, by A. K. Lobeck New York, Geographical press, Columbia university [1932]
map. 43½x43cm.

No scale.

1. Texas--1932. 2. Physical geography--Texas --1932.

NL 0431087 IU

GB 124 N4 L79
Lobeck, Armin Kohl, 1886-
... The superb position of New York City as a center for physiographic study, by A.K.Lobeck. New York, Published by the Academy, 1918.
cover-title, 49, [1] p. illus., maps (1 fold.) diagrs. 23½ cm. (Annals of the New York Academy of sciences. Vol.xxviii, p.1-50, June 29, 1918)
Bibliography: p.37-49.

NL 0431088 MiU MWelC NN ODW

Lobeck, Armin Kohl, 1886-1958
The trade of the world, by A. K. Lobeck ... Madison, Wis., Wisconsin geographical press, 1924.
4 p. illus. (maps) 2 diagr. on fold. sheet. 48cm.
Diagrams printed on both sides of sheet.

1. Commerce. I. Title.

Library of Congress HF499.L6 CA 24-541 Unrev'd

NL 0431090 DLC

Lobeck, Arnold.
... Contribution à l'étude des facteurs accessoires du développement (auximones) ... Weida, Impr. Thomas & Hubert, 1922.
49, ⌊1⌋ p. 23cm. (Université de Genève. Institut botanique. ⌊Publications⌋ X. sér., IV. fasc.)
"Bibliographie": p. ⌊48⌋-49.
Thèse—Univ. de Genève.

1. Bacillus bulgaricus. 2. Vitamines.

Agr 23-549

Library, U. S. Dept. of Agriculture 451G282 sér. 10, fasc. 4

NL 0431091 DNAL MiU

Lobeck, Arthur, 1872-
Beitraege zur kenntnis der flores-koso.
Inaug. diss. Leipzig, 1901

NL 0431092 ICRL PU CtY

Lobeck, Christian August, 1781-1860.
Aglaophamus; sive, De theologiae mysticae Graecorum causis libri tres, scripsit Chr. Augustus Lobeck ... idemque poetarum orphicorum dispersas reliquias collegit ... Regimontii Prussorum, sumtibus fratrum Borntraeger, 1829.
2 v. 21½cm.
Paged continuously.
"Carminum orphicorum reliquiae": v. 1, p. ⌊411⌋-783.

1. Greece—Religion. 2. Mysteries, Religious. 3. Orpheus. 4. Eleusinian mysteries. I. Title.

31-31309

Library of Congress BL785.L6 292

MH NN NjP NcD IEN OCU
CtY PBm PU PPPD ViU OU MiU NNUT MdBP ODW InU CU MB
NL 0431093 DLC DDO IaU TNJ NIC FTaSU GEU-T NRCR

Lobeck, Chr. Augustus.
Aglaophamus, sive De theologiae mysticae Graecorum causis libri tres. Idemque Poetarum Orphicorum dispersas reliquias collegit. Koenigsburg, Borntraeger Ff., 1829.
2 v. 22.5 cm.
Microfilm copy. Negative.
1. Dionysia. 2. Mysticism - Greece. 3. Mysteries, Religious. I. Title

NL 0431094 CSmyS

Lobeck, Christian August, 1781-1860, ed.

PA4413 .A5 1866
Sophocles.
Sophoclis Aiax. Commentario perpetuo illustravit Christ. Augustus Lobeck. Editio tertia. Berolini, apud Weidmannos, 1866.

VOLUME 337

PA85 .L8A2 LOBECK, CHRISTIAN AUGUST, 1781-1860.
Ausgewählte briefe von und an Chr.A.Lobeck und K. Lehrs, nebst tagebuchnotizen. Im auftrage des Vereins für die geschichte von Ost- und Westpreussen hrsg.von Arthur Ludwich... Leipzig, Duncker & Humblot, 1894.
2 v.in 1. 24cm. (On cover: Publication des Vereins für die geschichte von Ost- und Westpreussen)
Paged continuously.

NL 0431096 ICU NNF MH OCU TNJ CLSU CU

Lobeck, Christian August, 1781-1860.
Auswahl aus Lobecks akademischen reden. Hrsg. von Albert Lehnerdt ... Berlin, Weidmann, 1865.
viii, 230 p. 21½cm.
"Ueber Lobeck's literarischen nachlass": p.1-28; "Lobeck als akademischer redner": p.[29]-70.

I. Lehnerdt, Ludwig Moritz Albert, 1827- , ed.

NL 0431097 ViU PU PBm MH IU CtY CLSU NIC

Lobeck, Christian August, 1781-1860.
Commentationis de parogage nominum ionica p. I. n.p. 1885.

NL 0431098 NjP

Lobeck, Christian August, 1781-1860.
De adjectivorum motione anomala. n.p. 1831.

NL 0431099 NjP

Lobeck, Christian August, 1781-1860.
De aggravatione syllabarum in vocabulorum commissuris; p. III n.p. 1819.

NL 0431100 NjP

Lobeck, Christian August, 1781-1860.
De anomaliae verborum graecorum causis. n.p. 1837.
3 pt.

NL 0431101 NjP

Lobeck, Christian August, 1781-1860.
De aoristis quibusdam anthypotactis; p. II. n.p. 1819.

NL 0431102 NjP

Lobeck, Christian August, 1781-1860.
De atticistarum praeceptis ... quae Phrynichus sparsit. n.p. 1819.

NL 0431103 NjP

Lobeck, Christian August, 1781-1860.
De carminibus Orphicis dissertatio. n.p. 1824.
2 pt.

NL 0431104 NjP

Lobeck, Christian August, 1781-1860.
De compositione adjectiborum graecorum dissertatio I. n.p. 1816.

NL 0431105 NjP

Lobeck, Christian August, 1781-1860.
De epenthesi vocalium systoecharum in verbis II. conjug. contractis. n.p. 1845.

NL 0431106 NjP

Lobeck, Christian August, 1781-1860.
De metathesi aspirationis et quantitatis. n.p. 1852.

NL 0431107 NjP

Lobeck, Christian August, 1781-1860.
De methypallage et antistrophe. n.p. 1864.

NL 0431108 NjP

Lobeck, Christian August, 1781-1860.
De morte Bacchi. Viteberg, 1810.

NL 0431109 IEN NjP

Lobeck, Christian August.
De mysteriorum Graecorum argumentis. Diss. 1. Regimonti Prussorum.

NL 0431110 NjP

Lobeck, Christian August.
De nominibus adjectivi et substantivi ambiguis; diss. III. n.p. 1832.

NL 0431111 NjP

Lobeck, Christian August.
De nominibus graecae linguae monosyllabis dissertatio I. n.p. 1833.

NL 0431112 NjP

Lobeck, Christian August.
De nominibus graeci sermonis paragogis quorum character est ... labialis. n.p. 1842.

NL 0431113 NjP

Lobeck, Christian August.
De nominibus Graecorum verbalibus. Regiomonti Borussorum, 1844.
pt. 1.

NL 0431114 NjP

Lobeck, Christian August.
De nominibus in inos exeuntibus. n.p. 1836.

NL 0431115 NjP

Lobeck, Christian August.
De nominibus in ma exeuntibus dissertatio II. n.p. 1834.

NL 0431116 NjP

Lobeck, Christian August.
De nominum generis neutrius verbalium formatione diss. I. n.p. 1834.

NL 0431117 NjP

Lobeck, Christian August.
De nominum graecorum motione. n.p. 1834.

NL 0431118 NjP

Lobeck, Christian August.
De praeceptis grammaticorum quibusdam euphonicis. n.p. 1833.

NL 0431119 NjP

Lobeck, Christian August.
De nominum graecorum, terminationibus epentheticis disputatio III. n.p. 1840.

NL 0431120 NjP

Lobeck, Christian August.
De nominum verbal. descriptione. n.p. 1838.

NL 0431121 NjP

Lobeck, Christian August, 1781-1860.
De Orphei aetate. n.p. 1826.
2 pt.

NL 0431122 NjP

LOBECK, Christian August.
De Priscarum Gentium diebus Nuptiarum religiosis Opusculum post LXXII Annos iterum publicatum in Auditorio Maxim habendas indicit Ludovicus Friedlae[ ]er. Regimonti Prussorum, [1871].
4°. pp.8.

NL 0431123 MH

39 Lobeck, Christian August. 1781-1860.
De prosthesi et aphaeresi consonantium dissertatio prima. Regimonti Borussorum typis Hartungianis, 1846.
8 p. 4°.

NL 0431124 DLC NjP

Lobeck, Christian August.
De prosthesi et aphaeresi vocalium ὄ et ē. n.p. 1845.

NL 0431125 NjP

VOLUME 337

Lobeck, Christian August.
De productione compositorum; pars III.
n.p. 1817.

NL 0431126 NjP

Lobeck, Christian August, 1781-1860.
De Pythagoreorum sententiis mysticis.
n.p. 1827.

NL 0431127 NjP

Lobeck, Christian August, 1781-1860.
De Sanchuniathonis Theologia Punica.
Regiomonti Borussorum, 1829.

NL 0431128 NjP

Lobeck, Christian August.
De syllabarum productione; P. V.
n.p., 1819.

NL 0431129 NjP

Lobeck, Christian August.
De syllabis reduplicatis I. n.p., 1847.

NL 0431130 NjP

Lobeck, Christian August, 1781-1860.
De Syncope. n.p., 1849.
pt. 1.

NL 0431131 NjP

Lobeck, Christian August.
De verbis quintae conjugationis. n.p., 1843.

NL 0431132 NjP

Lobeck, Christian August.
De verborum graeci, sermonis usu punrorum descriptione diss. I. n.p. 1838.

NL 0431133 NjP

Lobeck, C.A.
De vocabulorum graecorum parathesi pars altera.
Program Diss. - Univ. of Koenigsberg, 1848.

NL 0431134 ICRL

Lobeck, Christian August.
Descriptionis verborum graecorum p. IV.
n.p., 1839.

NL 0431135 NjP

Lobeck, Christian August, 1781-1860.
De vocabularum graecoram syncope ...
see also his Disputationum de vocabulorum graecorum syncope ...

Lobeck, Christian August, 1781-1860
Dii vetervm adspectv corporvm exanimivm non prohibiti... Vitebergae, Ex officina meltzeriana, [1802?]
2 pts. in 1.
Diss.-Wittenberg?
t.-. for "Pars altera" names Henricus Leonhardus Heubner as joint author.

NL 0431137 MiU NjP

39 Lobeck, Christian August. 1781-1860.
Disputationum de vocabulorum graecorum syncope nona. Regimonti Borussorum, E.J. Dalkowski, 1851.
8 p. 4°.

NL 0431138 DLC

39 Lobeck, Christian August, 1781-1860.
Disputationum de vocabulorum graecorum syncope octava. Regimonti Borussrum, E.J. Dalkowski, 1841.
8 p. 4°.

NL 0431139 DLC

39 Lobeck, Christian August, 1781-1860.
Disputationum de vocabulorum graecorum syncope sexta. Regimonti Borussorum, typis Hartungianis, 1850.
8 p. 4°.

NL 0431140 DLC

Lobeck, Christian August.
Dissertatio de motione adjectivorum minum mobilium. n.p., 1831.

NL 0431141 NjP

Lobeck, Christian August.
Dissertatio de vocabulis singulari forma signatis. n.p., 1836.

NL 0431142 NjP

Lobeck, Christian August.
Dissertatio de syllabis duplicatis III.
n.p., 1847.

NL 0431143 NjP

Lobeck, Christian August.
Dissertationis de graecorum vocabulorum metathesi. n.p., 1850-51.
2 pt.

NL 0431144 NjP

Lobeck, Christian August, 1781-1860.
Dissertationis de graecorum vocabulorum syncope, part 5. Regimonti Borussorum, [1850?]
[3]-14 p.
Separate from Programm-Conditi Prussiarum regni memoriam anniversariam, 1850.

NL 0431145 MiU

Lobeck, Christian August.
Dissertationis de motione adjectivorum compositorum, p. III. n.p., 1835.

NL 0431146 NjP

Lobeck, Christian August.
Dissertationis de nominibus per al deflexis p. I. n.p., 1841.

NL 0431147 NjP

Lobeck, Christian August.
Dissertationis de proschematismo: 1-
n.p., 1852 - pt. 1-

NL 0431148 NjP

Lobeck, Christian August.
Dissertationis de prosthesi et aphaeresi literae alpha p. 3. n.p., 1845.

NL 0431149 NjP

39 Lobeck, Christian August. 1781-1860,
Dissertationis de syntaxi indeclinabilium paro prima. Regimonti Borussorum, E.J. Dalkowski, 1852.
8 p. 4°.

NL 0431150 DLC NjP

Lobeck, Christian August
Initia doctrinae de usu apostrophi ex tragicorum reliquis ducta. Vitebergae, 1804.
46 p.

NL 0431151 PBm

Lobeck, Christian August, 1781-1860.
Mittheilungen aus Lobecks briefwechsel. Nebst einem litterarischen anhange und einer zur feier seines gedächtnisses gehaltenen rede, hrsg. von. Ludwig Friedländer. Leipzig, B. G. Teubner, 1861.
4 p.l., 224 p. 19½cm.
"Gedachtnissrede auf Lobeck, gehalten in der aula zu Konigsberg am 29. november 1860": p.1-32.

I. Friedlander, Ludwig, 1824-1909, ed.

NL 0431152 ViU CtY NjP MU CLSU PU IEN

Lobeck, Christian August.
Monographia figurae etymologicae; p. I.
n.p. 1832.

NL 0431153 NjP

VOLUME 337

Lobeck, Christian August.
Observationum in Phrynichum. n.p., 1815.
3 pt.

NL 0431154 NjP

Lobeck, Christian August.
Observationum linguae graecae pars I.
n.p., 1817.

NL 0431155 NjP

Lobeck, Christian August, 1781-1860.
Paralipomena grammaticae graecae scripsit Chr. Augustus Lobeck ... Lipsiae, apud Weidmannos, 1837.
2 v. in 1. 21cm.
Paged continuously.
Each "Dissertatio" was also published separately.
CONTENTS.—pars prior. Dissertationes: De praeceptis euphonicis, De nominibus monosyllabis, De adjectivis immobilibus, De substantivorum I. declinationis paragoge ionica.—pars posterior. Dissertationes: De nominibus substantivi et adjectivi generis ambiguis, De nominum in μα exeuntium formatione, De motione adjectivorum minus mobilium, De figura etymologica.
1. Greek language—Grammar. 2. Greek language—Word formation. I. Title.
33-25848
Library of Congress PA254.L6 485

MiU OU ODW NIC NjNbS NcD ViU MdBP MH
NL 0431156 DLC CU WaU DDO CLSU CtY NjP NN PBm PU

Lobeck, Christian August, 1781-1860.
Pathologiae Graeci sermonis elementa, scripsit C. Augustus Lobeck... Regimontii Borussorum: Sumtu fratrum Borntraeger, 1853-62. 2 parts in 1 v. 8°.
Contents: Pars 1. De prosthesi et aphaeresi, de syncope, de parectasi, de metahesi, de parathesi et scriptura hyphen. Pars 2. De synaeresi, diaeresi et crasi deque affectionibus utrinque mixtis, de proschematismo, de apocope.
With this is bound his: 'Ρηματικόν, sive verborum Graecorum et nominum verbalium technologia. Regimontii, 1846. 8°.

364443A. 1. Greek language—Word formation.
N. Y. P. L. February 27, 1929

OCU ViU
NL 0431157 NN WU ODW PBm PU MH CtY CSt NIC MiU

Lobeck, Christian August.
Pathologiae sermonis graeci elementa.
n.p., 1844.

NL 0431158 NjP

Lobeck, Christian August, 1781-1860.
Pathologiae sermonis graeci prolegomena scripsit Chr. Augustus Lobeck. Lipsiae, apud Weidmannos, 1843.
x, 574 p. 21cm.

1. Greek language—Grammar—1800-1870.

NNF MiU MA MH NN PU PBm NIC
NL 0431159 ViU CU MChB NcD CSt MiU NjNbS CtY ICU

Lobeck, Christian August, 1781-1860.
Phrynichus. Eclobae nominum et verborum Atticorum, cum notis P.J. Nunnesii, D. Hoeschelii, J. Scaligeti et cornetii De Paniv, partim in tegrio, partim contractis. Lipsiae, Weidmann, 1820.
LXXX, 478 p.

NL 0431160 OO NRCR

Lobeck, Christian August.
Prolegomena. n.p., 1835.

NL 0431161 NjP

Lobeck, Christian August.
Prolegomena. n.p., 1856.

NL 0431162 NjP

Lobeck, Christian August.
Quaestionis de rectione verbi méllo pars I.
n.p., 1818.

NL 0431163 NjP

Lobeck, Christian August, 1781-1860.
'Ρηματικόν; sive, Verborum graecorum et nominum verbalium technologia; scripsit Chr. Augustus Lobeck. Regimontii, sumtu fratrum Borntraeger; [etc., etc.] 1846.
xii, 337 p. 21½cm.

7-16246
Library of Congress

ViU
NL 0431164 DLC CU CSt NIC NjNbS NN CtY PBm PU MiU

Lobeck, Christian August, 1781-1860.
Verborum graeci sermoni descriptionis p. 3. n.p., 1838.

NL 0431165 NjP

Lobeck, Engebret E.
see
Løbeck, Engebret Engebretsen, 1864-1922.

Lobeck (Erich) [1865-]. *Zur Prognose und Therapie der Hypopyonkeratitis. 38 pp. 8°. Greifswald, J. Abel, 1892.

NL 0431167 DNLM MiU

Lobeck, Erich, 1899-
... Die Verletzungen des Sehorgans, von Erich Lobeck ...
(*In* Handbuch der speziellen pathologischen Anatomie und Histologie. Berlin, 1937. 26cm. Bd. 11, Teil 3, p. [367]-539. illus. (part col.))
"Schrifttum" at end of each section.

NL 0431168 ICJ DNLM

Lobeck, Erich, Herman Max Wilhelm.
see Lobeck, Erich, 1865-

Lobeck, Fritz.
Farben anders gesehen. Strasbourg, P.-H. Heitz, 1950.
106 p. illus. 25 cm.

1. Color. I. Title.
QC495.L53 535.6 51-18267

NL 0431170 DLC

Lobeck, Fritz.
Farben anders gesehen; neue Ergebnisse zur Farbenlehre Goethes. [2. erweiterte Aufl.] Basel, Verlag Die Pforte, 1954.
126 p. illus., diagrs. 26 cm.
Includes bibliographical references.

1. Goethe, Johann Wolfgang von. Zur Farbenlehre. 2. Color. I. Title.
[QC495.L] A 56-3521
Harvard Univ. Library for Library of Congress [1]

NL 0431171 MH CU NRU

Lobeck, Fritz, 1897-
Fritz Lobeck
see under
Zürich. Kunsthaus.

Lobeck (Hans) [1858-]. *Künstlicher Diabetes durch centralen Vagusreiz. 29 pp. 12°. Greifswald, J. Abel, 1882.

NL 0431173 DNLM MiU

W 4 Lobeck, Hans, 1910-
F82 Ein Beitrag zur Osteogenesis imperfecta.
1938 Gelnhausen, Kalbfleisch, 1938.
31 p. illus.
Inaug.-Diss. - Frankfurt.
Bibliography: p. 28-31.

NL 0431174 DNLM

Lobeck, Helmut, 1924-
Subjektivismus und Objektivismus in Romantik und Biedermeier; studien zum Seinserlebnis Innerhalb der deutschen Bewegung. [n.p., 1948?]
112 l. 30 cm.
Inaug.-Diss. - Bonn.

NL 0431175 PBm

Lobeck, Immanuel Ludwig Otto, 1854-
Markgraf Konrad von Meissen ... Leipzig, Druck von W. Schuwardt & co., 1878.
90 p., 1 l. 21cm.
Inaug.-diss.—Leipzig.
Vita.

1. Konrad der Grosse, margrave of Meissen, 1098?-1157.
18-11423
Library of Congress DD147.5.K5L6

NL 0431176 DLC NIC

VOLUME 337

Lobeck, J. L. O.
see
Lobeck, Immanuel Ludwig Otto, 1854-

LOBECK, Jean.
Recherches sur les naphtisoindigotines. [Thèse]. Paris, Masson et cie., 1929.
pp. (6), 50+.

NL 0431178 MH-C CtY

FLGZ 148 no.25 Lobeck, Johann Elias.
... De usu feriarum saxonico ... Erfurti, G.H. Müller [1700]
19p. 20cm.
(Foreign law pamphlet collection, v.148, no.25)
Inaug.-disp. - Erfurt.

NL 0431179 CtY-L

Lobeck, Justo Florian.
De synaloephe I.
see his Dissertationis grammaticae de synalosphe pars prima.

Lobeck, Justo Florian
Dissertationis grammaticae de synalosphe pars prima, copulativae particulae complexionem continens... Regimentii Prussorum, 1339.
50 p.

NL 0431181 PBm NjP

LOBECK, Justo Florian.
Historiae litterarum Romanar m buvis enarratio. Jacobopoli Chilenorum, typis nationalibus, 1864.

NL 0431182 MH CtY

Lobeck, Justo Florian
Informe mandado publicar por la Facultad de Humanidades de la Universidad de Chile, acerca de dos textos de frances ... Santiago de Chile, Impr. Nacional, 1866
46 p.
Half title: Idioma frances

NL 0431183 MH

LOBECK, Justo Florian.
Ojeada retrospectiva sobre la marcha que, desde los tiempos antiguos hasta nuestros dias, se ha seguido al tratar de la mitologia clasica.-Estudio primen[ ]ido ante la facultad de humanidades i filosofía de la universidad de Chile en sesion del 6 de mayo de 1862. Santiago, 1862.
1.8°. pp23.
"Suplemento a los Anales de la universidad de Chile' correspondientes al año de 1862".

NL 0431184 MH DPU

Lobeck, Justo Florián.
Progymnasmata latina. Coleccion de ejercicios latinos i castellanos, destinada a los alumnos de la segunda clase de humanidades del Instituto nacional i colejios de la República de Chile, i arreglada conforme a la Gramática de don Francisco Bello, por el doctor Justo Florian Lobeck ... Santiago, Imprenta chilena, 1862.
xviii, 478 p. 17cm.

1. Latin language—Composition and exercises. I. Title.

Library of Congress PA2087.L79 10—23384

NL 0431185 DLC CtY WaU

Lobeck, Justo Florian, ed.
Bello, Francisco, 1817–1845.
Prosodia i métrica latinas, por D. Francisco Bello. 4. ed., rev. por encargo del rector del Instituto nacional, con órden del supremo gobierno, i considerablemente aum. por el doctor Justo Florian Lobeck ... Santiago de Chile, Imprenta chilena, 1862.

Lobeck, Justus Florianus.
Quaestionum Jonicarum liber. Fasciculus I. Regimontii Prussorum. Tag & Koch. 1850. 160 pp. 22 cm.
"Ita fructus sum, ut hoc loco de adjectivis in εις terminatis plenius exponerem." — *Page I.*
No more appears to have been published.

N1022 — Adjectives. Greek.

NL 0431187 MB NIC PPAmP MH IEN CtY

Lobeck, Konrad, 1914–
Die französisch-frankoprovenzalische dialektgrenze zwischen Jura und Saône ... von Konrad Lobeck ... [Winterthur, Buchdruckerei Winterthur ag., 1944.
8 p. l., [ix]–xii, 61, [1] p. 22½cm.
Abhandlung—Zürich.
"Teildruck. Die vollständige arbeit erscheint als band 23 der Romanica helvetica (series linguistica) ... Librairie E. Droz, Genève ... 1944."
Lebenslauf.
Includes bibliographies.

1. Franco-Provençal dialects. 2. Linguistic geography. I. Title.

Library of Congress PC3133.L6 46-18663

NL 0431188 DLC CtY ICU

Lobeck, Konrad, 1914–
Die französisch-frankoprovenzalische Dialektgrenze zwischen Jura und Saône. Genève, E. Droz, 1945.
xii, 317 p. 6 fold. maps. 25 cm. (Romanica helvetica; series linguistica, v. 23)
Issued in part as thesis, Zürich, 1944.
Includes bibliographies.

1. Franco-Provençal dialects. 2. Linguistic geography. I. Title. (Series: Romanica helvetica, v. 23)

[PC3133.L] A 48-6590*

Harvard Univ. Library for Library of Congress [1]

N NN CU
NL 0431189 MH MB LU CaBVaU CSt Cu-S OU MiU IaU RPB

Lobeck (Konrad Julius) [1876–]. *Beitrag zur Kenntnis der diffusen Sarkome der Pia mater. 34 pp., 2 l. 8°. Leipzig, B. Georgi, 1901.

NL 0431190 DNLM ICRL CtY

Lobeck, Margrit.
...Neue Weinachtsspiele. Bern, Troxler-Verlag, 1951. 74 p. 18cm.

1. Nativity plays, Swiss-German. 2. German language —Dialects—Switzerland.

NL 0431191 NN

QD305 .A2L8 Lobeck, Martin, 1878-
Ueber die einwirkung von halogenen auf dikarboxylglutarsaureester. (w_2-w_2^1 -propantetrakarbonsaureester.)
Weida i. Thur. 1905.
34p.
Inaug. diss. Leipzig.

NL 0431192 DLC MH PU CtY

Lobeck, Oskar, 1879–
Ultraviolette strahlen, ihre anwendung zur sterilisation von milch und ihre wirkung auf das in der milch enthaltene fett ... Weida i. Thür., Druck von Thomas & Hubert, 1905.
57, [1] p. 23cm.
Inaug.-diss.—Leipzig.
Vita.

1. Milk—Sterilization. 2. Spectrum, Ultra-violet.

12—13739

Library of Congress SF259.L77

NL 0431193 DLC ICJ CU PU CtY

Lobeck, Otto
Des Flavius Blondus Abhandlung...
see under Biondo, Flavio, 1388-1463.

Lobeck, Reinhard, 1902-
Die grossberliner stadtentwaesserung.
Inaug. Diss. Berlin, Tech. Hoch., 1927
Bibl.

NL 0431195 ICRL

Lobeck, Reinhard, 1902-
...Die Grossberliner Stadtentwässerung, von Dr.-Ing. Reinhard Lobeck... Berlin: J. Springer, 1928. 76 p. incl. tables. 8°. (Industriewirtschaftliche Abhandl. Heft 1.)
Bibliography, p. 76.

1. Irrigation—Germany—Berlin. 2. Canals—Germany—Berlin. I. Ser.
N. Y. P. L. February 16, 1932

NL 0431196 NN MH

Lobeck, Tobias, *fl.* 1750.
Atlas geographicus portatilis [sic], XXIX mappis orbis habitabilis regna exhibens. Cælo accurate expressit Tobias Conradus Lotterus, delineavit et excudit Tobias Lobeck. [Augustæ Vindelicorum, ca. 1762]
[4] l., [29] col. maps, [2] l. 12 cm.
Maps undated; issued also with 20 additional maps, two of which are dated 1762.
Issued also with German text, Kurzgefasste Geographie.

1. Atlases—Early works to 1800. I. Lotter, Tobias Conrad, 1717–1777, engr.

Map 51-849

NL 0431197 DLC MB RPJCB ICN CtY OCl OC

Lobeck, Tobias, *fl.* 1750.
Atlas geographicus portatilis [sic], XXIX mappis orbis habitabilis regna exhibens. Cælo accurate expressit Tobias Conradus Lotterus, delineavit et excudit Tobias Lobeck. [Augustæ Vindelicorum, 1762?]
[3] l., [49] col. maps. 12 x 15 cm.
The 29 maps, undated, called for by the title and Index mapparum are not in indicated order; 2 of the 20 additional maps are dated 1762.

1. Atlases—Early works to 1800. I. Lotter, Tobias Conrad, 1717–1777, engr.

G1015.L62 Map 51-854

NL 0431198 DLC NNH ViU CaOLU

VOLUME 337

Lobeck, Tobias, fl. 1750.
Atlas Geographicus portatilis XXX mappis bia habitabilis regina exhibens Caelo accurate expressit ... [Augusburg, Ca. 1780]
2 p.l., 35 maps., 1 l.
cf. Phillips (Atlases) 631.

NL 0431199 RPJCB

Lobeck, Tobias, *fl.* 1750.
Kurzgefasste geographie, in sich haltend einen aneinander hangenden entwurf aller theile des bevvohnten erdbodens, nebst compendieusen landcharten, welche einen kleinen sack-atlas ausmachen. Hrsg. von Tobias Lobeck ... Augspurg, Gedruckt bey A. Brinhauser [n. d.]
72 p., 1 l. front., xxix maps. 11½ x 14½cm.
Maps preceded by engraved t.-p.: Atlas geographicus portatilis [!] xxix mappis orbis habitabilis regna exhibens. Cælo accurate expressit Tobias Conradus Lotterus, delineavit et excudit Tobias Lobeck ...
1. Geography. 2. Atlases.
Library of Congress G121.L8 5-42719

NL 0431200 DLC InU MB

Lobeck, Tobias
Kurzgefasste geographie...
Augspurg, [c1750]

NL 0431201 RPJCB

Lobeck, T.
Kurzgefasste geographie, in sich haltend einen aneinander hangenden entwurf aller theile des bevvohnten erdbodens, nebst compendieusen landcharten, welche einen kleinen sackatlas ausmachen. 72 pp., 1 l., front., 29 col. maps. obl. 32°. Augspurg, A. Brinhauser [1762?] 630
Note.—Copy no. 1. Engraved frontispiece signed: Gottfr. Eichler jun., inv. et delin.—Tobias Lobeck sculpsit et excudit Aug: Vind:
Maps preceded by engraved title-page: Atlas geographicus portatilis, xxix mappis orbis habitabilis regna exhibens. Cælo accurate expressit Tobias Conradus Lotterus, delineavit et excudit Tobias Lobeck, chalcograph . . .
Atlas published also without text.
Maps not dated. Copy no. 3 of the "Atlas geographicus" . . . contains maps nos. [25] and [32], not in the "index mapparum," but dated 1762, which has been assigned to this copy.
British Museum catalogue has a under the date 1720 (?), but no other authority for this date is found.

NL 0431202 DLC NNC

912 Lobeck, Tobias, fl.ca.1750.
7621A Kurzgefasste geographie, in sich haltend einen aneinander hangenden entwurf aller theile des bewohnten erdbodens, nebst compendieusen land-charten, welche einen kleinen sack-atlas ausmachen. Hrsg. von Tobias Lobeck ... Augspurg [T. Lobeck, 1762?]
72, [44]p. pl., 42 col.map.
The maps, which are bound before the text, have special illus. t.-p., engr.: Atlas geographicus portatilis[!], XXIX. mappis orbis habitabilis regna exhibens. Cælo accurate expressit Tobias Conradus Lotterus, delineavit et excudit Tobias Lobeck.
Pasted in front of the Atlas are two maps, one of Berlin and environs, the other of Potsdam; inserted at end, before the Index mapparum, is a map of eastern United States, and at end of text, a map of Boston and vicinity.
1. Atlases. I. Lotter, Tobias Konrad, 1717-1777, engr.

NL 0431204 IU

*Ea 762l Lobeck, Tobias, fl.1750.
Kurzgefasste Geographie, in sich haltend einen aneinander hangenden Entwurf aller Theile des bewohnten Erdbodens, nebst compendieusen Landcharten, welche einen kleinen Sack-atlas ausmachen. Augspurg, Gedruckt bey J.M.Spaeth[1762?]
72p. 39 col.maps. 11x15cm.
Atlas also pub. separately with title: Atlas geographicus portatilis[!] XXIX mappis
Maps not dated. Maps no.2-3,5 listed in the "Index mapparum" wanting, but additional maps have been bound in. Frontispiece, engraved t.p. and p.1-2 of text wanting.

NL 0431206 CtY

Lilly Library G 1015 .L 79 1762? LOBECK, TOBIAS, fl. 1750
Vollständiger Sack-atlas aller Theile des bewohnten Erdbodens und derer Länder, in hauptund special Landcharten, nebst einem kurzgefasten Entwurf und Anweisung zur newesten Geographie. Hrsg. von Tobias Lobecks ... Augspurg, Gedruckt bey J. M. Späth [1762?]
1 p.l., 72 p. 48 maps 10.5 x 14 cm.
Maps preceded by engraved t. p. and front. "Index mapparum" bound following first map.
Contains 48 maps rather than 29 called for by engraved title and "Index mapparum." Final map dated 1762.
From the library of Bernardo Mendel.
In embossed boards.

NL 0431208 InU

Ca9 K6 +804l Lobeda, Germany (Thuringia)
Frohe Wünsche bey der Vermählungsfeyer ihro herzoglichen Durchlaucht Herrn Carl Friedrich Erbprinzen zu Sachsen Weimar und Eisenach mit ihro kaiserlichen Hoheit Maria Pawlowna Grossfürstin von Russland in Unterthänigkeit dargebracht von dem Rath und der Bürgerschaft der Stadt Lobeda. Im November 1804.
Jena, Gedruckt bey dem Hofbuchdrucker Göpferdt [1804] [4]pp. 34cm.
In verse.

NL 0431209 CtY

Lobedani, Johannes, respondent.
De inaudita philosophical Johannes Baptistae Helmontii ...
see under Micraelius, Johann, 1597-1658.

Lobedanius, A
Beschryving der vreugde-blyken
see under title

Lobedanius, Nicolaus
... De jure stapulae vulgo stapel-recht ... submittit Nicolaus Lobedanius ... Trajecti ad Rhenum, J. Broedelet, 1757.
1 p.l., 46 p., 1 l. 23cm.
Diss.- Utrecht.
Bibliographical footnotes.

NL 0431212 MH-L

Lobedank, Eberhard.
Goldene sonnen, roman von Eberhard Lobedank. Berlin, Globus verlag g. m. b. h. [°1940]
158, [1] p. 17½cm.
I. Title. 40-88055
Library of Congress PT2623.O15G6 1940
Copyright A—Foreign 46330
[2] 833.91

NL 0431213 DLC

Lobedank, Emil
Das ärztliche Gutachten im Rahmen des Reichs-versorgungsgesetzes...Berlin, Schostz, 1922.
92 p.

NL 0431214 PPC

Lobedank, Emil.
——. Die Augenkrankheiten, ihre Verhütung und Behandlung; gemeinverständlich dargestellt. 76 pp. 8°. München. O. Gmelin, 1902.

NL 0431215 DNLM PPC

von Lobedank (Emil). *Ein Fall von Retroflexio uteri gravidi mit beginnenden Incarcerationserscheinungen bei hochgradiger Osteomalacie. 18 pp. 8°. Strassburg, Heitz & Mündel, 1892.

NL 0431216 DNLM MBCo

Lobedank, Emil
—— Die Geschlechtskrankheiten. Gemeinverständliche Darstellung ihres Wesens, und Belehrung über zweckmässiges Verhalten der Erkrankten. 1 pl., 40 pp. 8°. München, O. Gmelin. 1904.

NL 0431217 DNLM

WS 100 L797g 1904 LOBEDANK, Emil
Die Gesundheitspflege des Schulkindes im Elternhause. Hamburg, Voss, 1904.
vii, 219 p.
Title

NL 0431218 DNLM DHEW

QS L797h 1903 LOBEDANK, Emil
Hilfstafel zum Gebrauch bei Sektionen und zur Abfassung des Sektionsprotokolls, eine zum Ablesen auf 2 m Entfernung eingerichtete Tafel als Ersatz eines Handbuchs. Leipzig, Konegen, 1903.
[8] p. (in portfolio)

NL 0431219 DNLM

Lobedank (Emil). Die hygienische Ausbildung des Offiziers; eine Zusammenstellung der wichtigsten Capitel der Gesundheitslehre. ix, 138 pp. 8°. Strassburg i. E., W. Heinrich, 1899.

NL 0431220 DNLM DNW

VOLUME 337

Lobedank. Emil
—— Die Infektionskrankheiten (ansteckende Krankheiten). Ihre Entstehung und Verhütung. iv. 103 pp. 8°. München, E. Gmelin, 1904.

NL 0431221 DNLM

Lobedank, Emil
—— Kurze praktische Anleitung zur Erkennung aller Formen des Kopfschmerzes. 71 pp. 8°. Würzburg, Curt Kabitzsch, 1914.

NL 0431222 DNLM

Lobedank, Emil.
Kurze praktische Anleitung zur Erkennung aller Formen des Kopfschmerzes, von Generaloberarzt a. D. Dr. Lobedank ... Zweite, verbesserte Auflage. Leipzig, C. Kabitzsch, 1921.
71, [1] p. incl. tables. 20½cm.
"Benutzte Lehrbücher": 1 p. at end.

NL 0431223 ICJ PPC

Lobedank, Emil.
Kurze praktische Anleitung zur Erkennung aller Formen des Kopfschmerzes, von Generaloberarzt a.D. Dr. Emil Lobedank ... Dritte verbesserte Auflage. Leipzig, C. Kabitzsch, 1931.
62 p. 20½cm.

NL 0431224 ICJ

UH L797m 1903
LOBEDANK, Emil, comp.
Der Militärarzt; ein Ratgeber bei der Berufswahl, für einjährig-freiwillige Ärzte, Studierende der Medizin und Abiturienten der höheren Lehranstalten. Leipzig, Thieme, 1903.
vi, 84 p.

NL 0431225 DNLM

Lobedank , Emil
—— Der physiologische Schwachsinn des Menschen. Eine medizinisch-philosophisch-soziale Studie für Aerzte, Juristen, Pädagogen und alle Gebildeten. 59 pp. 8°. München, Seitz & Schauer [1905].

NL 0431226 DNLM PPC MH-L

Lobedank, Emil
Das Problem der Seele und der Willensfreiheit in Theorie und Praxis. Beitrag zum Ende eines alten Streits. Von... Emil Lobedank ... Berlin, J. Guttentag, 1911.
55, [1] p. 23cm.

NL 0431227 MH-L DNLM

Lobedank, Emil
Rechtsschutz und Verbrecherbehandlung. Ärztlich-naturwissenschaftliche Ausblicke auf die zukünftige Kriminalpolitik.
— Wiesbaden. Bergmann. 1906. iv, 89, (1) pp. [Grenzfragen des Nerven- und Seelenlebens. Heft 46.] 8°.

H192 — Crime and criminals.

NL 0431228 MB DNLM PU ICJ PU-L MiU IaU

Lobedank, Emil
——. Der Revierdienst. Anleitung zur Wahrnehmung des Revierdienstes für Unterärzte und einjährig-freiwillige Aerzte. v, 99 pp. 12°. *Strassburg. R. Schultz & Co.*, 1901.

NL 0431229 DNLM

---

150 L78s
Lobedank, Emil.
Der stammbaum der seele ... Halle, 1907.
137p. diagrs.
"Literatur": p.[138]

NL 0431230 IU NN

Lobedank, Emil
—— Ueber die frühzeitige Erkennung und die Behandlung der Lungenschwindsucht (Lungentuberkulose) durch Tuberkulin. Gemeinverständliche Aufklärungsschrift mit einem Vorwort von O. Roepke. 38 pp. 8°. München, O. Gmelin, 1909.

NL 0431231 DNLM

Lobedank, Emil
—— Das Wesen des menschlichen Geisteslebens und das Problem der Strafe. 89 pp. 8°. Halle a. S., C. Marhold, 1914–15.
Forms Heft 1/2, v. 10, Jurist.-psychiat. Grenzfr.

NL 0431232 DNLM MH-L

Lobedanz, Arnold Troels Lund, 1861-1909.
Hjältarne från Napoleons tid, efter äldre och nyare källor. Bemyndigad öfversättning från danskan. Stockholm, Bonnier [1897]
220 p. illus., ports. 22cm.
Contents.- Ney.- Augereau.- Lannes.- Masséna.- Kléber.
1. France. Hist. 1789-1815. Biog. I. Ti

NL 0431233 MnU

Lobedanz, Arnold Troels Lund, *1861–1909.*
Murat og hans Hustru. Historisk Fortælling efter ældre og nyere Kilder. Af Arnold Lobedanz.
= Kjøbenhavn. Hagerup. 1899. 222, (1) pp. Portraits. 17 cm., in 8s.
Kilder, p. 11.

D7478 — Denmark. Lang. Works in ..ish. — Murat, Joachim, King of Naples. — Murat, Maria Annunciata Carolina Bonaparte, 1782–1839.

NL 0431234 MB

Lobedanz (Edmund). Das Seebad Marienlyst bei Helsingör, mit Umgebungen. 44 pp. 8°. *Copenhagen, Thiele,* [*n. d.*]

NL 0431235 DNLM

PT 7093 L79 1868
Lobedanz, Edmund, 1820-1882.
Album dänisch-norwegischer Dichtung; deutsch und mit biographisch-literarhistorischen Notizen. Leipzig, A. Fritsch, 1868.
344 p. port. 18cm.
With this is bound his Album schwedisch-finnischer Dichtung. Leipzig, 1868.
1. Danish poetry--Translations into German. 2. German poetry--Translations from Danish. 3. Norwegian poetry--Translations into German. 4. German poetry--Translations from Norwegian. I. Title.

NL 0431236 NIC

PT 7093 L79 1868
Lobedanz, Edmund, 1820-1882.
Album schwedisch-finnischer Dichtung; deutsch und mit biographisch-literarhistorischen Notizen. Leipzig, A. Fritsch, 1868.
276 p. port. 18cm.
With this is bound his Album dänisch-norwegischer Dichtung. Leipzig, 1868.
1. Swedish poetry--Translations into German. 2. German poetry--Translations from Swedish. 3. Finnish poetry--Translations into German. 4. German poetry--Translations from Finnish. I. Title.

NL 0431237 NIC

Lobedanz, Edmund, 1820-1882, tr.

Bjørnson, Bjørnstjerne, 1832–1910.
... Arne. Eine novelle von Björnson. Übersetzt von Edmund Lobedanz. Leipzig, Bibliographisches institut [1886]

Lobedanz, Edmund, 1820–1882, compiler.
Ausgewählte gedichte von Björnstjerne Björnson, Carl XV, C. Hauch, Th. Kjerulf und anderen neueren nordischen dichtern. Deutsch von Edmund Lobedanz. Leipzig, W. Friedrich, 1881.
sq. 16°. pp. viii, (1), 250.

Scandinavian poetry–Coll.

NL 0431239 MH IEN

Lobedanz, Edmund, 1820-1882, tr.

Bjørnson, Bjørnstjerne, 1832–1910.
... Der brautmarsch und andere erzählungen, von Björnstjerne Björnson. Uebersetzt und eingeleitet von Eduard [!] Lobedanz. Stuttgart, W. Spemann [1882]

Lobedanz, Edmund, 1820–1882.
Das französische element in Gottfried's von Strassburg Tristan. Von dr. E. Lobedanz. Schwerin, F. Herberger's buchdruckerei, 1878.
45 p. 22cm.

1. Gottfried von Strassburg, 13th cent. Tristan. 2. Tristan. I. Title.
[*Full name:* Edmund Adolph Johannes Lobedanz]

A 34–724

Title from Newberry Libr. Printed by L. C.

NL 0431241 ICN NIC MdBP CLSU MH CtY MWelC

PT 1526 L62 1878a
Lobedanz, Edmund, 1820-1882.
Das französische element in Gottfried's von Strassburg Tristan. Von dr. E. Lobedanz. Schwerin, F. Herberger's buchdruckerei, 1878.
45 p.
Photocopy.
1. Gottfried von Strassburg, 13th cent. Tristan. 2. Tristan. I. Title.

NL 0431242 CaBVaU

PT9831 .G5L6
Lobedanz, Edmund, 1820–1882, tr.

Tegnér, Esaias, *Bp.*, 1782–1846.
Die Frithiofs-Sage. Nach dem schwedischen Original in den Versmassen deselben neu übers. von Edmund Lobedanz. Stuttgart, W. Spemann [1881]

VOLUME 337

Lobedanz, Edmund, tr.
Die Frithjofssage. 1862
see under Tegnér, Esaias, 1782-1846.

[Lobedanz, Edmund] 1820-1882.
Holstenspiegel; ein beitrag zur beleuchtung der dänisch-holsteinischen frage, mit historischen beilagen aus holsteinischen schriften, von einem "deutschen" Schleswiger. Hrsg.von P.Hjort... Kjøbenhavn, Reitzel, 1850.
68 p. 22½ cm.

I.Hjort,Peder,1793-1871, ed. II.Title.

NL 0431245 NjP MH

4PT Ger. 8124 Lobedanz, Edmund, 1820-1882.
Ein neuer Glaube; biographisch -culturhistorischer Roman. Frankfurt a. M., Meidinger, 1859-
v. 1

NL 0431246 DLC-P4

Lobedanz Edmund Adolf Johannes, 1820-1882.
see Lobedanz, Edmund, 1820-1882.

Lobedanz, Gerhard.
Der einfluss von willensmängeln auf gründungs- und beitrittsgeschäfte, von dr. Gerhard Lobedanz. Berlin, Junker und Dünnhaupt, 1938.
236 p. 24cm. (*Added t.-p.:* Neue deutsche forschungen. Abt.: Bürgerliches recht, handels- und wirtschaftsrecht ... Bd. 4)
Half-title: Neue deutsche forschungen, hrsg. von Hans R. G. Günther und Erich Rothacker. Bd. 181.
Issued also as inaugural dissertation, Rostock.
"Schrifttumsverzeichnis": p. 231-236.
1. Mistake (Law)—Germany. 2. Corporation law—Germany. 3. Association and associations—Germany. 4. Partnership—Germany. I. Title.
39-13991

NL 0431248 DLC MH

M1503 .S319F4 1954
Lobedanz, Max. Fête galante.
Schierbeck, Poul, 1888-1949.
[Fête galante. Piano-vocal score. Danish & French]
Fête galante; opera i 3 akter. Op. 25. Tekst af Max Lobedanz. Adaptation française par Fred Fisher. Klaverudg. København, Edition Dania, 1954.

Lobedanz, Max, 1888-
...De Uvidende; Skuespil i 3 Akter. København: C. A. Reitzels Forlag, 1927. 117 p. 8°.

1. Drama, Danish. 2. Title.
N. Y. P. L. September 11, 1928

NL 0431250 NN

Lobegesang Jesu Christi: Sambt beygefügten Ausslegungen etlicher örter. 1636
see under Schneider, Michael, 1612-1639.

Lobeira, João de, *fl.* 1258-1285
see also
Amadís de Gaula.
On Lobeira's supposed authorship of the original *cf.* A. F. G. Bell, Portuguese literature, 1922, p. 68-70; J. Cejador y Frauca, Hist. de la leng. y lit. castellana, v. 1; H. Thomas in Bibliographical society, Trans., v. 11, p. 251-297.

Lobeira, Vasco de, *fl.* 1385-1403 (*supposed author of Amadís de Gaula*)
see
Amadís de Gaula.
Cf. A. F. G. Bell, Portuguese literature, 1922, p. 68-70; H. Thomas in Bibliographical society, Trans., v. 11, p. 251-297; J. Cejador y Frauca, Hist. de la leng. y lit. castellana, v. 1.

SF 768 .L6x
Lobel, B. L.
Enzymic correlates of development, secretary function and regression of follicles and corpora lutea in the bovine ovary, by B. L. Lobel and E. Levy. Copenhagen, Periodica, 1968.
63 p. illus. 24 cm. (Acta endocrinologica. Supplement. 132. 1968)

1. Ovaries. 2. Cattle--Physiology. 3. Enzymes. I. Levy, E., joint author. II. Title III. Series

NL 0431254 OKentU

Lobel, D. *Etude clinique et hématologique du cancer myéloïde du crâne à foyers multiples chez l'enfant (myélocytome, myélosarcome, chlorome) 60p. 8°. Par., 1934.

NL 0431255 DNLM

Lobel, Mrs. Edgar
see
Lobel, Mrs. Mary Doreen, 1900-

Lobel, Edgar, 1888-
Cardinal Pole's manuscripts, by E. Lobel.
(*In* British academy, London. Proceedings, 1931. London [1933] 26cm. [v. 17] p. [97]-103; IV double facsim.)
"Communicated January 1931."

1. Manuscripts, Greek. 2. Pole, Reginald, cardinal, 1500-1558.
A 33-2660
Title from Wisconsin Univ. Library of Congress [AS122.L5 vol. 17]
[2]

NL 0431257 WU CaBVaU DDO MH

Lobel, Edgar, 1888-
Esther iii. 1-3, translated into tragic iambics ...
see under Racine, Jean Baptiste, 1639-1699.

Lobel, Edgar, 1888-
A Greek historical drama. London, G. Cumberlege [1949?]
12 p. facsims. (1 fold.)

"From the Proceedings of the British academy, volume XXXV."

1. Greek drama (Tragedy) I. Title.

NL 0431259 NNC N MH IU

PA3323 L62
Lobel, Edgar, 1888- ed.
A Greek historical drama. London, G. Cumberlege [1950]
12 p. facsim.

"From the Proceedings of the British Academy. Volume XXXV."
Text comprises "parts of three columns of what is unmistakably a play ... in a piece of a papyrus roll from Oxyrhynchus written in the second or third century." (p.4)

NL 0431260 CU

Lobel, Edgar, 1888- *ed.*
A Greek historical drama.
(*In* British Academy, London (Founded 1901) Proceedings, 1949. London [1952] v. 35, p. [207]-216. facsim.)
Facsimile reproduces the text of "hitherto unpublished fragments of a Greek historical drama presumed written in the fifth century B. C."—British nat. bibl., 1950.
"The Egypt Exploration Society ... [allowed this text] to appear in isolation instead of as a constituent of a volume of P. Oxyrhynchus."
Bibliographical footnotes.

1. Oxyrhynchus papyri—Facsimiles. I. Title.
AS122.L5 vol. 35 A 53-2926
Wisconsin. Univ. Libr. for Library of Congress [2]†

NL 0431261 WU DLC NNC CaBVaU

Lobel, Edgar, 1888-
The Greek manuscripts of Aristotle's poetics, by E. Lobel. [London] Printed at the Oxford university press for the Bibliographical society, 1933.
4 p. l., 59 p. diagrs. 22 x 18cm. (Supplement to the Bibliographical society's Transactions. no. 9)

1. Aristoteles. Poetica. Manuscripts. I. Title.
Library of Congress PA3893.P5L6 34-10410
——— Copy 2. [3] 016.091

NL 0431262 MiU MH IU NN ViU OCl OO OU OCU ScU PBm PU PPT CU DLC CaBVaU OrU MeB OrPS CoU NNC PPRF MsU

PA 3893 P5L63
Lobel, Edgar, 1888-
The medieval Latin Poetics, by E.Lobell. Oxford, 1931.
26p. 23cm.
Cover-title.
"Communicated December 15, 1931."
Also issued in the Proceedings of the British Academy, v.17, p.[309]-334, 1933.

1.Aristoteles. Poetica. I.Title.

NL 0431263 CLSU NSyU NBC CSaT MU AAP

Lobel, Edgar, 1888-
The medieval Latin Poetics ... London, H. Milford [1932]
28 p.
"From the Proceedings of the British academy. vol. XVII."

NL 0431264 DDO

Lobel, Edgar, 1888-
The medieval Latin Poetics, by E. Lobel.
(*In* British academy, London. Proceedings, 1931. London [1933] 26cm. [v. 17] p. [309]-334)
"Communicated December 15, 1931."

1. Aristoteles. Poetica. I. Title.
A 33-2665
Title from Wisconsin Univ. Library of Congress [AS122.L5 vol. 17]
[2]

NL 0431265 WaPS WU CaBVaU OrPR OrCS GU NcGU KMK OCl MiU

VOLUME 337

PA 3893 P5L79+ **Lobel, Edgar, 1888-**
The medieval Latin poetics. London, H. Milford [1933]
28 p. 26cm.

"From the proceedings of the British Academy. Volume XVII."
"Communicated Dec. 15, 1931."

NL 0431266 NIC

Lobel, Edgar, 1888- ed.

Sappho.
Σαπφοῦς μέλη. The fragments of the lyrical poems of Sappho, edited by Edgar Lobel ... Oxford, The Clarendon press, 1925.

Lobel, Edgar, 1888- ed.

Alcaeus.
Ἀλκαίου μέλη. The fragments of the lyrical poems of Alcaeus, edited by Edgar Lobel. Oxford, The Clarendon press, 1927.

Lobel, Edgar, 1888-
The Oxyrhynchus papyri, part 22; edited with translations and notes, by E. Lobel and C. H. Roberts. London, Egypt Exploration Society, 1954.

181p. illus. (Egypt Exploration Society. Graeco-Roman memoirs, 31)

1. Oxyrhynchus papyri. (Series: Egypt Exploration Society. Graeco-Roman Branch. Publications. v. 31)

NL 0431269 PP

Lobel, Edgar, 1888- *ed.*
Poetarum Lesbiorum fragmenta ediderunt Edgar Lobel et Denys Page. Oxford, Clarendon Press, 1955.

xxxviii, 337 p. 23 cm.

"Catalogus manuscriptorum": p. ix-xi.

1. Greek poetry (Collections) I. Sappho. II. Alcaeus. III. Page, Denys Lionel, joint ed. IV. Title.

PA3432.L6 55—2058

OCIW OCU OU NBC PSC PSt PBL PPT NcD PHC TU ViU IaU CtY NNC MH DDO MB FU NN MoSU ICU OO NcU
NL 0431270 DLC WaSpG CaBVaU OrPR OrU PBm TxU DCU

W 4 P23 1944 **Lobel, Georges, 1918-**
Contribution à l'étude de l'épilepsie Bravais-Jacksonienne; relativité de sa valeur localisatrice. Paris, Arnette, 1944.
59 p. illus. (Paris. [Université] Faculté de médecine. Thèse. 1944. no. 195)

Series

NL 0431271 DNLM

Lobel, Ionel, 1911-
... Le collapsus cardiaque dans le coma diabetique ... Paris, 1936.
Thèse - Univ. de Paris.
"Bibliographie": p. [97]-102.

NL 0431272 CtY DNLM

Lobel, Johann Gottlob Friedrich
Der Halley'sche Comet in seiner Vierundzwanzigsten Wiederkunst seit dem Jahr 1835. Nürnberg, 1835.

NL 0431273 WU

Lobel, Léopold, 1881-
Manuel de sensitometrie. By L.L. and M. Dubois. Paris, Montel, 1929.

195 p.

NL 0431274 PPF

Lobel, Léopold.
...Manuel de sensitométrie. 3. éd. nouv. rédaction... Paris, P. Montel [1950] 215 p. illus. 18cm. (Collection art & technique)

At head of title: L. Lobel & M. Dubois.

572194B. 1. Photography—Sensitometer. I. Dubois, M., jt. au.
N. Y. P. L. April 10, 1951

NL 0431275 NN

Lobel, Léopold.
99791 La projection cinématographique. Guide pratique à l'usage des opérateurs projectionnistes par Léopold Löbel, ... Paris, H. Dunod et E. Pinat, 1912.
x, 111 p. incl. 163 illus., table. 25½cm.

NL 0431276 ICJ CLSU

Lobel, Léopold.
La technique cinématographique. Projection, fabrication des
108187 films, par Léopold Löbel, ... Paris, H. Dunod et E. Pinat, 1912.
xii, 324 p. incl. illus., tables, diagrs. 25½cm.

NL 0431277 ICJ NN MiU CLSU AAP NcU

Lobel, Léopold
La technique cinématographique: projection, fabrication des films. 2. éd., rev. et augm. Paris, Dunod, 1922.
xiv, 360 p. illus.

1. Motion-picture photography.

NL 0431278 NNC

Lobel, Léopold.
La technique cinématographique; projection, fabrication des films, par Léopold Lobel ... 3. éd., revue et augmentée. Paris, Dunod, 1927.

xii, 342 p. illus., diagrs. 25cm.

Bibliographical foot-notes.

1. Chronophotography.

NL 0431279 MiU NN

Lobel, Léopold.
La technique cinématographique; projection et fabrication des films muets et sonores, par Léopold Lobel ... 4. ed., rev. et augm. avec la collaboration de M. Dubois ... Paris, Dunod, 1934.

xiv, 383 p. illus., diagrs. 25½cm.

"Bibliographie relative au film parlant": p. [377]

1. Chronophotography. 2. Moving-pictures. 3. Moving-pictures, Talking. I. Dubois, M. II. Title.

36-13579

Library of Congress TR850.L65 1934

[2] 681.184

NL 0431280 DLC WU

Lobel, Léopold, 1881-
Sensitometry; the technique of measuring photographic materials, by L. Lobel and M. Dubois. [1st ed.] London, New York, Focal Press [1955]

263 p. illus. 19 cm. (The Manual of photo-technique)

"Translated and adapted by E. F. Teal from the French edition Manuel de sensitometrie."

1. Photographic sensitometry. I. Dubois, M., chemical engineer.

TR196.L63 56-2001 ‡

NL 0431281 DLC OrU FMU CoDU DSI ICJ MB PSt PP

Lobel, Loïcq de.
Le chemin de fer trans-Alaska-Sibérien (projet Loïcq de Lobel)
see under Syndicat français du trans-Alaska-Sibérien.

Lobel, Louis Willem Machiel.
Lepra bubalorum ... door Louis Willem Machiel Lobel ... Utrecht, Drukkerij fa. Schotanus & Jens, 1934.

5 p. l., [3]-234 p., 1 l. 24 pl. 24½cm.

Proefschrift—Utrecht.
"Literatuur": p. [231]-234.
"Stellingen" (1 leaf) laid in.

1. Buffaloes—Diseases. 2. Leprosy. I. Title.

36-36351

Library of Congress SF979.B9L6 1934

[2] 619.2

NL 0431283 DLC DNAL CtY ViU

Lobel, Manole, 1909-
... Valeur clinique de la sphygmoscopie rétinienne ... Paris, 1937.
Thèse - Univ. de Paris.
"Bibliographie": p. [175]-189.

NL 0431284 CtY

Lobel, Marco, 1909-
... Contribution à l'étude de la fontanelle à l'état normal et à l'état pathologique (rachitisme)... Paris, 1937.
Thèse - Univ. de Paris.
"Bibliographie": p. [35]-36.

NL 0431285 CtY

Lobel, *Mrs.* Mary Doreen, 1900-
The borough of Bury St. Edmund's; a study in the government and development of a monastic town, by M. D. Lobel. Oxford, The Clarendon press, 1935.

xi, [1], 208, [1] p. 2 fold. maps. 23cm.

1. Bury St. Edmunds. I. Title.

35-7835

Library of Congress DA690.B97L6

[3] 942.64

NL 0431286 DLC CaBVaU CtY PU PPPD NcD OCU MB NN

VOLUME 337

Lobel, *Mrs.* **Mary Doreen,** 1900–
... The history of Dean and Chalford, by M. D. Lobel. Oxford, Issued for the Society, 1935.
4 p. l., 175 p. pl., facsim. 23½cm. (*Half-title:* The Oxfordshire records society ... Oxfordshire records series—vol. xvii)
At head of title: The Oxfordshire records society.
1. Dean, Eng. 2. Chalford, Eng. 3. Manors. 35-14825
Library of Congress DA670.O9A3 vol. 17
[3] (942.57) 942.57

NL 0431287 DLC PU PHC OU MiU OCl

WZ 240 L796b 1598
L'OBEL, Matthias de, 1538-1616
Balsami, opobalsami, carpobalsami, & xylobalsami, cum suo cortice explanatio ... Londini, Excudebat Arnoldus Hatfield, impensis Joannis Norton, 1598.
[6], 40, [1] p. illus. 21 cm.
STC 16649.

NL 0431288 DNLM MH

L'Obel, Matthias de. Balsami, opobalsami, carpobalsami, & xylobalsami cum suo cortice explanationes & collectanea. [Londini. 1598.] (*In his* In G. Rondelletii methodicam pharmaceuticam officinam animadversiones, pars altera, 1605, pp. 516–529.)

NL 0431289 MH-A

Lobel, Matthias de, 1538-1616
Botanographi; sive, Plantarum historiae physicae, tam indeigenarum & Britanniae inquilinarum, quam exoticarum scriptoris. Quibus depravata & mutilata ex authoris mente corriguntur & restaurantur. Londini, T. Purfoot, 1605.
156p. 30cm.
Bound with the author's Dilvcidae simplicivm medicamenorvm explicationes, & Stirpivm adversaria. Londini, 1605

NL 0431290 WU PPPH

L'Obel Matthias de, 1538-1616, joint author.

QK41 .L7 Rare Bk Coll
Pena, Pierre, *fl.* 1535-1605.
Dilvcidae simplicivm medicamenorvm [!] explicationes, & stirpivm adversaria, perfacilis vestigatio, luculentaque accessio ad priscorum, præsertim Dioscoridis & recentiorum materiæ medicæ solidam cognitionem methodo exquisitissima, a notioribus summisque classium generibus ad vltimas vsque species digesta. Authoribus Petro Pena et Matthia de L'Obel, medicis. Quibus accessit altera pars, cum prioris illvstrationibvs, castigationibvs, avctariis, rarioribvs aliquot plantis, selectioribus remediis, svccis medicatis & metallicis, medicinae thesauris, opii ... formulis, operâ & studio eiusdem Matthiae de L'Obel. Londini, ex typographia T. Purfootij, 1605.

L'Obel, Matthias de, 1538–1616.
Icones stirpivm, || sev || Plantarvm || tam exoticarvm, || qvam indigenarvm, || in gratiam rei herbariæ ſtudioforum in duas partes digeftæ. || Cum feptem linguarum indicibus, ad diuerfarum nationum vfum. || [*Printer's mark.*] Antverpiæ, Ex officina Plantiniana, || ... , || M. D. XCI.
2 vol. in 1. Vol. 1: [8], 816 p. *,**, A–Z, a–z, AA–EE⁸; Vol. 2: 280, [54] p. and 1 blank leaf. Aa–Rr⁸, Ss⁴, +–++++++⁴ illus. 18×22cm.
Roman type.
A collection combining the illustrations published in the works of Dodoens, L'Écluse and de L'Obel, arranged by the latter. *cf.* Vander Haeghen, Bibl. belgica.
Vol. 2, p. 123–126, [49–54] and 1 blank leaf at end wanting.

NL 0431293 ICJ MoSB DDO MH-A NNBG

L'Obel, Matthias de, 1538–1616.
Matthiæ de L'Obel ... In G. Rondelletii ... methodicam pharmaceuticam officinam animadversiones, quibus depravata & mutilata ex authoris mente corriguntur & restaurantur. Accesserunt auctaria, in antidotaria vulgata censvrae beneuolæ, & Dilucidæ simplicium medicamentorum explicationes, Adversariorvmqve volumen, eorumq pars altera & illustramenta, quibus ambigua enodantur. Cum Lvdovici Myrei ... paragraphis vtiliss. ... Londini, excudebat prælum T. Purfootij, 1605.
2 pt. in 1 v. illus. 29cm.
Collation: pt. 1, 4 p. l., 156 p.; pt. 2, 8 p. l., 455, [1], 456–549 p.

The 2d part of this edition with title: Dilvcidæ simplicivm medicamenorvm [!] explicationes, & Stirpivm adversaria ... contains in preliminary leaves 3-8, p. 1–455, [1] the remainder of the first edition, published in 1570, by T. Purfoot, under title: Stirpivm adversaria nova [etc.] The letter to the professors of the University at Montpellier (p. [. 2) is set up in roman type, dated at end "Londini, pridie diuini natalitii" without the "1570" of the earlier issue; the dedication to Queen Elizabeth is omitted; the unnumbered supplementary leaf is replaced by p. 456–457 (without illus.), dated at end: Londini ... 1605.—Appended with continuous pagination and half-title ("Matthiæ de L'Obel ... Adversariorvm altera pars, cum prioris illvstrationibvs, castigationibvs, avctariis ... nec non commentariolis aliquot Rondelletianis nunquam antehac in lucem editis", p. [458]) are: Rariorum aliquot stirpium appendix (p. 460–515, dated at end: Londini, typis Purfootij, 1605, impensis authoris); Balsami [etc.] explanationes & collectanea (p. 516–526); Molle (p. 526–529); Cinnamomum eiusq genera (p. 529–532); Cassia, Xylo-cassia [etc.] (p. 532–534); Svccationes aliquot medicatae, ac primvm de lavdano opiato (p. 534–542); G. Rondelletii Tractatvs de hydrope nvnqvam antehac in lvcem editvs (p. 542–546); Eiusdem ... Elephantiasis noua methodica curandi ratio ... (p. 546–549) *cf.* Vander Haeghen. Bibl. belg.
1. Rondelet, Guillaume, 1507–1566. Dispensatorium seu pharmacopolarum officina ... 2. Pharmacy—Early works to 1800. 3. Botany. Medical. 4. Botany—Pre-Linnean works.
Library of Congress QK41.L7 6-45525

NL 0431296 DLC DNLM MH-A NIC DFo MiU MoSB

L'Obel, Matthias de, 1538–1616.
Kruydtboeck oft beschrÿuinghe van allerleye ghewassen, kruyderen, hesteren, ende gheboomten: devr Matthias de L'Obel ... t'Antwerpen, By Christoffel Plantyn, M.D.LXXXI.
2 v. in 1. illus. 35½cm.
Engraved t.-p.
1. Botany—Pre-Linnean works. 2. Botany, Medical. I. Title. 45-50910
Library of Congress QK41.L705

NL 0431297 DLC DNLM NNBG MShM MnU MiU MSM PU MoSB

Lobel, Matthias de.
Nova stirpium adversaria
see under Pena, Pierre, fl. 1535-1605.

L'Obel, Matthias de, 1538–1616.
Plantarum, sev Stirpivm historia, Matthiae de Lobel ... Cui annexum est adversariorvm volvmen ... Antverpiae, ex officina C. Plantini, 1576.
671, 457–471, 15, 24, [15] p. illus. 33cm.
This comprises L'Obel's "Stirpivm observaticnes" with "De succedaneis, imitatione Rondeletii".
457–471, 24, [15] p. are supplements and indexes to both the "Plantarvm, sev Stirpivm historia" and the "Nova stirpivm adversaria".
"Formvlae aliqvot remediorvm Gvillielmi Rondelletii ...": 15 p. after p. 471.
1. Botany—[Pre-Linnean works]
Agr 23-1445
Library, U. S. Dept. of Agriculture 452.2L78

PPAN PSC PPL MnU NNUT CSmH NNC NN MoSB IU MBH
NL 0431299 DNAL MH-A CLSU NIC DNLM CU NcD CtY-M

[L'Obel, Matthias de] 1538–1616.
Plantarvm sev Stirpivm icones. Antverpiæ, ex officina C. Plantini, 1581.
2 v. in 1. illus. 18½ x 23½cm.
A collection combining the illustrations published in the works of Dodoens, L'Écluse and de L'Obel, arranged by the latter, with the name of each plant in Latin, and an "Index synonymicvs stirpivm" in Latin, Dutch, German, French, Italian, Spanish, Portuguese and English. *cf.* Vander Haeghen, Bibl. belg.
1. Botany—Pre-Linnean works. I. L'Écluse, Charles de, 1526–1609. II. Dodoens, Rembert, 1517–1585.
Library of Congress QK41.L71 6-45523

NL 0431300 DLC MH-A PPL CU-A

Lobel, Matthias de.
Stirpium adversaria nova
see under Pena, Pierre, fl. 1535-1605.

L'Obel, Matthias de, 1538–1616.
Matthiæ de L'Obel ... Stirpium illustrationes. Plurimas elaborantes inauditas plantas subreptitiis Joh: Parkinsoni rapsodiis (ex codice ms. insalutato) sparsim gravatæ. Ejusdem adjecta sunt ad calcem Theatri botanici ἁμαρτήματα. Accurante Guil: How ... Londini, typis T. Warren, impensis J. Kirton, 1655.
19 p. l., 170, [4] p., 1 l. 19½ x 15cm.
A fragment of a large work planned by de L'Obel and pub. by the editor to discredit Parkinson who in his Theatrum botanicum, London, 1640, made use of the author's manuscript, without giving him due credit for it. *cf.* Dict nat. biog. & Vander Haeghen, Bibl. belg.
1. Parkinson, John, 1567–1650. 2. Botany—Pre-Linnean works. I. Howe, William, 1620–1656, ed.
6-45522
Library of Congress QK41.L72

NL 0431302 DLC MoSB WU MH-A DNLM ICJ MB

Lobel, Simca, 1908-
... Syndrome hyperfolliculinique ...
Paris, 1936.
Thèse - Univ. de Paris.
"Bibliographie": p. [83]-84.

NL 0431303 CtY DNLM

Lobel-Riche, 1877-
Armée française d'Orient, 1915–1917, en Macédoine. Douze lithographies originales du peintre-graveur Lobel Riche. [Paris, 1917]
4 p. l., 12 col. pl. 55cm.
In portfolio.
Each plate accompanied by guard sheet with descriptive letterpress.
Preface signed: Ph.-Emmanuel Glaser.
There were printed 200 numbered copies: nos. 1–30 "composés d'une double suite, 1. sur papier du Japon ... 2. sur papier de Chine," nos. 31–200 "sur vélin d'Arches." This copy is no. 61.
1. Macedonia. 2. European war, 1914- Pictorial works. I. Glaser, Ph. Emmanuel. II. Title: En Macédoine.
18-20413
Library of Congress NE2453.L6

NL 0431304 DLC

Lobel-Riche, 1877–
...Lobel-Riche. [Paris] Le Livre de Plantin [1946] 64 p., 89 pl. illus. 30cm.
At head of title: Robert Margerit.
Issued in portfolio, in slip case.
"Quatre cent quatre-vingt dix exemplaires...numérotés et signés...Lobel-Riche. 140."
"Bibliographie des ouvrages illustrés," p. [65-66]
564479B. I. Margerit, Robert.
N. Y. P. L. March 23, 1951

NL 0431305 NN

Lobelchik, Paltiel Jedidiah
see
Lubelchik, Paltiel Jedidiah.

Lobelia as a sure cure for venereal disease
see under [Kalm, Pehr] 1716-1779.

Lobelian (The) and Rhode Island Medical Review. Charles Gardner, proprietor; C. B. Peckham, editor. [Monthly.] v. 1, May, 1838, to April, 1839. 8°. *Newport.*

NL 0431308 DNLM

VOLUME 337

L'Obelisco, Rome.
See
Galleria dell' obelisco, Rome.

Lobelius, Matthias
see
L'Obel, Matthias de, 1538-1616.

Lobell, Conie, *pseud.*
see
Lope Bello, Consuelo, 1915-

Lobell, Griselda G., joint author.

PZ3 .L77967 Sh

Lobell, Nathan David, 1911-
The shadow and the blot, by N. D. and G. G. Lobell. [1st ed.] New York, Harper [1949]

SH234 C39 1954t no. 3

Lobell, Milton J
Metodos y artes pesqueros, por Milton J. Lobell, con la colaboración del Ing. Sigurd Stranger. [n.p.] Organización de las Naciones Unidas para la Agricultura y la Alimentación [1954?]
[2], vii, 144 l. illus., diagrs., tables. 33 cm. (Centro Latinoamericano de Capacitación Pesquera, 2d, México, 1954. Textos. T-3)
At head of title: ... Textos: Tecnología.
Bibliography: l. 141-144.

1. Fishing - Implements and appliances. 2. Fisheries. I. Title. (Series)

NL 0431313 DI

Lobell, Nathan David, 1911-
The shadow and the blot, by N. D. and G. G. Lobell. [1st ed.] New York, Harper [1949]
240 p. 21 cm.

I. Lobell, Griselda G., joint author. II. Title.

PZ3.L77967Sh 49-7822*

NL 0431314 DLC WaE OrP PP TxU

Lobell, William.
The Americans; a play in seven scenes and prologue, by William Lobell. New York, The Reader press, 1940.
x, 80 p. 21cm.
"First printing."

1. European war, 1914-1918—Drama. I. Title.
Library of Congress PS3523.O2A7 1940 40-5773
——— Copy 2.
Copyright D pub. 68667 [3] 812.5

NL 0431315 DLC

Lobell, William.
The fire door and other stories, by William Lobell. New York, The Reader press, 1937.
vii, 3-870 p. 21cm.
"First edition."

I. Title. 37-1374
Library of Congress PZ3.L7797Fi

NL 0431316 DLC

Lobell, William.
The steed success. New York, Reader Press, 1949.
758 p. 22 cm.

I. Title.
PZ3.L7797St 49-48225*

NL 0431317 DLC ViU

Lobelli, Giovanni Andrea, 1611-1683, ed.
Innocentia victrix sive Sententia comitiorum imperÿ Sinici pro innocentia Christianae religionis
see under title

Loben, Peter, Referendar: § 254 des Bürgerlichen Gesetzbuches und die Rechtsprechung des Reichsgerichtes. Mülheim a. Rh. 1909: Künstler. IX, 70 S. 8°
Leipzig, Jur. Diss. v. 29. Mai 1909
[Geb. 1. Nov. 84 Kerpen, Kr. Bergheim; Wohnort: Mülheim a. Rh.; Staatsangeh.: Preußen; Vorbildung: Gymn. Mülheim Reife O. 03; Studium: Bonn 2, München 1, Berlin 1, Bonn 2 S.; Rig. 30. Juni 06.] [U 09. 2594

NL 0431319 ICRL MH-L

Loben de Salazar, Don Francisco, pseud.
see Isla, Jose Francisco de, 1703- 1781.

Lobenberg, Alfred
Die unterschlagung an vertretbaren sachen
Inaug. Diss. Erlangen, 1931.
Bibl.

NL 0431321 ICRL

Lobenhofer, Eduard.
Fachrechnen ohne Algebra im Elektrohandwerk. München, R. Oldenbourg, 1943.
80 p. 17 cm.

1. Electric engineering—Tables, calculations, etc.
TK151.L85 50-51530

NL 0431322 DLC OU

Lobenhoffer, Wilhelm.
Funktionsprüfungen an transplantierten Nieren. Jena: G. Fischer, 1913. 1 p.l., 48 p., 1 pl. 8°.
Dissertation, Erlangen.
Repr.: Mitteilungen aus den Grenzgebieten der Medizin und Chirurgie. Bd. 26, Heft 2.
Bibliography, p. 46-48.

1. Kidneys.
N. Y. P. L. January 15, 1914.

NL 0431323 NN NIC ICRL DNLM NNC CtY

---

ar W 53580 no.5

Lobenhoffer, Wilhelm, 1879-
Über die Entwicklung der Abszessmembran bei Gehirnabszess. Erlangen, Buchdr. von Junge & Sohn, 1905.
19 p. 22cm.

Inaug.-Diss.--Erlangen.

NL 0431324 NIC DNLM ICRL

SPEC-M PS 623 .D7 1934#14

Lobensky, Louis.
The snatchers; a one-act drama in one scene. [Columbia, Mo., University of Missouri, 1934]
14 l. illus. (Dramatic prize plays. 1934, no. 14)
(A) The snatchers.
(S) Dramatic Arts Club, Columbia, Mo. Dramatic prize plays. 1934, no. 14.

NL 0431325 MoU

Lobenstein (Joh. Daniel). *Disput. inaug. med. exhibens ægrum dysuria cum tenesmo laborantem. 24 pp. 4°. *Giessæ, lit. vid. J. R. Vulpii*, 1724.

NL 0431326 DNLM

LOBENSTEIN, Max, 1905-
Über die herstellung einer löslichen stärke durch einwirkung von natriumhypochloritlauge auf stärke u.ihre eigenschaften. Inaug.-diss. Leipzig, Schwarzenberg & Schumann g.m.b.h., 1930.

pp.88. Illustr.
"Lebenslauf", p.88.

NL 0431327 MH-C CtY ICRL

Lobenstein, Maximilian Hofer von
see Hofer von Lobenstein, Maximilian, Freiherr, 1901-

Lobenstein, Theodor, 1878- Beiträge zur Kenntniss von Hydrazonen. Weida i. Th. 1909: Thomas & Hubert. 79 S. 8°
Leipzig, Phil. Diss. v. 7. Okt. 1909, Ref. Beckmann, Hantzsch
[Geb. 14. März 78 Hann.-Münden; Wohnort: Leipzig-Möckern; Staatsangeh.: Preußen; Vorbildung: Realgym. Kassel Reife O. 96; Studium: Göttingen 3, Leipzig 18 S.; Rig. 19. Juli 09.] [U 10. 3186

NL 0431329 ICRL OCU PU MH CtY

Lobenstein, Ger.
Festschrift der Stadt Lobenstein zur 700-Jahr-Feier
see under title

BR817 .S3S3

Lobensteinisches geseegnetes denckmahl/gestifftet von denen saltzburgischen emigranten. Oder: Eine kurtze erzehlung desjenigen guten/welches man an denen saltzburgischen emigranten in der...stadt Lobenstein wahrgenommen hat ... [Lobenstein|H.C.Simon/buchb.,1732.
24 p. 17cm. [With Schelhorn, J.G. Historische nachricht vom ursprunge...der evangelischen religion in den salzburgischen landen. Leipzig, 1732]
Signed: C.F.St.
1.Salzburgers-- Emigration, 1731-1735.

NL 0431331 ICU

VOLUME 337

Lobenstine, Belle Willson, 1883- ed.

Lobenstine, William Christian, 1831–1918.
Extracts from the diary of William C. Lobenstine, December 31, 1851–1858; biographical sketch by Belle W. Lobenstine. ⌊New York⌋ Priv. print., 1920.

Lobenstine, Edwin Carlyle, 1872- ed.

The China Christian year book.

Shanghai, Kwang Hsüeh publishing house, 19 -19; Christian literature society, 1923–

BJ18c
+937ℓ
Lobenstine, Edwin Carlyle, 1872- comp.
[Clippings (mounted) including illustrations, mainly from Shanghai newspapers, Aug.13-Dec. 14,1937]
4v. 28x35-38½x30cm.
Lettered on binding: Scrap book.

1. China - Hist. - 1937-

NL 0431334 CtY

Lobenstine, Edwin Carlyle, 1872–
The relation of church and mission in China, by E. C. Lobenstine; a statement prepared for the meeting of the International missionary council at Oxford, July 9th–16th, 1923. London, International missionary council ⌊1923⌋
35 p. 24½ᶜᵐ.

1. Missions—China. I. Title.

Library of Congress BV3415.L6 23-12762

NL 0431335 DLC CtY

Lobenstine, Edwin Carlyle, 1872-

Central China famine relief committee, *Shanghai.*
... Report and accounts from October 1, 1911, to June 30, 1912. Shanghai, Printed by the North-China daily news & herald, ltd., 1912.

Lobenstine, Ralph Waldo, 1874–
... Prenatal care, by Ralph W. Lobenstine ... and Harold C. Bailey ... New York, London, D. Appleton and company, 1926.
xiv, 211 p. illus., diagrs. 25ᶜᵐ. (Clinical pediatrics ... supervising editor, R. S. Haynes ... vol. I)
Includes bibliographies.

1. Pregnancy. 2. Obstetrics. I. Bailey, Harold Capron, 1879– joint author.

Library of Congress RJ23.C5 vol. I 26-16692

OC1JC OC1W-H MiU ICJ
NL 0431337 DLC CaBVaU OrU-M DNLM NcU-H PPHa PPC OU

Lobenstine, Ralph Waldo, 1874–
... Prenatal care, by Ralph W. Lobenstine ... and Harold C. Bailey ... *New York, London, D. Appleton and company, ᶜ1930.
xiv, 211 p. illus., diagrs. 25ᶜᵐ. (Clinical pediatrics ... supervising editor, R. S. Haynes ... vol. I)
*47 illustrations.
Includes bibliographies.

NL 0431338 ViU

Lobenstine, William Christian, 1831–1918.
Extracts from the diary of William C. Lobenstine, December 31, 1851–1858; biographical sketch by Belle W. Lobenstine. ⌊New York⌋ Priv. print., 1920.
9 p. l., 3-101 p. front. (port.) pl., facsim. 23ᶜᵐ.

1. Overland journeys to the Pacific. I. Lobenstine, Belle Willson, 1883– ed.

Library of Congress F593.L79 20-21415

NL 0431339 DLC ICU NIC

Lobensteinisches gesangbuch. 1769.
Geistlicher lieder-segen in sich haltend 1620. der besten und erbaulichsten alten und neuen lieder welche mit fleiss durchsehen, verbessert und nöthigen orts mit anmerckungen erläutert worden nebst einem vorbericht von D. G. S. 3. aufl. Lobenstein, Gedruckt bei G. F. Authenrieth, 1769.
12 p. l., 1395, ⌊21⌋ p. 17½ᶜᵐ.
"Vorbericht" signed: David Gottfried Schöber.
Without music.
First edition 1735.

1. Lutheran church—Hymns. 2. Hymns, German. I. Schöber, David Gottfried, 1696–1778, ed. II. Title.

Library of Congress BV481.L6L6 1769 42-43203

NL 0431340 DLC

Lobenthal, Günter Oeltze von

see

Oeltze von Lobenthal, Günter, 1911-

Lobenwein (Aloysius). *De ulno. 46 pp. 8°. *Patavii, Cartallier,* 1835.

NL 0431342 DNLM

QSB
qL797d
1814
LOBENWEIN, Johann Andreas, 1758-1820
De monstrosa genitalium deformitate et spina bifida; commentatio. [n. p., 1814]
54 p. illus.
Caption title.

NL 0431343 DNLM

Lobenwein (Joannes Andreas) [1758–1820]. *De paracentesi thoracis. 48 pp. sm. 4°. *Jenæ, ex off. Fickelscherrio-Stranckmanniana,* [1785].

NL 0431344 DNLM PPC

1848-1888.
Lober (César), *Contribution à l'étude des maladies du cœur. 39 pp. 4°. *Paris,* 1874. No. 199.

NL 0431345 DNLM

Lober, Cesar
——. *Paralysies, contractures, affections douloureuses de cause psychique. 116 pp. 8°. *Paris, O. Doin,* 1886.
Concours.

NL 0431346 DNLM

Lober, Cesar
——. Statistique médicale de la ville de Lille; de la mortalité des nouveau-nés et des moyens de la diminuer. (Ouvrage couronné; prix Pingreuon, 1879.) xiv, 88 pp., 6 tab. 8°. *Paris, O. Doin,* [1879].

NL 0431347 DNLM

HB
1323.I4
L797s
1880
LOBER, César, 1848-1888
Statistique médicale de la ville de Lille; de la mortalité des nouveau-nés et des moyens de la diminuer. Paris, Doin ⌊1880⌋
xiv, 88 p. illus.
"Ouvrage couronné par la Société des sciences de Lille, Prix Pingrenon 1879."
Title

NL 0431348 DNLM

Lober, Ernst: Rechtsgrund und Umfang der vertraglichen Haftung des Mieters für seine Gäste. [Maschinenschrift.] VII, 62 S. 4°. — **Auszug:** (Bernstadt i. Schl.) [1922]: (Siegert). 2 Bl. 8°
Breslau, R.- u. staatswiss. Diss. v. 10. Juni 1922 ⌊U 22. 1137

NL 0431349 ICRL

Lober, Eugen
see Lober, Julius Max Eugen, 1859-

D150.72
L78
Lober, Gertrude
Second purification of the free association test. Worksample 35, Form D. By Gertrude Lober. ⌊Boston⌋ Human engineering laboratory, 1939.
vii, 42 p. tables. 27ᶜᵐ. (Human engineering laboratory. Technical report no. 34)

Reproduced from type-written copy.
1. Mental tests.

NL 0431351 NNC

Lober, Heinrich, 1895–
Die Stadt Bayreuth unter dem Markgrafen Christian-Ernst, 1655–1712...von Heinrich Lober... Bayreuth: L. Ellwanger, 1930. viii, 250 p. incl. tables. 8°.
Dissertation, Erlangen, 1927.
Lebenslauf, last page.
Bibliography, p. 229–250.

539187A. 1. Municipal government—Germany—Bayreuth.
N. Y. P. L. July 23, 1931

NL 0431352 NN CtY PU MiU MH ICRL

Lober, John Baptiste, joint author.

Lesley, Robert Whitman, 1853–
History of the Portland cement industry in the United States, with appendices covering progress of the industry by years and an outline of the organization and activities of the Portland cement association, written by Robert W. Lesley ... in cooperation with his fellow members of the Committee on history, John B. Lober ... and George S. Bartlett ... Chicago, New York ⌊etc.⌋ International trade press, inc. ⌊ᶜ1924⌋

Lober ([Julius Max] Eugen) [1859–]. *Doppelseitige Tubo-Ovarialcysten. 32 pp. 8°. *Berlin, G. Lange,* 1886.

NL 0431354 DNLM

Lober, Mabel.

LC1045
.A25
no. 175
⌊**Foster, Terry Clarence**⌋ 1892–
... Manual for case workers; a handbook of instructions, policies, and procedures for the guidance of supervisors and agents of vocational rehabilitation. 1934. United States Department of the interior. Harold L. Ickes, secretary. Office of education. George F. Zook, commissioner. Washington, U. S. Govt. print. off., 1934.

VOLUME 337

Hk2
32lf

Lober, Vilma, 1920-
Die Frauen der Romantik im Urteil ihrer Zeit. [Gunzenhausen]1947.
vii, 91p. 19cm.
Inaug.-Diss. - Erlangen.
Bibliography: p. [85]-91.
Vita.

NL 0431356 CtY NIC DLC-P4

Lobera, Alonso.
Carta del p. Alonso Lobera de la Compañia de Jesus, rector del Colegio maximo de San Pablo, para los superiores de las casas, y colegios de esta provincia del Perù, sobre la muerte, y exemplares virtudes del padre Pedro Foronda, de la misma compañia. ₍Lima? 1759?₎
Microfilm copy, made in 1943, of the original in the Medina collection, Biblioteca nacional de Santiago de Chile. Positive.
Negative film in Brown university library.
Collation of the original, as determined from the film: ₍22₎ p.
Caption title.
Dated: Lima, y junio 6. de 1759.
Medina, La imprenta en Lima, 1130.
1. Foronda, Pedro, 1683-1759.
Microfilm AC-2 reel 214, no. 13 Mic A 49-1065
Brown Univ. Library
for Library of Congress ₍2₎†

NL 0431357 RPB DLC

Lobera, Alonso.
Riffa y planto de democrito y heraclito traduzido de Ytaliano en neuftia Lengua Vulgar... Valladolid, 1553.

NL 0431358 NNH

Lobera, Antonio
see Lobera y Abio, Antonio, d. 1760.

Case
F
40939
.516

LOBERA, ATHANASIO DE, d.1605.
Historia de las grandezas dela muy antigua ciudad y iglesia de Leõ, y de su obispo sant Froylan, con las del glorioso S. Atilano obispo de Çamora. Valladolid, D. Fernandez de Cordoua, 1596.
₍8₎, 422, ₍2₎ *l.* 20cm.
Titles and text within line borders; title vignettes (bishop's? arms) Initials.
In three parts, each with special t.-p.
Part 3 has title: Tercera parte. Trata la historia, de la vida y milagros del glorioso S. Atilano.

NL 0431360 ICN MoU NNH

Lobera, Cándido.
See
Lobera Girela, Cándido.

Lobera, Luis Dávila.
See
Lobera de Avila, Luis.

Lobera, Pedro Marino de
see Marino de Lovera, Pedro, 1520-1590.

Lobera de Avila, Luis.
Banncket der hofe und edelleut...
Franckfurt, C. Egenolff, 1551.

NL 0431364 NNNAM

Lobera de Avila, Luis
Bancket der Hofe und Edelleut. Des gesunden lebens Regiment...Franckfurt, Egen-off., 1556.
136 p.

NL 0431365 PPC

Lobera de Avila, Luis.
Banquete de nobles caballeros (1530) Madrid, 1952.
xvi, 193 p. illus., facsims. 24 cm. (Reimpresiones bibliográficas, 3)
"Se han tirado trescientos ejemplares ... numerados del 1 al 300. Núm. 118."
1. Medicine—15th-18th cent. 2. Hygiene—Early works to 1800. I. Title.
R128.6.L6 610 53-26886

NL 0431366 DLC CU TxU NN IU MU MH CU-S

Lobera de Avila, Luis.
Libꝛo de experiēcias de medicina y muy apꝛouado poꝛ sus effectos: ansi en esta nuestra España como fuera della. Hecho poꝛ el doctissimo y muy afamado y muy experimentado doctor Luys Dauila de Lobera ... Dirigido al reuerendissimo y muy yllustre señoꝛ don Luys Cabeça 8 Vaca obispo de Palēcia conde de Pernia ... Con pꝛeuilegio. ₍*Colophon:* Impresso en Toledo en casa de Iuan de Ayala, año M.D.XLIIII₎
Film copy, made in 1941, of the original in the Medina collection, Biblioteca nacional de Santiago de Chile. Positive.
Negative film in Brown university library.
Collation of the original, as determined from the film: xxxiiii numb. l.
₍*With his* Libꝛo delas quatro enfermedades coꝛtesanas. Toledo, 1544₎
First edition, Medina, Biblioteca hispano-americana, 121.
1. Medicine—1500-1800.
Brown univ. Library A 45-4338
for Library of Congress Film AC-2 reel 66, no. 6

NL 0431367 RPB DLC

WZ
240
fL797ℓ
1542

LOBERA DE AVILA, Luis
Libro de pestilencia curativo y preservativo: y de fiebres pestilenciales, con la cura de todos los accidentes dellas, y de las otras fiebres, y habla de phlebotomia, ventosas, sanguisuelas: y de las diez y nueve enfermedades subitas que son utilissimas. Y ciertas preguntas muy utiles en medicina en romance Castellano y Latin: y otras cosas muy necessarias en medicina y cirugia ... [Alcalá de Henares? Juan de Brocar? 1542?]
[10], xlii *ℓ.* 28 cm.
Imprint from Garcia Lopez, Ensayo de una tipografía Complutense, Madrid 1889, no. 185.

NL 0431368 DNLM NNH MnU NNNAM PBL

Lobera de Avila, Luis
——. Libro de pestilencia curativo y preservativo; y de fiebres pestilenciales, con la cura de todos los accidentes dellas y de las otras fiebres, y habla de phlebotomia, ventosas, sanguisuelas; y de las diez y nueve enfermedades subitas que son utilissimas. Y ciertas preguntas muy utiles en medicina en romance, castellano y latin; y otras cosas muy necessarias en medicina y cirugia. 9 p. l., 52 ff. fol. [*Alcala de Henares*, 1542?]
Bound with the following.

NL 0431369 DNLM PBL

WZ
290
L797L
1923

LOBERA DE AVILA, Luis
Libro del régimen de la salud, y de la esterilidad de los hombres y mujeres, y de las enfermedades de los ninos, y otras cosas utilísimas. Con una introducción y numerosas notas del Dr. Baltasar Hernández Briz. Madrid, Cosano, 1923.
355 p. illus. (Biblioteca clásica de la medicina española, t. 5)
A reissue, with notes, of the author's work published in 1551.
Title Series

CU-M MnU IU
NL 0431370 DNLM ICJ TxU CU NcD-MC MiU CLU CtY-M MH

B613
L784

Lobera de Avila, Luis.
Libro del regimiento de la salud, y de la esterilidad de los hõbres y mugeres, y đ las ẽfermedades đ los niños y otras cosas vtilissimas. ₍Valladolid, Sebastian Martinez₎ 1551.
xcvi *l.* 27cm.

NL 0431371 MnU KU-M

WZ
240
fL797v
1542

LOBERA DE AVILA, Luis
Libro delas quatro enfermedades cortesanas que son. Catarro. Gota arthetica sciatica. Mal de piedra y de riñones & hijada. E mal de buas: y otras cosas utilissimas. Nuevamente compuesto ... [Toledo, Juan de Ayala] 1544.
lxxxiii (i. e. lxxxii) *ℓ.*; xxxiiii *ℓ.* 28 cm.
Part [2] has separate title page: Libro de experiencias de medicina y muy aprovado por sus effectos: ansi en esta nuestra España como fuera della ...
The royal privilege on the verso of the title page to part [2] refers to both parts. Cf. Perez Pastor, La imprenta en Toledo. Madrid, 1887, no. 202.
Text of part [2] in Spanish and Latin. Salvá 2716, 2719 [this copy]
Bound with HIS Vergel de sanidad. [Alcala de Henares, 1542]

NL 0431373 DNLM PBL NNH

Lobera de Avila, Luis.
Libꝛo delas quatro enfermedades coꝛtesanas q̄ son: catarro, gota arthetica sciatica, mal de piedra y 8 riñones ꝛ hijada, e mal de buas: y otras cosas vtilissimas. Nueuamēte cōpuesto poꝛ el excellētissimo doctor Luys Lobera de Auila ... Dirigido al muy illustre señoꝛ don Juā de Çuñiga ... Cō pꝛiuilegio nueuamēte cōcedido. ₍*Colophon:* Impresso en Toledo en casa de Iuan de Ayala₎ 1544.
Film copy, made in 1941, of the original in the Medina collection, Biblioteca nacional de Santiago de Chile. Positive.
Negative film in Brown university library.
Collation of the original, as determined from the film: lxxxiij (*i. e.* lxxxii) numb. l.
Errors in foliation: leaves xxv, xliii, lvi, lxix, lxxxii misnumbered xxix, xlviii, lvii, lxviii, lxxxiij, respectively.
First edition.
Medina, Biblioteca hispano-americana, 121.
With this is bound the author's Libꝛo de experiēcias de medicina. Toledo, 1544.
1. Medicine—1500-1800.
A 45-4337
Brown univ. Library
for Library of Congress Film AC-2 reel 66, no. 6
₍2₎†

NL 0431375 RPB DLC PBL

WZ
240
L797ℓI
1558

LOBERA DE AVILA, Luis
Libro delle quatro infermita cortigiane, che sono catarro, gotta, artetica, sciatica: mal di pietre, & di reni: dolore di fianchi, et mal francese, & d'altre cose utilissime ... Con un trattato di esperienze certissime, & provate. Tradotto di Spagnuolo in Italiano per M. Pietro Lauro. [Venetia, Gio. Battista, & Marchio Sessa, 1558]
[23], 272, [11] *ℓ.* 16 cm.
Translations of HIS Libro delas quatro enfermedades cortesanas, and Libro de experiencias de medicina, both published in Toledo in 1544.
I. Lauro, Pietro, 16th cent., tr.

NL 0431376 DNLM PPC CtY-M CLU-M NNNAM

WZ
240
L797vG
1531

LOBERA DE AVILA, Luis
Ein nutzlich Regiment der Gesundtheyt, genant das Vanquete, oder Gastmal der edlen Diener von der Complexion, Eigenschafft, Schad, und Nutz allerley Speysz, Trancks, unnd von allem, damit sich der Mensch in Gesundtheyt enthelt, mit sampt einem kurtzen Regiment, wye man sich in der Pestilentz, pestilentzischen Fieber unnd Schweysz halten soll. Gemacht durch ... Ludovicum de Avila ... ehemals in lateynischer und hyspanischer Sprach beschriben, unnd durch ... Michaelem Krautwadel ... zů Landsperg verteűtscht ... [Augspurg, Heynrich Steyner, 1531]
[194] p. illus. 18 cm.
Imperfect: sig. A4 wanting; supplied in photocopy from College of physicians of Philadelphia library.
A translation of his Vanquete de nobles cavalleros ... issued by the same publisher the previous year.
I. Krautwadel, Michael, fl. 1531, tr.

NL 0431378 DNLM OrU-M NNH CtY-M DFo MiU NNNAM

VOLUME 337

WZ LOBERA DE AVILA, Luis
240 Remedio de cuerpos humanos y silva de experiencias y otras
fL797v cosas utilissimas; nuevamente compuesto ... [Alcalá de
1542 Henares? Juan de Brocar? 1542?]
[4], clxxxiii (i. e. clxxxii) ℓ. 28 cm.
Text in Spanish and Latin.
Contents. —Libro de anatomia. —Remedio de cuerpos [etc.]— Antidotario.
Bound (as issued?) with HIS Vergel de sanidad. [Alcala de Henares, 1542]
Cf. Garcia López, Ensayo de una tipografía Complutense, Madrid 1889, no. 184, who calls for 4 prel. leaves, 183 numbered leaves and one "para unas recetas y el colofon". This final leaf must be that seemingly misbound after leaf cii in the NLM copy of HIS Vergel de sanidad.
Salvá 2717 [this copy]

NL 0431380 DNLM NNH CLU-M MnU PBL

WZ LOBERA DE AVILA, Luis
240 Vergel de sanidad: que por otro nombre se llamava Banquete de
fL797v cavalleros, y orden de bivir: ansi en tiempo de sanidad como de
1542 enfermedad: y habla copiosamente de cada manjar que complexion, y propriedad tenga: y de sus provechos y daños ... Nuevamente corregido y añadido ... [Alcala de Henares, Joan de Brocar, 1542]
[10], cii, [1] ℓ. 28 cm.
Text in Spanish and Latin.
The final leaf, containing Latin verses on weights and measures, brief glossary of terms, and colophon, appears to belong to the Remedio de cuerpos humanos, with which this work seems to have been issued. Cf. Garcia Lopez, Ensayo de una tipografia Complutense, Madrid 1889, no. 184, and the note to the second work in this catalog.
Salvá 2715 [this copy]
With this is bound HIS Remedio de cuerpos humanos [Alcalá de Henares? 1542?]; Libro de pestilencia [Alcalá de Henares? 1542?]; Libro delas quatro enfermedades cortesanas [&] Libro de experiencias de medicina [Toledo] 1544.

NL 0431382 DNLM NNH NNNAM MnU PBL

Lobera Girela, Cándido.
Notas sobre el problema de Melilla. Melilla, Tip. El Telegrama del Rif, 1912.
156 p. port. 23 cm.

1. Melilla, Morocco. I. Title.

DT329.M4L6 76-220753

NL 0431383 DLC NN

Lobera Girela, Candido.
El problema rifeño. Melilla, El Telegrama del Rif, 1909.
40 p. 8°.

NL 0431384 NN

Lobera Girela, Cándido.
Problemas de Melilla; los derechos de arbitrios y las mercancías de tránsito, [por] Cándido Lobera Girela... [Melilla:] Tipografía "El Telegrama del Rif," 1917. 2 p.l., (1)8-69 p. 8°.

1. Morocco (Spanish). 2. Melilla. 3. Morocco.—History, 1911.
N. Y. P. L. October 9, 1918.

NL 0431385 NN

Lobera Girela, Cándido.
Problemas del protectorado; los Bienes Majzen, [por] Cándido Lobera Girela... Melilla: Tip. El Telegrama del Rif, 1916. 45 p. 8°.

1. Morocco (Spanish). 2. Morocco. —History, 1911.
N. Y. P. L. October 11, 1918.

NL 0431386 NN

Ayer LOBERA Y ABIO, ANTONIO, d. 1760.
4A El porque de todas las ceremonias de la
338 iglesia, y sus mysterios: cartilla de prelados, y sacerdotes, que enseña las ordenanzas ecclesiasticas.... Escrito, y compuesto por don Antonio Lobera, y Abio.... Figueras: Por Ignacio Portèr Impressor, y Librero [1758]
8 ℓ, 734 p. 21cm.
First edition. This copy formerly in the Bibliotheca Montereyensis-Angelorum Dioeceseos.

NL 0431387 ICN

Lobera y Abio, Antonio, *d.* 1760.
El porque de todas las ceremonias de la iglesia, y sus mysterios: cartilla de prelados, y sacerdotes, que enseña las ordenanzas ecclesiasticas, que deben saber todos los ministros de Dios. Escrito, y compuesto por don Antonio Lobera, y Abio ... En forma de dialogo symbolico, entre un vicario instruido, y un estudiante curioso ... Barcelona, F. Generas, impressor, y librero, 1760.
8 p. l., 734, [2] p. 20½cm.
First published, Figueras, 1758.

1. Catholic church. Liturgy and ritual. I. Title.

38-31861

Library of Congress BX1971.L6 1760

NL 0431388 DLC PPPD

PQ Lobera y Abio, Antonio, d. 1760
6171 El porqué de todas las ceremonias de la Igle-
.A195 sia y sus misterios. Cartilla de prelados y
L797 sacerdotes, que enseña las ordenanzas entre un vicario y un estudiante curioso compuso. Novisima ed., corr. Barcelona, Impr. de Sierra y Marti, 1791.
735 p. 22 cm.

NL 0431389 WU

LOBERA Y ABIO, Antonio.
El por qué de todas las ceremonias de la iglesia y sus mysterios, cartilla de prelados y sacerdotes, que enseña las ordenanzas eclesiasticas que deben saber todos los ministros de Dios, y en forma de dialogo simbolico entre un vicario instruido, y un estudiante curioso ... Decima impresión, corregida cuidadosamente y añadidas algunas notas ... En Madrid, En la Imprenta de Don Josef de Urrutia, 1791.
pp.[4],642,[2]. 22 cm.

NL 0431390 MH-P

Lobera y Abio, Antonio, d. 1760.
El porque de todas las ceremonias de la Iglesia y sus misterios. Cartilla de prelados y sacerdotes, que enseña las ordenanzas eclesiástas que deben saber todos los ministros de Dios, y en forma de diálogo simbólico, entre un vicario instruido y un estudiante curioso ... Mexico, Imprenta de la Voz de la Religion, 1851.

2 v. 17 cm.

1. Liturgy - Catechisms, question-books.
2. Liturgy - Popular works. I. Title: Las ceremonias de la Iglesia.

NL 0431391 PLatS

264.02 **Lobera y Abio, Antonio, d. 1760.**
L78p2 **El por qué de todas las ceremonias de la iglesia, y sus misterios. Cartilla de prelados y sacerdotes, que enseña las ordenanzas eclesiásticas que deben saber todos los ministros de Dios, y que en forma de diálogo simbólico entre un vicario instruido y un estudiante curioso, escribió y compuso. D. Antonio Lobera y Abio... 2. ed. Madrid, Libreria de D.M. Olamendi, 1867.**
526 p. 22 cm.
First publishe ed, Figueras, 1758.

1. Catholic church. Liturgy and ritual.
I. Title.

NL 0431393 LU PU

Lobera y Castro, Rafael
see Lovera Castro, Rafael.

863L784 LOBERA Y MENDIETA, José de.
OMa ... La muger mas pennitente, y espanto de caridad, la venerable hermana Mariana de Jesus, hija de la venerable orden tercera de penitencia de n. s. p. s. Francisco de la ciudad de Toledo... segunda parte. Madrid, J. de Zuñiga, 1748.
v. 20 cm.
At head of title: Comedia nueva.
I. Title.

NL 0431395 MnU

863L784 LOBERA Y MENDIETA, José de.
OM ...La muger mas penitente, y espanto de charidad, la venerable hermana Mariana de Jesus. Primera parte... [Barcelona? 1750?]
v. 20 cm.
Caption title.
At head of title: Comedia nueva.
I. Title.

NL 0431396 MnU NcU

F **[LOBERAN DE MONTIGNY, GABRIEL DE]**
39 **Les grandeurs de la maison de France.**
.515 **Paris, L. Bilaine, 1667.**
[20], 143p. geneal. tables. 24cm.
Bookplate of C. van Baviere.

NL 0431397 ICN

[Loberdos, Agapios, 1721-95]
'Ιστορία τῶν δύω ἐτῶν 1787, 1788, περιέχουσα τάς πράξεις τῶν παρόντων πολέμων μέσον τῶν 'Αουστρορώσσων καί τῶν 'Οθωμανῶν, συλλεχθεῖσα ἐκ τῶν διαφόρων εἰδήσεων ὁπού ἐκδίδονται εἰς τύπον εἰς τήν 'Ιταλικήν καί Γαλλικήν διάλεκτον καί μεταφρασθεῖσα εἰς τό κοινότερον τῶν καθ' ἡμᾶς 'Ελλήνων ἰδίωμα, παρά Α.Λ. Τόμος πρῶτος. 'Ενετίῃσι, Παρά Δημητρίῳ Θεοδοσίου, 1791
ις', 331 p.
No more published?

NL 0431398 MH

VOLUME 337

4 HJ- 225 Loderdos, Al I.
Ta epitokia en te Hellenike chrematagora.
1936.
95 p.
In Greek characters.

NL 0431399 DLC-P4 InU

Nbg 935l Loberdos, Al I
... 'Ο τόκος ἐν τῇ συγχρόνῳ οἰκονομίᾳ. 'Αθῆναι[Τύποις "Τὰ χρονικά"]1935.
119p.,3l. incl.tables. 25cm.
"Βιβλιογραφία": p. [9]-11.

NL 0431400 CtY

WK 500 L797p 1938 LOBERDOS, Ger.
Περὶ ὁρμονῶν τῆς ὑποφύσεως. 'Αθῆναι, Δρουκα, 1938.
8 p.
Title transliterated: Peri hormonōn tēs hypophyseōs.
1. Pituitary gland

NL 0431401 DNLM

[Loberdos, Joannes D.]
Hymnos eis tēn Henōsin. [n.p., 187-?]
100 p. 17 cm.
Lacks t.p.; title taken from section half-title.
1. Greek poetry, Modern - Texts.

NL 0431402 MdBP

Loberdos, Spyridon Pan
see Loberdos, Spyros Pangiōtou, 1877-1938.

Loberdos, Spyros Pangiōtou, 1877-1938
'Αποταμίευσις καὶ ταμιευτήρια.
'Εν 'Αθήναις. 1904. 93, (2) pp. [Σύλλογος πρὸς διάδοσιν ὠφελίμων βιβλίων. 'Εκδόσεις. 51.] 17 cm., in 8s.
Two copies.

K2086 — Greece. Language. Modern Greek. Works in Modern Greek. — S.r. — Savings banks.

NL 0431404 MB OCU

Loberdos, Spros Pangiōtou, 1877-1938.
'Ο ἐθνικὸς πλοῦτος. Α', Β'.
'Εν 'Αθήναις. 1901, 1902. 2 v. Tables. [Σύλλογος πρὸς διάδοσιν ὠφελίμων βιβλίων. 'Εκδόσεις. 24, 27.] 17 cm., in 8s.
Contents. — Α'. Γεωργικὰ προϊόντα. — Κτηνοτροφία. — 'Ορυκτὰ καὶ μέταλλα. Β'. Βιομηχανία. — Συγκοινωνία, ναυτιλία καὶ ἐμπόριον.
Bibliography, vol. 1, pp. 92, 93.
Relates to Greece.
Two copies of vol. Α'.

K2086 — S.r. — Greece. Geog. — Greece. Lang. Modern Greek. Works in Modern Greek.

NL 0431405 MB OCU

BX395 .C5L6 Loberdos, Spyridōn Pan., 1877-
'Ο μητροπολίτης Σμύρνης Χρυσόστομος. Σπυρίδων Λοβέρδος ἔγραψε. 'Αθῆναι, 1929
3 p.l., 9-221 p., 1 l. illus. 22½cm.
Title vignette (seal of the metropolitan of Smyrna)
Title, running title, captions, initials, tail-pieces, and paging in red.
Illustrated by Kōstēs Parthenēs. cf. verso of 2d prelim. leaf.

"'Εκδοσις τῆς 'Επιτροπῆς πρὸς συλλογὴν ἐργάνων δι' ἀνέγερσιν ἐθνικοῦ μνημείου εἰς τὸν μητροπολίτην Σμύρνης Χρυσόστομον."
Colophon: Τοῦ βιβλίου τούτου ἐτυπώθησαν δέκα χιλιάδες ἀντίτυπα ἐκ τῶν ὁποίων τετρακόσια ἠριθμημένα ἐπὶ χάρτου μαδαγασκάρης. 'Η ἐκτύπωσις συνεπληρώθη τὴν 20ὴν 'Ιανουαρίου 1929 ἐν τῷ τυπογραφείῳ τῆς ἑταιρείας "Π.Δ.Σακελλάριος".

1.Chrysostomos Kalaphatēs, metropolitan of Smyrna, 1868-1922. I.Parthenēs, Kōstēs 1879- illus.

NL 0431408 OCU MH

Loberdos, Spyros Panagiōtou, 1877-1938.
'Ο Μητροπολίτης Σμύρνης Χρυσόστομος. 2. ἔκδ. 'Αλεξάνδρεια, 'Εκδοτικος Οἶκος Γράμματα, 1930.
223 p. 22 cm.

1. Kalaphatēs, Chrysostomos, 1867-1922.
Title romanized: Ho Metropolitēs Smyrnēs Chrysostomos.

BX395.K33L6 1930 72-213637

NL 0431409 DLC

D 635 .L796 LOBERDOS, SPYROS Panyiōtou, 1877-1938.
'Ο πόλεμος καὶ ἡ οἰκονομικὴ ἐπέμβασις τοῦ Κράτους ⌜ὑπὸ⌝ Σπυρ. Λοβέρδου. 'Εν 'Αθήναις, Τυπογραφικὰ καταστήματα Ταρουσοπούλου, 1916.
38 p.

√1. European War, 1914-1918--Economic aspects.
√I. Title.
T.rom.: Ho polemos kai hē oikonomikē epembasis tou Kratous.

NL 0431410 InU

---

cl-g PA5610 .L73D65 Loberdou, Iōanna.
Δομίνικος· τραγωδία ⌜ὑπὸ⌝ 'Ιωάννας Λοβέρδου. 'Αθήνα, 'Αετός, 1952.
82 p. 23cm.

I.Title.
Title romanized: Dominikos.

NL 0431411 OCU

Loberg, Harry John.
Machine tool selling. 1st ed. New York, McGraw-Hill Book Co., 1949.
ix, 194 p. diagrs. 24 cm.
A summary of a sales refresher course sponsored by the National Machine Tool Builders' Assn. and the American Machine Tool Distributors' Assn., held at Cornell Univ. in July 1948.

1. Machine-tools—Trade and manufacture. 2. Salesman and salesmanship. I. Title.
HF5439.M26L6 658.896219 49-9896*

NL 0431412 DLC OrCS CU NcD OU PPD PP

Loberg, Harry John.
Machine tool selling. 2d ed. New York, McGraw-Hill, 1953.
194 p. illus. 24 cm.

1. Machine-tools—Trade and manufacture. 2. Salesmen and salesmanship. I. Title.
HF5439.M26L6 1953 53-9001 ‡
*658.851 658.896219

NcRS FTaSU OClW
NL 0431413 DLC WaS OrP OrCS PSt PPT TxU OCl OClW

LOBERG, O. N.
Norges fiskerier Udgivet af "Det Kongelige selskab for Norges vel". Kristiania, B.M. Bentzens bogtrykkeri, 1864.
1 p.l., XI, [1], 323, [1] p. 18 1/4 cm.

NL 0431414 MH CU DLC

Loberia, Argentine Republic.
...Monumento del general Bartolome Mitre; discursos y conferencia pronunciados en el acto de su inauguracion, 29 de marzo de 1942. [Loberia, 1942] 39 p. illus. 20cm.

1. Mitre, Bartolomé, pres. Argentine Republic, 1821-1906.
N. Y. P. L. March 29, 1943

NL 0431415 NN ICU DPU

Lobero, Antonio.
Memorie storiche della Banca di S. Giorgio
see under Banco di San Giorgio, Genoa.

Lobero, José.
In the Supreme Court of the State of California, Guillermo Abadie ... vs. José Lobero and wife and T.B. Dibblee
see under California. Supreme Court. [supplement]

Loberschiner, Fr. A
Das Kirchen-Vermögen oder die geistliche Art der Erwerbung und Verwaltung des Gotteshaus-und Pfründenvermögens, auf Grundlage der Oster. Concordats und der in Folge dessen geltenden Bestimmungen praktisch bearbeitet von Dr. Fr. A. Loberschiner. Budweis, L.E. Hansen, 1862.
iv, iv, 272p. 23cm.
1. Benefices, Ecclesiastical (Canon Law).
2. Benefices, Ecclesiastical--Austria. I. Title.
II. Title: Der Erwerbung und Verwaltung des Gotteshaus-und Pfründenvermögens.

NL 0431418 PLatS

Loberschiner, Fr. A., ed.
Versuch einer Erläuterung des zwischen Sr. Heiligkeit Papst Pius IX
see under Catholic Church. Treaties, etc., 1846-1878 (Pius IX)

Lobert, Alice.
See
Lobert-Dupont, Alice.

VOLUME 337

Lobert (Max) [1863-]. *Ein Fall von Thrombose der Pfortader. 35 pp. 8°. *Greifswald, J. Abel.* 1887.

NL 0431421 DNLM

Lobert-Dupont, Alice.
...Les adieux de Simone; un acte, en vers. L'urne pompéienne; un acte, en vers. Asnières (Seine): Édition asniéroise[, 1924?]. 52 p. 8°. (Her: Collection "Mes vingt rejetons." no. 5.)

1. Drama, French. 2. Title. 3. Title: L'urne pompéienne.
N. Y. P. L. September 10, 1925

NL 0431422 NN

Lobert-Dupont, Alice.
...Le mari idéal; comédie en un acte, en prose. La pavillonnette; comédie en un acte, en prose. Asnières: Édition asniéroise[, 1925?]. 94 p. 8°. (Collection "Mes vingt rejetons." no. 7.)

1. Drama, French. 2. Title. 3. Title: La pavillonnette.
N. Y. P. L. June 30, 1927

NL 0431423 NN

Lobert-Dupont, Alice.
...Thémadour; pièce en quatre actes, en vers. Asnières (Seine): Édition Asniéroise[, 1924?]. 115 p. port. 8°. (Collection "Mes vingt rejetons." no. 4.)

1. Drama, French. 2. Title.
N. Y. P. L. January 21, 1925

NL 0431424 NN

BX8022
.P7B2
LOBES, MICHAEL.
Kurtze historische erzehlung wie das heilsame reformations-werck, durch den dienst Herrn Christian Ketelhudten, als den ersten evangelischen prediger in Stralsund durch Gottes gnade angefangen und fortgesetzet worden... Alles...hrsg. von m. Michael Lobes... Stralsund, Gedruckt bey G.C.Schindler [1723]
[12], 75 p. 20cm. [With Balthasar, J.H. Erste[-andere] sammlung einiger zur pommerischen kirchen-historie gehörigen schriften. Greiffswald, 1723-25]
1. Ketelhodt, Christian, 1492-1546.

NL 0431425 ICU IU

Lobes, Vincenz Eduard Guldener von
see Guldener von Lobes, Vincenz Eduard, 1763-1827.

Lobet, Émile.
...À propos de l'orientation professionnelle, par Émile Lobet ... Bruxelles, M. Lamertin, 1934. 49 p. 19cm. (Documents pédotechniques. Année 13, no. 1.)

1. Occupations—Choice. I. Ser.
N. Y. P. L. January 22, 1948

NL 0431427 NN

Lobet, Émile, joint author.

HD7816
.B4L3
Laet, Maurice de, 1891-
Étude de la valeur économique des gestes professionnels [par] M. de Laet [et] É. Lobet. Préf. de Léon-Eli Troclet. Bruxelles, Visscher [1949]

Lobet, Émile.
Vocational guidance in Belgium.
(*In* International labour review. Mar. 1948. 24 cm. v. 57, p. [187]-204)

1. Vocational guidance[—Belgium]
[HD4811.I 65 vol. 57] (331.05) L 48-155 rev*

U. S. Dept. of Labor. Library
for Library of Congress [r50d2]

NL 0431429 DL PP

Lobet, J
Essai sur Jean Cousin.
[Auxerre. 1870.] 43-83, (1) pp. Portraits. Plates. [Almanach historique et statistique de l'Yonne. Année 1870. Partie 3.] 16 cm., in 8s.

L6696 — S.r. — Cousin, Jean, 1522-1594.

NL 0431430 MB

Lobet, J
Le nouveau Bois de Boulogne et ses alentours; histoire, description et souvenirs par J. Lobet. Ouvrage illustré de 26 vignettes par Thérond. Paris, L. Hachette et cie., 1856.
2 p. l., ii, 156 p. incl. illus., plates. 17½cm. (*On cover:* Bibliothèque des chemins de fer. 1. sér.)

1. Paris—Parks—Bois de Boulogne. 2. Paris—Suburbs.
5—14751
Library of Congress DC768.L79

NL 0431431 DLC

Lobet, J.
Plan topographique et historique du Bois de Boulogne et de ses environs. Paris, n.d.
24°

NL 0431432 NN

Lobet, J.
Quelques preuves sur Jean Cousin, peintre, sculpteur, géomètre et graveur, par J. Lobet: avec trente-trois gravures, marques, lettres ornées ou dessins du maître, dont trois portraits de Jean Cousin. Paris, Renouard (H. Loones et c^ie^, succ.) 1881.
2 p. l., 48 p. illus., VIII pl. (incl. front., port., fold. facsim.) 24½cm.
Frontispiece and portrait are mounted photos.
The author does not distinguish between Jean Cousin, 1490 (ca.)-1560? and his son, Jean Cousin, le jeune, 1522 (ca.)-1594?

1. Cousin, Jean, 1490 (ca.)-1560? 2. Cousin, Jean, le jeune, 1522 (ca.)-1594?
13—5237
Library of Congress ND553.C95L6

NL 0431433 DLC NcD PP PPPM

Lobet, Jean.
Des chemins de fer en France, et des différents principes appliqués à leur tracé, à leur construction et à leur exploitation, accompagné d'un examen comparatif sur l'utilité des différentes voies de communication, d'un résumé général de l'état actuel des chemins de fer dans tous les pays d'Europe, et d'un appendice sur les nouveaux systèmes de chemins de fer exécutés ou proposés jusqu'à ce jour, par J. Lobet ... Paris, Parent-Desbarres, 1845.
708 p. illus., fold. plates. 18cm.
1. Railroads—France. 2. Railroads—Europe.

A 29-717
Title from Bureau of Railway Economics TF505.L78
Printed by L. C.

NL 0431434 DBRE CtY PPL MH MH-BA MiU

Lobet (Léon). L'hypnotisme en Belgique, et le projet de loi soumis aux chambres législatives. 42 pp. 12°. *Verviers, Ve. J.-P. Massin,* 1891.

NL 0431435 DNLM

Lobet, Léon.

Mahaim, Ernest, 1865- *ed.*
Preisbildung gewerblicher erzeugnisse in Belgien. Mit beiträgen von prof. De Leener, ing. Max L. Gérard, ing. L. Lobet, gen.-insp. Ed. Mathus und ing. P. Stévart. Im auftrage des Vereins für sozialpolitik hrsg. von dr. Ernest Mahaim ... München und Leipzig, Duncker & Humblot, 1914.

Lobet, Marcel.
A la rencontre de Daniel-Rops. [n. p.] Sixaine [1946]
47, [1] p. port. 19 cm.
"Œuvres de Daniel-Rops": p. [48]

1. *Daniel-Rops, Henri, 1901- I. Title.
PQ2607.A53Z7 928.4 47-26644*

NL 0431437 DLC WaSpG NcD

PJ807
.L6
Lobet, Marcel.
Au seuil du désert; introd. a la poésie muselmane. Paris, A. Magné [1940]
78 p. 19cm. (Cahiers des poètes Catholiques, 26)

1. Mohammedan poetry. I. Title.
II. Series.

NL 0431438 MB OrU

Lobet, Marcel.
Chercheurs de Dieu. Préf. de Daniel-Rops. 3. éd., rev. et augm. Bruxelles, Écrits [°1942]
143 p. 19 cm. (Essais, 1)

1. Religion in literature. 2. French literature—Hist. & crit.
I. Title. (Series: Essais. Bruxelles, 1)
PN49.L55 1942 50-46029

NL 0431439 DLC

Lobet, Marcel
Les croisés belges à Constantinople. Bruxelles, Editions Durendal [1953?]

79 p.

NL 0431440 MH

Lobet, Marcel.
...Daniel-Rops, par Marcel Lobet. [Liége] La Sixaine [1946]
47 p. front. 19cm. (À la rencontre de...)

1. Daniel-Rops, Henry, 1901-
N. Y. P. L. February 10, 1948

NL 0431441 NN

VOLUME 337

LOBET, MARCEL.
Daniel-Rops. [Liége] La Sixaine [1946] 47 p. front. 19cm. (À la rencontre de...)

Film reproduction. Negative.

1. Daniel-Rops, Henry, 1901-

NL 0431442 NN

PJ 827 .L78 Lobet, Marcel.
Des Chants du désert au Jardin des roses. Préface d'Emile Dermenghem. [Bruxelles, Maison du poète [1949]
138 p. 20 cm.
Bibliography: p.133-134.

1. Arabic poetry--Hist.& crit. 2. Persian poetry--Hist.& crit. 3. Turkish poetry--Hist. & crit. I. Title.

NL 0431443 MiU NN ICU

LOBET, MARCEL.
L'épopée belge des croisades; Poitiers, Jerusalem, Byzance, Lepante. Liége, Éditions Soledi [194-?]
244 p.

NL 0431444 DDO

Lobet, Marcel
...L épopée belge des croisades. Poitiers, Jerusalem, Byzance, Lepante. Liege, Soledi 1944
244 p.

NL 0431445 PU

Lobet, Marcel.
...Godefroid de Bouillon; essai de biographie antilégendaire. Bruxelles, Éditions Les écrits [1943] 192 p. 20cm.
"Ouvrages consultés," p. [181]-185.

344620B. 1. Godfrey of Bouillon, 1058?-1100. 2. Crusades (First), 1096-1099.
N. Y. P. L. October 23, 1946

NL 0431446 NN WU

Lobet, Marcel.
Histoire mystérieuse et tragique des templiers. 3. éd. rev. et augm. Liége, Soledi, 1944.
274 p. 20 cm.
"Ouvrages consultés": p. [263]-266.

1. Templars.
CR4743.L6 1944 929.712 48-39991*

NL 0431447 DLC NN PU NcD

Lobet, Marcel.
... L'Islam & l'Occident; lettre-préface de Jérôme Tharaud ... et de Jean Tharaud. Thuillies (Belgique) Les Éditions Ramgal; [etc., etc., 1939]
4 p. l., 11-183 p. illus. (map) 18½cm.
"Bibliographie": p. 177-180.

1. Mohammedanism. 2. East.
43-26810
Library of Congress DS38.L6
[2] 297

NL 0431448 DLC CtY NN OrPR

Lobet, Marcel.
... La poésie et l'amour. Paris, La Colombe [1946]
3 p. l., [9]-196 p., 2 l. 18½cm.

1. Love poetry—Hist. & crit. I. Title.
PN1076.L6 A F 47-2640
Harvard univ. Library for Library of Congress [2]†

NL 0431449 MH DLC ICU CLU ViU WU CaBVaU

Lobet, Marcel.
...Une poignée de dattes; contes orientaux illustrés par Arlette Van Calck. Bruxelles, Renaissance du livre [1951] 61 p. illus. 22cm. (Collection "Les étoiles")

NL 0431450 NN

PN513 .L6
Lobet, Marcel.
La science du bien et du mal; essai sur la connaissance littéraire. [Bruxelles] Éditions des Artistes [1954]
161 p. 20 cm.

1. Literature—Hist. & crit. 2. French literature—Hist. & crit. I. Title.
A 54-4789
Illinois. Univ. Library for Library of Congress [1]

NL 0431451 IU WaU NN OCl PBL DLC

Lobet, Marcel.
La science du bien et du mal: essai sur la connaissance littéraire. [Paris] La Nef de Paris [1954]
161 p. 20cm.

NL 0431452 OCU NcD CoU

Lobet, Marcel.
La tragique histoire de l'ordre du Temple. Bruxelles, Office de publicité, 1954. 127 p. illus., ports. 19cm. (Collections Lebègue & nationale. no. 108)

Cover-title: Les templiers, moines et guerriers.
Bibliography, p. 123-125.

1. Templars—Hist.

NL 0431453 NN CtY MH NNC

Lobet den Herren. [Stuttgart, Quellverlag der Ev. Gesellschaft, 1947]
143 p. 15 cm.
"Herausgegeben im Auftrag des Kirchenbezirks Weisheim durch Stadtpfarrer Leopold."

1. Lutheran Church—Hymns. 2. Hymns, German. I. Leopold, ———, ed.
BV481.L6L62 A F 48-3350*
Yale Univ. Library for Library of Congress [1]†

NL 0431454 CtY DLC

Lobet den Herrn, altchristliche Kirchenlieder und geistliche Gedichte... 1928
see under Zoozmann, Richard, 1863-1934, ed.

Lobet den Herrn, der zu Zion wohnet
see under Kunze, Johann Christoph, 1744-1807.

Lobetantz, Martin, respondent.
Concordiae Joh Hus et Martini Lutheri ...
see under Mayer, Johann Friedrich, 1650-1712, praeses.

Lobethal (Julius) [1810-]. Bewijs dat de longtering kan genezen worden door aanwending eener nieuwe geneeswijze. Voor geneeskundigen en hulpbehoevenden. 78 pp. 16°. *Amsterdam, [s. d.]*

NL 0431458 DNLM

617.8 L797c Lobethal, Julius, b.1810.
Conspectus morborum auris humanae. Berolini, Typis Nietackianis, 1833.
[14],91,[5]p. 20cm.

Dissertatio inauguralis - Berlin.
Vita.
Bibliography: 3rd-7th prelim.leaf.

1. Ear - Diseases. I. Title.

NL 0431459 CLSU DNLM PPC

Lobethal, Julius, M.D.
Proof that consumption is curable; with a demonstration of a new healing method of chronic catarrh, etc...by Dr. J. Lobethal of Breslau, Prussia. From the German, translated...by R. Rohland. New York, 1875. 24 p. 12°.

Title from cover.

1. Tuberculosis. 2. Rohland, Robert, M.D., translator.
N. Y. P. L. April 18, 1912.

NL 0431460 NN DNLM PPC DLC

WC 262 L797u 1848 LOBETHAL, Julius, 1810-
Ueber die glückliche Behandlung der asiatischen Cholera durch die homöopathische Heilmethode. Breslau, Scholz, 1848.
32 p.
With this are bound: Kronser, V. N. Studien über die Cholera. Wien, 1848; Hildesheim, Wilhelm. Das Haar und seine Krankheiten. Berlin, 1846.

NL 0431461 DNLM

LOBETHAL, Rudolf, 1890-
Verwaltung und finanzpolitik in Preussen während der jahre 1808-1810. (Von der entlassung Steins bis zum amtsantritt Hardenbergs) Teil I. Die verwaltungsorganisation. Kap. I u. II Inaug.-diss. [Berlin, E. Ebering, 1914?]

"Lebenslauf" at end.

NL 0431462 MH CtY

Lobethan, Friedrich Georg August, b. 1753.
Einleitung zur theoretischen ehe-rechts-gelahrtheit. Von Friedrich Georg August Lobethan. Halle, Im verlag des Waisenhauses, 1775.
220 p., 1 l. 20cm.
Head-pieces.

1. Marriage law. 2. Marriage (Canon law) I. Title.
37-23249

NL 0431463 DLC

VOLUME 337

Lobethan, Friedrich Georg August, *b.* 1753.
Einleitung zur theoretischen ehe-rechts-gelahrtheit, von Friedrich Georg August Lobethan ... 2. verb. aufl. Halle, Waysenhaus, 1785.
xvi, 216 p. 20cm.

1. Marriage law. 2. Marriage (Canon law) I. Title.

37-23055

Library of Congress [2] 173.1

NL 0431464 DLC

Lobethan, Friedrich George August, b. 1753, ed.

Anhalt. *Laws, statutes, etc.*
Die fürstl. anhaltische erneuerte und verbesserte Landes und Process-ordnung, nebst der Gesinde-ordnung, mit erläuternden anmerkungen versehen, als ein blosses privat-werk hrsg. von Friedrich George August Lobethan ... Cöthen, J. A. Aue, 1804.

4K Ger 826 Lobethan, Friedrich Georg August, b. 1753.
Vollständige Abhandlung der Lehre von der Erbfolge. Halle, Im Verlag des Waisenhauses, 1776.
522 p.

NL 0431466 DLC-P4

Lobethan, Johann Konrad, 1688-1735.
...Herrlichkeit der Wiedergebohrnen im Reiche des Lammes ...aus dem V. and VIII. Cap. der Epistel des heiligen Pauli an die Römer...und in unterschiedlichen Predigten vorgetragen, und diese andere Auflage ist mit einem nützlichen Register, und erbaulichen anhange...[versehen?] [Franckfurt an der Oder, 1741.] 751 p. front. (port.) 12°.

Mutilated; end of title and imprint missing.

364904A. 1. Christian life.
N. Y. P. L. October 18, 1928

NL 0431467 NN

Music BV 481 L6 L79 Lobethan, Johann Konrad, 1688-1735 comp.
Neu-vermehrtes und neu-eingerichtetes Gesang-Buch, bestehend I. Aus den Psalmen Davids, wie sie D. Ambrosius Lobwasser in Reime gebracht, II. Aus ausserlesenen geistreichen Liedern, welche mit Fleiss gesammlet, und in eine fügliche Ordnung gebracht worden; auf gnädigsten Befehl. Cöthen, In Verlag des Waysenhauses, 1733.
[16], 1089, [27] p. front. 18cm.

Without music.

1. Hymns, German. 2. Lutheran Church--Hymns. I. Bible. O.T. Psalms. German. Paraphrases. 1733. Lobwasser. II. Title.

NL 0431469 NIC

M 2138 L79 1747 Lobethan, Johann Konrad, 1688-1735, ed.
Neu-vermehrtes und Neu-eingerichtetes Gesang-Buch, bestehend: I. Aus den Psalmen Davids, wie sie D. Ambrosius Lobwasser in Reime gebracht; II. Aus auserlesenen Geistreichen Liedern, wie sie mit Fleiss gesammlet und in eine fügliche Ordnung gebracht worden; nebst dem Chur-Pfältzischen Catechismo, Tauf- und Communion-Formuln und schönen Gebetern. 2. Aufl. Cöthen, Im Verlag des Waysenhauses, 1747.

Continued in next column

Continued from preceding column

183, 592, [10], 78+ p. 17cm.

CUL copy imperfect: all after p. 78 wanting.
Pref. signed: Johann Jacob Rindfleisch.
Unacc. melodies; shape-note notation.

NL 0431471 NIC

[LOBETTI, Pierfilippo.]
La costituzione ed il clero della diocesi di Cuneo. [Cuneo, 1848.]

Pamphlet.

NL 0431472 MH

Law Lobetti-Bodoni, Franco, joint author.

Mijno, Ulrico.
Prontuario alfabetico commentato della tariffa notarile in vigore [di] Ulrico Mijno [e] Franco Lobetti-Bodoni. Torino, Arduini, 1949.

F 945.1 L783 LOBETTI-BODONI, GIOVANNI
Castelli e monumenti del Saluzzese, con un disegno storico dei primi due secoli del Marchesato. Saluzzo, Lobetti-Bodoni, 1911.
108p. illus., plates, facsims. 40cm.

Head pieces; illuminated initials in red; titles of chapters in red; plates accompanied by guard sheets.
Bibliographies at ends of chapters.

NL 0431474 PU

LOBEZ, Agustin.
La ermita de los suspiros; leyenda fantástica. Valencia, Terraza, Aliena y compañía, 1878.

Cover reads:-Novela fantástica en verso.

NL 0431475 MH

Lobez, Agustin.
¡Madre mia del amparo! Comedia en un acto y en verso, original. Valencia, 1870. 32 p. 12°.

In: NPL p. v. 305, no. 4.

1. Drama (Spanish). 2. Title.
N. Y. P. L. May 1, 1911.

NL 0431476 NN

Lóbez, Florencio Ger y
see Ger y Lóbez, Florencio.

---

*GC7 A100 758l Lobgedichte auf den König von Preuszen, aus dem Englischen ...
London [i.e. Karlsruhe] 1758.
4°. 16p. 22.5cm.
False imprint.
Prose and verse.

NL 0431478 MH

Lob-Gedichte des so genannten Bauer-Hundes
see under [Neumeister, Erdmann] 1671-1756.

Lobgeois (Adolphe). *De l'hémoptysie. 30 pp. 4°. *Paris*, 1849, No. 65, v. 486.

NL 0431480 DNLM

Lobgeois (Auguste-Édouard). *De l'ulcération. Théorie nouvelle de l'ulcération. 23 pp. 4°. *Paris*, 1850, No. 50, v. 498.

NL 0431481 DNLM

QV L797r LOBGEOIS, Édouard
Rénovation radicale de l'art de guérir. Le tout résultant de la découverte: 1° du rôle normale des poumons et du foie dans l'animalité ... 2° du rôle anormal des mêmes appareils chez les races humaines ... Saint-Quentin [France] Moureau, 1882-
v.

NL 0431482 DNLM

Lobgesänge zu Ehren dem Heiligen und Gerechten in Israel. Hägerstown, Johann Gruber, 1808.
212 p.

NL 0431483 PPLT PPeSchw

Lobgesang auf Christus und Maria
see Marienpreis und lobgesang auf Christus.

LOB-GESANG zu Gott dem Herrn, welcher in Hiesiger Residentz Berlin, in der Juden-Synagoge, Andächtig Gehalten worden, wegen des Friedens-Schlusses...1742. Gedruckt auf Veranlassung der Hiesigen Juden Aeltesten (10)p f° in Hebr. a. Ger
1. Liturgy-Special. 2. History-Germany-Berlin.

NL 0431485 NNJ

Lo Bianca Salvatore
see Lo Bianco, Salvatore, 1865-1910.

33.19 L78 Lo Bianco, Antonio.
Agraria generale ed economia agraria corporativa. Milano, Hoepli, 1935.
197 p.

1. Agriculture. Economic aspects. Italy. 2. Italy. Agriculture.

NL 0431487 DNAL

VOLUME 337

Lo Bianco, Antonio.
Compendio delle limitazioni e delle servitù prediali del nuovo Codice civile italiano in confronto delle costruzioni civili, rurali, industriali ⌊di⌋ Antonio Lo Bianco ⌊e⌋ Giuseppe Lo Bianco. Applicazioni schematiche delle norme pratiche ad uso degli ingegneri, architetti, agrimensori, geometri e periti tecnici in genere. Milano, Hoepli, 1948.
110 p. illus. 16 cm.

1. Adjoining landowners—Italy. 2. Servitudes—Italy. I. Title.
55-31477 ‡

NL 0431488 DLC MH-L NNC

4K Ital.-54
Lo Bianco, Antonio.
La practica della consulenza tecnica dell' arbitrato e della perizia penale, secondo i nouvi codici di proceduro ... 6. ed. della "Perizia ed arbitrato." Publicazione postuma a cura del figlio dott. ing. Guiseppe Lo Bianco. Milano, U. Hoepli, 1947.
489 p.

NL 0431489 DLC-P4 MH-L

Lo Bianco, Antonio.
... La pratica della perizia e dell' arbitrato, norme di procedura indispensabili agli ingegneri, architetti, agrimensori, minerari, meccanici e periti in genere, con vari esempi di perizie, difese tecnico-legali ed arbitrati. 4. ed. completamente rifatta. Milano, U. Hoepli, 1935.
xii, ⌊4⌋ p., 1 l., ⌊3⌋-418 p. 16cm. (Manuali Hoepli)
At head of title: ... Prof. dott. ing. A. Lo Bianco ...

1. Evidence, Expert — Italy. 2. Arbitration and award — Italy. I. Title.
39-17165

NL 0431490 DLC

Lo Bianco, Antonio
La pratica delle limitazioni e delle servitù prediali; manuale pratico ad uso delle scuole d'ingegneria, delle scuole superiori di architettura, degli istituti tecnici di agrimensura, delle scuole di agronomia, degli ingegneri, architetti, capimastri, imprenditori di costruzioni, proprietari edili agricoltori e tecnici in genere. Corr. dagli articoli del Codice civile con breve commento e 106 vignette esplicative. 2. ed. Milano, Hoepli, 1950.

xii, 207 p. diagrs. 16cm.

At head of title: Antonio Lo Bianco, Giuseppe Lo Bianco.

NL 0431492 NNC

Lo Bianco, Antonio
... La pratica delle limitazioni e delle servitù prediali; manuale pratico ad uso delle scuole d'ingegneria, delle scuole superiori di architettura, degli istituti tecnici di agrimensura, delle scuole di agronomia, degli ingegneri, architetti, capimastri, imprenditori di costruzioni, proprietari edili, agricoltori e tecnici in genere. Corredato dagli articoli del Codice civile con

dagli articoli del Codice civile con breve commento, da 113 vignette esplicative e da massime della più moderna giurisprudenza. 3. ed. notevolmente ampliata. Milano, U. Hoepli, 1954.
xv, 251 p. 15cm.

At head of title: Dott. ing. Antonio Lo Bianco; dott. ing. Giuseppe Lo Bianco.
First edition has title: Compendio delle limitazioni e delle servitù prediali.

NL 0431495 MH-L

Lo Bianco, Antonio.
... La pratica delle servitù prediali; manuale pratico ad uso delle scuole d'ingegneria, delle scuole superiori di architettura, degli istituti tecnici di agrimensura, delle scuole di agronomia, degli ingegneri, architetti, capimastri, imprenditori di costruzioni, proprietari edili, agricoltori e tecnici in genere, corredato dagli articoli del Codice civile, dalla dottrina e dalla giurisprudenza, con breve commento. 70 vignette esplicative. Milano, U. Hoepli, 1934.
xi p., 3 l., ⌊3⌋-409 p. illus., diagrs. 15½cm. (Manuali Hoepli)
"Bibliografia": p. ⌊xv⌋

1. Servitudes—Italy. I. Title.
38-21881

NL 0431496 DLC

Lo Bianco, Antonio.
... La pratica delle servitù prediali; manuale pratico ad uso delle scuole d'ingegneria, scuole superiori di architettura, istituti tecnici di agrimensura, scuole di agraria, ingegneri, architetti, geometri, capimastri, imprenditori di costruzioni, proprietari edili, agricoltori e tecnici in genere. Secondo gli art. del Cod. civ., della dottrina e della giurisprudenza, con breve commento. 2. ed. ampliata, con 94 figure esplicative. Milano, U. Hoepli, 1938.
xxii, 492, ⌊1⌋ p. illus., diagrs. 15½cm. (Manuali Hoepli)

1. Servitudes—Italy. I. Title.
42-49065

NL 0431497 DLC

Lo Bianco, Antonio.
... Valutazioni di ricchezze naturali. Palermo, F. Ciuni, 1940.
207 p. diagr. 22cm.

1. Natural resources—Valuation. I. Title.
44-12360
Library of Congress HF5681.V3L6
⌊2⌋ 657

NL 0431498 DLC

Lo Bianco, Enrique Rioja y
see Rioja y Lo Bianco, Enrique, 1895-1963.

Lo Bianco, Francesco.
... La costituzione del principato, di Francesco Lo Bianco. ⌊Roma⌋ C. Colombo ⌊1942⌋
60 p., 1 l. illus. 24½cm. (Civiltà romana. 21)
At head of title: Mostra della romanità.
"Bibliografia": p. 56-60.

1. Rome—Pol. & govt.—B. C. 30-A. D. 68. I. Title.
44-12894
Library of Congress DG285.7.L6
⌊2⌋ 937.07

NL 0431500 DLC

Lo Bianco, Francesco.
... L'organizzazione dei lavoratori, di Francesco Lo Bianco. ⌊Roma⌋ C. Colombo ⌊1939⌋
43, ⌊1⌋ p. illus. 24½cm. (Civiltà romana. 16)
At head of title: Mostra della romanità.
"Note bibliografiche": p. 37-39.

1. Gilds—Rome. 2. Labor and laboring classes—Rome.
45-46963
Library of Congress HD6454.L6

NL 0431501 DLC NcD

Microfilm DG 44
Lo Bianco, Francesco.
L'organizzazione dei lavoratori, di Francesco Lo Bianco. [Roma] C. Colombo [1939]
illus. (Civiltà romana. 16)
Negative.
Filmed with Clausetti, Enrico. Fortificazioni e macchine belliche. [Roma, 1939]
"Note bibliografiche": p. 37-39.

1. Gilds--Rome. 2. Labor and laboring classes--Rome. I. Title. II. Series.

NL 0431502 ICU

Lo Bianco, Francesco Giovanni.
... Storia dei collegi artigiani dell' impero. Bologna, N. Zanichelli, 1934.
1 p. l., 138 p., 1 l. 23½cm.
At head of title: F. G. Lo Bianco.
"Bibliografia": p. ⌊129⌋-135.

1. Gilds—Rome.
HD6454.L62 338.64 A C 35-1513 rev †
Columbia univ. Libraries for Library of Congress ⌊r46c2⌋†

NL 0431503 NNC DLC CU

Lo Bianco, Francesco Giovanni.
... Un tentativo di fronte popolare in Italia. ⌊Roma⌋ Edizioni Roma ⌊1939⌋
2 p. l., 7-117 p., 1 l. 22cm.
On cover: (1921-1922)

1. Italy—Pol. & govt.—1922-1945. I. Title.
A 47-2984
Harvard univ. Library for Library of Congress ⌊2⌋

NL 0431504 MH

HX291 L797 Hoover Library
Lo Bianco, Francesco Giovanni.
Un tentativo di fronte popolare in Italia. Roma, Edizioni Roma ⌊1940⌋
117 p. 22cm.
On cover: 1921-1922.

1. Socialism in Italy. 2. Partito socialista italiano. 3. Italy - Pol. & govt. - 1922-1945. I. Title.

NL 0431505 CSt-H

Lo Bianco G
Chorus quick step, from the introduction of Verdis grand opera Ernani ... arranged for the pianoforte by Lo Bianco. Boston, G.P. Reed, cop. 1847.
3 p. f°.

NL 0431506 NN

Lo Bianco, G.
Galop and chorus of exultation from G. Verdi's grand opera Ernani ... arranged for the pianoforte by G. Lo Bianco. Boston, G.P. Reed, cop. 1847.
3 p. f°.

NL 0431507 NN

VOLUME 337

Lo Bianco, G

La tarantule. A favorite dance by Mad[lle] Fanny Elssler and Mons[r] Sylvain, as performed at the Park Theatre. Arr. for the piano forte. New York, Atwill, °1840.

5 p. 33 cm.

1. Tarantellas (Piano) I. Title.

M1.A13L M 59-1715

NL 0431508 DLC NN

Lo Bianco, H.

The Christmas message. Carol. (For Christmas.) [S. Accomp. for organ.]
(In Parish Choir, The. No. 206, pp. 822, 823. Medford, 1883.)

Apr. 16, 1902
E3963 — T.r. — Christmas carols.

NL 0431509 MB

Lo Bianco, Ottavio.
Alcune prose. Palermo, Stamp. G. Pedone, 1840.

NL 0431510 MH

Lo Bianco, Salvatore, 1865–

... The methods employed at the Naples Zoological station for the preservation of marine animals. By Dr. Salvatore Lo Bianco. Translated from the original Italian by Edmund Otis Hovey ... Washington, Govt. print. off., 1899.

42 p. front. 24½[cm]. (Part M of Bulletin of the United States National museum, no. 39)

At head of title: Smithsonian institution. United States National museum.

1. Zoological specimens—Collection and preservation. 2. Marine fauna. 3. Naples. Stazione zoologica. I. Hovey, Edmund Otis, 1862– tr.

S 13-151

Library, Smithsonian Institution Q11.U6

MoU OO DLC
ViU PPAmP PHC PBm PU PPAN PP OU OCU OCl PPFr OClMN
NL 0431511 DSI NN DNLM MB CaBVaU WaS OrP MdBP MU

Lo-Bianco (Salvatore). Metodi konservirovaniya morskikh zhivotnikh, upotreblyayemiye na zoologicheskoi stantsii v Neapolie. Perevel s italyanskavo i dopolnie N. V. Slyunin. [Method of conserving sea animals as practiced at the zoological station of Naples. Transl. from the Italian, with additions by Slyunin.] 47 pp. 8°. *S.-Peterburg*, 1892.
Repr. from: Med. pribav. k morsk. sborniku. St. Petersb., 1892.

NL 0431512 DNLM

Lo Bianco, Salvatore. 1865-
Notizie biologiche riguardanti specialmante il periodo di maturita sessuale digli animali de Golfo di Napoli. Del Dr. Salvatore Lo Bianco... [Naples, 1909?]
p.[513]-761.

Abdruck aus den Mittheilungen aus der zoologischen station zu Neapel. 19 bd. 4. hft. 1909."

NL 0431513 MiU

Lo Bianco, Salvatore.

Pelagische Tiefseefischerei der "Maja" in der Umgebung von Capri, von Dr. Salvatore Lo Bianco .... Mit einer Photogravüre, 41 Tafeln in Farbendruck und einer Karte. Jena, G. Fischer, 1904.

vi, [2], 91 p. front., xxxxi pl. (partly col., partly fold.), 1 fold. map. 28½[cm].
(*In* Beiträge zur Kenntnis des Meeres und seiner Bewohner, erster Band.)
Preface signed: Heinrich Schmidt.

NL 0431514 ICJ CSt CU PPAN

Lo Bianco, Salvatore, 1865–

Le pesche abissali eseguite de F. A. Krupp col yacht Puritan nelle adiacenze di Capri ed in altre località del Mediterraneo. Relazione del dr. Salvatore Lo Bianco ... [Naples, 1903]

p. [109]-279. pl. 8-9, fold. tab. 23½[cm].

"Abdruck aus den Mittheilungen aus der Zoologischen station zu Neapel. 16. bd., 1. u. 2. heft. 1903."

1. Fishing—Mediterranean. 2. Marine fauna—Mediterranean.

F 17-89

Library, U. S. Bur. of Fisheries

NL 0431515 DI

Lo Bianco, Salvatore, 1865-
Uova, larve e stadf giovanili di Teleostei
see under title

W 4 L99 1952/53 no. 136

LOBIDEL, François, 1928-
Le poumon du nouveau-né à propos de 110 observations recueillies en série à la Clinique obstétricale de Lyon. [Trévoux] 1953.
96 p. illus. (Lyons. [Université] Faculté mixte médecine et de pharmacie. Thèse, 1952/53, no. 136)
1. Infants - Newborn 2. Lungs

NL 0431517 DNLM

Lobien, Horst, 1904-
... Die quere gesichtsspalte und ihre operative behandlung ... Königsberg, Raabe, 1934.
19 p.

Inaug.-diss., Königsberg, 1933.
Lebenslauf.
"Literatur": p. 17.

1. Face - Abnormities and deformities.
2. Face - Surgery.

NL 0431518 NNC DNLM CtY

DO70.13 L78

Lobigs, Peter, 1913-
Pressenötigung ... von ... Peter Lobigs ... Düsseldorf, Leopold Odendahl, 1939.
65 p., 1 l. 21[cm].

Thesis, Cologne.
"Verzeichnis der benutzten bücher und schriften": p. 7-9.

1. Press law - Germany. 2. Liberty of the press - Germany.

NL 0431519 NNC CtY ICRL

Lobin, Yvette.

... Les tendances nationalistes de notre système français de droit international privé ... par Yvette Lobin. Marseille, Imprimerie M. Leconte, 1937.

199 p. 25[cm].

Thèse—Univ. d'Aix-Marseille.
"Bibliographie": p. [5]-6.

1. International law, Private. I. Title.

42-35353

Library of Congress JX6162.L6

NL 0431520 DLC CtY NNC

Lobineau, Guy Alexis, 1666–1727.

Histoire de Bretagne, composée sur les titres & les auteurs originaux, par dom Gui Alexis Lobineau ... enrichie de plusieurs portraits & tombeaux en taille douce; avec les preuves & pieces justificatives, accompagnées d'un grand nombre de sceaux ... Paris, M. David, 1707.

2 v. plates (incl. coats of arms) ports. 40[cm].

1. Brittany—Hist.

23-5263

Library of Congress DC611.B854L6

NL 0431521 DLC NcD CtY NNUT ICN

DC 611 .B854 L82

Lobineau, Guy Alexis, 1666–1727.

Histoire de Bretagne, composée sur les titres & les auteurs originaux, par dom Gui Alexis Lobineau ... enrichie de plusieurs portraits & tombeaux en taille douce; avec les preuves & pieces justificatives, accompagnées d'un grand nombre de sceaux ... Paris, Chez Louis Guerin, 1707.
2 v. plates (incl. coats of arms) ports. 40[cm].

NL 0431522 MiU

Rare Books Dept.

Lobineau, Guy Alexis, 1666–1727.

Histoire de Bretagne, composée sur les titres & les auteurs originaux, par dom Gui Alexis Lobineau ... enrichie de plusieurs portraits & tombeaux en taille douce; avec les preuves & pieces justificatives, accompagnées d'un grand nombre de sceaux ... Paris, Chez la Veuve François Muguet, 1707.
2 v. plates (incl. coats of arms) ports. 40[cm].

NL 0431523 CU OCl

Lobineau, Guy Alexis, 1666-1727.
Histoire de deux conquestes d'Espagne...
see under Luna, Miguel de, fl. 1600.

Lobineau, Guy Alexis, 1666-1727, ed.

Félibien, Michel, 1665–1719.

Histoire de la ville de Paris, composée par D. Michel Felibien, rev., augm. et mise au jour par D. Guy-Alexis Lobineau ... Justifiée par des preuves autentiques, & enrichie de plans, de figures, & d'une carte topographique. Divisée en cinq volumes in folio ... A Paris, Chez G. Desprez et J. Desessartz, 1725.

Lobineau, Guy Alexis, 1666-1727.
Inauguration du monument élevé à la mémoire de Dom Lobineau, 3 mai 1886
see under La Borderie, Arthur de, 1827-1901.

Lobineau, Guy Alexis. 1666-1727. Lettre à Dom Simon Bougis. 12 pp. (Soc. Bibilioph. fr. Mélanges. 1877.)

NL 0431527 MdBP

Lobineau, Guy Alexis, 1666-1727.
Les vies des saints de Bretagne, et des personnes d'une eminente pieté qui ont vécu dans la même province; avec une addition à l'histoire de Bretagne, par Dom Gui-Alexis Lobineau ... enrichies de figures en taille-douce. A Rennes, Par la Compagnie des Imprimeurs-libraires, 1724.
3 p. l., [5]-574 [i. e., 584], 16 p. illus., plate. 39[cm].

NL 0431528 NNC MH

VOLUME 337

D
9877
.52
LOBINEAU, GUY ALEXIS, 1666-1727.
Les vies des saints de Bretagne et des personnes d'une éminente piété qui ont vécu dans cette province... Nouvelle édition, revue, corrigée et considérablement augmentée, par m. l'abbé Tresvaux... Paris, Méquignon, 1836-38.
5v.

Contents.--t.1. III°, IV°, V° et VI° siècles.--t.2. VII° au XIII° siècle.--t.3. XIV°, XV°, XVI°, XVII° siècles, jusqu'en l'an 1634.--t.4. Depuis l'an 1634 jusqu'a l'an 1680.--t 5 Depuis l'an 1681 jusqu'a la fin du 18e siècle.

NL 0431529 ICN WaU CtY

Lobinger, Elizabeth Miller.
see Lobingier, Mrs. Elizabeth Erwin (Miller) 1889-

Lobinger, Magda.
...Un précurseur de la littérature comparée: Nicolas Martin, son style "biedermeier". Ses inspirations allemandes et hongroises. Par Magda Lobinger. Szeged, 1937. 83 p. 24½cm. (Études françaises; publiées par l'Institut français de l'Université de Szeged. [Tome] 17.)

Doctori értekezés — Szeged, 1937.
Added t.-p. in Hungarian: ...Nicolas Martin, az összehasonlitó irodalomtörténetirás előfutára.
Résumé in Hungarian.
"Bibliographie," p. [71]-72.

1. Martin, Nicolas, 1814-1877. 2. German literature—Foreign influence of. 3. Hungarian literature—Foreign influence on. 4. French literature—Foreign influence on, German. 5. French literature—Foreign influence on, Hungarian. I. Ser.
N. Y. P. L. February 19, 1941

NL 0431531 NN

Lobingier, Andrew Stewart, 1862-
Irrigation of the bladder in chronic cystitis of women. 13 pp. 12°. [Philadelphia, 1892.]
Repr. from: Med. News. Phila. 1892. lxi.

NL 0431532 DNLM

Lobingier, Andrew Stewart, 1862-
John Jones [by] Andrew Stewart Lobingier ... Chicago, Surgical pub. co., c1930.
cover-title, 4 p. port. 26½cm.

"Reprint from Surgery, gynecology and obstetrics, November, 1930, vol. LI, 740-743".

1. Jones, John, 1729-1791.

NL 0431533 NNC

Lobingier, Charles Sumner, 1866-1956

American bar association. *Comparative law bureau.*
... Bulletin for 1933 ... Washington, D. C., American bar association [1933]

LOBINGIER, Charles Sumner.
American Courts in China; second inaugural address as President of the Far Eastern American Bar Association. n.p., n.d.

(3)+23 p.
(Far Eastern Bar Association. Publications. 2).

NL 0431535 MH-L DS

Lobingier, Charles Sumner, 1866-1956.
American courts in China, by Charles Sumner Lobingier ... Second inaugural address as President of the Far-Eastern American bar association. [American bar association, 1919]
23 p. 23 cm. (Bar association publications. II)

NL 0431536 CtY-L

Lobingier, Charles Sumner, 1866-
The ancient and accepted Scottish rite of freemasonry, by Charles Sumner Lobingier ... Louisville, Ky., The Standard printing co., incorporated, 1932.
ix, 166 p. front., plates, ports., facsim., geneal. tab. 25½cm.

1. Freemasons—Hist. 2. Freemasons. Scottish rite. I. Title.
33-5464
Library of Congress HS765.L6
——— Copy 2.
Copyright A 60441 [2] 366.1

NL 0431537 DLC

Law

Lobingier, Charles Sumner, 1866-1956.
The beginnings of law; [a summation of results in legal anthropology] Washington, Mimeoform Press [19—]
142 p. 25 cm.

1. Law, Primitive. 2. Ethnological jurisprudence. I. Title.
340.1 61-32126 ‡

NL 0431538 DLC

LOBINGIER, CHARLES SUMNER. A bibliographical introduction to the study of Chinese law. [London, 1914.] [7] p. 8°.
From the Journal of the Royal Asiatic society, 1914, v. 45, p. 110-123.

NL 0431539 MSaE

Lobingier, Charles Sumner, 1866-
The connecting link in world law. By Charles Sumner Lobingier.
(*In* National university law review. Washington, D. C., 1929. 27cm. v. 9, no. 2, p. 3-53)

1. Jews—Law. I. Title.
37-11529
Library of Congress
——— Copy 2, detached.

NL 0431540 DLC

Pam.
Coll.
17268
Lobingier, Charles Sumner, 1866-
The early Malays and their neighbors; a brief survey of primitive cultural influences affecting the Filipinos, with an incidental review of the Philippine academy's work. (Read before the Royal Asiatic society at Shanghai, May 2, 1918.) [n.p., 1918]
14 p. 25½cm.

Caption title.
1. Malay race

NL 0431541 NcD

Lobingier, Charles Sumner, 1866-
The evolution of the civil law ... [n. p.] The author, 1915.
4 p. l., 105 p. 23½cm.

Interleaved.
Part of pages blank.
Contains bibliographies.
Heading for table of contents reads "Part 1: The Roman law."

1. Law—History and criticism.
A 18-106
Title from Columbia Univ. Printed by L. C.

NL 0431542 NNC TxU PPB CU-AL

Lobingier, Charles Sumner, 1866-
The evolution of the Roman law from before the Twelve tables to the Corpus juris. by Charles Sumner Lobingier ... 2d ed., 1923. [Omaha] The author [1923]
iv, iii, 319 p. tab., diagr. 23 x 19½cm.

1. Roman law—Hist. I. Title. 26-17643 Revised
Library of Congress
——— Copy 2. Pages iii-iv of 1st group (Foreword) are bound after p. iii of the 2d group.
[r38c2]

NL 0431543 PPB MH ViU OClW DLC WaU-L IdU CU-AL NBuU-L OkU PU-L PP

JX1706
.A58S65
1919
Lobingier, Charles Sumner, 1866-

U. S. *Congress. House. Committee on Foreign Affairs.*
Exchange of legation property at Bangkok, Siam. Authorizing the purchase of buildings and grounds for the Embassy of the United States at Santiago, Chile. Hearings before the Committee on Foreign Affairs, House of Representatives, Sixty-sixth Congress, first session, on S. 2250 and H. R. 10007. Statement of C. S. Lobingier. Washington, Govt. Print. Off., 1919.

Law
Lobingier, Charles Sumner, 1866- comp. and ed.

U. S. *Court for China.*
Extraterritorial cases ... Including the decisions of the United States Court for China from its beginning, those reviewing the same by the Court of appeals and the leading cases decided by other courts on questions of extraterritoriality. Compiled and edited by Charles Sumner Lobingier ... Manila, Bureau of printing, 1920-28.

Lobingier, Charles Sumner, 1866-1856.
The history of the conjugal partnership.
(In American law review. March-April-May, 1929. v. 63, no. 2. p. 250-84)

NL 0431546 C

Lobingier, Charles Sumner, 1866-
Institutes of civil law (Roman) [Manila? 19—]
1 v. (various pagings) 23 x 24 cm.
Caption title.
Syllabus of 29 lectures.
Blank leaves interspersed.
Includes bibliographical references.

1. Roman law—Outlines, syllabi, etc. I. Title.
49-57073*

NL 0431547 DLC

VOLUME 337

Lobingier, Charles Sumner, 1866-
Napoléon et son code. Traduit avec l'autorisation de l'auteur par J. Em. Lemière. Shanghai, Presse orientale, 1919.
40 p.

Originally published as "Napoleon and his code" in the Harvard law review, v. 32, 1918.
Author's bibliography: p. ₍35₎-40.

NL 0431548 NNC

Lobingier, Charles Sumner, 1866–
... Obsolete features of our federal Constitution, by Charles Sumner Lobingier, professor of comparative law in the National university, Washington, D. C. ... Washington, U. S. Govt. print. off., 1934.
v, 30 p. incl. tab. 23ᶜᵐ. (₍U. S.₎ 73d Cong., 2d sess. Senate. Doc. 100)
Presented by Mr. Norris. Ordered printed January 4, 1934.

1. U. S. Constitution. I. Title.

Library of Congress JK268.L55 34-26040
——— Copy 2. ₍3₎ 342.733

NL 0431549 DLC WaU-L MiU

Lobingier, Charles Sumner, 1866–
The people's law; or, Popular participation in law-making from ancient folk-moot to modern referendum; a study in the evolution of democracy and direct legislation, by Charles Sumner Lobingier ... with an introduction by George Elliott Howard ... New York, The Macmillan company, 1909.
xxi, 429 p. 22½ᶜᵐ. $4.00
Bibliography: p. 395-409.
1. Referendum. 2. Legislation.
Library of Congress JF425.L7 9-30393 Revised

PP NcD OCU MiU OCl OO ICJ MB NN ViU WaU-L OrP FMU NBuC NBuU-L NjP PU PU-L NIC PPL PPB
NL 0431550 DLC WaS Or OrU-L MtHi OrPR WaTC IdU

Lobingier, Charles Sumner, 1866-
Castile. *Laws, statutes, etc., 1252-1284 (Alfonso x)*
Las siete partidas, translation and notes by Samuel Parsons Scott ... introduction, table of contents and index by Charles Sumner Lobingier ... bibliography by John Vance. Chicago, New York ₍etc.₎ Pub. for the Comparative law bureau of the American bar association by Commerce clearing house, inc., Loose leaf service division of the Corporation trust company, 1931.

Lobingier, Charles Sumner, 1866–
Some original and peculiar features in the Nebraska constitution.
(*In* The annals of the American academy of political and social science. Phildelphia, 1899. vol. xv, no. 3, p. 433–437)
Signed: Charles Sumner Lobingier.

1. Nebraska. Constitution. I. Title.
Library of Congress H1.A4 vol. 15, no. 3 C D 17—39 b

NL 0431552 DLC CaBVaU OrU OrCS OCU OCl OClW ICJ NcD

Lobingier, Charles Sumner, 1866-
HS774 .A4 1931
Freemasons. *U. S. Scottish rite. Supreme council for the Southern jurisdiction.*
The Supreme council, 33°; Mother council of the world, Ancient and accepted Scottish rite of freemasonry, Southern jurisdiction, U. S. A. Louisville, Ky., The Standard printing co., incorporated, 1931.

Lobingier, Charles Sumner, 1866–
A treatise on Philippine practice including the law of evidence applicable to all courts and all laws relating to the primary courts, topically arranged and annotated, with appropriate decisions of the Supreme court and opinions of the attorney general, down to July 15, 1907. By Charles Sumner Lobingier ... Manila, The Oriental printing company, inc. ₍1907₎
2 p. l., 130, ix p. 23½ᶜᵐ.
1. Justices of the peace—Philippine Islands. 2. Evidence (Law)—Philippine Islands. ₍3. Municipal courts—Philippine Islands₎
Library of Congress 14-9660

NL 0431554 DLC WaU PPB

Lobingier, Charles Sumner, 1866-1956.
The value and place of Roman law in the technical curriculum, by Charles Sumner Lobingier. ₍Shanghai, n.d.₎
26 numb. l. 33½cm.
Caption title.
"Inaugural address as president of the Far Eastern American Bar Association."
Reproduced from typewritten copy.

NL 0431555 MH-L

Lobingier, Elizabeth Erwin (Miller) 1889–
Activities in child education for the church school teacher. With drawings by children. Boston, Pilgrim Press ₍1950₎
xiv, 226 p. illus. 23 cm.
Bibliography: p. 221–224.

1. Religious education of children—Occupations and busy work. I. Title.
BV1535.L55 268.68 50–7946

CoDuF
NL 0431556 DLC KyLxCB WaSp Wa Or MB PPEB PPD

Lobingier, Elizabeth Erwin (Miller) 1889–
Dramatization in the church school; a training course for leaders, by Elizabeth Erwin Miller (Elizabeth Miller Lobingier) ... Chicago, Ill., The University of Chicago press ₍1923₎
xiii, 89 p. front., plates (1 col.) 18ᶜᵐ. (*Half-title:* The University of Chicago publications in religious education ... Principles and methods of religious education)
"References" at end of most of the chapters.

1. Drama in education. 2. Religious education. I. Title.
Library of Congress BV1575.L6 23—5615

PP NcD CU MB NN OEac OOxM OU OCl NRCR
NL 0431557 DLC InAndC-T ICRL OrSaW OrP Or NcD PU

Lobingier, *Mrs.* Elizabeth Erwin (Miller)
The dramatization of Bible stories; an experiment in the religious education of children, by Elizabeth Erwin Miller ... Chicago, Ill., The University of Chicago press ₍©1918₎
xiv, 162 p. front., illus. 18½ᶜᵐ. (*Half-title:* The University of Chicago publications in religious education ... Principles and methods of religious education)

1. Drama in education. 2. Children's plays. 3. Religious education. I. Title.
Library of Congress BV1575.L63 18—10163

OOxM OClh OEac NN
NL 0431558 DLC NRCR MB WaU PPGi PPT PWcS NcD OU OCl

Lobingier, Elizabeth Erwin (Miller).
The dramatization of Bible stories; an experiment in the religious education of children, by Elizabeth Erwin Miller... Chicago: University of Chicago Press₍, 1919₎. xiv, 162 p. front., illus. 12°. (University of Chicago publications in religious education. Principles and methods of religious education.)

1. Drama in education. 2. Drama, Religious—Hist. and crit. 3. Education, Moral and religious. 4. Bible—Study and teaching. 5. Ser.
N. Y. P. L. December 19, 1924

NL 0431559 NN

Lobingier, Mrs. Elizabeth Erwin (Miller) 1889-
The dramatization of Bible stories. An experiment in the religious education of children. Chicago,Ill.: Univ.of Chicago Press,[1920]. xiv,162 p.,1 pl. illus. 12.(University of Chicago publications in religious education.- Principles and methods of religious education.)

NL 0431560 OCH

Epsteen Coll. in Rare Books Room
Lobingier, *Mrs.* Elizabeth Erwin (Miller) 1889–
The dramatization of Bible stories; an experiment in the religious education of children, by Elizabeth Erwin Miller ... Chicago, Ill., The University of Chicago press ₍1921₎
xiv, 162 p. front., illus. 18½ᶜᵐ. (*Half-title:* The University of Chicago publications in religious education ... Principles and methods of religious education)

NL 0431561 CoU

Lobingier, Mrs. Elizabeth Erwin (Miller) 1889-
The dramatization of Bible stories; an experiment in the religious education of children, ... Chicago, Ill., 1927.
xiv, 162 p. front., illus. 19 cm.
(Half-title: The University of Chicago publications in religious education ... Principles and methods of religious education)

NL 0431562 RPB

Lobingier, Mrs. Elizabeth Erwin (Miller) 1889-
The dramatization of Bible stories. An experiment in the religious education of children. [16th impression.]
Chicago. [1934.] xiv, 162 pp. Illus. Plates. [University of Chicago. Publications in religious education. Principles and methods of religious education.] 17.5 cm.

E238 — S.r. — Children's plays. — Bible stories. Dramatizations.

NL 0431563 MB MH

Lobingier, *Mrs.* Elizabeth Erwin (Miller)
Educating for peace ₍by₎ Elizabeth Miller Lobingier and John Leslie Lobingier. Boston, Chicago, The Pilgrim press ₍©1930₎
4 p. l., 216 p. 19½ᶜᵐ.
Includes bibliographies.

1. Peace—Study and teaching. I. Lobingier, John Leslie, 1884– joint author. II. Title.
Library of Congress JX1953.L6 30-16790
——— Copy 2.
Copyright A 24690 ₍3₎ 172.407

NjN
NL 0431564 DLC DAU OBlC OrP NRCR PPStarr PPPL NcD

Lobingier, Mrs. Elizabeth Erwin (Miller) 1889-
Foreign experiences of an American girl; by Elizabeth E. Miller. Meadville, Penn., The author, Messenger print, 1895.
viii, 148 p. 18ᶜᵐ. 8-11762
Library of Congress, no. D919.M64.

NL 0431565 DLC OrU

Lobingier, Mrs. Elizabeth Erwin (Miller) 1889-
Sargent, Walter, 1868–
How children learn to draw, by Walter Sargent ... and Elizabeth E. Miller ... Boston, New York ₍etc.₎ Ginn and company ₍©1916₎

VOLUME 337

Lobingier, *Mrs.* Elizabeth Erwin (Miller) 1889–
Hebrew home life; a children's reader, by Elizabeth Miller Lobingier. Chicago, Ill., The University of Chicago press [c1926]
viii, 81, [1] p. front., illus. (part col.) 19½cm. (*Half-title:* The University of Chicago publications in religious education ... Constructive studies)

1. Jews—Soc. life & cust. I. Title. 26—23666
Library of Congress BS1194.L6

NL 0431567 DLC WaTC IEG ODW OCl OO MB

Lobingier, Elizabeth Erwin (Miller) 1889–
Hebrew home life; a third-grade course of study suitable for primary departments of church schools, weekday schools of religion, and church vacation schools, by Elizabeth Miller Lobingier ... Teacher's manual. Chicago, Ill., The University of Chicago press [c1926]
xii, 144, [1] p. front., illus. 19½cm. (*Half-title:* The University of Chicago publications in religious education ... Constructive studies)
"Reading suggestions": p. 137-139.

1. Jews—Soc. life & cust. I. Title. 26—23665
Library of Congress BS1194.L62

NL 0431568 DLC IEG OCl NBuG

Lobingier, *Mrs.* Elizabeth Erwin (Miller) 1889–
Informal dramatization in missionary education; a manual for leaders of elementary groups, by Elizabeth Miller Lobingier ... New York, Friendship press, 1930.
32 p. 18½cm.
"Publications of the missionary education movement and the Friendship press": p. 29-32.

1. Drama in education. 2. Missions—Study and teaching. I. Title.
Library of Congress BV2086.L55 30-21312
Copyright A 25955 [2] 268.69

NL 0431569 DLC NcD

Lobingier, *Mrs.* Elizabeth Erwin (Miller) 1889–
Ship east—ship west, written and illustrated by Elizabeth Miller Lobingier. New York, Friendship press [c1937]
4 p. l., 87 p. incl. front., illus. 23½cm.
CONTENTS.—A bridge, a garden, a park, a gate (monuments of peace)—Gifts from other countries.—Child friends around the world.—The best way to settle quarrels.—How foolish war is!—Our flag.

1. Peace—Juvenile literature. I. Title. 37-36389
Library of Congress PZ7.L788h

NL 0431570 DLC InAndC-T IEG WaSp GU NcD OCl OO

Lobingier, *Mrs.* Elizabeth Erwin (Miller) 1889–
Stories of shepherd life; a second-grade course of study suitable for primary departments of church schools, week-day schools of religion, and church vacation schools, by Elizabeth Miller Lobingier ... a book for teachers. Chicago, Ill., The University of Chicago press [1924]
xix, 162 p. front., illus. 20cm. (*Half-title:* The University of Chicago publications in religious education ... Constructive studies)
"References" at end of most of the lessons.
Accompanied by loose-leaf portfolio containing printed reading lessons, pictures, and blank leaves for drawing, writing, and mounting pictures.
1. Bible stories. I. Title. II. Title: Shepherd life, Stories of. 24-10062
Library of Congress BS605.L6

NL 0431571 DLC Or MB PPABP PP NcD OOxM ODW OO OCl

Lobingier, Elizabeth Erwin (Miller)
Stories of shepherd life; a second-grade course of study suitable for primary departments of church schools, week-day schools of religion, and church vacation schools. A book for teachers Chicago, Ill., The University of Chicago press [1928]
Half-title: The University of Chicago publications in religious education. Constructive studies.

NL 0431572 MH

Lobingier, Mrs. Elizabeth Erwin (Miller) 1889-
William Tyndale; a dramatization...
[Chicago] University of Chicago press [c1925]
23 p.
Cover-title.
Reprinted from the Feb. issue of the International journal of religious education.

NL 0431573 OO

Lobingier, John Leslie, 1884–
The better church school. Boston, Pilgrim Press [1952]
152 p. 21 cm.

1. Sunday-schools. 2. Religious education. I. Title.
BV1520.L58 268 52—4583 ‡

NL 0431574 OrP PP PPEB NcD OO DLC CSaT KyLxCB KyU MH-AH Wa WaS WaT WaTC

Lobingier, John Leslie, 1884-
...Colonial education under the Dutch Reformed Church ... by John Leslie Lobingier. [Chicago, 1916.] 3 l., 72 f. 4°.
Typewritten.
Dissertation, University of Chicago, 1916.
Bibliography, p. [ii-iii.]

1. Education—Hist.—U. S.—New York. 2. Education, Sectarian—U. S.—New York. 3. Reformed Church in America.
N. Y. P. L. February 24, 1926

NL 0431575 NN

Lobingier, John Leslie, 1884- joint author.
Lobingier, *Mrs.* Elizabeth Erwin (Miller)
Educating for peace [by] Elizabeth Miller Lobingier and John Leslie Lobingier. Boston, Chicago, The Pilgrim press [c1930]

BV1548 L62
Lobingier, John Leslie, 1884-
How big is your world? A course plan for young people of high school age. Leader's book. [By] John Leslie Lobingier. Boston, Chicago, The Pilgrim press [c1931]
2p.l.,75p. 22cm.

1. Religious education. I. Title.

NL 0431577 NBuG NRCR NcD

BV1546 L6
Lobingier, John Leslie, 1884-
How big is your world? A course plan for young people of high school age. Student's book. [By] John Leslie Lobingier. Boston, Chicago, The Pilgrim press [c1931]
2p.l.,75p. 22cm.

I. Title. 1. Religious education.

NL 0431578 NBuG NcD

BV2090 .L79h 1947
Lobingier, John Leslie.
How to use "Great is the company". New York, Friendship Press, 1947.
31p. illus. 23cm.
Includes bibliography.

1. Missions--Study and teaching. 2. Bible--Use. I. Title. II. Wood, Violet. Great is the company.

NL 0431579 IEG

BV1520 .L6
Lobingier, John Leslie, 1884-
... Instructor's guide book, for use with The organization and administration of the Church school by Walter S. Athearn. Boston, Chicago, [c1924]

NL 0431580 DLC PPAmS

Lobingier, John Leslie, 1884–
Is war the way? A six-session course for individual reading, summer conferences, church study groups, by John Leslie Lobingier. Boston, Chicago, The Pilgrim press [c1935]
56 p. 19½cm.
Bibliography at end of each chapter; "Helps for the peace worker": p. 55-56.

1. Peace.
I. Title. 35-9533
Library of Congress JX1953.L63
—— Copy 2.
Copyright A 84054 [2] 172.4

NL 0431581 DLC OLak OO

Lobingier, John Leslie, joint author.
BV4590 .B6
Bosworth, Edward Increase, 1861-1927.
The Master's way; studies for men in the navy, by Edward Increase Bosworth ... and John Leslie Lobingier ... New York, National war work council of Young men's Christian associations, by Association press, 1918.

Lobingier, John Leslie, 1884–
The missionary education of adults [by] John Leslie Lobingier. New York, Missionary education movement of the United States and Canada [c1938]
vi p., 1 l., 182 p. 18½cm. (The Leader's handbook series)
"For further reading" at end of each chapter.

1. Missions—Study and teaching. 2. Religious education—Text-books for adults. I. Title. 38-7154
Library of Congress BV2090.L55
[a46d1] 266.07

NL 0431583 DLC KyLxCB KyU OrP NcD PPT MSohG

VOLUME 337

Lobingier, John Leslie, 1884–
Our church; a course of study for young people of the high-school age, by John Leslie Lobingier. Chicago, Ill., The University of Chicago press [°1927]
4 p. l., vii–viii, 121 p. illus. (maps) 19½ cm. (*Half-title:* The University of Chicago publications in religious education ... Constructive studies)
Part of pages blank for "Notes," etc.
Contains bibliographies.
1. Church—Study and teaching. I. Title.
BV602.L6 27—25560
NL 0431584 DLC NcD PU OLak OCl OO

Lobingier, John Leslie, 1884-
Our church; a course of study for young people of the high-school age, teacher's manual, by John Leslie Lobingier. Chicago, Ill., The University of Chicago press [°1927]
x, 79, [2] p. 19½cm. (*Half-title:* The University of Chicago publications in religious education ... Constructive studies)
Part of pages blank for "Teacher's notes".
"Worth reading": p. 8–12.
I. Title.
Library of Congress BV602.L62 27–25559
NL 0431585 DLC

BV602 L6 Lobingier, John Leslie.
Our church; a course of study for young people of high-school age, by John Leslie Lobingier. New York, London, Harper & brothers [c1927]
4p.l.,121p. illus.(maps) 19cm.
Part of pages blank for "Notes", etc.
"Sixth edition."
1. Religious education. I. Title.
NL 0431586 NBuG

Lobingier, John Leslie.
Projects in world-friendship, by John Leslie Lobingier ... Chicago, The University of Chicago press [1925]
xv, 177 p. front., illus. 18cm. (*Half-title:* The University of Chicago publications in religious education ... Principles and methods of religious education)
"Reading suggestions": p. 168–171.
1. Religious education. I. Title.
Library of Congress BV1475.L52 25—9231
NcD ODW OO OCl ViU ICJ
NL 0431587 DLC OrPR OrP NjNbS NRCR PU-Penn PJB PPPD

Lobingier, John Leslie, 1884–
What shall we do about missions? A six session course for young people, by John Leslie Lobingier. Boston, Chicago, The Pilgrim press [°1933]
2 p. l., 44 p. 20cm.
Bibliography: p. 41–43.
1. Missions—Study and teaching. I. Title.
Library of Congress BV2090.L56 33–16994
Copyright AA 119909 [2] 266.0714
NL 0431588 DLC NN

Lobingier, John Leslie, 1884–
World-friendship through the church school; a training course for church workers, by John Leslie Lobingier ... Chicago, Ill., The University of Chicago press [°1923]
xi, 91 p. 18cm. (*Half-title:* The University of Chicago publications in religious education ... Principles and methods of religious education)
"Readings" at end of each chapter.
1. Missions—Study and teaching. I. Title.
Library of Congress BV2090.L55 23–6909 Revised
PPEB OLak ODW OO OOxM ViU
NL 0431589 DLC OrP NRCR NjNbS PU-Penn PPABP PJB NcD

Lobingier, John Leslie, 1884–
Youth and the world outlook for young people's classes and societies [by] John Leslie Lobingier ... Boston, Chicago, The Pilgrim press [°1929]
64 p. 19cm. (Christian life series. no. III)
1. Missions—Study and teaching. I. Title.
Library of Congress BV2090.L57 29–8398
NL 0431590 DLC NcD MB OO

Lobingier (Kate Reynolds). Essential details in the conduct of labor. 14 pp. 16°. [*Denver*, 1893.]
NL 0431591 DNLM

Lobingier, Walter S., joint ed.
Pennsylvania. *Court of common pleas (Allegheny Co.)*
Rules of the Court of common pleas of Allegheny County, Pennsylvania. Pittsburgh, Pa., Smith bros. co. inc., 1923.

Lobingier, Walter S., joint ed.
Pennsylvania. *Supreme court.*
Rules of the Supreme court of Pennsylvania. Pittsburgh, Pa., Smith bros. co. inc., 1923.

Lobisser, Suitbert
see Lobisser, Swetbert, 1878-1943.

Lobisser, Switbert, 1878-1943 illus.
Haustrunk aus dem wunderbrünndl deutscher gedichte und lieder. [Wien] F. G. Speidel [1927]

Lobisser, Switbert, 1878–1943.
Das Lobisser buch. 3. u. 4. tausend. Klagenfurt, F. v. Kleinmayr, 1941.
148, [1] p. col. front., illus., plates, ports. 23½cm.
Library of Congress ND538.L55A3 46–40458
[2] 927.5
NL 0431596 DLC

LOBISSER, SUITBERT, 1878-1943.
... Suitbert Lobisser als Meister der Gebrauchsgraphik. Wien, Österreichische Exlibris-Ges. [1949] 29 p., 30 pl. 25cm. (Österreichische Exlibris-Gesellschaft. Sonderveröffentlichung. 2)
At head of title: Heinrich Neumayer.
486068B. I. Neumayer, Heinrich. II. Series.
NL 0431597 NN

Lobisser, Switbert, 1878-1943.
Switbert Lobisser; Verzeichnis seiner Holzschnitte. Graz, Leykam-Verlag, 1944. 94 p. 48 illus., port. 30cm. (Beiträge zur Kunstgeschichte Steiermarks und Kärntens. Bd. 7)
1. Lobisser, Suitbert, 1878-1943. I. Series.
NL 0431598 NN

Lobisser, Switbert, 1878–1943.
Switbert Lobisser; Verzeichnis seiner Holzschnitte, eingeleitet von Hermann Egger. 2., verm. Aufl. Graz, Leykam-Verlag, 1947.
128 p. (p. 49–128 plates) port. 30 cm. (Beiträge zur Kunstgeschichte Steiermarks und Kärntens, Bd. 7)
I. Egger, Hermann, 1873– (Series)
NE1217.L6E4 1947 51–32036
NL 0431599 DLC

Lobisser, Switbert, 1878-1943, illus.
Erkelenz, Carl Hanns, 1907– ed.
Vierzehn nothelfer, von dichtern dargestellt; herausgegeben von Carl Hanns Erkelenz. Mit vierzehn holzschnitten von Switbert Lobisser. Freiburg im Breisgau, Herder & co. g. m. b. h. verlagsbuchhandlung, 1937.

Lobit (Augustin). *Considérations sur l'étiologie et le traitement de l'hydrocèle vaginale. 38 pp. 4°. *Paris*, 1873, No. 390.
NL 0431601 DNLM

WBI L797b 1900 LOBIT, Jean
Biarritz, ses ressources hygiéniques et thérapeutiques. Biarritz, Lamaignère, 1900.
185 p. illus.
NL 0431602 DNLM

Lobit, Jean.
Biarritz, station bibernale. Notes climatologique et demographique sur Biarritz. 1896.
20764
NL 0431603 DAS

Lobit, Jean.
Contribution a l'etude de Biarritz-medical. Biarritz. 1897.
16 p. 8°.
P.4177 Author, gift. 10/8/98
NL 0431604 DAS

VOLUME 337

Lobit (Jean). Note climatologique et démographique sur Biarritz. 26 pp., 2 diag. 8°. *Biarritz, Lamaignère,* 1896.

NL 0431605 DNLM

Lobito, Angola. Camara municipal.

HE373
.A63L6
1941

Lobito, *Angola. Ordinances, etc.*
... Regulamento de trânsito na cidade do Lobito, aprovado pela Comissão administrativa da Camara municipal do Lobito, em sessão ordinária de 3 de abril de 1941. Luanda, Imprensa nacional, 1941.

Lobito, *Angola. Conselho de administração do porto do Lobito*
see
Angola. *Conselho de administração do porto do Lobito.*

Lobito, *Angola. Ordinances, etc.*
... Regulamento de trânsito na cidade do Lobito, aprovado pela Comissão administrativa da Camara municipal do Lobito, em sessão ordinária de 3 de abril de 1941. Luanda, Imprensa nacional, 1941.

10 p. 20½cm.

At head of title: Provincia de Benguela. Câmara municipal do Lobito.

1. Traffic regulations—Lobito, Angola. I. Lobito, Angola. Camara municipal.

Library of Congress HE373.A63L6 1941 44-10577

NL 0431608 DLC

Lobjois, André Amédée Émile, 1912-
... L'index et le virage de la cuti-réaction tuberculinique dans un service de médecine sociale infantile ... Angers, 1937.
Thèse - Univ. de Paris.
"Bibliographie": p. [139]-147.

NL 0431609 CtY

French
Rev.
DC
141
F87+
v.140

Lobjoy, François, 1743-1807.
Discours sur la présentation du traité de paix. 16 floréal an 10. [Paris, Impr. nat., an 10, i.e. 1802.]
3 p. 22cm.

At head of title: Corps législatif.
Reprinted in Archives Parlementaires, 2e série, v. 3, p. 603.

NL 0431610 NIC MnU

Lobko, U. A., joint ed.

SB251
.R9H6

Horians'kyĭ, M M *ed.*
Бавовник на Україні; посібник для агрономів та керівного складу колгоспів, МТС та радгоспів. Склала бригада за відповідальним редагуванням М. М. Горянського і У. А. Лобко. Київ, Держ. вид-во колгоспної і радгоспної літ-ри УСРР, 1935.

TP692
.5
.L6

Lobkov, Alekseĭ Mikhaĭlovich.
Сбор и транспорт нефти на промыслах. Допущено в качестве учеб. пособия для нефтяных вузов. Москва, Гос. научно-техн. изд-во нефтяной и горно-топливной лит-ры, 1955.

281 p. illus. 23 cm.

Bibliography: p. [278]

1. Petroleum—Storage. 2. Petroleum—Transportation. I. Title.
Title transliterated: Sbor i transport nefti na promyslakh.

TP692.5.L6 55-36932

NL 0431612 DLC

Lobkovic, Bohuslav Hasištejnský z
see **Lobkowitz, Bohuslaw Hassenstein,** *Freiherr* **von, 1460** *or* **61-1510.**

Lobkovic, Ferdinand Josef Jan Nepomuk, *kníže,* **1797-1868.**
Description of the collection of minerals belonging to the Prince of Lobkowitz in Bilin near Teplitz in Bohemia ... Vienna, W. Jacobi, 1869.

12 p. 21cm.

Signed: Jos. Rubesch.
"Translated from German by H. Berger."

1. Mineralogy—Catalogs and collections. I. Rubesch, Joseph. II. Berger, H., tr.

12-2652

Library of Congress QE386.L79

NL 0431614 DLC

Lobkovic, Jan Hasištejnský, 1450-1517.
Putování k Svatému hrobu. Dle rukopisu Pražské universitní knihovny, vydal, úvodem, ukazatelem míst a slovníkem opatřil Ferdinand Strejček. V Praze, Nákl. České akademie pro vědy, slovesnost a umění, 1902.

xxxii, 119 p. 27 cm. (Sbírka pramenův ku poznání literárního života v Čechách, na Moravě a v Slezsku. Skupina 1., řada 2. čís. 4)

1. Israel—Descr. & trav. I. Strejček, Ferdinand, 1878- ed. II. Title. (Series: Česká akademie věd a umění, Prague. Třída 3. Sbírka pramenů k poznání literárního života československého. Skupina 1., řada 2. čís. 4)

PG5000.C48 čís. 4 55-55614

NL 0431615 DLC ICU CSt DDO NIC MH NN NNC MiU

D 973
.L 79

LOBKOVIC, JAN HASIŠTEINSKÝ, kníže z, 1450-1517
Putování k svatému hrobu. Znova vydal Fr. Maleček. V Praze, Nákl. J. Otty, 1907.
180 p. (Světova knihovna, č.554-5)

At head of title: Jan Hasišteinsky z Lobkovic.
Travelling to the Holy Sepulchre [1493-1494]

1. Mediterranean sea--Desc. 2. Palestine--Descr. I. Title.

NL 0431616 InU

Lobkovic, Jiří Kristián, *kníže*
see
Lobkowicz, Jiří Kristián, *kníže,* **1835-1908.**

Lobkovic-Hasišteinský, Jan
see **Lobkovic, Jan Hasištejnský,** 1450-1517.

Lobkowicz, Jiří Kristián, kníže, 1835-1908.
Georg fürst von Lobkowicz und die selbstverwaltung im königreiche Böhmen
see under Bohemia. Zemský výb

Lobkowicz, Jiří Kristián, kníže, 1835-1908.
Jiří, kníže z Lobkowicz a samospráva v Království českém
see under Bohemia. Zemský výbor.

Lobkowicz, Maximilian, 1888-

Z6621
.P888

Prague. Národní a universitní knihovna.
Katalogy knihoven kolejí Karlovy university. [Redigoval Josef Bečka. Praha] 1948.

Lobkowitz, Albrecht, Freiherr von, 1892-
Ignaz Nöss; Volksschauspiel in fünf Aufzügen, von Freiherr von Lobkowitz. München: V. Höfling[, 1926]. 84 p. 24°. (Höflings Volkstümliche Bühne. Nr. 4267.)

1. Drama, German. 2. Title.
N. Y. P. L. November 29, 1927

NL 0431622 NN

Lobkowitz, Bohuslaw Hassenstein, *Freiherr von,* 1460 or 61-1510.
Carmina selecta. Bohuslai Hasisteinii a Lobkovic. [Pragae, Officinae Bremensis Monaci, 1922]
xxxi p. 27cm.

"Carmina selegit O. Jiráni, edidit Arthur Novák. Liber manu impressus est caracteribus et diligentia societatis Officinae Bremensis Monaci in centum, quae venalia sunt, exemplaribus. Ex aliis insuper xxx exemplaribus, quae ad editoris usum typis expressa non veneunt."
No.2.

NL 0431623 IU MH NN

Lobkowitz, Bohuslaw Hassenstein, *Freiherr* **von, 1460** (*or* **61)-1510.**
Epistolae. Accedunt Epistolae ad Bohuslaum scriptae. Edidit Augustinus Potuček. Budapest, Egyetemi Nyomda, 1946.

lii, 180 p. 25 cm. (Bibliotheca scriptorum medii recentisque aevorum. Saecula xv-xvi)

"Introductio" (chiefly bibliographical): p. [v]-lii.

I. Potuček, Augustin, 1872-1941. (Series)

A 50-2828

Illinois. Univ. Library
for Library of Congress [2]

NL 0431624 IU CtY MH ICN OU

Lobkowitz, Bohuslaw Hassenstein, Freiherr von, 1460 or 61-1510.
Das Geheimnis um die Erfindung von Pulver und Geschütz
see under Hassenstein, Wilhelm.

VOLUME 337

CT930 .L79 A3

Lobkowitz, Bohuslaw Hassenstein, Freiherr von, 1460 or 61-1510
Bohuslawa z Lobkowic a z Hasensteynu, List Panu Petrowi z Rosenberka o zprawě zemské poslaný, který po třech stech a sedmi letech z rukopisu wybral J. W. Zimmermann. W Praze, Wytistěn v. F. Fetterla z Wildenbrunu, 1818.
x, 76 p.
I. Petr z Rožmberka, b. 1462. II. Zimmermann, Jan Václav, 1788-1836, ed.

NL 0431626 ICU

Lobkowitz, Bohuslaw Hassenstein, Freiherr von, 1460 or 61-1510.
Listář Bohuslava Hasištejnské ho z Lobkovic. Nově uspořádal, doplnil a poznámkami opatřil Josef Truhlář. V Praze, Nákl. České akademie Císaře Františka Josefa pro vědy, slovesnost a umění, 1893. xvi, 245 p. 26cm.
All letters, but one, in Latin with summaries in Czech.

1. Letters, Czech, Neo-Latin. I. Truhlář, Josef, 1840-1914, ed.

NL 0431627 NN MiU MH MoU ICU

Case Y 682 .L 772

LOBKOWITZ, BOHUSLAW, 1462-1510.
...Lvcvbrationes oratoriae... His addita svnt, collecta per Thomam Mitem, diuersorum elogia D. Bohuslai vitam concernentia... Pragae, Excvdebant T.Mitis, et I.Caper, 1563.
[12], 160, [44] l. 16cm.
Initials, tail-pieces.
Contents.—De miseria humana.—De auaritia.—Oratio pro Petro Schotto.—Fragmentum de felicitate.—Fragmenti epistolarum libri V.—Vita autoris per Thomam Mitem collecta è diuersorum elogijs, & domini Bohuslai ad diuersos scriptis.

NL 0431628 ICN MH

Lobkowitz, Bohuslaw, Hassenstein, Freiherr von, 1460 or 61-1510.
Carro, Jean de, 1770-1857, ed.
Ode latine sur Carlsbad, composée vers la fin du quinzième siècle par le baron Bohuslas Hassenstein de Lobkowitz, avec une traduction polyglotte, une notice biographique sur ce poëte, des observations sur l'ode, et sur l'antiquité de ses thermes, par le chevalier Jean de Carro ... Avec le portrait de Lobkowitz et une vue des ruines de Hassenstein ... Prague, Impr. de Schoenfeld, 1829.

---

*ZC05 L7855 509o

Lobkowitz, Bohuslaw, 1462-1510.
Opuscula Bohuslai Boemi baronis de Hassenstayn que hoc volumine continentur. Ad Uladislaū Pānonie et Boemie regem in funere Anne regine coniugis elegia cōsolatoria. Elegia ad xiiij sanctos. quos vulgo auxiliatores vocant. de peregrinatione sua gracias agens. Ad Joannem Sturnū francū de Smalcaldia de auaricia libellus. Sūmos christianos principes cōtra Thurcas excitās adhortatorium carmen.
[Germany? 1509]
[39]p. 19.5cm.

Signatures: A-B6, C-D4.
Includes letters (dated Dec. 1508) by Jan Sturnus; though according to A. Potuček, editor of the 1946 ed. of Lobkowitz's letters, these were written by Lobkowitz in Sturnus's name.

NL 0431631 MH

Lobkowitz, Bohuslaw Hassenstein, *Freiherr* **von, 1460 or 61-1510.**
... Scripta moralia. Oratio ad Argentinenses. Memoria Alexandri de Imola. Edidit Bohumil Ryba. Lipsiae, B. G. Teubner, 1937.
vi, 44 p. diagr. 24 cm. (Bibliotheca scriptorum medii recentisque aevorum ... Redigit L. Juhász ... Saecula xv-xvi)
At head of title: ... Bohuslaus Hassensteinius baro a Lobkowicz.
"Oratio ad Argentinenses, quam pro Petro Schotto ... amicitiae causa scripsit, re vera nunquam esse habita videtur."—p. iv.
"De Bohuslai Hassensteinii vita et operibus": p. [iii]-iv; "De codicibus et editionibus Bohuslai operum, quae exceptis epistulis prosa oratione scripta sunt": p. iv-vi.
I. Schott, Peter, 1458?-1490. II. Tartagni, Alessandro, d. 1477. III. Ryba, Bohumil, 1900- ed.
A C 40-1902 rev
Illinois. Univ. Library for Library of Congress [r50c2]

NL 0431632 IU NN NNC PPJ MH OU ICN CtY

Lobkowitz, Bohuslaw Hassenstein, *Freiherr* **von, 1460 or 61-1510.**
Spisy Bohuslava Hasištejnského z Lobkovic. Vydal a poznámkami opatřil Bohumil Ryba. V Praze, Nákl. České akademie věd a umění, 1933–
v. 27 cm. (Sbírka pramenů k poznání literárního života československého. III. Třída České akademie věd a umění. Skupina druhá: Korespondence a prameny cizojazyčné, čís. 26)
In Latin.
Prefatory matter in Czech.
Contents.—sv. 1. Spisy prosaické.
I. Ryba, Bohumil, 1900– (Series: Česká akademie věd a umění, Prague. Třída 3. Sbírka pramenů k poznánfliterárního života československého. Skupina 2: Korespondence a prameny cizojazyčné, čís. 26)
PA8545.L58A6 1933 68-53622

NL 0431633 DLC CaBVaU MiU NN NIC ICU NNC MH MoU

Lobkowitz, Ferdinand Joseph Johann Nepomuck von, Prince, 1797-1868
see
Lobkovic, Ferdinand Josef Jan Nepomuk kníže, 1797-1868

Lobkowitz, George Christian, *fürst* **von**
see
Lobkowicz, Jiří Kristián, *kníže*, **1835–1908.**

Lobkowitz, Juan Caramuel
see Caramuel Lobkowitz, Juan, 1606-1682.

Lobkowitz von Hassenstein, Johann
see **Lobkovic, Jan Hasištejnský, 1450–1517.**

Lobl, Herbert Max
The opening of the gates; a study of Nazi foreign policy, 1933-1936
Honors thesis - Harvard, 1953

NL 0431638 MH

QE508 L6

Lobley, James Logan, 1834-1913
The age of the world. London, R. Ashley, 1914.
128 p.

1. Earth - Age.

NL 0431639 CU

Lobley, J[ames] Logan, 1834-1913.
The American fauna and its origin ...
[N.p.n.pub.1908?].
O.

NL 0431640 CaBViP

Lobley, James Logan, 1834-1913
Geology for all; a general conspectus of the subject adapted for all intelligent readers. London, Roper & Drowley, 1888.
161 p., illus.

NL 0431641 MiD DI-GS

Za889l

Lobley, James Logan, 1834-
Hampstead Hill: its structure, materials, and sculpturing, by J.Logan Lobley ... With The flora of Hampstead, by Henry T.Wharton ... The insect fauna of Hampstead, by the Rev.F.A.Walker ... and The birds of Hampstead, by J.Edmund Harting ... London, Roper and Drowley, 1889.
100p.incl.IXpl.(incl.front.,map,profiles)
21½cm.

NL 0431642 CtY PHC MH TxU

Lobley, James Logan, 1834–
Mount Vesuvius: a descriptive, historical, and geological account of the volcano, with a notice of the recent eruption, and an appendix, containing letters by Pliny the younger, a table of dates of eruptions, and a list of Vesuvian minerals. By J. Logan Lobley ... London, E. Stanford, 1868.
vi p., 1 l., 55 p. front., pl., map. 22½cm.

1. Vesuvius. 2. Volcanoes—Italy.
G S 10-308
Library, U. S. Geol. survey 220 (550) L785m

NL 0431643 DI-GS TxU PPFr OCl ICJ

Lobley, James Logan, 1834–1913.
Mount Vesuvius. A descriptive, historical, and geological account of the volcano and its surroundings. By J. Logan Lobley ... London, Roper and Drowley, 1889.
400 p. xx pl. (incl. front.) maps, profiles. 22½cm.
Catalogue of recorded eruptions: p. 378-379.

1. Vesuvius. I. Title.
Library of Congress QE523.V5L7 1-13224

NL 0431644 DNLM CtY MdBP TxU DLC NcU PPAN NIC ICJ MH MiHM PP MiU PPL

Lobley, Joseph Albert.
The church and the churches in southern India: a review of the Portuguese missions to that part of the world in the sixteenth century, with special reference to the Syrian Christians, and to modern missionary efforts in the same quarter... Cambridge, Deighton, Bell, 1870.
138 p. 23cm. (Maitland prize essay. 1870)

Bibliographical footnotes.

NL 0431645 NjPT

Ain loblich ordnūg der fürstlichen stat Wittemberg
see under [Karlstadt, Andreas Rudolf] 1480 (ca.)-1541.

VOLUME 337

Lobligeois (Charles). *De l'oblitération congéuitale des intestins. 80 pp. 4°. *Paris*, 1856, No. 259, v. 592.

NL 0431647 DNLM

Lobligeois (Félix) [1874-]. *Étude clinique et diagnostique des érythèmes scarlatiniformes et de la scarlatine vraie apparaissant au cours de la diphtérie. (Valeur diagnostique de l'examen du sang et de la diazoréaction de Ehrlich.) 77 pp. 8°. *Paris*. 1902. No. 149.

NL 0431648 DNLM

Lobligeois, Henri Louis.
... Réflexions sur la fortification permanente; avec 169 croquis dans le texte et 3 planches hors texte. Paris, Berger-Levrault, 1932.
xii, 275 p. illus., III fold. pl., diagrs. 22½cm.
At head of title: Lieutenant-colonel Lobligeois.

1. Fortification.
Library of Congress UG405.L64 33-21244
Copyright A—Foreign 21210
[2] 623.1

NL 0431649 DLC DNW

WX 2 A5V8 qP8L
LOBLOLLY.
[Portsmouth, Va.] U. S. Naval Hospital.
[1942?]-
v. illus., ports.
I. U. S. Naval Hospital, Portsmouth, Va.

NL 0431650 DNLM

... **Loblolly** pine (*Pinus taeda*) [Washington, Govt. print. off.] 1910.
4 p. 23cm. (U. S. Dept. of agriculture. Forest service. Circular 183. Forest planting leaflet)
1. Loblolly pine.
Agr 10-1427

Library, U. S. Dept. of Agriculture 1F76C no. 183

NL 0431651 DNAL

Loblov, Béla,
Cadenza to the Brahms violin concerto in D ... see under Brahms, Johannes, 1833-1897.

Lobman, Dawid.
Problemi di psicoanalisi, di Dawid Lobman. [Roma] De Carlo, 1946.
188 p., 1 l. 20½ x 12cm. (*Half-title:* La Specola, libri di varia cultura, vol. I)
"Nota bibliografica": p. 185-188.

1. Psychoanalysis.
BF173.L55 131.34 A F 47-986
Harvard univ. Library for Library of Congress [4]†

NL 0431653 MH DLC IaU

Lobman, Dawid.
Problemi di psicoanalisi. 2. ed. riv. e ampliata. [Roma] De Carlo, 1949.
239 p. 19 cm. (La Specola; libri di varia cultura, v. 1)
Bibliography: p. 233-237.

1. Psychoanalysis.
[BF173.L] 131.34 A 55-3852
Harvard Univ. Library for Library of Congress [1]

NL 0431654 MH DNLM

Lobman, Jerzy.
Chiny na własne oczy. [Wyd. 1. Warszawa] Czytelnik, 1954.
250 p. illus., port., maps (1 fold.) 24 cm.

1. China (People's Republic of China, 1949-)—Soc. condit. 2. China (People's Republic of China, 1949-)—Descr. & trav. I. Title.
HN673.5.L6 63-52940

NL 0431655 DLC

Lobmayer, Gerhard.
Ueber die Einwirkung von Salzsaeure auf Benzolazo-lutidin und Benzol-azo-4-lutidinkarbonsäure sowie über einige Schwefelderivate des Lutidins. Breslau, 1925.
Inaug. diss. - Breslau.

NL 0431656 ICRL

RC185 L798
Lobmayer, Géza.
... A tetanusról. Irta Lobmayer Géza ... [Budapest, Franklin-társulat nyomdája, 1914]
cover-title, [718]-727 p. 25½cm.
"Különnyomat az 'Orvosképzés' 1914. évi 10. füzetéből."

1.Tetanus.

NL 0431657 CSt-H CSt

DB926.3 C7 L63
Lobmayer, Iván
Történelmi kapcsolataink Horvátországgal. Budapest, A Magyar Külügyi Társaság Kiadása, 1941.
35 p. 21 cm. (Külügyi Könyvtar, 4)
Bibliography: p. 34-35.

1. Hungary - Relations (general) with Croatia. 2. Croatia - Relations (general) with Hungary. I. Title (1)

NL 0431658 CtY

Lobmeier, Georg, 1873-
Johann Georg Sulzer in seinem verhältnis zur physikalischen geographie ... Borna-Leipzig, Buchdr. R. Noske, 1907.
viii, 63 p., 1 l. 22½cm.
Inaug.-diss.—Erlangen.
Lebenslauf.
"Literaturverzeichnis": p. vii-viii.

8-25329* Cancel

NL 0431659 DLC NN CtY PU ICRL

Lobmeyr, Ludwig, and others.
Die Glasindustrie, ihre Geschichte, gegenwärtige Entwicklung und Statistik. In Gemeinschaft mit Albert Ilg und Wendelin Boeheim. Stuttgart. Spemann. 1874. x, 324, (1) pp. 23½ cm., in 8s.

M210 — Glass. — Ilg, Albert, jt. auth. — Boeheim, Wendelin, jt. auth.

NL 0431660 MB ICJ ICU NN DP MiU DSI MB NCorniC CtY

Lobmeyr, Ludwig
Versteigerung der Ölgemälde, Aquarelle und Handzeichnungen aus dem Nachlasse des Herrn Ludwig Lobmeyr ... den 22.Oktober und die darauffolgenden Tage ... im Künstlerhause, Wien ... Auskünfte und Katalogue von der Kunsthandlung C.J.Wawra. [Wien, 1917?]
xii, 51 p. plates (part col.)

NL 0431661 MH-FA

Lobmeyr-Hohenleiten,Oskar

Hugelmann, Karl Gottfried, 1879- *ed.*
Das nationalitätenrecht des alten Österreich. Unter mitarbeit von M. H. Boehm, N. Gürke, W. Haas, O. Lobmeyr-Hohenleiten, A. Manussi-Montesole, R. Pacher, G. Pockels, H. Steinacker, Th. Veiter und R. Wenedikter, herausgegeben von Karl Gottfried Hugelmann. Wien-Leipzig, W. Braumüller, universitäts-verlagsbuchhandlung, 1934.

Lobmiller, Hans, Rechtsanw.: Der Staat und das katholische Ordenswesen im Königreich Württemberg seit der Säkularisation bis zum Jahre 1848. (Die staatskirchenrechtl. Bestimmungen d. vor- u. frühkonstitutionellen Zeit in ihrem Einfluß auf d. Behandlung der Ordensfrage.) Eine rechtsgesch. Studie, nach d. Akten d. K. Geh. Haus- u. Staatsarchivs in Stuttg. u. d. Bisch. Ordinariats in Rottenburg verfaßt. Mit e. Anh. unveröff. Aktenstücke. Rottenburg a.N.: Bader 1914. 70, XIII S. 8° ¶Vollst. im Buchh. ebd.
Heidelberg, Jur. Diss. v. 27. Febr. 1914, Ref. F. Fleiner
[Geb. 8. Sept. 85 Wiesensteig; Wohnort: Tettnang; Staatsangeh.: Württemberg; Vorbildung: G. Rottweil Reife 04; Studium: Tübingen Phil. 2, Jura 7 S.; Rig. 5. Juni 12.] [U 14. 725

NL 0431663 ICRL MH-L CtY IU MH

Lobner, Joyce E.
The golden eagle child; a legendary play in one act, by Joyce E. Lobner. (In: Carter, L. H., compiler. The banner anthology of one-act plays by American authors. San Francisco, Cal. [, cop. 1929.] p. [235-]249. 8°.)

417918A. 1. Drama, American. 2. Indians, N. A.—Cal.—Drama. 3. Creation—Legends, Indian-American. 4. Title.
N. Y. P. L. June 25, 1929

NL 0431664 NN

4TA 213
Lobnitz,
Institution des ingénieurs civils et constructeurs de navire d'Écosse: Séance extraordinaire du 20 mai 1868: Lecture faite á Glascow sur la situation des travaux du canal de Suez et sur l'avenir de l'entreprise. Paris, Impr. et librairie centrales des chemins de fer A. Chaix, 1868.
40 p.

NL 0431665 DLC-P4

Lobnitz & company, ltd., Renfrew, Scot.
[Illustrated catalogue of steamers, yachts, dredgers, tugs, etc.] Renfrew, Lobnitz & co., 1901. 39 f. illus. 21cm.

267895B. 1. Shipbuilding—Gt. Br.—Scot.—Renfrew.
N. Y. P. L. January 24, 1945

NL 0431666 NN

VOLUME 337

Lobo, A. de Sousa Silva Costa
see
Sousa Silva Costa Lobo, Antonio de, 1840-

Lobo, A.E. Da Costa
see Costa Lobo, A.E. Da.

Lobo, A M de Souza
see Lobo, Antonio Maria de Souza, 1806-1844.

Lobo, Abelardo Saraiva da Cunha
see Saraiva da Cunha Lobo, Abelardo.

Lobo, Abilio, 1851?-1908, ed.

Á Volta do mundo; jornal de viagens e de assumptos geographicos, illustrado com milhares de gravuras representando paisagens, cidades, villas, monumentos, retratos ... etc., e um grande numero de cartas geographicas ... anno 1- ⌊15 nov.?⌋ 1880-
Lisboa, Empreza litteraria Luso-Brazileira, 1880-

Lobo, Abilio, 1851-1908, ed.
A Illustração universal; revista dos principaes acontecimentos de Portugal e do estrangeiro. anno 1- 9 fev. 1884-
Lisboa, Empreza litteraria luso-brazileira ⌊1884-

Lobo, Acacio.
Curso pratico de ingles comercial...
Lisboa, Livraria classica editora, 1938.

368 p.

NL 0431673 PP

651.74
L799c
1944

Lôbo, Acácio.
Curso prático de inglês comercial, compreendando correspondência e conversação. 10. ed., rev. e muito melhorada. Lisboa, Livraria Clássica Editora, 1944.

368p. 18cm.

1. English language - Business English. 2. Commercial correspondence. 3. English language - Text-books for foreigners - Portuguese. I. Title

NL 0431674 FU

Lobo, Ada Macaggi Bruno
see
Macaggi Bruno Lobo, Ada.

DP618
.C45

Lobo, Alvaro, 1550 or 1-1608, supposed author.

Chronica do cardeal rei d. Henrique, e Vida de Miguel de Moura, escripta por elle mesmo. Publicadas con algumas annotações pela Sociedade propagadora dos conhecimentos uteis. Lisboa, Typographia da Sociedade propagadora dos conhecimentos uteis, 1840.

LOBO, Alvaro, 1550 or 1 - 1608, comp.

Martyrologio dos santos de Portugal e festas geraes do reyno, recolhido dalguns autores e informações por algũs padres da Companhia de Jesu [Alvaro Lobo]. Coimbra, A. de Maris, 1591.

24°. pp.21,(58).
(Appended to: CATHOLIC CHURCH. Martyrologio romano. Coimbra, 1591.)

NL 0431677 MH

Lobo, Alvaro, 1550 or 1-1608, comp.
Martyrologio dos santos de Protugal e festas geraes do reyno, recolhido dalguns autores e informações por algũs padres da Companhia de Jesu [Alvaro Lobo]. Coimbra, A. de Maris, 1591.
21, (58) p. 24°. (In, or with, as issued: Catholic Church. Liturgy and ritual. Martyrology. Protuguese. Martyrologio romano ... Coimbra, 1591 [NC 0218936]

NL 0431678 MH

Lobo, Alvaro, 1550 or 1-1608, tr.
Martyrologio romano accommadado a todos os dias do anno conforme à nova ordem do calendario
see under Catholic Church, Liturgy and Ritual. Martyrology, Portugese.

Lobo, Americo, tr.

Marshall, John, 1755-1835.
Decisões constitucionaes de Marshall, presidente do Supremo tribunal dos Estados Unidos da America do Norte, traduzidas por Americo Lobo. Rio de Janeiro, Imprensa nacional, 1903.

Lobo, Americo, tr.

Longfellow, Henry Wadsworth, 1807-1882.
... Poemas norte-americanos de Henry W. Longfellow ... Rio de Janeiro, Imprensa nacional, 1887.

898.1
L799p

Lobo, Americo.
Poesias. ⌊Sapucaia, Estado do Rio (Brazil) Typ. Dª "A Sapucaia", 1918?⌋
118 p. 21 cm.

Contents. -A primeira saudade. -Antithese hugoana. -Canções francezas. -Doloras de Campoamor. -Cantos de Lord Lytton. -Poemas da escravidão (Longfellow) - Idyllios virgilianos. -Poesies.

NL 0431682 NcU

Z 770
.M2 L85

LÔBO, ANTÔNIO, 1870-1916
A bibliotheca do Maranhão em 1900. Maranhão, Typ. Frias, 1901.
121 p.

1. São Luís, Brazil (Maranhão)--Libraries. I. Title.

NL 0431683 InU

Lôbo, Antonio, 1870-1916.
Relatoria apresentado ao Sr. governador do estado do Maranhão ...
see under Maranhão (State) Bibliotheca publica do estado, Maranhão.

Lobo, Antonio Augusto da Silva
see
Silva Lobo, Antonio Augusto da, *d.* 1900.

Lobo, Antonio de Rosa Gama
see Rosa Gama Lobo, Antonio da, b. 1817.

Greenlee
4504
P855

LOBO, ANTÓNIO DE SANTA MARTA, b.1716.
Oraçaõ gratulatoria, com que se finalizou o solemne triduo, que o senado da camera desta sempre leal cidade do Porto fez celebrar em acçaõ de graças na cathedral da mesma cidade, tanto que recebeo o real avizo do milagroso prodigio, com que Deos conservou a vida ao nosso fidelissimo rey e senhor d. Joseph I. no horrorosissimo insulto com que foi accõmetido no dia tres de setembro proximo passado... Lisboa, M. Rodrigues, 1759.
27p. 20cm.

NL 0431687 ICN

Lobo, Antonio de Sousa Silva Costa,
see
Sousa Silva Costo Lobo, Antonio de, 1840-

Lôbo, Antônio Francisco Leal
see
Lôbo, Antônio, 1870-1916.

Lobo, António Maria de Souza, 1806-1844.
Obras dramaticas de A. M. de Souza Lobo. Porto, Na typografia de F. Guimarães, 1841 ⌊i. e. 1842⌋-
v. 22 cm.
CONTENTS.—⌊1⌋ O emparedado.
L. C. copy replaced by microfilm.
——— Microfilm. Microfilm 28469 PQ

I. Title: O emparedado.

[PQ9261.L538] 72-21931

NL 0431690 DLC InU

Lobo, Ari Maurell
see
Maurell Lobo, Ari, 1900-

VOLUME 337

HX314 .B826 Lobo, Aristides, tr.
Bukharin, Nikolaĭ Ivanovich, 1888–1938.
... ABC do comunismo, tradução de Aristides Lobo. Curitiba ₍etc.₎ Editôra Guaira limitada ₍194–₎

HV8661 .B285 1940 z Lobo, Aristides, tr.
Beccaria, Cesare Bonesana, *marchese* di, 1738–1794.
... Dos delitos e das penas. S₍ão₎ Paulo, Atena ₍194–₎

Lobo, Arturo Alonso
see
Alonso Lobo, Arturo, 1921–

Lobo, Arturo Gómez-
see
Gómez-Lobo, Arturo.

Lobo, Ayrton, 1903–
... Floriano. ₍Rio de Janeiro₎ D. N. P., 1939.
19, ₍1₎ p. 20½ᶜᵐ.
"Conferência realizada no Clube militar, na data centenária do nascimento de Floriano Peixoto."—p. 3.

1. Peixoto, Floriano, pres. Brazil, 1839–1895. I. Title.
₍Full name: Ayrton Bittencourt Lobo₎
Library of Congress F2537.P363 43-37746
₍2₎

NL 0431696 DLC NNC

Lobo, Barros
see Barros Lobo, Francisco.

Lobo, Bruno.
... De japonez a brasileiro (adaptação e nacionalisação do immigrante) Rio de Janeiro, Typ. do Dep. nacional de estatistica, 1932.
268 p., 2 l. illus. (incl. maps, facsim.) 23ᶜᵐ.
Added t.-p. in Japanese, at end of volume.

1. Japanese in Brazil. 2. Brazil—Emig. & immig. 3. Japan. I. Title.
₍Full name: Bruno Alvares da Silva Lobo₎
Library of Congress F2659.J3L7 33-309
₍3₎ 325.252

NL 0431698 DLC NcD

Lobo, Bruno.
Esquecendo os antepassados, combatendo os estrangeiros. ₍Rio de Janeiro₎ Editorial Alba, 1935.
192 p. 19 cm. (Série politico-social, 2)

1. Brazil—Emig. & immig. 2. Brazil—Foreign population. I. Title.
Full name: Bruno Alvares da Silva Lobo.
JV7462.L6 56-20584

NL 0431699 DLC

Lobo, Bruno
Esquecendo os antepassados, combatendo os estrangeiros Rio [de Janeiro] Branco [1935]
192 p. (Série político-social, 2)

NL 0431700 MH

Lobo, Bruno.
... Japonezes no Japão, no Brasil. Rio de Janeiro, Imprensa nacional, 1926.
178 p., 1 l. illus. (incl. maps) 22½ᶜᵐ.
An enlarged edition, published in 1932, has title: De japonez a brasileiro.

1. Japanese in Brazil. 2. Brazil—Emig. & immig. 3. Japan. I. Title.
₍Full name: Bruno Alvares da Silva Lobo₎
Library of Congress F2659.J3L8 41-13633
₍2₎ 325.2520981

NL 0431701 DLC CU

MANN QH 31 V9 L79 Lobo, Bruno.
Jubileu de Hugo de Vries; conferencia commemorativa, feita pelo Professor Bruno Lobo, na Sociedade Brasileira de Sciencias. Rio de Janeiro, Imprensa Nacional, 1918.
48 p. plates, port. 25 cm.
"Da 'Revista da Sociedade Brasileira de Sciencias', n. 2, 1918."
List of de Vries' principal publications: p. 6-9.

1. Vries, Hugo de, 1848-1935. I. Title. ₍II. Series: Academia Brasileira de Ciencias, Rio de Janeiro. Revista, no. 2₎

NL 0431703 NIC

Lobo, Bruno. A lagarta rosea da Gelechia gossypiella; [sobre os meios empregados no Egypto para combater]. Relatorio apresentado ao dr. J. G. Rereira Lima, ministro da agricultura, industria e commercio. Rio de Janeiro 1918. l. 8°. pp. 192. 3 maps, and other illus.
"Bibliographia," pp. 185-190.

NL 0431704 MH-A PPAmE

Lobo, Bruno.
Palavras. I.
— Rio de Janeiro. Escola. 1923. 1 v. 18 cm., in 8s.
Contents. — 1. Serie politico-social.
A collection of addresses.

N615

NL 0431705 MB ICarbS

Lobo, Bruno.
Relatorio apresentado ao exmo. sr. dr. Ildefonso Simões Lopes. Anno de 1920. Rio de Janeiro, Impr. nacional, 1921.
71 p. illus. 24 cm.
On cover: O Museo Nacional durante o anno de 1920.

NL 0431706 PU-Mu PU

Lobo, Bruno Alipio
see
Alipio Lobo, Bruno.

Lobo, Carlos Fernando Leckie.
A Organização Internacional do Trabalho. Suas origens. A parte dos Estados Unidos da América na sua criação. Rio de Janeiro, 1947.
130 p. 25 cm.
Bibliography: p. ₍125₎-130.

1. International Labor Organization.
HD7809.L62 50-35076

NL 0431708 DLC CtY MH NNC CU

Lobo, Ceferino E.
... Ensayos sobre crítica. [San Salvador, Talleres gráficos Cisneros] 1939.
76 p. 19 cm.
Contents. - Camilo Campos.- La enseñanza del costellano.

NL 0431709 DPU

0920.081 L786g Lobo, Chiquinha Neves.
Glórias brasileiras. S[ão] Paulo, 1943–
v. illus., mounted port. 21cm.
Vol. 1: Author's autograph presentation copy to Hecilda Clark.
CONTENTS.—1. sér. Rui Barbosa. Olavo Bilac. Machado de Assis. Santos Dumont. Carlos Gomes.

1. Brazil - Biog. I. Title.

NL 0431710 TxU

CT 181 .L82 Lôbo, Chiquinha Neves.
Vultos célebres. São Paulo, 1946-49.
2 v. illus.

1.Biography. I.Title.

NL 0431711 MiU

Lobo, Coimbra
see Coimbra Lobo,

Lobo, Constantino Botelho de Lacerdo
see Botelho de Lacerda Lobo, Constantina, 1754-1820?

Lobo, Costa.
see Costa Lobo,

Lobo, Crescencio.
The businessman's rupee interest tables, from 1 to 18 per cent. at 365 and 360 days per annum, by Crescencio Lobo ... With an introduction by Dayaram Sadhumal Hasrajani ... Bombay ₍C. Lobo₎ 1925.
4 p. l., ₍1₎, 26 p. 2 double tab. 24ᶜᵐ.

1. Interest and usury—Tables, etc. I. Title.
Library of Congress HG1638.I 4L6 43-21656
₍2₎ 332.82083

NL 0431715 DLC

VOLUME 337

Lobo, Daniel.
A nomenclature; or, Dictionary, in English, French, Spanish, and German, of the principal articles manufactured in this kingdom; more particularly those in the hardware and cutlery trades; the goods imported and exported, and nautical terms. Interspersed with phrases peculiar to trade and commerce in general, &c. &c. By Daniel Lobo ... London, Printed for the editor, 1776.
vii, 172, [3] p. 24cm.
1. Commercial products—Dictionaries. 2. English language—Dictionaries—Polyglot.
Library of Congress HF1041.L7 5-38163†
NL 0431716 DLC PU TxU

Lobo, Dr. David.
... Discurso ... Caracas Tip. American 1922.
NL 0431717 DPU

Film 9667 Lobo, Duarte, 1540-1643.
[Magnificat (1605) Selections]
[Eduardi Lupi] Cantica Beatae Virginis vulgo Magnificat 4 vocum. Antverpiae, ex officina Plantiniana, apud Joannem Moretum. 1605]
[2]p.
Contains 1p. of music: for superius and tenor with text "Anima mea Dominum".
Title from J.A.Stellfeld, Bibliographie des éditions musicales Plantiniennes, Bruxelles, 1949 (cf.p.144)
Microfilm (negative) made in 194-? of the original in the collection of Dr.Ivo Cruz, Conservatorio Nacional, Lisboa. 1 reel. 35mm.
On reel with the composer's Liber Processionum. Ulysipone, 1607.
1. Magnificat (Music)
NL 0431719 IaU

Lobo, Duarte, 1540-1643.
[Works, vocal]
Composições polifónicas. Transcritas em partitura por Manuel Joaquim. Lisboa, Instituto para a Alta Cultura, 1945-
score (v.) port., facsims. 32 cm.
CONTENTS.—t. 1. [Magnificats]
1. Choruses, Sacred, Unaccompanied—To 1800. 2. Magnificat (Music)
M3.L84 50-25275
NL 0431720 DLC CLU NcU IaU OOxM MH

AS242 .B3416 t. 5, fasc. 3 Lobo, Duarte, 1540-1643.
Stellfeld, Jean Auguste, 1881-1952.
Bibliographie des éditions musicales plantiniennes. [Bruxelles, Palais des académies, 1949]

Film 9667 Lobo, Duarte, 1540-1643.
[Masses, Liber 1 (1621)]
[Eduardi Lupi] liber Missarum 4, 5, 6 et 8 vocibus. Antverpiae, ex officinia Plantiniana Balthasaris Moreti, 1621.
134ℓ.
Title wanting: supplied from J.A.Stellfeld, Bibliographie des éditions Plantiniennes. Bruxelles, 1949 (cf.p.151)
Choirbook format; white mensural notation.
Contains 2 Mass antiphons (Asperges me and

Continued in next column

Continued from preceding column

Vidi aquam), 8 Masses, 2 motets.
Microfilm (negative) made in 194-? of the original in the collection of Dr.Ivo Cruz, Conservatorio Nacional, Lisboa. 1 reel. 35mm.
On reel with the composer's Liber Processionum... Ulysipone, 1607.
1. Masses - To 1800.
NL 0431723 IaU

Film 9667 Lobo, Duarte, 1540-1643.
[Liber Processionum et Stationum Ecclesiae Olysiponensis. Nunc denuó auctus, & in meliorem formam redactus ab Eduardo Lupo eiusdem Ecclesiae beneficiario & Musices praefecto. Ulysipone, apud Petrum Crasbeeck, 1607.
79ℓ.
Plainsong notation.
Microfilm (negative) made in 194-? of the original (M.I. 89) in the Biblioteca de Universidade, Coimbra, Portugal. 1 reel. 35mm.
On reel with the composer's Opuscula... Antwerpiae, 1602.- [Magnificat (1605) Selections]- [Masses, Liber 1 (1621)], Antverpiae, 1621.
1. Masses - To 1800.
NL 0431725 IaU

Film 9667 Lobo, Duarte, 1540-1643.
[Opuscula (1602)]
Eduardi Lupi lusitani civis Olisiponensis, in metropolitana eiusdem urbis Ecclesia beneficiarij & Musices praefecti Opuscula: Natalitiae Noctis Responsoria quaternis vocibus & octonis. Missa eiusdem Noctis octonis vocibus. Beatae Mariae Virginis Antiphonae octonis etiam vocibus. Eiusdem Virginis Salve choris tribus & vocibus undenis. Nunc primum in lucem edita. Superius. Antwerpiae, Ex officina Plantiniana, apud Ioannem Moretum, 1602.
(24p.)
1 part book.
Superius.
Microfilm (negative) made in 194-? of the original (M.I. 63) in the Biblioteca de Universidade, Coimbra, Portugal. 1 reel. 35mm.
On reel with the composer's Liber Processionum et Stationum Ecclesiae Olysiponensis, Ulisipone, 1607.
NL 0431727 IaU

Film 9668 Lobo, Duarte, 1540-1643.
[Masses, liber 2 (1639)]
[Eduardi Lupi] lusitani, civis olisioponensis, in metropolitana ejusdem urbis Ecclesiae. Beneficiarrii et musicae Praefecti. Liber II Missarum, IIII, V et VI vocibus. Antwerpiae, ex officina Plantiniana Balthasaris Moreti, 1639]
154ℓ. port.
t.-p. wanting: supplied from Stellfeld, J.A., Bibliographie des éditions musicales Plantiniennes. Brussels, 1949.
For 4-6 voices. Choirbook format; white mensural notation.
Microfilm (negative) made in 194-? of the original (M.I.-6) in the Biblioteca de Universidade, Coimbra, Portugal. 1 reel. 35mm.
On reel with: Magalhaes, Felipe de, [Masses (1636)] Lisbon, 1636.
1. Masses - To 1800.
NL 0431729 IaU

Lobo, Edmund.
... Clay speaks of the fire, by Edmund Lobo ... London, Williams and Norgate, ltd. [1946]
3 p. l., 58 p. 19cm.
At head of title: Poems, sonnets.
I. Title.
PR6023.O14C5 821.91 46-23192
NL 0431730 DLC

[Lobo, Edmund]
"There came past—" episode of a poet. Dublin, Wolf's head press [1952?] 14 p. 21cm.
Author's name on cover.
One of 50 copies printed.
NL 0431731 NN

Lobo, Eduardo Campos
see
Campos Lobo, Eduardo.

Lôbo, Eduardo de Barros
see
Barros Lôbo, Eduardo de, 1857-1893.

Lobo, Esmeralda de Abreu
see
Abreu Lobo, Esmeralda de

Lobo, Estevam.
...De viagem... Bello Horizonte: Imprensa official do estado de Minas, 1902. 211, ii p. 12°.
1. Europe—Descr. and trav., 1900-1918.
N. Y. P. L. January 19, 1926
NL 0431735 NN

Lobo, Estevam, joint ed.
Marshall, John, 1755-1835.
Decisões constitucionaes de Marshall, presidente do Supremo tribunal dos Estados Unidos da America do Norte, traduzidas por Americo Lobo. Rio de Janeiro, Imprensa nacional, 1903.

PQ 6534 .L6 M3 1773 Lobo, Eugenio Gerardo, 1679-1750.
Comedia famosa. Los martires de Toledo, y texedor Palomeque. [Valencia, Impr.de J.y T. de Orga, 1773]
32 p. 22 cm.
Caption title.
"N.188."
I.Title: Los martires de Toledo y texedor Palomeque.
NL 0431737 MiU

VOLUME 337

RARE BOOKS DEPT. Lobo, Eugenio Gerardo, 1679-1750.
Comedias y loas. [n.p., n.d.]
[308] p. 22cm.

Manuscript copy.
Title within double line border.

NL 0431738 CU

Lobo, Eugenio Gerardo, 1679-1750.
Difiniendo en realidad lo que es el chichesebo en oposito de las decimas, que compuso D. Eugenio Gerardo. Sevilla, F. de Leefdael. [n.d.]

NL 0431739 NNH

Lobo, Eugenio Gerardo, 1679-1750.
Jardin ameno de las nvsas, plantade entre las tareas do la milicid, y cvltivade entre los exercicios de la campaña. Por ... Evgenio Gerardo Lobo ... Zaragoza [17--]
4 p.l., 14 [2], 96 [4] p. 21 cm.
Originally pub.: Granada, N. Prieto.

NL 0431740 CU

Lobo, Eugenio Gerardo, 1679-1750.
...Los martyres de Toledo, y Texedor Palomeque... [Madrid,?] Librería de Quiroga, n.d.]
32p. 22cm.

Caption title.

NL 0431741 MWelC NcU

Lobo, Eugenio Gerardo, 1679–1750.
...Los martyres de Toledo, y texedor Palomeque. De Don Eugenio Gerardo Lobo. [Madrid, 1740] 16 l. 21cm.

Caption-title.
At head of title: Comedia nueva. Num. 227.

233575B. 1. Drama, Spanish. I. Title.
N. Y. P. L. March 3, 1944

NL 0431742 NN

864L78 Om1751 Lobo, Eugenio Gerardo, 1679-1750.
Los martyres de Toledo, y texedor Palomeque. [Madrid, Impr. de A. Sanz, 1751]
[36]p. 21cm.

Caption title.
"Comedia famosa, núm.21."

NL 0431743 IU

Lobo, Eugenio Gerardo, 1679-1750.
El mas justo rey de Grecia. [Barcelona n.d.]
(In [Comedias] [n.d.] v.4]

NL 0431744 RPB

Lobo, Eugenio Gerardo.
... El más justo rey de Grecia ...
[Barcelona, Juan Francisco Piferrer, n.d.]
28 p. 22 cm.
In: Teatro antiguo Borrás. v. 24, no. 19.
At head of title: Comedia fomosa. Núm. 163.

NL 0431745 NcU

Lobo, Eugenio Gerardo, 1679–1750.
...El más justo rey de Grecia. Comedia famosa, y nueva, de Don Eugenio Gerardo Lobo. [Sevilla, 172–?] 24 p. 21cm.

Caption-title.
At head of title: Num. 147.

233575B. 1. Drama, Spanish. I. Title.
N. Y. P. L. March 3, 1944

NL 0431746 NN

Lobo, Eugenio Gerardo, 1679-1750.
... El más justo rey de Grecia...
[Barcelona, Imprenta de Francisco Guriá, 1771]
[28] p. 22 cm.
In: Teatro antiguo Borrás. v. 24, no. 18.
At head of title: Comedia famosa, Núm. 152.

NL 0431747 NcD

PQ 6534 L7M4 1772 (Rare) Lobo, Eugenio Gerardo, 1679-1750.
El mas justo rey de Grecia. Comedia famosa. [Valencia, J. y T. de Orga, 1772]
28 p.

NL 0431748 ICU

863L786 OM LOBO, Eugenio Gerardio, 1679-1750.
... El mas justo rey de Grecia...
[Madrid, A. Sanz, 1783]

32 p. 21cm.

Caption title.
At head of title: "N. 79. Comedia famosa.

NL 0431749 MnU

Lobo, Eugenio Gerardo, 1679-1750.
El mas justo rey de Grecia, comedia famosa.
[Barcelona, J. F. Piferrer, 1790?]
28p. 22cm.

Caption title.
"Num.163."

NL 0431750 IU

864L78 Oma1822 Lobo, Eugenio Gerardo, 1679-1750.
El más justo rey de Grecia. [Valencia, Impr. de I. Mompié, 1822]
28p. 22cm.

Caption title.
"Comedia famosa, num.13."

NL 0431751 IU

PQ6534 L6 1720 Lobo, Eugenio Gerardo, 1679-1750.
Obras poeticas. Dedicadas en esta segunda edición al mismo autor, y añadidas de una tercera parte, y corregidas, y enmendadas. Cadiz, G. Peralta [1720?]
276 p.

Dedication signed: Geronimo Alonso de Morales y Peralta.

NL 0431752 CU ICU MoU MH

Lobo, Eugenio Gerardo, 1679–1750.
Obras poéticas de don Evgenio Gerardo Lobo... Dedicadas en esta segunda edición al mismo avtor. Y añadidas de vna tercera parte, corregidas, y emmendadas. Pamplona: J. Ezqverro, 1724. 4 p.l., 243 p. 8°.

Edited by G. A. de Morales y Peralta.

JANVIER COLLECTION.

1. Poetry (Spanish). 2. Morales y Peralta, Geronimo Alonso de, editor.
N. Y. P. L. September 11, 1915.

NL 0431753 NN NNH OU WU IaU NcD CU INS

PQ6534 L6 1725 Lobo, Eugenio Gerardo, 1679-1750.
Obras poeticas de don Eugenio Gerardo Lobo. Dedicadas en esta segunda edicion al mismo autor, y añadidas de una tercera parte, corregidas, y emmendadas. Barcelona, J. Llopis, 1725.
240 p.

Dedication signed: Geronymo Alonso de Morales y Peralta.

I. Morales y Peralta, Gerónimo Alonso de, ed.

NL 0431754 CU

Lobo, Eugenio Gerardo, 1679–1750.
Obras poeticas de don Eugenio Gerardo Lobo ... dedicadas en esta segunda edicion [!] al mismo autor. Y añadidas de vna tercera parte, y corregidas, y enmendadas ... En Pamplona: por Joseph Ezquerro. Año de 1729.
4 p. l., 260 p. 21½cm.

Dedication signed: Geronimo Alonso de Morales y Peralta.

I. Morales y Peralta, Gerónimo Alonso de, ed.

32-16573

Library of Congress PQ6534.L6 1729 861.49

NL 0431755 DLC

Ex 3175 .139 .1732 Lobo, Eugenio Gerardo, 1679-1750
Obras poeticas... Dedicadas en esta segvnda edicion[!] al mismo avtor. Y añadidas de vna tercera parte, corregidas, y emmendadas. En Barcelona, Por J. Llopis, Año de 1732.
252 p. 20 cm.

Dedication signed: Geronymo Alonso de Morales y Peralta.

NL 0431756 NjP NNH InU

861.39 L786A2 1758 Lobo, Eugenio Gerardo, 1679-1750.
Obras poeticas. Nueva edición, Corregida, y aumentada con muchas piezas postumas, en verso, y prosa, y otras inéditas de diversos autores. Madrid, Oficina de Joachin Ibarra, 1758.
2v. in 1. 21cm.

Title on spine: Obras de Gerardo Lobo.

NL 0431757 KU NNH NcD ICN MiDW NjP

Rare PQ 6534 L6 1769 Lobo, Eugenio Gerardo, 1679-1750.
Obras poeticas. Nueva ed., corr. y aumentada con muchas piezas posthumas, en verso y prosa, y otras ineditas de diversos autores. Madrid, M. Escribano, 1769.
2 v. 21cm.

Vol. 2 has title: Varias poesias y entre ellas muchas.

NL 0431758 NIC MiDW NcD CU InU CU-S IU

VOLUME 337

Lobo, E. G.
Obras poeticas. Nueva edicion.
Madrid, 1797.
2 vols. 8vo.

NL 0431759 NN

Lobo, Eugenio Gerardo, 1679–1750.
Obras poeticas lyricas, que su autor, el coronel d. Eugenio Gerardo Lobo ... ha cedido à la Congregacion de la milagrosa imagen de N. Señora de Peña sacra, que se venèra en el Real de Manzanares. Sacalas a luz la misma congregacion, y las dedica à esta Soberana Señora ... Corregidas, y enmendadas las que antes estaban impressas, y añadidas en mucho, que hasta aora no ha salido à luz ... En Madrid, en la Imprenta real, por Don Miguèl Francisco Rodriguez. Año de 1738.
14 p. l., 392, [6] p. pl. 21cm.

32-16572

Library of Congress PQ6534.L6 1738 861.49

NL 0431760 DLC CU MiU ICU CU-S NNH

Lobo, Eugenio Gerardo. Poesias. 27 pp.
(Coato, L. A. de, Poet. lir. del siglo 18, v. 1, p. 22.)

NL 0431761 MdBP

LOBO, E[ugenio] G[erardo], 1679-1750.
Poesías escogidas. Paris, Libreria de Rosa, 1837.
24°.

NL 0431761-1 MH

PQ 6534 L6 R3 1732

[Lobo, Eugenio Gerardo] 1679-1750.
Rasgo epico de la conquista de Oran qve a la diversion de los oficiales de los regimientos de qvardias españolas, y walonas dedica la ociosidad de vn compañero svyo. Barcelona, En la Imprenta de Maria Marti, 1732.
59p. 20cm.
1738 ed. is signed D.E.G.L. (i.e. Don Eugenio Gerardo Lobo).
Cf. Palau, v.4, p.251.
Bound in marble boards backed in vellum.

1. Africa--Colonization. 2. Oran. I. Title.

NL 0431762 NSyU

Lobo, Eugenio Gerardo, 1679-1750.
Relacion neuva. Quexas de amor, y silencia ... Madrid, 1738.

NL 0431763 NNH

Lobo, Eugenio Gerardo, 1679-1750.
Selva de las musas, que en elegante constraccion poëtiea, prorrumpe la facundio de D. Eugenio Gerardo Lobo ... Cadiz, G de Peralta, 1717.

NL 0431764 NNH

Lobo, Eugenio Gerardo, 1679-1750.
Sitio de campo-mayor, que con deseo de confagrarle con mas dichofo fin ã los pies de la ilustrissima señora la Sra Condessa de Atares, y de Villas Sevilla, F. de Leefdael [n.d.]

NL 0431765 NNH

Lobo, Eugenio Gerardo, 1679-1750.
Viendo en la celebre materna casa ...

NL 0431766 NNH

Lobo, Eulalia Maria Lahmeyer.
Administração colonial luso-espanhola nas Américas. Rio de Janeiro, Editôra Companhia Brasileira de Artes Gráficas, 1952.
444 p. maps (part fold.) 24 cm.
Errata leaf inserted.
Bibliography: p. [433]-444.

1. Spain — Colonies — America — Administration. 2. Portugal — Colonies—America—Administration. I. Title.

JL950.L6 55-43802

NL 0431767 NN MH TxU DLC ViU PSt MnU ICU CLSU LNHT IU FMU NcD

Lobo, Eusebio Badía y
see
Badía y Lobo, Eusebio.

Lobo, Fernando Abello
see
Abello Lobo, Fernando.

Lobo, Fernando Maria da Gama
see
Gama Lobo, Fernando Maria da

Lobo, Ferreira
see
Ferreira Lobo, José Joaquim, 1837-

Lobo, Francisco Alexandre, bp., 1763–1844.
Obras de d. Francisco Alexandre Lobo, bispo de Vizeu. Impressas á custa do seminario da sua dioceze ... Lisboa, Typographia de J. B. Morando, 1848–53.
3 v. port., form. 20½cm.
Edited by F. E. de Faria e Mello.
"Catalogo das obras do bispo de Vizeu": v. 1, p. ix-xviii.

1. Catholic church—Collected works. 2. Theology—Collected works—19th cent. I. Faria e Mello, Francisco Eleuterio de, 1780?-1851, ed.

38-33468

Library of Congress BX890.L56

NL 0431772 DLC CU MH

Lobo, Francisco Alexandre, 1763–1844.
Breves reflexões sobre a vida de Luiz de Camões, escrita por m. Charles Magnin, membro do Instituto, no principio de sua traducção dos Lusiadas. Por d. Francisco Alexandre Lobo ... Lisboa, Typ. da mesma academia [i. e. Academia real das sciencias] 1842.
8 p. 31½cm.

1. Camões, Luiz de, 1524?-1580. 2. Magnin, Charles, 1793-1862. I. Title.

33-36860

Library of Congress PQ9212.Z5L6 928.69

NL 0431773 DLC NN WU

Lobo, Francisco Alexandre, Bp., 1763–1844.
Cartas do exílio. Apresentação e notas de J. Henriques Mouta. Lisboa, União Gráfica, 1944–
v. port., facsims. 19 cm. (His Obras, 4)

I. Title.

DP645.L6A4 922.2469 49-58260*

NL 0431774 DLC

Lobo, Francisco Alexandre, 1763-1844, supposed author.
Discurso historico e critico ácerca do padre Antonio Vieira ...
see under title

Lobo, Francisco Alexandre, 1763–1844.
Memoria historica e critica acerca de Luiz de Camões, e das suas obras. Por Francisco Alexandre Lobo ... Lisboa, Typ. da mesma academia [i. e. Academia real das sciencias de Lisboa] 1820.
123 p. 25cm.
"Impressa no tomo VII. parte I. das Memorias da Academia real das sciencias de Lisboa."

1. Camões, Luiz de, 1524?-1580.

33-36856

Library of Congress PQ9212.L6
——— Copy 2. 928.69

NL 0431776 DLC

CT1378 V5L6 1897

Lobo, Francisco Alexandre, Bp., 1763-1844
Memoria historica e critica a'cerca do padre Antonio Vieira e das suas obras. Novamente editada ... pela Redacção da "Revista Catholica" Vizeu, 1897.
15,185 p. port.

1. Vieira, Antonio, 1608-1697.

NL 0431777 CU

[Lobo, Francisco Alexandre] 1763–1844.
Rezumida noticia da vida de d. Nuno Caetano Alvares Pereira de Mello, sexto duque de Cadaval ... Paris, Typ. de Casimir, 1837.
91 p. 21½cm.

1. Cadaval, Nuno Caetano Alvares Pereira de Mello, duque de, 1799-1837. I. Title.

33-7142

Library of Congress DP645.C3L6 923.2469

NL 0431778 DLC DCU-IA

Lobo, Francisco Barros
see Barros Lobo, Francisco.

Lobo, Francisco de Figueiredo da Gama
see Gama Lobo, Francisco de Figueiredo da.

Lobo, Francisco Miranda da Costa
see Miranda da Costa Lobo, Francisco, 1864-

VOLUME 337

Lobo, Francisco Rodrigues
see Rodrigues Lobo, Francisco, 17th cent.

Lobo, Francisco Rodriguez
see Rodrigues Lobo, Francisco, 17th cent.

LOBO, Francisco Roiz, pseud.
See FERREIRA DE VASCONCELLOS, Jorge, 16th cent.

XL .823 .C74J
[Lobo, Gaspar da Encarnação]
O jardineiro, anthologia, ou Tratado das flores, aos amantes da jardinagem O.C. D. G. da C.
Coimbra: Na Real Imprensa da Universidade. 1824. Com licença da Mesa do Desembargo do Paço.
3 p.ℓ., 110 p. 16cm. (8vo)
Title vignette: Portuguese arms.
Original marbled wrappers, stitched and untrimmed.
I. C., D. G. da. O jardineiro. II. Title.

NL 0431785 MB

Lobo, George Edmund, ed.
The Dublin art monthly...
see under title

Lobo, Gonzalo Roig
see Roig, Gonzalo, 1890-

Lobo, Haddock
O negro na vida social brasileira [por] H.Lobo & I. Aloisi. S.Paulo, S.E.Panorama, 1941
102 p. (Assuntos brasileiros; cadernos de ensaios, Ser.C, v.2)

NL 0431788 MH

Lobo, Helio, 1883-
... Antes da guerra (a missão Saraiva ou os preliminares do conflicto com o Paraguay) Rio de Janeiro [Imprensa ingleza] 1914.
260, [2] p., 1 l. 22cm.

1. Brazil—For. rel.—Uruguay. 2. Uruguay—For. rel.—Brazil. 3. Saraiva, José Antonio, 1823-1895. 4. Paraguayan war, 1865-1870. I. Title.
15-14983
Library of Congress F2687.L79

NL 0431789 DLC CU NIC LNHT KU NcD TxU DCU-IA

Lobo, Helio, 1883-
... Aos estudantes do Rio da Prata. Conferencias feitas nas universidades de Montevidéo e Buenos Aires sobre historia diplomatica e direito internacional no Brasil. Rio de Janeiro, Imprensa nacional, 1918.
xi p., 1 l., 172 p., 1 l. 20cm.
CONTENTS.—Brasil e Uruguay.—A America e a guerra.—A independencia argentina através as suas duas maiores glorias militares, San Martin a Belgrano.—Diplomatas e consules.—Ponto de partida.—Pela liberdade e o direito das gentes.—Cinco annos de glorias e sacrificios communs.—Epilogo.
1. Brazil—For. rel. 2. Spanish America—Hist.—Addresses, essays, lectures. I. Title.
43-32142
Library of Congress F2521.L7

NL 0431790 DLC NIC LNHT CtY DPU MH ICU IU NN

Lobo, Helio.
... O Brasil e seus principios de neutralidade. Rio de Janeiro, Imprensa nacional, 1914.
4 p. l., 140 p. 22½cm.

1. Brazil—Neutrality. 2. Brazil—For. rel.
16-17905
Library of Congress JX5365.L7

NL 0431791 DLC TxU CLU NIC CtY NcD NN

Lobo, Helio.
... Brasil, terra chara. Rio de Janeiro [Imprensa ingleza] 1913.
87 p., 1 l. 17cm.
CONTENTS.—A lição pan-americana.—A tarefa da codificação.—O Brasil no convivio das nações.

1. Brazil—For. rel. I. Title.
15-20363
Library of Congress F2537.L79

NL 0431792 DLC NNC IU TxU

Lobo, Helio, 1883-
... Brasilianos & yankees. Rio de Janeiro, Pimenta de Mello & c., 1926.
ix, 198 p. 19½cm.

1. Brazil—Relations (general) with U. S. 2. U. S.—Relations (general) with Brazil. I. Title.
29-1778 Revised
Library of Congress E183.8.B7L63

NL 0431793 DLC NIC FU CtY NN OU MH DCU-IA DPU

G869.8 Oc7Il
Lobo, Helio, 1883-
O cantor que venceu as sereias. [Rio de Janeiro, Impr. Nacional, 1929]
22p. 24cm.
Caption title.
"Conferencia realizada no Instituto Historico e Geographico de São Paulo."
1. Octaviano de Almeida Rosa, Francisco, 1825-1889. I. Title.

NL 0431794 TxU

Lobo, Helio, 1883-
Cerimonial da presidencia
see under Brazil. Presidencia.

Lobo, Helio, 1883-
Conferência Internacional do Trabalho (Genebra 1947)
see under Brazil. Ministério das Relações Exteriores. Serviço de Publicações.

Lobo, Helio, 1883-
Conferencias del Dr. Helio Lobo, dadas en el salón de actos públicos de la Universidad de Montevideo: Brasil y Uruguay. La democracia americana y la guerra. Montevideo, Talleres gráficos A. Barreiro y Ramos, 1918.
52 p. front. (port.) 23½cm.
At head of cover-title: Republica Oriental del Uruguay. Anales de la Universidad.

1. Brazil—Relations (general) with Uruguay. 2. Uruguay—Relations (general) with Brazil. 3. European war, 1914- —Addresses, sermons, etc.
20-12665
Library of Congress F2726.L79

NL 0431797 DLC TxU

Lobo, Helio, 1883-
... Cousas americanas e brasileiras. Rio de Janeiro, Imprensa nacional, 1923.
vi p., 3 l., [3]-562 p. 18½ cm.

1. United States—Relations (general) with Brazil. 2. Brazil—Relations (general) with U. S. 3. U. S.—Econ. condit.—1918- 4. Brazil—Econ. condit.—1918- I. Title.
25-12688
Library of Congress E183.8.B7L64

NL 0431798 DLC FMU NIC PLF TxU CtY NN

Lobo, Helio, 1883-
... Cousas diplomaticas. [Rio de Janeiro] Leite Ribeiro & Maurillo, 1918.
236 p. 24cm.
Author's autograph presentation copy "No instituto americano de direito internacional."
CONTENTS.—1. pte. A guerra maritima e as tradições internacionaes do Brasil (a proposito do torpedeamento do "Rio-Branco") (1854-1915)—2. pte. Esforço mallogrado (antecedentes de guerra do Paraguay) (1844-1856)—3. pte. Uma velha amizade internacional (Brasil Estados-Unidos) (1822-1916)—4. pte. A defesa da nacionalidade (uma pagina de historia colonial) (1500-1800)
1. Brazil—For. rel. 2. Brazil—For. rel.—U. S. 3. U. S.—For. rel.—Brazil. I. Title.
27-3884
Library of Congress E183.8.B7L65

NL 0431799 DLC NIC MH CU CtY TxU NN ViU

Lobo, Helio.
... De Monroe a Rio-Branco (paginas de diplomacia americana) Rio de Janeiro, Imprensa nacional, 1912.
4 p. l., [3]-155 p. 24½cm.
CONTENTS.—Entre George Canning e James Monroe.—A Assembléa do Isthmo.—A primeira Conferencia de Lima.—A Assembléa de Buenos Aires.—Tentativas de uma codificação.—A America latina e a diplomacia do imperio.

1. American republics—Pol. & govt. 2. Spanish America—For. rel. I. Title.
13-11557
Library of Congress JX1407.L7

NL 0431800 DLC ICJ MiU UU ViU NcU

Lobo, Helio.
... A democracia uruguaya. Rio de Janeiro, Imprensa nacional, 1928.
vi, 167, [1] p. 18cm.

1. Uruguay—Comm. 2. Uruguay—Indus. 3. Uruguay—Pol. & govt.—1830- 4. Education—Uruguay. I. Title.
29-6083
Library of Congress F2726.L792

NL 0431801 DLC IaU NN

Lobo, Helio, 1883-
... Docas de Santos, suas origens, lutas e realizações. Rio de Janeiro, Typ. do Jornal do commercio, Rodrigues & c., 1936.
4 p. l., [5]-695 p., 2 l. plates (1 fold.) ports., fold. tab. 25½cm.

1. Companhia das docas de Santos. 2. Santos, Brazil—Harbor. I. Title.
38-7317
Library of Congress HE556.S3L6
[2] [387.10981] 387.1220981

NL 0431802 DLC OCl

Lobo, Helio, 1883-
... O domínio do Canadá (ensaio de interpretação) Rio de Janeiro-São Paulo, Civilização brasileira s/a., 1942.
189 p., 1 l. 18cm.
"Bibliografia": p. [187]-189.

1. Canada.
43-50431
Library of Congress F1008.L8
[2] 917.1

NL 0431803 DLC CtY NN

VOLUME 337

Lobo, Helio, 1883–
... Genebra e a paz ... ⌜Rio de Janeiro, Est. de artes graf., C. Mendes Junior⌝ 1944.
cover-title, 46 p. incl. illus., ports. 23ᶜᵐ.
At head of title: Helio Lobo ⌜e⌝ Affonso Bandeira de Mello.
"Separata da revista do Instituto de estudos brasileiros."
Bibliographical foot-notes.
CONTENTS.—As instituições não politicas de Genebra e os planos de paz, por Hélio Lobo.—O espírito de Genebra e a reconstrução social do mundo, por Affonso Bandeira de Mello.
1. League of nations. I. Bandeira de Mello, Affonso de Toledo. II. Title.
46-16712
Library of Congress JX1975.L77
⌜2⌝ 341.1

NL 0431804 DLC DPU MH

Lobo, Helio, 1883– *ed.*
... Legislação relativa ao porto de Santos, precedida da legislação portuaria geral (1828–1937) Rio de Janeiro, Typ. do "Jornal do commercio", Rodrigues & cia., 1938.
3 p. l., ⌜3⌝–680 p. 28ᶜᵐ.
1. Harbors—Brazil—Regulations. 2. Santos, Brazil—Harbor. I. Brazil. Laws, statutes, etc. II. Title.
40-8644

NL 0431805 DLC DPU CtY NN CSt

Lobo, Helio, 1883–
... Manoel de Araujo Porto-Alegre; ensáio bio-bibliográfico. Rio de Janeiro, Empresa editora A B C limitada, 1938.
180 p. incl. front., illus. (incl. ports., facsim.) 18½ᶜᵐ. (*On cover:* Publicações da Academia brasileira. ⌜Classicos brasileiros⌝ III—Bibliografia. ⌜9⌝)
1. Araujo Porto-Alegre, Manuel de, barão de Santo Angelo, 1806–1879. 2. Araujo Porto-Alegre, Manuel de, barão de Santo Angelo, 1806–1879—Bibl.
39-4341
Library of Congress Z8041.8.L78
⌜2⌝ 928.69

NL 0431806 DLC TxU NBuU CU

Lobo, Helio, 1883–
Manuel de Araújo Pôrto-Alegre. ⌜Rio de Janeiro⌝ AGIR, 1945.
116 p. 20 cm. (Nossos grandes mortos, 3)
"Bibliografia do poeta": p. ⌜69⌝–93. "Bibliografia sôbre o poeta": p. 93–99.
1. Araujo Porto-Alegre, Manuel de, barão de Santo Angelo, 1806–1879. 2. Araujo Porto-Alegre, Manuel de, barão de Santo Angelo, 1806–1879—Bibl. I. Series.
F2505.N6 no. 3 928.69 A 48-1060*
New York. Public Libr. for Library of Congress ⌜1⌝†

NL 0431807 NN DLC NBuU MiU N FMU IU

947.094 L799 Lobo, Helio, 1883-
...No limiar da Asia;(a U.R.S.S. ensaio de interpretação) São Paulo, Companhia editora nacional, 1935.
2 p.l.,⌜3⌝-182 p.,1 l. 18½cm.
1.Bolshevism - Russia. 2.Russia - Politics and government - 1917- I.Title.

NL 0431808 CSt MH

Lobo, Helio, 1883–
... O pan-americanismo e o Brasil. São Paulo ⌜etc.⌝ Companhia editora nacional, 1939.
4 p. l., 150 p., 1 l. 18ᶜᵐ. (Biblioteca pedagogica brasileira. Sér. 5.ª: Brasiliana. v. 169)
1. American republics. 2. International American conferences. 3. Brazil—For. rel. I. Title.
40-29606
Library of Congress F1418.L64
⌜2⌝ 341.1

NL 0431809 NcD MH IaU DLC LU CaOTP MiEM CSt CU ICU ViU DPU PU

Lobo, Helio, 1883–
... A passo de gigante (Os Estados Unidos da America, alguns de seus tropeços passados e de seus problemas actuaes ...) Rio de Janeiro, Imprensa nacional, 1925.
xi, 380 p. 23½ᶜᵐ.
Includes bibliographies.
Summary of contents from t.-p.
CONTENTS.—O aspecto politico: democracia ou plutocracia?—A questão social: reforma ou revolução?—A marcha economica: cooperação internacional ou imperialismo?—A limitação dos armamentos: competição armada ou preponderancia commercial?—A prohibição do alcobol: verdade ou hypocrisia?
1. U. S.—Pol. & govt. 2. U. S.—Soc. condit. 3. U. S.—For. rel. I. Title.
25-12835
Library of Congress E743.L7

NL 0431810 DLC NIC UU FMU PLF CtY PU DCU-IA NN

Lobo, Helio, 1883–
Ás portas da guerra (Do Ultimatum Saraiva, 10 de Agosto de 1864, á Convenção da Villa União, 20 de Fevereiro de 1865) Rio de Janeiro, Impr. Nacional, 1916.
vii, 270 p. 19 cm.
At head of title: História diplomatica do Brasil.
"Volume ... inspirado em alguns papeis tidos até hoje em sigillo por nossa chancellaria."
1. Paraguayan War, 1865–1870. 2. Brazil—For. rel.—Uruguay. 3. Uruguay—For. rel.—Brazil. I. Title.
F2687.L8 50-50354

NL 0431811 DLC TxU NjP MH NN IU DCU-IA

Lobo, Helio, 1883–
Rio-Branco e o arbitramento com a Argentina; a questão do territorio de Palmas, também chamada das Missões. Rio de Janeiro, J. Olympio, 1952.
189 p. 23 cm. (Coleção Documentos brasileiros, 69)
1. Rio Branco, José Maria da Silva Paranhos, barão do, 1845–1912. 2. Misiones, Argentine Republic (Ter.)—Bound. 3. Brazil—Bound.—Argentine Republic. 4. Argentine Republic—Bound.—Brazil. I. Title.
F2554.A82L6 55-1857 ‡

NL 0431812 MH TxU NcD DPU ViU DLC LNHT CtY DAU ICU CaOTP NN WaU FU

LOBO,Helio.
Sabres e togas;a autonomia judicante militar. Rio de Janeiro,1906.
go.

NL 0431813 MH-L

Lobo, Helio, 1883–
... O tribunal arbitral brasileiro-boliviano. Rio de Janeiro, Imprensa nacional, 1910.
vii, 171 p. 24½ᶜᵐ.
1. Brazil—Claims vs. Bolivia. 2. Bolivia—Claims vs. Brazil. 3. Acre, Brazil (Ter.) I. Title.
14-7069 Revised 2
Library of Congress JX1532.Z7B7
——— Copy 3. Cover dated 1911. F2540.L65

NL 0431814 DLC LNHT N TxU NcU

LOBO,Helio.
O tribunal arbitral brasileiro-boliviano. Rio de Janeiro,1911.

NL 0431815 MH-L

Lobo, Helio, 1883–
... Um varão da republica, Fernando Lobo; a proclamação do regime em Minas, sua consolidação no Rio de Janeiro. São Paulo ⌜etc.⌝ Companhia editora nacional, 1937.
8 p. l., ⌜3⌝–249 p., 1 l. 18½ᶜᵐ. (Brasiliana. Biblioteca pedagogica brasileira. sér. 5.ª v. 88)
1. *Lobo, Fernando, 1851–1918. 2. Brazil—Pol. & govt.—1889– 3. Minas Geraes, Brazil—Pol. & govt. I. Title.
38-4490
Library of Congress F2537.L82
⌜3⌝ 923.281

NL 0431816 OU NN DLC CaBVaU CU ICU CaOTP IaU ViU DPU NcD

Lobo, Huertas.
Da animalidade à humanidade. [Lisboa] Empresa Contemporânea de Edições [194-]
44 p. (Colecção Testemunho, 1. Visão geral de prehistória, 1)

NL 0431817 MH

Lobo, Jacobo de la Pezuela y
see Pezuela y Lobo, Jacobo de la, 1811-1882.

Lobo, Jerone
see Lobo, Jeronymo, 1596-1678.

⌜Lobo, Jeronymo⌝ 1596–1678.
P. Hieronymi eines Jesuiten in Portugal Neue Beschreibung und Bericht von der wahren Beschaffenheit 1. Des Mohrenlandes, sonderlich des abyssinischen Kâyserthums. 2. Des Ursprungs Nyli. 3. Wo das Einhorn zufinden. 4. Warumb der Abyssiner Kâiser Priester Johannes geneñet werde. 5. Wie das Rothe Meer beschaffen, und woher es diesen Namen habe. 6. Von unterschiedlichen Arten der Palmenbâume, und von ihrer Tugend und Nutzbarkeit. Alles aus langwûriger Erfahrung zusammgetragen, und bey Weltkûndigem Leser zur angenehmen Nachricht in die teutsche Sprach ûbersetzt. Nûrnberg: Zu finden bey J. Hoffmann, Gedruckt bey C. Gerhard, 1670. 106 p. front., map. 14cm.
Imperfect: frontispiece wanting.
838356A. 1. Africa—Descr. and trav., to 1800. 2. Nile river. 3. Red sea. 4. Prester John. 5. Palms, Date. 6. Unicorn.
N. Y. P. L. April 26, 1938

NL 0431821 NN

1706 fLo Lobo, Jeronymo, 1596-1678.
Gedenk-waardige aanteekeningen, gehouden docr den eerwaarden vader Hieronymus Lobo op sijn voyagie, gedaan in het jaar 1636 aangaande het rijk der Abysinen... Waar by gevoegt zijn, de aanmerkingen op dese aanteekeningen, door den heer Thevenot... Nu alder-eerst uyt het Frans vertaalt. Leyden, P. vander Aa ⌜1706⌝
28 col. 2 illus. 33cm.
1. Ethiopia. Desc. & trav. 2.Africa, North. Desc. & trav. I. Thevenot. Michiel Melchisedech.

NL 0431822 MnU

VOLUME 337

Lobo, Jeronymo.
Gedenk-waardige aanteekeningen, gehouden door den Eerwaarden Vader Hieronymus Lobo op sijn voyagie, gedaan in het jaar, 1636. Aangaande het rijk der Abessinen; de oorsprongen en overvloeyingen des Nijls . . . Waar by gevoegt zijn, de aanmerkingen op dese aanteekeningen, door den Heer Thévenot . . . Nu alderëerst uvt het Frans vertaalt.

[1707.] (1) p., 28 col., (2) pp. [De aanmerkenswaardigste en alomberoemde zee- en landreizen. Deel 8.] F°.

Feb. 18, 1903
E7482 — Abyssinia. Geog. — Thévenot, Melchisédech, ed.

NL 0431823 MB

Lobo, Jeronymo, 1596–1678.
Gedenk-waardige aanteekeningen van den Eerwaarden Vader Hieronymus Lobo, aangaande het rijk der Abyssinen, de oorsprongen des Nijls, den eenhoorn, pellikaan, paradijs-vogel en de verscheyde soorten der dadel-boomen, door eygen ondervinding in sijn reys ondersogt en opgeteekent. [Leyden: P. vander Aa. 1707?] 50 p., 2 l. map, plates. 12°.

Caption-title.

1. Abyssinia.—Description and travel, to 1800.
N. Y. P. L. March 14, 1923.

NL 0431824 NN MB PU

Lobo, Jeronymo, 1596–1678.
P. Hieronymus Lobo's . . . Reise nach Habessinien, und zu den Quellen des Nils. Aus dem Französischen. Mit einer Einleitung, Anmerkungen, Zusäzzen, zweifachem Anhange, und einer Beschreibung von Habessinien, vermehrt und herausgegeben von Theophil Friedrich Ehrmann . . . Zürich: Orell, Gessner, Füssli und Cie., 1793–94. 2 v. map. 22cm.

From Legrand's translation of the Portuguese.
"Historisch-geographische Litteratur von Habessinien," v. 1, p. [3]–26.

840746-7A. 1. Ethiopia—Hist. 1762–1811, ed. and tr. II. Title: I. Ehrmann, Theophil Friedrich, Reise nach Habessinien.
N. Y. P. L. August 25, 1937

NL 0431825 NN ICU

Lobo, Jeronymo. 1593–1678. Relation de la rivière du Nil, de sa source et de son cours, et de l'inondation qu'elle fait dans la campagne d'Egypte, jusqu'à ce qu'elle tombe en la mer Mediterranée, et autres choses curieuses. Par un témoin oculaire. 48 pp. (Justel, H., *Rec. de divers voyages faits en Afrique et en l'Amérique.*)

NL 0431826 MdBP

[Lobo, Jeronymo,] 1596?–1678.
Relation de la riviere du Nil, de sa source et de son cours, et de l'inondation qu'elle fait dans la campagne d'Egypte, jusqu'à ce qu'elle tombe en la mer Mediterranée, & autres choses curieuses. Par un témoin oculaire, qui a demeuré plusieurs années dans les principaux royaumes de l'empire des Abissins. Traduit de l'original anglois . . . (In: Recueil de divers voyages faits en Afrique et en l'Amerique. Paris, 1674. 8°. [no. 2,] p. [205–] 252. fold. map.)

Map at end of volume.
Translation of the "Short relation of the river Nile," which was itself translated from the author's "Itinerario," by Sir Peter Wyche.
Contents: Relation de la riviere du Nil. De la fameuse licorne, des lieux où elle est nourrie, & comme elle est formée. La raison pourquoy l'empereur abissin est appellé Prestre Iean des Indes. Traité succinct de la mer Rouge, & de la cause de ce nom, par lequel on la connoist ordinairement. Discours des palmiers, de leur diversité, de leur fruit & de son utilité, & du terroir qui leur est propre.

1. Africa—Descr. and trav., to 1800. 2. Nile river. 3. Unicorn. 4. Prester John. 5. Red Sea. 6. Palms, Date. 7. Wyche, Sir Peter, 1628–1699?, translator. 8. Title.
N. Y. P. L. June 7, 1926

NL 0431828 NN OCl

[Lobo, Jeronymo] 1596?–1678.
Relation de la riviere du Nil, de sa source et de son cours, et de l'inondation qu'elle fait dans la campagne d'Egypte, jusqu'à ce qu'elle tombe en la mer Mediterranée, & autres choses curieuses. Par un témoin oculaire, qua a demeuré plusieurs années dans les principaux royaumes de l'empire des Abissins. Tr. de l'original anglois ...

(*In* Recueil de divers voyages faits en Afrique et en l'Amerique. Paris, 1684. 24cm. [no. 2] [205]–252 p. fold. map)

Translation of the author's "Short relation of the river Nile", which was itself translated from his "Itinerario" by Sir Peter Wyche.

CONTENTS.—Relation de la riviere du Nil.—De la fameuse licorne, des lieux où elle est nourrie, & comme elle est formée.—La raison pourquoy l'empereur abissin est appellé le Prestre Iean des Indes.—Traité succinct de la mer Rouge, & de la cause de ce nom, par lequel on la connoist ordinairement.—Discours des palmiers, de leur diversité, de leur fruit & de son utilité, & du terroir qui leur est propre.

1. Africa—Descr. & trav. 2. Nile river. 3. Red sea—Descr. & trav. 4. John, Prester. 5. Date-palm. 6. Animals, Mythical. I. Wyche, Sir Peter, 1628–1699?

CA 5—2070 Unrev'd
Library of Congress G159.R31

NL 0431830 DLC

Lobo, Jeronymo, 1596?-1678.
Relation du R. P. Jeranymo Lobo de l'empire des Abyssins, des sources du Nil, de la Licorne, &c. (In: Thévenot (M) Relations de divers voyages curieux ... Paris, 1696. new ed. f°. v. 2. [no. 10] 16 p., 1 plan. illus.)

NL 0431831 NN

Lobo, Jeronymo, 1596?–1678.
Relation historique d'Abissinie, du r. p. Jerome Lobo ... Traduite du portugais, continuée & augmentée de plusieurs dissertations, lettres & memoires. Par m. Le Grand ... Paris, La veuve d'A. U. Coustelier, & J. Guerin, 1728.

xiv, [4], 514, [8] p. front., 2 fold. maps. 25½ x 19cm.

Translated from the original manuscript.
Some issues appeared under title: Voyage historique d'Abissinie. Paris, La veuve d'A. U. Coustelier, & J. Guerin, 1728.

1. Ethiopia—Hist. 2. Ethiopia. 3. Ethiopia—Church history. I. Legrand, Joachim, 1653–1733, tr. II. Title.

44-52005
Library of Congress DT376.L75 1728 a

NL 0431832 DLC GU IU WU CLU-C MnU PBa MH

Lobo, Jeronymo, 1596–1678.
Relation de l'empire des Abyssins, des sources du Nil, de la licorne, &c.

(*In* Thevenot, M. Relations de divers voyages. Paris, 1696. 35½cm. v. 2 (no. 11) 16 p.)

Ethiopia
1. ~~Abyssinia.~~

CA 8-1372 Unrev'd
Library of Congress G159.T41

NL 0431833 DLC

E696 =T418r cop.5.4 Lobo, Jeronymo, 1596-1675.
Relations De L'Empire Des Abyssins, Des Sovrces Dv Nil, De La Licorne, &c. Par le R. P. Ieronymo Lobo.
A Paris, Chez André Cramoisy, ruë de la vieille Bouclerie proche le Pont S. Michel, au Sacrifice d'Abraham. MDCLXXIII. Avec Privilege Du Roy.
1 p.ℓ., 16 p. []1 A-B⁴ illus., 2 fold. maps. fol.
Also issued without special t.-p. as a part of Thévenot, Melchisédech, Relations de divers voyages curieux ..., 4. ptie., Paris, 1672-1674, and subsequent issues.
Also issued as a part of Almeida, Manuel de, Histoire de la haute Ethiopie ..., Paris, 1674, itself also issued as a part of Thévenot's Relations (as cited).
Bound in the Library's cop. 5.4 (35.5cm.)

Continued in next column

Continued from preceding column

of Thévenot's Relations.
Cut on t.-p.
Caption title (p. 1): Relations Dv R. P. Ieronymo Lobo De L'Empire Des Abyssins, Des Sources du Nil, de la Licorne, &c.
"... achevées d'estre imprimées pour la premiere fois le 11. Fevrier 1673." (p. 16).

On t.-p. verso: "Avertissement", 8 lines, and errata, 5 lines.
Camus: Thévenot, p. 355, and Lenox: Thévenot 71/2 record a variant t.-p. with the "Avertissement" in 24 lines and errata in 5 lines. The Library's copies of such a variant appear to be in 19th century type facsimile.
Also issued with t.-p. bearing imprint: Paris, G. Clousier, A. Cramoisy, 1673.

In this copy there are: 2 copies of p. 1-16 (exhibiting variants in leaves A1-4, B1-4), 3 (variant) copies of fold. map "Carte d' Ethiopie ...", and 2 (variant) copies of fold. map "Entrées de quelques ports ...". Further information concerning variant states is recorded in the Library's bibliographical files.

JCB(2)2:936. 54-56; Camus: Thévenot p. 355, XLII; Lenox: Thévenot 71-73; Bibl. Lindesiana 8837 IV 21-25; Backer 4:1896; cf. Streit 16, p. 585.

NL 0431838 RPJCB

[Lobo, Jeronymo] 1596?–1678.
Relazioni varie cavate da una traduzione inglese dell' originale portoghese. Firenze, P. Martini, 1693.
3 p. l., 112 p. front., fold. map. 17½cm.
Translated from the English of Sir Peter Wyche by Lorenzo Magalotti.
CONTENTS.—Del Nilo.—Perchè il Nilo inondi, e metta sotto la campagna d'Egitto ne' giorni del maggior caldo in Europa.—Dell' vnicorno; e di passaggio della fenice, dell' vccello di paradiso, e del pellicano.—Perchè l'imperatore degli Abissini si chiami comunemente il Pretegianni.—Del mar Rosso, e sua denominazione.—Della palma: sue varietà, frutto, utilita, e coltura.
1. Africa—Descr. & trav. 2. Nile River. 3. Red Sea—Descr. & trav. 4. John, Prester. 5. Date palm. 6. Animals, Mythical. I. Magalotti, Lorenzo, conte, 1637–1712, tr.

5-9457
Librarv of Congress DT7.L79

NL 0431839 DLC CU

[Lobo, Jeronymo] 1596-1678.
A Short Relation of the River Nile ... London, 1667.

NL 0431840 PU

[Lobo, Jeronymo] 1596?–1678.
A short relation of the river Nile, of its sourse and current; of its overflowing the campagnia of Ægypt, till it runs into the Mediterranean: and of other curiosities: written by an eye-witnesse, who lived many years in the chief kingdoms of the Abyssine empire. London, J. Martyn, 1669.
3 p. l., 105 p. 15cm.
Translated from Jeronymo Lobo's Itinerario by Sir Peter Wyche.
CONTENTS.—A short relation of the river Nile.—Of the famous unicorne, where he is bred, and how shap'd.—The reason why the Abyssine emperour is called Prester John of the Indies.—A short tract of the Red Sea, and of the cause of this name by which 'tis commonly known.—A discourse of palme-trees, of their variety, their fruit, (and the usefullnesse of it,) of their proper soyle.
1. Africa—Descr. & trav. 2. Nile River. 3. Red Sea—Descr. & trav. 4. John, Prester. 5. Date palm. 6. Animals, Mythical. I. Wyche, Sir Peter, 1628–1699? II. Title.
Library of Congress DT7.L8 4—36107

NL 0431841 DLC MWiW-C CSmH ViU CoU CtY KU MH InU

Af W97? 669sb Rare Books Col [Lobo, Jeronymo] 1596?-1678.
A short relation of the river Nile, of its source and current; of its overflowing the campagnia of AEgypt, till it runs into the Mediterranean: and of other curiosities. Written by an Eye-witness, who lived many years in the chief Kingdoms of the Abyssine Empire.
London, Printed for John Martin, Printer to the Royal Society, at the Bell in St. Paul's Church-yard, 1673. 4p.ℓ.,104p. 14½cm.
Signatures: A-G⁸.
Translated from Jeronymo Lobo's Itinerario by Peter Wyche.
1. Africa - Descr. & trav. 2. Nile River. 3. Red Sea - Descr. & trav. 4. John, Prester. 5. Date palm. 6. Animals, Mythical. I. Wyche, Sir Peter, 1628-1699? II. Title.

NL 0431842 TxU CLU-C MH NcD NN CtY

VOLUME 337

[Lobo, Jeronymo], 1596–1678.
A short relation of the river Nile; of its source and current; of
161061 its overflowing the campagnia of Ægypt, 'till it runs into the Mediterranean; and of other curiosities. With a new preface. Written by an eye-witness, who lived many years in the chief kingdoms of the Abyssine Empire. [By Jeronymo Lobo.] London, Printed for the Royal Society, 1669. Reprinted for, and sold by J. Lackington, 1791.
[2, v]–xi, [13]–113 p. 21½cm.
Published anonymously.
Translated from the Portuguese by Sir Peter Wyche.

161061 Contents.—A short relation of the river Nile.—The true cause of the river Nile's overflowing and drowning the campania of Egypt, in the height of summer in Europe.—Of the famous unicorn; where he is bred and how shaped.—The reason why the Abyssine Empire is called Prester John of the Indies.—A short tract of the Red Sea; and the cause of this name.—A discourse of palm-trees.

NL 0431844 ICJ RPB NN MWA MH MB MnU NIC CtY KyLoU

DT8 L62 1798
[Lobo, Jeronymo] 1596?-1678.
A short relation of the river Nile, of its sourse and current; of its overflowing the campagnia of Egypt, till it runs into the Mediterranean; and of other curiosities. With a new preface. Written by an eye witness, who lived many years in the chief kingioms of the Abyssine empire. London, Printed for Lackington, Allen, 1798.
113 p.

Translated from Jeronymo Lobo's Itinerario by Sir Peter Wyche.

NL 0431845 CU ViU

Lobo, Jeronymo, 1596?–1678.

Magalotti, Lorenzo, *conte*, 1637–1712.
Varie operette del conte Lorenzo Magalotti, con giuntà di otto lettere su le terre odorose d'Europa e d'America dette volgarmente buccheri, ora pub. per la prima volta. Milano, G. Silvestri, 1825.

Lobo, Jeronymo, 1596-1678.
Voyage historique d'Abissinie, du R.P. Jerome Lobo de la Compagnie de Jesus. Traduite du portugais, continue & augmentee de plusieurs dissertations, lettres & memoires. Par M.Le Grand... Amsterdam, Aux depens de la compagnie, 1728.
2 v.

NL 0431847 MiU OCl CtY

Lobo, Jeronymo, 1596–1678.
Voyage historique d'Abissinie, du R. P. Jerome Lobo de la Compagnie de Jesus. Traduite du portugais, continuée & augmentée de plusieurs dissertations, lettres & memoires. Par M. Le Grand ... A Paris, Chez la veuve d'A. U. Coustelier & J. Guerin, 1728.
xiv, [4], 514, [8] p. 26cm.
Caption and running title: Relation historique d'Abissinie ... (Apparently some copies appeared under this title. *cf.* Backer)
1. Abyssinia — Hist. 2. Abyssinia. 3. Abyssinia — Church history. I. Legrand, Joachim, 1653–1733, tr. II. Title. III. Title: Relation historique d'Abissinie.
Library of Congress DT376.L75 5-8165

NL 0431848 DLC NIC CSt CU-S MnU NN DCU-H

Lobo, Jeronymo. 1596–1678. Voyage to Abyssinia, 1622. 60 pp. (Pinkerton, J., *Voyages*, v.15, p.1.)

NL 0431849 MdBP OClWHi

Lobo, Jeronymo, 1596–1678.
A voyage to Abyssinia. By Father Jerome Lobo ... With a continuation of the history of Abyssinia down to the beginning of the eighteenth century, and fifteen dissertations on various subjects, relating to the history, antiquities, government, religion, manners, and natural history of Abyssinia, and other countries mention'd by Father Jerome Lobo. By Mr. Le Grand. From the French. London, A. Bettesworth, and C. Hitch, 1735.
xii, 396, [8] p. 20cm.
Title in red and black.
Translated by Dr. Samuel Johnson. *cf.* Fumagalli, Bibliografia etiopica, p. 14.
1. Ethiopia. 2. Ethiopia—Hist. I. Legrand, Joachim, 1653–1733. II. Johnson, Samuel, 1709–1784, tr. III. Title.
Library of Congress DT376.L77 1735 5—8164
[43c1]

NcU CtY PPL OCU ViU PBL TxU NN CSmH NjP WaU
NL 0431850 DLC IU IEN NcU PSt TU N NBuU NIC CU IaU

Lobo, Jeronymo, 1596–1678.
A voyage to Abyssinia, by Father Jerome Lobo ... Containing the history, natural, civil, and ecclesiastical, of that remote and unfrequented country, continued down to the beginning of the eighteenth century: with fifteen dissertations on various subjects, relating to the antiquities, government, religion, manners, and natural history, of Abyssinia. By M. Le Grand. Tr. from the French by Samuel Johnson, LL. D. To which are added, various other tracts by the same author, not published by Sir John Hawkins or Mr. Stockdale. London, Elliot and Kay; [etc., etc.] 1789.
2 p. l., 500 p. 21cm.
1. Ethiopia. 2. Ethiopia—Hist. I. Legrand, Joachim, 1653–1733. II. Johnson, Samuel, 1709–1784, tr. III. Title.
Library of Congress DT376.L77 1789 5—8163

OCl TU InU CSmH MB NN IU InU MH CU NjP CSt NBu OC
NL 0431851 DLC ViU TxU NIC IU MBU CtY PPAN PU NcU

Lobo, Jeronymo, 1596–1678.
... A voyage to Abyssinia, by Father Jerome Lobo, a Portuguese Jesuit. From the French.
(*In* Pinkerton, John, ed. A general collection of the best and most interesting voyages and travels ... London, 1808–14. 27½ x 21cm. v. 15 (1814) p. [1]–60. pl.)
"Translated by Dr. Johnson."—Foot-note, p. [1]
1. Ethiopia. 2. Ethiopia—Hist. I. Johnson, Samuel, 1709–1784, tr. II. Title.
CA 8—2066 Unrev'd
Library of Congress G161.P65 vol. 15

NL 0431852 DLC CaBViPA

916.3 L786v-Ej 1887
Lobo, Jeronymo, 1596-1678, S.J.
... A voyage to Abyssinia, by Father Jerome Lobo. Translated from the French by Samuel Johnson. London [etc.] Cassell & Company, limited, 1887.
192 p. 15 cm. (Cassell's national library. [no. 91])
Translation of his Voyage historique d'Abissinie.
1. Ethiopia. 2. Ethiopia--History. 3. Ethiopia--Church history. I. Johnson, Samuel, 1709-1784, tr. II. Jesuits (Works by)

NL 0431853 MoSU OCl PSt NIC

Lobo, Jeronymo, 1596-1678.
A voyage to Abyssinia, by Father Jerome Lobo. Translated from the French by Samuel Johnson. New York, Cassell & co., ltd. [1887]
"Cassell's national library, vol. II no. 92."

NL 0431854 MH

Lobo, Jeronymo, 1596?-1678.
... A voyage to Abyssinia. By Father Jerome Lobo ... From the French ... New York, Cossell [189-?]
14 cm.

NL 0431855 CU

Lobo, Jeronymo, 1596?–1678.
... A voyage to Abyssinia, by Father Jerome Lobo; tr. from the French by Samuel Johnson. London [etc.] Cassell & company limited, 1893.
192 p. 14½cm. (Cassell's national library. [no. 91])
1. Abyssinia. 2. Abyssinia—Hist. I. Johnson, Samuel, 1709–1784, tr.
20-13226
Library of Congress DT376.L77 1893

NL 0431856 DLC NN MiU

Lobo, João Bruno.
... Aguas termais em Goiaz, Caldas Novas, Caldas de Pirapitinga e Caldas Velhas, por João Bruno Lobo ... [Rio de Janeiro, 1938]
21 p., 1 l., incl. illus., plans, tables. plates. 23cm. ([Brazil] Laboratorio central da producão mineral. Avulso n.o 3 [i.e. 2])
At head of title: Ministerio da agricultura. Departamento nacional da producão mineral. Laboratorio central da producão mineral. Laboratorio central da producão mineral.
Series numbering corrected in ink.
"Separata do n.o 15, setembro-outubro, 1938, da revista 'Mineracao e metalurgia'"
1. Springs—Brazil. I. Title. II. Ser.

NL 0431857 ViU

Lobo, Jorge da Graça Ataíde, ed.

Law
Portugal. *Laws, statutes, etc.*
Trabalho, legislação em vigor, anotada [por] Jorge da Graça Ataíde Lobo. Luanda, Empreza Gráfica de Angola, 1955.

Lobo, José, ed.

Marshall, John, 1755–1835.
Decisões constitucionaes de Marshall, presidente do Supremo tribunal dos Estados Unidos da America do Norte, traduzidas por Americo Lobo. Rio de Janeiro, Imprensa nacional, 1903.

G981.4 L786f
Lôbo, José de Figueirêdo.
Fortificações coloniais da Bahia. Bahia, 1953. 67p. 24cm.
"Trabalho apresentado ao 1.º Congresso de Geografia e História da Bahia, realizado em março de 1949, e publicado nos Anais do referido Congresso."
Author's autograph presentation copy to [Jordão] Emerenciano.
Bibliography: p.[62]-63.

NL 0431860 TxU

Lobo, José Ignacio.

Festa jubilar do prof. dr. A. de Lemos Torres. S. Paulo [Empreza Cosmos de publicidade limitada] 1939.

Greenlee 4504 P855
LOBO, JOSÉ JUSTINIANO
Egloga pastoril em applauso do feliz nascimento do minino Jesus... Lisboa, Viuv. de I. Nogueira Xisto, 1768.
7p. 20cm.

NL 0431862 ICN

VOLUME 337

Lobo, José M Viguera
see
Viguera Lobo, José M

438 Lobo, José Teodoro de Souza.
Geografia elementar. 17a. ed. Livraria do Globo, Porto Alegre, 1941.
212 p. 19 cm.

NL 0431864 DPU

Lobo, Julio
El plan Chadbourne: nuestro cáncer social. Habana, Maza Caso y cia., 1933.
7 p. 24cm.

Cover title.
"Cortesía de la Revista 'Bohemia'."

1. Sugar trade - Cuba. 2. Chadbourne, Thomas Lincoln, 1871- I. Title.

NL 0431865 FU

981.04
L799a Lobo, Julio da Silveira.
Apontamentos para a historia do segundo reinado. [Rio de Janeiro?] 1895.
ii, 168 p. 18 cm.

Bound with Antonio Ferreira Vianna's "O antigo regimen". Rio de Janeiro, Cunha & Irmão, 1896.

1. Brazil—Pol. & govt.—1822-1889. I. Title.

NL 0431866 ICarbS

Lobo, Julio da Silveira, jr.
Homorrhagias post-partum; seu tratamento. 1892.
(In Rio de Janeiro-Faculdade de medicana Theses apresentada a Faculdade de medicina. v. 2)

NL 0431867 PU

Lobo, Leocadio.
... Primate and priest. [London, Press department of the Spanish embassy] 1937.
15 p. 22cm.

A reply to The martyrdom of Spain, a pastoral letter of His Eminence señor d. Isidro Gomá y Tomás. cf. p. 5.
No. [11] in a volume with binder's title: Pamphlets on the Spanish civil war: religious aspects.

1. Gomá y Tomás, Isidro, cardinal, 1869-1940. The martyrdom of Spain.

43-26137
Brief cataloging

Library of Congress DP269.P27 no. 11

NL 0431868 DLC MH

Lobo, Leopoldo Balcarcel
see
Balcarcel Lobo, Leopoldo.

Lobo, Luiz, 1873-
... História militar do Pará [por] Luiz Lobo ... Rio [de Janeiro, Bedeschi, 1943.
144 p. illus. (incl. ports.) 23½cm. (Biblioteca militar. Vol. LXV)
L. C. copy imperfect: p. 97-112 wanting.

1. Pará, Brazil (State)—Hist.

44-8068

Library of Congress F2586.L6
[2] 981

NL 0431870 DLC NN TxU CU OrPS

Lobo, Luiz Monteverde da Cunha
see Monteverde da Cunha Lobo, Luiz.

Lobo, Manuel, 1612-1686.
Relacion De La Vida, Y Virtudes Del V. Hermano Pedro de San Ioseph Bectancur. ... Con licencia. Impressa en Guatemala ... 1667.
Imperfect: wants 5 l.

NL 0431872 RPJCB

Lobo. Manoel da Gama
see
Gama Lobo, Manoel da.

Lobo, Manuel da Gama, 1658-1742, *praeses*.
Cæsareas conclusiones deductas ex elegantibus titulis D. de jure codillorum & C. de crimine expilatæ hæreditatis ex his quæ ibi suttiliter notavit sapientissimus d. d. præses Emmanuel a Gama Lobo, cujus nominis ingeniosum anagrama Malo Gamam Labeone v. quinquies eum explicat ... & defendit Felix Josephus a Costa ... [Ulyssipone Occidentali, P. Ferreyra, 1726]
[25] p. illus. 28 cm.
Signature: A[14].

I. Costa, Felix José da, b. 1701, respondent. II. Title.

PA8545.L6C3 55-51438

NL 0431874 DLC

Lobo, Mario.
Tres poemas y un nombre, voces hermanas de un corazón hermano. San José, Costa Rica, 1954.
78 p. illus. 20 cm.

I. Title.

PQ7489.L6T7 54-39955 ‡

NL 0431875 DLC FU TxU

W 4
S18
1910 LÔBO, Mario Ferreira de Souza
Da rõntgoscopia do estomago normal. Bahia, 1910.
vii, 123 p.
These - Bahia.

NL 0431876 DNLM

Lobo, Miguel, 1821-1876
Derrotero de las Islas Canarias. 2. ed. viii,95,[8]p. fold.maps. Cádiz, Imprenta de la Revista médica, 1860.

NL 0431877 OCl

F
1408
.25
.L6 Lobo, Miguel, d. 1876.
Un hijo de Inglaterra á quien le ha dado por viajar en las regiones americanas que fueron de España y por escribir sendos dislates sobre ellas y sus antiguos dominadores. Madrid, Impr. y Librería de M. Guijarro, 1874.
77 p.

#Hutchinson, Thomas Joseph, 1820-
#Latin America.
Un hijo de Inglaterra á quien le ha dado por viajar en las regiones ...

NL 0431879 MoU NcU MH

F1412
.L79 Lobo, Miguel, 1821-1876.
Historia general de las antiguas colonias hispano-americanas desde su descubrimiento hasta el año mil ochocientos ocho, por D. Miguel Lobo ... Madrid, M. Guijarro, 1875.
3 v. 26½ cm.

1. Latin America—History—To 1830.

F1412.L79 4-35434

NL 0431880 DLC TxU WU CU-B MnU NcD CU NN NjP

VK966
L7
1868 Lobo, Miguel, 1821-1876.
Manual de la navegacion del Rio de la Plata y de sus principales afluentes, con instrucciones para la recalada y derrotas de ida y vuelta á Europa, segun los documentos mas fidedignos, nacionales y extranjeros, por los señores Lobo y Riudavets. 2. ed. ampliada é ilustrada con una carta y vistas de costa. Madrid, Estab. tip. de T. Fortanet, 1868.
xv, 333 p. fold. map. 23 cm.
Based on the authors' translation of A Boucarut's Manuel de la navigation dans le Rio de la Plata, Paris, 1857.
1. Pilot guides—Rio de la Plata. I. Riudavets y Tudury, Pedro, joint author. II. Boucarut, Alcide, b. 1825.

VK966.L7 1868 4-9050

NL 0431881 DLC NN TxU CU

Lobo, Miguel, 1821-1876.
Priviléges et prééminences concédés aux gens de mer dans les XIIIe, XIVe, XVe, XVIe siècles depuis le règne de Sanche IV, surnammé le Brave [el Bravo] Paris, J. Corréard, 1864.
50 p., 1 l. 8°.

NL 0431882 NN

Lobo, Ovidio da Gama
see Gama Lobo, Ovidio da.

Lobo, Paul Allan, 1928-
Chemical processing at high temperature and high pressure. Ann Arbor, University Microfilms [1955]
([University Microfilms, Ann Arbor, Mich.] Publication no. 12,608)
Microfilm copy of typescript. Positive.
Collation of the original: ix, 103 l. illus.
Thesis—University of Michigan.
Abstracted in Dissertation abstracts, v. 15 (1955) no. 11, p. 2142.
Bibliography: leaves 101-103.

1. Pressure vessels. 2. Catalysis. I. Title.

Microfilm AC-1 no. 12,608 Mic 55-1020

Michigan. Univ. Libr. for Library of Congress [1]†

NL 0431884 MiU DLC

VOLUME 337

Lobo, Pedro José.
Bases e processos da economia de Macau; conferência pronunciada no Salão Nobre do Leal Senado da Câmara de Macau, no dia 21 de Maio de 1953, integrada no ciclo de conferências promovidas pelo Círculo Cultural de Macau. ⌈Macau⌉ Repartição Central dos Serviços Económicos, Secção de Propaganda e Turismo ⌈1953⌉
67 p. 22 cm.

1. Macao—Econ. condit. I. Title.

HC428.M25L6 55-40074

NL 0431885 DLC NN

Lôbo, Pelagio, 1888-
Recordações das arcadas. ⌈São Paulo⌉ Reitoria da Universidade de São Paulo, Departamento de Cultura e Ação Social, Divisão de Difusão Cultural, 1953.
294 p. 22 cm.

1. Law—Brazil—Biog. 2. São Paulo, Brazil (City) Universidade. Faculdade de Direito. I. Title.
Full name: Pelagio Alvares Lôbo.
58-45457

NL 0431886 DLC MH-L

Lobo, Rafael Pérez
see
Pérez Lobo, Rafael.

Lobo, Ramón
see Lobo y Regidor, Ramón.

WG
280
L799d
1948
LOBO, Renato Marques
Determinações cardíacas da esquistossomose mansônica. Salvador, Brasil, Livraria Progresso ⌈1948?⌉
238, vi p. illus.
Summary in English.
1. Heart - Diseases 2. Schistosomiasis

NL 0431889 DNLM TxU

Lobo, Roberto Haddock
see
Lobo, Roberto Jorge Haddock, 1902-

G330.981
H117h
1951
Lobo, Roberto Jorge Haddock, 1902-
História econômica e administrativa do Brasil para as escolas de comércio e administração e os cursos técnicos em geral. 2. ed., rev. [São Paulo] Edições Melhoramentos [1951]
204p. illus. 21cm.
Includes bibliography.

1. Brazil - Econ. condit. - 1918-

NL 0431891 TxU TNJ

Lobo, Roberto Jorge Haddock, 1902-
Pequena história da economia. São Paulo, Martins ⌈1943⌉
345 p. illus. 22 cm. (A Marcha do espírito, v. 8)

1. Economic history.

HC21.L6 1943 330.9 45-883 rev*

NL 0431892 DLC NN

Lobo, Roberto Jorge Haddock, 1902-
Pequena história do Brasil. Para o curso primário, com indicações dos principais fatos de nossa vida econômica. Illustrações de O.Storni. [São Paulo] Edições Melhoramentos [195-?]

NL 0431893 MH

Lobo, Roberto Jorge Haddock, 1902-
Pro Brasilia fiant eximia. São Paulo, Editora Bandeirante ⌈193-⌉
179 p. 19 cm.

I. Title.

PQ9697.L6P7 869.8 39-15901 rev*

NL 0431894 DLC CU TxU

WZ
100
qL799
LOBO, Rodolfo S
A collection of miscellaneous bio-bibliographical material on this person, together with abstracts, résumés, etc. of his works, may be found on the shelves under the above call number.

NL 0431895 DNLM

W
4
P252
1933/34
Lobo, Rodolfo S
Étude critique des méthodes d'extraction des toxiques organiques; application à la recherche des dérivés barbituriques. Paris, Jouve, 1934.
114 p. (Paris. Université. Faculté de pharmacie. Thèse. 1933/34. no. 9)
Bibliography: p. ⌈111⌉-114.

NL 0431896 DNLM CtY

Lobo, Roque Ferreira
see Ferreira Lobo, Roque, 1743-1828.

Lobo, Rosalio, plaintiff.

Segura, Francisco de P.
Amparo solicitado contra las sentencias del juez de 1ª instancia de Yautepec y Tribunal superior del estado de Morelos por Rosalío Lobo, Jorge Ayala y Narciso Garcés, patrocinados por sus abogados Francisco de P. Segura, Enrique J. Cervantes y Rafael O'Horan. Mexico, Imp. Hijas de J. F. Jens, 1897.

Lobo, Salvador González
see
González Lobo, Salvador.

Lobo, Saskia.
...Het kinderboek 1920-1924; een keur uit vijf jaren, samengesteld en toegelicht door Saskia Lobo... 's-Gravenhage, 1924.
30 p. 8°. (Centrale vereeniging voor openbare leeszalen en bibliotheken. Leeszaalwerk ⌈no.⌉ 4.)
Cover-title.

1. Juvenile literature—Bibl. 2. Ser.
N. Y. P. L. March 30, 1928

NL 0431900 NN

Lobo, Sebastião de Abreu.
Notas sobre a turbina maritima de Parsons ... Rio de Janeiro, Liga Maritima Brazileira, 1909.

NL 0431901 DPU

Lobo, Silva
see
Silva Lobo, Antonio Auguste da, d. 1900.

Lobo, Telesphoro de Souza
see
Souza Lobo, Telesphoro de

HJ9923
.B6A3
1941 c
Lobo, Ubaldo.
Brazil. *Laws, statutes, etc.*
... Ante-projeto de lei de contabilidade pública; exposição de motivos, justificação, ante-projeto, indices. Rio de Janeiro, Imprensa nacional, 1941.

4HE
1128
Lobo, Ubaldo
Contadoría Central de Transportes; transportes combinados terrestres aquaticos e aereos e a liquidação de suas contas. Rio de Janeiro, 1936.
94 p.

NL 0431905 DLC-P4

Lobo, Walter E 1905-
... Report on "Oxygen plant development" to February 28, 1945 ...
see under Kellogg, M.W., company.

B
0125L
Lobo Arraga, María Carmen del
⌈El⌉ General D. Manuel Obligado, apuntes para servir a su biografía (en el XVIII aniversario de su muerte). Buenos Aires, Mariani, 1914.
24 p. illus., port., (col.) 24 cm.

1. Obligado Ortiz, Manuel, 1838-1896.

NL 0431907 MiU

Lobo Azevedo, Ario
see Azevedo, Ario Lobo.

VOLUME 337

Lobo Bermejo, Mario N
Burgos y el Cid. Burgos [1955]

NL 0431909 WU

Lobo Cardoso, Manuel da Costa
see Cardoso, Manuel da Costa Lobo.

Lobo Carneiro, Fernando Luiz
see
Carneiro, Fernando Luiz Lobo.

Lobo Cayolla, Lourenço Caldeira da Gama
see
Cayolla, Lourenço, 1863-

Lobo de Almada Negreiros, Antonio de
see
Almada Negreiros, Antonio de, 1868-

Lobo de Andrade da Silva Leal, Sebastião Correia
see Silva Leal, Sebastião Correia Lobo de Andrade da, 1862-

PQ 9261 +L54 A82
Lobo d'Avila, Arthur, 1855-1945
Os amores do príncipe perfeito; romance histórico. [Lisboa] J. Romano Torres [19--?]
614p. illus. 27cm.
Bibliographical footnotes.

1. João II, King of Portugal, 1455-1495 - Fiction I. Title

NL 0431915 WU DLC-P4

869.8 L798ca
Lobo d'Avila,Arthur,1855-1945.
Os Caramurús; romance histórico da descoberta e independencia do Brazil. Lisboa, J.Romano Torres, 1900.
278 p. illus.

NL 0431916 MiU CtY ICN WU CSt NcU

Lobo d'Avila, Arthur, 1855-
... Cristóbal Colón, Salvador Gonsalves Zarco, infante de Portugal. Lisboa [Tip. da Emprêsa nacional de publicidade] 1939.
136 p., 4 l. incl. port., facsims., coat of arms. coat of arms. 24½cm.
At head of title: Arthur Lobo d'Ávila e Saul Santos Ferreira.
"Crêmos que o leitor ficará convencido, de que: Cristóbal Colón era na realidade Salvador Gonsalves Zarco-infante de Portugal."—p. 136.
1. Colombo, Cristoforo—Name. 2. Colombo, Cristoforo—Birthplace. 3. Colombo, Cristoforo—Coat of arms. I. Santos Ferreira, Saul, joint author.
[Full name: Arthur Eugenio Lobo d'Avila]
40-29771
Library of Congress E112.L847
[2] 923.9

NL 0431917 DLC NN MH-P

Lobo d'Avila, Arthur, 1855-
A descoberta da India; ou, O reinado de d. Manoel, drama historico em 5 actos, por Arthur Lobo d'Avila. Lisboa, 1897.
175, [1] p. 19cm.

1. Manuel, king of Portugal, 1469-1521—Drama. I. Title.
[Full name: Arthur Eugenio Lobo d'Avila]
37-36554
Library of Congress PQ9261.L54D4 1897
[2] 869.2

NL 0431918 DLC

Lobo d'Avila, Arthur, 1855-
... A descoberta da India; ou O reinado de d. Manuel; drama historico em 5 actos por Arthur Lobo d'Avila. Lisboa, Imprensa nacional, 1898.
iiii, 176 p., 1 l. 25cm.
At head of title: Quarto centenario do descobrimento da India. Concurso para um drama, aberto pela Commissão central executiva.
In verse.
"Justificação da tiragem: 3 exemplares em papel de linho branco nacional, 1:000 em papel de algodão de 1.ª qualidade."
Previously published Lisbon, 1897.
1. Manuel, king of Portugal, 1469-1521—Drama. I. Commissão central executiva para a celebração do quarto centenario do descobrimento da India. II. Title.
[Full name: Arthur Eugenio Lobo d'Avila]
37-36576
Library of Congress PQ9261.L54D4 1898
——— Copy 2. [3] 869.2

NL 0431919 DLC NcD CU WU

DS 498.3 .L79
Lobo d'Avila,Arthur,1855-1945.
A descoberta e conquista da India pelos portuguezes; romance histórico. Ed.illustrada por E.Casanova,A.Brandão e pelo auctor. Lisboa, J.Romano Torres, 1898.
223 p. illus.

1.Portuguese in India. 2.India--Disc.& explor. 3.India--Hist.--European settlements, 1500-1765. I.Title.
Full name: Arthur Eugenio Lobo d'Avila.

NL 0431920 MiU NcD NIC

Lobo d'Avila, Arthur, 1855-
... A descoberta e conquista da Índia pelos portuguesses, romance histórico ... 3. ed. Lisboa, J. Romano Torres & c.ª [1937?]
254 p., 1 l. pl., ports. 19cm.

1. Portuguese in India. 2. India—Disc. & explor. 3. India—Hist.—European settlements, 1500-1765. I. Title.
[Full name: Arthur Eugenio Lobo d'Avila]
41-26910
Library of Congress DS498.3.L6

NL 0431921 DLC NcU

4S 536
Lobo d'Avila, Arthur, 1899-1945.
Elogio historico do visconde de Coruche, Caetano da Silva Luz, lido na sessão solemne de 12 de abril de 1905, na Real Associação Central da Agricultura Portugueza, por Arthur Lobo d'Avila. Lisboa, 1906.
xliv p.

NL 0431922 DLC-P4

666.2 L786e
LOBO D'AVILA, ARTHUR, 1855-1945.
Esmaltes artisticos e industriais. Lisboa, Pereira, 1935.
9p.l.,[19]-159p. illus.,ports. 16cm.
(Biblioteca de ensino tecnico)

1. Enamel and enameling. I. Title.

NL 0431923 TxU

LOBO D'AVILA, ARTHUR, 1855-
Um infante de Portugal: Salvador Gonsalves Zarco, descobridor do Novo Mundo [de] Arthur Lobo d'Avila e Saul Santos Ferreira. [1.ed.] Lisboa [Tip. Silvas] 1942. 182 p. illus., port. 25cm.

No. 464 of 500 copies printed.
Bibliographical footnotes.

1. Gonsalves Zarco, Salvador. 2. Columbus, Christopher. 3. America—Discovery. I. Santos Ferreira, Saul, joint author.

NL 0431924 NN

Lobo d'Avila, Arthur, 1855-
... Malhados; peça em 3 actos. Lisboa, J. R. Torres, 1902.
112 p. front. (port.) 17cm.
On heavy paper.

I. Title.
[Full name: Arthur Eugenio Lobo d'Avila]
35-29276
Library of Congress PQ9261.L54M3
——— Copy 2. 869.2

NL 0431925 DLC MH

Lobo d'Avila, Arthur, 1855-1945.
Memórias de Artur Lobo d'Ávila (com interessantes apontamentos da sua viagem à China) 1855-1945. Coordenação e anotações de Reinaldo Ferreira (Néor X) e Saul dos Santos Ferreira. Lisboa [Impresso nas oficinas da papelaria Fernandes] 1946.
141, [2] p. 19cm.

I. Ferreira, Reinaldo, ed. II. Santos Ferreira, Saul dos, 1912- joint ed.
[Full name: Arthur Eugenio Lobo d'Avila]
46-21544
Library of Congress PQ9261.L54Z5
[2] 928.69

NL 0431926 DLC MH

40T 382
Lobo d'Avila, Arthur, 1855-1945
Memorias do Padre Vicente. Lisboa, Editores Lisboa & C.a, 1878.
261 p.

NL 0431927 DLC-P4

4PQ Port. 990
Lobo d'Avila, Arthur, 1855-1945.
Ministro ideal. Lisboa, A. M. Pereira, 1907.
324 p.

NL 0431928 DLC-P4

Lobo d'Avila, Arthur, 1855-
... Os ministros do senhor Moura. [Lisboa] Typ. do Diario de Lisboa, 1881.
413 p. 20½cm.

I. Title.
[Full name: Arthur Eugenio Lobo d'Avila]
34-8885
Library of Congress PQ9261.L54M5 869.3

NL 0431929 DLC

VOLUME 337

PQ9261 .L54R4

Lobo d'Avila, Arthur, 1855–1945.
O reinado venturoso; romance histórico portuguez da epocha manuelina. Ed. illustrada. Lisboa, Santos, Vieira [19–]
2 v. illus. 25 cm.
Issued in 12 pts.

1. Portugal—Hist.—Manuel, 1495–1521—Fiction. I. Title.
Full name: Arthur Eugenio Lobo d'Avila.

PQ9261.L54R4 OCAT 60–30583

NL 0431930 DLC NcU TxU

Lobo d'Avila, Arthur, 1855–
... Vasco, romance original. Lisboa, A. M. Pereira, 1903.
244 p. 20cm. (Collecção Antonio Maria Pereira. [48.° v.])

I. Title. [*Full name:* Arthur Eugenio Lobo d' Avila]

34–8884

Library of Congress PQ9261.L54V3 869.3

NL 0431931 DLC

869.8 L798ve Lobo d'Avila, Arthur, 1855-1945.
A verdadeira paixão de Bocage; romance historico sobre a vida do grande poeta [por] Artur Lobo d'Avila e Fernando Mendes. Lisboa, Secção Editorial de "O Seculo", 1926.
236 p. (O Romance popular)

1. Barbosa du Bocage, Manuel Marie de, 1765-1805--Fiction. I. Mendes, Fernando, joint author. II. Title.

NL 0431932 MiU NcU RP

Lobo d'Avila, Arthur Eugenio
see Lobo d'Avila, Arthur, 1855-1945.

Lobo d'Avila, Carlos, 1860–1895.
... Carteira d'um viajante, apontamentos a lapis, com um prologo do ex.mo sr. Pinheiro Chagas ... Lisboa, Typographia universal de T. Quintino Antunes, 1878.
xiii p., 1 l., 347 p., 1 l. 19cm.

1. Europe—Descr. & trav. 2. Switzerland—Descr. & trav. I. Title.

34–10104

Library of Congress D919.L7 914

NL 0431934 DLC

Lobo d'Avila, Joaquim Thomaz
see Avila, Joaquim Thomaz Lobo d'.

Lobo d'Avila da Silva Lima, José Caetano, 1885–
...Alguns problemas internacionaes... Lisboa: J. Rodrigues & c.a, 1931. 286 p. 26cm.
At head of title: Lobo d'Avila Lima.

152291B. 1. Law, International, 1914–
N. Y. P. L. January 28, 1942

NL 0431936 NN MH

Lobo d'Avila da Silva Lima, José Caetano, 1885-
... Contribution des Portugais au développement de la navigation aérienne; quelques voeux juridiques ... Lisboa, Centro tipografico colonial, 1928.
3 p.l., [9]-35 p. 25½cm.
"Mémoire présenté à la Section juridique du IVème Congrès international de navigation aérienne, Rome, 1927."
With author's autograph.

NL 0431937 MH-L

4K 2194 Lobo d'Avila da Silva Lima, José Caetano
Da concorrencia desleal. Coimbra, Imprensa da Universidade, 1910.
269 p.

NL 0431938 DLC-P4

Lobo d'Avila da Silva Lima, José Caetano.
... Da Sociedade das nações. Lisboa, J. Rodrigues & c.a, 1927.
viii, 191 p. 24½ x 19½cm.
At head of title: Lobo d'Avila Lima.

1. League of nations.

45–27448

Library of Congress JX1975.L78 [2] 341.1

NL 0431939 DLC MH

Lobo d'Avila da Silva Lima, José Caetano.
... Do cheque. Lisboa, Livraria profissional [1914?]
3 p. l., 173 p. 23½cm.
At head of title: Lobo d'Avila Lima.
Bibliographical foot-notes at end of most chapters.

1. Checks. I. Title.

33–32330

Library of Congress HG1691.L6 332.76

NL 0431940 DLC

Lobo d'Avila da Silva Lima, José Caetano, 1885-
Politica internacional. Coimbra, M.Marques, 1913.

NL 0431941 MH

JA 76 L62 Lobo d'Avila de Silva Lima, José Caetano
Politica social [por] Lobo d'Avila Lima. Coimbra, Moura Marques & Paraisos, 1912.
304p. 19cm.

1. Political science 2. Sociology I. Title

NL 0431942 WU CSt-H

Lobo d'Avila da Silva Lima, José Caetano.
... Portugal e a guerra das nações. Lisboa, Empresa lusitana, 1915.
332 p. 19cm.
At head of title: Lobo d'Avila Lima.
Cover dated 1916.
"Vão n'este modesto volume colligidas algumas d'entre as chronicas, que pelo espaço de dois annos viram a luz e tiveram fidalga hospitalidade nas columnas da imprensa sul-americana."—p. [5]

Continued in next column

Continued from preceding column

CONTENTS.—Portugal e a guerra das nações.—O imperialismo britannico em Moçambique.—Espheras de influencia e interesses.—"Regimen da porta aberta" em Angola.—A "politica do rail" em Africa.—O imperialismo anglo-germanico.—O "homen de Birmingham."—Uma critica á justiça moderna.—Parlamentos sociaes.—Economia mundial.—O custo da vida.—As contas do estado portuguez.—Terras de Santa Cruz.—Cosas de España.—Cousas de Portugal.

1. Portugal—For. rel. 2. World politics. 3. Economic conditions. I. Title.

45–29794

Library of Congress DP675.L58

NL 0431944 DLC MH

Lobo d'Avila da Silva Lima, José Caetano, 1885–
... Soccorros mutuos e seguros sociaes. Coimbra, Imprensa da Universidade, 1909.
xxiv, 492 p. 25cm.
"Dissertação inaugural para o acto de conclusões magnas na Faculdade de direito da Universidade de Coimbra."

1. Friendly societies. 2. Insurance, Industrial.

13–20527

Library of Congress HD7091.L7

NL 0431945 DLC ICJ

Lobo d'Avila Lima, Jose
see
Lobo d'Avila da Silva Lima, Jose Caetano, 1885-

Lobo da Costa, José Luiz
see Costa, José Luiz Lobo da.

946.903 L786c Lobo da Mesquita Gavião, Manoel, d. 1849, ed.
Collecção de documentos eneditos para a historia da Guerra Civil em Portugal no anno de 1847. Publicados e annotados por Manoel Lobo da Mesquita Gavião. Porto, Typographia do Nacional, 1849.
87p. fold. tables. 21cm.

1. Portugal - Hist. - 1826-1853 - Sources.

NL 0431948 TxU MH

Lobo da Silva, Arthur
see
Silva, Arthur Lobo da, 1876 *or* 7–

Lobo da Silveira, Eduard, graf von Oriolla
see Oriolla, Eduard, graf von, 1809-1862.

Lobo da Silveira, Joaquim José Antonio, conde de Oriola
Korrt beskrifning om Brasilien, af J. Lobo da Silveira ... Öfversättning af Martin Altén. Stockholm, Tryckt hos J. P. Lindh, 1809.
1 p. l., 86 p. 17½cm.

1. Brazil—Description and travel. I. Altén, Martin, 1764–1830, tr.

G S 34–506

U. S. Geol. survey. Libr. for Library of Congress Geo. F. Kunz collection K590 (410) L78 [a40b1]

NL 0431951 DI-GS

VOLUME 337

Lobo da Silveira, Joaquim José Antonio, *conde de Oriola.*
Skizze von Brasilien, von J. Lobo da Silveira ... Stockholm, Gedrukt bei J. P. Lindh, 1808.
4 p. l., 112 p., 1 l. 20cm.
"Literarischer beytrag": 3d prelim. leaf.

1. Brazil—Descr. & trav. 2. Natural resources—Brazil. I. Title.

F2508.L83 47-33770

NL 0431952 DLC NN

DP645 L6L6 Lobo de Avila, Rodrigo
O general Francisco de Paula Lobo d'Avila e os seus detractores; memoria redigida por seu filho Rodrigo Lobo d'Avila. Lisboa, Typographia Universal, 1865.
248 p.

1. Lobo de Avila, Francisco de Paula, 1801-1887.

NL 0431953 CU

Lobo de Barbosa Ferreira Teixeira Girao, Antonio, visconde de Villarinho de Sao Romao. 1785-1863

Manual pratico da cultura das batatas e do seu uso na economia domestica, colligido dos melhores agronomos francezes e inglezes, e seguido de algumas observações praticas do auctor, para melhor conhecimento dos nossos agricultores ... Lisboa, Typ. da [Academia real das sciencias] 1845.
2 p.l., vi, [7]-99, [4] p. fold.tab. 22 cm.

NL 0431954 MH-BA MH

4SB 505 Lobo de Barbosa Ferreira Teixeira Girao, Antonio, visconde de Villarinho de Sao Romao, 1786-1863.
Memoria historica e analytica sobre a Companhia dos Vinhos, denominada da Agricultura das Vinhas do Alto Douro. Lisboa, Impr. Nacional, 1833.
331 p.

NL 0431955 DLC-P4

Lobo de Barbosa Ferreira Teixeira Girão, Antonio, visconde de Villarinho de São Romão, 1785-1863.
Memoria sobre os pesos e medidas de Portugal, sua origem, antiguidade, denominação, e mudanças, que tem sofrido até nossos dias, bem como sobre a reforma que devem ter. Acompanhada de varias tabellas de reducção, ou comparação de todas as medidas e pesos do mundo conhecido, antigas e modernas, com as actuaes de Lisboa. Para uso do commercio, e boa inteligencia dos historiadores e geografos antigos e modernos. Por Antonio Lobo de Barbosa Ferreira Teixeira Gyrão. Lisboa: Na Imprensa nacional, 1833. iv, 111 p. 29½cm.

120429B. 1. Metrology—Portugal.
N. Y. P. L. February 25, 1942

NL 0431957 NN

Lobo de Barbosa Ferreira Teixeira Girão, Antonio, *visconde de Villarinho de São Romão,* 1785-1863.
Reflexões criticas, e artisticas sobre a edificação do novo theatro portuguez, denominado Theatro da gloria. Pelo visconde de Villarinho de S. Romão. [Lisboa, Typographia da Sociedad propagadora dos conhecimentos uteis, 1842]
7, 7, 8 p. 20cm.
Caption title.
In three pts. Pt. 2-3 have title: Reflexões criticas, e artisticas sobre a edificação do theatro portugues, hoje chamado, legalmente, Theatro de d. Maria II.

1. Lisbon. Theatro de d. Maria II. I. Title.

Library of Congress NA6840.L5M3 41-27482

NL 0431958 DLC

4SB 466 Lobo de Barbosa Ferreira Teixeira Girão, Antonio, visconde de Villarinho de São Romão, 1785-1863.
Tratado theorico e pratico da agricultura das vinhas, da extracção do mosto, bondade, e conservação dos vinhos, e da distillação das agoas ardentes. Lisboa, Na Imprensa Nacional, 1822.
239, lviii p.

NL 0431959 DLC-P4

Lobo de Barbosa Ferreira Teiaira Girao, Antonio, visconde de Villarinho de Sao Romao, 1785-1863.

Tratado theorico e pratico sobre a maneira de construir fogões de sala economicos e salubres. Lisboa, Typ. da mesma academia, [Academia real das sciencias], 1843.

NL 0431960 MH

Lobo de Barbosa Ferreira Teixeira Girão, Antonio, visconde de Villarinho de São Romão, 1785-1863.
... Viticultura e vinicultura, Traz os Montes — Alto Douro central, pelo visconde Villarinho de S. Romão ... Com 102 gravuras. Lisboa: Imprensa nacional, 1896. vi, 563 p. incl. tables. illus., plans (part col'd), plates. 34½cm.
At head of title: Ministerio das obras publicas, commercio e industria. Direcção geral de agricultura. Serviços ampelographicos.

124066B. 1. Viticulture—Portugal—Alto Douro. 2. Wine making—Portugal—Alto Douro. I. Portugal. Serviços ampelographicos.
N. Y. P. L. January 15, 1942

NL 0431961 NN

330(81) L799 Lobo de Barros, Nelson
O estado e a economia; plano industrial para o Brasil. [Rio, Editora Atlas] 1945
164 p.

Bibliography

1. Brazil - Econ. policy 2. Brazil - Indus.

NL 0431962 NNUN

Lobo de Barros, Nelson.
O estado e a economia plano industrial para o Brasil. Prefácio do Dr. Paulo Barra. [São Paulo] 1945. 164, [4] p. 22cm. (Monografias "Atlas" de economia. no.1)

Film reproduction. Master negative. Original discarded.
Positive in *ZT-46.
Bibliography, p. [165-168]

NL 0431963 NN

Lobo de Bulhões, Miguel Eduardo, 1830-1894.
Coelho, Eduardo, 1835-1889.
... O casamento do reino de Inglaterra com o reino de Portugal, por E. Coelho. Menina pobre, por M. Bulhões. Lisboa, Typographia universal de T. Q. Antunes, 1879.

[Lobo de Bulhões, Miguel Eduardo] 1830-1894.
Les colonies portugaises; court exposé de leur situation actuelle. Lisbonne, Imprimerie nationale, 1878.
4 p. l., 186 p., 1 l. 22½cm.
Preface signed: "L. de B."

1. Portugal—Colonies. I. Title.

Library of Congress JV4226.L8 9—34402

NL 0431965 DLC MH PSt CSt CtY-D NSyU CtY ViU NBuU

Lobo de Bulhões, Miguel Eduardo, 1830-1894.
336.39469 B933 A divida portugueza. Lisboa, Typo. portugueza, 1867.
112 p. 22cm.
With this is bound the author's: Les colonies portugaises. Lisbonne, 1878.

1. Debts, Public - Portugal. I. Title.

NL 0431966 CSt

336.469 B933 Lobo de Bulhões, Miguel Eduardo, 1830-1894.
A fazenda publica de Portugal; practicas vigentes e varias utopias do auctor. Lisboa, Impr. Nacional, 1884.
170 p. tables. 29cm.

1. Finance, Public Portugal.

NL 0431967 CSt MH

Lobo de Bulhões, Miguel Eduardo, 1830-1894.
... Historia e historias. Lisboa, Livraria Ferreira, 1878.
8 p. l., 329 p., 1 l. 19cm.
At head of title: Lobo de Bulhões.

1. Portugal—Soc. life & cust. 2. Portugal—Hist.—Addresses, essays, lectures. I. Title.

Library of Congress DP505.L6 38-9233
[2] 946.9004

NL 0431968 DLC

Lobo de Bulhões, Miguel Eduardo, 1830-1894.
Que sogra!! Comedia em tres actos. Imitação. Lisboa, Mattos Moreira & Ca., 1850.
75 p., 1 l. 16°.
In: NQM p.v. 96, no. 7.

NL 0431969 NN

861.5 L799p Lobo de Carvalho, Antonio
Poesias joviaes e satyricas. Colligidas e pela primeira vez impressas. Cadix, 1852.
xxiii, 231p. 16cm.

Bound with: Araujo, José Ignacio de. Poesias. Lisboa [Typ. de J. da Costa Nascimento Cruz] 1862.

NL 0431970 TNJ

Lobo de São Thiago, Sylvio
see São Thiago, Sylvio Lobo de.

4K 2696 Lobo Diaz, Leon
De la capacidad del fallido no rehabilitado. Santiago de Chile, 1927.
166 p.

NL 0431972 DLC-P4 MH-L

Lobo e Alpuim, Maria do Carmo Abreu Lima Noronha Texeira
see Lima Noronha Texeira Lobo e Alpuim, Maria do Carmo Abreu.

VOLUME 337

Lobo e Beça, Abilio Ayres Freitas
see Ayres Freitas Lobo e Beça, Abilio.

Lobo Guerrero, Bartolomé, abp., fl. 1622.

Lima (*Archdiocese*)
Constituciones sÿnodales del arçobispado de Los Reyes en el Perv. Hechas, y ordenadas por el illustrissimo, y reverendissimo ... arçobispo de la dicha Ciudad de los Reyes ... ¡Lima, Reimpression por J. J. Morel, 1754.

Lobo e Silva, Jaime d' Oliveira.
Anais de vila da Ericeira; Registo cronológico de acontecimentos referentes à mesma vila, desde 1229 até 1932. Coimbra, Imprensa da Universidade, 1933.
126 p. facsims

NL 0431976 MH ICN

Lobo Jiménez, Juan.
Album de las bellas.

NL 0431977 NNH

Lobo Lasso de la Vega, Gabriel, 1559-1619.
De Cortés valeroso y mexicana. pt. I.
Madrid, Pedro Madrigal, 1588.

NL 0431978 NNH

X40Z .L333 E Cutter Lobo Lasso de la Vega, Gabriel, 1559-1615
Elogios en loor de los tres famosos varones: don Iayme, rey de Aragon, don Fernando Cortes, marques del Valle, y don Aluaro de Baçan, marques de Santacruz. Cōpuestos por Gabriel Lasso dela Vega...Çaragoça, Alonso Rodriguez, 1601.
144 numb. l. illus. 15cm.
Contains bookplate of Jacob P.R. Lyell.
1. James I, king of Aragon 2. Cortés, Hernando, 1485-1547 3. Bazan, Alvard de, marquis de Santa Cruz, 1526-1588
I. Title

NL 0431979 WU RPJCB NNH NN

Lobo Lasso de la Vega, Gabriel, 1559-1615.
... Manojuelo de romances. Madrid, Editorial SAETA, 1942.
xiiii, 887 p. incl. pl., facsim. 14½cm. (*Half-title:* Colección literaria SAETA, dirigida por A. González Palencia. 6)
At head of title: Gabriel Lasso de la Vega.
"Prólogo" signed: Eugenio Mele ¡by¡ Angel González Palencia.
"Bibliografía": p. ¡xiii¡-xiiii.

I. Mele, Eugenio, 1875- ed. II. *González Palencia, Angel, 1889- joint ed. III. Title.

45-12285

Library of Congress PQ6411.L78A7

¡3¡ 861.39

NL 0431980 DLC CaBVaU PU MH CU WU UU ViU MoU MiU OU FU CLSU IU GU AU

Lobo Lasso de la Vega, Gabriel, 1559-1615.
Mexicana De Gabriel Lasso de la Vega, emendada y añadida por su mismo Autor. Dirigida A Don Fernando Cortes, tercero Marquis del Valle. ... Con Privilegio. En Madrid, por Luis Sanchez. Año. 1594. ...
8 p.l., 304 numb. l.

NL 0431981 RPJCB

863L33 Op1594f Lobo Lasso de la Vega, Gabriel.
Mexicana de Gabriel Lasso de la Vega, emendada y añadida por su mismo Autor. Dirigida a Don Ferdnando Cortes, tercero Marques del Valle. Lleva esta segvnda impression treze cantos mas que la primera ... En Madrid, 1594.
facsim.: 2pt.

Collation of original: 8p.l., 304 numb. l. incl. ports. Some leaves wrongly numbered.
Photographic reproduction of the copy in the John Carter Brown library.

NL 0431983 IU RPJCB

863L78 Op1936 Lobo Lasso de la Vega, Gabriel, 1559-1615.
Mexicana de Gabriel Lobo Lasso de la Vega, by Luis Avilés Pérez ... Urbana, Ill., 1936.
605(i.e.611) numb.l.

Thesis (Ph.D.)--University of Illinois, 1936.
Typewritten (carbon copy)
Vita.
Bibliographical foot-notes.

1936 Av5 ---- ---- Thesis copy.

I. Avilés Pérez, Luis, 1899- II. Title.

NL 0431984 IU RPJCB

863L33 Op1588r Lobo Lasso de la Vega, Gabriel
Primera parte De Cortés valeroso, y Mexicana, De Gabriel Lasso de la Vega... Madrid, 1588.
facsim: 208 l.

Collation of original: 8p.l., 193 numb.l., [7]l. incl 2 plates(ports.)
Photographic reproduction of copy in the Harvard college library.

NL 0431985 IU MH RPJCB ICN

Lobo Lasso de la Vega, Gabriel, 1559-1615.
Primera parte de Cortés valeroso, y Mexicana. Dirigida a don Fernando Cortés, nieto de don Fernando Cortés, marques del Valle, descubridor y conquistador del Nueuo Mundo. Madrid, P. Madrigal, 1588.
198 l. ports. 22 cm.
A poem.

1. Cortés, Hernando, 1485-1547—Poetry. I. Title.

PQ6411.L78A75 51-49498

NL 0431986 DLC ICN RPJCB NN MH NNH

FILM 863L78 Ot.1 Lobo Lasso de la Vega, Gabriel, 1559-1615.
The tragedies of Gabriel Lobo Lasso de la Vega (1587) Herbert Eugene Isar ¡editor¡ Ann Arbor, University Microfilms, 1955.

(¡University Microfilms, Ann Arbor, Mich.¡ Publication no.13,398)

Microfilm copy (positive) of typescript.
Collation of the original: lxxiii, 170l.
The editor's thesis--University of Pennsylvania.

Abstracted in Dissertation abstracts, v.15 (1955) no.10, p.1854.
Includes Tragedia llamada Honra de Dido restaurada and Tragedia de la destruycion de Constantinopla.
Bibliography: leaves i-viib.

I. Isar, Herbert Eugene, ed.

NL 0431988 IU

Lobo Leite Pereira, Francisco.
... Autoria da Geographia historica de capitania de Minas Geraes ... Rio de Janeiro, 1909.
10 p. 25.5 cm.
At head of title: Fernando Lobo Leite Pereira.
Signed: Francisco Lobo Leite Pereria.
"Parte do IX volume des Publicacões do Archivo publico nacional."

NL 0431989 CtY

Lobo Leite Pereira, Francisco.
Descobrimento e devassamento do territorio de Minas Geraes ... Bello Horizonte, Imprensa official do estado de Minas, 1902.
48 p., 1 l. 26.5 cm.

NL 0431990 CtY

Lobo Leite Pereira, Francisco.
Em busca das esmeraldas. Escassas noticias acerca da expedicão de Marcos de Azeredo em busca das esmeraldas, achando diamantes, e acerca de outras tentativas posteriormente feitas para aquelle fim até o anno de 1660. Traslados e excerptos de alguns escriptos em relação é empresa de Agostinho Barbalho Bezerra para descobrimento das esmeraldas, com algumas observações e annotações pelo

Dr. Francisco Lobo Leite Pereira. Ouro Preto, Imprenta official de Minas Geraes, 1897.
20 p. 27 cm.

NL 0431992 CtY

Lobo Leite Pereira (Joaquim). *A acção physiologica dos medicamentos será uma base segura para as indicações therapeuticas? 2 p. l., 124 pp. 4°. *Rio de Janeiro*, 1880.

NL 0431993 DNLM

Law Lobo Moraga, Sergio.

Guía sindical de Chile. 1951-
Santiago.

Lobo Neto, Roberto Jorge Haddock
see
Lobo, Roberto Jorge Haddock, 1902-

Lobo-Onell, C., joint author.

Chabanier, Henry Eugène Louis, 1891-
Diabète et chirurgie, par H. Chabanier et C. Lobo-Onell, avec la collaboration de m^lle E. Lélu. Préface du d^r M. Robineau. Paris, Masson et c^ie, 1936.

Lobo-Onell, C., joint author.

RC903 .C5 Chabanier, Henry Eugène Louis, 1891-
... Exploration fonctionnelle des reins, par H. Chabanier et C. Lobo-Onell, avec la collaboration de M. Lebert et E. Lélu. Préface du professeur Legueu. Paris, Masson et c^ie, 1930.

VOLUME 337

Lobo-Onell, C., joint author.

Chabanier, Henry Eugène Louis, 1891-
Les œdèmes, par H. Chabanier et C. Lobo-Onell ... Paris, Doin, 1946.

RC909 .C5
Lobo-Onell, C., joint author.

Chabanier, Henry Eugène Louis, 1891-
Physiopathologie et traitement du diabète sucré, par H. Chabanier, M. Lebert et C. Lobo-Onell; préface du professeur Legueu. Paris, Masson et c^ie^, 1929.

RC909 .C52
Lobo-Onell, C., joint author.

Chabanier, Henry Eugène Louis, 1891-
... Précis du diabète, par H. Chabanier et C. Lobo-Onell. Paris, Masson et c^ie^, 1931.

RC915 .C5
Lobo-Onell, C., joint author.

Chabanier, Henry Eugène Louis, 1891-
L'urémie, par H. Chabanier et C. Lobo-Onell; préface du professeur Jean Tapie. Paris, G. Doin & c^ie^., 1943.

Lobo Prabhu, J M
see
Prabhu, J M Lobo, 1906-

Lobo Ramalho, Robelia Sousa
see
Sousa Lobo Ramalho, Robelia.

Lobo Regidor, Manuel
see Lobo y Regidor, Manuel.

Lobo Regidor, Ramon
see Lobo y Regidor, Ramon.

Lobo Soropita, Fernao Rodrigues
see Rodrigues Lobo Soropita, Fernao, b. 1560.

869.2 L799e
[Lobo Sousa, A M de]
O emparedado; drama. [Porto, Typ. de Faria Guimarães, 1841]
x,64p. 22cm. (His Obras dramaticas)

NL 0432012 IEN

989.205 E74r%
Lobo Viana, Jose Feliciano.
A epopéa da Laguna. Rio de Janeiro, Imprensa Militar, estado-Maior do exercito, 1920.
1 v. (various paging)

1. Paraguayan war, 1865-1870. 2. Escragnolle Taunay, Alfredo de, 1843-1899. A retirada da Laguna. I. Title.

NL 0432013 ICarbS

989.205 O83Bℓ
Lobo Viana, Jose Feliciano.
Tuiutí é Osorio, Osorio é Tuiutí. Conferencia pronunciada no Circulo dos oficiais reformados do exército e da armada, na tarde de 24 de maio de 1939, em comemoração ao 37 aniversário da Batalha de Tuiuti. Rio de Janeiro, Oficinas Graficas Laemmert, 1940.
64p. map. (Biblioteca Militar)

1. Paraguayan War, 1865-1870. 2. Osorio, Manuel Luis, 1808-1879. 3. Tuiutí, Battle of, 1866. 4. Brazil--History, Military. I. Title.

NL 0432014 ICarbS

Lôbo Vilela, Antonio.
... Ao serviço da democracia, por A. Lôbo Vilela. Lisboa [Impresso na "Gráfica lisbonense", 1945.
113 p. 19^cm^. (Cadernos da "Seara nova." Estudos politicos e sociais)

1. Portugal—Pol. & govt.—1933- I. Title.

DP680.L6 946.9 47-18575

NL 0432015 DLC MH

Lôbo Vilela, António.
Ciência e poesia. [Lisboa] Portugália editora, 1955
125 p. 20 cm.

NL 0432016 MH NN

Lôbo Vilela, Antonio.
Linha geral (artigos políticos) Pref. de Câmara Reys. Lisboa [Seara Nova] 1946.
148 p. 19 cm. (Cadernos da "Seara Nova." Estudos políticos e sociais)

1. Social sciences--Addresses, essays, lectures. I. Title.

H33.L6 304 48-17508*

NL 0432017 DLC MH

Lôbo Vilela, Antonio.
Questões pedagógicas, reforma de ensino. Lisboa [Gráfica lisbonense] 1946.
103 p. 20 cm. (Cadernos da "Seara Nova", Secção de estudos pedagógicos)

NL 0432018 MH

Lobo Vilela, Antonio.
Sôbre o ensino das matemáticas elementares; conferência realizada no Liceu normal de Coimbra, a convite do Exme. Reitor, em 16 de maio de 1933. Coimbra, [Tip. Popular] 1933.
89 p. (Cadernos Presenca 4)

NL 0432019 MH

Lobo y de las Alas, Victor.
Stewart, Balfour, 1828-1887.
... Nociones de física, por el profesor Balfour Stewart ... Nueva ed. castellana, completamente reformada por el profesor d. Victor L. y de Las Alas ... Nueva York, D. Appleton y cía., 1901.

Lobo y Malagamba, Miguel
see Lobo, Miguel, 1821-1876.

M1503 .S227Q4
Lobo y Regidor, Manuel.
Santa Mariá, Antonio, 1861- FOR OTHER EDITIONS SEE MAIN ENTRY
... Quedar en seco, zarzuela en un acto. Letra de los sres. Lobo y Regidor, música del maestro A. Santamaría ... Madrid, P. Martín [189-]

LOBO Y REGIDOR, Ramón.
La apariencia; comedia en un acto. Madrid, R.Velasco, 1911.

On cover:-Sociedad de autores espanoles.

NL 0432023 MH

Lobo y Regidor, Ramon,
La buena moza
see under Foglietti Alberola, Luis, 1877-1918. [supplement]

He77 26 36
Lobo y Regidor, Ramón
De conquista; opereta en un acto, en prosa, original de Ramon y Manuel Lobo Regidor, música del maestro Ruisanz ... Madrid, R.Velasco, impr., 1896.
32p., 1ℓ. 20cm. [Binder's title: Teatro español, 36]
Without music.
"Estrenada ... en el teatro Eslava la noche del 23 de diciembre de 1895."
"Obras de los mismos autores": 1ℓ. at end.

NL 0432025 CtY MH

Lobo y Regidor, Ramón.
De conquista, opereta en un acto, en prosa, original de Ramón y Manuel Lobo Regidor, música del maestro Ruisanz. Madrid, R. Velasco, 1896.
32p.

Microcard edition.

NL 0432026 ICRL MoU LU

Lobo y Regidor, Ramón.
El estudiante Segovia
see under Jacopetti, composer, [supplement]

Lobo y Regidor, Ramón.
Generos del reino
see under San Felipe, composer.

Lobo y Regidor, Ramón.
El ramadán
see under Soriano, composer.

PQ6218 .S6 v.29
Lobo Regidor, Ramón
La receta de mamá; comedia en un acto y en verso, original de Ramón Lobo y José García-Plaza Madrid, P. Velasco, Impresor, 1896.
37p. 20cm.

On cover: Administración lírico-dramática.
Vol. 29 no. 14 in a collection with binder's title: Spanish plays; Comedias y dramas, v. 2.
i. García Plaza, José joint author. ii. Title.

NL 0432030 FMU NN CtY MH

Lobo Regidor, Ramón.
La receta de mamá, comedia en un acto y en verso, original de Ramón Lobo y José García-Plaza. Madrid, R. Velasco, 1896.
37p.

Microcard edition.

NL 0432031 ICRL LU OrU FU

VOLUME 337

Lobo Regidor, Ramón.
Sin titulo; juguete cómico en un acto y en prosa, original. Madrid: R. Velasco, 1909. 32 p. 12°.
In: NPL p. v. 359, no. 3.

1. Drama (Spanish). 2. Title.
N. Y. P. L. April 25, 1912.

NL 0432032 NN MH

Lobo y Regidor Ramón.
Un viaje redondo
see under Haynd, composer.
[supplement]

T976.411
L786l
The Lobo Land and Irrigation Company, Incorporated.
... Investigate us and our property at Lobo, Texas. [Crockett, Tex., 1910?]
[29]p. 18cm.
At head of title: The Lobo land & irrigation company, incorporated.
Cover title: Our responsibility.
Consists entirely of letters of testimonial regarding the members of the company.

1. Lobo, Tex.

NL 0432034 TxU

El lobo marino; drama. Traducido del francés por Isidoro Gil. Madrid, imprenta de Yenes, 1844.

(Sociedad de escritores dramáticos.)

NL 0432035 MH

Loboda, Andrii Mytrofanovych, 1871-1931, ed.
Vseukraïns'ka akademiia nauk, Kief. Etnografichna komisiia.
... Етнографічний вісник. Кн. 1- У Київі, з друкарні Всеукраїнської академії наук, 1925-

---

Loboda, Andrii Mytrofanovych, 1871-1931.
Русскій богатырскій эпосъ; опытъ критико-библіографическаго обзора трудовъ по русскому богатырскому эпосу. Кіевъ, Тип. Имп. Университета св. Владиміра (В. І. Завадзкаго) 1896.
236 p. 26 cm.
At head of title: А. М. Лобода.
Bibliographical references included in "Опытъ библіографическаго указателя" (p. 220-232)

1. Byliny—Hist. & crit. I. Title.
Title transliterated: Russkiĭ bogatyrskiĭ ėpos.

PG3104.L6 66-51128

NL 0432037 DLC

Loboda, Ivan.
They came again
see his Vony pryĭshly znovu.

Loboda, Ivan.
Вони прийшли знову; роман з фінляндсько-большевицької війни. Вінніпег, 1953.
132 p. port. 18 cm. (Клюб приятелів української книжки, кн. 16)
Added t. p.: They came again.

1. Russo-Finnish War, 1939-1940—Fiction. I. Title.
Title romanized: Vony pryĭshly znovu.

PG3979.L6V6 72-211630

NL 0432039 DLC CaBVaU NN

Loboda, Stefaniia Matveevna (Pashkovskaia) 1827-1887
see
Krapivina, S., pseud.

Loboda, Viktor Fedorovich.
Ордена и медали СССР; справочник. Москва, Воен. изд-во, 1950.
238 p. 23 cm.
At head of title: В. Ф. Лобода и И. П. Каргальцев.
Includes legislation of USSR.

1. Decorations of honor—Law and legislation—Russia. I. Kargal'tsev, I. P., joint author. II. Russia (1923- U. S. S. R.) Laws, statutes, etc. III. Title.
Title romanized: Ordena i medali SSSR.

51-29970

NL 0432041 DLC

G3476
.75S4
Lobodin, Mikhail Pavlovich.
Gruslanov, V
Серебряные трубы; рассказы. Москва, Воен. изд-во, 1955.

LOBODOWSKI, JÓZEF.
Komysze; powieść. Londyn, Gryf publications, 1955.
333 p. 22cm.

The first part of a trilogy of which "W stanicy" and "Droga powrotna" form the second and third parts respectively.

1. Russia--Hist., 1917- --Fiction. I. Title.

KU
NL 0432043 NN MH OU CU OCl CaBVaU CSt CtY NNC NjP

Łobodowski, Józef
Modlitwa na wojnę. Londyn, Wydawnictwo Światowego Związku Polaków z Zagranicy, 1947

Poems.

NL 0432044 NNC CU KU MiD MH CaBVaU

DK441
L799
Łobodowski, Józef
Por nuestra libertad y la vuestra; Polonia sigue luchando. Madrid, Editora Mundial [1945]
287 p. maps. 21cm.

1. Poland - Hist. - German occupation, 1939-1945. 2. World War, 1939-1945 - Poland. 3. World War, 1939-1945 - Territorial questions - Poland. I. Title.

NL 0432045 CSt-H

Łobodowski, Józef
Rozmowa z ojczyzną. [Wyd. 2. uzupełnione i poprawione] Warszawa, F. Hoesick, 1936.

NL 0432046 WaU

891.85
L799u
Łobodowski, Józef
Uczta zadżumionych. Paryż, Nakł. Subskrybentów i Autora, 1954.
179p. illus. 23cm.

Includes bibliography.

NL 0432047 IEN MU MiD CU NN CaBVaU

891.858
L786d
Łobodowski, Józef.
Z dymem pożarów. [Niceja] U Tyszkiewicza, 1941.
111 p. 19cm.

Poems.

NL 0432048 MiDW

Łobodowski, Józef.
Złota hramota. Drzeworyty: Jurij Kulcsyćkyj. Paryż, Instytut Literacki, 1954.
189 p. 22 cm. (Biblioteka "Kultury," t. 8)
Poems.

I. Title. (Series)

A 55-3197

Virginia. Univ. Libr. for Library of Congress

OCl MiU PP IU N NNC NcU
NL 0432049 ViU CU CtY MH NN PP C CSt MB IEN OU

Loboff, Peter.
The Volga-Don canal and the Donetz basin, by Peter Loboff ... [n. p., 19—?] 12 f. charts. 28cm.

1. Coal—Trade and stat.—Russia —Donetz valley. 2. Canals—Russia—Volga-Don.
N. Y. P. L. July 5, 1945

NL 0432050 NN

[Loboĭko, Ivan Nikolaevich] 1786-1861.
О важнѣйшихъ изданіяхъ Герберштейна Записокъ о Россіи, съ критическимъ обозрѣніемъ ихъ содержанія. Съ приложеніемъ портрета Герберштейна, рисунка и карты Россіи. Иждивеніемъ Вольнаго общества любителей россійской словесности. С. Петербургъ, въ Тип. К. Крайя, 1818.
3 p. l., 39 p. front. (port.) col. pl., fold. map. 20 cm.
Preface signed: Иванъ Лобойко.
"Извлеченіе изъ книги: Siegmund, freiherr v. Herberstein, mit besonderer rücksicht auf seine reisen in Russland, geschildert v. F. Adelung. St. Petersburg, 1818."

1. Herberstein, Sigmund, freiherr von, 1486-1566. Rerum moscoviticarum commentarii. I. Adelung, Friedrich von, 1768-1843. II. Title.
Title transliterated: O vazhnieĭshikh izdaniiakh Gerbershteĭna Zapisok o Rossii.

DK21.H54L6 18-11500 rev

NL 0432052 DLC

Lobón de Salazar, Don Francisco, pseud.
see Isla, José Francisco de, 1703-1781.

Lobos, Eleodoro, 1862-
... Al doctor Eleodoro Lobos
see under Buenos Aires. Universidad nacional. Facultad de ciencias económicas.

HD
472
.L79
Lobos, Eleodoro, 1862-
Apuntes sobre legislación de tierras, por E. Lobos. Buenos Aires, Imprenta y casa editora de Coni hermanos, 1900.
308 p. 18½cm.

1. Land tenure--Argentine Republic--Law. I. Title. II. Title: Legislación de tierras.

NL 0432055 MiU

Lobos, Eleodoro, 1862-
Informes presentados á la delegación argentina sobre marcas de fábrica ...
see under Inter-American High Commission

Lobos, Eleodoro, 1862-
... Límites interprovinciales. Reivindicación. Córdoba y San Luis ante la Corte Suprema de la nación. Buenos Aires, J. Peuser, 1906.
86 p. 25½cm.

At head of title: Estudio de los Doctores Lobos y Mayer.

NL 0432057 MH-L

VOLUME 337

Lobos, Eleodoro, 1862–
... La obra económica y financiera del doctor Eleodoro Lobos ... Buenos Aires, Impr. de la Universidad, 1925.
2 p. l., xi, 704 (i. e. 702) p. incl. tables. 24½cm. (Biblioteca de ciencias económicas)
Page 702 incorrectly numbered 704.
1. Land tenure. 2. Land tenure—Argentine Republic—Law. 3. Finance—Argentine Republic. 4. Argentine Republic—Econ. condit.—1918–
Library of Congress HD473.L6 27-12132
NL 0432058 DLC NcU DCU-IA TxU

Argentina NJb58 S61 917ℓ
Lobos, Eleodoro, 1862-
Organización del crédito y los proyectos financieros; conferencia pronunciada por el Dr. Eleodoro Lobos, el 18 de julio de 1917 en el Instituto popular de conferencias. Buenos Aires,Talleres heliográficos de R. Radaelli,1917.
77p. 18cm.
NL 0432059 CtY MH-BA

Lobos, Fabian.
Juicios criticos sobre los principales métodos caligráficos... Santiago de Chile, Esmeralda, 1904.
18 p. 24cm.
NL 0432060 DGW-C DPU

Lobos, Fabian.
Teoría i práctica de la letra derecha, ed. 1911.
NL 0432061 DPU

Lobos, Fabian.
... Teoría i práctica de la letra derecha ... Valparaiso, Scherrer y Herrmann, 1912.
87 p. 25cm.
At head of title: Lecciones de caligrafía.
NL 0432062 DGW-C

Lobos, Fabian.
... Teoría i práctica de la letra inglesa ... Valparaiso, Scherrer y Herrmann, 1912.
76 p. 25cm.
At head of title: Lecciones de caligrafía.
NL 0432063 DGW-C

Lobos, Fabian.
... Teoría i práctica de la letra redonda francesa ... Valparaiso, Scherrer y Herrmann, 1912.
47 p. 25cm.
At head of title: Lecciones de caligrafía.
NL 0432064 DGW-C

Lobos, Heitor Villa-
see Villa-Lobos, Hector.

Lobos, Jorge Luque
see Luque Lobos, Jorge.

Lobos, Marcelo L.

Mayer, Carlos Marcelo, 1879–
... Impuesto a los réditos; recopilación de leyes, decretos, resoluciones y jurisprudencia. Buenos Aires ₍Librería y editorial "El Ateneo"₎ 1939.

Lobos, R. Villa-
see Villa-Lobos, Raul, 1862-1899.

Lobos, Roberto Alarcón
see
Alarcón Lobos, Roberto.

W 4 C532 1945
LOBOS BRIONES, Mario.
Formolgelificación del suero bovino, su importancia en la obtención de un substituto del plasma humano. ₍Santiago de Chile₎ 1945.
18 p. illus.
Tesis - Univ. de Chile.
1. Blood substitutes 2. Serum Title
NL 0432070 DNLM

G868.8 L7875s
Lobos Flores, Heraclio.
Superando la valla del error. [Santiago, 19--]
64p. 18cm.
Cover title.
NL 0432071 TxU

Lobos Hernández, Hugo Américo.
Algunas observaciones sobre la protección de la familia en el derecho guatemalteco. Guatemala, 1953.
58 p. 23 cm.
Tesis (licenciatura en ciencias jurídicas y sociales)—Universidad de San Carlos de Guatemala.
1. Domestic relations—Guatemala.
57-32830 ‡
NL 0432072 DLC

Lobos Porto,
... Azorín, el hombre y la obra. Córdoba, República argentina, 1939.
57 p., 2 l. 18½cm.
"Bibliografía consultada": p. 55-57.
1. Martínez Ruiz, José, 1873–
Library of Congress PQ6623.A816Z67 41-27012 Provisional
NL 0432073 DLC NBuU PPiU ViU

Lobos Porto,
... José de San Martín, figura de epopeya. Córdoba, República argentina. ₍Talleres gráficos del Colegio Pío x de Córdoba₎ 1942.
2 p. l., 7-16 p. 18cm.
1. San Martín, José de, 1778-1850.
New York. Public library for Library of Congress ₍2₎ A 44-1153 Provisional
NL 0432074 NN

Lobos Porto,
... Piedra y nube (poemas de Sañogasta) Córdoba ₍República argentina₎ 1938.
92 p., 2 l. 19cm. (Colección "Elea")
I. Title.
Library of Congress PQ7797.L548P5 45-41513
₍2₎ 861.6
NL 0432075 DLC

LOBOSCO, Angela.
Rojo y azul; versos. Buenos Aires, 1921.
NL 0432076 MH

GB2401 U56 no.23
Lobotskiĭ, I͡U B
Blasting operations. (Vzryvnye raboty) Translated by Jaroslav Jan Peel. Wilmette, Ill., [1953]
3 p. diagrs. 27 cm. (U.S. Army. Corps of Engineers. Snow, Ice and Permafrost Research Establishment. Translation 23)
Title-page on verso of cover.
1. Blasting. I. Peel, Jaroslav Jan, tr. (Series)
NL 0432077 DI DAS

Lobov, Nikolaĭ Fedorovich.
Опыт передовых поливальщиков. Ростов-на-Дону, Ростовское книжное изд-во, 1953.
27 p. illus. 21 cm. (Библиотека колхозника)
1. Irrigation farming. I. Title.
Title transliterated: Opyt peredovykh polival'shchikov.
SB112.L6 58-36116 ‡
NL 0432078 DLC

G7010 .J3 1947 .A3
Lobova, Elena Vsevolodevna.
Akademii͡a nauk SSSR. *Pochvennyĭ institut imeni V. V. Dokuchaeva.*
Почвенная карта Европейской части СССР. ₍Составлена Е. В. Лобовой и Н. Н. Розовым при участии Н. Н. Лебедева. Под общей ред. Л. И. Прасолова. ₍Москва?₎ Изд-во Академии наук СССР, 1947.

Lobovikov, V V
Сборник задач по планированию хозяйственной деятельности торга; учебное пособие для техникумов системы Министерства торговли СССР. Москва, Гос. изд-во торговой лит-ры, 1955.
137 p. 23 cm.
1. Russia—Comm. I. Title.
Title transliterated: Sbornik zadach po planirovanii͡u khozi͡aĭstvennoĭ dei͡atel'nosti torga.
HF3626.L58 57-21090
NL 0432080 DLC

Lobpreis, Anton.
... De fracturis extremitatum inferiorum praemissa diagnosis et therapiae brevi expositione cum tabulis litho impressis ... submittit Antonius Lobpreis ... Vindobonae, Ex typographia F. Ullrich ₍1832₎
vi, 95, ₍3₎ p. fold. plates. 21cm.
Inaug. Diss.—Vienna.
Text in German.
NL 0432081 ICJ DNLM

JV4026 .C5
Lobra y Cadrana, Rafael Maria de, 1841-1918.
Cepeda, Francisco.
... Conferencias de Abuli celebradas con el jefe de la minoria autonomista parlamentaria, don Rafael M. de Lobra sobre politica antillana, sus relaciones con la política peninsular y procedimientos que deben seguirse en interés de la reforma colonial, por Francisco Cepeda. Ponce, Tip. de la "Revista de Puerto-Rico," 1890.

VOLUME 337

Lobrani (V.) Études sur le fonctionnement du service des aliénés du département de la Seine, et projet de réformes à introduire dans l'organisation de ce service. 93 pp. 8°. *Paris, Seringe frères & Noailles*, 1882.

NL 0432083 DNLM

Lobrano, Gustav Stubbs, joint author.

Flick, Alexander Clarence, 1869–
Samuel Jones Tilden; a study in political sagacity, by Alexander Clarence Flick, assisted by Gustav S. Lobrano ... New York, Dodd, Mead & company, 1939.

Lobre, Marthe Francillon-
see Francillon-Lobre, Marthe.

Lobred vnd Gratulation der glücklichen Ankunfft der ... Herrn Maximiliani Hertzog in Obern vnd Nidern Bayrn, &c.
see under [Keller, Jakob] 1568-1631.

DD404 .L8 Lobrede auf Friedrich den Grossen, König von Preussen. Berlin, 1786.
24 p.

1. Friedrich II, der Grosse, King of Prussia, 1712-1786.

NL 0432087 ICU

Lobrede auf J.J. Rousseau über dessen weltbürgerlichen Einfluss und den Charakter seiner Schriften
see under [Escherny, François Louis, comte d'] 1733-1815.

Lobrichon, Pierre, 1911-
... Contribution à l'étude des variations de la voûte plantaire au cours du cycle menstruel et de leur rapport avec le système endocrinien ... Paris, 1937.
Thèse - Univ. de Paris.
"Bibliographie": p. [98]-99.

NL 0432089 CtY

Lobrin, Artemio M
Notes on the law on taxation in the Philippines. Manila, Philaw Pub. Co., 1950.
687 p. 26 cm.

1. Taxation—Philippine Islands—Law.

56-15624 ‡

NL 0432090 DLC MH-L

845L78 O.f Lobry, A J A
... Une famille au dix-neuvième siècle, 1870-1900. Notes pour servir à l'étude de la bourgeoisie. Paris [etc.] Berger-Levrault, 1918.
182p.

NL 0432091 IU

Lobry, A J A 321.91 S100
... Notes pour servir à l'étude de la bourgeoisie. **Les provinciaux.** Paris, Berger-Levrault, 1921.
[8], 257 p. 19cm.
At head of title: A.-J.-A. Lobry.
Half-title: Les provinciaux.

NL 0432092 ICJ

Lobry (Bélisaire-Socrate). * Sur l'influence des boissons alcoholiques, considérée comme cause de maladies. 22 pp. 4°. *Paris*, 1821, No. 31, v. 163.

NL 0432093 DNLM

Lobry, Frédéric.
Airs du Mariage de Figaro
see under Mozart, Johann Chrysostom Wolfgang Amadeus, 1756-1791.

LOBRY, FRÉDÉRIC.
[VARIATIONS, AU CLAIR DE LA LUNE]
Variations pour le piano-forte sur l'air: Au clair de la lune, par Frédéric Lobry. Paris, Janet et Cotelle [1822] Pl.no.991. 9 p. 33cm.

1. Piano.

NL 0432095 NN

Lobry, Louis.
... De la fréquence des hémoptysies tuberculeuses chez les aortiques ... Paris, 1921.
31 p. 23.5 cm.
Thèse - Univ. de Paris.

NL 0432096 CtY DNLM

Lobry (Louis-Hippolyte-Alziere) [1877–].
*Sur l'électrolyse de quelques acides minéraux. 42 pp. 8°. Lille, 1911. No. 25.

NL 0432097 DNLM

Lobry de Bruyn, De la nécessité d'enseigner l'hygiène aux jeunes gens. Mémoire dédié aux membres du Congrès d'hygiène et de sauvetage à Bruxelles, septembre 1876. 31 pp. 8°. *Leide, De Breuk & Smits*, 1876.

NL 0432098 DNLM

Lobry van Troostenburg de Bruyn, Cornelis Adriaan
see
Bruyn, Cornelis Adriaan Lobry van Troostenburg de, 1889–

Lobsan mingyur
see Blo-bsaṅ min -'gyur rdo-rje, lama.

Lobscheid, E
Ueber die Bestimmung der magnetischen Inclination von Marburg. Marburg, 188o.

NL 0432101 NjP

Lobscheid, William.
... A Chinese and English dictionary, by the Revd. W. Lobscheid ... Hongkong, Noronha & sons; [etc., etc.] 1871.
ix, 592 p. 26½cm.
Added title in Chinese.

1. Chinese language—Dictionaries—English. 2. English language—Dictionaries—Chinese.

Library of Congress PL1455.L7 1-3477

MSaE HU
NL 0432102 DLC NIC OU MdBP PPAmP NIC NN ICJ MnHi

MR2 L79 Lobscheid, William
The Chinese and English guide through China and Eastern Asia. Hongkong, printed at Noronha's office, 1864.
102p. 21.5cm.
Cover-title reads: Topography of China and neighbouring states; with degrees of longitude and latitude.
Reprinted from the Chinese repository.

NL 0432103 NNUT

5988.07 7019 Lobscheid, William.
Chinese-English grammar, by William Lobscheid. Hongkong, Printed at Noronha's Office, 1864.
2v. 22cm.

E.A.L. copy incomplete: v.2 wanting.
Title also in Chinese.
"The English is Cornwell's Grammar for Beginners with little alterations; the Chinese is Canton Colloquial."

1. English language--Grammar. 2. English language--Text-books for foreigners--Chinese. I. Titl.

NL 0432104 CU-E

Lobscheid, William.
The Chinese: what they are, and what they are doing. By the Rev. W. Lobscheid ... San Francisco, A. L. Bancroft & co., printers, 1873.
21 p. 22cm.

1. China—Soc. life & cust. 2. National characteristics, Chinese.

43-21229

Library of Congress DS721.L7

NL 0432105 DLC NIC CtY NN

Lobscheid, William.

... **Commercial** press English and Chinese pronouncing dictionary. Comprising 100,000 words and phrases, with translations, pronunciations, etymologies, definitions, illustrations, etc., etc., also a copious appendix. 3d ed. Shanghai, Printed at the Commercial press, 1903.

Lobscheid, William.
... English and Chinese dictionary, with the Punti and Mandarin pronunciation. By the Rev. W. Lobscheid ... Hongkong, the Daily press, 1866-69.
4 pts. in 2 v. 33 1/2cm.
Paged continuously.
CONTENTS.—[v. 1] A-H.—[v. 2] I-Z.

NL 0432107 MB CU NIC CtY OCl MH ICN MdBP MSaE

5196.9 7019.5 Lobscheid, Wilhelm.
An English and Chinese dictionary... as revised and enlarged by Tetsujiro Inouye. Tokyo, J. Fujimoto, 16th year of Meiji [1883]
1357 p.

Added t.p. in Japanese.

NL 0432108 CU-B PP

VOLUME 337

PL 1455 L6 Lobscheid, William
An English and Chinese dictionary, by the Rev. W. Lobscheid. Rev. and enl. by Tetsuziro Inouye. Tokio, Zen-Rin Yaku-Sho Kwan, 1900.
1357 p.
Added title page in Chinese.

1. English language - Dictionaries - Chinese.

NL 0432109 NBuU

Lobscheid, William, comp.
An English and Chinese dictionary, by W.Lobscheid as rev. and enl. by Tetsuziro Inouye. 2d ed. (6),1357 p.facsim. Tokio,Z.Huzimoto,32nd year of Meiji [i.e.1900].

Preface and added title-page in Chinese.
First edition, 1866-68.

NL 0432110 OCl

Wason PL1455 L79E5+ 1903 Lobscheid, William.
An English and Chinese dictionary. Rev. and enl. by Tetsuziro Inouye. Shanghai, Cho Sing, 1903.
1357 p. 25 cm.

Added t. p.: 增訂英華字典

1. English language--Dictionaries--Chinese. I. Inoue, Tetsuzirō, 1856-1944. II. Title.

NL 0432111 NIC NBuU CU

Lobscheid, William. *3033-34
[English-Chinese dictionary.]
— [Tokyo. Seishido. 186–?] (2), 1357, (1) pp. 26½ cm., in 8s.
Includes an appendix containing Trimetrical classic, Proverbs, etc.

K5117 — English language. Dict. Ch...se. — China. Lang. Dict. English. — Proverbs. Chinese.

NL 0432112 MB

Lobscheid, William
Evidence of the affinity of the Polynesians and American Indians with the Chinese and other nations of Asia, derived from the language, legends & history of those races. (6),64 p. Hongkong, Printed by De Souza & co.1872.

Binder's title: Affinity of the Polynesians.
"Table of the most important events of China and the new world from the first appearance of the Tolteks to the fall of Mexico and Peru", p.[63]-64.

NL 0432113 ICN OCl

Lobscheid, William.
The evils of Hongkong and their cure. By the Rev. W. Lobscheid. Hongkong, Printed by De Souza & co. [1871]
2 p. l., 12 p. 18cm.

1. Crime and criminals—Hongkong. 2. Hongkong—Soc. condit. I. Title.

Library of Congress HV7090.H6L6 44-34967

NL 0432114 DLC

Lobscheid, William.
A few notices on the extent of Chinese education, and the government schools of Hongkong; with remarks on the history and religious notions of the inhabitants of this island. By the Rev. W. Lobscheid... Hongkong, "China Mail" off., 1859. 48 p. 21cm.

1. Education—China—Hongkong.
N. Y. P. L. March 10, 1948

NL 0432115 NN CtY MSaE

Lobscheid, William.
Grammar of the Chinese language.
2 v. Hongkong, 1864.

NL 0432116 ODW

Lobscheid, William.
Grammar of the Chinese language. 2 pt.in 1 v. Hongkong,Printed at the office of the "Daily Press," 1904.

NL 0432117 OCl PU

Lobscheid, William.
Hülfsbuch zum richtigen verständniss der apostolischen kirchenlehre, von W. Lobscheid ... San Francisco, Gedruckt in der druckerei des "California democrat", 1873.
cover-title, iii, [1], 25 p. 23cm.

1. Lutheran church—Catechisms and creeds—German. I. Title.

Library of Congress BX8070.L37 36-33257

NL 0432118 DLC

Lobscheid, William, tr.
The political, social and religious constitution of the natives on the west coast of Formosa...
see under [Commelin, I.]

Lobscheid, William.
Eine politische Rundschau, mit besonderer Beziehung auf die chinesische Gesandtschaft. Berlin, Stilke & Van Muyden, 1870.
8 p. 23 cm.

1. World politics—Addresses, essays, lectures. I. Title.

D393.L6 50-44834

NL 0432120 DLC

Nk172 I61 866l Lobscheid, William, comp & tr.
The religion of the Dayaks; collected and translated into English, by the Rev. W.Lobscheid. And The political, social and religious constitution of the natives on the west coast of Formosa, before and during the occupation of the island by the Dutch ... Tr. from an old Dutch work, by the Rev. W.Lobscheid. 3d ed. Hongkong, Printed by J.de Souza,1866.
2p.l.,12p.,2l.,14p. 21½cm.
"The political, social and religious constitution ... " tr. from pt. 20 of I.Commelin's Begin ende voortgangh van de Vereenighede Nederlandsche geoctroyeerde Oost-Indische compagnie. Cf. British museum catalogue.

NL 0432122 CtY OCl

Lobscheid, William, ed.
Select phrases in the Canton dialect
see under Kerr, John Glasgow, 1824-1901.

Lobsenz, Amelia.
Kay Everett calls CQ. New York, Vanguard Press [1951]
213 p. illus. 22 cm.
Bibliography: p. 212-213.

I. Title.

PZ7.L783Kay 51-10459

NL 0432124 DLC

Lobsenz, Amelia.
Kay Everett works DX. New York, Vanguard Press [1952]
176 p. 22 cm.

I. Title.

PZ7.L783Kc 52-11129 ‡

NL 0432125 DLC WaSp Or IU

Lobsenz, Johanna.
The older woman in industry, by Johanna Lobsenz. New York, C. Scribner's sons, 1929.
xvi, 281 p. incl. tables, diagrs. 19½cm.
"Publications consulted": p. 272.

1. Woman—Employment. I. Title.

Library of Congress HD6053.L6 29-7387

MiU OCl NcD OOxM NN MB ICJ WaS
NL 0432126 DLC DL NBuU CU PU-Penn PP PBm Or OU OO

Lobsenz, Norman M 1919–
The minister's complete guide to successful retirement. Great Neck, N. Y., Channel Press [1955]
192 p. illus. 21 cm.

1. Clergy—Retirement. I. Title.

BV4382.L6 *253.2 56-56 rev ‡

NL 0432127 DLC PP PCC WaTC PPEB NcD

Lobsien, Marius
... Untersuchungen über die methode der effiktiven wellenlängen, von Marius Lobsien. Bergedorf, 1936.
cover-title, p. (201)-212. tables, diagr. 29 cm. (Astronomische abhandlungen der Hamburger sternwarte in Bergedorf... bd. IV, nr. 8)
"Als dissertation von der Mathematisch-naturwissenschaftlichen facultät der Hanseischen universität zu Hamburg genehmigt. (A.N. 6203)".

NL 0432128 DN-Ob

Lobsien, Marx.
Das censieren. Kritische anmerkungen, von Marx Lobsien ... Langensalza, H. Beyer & söhne, 1898.
19, [1] p. 21½cm. (Pädagogisches magazin, hft. 106)

1. School discipline. 2. Marking. I. Title.
E 12-1066

Library, U. S. Bur. of Education LB3014.L7

NL 0432129 DHEW

Lobsien, Marx.
Einfluss des Antikenotoxin auf die geistige Leistungsfähigkeit der Schüler. (In: Internat. Congress on School Hygiene, 4. Buffalo, 1913. Transac. Buffalo, 1914. 8°. v. 3, p. 356-363.)

1. Fatigue (Mental).
N. Y. P. L. July 2, 1917.

NL 0432130 NN

Lobsien, Marx.
Die experimentelle ermüdungsforschung. Von Marx Lobsien ... Langensalza, H. Beyer & söhne, 1914.
viii, 160 p. incl. diagrs. plates. 24½cm. (*Added t.-p.:* Beiträge zur kinderforschung und heilerziehung. hft. 108)
Plates printed on both sides.
"Literaturverzeichnis": p. 154-160.

1. Fatigue. I. Title.
E 26-96

Library, U. S. Bur. of Education LB1075.L77

NL 0432131 DHEW PU NN

VOLUME 337

Lobsien, Marx.
Experimentelle praktische schülerkunde, von Marx Lobsien ... mit einem beitrag über das pathologische kind von dr. O. Mönkemöller ... mit 16 figuren im text und einer tafel. Leipzig und Berlin, B. G. Teubner, 1916.
2 p. l., 295, [1] p. incl. illus., tables, form, diagrs. pl. 22½cm. mk. 5
Plate attached to cover.
"Literatur": p. [287]-289.

1. Child study. 2. Mental tests. 3. Children, Abnormal and backward. I. Mönkemöller, Eduard Otto, 1867- II. Title. 22-18864
Library of Congress LB1115.L6

NL 0432132 DLC DNLM NIC

BF 371 L62 1913 Lobsien, Marx.
Das Gedächtnis; eine übersichtliche Darstellung der Ergebnisse der neuesten Forschungen. Osterwieck/Harz, A. W. Zickfeldt, 1913.
268 p. (Der Bücherschatz des Lehrers, v. 21)

1. Memory. I. Title. II. Series.

NL 0432133 CaBVaU NNF CtY ICRL NNU-W ICJ

Lobsien, Marx.
Die Gleichschreibung als Grundlage des deutschen Rechtschreibunterrichts. Ein Versuch ... Langensalza, H. Beyer & Söhne, 1904.
43 p. 8°. (Paedagog. Mag. Hft. 219)

NL 0432134 NN

Lobsien, Marx.
... Intelligenzprüfungen auf grund von gruppenbeobachtungen, von Marx Lobsien... Langensalza, J. Beltz, 1914.
2 p. l., 59, [1] p. (Aktuelle fragen aus der padagogik der gegenwart... hrsg. von Max Reiniger... band 8.)

NL 0432135 OU

LB1051 .L77 Lobsien, Marx.
Die lernweisen der schüler; psychologische beiträge zur geistigen ökonomie des unterrichtens, von Marx Lobsien. Mit zwei figuren und einer tafel im text. Leipzig, Ernst Wunderlich, 1917.
2p.l., 89p. table, diagrs. 22½cm.

1. Education. 2. Educational psychology.

NL 0432136 NNU

LB1573 .L77 Lobsien, Marx.
Die mechanische leseschwierigkeit der schriftzeichen auf psychophysischer und experimenteller grundlage, von Marx Lobsien... Langensalza, H. Beyer & söhne, 1898.
63p. tables. 21cm.
Bibliographical foot-notes.

1. Reading, Psychology of. 2. Reading (Elementary) I. Title.

NL 0432137 NNU-W

LOBSIEN, Marx.
Schülerkunde auf grund von versuchen. 2e aufl. Leipzig und Berlin, B.G. Teubner, 1923.

Tables and charts.
"Schrifttum", pp. [204]-208.

NL 0432138 MH IU NNU-W

Lobsien, Marx.
Schuelerlandurlaub und geistige Erholung auf Grund von Versuchen, von Max Lobsien... Langensalza: H. Beyer & Söhne, 1925. 31 p. 8°. (Pädagogisches Mag. Heft 1050.)
Bibliographical footnotes.

1. Education—Psychology in—Special phases. 2. Vacations. 4. Ser.
N. Y. P. L. June 1, 1926

NL 0432139 NN

Lobsien, Marx.
Schwankungen der psychischen Kapazität. Einige experimentelle Untersuchungen an Schulkindern.
— Berlin. Reuther & Reichard. 1902. (5), 110 pp. Charts. [Sammlung von Abhandlungen aus dem Gebiete der pädagogischen Psychologie und Physiologie. Band 5, Heft 7.] 8°.

E8100 — Children. Study. — Psychology. — S.r.

NL 0432140 MB DNLM PU MH MWelC

Lobsien, Marx.
Über den einfluss des antikenotoxin auf die hauptkomponenten der arbeitskurve. Einige experimentelle beobachtungen von Marx Lobsien ... Langensalza, H. Beyer & söhne, 1912.
28 p. diagrs. 24cm. (Added t.-p.: Beiträge zur kinderforschung und heilerziehung. hft. 96)
Bibliographical foot-notes.

1. Fatigue. I. Title.
E 14-60
Library, U. S. Bur. of Education LB1075.L78

NL 0432141 DHEW PU

Lobsien, Marx.
Ueber den Vorstellungstypus der Schulkinder. Untersuchungen nach der kraepelinschen Methode. Langensalza: H. Beyer & Söhne, 1911. 2 p.l., 67 p. 8°. (Pädagogisches Magazin. Heft 457.)

1. Education.—Psychology: Special phases.
N. Y. P. L. February 24, 1912.

NL 0432142 NN

Lobsien, Marx.
Über lesbarkeit von fraktur und antiqua. Experimentelle untersuchungen, von Marx Lobsien. Langensalza, H. Beyer & söhne, 1918.
32 p. 23½cm. (Added t.-p.: Beiträge zur kinderforschung und heilerziehung. hft. 149)

1. Type and type-founding. I. Title.
E 22-441
Library, U. S. Bur. of Education Z250.L78

NL 0432143 DHEW

LB1139 .W9L7 Lobsien, Marx.
Über schreiben und schreibbewegungen. Von Marx Lobsien ... Langensalza, H. Beyer & söhne (Beyer & Mann) 1907.
[3], 64 p. diagrs. 21½cm.
"Pädagogisches magazin heft 298."

NL 0432144 ICU

LB1075 .L77 Lobsien, Marx.
...Was muss der lehrer von der experimentellen ermüdungsforschung wissen? Von Marx Lobsien... Altona und Hamburg, Hammerich & Lesser, 1919.
64p. tables, diagrs. 23cm. (At head of title: Padagogik der neuzeit; erziehungswissenschaftliche abhandlungen für freunde der jugend... hrsg. A. Bielfeldt-Altona)
Bibliographical foot-notes.
1. Fatigue. 2. Educational psychology.

NL 0432145 NNU-W

Lobsien, Marx.
Wie die schüler die schulfächer beurteilen. Leipzig, Wunderlich, 1926.
60 p.

NL 0432146 OOxM

Lobsien, Marx.
Das 10 Minuten-Turnen. Eine experimentell-statische Untersuchung über die Bedeutung der "Übungen für das tägliche Turnen" für die geistige Frische der Schulkinder. Langensalza: H. Beyer & Söhne, 1912. 26 p. 8°. (Pädagogisches Magazin. Heft 471.)

1. Physical education in schools, Germany.
N. Y. P. L. October 4, 1912.

NL 0432147 NN

PT 1173 L6 Lobsien, Wilhelm, 1872-
Aus silbernen Schalen; Gedichte neuerer Dichter, gesammelt von Wilhelm Lobsien. Buchschmuck von Mary Freiin Knigge. Bremen, Niedersachsen-Verlag, C. Schünemann [1905]
128p. 20cm.

1. German poetry - 19th cent. 2. German poetry (Collections) I. Title

NL 0432148 WU IaU

830.81 L78a Lobsien, Wilhelm, 1872 -
Aus silbernen schalen; gedichte neuerer dichter. Buchschmuck von Mary Freiin Knigge. Bremen [191-?]
128p.

Pages have ornamental borders.

NL 0432149 IU

PT 2623 O18 B5 Lobsien, Wilhelm, 1872-
Binne Hayens' Kampf um Gott; eine Hallignovelle. Heilbronn, E. Salzer, 1933.
109p. 16cm.

NL 0432150 WU

PT 2623 O18 D8 Lobsien, Wilhelm, 1872-
Dünung; Gedichte. Bremen, C. Schünemann [1905]
179p. 23cm.

NL 0432151 WU

Lobsien, Wilhelm
Ebba Enevold's Liebe. Hamburg, Hermes, 1919.

370 p.

NL 0432152 PPG

PT3803 S7L5 Lobsien, Wilhelm, 1872-
Die erzählende Kunst in Schleswig-Holstein von Theodor Storm bis zur Gegenwart. Altona, C. Adolff, 1908.
160 p.

1. German literature - Schleswig-Holstein - Hist. & crit.

NL 0432153 CU TxU CU

Lobsien, Wilhelm, 1872-
Friesenblut [von] Wilhelm Lobsien. [n. p., 1925?]
cover-title, 87 p. 18cm.
Contents.—Halligleute.—Heimgeholt.—Wattentod.

I. Title.
PT2623.O18F7 46-44839

NL 0432154 DLC

VOLUME 337

PT 2623 O18 G4
Lobsien, Wilhelm, 1872-
Gesa Früddens Weg; eine Hallignovelle. Heide, Westholsteinische Verlagsanstalt Boyens [1944]
146p. illus. 19cm.

NL 0432155 WU

Lobsien, Wilhelm, 1872-
Hafen binnen, Halliggeschichten. Berlin, M. Warneck [1932]
46 p. 17 cm.

I. Title.

PT2623.O18H25 52-47397

NL 0432156 DLC

Lobsien, Wilhelm, 1872-
Der Halligpastor. Roman, von Wilhelm Lobsien. Berlin, M. Warneck, 1914.
358 p. 20cm. M. 4

I. Title.

Library of Congress PT2623.O18H3 1914 14-10723

NL 0432157 DLC PPG NN

Lobsien, Wilhelm, 1872-
Der Halligpastor; roman. Heide in Holstein, Westholsteinische verlagsanstalt Boyens [1952]
283 p. 21cm.

NL 0432158 OCU NN

Lobsien, Wilhelm, 1872-
Heilige not; bilder aus Deutschlands kampf gegen die Russen, von Wilhelm Lobsien; mit sechs vollbildern und reichem buchschmuck von professor Walter Klemm und einer reliefkarte des östlichen kriegsschauplatzes. Weimar, G. Kiepenheuer, 1914.
3 p. l., [3]-178 p. incl. front. (port.) illus., plates. fold. map. 19½cm. (Half-title: Heldenkämpfe 1914-1915, bd. 1)

1. European war, 1914- —Campaigns—Eastern I. Title.

Library of Congress D551.L6 21-8895

NL 0432159 DLC NjP NN

Lobsien, Wilhelm, 1872-
Heilige not; bilder aus Deutschlends kampf gegen die Russen, von Wilhelm Lobsien ... Wiemar, G. Kiepenheuer, 1915.
2 p. l., 178 p. illus., fold. map. 19½ cm. (Half-title: Heldenkampfe, 1914-1915. Band i.)

NL 0432160 DNW CtY MiU

Lobsien, Wilhelm, 1872-
Jodute! ein kampf um Lübecks freiheit, von Wilhelm Lobsien ... Mainz, J. Scholz [°1911]
190 p. illus. 19½cm. (Half-title: Mainzer volks- und jugendbücher. [19])
Series title also on t.-p.

I. Title.

Library of Congress 12-17295

NL 0432161 DLC

Hky L781 J58
Lobsien, Wilhelm, 1872-
Jodute. Köln, H. Schaffstein [c1925]
182p. illus. 21cm.
A story.

NL 0432162 CtY

Lobsien, Wilhelm, 1872-
Klaus Störtebeker; Erzählung aus der Zeit der Vitalienbrüder, von Wilhelm Lobsien. Mit vier farbigen Bildern von Ludwig Eberle. Stuttgart: K. Thienemann [1927] 125 p. col'd front., col'd plates. 21cm.

999154A. 1. Juvenile literature—Fiction, German. 2. Störtebeker, Klaus, d. 1401—Fiction. I. Title.
N. Y. P. L. June 26, 1939

NL 0432163 NN PPG

Lobsien, Wilhelm, 1872-
Klaus Störtebeker, erzählung aus der zeit der Vitalienbrüder, von Wilhelm Lobsien. Mit vier farbigen bildern von Ludwig Eberle. Stuttgart, K. Thienemann [1941]
110 p., 1 l. col. front., col. plates. 21cm.
"78.-88. tausend."

1. Störtebeker, Klaus, d. 1401—Fiction.

PT2623.O18K5 1941 833.91 A F 47-1284

Yale univ. Library for Library of Congress [4]†

NL 0432164 CtY NN DLC

Lobsien, Wilhelm, 1872-
... Klaus Störtebeker, erzählung aus der zeit der Vitalienbrüder. Mit 4 farbigen bildern von Ludwig Eberle. Stuttgart, K. Thienemann [1943]
118 p., 1 l. col. front., col. plates. 21cm.
"89.-103. tausend."

1. Störtebeker, Klaus, d. 1401—Fiction.

PT2623.O18K5 1943 833.91 47-34538

NL 0432165 DLC PU WU IU CU

Lobsien, Wilhelm, 1872-
Koog und kogge, ein geschichtenkranz um Nordfriesland und die Halligen, von Wilhelm Lobsien. Heide in Holstein, Westholsteinische verlagsanstalt Boyens & co. [°1943]
271 p. 19½cm.
"11. bis 20. tausend."

I. Title.
PT2623.O18K6 833.91 A F 46-1227

Smith college. Library for Library of Congress [4]†

NL 0432166 MNS OU IaU ICRL TxU ViU CtY RPB DLC MB

Lobsien, Wilhelm, 1872-
Landunter: Halligroman. Berlin, Warneck, 1922.
349 p.

NL 0432167 PPG

PT 2623 O18 L3
Lobsien, Wilhelm, 1872-
Landunter; Halligroman. Berlin, M. Warneck, 1928.
349p. 20cm.

NL 0432168 WU

Lobsien, Wilhelm, 1872- joint ed.

Janssen, Albrecht, 1886- ed.
Die Nordseeinseln; ein heimatbuch hrsg. von Albrecht Janssen und Wilhelm Lobsien; buchschmuck und einband von Ernst Petrich; 16 zum teil farbige kunstbeilagen nach werken friesischer meister, 13 künstleraufnahmen von Theodor Möller u. a. und 3 karten. Leipzig, F. Brandstetter, 1925.

PT 2623 O18 P5
Lobsien, Wilhelm, 1872-
Pidder Lyng. Stuttgart, K. Thienemann [c1909]
148p. illus. 21cm.

NL 0432170 WU PPT

Lobsien, Wilhelm, 1872-
Pidder Lyng, der liekendeeler von Sylt, von Wilhelm Lobsien ... Mainz, J. Scholz [1910]
222 p. illus. 19½ x 15½cm. (Half-title: Mainzer volks- und jugendbücher)
Series title also on t.-p.

10-15183

NL 0432171 DLC

Lobsien, Wilhelm, 1872-
Pidder Lyng; ein Spiel in einem Aufzug, von Wilhelm Lobsien. Dresden: C. L. Ungelenk, 1931. 30 p. 16cm. (Neue Volks- und Laienspiele. [Nr.] 8.)

648822A. 1. Drama, German. I. Title.
N. Y. P. L. June 19, 1933

NL 0432172 NN

Lobsien, Wilhelm, 1872-
Das Rosendach; die Geschichte einer nordschleswigschen Jugend. Berlin, M. Warneck, 1923.
198 p. 19 cm.

I. Title.

PT2623.O18R6 52-47417

NL 0432173 DLC

Lobsien, Wilhelm, 1872-
Schleswig-Holstein. Berlin, L. Simon [194-?]
39p. illus. (Die deutschen Bücher)

NL 0432174 OCl

Lobsien, Wilhelm, 1872-
Segnende erde, roman aus Deutschlands dunklen tagen, von Wilhelm Lobsien. Heide in Holstein, Westholsteinische verlagsanstalt Boyens & co. [1943]
258 p. 20½cm.
"16. bis 25. tausend."
"Der vorliegende roman 'Segnende erde' ist eine umarbeitung der erzählung 'Der pilger im nebel'."

I. Title.
PT2623.O18P5 1942 833.91 A F 46-1228

Smith college. Library for Library of Congress [4]†

NL 0432175 MNS IaU ICRL CtY ViU TxU RPB DLC MB

Lobsien, Wilhelm, 1872-
Sonnwendfeuer, ein Spiel aus der Nordmark. Dresden, C. L. Ungelenk, 1933.
35 p. diagr. 15 cm. (Neue Volks- und Laienspiele, 33)

I. Title. (Series)

PT2623.O18S6 52-47556

NL 0432176 DLC

Lobsien, Wilhelm, 1872-
Um Recht & Freiheit. Koln, Schaffstein, 1925.
201 s.

NL 0432177 PPG

VOLUME 337

Lobsien, Wilhelm, 1872–
Unter Schwedens reichsbanner, von Wilhelm Lobsien ... Mainz, J. Scholz [1913]
210 p. illus. 19½cm. (Mainzer volks- und jugendbücher. [buch 22]) M. 3

I. Title.

Library of Congress PZ31.M3 vol. 22 13-15892

NL 0432178 DLC WU

Lobsien, Wilhelm, 1872–
Uthörn, geschichten aus Nordfriesland, von Wilhelm Lobsien. 24. bis 33. tausend. Heide in Holstein, Westholsteinische verlagsanstalt Boyens & co. [1943]
190 p. 20½cm.

I. Title.
PT2623.O18U8 833.91 A F 46-1229
Smith college. Library for Library of Congress [4]†

NL 0432179 DLC MB MNS OrU IaU CtY ScU OU ICRL TxU ViU RPB

Lobsien, Wilhelm, 1872–
Wellen und winde; Nordseegeschichten. n.d.

NL 0432180 OCl

Lobsiger, Ernst
Die auswärtige armenpflege des kantons Bern ... von ... Ernst Lobsiger ... Thun, Fritz Weibel, 1939.
x, 162 p. 22½cm.
Diss.- Bern.
"Literaturverzeichnis": p. ix-x.

NL 0432181 MH-L CtY

JV8281 Z9L6 Lobsiger, Georges
L'émigrant et ses préoccupations. Berne, Kümmerly & Frey [1951]
114 p. fold.col.map. (K & F petite bibliothèque géographique de l'émigrant et de l'homme d'affaires, ed. sous les auspices de l'Office Fédéral de l'Industrie, des Arts et Métiers, et du Travail. Section de la Main-d'Oeuvre et de l'Émigration. 6)
Published also in German under title: Vademecum für Auswanderer.
Bibliography: p.105-108.

NL 0432182 CU

Lobsiger, Marguerite (Dellenbach)
see
Lobsiger-Dellenbach, Marguerite E

Lobsiger-Dellenbach, Marguerite E
La conquête du massif alpin et de ses abords par les populations préhistoriques. Grenoble, 1935.
268 p. illus., 4 fold. maps. 26 cm.
Thèse—Université de Grenoble.
"Répertoire, avec indications bibliographiques, des stations paléolithiques, mésolithiques et néolithiques, rencontrées dans le massif alpin": p. [140]-246.
"Bibliographie générale": p. [247]-254.

1. Alps—Antiq. 2. Man, Prehistoric—Europe. I. Title.

GN803.L65 42-32795 rev*

NL 0432184 DLC CtY NNC

NB 159 .D3 L7 LOBSIGER DELLENBACH,MARGUERITE E
Figurines en terre modelée du Dahomey. Genève, Ville de Genève Musée d'ethnographie, 1946.
26 p. illus.
Reprinted from Archives suisses d'anthropologie générale, v.11, p. 215-238, 1945.

1. Terra-cottas--Dahomey. I. Geneva--Musée ethnographique. II. Title. Art cds.

NL 0432185 InU

Lobsiger-Dellenbach, Marguerite E
Gravures sur bambous, Nouvelle Calédonie, par Marguerite Dellenbach et Georges Lobsiger.
(IN: L'Ethnographie. Paris. 29cm. Nouv. sér., no 35-36 (15 juil. 15 déc. 1938) p.[35]-49. illus.)
Bibliography, p. 49.

1. Decorative art, Primitive-- New Caledonia.
2. Bamboo work.

NL 0432186 NN

Q115 .M685 Lobsiger-Dellenbach, Marguerite E.
Mission scientifique genevoise, *1952.*
Himalaya du Népal; rapports sur les travaux de la mission scientifique déléguée par les autorités cantonales et municipales de Genève, mars-juillet 1952 [par] Marguerite Lobsiger-Dellenbach, Augustin Lombard [et] Albert Zimmermann. Genève, Jeheber [1952]

Lobsiger-Dellenbach, Marguerite E
Népal; catalogue de la collection d'ethnographie Népalaise
see under Geneva. Musée d'ethnographie.

Lobsiger-Dellenbach, Marguerite E
Recherches ethnologiques au Népal (vallée de Katmandou) par Marguerite Lobsiger-Dellenbach. Genève, Société général d'impr., 1955.
141 p. illus., plates. 25 cm.
Cover title.
"Tirage à part du Globe, organe de la Société de géographie de Genève, tomes quatre-vingt-douze et quatre-vingt-treize, 1953 et 1954."
Observations made by the author as member of the Mission scientifique genevoise, 1952.

1. Ethnology—Nepal—Kathmandu. I. Mission scientifique genevoise, 1952. II. Title.

DS485.N4L6 68-122308

NL 0432189 DLC NRU

---

ar X 3222 no.27 Lobspruch der Stadt Gross-Glogau; zum ersten Male nach einer Handschrift aus dem 16. Jahrhundert vollständig hrsg. von F.W. v. Rascek. Gross-Glogau, C. Flemming, 1865.
22 p. 27cm.
Separate from "Programm" (Schulnachrichten)--Königl. Katholisches Gymnasium, Gross-Glogau.
No. 27 in a vol. lettered: Programmes: German literature. II.

NL 0432190 NIC

Ein Lobspruch der Stat Nürnburg
see under [Sachs, Hans] 1494-1576.

Lobspruch vber die herrliche Victori
see under [Wijnandts, Willem] fl. 1629.

Ein lobspruech der stat Salzpurg
see under [Sachs, Hans] 1494-1576.

Wing ZP 947 .S 389 LOBSPRÜCHE und -Lieder auf Hamburg. [Hamburg,1925]
[28]l. 23cm.
"Aus Anlass der Deutschen Lehrerversammlung zu Hamburg ... wurde dies Buch ... in der Staatlichen Kunstgewerbeschule gedruckt ... Buchgestaltung und Ausführung durch Johannes Schulz."

NL 0432194 ICN

Lobstein (Charles) [1864–]. *Contribution à l'étude des amputations spontanées dans les traumatismes. 33 pp., 1 l. 4°. *Paris,* 1890, No. 2-0.

NL 0432195 DNLM

MZ76 C665 XL78f Lobstein, E., ed.
François Coillard, der Gründer der Sambesimission zur Jubelfeier des 100 Jähr. Bestehens der Pariser Evang. Missionsgesellschaft (4. November 1822) Hrsg. im Auftrage des Strassburger Hilfscomité, von E. Lobstein. Paris, Société des missions évangéliques [1922?]
32 p. illus., map, port. 19 cm.

1. Coillard, François, 1834-1904. 2. Africa, South - Missions. 3. Société des missions évangéliques, Paris. 4. Barotseland - Missions. 5. Basuto (African people) Afr

NL 0432196 CtY-D

[Lobstein, Ed.]
Jean-Frédéric Lobstein, pasteur à Odessa, Épinal, Genève, Bâle, 1808-1855; un prédicateur du réveil... Paris, Fischbacher, 1928.
68 p. facsims. 22cm.
At head of cover title: Ed. et El. Lobstein.
Bibliographical footnotes.
1 Lobstein, Jean Frédéric, 1808-1855

NL 0432197 NjPT

Lobstein, Ed. joint author.
Paul Lobstein; esquisse biographique
see under Lobstein, Elisabeth (Kopp)

Lobstein, **Eduard,1826-1897.**
Die Abtei und Stadt Weissenburg im Elsass; historische Skizze... 2. Aufl. Strassburg, R. Schultz, 1886.
24 p., 26cm.

NL 0432199 NjPT

4-R512 L64L6 Lobstein, Eduard, 1826- **1897.**
J. Fr. Lobstein sen., Professor der Anatomie und Chirurgie; ein Lehrer Goethe's in Strassburg. Nebst einem Anhang: Zur Geschichte des Bürgerhospitals von Strassburg. Heidelberg, C. Winter, 1880.
vii,94 p.
Bibliographical footnotes.

1. Lobstein, Johann Friedrich, 1736-1784.
2. Strassburg. Bürgerhospital.

NL 0432200 CU OCIW PPC

WZ 100 L7998L 1878 LOBSTEIN, Eduard,**1826-1897.**
Joh. Friedr. Lobstein, Professor der innern Klinik und pathologischen Anatomie, der Gründer des anat.-pathol. Museums zu Strassburg; sein Leben und Wirken. Ein Beitrag zur Säcular-Feier seiner Geburt. Strassburg, Trübner, 1878.
xi, 267 p.
1. Lobstein, Johann Georg Christian Friedrich Martin, 1777-1835

NL 0432201 DNLM PPC

VOLUME 337

Lobstein, Elisabeth (Kopp)
Jean-Frédéric Lobstein, pasteur à Odessa, Épinal, Genève, Bâle, 1808-1855
see under [Lobstein] Ed.

BR139 L6L6 Lobstein, Elisabeth (Kopp)
Paul Lobstein; esquisse biographique retracée d'après son journal intime, ses agendas, sa correspondance, ses publications [par El & Ed. Lobstein] Strasbourg, Librairie Istra, 1926.
viii, 285 p. illus.

Cover title: Paul Lobstein, professeur à l'Université de Strasbourg, 1850-1922; un Alsacien idéal.
Bibliography: p. [272]-280.

1. Lobstein, Paul, 1850-1922. I. Lobstein, Ed. joint author.

NL 0432203 CU MH NNUT OO

Lobstein, Émile.
Les mines de diamant du Cap, par Émile Lobstein. Paris, Imprimerie E. Buttner-Thierry, 1889.
20 p. tables. 24cm.
"Notice d'après une étude publiée par l'auteur dans Le Génie Civil."

1. Diamond mines and mining—South Africa.

G S 34-789

Libr., U. S. Geol. Surv., Geo. F. Kunz Collection K481 (780) L78m

NL 0432204 DI-GS

LOBSTEIN, ERNEST, Prof.
Researches biochimiques sur le bacille tuberculeux. Strasbourgh, Editions de la Gazette medicale, 1922.
199 p.

NL 0432205 CtY

ML410 R85L6 Lobstein, Ernest Charles.
Rouget de Lisle, Verfasser der Marseillaise; eine biographische Studie aus Anlass seines hundertsten Todestages, 1760-1836 [Strasbourg-Robertsau, A.Weber, pref. 1936]
44p. 21cm.

1. Rouget de Lisle, Claude Joseph, 1760-1836. I. Title.

NL 0432206 IaU

Lobstein (Ernst). *Zur Casuistik des Gallenstein-Ileus. [Heidelberg.] 1 p. l., 37 pp. 8°. Tübingen, H. Laupp, 1895.

NL 0432207 DNLM

Lobstein, Eugène Michel.
Considérations hygiéniques sur le chauffage...par Eugène-Michel Lobstein... Strasbourg: Berger-Levrault, 1847. 2 p.l., 27 p. sq. 8°.
Dissertation, Strassburg.

1. Heating.
N. Y. P. L. October 16, 1915

NL 0432208 NN DNLM

Lobstein, Frédéric
See
Lobstein, Jean Frédéric, 1808-1855.

Lobstein, Friedrich Eduard
see Lobstein, Eduard, 1826-1897.

LB3407 .A43 Lobstein, Hella, joint author.
Allendy, René Félix, 1889–
... El problema sexual en la escuela, traducción del francés por H. Almendros. La Habana, Cultural, s. a., 1940.

LB3407 .A425 Lobstein, Hella, joint author.
Allendy, René Félix, 1889-1942.
Sex problems in school [by] René Allendy [and] Hella Lobstein. Tr. from the French by Egon Larsen. London, New York, Staples Press [1948]

Lobstein, Jean.
Organisation scientifique de la production et du travail. Certificat d'aptitude à l'administration des entreprises, par J. Lobstein. Paris, Centre de documentation universitaire [195-]
iv, 111 p. 27 cm.
Cover title.
Bibliography: p. [i]-iv.

1. Industrial management. I. Title.

HD33.L65 64-51355

NL 0432213 DLC

Lobstein, Jean.
La révolution fiscale et administrative. Avant-propos de C.-J. Gignoux. Paris, Société d'éditions économiques & sociales [194-]
16 p. 21 cm.

1. Finance—France. I. Title.

HJ1091.L55 336.44 48-39468*‡

NL 0432214 DLC

Lobstein, Jean.
... La révolution sociale et économique ... Paris, Société d'éditions économiques & sociales [1944?]
33, [1] p., 1 l. 21cm.
"2e édition."—p. 33.

1. Economics. I. Title.

45-19984
Library of Congress HB173.L75 1944
[2] 330.1

NL 0432215 DLC

Lobstein, Jean Frédéric, 1777-1835
see
Lobstein, Johann Georg Christian Friedrich Martin, 1777-1835.

Lobstein, Jean Frédéric, 1808-1855.
L'année chrétienne; ou, Une parole sainte; méditée pour chaque jour, par F. Lobstein... Genève: E. Beroud, 1856. 456 p. 2. ed. 12°.

1. Meditations (Religious).
N. Y. P. L. March 31, 1919.

NL 0432217 NN

BV4834 .L787 Lobstein, Jean Frédéric, 1808-1855.
Die christlichen festtage in zwanzig betrachtungen ... Basel, Bahnmaier's buchhandlung (C. Detloff), 1863.
iv, 244 p.
Zweiter (ergänzungs-) band von Lobstein's Weckstimmen.

1. Meditations.

NL 0432218 ICU

Lobstein, Jean Frédéric, 1808-1855.
Les fêtes chrétiennes exposées en vingt méditations. Toulouse, Société des Livres Religieux, 1855.
368 p. 12°.

NL 0432219 NN

Lobstein, Jean Frédéric, 1808-1855.
Gottes arbeiten an den seelen; aus den Französischen übersetzt, hrsg. von dem Christlichen verein im nordlichen Deutschland. Eisleben, Kloppel, 1859.
196 p.

NL 0432220 PPLT

BV4834 .L79 LOBSTEIN, Jean Frédéric, 1808-1855.
Klippen auf dem heilsweg. Von J.F.Lobstein... Mit einem kurzen lebensabriss des sel.verfassers. 2.autorisirte aufl. Basel und Biel, Bahnmaier, 1860.
[1], xvii, [1], 135, [1]p. 19½cm.

1. Meditations.

NL 0432221 ICU

Lobstein, Jean Frédéric, 1808-1855.
Quelques maladies spirituelles décrites en douze méditations Bibliques. Toulouse, Société des Livres Religieux, 1853.
195 (1) p. sm. 16°.

NL 0432222 NN

Lobstein, Jean Frédéric, 1808-1855.
Quelques travaux de Dieudans les ames. Douze méditations faites à l'oratoire de Genève, par F. Lobstein. Toulouse, Société des Livres Religieux, 1854.
256 p. sm. 16°.

NL 0432223 NN

Lobstein, Jean Frederic, 1808-1855, arr.
Sept célebres quatuors de J. Haydn, arrangés pour piano et violon
see under Haydn, Joseph, 1732-1809.

Lobstein, Joh. Franz.
Beiträge zur geschichte der musik im Elsass, und besonders in Strassburg, von der ältesten bis auf die neueste zeit, von J. F. Lobstein ... (Mit 3 lithographien.) Strassburg, Gedruckt bei P. H. Dannbach, 1840.
viii, 147 p. 3 fold. pl. 22cm.
"Einiges bereits in der Leipziger Allgemeinen musikalischen zeitung (1839), so wie in A. Stöbers Erwinia mitgetheilt."—Vorwort.

1. Music—Alsace—Hist. & crit.

9-11090
Library of Congress ML283.A5L7

NL 0432225 DLC NcRS IaU CU OClW

LOBSTEIN, Joh. Franz.
Manuel du notariat en Alsace, ou Notices sur la composition de toutes les études de cette ancienne province (Haut- et Bas-Rhin, partie des Vosges et de la Vavière-Rhénane), &c. Strasbourg, Treuttel et Wurtz, 1844.

NL 0432226 MH

Lobstein (Joh. Fridericus) [1736-84]. *De nervo spinali ad par vagum accessorio. 50 pp., 2 pl. 4°. Argentorati, typ. vid. Pauschingerianæ, [1760].

NL 0432227 DNLM

VOLUME 337

Lobstein, Johann Friedrich, 1777-1835
see
Lobstein, Johann Georg Christian Friedrich Martin, 1777-1835

Lobstein, Johann Friedrich, 1808-55.
SEE
Lobstein, Jean Frédéric, 1808-55.

Lobstein, Johann Friedrich Daniel, 1777-1840.
Dialogues between patients and the physician, on the several principal diseases in this country ... by J. F. Daniel Lobstein ... New-York, The author, 1839.
iv, [5]-143, [1] p. 22½cm.

1. Medicine, Popular.

Library of Congress RC81.L82 7-10387†

NL 0432230 DLC MnU WU-M ViU-M DNLM NcD-MC PPC

Lobstein, Johann Friedrich Daniel, 1777-1840.
*Dissertation sur la fièvre puerpérale. iii, 44 pp. 4°. Paris, 1803, No. 63. c.

NL 0432231 DNLM PPC

1887 Lobstein, Johann Friedrich Daniel, 1777-1840.
Doctor Lobstein has the honour to inform the physicians and literati of the United States, that he is writing a new work, entitled, Treatise upon the semeiology of the eye. [New York? 1829?]
8 p. 8°.

NL 0432232 DLC

Lobstein, Johann Friedrich Daniel, 1777-1840.
A general guide for practising physicians, in the examination of the sick. With an appendix of medical formulæ. By J. F. Daniel Lobstein ... 2d ed. Philadelphia, L. D. Belair, 1823.
vi, [7]-124 p., 1 l. 14½cm.

1. Medicine — Practice. 2. Medicine — Formulae, receipts, prescriptions.

35-36254

Library of Congress RC50.L6 1823

NL 0432233 DLC PPPH MH-M PPL PPC PU NN OClW-H OO CtY-M DNLM MBCo

---

QV L799r 1815 LOBSTEIN, Johann Friedrich Daniel, 1777-1840
Recherches et observations sur le phosphore; ouvrage dans lequel on fait connaître les effets extraordinaires de ce remède dans le traitement de différentes maladies internes. Strasbourg, Levrault, 1815.
xi, 107 p.

NL 0432234 DNLM MB

Lobstein, J[ohann] F[riedrich] Daniel, 1777-1840.
Remarks on the pernicious effects and fatal consequences of blood-letting; and designed by the author for the prolongation of the lives of his fellow beings. By J. F. Daniel Lobstein ... New-York, Printed by W. Mitchell, 1832.
16 p. 21cm.

1. Bloodletting.

Library of Congress RM711.L78 5-472†
——— Copy 2. [Theological pamphlets, v. 44, no. 13]

NL 0432235 DLC CtY-M DNLM

WQ L799r 1816 LOBSTEIN, Johann Friedrich Daniel, 1777-1840
Remarques de M.r J.-Frédéric Lobstein sur la critique de ses observations d'accouchemens, insérées dans le Journal de médecine, rédigé par M. Leroux, mois de novembre 1816. [Paris? 1816?]
48 p.
Caption title.

NL 0432236 DNLM

Lobstein, Johann Friedrich Daniel, 1777-1840.
Researches and observations on the use of phosphorus, in the treatment of various diseases. By J. F. Daniel Lobstein ... Philadelphia, The author, 1825.
v p., 1 l., [vii]-xi, [13]-114 p. 21½cm.
Advertising matter: p. [109]-114.

1. Phosphorus—Therapeutic use.

34-38256

Library of Congress RM666.P7L62

NL 0432237 DLC KU-M DNLM PPAN PPC PHi PPGi MiU MB ICJ

RM666 P7 825l Lobstein, Johann Friedrich Daniel, 1777-1840.
Researches and observations on the use of phosphorus, in the treatment of various diseases. Philadelphia, R. Wright, 1825.
107p. 24cm.

NL 0432238 CtY-M DNLM

Lobstein, Johann Friedrich Daniel, 1777-1840
Sur la critique de ses observations d'accouchemens. 48 pp. 12°. [Paris, Migneret, 1816.]
Repr. from: J. de méd., Par., 1816.

NL 0432239 DNLM

Lobstein, J[ohann] F[riedrich] Daniel, 1777-1840.
Topographie physique et médicale, de la ville de Philadelphie, avec des tableaux statistiques . . . Philadelphie, J. F. Hurtel, 1823.
8 pp. 12°.
Prospectus.
F158.44.L7 1-10662—M 1

NL 0432240 DLC

Lobstein, Johann Friedrich Daniel, 1777-1840.
A treatise upon the semeiology of the eye, for the use of physicians; and of the countenance, for criminal jurisprudence. By J. F. Daniel Lobstein ... New-York, C. S. Francis; Philadelphia, Towar & Hogan; [etc., etc.] 1830.
3 p. l., [v]-xxiii, [25]-175 p. 21½cm.

1. Eye. 2. Semiology.

(Toner) 7—24984

Library of Congress RC73.5.L79

NL 0432241 DLC PPC PPL DNLM OO PU ICJ Nh

WW L799t 1830 LOBSTEIN, Johann Friedrich Daniel, 1777-1840
A treatise upon the semeiology of the eye, for the use of physicians; and of the countenance, for criminal jurisprudence. New York, Seymour, 1830.
175 p.

NL 0432242 DNLM NcD-MC

QV L799r 1817 LOBSTEIN, Johann Friedrich Daniel, 1777-1840
Untersuchungen und Beobachtungen über den Phosphor und die ausserordentlichen Würkungen, die dieses Heilmittel in verschiedenen innern Krankheiten hervorbringt. Aus dem Französischen übers. und mit einigen Zusätzen begleitet vom Verfasser der Rezepte und Kurarten der bessern Aerzte jeder Zeit. Leipzig, Engelmann, 1817.
xii, 147 p.
Translation of Recherches et observations sur le phosphore.

NL 0432244 DNLM

Lobstein, Johann Georg Christian Friedrich Martin, 1777-1835,
———. Compte rendu à la Faculté de médecine de Strasbourg sur l'état actuel de son muséum anatomique, suivi du catalogue des objets qu'il renferme. 144 pp. 8°. Strasbourg, F.-G. Levrault, 1820. [F., v. 744.]

NL 0432245 DNLM PPC

QS L799c 1824 LOBSTEIN, Johann Georg Christian Friedrich Martin, 1777-1835
Compte rendu à la Faculté de médecine de Strasbourg sur les travaux anatomiques exécutés à l'amphithéatre de cette faculté pendant les années 1821, 1822 et 1823; suivi d'un premier supplément au catalogue de son muséum anatomique. Strasbourg, Levrault, 1824.
78 p.
I. Strasbourg. Université. Faculté de médecine

NL 0432246 DNLM

Lobstein, Johann Georg Christian Friedrich Martin, 1777-1835.
De nervi sympathetici humani fabrica usu et morbis. Commentatio anatomico-physiologico-pathologica, tabulis æneis et lithographicus illustrata. Auctore Joh. Frid. Lobstein ... Parisiis, [etc.], F. G. Levrault, 1823.
xij, 174, viij p. x pl. (part col., 1 fold.) 30½cm.
Bibliographical foot-notes.

NL 0432247 ICJ DNLM PP PPC IU-M CtY WaU WU NIC MnU WU-M

19th c.
WL L799D 1821 Lobstein, Johann George Christian Friedrich Martin, 1777-1835.
Discours sur la prééminence du système nerveux dans l'économie animale, et l'importance d'une étude approfondie de ce système; prononcé à la séance publique de la Faculté de médicine de Strasbourg pour la distribution des prix de l'année scolaire de 1819-1820. Strasbourg, Levrault, 1821.
46 p. 22 cm.
1. Nervous System. I. Title.

NL 0432248 WU-M DNLM

Lobstein, Johann Georg Christian Friedrich Martin, 1777-1835.
Dissertation sur la nutrition du foetus, presentée et soutenue à l'École spéciale de médicine de Strasbourg, le 12 Messidor an 10, à trois heures après-midi Strasbourg, Levrault, an X 1802.
150 p.

NL 0432249 PPC

QZ L789e 1835 LOBSTEIN, Johann Georg Christian Friedrich Martin, 1777-1835
Essai d'une nouvelle théorie des maladies, fondée sur les anomalies de l'innervation. Paris, Levrault, 1835.
48 p. illus.

NL 0432250 DNLM NcD-MC

VOLUME 337

Lobstein, Johann Georg Christian Friedrich Martin, 1777–1835.
Essai sur la nutrition du foetus, par J. Fréderic Lobstein, ... Strasbourg, Levrault frères, an x (1802).
xvj, 150, [2] p. 2 pl. 27x21½cm.
Bibliographical foot-notes.

NL 0432251 ICJ ViU NjP MiU NIC DNLM

RD761 .S33 1804
Lobstein, Johann Georg Christian Friedrich Martin, 1777–1835.
Fragment d'anatomie physiologique sur l'organisation de la matrice dans l'espèce humaine ... par Jean Frédéric Lobstein. Paris Levrault, 1803.
2 p. l., 32 p. 21cm. (With Scarpa, Antonio. Mémories de physiologie et de chirurgie-partique. Paris, 1804)
1. Uterus.

NL 0432252 ViU DNLM

Lobstein, Johann Georg Christian Friedrich Martin, 1777–1835.
Lehrbuch der pathologischen Anatomie, von Dr. J. F. Lobstein ... Deutsch bearbeitet von A. Neurohr ... Erster-[zweiter] Band. Stuttgart, F. Brodhag'sche Buchhandlung, 1834–1835.
2 vol. 20cm.

NL 0432253 ICJ DNLM FU-HC CtY-M

Lobstein, Johann Georg Christian Friedrich Martin, 1777-1835.
——. Mémoires de médecine pratique. 103 pp. 8°. *Strasbourg & Paris, F.-G. Levrault*, 1832. [P., v. 488.]

NL 0432253-1 DNLM

WL L799d 1834
LOBSTEIN, Johann Georg Christian Friedrich Martin, 1777-1835
Memoria anatomico-fisiologico-patologica su la struttura, le funzioni e le malattie del nervo grande simpatico dell'uomo. Tr. dal latino, corr. di note e commenti del dottore Domenico Branca. Milano, Molina, 1834.
xvii, 187 p. illus. (Biblioteca di medicinae chirurgia pratica. Classe medica)

Translation of De nervi sympathetici humani fabrica, usu et morbis commentatio anatomico-physiologico-patholigica.
I. Branca, Domenico, ed.

NL 0432255 DNLM

Lobstein, Johann Georg Christian Friedrich Martin, 1777-1835.
——. Memoria physiologica, impressa em Paris no anno de 1823, vertida da lingua latina em vulgar ... por A. F. Braga. 45 pp., 1 l., port. 8°. *Porto, Viuva A. Ribeiro & filhos*, 1826. [P., v. 1256.]

NL 0432256 DNLM

Lobstein, Johann Georg Christian Friedrich Martin, 1777-1835
Observations anatomico-physiologiques sur la circulation du sang dans l'enfant qui n'a pas respiré. Paris, Levrault, 1803.
2l., 36p. 20cm.

"Extrait du Magasin Encyclopedique, ann. IX."

1.Blood circulation. 2.Fetus.

NL 0432257 NcD-MC

Lobstein, Johann Georg Christian Friedrich Martin, 1777-1835.
——. Observations d'accouchemens, recueillies à la salle des accouchées de l'hôpital civil de Strasbourg. 59 pp. 8°. [*Strasbourg*], *Migneret*, [1816].

NL 0432258 DNLM NN

Lobstoin, Johann Georg Christian Friedrich Martin, 1777-1835.
——. Plan raisonné d'un cours de médecine légale. 1 p. l., 31 pp. 4°. *Strasbourg, Levrault*, 1814.
Concours.

NL 0432259 DNLM

QS L799r 1804
LOBSTEIN, Johann Georg Christian Friedrich Martin, 1777-1835
Rapport sur les travaux exécutés à l'amphithéatre d'anatomie de l'École de médecine de Strasbourg pendant le premier semestre de l'an XII; présenté à l'assemblée des professeurs de cette école. Strasbourg, Levrault, 1804.
46 p.
I. Strasbourg. Université. Faculté de médecine

NL 0432260 DNLM

Lobstein, Johann Georg Christian Friedrich Martin, 1777-1835.
——. Rapports sur les travaux exécutés à l'amphithéâtre d'anatomie de Strasbourg. 89 pp. 4°. *Strasbourg, Levrault & Cie.*, 1805.

NL 0432261 DNLM

Lobstein, Johann Georg Christian Friedrich Martin, 1777-1835.
——. Sur les avantages des établissemens cliniques. Séance publique de la Faculté de médecine de Strasbourg du 27 décembre 1829. 31 pp. 4°. *Strasbourg, F.-G. Levrault*, 1830.

NL 0432262 DNLM

Lobstein, Johann Georg Christian Friedrich Martin, 1777–1835.
Traité d'anatomie pathologique; par J. F. Lobstein, ... Tome premier-[second], ... Paris, [etc.], F. G. Levrault; [etc., etc.], 1829–1833.
2 vol. 21cm. *and* atlas of [2], 4, 8 p., xvi pl. (part col.) 52½cm.
Atlas has lithographed t.-p.
Contents.—t. 1. L'anatomie pathologique générale. xij, 568, [2] p.—t. 2. L'anatomie pathologique spéciale. [4], 656 p.
Atlas has shelf number SA616.078 I901

NL 0432263 ICJ DNLM WU-M

MICRO 23
Lobstein, Johann Georg Christian Friedrich Martin, 1777-1835.
Traité d'anatomie pathologique. Paris, Levrault, 1829-33.
2 v. and atlas.
Microfilm from NLM copy.

1. Anatomy--Pathological. I. Title.

NL 0432264 CU-M

Lobstein, Johann Georg Christian Friedrich Martin, 1777–1835.
A treatise on the structure, functions and diseases of the human sympathetic nerve ... By John Fred. Lobstein ... Tr. from the Latin, with notes, by Joseph Pancoast, M. D. Philadelphia, J. G. Auner, 1831.
viii, [9]–157, [6] p. VI pl. 22cm.
Original ed. published 1823 under title: De nervi sympathetici humani fabrica, usu et morbis commentatio ...
1. Nervous system, Sympathetic. 2. Nervous system—Diseases. I. Pancoast, Joseph, 1805–1882.
7—26651
Library of Congress RC343.L85

ICJ NjP
NL 0432265 DLC DNLM KyU PPJ PPHa PU PPL ViU MiU

WQ L799e 1804
LOBSTEIN, Johann Georg Christian Friedrich Martin, 1777-1835
Ueber die Ernährung des Fötus. Aus dem Französischen übers. von Theodor Friedr. Arn. Kestner. Halle, Societäts-Buchhandlung, 1804.
xviii, 214 p.
Translation of Essai sur la nutrition du foetus.

NL 0432266 DNLM

Lobstein, Johann Georg Christian Friedrich Martin, 1777-1835.
——. Versuch einer neuen Theorie der Krankheiten gegründet auf die Anomalien der Nervenkraft. Teutsch bearbeitet von A. Neurohr. 96 pp., 1 tab. 8°. *Stuttgart, F. Brodhag*, 1835.

NL 0432267 DNLM

Lobstein, Johann Michael, 1740-1794.
Codex Samaritanus Parisinus sanctae Genovefae. Praemissa commentatio de Samaritanae gentis religione aevi recentioris... Francofurti ad Moenum, Typis Eichenbergianis, 1781.
152 p. 20 cm.

NL 0432268 NjP

Lobstein (Karl). *Ueber multiple Eitermetastasen in den Muskeln bei puerperaler Pyämie. 54 pp. 8°. *Strassburg, C. Müh & Co.*, 1894.

NL 0432269 DNLM MH

Lobstein, M
see Treslong, H van.

Lobstein, Paul, 1850-1922.
Die altkirchliche christologie und der evangelische heilsglaube. Leipzig, 1896.
36 p. 8°. (Hefte zur "Christlichen welt," 24)

NL 0432271 MH NNUT

Div.S. 232 L799B
Lobstein, Paul, 1850-1922.
Le bilan dogmatique de l'orthodoxie régnante. Paris, Fischbacher, 1891.
47 p. 23 cm. (His Études christologiques)

Bibliographical footnotes.

1. Jesus Christ. Person and offices.

NL 0432272 NcD CtY-D

Lobstein, Paul, 1850-1922.
Calvin und Montaigne. Rede zum vierhundertjährigen jubiläum Calvins, gehalten in der Aula d der Kaiser Wilhelms-universität von d.P. Lobstein. ... Strassburg, E. van Hauten, 1909.
20 p.

NL 0432273 OO OCl

Div.S. 232 L799C
Lobstein, Paul, 1850-1922.
La christologie traditionnelle et la foi protestante. Paris, Fischbacher, 1894.
53 p. 23 cm. (His Études christologiques)

Bibliographical footnotes.

1. Jesus Christ. History of doctrines.

NL 0432274 NcD

VOLUME 337

BX 9418 L6 Lobstein, Paul, 1850-1922.
La connaissance religieuse d'après Calvin; étude d'histoire et de dogmatique. Paris, Librairie Fischbacher, 1909.
64 p. 23cm.

1. Calvin, Jean, 1509-1564--Theology. I. Title.

NL 0432275 CSaT NcD FTaSU PPiPT

Lobstein, Paul, 1850-1922.
La doctrine christologique
see his Études christologiques. La doctrine christologique.

BV823 .L8 LOBSTEIN,PAUL,1850-
La doctrine de la sainte cène. Essai dogmatique,par P.Lobstein... Lausanne,Impr.G.Bridel,1889.
[5],206 p. 22cm.

1.Lord's supper.

NL 0432277 ICU NcD CtY-D PPPD MH

Div.S. 265.3 L799Do Lobstein, Paul, 1850-1922.
Le dogme de la naissance miraculeuse du Christ. Paris, Fischbacher, 1890.
51 p. 23 cm. (His Études christologiques)

Bound with the author's La doctrine de la sainte Cène. Lausanne, 1889.
Bibliographical footnotes.
1. Virgin birth. I. Title.

NL 0432278 NcD

RC63 L79g Lobstein, Paul, 1850-1922.
Einleitung in die evangelische Dogmatik, von D.P.Lobstein ... Aus dem französischen übersetzt von Pfarrer A.D.Maas. Vom Verfasser durchgesehene und stark vermehrte Ausgabe. Freiburg i.B. [etc.] J.C.B.Mohr(P.Siebeck)1897.
x,292p. 23cm.

NL 0432279 NNUT OrPR NcD CtY-D PPLT

Lobstein, Paul, 1850-
Essai d'une introduction a la dogmatique Protestante. Paris, Librairie Fischbacher, 1896.
250p. O.

NL 0432280 NcD NNUT

Lobstein,Paul,1850-1922.
Die ethik Calvins in ihren grundzügen entworfen. Ein beitrag zur geschichte der christlichen ethik von lic.theol.P.Lobstein ... Strassburg, C.F.Schmidt (F.Bull) 1877.
2 p.l.,151,[3] p. 24cm.
Bibliographical footnotes.

1.Calvin,John,1509-1564.

BX9421.L8

NL 0432281 MiU PPiPT MnCS NRCR NcD PPLT CtY MH NNUT

BR75 L786e Lobstein, Paul, 1850-1922.
Études christologiques: La doctrine des fonctions médiatrices du Sauveur. Paris, Librairie Fischbacher, 1891.
29 p. 23 cm.

Bibliographical footnotes.

NL 0432282 CtY-D NcD

232.3 L799e Theol. Lobstein, Paul, 1850-1922.
Études christologiques: la doctrine des fonctions médiatrices du Sauveur. Paris, Librairie Fischbacher, 1892.
29 p. 22cm.

1. Atonement.

NL 0432283 TxDAM

608.2 C16.9 L799et LOBSTEIN, Paul, 1850-1922.
Etudes sur la pensée et l'oeuvre de Calvin. Neuilly (Seine) Editions de "La Cause" [1927]
185p. 19cm.

NL 0432284 MH-AH OCU IaU

Lobstein, Paul, 1850-
An introduction to Protestant dogmatics, by Dr. P. Lobstein ... Authorized translation from the original French ed. by Arthur Maxson Smith, PH. D. [Chicago] The translator, printed at the University of Chicago press [1902]
xxi, 275 p. 20½cm.

Library of Congress 3—2198

NL 0432285 DLC NNUT OO PPWe

Lobstein, Paul, 1850-
An introduction to Protestant dogmatics, by Dr. P. Lobstein... Authorized tr. from the original French ed. by Arthur Maxson Smith, Ph.D. Chicago, The University of Chicago press [1910]
275 p.

NL 0432286 MiU OCl PPPD PCC

Lobstein, Paul, 1850-1922, ed.
Calvin, Jean, 1509-1564.
Ioannis Calvini Opera quae supersunt omnia. Ad fidem editionum principum et authenticarum ex parte etiam codicum manu scriptorum, additis prolegomenis literariis, annotationibus criticis, annalibus Calvinianis indicibusque novis et copiosissimis, ediderunt Guilielmus Baum, Eduardus Cunitz, Eduardus Reuss ... Brunsvigae, apud C. A. Schwetschke et filium, 1863-1900.

BT 317 .L79 1896 Lobstein,Paul,1850-1922.
Die lehre von der übernatürlichen geburt Christi. Christologische studie,von P.Lobstein ... 2.stark verm.aufl. Freiburg i. B. und Leipzig, J.C.B.Mohr (P.Siebeck) 1896.
2 p.l.,65 p. 23cm.
"Die erste auflage ... ist ... erschienen unter dem titel: 'Etudes christologiques.--Le dogme de la naissance miraculeuse du Christ,Paris,1890.' Die gegenwärtige veröffentlichung ist ... eine deutsche wiedergabe der ... französischen studie,für deren uebersetzung ich herrn Arendt in Pankow bei Berlin meinen ... dank ausspreche."--Vorwort.
1.Jesus Christ--Nativity. I.Arendt.

NL 0432288 MiU NcD PPPD

FX92 L786n Lobstein, Paul, 1850-1922.
La notion de la préexistence du fils de Dieu; fragment de christologie expérimentale. Paris, Librairie Fischbacher, 1883.
159 p. 22 cm.

Bibliographical footnotes.

NL 0432289 CtY-D CU MB NcD NNUT NCRC

WC 17856 Lobstein, Paul, 1850-1922.
Par le Christ à Dieu; études religieuses, histoire et doctrine. Neuilly, "La Cause" [1931]
290 p. illus.

1. Christianity - Addresses, essays, lectures. I. Title (1)

NL 0432290 CtY MH-AH

Lobstein, Paul, 1850-1922.
Paul Lobstein; esquisse biographique ...
see under Lobstein, Elisabeth (Kopp)

---

arW 34607 Lobstein, Paul, 1850-1922.
Petrus Ramus als Theologe; ein Beitrag zur Geschichte der protestantischen Theologie. Strassburg, C. F. Schmidt, 1878.
86 p. 25cm.

1. La Ramée, Pierre de, 1515?-1572.

NL 0432292 NIC MH-AH NcD NNC-T

Lobstein, Paul, 1850-1922.
The virgin birth of Christ; an historical and critical essay by Paul Lobstein ... Translated into English by Victor Leuliette ... Edited, with an introduction, by the Rev. W. D. Morrison ... London and Oxford, Williams & Norgate; New York, G. P. Putnam's sons, 1903.
138 p. 19cm. (On cover: Crown theological library)

1. Virgin birth. I. Leuliette, Victor, tr. II. Morrison, William Douglas, 1853- ed.
5—15331

Library of Congress BT317.L7
[a36d1] 232.921

NL 0432293 PPM NIC KyLxCB KyU DLC MBrZ MB MH OClW OCl ODW PPWe PBm PPPD

Lobstein, Paul, 1850-1922.
The virgin birth of Christ, an historical and critical essay, by Paul Lobstein ... translated into English by Victor Leuliette ... Edited, with an introduction, by the Rev. W. D. Morrison ... New York, G. P. Putnam's sons; London, Williams and Norgate, 1903.
138 p. 19cm. (On cover: Crown theological library)
Bibliographical references included in "Notes" (p. 113-138)

1. Virgin birth. I. Leuliette, Victor, tr. II. Morrison, William Douglas, 1853-1943, ed.
44-14051

Library of Congress BT317.L7 1903 a

NL 0432294 DLC NcD

Lobstein, Paul, 1850-1922.
Wahrheit und dichtung in unserer religion. Tübingen, J.C.B. Mohr, 1905.
35 p. 21 cm.

"Die seiten 1-35 dieses sonderabdrucks entsprechen den seiten 507-536 des jahrgangs 1904 der Zeitschrift für theologie und kirche."

NL 0432295 CtY-D

Lobstein, Paul, 1850-1922. 3454-38
Zum evangelischen Lebensideal in seiner lutherischen und reformierten Ausprägung.
(In Theologische Abhandlungen . . . Pp. 157-181. Tübingen, 1902.)

NL 0432296 MB NNUT

LOBSTEIN, RENÉ.
... ESSAI SUR LA LÉGISLATION COLONIALE DE L'ALLEMAGNE ... PARIS, A.CHEVALIER-MARESCQ & CIE, 1902.
2 P.L., 190 P. 23½ CM.
[INTERNATIONAL LAW PAMPHLETS, VOL. 23.]
THÈSE UNIV. DE PARIS.

NL 0432297 MdBJ MH CtY

VOLUME 337

Lobstein, René.
Essai sur la législation coloniale de l'Allemagne; par René Lobstein ... Paris, A. Chevalier-Marescq & c^ie, 1902.
2 p. l., 190 p. 25^cm.
"Bibliographie": p. [185]-188.

1. Germany—Colonies—Law. 2. Germany — Colonies —Administration.

Library of Congress JV2062.L8 3—16335

NL 0432298 DLC ICJ

Lobstein, René.
... Les origines du droit dynastique allemand...
Lyon, 1914.
25 cm.
Thèse - Univ. de Lyon.

NL 0432299 CtY NjP

The lobster bite. [New York: Amer. Temperance Union, 186-?]
4 p. 12°.
Caption-title.
In: VTZ p. v. 131, no. 7.

BLACK TEMPERANCE COLL.
1. Temperance.—Addresses, essays, lectures.
N. Y. P. L. December 19, 1918.

NL 0432300 NN

The LOBSTER fishery. [Ottawa, I.B. Taylor, 1874?]
pp.13. F 6411.5

NL 0432301 MH

The lobster; is it cruel to cook him alive?
see under Park, William D. & Son.

---

*EB7 A100 710l2
Lobsters.
[London? ca.1710]
broadside. 1 illus. 32x20.5cm.
Engraved throughout; illus. of lobsters signed "A B Flamen sc", but it is rather a reverse copy, presumably by another hand, of plate no.7 in his "Diuerses especes de poissons d'eau douce".
Text is political satire in acrostic verse; date is conjectural.
At head: (Nam vos mutastis & illas) Ovid.

NL 0432303 MH

Lobsters and lobster problem
see under [Field, George Wilton] 1863-

Lewis Walpole 659 807B
The Lobster's voyage to the Brazils. Illustrated with elegant and appropriate engravings. London, J.Harris[etc.] 1808.
16p. front., plates. 13cm. [Bound with The elephant's ball. 1808]
Illustrated by W.Mulready. - cf.DNB.
In verse.
In case labelled: Butterfly's ball & sequels.

NL 0432305 CtY

Lo Bue, Francesco, 1914-1955.
... Che cosa è il Nuovo Testamento. Breve introduzione alla letteratura del cristianesimo nascente. Torre Pellice Libreria editrice Claudiana, 1954.
160 [1] p. 20^cm.
"Nota bibliografica": p. [161]

NL 0432306 NjPT

Lobund
see Notre Dame, Ind. University. Laboratories of Bacteriology.

Lobund reports
see L.O.B.U.N.D. reports

Lobunez, Walter.
The dipole moments and structures of organic peroxides and related substances.
[Philadelphia] 1954.
39 numb. l. diagrs., tables. 29 cm.
Thesis (Ph.D.) - University of Pennsylvania, 1954.
Typewritten.
Bibliography: l. 4.

NL 0432309 PU PU-El

Lobut, Henri. L347.4 P701
... L'antichrèse autrefois et aujourd'hui, son évolution historique, son rôle dans la pratique. ... Par Henri Lobut, ... Paris, A. Rousseau, 1897.
xvi, 269 p. 25½^cm.
Thèse — Univ. de Paris.

NL 0432310 ICJ

Lobwasser, Ambrosius, 1515-1580, tr.
Catechismus oder kurtzer Unterricht Christlicher Lehre
see under Heidelberg catechism.

Lobwasser, Ambrosius, 1515-1585.
Beust, Joachim von, 1522-1597.
Christiados libellus. Denuò recognitus, & locupletatus ab autore Ioachimo à Beust ... Witebergæ, typis G. Kelneri, sumptibus hæredum S. Selfischij, 1616.

M2138 .C57C5 1761 Case
Lobwasser, Ambrosius, 1515-1585.
Chur-pfälzisches gesangbuch. 1761.
Chur-pfälzisch-allgemeines reformirtes gesang-buch, bestehend aus denen Psalmen Davids, nach d. Ambrosii Lobwassers hin und wieder verbesserter uebersetzung, und 700. auserlesenen liedern, samt deren inhalt und verschiedenen neuen melodien ... Zum öffentlichen kirchen-gebrauch und besonderer haus-andacht herausgegeben, auch denen nöthigen registern und chur-pfälzischen kirchen-agendis versehen ... Franckfurt am Mayn, Bey J. B. Andreä, 1761.

Lobwasser, Ambrosius, 1515-1585.
Des Königs und Propheten Davids geistreiche Psalmen ... [harmonized by Crüger]
Berlin, Salfeldische Witwe [1700]
see under Crüger, Johann, 1598-1662.

Lobwasser, Ambrosius, 1515-1585.
Des Königs und Propheten Davids Psalmen...
Basel, 1730 (also 1743)
see under Bible. O.T. Psalms. German. Paraphrases. 1730. Lobwasser. (also 1743)

---

tPT1743 L72D4 1634
Lobwasser, Ambrosius, 1515-1585.
Deutsche zierliche Epigrammata. Von allen Ständen und Leuten in gemein.
[n.p.], 1634.
[95] p. 15cm.
Engraved title-page with author's portrait.

NL 0432316 CU

Lobwasser, Ambrosius, 1515-1585.
Einstimmiges Psalmbuch... (Bern, 1756)
see under Bible. O.T. Psalms. German. Paraphrases. 1756. Lobwasser.

Lobwasser, Ambrosius, 1515-1585.
(Die) CL [i.e. Hundertfünfzig] Psalmen Davids ...
see under Bible. O.T. Psalms. German. Paraphrases. 1696. Lobwasser. Also with later dates through at least 1786.

Lobwasser, Ambrosius, 1515-1585.
Reformed church in the United States.
Das neue und verbesserte gesangbuch, worinnen die Psalmen Davids samt einer sammlung alter und neuer geistreicher lieder, sowohl für privat und hausandachten, als auch für den öffentlichen Gottesdienst enthalten sind. Nebst einem anhang des Heydelbergischen catechismus, wie auch erbaulicher gebäter. Nach einem synodal schluss zusammen getragen und eingerichtet vor die Evangelisch-Reformirten gemeinen in den Vereinigten Staaten von America. 3. aufl. Germantaun, Gedruckt bey M. Billmeyer, 1807.

Lobwasser, Ambrosius, 1515-1585.
Neu-eingerichtetes Gesang-Buch, in welchem die Psalmen Davids ...
see under Bible. O.T. Psalms. German. Paraphrases. 1756. Lobwasser. (Cassel, J.E. Hüter) Also 1759 (Mengeringhause C. Konerts Witwe)

Lobwasser, Ambrosius, 1515-1585.
Neu-eingerichtetes Gesang-Buch, welches in sich hält die Psalmen Davids ... (Cassel, 1754)
see under Bible. O.T. Psalms. German. Paraphrases. 1754. Lobwasser.

Lobwasser, Ambrosius, 1515-1585.
Neu-verbessertes Kirchen-Gesang-Buch, in sich haltend die Psalmen Davids ...
see under Bible. O.T. Psalms. German. Paraphrases. 1753. Lobwasser. (Franckfurt a.M.) Also 1760 (Hanau)

Lobwasser, Ambrosius, 1515-1585.
Neu-verbessertes Kirchen-Gesang-Buch, verfassend die 150 Psalmen Davids ... [etc.]... revidiret und approbiret durch den christlidren Synodum Generalem der reformirten Kirchen in... Cleve, Gülich, Berg and Marck. (Basel, 1770-71 ([Wesel?] 1783)
see under Evangelisch-Reformierte Kirche in Jülich-Cleve-Berg und Mark.
[for the 1770-71 ed., in supplement]

Lobwasser, Ambrosius, 1515-1585.
Neu-vermehrt und vollständiges Gesangbuch, worinnen sowohl die Psalmen Davids...
als auch [etc.]
see under Reformed Church in the United States [for editions printed or distributed in this country] Also under title [for editions printed in Marburg for European use]

VOLUME 337

Lobwasser, Ambrosius, 1515-1585.
(Die) Psalmen Davids...
see under Bible. O.T. Psalms. German. Paraphrases. 1594. Lobwasser. Also, under similar headings, numerous later editions, through at least 1751.

M2138 .B395P8 1792 Case
Lobwasser, Ambrosius, 1515–1585.
Berner Gesangbuch.
Die Psalmen und Fest-Lieder für den öffentlichen Gottesdienst der Stadt und Landschaft Bern. Bern, D Brunner, 1792.

Lobwasser, Ambrosius, 1515-1585.
Psalmodia sacra ... Hanau, J. Lasche, 1660
see under Bible. O.T. Psalms. German. Paraphrases. 1660. Lobwasser.

Lobwasser, Ambrosius, 1515-1585.
Psalmodia sacra ... [harmonized] Berlin, C. Runge, 1658.
see under Crüger, Johann, 1598-1662.

M2142 .L2P8 1596 Case
Lobwasser, Ambrosius, 1515–1585.
Bible. *O. T. Psalms. Latin. Paraphrases. 1596. Spethe.*
Psalmorvm Davidis, prophetæ regii, paraphrasis metrorhythmica, ad melodias gallicas, et rhythmos germanicos d. doct. Ambrosii Lobwasseri, χαδ δύναμιν concinne ac proprie accommodata, exercitium scholasticæ iuuentuti matutinum & vespertinum futura. Cum argumentis, diuersa metri ratione, & quatuor vocum symphoniis avctore Andrea Spethe ... Heidelberg, apud Petrum Mareschallum, D.M.XCVI.

Lobwasser, Ambrosius, 1515-1585.
Ils Psalms da David, suainter la melodia francêsa... Basel, 1661 (also:[Zernez] 1776)
see under Bible. O.T. Psalms. Raeto-Romance (Upper Engadine) Paraphrases. 1661. Wietzel. (also with date 1776)

Lobwasser, Ambrosius, 1515-1585.
Ils Psalms de David, segond melodia de A. Lobvasser: sco eir otras usadas festales. Scuol, 1762
see under Bible. O. T. Psalms. Raeto-Romance (Lower Engadine) Paraphrases. 1762. Nicolai.

Lobwasser,, Ambrosius, 1515-1585.
Der Psalter des Königlichen Propheten Davids...
see under Bible. O.T. Psalms. German. Paraphrases. 1573. Lobwasser. and later editions under similar headings.

Lobwasser,Ambrosius,1515-1585.
Sermo versibvs comprehensvs et habitvs ab Ambrosio Lobassero ... cvm novis magistris scolastici honores decernerentvr Lipsiae,anno M.D.XLIX. Hvic addita est,Forma declarationis et renvntiationis illorvm. Lipsiae, in officina V.Papae [1549?]
[23] p. 19½ x 14½cm.
Signatures: A-C⁴ (C[4] verso blank)
Initials.
The Forma declarationis has caption title: Oratio postea habita a m.rectore academiae,vt mos est,qva creati declaratiqve magistri hi fvervnt.
1.Leipzig. Universität.

NL 0432333 MiU

---

*GC5 L7867 548s
Lobwasser, Ambrosius, 1515-1585.
Silvvla carminvm, inter qvae praecipva est ode Asclepiadea cvm acrostichide epithalamii compositi Avgvsto principi Sax. Avtore m. Ambrosio Lobassero.
Lipsiae anno M.D.XLVIII.
8°. [15]p. 15cm.
Signature: A⁸.
Includes a poem addressed to the author by Joachim Camerarius.

NL 0432334 MH

Lobwasser, Ambrosius, 1515-1585.
Transponiertes Psalmenbuch...
Bern, 1745 (also 1755)
see under Bible. O.T. Psalms. German. Paraphrases. 1745. Lobwasser. (also 1755)

Lobwasser, Ambrosius, 1515-1585.
Vermehrtes und zum Theil verbessertes Gesang-Buch... Marburg, J.M. Stock, 1742 [his Die Psalmen Davids, and other material]
see under Bible. O.T. Psalms. German. Paraphrases. 1742. Lobwasser.

Lobwasser, Ambrosius, 1515-1585.
Vierstimmiges Psalmbuch... Bern, 1757 (also 1763)
see under Bible. O.T. Psalms. German. Paraphrases. 1757. Lobwasser. (also with date 1763)

Beinecke Library 1971 344
Lobweiler, Bros
Auss Leiptzig/ vom 13. Februarij. Kurtzer Bericht/ was sich bey angehendem von Churfl. Durchleucht. zu Sachsen/ ꝛc.ꝛc.ꝛc. aussgeschriebenem/ der evangelischen vnd protestirenden Churfürsten vnd Stånden hocherwüntschtem Convent vernemmen lassen. Auss einem Schreiben Bros. Lobvveiler an seine gnådige Herrschafft/ sampt beygefügtem Provisional vidimus vber die bey dieser Occasion durch Matthiam Hoe von Hoenegg/ ... in der Kirchen zu S.Thomas zu Leiptzig gehaltener stattlicher

Anmahnungs-Predig/ wie dieselbe erstlich gedruckt zu Leiptzig/ bey Gregorio Ritschen/ Anno 1631.
47 p. 19 cm.
Bound with: Oedickhof, Johann. Recepisse, dass D.Matthiae Hoe ... Leipzigsche Schlusspredig ...
Signatures: a-f⁴

1. Hoë von Hoënegg, Matthias, 1580-1645. Convent Predigt der evangelischen Stände zu Leipzig, über den 83. Psalm. 2. Theology, Doctrinal - Protestant authors.

NL 0432340 CtY

Lobysevich, Fedor Ivanovich.
Описаніе Хивинскаго похода 1873 года. По матеріаламъ особой коммиссіи, учрежденной тотчасъ послѣ похода. Составлено Ф. И. Лобысевичемъ. Подъ ред. В. Н. Троцкаго. С.-Петербургъ, Общественная польза, 1898.
ii, 277 p. illus., fold. col. maps, ports. 33 cm.

1. Russo-Khivan expedition, 1873. I. Trofskil, Vitalii Nikolaevich, 1835-1901, ed. II. Title.
Title romanized: Opisanie Khivinskago pokhoda.

DK889.L62 CA 13-184

NL 0432341 DLC

PQ4673 .K6 Rare Bk. Coll.
Lobysevich, Stepan, tr.
(Liubov' Palirifa i Dirfil ...)
Любовь Палиріа и Дирфіл. Перевелъ съ французскаго на россійскій Степанъ Лобысевичъ. Въ Санктпетербургѣ, При Морскомъ шляхетномъ кадетскомъ корпусѣ, 1774.

Lobzan Tandsin
see **bLo-bzaṅ bsTan-'jin,** *fl.* 1650–1735.

Lobzang Mingyur Dorje, Lama
see Blo-bsaṅ min-ʼgyur rdo-rje, Lama.

Loc**, baron de, pseud.
Essai sur la necessité de conférer les emplois selon les talens
see [Locella, Alois Emmerich, Freiherr von] 1733-1800.

Loc, Alf, *pseud.*
see
Lo Cascio, Alfred, 1910–

Loc, Phan-van-
see
Phan-van-Loc.

La loca de Londres
see under [Lafont, Charles] 1809-1864.

Micro-card
La loca del Guadalquivir. Drama en siete cuadros. Precedido de un prólogo. Madrid, Impr. de Cristóbal González, 1860. [Louisville, Ky., Falls City Microcards, 1960]
2 cards. [Four Centuries of Spanish Drama]
Microprint copy.
Collation of the original: 100 p. 22 cm.

NL 0432349 LU OrU FU NN ICRL

La loca fingida
see under Breton de los Herreros, Manuel, 1796-1873.

Loca hebraica ex Sacra Scriptura selecta, quae ad demonstranda religionis christianae dogmata adhiberi solent
see under [Eichenlaub, Candidus Bernard, O.S.B.] 1862-1940.

He77 027 6
La loca; 6, El castillo de las siete torres, drama en cinco actos, arreglado al teatro español por los Sres.S.G., y V.y S.y L. [Madrid,1851]
16p. 27cm. (Biblioteca dramatica)
Binder's title: Teatro español. 3.ser., v.6.
Caption title.

1. Napoléon I, Emperor of the French, 1769-1821 - Drama. I. G., S

NL 0432351 CtY

Ločšk, Karel.
Mistr Jan Hus; k 6.červenci 1903. Praha, Nakl. K.Ločska, 1903
16 p.
"Částečný výtěžek ve prospěch Husova fondu"

NL 0432352 MH

VOLUME 337

051 L786 The Local. v.1, Feb.16, 1878- Scottsburg, Or. nos. in v. 25cm.

NL 0432353 OrU

The LOCAL agent; monthly educational insurance magazine for fire, casualty and surety agents. v.14-41, no.9; 1942-Sept.1969. St. Louis, Commerce pub. co. v. illus. 29cm.
Subtitle varies (sometimes omitted).
For later file, which continues its numbering see: American agent & broker.

1. Insurance--Per. and soc. publ.--U.S.

NL 0432354 NN ICRL

Film 1122 no. 3 LOCAL anaesthesia by beta-eucaine, hydrochloricum and lacticum, in combination with suprarenal substances. [By H. Braun, et al. n. p.] 1905.
52 p.
Film copy.
Includes articles which appeared originally in various medical journals.
I. Braun, Heinrich, 1862-1934

NL 0432355 DNLM

... Local and business directory [of Holyoke, Mass.] for 18 Containing a history of the town ... Holyoke, Mass., C. H. Lyman, 18
v. front. (fold. plan) 20½cm.

1. Holyoke, Mass.—Direct. I. Lyman, Charles H., Holyoke, Mass., pub.

8-32979

Library of Congress F74.H73A18

NL 0432356 DLC

Local and Greenwich time of high water on full and change days, with the rise of the tide at springs and neaps, for the principal ports of the world see under Gt. Brit. Hydrographic office.

The local Anti-Saloon League; its organization, constituency, work, and value. (Revised and reprinted.) [n. p.] 1900. 4 l. 16°.

1. Temperance.—Societies.
N. Y. P. L. May 2, 1921

NL 0432358 NN

LOCAL arbitration proceedings between Boston newspaper publishers and Boston typographical union, no.13, February 5,6,8,1912. Boston, Allied print.trades council, n.d.

Pamphlet. Soc 1561.01

NL 0432359 MH

Local assessors, State conference of see State conference of local assessors in the State of New York.

The Local authorities diary and Abridgment of the year's changes in the law ... [1925- London, E. Benn limited, 1924-
v. 22½cm.
The Abridgment has caption title: Fletcher Moulton's abridgment for 1925-
Editors: 1925- R. A. Glen, H. F. Moulton, G. Olver.

1. Local government—Gt. Brit.—Year-books. 2. Law—Gt. Brit. 3. Law reports, digests, etc.—Gt. Brit. I. Glen, Randolph Alexander, 1875- ed. II. Moulton, Hugh Fletcher, 1876- joint ed. III. Olver, Graham Thomas Walters, joint ed. IV. Title: Abridgment of the year's changes in the law. V. Title: Fletcher Moulton's abridgment for 1925-

28-1384

NL 0432361 DLC

Local business directory and views. [San Francisco, Bardell art printing co., °1915]
cover-title, 1 p. l., 24 mounted col. pl. 22 x 30cm.
Views only.

1. San Francisco. Panama-Pacific international exposition, 1915.

15-19602

Library of Congress TC781.C1L7

NL 0432362 DLC

Local Cartage National Conference.
Directory of local truck operators see under title

Local climatological data, Blue Hill Obs. see under U.S. Weather Bureau.

Local collections; or, Records of remarkable events, connected with the borough of Gateshead. 1837- Gateshead-on-Tyne, W. Douglas, 1840-
v. in front., illus., map, plans. 28½cm.
"Only sixty copies printed.—To be continued annually."
A volume for 1844 is mentioned in Gross's Bibliography of English municipal history.

1. Gateshead, Eng.—Hist.

3—4622

Library of Congress DA690.G25L8

NL 0432365 DLC

Local community fact book: Chicago metropolitan area. 1938- [Chicago]
v. illus. 29 cm.
Vols. for 1960- issued as Chicago Community Renewal Program study.
Supersedes the District fact book, edited by E. L. Burchard and M. J. Arvin.
Title varies slightly.
Vol. for 1938 prepared for the Chicago Recreation Commission with the assistance of the Social Science Research Committee, University of Chicago, and others.
Vols. for 1949- issued by the Chicago Community Inventory, University of Chicago.

Editors: 1938-49, L. Wirth (with M. Furez, 1938; E. H. Bernert, 1949)—1950- E. M. Kitagawa (with P. M. Hauser, 1950; K. E. Taeuber, 1960)

1. Chicago — Descr. — Period. 2. Chicago — Stat. — Period. I. Wirth, Louis, 1897-1952, ed. II. Furez, Margaret, ed. III. Sheldon, Eleanor Bernert, 1920- ed. IV. Kitagawa, Evelyn Mae, 1920- ed. V. Hauser, Philip Morris, 1909- ed. VI. Taeuber, Karl E., ed. VII. Chicago Recreation Commission. VIII. Chicago. University. Chicago Community Inventory. (Series: Chicago. Community Renewal Program. Study)

F548.1.L6 54-2000 rev

NL 0432367 DLC IEN MiU CU NcD

Local control survey of Massachusetts see Massachusetts geodetic survey.

Local Co-Operative Stores of Illinois.
Proceedings; first convention of the Local Co-Operative Stores of Illinois, and first annual convention of the Co-Operative Society of Illinois. [Peoria? Ill., 1915]
64 p. 24 cm.

Cover title.

1. Cooperation - Illinois - Societies. I. The Co-Operative Society of Illinois.

NL 0432369 WHi

Local Council of ______ in affiliation with the National Council of Women of Canada. British Columbia.
Constitution and standing orders of the local councils of British Columbia.... Victoria, B.C.Colonist Presses, 1911.
22 p. 13cm.

NL 0432370 CaBViPA

A local council of social service see under National Council of Social Service.

Local Council of Women, Regina, Sask.
[History of the Regina Council of Women.] Regina, 1926. 64 p. 16°.

403429A. 1. Woman—Assoc. and org.—Canada—Regina.
N. Y. P. L. March 14, 1929

NL 0432372 NN

Local Council of Women, *San Francisco.* 379.794 S1057
The socialization of the public school. Report of Committee appointed by The Local Council of Women for the Establishment of Municipal Social Centers. San Francisco, California, 1905.
3 pt. in 1 vol. 21½cm.
cover-title.
"References in part," at end of pt. 2, 3.
Contents. — Legislative provisions for education and recreation. 1904. — The socialization of the public school. Conditions in cities other than San Francisco, and in foreign countries. 1904. — Physical conditions in the San Francisco public schools. Ideal school administration. 1905.

NL 0432373 ICJ CU ICU

HC L8115go Local Council of Women, Swift Current, Sask.
Golden furrows. Format and editorial work by Dave and Alice Belbeck, from material supplied by LCW's Archives Committee. Swift Current, Sask., 1954.
55 p. illus., ports.

On cover: An historical chronicle of Swift Current.
"Saskatchewan Golden Jubilee, 1905-1955"

NL 0432374 CaOTU WHi

Local council of women, Victoria, British Columbia.
Address delivered at the - annual meeting, by the president, 19 - 19 , and constitution. [Victoria, Colonist,19 -19].
v.0.

NL 0432375 CaBViPA

Local Council of Women of Victoria and Vancouver Island. Meeting, 13th, Victoria, B.C., 1907.
[Proceedings. Victoria, 1907]
7 p. 17 cm.

Cover title.
Meeting held Nov.11-12, 1907.

NL 0432376 CaBViP

VOLUME 337

KG
195
L62
C68
The LOCAL courts' and municipal gazette. v.1-8; 1865-72. Toronto, W.C. Chewett [etc.] 8 v.

Supersedes, in part, the Upper Canada law journal.

1. Law reports, digests, etc. - Ontario.

NL 0432377 CaBVaU CaOTU WaU-L

Local defence volunteers (*Gt. Brit.*)
see
Gt. Brit. *Home guard.*

Local designations of Confederate troops (n.p., n.d.)
169 p. 21cm.
Interleaved

NL 0432379 DNW GEU NcU NcD

The LOCAL elections,liberal-conservative campaign pamphlet containing facts and figures for the consideration of the people relative to the issues to be decided on 5th June; also the speech of W.R.Meredith,delivered at the mass meeting held Apr.25th,1879. Toronto, Williams,Sleeth & Macmillan,1879.

pp.39.
Title taken from cover.
"Speech delivered by W.R.Mereidth",pp. 27-39.
Can 2435.15

NL 0432380 MH

Microfilm
R
Local 439 news. Toronto.

Library has
v.1- March 9, 1944-

Microfilm. Positive.
Frequency varies: v.1, no.1-no.3, War worker.
Official organ of Local 439, UAW-CIO.
On reel with v.13-15 of United automobile worker. Canadian ed.

I. International Union, United Automobile, Aircraft and Implement Workers of America. Local no. 439.

NL 0432381 MiD

Local events and incidents at home
see under [Irving, John Beaufain] 1800-1881.

The local examinations statute
see under [Griffiths, John] 1806-1885.

Local fire, lightning, tornado, windstorm, and hail protection association.
Constitution and by-laws of the Local fire, lightning, tornado, windstorm, and hail protection association. [Halloway, Minn.] W. H. Pfeiffer [1915]
[5] p. 22½cm.

15-18860
Library of Congress HG9969.U6L6

NL 0432384 DLC

Local gleanings; an archæological & historical magazine, chiefly relating to Lancashire & Cheshire. Ed. by J. P. Earwaker ... v. 1; July 1879–June 1880. Manchester [Eng.] J. E. Cornish; [etc., etc., 1879–80]
xxxii, 480 p. plates, port., facsim. 24½cm. monthly.
No more published.

1. Lancashire, Eng. 2. Cheshire, Eng. I. Earwaker, John Parsons, 1847-1895, ed.

4—14504
Library of Congress DA670.L19L8

NL 0432385 DLC MdBP OCl MH NcD PHi

Local government; a handbook for citizens of Chapel Hill and Orange County, North Carolina
see under [Chapel Hill, N.C. League of Women Voters]

Local government abroad. v.1- ; Oct. 1927-
London, Municipal Journal Ltd.
v. quarterly.

Ceased Jan. 1930.
Absorbed by Municipal review.
"In connection with the International Union of Local Authorities."

NL 0432387 ICRL IU

Local government acts, 1929
see under Gt. Brt. Laws, statutes, etc., 1910-1936 (George V)

LOCAL government administration.
Melbourne. v. illus. 24cm.

Bimonthly.
"Official organ of the Institute of municipal administration, Australia.

1. Government, Local--Per. and soc. publ. --Australia. 2. Municipal government--Per. and soc. publ. --Australia. I. Institute of municipal administration (Australia).

NL 0432389 NN

Local government administration ... v. 1- June 1935-
[Westminster, 1935-
v. illus., diagrs. 25cm. quarterly.
Organ of the International union of local authorities; published by the British and American committees of the union.
Includes translations of many articles in "L'Administration locale" as well as original articles.

1. Local government—Period. 2. Municipal government—Period. I. International union of local authorities.

42-44739
Library of Congress [2] 352.0005

NL 0432390 DLC ICRL I P MiU-L NNU NN ICU TxU

Local Government and Shires Associations of N.S.W.
see Local Government Association of New South Wales.

The **Local** government annual and official directory.
London, Local Governmental Journal.
v. 19 cm.
Began publication in 1892. Cf. Willing's press guide.

1. Local government—Yearbooks. 2. Local government—Gt. Brit. I. Local government journal.

JS3003.L58 352.042 52-20717

NL 0432392 DLC NN MB RPB

Local Government Association of New South Wales.
Annual conference. Proceedings.
Sydney.
v. 21 cm.

1. Local government—Societies. 2. Local government—New South Wales.

JS8141.A1L6 352.094 51-38412 ‡

NL 0432393 DLC

Local Government Association of New South Wales.
A history of local government in New South Wales
see under Larcombe, Frederick Arthur.

Local government association of New South Wales.

Browning, Robert Jardine, *ed.*
Local government law & practice, New South Wales; being the Local government acts, 1919–1922, annotated and explained, including opinions issued to councils by the Local government association, by R. J. Browning ... J. Young ... [and] A. R. Bluett ... Sydney [etc.] The Law book co. of Australasia, limited, 1924.

JS3081
1949
.M3
Local Government Association of New South Wales.
Mainerd, A
Local government overseas; address to the annual conference of the Local Government Association, following visit early in 1949 to England and America. [Sydney, 1949?]

Local Government Association of New South Wales. Proceedings
see its Annual conference. Proceedings.

Local Government Association of New South Wales
see also **Local Government Summer School,** *Sydney University.*

JS7649
R4L79
f
Local Government Association of Rhodesia.
Local government information
[Salisbury, Rhodesia]
v. 33cm. annual.
Cover title.
Processed.

1. Local government - Rhodesia, Southern - Stat. I. Title.

NL 0432399 CSt-H

JS7649
R4L81
f
Local Government Association of Southern Rhodesia. Conference.
Report of proceedings.
[Salisbury]
v. 33cm. annual.
Cover title.

1. Local government - Rhodesia, Southern Congresses.

NL 0432400 CSt-H

Local Government Board (*Ireland*)
see **Ireland.** *Local Government Board.*

Local Government Board for Scotland
see **Scotland.** *Local Government Board.*

VOLUME 337

Local government boundary commission (*Gt. Brit.*)
see
Gt. Brit. *Local government boundary commission.*

JS7
.G53

The Local government chronicle.

Gt. Brit. *Local Government Board.*
Decisions of the Local Government Board, collected from all sources, and reprinted from the Local government chronicle. 1902/03–1916. London, C. Knight.

HJ9423
.L6

Local government chronicle.

Local government finance.
London, C. Knight.

The **Local** government chronicle and magisterial reporter.
[London, C. Knight & co., ltd.,
nos. in v. 28½cm. weekly.
"Established 1855."

1. Local government—Period. 2. Local government—Gt. Brit.
45-52998
Library of Congress JS3001.L6
[2] 352.042

NL 0432406 DLC NBuU-L DNLM WaU-L NNC-L DL

Local government ... comprising statutes, orders, forms, cases, and decisions of the local government board. 1908–
London, Butterworth & co. [etc.] 1910–
v. 26cm.
Editors: 1908– Alexander Macmorran. K. M. Macmorran.

1. Local government—Gt. Brit. I. Macmorran, Alexander, 1852– ed. II. Macmorran, Kenneth M., ed.

Library of Congress JS3111.L7 10—19461

NL 0432407 DLC MH-L NjP GU ICRL PU MiU

TD884
L8
1950

Local Government Conference on Air Pollution and Smoke Prevention Problems in Allegheny County, Pittsburgh, 1950.
Proceedings... October 27, 1950. Pittsburgh, 1950.
54 p. 23 cm.
Cover title.
At head of title: University of Pittsburgh. Institute of Local Government.

1. Air pollution.— Congresses. I. Pittsburgh. University. Institute of Local Government.

NL 0432408 DI IEN

Pamphlet
TD
2+

Local Government Conference on Refuse Disposal Methods, University of Pittsburgh, 1954.
Proceedings. University of Pittsburgh, April 22, 23, 1954. [Pittsburgh, 1954]
106 p. illus. 28cm.

1. Refuse and refuse disposal--Congresses.

NL 0432409 NIC MiD

The LOCAL government directory; almanac and guide... Year

London: C. Knight and Co. Ltd., 1 19cm.
v.

1. Government, Local—Gt.Br.—Yearbooks.

NL 0432410 NN

Local government (Dublin) tribunal
see
Ireland (*Eire*) *Local government* (*Dublin*) *tribunal.*

TA1
.A96

Local Government Engineers' Association of New South Wales.
The Australasian engineer.
Sydney.

HJ101
q073

Local government finance.
May 1949-
Eugene, University of Oregon, Bureau of Governmental Research and Service, 1949-
v. 28cm.

Published in cooperation with the Oregon Finance Officers Association.
Name changes: 1949-68, Oregon Finance Officers Association. News letter.- 1969- Local government finance.

1.Finance, Public - Oregon. 2. Finance - Soc. I.Oregon. University.

NL 0432413 OrCS

Local government finance.
[London,
v. ports. 26cm. monthly.
Publication began in 1806.
At head of title, : The Institute of municipal treasurers and accountants (incorporated)

1. Municipal finance—Period. 2. Municipal finance—Gt. Brit. I. Institute of municipal treasurers and accountants.
45-52999
Library of Congress HJ9103.L6
[2] 352.105

NL 0432414 DLC NcU PPiU KyU TxU MoU NBuU-L N

Local government finance.
London, C. Knight.
v. 22 cm. annual.
Editors: 19 F. J. Alban and N. E. Lamb.
"Being articles, queries and answers appearing in 'The Local government chronicle.'"

1. Local finance—Yearbooks. 2. Local finance—Gt. Brit. I. Alban, Frederick John, ed. II. Local government chronicle.

HJ9423.L6 352.1 51–20917 ‡

NL 0432415 DLC

Local government for the territory of Utah
see under U.S. Congress. House. Committee on the Territories.

Local government forms and precedents in England and Wales. Consulting editor: A. Norman Schofield; editor: A. V. Risdon. London, Butterworth, 1953–
v. 26 cm.
——— General index. London, Butterworth, 1957.
283 p. 26 cm.
JS3161.L6 Index

1. Municipal government—Gt. Brit.—Forms, blanks, etc. I. Schofield, Alfred Norman, ed.
JS3161.L6 352.042 57–26401 rev

NL 0432417 DLC

Local government functions survey (*New Jersey*)
see
Survey of local governmental functions (*New Jersey*)

Local government handbook [1924]– prepared by the Joint research and information department of the Trades union congress and the Labour party. London, The Labour joint publications department, 1924–
v. 19cm.
Includes bibliography and a list of local government societies.

1. Local government—Gt. Brit. 2. Municipal government—Gt. Brit. I. Trades union congress. II. Labor party (Gt. Brit.)
26-12307
Library of Congress JS3003

NL 0432419 DLC PP NN

Local government handbook [1945-]
see under Labour Party (Gt. Brit.)

Local government in Branch county
see under [Ford, Robert Spivey] 1902-

Local government in Cheboygan county ...
see under [Ford, Robert Spivey] 1902-

Local government in Genesee county ...
see under [Landers, Frank Michael]

Local government [in Scotland]
see under [Goudy, Henry] 1848-1921

Local government information
see under Illinois. University. Institute of Government and Public Affairs.

Local government journal.
[London,
v. illus. 27½cm. monthly.
Publication began Feb. 10, 1872. *cf.* Union list of serials.
Running title : Local government journal & officials' gazette.

1. Local government—Period. 2. Local government—Gt. Brit.
45-25080
Library of Congress JS3001.L63
[2] 352.042

NL 0432426 DLC NcU NN

VOLUME 337

Local Government Journal.
The housing acts, 1914. Being the text of the Housing act, 1914, and the Housing (no. 2) act, 1914 ...
see under Gt. Brit. Laws, statutes, etc., 1910-1936 (George V)

Local government journal.
JS3003 .L58 The Local government annual and official directory.
London, Local Governmental Journal.

US 869 L Local government law service newsletter; news and comments on local government law.
v. 1, n. 1- Jan. 1951-
Philadelphia, Section of local government law, American bar association, 1951-
v. 28 cm. 10 nos. per year.
Title varies: Jan. 1951-June 1961, Municipal law service letter.
Includes Committee reports supplement (annual)

NL 0432429 MH-L WaU-L GU NNC-L NcU DLC

The Local government manual and directory. 1923-
London, Shaw & Sons Ltd.
v. 20 cm. annual.
Continues Shaw's local government manual and directory ...

1. Local government—Great Britain—Yearbooks.
JS3003.M8 352.042 72-622949

NL 0432430 DLC DNLM PP DS

Local government. Memorandum ... [1877]
see under [Wright, Sir Robert Samuel] 1839-1904.

The Local government news. v. 1-8; Jan. 1924 - Dec. 1931. London, The Fabian Society, 1924-1931.
8 v. in 4. 28 cm. monthly.

NL 0432432 NcD

331.805 INA Local 974 news.
East Peoria, Ill.
v. illus. 42cm. irregular.
Vol. 4 omitted in numbering.
"Official publication of Local 974, UAW-CIO."
Title varies: May 11, 1955, The 974 news.

NL 0432433 IU

The local government of Jamaica and British Guiana. [London, Jackson and Walford, 1848]
19 p. 22cm.
Volume of pamphlets.

1. Local government - Jamaica. 2. Local government - British Guiana.

NL 0432434 NNC

Local government of the metropolis; a sketch of the municipal institutions of London, including the city of London Corporation ... with the outline of a plan for an improved system of local administration. London, J. Macrone, 1836.
35 p. 21 cm.
Reprint of "Municipal reform as required for the metropolis", signed W.E.H., from the London and Westminister Review, April 1836.

1. London. Corporation. 2. London - Pol. & Govt.

NL 0432436 MdBP

Local Government Officer
see L.G.O.: Local government Officer.

S 352.0755 qL811 Local Government Officials' Conference, Charlottesville, Va.
Proceedings. [Charlottesville, Bureau of Public Administration, University of Virginia, 1952-55.
4 v. in 1. 29 cm.
"A cooperative training program sponsored jointly by the League of Virginia counties, Virginia Court Clerks' Association, Virginia State Sheriffs' and City Sergeants' Association, Commissioners of the Revenue Association of Virginia, Treasurers Association of Virginia, Association of Commonwealth's Attorneys of Virginia [and] University of Virginia."
1. Local government. Virginia. I. League of Virginia Counties. II. Virginia. University. Bureau of Public Administration.

NL 0432439 N

Local Government Officials' Conference, *Charlottesville, Va., 1952.*
Proceedings. [Charlottesville] Bureau of Public Administration, University of Virginia, 1952.
vi, 71 p. 28 cm.
"A cooperative training program sponsored jointly by the League of Virginia Counties, Virginia Court Clerks' Association, Virginia State Sheriffs' and City Sergeants' Association, Commissioners of the Revenue Association of Virginia, Treasurers' Association of Virginia, Association of Commonwealth's Attorneys of Virginia [and] University of Virginia."
1. Local government—Virginia.
A 53-9525
Virginia. State Library for Library of Congress [1]

NL 0432440 Vi WaU-L ViU-L

JS451 .V8L623 1952 Local Government Officials' Conference, Charlottesville, Va., 1952.
[Programs, statistics and resumé of proceedings of the Conference held at the University of Virginia, June 25-28, 1952. Charlottesville? Va., 1952]
8 pieces (in slip-case) 28cm.
Mimeographed.
Resumé of proceedings, "Local Government Officials Share Experiences", composed for publication in "Virginia and the Virginia County."
1. Local government—Congresses. 2. Local government—Va.

NL 0432441 ViU

Pamphlet JS 44+ Local Government Officials' Conference, Charlottesville, Va., 1954.
Proceedings. August 23-25, 1954. A cooperative training program sponsored jointly by the League of Virginia Counties [and others. Charlottesville] Bureau of Public Administration, University of Virginia, 1954.
vi, 86p. illus. 28cm.
1. Local government--Virginia.

NL 0432442 NIC NN

Pamphlet JS 71+ Local Government Officials' Conference, Charlottesville, Va., 1955.
Proceedings, August 29-31, 1955. A cooperative training program sponsored jointly by the League of Virginia Counties, League of Virginia Municipalities [and others. Charlottesville] Bureau of Public Administration, University of Virginia, 1955.
vi,68 p. illus. 28cm.
1. Local gove rnment--Virginia--Congresses.

NL 0432443 NIC

Local government officier and contractor
see L. G. O.: Local government officier and contractor.

UK 008 L73 Local government review. v.1- Jan. 28, 1837- London.
v. biweekly, 1837; weekly, 1838-
Title varies: 1837-45, Justice of the peace and county, borough, poor law union and parish law recorder; 1846-1926, Justice of the peace; 1927-Nov. 13, 1971, Justice of the peace and local government review; Nov. 20, 1971- Local government review.
Caption title, 1846- : And county, borough, poor law union and parish law recorder.

NL 0432445 NBuU-L

Local government review. London
see also Justice of the peace and local government review.

The Local government review. v. 1-(no. 1-12;) Jan. 1949-
[Quezon City, Philippines]
(1) v. illus., ports. 26 cm. monthly.

1. Local government—Philippine Islands—Period.
JS7301.A1L6 55-23922

NL 0432447 DLC

Local government service. London
see
The Municipal officer.

Local government services and industrial development in the southeast. [A joint statement by: University of Alabama, Bureau of Public Administration, and others. University? Ala., 1952]
27 p. 21 cm.

1. Industries, Location of—Southern States. 2. Municipal government—Southern States. I. Alabama. University. Bureau of Public Administration.
HC107.A13L6 338.975 52-62959 ‡

PSt IU NcD MsU FMU IdPI OrPR OrU Wa WaE WaS WaPS WaSp WaSpG WaT WaTC WaWW OrU-M MtBuM CaBVaU IdB IdU MtBC NN MtU OrCS OrP
NL 0432449 DLC Or DI FTaSU OrU TxU OrStbM OrSaW

Local government; speaker's handbook
see Labour Party (Gt. Brit.) Research Dept.
Speakers' notes, local elections.

VOLUME 337

Local Government Summer School, *Sydney University.*
Proceedings.
[Sydney]
v. diagrs. 22 cm.
First school held 1945.
School sponsored by Local Government Assn. of New South Wales and Shires Assn. of New South Wales.

1. Local government—Societies, etc. 2. Local government—Australia.
JS8001.L6 352.094 49-17108*

NL 0432451 DLC

Local government yearbook. Cleveland.
see under Cleveland Bureau of Governmental Research.

A local guide and directory, with compliments of the merchants of Queens Village. [Queens Village, Queens review print]n.d. [20]p. Cover title.

NL 0432453 NJQ

The LOCAL guide, conducting to whatever is worthy of notice in the colonies of Deméràry and Essequebo. George-town, Deméràry, W. Baker, 1819.
17 cm.

NL 0432454 MH

The local guide: Demerary and Essequebo...
George-town: Royal Gazette Office 12?.
v.

1. Demerara—Registers. 2. Demerara—Gov. 3. Essequibo—Registers. 4. Essequibo—Gov. 5. Commerce—Regulations—Guiana, British.
N. Y. P. L. September 11, 1925

NL 0432455 NN

Local guide of British Guiana. Containing historical sketch, statistical tables, and the entire statute law of the colony in force, Jan. 1, 1843.
= Demerary. Baum & Dallas. 1843. 828 pp. Map. Sm. 8°.

F4019 — Guiana, British. Geog. Guide-books.

NL 0432456 MB

LOCAL health units for the nation.
New York. v. 29cm.

Irregular.
"Bulletin of National advisory committee on local health departments."
Issued by the National health council (Nov. 1947-Jan. 1948 by the American public health association).

Title varies: Nov. 1947-May, 1948, Bulletin on local health units.
Ceased publication with v.13, no.2, Dec. 1959?

1. Hygiene, Public--Assoc. and org.--U.S. I. American public health association. II. National health council. III. National advisory committee on local health departments.

NL 0432458 NN CU

The Local historian. v. 1-
Aug./Sept. 1952-
[London, etc., National Council of Social Service, etc.]
v. illus., maps, plates, ports. 22-24 cm.

Bimonthly, 1952-June/July 1956; quarterly, autumn 1956-
Journal of the Standing Conference for Local History, autumn 1961-
Title varies: 1952-67, The Amateur historian.
Issues for autumn 1961- include the Standing Conference for Local History Bulletin.

1. Gt. Brit.—History, Local—Periodicals. I. National Council of Social Service. II. Standing Conference for Local History. III. Standing Conference for Local History. Bulletin. IV. Title: The Amateur historian.

DA20.A44 63-54841

NL 0432459 DLC NIC TxU MiU IU

T929.105
L786 **Local history & genealogical society, cooperating with the Dallas Public Library. v.1-**
Feb. 1955-
[Dallas, Tex., Local History & Genealogical Society]
v. 28cm.

Newsletter of the organization of the same name. Cf. New serial titles, 1963.

1. Genealogy - Period. 2. Texas - Geneal. I. Local History and Genealogical Society, Dallas.

NL 0432460 TxU PHi CL NN

The local history of Andover, Vt.
see under Hemenway, Abby Maria, ed.

Local hits, or, High life in New Orleans. A comedy in one act. New Orleans, Printed at the office of The Orleanian, 1850.
52 p. 18cm.

Errata on p. 52.

NL 0432462 NcD NN

Local housing authority conference.
Report.

New York [
v. 27cm.

At head of title: , National housing agency, Federal public housing authority, Region II.

1. Housing - U. S. I. U. S. Federal public housing authority.

NL 0432463 NNC-A

Local improvements by special assessment in Illinois
see under [Cushing, Royal B] 1875-

Local indexes in Georgia libraries
see under [American library association. Junior members' round table. Georgia]

Local institutions. Baltimore, Johns Hopkins University, 1883.
CB
ALS
OTm
1 v. (various pagings) (Johns Hopkins University studies in historical and political science. [1st ser.])
Contents.-1. An introduction to American institutional history, by E. A. Freeman.-2. The Germanic origin of New England towns, by H. B. Adams. -3. Local government in Illinois, by Albert Shaw. Local government in Pennsylvania, by E. R. L. Gould.-4. Saxon tithingmen in America, by H. B.

1. Local govern ment - U. S. (Series)

Continued in next column

Continued from preceding column

Adams.-5. Local government in Michigan and the Northwest, by E. W. Bemis.-6. Parish institutions of Maryland, by Edward Ingles.-7. Old Maryland manors, by John Johnson,-8. Norman constables in America, by H. B. Adams.-9-10. Village communities of Cape Anne and Salem, by H. B. Adams.-11. The Genesis of a New England state, by Alexander Johnston.-12. Local government and free schools in South Carolina, by B. J. Ramage.

NL 0432467 CSt-Law NBuC

Local Interclerical Office, *The Hague*
see **Plaatselijk Interkerkelijk Bureau,** *The Hague.*

332.1
L78 **Local issues. Joint stock banks and Bank of England notes, &c contrasted. By a merchant. London, 1834.**
16p.

NL 0432469 IU

Local joint executive board of New York city.
Guide to union restaurants, cafeterias, bars, and hotels affiliated with American federation of labor, New York state federation of labor, Central trades & labor council, New York state culinary alliance & Bartenders international league of America. Compiled and published August 12, 1939, by Local joint executive board of New York city... New York, N. Y. [1939]
189 p. 13½cm.

Cover-title.

1. Restaurants—U. S.—N. Y.—New York.
N. Y. P. L. August 23, 1940

NL 0432470 NN

The local loans of England and Wales, Author of
see Dalton, Sir Cornelius Neale, 1842-

Local loiterings, and visits in the vicinity of Boston
see under [Dix, John] 1800?-1865?

Local London, a municipal directory for the metropolis and its suburbs ... An official reference to the several corporations, councils, and boards within the county and city of London, and to sixty adjoining areas of the counties of Middlesex, Surrey, Kent, Essex, and Hertford; also to the principal legal, educational, charitable and other institutions therein. Comp. from the latest official records. Pub. yearly in June. Westminster, P. S. King & son [19
v. fold. map. 19½cm.

1. London—Direct.

20-18093

Library of Congress DA679.A3

NL 0432473 DLC

Local merchant in command
see under Institute of distribution, inc., New York.

Local notes and gleanings; Oldham
see under Shaw, Giles.

Local notes and queries from the "Manchester Guardian," 1874-[1876]
see under The Guardian, Manchester, Eng.

VOLUME 337

Local notes for 1881-1882
see under Cossins, James.

Local option. A candid view by a careful observer. [n. p., 187–?] 2 l. 12°.
In: VTZ p. v. 92, no. 11.

BLACK TEMPERANCE COLL.
1. Local option.
N. Y. P. L. June 21, 1918

NL 0432478 NN

LOCAL OPTION AND SELF-GOVERNMENT LEAGUE OF ARKANSAS.
For Arkansas citizens to decide. State wide prohibition and local option examined and compared. [Little Rock, Arkansas, Democrat Print. and Litho. Co., 1912.]
23 x 9.5 cm. pp.16.

NL 0432479 MH

FILM
1417
"Local option," considered as to its principles—as to its effects on the cause of temperance, and as to its operation on the rights and the morals of the people. [n. p., 1880?]
Microfilm copy (negative) made in 1952 by the University of Virginia Library from the Thomas Balch copy.
Collation of original from the film: 16 p.
1. Local option—Va.—Controversial literature. 2. Local option—U. S.—Controversial literature.

NL 0432480 ViU

The local option debate and division list, June 14th, 1881. [Manchester: United Kingdom Alliance, 1881?] 15 p. 8°.
Caption-title.
Repr.: Alliance news, June 21st, 1881.
In: VTZ p. v. 186, no. 11.

BLACK TEMPERANCE COLL.
1. Local option, Gt. Br.
N. Y. P. L. May 28, 1919.

NL 0432481 NN

"Local option" exposed
see under [Wasson, Emund Atwil] 1864-

The Local option movement in the state of New York
see under Thomann, Gallus.

Local option. Facts and figures for the people. [n. p., 1872?] 4 p. 8°.
Caption-title.
In: VTZ p. v. 91, no. 30.

BLACK TEMPERANCE COLL.
1. Local option.
N. Y. P. L. June 6, 1918

NL 0432484 NN

Local option in taxation. Amendment to the constitution of Ohio. Proposed by Mr. Locke. [Columbus, 1895?]
5 p.

NL 0432485 OClWHi

Local option. Its history and practical operation. [n. p., 1873?] 8 p. 8°.
Caption title
In: VTZ p. v. 91, no. 2.

BLACK TEMPERANCE COLL.
1. Local option.
N. Y. P. L.

NL 0432486 NN

Local option tested; comparison between license and no-license cities
see under [Muller, George]

...**Local** option: what it is, and the beneficial results of its operation in Maryland and elsewhere; its legislative history. Also a chapter on the Revenue from liquor licenses, and a recent letter from Honorable Neal Dow as to the working of prohibition in Maine. Baltimore: J. Young [1880?]. 15 p. 8°.
In: VTZ p. v. 71, no. 13.

BLACK TEMPERANCE COLL.
1. Local option, U. S.: Md.
N. Y. P. L. March 21, 1918

NL 0432488 NN

Local organizing commission of the Internationa congress of navigation. 12th, Phila., 1912
see
International congress of navigation, 12th, Phila., 1912. Local organizing commission.

HE4775
f.L8
Local passenger traffic. Germany. 1902-1908.
[Pamphlets, clippings, etc.]
12 items in 1v. illus., tables, diagrs. 32cm.
Typewritten t.-p.

NL 0432490 ICU

The Local Philosopher.
Knotty Walk ...
see under title

Local planning administration. Chicago.
see under Segoe, Ladislas.

Local planning administration. [Washington] 1951-59
see Principles and practice of urban planning.

Local Planning Institute, *Grand Rapids, 1946*
see **Grand Rapids Local Planning Institute,** *1946.*

Local planning is practical
see under New England Council. Community development committee.

Local preacher's and lay worker's conference.
Minutes of the annual session. Franklinton, 1898.
v.29.
Methodist Episcopal Church, South.

NL 0432496 Nh

Div.S.
287.105
L811
The Local preacher's' magazine. v. 1-2, Jan. 1851- 1852; new ser., v. 1- 1853-
London, Aylott and Jones.
v. in 22 cm. monthly.
Title varies: 1851-52, The Local preachers' magazine, and Mutual Aid Association register (varies slightly)
1. Wesleyan Methodist Church. Period. 2. Methodist Church. Period. I. Wesleyan Methodist Local Preachers' Mutual Aid Association.

NL 0432497 NcD KyWAT MB

The **Local** preachers' magazine and Christian family record
see The **Local** preachers' magazine.

The **Local** preachers' magazine and mutual aid reporter
see The **Local** preachers' magazine.

The local press on the Erie railway management. January, 1872. Albany, Weed, Parsons and company, printers, 1872.
74 p. 23cm.

1. Erie railroad company.
A 15-358
Title from Bureau of Railway Economics. Printed by L. C.

NL 0432500 DBRE CtY OClWHi OCl NN

Local rating; memorandum on the proposal of the Departmental Committee on Local Taxation that the assessments for local rates should be made by the Valuation Staff of the Inland Revenue Department, compiled by a body of surveyors. London: P. S. King & Son, 1914. 2 p.l., 52 p. 12°.

1. Taxation (Local), Gt. Br., 1914.
N. Y. P. L. September 13, 1915

NL 0432501 NN

Local Register, The, and chronological account of occurrences and facts connected with the town and neighbourhood of Sheffield [to 1830. Added, the [annual] Continuation of the Sheffield Local Register, to 1878].
— Sheffield. Thomas. 1830–1878. xl, 1107, (1) pp. 24°.

F3383 — Sheffield, Yorkshire, England. Hist. — Annuals.

NL 0432502 MB

HG4961
.C6
Local Securities Manual Company, Cleveland.
Cleveland securities manual.
Cleveland, Local Securities Manual Co.

HG4961
.P89
Local Securities Manual Company, Cleveland.
A Public service securities manual.
Cleveland.

Local security force (*Ireland* (*Eire*))
see
Ireland (*Eire*) *Local security force.*

VOLUME 337

The Local self-government gazette.
v. 1

Park Town, Madras, 1915 8°.
v. illus., plans, plates.

Monthly.
Editors: v. 1. K. C. Desikachariar and P. D. Aiyangar.

1. Municipal government—Per. and soc. publ.
N. Y. P. L. December 3, 1927

NL 0432506 NN

Local self-government year-book.
1928

Bombay, India, 1928 8°.
v. tables.

Published by the Local Self-Government Institute, Poona, India.
Editor : 1928 , S. R. Bhagwat.

1. Municipal government—India— Bombay (presidency).
N. Y. P. L. February 7, 1929

NL 0432507 NN

X Per L811S Local Self-Government Institute (Bombay State)
Quarterly journal. v. 1- (no. 1-); July, 1930-
[Bombay]
v. in illus. 25 cm.

Issued in cooperation with the All-India Institute of Local Self-Government.

1. Local government. Periodicals.
I. All-India Institute of Local Self-government.

NL 0432508 NcD NSyU IU P ICRL TxU MiU DLC

Local Self-Government Institute, Poona, India
Local self-government year-book
see under title

Local self-government institute, Punjab, India.
Training class for officers of local self-government service. [Lahore, Artistic printing works]

14 p.
At head of title: The Punjab local self-government institute.

NL 0432510 MH-PA

US 982 LOC Local self-government league.
... Plans to amend national prohibition without repealing either the eighteenth amendment or the Volstead act, also to divorce prohibition from politics. Baltimore, Local self-government league, Chamber of commerce, 1931.

cover-title, 46 p. 23 x 10½cm.

NL 0432511 MH-L

331.805 UNIS Local 65.

Chicago.
v. illus. 42cm. monthly.

"Dedicated to the advancement of southwestern Chicago steelworkers."
Issued by Local 65, United Steel Workers of America, CIO.

NL 0432512 IU

Local taxation, and assessment laws for city taxes, streets, sewers, &c., with notes, extracts and remarks on municipal government... Pittsburgh, Stevenson & Foster, 1875.
76 p.

NL 0432513 OClWHi

Local taxation for provincial requirements
see under [Colvin, A.]

C.6892 The Local taxes of the United Kingdom, containing a digest of the law, with a summary of statistical information concerning the several local taxes in England, Scotland, and Ireland. London, C.Knight and co., 1846.
280 p.

NL 0432515 MH

Local traveller's time table guide for Chicago and suburbs.
Chicago, Ill., Wakeman-Rivera publishing co. [18
v. 15½cm. monthly.

1. Railroads—Chicago—Time tables.

CA 9-4082 Unrev'd

Library of Congress HE2729.C5L8

NL 0432516 DLC

331.805 BUIJ Local 25 voice.

Chicago.
v. illus. 46cm. monthly

Published by the Chicago Office, Theater and Amusement Building Janitors' Union, Local 25 of the Building Service Employees' International Union, A.F.L.
Articles in English and Polish.

NL 0432517 IU

Local union directory of the American Federation of Labor and railroad brotherhoods.

[Dayton]
v. 45 cm.
"Compiled and published by the Labor union newspaper."

1. Trade-unions—U. S.—Direct. I. American Federation of Labor. II. Labor union.

HD6504.D3L6 331.88058 49-25999*

NL 0432518 DLC

Local union, no. 298, U.B. of carpenters and joiners of America
see United Brotherhood of Carpenters and Joiners of America. Local union, no. 298, Highland Park, Ill.

Locale belangen.
Nn96 I61 L786

Semarang, Vereniging voor Locale Belangen.
illus. plates, 25cm. semimonthly.

Issues for Aug. 1 - Dec. 16, 1926 called 14e jaargang, afl. 1, 28-36, but constitute 13e jaargang, afl. 27-36.
Began publication 1913/14?
With v.8 - 15 are bound Its supplements, Mededeeling no. 43, 47-71.

1. Indonesia - Social condit. - Period.
2. Local govt. - Indonesia - Period.
I. Vereniging voor Locale Belangen.

NL 0432521 CtY

Nn96 I61 L786A Locale belangen. Mededeeling.

Semarang, Vereniging voor Locale Belangen.
illus. 25cm.

Supplement to Locale belangen.
No. 61 erroneously numbered 58.
No. 43, 47-71 bound with Locale belangen, v. 8, 10-15.

1. Indonesia - Social condit. - Period.
2. Local govt. - Indonesia - Period.
I. Vereniging voor Locale Belangen.
Bd. w.: Locale belangen. Mededeeling.

NL 0432523 CtY

DH811 G4S62 no.6 Locale standenvertegenwoordiging in het Graafschap Vlaanderen; een tractaat uit de XVIIIe eeuw (1774-1775) uitg. door J. Dhondt. Gent, 1950.
64 p. (Maatschappij voor Geschiedenis en Oudheidkunde te Gent. Verhandelingen, Nr. 6)

Text in French.

I. Dhondt, Jan, 1915- ed.

NL 0432524 CU

UTA4 +L63 Locale techniek. le- jaarg.
jan.-apr. 1932-
Bandoeng.
illus. 30cm. quarterly.

"Technisch orgaan van de Vereeniging voor Locale Belangen te Semarang."

1. Engineering - Period. 2. Engineering - Indonesia. 3. Indonesia - Public works.
I. Vereniging voor Locale Belangen.

NL 0432525 CtY

Locale verordeningen, andere beschikkingen van locale raden en gewestelijke verordeningen.

[n. p.]
v. 21 cm.
"Extra-bijvoegsel der Javasche courant."

1. Local government—Java. I. Java. Javasche courant. Supplement.

49-53487*‡

NL 0432526 DLC NIC

Locales und provinzielles: in plattdeutschen reimen. Münster 1845. 34p.18cm.
Postscript signed L.T.

Has bound in:
Der westfälische landwehrmann. [1848].
Zumbroock, F[erdinand]. Poetische versuche in plattdeutscher mundart. 1849.

NL 0432527 CU

T3 .G465 Local-Gewerbe-Verein zu Hannover.
Verhandlungen ... Jahrg. 1858-59.
Hannover, 1859-60.
2 v.

NL 0432528 DLC

B A259ℓ [Locali, Gaudenzio]
Istruttiva narrazione di alcune memorie della vita, morte, e traslazione di s. Agabio, secondo vescovo e protettore della città e diocesi di Novara Con alcune memorie de'vescovi successori. Vercelli, Dalla Stamperia patria, 1789.
134, [10]p.

Title vignette (device of printer?); tail-piece.
"Memorie de'vescovi di Novara": p.[83]-134;
"Iscrizioni del chiarissimo padre Giuseppe Draghetti": [10]p. at end.

NL 0432529 IU

VOLUME 337

M-R747.C7
C73
1942
Localio, Arthur Silvio, 1911-
... Wound healing; a consideration of the different factors with experimental observations ₍by₎ Arthur S. Localio ... ₍New York, 1942₎
1 p. l., 124, ₍12₎ numb. l. 21 mounted plates, 11 tables, 3 charts, VI diagrs. 28cm. (Columbia university. College of physicians and surgeons. Theses for the degree of Doctor of medical science, 1942)

"Med. Sc. D. (Surgery) June 2, 1942."

Type-written copy.
Bibliography: ₍12₎ l. at end.

1. Wounds - Healing. 2. Sutures.

NL 0432531 NNC

Localities
see under [Heath, William] 1795-1840.

Locamer, Georg David, 1588-1637, praeses
... De jure et privilegiis fisci ... Argentorati, P. Ledertz, 1622.
₍50₎ p. 20cm.
Diss. - Strasbourg (J. B. Gomer, respondent)

NL 0432533 MH-L

Locamer, Georg David, 1588-1637, praeses
... De jurisdictione ... Argentorati, P. Ledertz ₍1627₎
₍16₎ p. 18cm.
Diss. - Strasbourg (G. Oelhafen von Schöllenbach, respondent)

NL 0432534 MH-L

Locamer, Georg David, 1588-1637, praeses
... De praecipuis ad causam feudorvm efficientem pertinentibus ... Argentorati, P. Ledertz, 1621.
₍24₎ p. 18cm.
Diss. - Strasbourg (Johann Löw, respondent)
At head of title: Disputationum feudalium prima.

NL 0432535 MH-L

Locamer, Georg David, 1588-1637, praeses
... De successione ab intestato ... Argentorati, P. Ledertz, 1629.
₍16₎ p. 18cm.
Diss. - Strasbourg (J. S. Osswald, respondent)

NL 0432536 MH-L

Locamer, Georg David, 1588-1637, ed.

Corpus juris civilis. *Institutiones.*
Imp. Cæs. Justiniani Institutionum libri IV. Cum annotationibus Georgii-Davidis Locameri ... Argentorati, sumptibus Eberhardi Zetzneri, 1632.

Locamer, Georg David, 1588-1637.
... In imp. Caes. Justiniani institutionum libros IV, annotationes, auctae & accuratae, junctisque titt. digest: de verb. signif. & de regulis iuris: studio Johannis Rebhan ... Argentorati, sumptibus Eberhardi Zetzneri, 1656.
7 p.l., 618, ₍6₎, 86 (i.e. 88), ₍4₎ p. 14cm.
Added engraved t.-p.

NL 0432538 MH-L

HC
547
M2
L6
Locamus, P
Madagascar et ses richesses; bétail, agriculture, industrie, par P. Locamus. Paris, A. Challamel, 1896.
194p. illus. 19cm.
Bibliographical footnotes.

1. Madagascar - Econ. condit. I. Title

NL 0432539 WU IaU IEN MH CSt CU MH MBU

Locanda, José María Bongoa y
see Bongoa y Locanda, José María.

La locanda: commedia per musica
see under Paisiello, Giovanni, 1740-1816.

... A locandiera, ornada segundo o gosto dos comicos theatros portuguezes
see under [Goldoni, Carlo] 1707-1793.

Il locandiere deluso; intermezzo in un'atto, da rappresentarsi nel Regio Teatro di via del Cocomero nel carnevale dell'anno 1795. Firenze, nella stamperia di Ant. Gius. Pagani e comp., 1794.

NL 0432543 MH

Locangeli, Charles.
Modèle qui offre la restauration du Colisée de Rome, tel qu'il était originairement de la soixantième partie de la réalité mesure linéaire, fait par Charles Locangeli ... Rome, Marini, 1829.
20 p. 20cm.

1. Rome (City) Colosseum.

NL 0432544 NNC

W 4
M79
1749
L.1
LOCANO, Giorgio.
Dissertatio physiologica, de mechanico feminarum tributo ... Monspelii, Apud Joannem Martel, 1749.
43 p. 17 cm.
Diss. - Montpellier.

NL 0432545 DNLM

Locano, Giorgio.
Tentamen medico-anatomicum, de novo spinalis medullae ductu in quo praeter ejusdem ductus, historiam anatomicam, plures quoque morbi ab ejusdem existentia pendentes recensentur et explicantur. Melitae in Palatio, Capaci, 1761.
140 p.

NL 0432546 PPC

Locano, Pierre
see Lozano, Pedro, 1697-1752.

Locard,
Histore de l'établissement du Christianisme ...
see under Serieys, Antoine, 1755-1829.

Locard, Arnould, 1841-1904
Catalogue des mollusques vivants terrestres et aquatiques du Département de l'Ain. Lyon, Paris, 1881.
151 p. 27 cm. (Académie des Sciences, Belles-Lettres et Arts de Lyon. Classe des Sciences. Mémories. ser. 2, v. 25, 1881-82)

1. Mollusks - France. I. Series.

NL 0432549 ICF PPAN DSI

594
L786c
Geol
Lib'y
LOCARD, ARNOULD, 1841-1904.
Catalogue général des mollusques vivants de France; mollusques marins. Lyon, H. Georg, 1886.
x, 778p., 1l. 27cm. (Prodrome de malacologie française)

1. Mollusks - France - Catalogs and Collections.

NL 0432550 TxU MH ICF

Locard, Arnould, 1841-
Catalogue général des Mollusques vivants de France; Mollusques terrestres, des eaux douces et des eaux saumatres. Lyon, H. Georg, 1882.
vi, 462 p. 26 cm.
Running title: Prodrome de malacologie francaise.

NL 0432551 CtY ICF MH DNLM

Locard, Arnould, 1841-1904.
Conchyliologie Francaise. Les coquilles terrestres de la France. Paris, 1894.

NL 0432552 PPAN

Locard, Arnould, 1841-1904.
Conchyliologie portugaise. Coquilles terrestres des eaux douces et saumatres. Lyon, H. Georg, 1899.
1 p.l., iv, 303 p. f°. (Museum d'histoire naturelle de Lyon, Archives t. 7. [no. 1.])

NL 0432553 NN PPAmP

Locard, Arnould, 1841-1904
Contributions à la faune malacologique française. pts. 1-16, 1881-90. Paris, 1889-90.
3 v. illus., plates (part fold.) 27 cm.

1. Mollusks - France.

NL 0432554 ICF PPAN

Locard, Arnould, 1841-1904
Les coquilles des eaux douces et saumâtres de France; description des familles, genres et espèces, Paris, J. B. Baillière et fils, 1893.
327 p. illus. 26 cm.
At head of title: Conchyliologie française.

1. Mollusks - France. I. Conchyliologie française.

NL 0432555 ICF DSI PPAN ICJ MdBP DNLM

VOLUME 337

Locard, Arnould, 1841-1904.
Les coquilles marines au large des côtes de France. Faune pélagique et faune abyssale. Description des familles, genres et espèces. 198 p. Q. (Conchyliologie française.) Paris: J.-B. Baillière & fils, 1899.

NL 0432556 ICJ DSI

Locard, Arnould, 1841-1904
Les coquilles marines des côtes de France; description des familles, genres et espèces. Paris, J. B. Baillière et fils, 1892.
384 p. illus. 26 cm. (Société Linnéenne de Lyon. Annales. n.s., v. 37, 1891)

1. Mollusks - France. I. Series.

NL 0432557 ICF ICJ DSI CaBVaU TxU Wal' PPAN

Locard, Arnould, 1841-1904.
Les coquilles marines des côtes de France, description des familles, genres et espèces. Paris, Baillière, 1897.
384 p.

NL 0432558 PU-Z

Locard, Arnould, 1841-1904.
Les coquilles sacrees dans les religions indoues. Paris, Ernest Leroux, 1884.

Ann. du Mus. Guimet. Tome VII.

NL 0432559 DCU-H CtY

Locard, Arnould, 1841-1904
Les coquilles terrestres de France; description des familles, genres et espèces. Paris, J. B. Baillière et fils, 1894.
370 p. illus. 26 cm.
At head of title: Conchyliologie française.

1. Mollusks - France. I. Conchyliologie française.

NL 0432560 ICF CaBVaU CLU ICJ DSI

Locard, Arnould, 1841-1904
Les coquilles terrestres, des eaux douces et saumâtres. Lyon, A. Rey, 1899.
303 p. illus., plates. 35 cm. (Lyons. Museum d'Histoire Naturelle. Archives. v. 7)
At head of title: Conchyliologie portugaise.

1. Mollusks - Portugal. I. Conchyliologie portugaise.

NL 0432561 ICF

Locard, Arnould, 1841-1904.
De la valeur des caractères specifiques en malacologique. Lyon, 1883.

(Conch. T. 8. vol. 22)

NL 0432562 PPAN

Locard, Arnould, 1841-1904.
Des ravages causés par le liparis dispar sur les platanes des promenades publiques de Lyon en 1878. Lyon, 1878.

(B. T. 8. vol. 15).

NL 0432563 PPAN

QE 755 F8 L6
Locard, Arnould, 1841-1904.
Description de la faune de la mollasse marine et d'eau douce du Lyonnais et du Dauphiné. Lyon, Pitrat Ainé, 1878.
vi, 278 p. illus. 38 cm.

"Extrait des Archives du Muséum d'Histoire naturelle de Lyon, T. 2."

1. Paleontology - France. 2. Paleontology - Tertiary.

NL 0432564 OU DNLM

Locard, Arnould, 1841-1904.
Description de la faune des terrains tertiaires moyens de la Corse. 1872
1162

NL 0432565 DI-GS

QE736 L6 Paleo. Library
Locard, Arnould, 1841-1904.
Description de la faune des terrains tertiaires moyens de la Corse. Description des échinides par Gustave Cotteau. Paris, F. Savy, 1877.
ix, 374 p. plates.

"Lu à la Société d'Agriculture, Histoire naturelle et Arts utiles de Lyon, dans sa séance du 23 février 1877."
Includes bibliographies.

1. Paleontology - Tertiary. 2. Paleontology - Corsica. 3. Sea-urchins, Fossil. I. Cotteau, Gustav Honoré, 1818-1894.

NL 0432566 CU DSI IU MiU NjP CSt PPAN

---

564 L78de
Locard, Arnould, 1841-1904.
Description de la faune malacologique des terrains quaternaires des environs de Lyon. Lyon, H. Georg, 1879.
xiv, 207p. plate. 27cm.

1. Mollusks, Fossil. 2. Paleontology—Quaternary. 3. Paleontology—Lyon. I. Title: Faune malacologique des terrains quaternaires des environs de Lyon.

NL 0432567 IU DNLM

QE 801 L6
Locard, Arnold, 1841-1904.
Description de la faune malacologique des terrains quaternaires des environs de Lyon. Lyon, H. Georg; Paris, J.-B. Baillière, 1879.
xiv, 207 p. illus. 27 cm.

Bibliographical footnotes.

1. Mollusks, Fossil - France - Lyons. 2. Paleontology - Quaternary.

NL 0432568 OU

Locard, Arnould, 1841-
... Description des mollusques fossiles des terrains tertiaires inférieurs de la Tunisie, recueillis en 1885 et 1886 par M. Philippe Thomas ... par Arnould Locard. Paris, Imprimerie nationale, 1889.
2 p. l., ii, 65 p. 25cm. and atlas, 1 p. l., pl. vii-xi. 37½cm. (Half-title: Exploration scientifique de la Tunisie, publiée sous les auspices du ministère de l'instruction publique. Paléontologie. Mollusques fossiles)

1. Mollusks, Fossil. 2. Paleontology — Tertiary. 3. Paleontology — Tunis.

G S 9-38

Library, U. S. Geol. survey 502(730) F85 (v. 3)

NL 0432569 DI-GS CU FU IU PPAN MiU ICJ

QL425 .F8L8
Locard, Arnould, 1841-1904.
Études sur les variations malacologiques d'après la faune vivante et fossile de la partie centrale du bassin du Rhône, par Arnould Locard ... Lyon, H. Georg; [etc., etc.] 1880-81.
2 v. v pl. 26cm.
Plates accompanied by leaves with descriptive letterpress.
"Bibliographie": v. 2, p. [551]-556.

1. Mollusks—Rhône River.

NL 0432570 ICU ICF CLU DNLM MH DSI

S21j 018
Locard, Arnould, 1841-1904.
Expéditions scientifiques du Travailleur et du Talisman pendant les années 1880, 1881, 1882, 1883 ... Mollusques testacés ... Paris, Masson et cie., 1897-98.
2v. 40pl. 32½cm
Bibliographical foot-notes.

NL 0432571 CtY

QH71 .L9A5
Locard, Arnould, 1841-1904.
Lyons. Muséum d'histoire naturelle.
Guide aux collections de zoologie, géologie et minéralogie, par Arnould Locard. Lyon, Impr. Pitrat aîné, 1875.

QL 403 +L6
Locard, Arnould, 1841-1904
Histoire des mollusques dans l'antiquité. Lyon, H. Georg, 1884.
242p. illus. 28cm.
Bibliographical footnotes.

1. Mollusks I. Title

NL 0432573 WU PPAN ICF

Locard, Arnould, 1841-1904.
Les huîtres et les mollusques comestibles, moules, praires, clovisses, escargots, etc.; histoire naturelle, culture industrielle, hygiène alimentaire, par Arnould Locard ... Paris, J.-B. Ballière et fils, 1890.
383 p. 97 illus. 18½cm.
On half-title: Bibliothèque scientifique contemporaine.

1. Mollusks. 2. Oyster. 3. Oyster-culture. 3. Shell-fish fisheries. 5. Shell-fish culture.

A 18-1510

Title from Harvard Univ. Printed by L. C.

NL 0432574 MH PPAN MB

---

594 L811m
Locard, Arnould, 1841-
Malacologie Lyonnaise; ou Description des mollusques terrestres & aquatiques des envirc. de Lyon d'apres la collection Ange-Paulin Terver, donnée au Museum de Lyon par la Famille Terver en 1876. Lyon, H. Georg, 1877.
151p.

1. Mollusks. I. Terver, Ange-Paulin. Title.

NL 0432575 ICarbS PPAN DNLM MH DI-SI

Locard, Arnould, 1841-1904.
... Manuel pratique d'ostréiculture ... Les huitres et les mollusques comestibles, moules, praires, clovisses, escargots, etc.: histoire naturelle, culture industrielle, hygiène alimentaire. Paris, J.-B. Baillière & fils, 1900.
383 p. 97 illus. 18 cm. (Half-title: Bibliothèque des connaissances utiles)
1. Mollusks. 2. Oysters. 3. Oyster-culture. 4. Shell-fish fisheries.

NL 0432576 CU

Locard, Arnould, 1841-1904.
Minéraux utiles et pierres précieuses, leurs applications aux arts et à l'industrie, par Arnould Locard ... Tours, Alfred Cattier, 1892.
viii, [9]-223, [1] p. incl. front., illus. 23cm.

1. Mineralogy. 2. Precious stones.

G S 34-382

U. S. Geol. survey. Libr. for Library of Congress Geo. F. Kunz collection K480 L79m [a40b1]

NL 0432577 DI-GS MB

VOLUME 337

Locard, Arnould, 1841-1904.
Mollusques testacés. t. 1. Paris, Masson & cie. 1897.
v. pls. 4°. [Expéditions scientifiques du Travailleur et du Talisman].

NL 0432578 MB MH CU ICJ PPAN

Locard, Arnould, 1841- joint author.

Falsan, Albert, 1833-
Monographie géologique du Mont-d'Or lyonnais et de ses dépendances, par Albert Falsan et Arnould Locard ... Ouvrage couronné par l'Académie de Lyon. Paris, F. Savy; [etc., etc.] 1866.

Locard, Arnould, 1841-1904.
Note sur les pluies de boue dans la region Cygunaise lue...1860. par M.A. Locard. Lyon, 1880.

(P. S. T. vol 27)

NL 0432580 PPAN

Locard, Arnould, 1841-1904.
Nouvelles recherches sur les argiles laciestres des terrains quaternaires des environs de Lyon par Arnould Locard. 1880.

(G. T. 8. vol. 30)

NL 0432581 PPAN

LOCARD, Arnould, 1841-1904.
La pêche en eaux douces. Paris, J.B. Baillière et fils, 1927.

Illustr.
Half-title: Bibliothèque des connaissances utiles.

NL 0432582 MH

[Locard, Arnould] 1841-1904.
La pêche et les poissons des eaux douces. Avec figures intercalées dans le texte. Description des poissons, engins de pêche, lignes amorces, esches, appats, pêche à la ligne, pêches diverses, nasse, filets, etc. Paris, J. B. Baillière et fils, 1891.
252 p. illus. 17½cm. (Bibliothèque des connaissance utiles)

1. Fishes—France. 2. Fishing—Implements and appliances. 3. Fishery law and legislation—France. I. Title.

A 18-1511

Title from Harvard Univ. Printed by L. C.

NL 0432583 MH

Locard, Arnould, 1841-1904.
Recherches historiques sur la coquille des imprimeurs, par Arnould Locard. [no imprint]
[13]-70 p. illus. 27½cm.
Bibliographical foot-notes.
Caption title.

1. Coquille (Printer's term)

NL 0432584 MiU

442.5
L81r
Locard, Arnould, 1841-1904
Recherches historiques sur la coquille des imprimeurs. (Tiré à 100 exemplaires) Lyon, Rey, 1892.
62p. illus. Q.

Bibliographical foot-notes.

NL 0432585 IaU

560.944
L78r
Locard, Arnould, 1841-1904.
Recherches paléontologiques sur les dépots tertiaires à Milne-Edwardsia et Vivipara du pliocène inférieur du département de l'Ain. Mâcon, Protat, 1883.
166p. plates. 25cm.

"Extrait des Annales de l'Académie de Macon, IIe série, tome VI."

NL 0432586 IU PPAN

Locard, Arnould, 1841-1904.
Sur quelques cas d'albinisme et de melanisme chez les mollusques terrestres et d'eau douce de la faune francaise. Lyon, 1883.

(Conch. T. 8. vol. 22)

NL 0432587 PPAN

LOCARD, EDMOND, 1877-1966.
A-t-elle empoisonné son mari? Affaire Lafarge. Paris, Éditions de la Flamme d'or [1954] 127 p. 18cm. (Causes célèbres, 3)

1. Lafarge, Marie Fortunée (Cappelle) Pouch-, 1816-1852. 2. Poisoning--Trials--France. I. Title.

NL 0432588 NN

Locard, Edmond, 1877-1966.
... L'affaire Dreyfus et l'expertise de documents écrits, par le docteur Edmond Locard ... Lyon, J. Desvigne et cie, 1937.
cover-title, 66 p. illus. (facsims.) diagrs. 24cm. (Bibliothèque de la Revue internationale de criminalistique ...)

1. Dreyfus, Alfred, 1859-1935. 2. Writing—Identification. I. Title.

39-13678

NL 0432589 DLC NN MH

Locard, Edmond, 1877-1966.
Confidences; souvenirs d'un policier. Lyon, J. Desvigne [1951]
249 p. 19 cm.

1. Crime and criminals—France—Lyons. I. Title.

HV7915.L6 52-35778 ‡

NL 0432590 DLC MH IU

Locard, Edmond, 1877-1966.
... Le crime et les criminels. Paris, La Renaissance du livre [192-]
278 p., 1 l. plates (incl. facsims.) ports. 18½cm.
Bibliography: p. 9.

1. Crime and criminals.

46-37399

Library of Congress HV6241.L6

NL 0432591 DLC PU-L MH CtY NN PU

Locard, Edmond, 1877-1966.
Le crime et les criminels. 10. éd.
278p. 12° Par. [1920?]

NL 0432592 DNLM MH

Locard, Edmond, 1877- Soc 2931.1
Les crimes de sang et les crimes d'amour au xviie siècle. Lyon, etc. A. Storck & cie. 1903.

Crime||

NL 0432593 MH DNLM

Locard, Edmond, 1877-
La criminalistique, à l'usage des gens du monde et des auteurs de romans policiers [par] Edmond Locard ... Lyon, J. Desvigne et cie., 1937.
2 p. l., [7]-156 p., 2 l. 23cm.

1. Criminal investigation. I. Title.

39-11424

Library of Congress HV8073.L58
[2] 364

NL 0432594 DLC NNC

Locard, Edmond, 1877-
La défense contre le crime. Paris, Payot, 1951.
152 p. 23 cm. (Bibliothèque scientifique)

1. Crime and criminals. I. Title.

HV6251.L6 364.2 51-5467

NL 0432595 DLC CtY ICU DNLM OU

Taxl6
F6
902l
Locard, Edmond, 1878-
... Le XVIIe siècle médico-judiciaire. Lyon, A.Storck & cie, 1902.
2p.l.,xiv,479,[1]p. 24cm.

1. Medical jurisprudence - France.

NL 0432596 CtY RPB MH NN DNLM

BF892
.B3
Locard, Edmond, 1877- joint author.

Barraud, J
L'écriture ment-elle? Introduction pratique à la graphologie [par] J. Barraud en collaboration avec E. Locard. Lyon, Gutenberg [1945]

Locard, Edmond, 1877-
... Edgar A. Poe as a detective... [New York, 1941?]
25 f. 27½cm.

Reproduced from typewritten copy.
Issued in loose-leaf binder.
Translation by John H. Hulla of an excerpt from "La Revue hebdomadaire, no. 31, 30e année, 30 juillet, 1921."

145285B. 1. Poe, Edgar Allan, 1809-1849. I. Hulla, John H., tr.
N. Y. P. L. March 6, 1942

NL 0432598 NN

Locard, Edmond, 1877-
... L'enquête criminelle et les méthodes scientifiques. Paris, E. Flammarion, 1920.
300 p. diagrs. 19cm. (Bibliothèque de philosophie scientifique) fr. 5.75

1. Evidence, Criminal. 2. Crime and criminals—France.

20-12821

Library of Congress HV8073.L6

NL 0432599 DLC ICU CU WaT PU-L ICJ

Locard, Edmond, 1877-1966.
L'enquête criminelle et les méthodes scientifiques. Paris., Flammarion, 1925.

300 p.

NL 0432600 PU

652M
L783.2
LOCARD, EDMOND, 1877-
...L'expertise des documents écrits. Les correspondances secrètes. Les falsifications, par le dr.Edmond Locard... Lyon, J.Desvigne et cie, 1935-1936.
2v. illus., facsims., diagrs. 25½cm. (Traité de criminalistique. [t.5-6])

Continuously paged.
Date on cover (v.2): 1937.
"Bibliographie cryptographique": t.2, p.905-931.

NL 0432601 PU

VOLUME 337

LOCARD, EDMOND, 1877-
Le fiancé de la guillotine (Lacenaire). Paris, Editions de la flamme d'or [1954] 137 p. 19cm. (Causes célèbres. 7)

1. Lacenaire, Pierre François, 1800-1836. I. Title. II. Les causes célèbres.

NL 0432602 NN MH

LOCARD, Edmond, 1877-1966.
L'identification des criminels par l'examen des glandes sudoripares. Paris, 1912.

12 p.
"Extrait de la Province médicale", 1912.

NL 0432603 MH-L

Locard, Edmond, 1877-
... L'identification des récidivistes, par Edmond Locard ... Avec 85 figures dans le texte. Paris, A. Maloine, 1909.
2 p. l., lv, 428 p. illus., diagrs. 24½cm. (Bibliothèque de criminologie, pub. sous la direction du professeur A. Lacassagne)

1. Crime and criminals—Identification.
46-37398
Library of Congress HV8073.L64

NL 0432604 DLC DNLM ICJ

Locard, Edmond, 1877-
... La investigación criminal y los métodos científicos; traducción por Germán Salgado ... Buenos Aires [Talleres gráficos argentinos L. J. Rosso] 1937-38.
2 v. diagrs. 23cm. (Biblioteca policial ... año III, núm. 29, 33)
At head of title: Dr. Edmundo Locard.
Vol. 2 printed by Imprenta López.
Bibliographical foot-notes.

1. Criminal investigation. 2. Evidence, Criminal—France. 3. Crime and criminals—France. I. Salgado, Germán, tr.
45-20300
Library of Congress HV8073.L62
[2] 351.74

NL 0432605 DLC

Locard, Edmond, 1877-

Ashton-Wolfe, Harry, 1881-
The invisible web; strange tales of the French sûreté, by H. Ashton-Wolfe ... from documents supplied by Dr. Edmond Locard of the sûreté at Lyons, France. [London] Hurst & Blackett, ltd. [1929]

Locard, Edmond, 1877-1966.
Die kriminaluntersuchung und ihre wissenschaftlichen methoden. Bearbeitet von Willy Finke. Berlin, 1930.

NL 0432607 MH-L

Locard, Edmond, 1877-1966.
Laboratoires de police et instruction criminelle. Lyon: A. Rey, 1913. 40 p. illus. 8°.
Repr.: Bull. de la Soc. d'anthropologie de Lyon. Séance du 7 décembre 1912

1. Criminals.—Identification.
N. Y. P. L. January 14, 1914.

NL 0432608 NN

LOCARD, EDMOND, 1877-
Le magistrat assassiné: affaire Fualdès. Paris, Éditions de la Flamme d'or [1954] 126 p. 18cm. (Causes célèbres. 1)

1. Fualdès, Joseph Bernardin, d. 1817. 2. Murder--Trials--France

NL 0432609 NN MH

Locard, Edmond, 1877-1966.
La malle sanglante de Millery, par E. Locard. Paris: Gallimard [cop. 1934] 219 p. 12°.

1. Title. 2. Crime. 3. Detectives.
N. Y. P. L. August 30, 1935

NL 0432610 NN

Locard, Edmond, 1877-
Manual de técnica policíaca, por Edmond Locard ... traducido de la segunda edición francesa por A. Bon. 2. ed. rev. Barcelona, J. Montesó, 1943.
448 p. illus., plates, diagrs. 22cm.
"Bibliografía" at end of each chapter.

1. Criminal investigation. I. Bon, A., tr.
44-51843
Library of Congress HV8073.L67 1943
[2] 351.74

NL 0432611 DLC DPU

Locard, Edmond, 1877-
... Manuel de technique policière, (enquête criminelle) avec 43 figures. Paris, Payot, 1923.
2 p. l., [7]-291 p. illus., plates, fold. tab. 19½cm.
Bibliography at end of each chapter.

1. Criminal investigation. I. Title.
23-16406
Library of Congress HV8073.L65
[a45c1] 351.74

NL 0432612 DLC CtY CU OClW

Locard, Edmond, 1877-
... Manuel de technique policière ... 3. éd., entièrement refondue et augm. Avec 43 figures. Paris, Payot, 1939.
363, [3] p. illus., plates, diagrs. 22cm. (Bibliothèque scientifique)
"Bibliographie" at end of most of the chapters.

1. Criminal investigation.
45-52122
Library of Congress HV8073.L65 1939
[2] 351.74

NL 0432613 DLC DNLM NN

Locard, Edmond, 1877-
Manuel de technique policière ... 4. éd., corr. Paris, Payot, 1948 [c1923]
310 p. illus. 23 cm. (Bibliothèque scientifique)

1. Criminal investigation.

HV8073.L65 1948 57-41794 ‡

NL 0432614 DLC DNLM MH-L

Locard, Edmond, 1877-
... Manuel du philatéliste. Paris, Payot, 1942.
2 p. l., [7]-359 p. 23cm.

1. Postage-stamps—Collectors and collecting.
45-17341
Library of Congress HE6215.L63
[2] 383.22

NL 0432615 DLC CU CtY IU MH CU NjP

Locard, Edmond, 1877-
Mata-Hari. Paris, La flamme d'or [1954] 126 p. illus. 18cm. (Causes célèbres. 5)

1. Zelle, Margaretha Geertruida, 1876-1917.

NL 0432616 NN

614.23 LOCARD, Edmond, 1877-
L786m La médecine judiciaire en France au XVIIe siècle. Lyon, A. Storck, 1902. xiv, 479, [1] p.

Thèse - Lyon. Faculté de médecine et de pharmacie.

1. Medical jurisprudence - France.

NL 0432617 WaU

ar W Locard, Edmond, 1877-
23869 Les méthodes de laboratoire dans l'expertise en écriture. Bruxelles, Veuve F. Larcier, 1921.
30 p. illus. 25cm.

"Extrait de la Revue de droit pénal et de criminologie et archives internationales de médecine légale (Janvier 1921)."

1. Writing-- Identification.

NL 0432618 NIC

Locard, Edmond, 1877-
Note sur l'identification des suspects. La Plata (Rep. argentina) Taller de impresiones oficiales, 1937.
FL2 29 p. 27cm. (Biblioteca de la Revista de
R456 identificación y ciencias penales. no.25, enero
I19b de 1937)
no.25 "Publicado en el tomo XIII de la Revista de identificación y ciencias penales, enero-junio de 1936."
1. Crime and criminals - Identification. 2. Finger-prints. 3. Identification. Series.

NL 0432619 MiU-L

Locard, Edmond, 1877-
Peut-on correspondre avec l'au delà? Étude critique sur le spiritisme. Lyon, Éditions Gutenberg [1945]
cover-title, 45 p. 21 cm.
Half-title: Le spiritisme.

1. Spiritualism. I. Title.
BF1302.L6 133.9 A 48-1262*
Harvard Univ. Library for Library of Congress [1]†

NL 0432620 MH DLC IaU

Locard, Edmond, 1877-
La police; ce qu'elle est, ce qu'elle devrait être, par le Docteur Edmond Locard... Paris: B. Grasset, 1918. 64 p. 12°. (Le fait de la semaine. 6e année, no. 11.)
On cover: Pour la rénovation française.
Contents: Avant-propos. Organisation administrative de la police. La police judiciaire. La police d'ordre. La police politique. La police des mœurs. Contre-espionnage. Conclusions.

1. Police, France. 2. Series.
N. Y. P. L. September 18, 1918.

NL 0432621 NN

Locard, Edmond, 1877-
...La police; ce qu'elle est; ce qu'elle devrait être. Paris: Payot & Cie, 1919. 2 p.l., (1)8-238 p., 1 l. 12°. (Bibliothèque politique et économique.)

NL 0432622 NN PU-L MH

VOLUME 337

Locard, Edmond, 1877-
La police et les méthodes scientifiques, par le docteur Edmond Locard. Paris, Les Éditions Rieder, 1934.
82 p., 1 l. XLVIII pl. (incl. facsims.) on 24 l. 20cm. (Half-title: Bibliothèque générale illustrée. 24)

1. Crime and criminals. 2. Police.
A 35-742
Title from N. Y. Pub. Libr. Printed by L. C.

NL 0432623 NN

Locard, Edmond, 1877-
...The police method of Sherlock Holmes. Translated, 1942, by John Hugh Hulla... [New York, 1942] 51 f. col'd illus. 28cm.

Original issued in: La Revue hebdomadaire, année 31, tome 2, Paris, February, 1922.

224957B. 1. Doyle, Sir Arthur Conan, 1859-1930—Characters. I. Hulla, John Hugh, tr.
N. Y. P. L. June 8, 1943

NL 0432624 NN

Locard, Edmond, 1877-
La policía, lo que es, lo que debiere ser. Traducción directa del francés, con autorización, por Enrique Fentanes. Buenos Aires, 1937.
157 p. 23 cm. (Biblioteca policial, año III, núm. 21)

1. Police—France. I. Title. (Series)
HV8203.L63 351.74 45-29311 rev*

NL 0432625 DLC

Locard, Edmond, 1877-
...Policías de novela y policías de laboratorio. Traducida del frances, con autorizacion, por el coronel (R.) Luis Jorje Garcia... [Buenos Aires] 1935. 220 p. 24cm. (Biblioteca policial. núm. 1.)

"Bibliografía," p. 219-220.

1. Detective stories—Hist. and crit. 2. Criminal investigation.

NL 0432626 NN

Locard, Edmond, 1877-
... Policiers de roman et policiers de laboratoire. Paris, Payot, 1924.
2 p. l., [7]-277 p., 1 l. 18½cm.
"Bibliographie": p. [275]-277.

1. Detectives. I. Title.
Library of Congress HV7909.L6 25-1669

NL 0432627 DLC

Locard, Edmond, 1877-1966.
La poroscopie procédé nouveau d'identifacatio[n] des criminels par les traces des orifices sudoripares. Lyon, A.Rey, 1913.

20 p. 4° Ill.
"Extrait des archives d'anthropologie criminelle, de médicine légale et de psychologie normale et pathologique, nos 235, 15 juillet 1913."

NL 0432628 MH-L

ar W 23868 Locard, Edmond, 1877-
La preuve judiciaire par les empreintes digitales. Données physiologiques. Pratique policière. Nature et valeur de la preuve. Calcul des chances d'erreur jurisprudence comparée. Lyon, A. Rey, 1914.
32 p. 25cm.

"Extrait des Archives d'anthropologie criminelle, de médecine légale et de psychologie normale et pathologique, no 245, 15 mai 1914."

1. Fingerprints.

NL 0432629 NIC

Locard, Edmond, 1877-
Rio de Janeiro (*Federal district*) *Secretaria da policia.*
Relatorio apresentado ao Exmo Snr. Dr. J. J. Seabra, ministro da justiça e dos negocios interiores pelo chefe de policia do Districto federal A. A. Cardoso de Castro. Rio de Janeiro, Typ. Rebello Braga, 1904.

Locard, Edmond, 1877- ed.

Revue internationale de criminalistique ... 1.- année; juil. 1929-
Lyon, J. Desvigne et ses fils, 1929-

Locard, Edmond, 1877-1966.
... Руководство по криминалистике; перевод проф. С. В. Познышева и Н. В. Терзиева; под редакцией С. П. Митричева. Москва, Юридическое издательство НКЮ СССР, 1941.
543, [1] p. illus., facsims., tables, diagrs. 23cm.
At head of title: Всесоюзный институт юридических наук НКЮ СССР. Эдмонд Локар.
"Является переводом части 'Руководства'."
Errata slip mounted on t.-p.
Bibliographical foot-notes.
1. Criminal investigation—France. 2. Crime and criminals—France. 3. Evidence, Expert—France. 4. Writing—Identification. 5. Forgery. I. Mitrichev, S. P., ed. II. Poznyshev, Sergeĭ Viktorovich, 1870- tr. III. Terziev, N. V., joint tr. IV. Moscow. Vsesoiuznyĭ institut iuridicheskikh nauk. *Title transliterated:* Rukovodstvo po kriminalistike.
Library of Congress HV8073.L684 44-18979
[2]

NL 0432632 DLC CtY

Locard, Edmond, 1877-1966.

Meyer, Josef Bernhard.
Die sicherungstechnik der wertpapiere unter besonderer berücksichtigung der sicherheitspapiere, der graphischen und schreibtechnischen sicherungsmethoden, von dipl. ing. chem. J. B. Meyer, mit einem vorwort und einem beitrag von dr E. Locard ... und 32 textabbildungen. Zürich-Oerlikon, Pacoverlag, 1935.

Locard, Edmond, 1877-1966.
Traité de criminalistique ... par le dr. Edmond-Locard ... Lyon, J. Desvigne et ses fils, 1931-36.
6 v. illus. (incl. tables) facsims., diagrs. 25½cm.
Includes bibliographies.
CONTENTS.—[t. 1-2] Les empreintes et les traces dans l'enquête criminelle.—[t. 3-4] Les preuves de l'identité.—[t. 5-6] L'expertise des documents écrits. Les correspondances secrètes. Les falsifications.

1. Criminal investigation—France. 2. Crime and criminals—France. 3. Evidence, Expert—France. 4. Writing—Identification. 5. Forgery. I. Title.
32-10301 Revised
Library of Congress HV8073.L68
——— 2d set. [r39c2] 364

NL 0432634 DLC MH-L MiU-L NN

Locard, [E
Comparaison du prix de revient des citernes et des cuves en maçonnerie avec celui des foudres, cuves et tonneaux en bois. Par M. Locard ... Lu à la Société d'agriculture, d'histoire naturelle et des arts utiles de Lyon, dans sa séance du 23 mars 1849. [Lyon, Impr. de Barret, 1849]
7 p. fold. pl. 21cm.
(Rural economy pamphlets, v. 7, no. 9)
Caption title.
"Extrait des Annales de la Société nationale d'agriculture, d'histoire naturelle et des arts utiles de Lyon.—1849."
1. Wine and wine making.
5-38744†
Library of Congress S405.R94

NL 0432635 DLC

Locard, Eugene
Cours de dessin linéaire appliqué aux arts et à l'industrie; 2. éd. Paris, 1880.

NL 0432636 NjP

TF 258 .L79 Locard, Eugène.
Recherches sur la résistance des rails en fer forgé. Lyon, Impr.de Barret, 1854.
74 p. plate. 25 cm.

1. Railroads—Rails.

NL 0432637 MiU

625.14 L78re Locard, Eugene.
Recherches sur la résistance des rails en fer forgé. Lyon, 1857.
74p. pl., tables.

NL 0432638 IU

TF 258 .L78 Locard, Eugène.
Recherches sur les rails et leurs supports. Extrait des ouvrages anglais de P.Barlow et N. Wood, suivi de la description des rails et des coussinets employés sur les principaux chemins de fer d'Europe et d'Amerique ... Paris, Carilian-Goeury et V.Dalmont, 1853.
viii,616 p. 22 cm. and atlas (15 pl.)
29 x 23 cm.

1. Railroads—Rails. I. Barlow, Peter, 1776-1862. II. Wood, Nicholas, 1793-1865.

NL 0432639 MiU DP CSt IU

Locard, Fredereta
A compendious French grammar
see under Edgren, August Hjalmar, 1840-1903.

4-XHD Ed3s Locard, Fredereta.
...Supplementary exercises for Edgren's French grammar...Boston, 1897.

[2], LXV-LXXIII, 273-295 p. 19cm.
(Heath's Modern language series.)

NL 0432641 RPB

Locard, Henri.
Commentaire de la loi du 26 mars 1891 (loi Bérenger) sur l'atténuation et l'aggravation des peines, par Henri Locard ... Paris, A. Durand et Pedone-Lauriel, 1891.
2 p. l., 190 p. 22 cm.

NL 0432642 NNC

Locard, Jacques.
... L'analyse des traits de crayon en criminalistique. Lyon, 1936.
211, [1] p. illus., diagrs. 25cm.
On label mounted on cover: J. Desvigne & cie, Lyon.
Published in part also as thesis, Lyons.
"Bibliographie": p. [201]-206.

1. Chemistry, Legal. 2. Graphite. 3. Writing—Identification. 4. Pencils. I. Title.
39-14685
Library of Congress HV8076.L6
[2] 364

NL 0432643 DLC

VOLUME 337

Locard, Jacques.
... Contribution à l'étude de l'oxydation du graphite en milieu alcalin ... [Trévoux] Imprimerie de Trévoux, G. Patissier, 1936.
211 p., 1 l. illus. 25½cm.
Thèse—Univ. de Lyon.
Published also without thesis note under title: L'analyse des traits de crayon en criminalistique (Lyon, 1936)
"Bibliographie": p. [201]-206.
1. Chemistry, Legal. 2. Graphite. 3. Writing—Identification. 4. Pencils. I. Title.
41-21567
Library of Congress HV8076.L6 1936 a
[2] 364

NL 0432644 DLC CtY

Locard, Jacques.
Cours de police scientifique. [2. éd. Lyon, J. Desvigne, 1951]
93 p. illus. 25 cm.
1. Criminal investigation. I. Title.
HV8073.L7 1951 52-28711 ‡

NL 0432645 DLC

Locard, Jacques.
Manuel de photographie judiciaire. [n. p., n. d.]
52 p. illus. 27 cm.
1. Photography, Legal. 2. Photography—Handbooks, manuals, etc. I. Title: Photographie judiciaire.
TR830.L6 56-33212 ‡

NL 0432646 DLC

PQ2623 .O2V3
Locard, Jacques.
Variations. Lyon, J. Desvigne [1950]
221 p. 19 cm.
CONTENTS.—Minna.—Simone.—Irène.
I. Title.
A 52-6786
Illinois. Univ. Library for Library of Congress [1]

NL 0432647 IU MH DLC

Locard, Paul, 1871 –
Histoire de la musique ... France.
(In Encyclopédie de la musique et dictionnaire du Conservatoire ... Paris [1913]-31. 29½cm. 1. ptie. [v. 3] (c1914) p. [1176]-1814. illus. (incl. facsims., music))

Locard, Paul, 1871 –
... Léon Boëllmann, par Paul Locard ... Strasbourg, J. Noiriel (F. Staat succ.) 1901.
1 p. l., 13 p. illus., plates. 32½ x 25½cm. (Biographies alsaciennes [IX])
Extrait de la Revue alsacienne illustrée, vol. III, no. III (1901)
1. Boëllmann, Léon, 1862-1897.
4-18222

NL 0432649 DLC

Locard, Paul, 1871 –
... Les maîtres contemporains de l'orgue. Paris, Édition du Courrier musical [1901]
48 p. 3 port. 19cm.
Imprint covered by label of Librairie Fischbacher.
Subject entries: Organists, French.
3-16800
Library of Congress, no. ML396.L81.

NL 0432650 DLC OBerB

Locard, Paul, 1871–
Le piano. [1. éd.] Paris, Presses universitaires de France, 1948.
126, [2] p. 18 cm. ("Que sais-je?" Le point des connaissances actuelles, 263)
"Bibliographie": p. [127]
1. Piano—Hist. 2. Piano music—Hist. & crit. (Series)
ML650.L6 786.2 48-24371*

NL 0432651 DLC MiU NcU OU

Locarni, G[iuseppe].
Il tempio israelitico di Vercelli. Torino: Camilla & Bertolero, 1889. 2 p.l., (1)8-15 p., 4 pl. 8°.
Repr.: Ingegneria civile e le arti industriali. v. 14.
1. Jews in Italy: Vercelli. 2. Synagogues, Italy: Vercelli.
N. Y. P. L. January 6, 1914

NL 0432652 NN

Locarnini, Guido.
Die literarischen Beziehungen zwischen der italienischen und der deutschen Schweiz. Bern, A. Francke [1946]
382 p. 23 cm.
"Bibliographie": p. [363]-380.
1. Swiss literature—Hist. & crit. I. Title.
PQ5961.L6 809 50-27160

UU ICN TU MH PU CU OCU NcD NcU IaU FTaSU NN
NL 0432653 DLC MH RPB NNC CtY NcD CLU ICU NIC CLSU

LOCARNINI, GUIDO.
Il problema etnico ticinese [a cura della] Nuova società elvetica. Bellinzona, S.A. Grassi, 1955. 101 p. illus. 23cm.
Bibliographical footnotes.
1. Ethnology--Switzerland--Ticino. 2. Ticino, Switzerland (Canton)--Population. 3. Ticino, Switzerland (Canton)--Hist. I. Neue helvetische Gesellschaft.

NL 0432654 NN MH MdBJ MU

Locarno, Dario G
... Il libro dei sogni; ossia, Morfeo. La vera interpretazione di tutti i sogni con tutte le voci moderne e scientifiche delle ultime invenzione e scoperte con relativi numeri. Oroscopo per uomo e donna. I quattro temperamenti dell' uomo. I giorni buoni e cattivi della luna. Segnali di buono e cattivo augurio. Tavola dei giorni fasti e nefasti. Calcoli matematici per cabalisti, con tavole di numeri e loro potenza. Proverbi con relativi numeri, ecc. New York, N. Y., Italian American press, 1944.
255, [1] p. 18½cm.
1. Dreams. 2. Fortune-telling. 3. Astrology. I. Title.
45-13446
Library of Congress BF1094.L6
[2] 135.382

NL 0432655 DLC

Locarno, Giovanni da.
Saggio sullo stile dell'oratoria sacra nel Seicento esemplificata sul P.Emmanuele Orchi, Romae, Institutum historicum Ord.Fr.Min.Cap., 1954
xvi, 250 p. (Bibliotheca Seraphico-Capuccina, Sectio historica, 14)

NL 0432656 MH

Locarno. Circolo di coltora
see Circolo di coltora, Locarno.

341.24 L811
Locarno. Conference, 1925
Accordi di Locarno. Milano, ISPI [1936]
40 p.

NL 0432658 NNUN

Locarno. Conference, 1925.
... Final protocol of the Locarno conference, 1925 (and annexes) together with treaties between France and Poland and France and Czechoslovakia, Locarno, October 16, 1925 ... London, Printed & pub. by H M. Stationery off., 1925.
61 p. 24½cm. ([Gt. Brit. Foreign office] Miscellaneous no. 11 (1925))
Gt. Brit. Parliament. Papers by command. Cmd. 2525.
I. France. Treaties, etc., 1924– (Doumergue) II. Poland (1918–) Treaties, etc., 1922?– (Wojciechowski) III. Czechoslovak Republic. Treaties, etc., 1918– (Masaryk) IV. Title.
26-2290
Library of Congress JX1931 1925 b

NL 0432659 DLC CaBVaU

Locarno conference, 1925.
Final protocol of the Locarno conference, 1925 (and annexes), together with treaties between France and Poland and France and Czechoslovakia, initialled at Locarno, October 16, 1925; signed at London, December 1, 1925; not ratified at date of publication herein.
(In American journal of international law. Concord, N. H., 1926. v. 20, suppl., p. 21-33)
Translation reprinted from Gt. Brit. Foreign office. Misc. 1925, no. 11 (Cmd. 2525)
1. Arbitration, International. 2. [Arbitration treaties] I. France. Treaties, etc., 1924– (Doumergue) II. Poland (1918–) Treaties, etc., 1922?-1926 (Wojciechowski) III. Czechoslovak Republic. Treaties, etc., 1918– (Masaryk)
A 26-386
Title from Carnegie Endow. Int. Peace. Printed by L. C.

NL 0432660 NNCE CaBVaU OCl

Locarno. Conference, 1925.
... Final protocol of the Locarno conference, 1925, and treaties between France and Poland and France and Czechoslovakia ... Worcester, Mass., New York city, Carnegie endowment for international peace, Division of intercourse and education [1926]
93 p. incl. maps. 19½cm. (International conciliation ... January, 1926, no. 216)
French and English on opposite pages.
"From war to peace: the new security, reprinted from the London Times, December 1, 1925": p. 83-92.
"References": p. 93.
I. France. Treaties, etc., 1924-1931 (Doumergue) II. Poland (1918–) Treaties, etc., 1922-1926. (Wojciechowski) III. Czechoslovak republic. Treaties, etc., 1918-1935 (Masaryk) IV. Title. V. Title: Protocol of the Locarno conference, 1925.
26-4492
Library of Congress JX1907.A8 no. 216

OO PPTU
NL 0432661 DLC WaU-L PBm MiU OrPR WaS CaBVaU OCl

Locarno. Conference, *1925.*
Gesetz über die Verträge von Locarno, und den Eintritt Deutschlands in den Völkerbund vom 28. November 1925, sowie dem Wortlaut des Notenwechsels zwischen der deutschen Regierung und dem Generalsekretär des Völkerbundes vom 14. bis 17. März 1936; mit einer Einleitung von Viktor Brune. Berlin, Freiheitsverlag, 1936.
77 p. 21 cm.
French and German.
1. Germany—For. rel.—1918– 2. Arbitration, International. 3. League of Nations—Germany.
JX1931 1925cb 53-50007

NL 0432662 DLC MiU

Locarno. Conference, 1925.
Roels, Edgar.
La guerre aux traités. par Edgar Roels. Paris, F. Alcan. 1932.

Locarno. Conference, 1925.
Locarno a Svaz národů
see under title

Locarno. Conference, 1925
...The Locarno agreements and the League of Nations. [Nancy: Berger-Levrault, 1926.] 25 p. f°. (League of Nations. Monthly summary. Suppl. Dec., 1925.)
Caption-title.
Treaty signed by representatives of Germany, Belgium, France, Great Britain, Italy, Poland and Czecho-Slovakia, October 16, 1925.
1. Locarno, Treaty of, 1925. 2. Belgium. Treaties, 1925. 3. France. Treaties, 1925. 4. Great Britain. Treaties, 1925. 5. Italy. Treaties, 1925. 6. Treaties, 1925, October 16. 7. Ser.
N. Y. P. L. September 17, 1926

NL 0432665 NN

VOLUME 337

Locarno. Conference, 1925.
...The Locarno agreements; unofficial translations of the text of the final protocol of the Locarno Conference, the text of the treaty of mutual guarantee (commonly called the Security pact) and the text of the other documents initialled at Locarno, Oct. 16th, 1925 ⌜London:⌝ League of Nations Union⌜, 1925⌝. 15 p. 12°.

At head of title: no. 185, November, 1925.

1. Locarno, Treaty of, 1925. 2. League of Nations Union.
N. Y. P. L. January 31, 1927

NL 0432666 NN

Locarno. Conference, 1925.
... Locarno conference, 1925. Final protocol (and annexes) together with treaties between France and Poland and France and Czechoslovakia. Locarno, 16th October, 1925 ... ⌜Melbourne⌝ Printed and pub. for the government of the commonwealth of Australia by H. J. Green, government printer for the state of Victoria ⌜1926⌝
16 p. 33cm.
At head of title: 1926. The Parliament of the commonwealth of Australia.
I. France. Treaties, etc., 1924– (Doumergue) II. Poland (1918–) Treaties, etc., 1922?–1926 (Wojciechowski) III. Czechoslovak Republic. Treaties, etc., 1918– (Masaryk)

26-16499
Library of Congress JX1931 1925 bc

NL 0432667 DLC

Locarno. Conference, 1925
Locarno Conference, 1925, [including English text of the] Treaty of Mutual Guarantee

1 folder. ([Gr.Brit.Public Record Office. Papers on deposit at the Public Record Office] F.O.840)
Correspondence and papers relating to the Treaty of Mutual Guarantee
Microfilm, positive

NL 0432668 MH

Locarno. Conference, 1925.
X1951 Locarno; tekst van de oorkonden van Locarno
.925 in het Fransch en in Nederlandsche vertaling,
.2 bewerkt door C.A. Kluyver... 's-Gravenhage, M. Nijhoff, 1926.
xi p., 1 l., 120 p. 23½cm.
Contains the final protocol of the Locarno conference with annexes, the treaty between France and Poland and that between France and Czechoslovakia, and articles 10-16 of the Covenant of the League of nations.
"Literatuuropgave": p.⌜119⌝-120.
I.France.Treaties,etc.,1924-1931(Doumergue)

NL 0432669 CSt-H

Locarno. Conference, 1925.
... Locarnoavtalen, jämte svensk översättning. Stockholm, Kungl. boktryckeriet, P. A. Norstedt & söner, 1926.
1 p. l., 21, ⌜1⌝ p. 24cm.
At head of title: Aktstycken utgivna av Kungl. Utrikesdepartementet.
Includes also the treaty between France and Poland (Locarno, Oct. 16th, 1925)

I. France. Treaties, etc., 1924–1931 (Doumergue) II. Poland (1918–) Treaties, etc., 1922?–1926 (Wojciechowski)

32-16015
Library of Congress JX1931 1925 cd
⌜3⌝ 341.1

NL 0432670 DLC

Locarno. Conference, 1925.
... Protocol of the Locarno conference. Final protocol of the Locarno conference, 1925 and annexes together with treaties between France and Poland and France and Czechoslovakia ... Washington, Govt. print. off., 1925.
iii, 27 p. 23½cm. (⌜U. S.⌝ 69th Cong., 1st sess. Senate. Doc. 21)
Presented by Mr. Walsh. Ordered printed December 15, 1925.
I. France. Treaties, etc., 1924– (Doumergue) II. Poland (1918–) Treaties, etc., 1922?– (Wojciechowski) III. Czechoslovak Republic. Treaties, etc., 1918– (Masaryk) IV. Walsh, Thomas James, 1859– V. Title.

25-27508
Library of Congress JX1931 1925 c

NL 0432671 DLC OO OOxM MiU DAL ICJ

Locarno, Switzerland. Conference, 1925.
Das Schlussprotokoll von Locarno und seine Anlagen. Frankfurt am Main: L. Sänger, 1926. 41 p. 4°.

French and German on opposite pages.
Treaties signed by Germany, Belgium, Great Britain, France, Italy, Poland and Czecho-Slovakia, 16 October 1925.

521221A. 1. Locarno, Treaty of, 1925. I. Treaties, 1925, October 16.
N. Y. P. L. June 8, 1931

NL 0432672 NN ICJ CtY

Locarno. Conference, 1925.
... Treaty of mutual guarantee between the United Kingdom, Belgium, France, Germany and Italy. Locarno, October 16, 1925. <Ratifications deposited at Geneva, September 14, 1926> ... London, H. M. Stationery off., 1926.
11 p. 24½cm. (⌜Gt. Brit. Foreign office⌝ Treaty series, 1926, no. 28)
Parliament. Papers by command. Cmd. 2764.
French and English on opposite pages.
1. Arbitration, International. 2. ⌜Arbitration treaties⌝ I. Gt. Brit. Treaties, etc., 1910– (George V) II. Belgium. Treaties, etc., 1909– (Albert I) III. France. Treaties, etc., 1924– (Doumergue) IV. Germany (1918–) Treaties, etc., 1918– V. Italy. Treaties, etc., 1900– (Victor Emmanuel III) VI. Title.

A 27-63
Title from Carnegie Endow. Int. Peace JX636.A3 1926 no. 28 Printed by L. C.

NL 0432673 NNCE CaBVaU DLC

Locarno. Mostra d'arte Ticinese.
Mostra d'arte Ticinese del '600 e '700 nel Castello di Locarno. Maggio Ottobre 1938. Locarno, Vito Carminati, 1938.
66,2 p. 48pl.

NL 0432674 OClMA

Locarno. Societa ticinese di scienze naturali
see
Societa ticinese di scienze naturali.

Locarno. Universal peace congress, 30th, 1934
see Universal peace congress. 30th, Locarno, 1934.

Locarno. ⌜Geneva? 1926?⌝
9 numb. l. 33 1/2 cm.
Caption title.
Mimeographed.

NL 0432677 CSt-H

JX1931 Locarno a Svaz národů. V Praze, Nákl. 'Orbis', 1925.
1925 133 p. (Časové otázky, sv. 3 [a])
L62
Texts in French and Czech.

Contents. - Ministr Beneš o konferenci locarnské. - Locarnská ujednání. - Úmluva o Spolecnosti národů. - Smlouva francouzsko-československá.

1. Locarno. Conference, 1925. I. Locarno. Conference, 1925. II. League of Nations. Covenant. III. Czechoslovak Republic. Treaties, etc., 1924- (Masaryk) IV. France. Treaties, etc., 1924- (Doumergue) V. Benes, Edvard, Pres. Czechoslovak Republic, 1884-1948.

NL 0432678 CU MH

... **Locarno** and the Balkans ...: A turning point in history, by James T. Shotwell, The possibility of a Balkan Locarno, by David Mitrany ... Worcester, Mass., New York city, Carnegie endowment for international peace, Division of intercourse and education ⌜1927⌝
36 p. 19½cm. (International conciliation ... April, 1927, no. 229)
The address by Dr. Shotwell was delivered before the Institute social de Bucarest, in October, 1925.
Bibliography: p. 35-36.
1. Locarno. Conference, 1925. 2. Balkan peninsula—Hist. 3. Eastern question (Balkan) I. Shotwell, James Thomson, 1874– II. Mitrany, David, 1888– III. Title: A turning point in history. IV. Title: The possibility of a Balkan Locarno.

27-11057
Library of Congress JX1907.A8 no. 229

OCl OO OU
NL 0432679 DLC WaU-L CaBVaU OrPR TxU PHC PPT MB MiU

... The **Locarno** conference, October 5-16, 1925. Boston, World peace foundation ⌜1926⌝
75 p. incl. map. 20½cm. (World peace foundation. Pamphlets. vol. IX, no. 1. 1926)

1. Locarno. Conference, 1925.

26-6450
Library of Congress JX1908.U52 vol. IX, no. 1

OO OCU OClCC NcU
NL 0432680 DLC WaU-L OrU WaTC PPT PPD PHC PCC OOxM

Locarno e le sue valli... Neuchâtel, Éditions de la Baconnière ⌜194-?⌝ 32 p. 48 pl. 17cm. (Città e régioni d'arte svizzere. ⌜v. 4⌝)

Text in Italian, German, English and French.

1. Art, Swiss—Locarno. 2. Locarno, Switzerland—Views. I. Ser.
N. Y. P. L. September 14, 1951

NL 0432681 NN

The Locarno treaties, their importance, scope and possible consequences
see under [Farmers' loan and trust company, New York]

B **Locas, Clément.**
65 **Nationalisme et droit. Montréal, Fides, [1954].**
L6 **149 p. 21 cm. (Philosophie et problèmes contemporains, 11)**
Dissertatio (Ph.D.)—Pontificium Institutum, "Angelicum", Rome.

1. Law - Philosophy. 2. Nationalism. I. Philosophie et problèmes contemporains, 11.

NL 0432683 IMunS NN OCU CaOTU

Lo Cascio, Alfred, 1910–
Bloods of the equator, by Alfred LoCascio, jr. Boston, Meador publishing company, 1939.
202 p. 21cm.

I. Title.

39-24227
Library of Congress PZ3.L7793Bl

NL 0432684 DLC NcD OOxM MB

⌜**Lo Cascio, Alfred**⌝ 1910–
Hey, taxi! By Alf Loc ⌜*pseud.*⌝ Boston, Meador publishing company, 1940.
36 p. incl. front., illus. 17½cm.

I. Title.

40-30666
Library of Congress PS3523.O22H4 1940
——— Copy 2.
Copyright ⌜2⌝ 817.5

NL 0432685 DLC

Lo Cascio, Alfred, 1910–
The tom-toms speak, by Alfred LoCascio, jr. ... Boston, Meador publishing company, 1940.
163 p. incl. front. 20cm.

I. Title.

40-10772
Library of Congress PZ3.L7793To

NL 0432686 DLC

Locascio, Franc. Resoconto delle inoculazioni vacciniche praticate da aprile ad ottobre corrente anno 1878. 44 pp. 8°. *Palermo*, 1878.

NL 0432687 DNLM

VOLUME 337

LOCASCIO, Francesco.
Historia delle guerre civili di Messina dell' anno 1672 sino al 1678. Descritta da D Francesco lo Cascio Palermitano, capellano del monasterio detto di Saladino.

258, [11]p. 35cm.

Note in pencil on t.-p.: Phillipps manuscript 21647.

1. Sicily. Hist. 2. Manuscripts, Italian. Examples.

NL 0432688 MnU

QC 385 L6 LoCascio, Girolamo, 1894-
Elementi di diottrica oculare. [Napoli] Istituto editoriale del Mezzogiorno [1955]
362 p. illus. 25 cm.

Bibliography: p. [361]-362.

1. Refraction. 2. Optics, Geometrical.

NL 0432689 OU

Lo Cascio, Girolamo, 1894–
Lezioni di clinica oculistica raccolte nel 1936 dal dott. R. Campos. 3. ed. riv. ed ampliata dal dott. A. Santoni ... Napoli, Humus [194–?]
264 p. illus. 21 cm.
Contains signature of A. Santoni.

1. Eye—Diseases [and defects] I. Campos, Raffaele, ed. II. Santoni, Armando, ed.

Med 48-1410
U. S. Army Medical Libr. for Library of Congress [WW140L811L 1940] [1]

NL 0432690 DNLM MnU NNC

Lo Cascio, Girolamo, 1894–
... Lezioni sul tracoma, tenute dal prof. G. Lo Cascio, raccolte e pubblicate dal dott. Antonino de Crecchio. Napoli, G. U. F. "Mussolini," Sezione editoriale, 1940.
2 p. l., 61 p. plates. 24½cm.
At head of title: R. Università di Napoli.

1. Conjunctivitis, Granular. I. Crecchio, Antonino de, ed. II. Naples. Università. III. Gruppo universitario fascista "Mussolini," Naples.

45-40872
Library of Congress RE321.L6 [2] 617.77

NL 0432691 DLC

Lo Cascio,Girolamo,1894-
Paratiroidi e occhio. 24cm. Le Caire, 1938. p.401-71.

NL 0432692 DNLM

Lo Cascio, Girolamo, 1894–
La respirazione della retina durante l'adattamento al buio; memoria di Girolamo Lo Cascio e Alma Bordiga.
(*In* Atti della Reale Accademia d'Italia. Memorie della Classe di scienze fisiche, matematiche e naturali. Roma. 25 cm. v. 14 (1944) p. [505]-525. diagrs.)
Bibliography: p. 525.

1. Retina. I. Bordiga, Alma, joint author.

[AS222.R5325 vol. 14] A 58-810
Illinois. Univ. Library for Library of Congress [1]

NL 0432693 IU

Law Lo Cascio, Italo, ed.
Italy. *Laws, statutes, etc.*
Manuale d'uso della nuova tariffa doganale; tabelle aggiornate al 31 luglio 1950 (a cura del dott. Italo Lo Cascio) [1. ed.] Roma, Tip. F. Failli, 1950.

Lo Cascio, Manlio.
Diritto militare e disciplinare (Conferenze tenute al 15° Corso superiore S. G. A.) Anno accademico, 1951–52. [Roma, Associazione culturale aeronautica, 1952]
232 p. 25 cm.
At head of title: Scuola di guerra aerea, Firenze. Corso superiore e normale.

1. Military law—Italy. 2. Military discipline—Italy. 3. Military offenses—Italy.

A 53-7214
Michigan. Univ. Libr. for Library of Congress [1]

NL 0432695 MiU

Locascio, Michael.
Dedications. New York, Vantage Press [°1954]
23 p. 23 cm.
Poems.

I. Title.

PS3523.O222D4 811.5 54-12643 ‡

NL 0432696 DLC

Law Locascio, Pietro, ed.
FOR OTHER EDITIONS SEE MAIN ENTRY
Italy. *Laws, statutes, etc.*
Codice penale vigente nella Repubblica italiana. Ed. accuratamente riscontrata sul testo ufficiale, aggiornata secondo le più recenti riforme di materia penale, completata con le disposizioni di coordinamento e transitorie, corredata di un indice analitico, con l'aggiunta di nozioni di polizia giudiziaria. A cura dei dott. Arnaldo Pacelli e Pietro Locascio. 11. ed. Roma, Casa editrice mediterranea, 1952.

Law Locascio, Pietro, joint ed.
Italy. *Laws, statutes, etc.*
Codice penale vigente nello Stato italiano. Ed. accuratamente riscontrata sul testo ufficiale, aggiornata secondo le più recenti riforme in materia penale, completata con le disposizioni di coordinamento e transitorie e corredata di un indice analitico. Con l'aggiunta di nozioni di polizia giudiziaria. A cura dei dott. Arnaldo Pacelli e Pietro Locascio. Roma, Casa Editrice Mediterranea, 1947.

PQ4827 018 A73 Lo Cascio, Renzo
Amara terra. [Palermo] G. B. Palumbo, 1949.
89p. 25 cm.
Verse.

NL 0432699 RPB

LO CASCIO, RENZO.
Lettura del Poliziano, le "Stanze per la giostra." Palermo, S.F. Flaccovio [1954] 253 p. 23cm. (Collano di saggi e monografie. 6)

1. Poliziano, Angelo Ambrogini, known as, 1454-1494. I. Series.

RPB
NL 0432700 NN IU CSt IaU ICU InU NIC NcD NcU CtY CU

PQ4827 018 R5 Lo Cascio, Renzo
Il ritorno. [Palermo] G.B.Palumbo, 1949.
37p. 25 cm.

NL 0432701 RPB

Locascio, Santiago.
... Juan Bautista Alberdi (crítica histórica) Prólogo de Antonio R. Zúñiga ... B[ueno]s Aires [etc.] Maucci hermanos e hijos, 1916.
3 p. l., [ix]-xv, 153 p., 2 l. 18½cm.
Portrait on cover.

1. Alberdi, Juan Bautista, 1810-1884.

37-6945
Library of Congress F2846.A326 [2] 923.482

NL 0432702 DLC CU NcU CoU InU TxU

Lo Cascio Loureiro, Hortensia.
... Historia de Madrid (episodios 1561–1932) e Historia documentada de la antigua Iglesia hospital de s. Pedro y s. Pablo, de Madrid, titulada de los italianos. Madrid, Imprenta de Comercio, 1932.
175 p. 22cm.

1. Madrid — Hist. 2. Madrid. Iglesia hospital de san Pedro y san Pablo.

34-6482
Library of Congress DP354.L6 [2] 946.4

NL 0432703 DLC NNC MH

Lo Casto, B G. Dn 127.55F
Ricostruzione della "valle inferna." Catania, N. Giannotta, 1901.
f°. pp. (8), 29. 4 plates.

Lo Casto, B G. Dn 127.55F
Ricostruzione della "valle inferna." Catania, N. Giannotta, 1901.
f°. pp. (8), 29. 4 plates.

Dante-Div. Com.-Inf.||

NL 0432704 MH

Locataire, *pseud.*
see Cooze, Frank Ivan, 1907–

LOCATELLI, ____,condesa de.
Un drama contemporáneo; narración. Madrid, E.Teodoro,1883.

At head of title:-Biblioteca de la madre y el niño.
Span 5792.9.31

NL 0432706 MH

[Locatelli, Agostino.]
Cenni biografici sulla straordinaria carriera teatrale percorsa da Gio. Battista Rubini da Romano, cantante di camera... Milano: F. Colombo, 1844. 88 p. 8°.
Preface signed: Locatelli, Agostino.

JUILLIARD FOUNDATION FUND.
509663A. 1. Rubini, Giovanni Battista, 1795–1854. I. Title.
N. Y. P. L. July 22, 1931

NL 0432707 NN MH

914.524 L787g Locatelli, Agostino.
Guida artistico-monumentale di Bergamo e sua provincia con storia patria ... Bergamo, A spese dell'autore, 1854.
190p. fold.plan.

1. Bergamo--Descr. 2. Art--Bergamo. 3. Bergamo (Province)--Descr. & trav.

NL 0432708 IU

VOLUME 337

Locatelli, Agostino.

Fabietti, Ettore.
... Manuale per le biblioteche popolari, con aggiunto un Saggio di catalogo modello di E. Fabietti e A. Locatelli. Milano, Consorzio delle biblioteche popolari, 1908.

Locatelli, Agostino, joint author.

Fabietti, Ettore.
... Saggio di catalogo modello per una biblioteca popolare di centro urbano e per una bibliotechina di piccolo centro rurale. Milano, Consorzio delle biblioteche popolari (Riparto provincia) 1908.

Locatelli, Aldo.
... Corso di meccanica e macchine per allievi delle scuole tecniche industriali e tecnici d'officina ... Torino, Editrice Libraria italiana, 1943-
v. illus., diagrs. 19cm.
Vol. 1: 6. ristampa della 8. ed.; v. 2: 7. ed. riveduta (3. ristampa)
CONTENTS.—v. 1. Meccanica teorica ed applicata.—v. 2. Macchine idrauliche e termiche.
1. Mechanics, Applied. 2. Hydraulic machinery. 3. Heat-engines.
45-14113
Library of Congress TA350.L6
[2] 621

NL 0432711 DLC

Locatelli, Aldo.
Esercitazioni di meccanica e macchine, oltre 700 esercizi dei quali più di 300 completamente svolti. Tabelle riassuntive di meccanica e tabelle numeriche di uso più frequente. 2. ed. riv. Torino, S. Lattes, 1948.
432 p. illus., tables. 20 cm.
1. Mechanical engineering—Problems, exercises, etc. 2. Mechanics, Applied.
TJ170.L6 1948 621.076 49-26610*

NL 0432712 DLC

Locatelli, Alessandro. Ott 413.1
Racconto historico della veneta guerra in Levante diretta dal valore del principe Francesco Morosini contro l'Impero Ottomano. Opera postuma. Colonia, G. Albrizzi, 1691.
2 pt. l. 8°. 55 engraved plates.
Turkey-Hist. 1682-99||

NL 0432713 MH ICN ICU MdBP NN

Locatelli, Amilcare.
...L'"affare" Dreyfus (la più grande infamia del secolo scorso). Milano: Edizioni "Corbaccio," 1930. 554 p. illus. (incl. facsims., plans), plates, ports. 8°.
582787A. 1. Dreyfus case.
N. Y. P. L. June 9, 1932

NL 0432714 NN CU MH OCl

Locatelli, Amilcare.
Come si vota nelle elezioni amministrative. Milano, Società editrice Avanti! [1946?]
20 p. 17 cm. (Travet rosso)
1. Election law—Italy. I. Series.
JN5623.L6 A F 48-3403*
California. Univ. Libr. for Library of Congress [1]†

NL 0432715 CU MH MiU DLC

Locatelli, Amilcare.
... Francesco Le Vaillant attraverso l'Africa australe (fra Gonachesi, Cafri e Boschimani) Torino-Milano [etc.] G. B. Paravia & c. [1931]
2 p. l., 304 p. front. (fold. map) plates. 19½cm. (I grandi viaggi di esplorazione)
Illustrated cover in colors.
Head and tail pieces.
The plates are from Le Vaillant's Voyage dans l'intérieur de l'Afrique.
1. Le Vaillant, François, 1753-1824. 2. Africa, South—Description and travel. I. Title.
A C 32-119
Title from N. Y. Pub. Libr. Printed by L. C.

NL 0432716 NN

Locatelli, Amilcare.
...Serpa Pinto; dall' Oceano Atlantico all' Oceano Indiano. Torino: G. B. Paravia & c., 1928. 306 p. front., maps, plates, ports. 12°. (I grandi viaggi di esplorazione.)
Plates printed on both sides.
Bibliographical footnotes.
451640A. 1. Africa, Central—Descr. and trav., 1875-1900.
N. Y. P. L. January 17, 1930

NL 0432717 NN MiD

Locatelli, Amilcare.
...La spedizione di La Pérouse nel grande oceano. Torino: G. B. Paravia & c., 1929. 272 p. front. (port.), map, plates. 12°. (I grandi viaggi di esplorazione.)
Bibliographical footnotes.
454634A. 1. Lapérouse, Jean François de Galaup, comte de, 1741-1788. 2. Voyages around the world, 1700-1800.
N. Y. P. L. March 5, 1930

NL 0432718 NN ICN

Locatelli, Anton Felice. 331.91 R100
... Le leggi sul lavoro e il diritto internazionale operaio con prefazione del prof. Enrico Catellani. Padova, Fratelli Drucker, 1911.
xi, 168, [4] p. 20½cm.
At head of title: Anton Felice Locatelli.

NL 0432719 ICJ

Locatelli, Antonio.
... Le ali del prigioniero. Milano, Fratelli Treves, 1924.
3 p. l., 314 p. front. (port.) 19cm.
3. migliaio.
1. European war, 1914-1918—Prisoners and prisons, Austrian. 2. European war, 1914-1918—Aerial operations. I. Title.
24-7967
Library of Congress D627.A8L5 1924

NL 0432720 DLC NN

Locatelli, Antonio. 2308E.85
Le ali del prigioniero.
— Milano. Treves. [1929.] (5), 314 pp. Portrait. 18 cm., in 8s.
Autobiographical account of an Italian aviator's experiences in the World War, with special reference to Austrian prisons.
D2434 — T.r. —European War, 1914-1919. Italy. — European War, 1914-1919. Personal narratives. — European War, 1914-1919. Aeronautics. — European War, 1914-1919. Prisons. Austrian.

NL 0432721 MB

[LOCATELLI, ANTONIO.]
I cavalieri d'Italia a Pozzuolo del Friuli. Omaggio. [Lonigo: Tip. G. Gaspari, 1930.] 20 p. 23½cm.
Signed: Antonio Locatelli.
696635A. 1. European war, 1914-1918—Regt. hist.—Italy—Cav.—2. Brigade. 2. Army, Italian—Regt. hist. I. Title.

NL 0432722 NN

Locatelli, Antonio.
La spedizione di La Pérouse nel Grande Oceano.
Torino, G.B. Parsvia, 1933.

NL 0432723 ICN

LOCATELLI, Antonio.
Il volo su Vienna. La traversata delle Ande. Bergamo, C. Conti & c., [1919].

NL 0432724 MH

Locatelli, Antonio, fl.1820-1837.
Avventure di Pippetto Spasimi; commedia di un atto solo di Antonio Locatelli.
PQ 1231 [Venezia, Rizzi, 1820]
.A8 G5 44 p. 16cm. (Giornale teatrale.
fasc.2 fasc. II [pt. 2])

NL 0432725 MdBJ

Locatelli, Antonio, fl.1820-1837, ed.
Iconografia italiana degli uomini e delle donne celebri dall'epoca del risorgimento delle scienze e della arti fino ai nostri giorni. Milano, Locatelli, 1836
4 v. ports.
Large paper edition
Vol.2-4 are without title pages
1. Italy - Biography. I. Title

NL 0432726 MH ICN

---

q920.045 [Locatelli, Antonio] fl.1820-1837, ed.
L787i Iconografia italiana degli uomini e delle donne celebri dall'epoca del risorgimento delle scienze e delle arti fino ai nostri giorni. Milano, 1837.
v. ports.
Dedication signed: Antonio Locatelli.
Vol.2 has no t.-p.

NL 0432727 IU CSmH InU

Locatelli, Antonio, fl.1820-1837.
Il perfetto cavaliere; opera corredata di stampe miniate rappresentanti le varie specie de vavalli, invominciando dal celvaggio, co loro differenti mantelli ed accompagnata dalla storia naturale del cavallo seritta da Buffon...
Milan, Sonzogno, 1825.
576 p.

NL 0432728 PU-V

Locatelli, Antonio Maria.
... A new life of St. Anthony of Padua, by the Promoter of the Universal association of St. Anthony, with the help of the learned of the same society. First English translation from the Italian text, by Prof. Arthur de Rénoche. Padua, Printing office Antoniana, 1902.
xx, 202 p., 1 f. illus.

NL 0432729 MdSsW

Locatelli, Basilio.
La commedia in commedia; commedia... (In: Apollonio, Mario, ed. Commedia italiana. [Milano] 1947. p. [567]-576.)
456666B. 1. Drama, Italian. I. Title.
N. Y. P. L. October 28, 1948

NL 0432730 NN

VOLUME 337

B S2531ℓ Locatelli, Carlo, 1836-1923.
S. Satiro. Milano, Libreria editrice ditta S. Majocchi, 1875.
75p. 19cm.

1. Satiro, Saint, 338(ca.)-375.

NL 0432731 IU

Locatelli, Carlo, 1836-1923
Vita di S. Ambrogio ... Nuova edizione illus. Milano, Serafino Majocchi, 1874.

637 p. 24 cm.

NL 0432732 PLatS CU

Locatelli, Carlo, 1836-1923.
La vita di San Carlo narrata alle famiglie ... Milano, Serafino Majocchi, 1882.

637 p. front., illus., plates, 23 cm.

NL 0432733 PLatS IU

Locatelli, Emo.
... Appunti ad un'annotazione nel casellario giudiziale d'una sentenza di non farsi luogo a procedere in seguito a recesso da querela per diffamazione anteriore al r. decreto 1 dicembre 1889. Querela: Montemezzi contro Locatelli - Udienza 6 dicembre 1888 del Tribunale di Verona. Verona, G. Annichini, 1892.

25 p., 1 l. 23cm.
Author's autograph presentation copy to Luigi Lucchini.

NL 0432735 MH-L

MICD 862 Locatelli, Federico.
El rey de la Alpujarra, zarzuela cómica en un acto dividido en tres cuadros, original y en prosa ... música del maestro Amadeo Vives. Madrid, R. Velasco, 1900.
32 p.

NL 0432736 MoU MH NN MiEM

Locatelli, Federico.
El rey de la Alpujarra, zarzuela cómica en un acto dividido en tres cuadros, original y en prosa ... música del maestro Amadeo Vives. Madrid, R. Velasco, 1900.
32p.

Microcard edition.

NL 0432737 ICRL

[Locatelli, Francesco] 1687-1770.
Lettres moscovites ... Konisberg, 1736.
2 p. l., 363 p. 16cm.

1. Russia—Descr. & trav. I. Title.

42-27696

Library of Congress DK23.L6

NL 0432738 DLC ICN

[Locatelli, Francesco] 1687-1770. Slav 3077.36.2
Lettres moscovites. Paris, au depens de la compagnie, 1736.
pp. (4), 363.

NL 0432739 MH MU InU

PR3633 .A3 1735a v. 4 [Locatelli, Francesco] 1687-1770.
Lettres moscovites: or, Muscovian letters. Containing, an account of the form of government, customs, and manners of that great empire. Written by an Italian officer of distinction. Tr. from the French original, printed at Paris 1735, by William Musgrave ... London, 1736.
[1], xii, 190 p. 20cm. (In Pope, Alexander. Mr. Pope's literary correspondence ... London, 1735-37. v. 4)

1. Russia—Soc. life & cust. 2. Russia—Pol. & govt.

NL 0432740 ICU NN PPL IU MH

[Locatelli, Francesco] 1687-1770.
Die so genannte Moscowitische Brieffe, oder Die, wider die löbliche russische Nation von einem aus der andern Welt zurück gekommenen Italiäner ausgesprengte abendtheurliche Verläumdungen und Tausend-Lügen; aus dem Frantzösischen übersetzt, mit einem zulänglichen Register versehen, und dem Brieffsteller so wohl, als seinen gleichgesinnten Freunden, mit dienlichen Erinnerungen wieder heimgeschickt von einem Teutschen. Franckfurth [etc.] J. L. Montag, 1738. 69 l., 816 p., 64 l. front. 17cm.

157608A. 1. Russia—Social life, 18th cent. I. Title. II. Title: Moscowitische Brieffe.
N. Y. P. L. Card revised August 22, 1944

NL 0432741 NN MnU NjP CtY MH

Locatelli, Giampietro.
Museo capitolino o sia descrizione delle statue, iscrizioni, ed altre antichità, e de'quadri de'più bravi pennelli, che si custodiscono ne' palazzi di Campidoglio. [Rome, 1771]

135 p.
Bound with: Rossini, G.P. the Elder. Il Mercurio errante delle grandezze di Roma... Roma, 1771.

NL 0432742 DDO

WZ 250 L8112dp 1631 LOCATELLI, Giovanni Battista, fl. 1631
Della peste trattato ... Rovigo, Giacinto e Marin Bissuccio, 1631.
[8], 189, [7] p. 26 cm.

NL 0432743 DNLM

945.08 M499Bℓ Locatelli, Giuliano.
Francesco Melzi, precursore dell'Unità italiana. [Milano, n.d.]
[153]-164p. 25cm.

Caption title.
Offprinted or extracted from Archivio storico lombardo; giornale della Società storica lombarda

1. Melzi d'Eril, Francesco, 1753-1816. 2. Italy - Hist. - 1789-1870.

NL 0432744 TxU

Locatelli, Giuliano.
... Il marxismo. Milano, Edizioni Allegranza [1945]
139, [1] p., 2 l. 17½cm. (Dottrine rivoluzionarie [a cura di Leopoldo Marchetti e Anna Allegranza])
Bibliography included in "Note" at end of each chapter.

1. Socialism. 2. Marx, Karl, 1818-1883.
HX291.L56 A F 47-3758
New York. Public library for Library of Congress [2]†

NL 0432745 NN CtY CU DLC WU

Locatelli, Giuseppe, M.D.
1824. [P., v. 2145.] Tesi. 2l. 4°. Genova,

NL 0432746 DNLM

Locatelli, Giuseppe, M.D.
Tesi. 3l. 4°. Genova, 1824. [P., v. 2145.]

NL 0432747 DNLM

Locatelli, Giuseppe, 1856-1939.
see Locatelli Milesi, Giuseppe, 1856-1939.

BX1518 .L8 Locatelli, Joseph, 1749-1800.
Babylon Bohemiae ab anno 1780 usque ad annum 1790. Edidit Antonius Podlaha. Pragae, Sumptibus s. f. Metropolitani Capituli Pragensis, 1905.
152 p. (Editiones Archivii et Bibliothecae s. f. Metropolitani Capituli Pragensis, 1)

1. Catholic Church in Bohemia. I. Podlaha, Antonín, 1865-1932, ed. II. Title.

NL 0432749 ICU MiU

Locatelli, Joseph von.
Nachricht eines newen Instruments, mit welchem Waitz, Korn, vnd all anders Getraidt, oder Acker Früchte ... gesähet werden. Erfunden vnd geoffenbahret von Joseph von Locatelli ... Gedruckt zu Wienn, bey Johann Jacob Kürner [166-?]
12 p. plate. 20cm.

NL 0432750 NNC

DB 879 .P8 E23 v.6 **Locatelli, Joseph, 1749-1800.**
Regimen Leopoldinum, 1790-1792. Memorabilia, 1792-1799. Edidit Antonius Podlaha. Pragae, Sumptibus S.F.Metropolitani Capituli Pragensis, 1906.
110, vii p. (Editiones Archivii et Bibliothecae S.F.Metropolitani Capituli Pragensis, 6)

1. Bohemia--Pol & govt. 2. Catholic Church in Bohemia. I. Title. II. Title: Memorabilia, 1792-1799.

NL 0432751 MiU

RS 87 .L82 Locatelli, Lodovico, ca. 1600-1657
Theatro d'arcani del medico Lodovico Locatelli ... nel qvale si tratta dell' arte chimica, & suoi arcani, con gli afforismi d' Ippocrate, commentati da Paracelso, & l'espositione d' alcune cifre, & caratteri oscuri de filosofi ... Milano, Per G. P. Ramellati, 1644.
29 p. l., 456 p. 19 cm.
Added t.p., engraved. Title within architectural border.
1. Pharmacy--Early works to 1800. I. Title.

NL 0432752 MiU DFo WU CtY-M PPC NNNAM DNLM

WZ 250 L8114t 1667 LOCATELLI, Lodovico, ca. 1600- 1657
Theatro d'arcani ... nel quale si tratta dell'arte chimica, & suoi arcani. Con gli Afforismi d'Ippocrate commentati da Paracelso et l'espositione d'alcune cifre, & caratteri oscuri de filosofi ... Venetia, Paolo Haglioni, 1667.
[16], 392, [22] p. diagr. 16 cm.
Contents as in the 1644 Milan edition, some preliminary matter omitted.
Södhoff 397.

I. Forberger, Georg, 16th cent., tr. II. Hippocrates.

[Aphorismi. Bks. 1, 2, 4. Latin. 1667] III. Paracelsus, 1493- 1541. Erklärung über etliche Aphorismen des Hippokrates

NL 0432754 DNLM WU CtY-M FU

VOLUME 337

[LOCATELLI, Luigi].
La barcaccia di Bologna; poema giocoso del abate Sabinto Fenicio [pseud.]. Aggiuntovi Il burchiello di Padova; poemetto di Poliseno Fegejo P.A.[pseud.for Carlo Goldoni]. Tomo 14. n.p., Cino Bottagriffi e c., 1760.
pp.96.
"Il burchiello di Padova", pp.73-96.
Ital 8160.5.31

NL 0432755 MH NIC

W 1 RI3631 n. 2 1955
LOCATELLI, Luigi, M.D.
Considerazioni statistiche e critiche sui tumori maligni osservati nel settorato dell'Ospedale maggiore de Bergamo dall'anno 1923 al 1954. Padova, Istituto di anatomia e istologia patologica dell'Università di Padova, 1955.
43 p. illus. (Rivista di anatomia patologica e di oncologia. Supplemento, n. 2)
1. Neoplasms - Italy 2. Neoplasms - Stat. Series

NL 0432756 DNLM

WC 605 qL811t 1949
LOCATELLI, Luigi, M.D.
Il tifo nella Bergamasca; studio clinico, statistico, epidemiologico, topografico. Bergamo, S. E. S. A., 1949.
57 p. illus. (Collana scientifica)
1. Typhus - Italy

NL 0432757 DNLM

LOCATELLI, LUIGI, 1872-1949.
Bibliografia tassiana. Bergamo, Centro di Studi tassiani [1953- pts. 25cm.

Issued as a supplement to Studi tassiani, v. 3- (1953-
Compiled from notes and records deposited in the Civica biblioteca di Bergamo.
Part 4 has also special t. p.

1. Tasso, Torquato, 1544-1595-- Bibl.

NL 0432758 NN IU

HJ2763 .P58
Locatelli, Paolo.
Sorveglianti e sorvegliati; appunti de fisiologia sociale. Milano, G. Brigola, 1876.
175p. 19cm.
Bound with: Pianciani, Luigi. Della amministrazione italiana. 1876.

1.Police - Italy. 2.Crime and criminals - Italy. I.Title.

NL 0432759 NNU

364.25 L787s2
Locatelli, Paolo
Sorveglianti e sorvegliati. Appunti di fisiologia sociale presi dal vero da Paolo Locatelli. 2. ed. riveduta con aggiunte. Milano, Libreria Fratelli Dumolard, 1878.
281 p. 19 cm.

1. Crime and criminals--Italy. 2. Criminal justice, Administraton of--Italy. I. Title

NL 0432760 VtU

LOCATELLI, Paolo Maria.
Discorso per la fondatrice dell'Ordine della Visitazione di Maria canonizzata Santa Giovanna Francesca Fremiot di Chantal recitato nel solenne ottavario in Arona...1768. In Milano, per Federico Agnelli, [1768?].

17 cm. pp.31.

NL 0432761 MH

LOCATELLI, Pasino.
Bernardo Tasso; discorso letto nella festa scolastica del 17 marzo 1872. Bergamo, dalla tipografia Pagnoncelli, 1872.

Pamphlet.
At head of title: Illustri Bergamaschi, 3.
Ital 7770.79

NL 0432762 MH

Locatelli, Pasinio.
Cenni biografici del dott Luigi Fantoni. Bergamo, 1875?

NL 0432763 NIC

Locatelli, Pasino
I dipinti di Lorenzo Lotto nell'oratorio Suardi in Trescore Salneario. Bergamo, 1891.

52 p.

NL 0432764 PBm

N6922 L6
Locatelli, Pasino
Illustri bergamaschi; studi critico-biografici. Bergamo, Dalla tip. Pagnoncelli, 1867-79.
3 v.

Contents. - 1-2. Pittori. - 3. Intarsiatori, architetti e scultori.

1. Artists, Italian - Bergamo. 2. Art - Bergamo. I. Title.

NL 0432765 CU MH IU

Locatelli, Pasino.
... Notizie intorno a Giacomo Palma il vecchio ed alle sue pitture; con riproduzione in fototipia di diciotto dipinti. Bergamo, Fratelli Cattaneo succ. Gaffuri e Gatti, 1890.
94 p., 1 l. front., pl., port. 30cm.
8-11233

NL 0432766 DLC PSt

LOCATELLI, PASINO.
Studi critico-biografici. Pittori. Bergamo, dalla tipografia Pagnoncelli, 1867.
x, 474p. 19cm. (Illustri Bergamaschi)

NL 0432767 ICN

Locatelli, Pasino, tr.
Il vangelo di S. Matteo, volgarizzato in dialetto bergamasco
see under Bible. N.T. Matthew. Italian (Bergamo) 1860. Locatelli.

Locatelli, Pietro
see Locatellus, Petrus.

Locatelli, Pietro Antonio, 1695-1764.
L'arte del violino. XII concerti. Cioé, violino solo, con XXIV capricci ad libitum ... Violino primo, violino secondo, alto, violon cello solo, è basso ... Opera terza. Amsterdam, M. Carlo le Cene, [1733?]
2 p.l., 98 p. f°.
Violin solo part only. Other parts on film.

NL 0432770 NN

FILM 9850 M Music Library
Locatelli, Pietro, Antonio 1695-1764.
[L'arte del violino]
L'arte del violino. XII concerti cioè violino solo, con XXIV capricci ad libitum, che si potrà finire al segno ... Opera terza. Amsterdam, A spesa di Michele Carlo le Cene [1733]
6 parts. On film (Positive)

Microfilm. Original in British Museum.
For violino solo, violino primo, violino secondo, alti, violoncello solo, and basso.

NL 0432771 CU NN

Locatelli, Pietro Antonio, 1695–1764.
L'arte del violino; XII concerto [sic] con XXIV capricci ad lib. che si potra finire al segno, op. 3. Paris, Des Lauriers [ca. 1780]
part. 33 cm.
Part for solo violin.
The concertos for violin and string orchesrta; the caprices for violin.

1. Concertos (Violin with string orchestra)—To 1800—Parts (solo) 2. Violin music—To 1800. I. Title.
M1112.L63 op. 3 72-224441
[M42]

NL 0432772 DLC

MT273 L81A7 1920
Locatelli, Pietro Antonio, 1695-1764.
[L'arte del violino]
L'arte del violino, 25 capricci. L'art du violon. The art of the violin. Die Kunst des Violinspiels. (Franzoni) [Milano, New York] Ricordi [1920]
79 p. 31cm. (Edizioni Ricordi 110)

1. Violin - Studies and exercises. I. Franzoni, Romeo, ed.

NL 0432773 CSt

Locatelli, Pietro Antonio, 1695-1764.

...Composizioni; per pianoforte a quattro mani a cura di Alceo Toni. Milano: Soc. anonima notari [1921?] 3 no. in 1 v. 23cm. (Raccolta nazionale [delle musiche italiane] Quaderno 205, 155–156.)
Score: piano, 4 hands.
At head of title: P. Locatelli e F. G. Bertoni.
Each number has special t.-p.
On cover: N. 16. I classici della musica italiana.
CONTENTS.—Locatelli, P. Concerto grosso n. 12, Op. 1.—Bertoni, F. G. Quartetto n. 3.—Bertoni, F. G. Quartetto n. 5.

JUILLIARD FOUNDATION FUND.
826823A. 1. No subject. I. Toni, Alceo, 1884- , ed. II. Ser.
N. Y. P. L. July 31, 1936

NL 0432774 NN IEN

Mus M 1040 L6
Locatelli, Pietro Antonio, 1695-1764.
[Concerto grosso, op.7, no.12, F major]
Concerto grosso, F major, for 4 solo violins and string orchestra. Op.7, no.12. Edited by Newell Jenkins. London, New York, Eulenburg [n.d.] Pl. no. E.E. 6122.
miniature score (62p.) (Edition Eulenburg, 1219)

1. Concerti grossi - Scores.

NL 0432775 FTaSU

M1040 .L6 1919
Locatelli, Pietro Antonio, 1695-1764.
[Concerti grossi. op. 1, F minor. Selections]

Concerto grosso F-moll mit Pastorale. [Aus "Concerti grossi" Op. 1; 1721. Bearb. von Arnold Schering] Leipzig, C. F. Kahnt [1919] Pl. no. 8119.
score (21 p.) and parts. 34cm. (Perlen alter Kammermusik deutscher und italienischer Meister ... Nr. 23)
Score and parts: vl. I, vl. II, vla. I, vla. II, cello, concertino; vl. I, vl. II, vla. I, vla. II, cello & bass (2 copies) harpsichord.
1. Concerti grossi—To 1800—Scores and parts. I. Schering, Arnold, 1877-1941,

NL 0432776 ViU ICN

VOLUME 337

Locatelli, Pietro Antonio, 1693–1764.
Concerto grosso for string orchestra with piano (or harpsichord), by Pietro Locatelli. [Op. 1, no. 2.] Arranged for concert use by Sam Franko... New York: G. Schirmer, Inc.[, 1928.] Publ. pl. no. 33733. 19 p. f°.

Score.

JUILLIARD FOUNDATION FUND.

1. Concertos—Concerti grossi. 2. Franko, Sam, 1857– , editor.
N. Y. P. L. November 21, 1928

NL 0432777 NN IU

Locatelli, Pietro Antonio, 1693–1764.
...Concerto grosso für Streichorchester mit Klavier, bearbeitet von Arthur Egidi. Partitur, zugleich Klavierstimme, 4 Streicherstimmen. Op. 1, no. 6. Berlin-Lichterfelde: C. F. Vieweg, G.m.b.H.[, 1927.] Publ. pl. no. V. 1692. 5 parts in 1 v. f°. (Musikschaetze der Vergangenheit; Vokal- und Instrumental-Musik des XVI bis XVIII. Jahrhunderts.)

Score and 4 parts.

1. Concertos—Concerti grossi. I. Egidi, Arthur, 1859–
N. Y. P. L. January 13, 1931

NL 0432778 NN

Locatelli, Pietro Antonio, 1693–1764.
[Concerti grossi. Op. 1, no. 8]
...Concerto grosso Nr. 8 (F-moll) mit Pastorale aus Op. 1. 1721. Für 2 Solo-Violinen, 2 Solo-Violen, Solo-Violoncello, Streichquintett u. Klavier (auch mit einfacher Besetzung ausführbar)... Leipzig: C. F. Kahnt [cop. 1919] Publ. pl. no. C. F. K. 8119. 21 p. 34cm. (Perlen alter Kammermusik deutscher und italienischer Meister.)

Score (including realized basso continuo).
"Für den praktischen Gebrauch bearbeitet von A. Schering."

CARNEGIE CORPORATION OF NEW YORK.

1. Concerti grossi—Full score. I. Schering, Arnold, 1877– ed.
N. Y. P. L. October 18, 1935

NL 0432779 NN MH CSt MiU ICU MB

Locatelli, Pietro Antonio, 1693–1764.
[Concerti grossi. Op. 1, no. 12. Arr. for piano, 4 hd.]
...Concerto grosso n. 12, Op. 1, per quattro violini obbligati. Riduzione per pianoforte a 4 mani di Alceo Toni... (In his: Composizioni. Milano [1921?] 23cm. ⟨Raccolta nazionale [delle musiche italiane] Quaderno 205, p. [1]–24⟩.)

Score: piano, 4 hands.
From his: XII concerti grossi à quattro, e à cinque... Opera prima. Amsterdam: J. Roger [1719?]

JUILLIARD FOUNDATION FUND.

826823A. 1. Piano—4 hands—Arr. 2. Concerti grossi—Arr. for piano, 4 hands.
N. Y. P. L. August 7, 1936

NL 0432780 NN ICN IaU

M 2 C13 no.16 pt.1
Locatelli, Pietro Antonio, 1695–1764.
[Concerto grosso, op. 4, no. 12, F major; arr.]
Concerto grosso n. 12, op. 1 [i.e. 4] per quattro violini obbligati. Riduzione per pianoforte a 4 mani di Alceo Toni. Concerto grosso n. 12, op. 1. [i.e. 4] Reduction for the pianoforte 4 hands by A. Toni. Milano, Notari, c1921.
24 p. 24cm. ((I classici della musica italiana, no. 16)

"P. Locatelli e F.G. Bertoni. Composizioni per pianoforte a quattro mani [pt. 1]" "Quaderno n. 125"

1. Concerti grossi arranged for piano (4 hands)

NL 0432782 NIC NN

Locatelli, Pietro Antonio, 1695–1764
Concerti grossi, op.1, no.6
Concerto grosso, op.1, no.6, für Streichorchester mit Klavier. Bearb. von A.Egidi. Berlin, Vieweg [19-] Pl.no.V.1692

Score (12 p.) (Musikschätze vergangener Zeiten)
Cover title also in English
Bass realized for keyboard instrument

NL 0432783 MH

Locatelli, Pietro Antonio, 1695–1764.
[Concerti grossi, op. 1, no. 9]
...Concerto grosso (Op. 1, n. 9) per orchestra d'archi. Libera elaborazione di Ettore Bonelli... Padova, G. Zanibon, 1948. Pl.nos. G.3728 Z.–G.3729 Z. 1 v. 34cm.

Score, string orchestra (20 p.) and parts.
Duration: 12 minutes.

1. Concerti grossi—To 1800. 2. Orchestra—To 1800. I. Bonelli, Ettore.

NL 0432784 NN CLU MH OCl

Locatelli, Pietro Antonio, 1693–1764.
Concerto per quattro violini, con accompagnamento d'orchestra d'archi ed organo. Op. 1, n. 12. Di Pietro Locatelli. Con le arcate, i segni vari d'esecuzione ed il basso continuo elaborato per organo da Alceo Toni. Partitura... Milano: G. Ricordi e C., 1929. Publ. pl. no. 120864. 35 p. 8°.

JUILLIARD FOUNDATION FUND.

1. Concertos—Concerti grossi. I. Toni, Alceo, 1884– , arranger.
N. Y. P. L. October 28, 1930

NL 0432785 NN

-VM 1105 L 81c
LOCATELLI, PIETRO, 1693-1764.
[Concerto, no.10, piano & string] X° concerto da camera per orchestra d'archi e pianoforte. Revisione e realizzazione del basso di Gino Marinuzzi. Partitura. Milano, G.Ricordi e C., 1929.
miniature score(35p.) 23cm.

NL 0432786 ICN

Locatelli, Pietro Antonio, 1693–1764.
...X.° concerto da camera per orchestra d'archi e pianoforte; revisione e realizzazione del basso di Gino Marinuzzi. [Op. 1, no. 10.] Partitura. Milano: G. Ricordi e C., 1929. Publ. pl. no. E. R. 1005. 35 p. 8°.

Score.

DREXEL MUSICAL FUND.

1. Concertos—Concerti grossi. I. Marinuzzi, Gino, 1882– , editor.
N. Y. P. L. July 7, 1931

NL 0432787 NN

Locatelli, Pietro Antonio, 1695–1764.
[Concerto, op. 4, pt. 2, no. 4, E♭ major]

x° [i. e. Decimo] concerto da camera, op. 4 (1735). Trascrizione di Giacomo Benvenuti. Milano, Carisch, 1952.

score (24 p.) 31 cm.
Concertino: string quartet.
Continuo realized for harpsichord.

1. Concerti grossi—To 1800—Scores.

M1145.L8 op. 4, pt. 2, no. 4 M 55–662 rev 2

NL 0432788 DLC NN NIC

Locatelli, Pietro Antonio, 1695–1764.
[Sonatas, flute & continuo, op. 2]

XII [i. e. Dodici] sonate à flauto traversiere solo è basso. Opera secunda. Nouv. ed. [Paris] Le Clerc le cadet [173-?]

50 p. 34 cm.

1. Sonatas (Flute and harpsichord)—To 1800.

M242.L 46–30919 rev*

NL 0432789 DLC CtY NRU-Mus

Locatelli, Pietro Antonio, 1695–1764.
[Sonatas, violin & continuo, op. 6]
XII sonate à violino solo è basso da camera. Opera sesta. Amsterdam [1746?]

score (64 p.) 34 cm.
"Opere del autore date alla stampa": [1] p. preceding p. 1.
CONTENTS.—B♭ major.—F major.—B major.—E major.—C major.—D major.—F minor.—C major.—B minor.—G major.—E flat major.—D minor.

1. Sonatas (Violin and harpsichord)—To 1800.

M219.L8 op. 6 1746 46–30921 rev*

NL 0432790 DLC MiU

Locatelli, Pietro Antonio. 1695-1764.
XII sonate a violino solo è basso da camera... Opera sesta.
= Paris. Le Clerc. [1750?] 65 pp. 31 cm.

K198 — Violin. Music. — Sonatas. Violin and harpsichord.

NL 0432791 MB CtY

LOCATELLI, PIETRO Antonio, 1695-1764.
[SONATAS, FLUTE & CONTINUO, OP. 2, NO. 4-6]
Drei Sonaten für Querflöte und Basso continuo, hrsg. von Gustav Scheck; Generalbass-Aussetzung von Walter Upmeyer. Kassel, Bärenreiter-Verlag [Vorwort 1944] score (19 p.) and 2 parts. 29cm. (Hortus musicus. 35)

The unfigured bass is realized for keyboard instrument; includes part for violoncello (viola da

CONTENTS. — [G major] — [D major] — [G minor]

1. Flute and piano--To 1800. I. Scheck, Gustav, ed. II. Upmeyer, Walter, 1876- , ed. III. Series.

NL 0432793 NN FTaSU CLSU NcU OrSaW NBC NcD

Locatelli, Pietro Antonio, 1695–1764.
[Sonatas, flute & continuo, op. 2, no. 4–6]

Drei Sonaten, für Querflöte und Basso continuo. Hrsg. von Gustav Scheck; Generalbass-Aussetzung von Walter Upmeyer. Kassel, Bärenreiter-Verlag [1949]

score (19 p.) and parts. 29 cm. (Hortus musicus, 35)
Bärenreiter-Ausgabe, 626.
CONTENTS.—[G major]—[D major]—[G minor]

1. Sonatas (Flute and harpsichord)—To 1800. I. Scheck, Gustav, 1901– ed. (Series)

M242.L M 53–418

NL 0432794 DLC MB CSt IU ICN OOxM OrCS

*M2 .H77 no.35 1954
Locatelli, Pietro Antonio, 1695-1764.
[Sonatas, flute & continuo, op. 2, no. 4-6]
Drei Sonaten, für Querflöte und Basso continuo. Hrsg. von Gustav Scheck; Generalbass-Aussetzung von Walter Upmeyer. Kassel, Bärenreiter-Verlag [1954?]
score (19 p.) and 2 parts. 29cm. (Hortus musicus, 35)
CONTENTS.—[G major]—[D major]—[G minor]

1. Sonatas (Flute and harpsichord)—To 1800. I. Scheck, Gustav, 1901, ed. II. Series.

NL 0432796 MB

Locatelli, Pietro Antonio, 1695–1764.
...[Sonata. Op. 8, no. 1.] Largo aus der F dur-Sonate, Op. 8, Nr. 1... Leipzig: C. F. Peters[, 1932]. Publ. pl. no. 10936. 2 parts. 30½cm. (Alte Meister Weisen; Original-Werke für Violine und Klavier, herausgegeben von M. Jacobsen und M. Ettinger. Nr. 3.)

Violin and piano (realized from basso continuo) in score. Violin part.
From his: X sonata, VI a violino solo e basso, e IV a tre. Op. 8. Amsterdam, 1731.
Edition Peters, Nr. 4227.

CARNEGIE CORPORATION OF NEW YORK.

1. Violin and piano (basso continuo). I. Ser.
N. Y. P. L. November 2, 1932

NL 0432797 NN

VOLUME 337

Locatelli, Pietro Antonio, 1695-1764.
Opera quarta. Parte Prima. VI introduttione teatrali. Parto seconda. VI concerti. Violino primo, secondo, alto, à violoncello solo, Violino primo, secondo, alto, à basso, ripeni... Amsterdam: M. Carlo le Cene, [1735?] 33 p. f°.

Violino primo solo only.

NL 0432798 NN

---

q787.1 L78s Locatelli, Pietro, 1695-1764.
... Sarabanda und Allegro scherzoso ... mit klavierbegleitung und vortragszeichen versehen von Alfred Moffat. Mainz, B. Schotts söhne; [etc., etc., 190-?]
2v. (Sonaten-studien für die violine mit beziffertem bass ... no.4)

Plate no.: 26508.
Contents.- [v.1] Piano.- [v.2] Violin.

1. Violin music. I. Moffat, Alfred Edward, 1866-

NL 0432799 IU

M 312.4 L811 Locatelli, Pietro Antonio, 1695-1764.
VI sonate ... a tre: due violini o flauti e basso... Opera quinta. Gravées par De Gland... Paris: Le Clerc, [1737]. 34 1/2 cm.

Separate parts.

NL 0432800 NRU-Mus

Locatelli, Pietro Antonio, 1695-1764.
[Trio-sonatas, flutes & continuo, op. 5]

VI sonatas for two German flutes or two violins, with a thorough bass for the harpsicord or violoncello. Opera terza [i. e. quinta] London, I. Walsh [1745]
parts. 32 cm.

1. Trio-sonatas.

M317.L75 op. 5 46-31287 rev*/M

NL 0432801 DLC MiU CtY

LOCATELLI, PIETRO Antonio, 1695-1764.
[SONATAS, 2 VIOLINS & CONTINUO, OP 5]
VI sonatas for two German flutes or two violins with a thorough bass for the harpsicord or violoncello. Composed by Sigr. Pietro Locatelli. Opera terza. London, Printed for I. Walsh [1745]
3 parts.

Microfilm.

Actually op.5. See British union catalog.

1. Chamber music, 18th cent.--Trios. 2. Piano in trios (Piano, 2 flutes)--To 1800. 3. Piano in trios (Piano, 2 violins)--To 1800.

NL 0432803 NN

Locatelli, Pietro Antonio, 1695-1764.
[Sonatas, 2 flutes, op. 4 (Walsh)]

Six sonatas or duets for two German flutes or violins. Opera quarta. London, Printed for I. Walsh [1745?]
score (27 p.) 31 cm.

CONTENTS.—No. 1, E minor.—No. 2, G minor.—No. 3, G major.—No. 4, D minor.—No. 5, B minor.—No. 6, D major.

1. Sonatas (2 flutes)—To 1800.

M289.L M 57-1402

NL 0432804 DLC

LOCATELLI, PIETRO Antonio, 1695-1764.
[SONATAS, FLUTE & CONTINUO, OP.2. SELECTIONS]
Solos for a German flute or violin with a through bass for the harpsicord or bass violin. Compos'd by Pietro Locatelli. Opera seconda... London, Printed for and sold by I. Walsh [1737] score(27 p.)

Microfilm.
For flute or violin and figured bass.

Contains op.2: no. 2, 1, 9, 10, 4 and 7.

1. Flute and piano--To 1800. 2. Violin and piano--To 1800.

NL 0432806 NN

---

f787.1 L81s.DS Locatelli, Pietro Antonio, 1693-1764
...Sonata da camera for violin & piano. F. David's edition, ed. and rev. by Emile Sauret. London, Augener [c1920]
2v. F. (Augener's edition, no.7437)

Contents: [v.1.] Violin & piano.- [v.2] Violin.

NL 0432807 IaU MeB NcD OrU

M787.1 L767s2 Locatelli, Pietro Antonio, 1695-1764.

Sonata da camera, G minor, Violine & Piano. Bearb. von Ferdinand David. Leipzig, Breitkopf & Härtel, n.d.
score (9p.) and part. 36cm. (Edition Breitkopf nr.3358)

1. Sonatas (Violin and piano) 2. Violin music. I. David, Ferdinand, 1810-1873, ed. II. Series.

NL 0432808 OrU

Locatelli, Pietro Antonio, 1693-1764.
[Sonatas. Violin & piano. Op. 6, no.]
...Sonata da camera, G moll... Für Violine mit beziffertem Bass. Für Violine und Klavier bearbeitet von Ferd. David, revidiert von H. Petri... Leipzig: Breitkopf & Härtel [ca. 1900] Publ. pl. no. E. B. 3358. 2 parts in 1 v. 30½cm. (Edition Breitkopf. Nr. 3358.)

Score (9 p.): violin and piano (realized from basso continuo).
From his: XII sonate a violino solo e basso, da camera... Opera sesta. Amsterdam: Appresso l'autore [1737]
"Nach einem Manuskript in der Privatbibliothek S. M. des Königs von Sachsen bearbeitet."

1. Violin and piano—To 1800. 2. Sonate da camera—To 1800. I. David, Ferdinand Victor, 1810-1873, ed. II. Petri, Henri, 1856-1914, ed.
N. Y. P. L. October 7, 1936

NL 0432809 NN CtY

---

q787.3 L78s Locatelli, Pietro Antonio, 1695-1764.
[Sonata (en Ré) rifatta da Alfredo Piatti. Mainz, B. Schott's söhne [19--]
2v. (Cello-bibliothek)

Contents:-
v.1 Piano.
v.2 Violoncello.

NL 0432810 IU

Locatelli, Pietro Antonio, 1695-1764. **M.432.42.4
Sonata in B. Für Violine & Klavier. Nach der Original-Ausgabe ... bearbeitet von Alfred Moffat.
= Mainz. Schott. 1909. 11 pp. [Kammer-Sonaten für Violine & Klavier des 17ten & 18ten Jahrhunderts. No. 18.] 33½ cm.

H8661 — Violin. Music. — Sonatas. Violin and pianoforte.

NL 0432811 MB

Locatelli, Pietro Antonio, 1695-1764.

... Sonata in D major, for cello and piano. (A. Piatti) New York city, International music company [1943]
cover-title, 12 p. and pt. 30½cm.

At head of title: Locatelli.
Publisher's plate no.: 530.

1. Sonatas (Violoncello and harpsichord)—To 1800. I. Piatti, Alfredo, 1822-1901, ed.

Library of Congress M231.L8 Dmaj.P5 44-9969

NL 0432812 DLC OrU MH

M 787.1 L786s Locatelli, Pietro Antonio, 1695-1764.
[Sonata, violin & continuo, op.6, no.7, F minor]
Sonata in F minor, for violin and piano. Harmonized by L. A. Zellner, revised and edited by Maud Powell. New York, G. Schirmer, ©1946.
score(15 p.) and part. 30cm. (Schirmer's library of musical classics, v.1096)

1. Sonatas (Violin and harpsichord) - To 1800.

NL 0432813 MiDW

Locatelli, Pietro Antonio, 1695-1764
[Sonata, violin & continuo, op.6, no.12, D minor; arr.]
Sonata in G minor, op.6, no.12 for viola and piano, edited by Paul Doktor. International Music Co. [c1953]
score (12 p.) & part.

NL 0432814 OrP CaOTP LU IEN

Locatelli, Pietro Antonio, 1695-1764.
[Sonata, violin & continuo, op. 6, no. 6, D major]

Sonata in re magg. [Accompagnamento di pianoforte, digitazione, ornamenti di] Cesare Barison. Trieste, C. Schmidl, °1909.
score (15 p.) and part. 32 cm. (Tesori musicali italiani)

Edition Schmidl, no. 4594.
Unfigured bass realized for piano.

1. Sonatas (Violin and harpsichord)—To 1800.

M219.L8 op. 6, no. 6 1909 65-68033/M

NL 0432815 DLC

Locatelli, Pietro Antonio, 1695-1764.
Sonata no.1 for flute and bass, by Pietro Locatelli... Edited for flute & piano by J.H. Feltkamp. [London:] Oxford Univ. Press, 1928. 2 parts in 1 v. f°

Flute and piano in score, and flute part.
Cover-title.

1. Flute and basso continuo. 2. Flute and piano. I. Feltkamp, J. H., editor.

NL 0432816 NN MB

Locatelli, Pietro Antonio, 1695-1764
[Sonata, flute & piano]
Sonata per il flauto traverso [herausgegeben von Alexander Kowatscheff] Zürich, Hug [c1947]
score (8 p.) & part. (Peters edition no.6032)

NL 0432817 OrP MH NN IaU

VOLUME 337

Locatelli, Pietro Antonio, 1695-1764.
[Sonata, violin & continuo, op. , no.6, D major]
Sonata VI, per violino e basso. Realizzazione per violino e pianoforte di Ottorino Respighi... Milano, New York, G.Ricordi, c1921.
score (14p.) and part. 32cm.

Publisher's plate no.: E.R.240.

1.Sonatas (Violin and piano) - To 1800. I.Respighi, Ottorino, 1879-1936.

NL 0432818 CLSU MH

Locatelli, Pietro Antonio, 1695-1764.
Sonatas or duets, Six, for two German flutes or violins. Opera quarta. [Score]. London: Printed for I. Walsh, [1735?]. 27 p. 31cm.

NL 0432819 NRU-Mus

Locatelli, Pietro Antonio, 1695-1764.
[Trio-sonata, flutes & continuo, op. 5, no. 1, G major]

Sonate à deux violons ou deux flûtes traversières. [Réalisation de] Claude Crussard. [Lausanne] Foetisch, 1955.

score (19 p.) 31 cm. (Flores musicae, 6)

With realization of the figured bass for harpsichord.
Duration: 13 min.

1. Trio-sonatas. (Series)

M2.F66 vol. 6 M 57-1745

NL 0432820 DLC NIC ICU NcD NcRS MoU OU CoU

Locatelli, Pietro Antonio, 1695-1764.
[Sonatas. Violin & piano. Op. 6, no. 1]
...Sonate...B-dur... Mainz [etc.] B. Schott's Söhne [1910] Publ. pl. no. 28779. 2 parts in 1 v. 31cm. (Kammer-Sonaten des 17ten und 18ten Jahrhunderts. Heft 18.)

Score (including realized basso continuo) and violin part.
From his: XII sonate a violino solo e basso, da camera... Opera sesta. Amsterdam: Appresso l'autore [1737]
"Arrangement von Alfred Moffat."
"Edition Schott. Nr. 2145I."

Carnegie Corporation of New York.

1. Violin and piano. 2. Sonatas—Violin and piano. I. Moffat, Alfred Edward, 1866- , arr.
N. Y. P. L. October 9, 1935

NL 0432821 NN

Locatelli,Pietro Antonio,1695-1764.
[Sonata,violin & continuo,op.6,no.6,D major; arr.]
Sonate,D-dur. [Arr.von Alfred Piatti. Neuausg.: Eugen Rapp] Mainz, B.Schott's Söhne; New York, Schott Music Corp. (Associated Music Publishers) [c1949]
score (13 p.) and part. 31 cm. (Cello-Bibliothek; klassische Sonaten für Violoncello und Klavier,Nr.1)
Arr.for violoncello and piano.

1.Sonatas (Violoncello and piano), Arranged.

NL 0432822 MiU LU

Locatelli, Pietro Antonio, 1695-1764.

...Sonate, E-moll, für 2 Flöten. Sonata in E-minor... Leipzig: W. Zimmermann [1934] Publ. pl. no. Z. 11603. 7 p. 31cm.

Score: flute I-II.
"'Duetto a due flauti a traverso,' published about 1725... In republishing...the editor resorted to a compiled work in the Berlin Government Library (Staatsbibliothek Mus. 30 248)."
"Herausgegeben von Kurt Schlenger."
A second score in pocket.

Carnegie Corp. of New York.

1. Flute—2 flutes—To 1800. 2. Sonatas—2 flutes—To 1800.
I. Schlenger, Kurt, 1909- , ed.
N. Y. P. L. April 12, 1937

NL 0432823 NN MH NcU OOxM

Locatelli, Pietro Antonio, 1695-1764.
[Sonatas. Violin & piano. Op. 8, no. 2]
...Sonate en ré majeur... Paris [etc.] H. Lemoine & cie., cop. 1913. Publ. pl. no. 21569. P. 1280 HL. 2 parts in 1 v. 35½cm. (L'école du violon au XVIIme et au XVIIIme siècle: Les maitres italiens du violon au XVIIIme siècle.)

Score (including realized basso continuo) and violin part.
With reproduction of original t.-p. with imprint: Amsterdam: Apresso l'autore [1731]
Cover-title.
"Réalisation de la basse chiffrée par Joseph Jongen."
"Collection Joseph Debroux." "Panthéon. no. ...1280."

1. Violin and piano. 2. Sonatas—Violin and piano. I. Jongen, Joseph, 1873-
N. Y. P. L. October 18, 1935

NL 0432824 NN

LOCATELLI, PIETRO ANTONIO, 1695-1764.
[Sonata, violin; no. G major, op.6, no.]
Sonate en Sol Paris,M.Senart[18--]
3 pt.in 1v. 35cm. (Nouvelle édition française de musique classique)

"Pour violon et basse continue au clavecin."
Violin part laid in.
"Révision par Vincent d'Indy."
Contents.—Allemande.—Siciliano.—Gigue.

NL 0432825 ICN

Locatelli, Pietro Antonio, 1695-1764.
...Sonate en Sol, pour violon et basse continue au clavecin. 1re [-3me] partie. Extraite du Recueil des six sonates, Op. 6 (1737). Révision par Vincent d'Indy. [Paris: Édition M. Senart & cie., 1910?-192-?] Publ. pl. no. 179, S. et cie. 73, S. R. & cie. 180. 6 parts in 1 v. f°.

Violin and piano in score and violin part.
Caption-title.
Title-page reads: Nouvelle édition française de musique classique, publiée sous la direction ... de Vincent d'Indy. Piano et violon.

Partie 2 has title: Sicilienne, extraite de la Sonate en Sol.
Imprint varies. Partie 3 has imprint: Paris, Édition M. Senart, B. Roudanez & cie.
Partie 1-2 reprinted from plates of 1910?, with later t.-p.

1. Violin and basso continuo. 2. Violin and piano. I. Indy, Vincent d', 1851-1931, editor.
N. Y. P. L. May 12, 1932

NL 0432827 NN

Locatelli, Pietro Antonio, 1695-1764.
[Sonatas. Violin & piano. Op. 6, no. 10]
Sonate [G dur] von Pietro Locatelli... Bearbeitung von A. Moffat. Berlin: N. Simrock G.m.b.H. [1899] Publ. pl. no. 11220. 2 parts in 1 v. 34cm. (Meister-Schule der alten Zeit. 7.)

Score (including realized basso continuo) and violin part.
From his: XII. sonate a violino solo e basso, da camera... Opera sesta. Amsterdam: Appresso l'autore [1746] —cf. *Altmann. Kammermusik-Katalog. 4. ed.; Brit. Mus. Cat. of printed music (1487-1800).*
Caption-title.

Carnegie Corporation of New York.

1. Violin and piano. 2. Sonate da camera. I. Moffat, Alfred Edward, 1866- , ed.
N. Y. P. L. November 14, 1935

NL 0432828 NN

---

32 **Locatelli, Pietro Antonio, 1695-1764.**
Sonate in D moll. Arrangement von Alfred Moffat. Für violine und pianoforte. Leipzig, Brussels, etc. Breitkopf & Härtel, 1898.
9 p. fol. (Breifkopf & Härtels violin-bibliothek.)

NL 0432829 DLC

Locatelli, Pietro Antonio, 1695-1764.
[Sonatas. Violin and piano. Op. 6, no. 9.]
...Sonate in h moll... Berlin: N. Simrock G.m.b.H.[, etc., etc.], 1920. Publ. pl. no. 14060. 2 parts in 1 v. 34½cm. (Alte Sonaten für Violine und Klavier. [Nr.] 4.)

Score (including realized basso continuo) and violin part.
From his: XII sonate a violino solo e basso da camera. Opera sesta. Amsterdam, 1728-37]. — *cf. Altmann. Kammermusik-Katalog. 4. ed.; Scheurleer. Cat. 1923-25.*
"Ausgabe von Paul Klengel."

Juilliard Foundation Fund.

1. Violin and piano. 2. Sonatas—Violin and piano. I. Klengel, Paul K., 1854- , editor.
N. Y. P. L. January 17, 1935

NL 0432830 NN

Locatelli, Pietro Antonio, 1695-1764.
[Sonata, violin & harpsichord, F minor]
Sonate, Le tombeau, en fa mineur, pour violon et piano. Revision et realisation de l'accompagnement par E. Ysaÿe. Bruxelles, Schott Freres [°1928]
score (13p.) and part.

1. Sonatas (Violin and harpsichord)--To 1800.

NL 0432831 IEN CU-S

Locatelli, Pietro Antonio, 1695-1764.
[Sonatas. Violin & piano. Op. 6, no. 1. Tema con variazione. Arr. for vln & lute]
[...] Thema mit Variationen für Geige und Laute; herausgegeben und bearbeitet von Heinz Bischoff. Augsburg: Bärenreiter-Verlag [1925] 8 p. 29½cm. (Bärenreiter Ausgabe. Nr. 71.)

Violin and lute (realized from basso continuo) in score.
From his: XII sonate a violino solo e basso, da camera... Opera sesta. Amsterdam: Appresso l'autore [1737]
Cover-title.

Juilliard Foundation Fund.

1. Violin and lute. 2. Lute and violin. I. Bischoff, Heinz, ed.
N. Y. P. L. October 9, 1935

NL 0432832 NN

Locatelli, Pietro Antonio, 1695-1794.
Thematische catalogus
see under Koole, Arend Johannes Christiaan, 1908-

Locatelli, Pietro Antonio, 1695-1764.
[Sinfonia, string orchestra, F minor]

Trauersymphonie für Streichquartett (bezw. Orchester) mit obligatem Klavier (Orgel, Harmonium) Leipzig, C. F. Kahnt Nachfolger, °1904.
score (15 p.) 34 cm. (Perlen alter Kammermusik ...)
"Composta per l'essequie della sua donna che si celebrarono in Roma."
"Nach dem auf der Grossherzogl. Bibl. Darmstadt befindlichen Handschriftenmaterial (Partitur und Stimmen) zum ersten Mal herausgegeben von A. Schering."
Originally for 2 violins, viola with continuo. The bass is realized for organ.
1. String orchestra music—To 1800—Scores. I. Schering, Arnold, 1877-1941, ed. II. Title. (Series)
M1145.L8S58 51-45028

NL 0432834 DLC MB ICU MH ViU

Locatelli, Pietro Antonio, 1695-1764.

...Trauersymphonie für Streichquartett oder Streichorchester und Klavier (Orgel oder Harmonium)... Leipzig: C. F. Kahnt [1906] Publ. pl. no. 4315. 15 p. 34cm. (Perlen alter Kammermusik deutscher und italienischer Meister.)

Score (including realized basso continuo).
"Nach dem Handschriftenmaterial (Partitur und Stimmen) zum ersten Mal herausgegeben von A. Schering."
"Composta per l'essequie della sua donna che si celebrarono in Roma."

Carnegie Corporation of New York.

1. Symphonies—Full score. 2. Funerals—Music. I. Schering, Arnold, 1877- , ed.
N. Y. P. L. October 24, 1935

NL 0432835 NN ICN

Locatelli, Pietro Antonio, 1695-1764.
...Trio in G dur, Op. 3, No. 1, für 2 Violinen (Flöten), Violoncell und Pianoforte... Leipzig: Breitkopf & Härtel[, 1906]. Publ. pl. no. K. M. 1835/36. 4 parts in 1 v. f°. ("Collegium musicum"...herausgegeben von Hugo Riemann. Nr. 21.)

Score, including realization of basso continuo, and 3 string parts.
On cover: Breitkopf & Härtels Kammermusik-Bibliothek. Nr. 1835/36.

Juilliard Foundation Fund.

1. Trios—Two violins and basso continuo. 2. Quartets—Piano, two violins and violoncello. 3. Ser.
N. Y. P. L. April 30, 1928

NL 0432836 NN MiU MH CtY ViU

VOLUME 337

M
412.4
.L81
Locatelli, Pietro Antonio, 1695-1764.
[L'arte del violino. Trio, piano & strings no. 1]
Trio in G major - opus 3, no. 1; for two violins and piano (or two flutes and piano) (With cello ad libitum). [Edited by Hugo] Riemann. New York, International Music [c1952] score (20 p.) and 3 parts 31 cm.

NL 0432837 DCU ICU

Locatelli, Pietro Antonio, 1695-1764.
[Trio-sonata, flutes & continuo, op. 5, no. 4, C major]
Trio-Sonate C-dur; für 2 Violinen oder 2 Flöten und Generalbass, op. v, Nr. 4. [Bearb. von Hans Albrecht] Lippstadt, Kistner & Siegel; sole agent for the USA: Concordia Pub. House, St. Louis [Vorwort 1951] Pl. no. 30102.
score (9 p.) and parts. 30 cm. (Organum. 3. Reihe: Kammermusik, Nr. 46)
Figured bass realized for harpsichord.
1. Trio-sonatas. I. Albrecht, Hans, 1902- ed. (Series)
M2.O78 Reihe 3, Nr. 46 64-56147/M

NBC
NL 0432838 DLC CoU IU ICU PPT NcD NN NcU MH NIC MiU

Locatelli, Pietro Antonio, 1695-1764.
[Sonatas. 2 violins & piano.
...Trio-Sonate, D moll... 2 Violinen, Violoncello (ad lib.) & Piano (Alfred Moffat)... Leipzig: N. Simrock [cop. 1931] Publ. pl. no. 11773. 4 parts in 1 v. 31cm. (Trio-Meisterschule. Nr. 2.)
Score (including realized basso continuo) and 3 parts. Violoncello doubles bass. On cover: Elite Edition. No. 731 (S.). "E[dition] S[imrock] 731."
CARNEGIE CORPORATION OF NEW YORK.
1. Chamber music, 18th cent.—Trios. 2. Piano—Trios—Piano and 2 violins—Early. 3. Sonatas—Trios. I. Moffat, Alfred Edward, 1866- ed.
N. Y. P. L. November 14, 1935

NL 0432839 NN

Locatelli, Pietro Antonio, 1695-1764.
[Trio-sonata, flutes & continuo, op. 5, no. 5, D minor]
Trio-Sonate D-moll; für 2 Violinen, oder 2 Flöten und Generalbass, op. v, Nr. 5. [Bearb. von Hans Albrecht] Lippstadt, Kistner & Siegel; sole agent for the USA: Concordia Pub. House, St. Louis [Vorwort 1953] Pl. no. 30156.
score (11 p.) and parts. 30 cm. (Organum. 3. Reihe: Kammermusik, Nr. 50)
Figured bass realized for harpsichord.
1. Trio-sonatas. I. Albrecht, Hans, 1902- ed. (Series)
M2.O78 Reihe 3, Nr. 50 64-56018/M

NL 0432840 DLC PPT NN MH IU NBC NcD NIC MiU CoU

M785.73
L811t
Music
lib.
Locatelli, Pietro Antonio, 1695-1764.
[Trio-sonata, violins & continuo, D minor]
Trio-Sonate [für zwei Violinen und piano. Mit Violoncello ad lib. nach der Originalausgabe für zwei Violinen mit beziffertem Bass ... d-moll ...] Hrsg. von Alfred Moffat. Hamburg, N. Simrock [19] Pl. no. 11778. score (7p.) and 2 parts. 33cm. (Trio-Sonaten alter Meister ... 2)
Caption title.
Figured bass realized for piano; violoncello continuo part included. Violin parts on 1 fold. leaf.

NL 0432841 NcU

Locatelli, Pietro Antonio, 1695-1764.
[Sonatas. 2 violins & piano. Op. 5, no. 1]
...Trio-Sonate, G dur... 2 Violinen, Violoncello (ad lib.) & Piano (Alfred Moffat)... Leipzig: N. Simrock [cop. 1910] Publ. pl. no. 12618. 4 parts in 1 v. 31cm. (Trio-Meisterschule. Nr. 22.)
Score (including realized basso continuo) and 3 parts. Violoncello doubles bass. From his: Sei sonate à tre, o due violini o due flauti traversieri, e basso per il cembalo. Opera quinta. Amsterdam: Appresso l'autore [1736] On cover: Elite Edition. No. 631(S.). "E[dition] S[imrock] 751."
1. Chamber music, 18th cent.—Trios. 2. Piano—Trios—Piano and 2 violins—Early. 3. Sonatas—Trios. I. Moffat, Alfred Edward, 1866- ed.
N. Y. P. L. November 14, 1935

NL 0432842 NN

Locatelli, Pietro Antonio, 1695-1764.
[Trio-sonata, flutes & continuo, op. 5, no. 1, G major]
Trio-sonate G-dur; für 2 Violinen oder 2 Flöten und Generalbass, op. v, no. 1. [Bearb. von Hans Albrecht] Lippstadt, Kistner & Siegel; sole agent for the USA: Concordia Pub. House, St. Louis [Vorwort 1954] Pl. no. 30189.
score (23 p.) and parts. 30 cm. (Organum. 3. Reihe: Kammermusik, Nr. 52)
Figured bass realized for harpsichord.
1. Trio-sonatas. I. Albrecht, Hans, 1902- ed. (Series)
M2.O78 Reihe 3, Nr. 52 64-56016/M

ICarbS
NL 0432843 DLC PPT CoU MiU NcD NIC NBC MH NN IU

Locatelli, Pietro Antonio, 1695-1764.
Twee sonates voor viool met pianobegeleiding, van Pietro Locatelli ... Bewerkt door Julius Röntgen. Met eene inleiding door dr. D. F. Scheurleer ... Amsterdam, G. Alsbach & cie.; Leipzig, Breitkopf & Härtel, 1911.
2 pt. in 1 v. port. 30½cm. (Vereeniging voor Noord-Nederlands muziekgeschiedenis. Uitgave xxxi)
Score (1 p. l., 27 p.) violin and piano, realized from basso continuo. Violin part (14 p.)
Publisher's plate nos.: 41, 42.
Sonata 1 in G major, from Op. 8 according to Scheurleer's preface, is Op. 2, no. 5, the Andante from Op. 6, no. 12; sonata 2 in F minor, from Op. 4 according to Scheurleer, is Op. 6, no. 7. cf. Altmann. Kammermusik-katalog.
1. [Violin and pianoforte—Early—Sonatas] I. Röntgen, Julius, 1855-1932, ed. A 44-603
New York. Public library for Library of Congress M2.V48 vol. 31 [3] † (780.82) 787.1

NL 0432845 NN MH DLC PP MB PU-Music

M
1040
.L82
C71
Locatelli, Pietro Antonio, 1695-1764.
[Concerti grossi, op. 1]
XII concertos in eight parts, for two violins and other instruments; with a through bass for the harpsichord. Opera prima. London, Printed for and sold by I. Walsh [1736?] Publ. no.: 600. 8 parts in slip-case. 35 cm.
For 2 violins, viola, and bass (concertino), strings and continuo.
CONTENTS.--F major.--C minor.--B♭ major.--E minor.--D major.--C minor.--F major.--F minor.--D major.--C major.--C minor.--G minor.
1. Concerti grossi--To 1800--Parts.

NL 0432846 MiU

FILM
A145
M
Locatelli, Pietro Antonio, 1695-1764.
[Concerti grossi, op. 1]
XII concertos in eight parts, for violins and other instruments; with a thorough bass for the harpsichord. Opera prima. London, Printed for and sold by I. Walsh [1736]
8 parts on 1 reel. On film (Negative)
Microfilm. Original in the British Museum.

NL 0432847 CU

---

m781.32
L811c
Locatelli, Pietro Antonio, 1695-1764.
[Caprices, violin]
Vingt-six caprices; réalisés d'après les documents originaux revus et augmentés. Paris, Alphonse Leduc [c1919] 59p. 33cm.
At head of title: Enseignement complet du violon, par G. Catherine. Études et exercises.
1. Violin - Studies and exercises. LC.

NL 0432848 CLSU

Locatelli, Roberto.
Brujo aymará
see under Iglesias Villoud, Hector, 1913-

Locatelli, Roberto.
Danza de los "Laikas" para piano
see under Iglesias Villoud, Hector, 1913-

Locatelli, Sebastiano, fl. 1664.
... Voyage de France; mœurs et coutumes françaises (1664-1665) Relation de Sébastien Locatelli ... tr. sur les manuscrits autographes et pub. avec une introduction et des notes par Adolphe Vautier ... Paris, A. Picard et fils, 1905.
lxxiv, 348 p., 1 l. 25½cm. (Bibliothèque de la Société des études historiques. fasc. iv. Fondation Raymond)
"Notice bibliographique": p. [lvii]-lxxiv.
1. France—Soc. life & cust. 2. France—Descr. & trav. I. Vautier, Adolphe, 1865- ed. and tr.
22-20795
Library of Congress DC126.L7

NL 0432851 DLC CtY MB NcU NcD CaBVaU OU OCl

AC
45
L81a
Locatelli, Tommaso
L'appendice della Gazzetta di Venezia, prose scelte di Tommaso Locatelli. Venezia, Co'tipi del gondoliere[etc.] 1837-80. 16v. in 7. port. 16cm.
No more published?
I. Gazzetta di Venezia.

NL 0432852 NRU MH CtY

WG
27963
Locatelli, Ugo, 1875-
Ueber einige neue Purpursäuren. Göttingen, 1903.
59 p.
Inaug.-Diss. -Göttingen.

NL 0432853 CtY MH

Locatelli, Víctor H
... La lucha contra el cáncer en la República argentina; tesis de doctorado del dr. Víctor H. Locatelli. Buenos Aires, Imprenta: Aniceto López, 1941.
60 p., 2 l. 27cm.
At head of title: Universidad nacional de Buenos Aires. Facultad de ciencias médicas.
"Bibliografía": 1st leaf at end.
1. Cancer—Argentine republic. I. Title.
45-53750
Library of Congress RC261.L798

NL 0432854 DLC

Locatelli, Víctor H.
... Terapéutica ... Buenos Aires, "El Ateneo", 1927-
v. 23cm.
At head of title: V. H. Locatelli y R. R. del Lago.
1. Therapeutics. 2. Medicine—Formulae, receipts, prescriptions. I. Lago, Raúl R. del, joint author.
30-11920
Library of Congress RM101.L6

NL 0432855 DLC

UG
400
.L8
Locatelli, Vincenzo.
Invito generale del cap. Vincentio Locatelli da Cremona ... Alli professori del reparare, fortificare, & edificare luoghi, & a quelli che dapoi construtti detti luoghi accettano carico di defenderli contra la tremenda offesa hoggidi usata da Maumetani, cioè, de canoni, colubrine, basilichi, zappa, & pala ... [Bologna, 1575]
[36] p. 1 illus. (diagr.) 18½ x 14cm.
Signatures: 1 leaf unsigned, B4, C2, D4, 2 leaves unsigned, E4, F1.
Title (surmounted by arms of Pope Gregory XIII) on recto and verso of first leaf.
Head and tail pieces; initials.
In two parts, apparently published separately. The first (1 leaf unsigned, sig. B4, C2, D4) has colophon at end (p. [22]): In Bologna, Per Alessandro Benacci, MDLXXV. The second (2 leaves unsigned, sig. E4, F1) dated at end Di Lucca di 20. di luglio 1575, has caption title only: Diligenza fatta dal capit. Vincentio Loccatelli ... per porre in esecvtione qvanto ha proposto del suo Inuito generale ... publicato il di 12. febraio 1575.
Label on inside of front cover: Biblioteca Riccardi in Modena. Stamped below coat of arms at head of title: Ex bibliot: com: Fran: M: Cardelli Romae. Manuscript note on first page of 2d part: Ex dono ipsius autoris ...
1. Fortification--Early works to 1800. I. Title.

NL 0432858 MiU

VOLUME 337

ND623
.B568L6
Locatelli-Milesi, Achille, 1883-

Bonfanti, Arturo, 1905-
Bonfanti, 20 riproduzioni in nero e 2 tavole a colori, presentazione di Achille Locatelli Milesi. Bergamo, Edizioni Orobiche [1945]

Locatelli-Milesi, Achille, 1883-

Fornara, Carlo, 1871-
... Fornara; con otto tavole colorate, testo di Achille Locatelli Milesi. Bergamo, Istituto italiano d'arti grafiche [1939]

Locatelli Milesi, Achille, 1883-
Fra Galgario, con 56 tavole in nero e 4 tricromie. Bergamo, Orobiche [c1945,
57 p. LX ports. (part col.) 24cm. (Collan di monografie su artisti bergamaschi, a cura della Banca mutua popolare di Bergamo. 3)

"Bibliografia": p. 57.

1. Galgario, Fra Vittore Ghislandi, 1655-1743. I. Collana di monografie su artisti bergamaschi. 3.

NL 0432861 NNC MdBWA MH NN MiU ICU PPiU CU NjP

Locatelli-Milesi, Achille, 1883-
Giovanni Carnovali, il Piccio
see under Carnovali, Giovanni, 1804-73.

759.5
Se31
Locatelli-Milesi, Achille, 1883-
... L'opera di Giovanni Segantini. Milano, L. F. Cogliati, 1906.
35p. front.(mounted port.) mounted plates.

1. Segantini, Giovanni, 1858-1899.

NL 0432863 IU IaU TU

Locatelli-Milesi, Achille, 1883-
Il Piccio. Catalogo [a cura di N. Zucchelli]
see under Bergamo. Palazzo comunale di via T. Tasso.

BX
4705
.L619
L6
Locatelli-Milesi, Achille, 1883-
La signora di Monza nella realtà. Milano, Fratelli Treves [c1924]
239 p. 19cm.

1. Leyva, Marianna de, known as Signora di Monza, 1575-1650 I. Title

NL 0432865 WU NN NNC MH CaBVaU

Locatelli-Milesi, Giuseppe, 1856-1939.
I Bergamaschi in Polonia nel 1863; ricordi della spedizione di Francesco Nullo. Bergamo, Agenzia giornalistica Manighetti, 1893.
p. 81 (20.)
"Lettura fatta all'Ateneo di Bergamo il 12 febbraio 1893."
Later edition, 1913, has title: La spedizione di Francesco Nullo in Polonia (1863)

NL 0432866 MH

Locatelli-Milesi, Giuseppi, 1856-1939.
La colonna Camozzi e la insurrezione bergamasca del 1849. Bergamo, F. e P. Fratelli Bolis 1904.
Front. 1.8°.

NL 0432867 MH

Locatelli-Milesi, Giuseppe, 1856-1939.
L'epopea garibaldina del 1860; lettura fatta all'Ateneo di scienze, lettere ed arti in Bergamo nella seduta pubblica del 15 maggio 1910. Bergamo, Istituto italiano d'arti grafiche, 1910.
68 p. Ports. and other illustr.
At head of title: Giuseppe Locatelli Milesi.

NL 0432868 MH

Locatelli-Milesi, Giuseppe, 1856-1939.
L'epopea garibaldina del 1860. Da ricordi e confidenze di Ergisto Bezzi. Trento, Soc. tip. ed. trentina, 1910.
55 p. Ports.
Cover serves as title-page.
At head of title: G. Locatelli Milesi.

NL 0432869 MH

LOCATELLI MILESI, GIUSEPPE, 1856-1939.
Ergisto Bezzi, il poema di una vita; studio storico biografico, con 84 lettere di Giuseppe Mazzini. Milano, Sonzogno, 1916. xiv, 447 p. illus. 23cm.

Bibliografia, p. [443]

1. Bezzi, Ergisto, 1835-1920. 2. Italy--Politics, 1849-1870. I. Mazzini, Giuseppe, 1805-1872.

NL 0432870 NN CU MH IU

Locatelli Milesi, Giuseppe, 1856-1939

Venanzio, Alessandro, 1836-1911.
... Nella Siberia orrenda; faville di italico eroismo sulle steppe e nelle galere siberiane. Narrazione di Alessandro Venanzio, compagno di Nullo nella spedizione in Polonia del 1863. Seconda edizione, con introduzione, aggiunte e note di Carlo Rugarli. Milano, Antonio Vallardi [1933]

945.24
L787r
Locatelli Milesi, Giuseppe, 1856-1939.
La rivoluzione di Bergamo del 1797: cenni storici. Bergamo, 1897.
139p.

NL 0432872 IU

Locatelli-Milesi, Giuseppe, 1856-1939.
La spedizione di Francesco Nullo in Polonia, 1863. Con prefazione di Stefan Zeromski. Roma, Agenzia polacca di stampa, 1913.
viii, 71, (1) p. Port.
At head of title: Giuseppe Locatelli-Milesi.
An earlier edition, 1893, has title: I Bergamaschi in Polonia nel 1863; ricordi della spedizione di Francesco Nullo.

NL 0432873 MH

DG975
.B52L6
Locatelli Milesi, Sereno.
Bergamo vecchia e nuova, e La bergamasca; itinerari, incontri, ricordi. [3. ed. augm. ed aggiornata. Bergamo] Edizioni Orobiche [1945]
568 p. map. 22cm.
Bibliography: p. 611-614.

1. Bergamo—Descr. 2. Bergamo—Hist.

NL 0432874 MB MH

Locatelli Milesi, Sereno
... In corte d'assise (arringhe) Milano, Studio editoriale lombardo, 1915.
4 p.l., 11-214 p. front. (port.) 22cm. (On cover: Oratori d'Italia, 2)

NL 0432875 MH-L

Y
712509
.51
LOCATELLI-MILESI, SERENO.
...Sonetti bergamaschi. Prefazione di Giacinto Gambirasio. Bergamo,"Giopì",1938.
99p.

"Pubblicazioni del Ducato di Piazza pontida e del 'Giopi'": p.98-99.

NL 0432876 ICN

QA75
.N314
Rare bk.
Coll.
Locatello, Marco, tr.

Napier, John, 1550-1617.
Raddologia, ouero Arimmetica virgolare in due libri diuisa; con appresso vn' espeditissimo prontvario della molteplicatione, & poi vn libro di Arimmetica locale ... Auttore, & inuentore il baron Giovanni Nepero, tradottore dalla latina nella toscana lingua il cavalier Marco Locatello; accresciute dal medesimo alcune considerationi gioueuoli. Verona, appresso A. Tamo, 1623.

B156.4
L787
Locatellus, Petrus
Conivrationes potentissimæ, et efficaces ad expellendas et fugandas aereas tempestates, à dæmonibus per se, siue ad nutum cuiusuis diabolici ministri excitatas, ex diuersis, & probatis auctoribus collectæ, vt Sacerdotes & alij commodè tam diu coniurare possint, quam diu videant tempestatis periculum imminere. A. R. Pres. Petro Locatello tit. S. Cassiani Bergomi collectæ ... Placentiæ, apud Ioannem Bazachium, 1609.
[4], 54 p. 17cm.

Title-vignette.
Manuscript notes.

NL 0432878 NNC

Locatellus, Petrus.
Exorcismi potentissimi & efficaces ... Labaci,1680.

NL 0432879 NIC

Locati (Alexandre). Description de la voiture et wagon hôpital, des cacolets et brancards, pour le transport des blessés et malades, particulièrement en guerre. Dessins et modèles construits d'après les expériences faites dans la dernière guerre en Tyrol et les indications du Dr. Bertani. 24 pp., 4 pl. roy. 8°. *Turin, J. Favale & Cie.* 1867.

NL 0432880 DNLM

Locati, Antonio, 1503-1587.
see Locati, Umberto, bp. of Bagnarea, 1503-1587.

TA460
.L6
Locati, Luigi.
La fatica dei materiali metallici. Milano, Hoepli, 1950.
viii, 333 p. illus., diagrs. 26 cm.
Bibliography at end of each part.

1. Metals—Fatigue. 2. Strength of materials. I. Title.

A 51-1107

Illinois. Univ. Library for Library of Congress [1]

NL 0432882 IU NN DLC

VOLUME 337

Locati, Luigi.
Tecnologie aeronautiche; materiali e processi per motori e velivoli ad uso degli ingegneri della Scuola di ingegneria aeronautica del Politecnico di Torino. Torino, Levrotto & Bella [195-]
168 p. illus. 25 cm.

1. Aeroplanes — Materials. 2. Aeroplanes — Design and construction. I. Title.

TL698.L6 62-66193 ‡

NL 0432883 DLC

Case F 359695 .516 LOCATI, UMBERTO, bp. of Bagnorea, 1503-1587.
Cronica dell'origine di Piacenza, già latinamente fatta per il r. p. Omberto Locati, & hora dal medesimo ridotta nella volgare nostra fauella. Cremona, V. Conti, 1564.
393, [15] p. 21m.

Title vignette (printer's device) Initials, head and tail pieces.

NL 0432884 ICN

Locati, Umberto, 1503-1587.
Cronica dell' origine di Piacenza. Già latinamente fatta, & hora dal medesimo ridotta. Cremona, V. Conti, 1564 [1565].
sm. 4°. pp. 393 +.
The note to the reader on pages 392-394, and the colophon are dated 1565.

Print. spec.|Piacenza, Italy||

NL 0432885 MH IU CtY

Locati, Umberto, 1503-1587.
De Placentinae urbis origine, successu, et laudibus seriosa narratio. Cermonae, apud Vincentium Conctum, 1564.
sm. 4°. pp. 221 +.

Piacenza|Print. spec.|

NL 0432886 MH IU CLU NjP ICN

2945 fG757 v.3 Locati, Umberto, bp. of Bagnarea, 1503-1587
De Placentinae vrbis origine, svccessv, et lavdibvs, seriosa narratio.

(In Graevius, J.G. Thesavrvs antiqvitatvm et historiarvm Italiae. Lvgdvni Batavorum, 1704. v.3, pt.2, col. [1]-104 (at end))

1. Piacenza, Italy. Hist.

NL 0432887 MnU

WZ 240 L811i 1576 LOCATI, Umberto, Bp. of Bagnorea, 1503-1587, comp.
Italia travagliata novamente posta in luce, nellaqual si contengono tutte le guerre, seditioni, pestilentie, & altri travagli, liquali nell'Italia sono stati dalla venuta d'Enea Troiano in quella, infina alli nostri tempi: da diversi authori racolti. Per il ... vescovo di Bagnarea: con somma diligentia corretta & stampata ... Venetia, Daniel Zanetti, & compagni, 1576.
[12], 219 ℓ. 20 cm.

NL 0432888 DNLM ICN IU CtY DFo

Locati, Umberto, bp. of Bagnarea, 1503-1587.
Opvs qvod Ivdiciale Inqvisitorvm dicitvr, per F. Vmbertvm Locatvm Placentinvm, inqvisitorem, sacrae theologiae professorem ex diversis eivsdem sacrae theologiae, & I. V. D. extractum. Cvm additione nonnvllarvm quaestiuncularum & decisionum quorumdam notabilium casuum tam in vrbe, quam Placentiae discussorum, ac formvlis agendorvm in fine positis. Cvm dvplici indice. Romae, apud Haereses Antonij Bladij impressores camerales, 1568.
4 p. l., 595, [27] p.

NL 0432889 NNC

---

g BX 1701 L6 Locati, Umberto, *Bp. of Bagnoregio*, d. 1587.
Opvs qvod ivdiciale inqvisitorvm dicitvr... per...Vmbertvm Locatvm...nuper extractum, ac plusculumquam prius fuerat excusum, nunc auctum & correctum.... Romae, apud haeredes Antonii Bladii, 1570.
[42] 511 p.

Title vignette; initials.

1. Inquisition.

NL 0432890 CU-L ICU NNC

BX 1710 L81 Locati, Umberto, bp. of Bagnarea, 1503-1587.
Praxis ivdiciaria inqvisitorvm ... Ex diuersis eiusdem sacrae theologiae, ac I. V. D. collecta ... Editio secunda multis in locis ab eodem auctore aucta ... Venetiis, apud Damianum Zenarium, 1583.
[48], 527 p. 22cm.

The original edition (Rome, 1568) was published in Rome under the title Opus quod judiciale inquisitorum dicitur.

NL 0432891 NIC OCH OCU MH NNC

Locating a medical school by popular vote
see under [Association to retain the medical school and hospital at the University of Virginia]

Location and detailed description of early Catholic church property in the archdiocese of Milwaukee, Wis.
see under [LaVies, John Gregory] 1877-

Location data for Consolidated Presbyterian College from Fayetteville, North Carolina
see under (Fayetteville Steering Committee)

Location of automotive Diesel troubles made easy
see under Henley, Norman W., Publishing Co.

... The location of Pequehan ...
see under [Landis, David H] 1864-

The location of seventeenth-century documents described in the first nine Reports of the Historical manuscripts commission
see under [Upton, Eleanor Stuart]

F592 D6L6 The location of site of Breen Cabin; General C.F. McGlashan, Donner Party historian, declares present pioneer monument covers exact spot where hut stood. Array of interesting facts presented relating to early investigation of sites of various cabins occupied by members of ill-fated pioneer party. Oakland, Calif., 1920.
14 p. (incl. cover) 23cm.

Cover title.
Includes a letter dated June 2, 1920, Truckee, Calif. from General McGlashan to J.R. Knowland, Chairman Historic Landmarks Committee, Native Sons of the Golden West.

NL 0432898 CU-B

... The location of Susquehannock Fort ...
see under [Landis, David H] 1864-

Location of the Crosby and Illinois iron claims in King county, Washington. n.p., n.d.
29 x 34 cm.

NL 0432900 WaS

Location of the overland mail
see under Missouri Republican, St. Louis.

LOCATIONS of financial institutions in New York state. New York. v. 29cm.

"Locations of main offices and branches of commercial banks, savings banks and savings and Loan associations in New York state... by community and county, indicating population."
Prepared by the Savings banks association of New York state.
1. Banks and banking--Direct.--U.S.--New York. I. Savings banks association of the state of New York.

NL 0432902 NN

Loccatelli, Vincenzio. Gubbio, 1840.
Prospetto della storia di Gubbio.

NL 0432903 NIC

Loccatelli, Vincenzo. **FR56.L78
Vita di Santa Chiara di Asisi . . .
— Asisi. Sgariglia. 1854. 368 pp. Table. Plate. 22.5 cm., in 8s.
Appendice: — Dei documenti che servono alla vita di S. Chiara: Regola delle Povere Dame approvata da Innocenzio IV; Albero genealogico della famiglia Scefi, conti di Sasso Rosso; Nomi dei ventiquattro nobili asisani, che nel 1253 assistettero come testimoni alla canonizzazione di S. Stanislao Vescovo di Cracovia, Stemma Scefi, Taccoli e Ciofi; Lettera della B. Agnese a Santa Chiara sua sorella; Intorno al recipiente, dove S. Chiara conservava l'Eucaristia; Orazione alle Cinque Piaghe, composta da S. Chiara; Testamento spirituale della Santa; Lettere di Papa Gregorio IX. alla medesima; Deposizione erronea intorno alla sepoltura della Santa; Lettera pastorale di Monsig. Luigi Landi Vittori, Vescovo di Asisi, in occasione dell' invenzione delle sacre spoglie di S. Chiara; Saggio di corrispondenza epistolare fra l'Abbadessa di S. Chiara di Asisi ed altre communità oltramontane.
Contains MS. notes by Sabatier, also MS. presentation inscription from Leonello Leonelli to Sabatier.
1. Clara, Saint, 1194-1253. 2. Clarisses.

NL 0432905 MB

Loccatelli, Vincenzo
Vita di Sa. Chiara di Assisi, scritta da Vincenzo Loccatelli ... Napoli, A. Festa, 1855.
554 p., 1 f. (Raccolta di Vite di Santi, per cura di Francesco Festa. v.X).

NL 0432906 MdSsW

Loccatelli Paolucci, Tommaso, *Priore*. **FR28.V831
Del Martire S. Vittorino secondo vescovo di Asisi. Cenni storici pubblicati nella fausta promozione della . . . Paolo C.te Fabiani . . . a pontefice della medesima serafica città.
Asisi. Sensi. 1872. 32 pp. 23 cm., in 4s.

E3625 — Vittorino, Saint, Vescovo di Assisi.

NL 0432907 MB

Loccatelli Paolucci, Tommaso, *Priore*. **FR28.Sa1
Del vescovo e martire San Sabino, brevi memorie dedicate a . . . Mons. Gaetano Lironi . . .
Assisi. Sensi. 1883. 39 pp. 21.5 cm.

E3625 — Sabinus, Saint, Bishop of Faenza and Assisi, -303.

NL 0432908 MB

VOLUME 337

Loccatelli Paolucci, Tommaso, *Priore*.
Della badia di S. Pietro di Assisi.
— Assisi. Sensi. 1885. viii, 55, (1) pp. 22 cm.
Bound with the original paper covers.
The author's name appears only on page v.

E3481 — Assisi, Italy. Churches. San Pietro.

NL 0432909 MB

Loccatelli Paolucci, Tommaso, *Priore*.
Illustrazione dell' antica badia di S. Benedetto al Monte Subasio.
— Assisi. Sensi. [1880.] 46, (1) pp. 23 cm.
Bound with the original paper covers.
The author's name appears only on page 46.

E3481 — Monte Subasio, Italy. Abbey of St. Benedict.

NL 0432910 MB

Loccatelli Paolucci, Tommaso, *Priore*.
Illustrazione della casa di S. Francesco di Assisi, detta volgarmente la Chiesa Nuova.
— Perugia. Santucci. 1865. 23 pp. Plates. 21.5 cm.
Bound with the original paper covers.
Contains MS. notes by Paul Sabatier.

E3481 — Assisi, Italy. Churches. Chiesa Nuova.

NL 0432911 MB

Loccatelli Paolucci, Tommaso, *Priore*. **FR63.L78
Lettera . . . al M. R. P. Reginaldo da Carignano, M.O.
— Foligno. Campitelli. 1843. 13, (1) pp. 21 cm.
Su due opuscoli stampati in Perugia pel Bartelli, contenente l'uno alcune tesi De militante Christi ecclesia, intitolato l'altro Theses a censuris vindicatae.

E3558 — Carignano, Reginaldo da, Pater, M.O. — Letters. Colls. — Roman Catholic Church. Doctrinal and controversial works.

NL 0432912 MB

Loccatelli Paolucci, Tommaso, *Priore*. No. 1 in **FR77.As7lo.Vol. 1
Serie quadruplice dei vescovi della città serafica . . .
— Assisi. Sensi. 1872. 26 pp. Coat of arms. Tables. 23.5 cm.
The author's name appears only on page 26.
Bound with the original paper covers.
Contains MS. notes and insertions by Paul Sabatier.

E3528 — Assisi, Italy. Hist. Relig. — Assisi, Italy. Biog. and geneal.

NL 0432913 MB

Loccatelli Paolucci, Tommaso, *Priore*. **FR28.B51
Suor Diomira Bini di Assisi, Terziaria di S. Francesco . . .
Assisi. Tip. Metastasio. 1887. 81 pp. 23.5 cm., in 8s.
Litanie della SS. Vergine scritte da Suor Diomira, pp. 70-72.
Saggio di notizie sulla famiglia Bini, pp. 73-81.

E3625 — Bini, Diomira, Suor, 1574-1608.

NL 0432914 MB

Loccatelli Paolucci, Tommaso, *Priore*. **FR56.L79
Vita breve di S. Chiara di Assisi.
Assisi. Sensi. 1882. viii, 243, (1) pp. 18 cm.
Contains a MS. note by Paul Sabatier, and a MS. presentation inscription to him from Chan. Elisei d'Assisi.

E3625 — Clara, Saint, 1194-1253.

NL 0432915 MB CU

1598-1677.
Loccenius, Joannes, Antiqvitatvm Sveo-Gothicarum, Libri tres. Holmiæ, Henricus Käyser, 1647. 12°. pp. (18) + 372 + (4). IcB7L811
Engraved t.-p.; has a second t.-p. without date.

NL 0432916 NIC

Loccenius, Joannes, 1598-1677.
Johannis Loccenii Antiquitatum sveo-gothicarvm, cum hujus ævi moribus, institutis ac ritibus indigenis pro re nata comparatarum libri tres. Ed. secunda, emendatior & auctior. Holmiæ, ex officinâ J. Janssonii [1670?]
3 p. l., 168 p. 16cm. (With his Rerum svecicarum historia ... Holmiæ, 1654)
"Explicatio peregrinarum aliquot dictionum iuris feudalis": p. 162-168.

1. Sweden—Antiq.

Library of Congress DL646.L8 5-13692†

NL 0432917 DLC PBa

Loccenius, Joannes, 1598-1677.
Johannis Loccenii Antiquitatum sveo-gothicarum, libri tres. In qvibus prisci sveonum et gothorum mores, statvs regni atqve institvta, cum hodiernis, pro re nata, comparantvr; leges patriae passim, varia qve auctorvm loca illvstrantvr et explicantvr. Editio tertia emendatior & auctior. Accedit nunc index rervm et verborvm. Vpsaliae, Henricus Curio, 1670.
[8] 210, [14] p. 16 cm.

NL 0432918 KyU PU-L PBa NN NIC MH

1616
.592
.2
Loccenius, Joannes, 1598-1677.
...Antiqvitatum sveo-gothicarum libri tres; in qvibus prisci Sveonum & Gothorum mores, status regni atqve instituta, cum hodiernis pro re nata moribus & instituti comparantur. Ed.4., emendatior & auctior. Francofurti & Lipsiae, Impensis viduae & haered.J.Wildii, 1676.
8 ℓ.,139,[1] p. 20½ cm.
1.Sweden-Antiq.

NL 0432919 NjP ICN MH

Loccenius, Joannes, 1598-1677.
Johannis Loccenii Jc. De iure maritimo & navali libri tres. Holmiæ: Ex officinâ J. Janssonii, 1650. 288 p. nar. 12°.
Added, engr. t.-p. with date 1651.

239945A. 1. Law, Maritime.
N. Y. P. L. August 26, 1926

NL 0432920 NN WU MB MiU-L MH

J
84
.516
LOCCENIUS, Joannes 1598-1677.
De iure maritimo & navali libri tres.
Holmiae, Ex officina J.Janssonii, 1651.
288p. 14cm.

Added t.-p., engraved.
With this is bound: Graswinckel, Dirk. Stricturae ad censuram. Amstelaedami, 1654.

NL 0432921 ICN MWA DS

Loccenius, Joannes, 1598-1677.
Johannis Loccenii JC. De jure maritimo. & navali, libri tres. Editio secunda, emendatior & auctior. Holmiae, ex officina J. Janssonii, 1652.
334, [6] p. 12½cm.

1. Maritime law.

NL 0432922 MiU NN CLL NNC MiU-L MH-L

LOCCENIUS, Joannes, 1598-1677.
De jure maritimo & navali libri tres. Holmiae, 1664.

Ed. 3a.
Bound with his Sveciae Regni jus maritimum, 1674.

NL 0432923 MH-L

JX
4410
L78
Loccenius, Joannes, 1598-1677.
Ioan. Loccenivs De iure maritimo. Amstelodami, apud Henricum et Theodorum Boom, 1669.
3 p.l., 3-334, [2] p. 13 cm.

Decorated title-page.

NL 0432924 NNC

FF
ALS
ORJ
Loccenius, Joannes, 1598-1677.
Joannis Locceni. De jure maritimo et navali, libri tres. Editio tertia & ultima. Noviter & acuratius recusa novoq rerum & verborum indice aucta. Holmiae, apud J. Moris [1693?]
334 p.

1. Maritime law. 2. Maritime law - Sweden.
I. Title: De jure maritimo et navali.

NL 0432925 CSt-Law

IB
1637
L6
D4
Loccenius,Joannes,1598-1677.
De ordinanda republica,dissertationum libri quatuor. Accedunt duæ Salvstii epistolæ,de ordinandâ repub.& una Ciceronis epistola de provinciâ rectè administrandâ. Cum eiusdem notis politicis. Lugduni Batavorum, Apud Iacobum Marci, 1637.
552p. 13cm.
Bound in vellum.
Colophon: Lugdvni Batavorvm,Ex officina Iohan. Iansonii à Dorp. Anno cIↃ IↃc XXXVII.
Printer's device on t.p.
Provenance: Jan Novotny.

NL 0432926 NSyU CSmH

LOCCENIUS,Joannes, 1598-1677.
De studio juris dissertatiuncula epistolica.

In GROTIUS,H.et al. Dissertationes de studiis instituendis,1645.

NL 0432927 MH-L

European Tracts
S4
1628
L78
Loccenius, Joannes, 1598-1677
Dissertationes duae, I. De Scythis veteribus, eorumque ortu ... II. De Svecis ac Gothis separatim, eorum politiae vel regni constitutione ... Authore Joanne Loccenio ... Upsaliae, typis Eschilli Matthiae, 1628.
[94] p. 15 cm.
Signatures: $)(^4$A-E^{8}F^4 (F$_4$ blank? wanting)

NL 0432928 CtY

LOCCENIUS,Joannes, 1598-1677.
Explicatio peregrinarum aliquot dictionum feudalium.

Appended to BRISSON,B. De verborum...significatione,1743.

NL 0432929 MH-L

VOLUME 337

948.5
L787

Loccenius, Joannes, 1598-1677.
JOHANNIS LOCCENII/ HISTORIAE/ SVECANAE,/ A primo REGE SVECIAE/ usqve ad/ CAROLUM XI./ REGEM SVECIAE,/ deductae,/ LIBRI NOVEM,/ Secundâ Editione multò auctiores & emendatiores./ Accedunt/ ANTIQVITATUM SVEO-/ GOTHICARVM,/ cum hodiernis institutis comparatarum,/ LIBRI TRES/ locupletiores,/ eodem AUVCTORE./ FRANCOFURTI & LIPSIAE,/ Impensis Viduae & Haeredum JOACHIMI WILDI./ ANNO M.DC.LXXVI./
2 pts.([30]139[1-1]:954[59] p.) 21 x 16 cm.

Main title in red & black. Part I has special t.p.; pt. II has no t.p.
With this is bound: Anatomia Societatis Jesu; & Schurtzfleisch,Conrad Samuel,1641-1708. De viticis ecclesiae;& Hartnack,Daniel, 1602-1708.Bellorum quae Christianos inter & Turcas gesta sunt; & Heinricius,Joachim. Oratione panegyrica; & Acker,Johann Heinrich. Historia reformationis ecclesiae.
Provenance: B1 Whittingham,Maryland Diocesan Library.

NL 0432931 NNG CtY MnU

Loccenius, Joannes, 1598-1677.
Lexicon ivris Sveo-Gothici collectore Johanne Loccenio. Accedit index explicationis dictionum feudalium. Editio secunda emendatior & auctior, addito etiam novo indice, continente simul veterum juris Sveo-Gothici verborum interpretationem Sveticam. Upsaliae, excudit Henricus Curio... 1665.
2p.ℓ.,267,[1],18p. 17cm.
"Cum Regio privilegio."
Signatures: 2 leaves unsigned,A-Q8,R6,Aa8.
Manuscript notes in text.

1. Dictionaries, Law - Swedish

NL 0432932 CtY-L MH

Loccenius, Joannes, 1598-1677.
Lexicon juris Sueo-Gothici labore & studio Johannis Loccenii ic. ... Edition tertia, multo emendatior & auctior. Accedit appendix seu explication verborum Gotho-Teutonicorum iuris feudalis. Holmiae, Typis & sumptibus, Henrici Keysers, 1674.

NL 0432933 CLL CtY PBa PU-L NN MH-L

Loccenius, Joannes, 1598-1677.
Общество пчелъ; или, Краткое сравненіе правительства пчелъ съ правленіемъ гражданскимъ. Переведено съ латинскаго на россійскій языкъ Иваномъ Мошковымъ. Въ Санктпетербургѣ, 1772.
80 p. 20 cm.
Bound with Tatishchev, V. N. Духовная. Въ Санктпетербургѣ, 1773.

1. Public administration. I. Title.
Title transliterated: Obshchestvo pchel.

DK127.5.T3A58 56-48096

NL 0432934 DLC

Beinecke Library
Bg4
632Lq

Loccenius, Joannes, 1598-1677
Periodus imperiorum, thet är: Om the fyra forna stora rikens uphof, tilwärt och undergång. Af ... Joh. Loccenio, år 1632. å Latinska tungomålet för fattad ... men nu först å Swenskan öfwersatt ... Stockholm, Kongl. tryckeriet, 1758.
6 p.ℓ., 172, [8] p. 16 cm.

1. History, Ancient. I. Title.(1)

NL 0432935 CtY

Loccenius, Joannes, 1598-1677.
Politicarvm dissertationvm syntagma. Autore Ioh: Loccenio. Amstelodami, apud I. Ianssonium, 1644.
11 p. l., 504 p. 13½cm.
Engraved t.-p.
Mutilated: pieces cut out of the cover and foot of t.-p.
With this is bound Puteanus, Erycius. Civilis doctrinae lineae ... 1645.

NL 0432936 MiU CSmH NSyU

Loccenius, Joannes, 1598-1677, ed.
Q. Curtii Rufi De rebus gestis Alexandri Magni
see under Curtius Rufus, Quintus.

Loccenius, Joannes, 1598-1677.
Johannis Loccenii Rerum svecicarum historia a rege Berone Tertio usque ad Ericum Decimum Quartum deducta, & pluribus locis, quam antehac, auctior edita. Accedunt Antiquitates sveo-gothicæ. Holmiæ, ex officinâ J. Janssonii, 1654.
4 p. l., 426 (i. e. 428) p. 16cm.
Pages 76-77 omitted in numbering.
"Authorum index, quorum ope vsus sum": p. 425-426.
"Antiquitates sveo-gothicæ" has special t.-p., separate pagination and signatures.

1. Sweden—Hist.

5-13693

Library of Congress DL646.L8

NL 0432938 DLC DSI OCl PBa

Loccenius, Joannes, 1598-1677.

Heineccius, Johann Gottlieb, 1681-1741, *ed.*
Scriptorvm de ivre navtico et maritimo fascicvlvs Io. Franc. Stypmanni Ivs maritimvm et navticvm, Reinoldi Kvricke De adsecvrationibvs diatriben et Io. Loccenii Ivs maritimvm complexvs. Praefationem de ivrisprvdentia, divinarvm hvmanarvmqve rervm notitia, praemisit Io. Gottl. Heineccivs, ic. Halae Magdebvrgicae, svmtibvs Orphanotrophei, 1740.

Loccenius, Joannes, 1598-1677.
Sveciæ regni jus maritimum, lingvâ sveticâ conscriptum, à Johanne Loccenio jc. in lingvam latinam translatum. Accedunt Johannis Loccenii jc. De jure maritimo libri tres, cum regni Sveciae & aliorum populorum legibus maritimis collati: variorum casuum decisionibus additis. Holmiæ, typis & impensis Nicolai Wankivii, Reg. Maj. typogr., MDCLXXIV.
8 p. l., 62 (i. e. 562), [2] p. 15½cm.
Page 562 incorrectly numbered 62.
"Johannis Loccenii jc. De jure maritimo libri tres ... Editio tertia, emendatior & auctior", with special undated t.-p.: p. [133]-562.
1. Maritime law. 2. Maritime law—Sweden. I. Sweden. Laws, statutes, etc. II. Title. III. Title: De jure maritimo libri tres.

32-19396

Library of Congress [2] [349.485077] 347.709485

NL 0432940 DLC MH-L NjP

Loccenius, Joannes, 1598-1677, ed. and tr.
FOR OTHER EDITIONS SEE MAIN ENTRY

Sweden. *Laws, statutes, etc., 1319-1371 (Magnus Eriksson)*
Sveciæ regni leges civiles aut civitatum, secundum potentissimi & serenissimi principis ac domini, domini Gustavi Adolphi, Sueonum, Gothorum & Vandalorum regis, magni principis Finlandiæ, ducis Esthoniæ & Careliæ, domini Ingermanniæ &c. mandatum publicatæ & typis excusæ a. 1618. A Johanne Loccenio jc. in latinam linguam traductæ, & brevibus notis illustratæ. Accedunt Regulæ juris sveogothici, atque index. Cum S.mæ R.giæ Maj.tis privilegio. Londini Scanorum, sumtibus Adami Junghans imprimebat Vitus Haberegger/ Acad. carol. typogr. Anno M.DC.LXXV.

Loccenius, Joannes, 1598-1667, ed. and tr.

Sweden. *Laws, statutes, etc., 1599-1611 (Charles IX)*
Sveciæ regni leges provinciales, prout quondam a potentissimo & serenissimo principe ac domino, Domino Carolo IX Sueonum, Gothorum, Vandalorum ... &c. rege, post recognitionem, confirmatæ, & anno 1608, publicatæ sunt, a Johanne Loccenio jc. in latinam linguam traductæ, & brevibus notis illustratæ ... Holmiæ, Typis Nicolai Wankijf, 1672. FOR OTHER EDITIONS SEE MAIN ENTRY

Beinecke Library
Bu64n
647Lq

[Loccenius, Joannes] 1598-1677
Swenske och Göthiske samle handlingar. Stockholm, Trocht hos Benj.G.Schneider, 1728.
32 p.ℓ., 358, [33] p. 14 cm.
His Antiquitatum sveo-gothicarum libri tres, translated by N.H.Dal, with some additions by the translator.
Title vignette.
1. Sweden - Antiq. I. Dal, Nils Hufwedsson, 1690-1740, tr. II. Title: Svenske och Göthiske samle handlingar.

NL 0432943 CtY IU

JN 7741
.L81
(Rare)

Loccenius, Joannes, 1598-1677.
...Synopsis juris, ad leges sveticas accommodata. Cui accedunt qvaestiones practicae et exercitationes juris. Editio secunda, emendatior & auctior. Holmae, Typis & sumtibus H. Keyser, 1653.
227 p.

1. Law--Sweden. I. Title.

NL 0432944 ICU

Loccenius, Joannes, 1598-1677.
Synopsis juris publici svecani. Gothoburgi, 1673.
948 p.
I. Sweden. Laws, statutes, etc.

NL 0432945 PPAmSwM

Locchi, Domenico.
... Nuovissimo atlante geografico (39 tavole) Torino [etc.] G. B. Paravia & c. [1943]
2 p. l., 38 double col. pl. (maps, diagr.) 28cm.
At head of title: D. Locchi.

1. Atlases.

Map 46-311

NL 0432946 DLC NN DLC

AA
1114
M34
L78

Locchi, Oreste Tarquinio
La provincia di Pesaro ed Urbino. Roma, Edizioni di "Latina Gens", 1934.
845 p. illus., maps. 25 cm.

1. Pesaro e Urbino - Description - Guidebooks.

NL 0432947 NNC-A IMunS NN

W 4
S24
1925

LOCCHI, Renato
Ossificações tentoriaes, peritrigeminaes e suprapetrosas no craneo humano; observações e pesquizas. S. Paulo, Secção de obras d' "O estado de S. Paulo," 1925.
135 p. illus.
These inaug. - São Paulo.

NL 0432948 DNLM MH

PQ
4827
O3
C3

Locchi, Vittorio, 1889-1917.
Le canzoni del Giacchio. [Milano, L'Eroica, 1919]
51p. illus. 19cm. (I Gioielli de L'Eroica, No.9)
Title and illustrations within ornamental border in buff.
Introduction by Italo Marinelli.
Ornamentations by A. Cermignani.

NL 0432949 CtU TU

VOLUME 337

Locchi, Vittorio, 1889-1917.
...The feast of Saint Gorizia, by Vittorio Locchi; translated [into English verse] by Lorna De Lucchi. Milano: [La Soc. editoriale milanese,] 1919. 55, 6-55(1) p., 3 l. col'd illus. 16°. (The jewels of the Eroica. [no.] 2.)

Cover-title.
Added t.-p. in Italian.
Text in English and Italian on opposite pages.

1. European war, 1914- —Poetry. 2. Poetry (Italian). 3. Lucchi, Lorna de, translator. 4. Title. 5. Series.
N. Y. P. L. November 26, 1919.

NL 0432950 NN CU PU

855L78 Locchi, Vittorio, 1889-1917.
Os ... La sagra di Santa Gorizia. La Spezia, "Arti grafiche" 1917.
61p. (I gioielli del "L'Eroica" 2)

NL 0432951 IU TxU

Locchi, Vittorio, 1889-1917.
... La sagra di Santa Gorizia. Milano, 1919.
2 p. l., [1], 6-55, 6-55, [2] p., 2 l. 16½cm. (I gioielli del "L'Eroica." 2)
Half-title: The feast of Saint Gorizia by Vittorio Locchi, tr. into English verse by Lorna de' Lucchi, with introduction by Ettore Cozzani. English and Italian on opposite pages.

I. Lucchi, Lorna de', tr. II. Title. III. Title: The feast of Saint Gorizia.
Library of Congress PQ4827.O3S3 1919 20-5563

NL 0432952 DLC NIC NjP MB CtY OU MiU PBm PPL

D855L78
W
Locchi, Vittorio, 1889-1917.
... La sagra di santa Gorizia. [5. ed.] Milano [1923]
2 p. l., 7-61, [3] p. illus. 16cm. (I gioielli dell'Eroica, 2)

At head of title: V. Locchi.
Preface signed: Ettore Cozzani.

I. Cozzani, Ettore, 1884- ed. II. Title.

NL 0432953 NNC TU

Locchi, Vittoro, 1889-1917.
La sagra di Santa Gorizia. Milano, L'eroica, 1928.
61 p.

NL 0432954 PP

Locchi, Vittorio, 1889-1917.
...I sonetti della malinconia. Milano, 1919. 57 p. illus. 19cm. (I gioielli del "L'Eroica". 5.)

1. Sonnets, Italian. I. Title.
N. Y. P. L. January 23, 1948

NL 0432955 NN

PQ Locchi, Vittorio, 1889-1917.
4827 La Sveglia. Il Testamento. Milano
O3 [L'Eroica] 1918.
S8 59p. illus. 17cm. (I Gioielli del L'Eroica, 4)
Title within ornamental border, head-pieces, intial.
Pref. by Ettore Cozzani.
Ornamenti di Mantelli.

NL 0432956 CtU TU

PQ Locchi, Vittorio, 1889-1917.
4827 Tersite. Milano, L'Eroica [1941]
O3 84p. illus. 17cm. (I Gioielli de
T4 L'Eroica, N°.35)
Pref. by Ettore Cozzani.
Disegni di A. e V. Migliorati.

NL 0432957 CtU

Locchi, Vittorio, 1889-1917.
... L'uragano. [Milano, "L'Eroica", 1922]
4 p.l., [3]-123, [3] p. 22 cm. (Il teatro de "L'Eroica", 1)
Ornamented t.-p.

NL 0432958 CU TU

Locchi, Vittorio, 1889-1917.
...L'uragano. [Milano: "L'Eroica," 1934] 152 p. illus. 16½cm. (L'Eroica. I gioielli de "L'Eroica." no. 30-31.)

Drama in 3 acts; first performed in Florence in 1922.

802731A. 1. Drama, Italian. I. Title.
N. Y. P. L. March 4, 1936

NL 0432959 NN

WC LOCCI, Armando R
310 Brucelosis; consideraciones clínicas y
L811b epidemiológicas. Rosario, 1941.
1941 164 p. illus.
1. Brucellosis

NL 0432960 DNLM

Loccoz, Olimpia Schneider Moenne-
see
Schneider Moenne-Loccoz, Olimpia.

Loccum, Ger. Evangelische Akademie
see
Evangelische Akademie, *Loccum, Ger.*

Die Loccumer Historienbibel
see under Liljebäck, Erik Nilsson.

Locela, Rafael Lasala y
see Lasala y Locela, Rafael, Bp., 1716-1792.

Z943.032 [Locelius, Jacobus]
L787 Erschröckliche, vnerhörte neüwe zeittung, welche sich newlich in disem M.D.LXII. jare, zů Dreszigk, zwischen Zeitz und Naumburgk, vnter dem ehrenfesten, gestrengen Heinrichen von Bünaw, dem eltern gelegen, zůgetragen, und von dem pfarherren desselbigen orts, an etliche namhafftige personen glaubwirdig, wie folget, geschriben. [n.p. 1562]
[7] p. 19cm.
Signature: Ar.
Signed: Jacobus Locelius
1. Germany. History, 1556-1648. 2. News-letters, German. I. Title.

NL 0432965 MnU

U [LOCELLA, ALOYS EMMERICH, Freiherr VON] 1733-
139 1800.
.095 Essai sur la nécessité de conférer les emplois selon les talens, par Mr. le baron de Loc**. Europe[Strasburg?]1760.
66p. 21cm. (with Bilistein, Charles Léopold Andreu de. Institutions militaires pour la France. 1762)

NL 0432966 ICN MH

DG88 LOCELLA,ALOYS EMMERICH,freiherr VON,1733-1800.
.L76 Aloysii l.b.a Locella Tria tentamina ad illvstran-
(Cl) das Leges XII tabvlarvm. Viennae Avstriæ,apvd I.T. Trattner,1754.
[12],209,[9]p. 21½cm.
Title in red and black.

1.Leges XII tabularum. 2.Roman law.

NL 0432967 ICU

Locella, Alois Emmerich, freiherr von, 1733-1800, ed.

Xenophon, *of Ephesus.*
Xenophontis Ephesii De Anthia et Habrocome Ephesiacorvm libri v. Graece et latine recensvit svpplevit emendavit latine vertit adnotationibvs aliorvm et svis illvstravit indivibvs instrvxit Aloys. Emeric. liber baro Locella ... Vindobonae, apvd A. Blvmaver, 1796.

LOCELLA,Guglielmo,barone,1848-1908.

See LOCELLA,Wilhelm,freiherr von,1848-1908.

Locella, Marie (von Tiedemann) freifrau von, 1855- ed.
Locella, Wilhelm, *freiherr* von, 1848-1908.
Dante's Francesca da Rimini in der literatur, bildenden kunst und musik, nach den plänen und entwürfen des professors baron Guglielmo Locella bearb. und hrsg. von baronin Marie Locella; mit 19 kunstbeilagen und 75 abbildungen im text. Eszlingen a. N., P. Neff (M. Schreiber) 1913.

Locella, Wilhelm, *freiherr* von, 1848-1908.
Dante in der deutschen kunst; 20 handzeichnungen deutscher künstler zu Dantes Göttlicher komödie, nebst vier Dante-portraits, mit erläuterndem text hrsg. von baron G. Locella. Dresden, L. Ehlermann, 1890.
3 p. l., 30 p., 1 l. xx pl. (3 double) 4 port. 43½cm.
Portraits: "Dante-bildnis nach Giotto (codex ricardianus); Dantebüste aus dem National-museum zu Neapel; Dante-bildnis nach dem fresko-gemälde von Giotto vor ... [und] nach der restauration."

1. Dante—Iconography. 2. Drawings, German. I. Title.
Library of Congress PQ4329.L6 20—19387

NL 0432971 DLC CtY MiU MH NIC

LOCELLA, Wilhelm, freiherr von, 1848-1908.
Dante nell' arte tedesca. Venti disegni di artisti tedeschi ad illustrazione della Divina commedia e quattro ritratti di Dante. U. Hoepli: Milano. 1891 [1890]. (8), 30 pp. F°.

NL 0432972 MB RPB

VOLUME 337

Locella, Wilhelm, *freiherr* **von,** 1848–1908.
Dante's Francesca da Rimini in der literatur, bildenden kunst und musik, nach den plänen und entwürfen des professors baron Guglielmo Locella bearb. und hrsg. von baronin Marie Locella; mit 19 kunstbeilagen und 75 abbildungen im text. Eszlingen a. N., P. Neff (M. Schreiber) 1913.
3 p. l., 205 p. illus., xix pl. (3 col., incl. front.) 27cm.
1. Dante Alighieri. Divina commedia. Inferno. Canto v. 2. Francesca da Rimini, d. ca. 1285. 3. Dante Alighieri—Illustrations. 4. Dante Alighieri—Music. I. Locella, Marie (von Tiedemann) freifrau von, 1855– ed.
14—11942
Library of Congress PQ4410.F8L7

NL 0432973 DLC CU-S CLU OKentU CtY OC1W NjP NN MB

LOCELLA, Wilhelm, freiherr von, 1848–1908.
Dante's Francesca da Rimini in der weltliteratur und kunst; ein vortrag. Erlangen, 1906.
pp.(8).
"Separatabdr.aus d.Verhandlungen des xii. deutschen neuphilologentages, München, 1906."

NL 0432974 MH

Locella, Wilhelm, *freiherr* **von,** 1848–1908, *ed.*
Novelle italiane di quaranta autori dal 1300 al 1847. Pubblicate per cura di G. Locella. Leipzig, F. A. Brockhaus, 1879.
3 p. l., 441, [1] p. 18cm. (*Half-title:* Biblioteca d'autori italiani, t. 17)
1. Italian fiction (Collections)
1–23765 Revised
Library of Congress PQ4252.L7

NL 0432975 DLC MdBP MH OC1 PBm

Wilhelm, freiherr von, 1848–1908.
Locella,
Nuovo dizionario tascabile: Italiano Tedesco e Tedesco Italiano. New York: Brentano's [18—?]. vi, 222(1) p. 4. ed. 16°.
Neues italianisch-deutsches und deutsch-italianisches Taschenwörterbuch.
1. German language. 2. Dictionaries.
N. Y. P. L. June 15, 1913.

NL 0432976 NN

Locella, Wilhelm, freiherr von, 1848–1908.
Nuovo dizionario tascabile Italiano tedesco e tedesco Italiano di G. Locella. 2nd ed. Leipzig, Bernhard Tauchnitz. 1879.
218 p. & 222p.

NL 0432977 OC1JC

Wilhelm, freiherr von, 1848–1908
Locella,
Nuovo dizionario tascabile italiano tedesco e tedesco italiano, di G. Locella... Neues italienisch-deutsches und deutsch-italienisches Taschenwörterbuch. Von G. Locella... New York: Brentano's [189–?]. vi, 218, 222 p. 4. ed. 16°.
44098A. 1. Italian language.—Dictionaries: German. 2. German language.—Dictionaries: Italian.
N. Y. P. L. May 31, 1922.

NL 0432978 NN

Locella, Wilhelm, freiherr von, 1848–1908.
Nuovo dizionario tascabile Italiano-Tedesco e Tedesco-Italiano... 8th ed. N.Y., Macmillan, n.d.
242 p.

NL 0432979 OC1W

Locella, Wilhelm, freiherr von, 1848–1908.
Alfieri, Vittorio, 1749–1803.
Tragedie scelte di Vittorio Alfieri ... Cogli argomenti e pareri relativi alle medesime dell'autore. Pubblicate per cura di G. Locella. Leipzig, F. A. Brockhaus, 1878.

Locella, Wilhelm, freiherr von, 1848–1908, ed.
Foscolo, Ugo, 1778–1827.
Le ultime lettere di Jacopo Ortis ed altre opere scelte di Ugo Foscolo. Pubblicate per cura di G. Locella. Leipzig, F. A. Brockhaus, 1878.

Locella, Wilhelm, *freiherr* **von,** 1848–1908.
Zur deutschen Dante-litteratur, mit besonderer berücksichtigung der übersetzungen von Dantes Göttlicher komödie. Mit mehreren bibliographischen und statistischen beilagen von bar. G. Locella. Leipzig, B. G. Teubner, 1889.
iv p., 1 l., 108 p. 2 fold. tab. 19cm.
CONTENTS.—Vorwort.—Allgemeiner überblick.—Die deutschen übersetzungen der Divina commedia und ihre verfasser.—Bibliographie der deutschen übersetzungen der Divina commedia und kurze biographische notizen der übersetzer.—Der xxvii. gesang der Hölle mit dem kommentar Philalethes' in italienischer sprache.—Beschreibung und inhaltsangabe der Dante-albums der Kgl. öffentlichen bibliothek zu Dresden.—Namensverzeichnis.—Graphische darstellung einer vergleichenden statistik der deutschen Dante-litteratur (Tabelle I).—Graphische übersicht der deutschen übersetzungen von Dantes Divina commedia (Tabelle II)
1. Dante—Bibl. 2. Dante—Translations. 3. Literature, Comparative—Italian and German. 4. Literature, Comparative—German and Italian.
3–6391 Revised
Library of Congress Z8215.L81

NL 0432983 DLC WU CtY NIC MH

PQ2623 .O24F7
Lo Celso, André.
Frissons. Illus. de Bablet [et al.] Paris, La Revue moderne [1951]
88 p. illus. 19 cm.
Poems.
I. Title.
A 52–918
Illinois. Univ. Library for Library of Congress [1]

NL 0432984 IU DLC

Lo Celso, Angel T 1900–
Arquitectura y construcciones rurales. Buenos Aires, Dirección General de Publicidad de la Universidad Nacional de Córdoba; distribuidor: Librería y Editorial "El Ateneo," 1953.
487 p. illus. 23 cm.
1. Farm buildings—Argentine Republic. I. Title.
NA8206.L6 56–28014 ‡

NL 0432985 DLC

Lo Celso, Angel T 1900–
... Euritmia arquitectónica, ensayo de una expresión estética; prólogo del arq. Juan Kronfuss. Córdoba (R. A.) [Impr. de la Universidad nacional] 1943.
xix, [3]–206 p., 2 l. illus., diagrs. 24cm.
"Se formó con las separatas de la Revista de la Universidad, correspondientes a los nros. 3–4, 5–6, 7–8 y 9–10 del año 1941 y nros. 1–2, 3–4, 5–6, 7–8 y 9–10 del año 1942."
1. Esthetics. 2. Rhythm. 3. Architecture—Composition, proportion, etc. I. Title.
44–6063
Library of Congress N76.L6
[3] 720.1

NL 0432986 DLC

G720.1 L787e 1950
Lo Celso, Angel T 1900–
Euritmia arquitectónica, ensayo de una expresión estética; prólogo del arq. Juan Kronfuss. [2. ed.] Córdoba, República Argentina, Impr. de la Universidad, 1950.
442p. illus., diagrs. 24cm.
1. Aesthetics. 2. Rhythm. 3. Architecture - Composition, proportion, etc. I. Title.

NL 0432987 TxU

G720.1 L787f
Lo Celso, Angel T 1900–
Filosofía de la arquitectura. Córdoba, República Argentina, Impr. de la Universidad, 1952.
xvii, 317p. illus. 23cm.
1. Architecture. I. Title.

NL 0432988 TxU

Lo Celso, Angel T 1900–
Por rutas de América, un viaje al Perú; VI Congreso Panamericano de Arquitectos. Prólogo del Arq. Angel Guido. [Córdoba, República Argentina, Distribuidor: Editorial "Assandri," 1948]
xv, 166 p. illus., group ports. 24 cm.
"Se formó con las separatas de la Revista de la Facultad de Ciencias Exactas, Físicas y Naturales, correspondiente a nº 4 del año x (1947) y nros. 1, 2, 3 y 4 del año xi (1948)"
CONTENTS.—El Cuzco.—Machupijchu.—Saccsahuaman.—Lima.—Arequipa.—El Congreso Panamericano de Arquitectos.—Pachacamac.—Una visita al Instituto y Museo de Antropología de Lima.—Señorío, tradición y calor popular.—Pintura colonial del Cuzco.
1. Architecture—Peru. 2. Peru—Descr. & trav. I. Pan American Congress of Architects. 6th, Lima, 1947. II. Title.
NA910.L6 720.985 50–26190

NL 0432989 DLC CtY

Lo Celso, Angel T 1900–
Realidad y abstracción en el arte de la pintura. Buenos Aires, Impr. de la Universidad Nacional de Córdoba; distribuidor: Librería y Editorial "El Ateneo," 1955.
x, 477 p. illus. (part mounted col.) 24 cm.
1. Painting—Hist. 2. Art, Modern—20th cent. 3. Art, Abstract. 4. Painting, French. I. Title.
ND195.L6 57–19533

NL 0432990 DLC TxU MiU

Lo Celso, Angel T 1900–
Sentido espiritual de la arquitectura en América. Córdoba, Universidad Nacional, 1948.
89 p. illus. 24 cm. (Publicaciones de la Facultad de Filosofía y Humanidades, no. 2)
1. Architecture. 2. Aesthetics. 3. Architecture—America. I. Title. (Series: Córdoba, Argentine Republic. Universidad Nacional. Facultad de Filosofía y Humanidades. Publicaciones, nueva ser., no. 2)
NA2500.L57 1948a 720.1 53–28871

NL 0432991 DLC TxU CtY

JA 79 L615 LAC
Lo Celso, Juan A
Etica política bajo el signo de la revolución; conferencia [por] Juan A. Lo Celso. Rosario, Ateneo de la Juventud Revolucionaria 4 de Junio, 1947.
15p. 23cm.
"Pronunciada el 28 de marzo de 1947 en el salón de la Biblioteca Argentina de Rosario, inaugurando el ciclo 1947 del Ateneo."
1. Political ethics - Addresses, essays, lectures. I. Title.

NL 0432992 TxU

Lo Celso, Rogasiano M
... Responsabilidad civil de los gestores en las sociedades anónimas ... Prólogo del doctor Salvador Arteabaro. Buenos Aires, Editorial Depalma, 1944.
3 p. l., [ix]–xiv, 160 p., 1 l. 23½cm.
"Obra premiada por unanimidad con medalla de oro y diploma, en el certamen de trabajos jurídicos del año 1942, organizado por el Colegio de abogados de Rosario."
1. Directors of corporations—Argentine republic. I. Title.
45–15652

NL 0432993 DLC CtY

VOLUME 337

Locet, Daluce, pseud.
see Colet, Claude, 16th cent.

Locet, Pamanchoys, pseud.
see Colet, Claude, 16th cent.

A
L787
Locey, Cyrus T 1835-1920.
[Diary of Cyrus T. Locey, 1858-1859, 1873-1911, and miscellaneous papers, including the organization papers of the Eldorado grange, Malheur county, Oregon]
2 boxes.

Copy. The copy is made part in photostat, part in microfilm, and part in typed form.

1. Malheur county, Ore. History. 2. Patrons of husbandry. Oregon state grange.

NL 0432996 OrU

Loch, Major

Taylor, Meadows *i. e.* **Philip Meadows,** 1808-1876.
Architecture at Beejapoor, an ancient Mahometan capital in the Bombay Presidency, photographed from drawings by Capt. P. D. Hart, B. E., A. Cumming, C. E., and native draftsmen; and on the spot by Colonel Biggs ... and the late Major Loch ... With an historical and descriptive memoir by Captain Meadows Taylor ... and architectural notes by James Fergusson ... Pub. for the Committee of architectural antiquities of Western India under the patronage of Kursondas Madhowdas. London, J. Murray, 1866.

Loch, Albert, 1913-
... Über das Verhältnis der sozialen Lage und Kiefer- und Zahnreihenanomalien bei den Schulkindern in St. Wendel-Saar ... [n.p.] 1936.
Inaug.-Diss. - Greifswald.
Lebenslauf.
"Quellenangabe": p. 15.

NL 0432998 CtY MiU

Loch, Alexander: Bericht über 200 in den ersten beiden Kriegsjahren an Hals, Nase und Ohren untersuchte und behandelte Verwundete aus dem Düsseldorfer Lazarett für Kieferverletzte. Berlin: Karger 1917. 98 S., 3 Bl. Tab. 8°
¶ Aus: Beiträge z. Anat. ... d. Ohres, d. Nase u. d. Halses. Bd 9.
Gießen, Med. Diss. v. 27. März 1917, Ref. v. Eicken
[Geb. 2. Mai 86 Oberstein a. N.; Wohnort: Düsseldorf; Staatsangeh.: Oldenburg; Vorbildung: Kaiser-Wilhelm-G. Trier Reife 04; Studium: Naturw. Heidelberg 1, Med. München 2, Kiel 4, Straßburg 4 S.; Coll. 12. Aug. 16; Approb. 15. Dez. 10.] [U 17. 870

NL 0432999 ICRL DNLM

Loch, Alfred.
Begriff und privatrechtliche Natur des Kettenhandels. Goettingen, 1923.
32 p.
Inaug.-Diss. Goetingen
Bibl.

NL 0433000 ICRL

Loch, Artur.
Der elektrische Vollbahnbetrieb auf den deutschen Reichsbahnen unter besonderer Berücksichtigung der schlesischen Gebirgstrecken. I. T. Beschreibung der gesamten Einrichtungen einschliesslich der Lokomotiven und Triebwagen. Beilefeld, Velhagen & Klasing, 1923.
103 p. illus., 2 plates (attached inside back cover) map. (Verband deutscher Eisenbahnfachschulen [Berlin] Bd. 25, I. T.
No more published?

NL 0433001 ICJ

Loch, Catharine Grace, 1854-1904.
Catharine Grace Loch, Royal red cross, Senior lady superintendent Queen Alexandra's Military nursing service for India: a memoir, with an introduction by Field-marshal the Earl Roberts ... With two portraits. London, New York [etc.] H. Frowde, 1905.
xiii p., 1 l., 359, [1] p. front., ports. 19½cm.
Edited by A. F. Bradshaw.

1. India. Army—Sanit. aff. I. Bradshaw, A. Frederick, 1834- ed.

6-28430

Library of Congress UH347.L8

NL 0433002 DLC ICRL PPL ICJ

Loch, sir Charles Stewart, 1849-1923.

Bosanquet, Bernard, 1848-1923, *ed.*
Aspects of the social problem, by various writers. Ed. by Bernard Bosanquet. London and New York, Macmillan and co., 1895.

Loch, Charles Stewart, 1849-
Charity and social life; a short study of religious and social thought in relation to charitable methods and institutions, by C. S. Loch ... London, Macmillan and co., limited, 1910.
xii, 496 p. 19cm.
"The book is for the most part a reprint of an article on 'Charity and charities' which was first published in 1902 in the supplementary volumes of the Encyclopaedia britannica."—Pref.

1. Charity. 2. Charity organization. 3. Charities—Gt. Brit. I. Title.

10-24532

Library of Congress HV16.L7

NL 0433004 CtY OU OO MiU OCl PHC PBm NjP ICJ NN MB ViU NN NjR DLC CaBVaU IdU OrP UU FMU CU MtU NcU NcD

Loch, *Sir* **Charles Stewart,** 1849-1923.
Charity organisation, by C. S. Loch ... London, S. Sonnenschein & co., 1890.
4 p. l., 106 p. 19½cm. (Social science series. 16)
"Reprint of a paper entitled De l'organisation de l'assistance, written for the Congrès international d'assistance held in Paris in July and August, 1889."—Pref.

NL 0433005 NcD RP NIC OrP NjP OrU FMU LU MH PPL MiU OO

Loch, *Sir* **Charles Stewart,** 1849-1923.
Charity organisation, by C. S. Loch ... 2d ed. London, S. Sonnenschein & co., 1892.
4 p. l., 106 p. 19½cm. (Social science series. 16)
"Reprint of a paper entitled De l'organisation de l'assistance, written for the Congrès international d'assistance held in Paris in July and August, 1889."—Pref.

1. Charity organization. 2. Charities—Gt. Brit. 3. Poor laws—Gt. Brit. I. Title.

1-18582 Revised

Library of Congress HV40.L8
— Copy 2. H31.S7 vol. 16
[r26c2]

NL 0433006 PBm PU ICJ DLC Nh NIC WaWW WaS OrU OU OCl PPM

Loch, C[harles] S[tewart], 1849-1923.
Charity organisation. London: Swan Sonnenschein & Co., Ltd., 1905. 4 p.l., 106 p. 3. ed. 12°.

NL 0433007 NN IdU MH CU CaBVaU PSC PP

Loch, C. S. Confusion in medical charities.
13 pp. (*Nineteenth Cent.* v. 32, 1892, p. 298.)

NL 0433008 MdBP

Loch, *Sir* **Charles Stewart,** 1849-1923.
Criticisms of "General" Booth's social scheme, from three different points of view. By C. S. Loch, Bernard Bosanquet, and the Rev. Canon Philip Dwyer. London, Swan Sonnenschein & co., 1891.
100, [2] p., 1 l., [2], 99, [iii]-vi p., 1 l., 72 p. 18½ cm.
"Contains, with a few slight modifications and additions, a series of short papers on General Booth's social scheme, which were submitted to the Council of the London charity organisation society and received their approval."—Pref. The papers were first published separately by same publisher; paper by Loch is 2d edition.
CONTENTS.—General Booth's social scheme [by] C. S. Loch.—Booth's submerged tenth [by] Canon Dwyer.—"In darkest England" [by] B. Bosanquet.
1. Booth, William, 1829-1912. In darkest England. 2. Poor—Gt. Brit. 3. Agricultural colonies. 4. Unemployed. I. Bosanquet, Bernard, 1848-1923. II. Dwyer, Philip.
Washington, D. C. Pub Library W 10—55

NL 0433009 NcU CtY PPM PPL OClW PU MB NjP NcD PPFr DWP WaWW WaS RPB MU CU ICarbS Nh PPL

LOCH, Charles Stewart, 1849-1923.
Cross purposes in medical reform. A paper, etc. [London, 1884?]

NL 0433010 MH

Loch, Charles stewart, 1849-1923.

Gt. Brit. *Local government board.*
Elberfeld poor law system. Reports on the Elberfeld poor law system and German workmen's colonies. Presented to both houses of Parliament by command of Her Majesty, March 1888. London, Printed for H. M. Stationery off., by Eyre and Spottiswoode. 1888.

Loch, Charles Stewart, 1849-1923.
The Elberfield system [of poor relief].
London. [1903.] 237-264 pp. [Charity Organization Society, London. Occasional papers. Ser. 3, no. 20.] 21½ cm.

L1324 — Elberfeld, Germany. The poor. — S.r.c.

NL 0433012 MB

Loch, Sir Charles Stewart, 1849-1923.

HD5767
.S6
Spencer, Mary G
Employment pictures from the census, by M. G. Spencer and H. J. Falk. With a pref. by C. S. Loch. London, P. S. King, 1906.

Loch, Sir Charles Stewart, 1849-1923.
An examination of "General" Booth's social scheme. Adopted by the council of the London charity organisation society... 2. ed. London, Swan Sonnenschein & co., 1890. 100 p. 19cm.

255391B. 1. Charities, Work providing—Gt. Br. 2. Salvation army—Gt. Br. 3. Booth, William, 1829-1912. In darkest England, and the way out.
N. Y. P. L. June 5, 1944

NL 0433014 NN MWelC IU

Loch, *Sir* **Charles Stewart,** 1849-1923.
A great ideal and its champion; papers and addresses by the late Sir Charles Stewart Loch. London, G. Allen & Unwin ltd. [1923]
2 p. l., 7-223, [1] p. 19cm.
"This book, compiled by colleagues and friends of the late Sir Charles Stewart Loch, consists of papers, addresses and extracts from addresses delivered by him as secretary to the Council of the Charity organisation society."—Pref.

1. Charity—Addresses, essays, lectures. 2. Charity organisation society, London. I. Title.

24-16012

Library of Congress HV15.L6

NL 0433015 DLC FMU MU CtY OClW ICJ NN

VOLUME 337

LOCH,[Charles] S[tewart],1849-
How to help cases of distress; a handy reference book for almoners and others. 4th ed. London,Charity Organization Society,etc.,[1890]

"A reprint of the introduction to the 'Charities register and digest'."
Soc 2115.75.4

NL 0433016 MH PPPSW

Loch, Charles Stewart, 1849-
How to help cases of distress; a handy reference book for almoners and others. By C. S. Loch, ... Fifth edition, June 1895. London, Charity Organisation Society and Longmans, Green, & Co., [1895].
viii, ccviii p. 22cm.
"Books for reference & reading concerning charity and questions bearing upon charitable work," p. cxcvi-cxcix.

NL 0433017 ICJ FMU

Loch, *Sir* Charles Stewart, 1849–1923.
In memoriam Miss Octavia Hill, by C. S. Loch ... Boston, The Associated charities, 1913.
cover-title, 15 p. 19cm.
"Reprinted by permission from the Charity organization review (London) for September and October, 1912."

1. Hill, Octavia, 1838–1912.

26-2881

Library of Congress HV28.H45L6

NL 0433018 DLC NN PPPSW

Loch, Charles Stewart, 1849- ed.
Methods of social advance; short studies in social practice by various authors, ed. by C. S. Loch ... London, New York, Macmillan and co., limited, 1904.
4 p. l., 192 p. 20½cm.
"Most of the papers have appeared in the Charity organisation review."—Pref.
CONTENTS.—Loch, C. S. Introduction: Distress and its prevention.—Cautley, E. Out-patient departments and the rearing of children.—Nussey, H. G. The work of a hospital almoner.—Mudd, E. E. Charitable action in phthisical cases.—Duke, O. T. Physical education.—Motion, J. R. A policy of hustling; or, The lock and key.—Haggard, H. R. Agriculture and the unemployed question.—Bosanquet, H. Past experience in relief works.—Martineau, J. Emigration and want of employment.—Nunn, T. H. Municipal labour bureaux.—Livesey, G. Industrial partnership and the prevention of distress.—Brady, M. K. and Durham, F. H. Apprenticeship.—Bosanquet, H. Wages and housekeeping.—Loch, C. S. The separate payment of rates.—Mackay, T. Poor law reform.—Loch, C. S. A charities board.—Urwick, E. J. A school of sociology.—Loch, C. S. 'If citizens be friends.'

4-16346

OO OCl MB ICJ NN
NL 0433020 DLC CU NIC KEmT NcD PPL PBm PU OO ODW

331.254 Loch, Sir Charles Stewart, 1849-1923
L81n The national insurance bill; a paper, approved by the council of the Charity organisation society... London [Charity organisation society] 1911.
cover-title, 48p. tables. O.

NL 0433021 IU MH IaU

Loch, Charles Stewart, 1849-
Old-age pensions; a collection of short papers. London, Macmillan and company, limited; New York, The Macmillan company, 1903.

Loch, Charles Stewart, 1849-
Old age pensions and pauperism; an inquiry as to the bearing of the statistics of pauperism quoted by the Rt. Hon. J. Chamberlain, M. P. and others, in support of a scheme for national pensions. [By] C. S. Loch ... London, S. Sonnenschein & co., 1892.
59 p. 22½cm.

1. Old age pensions. 2. Poor.

1-18583

Library of Congress HD7106.G8L7

NL 0433023 DLC ICJ

Loch, Sir Charles Stewart, 1849-1923.
The prevention and relief of distress: a handbook of information respecting the statutory and voluntary means available for the relief of distress and the improvement of social conditions; being Sir Charles Loch's 'How to help cases of distress,' revised, re-arranged, and brought up to date for the Charity Organisation Society. Westminster [London]: P. S. King & Son, Ltd., 1922. vii, 140 p. 12°.

NL 0433024 NN PU CU MH CtY ICU

Loch, Sir Charles Stewart, 1849-1923
The prevention and relief of distress; a handbook of information respecting the statutory and voluntary means available for the relief of distress and the improvement of social conditions in the county of London; being Sir Charles Loch's 'How to help cases of distress' revised, re-arranged, and brought up to date for the Charity Organisation Society. [London:] P. S. King & Son, Ltd., 1931. vii, 185 p. incl. tables. 12°.

587982A. 1. Charities—Handbooks. 2. Charities, Private—Gt. Br.—Eng.—London. I. Loch, Sir Charles Stewart, 1849-1923.
N. Y. P. L. August 13, 1932

NL 0433025 NN

HV 250 LOCH,Sir CHARLES STEWART,1849-1923
.L9 L8 The prevention and relief of distress; a handbook of information respecting the statutory and voluntary means available for the relief of distress and the improvement of social conditions in the county of London, being Sir Charles Loch's 'How to help cases of distress,' rev., re-arranged, and brought up to date for the Charity Organisation Society Westminster, P. S. King and Charity Organisation Society, 1932.
185 p.

NL 0433026 InU

Loch, Charles Stuart, 1849-1923.
The prevention and relief of distress, a handbook of information respecting the statutory and voluntary means available for the relief of distress and improvement of social conditions in the county of London... London, P.S. King & son, Ltd. and Charity organization soc., 1934.

NL 0433027 PPPSW

HV245
.A2A32
1935 Loch, Sir Charles Stewart, 1849-1923.
The prevention and relief of distress; a handbook of information respecting the statutory and voluntary means available for the relief of distress and the improvement of social conditions in the county of London; being Sir Charles Loch's 'How to help cases of distress', rev., re-arranged, and brought up to date for the Charity organisation society. Special features: London relief and assessment codes, July 1935, Housing act, July 1935, National health insurance and contributory pensions

Continued in next column

Continued from preceding column

act, August 1935. Westminster, P. S. King & son, ltd.; [London] Charity organisation society, 1935.
vii, 234 p. 18½cm.
"Embodies most of the material ... which was contained in Sir Charles Loch's introduction to the 'Charities register and digest,' published and annually revised by the Charity organisation society."--Pref.

1. Charities—Gt. Brit. 2. London—Charities. 3. Poor—Gt. Brit. I. Charity organisation society, London. II. Title.

NL 0433028 DLC IU MH

Loch, Charles Stewart, 1849-1923.
The school board& children in want of food. [London., 1890?]
7 p.

NL 0433029 PBm

Loch, *Sir* Charles Stewart, 1849-
The state and the unemployed.
(In Charity Organisation Society, London. Occasional papers. Ser. 2, no. 21, pp. 241-259. [London.] 1907.)

L6307 — Unemployed, The.

NL 0433030 MB MH

Loch, C[harles] S[tewart], 1849-1923.
Statistics of population and pauperism ... England and Wales, 1851-1901. [London] 1905.
24 p. 4°. (Institut international de statistique, 10.sess., Londres, 1905)
Suggested resolutions in regard to statistical returns of pauperism... 1 l. 4°., and 1 diagram ob. 4°., inserted.
n.t.-p.

NL 0433031 NN

---

361 Loch, Sir Charles Stewart, 1849-1923.
L787gDb Een strijder voor een hoog ideaal; opstellen en toespraken. Vertaald door J. F. L. Blankenberg. Haarlem, H. D. Tjeenk Willink, 1924.
252p. port. 20cm.

1. Charity--Addresses, essays, lectures. 2. Charity Organization Society, London. I. Blankenberg, J. F. L., tr. II. Title.

NL 0433032 IU

HV16
.L7
1938 Loch, Sir Charles Stewart, 1849-1923.
Three thousand years of social service, being a reprint of "Charity and social life." London, Charity Organization Society, 1938.
496 p. illus.

First ed. published in 1910 under title: Charity and social life.

1. Charity. 2. Charity organization. 3. Charities - G. Brit. I. Title. II. Title: Charity and social life.

NL 0433033 NbU LU

VOLUME 337

LOCH, DAVID, d. 1780.
A curious and entertaining collection of letters, concerning the politics of Edinburgh, and some hints as to the trade of Scotland; particularly the woolen and linen manufacturers... With curious observations on some political schemes, transmitted to the printer by several gentlemen. Likeways, a plan to the public, in order to reduce the prices of all the necessaries of life. Edinburgh, 1774. 34 p. 23cm.
1. Wool--Trade and stat.--Gt. Br.--Scotland. 2. Linen--Trade and stat.--Gt. Br.--Scotland. I. Title.

NL 0433034 NN

Loch, David, *d.* 1780.
Essay on the trade, commerce, and manufactures of Scotland. By David Loch ... Edinburgh, Printed for the author, 1775.
2 p. l., vii, 92 p. 22½cm.

1. Scotland—Econ. condit.
10-12188
Library of Congress HC257.S4L7

NL 0433035 DLC CLU CtY OClW MH-BA MiU-C NjP

Loch, David, *d.* 1780.
Essays on the trade, commerce, manufactures, and fisheries of Scotland; containing, remarks on the situation of most of the sea-ports; the number of shipping employed; their tonnage: strictures on the principal inland towns; the different branches of trade and commerce carried on; and the various improvements made in each: hints and observations on the constitutional police; with many other curious and interesting articles never yet published. By. David Loch ... Edinburgh, Printed by W. and T. Ruddiman, for the author, 1778–79.
3 v. 17cm.
1. Scotland—Indus.—Hist. 2. Scotland—Economic conditions.
5-21402†
Library of Congress HC257.S4L8

NL 0433036 DLC MH-BA CtY MiU NN

Loch, David, *d.* 1780.
Letters concerning the trade and manufactures of Scotland; particularly the woolen and linen manufactures. Humbly submitted to the consideration of the honourable convention of the Royal boroughs of Scotland. By David Loch, merchant. Edinburgh, Printed for the author, 1774.
1 p. l., ii, 29 p. 19cm.
1. Scotland—Manufactures.

NL 0433037 MiU PU CtY NN MH-BA

774
L73
Loch, David, d.1780.
Letters concerning the trade and manufactures of Scotland; particularly the woollen and linen manufactures. Humbly submitted to the consideration of the honourable convention of the Royal boroughs of Scotland. 3d ed., with large additions ... Edinburgh, Printed for the author, 1775.
1p.ℓ.,24p. 26x21cm.

NL 0433038 CtY MH-BA

Loch, David, d.1780.
A tour through most of the trading towns and villages of Scotland; containing notes and observations concerning the trade, manufactures, improvements, &c. of these towns and villages. By David Loch. By order of the Honourable Board of trustees for fisheries, manufactures, and improvements in Scotland. Edinburgh, Printed by W. and T. Ruddiman, 1778.
1 p. l., 72 p. 22½cm.
1. Scotland—Description and travel. 2. Scotland—Industry.
A 18—1512
Harvard univ. Library for Library of Congress [a40b1]

NL 0433039 MH

PA
2338
L81
Loch, Eduard, 1840-
De usu alliterationis apud poetas Latinos. Halis Saxonum [1865]
60 p. 20cm.
Inaug.-Diss.--Halle.
Full name: Johann Eduard Loch.
1. Alliteration. 2. Latin language--Metrics and rhythmics.

NL 0433040 NIC MiU NjP

LOCH, Eduard, 1840-
Zum gebrauch des imperativus bei Plautus [Progr.], Memel, 1871.
4°. pp.26. Lp 26.821

NL 0433041 MH MiU PBm CU NIC

PA2185
.L8
Loch, Eduard, 1868-
De genetivi apud priscos scriptores Latinos usu. Bartenstein, 1880.
34 p.
Programm--Gymnasium, Bartenstein.
1. Latin language--Case.

NL 0433042 ICU NjP PU MH NIC

Loch, Eduard, 1868-
De titulis graecis sepulcralibus. ... Regimonti, ex officina Leupoldiana, 1890.
cover-title, 1 l., 62, [2] p. 21½cm.
Inaug.-diss.—Königsberg.
Vita.
1. Inscriptions, Greek.

NL 0433043 MiU CtY CU NIC MH ICRL

Loch, Eduard, 1868-
Geschichte des Corps Masovia 1830-1930
see under title

M1961
.C5 I 5
1934
Loch, Eduard, 1868- ed.
Clericus, Ludwig, 1827–1892, *comp.*
Das illustrierte Liederbuch der Albertina, von Ludwig Clericus. Königsberg i. Pr., 1850. Neu herausgegeben von dr. Eduard Loch. Königsberg Pr., Gräfe und Unzer, 1934

Loch, Elizabeth (Villiers) *baroness, ed.*
Sister Henrietta, C. S. M. and A. A. Bloemfontein. Kimberley. 1874–1911. Ed. by Dowr. Lady Loch and Miss Stockdale. With 2 portraits. London, New York [etc.] Longmans, Green, and co., 1914.
4 p. l., 157 p. 2 port. (incl. front.) 20cm.
Contents.—Home life. [By] C[hristine] S[tockdale]—Account of her death. [By] F. S[tockdale]—Appreciation. [By] Lady Loch.—Extracts from letters.—Diary during the war.—Hospital work in Kimberley. [By] G. A. Hodgson.
1. Stockdale, Henrietta, 1847-1911. I. Stockdale, Christine, joint ed. II. Hodgson, G. A. III. Title.
14-12504

NL 0433046 DLC

MZ54
L787s
[Loch, Elizabeth (Villiers)] baroness
Sketch of women's work in South Africa. Cape Town, Townshend, Taylor & Snashall, printers, 1893.
viii, 86 p. illus., port. 21 cm.
1. Africa, South - Missions. 2. Women - Missions - Africa. I. Title.

NL 0433047 CtY-D

Loch, Eric Erskine, 1891-
... Fever, famine, and gold; the dramatic story of the adventures and discoveries of the Andes-Amazon expedition in the uncharted fastnesses of a lost world in the Llanganatis mountains. New York, G. P. Putnam's sons [c1938]
xiv, 257 p. front., illus. (map) plates, ports. 21½cm.
At head of title: Captain E. Erskine Loch, D. S. O.
Maps on lining-papers.
1. Andes-Amazon expedition, 1935–1937. 2. Ecuador—Descr. & trav. 3. Llanganati. I. Title.
38-22936
Library of Congress F3714.L63
——— Copy 2.
Copyright A 119875 [5-5] 918.6

NL 0433048 DLC CU MH Wa WaS NcC NcD OCl OEac OClh NN

823.912
D361P
Loch, Frederick Sydney.
Pelican pool; a novel. Sydney, Angus & Robertson, 1917.
322 p. 19 cm.
By Sydney De Loghe, pseud.

NL 0433049 NcD HU

D
640
L789s
[Loch, Frederick Sydney]
The straits impregnable, by Sydney De Loghe [pseud.] Melbourne, Australasian Authors Agency, 1916.
212 p.
1. European War, 1914-1918 - Personal narratives, Australian. 2. European War, 1914-1918 - Campaigns - Turkey and the Near East - Gallipoli.

NL 0433050 CLU NcD TxU MiU

Loch, Frederick Sydney.
The Straits impregnable, by Sydney De Loghe. London, J. Murray, 1917.
viii, 298 p. 20 cm.
1. European War, 1914-1918—Personal narratives, English. I. Title.
D640.L62 17-12512 rev

NL 0433051 DLC KU WU NcU NjP

Loch, Gerhard: Ueber die Kombination von Pancreascarcinom mit Pancreasatrophie m. bes. Berücks. d. Frage d. Auftretens von Diabetes mellitus b. Pancreascarcinom. Aus d. med. Universitätskl. zu Breslau. [In Maschinenschrift.] 29, 10 S. 4°(2°). — Auszug: Breslau 1921: Breslauer Genossensch.-Buchdr. 2 Bl. 8°
Breslau, Med. Diss. v. 25. Juni 1921, Ref. Minkowski
[Geb. 5. Jan. 94 Zaumgarten, Kr. Breslau; Wohnort: Breslau; Staatsangeh.: Preußen; Vorbildung: König Wilhelm-G. Breslau Reife 14; Studium: Breslau 14 S.; Coll. 22. Juli 20; Approb. 31. Mai 21.] [U 21. 3002

NL 0433052 ICRL

VOLUME 337

Loch, Gordon, 1887–
The family of Loch by Gordon Loch. Edinburgh, Priv. print. by T. and A. Constable ltd., 1934.
xxviii, 517 p. plates, ports., fold. plan, map, facsims. (part double) fold. geneal. tables, col. coats of arms. 29cm.
"This edition is limited to 111 copies, of which this copy is no. 70." Plates accompanied by guard sheets with descriptive letter-press.

1. Loch family.
[Full name: Percy Gordon Loch]
34-35185
Library of Congress CS479.L73
[2] 929.2

NL 0433053 DLC NcD

E 7 L 783 LOCH, GORDON, 1887–
The family of Loch. Edinburgh, T. and A. Constable, 1934.
2 v. illus., facsims., geneal. tables. 29cm.

Xerox copy.

NL 0433054 ICN

DS757 .5 .L65 LOCH, GRANVILLE GOWER, 1813-1853.
The closing events of the campaign in China: the operations in the Yang-Tze-Kiang; and the treaty of Nanking. By Capt. Granville G. Loch... London, J. Murray, 1843.
xii, 227, [1] p. fold. map. 20½cm.

1. China--Hist.--War of 1840-1842. 2. China--Descr. & trav.

NL 0433055 PPL FTaSU CU NIC ICN ICU CoU MiU CtY MSaE NcD NN CtY MH PU

Loch, Granville Gower, 1813-1853.
Letzte Ereignisse des Feldzuges in China mit statistischen und sittenschildernden Beobachtungen. Nachtrag zu dem "Krieg in China" von C. Richard. Aachen, J. A. Mayer, 1844.
vii, 176 p. 23cm.

1. China—Hist.—War of 1840-1842. I. Richard, C. Der Krieg in China. II. Title.

NL 0433056 MB MnU

Loch, Hans.
Auf seltsamen Pfaden; Streifzüge durch das Russland von gestern und heute. Berlin, Verlag Kultur und Fortschritt, 1955.
290 p. illus. 21 cm.

1. Russia—Descr. & trav.—1945– I. Title.

DK28.L54 56-29131 ‡

NL 0433057 DLC DS NN NNC

Loch, Hans.
Auferstehung einzigartiger Kunst durch edle Freundestat. [1. Aufl.] Berlin, Verlag Kultur und Fortschritt, 1955.
51 p. illus. 21 cm.

1. Dresden. Gemälde-Galerie. 2. Paintings—Exhibitions. 3. World War, 1939-1945—Art and the war. I. Title.

N2280.L6 56-43330 ‡

NL 0433058 DLC MH

Loch, Hans.
Ein Bürger sieht die Sowjetunion. Leipzig, P. List [1953]
197 p. illus. 20 cm.

1. Russia—Descr. & trav.—1945– I. Title.

DK28.L55 914.7 54-15186 ‡

NL 0433059 DLC NN NNC

DD257 .25 .L6 Loch, Hans.
Entscheidende Tage. Berlin, Verlag Kultur und Fortschritt, 1953.
90 p. illus., ports. 21 cm.

1. German reunification question (1949–) 2. Germany (Democratic Republic, 1949–)—Relations (general) with Russia. 3. Russia—Relations (general) with Germany (Democratic Republic, 1949–) I. Title.

A 54-5311

Wisconsin. Univ. Libr. for Library of Congress [1]

NL 0433060 WU MH NN DLC

Loch, Hans.
Mit Bleistift und Kamera durch den russischen Alltag. Berlin, Verlag Kultur und Fortschritt, 1954.
352 p. illus. 22 cm.

1. Russia—Descr. & trav.—1945– I. Title.

DK28.L56 55-16458 ‡

NL 0433061 DLC NN NNC

Loch, Henry Brougham Loch, *baron*, 1827-1900.
... Basutoland. Report by Sir H. B. Loch of his visit to Basutoland in April 1890; with a despatch from the Secretary of State ... London, Printed for H. M. Stationery Off. by Eyre and Spottiswoode, 1890.
12 p. 33cm. ([Great Britain. Colonial Office] Her Majesty's colonial possessions. no. 102)
Numbered also as Papers by command <C.-5897.-82> In Sessional papers of the House of Commons, 1890, v. 48.

NL 0433062 ICJ MdBP

951.034 L787 LOCH, Henry Brougham Loch, baron, 1827-
Personal narrative of occurrences during Lord Elgin's second embassy to China, 1860. London, J. Murray, 1869.
viii, 298 p. illus., port., map. 20cm.

1. China. History. 1857-1861. 2. Elgin, James Bruce, 8th earl of, 1811-1863. I. Title.

NL 0433063 NIC CU MnU MB MdBJ MnU MdBP ODW OC1W MSaE InU

Loch, Henry Brougham Loch, *baron.*
Personal narrative of occurrences during Lord Elgin's second embassy to China in 1860. By the late Henry Brougham Loch (Lord Loch) ... 3d ed., with illustrations, and a preface by Lady Loch. London, J. Murray, 1900.
xii, 185 p. front. (port.) 2 pl., fold. map. 20½cm.

1. China—Hist.—Foreign intervention, 1857-1861. 2. Elgin, James Bruce, 8th earl of, 1811-1863.

Library of Congress DS760.L81 1-13223

NL 0433064 PPL OCl MiU DLC NcD DN FTaSU CoU CSt-H GU NBC CaBVaU

[Loch, James, 1780-1855.
An account of the improvements on the estate of Sutherland, belonging to the Marquis and Marchioness of Stafford. London, Printed by E. Macleish, 1815.
20 p. 23cm.

NL 0433065 NNC

Loch, James, 1780-1855.
An account of the improvements on the estates of the Marquess of Stafford, in the counties of Stafford and Salop, and on the estate of Sutherland. With remarks. By James Loch, esquire. London: Longman, Hurst, Rees, Orme, and Brown, 1820. xx, 236, 118 p. incl. front., fold. maps, plates (part fold.). 8°.

1. Agriculture, Gt. Br.: England: Staffordshire. 2. Agriculture, Gt. Br.: England: Salop. 3. Agriculture, Gt. Br.: Scotland: Sutherland.
N. Y. P. L. July 2, 1919.

NL 0433066 NN DNAL MH-BA ICU MH NcD MdBP IEN CtY

Loch, James, 1780-1855.
Brougham and his early friends. Letters to James Loch, 1798-1809
see under Brougham and Vaux, Henry Peter Brougham, baron, 1773-1868.

Loch, James, 1780-1855.
Dates and documents relating to the family and property of Sutherland extracted chiefly from the originals in the Charter room at Dunrobin. not pub. 1859.
73 p.

NL 0433068 OClWHi

Loch, James, 1780-1855.
Memoir of George Granville, late duke of Sutherland, K. G.; by James Loch ... London, 1834.
83 p. front. (port.) illus., pl. 33cm.
Not published.

1. Sutherland, George Granville Leveson Gower, 1st duke of, 1758-1833.

Library of Congress DA880.S96L8 5-659†

NL 0433069 DLC MH-BA CaBVaU CtY OClWHi ViU NcD NN

Loch, Johann Eduard.
see Loch, Eduard, 1840-

Loch, Joice Mary Nankivell, 1893-
The fourteen thumbs of St. Peter, by Joice M. Nankivell. London, J. Murray [1926]
320 p. 19½ cm.

1. Russia—History—Revolution, 1917-1921—Fiction. I. Title.

PZ3.L7799Fo 27-1585

NL 0433071 DLC

Loch, Joice Mary Nankivell, 1893-
The fourteen thumbs of St. Peter, by Joice M. Nankivell. New York, E. P. Dutton & company [1927]
xii, 308 p. 19½ cm.

1. Russia—History—Revolution, 1917-1921—Fiction. I. Title.

PZ3.L7799Fo 3 27-3016

NL 0433072 DLC

VOLUME 337

Loch, Joice Mary Nankivell, 1893-
Ireland in travail, by Joice M. Nankivell ... and Sydney Loch ... London, J. Murray, 1922.
viii, 304 p. 19½ cm.

1. Ireland—Hist.—1910-1921. 2. Sinn Fein. I. Loch, Sydney, joint author. II. Title.

DA962.L58 22-20134 rev 2

NL 0433073 DLC

Loch, Joice Mary Nankivell, 1893-

[House, *Mrs.* Susan Adeline (Beers)] 1850-
A life for the Balkans; the story of John Henry House of the American farm school, Thessaloniki, Greece, as told by his wife to J. M. Nankivell, with an introduction by John H. Finley. New York [etc.] Fleming H. Revell company [°1939]

Loch, Joice Mary Nankivell, 1893-
The river of a hundred ways; life in the war-devastated areas of eastern Poland, by Joice M. Nankivell and Sydney Loch ... London, G. Allen & Unwin ltd. [1924]
256 p. 19 cm.
"This book does not try to give a history of the work of the Society of Friends' relief mission in Poland. It aims, instead, at giving a glimpse of the field, the ups and downs in a Mission member's day."—p. 9.

1. Reconstruction (1914-1939) — Poland. 2. Friends, Society of. I. Loch, Sydney, joint author. II. Title.

DK440.L6 25-7386 rev 2

NL 0433075 DLC

Loch, Joice Mary Nankivell, 1893-
Tales of Christophilos; illustrated by Panos Ghikas. Boston, Houghton Mifflin, 1954.
119 p. illus. 24 cm.

I. Title.

PZ9.L78Tal 53-10988

NL 0433076 DLC

Loch, M.G., tr.
The growth of modern nations; a history of the particularist form of society
see under Tourville, Henri de, 1843?-1903

Lbb89 D7 931l
Loch, Max, 1899-
Über Eidetik und Kinderzeichnung ... Ochsenfurt, a.M., 1931.
101p.,1l. 11pl.on 6l. 22½cm
Inaug.-Diss. - München.
Lebenslauf.
"Literatur": p.99-100.

NL 0433078 CtY PU CU

Loch, Otto, 1906-
... Welche gynäkologischen Erkrankungen sind die wichtigsten für die Tätigkeit des praktischen Arztes? ... [n.p., 1933].
Inaug.-Diss. - Leipzig.
Lebenslauf.
"Literatur": p. 13.

NL 0433079 CtY

Loch, Philipp
Charles Sorel als literarischer kritiker... Würzburg, Mayr, 1933.
70 p.

NL 0433080 PBm CtY PU

Loch (Rudolf). *Ein Fall von Neuroma verum nervi optici. [Greifswald.] 31 pp. 8°. *Danzig, A. W. Kafemann.* [1874].

NL 0433081 DNLM

Loch, Sophy, joint ed.

Jones, Emily G.
A manual of plain needlework and cutting-out, by the late Emily G. Jones ... Rev. (September 1896) by Miss Heath and Miss Loch ... with original plates and illustrations. New impression. London, New York and Bombay, Longmans, Green, and co., 1899.

Loch, Sophy, joint author.

Longman, Eleanor D.
Pins and pincushions, by E. D. Longman and S. Loch ... With 43 plates. London, New York [etc.] Longmans, Green and co., 1911.

BX 385 A8 L6
Loch, Sydney
Athos: the holy mountain. New York, Nelson [n.d.]
264 p. illus.

1. Athos (Monasteries) I. Title.

NL 0433084 CaBVaU

DA962 .L58
Loch, Sydney, joint author.

Loch, Joice Mary Nankivell, 1893-
Ireland in travail, by Joice M. Nankivell ... and Sydney Loch ... London, J. Murray, 1922.

DK440 .L6
Loch, Sydney, joint author.

Loch, Joice Mary Nankivell, 1893-
The river of a hundred ways; life in the war-devastated areas of eastern Poland, by Joice M. Nankivell and Sydney Loch ... London, G. Allen & Unwin ltd. [1924]

Loch, Sydney.
Three predatory women, by Sydney Loch. London, G. Allen & Unwin ltd. [1925]
316 p.

NL 0433087 MiU CtY

Loch, Sydney.
Three predatory women, by Sydney Loch. New York, George H. Doran company [°1926]
vi p., 1 l., 9-297 p. 19½cm.

I. Title.
Library of Congress PZ3.L78Th 26-3572

NL 0433088 OrPR OrP OrCS MtU MtBC IdU Wa CaBVaU IdB WaPS WaS WaSp WaSpG WaT WaTC WaWW OrU DLC OrU-M OrSaW OrStbM Or OCl IdPI WaE

Loch, Valentin, 1813-1893, ed
Biblia sacra vulgatae editionis... Edidit Valentinus Loch. Ratisbonae, 1849
see under
Bible. Latin. 1849. Vulgate.

Later editions by Loch were published 1862-1863, 1863, 1873, 1883, 1888, 1895, 1899, 1902, 1903. (1872)

NL 0433089

Loch, Valentin, 1813-1893, tr.
Die Heiligen Schriften des alten und Neuen Testamentes

see

Bible. German. 1851. Loch
and other editions indicated by addition of the name of Loch after the date in the heading.

PA 2822 L81
Loch, Valentin, 1813-1893.
Materialen zu einer lateinischen Grammatik der Vulgata. Bamberg, Druck der W. Gärtner'schen Officin. [1870]
34 p. 22cm.

Accompanies "Programm" (Jahresbericht)-- K. Bayer. Lyceum, Gymnasium und Lateinische Schule, Bamberg.

NL 0433091 NIC NjP

Loch, Valentin, 1813-1893, ed.
Novum Testamentum...Ratisbonae, 1862
see under
Bible. N.T. Latin. 1862. Vulgate.

and later editions edited by Loch.

Loch, Valentin, 1813-1893.
'Hē palaia diathēkē kata tous hebdomēkonta. Vetus Testamentum graece...edidit...Valentinus Loch. Ratisbonae, G. J. Manz, 1866
see under Bible. O.T. Greek. 1866. Septuagint. (also 1886)

Loch, Valentin, 1813-1893.
Perikopenbuch, oder Sammlung der Episteln und Evangelien auf alle Sonntage... [in the Loch-Röschl translation] Regensburg, 1896
see under Bible. N.T. Epistles and Gospels, Liturgical. German. 1896. Loch.

Loch, Valentin, 1813-1893, ed.

Bible. *N.T. John. Latin. 1877. Vulgate.*
Sanctum Jesu Christi Evangelium secundum Joannem. Ad usum scholarum notis illustravit professor quidam Seminarii Dominae Nostrae Angelorum ... [Suspension Bridge, N. Y.] sumtibus et typis ephemeridis Niagara index dictae, 1877.

VOLUME 337

Loch, William Adam, *b.* 1814.
A practical legal guide for sailors and merchants during war. With appendices containing the orders in council, and other official documents relating to the present war. By William Adam Loch ... London, Longman, Brown, Green, and Longmans, 1854.
2 p. l., [viii]-xii, 277, [1] p. 22cm.

1. War, Maritime (International law)

10-20063

Library of Congress JX5211.L7

NL 0433096 DLC NN DN MdBP

W 4 B51 1939 **Loch, Wolfgang,** 1915-
Über die Bedeutung verschiedener Substrate für den Ablauf des Erregungsstoffwechsels am Speicheldrüsengewebe. Berlin, Hammer, 1939.
22 p. illus.

Inaug.-Diss. - Berlin.
Bibliography: p. 22.

NL 0433097 DNLM

Loch Etive and the sons of Uisnach
see under Smith, Robert Angus, 1817-1884

Loch Garman, Ire. (County)
see Wexford, Ire. (County)

Loch Garman. Baile Átha Cliath, Oifig an tSoláthair [1945]
viii, 187 p. (Stair na gComndae, 6)

NL 0433100 MH

LOCH Lein; irisleabar míosamail. Cill Airne.
24 x 18.5 cm.
Illustr.
Book I, no.1-[11; II, 1-3] (Jan.-Jun., Aug.-Dec.1903; Mar., May, July 1904)
No more published.
"Henceforth "Loc Léin" will appear in the first week of each alternate month." Banba. Mar.1904 issue.

NL 0433101 MH

Loch Lomond and the Firth of Clyde. Issued with the approval and co-operation of the Dunbartonshire Development Board. London, Century Press [1952?]
30 p. illus. 19 cm.

1. Clyde, Firth of. 2. Lomond, Loch.

DA880.C6L67 914.141 52-41069 ‡

NL 0433102 DLC

Loch Lomond: chromo views and guide book. Lond., Nelson, n.d.
21 p. illus. map, S.
I. Scotland-Description & travel.

NL 0433103 NcU

Loch Raven, Md. Training school for boys
see
Maryland. Training school for boys, Loch Raven.

---

*BROADSIDE 1860 (1954) .L63 Loch Willow School, Augusta Co., Va.
[Program and circular. Staunton, Va., 1860]
broadsides (2 pieces) various sizes.
Photocopy (negatives) made in 1954 by the Univ. of Virginia Library from the originals in the McCue family papers.
Jed. Hotchkiss, Principal.

1. Private schools—Va.—Augusta Co. I. Hotchkiss, Jedediah, 1827-1899.

NL 0433105 ViU

Lochaber A much admired Song with an Accompanyment for the Harp or Piano Forte. Dublin. Published by B. Cooke at his Piano Forte and Music Warehouse No.4. Sackville Street

First line: Farewell to Lochaber and farewell my Jean

(IN English popular music of the 1790's)
784.8 E58 Library Assoc. of Portland (Oregon)

NL 0433106 OrP MBHM

Lochaber. A two part song [M.-S., Bar.]. Set for the German flute [and pianoforte].
[London? 1750?] (1) p. 32½ cm.

K3279 — Duets. Vocal.

NL 0433107 MB

Lochac, Emmanuel, 1886-1956.
La bouteille dans le vide. Aigues-Vives (Gard) Marsyas, 1954.
22 p. 20 cm.

1. Aphorisms and apothegms. I. Title.

A 55-4430

Illinois. Univ. Library for Library of Congress [3]

NL 0433108 IU

Lochac, Emmanuel, 1886-1956.
...Hier nous attend... Aigues-Vives, Marsyas, 1946. 86 p. 19cm.

Poems.

NL 0433109 NN

PQ 2623 .O23 O5 Lochac, Emmanuel, 1886-1956.
L'Oiseau sur la pyramide; tercets. Préface de Jean Royère. Paris, A. Messein, 1924.
70 p. 19cm. (Collection La phalange)

NL 0433110 NNC NcD

LOCHAC, Emmanuel, 1886-1956.
Le promenoir des élégies. Paris, A. Messein, 1929.

pp.62.
"Collection la Phalange."

NL 0433111 MH NcD

M2 .L78q **Lochamer** Liederbuch.
Die einstimmigen Weisen des Lochamer Liederbuches. Nach der Quelle bearb. und zum Singen und Spielen mit Begleitstimmen hrsg. von Ernst Rohloff. Halle (Saale) Mitteldeutscher Verlag [1953]
score(54 p.) and part. 30 cm.

I. Rohloff, Ernst Franz 1884- ed.

NL 0433112 NjP

Lochamer Liederbuch.
Das Locheimer Liederbuch. I. T.: Die mehrstimmigen Sätze, hrsg. von Konrad Ameln. Augsburg, Bärenreiter Verlag [c1925]
score (32 p.) 19 x 26 cm. (Deutsche Liedsätze des fünfzehnten Jahrhunderts für Singstimmen und Melodieinstrumente, Bd. 1)
No more published.
For 2-3 voices.

1. Part-songs, German—To 1800. I. Ameln, Konrad, 1899- ed. II. Series.

M2.L782 M 61-2227
—— —— Copy 2. ML30.4c no. 2274 Miller

NL 0433113 DLC NN

FILM MS M786.8 L78l Lochamer Liederbuch.
[Locheimer Liederbuch and the Fundamentum organisandi of Conrad Paumann, both in German organ tablature]
score([2], 92p.) [2]p.
For modern transcription cf. Chrysander, Jahrbücher, II, 1-234.
Microfilm of Ms. 40613. Kassel, Musikeschichtliches Archiv, 1967. 1 reel. 35mm.

NL 0433114 IU

Lochamer liederbuch
Das Locheimer liederbuch, nebst der Ars organisandi von Conrad Baumann, als documente des deutschen liedes sowie des frühesten geregelten contrapunktes und der ältesten instrumentalmusik aus den urschriften kritisch bearb. von Friedrich Wilhelm Arnold. 234, [v]-viii p. [Leipzig, 1864]

Caption-title.
With help by Heinrich Bellermann and Friedrich Chrysander.

NL 0433115 OCl

PT1163 .A2L8 **Lochamer liederbuch.**
Das Locheimer liederbuch nebst der Ars organisandi von Conrad Paumann; als dokumente des deutschen liedes sowie des frühesten geregelten kontrapunktes und der ältesten instrumentalmusik aus den urschriften kritisch bearb. von Friedrich Wilhelm Arnold ... Leipzig, Breitkopf & Härtel, 1926.
iv, 234 p. illus., 3 facsim. 23½cm.

"Neudruck aus den 'Jahrbüchern für musikalische wissenschaft' (Friedr. Chrysander) II. bd. 1867."
An edition of the Codex z b. 14 of the Fürstlich Stolbergsche bibliothek, Wernigerode.
CONTENTS.—Einleitung.—Das Locheimer liederbuch uebertragen und bearb. von Fr. W. Arnold und Heinrich Bellermann.—Conrad Paumann's Fundamentum organisandi. Aus der tabulatur übertragen von F. W. Arnold. Revidiert von Heinrich Bellermann.—Nachwort der herausgeber Fr. Chrysander und H. Bellermann.

1. Songs, German. 2. Organ music.

NL 0433117 ICU MiDW MH InU MoU NIC

VOLUME 337

Lochamer liederbuch.
Das Locheimer liederbuch nebst der Ars organisandi von Conrad Paumann; als dokumente des deutschen liedes sowie des frühesten geregelten kontrapunktes und der ältesten instrumentalmusik aus den urschriften kritisch bearb. von Friedrich Wilhelm Arnold ... Leipzig, Breitkopf & Härtel, 1926.
iv, 234 p. illus., 3 facsim. 23½cm.
Photocopy.

NL 0433118 ICU NjP

784.4943 L812 1926 Lochamer Liederbuch.
Locheimer Liederbuch, Neudeutsche Fassung von Karl Escher, Bearbeitung der Melodien von Walter Lott. Leipzig, Steingraber, 1926
94 p. music. 21 cm.

1. Locheimer Liederbuch. 2. Folk-songs, German. 3. Songs, German. I. Escher, Karl. II. Lott, Walter. III. Title.

NL 0433119 ICarbS NIC ICU

Lochamer Liederbuch.
Locheimer Liederbuch und Fundamentum Organisandi des Conrad Paumann, in Faksimiledruck hrsg. von Konrad Ameln. Berlin, Wölbing-verlag, 1925.
92, 24 p. illus., facsims. plates. 25 cm.
"Der Kodex Zb. 14 der Fürstlich Stolbergschen Bibliothek."
"Es wurde eine einmalige Vorzugsausgabe von 300 numerierten Exemplaren in Lederband, die übrige Auflage von 700 Exemplaren in Halbpergament angefertigt."
"Literatur-Nachweis": p. 16.
1. Part-songs, German—To 1800. 2. Organ music—To 1800. I. Paumann, Conrad, 1410 (ca.)-1473. II. Ameln, Konrad, 1899- III. Wernigerode. Fürstlich Stolberg. Wernigerödische Bibliothek. MSS. (Zb. 14)
M2.L78 26-7775

OOxM OC1W OO MB
NL 0433120 DLC CaBVaU FTaSU NIC WaU MiU WaU CtY

M2 .L76 Lochamer Liederbuch.
Locheimer Liederbuch und Fundamentum Organisandi des Conrad Paumann. In Faksimiledruck hrsg. von Konrad Ameln. Kassel, Bärenreiter [1925?]
facsim. (92p.), 24p. illus. 24cm.
"Der Kodex Zb.14 der Fürstlich Stolbergschen Bibliothek in Wernigerode."
Bibliography: p.16.

NL 0433121 NcU RPB NcRS

Lochan Prasad Kavya-vinod
see
Kavya-vinod, Lochan Prasad, *pandit.*

Lochana-prāsada Kavyavinoda
see
Kavya-vinod, Lochan Prasad, *pandit.*

WZ 240 L812j 1585 LOCHANDER, Martinus, fl. 1584
Julianum hospitale, arte rara, singulari pietate, immensoque sumtu a ... domino Julio Dei gratia episcopo Wirtzburgensi ... anno ... millesimo, quingentesimo septuagesimo sexto, quarto non. Martii in pauperum usus ... extructum, carmine adumbratum a M. Martino Lochandro Gorliciense Silesio. Wirtzburgi, Ex officina Henrici Aquensis, 1585.
[7], 40 p. illus. 20 cm.
With this are bound: Mermann von Schönburg, Thomas. Ad reverendum ... Wolfgangum Theodoricum de Hutten. Ingolstadii, 1573. —Engerd, Johann. Congratulatio inscripta pietate ... reverendo ... Joanni Baptistae Riednero.

Continued in next column

Continued from preceding column

Ingolstadii, 1574. —Carmina gratulatoria ... diversis autoribus inscripta reverendo ... Joanni Baptistae Ridnero. Ingolstadii, 1575. —Gasser, Petrus. Elegia de lapsu primorum parentum tristissimo. Friburgi Brisgoiae, 1574.

NL 0433125 DNLM

Lochandhu, a tale of the eighteenth century
see under [Lauder, Sir Thomas Dick] bart., 1784-1848.

Lochard, A
... A propos de l'organisation de la production en économie stalinienne. Paris, Recueil Sirey [1945]
60 p. 25½cm.

1. Russia—Economic policy. 2. Economic policy. I. Title.
HC335.L64 47-16744

NL 0433127 DLC NNUN NN IU

Lochard (Gustave). *Étude sur les positions occipito-postérieures. 57 pp., 1 l. 4°. *Paris, 1881, No. 243.*

NL 0433128 DNLM

Bonaparte Collection No.3093 LOCHARD, JOSEPH.
Éphémérides du Béarn et du pays basque... Paris, Dumoulin, 1866.
192p. 23½cm.

Author's autograph presentation copy.

NL 0433129 ICN

DC 195 B36 L81 Lochard, Joseph, ed.
Quelques pages d'un manuscrit sous la Terreur en Béarn, 1793-1794, documents inédits des archives des Basses-Pyrénées. Paris, E. Lechevalier, 1893.
viii, 220 p. 21cm.

1. Béarn, France--Hist. 2. France--Hist.--Revolution--1793-1794.

NL 0433130 NIC MH

Lochard, Paul, 1835-1919.
Les chants du soir, poésies. Paris, Impr. typographique Kugelmann, 1878.

210p. 18cm.

With this is bound: Rose, S. L. Les soupirs. Paris, 1884.

I. Title. II. Rose, Samuel Luzincourt, 1857- Les soupirs.

NL 0433131 FU

Lochard, Paul, 1835-1919.
... Les feuilles de chêne. Paris, Ateliers haïtiens, 1901.
2 p. l., [7]-190, [2] p. 22cm.
"Préface" (p. [7]-22) signed: A. Firmin.

I. Firmin, Anténor, 1850-1911. II. Title. 25—20873
Library of Congress PQ3949.L6F4

NL 0433132 DLC FU NN DHU

Lochart, Arthur John.
The masque of minstrels, and other pieces, chiefly in verse by two brothers. Bangor, 1887.
361 p. 2 por. D.
Presentation copy with author's signature.
By A.J. & B.W. Lochart.

NL 0433133 RPB

Lochart, Hamilton

76 L8124t Harris Collection The true republican; or, A dialogue between the king and the farmer; by way of argument ... and a second dialogue between the farmer and his wife, after his escape from the king and his nobles ... by Hamilton Lochart, School-master, Sadsbury township, Chester county [Pa.] [n.p.] Printed for the author, 1806.
vi, 153p. 17 cm.

1. Dialogues. I. Title.

NL 0433134 RPB

Lochbihler, Christian.
Der wohlerfahrene thier-arzt, als heilender, berathender und warnender freund bei allen krankheiten und lähmungen der ... pferde und maulthiere ... Mit einem anhange versehen. Hrsg. von Christian Lochbihler ... 1. aufl. ... St. Louis, Mo., 1878.
1 p. l., ii, [7]-299, [2] p. illus. 23½cm.

1. Horse—Diseases.
Library of Congress SF953.L8 CA 17-2335 Unrev'd

NL 0433135 DLC

Lochbrunner, Emil
Veränderungen des blutbildes durch röntgenstrahlen.

Inaugural dissertation, Universitat zu München, 1933.

NL 0433136 PPWI CtY

Lochbrunner (Franz Jos.) *Ueber die Eklampsie der Schwangeren, Gebärenden und Wöchnerinnen. 46 pp. 8°. *München, C. Wolf u. Sohn, 1875.*

NL 0433137 DNLM

Lochbrunner, Margarete (Paulenbach) 1892-
Dantes Weg durch die drei Seelenreiche; eine Einführung in die Göttliche Komödie. Marburg-Lahn, Simons Verlag, 1948.
64 p. (Schriften der Deutschen Dantegesellschaft, 8)

NL 0433138 MH RPB IU

Lochbrunner, Siegfried, 1921-
Abschreibung und Finanzierung. München, 1951.
137, [23] l. col. diagrs. 30 cm.
Typescript (carbon copy)
Inaug.-Diss.—Munich.
Vita.
Bibliography: leaves [1]-[4] at end.

1. Depreciation. I. Title.
HG4028.D4L6 56-17778

NL 0433139 DLC

Lochbrunner-Paulenbach, Margarete, 1892-
see Lochbrunner, Margarete (Paulenbach) 1892-

VOLUME 337

Lochbühler, Josef
Ist die resistenz isolierter roter blutkörperchen gegen strahlenwirkung (sichtbare und ultraviolette strahlen) durch vorbehandlung des ganzen tieres mit arzneimitteln beeinflussbar?

Inaugural dissertation, 1932.

NL 0433141 PPWl CtY

Loche. Précis sur le nouveau traitement des maladies des yeux. 63 pp. 8°. *Londres*, 1783.

NL 0433142 DNLM

Loche (Charles) [1865–]. *Essai sur le traitement des affections de l'estomac et du duodénum. 86 pp. 4°. *Paris*, 1893, No. 302. —— The same. 86 pp. 8°. *Paris, G. Steinheil*, 1893.

NL 0433143 DNLM

Loche (Fernand). *Des indications de l'accouchement prématuré artificiel et des moyens de le provoquer. 47 pp. 4°. *Paris*, 1863, No. 162.

NL 0433144 DNLM PPC

LOCHE, Gustave Gabriel.
Histoire naturelle des mammifères. (Exploration scientifique de l'Algérie, etc. - Sciences physiques, 1867, 4°, Zoologie) 7 col. plates.

NL 0433145 MH-Z NN

LOCHE, Gustave Gabriel.
Histoire naturelle des oiseaux. (Exploration scientifique de l'Algérie, etc. - Sciences physiques, 1867, 4°, Zoologie.)

15 col. plates.

NL 0433146 MH-Z NN

Loche, Jules, comte de Mouxy de
see Mouxy de Loche, Jules, comte de.

Loche, L E.
Des mécanismes élémentaires, par L.-E. Loche ... ouvrage illustré de 395 figures. Paris, H. Dunod et E. Pinat, 1919.
3 p. l., [iii]–xii, 257, [1] p. illus., diagrs. 21½cm. fr. 10

1. Machinery, Kinematics of. I. Title.
19–18315
Library of Congress TJ175.L6

NL 0433148 DLC PPF ICJ

Loche, L E 621.81 S002
Théorie simplifiée des mécanismes élémentaires, par L.-E. Loche, 14661 ... Ouvrage illustré de 160 figures. Paris, Dunod, 1920.
xi, 172 p. diagrs. 21½cm.

NL 0433149 ICJ

Loche, Victor Jean François, 1806–1863.
Catalogue des mammifères et des oiseaux observés en Algérie. Par le capitaine Loche. Rédigé d'après la classification de S. A. le prince Charles-Lucien Bonaparte.
Paris. Bertrand. [1858.] xi, 158 pp. 21½ cm., in 8s.

L3292 — Algeria. Zool. — Mammalia. — Ornithology.

NL 0433150 MB IU ICF-A

LOCHEAD, D C
Bovine tuberculosis in humans ... paper read before the second annual midwest tuberculosis conference at Omaha, Nebraska, June 29, 1926. Springfield, State, 1926.
20 p.

NL 0433151 Or

448
L78 Lochead, D C
Bovine tuberculosis in humans. Springfield, Dept. of Agriculture, 1927.
20 p.

1. Tuberculosis of bovine origin. I. Illinois. Dept. of Agriculture.

NL 0433152 DNAL

Lochead, John H[utchison], 1909–
Control of swimming position by mechanical factors and proprioception. N.p. Quarterly review of biology, 1942.
pp. 12-30, diagrs. O.

NL 0433153 CaBViP

Lochead, William.
Observations on the natural history of Guiana: in a letter to the Rev. Dr. Walker.
(*In* Royal society of Edinburgh Transactions. Edniburgh, 1798. 28cm v. 4, pt. 2, 1, p. 41-63)

CA 5—331 Unrev'd
Library of Congress Q41.E2 vol. 4

NL 0433154 DLC OCl

Lochée (Alfred) [1811–90]. An address to the students of the Missionary College of Saint Augustine, Canterbury, preparatory to their commencing the study of practical medicine. 2. ed. 24 pp. 8°. *Canterbury, College Press*, 1856. [P., v. 2192.]
For Biography, see Brit. M. J., Lond., 1890, i, 1108.

NL 0433155 DNLM

WX
L812d
1841 **Lochée, Alfred, 1811-1890.**
A descriptive and tabular report of the medical and surgical cases treated in the Kent and Canterbury Hospital, from Oct. 16, 1838, to Oct. 16, 1840. Canterbury, Kentish Observer, 1841.
85 p.
1. Kent and Canterbury Hospital, Canterbury, Eng.

NL 0433156 DNLM

WX
L812d
1842 LOCHÉE, Alfred, 1811-1890
A descriptive and tabular report of the medical and surgical cases treated in the Kent and Canterbury Hospital, from Oct. 16, 1840, to June 1, 1842, with remarks upon its present condition and future prospects, illustrated by tables of expenditure, &c., and preceded by an essay on the origin and progress of hospitals, for the sick, from the earliest times. Canterbury, Kentish Observer Office, 1842.

125 p.
1. Canterbury, Eng. Kent and Canterbury Hospital

NL 0433158 DNLM

Lochée, Lewis.
Elements of field fortification. By Lewis Lochée ... London, The author, sold by T. Cadell [etc.] 1783.
xiii, 164 p. VII fold. pl. 21½cm.

1. Fortification, Field.
18–17957
Library of Congress UG403.L8

NL 0433159 DLC NcU NN

U
26
.516 LOCHÉE, LEWIS.
Elements of fortification. London, The author, 1780.
xxvi, 221p. fold. illus. 24cm.

NL 0433160 ICN

Lochée, Lewis.
An essay on castrametation. By Lewis Lochée ... London, The author, sold by T. Cadell, 1778.
v, [2], 78 p. IX fold. pl. 21½cm. [With his Elements of field fortification. London, 1783]

1. Camps (Military)
18–17959
Library of Congress UG403.L81

NL 0433161 DLC MiU

Lochée, Lewis.
An essay on military education. By Lewis Lochée, master of the Military academy, Little Chelsea ... 2d ed London, Printed for the author, sold by T. Cadell, 1776.
2 p. l., 106 p. 20½cm.
"Sketch of the ... principles of righteous government, and of the British constitution... chiefly taken from a celebrated writer": p. 78–106.

1. Military education. 2. Gt. Brit.—Pol. & govt.
18–12966
Library of Congress U404.L6

NL 0433162 DLC CSt ViW

949.3
L812h.3 Lochée, Lewis.
Histoire de la dernière Revolution Belgique. 3. éd. Lille, J. Roelenbosch, 1791.
91, 27p. 24cm.

"La justification du Général de Schoenfeldt; au peuple Belgique. 27p. at end."

NL 0433163 IEN

VOLUME 337

944.04
Z1
v.1
Lochée, Lewis.
Observations sur la révolution belgique, et réflexions sur un certain imprimé adressé au peuple belgique, qui sert de justification au baron de Schoenfeldt. [n.p.] 1791.

120 p. 21cm. [French historical pamphlets, 1791-1798. v.1, no. 1]
1. Belgium. Hist. 1789-1790. 2. Schoenfeldt, Nicolas Henri, baron, 1733 1795. I. Title.

NL 0433164 MnU

U
512
.M43
L79
Lochée, Lewis.
A system of military mathematics. London, 1776.
2v. fold.plates.

NL 0433165 IU MiU

Locheimer Liederbuch
see Lochamer Liederbuch.

Lochelongue, André
Recherches sur les granulations toxiques des polynucléaires. Intéret de ce test hématologique dans l'evolution des états tuberculeux.
Toulouse, 1943
Thèse - Toulouse

NL 0433167 CtY-M

Lochelongue, Jean.
... Le partage d'ascendant par testament en droit français moderne ... par Jean Lochelongue ... Paris, Dalloz, 1937.
185, [1] p. tables (1 fold.) 24cm.
Thèse—Poitiers.
"Bibliographie": p. [177]-179.

1. Wills—France. 2. Inheritance and succession—France. I. Title.
42-10405

NL 0433168 DLC CtY-L

Lochelongue, Jean.
... Le partage d'ascendant par testament en droit français moderne; son aspect pratique. Paris, Dalloz, 1937.
185, [1] p. fold. tab. 24cm.
"Bibliographie": p. [177]-179.

1. Wills—France. 2. Inheritance and succession—France. I. Title.
41-36368

NL 0433169 DLC

Lochelongue (Joseph). * Aperçu sur le mode d'emploi et les indications des injections massives salines dans les affections médicales et les intoxications. 106 pp. 8°. *Paris*, 1896, No. 6.

NL 0433170 DNLM

Lochelongue, Joseph.
... Le liquide céphalo-rachidien et ses anomalies (technique et applications cliniques) 15 figures.—4 planches en couleurs. Paris, A. Malvine et fils, 1918.
2 p. l., iv, [5]-281 p. illus., iv col. pl., diagrs. 19cm. fr. 5

1. Cerebrospinal fluid.
18-11444
Library of Congress RC385.L6

NL 0433171 DLC PPC CtY DNLM ICJ

Lochem, Johannes van.

Albergen, *Netherlands (Priory of Augustinian canons)*
... Albergensia. Stukken betrekkelijk het klooster Albergen. Zwolle, De erven J. J. Tijl, 1878.

Lochemes, Josephine Rose
see
Lochemes, Mary Frederick, *sister*, 1904–

Lochemes, Mary Frederick, *sister*, 1904–
... The church in Latin America; a brief history of the Catholic church from colonial times in Mexico, Middle America, and South America, by Sister Mary Frederick Lochemes ... and Sister Mary Patrice McNamara ... Wichita, Kan., The Catholic action bookshop, 1945.
56 p. 23cm. (The Catholic action series of textbooks for religious discussion clubs)
Map on p. [2] of cover.
"Reference list": p. [3] of cover.
1. Catholic church in Spanish America. I. McNamara, Mary Patrice, sister, joint author.
45-9951
Library of Congress ° BX1426.L6
[3] 282.8

NL 0433174 DLC KAS TxU OrStbM NcD MiDP

Lochemes, Mary Frederick, *sister*, 1904–
... Robert Walsh: his story ... by Sister M. Frederick Lochemes ... Washington, D. C., The Catholic university of America press, 1941.
ix, 258 p. 23cm.
Thesis (PH. D.)—Catholic university of America, 1941.
"Publications of Robert Walsh": p. 229-230. "Bibliographical note": p. 231-243.

1. Walsh, Robert, 1784-1859.
[*Secular name:* Josephine Rose Lochemes]
A 42-367
Catholic univ. of America. Library
for Library of Congress CT275.W257L6
[2]† 920.5

NL 0433175 DCU NcD CU OClWHi OU DLC MBtS

Lochemes, Mary Frederick, *sister*, 1904–
Robert Walsh: his story, by Sr. M. Frederick Lochemes ... New York, American Irish historical society, 1941.
xiii, 258 p. front., ports., facsims. 23½cm.
Issued also as thesis (PH. D.) Catholic university of America.
"Publications of Robert Walsh": p. 229-230. "Bibliographical note": p. 231-243.

1. Walsh, Robert, 1784-1859. I. American-Irish historical society.
[*Secular name:* Josephine Rose Lochemes]
42-15055
Library of Congress CT275.W257L6 1941 a
920.5

NL 0433176 DLC WU TU Vi ViU NcU PU PPAmP

Lochemes, Mary Frederick, *sister*, 1904–
We saw South America; a diary of two Franciscan nuns [by] Sister M. Frederick Lochemes ... Milwaukee, The Bruce publishing company [1946]
xii, 308 p. plates, ports. 20½ cm.

1. South America—Descr. & trav. I. Title.
F2223.L82 918 47—331

NL 0433177 DLC OClJC PU NcU Or OrStbM

[**Lochemes, Michael Joseph**] 1860–
Dreiguds un noschens, vun Meik Fuchs [*pseud.*] Neue edischen mit impruvments. Milwaukee, Wis., M. H. Wiltzius & co., 1898.
170 p. illus. 19cm.

I. Title.
98-2258 Revised 2
Library of Congress PF5938.L7 1898

NL 0433178 DLC NN

[**Lochemes, Michael Joseph**] 1860–
Dreiguds un noschens. Altes un neues vun Meik Fuchs [*pseud.*] Milwaukee, Wis. Hoffmann brothers, 1890.
152 p. illus. 18cm.

I. Title.
25-1724 Revised
Library of Congress PF5938.L7 1890

NL 0433179 DLC NN IU

Lochemes, Michael [Joseph, 1860-
Der Pelkelpeter: ein Märchenspiel, von Dietrich Waldvogel, [pseud. i.e. Rev. Michael Joseph Lochemes] Chicago: Mühlbauer & Behrle, 1885?
20p. 12°. (Dramatisch deklamatorische Jugend-bibliothek. xviii, Heft.)

NL 0433180 NN

3A
327
LOCHEMES, MICHAEL JOSEPH, 1860-
Gedichte eines Deutsch-Amerikaners. Milwaukee, Wiltzius, 1906.
viii, 205 p. 16cm.

NL 0433181 ICN OCU NN

Lochemes, Michael Joseph, 1860-
Hoffnung und Erinnerung
see under Rothensteiner, John Ernest, 1860-1936.

Lochemes, Michael Joseph, 1860–
Outline of Catholic pedagogy; adapted for the use of teachers and students, by M. J. Lochemes. Racine, Wis., 1915.
2 p. l., 77 p. 19½cm.

1. Catholic church—Education.
15-13577
Library of Congress LC485.L7

NL 0433183 DLC

Lochemes, Michael Joseph, 1860-
Outline of Catholic pedagogy; adapted for the use of teachers and students, by M.J. Lochemes. Racine, Wis., 1916.
vii,151p. 20cm.
Pub. by Convent of St. Catherine of Siena.

1. Education 2. Church and education I. Racine, Wisc. Convent of Saint Catherine of Siena.

NL 0433184 KAS

VOLUME 337

Lochemes, Michael Joseph, 1860-
Recollections of Oberammergau. By M. J. Lochemes ... Dayton, O., G. A. Pflaum [1892]
64 p. incl. front., illus. 18½cm.

1. Oberammergau passion-play.
11-15818
Library of Congress PN3238.L6

NL 0433185 DLC NN MB

Lochemes, Michael Joseph, 1860-
Theodotus. Ein drama in fünf akten, von M. J. Lochemes. Chicago, Ill., Muehlbauer u. Behrle, 1895.
117 p. 18cm.
Line borders.

I. Title.
Library of Congress PT3919.L7T5 1895 18-9021

NL 0433186 DLC

Lochenies, G
Manuel de sténographie. Bruxelles, Assoc. sténographique unitaire de Belgique [1952] 110 p. 27cm.
At head of title: Système Prévost-Delaunay.

1. Shorthand—Systems, Belgian, 1952. I. Association sténographique unitaire de Belgique.

NL 0433187 NN

Lochepierre, Florentin de Thierriat
see **Thierriat, Florentin de.**

Locher, A.
With Star and Crescent: a full and authentic account of a recent journey with a caravan from Bombay to Constantinople, comprising a description of the country, the people, and interesting adventures with the natives, by A. Locher ... Philadelphia, Aetna publishing company, 1889.
634 p. incl. front., plates. 20½cm.

1. Arabia—Descr. & trav. 2. Asia, Western—Descr. & trav. I. Title.
5-6845
Library of Congress DS48.2.L8

WaSp WaS WaPS WaE Wa
MtBC MtU OrCS OrPR OrP OrU NN WaWW WaTC WaT WaSpG
MtBuM OrU-M OrSaW OrStbM Or IdPI DGU CaBVaU IdB IdU
NL 0433189 DLC MiU OClWHi ViU PPL OCl OClW MoU MsU

Locher, A.
With star and crescent; a full and authentic account of a recent journey with a caravan from Bombay to Constantinople, comprising a description of the country, the people, and interesting adventures with the natives, by A. Locher ... Philadelphia, Ætna publishing company, 1890.
634 p. incl. front., plates, ports. pl. 20½cm.

1. Arabia—Descr. & trav. 2. Asia, Western—Descr. & trav. I. Title.
34-39657
Library of Congress DS48.2.L8 1890
[42b1] 915

LU
NL 0433190 DLC ABS CoU Wa CU WaU FTaSU ICRL CLSU

Locher, A
With Star and Creseent; a full and authentic account of a recent journey with a caravan from Bombay to Constantinople, comprising a description of the country the people, and interesting adventures with the natives... Phila., Etna publishing co. 1892.

624 p.

NL 0433191 PPT

230.06
T390
v.29
Locher, A *of Switzerland.*
Vom Frauenstimmrecht insbesondere in kirchlichen Angelegenheiten. Zürich, O. Füssli, 1903.
46 p.
Bound with other pamphlets.

1. Women in church work.

NL 0433192 TxDaM-P

Locher, Adolf, d. 191-?
Mittellos in Amerika; Selbsterlebtes von Adolf Locher. Nach dessen Tagebuchblättern bearbeitet von Friedrich Wencker... Minden in Westfalen: W. Köhler, 1925. 192 p. 12°.
p. 189-192, advertising matter.

1. United States—Descr. and trav., 1910- . 2. Wencker, Friedrich, 1893- , editor. 3. Title.
N. Y. P. L. May 20, 1927

NL 0433193 NN

Locher, Adolph.
Dr. J. G. Eduard Stehle (1839-1915); erinnerungen von P. Adolph Locher ... Mit titelbild und 12 textillustrationen. Einsiedeln, Schweiz, M. Ochsner [1918]
2 p. l., [7]-88 p. front. (port.) illus. (incl. facsim. music) 17cm.
"Kompositionen von dr. J. G. Eduard Stehle": p. [82]-88.

1. Stehle, Johann Gustav Eduard, 1839-1915.
21-9951
Library of Congress ML410.S814L6

NL 0433194 DLC

Locher, Adolph.
... Jean-Gustave-Édouard Stehlé, organiste et compositeur, 1839-1915; directeur de musique à Rorschach (Suisse) 1869-1874; maître de chapelle et organiste de la Cathédrale de St-Gall (Suisse) 1874-1913. Avec 6 gravures hors texte. Strasbourg, F. X. Le Roux & cie, s. a., 1928.
3 p. l., 162 p. front., illus. (facsim.) plates, ports. 20cm.
At head of title: A. Locher.
"Principales œuvres de J.-G.-Éd. Stehlé": p. [157]-158.

1. Stehle, Johann Gustav Eduard, 1839-1915.
29-21469
Library of Congress ML410.S814L62

NL 0433195 DLC NN

Locher, Agatho, tr.

HN37
.C3U7
Ušeničnik, Aleš, 1868-
Die soziale Frage. Aus dem Slovenischen übertragen von Agatho Locher. Winterthur, Konkordia [1940]

Locher, Albert, 1900-
... Ueber die Wirkung des Jods bei Sporotrichose. Das Verhalten von Sporotrichonkulturen gegen freies Jod... Zürich, 1929.
Inaug.-Diss. - Zürich.
Curriculum vitae.
"Abdruck aus der Zeitschrift für Immunitätsforschung und experimentelle Therapie, Bd. 64, 1929 ... Jena."
"Literatur": p. 454.

NL 0433197 CtY

Locher, Albert, 1904-
Der schutz der persoenlichkeit durch die §138 absass 1, 823 und 826 B.G.B.
Inaug. diss. Tuebingen, [n.d.]

NL 0433198 ICRL MH

Locher, Alfred, 1895-
Die verletzung von lieferungsvertraegen ueber heeresbeduerfnisse...
Inaug. diss. Zürich, 1920
Bibl.

NL 0433199 ICRL

LOCHER, ANGELA.
...Begegnungen. Luzern, Caritas [1952] 64 p. 20cm.
3. Aufl.

NL 0433200 NN CtY

Locher, Arthur, 1899-
Zur Kenntnis des 1-Nitro-2-methylanthrachinons...von Arthur Locher... Weida i. Thür.: Thomas & Hubert, 1925. 52 p. diagrs. 8°.
Dissertation, Zürich, 1925.
Vita.

1. Nitro-methyl-anthraquinone.
N. Y. P. L. August 26, 1926

NL 0433201 NN CtY ICRL

786.6
L78eDi
Locher, Carl, 1843-1915.
Beschrijving der registers van het orgel en hunne klankkleur. Vrij naar het hoogduitsch voor Nederland bewerkt door Corns. Immig Jr. (Geautoriseerde uitgave) Dordrecht, J. de Zeeuw, 1900.
ii, 103p. illus. 22cm.

First published 1887 under title: Erklärung der Orgel-Register.

1. Organ. 2. Organ--Construction.

NL 0433202 IU

Locher, Carl, 1843-1915.
Dictionary of the organ: organ registers, their timbres, combinations, and acoustic phenomena, by Carl Locher ... Authorized translation from the 4th (1912) German edition, by Claude P. Landi, L. R. A. M. New York, E. P. Dutton & co.; London, K. Paul, Trench, Trübner & co., ltd., 1914.
xi, 207 p. illus. 19cm.
Printed in Great Britain.
Original has title: Erklärung der orgel-register.
"A short sketch of the art of organ-building in England": p. 199-202.

1. Organ. 2. Organ—Construction. I. Landi, Claude P., tr.
15-22074
Library of Congress ML595.L83

NL 0433203 DLC ICJ WU PP PPLas MB PSt OCl

VOLUME 337

ML595 L6 Music Library
Locher, Carl, 1843-1915.
Erklärung der Orgel-Register, mit Vorschlägen zu wirksamen Register-Mischungen. Bern, Nydegger & Baumgart, 1887.
xii, 77 p. illus.

1. Organ-pipes. 2. Organ - Registration. I. Title.

NL 0433204 CU MH InStme GU IU

Locher, Carl, 1843-1915.
Erklärung der orgel-register und ihrer klangfarben, von Carl Locher ... 2., sehr verm. aufl. mit vielen neuen angaben zu registermischungen und mit praktischen ratschlägen für kirchenbehörden. Bern, Nydegger & Baumgart, 1896.
xii, 107 p. front. (port.) illus. 19½cm.
Appended: Press notices and reviews of the work (12 p.)

Subject entries: 1. Organ. 2. Organ—Construction.
8-14740
Library of Congress, no. ML681.L81.

NL 0433205 DLC

ML552 .L8
Locher, Carl, 1843-
An explanation of the organ stops with hints for effective combinations, by Carl Locher ... Tr. with the author's permission by Agnes Schauenburg ... London, K. Paul, Trench & co., 1888.
xi, 77 p. illus. 23cm.

1. Organ-pipes. 2. Organ—Construction.

NL 0433206 MB MiD CLU ICarbS NIC NcGU ICU MiU MH Wa NNUT PP OO OU OCU NN IU

Locher, Carl , 1843-1915.
Les jeux d'orgue et leurs timbres, leurs combinaisons et les phénomènes acoustiques qu'ils présentent, par Charles Locher ... 2.éd. refondue en considérablement augmentée,avec un portreit et 12 [i.e.10] figures dans le texte. Traduction de Jean Bovet ...
Paris,Librairie Fischbacher,1909. viii,166pp. front.(port.) 10 illus. 22½cm.
Topics arranged in alphabetical order.

1. Organ. 2.Organ - Construction. I. Bovet, Jean, tr. I. Title.

NL 0433207 CtY-Mus NcU NcD IEN CaBVaU

Locher, Carl, 1843-1915.
Les jeux d'orgue. Leur caractéristique et leurs combinaisons les plus judicieuses. Par Charles Locher. Traduction libre revue par l'auteur.
= Paris. Fischbacher. 1889. (5), 78 pp. Illus. 23 cm., in 4s.
An English translation of this work may be found on shelf-number 4046.73.

NL 0433208 MB CtY NNC OU IU

Locher, Carl, 1843-1915.
... Manuale dell' organista. I registri dell' organo, con speciale riguardo al differente loro timbro di voce e relativi fenomeni acustici ad uso degli organisti ed organari. Disposizione del monumentale organo del Duomo di Milano e statistica dei più grandi organi del mondo. In appendice: L'organo e i suoi amalgami dalla metà del sec. XVI ai giorni nostri, di Ferruccio Vignanelli ... 2. ed. italiana, riveduta, ampliata ed illustrata a cura di Ernesto Locher. Milano, U. Hoepli, 1940.
3 p. l., [ix]-xxii p., 1 l., 291 p., 1 l. incl. illus., plates, ports. 15½cm. (Manuali Hoepli)
At head of title: Carlo Locher.
1. Organ. 2. Organ—Construction. I. Locher, Ernesto, ed. II. Vignanelli, Ferruccio. III. Title: I registri dell'organo.
Library of Congress ML595.L838 1940 45-43022
[2] 786.6

NL 0433209 DLC

ML595 .R3L8
Locher, Carl, 1843-
... Die orgel-register und ihre klangfarben, sowie die damit verwandten akustischen erscheinungen und wirksamen mischungen; ein handbuch für organisten von Carl Locher ... Illustrationen aus den xylographischen anstalten von Vieweg & sohn in Braunschweig und von Emil Singer in Leipzig. 3. stark verm. aufl. Bern, E. Baumgart, 1904.
xvi, 141 p. front. (port.) illus. 20½cm. (Nr. 1046 Universalkatalog der kirchenmusikalischen werke für den Allgemeinen deutschen Cäcilienverein)
First published in 1887 under title: Erklärung der orgel-register.

1. Organ. 2. Organ—Construction.

NL 0433210 ICU IU ICN WU

Locher, Carl, 1843-
Die orgel-register und ihre klangfarben, sowie die damit verwandten akustischen erscheinungen und wirksamen mischungen, mit dem bilde des verfassers; ein nachschlagewerk für organisten, physiker und physiologen, von Carl Locher ... 4. stark verm. aufl., mit berücksichtigung der modernen anlagen und spielhilfen. Bern, E. Baumgart, 1912.
xvi, 181 p. incl. front. (port.) illus. 23cm.
First published 1887 under title: Erklärung der orgel-register.
1. Organ. 2. Organ—Construction.
18-16121
Library of Congress ML595.L83

NL 0433211 DLC MiU

Locher, Carl, 1843-1915.
Die orgel-register und ihre klangfarben, sowie die damit verwandten akustischen erscheinungen, nebst vorschlägen zu wirksamen mischungen, mit berücksichtigung der modernen anlagen und spielhilfen; mit 11 in den text gedruckten illustrationen; ein nachschlagewerk für organisten, physiker und physiologen, von Carl Locher ... 5., abermals verm. und verb. aufl., besorgt von Jos. Dobler ... Bern und Biel, E. Kuhn; [etc., etc., 1923]
viii, 139, [1] p. illus. 23cm.
First published 1887 under title: Erklärung der orgel-register.
1. Organ. 2. Organ—Construction. I. Dobler, Josef, 1875- ed.
25-13393
Library of Congress ML595.L83 1923

NL 0433212 DLC IaU

786.6 L78eSh 1909
Locher, Carl, 1843-1915.
Orgelstämmorna och deras klangfärger, jämte råd och anvisningar beträffande lämpliga stämblandningar. Bemyndigad översättning från tyska originalets 3. uppl. av C. F. Hennerberg. Med porträtt av förf. och förord av G. Hägg. Stockholm, P. A. Norstedt [1909]
viii, 120p. illus., port. 22cm.

Translation of Erklärung der Orgel-Register.

NL 0433213 IU

Locher, Charles Hunter, joint author.

Ackerman, Adolph John.
Construction planning and plant, by Adolph J. Ackerman ... and Charles H. Locher ... 1st ed. New York and London, McGraw-Hill book company, inc., 1940.

Locher, Charlotte Joahne Sophie
Untersuchungen ueber den farbensinn von eichhoernchen.
56 p.
Leiden. Diss. 1933.

NL 0433215 PU NcD CtY

PL8751 .Z5C48
Locher, Christian Wilhelm.

Christaller, Johann Gottlieb, 1827-1895.
A dictionary, English, Tshi (Asante), Akra; Tshi <Chwee> comprising as dialects: Akán (Asànté, Akém, Akuapém, &c.) and Fànté; Akra <Accra> connected with Adangme; Gold coast, W. Africa. Enyiresi, otšüi ko gã wiemoi-ašiŝitšõmo-wolo. By the Rev. J. G. Christaller, Rev. Ch. W. Locher, Rev. J. Zimmermann ... Basel, The Basel evang. missionary society; [etc., etc.] 1874.

Locher, E.
Album des portraits et costumes Suisses des plus belles femmes en habits de fete. Dessines par E. Locher de Fribourg. Ce Recueil a ete grave, precieusement colorie et dedie a Son Altesse Madame la Princesse Royale Charlotte de Saxe Cobourge, nee Princese de Galles, l'annee 1824, par son tres-humble serviteur J.P. Lamy.
Portrait and 36 very fine water-color drawings of the costumes of Swiss women, all neatly mounted on stiff gray paper.

4 to., old red straight-grained morocco gilt, with flap. Bale (1824)

NL 0433218 CSmH

Wason BV3300 L81
[Locher, E A]
M. Gilles Delamotte, missionaire manceau, martyrisé en Cochinchine. S. N. D. B. Le Mans, Leguicheux-Gallienne, 1880.
42 p. 22cm.

Signed by author.

1. Delamotte, Gilles Joseph Louis, 1799-1840. 2. Martyrs--Indochina, French. 3. Missions--Indochina, French.

NL 0433219 NIC

Locher, Edouard.
1914/1922, catalogue spécial des timbres de la guerre, de l'armistice, et de nouveautés ... édité par la maison de timbres-poste Edouard Locher ... [Dubendorf-Zurich, Imprimerie H. Grapentien, 1922?]
cover-title, 216 p. 20 cm.
Caption title: Catalogue complet des timbres-poste relatifs à la guerre et à l'armistice 1914/1922.
1. Postage-stamps - Catalogs. 2. European war, 1914-1918.

NL 0433220 CU

Locher, Eduard, 1840-1910.
Neues bahnsystem für die Jungfrau-bahn, von Ed. Locher. Zürich, Druck von Orell Füssli & co., 1890.
15 p. front. 22cm.

1. Jungfraubahn.
CA 7-4352 Unrev'd
Library of Congress TF688.J9L8

NL 0433221 DLC

Locher, Edward William,
A study of the elements of mystery and terror in the tales of E.T.W.Hoffmann and E.A. Poe. 1908.

NL 0433222 CU

VOLUME 337

PT915 Locher, Emma.
.L8 Die Venedigersagen ... Tübingen, Druck von H. Laupp, jr., 1922.
178 p. 23cm.
Inaug.-diss.—Freiburg in der Schweiz.
"Verzeichnis der benutzten literatur": p. [171]-178.

1. Legends. 2. Legends, German.

NL 0433223 ICU

Locher, Ernest, 1899-
La culture caféière dans l'état de São Paulo combinée avec la sériciculture ... par Ernest Locher ... Berne, Imprimerie H. Schenk, 1931.
158, [1] p. diagrs. 23cm.
Inaug.-Diss.—Zürich.
Vita.
"Littérature": p. 157-158.

NL 0433224 ICJ DNAL CtY

Locher, Ernesto, ed.

ML595 Locher, Carl, 1843-1915.
.L838 ... Manuale dell' organista. I registri dell' organo, con speciale riguardo al differente loro timbro di voce e relativi fenomeni acustici ad uso degli organisti ed organari. Disposizione del monumentale organo del Duomo di Milano e statistica dei più grandi organi del mondo. In appendice: L'organo e i suoi amalgami dalla metà del sec. XVI ai giorni nostri, di Ferruccio Vignanelli ... 2. ed. italiana, riveduta, ampliata ed illustrata a cura di Ernesto Locher. Milano, U. Hoepli, 1940.
1940

Locher, Ernst.
Schiessen und Treffen mit Infanteriewaffen; Kurzgefasste militärische Schiess- und Waffenlehre. Frauenfeld, Huber [1948]
108 p. diagrs., tables (in pocket) 20 cm.

1. Shooting, Military.

UD330.L6 356.18 49-26191*

NL 0433226 DLC

Locher, Eugen, 1890-
Handels-wechsel- und seerecht. (In Das Gesamte deutsche recht, 1, p. 1181-1401)

NL 0433227 MH-L

Locher, Eugen, 1890-
... Krisennotrecht. Antrittsrede des neuen rektors, professor dr. Eugen Locher, gehalten am 4. november 1932. Erlangen, Verlag von Palm & Enke, 1932.
47 p. 24cm. (Erlanger universitäts-reden, 15)
"Bericht über das studienjahr 1931/32": p. [37]-47.
Bibliographical foot-notes.

1. Panics—1929. 2. Germany—Economic policy. I. Title.
A O 33-425 Revised
Stanford univ. Library for Library of Congress AS182.E849 no. 15
[r43c2]† (378.43) 338.53

NL 0433228 CSt DLC PU

K47L Locher, Eugen, 1890-
7AK1 Die Neugestaltung des Liegenschaftsrechtes.
A Berlin, Deutscher Rechtsverlag «1942»
18 192p. 22cm. (Arbeitsberichte der Akademie für Deutsches Recht, Nr. 18)

1. Real property (Germanic law) I. Title

NL 0433229 WU NNC MH IEN

Locher, Eugen, 1890-
Das Recht der Wertpapiere. Tübingen, Mohr, 1947.
159 p. forms. 23 cm.

1. Negotiable instruments—Germany.

50-15981

NL 0433230 DLC MiU-L

Locher, Eugen, 1890-
Das württembergische Hofkammergut; eine rechtsgeschichtliche studie, von dr. Eugen Locher ... Stuttgart, F. Enke, 1925.
57 p. 25cm. (Added t. p.: Tübinger abhandlungen zum öffentlichen recht ... 4. hft.)

1. Württemberg—Kings and rulers. 2. Württemberg—Constitutional law. 3. Law—Württemberg—History and criticism. I. Württemberg. Hofkammergut. II. Title.
A 31-234
Title from Carnegie Endow. Int. Peace JX77.T8 hft. 4
Library of Congress DD801.W657L6
[a35c1] 342.4347

NL 0433231 DGW-C DLC MH NN

Locher, Felix.
...Das praktische Färben, Blondieren und Tönen der Haare. Ein Buch aus der Praxis für die Praxis. [Wien] Verlag des Österreichischen Gewerkschaftsbundes, 1949. 120 p. illus. 21cm.

528002B. 1. Hair dyes. 2. Hair dressing.
N. Y. P. L. June 16, 1950

NL 0433232 NN

Locher, Felix, 1878-
Das prinzip der firmenwahrheit im schweizerischen obligationenrecht...
Inaug. diss. Leipzig, 1908 (Winterthur)
Bibl.

NL 0433233 ICRL MH

Locher, Felix, 1882-
Telecurve world map; great circle routes, true directions, distances, standard time & date around the world. Focal point, Los Angeles area. [Wall ed.] Los Angeles, Telecurve Co.; world-wide distributors: Coast Visual Education Co., °1950.
col. map 55 x 108 cm.
Scale ca. 1 : 40,000,000.
Directions for use in margin, with "World index" and 4 miniature reproductions from the Telecurve filmstrip "Global geography shortcuts."
Accompanied by "Telecurve timeband," a graduated strip for determining comparative time data.
1. World maps. 2. Distances—Maps. I. Telecurve Company, Los Angeles. II. Coast Visual Education Company, Los Angeles. III. Title.
G3200.P1 1950.L6 Map 50-537

NL 0433234 DLC

Locher, Felix, 1882-
United States standard time zone Telecurve map. Hollywood, Coast Visual Education Co., Telecurve Division, °1951.
col. map 33 x 59 cm.
Scale ca. 1 : 9,600,000; "each vertical degree of latitude equals 69 statute miles."
With marginal text: Standard time zones around the world.

1. Time—Systems and standards—Maps. I. Coast Visual Education Company, Los Angeles. II. Title. III. Title: Telecurve map.
G3701.B2 1951.L6 Map 51-1153

NL 0433235 DLC

Locher, Foppe.
... Die siedlerheimstätte in Ostpreussen, erfahrungen und aufgaben. Berlin, Verlag der Deutschen arbeitsfront, g. m. b. h., 1938.
47 p. illus. (plans) 29½cm.
At head of title: F. Locher.
"1. auflage. 1. bis 3. tausend."

1. Architecture, Domestic—Prussia, East (Province) 2. Architecture, Domestic—Designs and plans. 3. Labor and laboring classes—Dwellings. I. Deutsche arbeitsfront. II. Title.
43-33932
Library of Congress NA7554.L6
[3] 728.68

NL 0433236 DLC

Locher, Franz.
Allgemeine erdkunde, 2e. aufl. Regensburg, Manz, 1859.
823 p. 8°.

NL 0433237 MWC

Locher, Franz
Allgemeine Geographie, oder Lehrbuch der Erdkunde für Gymnasien, Real-und höhere Bürger-Schulen, so wie zum Selbstunterricht. Statistisch, historisch und ethnographisch bearbeitet. Regensburg, Friedrich Pustet, 1852.
iv, 843 p. 23 cm.

1. Geography - Textbooks.

NL 0433238 PLatS

Locher (Franz) [1881-]. *Ueber die Wirkung einiger photodynamischen Substanzen auf Hefe, Acetondauerhefe und Hefepressaft. 22 pp. 8°. München, Wolf & Sohn, 1906.

NL 0433239 DNLM

Locher, Franz von, 1818-1892.
Ueber die Helmkleinode. Bedeutung, Recht und Geschichte. (In Koeniglich-bayerische Akademie der Wissenschaften, Munich. Philosophisch-philologische und historische Classe. Sitzungsberichte. 1885, pp. 147-197. München. 1885.)

K6581 — Helmets. — Heraldry. — Gems.

NL 0433240 MB

Locher, Fred.
Hydraulic studies of a water jet-pump for the Keswick Dam fish-trap. [Boulder, University of Colorado Libraries, Dept. of Microphotography, 1945]
Microfilm copy of typewritten ms. Positive.
Collation of the original, as determined from the film: iv, 60 l. illus.
Thesis (M. sc.)—University of Colorado.
Bibliography: leaf 59.

1. Pumping machinery. I. Keswick Dam fish-trap.

Microfilm AC-5 Mic 50-187

NL 0433241 DLC

Locher, Friedrich, 1820-1911
Der Bolligerhandel und was drum und dran hängt, von dr. Friedrich Locher ... Zürich, E. Speidel, 1898.
66 p. 21½cm.

NL 0433242 MH-L

VOLUME 337

[Locher, Friedrich] 1820-1911.
Die freiherren von Regensberg. Pamphlet eines schweizerischen juristen. Bern, Haller'sche verlagsbuchhandlung, 1866-
pts. in v. facsim., fold. geneal. tab. 21½cm.
Parts 1 and 2 in 1 v., with general t.-p. and contents and continuous paging.
p. 181-208, pt. 6, omitted in numbering.
CONTENTS.—I [th.] Einst. Die freiherren der ältern linie. 1866.—II [th.] Jetzt. Die freiherren der gegenwart. 1866.
—— VI. th. Die neuesten freiherren. 1869.
I. Title.
5—15634
Library of Congress DQ799.6.L8

NL 0433243 DLC

Locher, Friedrich, 1820-1911.
Geld und Recht oder Wie man eine Million stiehlt. Zürich, Schmidt, 1891.
iv, 192 p.

NL 0433244 NNC

Locher, Friedrich, 1820-
Nach den oasen von Laghuat. Bern, Haller, 1864.
pp. viii, 208.

Laghouat||

NL 0433245 MH PPG

[Locher, Friedrich] 1820-1911.
Othello, der justizmohr von Venedig. Vom verfasser der "Freiherren von Regensberg". Bern, Haller, 1867.
46 p. 8°.
"A letter by F. Locher refuting 21 accusations preferred against him by Dr. Ullmer."—Brit. mus.

I. Title.
1—20820

NL 0433246 DLC

[Locher, Friedrich] 1820-
Der prinzeps und sein hof ... Vom verfasser der "Freiherren von Regensberg." Bern, In commission der Haller'schen verlagsbuchhandlung, 1867.
56 p. 21½cm.
First published, Bern, 1867, as the second half of part four of the author's Freiherren von Regensberg.

1. Zürich—Pol. & govt.

Library of Congress DQ799.6.L815
5-8212†

NL 0433247 DLC

DQ 178 L6 1901
Locher, Friedrich, 1820-1911.
Republikanische Wandelbilder und Portraits. Hrsg. und verlegt von seiner Tochter Emma Locher. Zürich, Th. Schröter [1901?]
380p. 21cm.

1. Locher, Friedrich, 1820-1911. I. Title.

NL 0433248 MU IEN

Nx42 881l
Locher, Friedrich, 1820-1911.
Wetterleuchten. Der Staatssozialismus und seine Consequenzen ... Zürich, Trüb'sche Buchhandlung, 1881-83.
5v. in 1. 21½cm.
Vols. 3-4 have imprint: Zürich, In Kommission bei T. Schröter's Verlagsbuchhandlung (slight variations)
Title appears only on cover of v.3, pt.1; t.-p. reads: Zwanglose Blätter; sechste und siebente Prise.

NL 0433249 CtY

FL8 S9.9 L812g 1934
Locher, Fritz
Die Gesetzgebung betreffend die staatliche Beaufsichtigung der privaten Versicherungsunternehmungen in der Schweiz. Leipzig, C. Schwarze, 1934.
71 p. 21cm.
Cover title.
Inaug.-Diss. - Leipzig.
Bibliography: p.5-[7]

1. Insurance companies - Switzerland. 2. Insurance - Switzerland - State supervision. I. Title.

NL 0433250 MiU-L

Locher, Fritz
Das Zunfthaus zur Zimmerleuten im Zeitraum von sechs Jahrhunderten, 1357-1937. [Zürich, Buchdruckerei Schulthess, 1937].
33 p. illus. (part col.)

1. Zunfthaus zur Zimmerleuten, Zurich. X ref.: Zurich. Zufthaus zur Zimmerleuten (to 1)

NL 0433251 MH

QD341 .A8L76
Locher, Fritz, 1897-
Zur kenntnis der aminosäuren ... Winterthur, Buchdr. Geschwister Ziegler, 1922.
71 p. 22cm.
Inaug.-diss.—Zürich.
Lebenslauf.

1. Amino acids.

NL 0433252 ICU OCU CtY DLC ICRL

G271.5 L788c
Locher, G
A Companhia de Jesus; centenario da sua restauração, 1814-7 de agosto-1914. Pôrto Alegre, Typographia do Centro, 1914.
62p. ports. 22cm.

1. Jesuits. 2. Jesuits in Brazil.

NL 0433253 TxU

Locher, Gabriel, O.S.B., 1884-
Aus verborgenheit ans Licht; kurzes Lebensbild der Dienerin Gottes Schwester Maria Fortunata Viti, Benedikterin. Druck und Verlag der Benedikterabtei Seckau, [1937]
viii, 240p. front. (port.) illus. 19cm.

NL 0433254 PLatS

Locher, Gabriel, 1884-
A brief biography of Sister Mary Fortunata Viti of Santa Maria dei Franconi, Veroli, Italy, lay sister in the Benedictine convent, 1827-1922; a hidden life of sanctity brought from obscurity to light, translated from the second German edition of Rev. Gabriel Locher ... by Rev. Stephen Radtke ... Clyde, Mo., Benedictine convent of perpetual adoration [1940]
vi, 216, [2] p. front. (port.) plates, facsim. 18½cm.

1. Viti, Maria Fortunata, suora, 1827-1922. I. Radtke, Stephen John, 1885- tr. *Translation of* Aus verborgenheit ans licht.
43-29161
Library of Congress BX4705.V67L62
[2] 922.245

NL 0433255 DLC PLatS OrStbM

Locher, Gabriel, O.S.B., 1884-
... La serva di Dio Suor Maria Fortunata Viti Benedettina conversa nel monastero di S. Maria dei Franconi in Veroli. Profilo biografico a cura della postulazione della causa di beatificazione. Roma, [Tipografia dei Monasteri Subiaco] 1935.
129 p. front. (port.), illus., plates, 20 cm.

1. Viti, Maria Fortunata, O.S.B., Sister, 1827-1922.

NL 0433256 PLatS

Locher, Gabriel, O.S.B., 1884-
Vita della serva di Dio Suor Maria Fortunata Viti conversa Benedettina di S. Maria in Veroli. [Veroli, 1940]
xii, 308 p. illus. 21 cm.

1. Viti, Maria Fortunata, O.S.B., Sister, 1827-1922.

NL 0433257 PLatS InStme

BX 4854 .I4 L8
LOCHER, GERRIT PAUL HENDRIK
De kerkorde der Protestantse Kerk in Indonesië; bijdrage tot de kennis van haar historie en beginselen. Leiden, 1948.
255 p.

Proefschrift--Leiden.

1. Protestantism--Indonesia. I. Title.

NL 0433258 InU

BR1220 L6
Locher, Gerrit Paul Hendrik
De kerkorde der Protestantse kerk in Indonesië, door G.P.H. Locher. [Amsterdam] Druk Kampert & Helm [1949]
255 p. (Bijdragen tot de zendingswetenschap, deel 2)

Bibliographical footnotes.

1. Protestant churches - Indonesia. 2. Indonesia - Church history. I. Title. (Series)

NL 0433259 CU CtY-D PPLT NIC NjPT MH OrU

Div.S. 922.4492 K79L
Locher, Gottfried Wilhelm
Aus dem Leben und Wirken des Dr. Herm. Fried. Kohlbrügge. Zwei Vorträge, gehalten anlässlich des 50jähr. Gedächtnistages seines Heimganges am 5. März 1875, von G. W. Locher. [n. p.] Verlag der Niederl. Reform. Gem. [n. d.]
46 p. port. 23 cm. [1925?]

1. Kohlbrügge, Hermann Friedrich, 1803-1875.

NL 0433260 NcD

VOLUME 337

E99 .K9L8 LOCHER,GOTTFRIED WILHELM, 1908-
The serpent in Kwakiutl religion,a study in primitive culture... Leiden,1932.
xii,118,3 p. illus.,pl. 24cm.
Proefschrift--Leyden.
Bibliography:p.[115]-118.

1.Kwakiutl Indians--Religion and mythology. 2.Serpent-worship.

NL 0433261 ICU PU OCl CtY NjP WaU

Locher, Gottfried Wilhelm, 1908-
The serpent in Kwakiutl religion, a study in primitive culture, by Dr. G. W. Locher. Leyden, E. J. Brill ltd., 1932.
viii, 118 p., 1 l. illus., pl. 24½cm.
Bibliography: p. [115]-118.

1. Kwakiutl Indians—Religion and mythology. 2. Serpent-worship. I. Title.

Library of Congress E99.K9L6 33-12205
[2] 970.6

CaBVaU CaBViPA
IaU FU CoU OCU PU MH-P CaOTP TNJ-R OrPR CaBVa
NL 0433262 DLC OrCS OrU TxU MoU ICarbS NcD NN NBuU

GN590 L6 ANTHRO Locher, Gottfried Wilhelm, 1908-
De sociologie en cultuurkunde van Zuidoost-Azië en het Zuidzeegebied in haar betrekking tot de algemene cultuurwetenschap. Groningen, J.B. Wolters, 1955.
22 p.
Rede - Leyden (Aanvarding van het ambt van buitengewoon hoogleraar in de sociologie en cultuurkunde van Zuidoost-Azië en het Zuidzeegebied) 1955.
"Aantekeningen" (bibliographical): p.21-22.

1. Ethnology - Asia, Southeastern. 2. Acculturation.

NL 0433263 CU NIC CtY CU

BT10 .S88 v.5 Locher, Gottfried Wilhelm, 1911
Der Eigentumsbegriff als Problem evangelischer Theologie. Zürich, Zwingli-Verlag, 1954.
169 p. (Studien zur Dogmengeschichte und systematischen Theologie, Bd.5)
Includes bibliography.

1. Christianity and economics. 2. Property.

NL 0433264 ICU MH NjPT IaU NcD CtY-D NjP

BX 4801 K5 v.26 Locher, Gottfried Wilhelm, 1911-
Die evangelische Stellung der Reformatoren zum öffentlichen Leben. Zürich, Zwingli-Verlag [1950]
40 p. 21cm. (Kirchliche Zeitfragen, Heft 26)

1. Reformation. 2. Protestantism. I. Title. (Series)

NL 0433265 CSaT MH-AH CSt IaU TxFTC

Locher, Gottfried Wilhelm, 1911-
Die Theologie Huldrych Zwinglis im Lichte seiner Christologie. Zürich, Zwingli-Verlag, 1952-
v. 23 cm.
Inaug.-Diss.—Zürich.
Published also as Studien zur Dogmengeschichte und systematischen Theologie, Bd. 1.
Vita.
Bibliography: v. 1, p. 170-178.

1. Zwingli, Ulrich, 1484-1531. 2. Jesus Christ—History of doctrines.

BR345.L6 55-44745

NL 0433266 DLC

Locher, Gottfried Wilhelm, 1911-
Die Theologie Huldrych Zwinglis im Lichte seiner Christologie. Zürich, Zwingli-Verlag, 1952-
v. 23 cm. (Studien zur Dogmengeschichte und systematischen Theologie, Bd. 1)
"Literatur": v. 1, p. 170-178.
CONTENTS.—1. T. Die Gotteslehre.

1. Zwingli, Ulrich, 1484-1531. 2. Jesus Christ—History of doctrines. I. Title.

Harvard Univ. Library for Library of Congress [1] A 53-2792

CSt RPB ViU GDC ViHarEM KyLxCB PPiPT MU MoU MB
NL 0433267 MH CLSU CtY OO ICU MH-AH NjPT NcD IaU

PA3873 .A97A4L8 **Locher, Hans, 1824-1873.**
Aretäus aus Kappadocien. Mit uebersetzung seiner vorzüglichsten und interessantesten pathologischen und therapeutischen schilderungen. Eine monographie von dr.Hans Locher... Zürich,F.Schulthess,1847.
[6],258,[1]p. 20½cm.

1.Medicine--Early works. 2.Medicine,Greek and Roman.

NL 0433268 ICU

Locher, Hans, 1824-73.
——. Die chirurgischen und medizinischen Krankheiten des Schädels und Gehirns und psychiatrische Klinik. xvii, 469 pp. 8°. Erlangen, F. Enke, 1869.
2. title-page of v. 2 of the preceding.

NL 0433269 DNLM

RC756 .L8 LOCHER,HANS,1824-1873.
Die erkenntniss der lungen-krankheiten vermittelst der percussion und auscultation. Ein lehrbuch bearb. für studirende und praktische aerzte von dr.Hans Locher... Zürich,F.Schulthess,1853.
[8],312 p. 20½cm.

1.Lungs—Diseases—Diagnosis. 2.Percussion. 3. Auscultation.

NL 0433270 ICU KU-M FU-HC WU DNLM PPC

WB L812m 1867 LOCHER, Hans, 1824-1873.
Medizinisch-chirurgische Klinik; Vorlesungen über sämmtliche Fächer der praktischen Medizin. Erlangen, Enke, 1867-69.
2 v.
Contents. —Bd. 1. Die Medizinischen und chirurgischen Krankheiten der Haut.

NL 0433271 DNLM PPC MB

Locher, Hans, 1824-73.
——. Die medizinischen und chirurgischen Krankheiten der Haut. xxii, 438 pp. 8°. Erlangen, F. Enke, 1867.
2. title-page of v. 1 of the following:

NL 0433272 DNLM

WZ 100 P221L 1851 Locher, Hans, 1824-1873.
Theophrastus Paracelsus Bombastus von Hohenheim, der Luther der Medicin und unser grösster Schweizerarzt... Mit einem Holzschnitte von C. Staub. Zürich, Meyer und Zeller, 1851.
vi, 68 p. port. 22 cm.
Cover title.

1. Paracelsus, 1493-1541. I. Title.

NL 0433273 WU-M DNLM PPC PU-S

Locher (Hans) [1824-73]. *Ueber das Leben und die Schriften des Aretäus aus Kappadocien. 37 pp. 8°. Zürich, F. Schulthess, 1847.

NL 0433274 DNLM MiU

LOCHER,Hans, 1824-1873.
Ueber den schlaf und die träume,das nachtwandeln und die visionen. Zürich,1853.

NL 0433275 MH

Locher, Hans, 1824-1873.
Zur Lehre vom Herzen. Gratulationsschrift, der Medicinisch-Chirurgischen Gesellschaft des Kantons Zürich an ihrem fünfzigjährigen Stiftungsfeste den 7. Mai 1860, überreicht von Dr. Hans Locher, ... Erlangen, F. Enke, 1860.
[6], 132 p. 21½cm.

NL 0433276 ICJ DNLM

Locher, Harry O.
Helps to successful contracting. by Harry O. Locher ... 1st ed. New York and London. McGraw-Hill book company, inc., 1934.
xiv, 222 p. 2 diagr. 19½cm.

1. Contractors' operations. I. Title.
Library of Congress TA210.L55 34-13707
—— Copy 2.
Copyright A 71666 [5] 620.03

IdU WaS
NL 0433277 DLC PP OCl MiU NN NcRS NcD NIC TU Or

Locher, (Harry O) & Co.
There are few branches of industry which today present more practical interest than that pertaining to the application of hydraulic cement ...
see under James River Cement Works, Balcony Falls, Va.

Locher, Hugo,
Die behandlung des abwassers aus schlachthoefen... Inaug. diss. Stuttgart, tech. hoch.,1931.
Bibl.

NL 0433279 ICRL

Locher, I. H. *Map 1036.r19
Eisenbahn & Reisekarte mit Bäder & Kurorten der Schweiz. Zürich. [1873?] Size, 17⅝ × 25¾ inches. Scale, none. Folded.

L6188 — Switzerland. Geog. Maps.

NL 0433280 MB

Map G 6035 B5 Locher, J. H.
Panorama du Mont Righi. Zurich, [n.d.]
map 56 x 8 cm. in folder 13 cm.
No scale given.

1. Mont Rigi--Maps.

NL 0433281 NIC

VOLUME 337

Locher, Jacob, 1471-1528 Analyse de la Tragedia de Thurcis et Suldano, de L. 14 pp. (*Journ. asiat.* 2 s. v. 7, 1831, p. 303.)

NL 0433282 MdBP

LOCHER Jacob, 1471-1528.
Carmen de Sancta Catharina. - Bâle, Jean Bergman de Olpe, 1496.

Petit in-4, 6 ffnc.; car.rom.et goth.; 30 ll.ll.; signat.a, l cahier fig.sur bois.

NL 0433283 MH

LOCHER, Jacob, 1471-1528.
[Carmen de Sancta Catharina. Basel, J. Bergmann, 1496].

4°. ff.6. Wdcts.
Hain *10164.

NL 0433284 MH

Locher, Jacob, 1471-1528.
Carmen heroicum de partu monstrifero. Ingolstadt ⌊Johann Kachelofen, after 26 Nov. 1499⌋

⌊4⌋ l. woodcuts: illus. 4°. 21.4 cm.

Leaf ⌊1a⌋ (t.-p.): Monstrosa hois forma.
Hain. Repertorium, *10162. Brit. Mus. Cat. (xv cent.), III, p. 679 (IA.13546) Schramm. Bilderschmuck d. Frühdr., v. 16, p. 12, 17 and illus.

1. Monsters. I. Title: Monstrosa hominis forma.
Incun. X.L78 Rosenwald Coll. 48-43290

NL 0433285 DLC

FILM 4298 AC Roll 23
Locher, Jacob, 1471-1528.
Carmen heroicum de partu monstrifero. Ingolstadt ⌊Johann Kachelofen, after 26 Nov. 1499⌋

NL 0433286 CU

Rare Book Room Gk18 518L
Locher, Jacob, 1471-1528.
Compendivm rhetorices / ex Tulliano thesauro diductum ac concionatum: per Iacobum Locher Philomusum ... Anno. M.D.XVIII. R. Beck. [Colophon: Excusum Argentinae per Renatum Beck Anno.1518]
[35]p. 18cm.
Signatures: A-B4C6D4.

NL 0433287 CtY

Locher, Jacob, 1471-1528.
Continentur in hoc opusculo a Iacobo Locher Philomuso facili syntaxi concinnato: Vitiosa sterilis mule ad musam, roscida lepiditate predictam, comparatio. Currus sacre theologie triumphalis, ex Veteri Instrumento & Noue Testamento ornatus. Elogia quattuor Doctorum Ecclesie, cum epigrãmatibus & duabus prefationibus. ⌊Nurnberge, Impressum per I. Veissenburger, 1506⌋
⌊63⌋ p. illus. 20 cm.
Signatures: A-D6, E8.
Illus. attributed to Wolf Traut by Dodgson. cf. Brit. Mus. Dept. of Prints and Drawings. Cat. of early German and Flemish woodcuts. London, 1903-11, v. 1, p. 505.

I. Traut, Wolf, d. 1520, illus.
PA8547.L4C6 Rosenwald Coll. 49-38090*

NL 0433288 DLC MiU

Film 2949 .594
Locher, Jacob, 1471-1528.
Continentur In hoc opusculo a Jacobo Locher Philomuso facili syntaxi concinnato. (Nurnberge, 1506)
(62) p. illus. 22 cm.

Microfilm (negative) of the original in University of Michigan library. 1 reel.

NL 0433289 NjP

Locher, Jacob, 1471-1528, comp.
Deliciae poeticae; or Parnessaus display'd
see under title

Locher, Jacob, 1471-1528.
Epistola dedicatoria...
see under Claudianus, Claudius, fl. 400.

Locher, Jakob, 1471-1528.
⌊Epitoma rhetorices⌋ ⌊Freiburg im Breisgau, Friedrich Riedrer, 1496?⌋ 20 l. 20cm. (4°.)

l. 1a: Epithoma Rhetorices graphicum‖ a Jacobo Locher philomuso congestum.‖ Carmen eiusdē ad diuam Catharinam‖ Epigramma ad lectores.‖ ⌊8 lines of verse⌋ l. 20a: ...Et procul ignotos aduolitasse viros‖
Hain-Copinger 10156. BMC, III, 697. IA. 14224. Stillwell: Second census, L232.
Gothic type (Proctor 3220); 36 lines. With initial indicators, initials and signature marks; without catchwords and foliation.

Signatures: a-b8, c4.
"Jacobus Locher...‖...Federico Riedrer. S. D.," l. 20a. dated: Uale Friburgi. vj.kl.‖martii āno. 1.4.9.6. ...
With stamp of Richard Heber and bookplate of James P. Lyell.

53R0868. 1. Rhetoric.

NL 0433293 NN

Beinecke Library Gr12 L788 E9
Locher, Jacob, 1471-1528.
Exhortatio heroica Iacobi Locher Philomusi ad principes Germanię & status pro serenissimo Romanorum ac Hispaniarū rege Carolo, cōtra hostes Sacrosancti Imperii detestabiles ... [n.p., 1521]
[11] p. 21 cm.
Signatures: A6.
Dedication to Leonardo de Eck: "datū in oppido Vlmano tertio nonas Augusti, anno xxi."
In verse.

NL 0433294 CtY MH ICN

Locher, Jacob, 1471-1528.
In hoc libello Iacobi Locher Philomusi Sueui infrascripta poematia continentur: ❡Epiodion de morte Plutonis: & Dęmonū: ❡Encomion paupertatis heroicum: ❡Carmen de pace: cum uariis epigrãmatibus & elegidiis: ❡Nuthesię tres moralia p̃cepta continentes.e gręco Phocylide ad latinos elegos traductę ... ⌊Augustę, 1513⌋
⌊55⌋ p. 19½cm.
Colophon: Siluanus Othmar impressit Augustę apud ędem Diuę Vrsulę ad Lichum.anno M D XIII ...
Signatures: a8, b-e4-6.
I. Phocylides, of Miletus, fl. 544 B.C. Spurious and doubtful works. Car adminitorium.

NL 0433295 MiU DNLM CtY TxU DFo ICN IU ICU

---

*GC5 L7884 505ℓ
Locher, Jacob, 1471-1528.
Ludicrū drama: plautino more fictum: a Jacobo locher philomuso: de sene amatore: filio corrupto: & dotata muliere ...
[Germany, ca.1505?]
[8]p. 20.5cm.
Woodcut illus. on t.-p.
Based on the Asinaria of Plautus.

NL 0433296 MH DFo

Locher (Jacob) 1471-1528 [*Fol. 1a, title:*] Monstrosa hominis forma. [*Fol. 2b incipit:*] Carmen heroicum de partu monstrifero in oppido Rhain ad ripam lyci adjacente ab egena femina edito Anno domini Nonagesimonono supra milesimum XV. Kalendas Decembris. [*Fol. 2a, ad finem:*] ex Ingelstadensi Gymnasio sexto kalendas decembris, M.cccc,lxxxix. [*Fol. 4b, ad finem:*] Impressus hic libellus in Ingelstadnsi [*sic*] studio.

NL 0433297 DNLM

Incun. 1497 .B72 Rosenwald Coll.
Locher, Jacob, 1471-1528, tr.
FOR OTHER EDITIONS SEE MAIN ENTRY
Brant, Sebastian, 1458-1521.
Das Narrenschiff. Latin. Strassburg, Johann (Reinhard) Grüninger, 1 June (Kal. Iun.) 1497.

Locher, Jacob, 1471-1528.
Der neū Layenspiegel von rechtmässigen Ordnungen in bürgerlichen und peinlichen Regimenten
see under Tengler, Ulrich, d. 1511?

Incun. 1498 .H6 Rare bk. coll.
Locher, Jacob, 1471-1528, ed.
Horatius Flaccus, Quintus.
Opera. Strassburg, Johann (Reinhard) Grüninger, 12 Mar. (IV Id. Mar.) 1498.

Rare PA 8547 L4 O6 1496
⌊Locher, Jacob⌋ 1471-1528.
Oratio de studio humanarum disciplinarum et laude poetarum. ⌊Freiburg im Breisgau, Friedrich Riedrer, 1496-97⌋
⌊8⌋ l. 20cm.

Signatures: a-b4.
Leaf ⌊1a⌋ (Title): Oratio de studio humanarum disciplinarum: et laude poetarum extemporalis.
Leaf ⌊8a⌋, line 5: Finis opusculi. Followed by two poems: "Ad vdalricum zasium Endecasyllabon Jacobi philomusi", and "Tetrastichon eiusdem Ad gabrielem lorch".
Hain. Repertorium, no. *10166; Proctor, 3222; Klebs, 612.1; Brit. Mus. Cat. (XV. cent.) III, p. 697 (IA. 14230)
Ex libris Frid. Zarncke.

NL 0433302 NIC DLC

Locher, Jacob, 1471-1528.
Panegyricus ad Maximilianum. Tragoedia de Turcis et Soldano. Dialogus de heresiarchis. Strassburg, Johann (Reinhard) Grüninger, 1497.
⌊62⌋ l. woodcuts: illus. 4°. 21.3 cm.
Leaf ⌊1a⌋ (t.-p.): Libri Philomusi. Panegyrici ad Regē. Tragediā de Thurcis et Suldano. Dyalogͤ de heresiarchis.
Includes also letters and verses by Locher.
Hain. Repertorium, *10153. Brit. Mus. Cat., I, p. 112 (IA. 1468) Schramm. Bilderschmuck d. Frühdr., v. 20, p. 5, 23 and illus.
In last line of colophon, Hain and Brit. Mus. have: christo; L. C. copy: chistro.

Ex libris De St Genies.

Incun. 1497.L6 Rosenwald Coll. 48-43528
——— Copy 2. 19.6 cm. Last line of colophon: chistro; last line of leaf ⌊51a⌋: τεχὸς (omitted in copy 1) Ex libris Robert Hoe.
——— Copy 3. 19.1 cm. Last line of colophon: christo; last line of leaf ⌊51a⌋: τεχὸς; other slight variations from copy 1 and 2. Inscription on t.-p.: Sum Joannis Kapler P. H. anno 1630.

NL 0433304 DLC IU CtY ICN MH

VOLUME 337

Rare Book Room Grl2 L788 P3 [Locher, Jacob] 1471-1528, comp.
Papyrotheca. Prologus epistolicus Philomusi [pseud.] ad nobilē ... doctorē Leonardū de Eck. Orator M. Tullij Cicerōis ad Brutū Oratio Philomusi de passione dominica: et Elegia eiusdem. Orationes tres ... Thome Rosēpuschij ... [Colophon: Excusa in officina Millerana Augustae Vindelicorū. VI.Nonas Martias.Anno.1517]
[139]p. 21cm.
Signatures: a-f⁴.⁸g-h⁴i⁶Aa-Bb⁶Cc-Dd⁴.

NL 0433305 CtY

*G.405 .142 Locher, Jacob, called Philomusus, 1471-1528.
Poemation de Lazaro mendico: diuite purpurato & inferno Charonte. [Augsburg, Silvan Otmar, 1512?]
[22] p. woodcuts. 22 cm.

NL 0433306 MB

Locher, Jacob, 1471-1528.
Rosarium celestis curie: ɛ patrie triumphantis, a Iacobo Locher Philomuso poeta & oratore laureato confectum. Hexasticon eivsdem ad lectorem [10 lines, [Viennae Austriae, 1516, [15] p. illus. 21cm.
Colophon: Impressum Viennae Austriae per Ioannem Singrenium.anno dñi.M.D.XVI.
Signatures: A-B⁴.
Wood-cut on verso of t.-p.; initials (woodcuts)

NL 0433307 MiU DLC PU

LOCHER, Jacob, called Philomusus, 1471-1528.
Spectaculum a Jacobo Locher, more tragico effigiatum. Eiusdem Iudiciū Paridis de pomo aureo, de triplici hominum vita, de tribus deabus. [Ingolstadt?, 1502?]
sm.4°. pp.(147), Wdcts.

NL 0433308 MH ICN DFo

Locher, Jacob, 1471-1528, tr.

Brant, Sebastian, 1458-1521.
Stvltifera navis mortalivm, in qva fatvi affectvs, mores, conatvs atqve stvdia, quibus vita hæc nostra, in omni hominum genere, scatet, cunctis sapientiæ cultoribus depinguntur, & uelut in speculo ob oculos ponuntur. Liber salutaribus doctrinis & admonitionibus plenus. Olim à clariss. viro d. Sebastiano Brant iurisconsulto, germanicis rhythmis conscriptus, & per Iacobvm Locher Sueuum latinitati donatus: nunc uerò reuisus & elegantissimis figuris recens illustratus. Basileæ [1572]

PT1509 .N4 1570 Rare bk. coll. Locher, Jacob, 1471-1528, tr.

Brant, Sebastian, 1458-1521.
Stultifera Nauis, qua omnium mortalium narratur stultitia, admo- ‖ dum vtilis & necessaria ab omnibus ad suam salutem perlegenda, ‖ è Latino sermone in nostrum vulgarem versa, & iam diligenter ‖ impressa. An. Do. 1570. ‖ The Ship of Fooles, wherein is shewed the folly ‖ of all States, with diuers other workes adioyned vnto the same, ‖ very profitable and fruitfull for all men. ‖ Tr. out of Latin into Englishe by Alexander ‖ Barclay Priest. ‖ [Colophon: Imprinted at London in Paules Church- ‖ yarde by Iohn Cavvood printer to the ‖ Queenes Maiestie, [1570]

Rare Book Room Zi 7774 Locher, Jacob, 1471-1528.
Theologica emphasis. [Basel, Johann Bergmann, 1496]
26ff. 22cm. 4°.
Hain 10154; British Museum, XV cent., vol.3, p.795.
For fuller description see collation slip in volume.

NL 0433311 CtY

Locher, Jens, 1889-
Aargang 1929; lystspil i 3 akter af Jens Locher. København, C. M. Woel, 1930.
160 p. 22cm.

I. Title.

Library of Congress PT8175.L56A63 1930 30-27721
Copyright D pub. 5016 [2] 839.8126

NL 0433312 DLC

4PT Den 276 Locher, Jens, 1889-
Familien Hansen. Med forord af Axel Garde. København, Westermann, 1944.
126 p.

NL 0433313 DLC-P4

Locher, Jens, 1889-
...Fodboldpræsten. København, De Unges forlag, 1950.
202 p. 22cm.
Novel.

NL 0433314 NN

Locher, Jens
Hannes hændelser. [København] Hasselbalch, 1950
54 p.

NL 0433315 MH

PN6222 .D4S8 Locher, Jens, 1889- ed.
Svikmøllen.
[København] S. Hasselbalch [19

Locher, Jens, 1889-
Sol staar op—! Skuespil i fem akter. [København] S. Hasselbalch [°1926]
130 p. 20½cm.

I. Title.

Library of Congress PT8175.L56S6 1926 28-23222

NL 0433317 DLC NN

Locher, Joachim Albert
... De subscriptione ... subjicit Joachimus Albertus Locher. Lipsiae, J. Georg [1668]
[22] p. 17½cm.
Diss. - Leipzig.

NL 0433318 MH-L

Locher (Joannes) [1797-]. *De putrescentia uteri. 34 pp. 8°. Berolini, typ. A. G. Schadii, [1819].

NL 0433319 DNLM MBCo

Locher, Joannes Georgius.
Disquisitiones mathematicae de controversiis et novitatibus astronomicis.
Ingolstadt, 1614.
4to.

NL 0433320 NN

Locher (Joannes Henricus). *Diss. exhibens magnum lienis in hydrophobia momentum. 23 pp., 1 pl. 4°. Gottingæ, C. Herbst, 1822.

NL 0433321 DNLM

BR 350 .L7 A33 Locher, Johann, d.1524.
Ein gnadenreichs Priuilegium christlicher Freyheyt, von Gott verlyhen: allerley Speyss: allwegen und mit güter Gewissen zügeniessen; wider alten Gebrauch der trutzigen Romanisten. Durch Johann Locher von München. [Zwickaw, Gedruckt durch Jörg Gastel, XXIIII i.e. MDXXIIII]
[27] p. 20½ cm.
Signatures: A-B⁴, C², D⁴ (D4 verso blank)
Title within ornamental border by Hans Weiditz. Cf.A.F.Johnson, German Renaissance title-borders, no.30 (in Bibliographical Society, London. Facsimiles and illustrations, no.1)
1.Fasting.

NL 0433322 MiU

H 284.3 L78m 1524 Locher, Johann, d. 1524.
Miglichen bericht an die zū Zwickaw: vō wegē yrer wunderbarlichen vnd vnerhorten handlung: mit dysen angetzeygt werden. Die gütten vnd posen Christen, wie sie sich gegen Gottes wort halten. Anno dñi. M. D. XXIIII. Durch Johann Locher von Minchen [Zwickaw, Georg Gastel, 1524]

Colophon, D3 recto.
A-C⁴, D³ (D3 verso blank).
4to. 18.5 x 14cm. Black letter.
[30]p.

Title within woodcut border.
Cards.
Wormhole.
Listed in BMC of German Books, p. 522.

1. Zwickau Prophets. 2. Anabaptists - Zwickau. I. Title.

NL 0433324 ViHarEM

Rare Book Room Me45 L788 A2 1524 Locher, Johann, d. 1524.
Vom Aue Maria Leuthen den Glaubigen vast fürderlich. Anno &c. XXiiij. Durch Johann Locher von München. [Zwickau, Jörg Gastel, 1524]
[7]p. 20cm.
Signature: A⁴.

NL 0433325 CtY

Locher, Johann Emanuel, 1769-1815
[Swiss costumes, by Johann Emanuel Locher and Markus Dinkel] 12 col.pl. New York, G. E. Stechert & co. [1935]

From a calendar by Stechert.

NL 0433326 OCl

W 4 L68 1761 L.1 LOCHER, Johann Georg
Dissertatio physiologico-medica inauguralis de secretione glandularum in genere ... Lugduni Batavorum, Apud Johannem Luzac, 1761.
61 p. 24 cm.
Diss. - Leyden.

NL 0433327 DNLM

VOLUME 337

Locher, Johann Jakob, 1771-
Cogitata quaedam de operatione labii leporini. Ienae, Fiedler [1792]
36, 8 p.

Inaug.-diss, Jena.

1. Harelip.

NL 0433328 NNC DNLM NNC-M

Locher, Johann Joseph, b. 1711.
Speculum Academicum Viennense, seu Magistratus antiquissimae et celeberrimae Universitatis Viennensis, a primo ejusdem auspicio ad nostra tempora chronologice, historice, et lemmatice exhibitus a Joanne Josepho Locher. Viennae, sumptibus Leopoldi Joannis Kaliwoda, 1773.
[12], 437, [70] p. 21 cm.

1.Vienna. Universität. History. 2.Vienna. Universität. Faculty. I.Title.

NL 0433329 MnU

RN66 B282 X78 Locher, Johannes Caspar Stephanus.
Deutschkirche "Duitsche christenen" en Karl Barth. Wageningen, H. Veenman [1933]
22 p. 25 cm.

1. Barth, Karl, 1886- 2. Deutsche christen. I. Title.

NL 0433330 CtY-D

Locher, Johannes Caspar Stephanus.
Kohlbrugge en de afscheiding... Amsterdam, Vereeniging tot uitgave van Gereformeerde geschriften, 1934.
54 p. 24cm.

NL 0433331 NjPT NjNbS

GT6 L788l Locher, Johannes Caspar Stephanus.
De leer van Luther over Gods woord. Amsterdam, Scheffer & co., 1903.
xi, 364 p. 24 cm.

Proefschrift - Leiden.
Bibliographical footnotes.

1. Luther, Martin, 1483-1546.

NL 0433332 CtY-D MH-AH PU ICU

Div.S. 270.6 L973ZL0 Locher, Johannes Caspar Stephanus.
De leer van Luther over Gods Woord. Door J. C. S. Locher. Amsterdam, Scheffer, 1903.
xi, 357 p. 24 cm.

Bibliographical footnotes.

1. Luther, Martin. Theology. I. Title.

NL 0433333 NcD

Div.S. 230 L861ZL Locher, Johannes Caspar Stephanus.
Toelichting en verweer. Opmerkingen aangaande verschillende punten der waarheid, naar aanleiding van de dissertatie van Dr. J. van Lonkhuijzen: Hermann Friedrich Kohlbrügge en zijn prediking. Amsterdam, Maatschappij tot Uitgave van Gereformeerde Geschriften, 1908.
v, 191 p. 24 cm.

"Toelichting bij de aanhalingen in dit werk voorkomende": p. [iii]-v.

1. Lonkhuyzen, Jan van. Hermann Friedrich Kohlbrügge en zijn prediking. I. Title.

NL 0433334 NcD MH-AH NjNbS

Locher, Johannes Ludovicus.
De anthrace venenato. Tubingae, Fuesianis, 1786.

24 p.

Inaugural dissertation.

NL 0433335 PPC

Locher, Josef.
Geld- und Währungs-Regelung. Das Gesetz des Geldumlaufs. Ursache der Krisen. [Stuttgart, Schwabenverlag] 1947.
32 p.

NL 0433336 MH-BA MH IU

Locher, Karl, 1843-1915.
see Locher, Carl, 1843-1915.

Locher, Kaspar Theodore, 1920-
German histories of American literature; a chronological and critical description of all German historical accounts of American literature which appeared between 1800 and 1950. Chicago, University of Chicago Press, 1955.
7 cards. 7½ x 12½ cm.
Microprint copy of typescript.
Collation of the original: vi, 271 l.

1. American literature—Hist. & crit.—Bibl. 2. Criticism—Germany. I. Title. II. Title: A chronological and critical description of all German historical accounts of American literature.

Microfilm Z1225 Micp 56-1

NL 0433338 TU NN FU ViU UU NjP DLC OrU OrPR MiU NcD OOxM OClW NcU OU

PS3999 Locher, Kaspar Theodore, 1920-
The reception of American literature in German literary histories in the nineteenth century. 1949.
459 l.

Typewritten.
Thesis—Univ. of Chicago.

1. American literature—Hist. & crit. 2. Literature, Comparative—American and German. 3. Literature, Comparative—German and American.

NL 0433339 ICU

FILM 810.9 L78r Locher, Kaspar Theodore, 1920-
The reception of American literature in German literary histories in the nineteenth century. Chicago, 1949.
Microfilm copy (positive)
Collation of the original: 459l.
Thesis--University of Chicago.
Bibliography: leaves [405]-444.

NL 0433340 IU InU NN NIC

Law Locher, Kurt.

Sandström, Karl Gustaf Armand, 1895-
The double taxation conventions between Sweden and Switzerland of October 16th, 1948. Die Doppelbesteuerungsabkommen zwischen der Schweiz und Schweden vom 16. Oktober 1948. By K. G. A. Sandström & Kurt Locher. Amsterdam, International Bureau of Fiscal Documentation, 1951.

Locher, Kurt.
Handbuch der schweizerisch-amerikanischen Doppelbesteuerungsabkommen, Einkommens und Erbschaftssteuern. Basel, Verlag für Recht und Gesellschaft, 1952 [i. e. 1951-52]
1 v. (loose-leaf) 23 cm.
Includes texts of Einkommenssteuerabkommen and Erbschaftssteuerabkommen in English and German.

1. Taxation, Double—U. S. 2. Taxation, Double—Switzerland. 3. Income tax—U. S.—Law. 4. Income tax—Switzerland—Law. 5. Inheritance and transfer tax—U. S. 6. Inheritance and transfer tax—Switzerland.

New York Univ. Libraries for Library of Congress [1]† A 53-6776

NL 0433341 NNU DLC NNC

Locher, Kurt.
Handbuch und Praxis der schweizerisch-amerikanischen Doppelbesteuerungsabkommen, Einkommens-und Erbschaftssteuern. Basel, Verlag für Recht und Gesellschaft, 1955.
(6 Lieferungen; loose leaves)

NL 0433342 NNU-W

*HJ3564 .A3L6 Locher, Kurt.
Das interkantonale Doppelbesteuerungsgerecht. Basel, Verlag für Recht und Gesellschaft, 1954.
1 v. (various pagings) 23cm. (Die Praxis der Bundessteuern, 3. T.)
Title and section headings repeated in French.

1. Taxation, Double—Switzerland. 2. Taxation—Switzerland—Law. I. Title. II. Series.

NL 0433343 MB ViU

Locher, Kurt.
Die rechtliche Stellung und der Schutz der Gesellschaftsgläubiger im schweizerischen Aktienrecht ... von ... Kurt Locher ... Affoltern am Albis, J. Weiss, 1941.
xiii p., 1 l., [3]-105 p. 23cm.
Inaug.-Diss. - Bern.
"Literatur-Verzeichnis": p.ix-xiii.

NL 0433344 MH-L ICRL

Locher, Louis
see Locher-Ernst, Louis, 1906-

WG 23688 Locher, Max.
Über Condensationsproducte der Dioxyweinsäure mit aromatischen Hydrazinen. Winterthur, 1887.
43 p.
Inaug.-Diss. - Basel.

NL 0433346 CtY

VOLUME 337

Locher, Maximilian, *18th cent.*
Maximiliani Locher ... Observationes practicae circa inoculationem variolarum in neo-natis institutam. Vindobonæ, typ. J. T. nob. de Trattnern, 1768.
48 p. 20cm.
——— Maximiliani Locher ... Continuatio experimentorum de inoculatione variolarum. Vindobonæ, typ. J. T. nob. de Trattnern, 1768.
41 p. 20cm. [With his Observationes practicae circa inoculationem variolarum in neo-natis institutam. Vindobonæ, 1768]
——— Maximiliani Locher ... Continuatio altera experimentorum de inoculatione variolarum. Vindobonæ, typ. J. T. nob. de Trattnern, 1768.
56 p. 20cm. [With his Observationes practicae circa inoculationem variolarum in neo-natis institutam. Vindobonæ, 1768]
1. Smallpox, Inoculation of.
34-40151
Library of Congress RM786.L6
NL 0433348 DLC NNNAM

18th cent. LOCHER, Maximilian, 18th cent.
Observationes practicae circa luem veneream, epilepsiam et maniam, tria morborum genera in praedicto nosocomio prae aliis maxime obvia. His accedunt casus varii, qui ulteriorem cicutae usum internum et externum in morbis curatu difficillimis confirmant. Viennae, Typ. J.T. Trattner, 1762.
108p. 19cm.
NL 0433349 CtY-M KU-M DNLM WU

Locher, Maximilian, 18th cent.
Observations sur l'usage interne du colchique d'automne, du sublimé corrosif, de la feuille d'oranger, du vinaigre distillé, &c.
see under Störck, Anton, freiherr von, 1731-1803.

Locher, P. Adolph.
See
Locher, Adolph.

Locher, Pablo
see Locher, Paul.

Locher, Paul.
El capitan azul. Drama en tres actos, escrito en frances, por Mr. Pablo Locher, traducido libremente por Don Antonio María de Ojeda. Sevilla: M. Caro, 1839. 83(1) p., front. 8°.
1. Drama (French). 2. Ojeda, Antonio María de, translator. 3. Title.
N. Y. P. L. April 1, 1916.
NL 0433353 NN MH

Locher, Paul, 1858–
Ein Buchdruckerleben; Erinnerungen eines alten Buchdruckers, von Paul Locher. Berlin: Fr. Zillessen, 1925. 175 p. 12°.
262562A. 1. Printing—Hist.—Germany, 19th cent.
N. Y. P. L. October 1, 1926
NL 0433354 NN

W 4 B52 1952 LOCHER, Robert.
Das elektrophoretische Serumeiweissbild bei der Krebskrankheit. Innsbruck [1952?]
25 p. illus.
Inaug.-Diss. - Bern.
1. Blood proteins 2. Neoplasms - Diagnosis
W4 B52
NL 0433355 DNLM

Pamph. v.610 LOCHER, Th J d.1882.
Noch perfectionisme noch antinomianisme. Korte verklaring van Heidelb. Catechismus: Vr. en Antw. 114 en 115 en van Romeinen VII, door Th. J. Locher. Utrecht, C. Van Bentum, 1881.
70p. 19cm.
NL 0433356 MH-AH

Locher, Theo, 1921–
Bernische Kartierung zur Zeit der Dufourkarte und Vorarbeiten zum bernischen Kataster. [Bern, 1954]
87 p. illus. 24 cm.
Inaug.-Diss.—Bern.
Vita.
Cover title.
"Separat-Abdruck aus dem 'Jahresbericht der Geographischen Gesellschaft von Bern, 1953/54.'"
Bibliography: p. 78-79.
1. Cartography—Switzerland—Bern (Canton) I. Title.
GA1025.B4L6 64-30104
NL 0433357 DLC

Locher, Theodor, 1899-
Ueber die differential-diagnose: Tertiaere syphilis und tuberkulose der haut.
Inaug. diss. Marburg, 1927.
Bibl.
NL 0433358 ICRL CtY

DB 200.7 .L82 Locher, Theodor Jakob Gottlieb, 1900-
Die nationale Differenzierung und Integrierung der Slovaken und Tschechen in ihrem geschichtlichen Verlauf bis 1848. Haarlem, H.D.Tjeenk Willink, 1931.
208 p. 23 cm.
Proefschrift--Leiden.
Bibliographical footnotes.
"Stellingen" ([3] p.) laid in.
1.Slovaks. 2.Czechs.
MU ICU CaBVaU
NL 0433359 MiU NcU InU IU WU NRU FMU CSt-H PU NN

Locher, Theodor Jakob Gottlieb, 1900–
Nederland en het komende Duitsland, een pleidooi tegen annexatie. Amsterdam, J. M. Meulenhoff [1945]
31 p. 24 cm. (Tijd- en strijdvragen)
1. World War, 1939-1945—Territorial questions—Netherlands 2. Netherlands—Bound.—Germany. 3. Germany—Bound.—Netherlands. I. Title. II. Series.
D821.N4L6 A F 48-971*
New York. Public Libr. for Library of Congress [2]†
NL 0433360 NN WaU DLC MiU

Locher, Theodor Jakob Gottlieb, 1900–
Over de verhouding van oost en west in de europese geschiedenis; rede uitgesproken bij de aanvaarding van het ambt van hoogleraar in de algemene geschiedenis aan de Rijksuniversiteit te Leiden op 29 maart 1946, door dr Th. J. G. Locher. Amsterdam, J. M. Meulenhoff [1946]
1 p. l., 24 p. 22½cm.
On cover: Inaugurele rede.
Bibliographical references in "Aantekeningen" (p. 21-24)
1. Europe—Civilization. 2. Russia—Civilization. I. Title.
D8.L6 A F 46-1003
Harvard univ. Library for Library of Congress
NL 0433361 MH NIC NcU CtY DLC CLU

D377.3 L812 Hoover Library Locher, Theodor Jakob Gottlieb, 1900-
Het panslavisme bij de Tsjechen en Slovaken [n.p., 1932]
[41]-54 p. 25cm.
Caption title.
Bijlage A to Verslag van het eerste Congres van nederlandsche historici, 14 Mei, 1932.
1.Panslavism .Czechs. 3.Slovaks.
NL 0433362 CSt-H

Locher, Theodor Jakob Gottlieb, 1900–
Peter de Grote. Amsterdam, Ploegsma, 1947.
266 p. port. 20 cm. (Daad en droom; een reeks biografieën, deel 2)
"Geraadpleegde bronnen en literatuur": p. 264-266.
1. Peter I, the Great, Emperor of Russia, 1672-1725. 2. Russia—Hist.—Peter I, 1689-1725. (Series: Daad en droom, deel 2)
A 48-8972*
Harvard Univ. Library for Library of Congress [1]
NL 0433363 MH NN CaQMM

D16.4 G3L6 Locher, Theodor Jacob Gottleib, 1900-
Die Überwindung des Europäozentrischen Geschichtsbildes. Weisbaden, Steiner, 1954.
18p. 24cm. (Institut für Europäische Geschichte, Mainz. Vorträge)
1. Europe. History. Study and teaching.
ICU InU ICN NIC CaBVaU
NL 0433364 IaU OU LU CU MU MoU MiU NNC NcD NN IU

Locher, Theodorico, respondent.
Patrocinivm votorvm catholicorvm adversvs impios & sacrilegos apostatas ...
see under Forer, Laurent, , 1580-1659, praeses.

Locher, Walter.
Die theorie der konsumentenrente, von Walter Locher ... Stuttgart, W. Kohlhammer, 1933.
4 p. l., 45 p. diagrs. 24cm. (Added t.-p.: Tübinger wirtschaftswissenschaftliche abhandlungen. [neue folge] ... hft. 3)
"Literaturverzeichnis": p. [44]-45.
1. Consumption (Economics) 2. Value. 3. Supply and demand. I. Title. II. Title: Konsumentenrente, Die theorie der.
33-39134
Library of Congress HB801.L6
330.1
NL 0433366 DLC OU

Locher, Walter E.
A study of the behavior of magnetized iron under torsion. Thesis, 1934.
NL 0433367 OClW

W 4 W951 1955 LOCHER, Walter Josef, 1927-
Zur Kenntnis der papillären Cystadenolymphome. Würzburg, 1955.
30 p. illus.
Inaug.-Diss. - Würzburg.
1. Adenolymphoma - Salivary
2. Parotid gland - Neoplasms
NL 0433368 DNLM

VOLUME 337

Locher, Werner, 1904-
... Scherbenkobalt und Nervarsen. Vergleichend histologische Untersuchungen ihrer Wirkung auf die Wurzelhaut des Menschen und des Hundes ... Zürich, 1930.
Inaug.-Diss. - Zürich.
Curriculum vitae.
Published also in Schweizerische Monatsschrift für Zahnheilkunde, Band XL, No. 1.
"Literaturverzeichnis": p. 44-46.

NL 0433369 CtY

WB L814g 1832 LOCHER-BALBER, Hans, 1797-1873
Grundzüge der Propädeutik zum Studium der Medicin. Zürich, Orell, Füssli, 1832.
xv, 360 p.

NL 0433370 DNLM

Locher-Balber (Hans) [1797-1873]. Vortrag gehalten zur Feier des zehnjährigen Stiftungstages einer Gesellschaft ärztlicher Freunde in Zürich, den 27. März 1846. 23 pp. 8°. [Zürich, Orell, Fussli & Co.], 1846.

NL 0433371 DNLM

Locher-Ernst, Louis, 1906-
Differential- und Integralrechnung im Hinblick auf ihre Anwendungen; ein Lehr- und Übungsbuch zur Infinitesimalrechnung und zur analytischen Geometrie. Basel, Birkhäuser, 1948.
595 p. diagrs., tables. 25 cm.

1. Calculus.

QA303.L68 517.1 48-27726*

NL 0433372 DLC CSt CtW ScCleU OU NRU CtY TxU NjP

Locher-Ernst, Louis, 1906-
Einführung in die freie Geometrie ebener Kurven. Basel, Birkhäuser [1952]
85 p. illus. 23 cm. (Elemente der Mathematik vom höheren Standpunkt aus, Bd. 1)

1. Curves, Plane. I. Title.

QA483.L6 53-751

OrStbM OrU-M
WaWW WaTC WaT WaSpG WaSp WaS WaPS WaE Wa Or OrSaW CaBVaU IdB IdPI IdU MtBC MtU OrCS OrP OrPR OrU MH CtY OrU CSt CoU CLU NjR WaU MoU ICarbS MtBuM
NL 0433373 DLC CLSU NBC ICU NN NcD TU OCU TxU OU

Locher-Ernst, Louis, 1906-
Geometrisieren im bereiche wichtigster kurvenformen; eine erste einführung in das geometrische denken, von dr. Louis Locher-Ernst ... Mit 51 abbildungen. Zürich-Leipzig, Orell Füssli verlag [°1938]
64 p. diagrs. 23½ cm.
"Das vorliegende heft stellt eine überarbeitung der nachschrift von sechs vorträgen dar, die in der zeit vom 19. bis 24. september dieses jahres am Goetheanum, freie hochschule für geisteswissenschaft, Dornach, gehalten wurden."—Vorwort.

1. Mathematics—Philosophy. 2. Anthroposophy. I. Title.

A C 39-1942 rev

Michigan. Univ. Libr. for Library of Congress QA9.L8 [r49c1]

NL 0433375 MiU OrCS CtY

Locher-Ernst, Louis, 1906-
Mathematik als vorschule zur geist-erkenntnis; dreizehn vorträge ... Zürich, Archimedes verlag [c1944]

120p. tables,diagrs. 23cm.
Pages 118-120, advertising matter.

NL 0433376 CLSU

Locher-Ernst Louis, 1906-
Projektive geometrie und die grundlagen der euklidischen und polareuklidischen geometrie ... von dr. Louis Locher-Ernst ... Zürich-Leipzig, Orell Füssli [1940]
xv, 290 p. diagrs. 20 cm. (His: Urphänomene der geometrie, 2. t.)
1. Geometry, Projective.

NL 0433377 CU MH IU

BP595 .S9 Locher-Ernst, Louis, 1906- ed.
Sternkalender; erscheinungen am sternenhimmel.
Zürich, Kreuzlingen, Archimedes verlag, P. Christiani & cie.; [etc., etc., 19

518.5 L78u Locher-Ernst, Louis, 1906-
Über gruppen konformer raumabbildungen und modulfunktionen des raumes. Zürich, 1930.
26p.

Inaug.-diss.--Zürich.
Curriculum vitae.

NL 0433379 IU ICRL MiU RPB CtY DLC

Locher-Ernst, Louis, 1906-
Urphänomene der Geometrie. Zürich, Orell Füssli [°1937]-
v. diagrs. 21 cm.
"Die vorliegenden Ausführungen sind aus einer Vortragsreihe entstanden."—v. 1, p. ix.

1. Geometry, Projective. I. Title.

QA471.L6 516.57 38-30576 rev

NL 0433380 DLC OrCS MH CtY OU RPB

Locher-Werling, Emilie.
„Es Sachsilüüte". Ein Zürcherisches Dialektstück in 3 Akten. Aarau, H.R. Sauerländer & Co., 1908.
82 p. 12°.

NL 0433381 NN

Locher-Werling, Emilie.
„Esperantø". Szene in Zürcher Dialek. Aarau, H.R. Sauerländer & Co., 1908.
15 p. 16°.

NL 0433382 NN

Locher-Werling, Emilie.
"Manöverläbe." Lustspiel in drei Bildern in Zürcher Dialekt. Aarau: H. R. Sauerländer & Co., 1910. 82 p., 1 l. 12°.

1. Drama (Swiss-German). 2. Title.
N. Y. P. L. May 16, 1911.

NL 0433383 NN

Locher-Werling, Emilie.
„Si ischt scho verseh." Lust-Spiel in 2 Akten, in Zürcher Dialekt. Aarau, H.R. Sauerländer & Co., 1907.
32 p. 12°.

NL 0433384 NN

Locher-Werling, Emilie.
D' Stüürschrub, oder; 's hät alles zwo Syte; Lustspiel in zwei Aufzügen in Zürcher Dialekt, von Emilie Locher-Werling... Aarau: H. R. Sauerländer & Co., 1915. 41(1) p. 2. ed. 12°.

1. Drama (Swiss-German). 2. Swiss dialects: Zurich. 3. Title.
N. Y. P. L. June 1, 1920.

NL 0433385 NN

Locher-Werling, Emilie.
Sulaglin e Sturniclin; duos sourinas chi nu's sumaglian ne brich ne zich. Rumauntsch da L. Liun. n.p. [193-]

[32] p. color illus. 33 cm.

NL 0433386 MH

Locher-Werling, Emilie.
Trutta e Blondina; l'historia de duas soras. Romontsch da G.F. [Gian Fontana] n.p. [193-]

[32] p. color illus. 33 cm.

NL 0433387 MH

Locher-Wild, Hans.
Ueber familienanlage und erblichkeit, eine wissenschaftliche razzie, von Dr. Hans Locher-Wild ... Zürich, Orell Füssli & co., 1874.
319 p. 23 cm.

NL 0433388 NcD CU

HD 9715 S94L62 Locher et cie.
Hundert Jahre Technik, 1830-1930. [Zürich, 1930]
444p. illus. 33cm.

On spine: Die Baufirme Locher et cie in Zürich.

1. Construction industry - Switzerland.
I. Title.

NL 0433389 MU DLC-P4

[Locher & Cie, Zurich]
Der Pelikan, 1675-1931. [Zürich, Gedruckt in der Buchdruckerei Berichthaus, 1932?]
24p., illus., 14 plates, 4 plans, 32cm.

NL 0433390 MH

823.91 B471Bl Locherbie-Goff, Margaret.
La jeunesse d'Arnold Bennett (1867-1904). Avesnes-sur-Helpe [France] Editions de L'Observateur, 1939.
322p. illus. 25cm.

Includes text of Bennett's Rosalys.

1. Bennett, Arnold, 1867-1931. I. Bennett, Arnold 1867-1931. Rosalys. II. Title.

NL 0433391 ICarbS

VOLUME 337

Locherbie-Goff, Margaret.
La jeunesse d'Arnold Bennett (1867-1904) Avesnes-sur-Helpe (Nord), Éditions de "L'Observateur", 1939 [i.e. 1941]
322 p. plates, ports., map (fold.)

Thesis, Lille.
Bibliographical footnotes.
"Errata" inserted following t.-p.

1. Bennett, Arnold, 1867-1931.

NL 0433392 NNC MH CtY ICU

---

f604.7
D92.9
L812cl
1740
LOCHERER, Alipius.
Clypeus philosophico-Scotisticus, cursus philosophicus, juxta mentem et doctrinam ... Joannis Duns-Scoti elaboratus ... ab Alipio Locherer. Crembsii, Typis Ignatij Antonij Praexl, 1740.
7p.l.(incl.port.),636,[3]p. 32.5cm.

NL 0433393 MH-AH

Locherer, Johann Nepomuk, 1773-1837.
Lehrbuch der christlich-kirchlichen Archäologie... Frankfurt a.M., Andrea, 1832.
viii, 194 p. 19cm.

NL 0433394 NjPT NjP

Locherer, Johann Nepomuk, 1773-1837.
Lehrbuch der Patrologie; für academische Vorlesnugen bestimmt von Dr. Johann Nepomuk Locherer... Mainz, Florian Kupferberg, 1837.

viii, 224p. 21cm.

1. Fathers of the Church--History and criticism.

NL 0433395 PLatS

Loches, Joannes Daniel de. * De testamentis **privilegiatis.** 19 pp., 1 l. 4°. *Lugd. Bat., S. Luchtmans et fil.*, 1755. [P., v. 997.]

NL 0433396 DNLM

LOCHES, Joannes Gerardus de.
Specimen juridicum inaugurale de abigeis eroumque poena jure romano et hollandico. Lugduni Batav.,1790.

(4)+22+2 p.
Diss.-Inaug.-Leyden.

NL 0433397 MH-L

Lochet, Jean.
Des effets de la pluralité d'établissements en matière de sociétés par actions en droit français. Paris, 1930.

NL 0433398 MH-L

Ndh95
F6
929m
Lochet, Jean.
... Des effets de la pluralité d'établissements en matière de sociétés par actions en droit français ... Paris,Rousseau et cie.,1929.
2p.l.,[7]-215p. 24cm.
"Bibliographie": p.[203]-208.
Thèse - Univ. de Paris.

1.Corporation law - France. 2.Stock companies - France. 3.Corporation law.
Card for Law school.

NL 0433399 CtY MH-L

842
J774
Rare
Books
Col
[Lochet, Jerôme]
Le fabricisme ou Histoire secrette de la révolution de Liege, drame, en trois actes. A Munsterbilsen, Chez le Sieur Clairvoyant, imprimeur pacifique, 1791.
36,[1]p. 20cm. [With Ioseph sur le trone. Liege, 1695]

NL 0433400 TxU

Lochet, Louis.
... L'apôtre dans le mystère de l'Église ... Montréal, Fides, 1951.
71 p. 19 cm. (Textes d'action catholique, 3)

NL 0433401 NcD

Lochet, Louis.
Fils de l'Église. Paris, Éditions du Cerf, 1954.
257 p. 23 cm. (Problèmes modernes d'apostolat)

1. Catholic Church. I. Title.

A 55-6903

Catholic Univ. of America. Library
for Library of Congress [3]

NL 0433402 DCU OrStbM MH-AH

BX
2348.
Z5
L7
1955
Lochet, Louis.
L'Union à dieu ame de tout apostolat...
2. éd. Montréal, Fides [1955]
48p 19cm (Textes d'action catholique. Nouvelle série. 1)

1. Catholic action. 1. Title.

NL 0433403 MnCS

Rs10
Bor951
Lochet, Robert.
Contribution à l'étude de la diffusion moléculaire de la lumière (effet Rayleigh) dans les solutions étendues d'électrolytes forts. Paris, 1952 (i.e. 1953)

Thèse - Bordeaux.

NL 0433404 CtY

Rs10
Bor951
Lochet, Robert.
Contribution à l'étude de la diffusion moléculaire de la lumière (effet Rayleigh) dans les solutions étendues d'électrolytes forts. Paris,1952[i.e.1953]

Thèse - Bordeaux.

NL 0433405 CtY

Lochgilphead, Scot. Argyll and Bute District Lunatic Asylum
see Argyll and Bute District Lunatic Assylum, Lochgilphead, Scot.

SF247
.L6
Lochhead, A. Grant.
Bacteriological investigations of milking machines.
Ottawa, 1929.
8° 1 pam.

NL 0433406 DLC

Lochhead, A. Grant, and **D. A. Heron.**
Microbiological studies of honey. I. Honey fermentation and its cause. II. Infection of honey by sugar-tolerant yeasts. By A. Grant Lochhead...and Doris A. Heron... Ottawa: Published by authority of the Hon. W. R. Motherwell, minister of agriculture, 1929. 47 p. illus. 8°. (Canada. Agriculture Dept. Bull. n. s., no. 116.)

Cover-title.
Bibliography, p. 35-36.

1. Honey. 2. Heron, Doris A., jt. au. 3. Ser.
N. Y. P. L. December 17, 1929

NL 0433407 NN DLC

914.15
L812s
Lochhead, Alexander.
Sprigs of Shillelah; adventures in Ireland. Dundee, J. Leng, 1907.
159p. 19cm.

"Reprinted from the People's friend."

1. Ireland. Descr. & trav. I. Title.

NL 0433408 IEN PPL

Lochhead, James.

Marshall, Francis Hugh Adam, 1878–
The physiology of reproduction, by Francis H. A. Marshall ... With contributions by William Cramer ... James Lochhead ... and Cresswell Shearer ... 2d and rev. ed. London, New York [etc.] Longmans, Green, and co., 1922.

Lochhead, Jewell, 1888–
The education of young children in England, by Jewell Lochhead ... New York city, Teachers college, Columbia university, 1932.
vi, 226 p., 1 l. 23cm.

Thesis (PH. D.)—Columbia university, 1932.
Vita.
Published also as Teachers college, Columbia university, Contributions to education, no. 521.
Bibliography: p. 219-226.

1. Education—England. 2. Education of children. 3. Public schools (Elementary)—England. 4. School management and organization—Gt. Brit. 5. Kindergarten. 6. Nursery schools. 7. Teachers, Training of—Gt. Brit. I. Title.

32-35055

Library of Congress LA633.L6 1932
Columbia Univ. Libr. [3] 372.20942

NL 0433410 NNC DLC

Lochhead, Jewell, 1888–
The education of young children in England, by Jewell Lochhead ... New York city, Teachers college, Columbia university, 1932.
vi, 226 p. 23½cm. (Teachers college, Columbia university. Contributions to education, no. 521)

Issued also as thesis (PH. D.) Columbia university.
Bibliography: p. 219-226.

1. Education—England. 2. Education of children. 3. Public schools (Elementary)—England. 4. School management and organization—Gt. Brit. 5. Kindergarten. 6. Nursery schools. 7. Teachers, Training of—Gt. Brit. I. Title.

32-35056

Library of Congress LA633.L6 1932 a
——Copy 2. LB5.C8 no. 521
Copyright A 58074 [17] 372.20942

MiU OU OO ODW OCl MB AU MtU ViU OrPR OrP OrU PSt
NL 0433411 DLC KEmT ICRL NcU NcD PPPL PBm PPT OCU

VOLUME 337

Lochhead, John, 1876–
A reach of the river; a family chronicle, 1880–1954. [Gillingham] Dorset, Priv. print. at the Blackmore Press [1955]
470 p. illus. 23 cm.

1. Lochhead family. I. Title.

CS439.L627 1955 56-25333 ‡

NL 0433412 DLC NN

Lochhead, John Lipton.

FOR OTHER EDITIONS SEE MAIN ENTRY

VK23 .D3 1939 **Dayton, Fred Erving,** 1880–
Steamboat days. Illustrated by John Wolcott Adams. New York, Tudor Pub. Co. [1939]

Lochhead, Margaret Szabo, 1906–
... Methods of hatching eggs of the blue crab, [by] Margaret S. Lochhead and Curtis L. Newcombe. [Williamsburg? Va., 1942?]
cover-title, p. 76–86 incl. table. 23cm. (Virginia fisheries laboratory and Department of biology, College of William and Mary. Contribution no. 9)
"Literature cited": p. 86.
"Reprinted from The Virginia journal of science, vol. III, nos. 2 & 3, 1942."
1. Crabs. 2. Wild life, Conservation of. I. Newcombe, Curtis Lakeman, 1905– joint author. II. Title: Hatching eggs of the blue crab. III. Title: The blue crab. IV. Ser.

NL 0433414 ViU

W.C.L. 821.91 L812F Lochhead, Marion Cleland.
Feast of Candlemas and other devotional poems; with a foreword by the Bishop of Glasgow and Galloway. Edinburgh, Moray Press [1937]
63 p. 20 cm.

NL 0433415 NcD NNC NN PU

821.9 L812fi Lochhead, Marion Cleland.
Fiddler's bidding. Edinburgh, Oliver and Boyd, 1939.
19p. 16cm.

NL 0433416 IEN LU

823.9 L812i Lochhead, Marion Cleland.
Island destiny. Edinburgh, Moray Press [1936]
287p. 19cm.

NL 0433417 IEN NN

Lochhead, Marion Cleland.
John Gibson Lockhart. [1st ed.] London, Murray [1954]
324 p. illus. 22 cm.

1. Lockhart, John Gibson, 1794–1854.

PR4891.L4L6 928.2 54-12712

WaWW WaTC MtBuM
MB GU MsU FMU WaS WaSp WaSpG WaT OrStbM Or CaBViP
PBL PU OOxM OO OU MiU OrU-M OrSaW NcGU CoU ICU AU
MH NN LU CtY IaU ViU TxU NcD IU NcU PPT AAP PP PSt
WaTC MtBC IdPI IdU IdB NBuC CaBVaU WaU ScU InStme
NL 0433418 DLC WaE WaPS OrU Wa OrP OrPR MtU OrCS

Lochhead, Marion Cleland.
A lamp was lit; the Girls' Guildry through fifty years. Edinburgh, Moray Press [1949]
104 p. plates, ports. 19 cm.

1. Girls' Guildry. I. Title.

HS3365.G7L6 267.81 50-35740

NL 0433419 DLC

823.9 L812o Lochhead, Marion Cleland.
On Tintock tap, being lowland and other tales for children. Illustrated by Mildred R. Lamb. Edinburgh, Moray Press [1946]
viii,200p. illus. 19cm.

NL 0433420 IEN

821.9 L812p Lochhead, Marion Cleland.
Painted things, and other poems. London, Gowans and Gray, 1929.
63p. 19cm.

NL 0433421 IEN MH

Lochhead, Marion Cleland.
Poems. London, etc., Gowans and Gray, Ltd., 1928.
48 p. sq. 12°.

NL 0433422 MH

Lochhead, Marion Cleland.
Saint Mungo's bairns, being the story of Glasgow told for children. Illus. by Nan Muirhead Moffat. Edinburgh, Moray Press [1948]
ix, 253 p. illus. 19 cm.

1. Glasgow—Hist.—Fiction. I. Title.

PZ9.L79Sai 49-27389*

NL 0433423 DLC

Lochhead, Marion Cleland.
The Scots household in the eighteenth century; a century of Scottish domestic and social life. Edinburgh, Moray Press [1948]
410 p. plates, ports. 22 cm

1. Scotland—Soc. life & cust. 2. Scotland—Hist.—18th cent. I. Title.

DA812.L6 941.07 51-3078

WaPS WaS WaSp OrPR OrU OrCS MtU MtBC
Wa WaE IdB IdPI IdU OrP WaWW NIC CaOTP WaSpG WaT WaTC
CBBD TU CaBVaU CaBViP Or OrStbM OrSaW OrU-M MtBuM
NL 0433424 DLC NcU NN InU ICN ICU NcU MH TxU CtY PBm

Lochhead, Robert Knight.
... Valuation and surplus, by R. K. Lochhead ... Cambridge [Eng.] Pub. for the Institute of actuaries Students' society, at the University press, 1932.
xiii, 99 p. 22cm. (Institute of actuaries Students' society's Consolidation of reading series)
"Summary of references": p. [97]–99.

1. Insurance, Life—Finance. 2. Insurance, Life—Rates and tables. I. Title.

Library of Congress HG8846.L6 33-5758
[3] 368.3

NL 0433425 DLC NN CU MiU PPProM

Lochhead, Robert Norman.
With rod well bent... London, Jenkins [1951]
176 p. illus. 22 cm.

NL 0433426 NjP

Lochhead, William, 1864–1927.
Class book of economic entomology, with special reference to the economic insects of the northern United States and Canada, by William Lochhead ... with 257 illustrations. Philadelphia, P. Blakiston's son & co. [c1919]
xiv, 436 p. incl. front. (ports.) illus. col. pl. 20cm. $2.50
Bibliography: p. 407–408.

1. Insects, Injurious and beneficial. 2. Insects—U. S. 3. Insects—Canada. I. Title: Economic entomology.

Library of Congress SB931.L8 19–6649

DNLM PPFr PBm CU PPLas MiU ODW OO OC1W
NL 0433427 DLC NjP CaBVaU Or WaS CaBViP ViU NcD

---

443 L782 Lochhead, William, 1864-1927.
An introduction to heredity and genetics; a study of the modern biological laws and theories relating to animal & plant breeding. [n.p., 1920]
185 p.

1. Evolution. 2. Heredity. 3. Plant-breeding. 4. Domestic animals. Breeding.

NL 0433428 DNAL IU CaBVaU

Lochhead, William, 1864–1927.
... Outlines of nature studies, by William Lochhead ... Toronto, Ont., Ontario dept. of agriculture, 1905.
cover-title, 48 p. 21½cm. (Ontario agricultural college. MacDonald institute. Bulletin 142)

1. Nature study—Outlines, syllabi, etc.

E 15-1443

Library, U. S. Bur. of Education QH53.O7L7

NL 0433429 DHEW PU DLC

Lochhead, William, 1864–1927.
... The San José and other scale insects. Prepared for the use of fruit growers and scale inspectors, by Wm. Lochhead ... Toronto, Warwick bro's & Rutter, printers, 1900.
48 p. illus. 22cm.
At head of title: Ontario department of agriculture.

1. San José scale. 2. Scale-insects. I. Ontario. Dept. of agriculture.

Library of Congress SB945.S2L7 12–36766

NL 0433430 DLC NIC NcRS MiU ICJ

Lochhead, William, 1864–1927.
A synopsis of economic entomology. [Ste. Anne de Bellevue, Que.] Macdonald College [n.d.]
113 p. 23 cm.

1. Insects, Injurious and beneficial.
I. Titlo.

NL 0433431 CaBVaU

VOLUME 337

Lochhead, William, 1864-1927, ed.

Harrison, Francis Charles, 1871-
... The weeds of Ontario, by F. C. Harrison ... Rev. by Wm. Lochhead ... Toronto, Ontario Dept. of agriculture, 1903.

Lochiel; or, The field of Culloden ...
see under [Carey, David] 1782-1824.

"LOCHIEL'S warning." Edinburgh, J. Johnstone, [1843].

24°. pp.11.
The date is taken from the end of the article "From the "Witness' of the 3d June".

NL 0433434 MH

Lochinvar, John Gordon, 1st viscount Kenmure, lord
see Kenmure, John Gordon, 1st viscount, lord Lochinvar, 1599?-1634.

Lochinvar, *Sir* **Robert Gordon, of**
see
Gordon, *Sir* **Robert,** *of Lochinvar, d.* 1627?

759.5 [Lochis, Guglielmo] conte.
L788p La pinacoteca e la villa Lochis alla Crocetta di Mozzo presso Bergamo, con notizie biografiche degli autori dei quadri. Milano, V. Guglielmini, 1846.
222p.

Dedication by Conte Guglielmo Lochis.

1. Paintings--Mozzo, Italy. 2. Painters, Italian. I. Title.

NL 0433437 IU

ND [Lochis, Guglielmo, conte] collector.
614 La pinacoteca e la villa Lochis alla
.L6 Crocetta di Mozzo presso Bergamo, con notizie biografiche degli autori dei quadri. 2. ed. Bergamo, Tip. Natali, 1858.
294 p.

#Painters, Italian.
#Paintings, Italian.
La pinacoteca e la villa Lochis alla Crocetta di Mozzo presso Bergamo.

NL 0433438 MoU IU

720.945 Lochis, Ottavio, conte.
L788i Illustrazione dell'origine e del progresso dell'arti belle sino al secolo XVI ... Bergamo, P. Cattaneo, 1851.
143p.

1. Architecture--Hist. 2. Art--Hist.

NL 0433439 IU

Lochlainn, Colm O
see O'Loughlin, Colm.

Lochlan, Helen Beatrice.
Irene Ashton; or, The stolen child; drama in five acts ... Boston, 1911.
15 p. 19 cm.

NL 0433441 RPB

Lochlan, Helen B[eatrice]
The spirit of Christmas. A prelude to the distribution of presents on Christmas Eve at the Independent Liberal church, Greenwich, Mass., Dec. 25th, 1893. Greenwich, Mass., 1893.
[7] l. 16 cm.
Cover title.

NL 0433442 RPB

The Lochleven angler
see under Burns-Begg, Robert, 1833-1899.

Case
F The Lochlomond expedition M.DCC.XV.
434 Reprinted and illustrated from original
.52 documents. Glasgow, 1834.

Bookplate of Johannes Georgius Home Drummond, of Abbots grange.
A reprint by James Dennistoun; the original tract is in the National library of Scotland and is believed to be unique. The author is unknown.-cf. Halkett & Laing.
With reproduction of original t.-p.

NL 0433444 ICN OCl

Lochlons, Colin, *pseud.*
see **Jackson, Caary Paul,** 1902-

Lochmaier, Michael, 15th Cent.
Celeberrimi sacre theologie necnō iurispontificij doctoris ... Michaelis lochmair sermones de sanctis perutiles: cum vigintitribus sermonibus magistri Pauli wann annexis feliciter incipiunt.
— *Colophon:* Impressiq; in imperiali oppido Hagenaw per Henricū Gran finiunt feliciter. xxiiij. die mensis Martij. Anno salutis post Millesimū quingentesimum. (252) ff. 50-52 lines. Black-letter. Ornamental rubricated capitals, with guide letters. 27 cm., in 8s; a, b, c, f, m, n, s, x, A, D in 6s.
See Hain-Copinger, no. 10174.
Fol. (252) is blank.

E2253 — Double main card. — Lochmaier, Michael. (M1) — Wann, Paul. (M2) — Sermons. Colls. (1, 2) — Saints. (1, 2) — Incunabula. (1)

NL 0433446 MB PP

LOCHMAIER, Michael, 15th cent.
Celeberrimi sacre theologie...Michaelis Lochmair sermones de sanctis perutiles: cum viginitribus sermones ... Pauli Wann annexis filiciter incipiunt.

Colophon: Hagenaw, 1500.

NL 0433447 MH-AH

Rare
BX Lochmaier, Michael, 15th cent.
1756 Celeberrimi sacre theologie necnō iuris-
L81+ pōtificij doctoris ... Michaelis lochmair
1507 sermōes de sanctis perutiles: cū vigintitribus sermōibus magistri Pauli wann annexis, feliciter incipiunt. [Hagenaw, Impressi per Henricum Gran, 1507]
[252] l. 28cm.

Signatures: A-B6, a-f8.8.6, g-18, m-n6, o-p8, q-z A-D8.8.6, E-I8.
Last leaf (blank) wanting.

Reprint of the 1497 edition.
With manuscript marginal notes.
Manuscript note on t. p.: Monasterij Weissenaw.

1. Catholic Church--Sermons. 2. Sermons, Latin. 3. Saints. I. Wann, Paulus, d. 1489. II. Title: Sermones de sanctis.

NL 0433449 NIC

BV Lochmaier, Michael, 15th cent.
4009 Parrochiale curatorum... Paris, Chez Francoys
L7 Regnault [n.d.]
Cage
[8] clxxi [1] l. 8vo.

NL 0433450 DFo

Rare
BX Lochmaier, Michael, 15th cent.
1939 Parochiale curatorum. [Nuremberg, Fried-
C665 rich Creussner, not before 1493]
L81 [164] l. 20cm.
1493
Signatures: A8, B6, a-b8, c6, d-t8.
Leaf [1a] (title): Prestantissimi sacre theologie. necnon iuris pontifitij doctoris et artium magistri. ac ecclesie Patauiensis canonici dñi Michaelis lochmaier parrochiale curatorum feliciter incipit.
Leaf [15a] Between the table and the text there is a second t. p. (Tractatus Inparrochiale curatorum), chiefly occupied by a large colored woodcut, lettered: Hec est Stella maris.
Large marginal woodcut on leaf [16a]
Hain. Repertorium (with Copinger's Supplement) *10167; Proctor 2189; Brit. Mus. Cat. (XV cent.) II, p. 455 (IA. 7812); Stillwell L 236.

NL 0433452 NIC NcU PP-W

Lochmaier, Michael, 15th cent.
[Parochiale curatorum] [Haguenau, Heinrich Gran for Johannes Rynmann, 20 Aug. 1498] 152 l. 20cm. (4°.)

l. 1a: Prestātissim [sic] sacre theologie.|| necnō iurispontificii doctoris|| et artium magistri. ac ecclesie|| Patauiēsis canonici domini|| Michaelis Lochmaier paro-||chiale curatoꝝ...
Colophon, l. 152a: ... imp[re]ssus ac dili||gēter reuisus p sollertē Henri||cū Gran. ī...Ha||genow: expēsis ꝛ sūptibꝫ...||...Joh[ann]is Rymman...||...M .cccc.||xcviij. xx.die mēsis Augusti.||

Hain-Copinger 10169. BMC, III, 686. IA.13776. Stillwell: Second census, L237.
Gothic type (Proctor 3196); 2 columns, 34 lines. With headlines, initial indicators, marginalia and signature marks; without catchwords and foliation.
Signatures: A-B6, a-o8, p-s6.6. Sig. a1 blank.
Leaf 13 (blank) wanting.
With bookplate of Raimond van Marle.
With portions of a vellum ms. used as end papers.

53R0867. 1. Catholic church, Roman —Doctrine and discipline.

NL 0433454 NN DLC PP MH NcU

FILM Lochmayer, Michael, 15th cent.
4298 Parochiale curatorum. Hagenoae,
AC Henricus Gran; impens. Johannis Ryn-
Roll mann, 20 August, 1498.
128 152 l.
Hain-Copinger 10169.

NL 0433455 CU CaBVaU

VOLUME 337

Lochmaier, Michael, 15th cent.
Parochiale curatorũ; libellus per q̃z utilis sacerdotibus etiã eruditis mediocriter quo docentur quid eorũ officium requirat. ₍Basileae, Hysch. 1519.₎
135 ff.

NL 0433456 PPLT

Lochmair, Michael, 15th cent
Practica electionum prelatorum. F. a 2 Practica electionũ prelatorum. Passau, Johannes Petri, 1490.

NL 0433457 PP

Rare Book Room Z1 2845 Lochmaier, Michael, 15th cent.
Sermones de sanctis, cum vigintitribus Pauli Wann sermonibus. [Passau,Johann Petri,1490-91]
402ff. 26cm.
Fol.19 and 402, both blank, wanting.
Hain-Copinger 10172; British museum, XV cent., vol.2, p.617.

NL 0433458 CtY NcU DLC MiU ICN IU

Lochmaier, Michael, 15th cent.
Sermones de sanctis perutiles, cum viginti tribus sermonibus magistri Pauli Wann annexis. (Hagenau, Gran, 1497.)

NL 0433459 MA

Hain 10174 Lochmaier, Michael, 15th cent.
Sermones de sanctis. Hagenau, Heinricus Gran, 1500.

NL 0433460 DLC MH

f604.7 L81.4ses 1507 LOCHMAIER, Michael, 15th cent.
... Sermões de sanctis perutiles: cũ vigintitribus sermoibus magistri Pauli wann annexis. faliciter incipiunt. [Hagenau, 1507].
[502]p. 29.5cm.
At head of title: Celeberrimi sacre theologie ... Michaelis lochmair.
Colophon: Expensis prouidi viri Joannis Rynman: diligeter reuisi et emendati. Impressique in imperiali oppido Hagenarv per industria Henricum Gran finiunt feliciter.

Anno salutis nostre millesimo quingetesimo septimo xiiij. die mensis Martij.
Signatures: A-B⁶, a-b⁸, c⁶, d-e⁸, f⁶, g-l⁸, m-n⁶, o-r⁸, s⁶, t-v⁸, x⁶, y-z⁸, A⁶, B-C⁸, D⁶, E-I⁸. (last leaf blank, wanting.)

NL 0433462 MH-AH

Lochmair, Michael, 15th cent.
see Lochmaier, Michael, 15th cent.

Lochman, A. R , b. 1802.
Rosa of Linden Castle....
See under
[Schmid, Christophe von] 1768-1854.

Lochman, Augustus Hoffman, 1802-1891, tr.

Redenbacher, Wilhelm, 1800-1876.
The emerald. From the German of William Redenbacher, by A. H. Lochman ... Philadelphia, Lutheran board of publication, 1872.

Lochman, Augustus Hoffman, 1802-1891, ed.

Lochman, Johann Georg, 1773-1826.
Hinterlassene predigten, von Johann Georg Lochman ... Zum druck befördert von Augustus H. Lochman. A. M. Harrisburg, G. S. Peters, 1828.

Lochman, Augustus Hoffman, 1802-1891.

F157 .Y6Y6 **York,** *Pa. Centennial committee of arrangements.*
The historical sketch, and account of the centennial celebration at York, Pa., July 4, 1876. Containing an accurate account of the proceedings from the time of the passage of the resolution by the Town council to celebrate the nation's birth ... up to the close of the celebration; the ... prayer offered by ... Dr. A. H. Lochman; the ... historical sketch prepared by John Gibson, esq.; the ... poem by E. N. Gunnison, esq. and the ... oration delivered by George W. McElroy, esq. York, Penna., Democratic press print, 1876.

882 L512pr 1885 LOCHMAN, Augustus Hoffman, 1802-1891.
Practical sermons and addresses, by A.H. Lochman... Printed at the request of many of his friends and former parishioners, York, Pa., Teachers' Journal Office, 1885.
360p. front.(port.) 20.5cm.

NL 0433468 MH-AH PPLT IU

Lochman, Charles L.
Address for the fiftieth anniversary of an Odd fellows' lodge, and other poems, chiefly occasional. By Charles L. Lochman. Bethlehem, Pa., The author, 1897.
63, ₍1₎ p. 20cm.

1. Odd fellows, Independent order of. Hamburg, Pa. Symmetry lodge, no. 103. 2. Odd fellows, Independent order of. Pennsylvania. I. Title.

Library of Congress PS2248.L79A7 33-35318
Copyright 1897: 41287 811.49

NL 0433469 DLC PPHi

Lochman, Charles L.
Dose and price labels of all the drugs and preparations of the United States pharmacopœia of 1880 ... 2d ed., rewritten and thoroughly rev. and enl. ... By C. L. Lochman ... Philadelphia, Dunlap & Clarke, printers, 1887.
xv p., 181 numb. l., 1 l., 183-201 p. 23½ x 11½cm.

1. Labels (Pharmacy)

Library of Congress RS356.L82 7-32645†

NL 0433470 DLC DNLM PPC

Lochman, Charles L.
Dose and price labels of all the drugs and preparations of the United States Pharmacopoeia of 1880... 3d ed., rev. and enl. ... Philadelphia, Dunlap & Clarke, printers, 1889.

NL 0433471 OClW PPC

615.4 L81d Ed.4 Lochman, Charles L.
Dose and price labels of all the drugs and preparations of the United States pharmacopoeia of 1880... 4th ed., rev. and enl. Milwaukee, Wis., Jerman ₍c1890₎
181l., ₍183₎-201p. 22 x 9 1/2 cm.

NL 0433472 IaU

Lochman, Charles L.
Dose and price labels of the principal articles of the materia medica and preparations, used in the United States; with some useful hints and formulas ... By C. L. Lochman ... Allentown, Pa., C. L. Lochman and Haines & Worman, 1877.
1 p. l., ₍5₎-6 p., 93 l. 23 x 10½cm.

1. Labels (Pharmacy)

Library of Congress RS356.L81 7-32644†

NL 0433473 DLC DNLM

Lochman, Charles L., tr.

RS141 .4 .P53 1884 **Pharmacopoea Germanica.** *English.*
Pharmacopoea Germanica. Editio altera. The German pharmacopoeia. 2d ed., which, by authority of the Federal Council of the German Empire, replaces the 1st ed. on Jan. 1, 1883. Translated by C. L. Lochman. New York, J. H. Vail, 1884.

Lochman, Charles L.
Photographic illustrations of the maples of North America, native and cultivated. Together with the hickories and walnuts of North America, by Charles L. Lochman ... Bethlehem, Pa., C. L. Lochman, 1899.
2 p. l., 41 mounted pl. 26½ x 20cm.

1. Walnut. 2. Hickory. 3. Maple. 4. Trees—North America. I. Title.

Library of Congress QK495.A17L8 99-2946 Revised

NL 0433475 DLC

Lochman, Charles L.
Photographs of medicinal plants from natural specimens. [No imprint]
88 mounted photos.
Binder's title.

NL 0433476 MiU PPAN

Lochman, Christina, 1907–
... Early Upper Cambrian faunas of central Montana, by Christina Lochman ... and Donald Duncan ... (With descriptions of *Brachiopoda by* W. Charles Bell) ₍New York₎ The Society, 1944.
ix, 181 p. illus. (map) 19 pl. (incl. front.) on 10 l., diagr. 24½ cm. (Geological society of America. Special papers, no. 54)
"First part of an Upper Cambrian faunal study designed to supplement Deiss' stratigraphic work on the revision of the type Cambrian formations and sections of central Montana (in Geological society of America. Bulletin. v. 47, p. 1257-1342. August 18, 1936)"—p. 1.
"References cited": p. 154-155.

1. Paleontology—Cambrian. 2. Paleontology—Montana. 3. Brachiopoda, Fossil. I. Duncan, Donald Cave, 1911– joint author. II. Bell, William Charles, 1911– III. Deiss, Charles Frederick, 1903– Revision of type Cambrian formations and sections of Montana and Yellowstone national park.

QE726.L57 560.9786 44-5962

MU MoU CoU ViU OCU PSt PBm NIC
NL 0433478 DLC WaTC MtBC CaBVaU WaTC IdPI OU PU

VOLUME 337

Lochman, George, 1773-1826
see Lochman, Johann Georg, 1773-1826.

Lochman, Jan Milič.
Náboženské myšlení českého obrození; kořeny a počátky. V Praze, Komenského evangelická fakulta bohoslovecká, 1952-
v. 22 cm. (Spisy Komenského evangelické fakulty bohoslovecké. Řada A, sv. 19
Includes bibliography.

1. Bohemia—Church history. I. Title.

BR817.B6L6 60-17036 ‡

NL 0433480 DLC CaBVaU CtY-D ICU MH-AH MH

Lochman, Johann Georg, 1773-1826.
Hinterlassene predigten, von Johann Georg Lochman ... Zum druck befördert von Augustus H. Lochman. A. M. Harrisburg, G. S. Peters, 1828.
vi, [7]-332, [2] p. 17½cm.

I. Lochman, Augustus H., ed.

5-17670

NL 0433481 DLC PPeSchw PLF ViHarEM MH-AH CtY-D PHi PPLT

Lochman, Johann Georg, 1773-1826.
The history, doctrine and discipline of the Evangelical Luteran church. By George Lochman ... Harrisburg [Pa.] Printed and sold by John Wyeth. 1818.
v (i.e. iv), [5]-164 (i.e. 168) p. 17cm.
Pages 98, 109-164 numb. 86, 105-164 respectively.
Bibliography in author's preface: p. iv.
Part II has half-title: The doctrine of the Evangelical Lutheran Church, containing the Augsburg Confession, with explanatory notes & remarks.
Part III has half-title: The discipline of the Evangelical Lutheran Church.
1. Lutheran church—Hist. 2. Lutheran church—Doctrinal and controversial works. I. Augsburg confession.

NL 0433482 ViU N PHi PSt PPPD MH-AH NNC MdBP DLC MiU-C NcD ICU CSmH

Microfilm BX 179 reel 5
Lochman, Johann Georg, 1773-1826.
The history, doctrine and discipline of the Evangelical Lutheran church. Harrisburgh, J. Wyeth, 1818.
(Microfilm corpus of American Lutheranism, reel 5, no.7)
Positive: original in Univ. of Chicago Library.

NL 0433483 ICU CBPL ICRL

Microfilm BX 179 reel 6
[Lochman, George], 1773-1826.
Principles of the Christian religion in questions and answers, designed for the instruction of youth in evangelical churches. 2d ed. Harrisburg, Printed by J. S. Wiestling, 1825.
(Microfilm corpus of American Lutheranism, reel 6, no.11)
Positive; original in Library of Theological Seminary of Evangelical Lutheran Church, Philadelphia.
I. Title.

NL 0433484 ICU ICRL CBPL

Lochman, Johann Georg, 1773-1826.
Principles of the Christian religion in questions and answers... 2d. ed. Harrisburg (Pa.), Wiestling, 1825.
47 p.

NL 0433485 PPLT

Lochman, Johann Georg, 1773-1826.
Principles of the Christian religion in questions and answers... Germantown (Pa.) Billmeyer, 1827.
51 p.

NL 0433486 PPLT

BF698 .L57
Lochman, Margaret.
Inner life of humanity, by Margaret Lochman ... [New York] Margaret Lochman [c1936
v. 20cm.

1. Personality. I. Title.

NL 0433487 DLC NN

Lochmann, Curt
Ueber die gerbwirkung einiger komplexer chromsalze.
Inaug. diss. Darmstadt tech. hoch., 1924.

NL 0433488 ICRL

Lochmann, E.
Einiges über Erweiterung und Betrieb des Rohrnetzes. (In Betriebsführung, Die, von Wasserwerken. Pp. 205-219. Leipzig. 1909.)

H2117 — Conduits.

NL 0433489 MB

LOCHMANN, Eduard, 1872-
Friedrich der Grosse und die katholische kirche in Schlesien seit dem beginn des siebenjährigen krieges. Inaug.-diss., Göttingen. Osnabruck, 1903.
"Lebenslauf", after p.74.

NL 0433490 MH CtY

Lochmann, Ernst Ferdinand, 1820-1891.
Alkohol. Af professor dr. Lochmann ... Kristiania, Grøndahl & søns bogtrykkeri, 1884.
54 p. 18½cm. [With Utheim, John. Fra fremmede lande. Kristiania, 1878]
Udg. af Selskabet for folkeoplysningens fremme, som 1. tillægshefte til "Folkevennen" for 1884.

1. Alcohol. I. Selskabet for folkeoplysningens fremme, Christiania. II. Folkevennen.

17-7294

Library of Congress DS8.U8

NL 0433491 DLC

LOCHMANN, Ernst Ferdinand, 1820-1891.
Den nyare naturaskadningen. Öfversatt fran norskan af Andrea Butenschön. Stockholm, [1890.]

NL 0433492 MH

Lochmann (Ernst Ferdinand) [1820-1891]. Om Spedalskheden. 39 pp. 8°. *Christiania, Steenske Bogtrykkeri*, 1871.

NL 0433493 DNLM NN

448.2 L78
Lochmann, Ernst Heinrich.
Über das Vorkommen der Dyspepsiecoli-Typen O111: B4 und O55: B5 in Vorzugsmilch zugleich ein Überblick über das gesamte Coli-Problem. Hannover, 1955.
76 p.
Inaug.-Diss. - Tierärztliche Hochschule, Hannover.
1. Milk. Bacteriology.

NL 0433494 DNLM

Lochmann (Felix). *Zur Anatomie und Physiologie der Umbilicalgefässe. 22 pp. 8°. *Heidelberg, P. Wiese*, 1900.

NL 0433495 DNLM ICRL

Lochmann, Ferdinand, 1820-1891
see Lochmann, Ernst Ferdinand, 1820-1891.

FLGZ 418 no.19
Lochmann, Gotthelf Friedrich.
De ivrisdictione patrimoniali ... Lipsiae, litteris vidvae Langenhemiae [1766]
1p.l.,36p. 20cm.
(Foreign law pamphlet collection, v.418, no.19)
Disputatio - Leipzig.

NL 0433497 CtY-L MH

Lochmann, Gotthelf Friedrich, respondent.
De nobili vasallo in dominum committente
see under Hommel, Karl Ferdinand, 1722-1781, praeses.

Lochmann, Gotthelf Friedrich, praeses.
Observationes ad svccessionem fevdalem in Saxonia Electorali spectantes ... Lipsiae, Ex Officina Langenhemia [1767]
34, [2] p. 26cm.
Diss. - Leipzig (G. G. Hunger, respondent)

NL 0433499 MH-L

VOLUME 337

Lochmann, Gustav.
Als der Ami kam; Fulda in der Stunde der Entscheidung. Fulda, Fuldaer Verlagsanstalt, 1955.
190 p. illus. 20 cm.

1. Fulda, Ger.—Hist. 2. World War, 1939-1945—Germany—Fulda. I. Title.
DD901.F9L6 56-32128 ‡

NL 0433500 DLC MH NN

Lochmann, Heinrich Ludwig, 1891-
Zur entwicklungsgeschichte der Siphonophoren
see Lochmann, Ludwig, 1891-

WBA L812s 1850
LOCHMANN, J J
Sympathetischer Wunder-Doktor in vielen bewährten Heilmitteln gegen viele gefährlichen und schmerzvollen äusserlichen und innerlichen Krankheiten der Menschen und Thiere, nebst einer Sammlung der besten und bewährtesten natürlichen Mittel und Recepte für alle Vorkommnisse des menschlichen Lebens, aus alten und seltenen Büchern gesammelt. Baltimore, Lippe [185-?]
126 p.
Title

NL 0433502 DNLM

Lochmann, Jean Jacques, 1802-1897.
... Astronomisch-geodätische arbeiten in der Schweiz
see under Schweizerische geodätische kommission.

Lochmann, Jean Jacques, 1802-1897.
Vaud (Canton) Bibliothèque cantonale et universitaire, *Lausanne.*
Catalogue de la Bibliothèque cantonale vaudoise ... Lausanne, 1853-56.

QB296 .S948
Lochmann, Jean Jacques, 1802-1897.
Schweizerische geodätische kommission.
Das schweizerische dreiecknetz, hrsg. von der Schweizerischen geodätischen kommission. 1.-9. bd. Zürich, Commission von S. Höhr, 1881-1901.

Lochmann (Joh.) *De typho abdominale. 26 pp. 8°. *München, J. G. Weiss,* 1859.

NL 0433506 DNLM

A30 L4 1692L
Lochmann, Johann Martin.
Dissertatio moralis de jure necessitatis. Lipsiae, 1692.
Inaug.-diss. - Leipzig.

NL 0433507 CtY

Lochmann, Johannes, 1700-1762.
Scheuchzer, Johann Jacob, 1672-1733.
Alphabethi ex diplomatibus et codicibus thuricensibus specimen; publicatum a Johanne Jacobo Scheuchzer ... et Johanne Lochmann ... Tiguri, typis Gessnerianis, sumptibus Lochmanni, 1730.

Lochmann, Ludwig: 1891 Aus d. Zool. Inst. zu Leipzig. Zur Entwicklungsgeschichte der Siphonophoren. Mit 5 Fig. im Text u. Taf. VII. Leipzig & Berlin: W. Engelmann 1913. S. 258—289, 1 Taf. 8° ¶ Aus: Zeitschrift f. wiss. Zool. Bd 108.
Leipzig, Phil. Diss. v. 18. Mai 1914, Ref. Chun, Pfeffer
[Geb. 9. Febr. 91 Köthen; Wohnort: Leipzig; Staatsangeh.: Anhalt; Vorbildung: G. Köthen Reife 09; Studium: München 3, Leipzig 5 S.; Rig. 1. Juli 13.] [U 14. 4225

NL 0433509 ICRL CtY OCU PU MH

Lochmann, Philipp, respondent.
... De conditionibus ...
see under Hilliger, Oswald, 1583-1619, praeses.

Lochmann, Robert Ferdinand Werner, 1901-
see Lochmann, Werner, 1901-

W 4 B51 1940
Lochmann, Rudolf, 1912-
Missbildungen der Hand bei genuiner Epilepsie. [n.p., 1940]
19 p. illus.

Inaug.-Diss. - Friedrich Wilhelms Univ., Berlin.
Bibliography: p. 17.

NL 0433512 DNLM

Lochmann, Werner,1901-
Zahnheilkundiges bei Giovanni Micaele Savonarola.
Inaug. diss. Leipzig,1926.
Bibl.

NL 0433513 ICRL CtY DNLM

Lochmann, Wilhelm: Ein Fall von Volvulus bei einem Neugeborenen. [Maschinenschrift.] 22 S. 4°. — Auszug: Greifswald 1922: Adler. 4 S. 8°
Greifswald, Med. Diss. v. 24. Mai 1922 [U 22. 3614

NL 0433514 ICRL

Lochmel', I F
Abriss der Geschichte des Kampfes der weissruthenischen Nation gegen die polnischen Herren; dienstliche Uebersetzung aus dem Russischen ausgeführt von Irene Pflug. Berlin, Publikationsstelle in Berlin-Dahlem, 1943.
126 p. 31 cm.
"Nur für den Dienstgebrauch."

1. White Russia—Hist. I. Title.
DK508.7.L615 52-53850

NL 0433515 DLC

DK507 .L6
Lochmel', I F
Очерк истории борьбы белорусского народа против польских панов. Москва, Воен. изд-во, 1940.
162 p. 20 cm.
—— Microfilm copy (positive)
Negative film in the Library of Congress.
Microfilm Slavic 107 AC

1. White Russia—Hist. I. Title.
Title transliterated: Ocherk istorii bor'by belorusskogo naroda.
DK507.L6 59-43836

NL 0433516 DLC

Lochmel', I. F., ed.
Akademiia navuk BSSR, *Minsk. Instytut historyi.*
Заходняя Беларусь пад панскім гнётам і яе вызваленне. Пад рэдакцыяй Н. М. Нікольскага і І. Ф. Лочмеля. Мінск, Выдавецтва Акадэміі навук БССР, 1940.

Lochmer, Aleksander.
see
Lochmer, Šandor.

Lochmer,Šandor.
Džepni rječnik hrvatskoga i engleskoga jezika sa točnim izgovorom svake riječi,priredio prof. Aleksander Lochmer. Pučko izdanje. Zagreb, Tisak i naklada knjižare L.Hartmana, 1911.
230 p. 15½cm.

1.Croatian language—Dictionaries—English.

NL 0433519 MiU CU OCl NN

PG1377 .E5
Lochmer, Šandor.
Engleski učitelj; džepni riječnik za srbe i hrvate, sa tačnim izgovorom svake riječi, po A. [i. e. Š.] Lochmeru. Chicago, Palandech's Pub. House [19—]

Lochmer, Šandor.
Englesko-Hrvatski razgovori za svakdanju porabu, 1891.
[287 p.

NL 0433521 OCl

Lochmer, Šandor.
Englesko-hrvatski rječnik izradio prof. Šandor Lochmer. U Senju, Naklada I. P. Hreljanovića, 1906.
3 p. l., 1112 p. 19½cm.
Added t.-p. in English.
Imprint covered by label: C. N. Caspar co., Milwaukee, Wisconsin.

1. English language—Dictionaries—Croatian. 2. Croatian language—Dictionaries—English.

Library of Congress PG1377.L6 32-9881
[2] 491.8332

NN
NL 0433522 DLC WaS IEN ICU IU MH OCl OU PSt NBuG

Lochmer, Šandor.
O Engleskom Izgovoru. Na Rieci 1887.
Dissertations. Engl. Philol. v.15 no.9.
26 p.

NL 0433523 MiU

VOLUME 337

Lochmer, Šandor.
Gramatika engleskoga jezika za skolu i samouke. Zagreb, 1909.
[347p.]

NL 0433524 OCl

Slavic-American Imprints Coll. 422.14 L635
Lochmer, Šandor.
Laki način Engleski bez učitelja; Vježbe i razgovori za u kratko vrijeme naučiti, razumijevati i govoriti Engliski, priredio prof. Alexander Lochmer. 2. ed. Chicago, Palandech's Publishing House [n.d.]
93 p. 22 cm.
English translation of title: The easy method of learning English without teacher; exercises and dialogues to learn, understand and speak English in a short time. Arranged by prof. Alexander Lochmer.

NL 0433525 IEdS MiD

Lochmer, Šandor.
Laki način engelski bez učitelja u kratko vrijeme naučiti, razumijevati i govoriti. Vježbe, razgovori i hrvatsko-engleski rječnik sa točnim izgovorom svake riječi. Savjeti za putnike u Ameriku. 2. . . . izdanje.
— Zagreb. Hartman. 1911. (7), 158 pp. 22½ cm., in 8s.

H8308 — English language. Gram. For Croatians. — English language. Conv. For Croatians. — Serbo-Croatian language. Dict. English.

NL 0433526 MB WaS OrP OCl

Lochmer, Sandor.
Laki način engleski bez učitelja u kratko vrijeme naučiti, razumijevati i govoriti. Vježbe razgovori i hrvatsko-engleski riječnik sa točnim izgovorom svake riječi. Savjeti za putnike u Ameriku. Priedio prof. Alexander Lochmer. Drugo sasvim popravljeno izčanje. Chicago, Ill.: J. Žagar & co., 1926. 171 p. 23½cm.
Cover-title: Gramatika i riječnik; ili, Laki način engleski bez učitelja.

44100B. 1. Croatian language—English. 2. Croatian language—Conversation and phrase books, Dictionaries, English. I. Title.
N. Y. P. L. April 17, 1940

NL 0433527 NN MiD OCl

Lochmeyer, Michael.
See
Lochmaier, Michael, 15th cent.

Lochmüller, Benedikt, 1894-
Brand im Tempel, Hölderlin-Epos. [Bayreuth, Gauverlag Bayreuth [1943]
248 p. 23 cm.

1. Hölderlin, Friedrich, 1770-1843—Poetry. I. Title.
PT2623.O19B7 55-47938 ‡

NL 0433529 DLC CtY

834L782 Ob
Lochmüller, Benedikt, 1894-
... Brand im tempel; Hölderlins schicksalsbuch. Dresden, W. Jess [1931]
208p.
In verse.

1. Hölderlin, Johann Christian Friedrich, 1770-1843--Poetry. I. Title.

NL 0433530 IU CtY

Lochmüller, Benedikt, 1894-
... Hans Schemm ... Bayreuth, Deutscher volksverlag [1935-40]
2 v. front. (v. 2) plates, ports., facsim. 21 cm.
Vol. 2 has imprint: München, Deutscher volksverlag.
Vol. 1: 1. auflage, 1.-20. tausend; v. 2: 1. auflage.
"Quellennachweis": v. 2, p. 738-740.

1. *Schemm, Hans, 1891-1935.
DD247.S34L6 923.243 36-4067 rev

NL 0433531 DLC IaU MiU RPB CU NN MH

PA 6322 .L6
Lochmüller, Hans, 1870-
Quaestiones grammaticae in Ciceronis libros oratorios. Landshut, Druck von Thomann [1901]
38 p.
Thesis, Munich.

1. Cicero, Marcus Tullius. Works, Rhetorical.

NL 0433532 NNC PU NjP MH CU

Lochmueller, Kurt.
Die gelierfaehigkeit der pektine.
Inaug. diss. Muenchen, tech. hoch., 1927.

NL 0433533 ICRL

338.1 L789z
Lochmüller, Wilhelm, 1882-
Zur entwicklung der deutschen baumwollindustrie ... Jena, G. Fischer, 1906.
32p.
Inaug.-diss.--Jena.
Lebenslauf.
Part of the complete work, which appeared as Abhandlungen des Staatswissenschaftlichen seminars zu Jena, 3.bd., 3.hft.
Bibliographical foot-notes.
1. Cotton growing and manufacture--Germany.
2. Cotton trade--Germany.

NL 0433534 IU ICRL MH

Lochmüller, Wilhelm, 1882-
Zur entwicklung der baumwollindustrie in Deutschland. Von dr. W. Lochmüller. Mit 3 kurven im text. Jena, G. Fischer, 1906.
vi p., 1 l., 127 p. diagrs. 24 cm. (*Added t.-p.: Abhandlungen des Staatswissenschaftlichen seminars zu Jena ... 3. bd., 3 hft.*)
Appeared in part as the author's inaugural dissertation, Jena, 1905 (33 p.)
"Benutzte literatur": p. [125]-127.

1. Cotton manufacture—Germany. 2. Cotton trade—Germany.
HD9883.5.L6 15-27676

NL 0433535 DLC PU ICJ NN MB CU NcD

DD 228.6 .L81
LOCHMÜLLER, WILLY.
Unsere Zukunft liegt auf dem Balkan! Afrikanische oder europäische Politik? Leipzig, B. Volger, 1913.
40 p.

1. Germany--Foreign relations--1870-1940.

NL 0433536 InU

Lochnell [pseud.]
Saxon Lyrics & Legends after Aldhelm. London & New York [1886]
16°.
These poems are "written in imitation of what Aldhelm might have sung lond ago" cf. Introd. p. 8.

NL 0433537 CtY

Lochnell [pseud.]
Saxon lyrics and legends, after Aldhelm, by Lochnell [pseud.] Cleveland, O., At the Clerk's press, 1911. xi(i), 93(1) p., 1 l. 14cm.
No. 86 of 97 copies printed.
"Done into type and imprinted at the private press of Charles C. Bubb, a clerk in holy orders."
"Written in imitation of what Aldhelm might have sung long ago."—*Introd., dated at Comballaz, 1885.*
Erratum slip tipped in between p. x and xi.
Printer's autographed presentation copy to Mrs. E. W. Worthington.

52R0706. I. Aldhelm, Saint, bp. of Sherborne, 640?-709. II. Title.

NL 0433538 NN OClW

LOCHNER, Adolf Heinrich Johannes.
See LOCHNER, Johannes.

Lochner, Albert.
Darlehen und Anleihe im internationalen Privatrecht. Stuttgart, Kohlhammer [1954]
108 p. 24 cm. (Göttinger Studien zum Völkerrecht und internationalen Privatrecht, 4)
Includes bibliography.

1. Conflict of laws—Loans—Germany (Federal Republic, 1949-) I. Title.
55-25999 ‡

NL 0433540 DLC NIC CU-AL DS

NK2552 L63 Restricted Circulation
Lochner, Anton.
Germanische Möbel; eine Sammlung kunstgewerblicher Vorbilder aus der Zeit von 1450 bis 1800, meist aus den Museen Nürnbergs. 2. Aufl. Berlin, M. Spielmeyer [18--]
100 plates (in portfolio)
Library's copy lacks plates 21-22, 25-26.

1. Furniture, German. I. Nürnberg. Museums.

NL 0433541 CLobS

Lochner, Anton.
Germanische moebel; eine sammlvng kvnstgewerblicher vorbilder aus dem mittelalter von 1450 bis 1800, meist' aus den museen Nvernbergs; in 100 tafeln nach der natur aufgenommen, in feder gezeichnet und hrsg. von Anton Lochner. Nvernberg, A. Lochner [1897]
[4] p. 100 pl. 44½cm.
Imprint covered by label: Berlin, Spielmeyer.

NL 0433542 NNC MB

Lochner, Arthur.
Der Spezifikationskauf ... von Arthur Lochner ... Aachen, C.H. Georgi, 1898.
53 p. 22cm.
Inaug.-Diss. - Erlangen.
"Litteratur": p.[3]-[5]

NL 0433543 MH-L ICRL NIC MH

VOLUME 337

Lochner, Carl Friedrich, 1694-1748, respondent.

Sonntag, Christoph, 1654-1717, *praeses.*
Collectionem meditatam de asiarchis, Act. XIX, 31 ... publice ventilabit ... Carolvs Fridericvs Lochnervs ... [Altdorfii] literis Jod. Gvil. Kohlesii [1712]

Lochner, Carl Friedrich, 1694-1748, respondent.

Zeltner, Gustav Georg, 1672-1738, *praeses.*
... Evangelivm τετραγράμματον e Novo Testamento exvlans ... Altdorfii Noricorvm, exscripsit J. G. Kohlesius, CIↃ IↃCC XII.

Lochner, Carl Friedrich, 1694-1743, respondent.

Sonntag, Christoph, 1654-1717, *praeses.*
Stromata thesivm et antithesivm, circa varios ll. theologicos contexta ... [Altdorfii] literis Magni Danielis Meyeri [1712]

Lochner, Flavia, *sister.*
... A study of the musculature of the body-wall and septa of the earthworm, *Lumbricus terrestris L.* ... by Sister M. Flavia Lochner ... Washington, D. C., Catholic university of America, 1937.
xii, 40 p. plates. 23cm. (The Catholic university of America. Biological series no. 22)
Thesis (PH. D.)—Catholic university of America, 1937.
"Literature": p. 1-6; Bibliography: p. 33-36.
1. Earthworms. 2. Muscles. I. Title: Musculature of the body-wall and septa of the earthworm, *Lumbricus terrestris L.*
37-23207
Library of Congress QL391.O4L6 1937
——— Copy 2.
Copyright A 108585 [3] 595.16

NL 0433547 DLC CU NcU NcD OCl OU PU

Lochner (Friedrich). *Ueber die zuckerbildende Substanz der Leber. 20 pp. 8°. *Erlangen, A. E. Junge,* 1858.

NL 0433548 DNLM MiU

Lochner, Friedrich, 1602-1673.
Lustgedicht zu hochzeitlichem Ehrenbegängniss Herrn D. Johann Röders und Jungfer Maria Rosina Schmidin auf der siebenröhrigen Schilffpfeiffen Pans wolmeinend gespielet von den Pegnitzhirten
see under title

BX 8076 M6 T8 L6
Lochner, Friedrich, 1822-1902.
Geschichte der Evang.-Luth. Dreieinigkeits-Gemeinde U. A. C. zu Milwaukee, Wis. Im Auftrag der Gemeinde zur Feier ihres fünfzigjährigen Jubiläums den 17. Oktober 1897. Milwaukee, Germania Pub. Co., 1897.
89p. ports.,plates.
With this is bound Geschichte der Gründung und Ausbreitung der zur Synode von Missouri, Ohio un d andern Staaten gehöenden Evange lisch-Lutherischen Gemeinden U. A. C. zu Chicago, Illinois. 1896. and Kurze Chronik der Evangelisch-Lutherischen Immanuels-Gemeinde U. A. C. zu Chicago, Ill., 1854-1904. 1904. and Graebner, Augustus Lawrence. Half a century of sound Lutheranism in America. 1893.
1. Milwaukee Trinity Evangelical Lutheran Church. I. Tit le. a.a. for bound withs.

NL 0433551 MoSCS ICN NN

764.9 Luth L812ha 1895
LOCHNER, Friedrich, 1822-1902.
Der Hauptgottesdienst der evangelisch=lutherischen Kirche. Zur Erhaltung des liturgischen Erbtheils und zur Befoerderung des liturgischen Studiums in der americanisch=lutherischen Kirche erlaeutert und mit altkirchlichen Singweisen versehen, von Friedrich Lochner. St. Louis, Concordia, 1895.
ix,294p. music. 22cm.

NL 0433552 MH-AH PPLT IEN

Lochner, Friedrich Carl Johann, 1822-1902
see Lochner, Friedrich, 1822-1902.

Lochner, Friedrich, 1822-1902.
Liturgie für einen Charfreitags-Gottesdienst, dargeboten von Friedrich Lochner. [Five-line German Biblical quotation: Ps. 22, 28 u. 31] Milwaukee, Wis., Schnellpressen-Druck des "Herold" 1871.
cover-title, 20 p. 15½cm.
1. Lutheran church. Liturgy and ritual. 2. Good Friday.

NL 0433554 ViU

Lochner, Friedrich, 1822-1902, ed.
Liturgische Monatsschrift
see under title

---

770 L816p
LOCHNER, Friedrich, 1822-1902.
Passion= und Osterbuch. Andachten zur haeuslichen Feier der heiligen Passions= und Osterzeit. Aus den aelteren Schaetzen der rechtglaeubigen Kirche gesammelte und bearbeitet. St. Louis, Mo., Lutherischer Concordia Verlag, 1879.
2v. 19cm.
A-H has vol2: Osterbuch.

NL 0433556 MH-AH

48V 845
Lochner, Friedrich, 1822-1902.
Predigten über die Episteln der Sonn- und Festtage des Kirchenjahres, nebst ein Paar Gelegenheitspredigten, gehalten und auf Verlangen dem Druck übergeben. Milwaukee, G. Brumder [18]
832 p.

NL 0433557 DLC-P4

WG 23658
Lochner, Friedrich, 1863-
Reductions-Stufen der Anthra- und Isoanthraflavinsäure. Berlin, 1889.
38 p.
Inaug.-Diss. - Berlin.

NL 0433558 CtY ICRL

Lochner, Fritz.
Wir helfen uns selbst! Fort mit der Bremse, aufwärts geht unser Weg! Gemeinverständliche Darstellung unserer wirtschaftlichen Lage und der Wege zur Rettung, von Fritz Lochner. Kaiserslautern: Thiemesche Druckereien, G.m.b.H., 1931. 39 p. 8°.

637325A. 1. Economic history—Germany, 1918-
N. Y. P. L. May 31, 1933

NL 0433559 NN

Lochner, Georg.
Das gastrecht des schiffe nach dem abkommen der 2. genfer general-verkehrs-konferenz ueber die internationale rechtsordnung in den seehaefen vom 9. Dezember 1923.
Inaug. diss. Wuerzburg, nd.
Bibl.

NL 0433560 ICRL CtY MH

Lochner (Georg Friderich) [1802-55]. *De crisium doctrina et notione. 54 pp. 8°. *Erlangæ, typ. Kunstmannianis,* [1827].

NL 0433561 DNLM

WX L817s 1844
LOCHNER, Georg Friedrich, 1802-1855.
Statistisch-medizinischer Bericht über die Kranken- und Versorgungs-anstalten Nürnbergs, von Lochner und Bock; nebst Bemerkungen über die im Sebastian-Spital eingeführte methodische Behandlung der Syphilis von Letzterem. Nürnberg, Bauer und Raspe, 1844.
iv, 96 p.

NL 0433562 DNLM

Lochner, Georg Wolfgang Karl, 1798-1882.
Bild-Werke aus dem Mittelalter
see under Fleischmann [C.W.]

LOCHNER Georg Wolfgang Karl, 1798-1882.
Commentatio qua enarantur fata et rationes earum familiarum Christianarum in Polonia quae ab ecclesia romano-catholica alienae fuerunt ind ab eo tempore,quo fratres bohemi,qui dicuntur,eo migraverant. [Leipzig,1832].
4°.
Acta soc.iabl.,IV.fasc.II.

NL 0433564 MH

Lochner, Georg Wolfgang Karl, 1798-1882, ed.
Das deutsche mittelalter in den wesentlichsten zeugnissen seiner geschichtlichen urkunden, chroniken und rechtsdenkmäler. Zugleich als handbuch für den geschichtsunterricht in höhern bildungsanstalten, hrsg. von Georg Wolfgang Karl Lochner ... Nürnberg, Bauer und Raspe, 1851.
2 v. in 1. 21 cm.
1. Germany - Soc. life & cust. 2. Germany - Hist. - 1273-1517. I. Title.

NL 0433565 CU MH DLC-P4

BX4921 L6
Lochner, Georg Wolfgang Karl, 1798-1882.
Entstehung und erste Schicksale der Brüdergemeinde in Böhmen und Mähren; und, Leben des Georg Israel, ersten Aeltesten der Brüdergemeinde in Gross-Polen. Als Beiträge zu einer slavischen Kirchengeschichte. Nürnberg, F. Campe, 1832.
x,164p. 21cm.
Bibliographical footnotes.
1. Bohemian Brethren - Hist. 2. Israel, Georg, 1505-1588. I. Title. II. Title: Leben des Georg Israel.

NL 0433566 IaU NjPT

VOLUME 337

DC163 L6 **Lochner, Georg Wolfgang Karl, 1798-1882.**
Die französische Revolution vom ersten Ausbruch bis zur weitesten Ausdehnung, von 1789 bis 1807. Nürnberg, F.Campe, 1848.
447p. 19cm.

1. France - Hist. - Revolution, 1789.

NL 0433567 IaU

Br106 N8 873L Lochner, Georg Wolfgang Karl, 1798-1882.
Geschichte der Reichsstadt Nürnberg zur Zeit Kaiser Karls IV, 1347-1378. Berlin, F. Lobeck, 1873.
212 p. 21 cm.

1. Nuremberg - Hist.

NL 0433568 CtY MH

DD 901 N94 L6 1873a **Lochner, Georg Wolfgang Karl, 1798-1882.**
Geschichte der Reichsstadt Nürnberg zur Zeit Kaiser Karls IV, 1347-1378. Berlin, F. Lobeck, 1873.
212 p.

Photocopy. [Cambridge, Mass.] Harvard University Library, Reproduction Service, 1968. 25 cm.

1. Nuremberg - History. I. Title.

NL 0433569 OU

D117 L6 Lochner, Georg Wolfgang Karl, 1798-1882.
Geschichte des Mittelalters. Nürnberg, F.N.Campe, 1839-40.
2 v. in 1. 21cm.
Contents.-1.Bd.Die Zeit vor und Während der Kreuzzüge.-2.Bd.Vom Ende der Kreuzzüge bis zum Ende des Basler Concils.

1.Middle Ages - Hist.

NL 0433570 CSt

Lochner, Georg Wolfgang Karl, 1798-1882.
Historisch-genealogische tafeln zur geschichte des koenigreichs Bayern, etc. Nürnberg, F. Campe, 1828.
obl. 8°. pp. (6). 13 geneal. tables.

Bavaria-Biog.

NL 0433571 MH

Lochner, Georg Wolfgang Karl, 1798-1882, ed.

Neudörfer, Johann, 1497-1563.
Des Johann Neudörfer schreib- und rechenmeisters zu Nürnberg nachrichten von künstlern und werkleuten daselbst aus dem jahre 1547, nebst der fortzetzung des Andreas Gulden, nach den handschriften und mit anmerkungen hrsg. von dr. G. W. K. Lochner ... Wien, W. Braumüller, 1875.

---

arW 37419 **Lochner, Georg Wolfgang Karl,** 1798-1882.
Leben und Gesichte der Christina Ebnerin, Klosterfrau zu Engelthal. Nürnberg, F. Schmid, 1872.
iv, 54 p. 23cm.

1. Ebnerin, Christina.

NL 0433573 NIC CU

Lochner, Georg Wolfgang Karl, 1798-1882.
Lebensläufe berühmter und verdienter Nürnberger. Nürnberg, Schrag, 1861.
8°
66.

NL 0433574 PPLT

914.332 L78n **Lochner, Georg Wolfgang Karl, 1798-1882.**
Nürnberg's Vorzeit und Gegenwart. In einer Reihe von Aussätzen verfasst und redigirt von Georg Wolfgang Karl Lochner. Nürnberg, Campescher Druck, 1845.
xiv, 381p. fold.illus., fold.map. 18cm.

"Erinnerungsgabe der dreiundzwanzigsten Versammlung deutscher Naturforscher und Aerzte gewidmet von der Stadt Nürnberg."

NL 0433575 IU CtY MH

Lochner, Georg Wolfgang Karl, 1798-1882.
Observationes ad Caesaris commentariorum locos quosdam. 1828.

NL 0433576 IaU

CS2547 .L8 **Lochner, Georg Wolfgang Karl,** 1798- 1882.
Die personen-namen in Albrecht Dürer's Briefen aus Venedig. Von Georg Wolfgang Karl Lochner. Nürnberg, F. Korn, 1870.
52 p. 23cm.

1. Dürer, Albrecht, 1471-1528.

NL 0433577 ICU

Pamph. v.449 LOCHNER, Georg Wolfgang Karl, 1798-1882.
Philippus Melanchthon und das Gymnasium zu Nuernberg in ihrem wahren Verhaeltniss betrachtet. Nuernberg, Sebald, 1853.
8p. 23cm.

NL 0433578 MH-AH

Lochner, Georg Wolfgang Karl, editor.
Der spruch von Nürnberg; etc.
see Rosenblüt, Hans, 15th cent.

LOCHNER,Georg Wolfgang Karl,1798-1882.
Die stadt Nürnberg im ausgang ihrer reichsfreiheit. Nürnberg,Bauer & Raspe,1858.

pp.48.
"Erweiteter abdruck aus dem maiheft der Zeitschrift für deutsche kulturgeschichte."

NL 0433580 MH

Lochner, Georg Wolfgang Karl, 1798 1882.
Ueber den antheil Johann III Sobiesky's, königs von Polen, Johann Georgs III, kurfürsten von Sachsen und ihrer heere an dem entsatze von Wien im jahre 1683. Nürnberg, F. Campe, 1831.
nar. 8°. pp. iv, (1), 110.
"Eine von der Fürstlich Jablonowskischen gesellschaft der wissenschaften zu Leipzig gekrönte preisschrift."

Vienna-Siege, 1683 | Jan III Sobieski, king of Poland
Johann Georg III, elector of Saxony | Fürstlich Jablonowskische gesell schaft der wissenschaften, Leipzig

NL 0433581 MH ICN

LOCHNER,Georg Wolfgang Karl, 1798-1882.
Über die theilnahme der stadt Nürnberg am dreissigjaehrigen kriege. Von 1613 bis auf Gustav Adolphs erste ankunft zu Nürnberg 1632 merz 21. [Progr.] Nürnberg,druck der Campeschen officin,1832.

4°. pp.36,xx.

NL 0433582 MH

Lochner, Gustav, 1875-
Ueber Prostatektomie ... Leipzig, 1905.
Inaug.-Diss. - Leipzig.
Lebenslauf.
Bibliographical foot-notes.

NL 0433583 CtY ICRL DNLM

Lochner, Hans.
Ausschluss von Mitgliedern freier **Vereine ... von Hans Lochner ... Erfurt,** Ohlenroth, 1896.
39 p. 23cm.
Inaug.-Diss. - Göttingen.
Bibliographical footnotes.

NL 0433584 MH-L

Lochner, Hans.
Die Pilgerfahrten Nürnberger Bürger
see under Kamann, Johann.

HF5363 .M78 1944 Lochner, Hans, 1889-

FOR OTHER EDITIONS SEE MAIN ENTRY

Müller, Kurt, *of Halle.*
... Das grundwissen des kaufmanns, eine betriebslehre, hrsg. von dipl.-hdl. dr. H. Lochner ... 7. und 8. aufl. Leipzig, G. A. Gloeckner, 1944.

Lochner, Hans, 1889-
Das kaufmännische Grundwissen; eine Betriebslehre mit Scheck- und Wechsellehre. Nürnberg, L. Liebel, 1949.
248 p. illus. 22 cm. (Die Schule des Kaufmanns, Bd. 3)

1. Commerce—Handbooks, manuals, etc. (Series)

HF1010.L6 51-21324

NL 0433587 DLC

Lochner, Hansmartin, 1926-
Die katholischen Zeitschriften Bayerns, 1900-1918. München, 1954.
ix, 366 l. mounted diagrs., mounted facsims. 30 cm.
Typescript (carbon copy)
Inaug.-Diss.—Munich.
Vita.
Bibliography: leaves 364-366.

1. German periodicals—Bavaria. 2. Press, Catholic. I. Title.

PN5217.B38L6 56-38006

NL 0433588 DLC

VOLUME 337

B.F.
839.313
L812b
Lochner, Helena J. F.
Die berg se geheim. Geïllustreer deur die skryfster ... 2. druk. Kaapstad, Nasionale pers, 1936.
2 p. l., 53 p., incl. front. 18cm. [Verhaaltjies vir laer skole. no. 13]

Contains the autograph of the author.

NL 0433589 IEN

Lochner, Helena J. F.
Die Gelende velskoene'n sprokie.
Kaapstad, Nasionale Pers, 1938.

NL 0433590 IEN

B.F.
839.313
L812p
Lochner, Helena J. F.
Pinkie, die Hottentotjie en Apie vang diewe. Vir kinders van 7 tot 10 jaar ... 3. druk. Kaapstad, Nasionale pers, 1936.
2 p. l., [3]-52 p. illus. 18cm. [Verhaaltjies vir laer skole. no. 6]

Contains the autograph of the author.

I. Title. II. Title: Apie vang diewe.

NL 0433591 IEN

Lochner, Herbert Max, 1901-
Über die kontrastdarstellung der gallenblase ... Halle-Saale, 1927.

Halle diss. 1927

NL 0433592 MiU ICRL

Lochner, Hermann.
Die fernsprechtechnik und ihre physikalischen grundlagen; gemeinverständliche einführung unter besonderer berücksichtigung der im heere verwendeten apparate; im auftrage des Reichswehrministeriums bearbeitet von Hermann Lochner. Mit 66 farbigen tafeln nach zeichnungen des verfassers. München, Druck von Meisenbach, Riffarth & co., a.-g., 1924.
viii, 200 p. col. illus. 18cm.

1. Telephone.
Library of Congress TK6162.L6 25-24467

NL 0433593 DLC

Lochner, Jacob Hieronymus, 1683-1764.
... De suggestionibus satanae...
see under Fecht, Johann, 1636-1716, praeses.

Lochner, Jacobus Hieronymus, 1649-1700.
Die wohlerwehlte Herrlichkeit bey dem Thürhüten im Gottes-Hauss aus des LXXXIVsten Psalms 11ten vers. ... Zu Gedächtniss des weiland ... Herrn M. Caroli Friderici Lochners ... forgestellet von der ... beständigen Bruder-Liebe Jacobi Hieronymi Lochners ... Bremen, 1699.
8 p.l., 64, [16] p. 17 cm.

NL 0433595 CtY

FILM
4333
PT
Reel
131
Lochner, Jacobus Hieronymus, 1649-1700.
Die wohlerwehlte Herrlichkeit bey dem Thürhüten im Gottes-Haus aus des LXXXIVsten Psalms 11ten vers. Zu...Gedächtniss des weiland...Herrn M. Caroli Friderici Lochners...für gestellet von der...beständigen Bruder-Liebe Jacobi Hieronymi Lochners...Bremen, Gedruckt bey Herman Brauer, 1699.
8p.ℓ.,64,[16]p. 17cm.
(German Baroque Literature, No.568, reel No. 131 Research Publications, Inc.)
Microfilm.

NL 0433596 CU

Lochner, Johann Carl, respondent.
Triumphus bonae caussae theologicae consideratus
see under Baier, Johann David, 1681-1752, praeses.

Lochner, Johann Heinrich, 1695-1715.

QH71
.B35B4
Rare bk. coll.
Besler, Basilius, 1561-1629.
Rariora mvsei Besleriani quae olim Basilivs et Michael Rvpertvs Besleri collegerunt, aeneisqve tabvlis ad vivvm incisa evvlgarvnt: nunc commentariolo illustrata a Johanne Henrico Lochnero ... denvo lvci pvblicae commisit et lavdationem ejvs fvnebrem adjecit maestissimus parens Michael Fridericvs Lochnervs ... [Nuremberg] 1716.

PF3144
L6
1735
[Lochner, Johann Hieronymus]
Chloreni Germani [pseud.] neu verbesserte teutsche orthographie, oder: Gründliche anweisung recht, und nach der unter den heutigen gelehrten üblichen art, zu schreiben. Nebst einer kurzen untersuchung der teutschen sprach, so viel hierzu gehöret: Insonderheit der vornemsten strittigen, gleichlautenden, oder sonst merkwürdigen, wörter. Wie alles, so wol anfängern zur genugsamen nachricht, als bey geübten zur grundlegung eines collegii, dienen kan. Frankfurt und Leipzig, G.C. Weber, 1735.
7 p.l.,815 p. front. 16cm.

NL 0433600 CU

Lochner, Johann Hieronymus, ed.
Samlung merkwürdiger Medaillen, erstes Jahr 1737 [ ] in welcher wöchentlich ein curiöses Gepräg, meistens von modernen Medaillen, ausgesuchet, und nicht nur fleisig in Kupfer vorgestellet, sondern auch durch eine historische Erläuterung hinlänglich erkläret, nun aber, so wol mit vollständigen Registern, als einer Vorrede von dem Leben des berühmten Medailleur Raimund Falz, an das Licht gegeben worden, durch Johann Hieronymus Lochner. Nürnberg, P. C. Monath [1737]
v. in illus. 21cm.

Issued in weekly parts.
Title-pages vary.

I. Medals. I. Title.
N. Y. P. L. July 6, 1945

NL 0433601 NN

Lochner, Johann Michael Friedrich, 1728-1765, respondent.

Schwarz, Christian Gottlieb, 1675-1751, *praeses.*
Exercitatio academica De antiqvo ritv legitimandi liberos illegitimos per pallivm qvam praeside Christiano Gottlib. Schvvarzio ... in circvlo academico ventilandam, proponit Iohannes Michael Fridericvs Lochnervs ... Altorfii, ex officina Iohannis Adami Hesselii [1747]

Lochner, Johann Michael Friedrich, 1728-1765.
Otia das ist verschiedene zur iurisprudenz und litteratvr gehörige materien. Nebst sr. magnificenz des hochberühmten herrn prof. Schvvarzens vorrede von den verschiednen meinungen vom ursprung der kaiserlichen hohen gerechtsamen und der landes hoheit teutscher fürsten. Hrsg. von Johann Michael Friedrich Lochner. Nürnberg, Stein und Raspe, 1751.

2 p.l., [36], 295, [9] p. 17cm.
Includes bibliographies.

NL 0433604 MH-L

Lochner, Johannes, ed.
Gallée, Johan Hendrik, 1847-1908.
Altsächsische grammatik, von Johan Hendrik Gallée. 2. völlig umgearb. aufl. Eingeleitet und mit registern versehen von Johannes Lochner ... Halle, M. Niemeyer; [etc., etc.] 1910.

Lochner, Johannes, ed.

B2750
.K29
Philosophische monatshefte der Kant-studien, im auftrage der Kant-gesellschaft ... 1.-2. jahrg.; 1925-26. Berlin, R. Heise [1925-26]

Lochner, Johannes, joint ed.
Leisewitz, Johann Anton, 1752-1806.
Johann Anton Leisewitzens tagebücher, nach den handschriften hrsg. von Heinrich Mack und Johannes Lochner ... Weimar, Gesellschaft der bibliophilen, 1916-

---

Lochner, Johannes, 1879-
Thomas Prischuchs Gedichte auf das Konzil von Konstanz. (Kapitel I bis III.)...von Johannes Lochner... [Berlin: E. Ebering, G.m.b.H., 1905.] 53 p. pl. 8°.

Dissertation, Berlin.
Lebenslauf.
Bibliographical footnotes.

1. Prischuch, Thomas, fl. 1460.
N. Y. P. L. August 17, 1922.

NL 0433608 NN ICRL CtY PU MH

Lochner, Johannes, 1879-
... Thomas Prischuchs gedichte auf das Konzil von Konstanz. Von Dr. Johannes Lochner. Berlin, E. Ebering, g. m. b. h., 1906.
167 p. incl. pl. 24½cm. (Berliner beiträge zur germanischen und romanischen philologie ... XXIX. Germanische abteilung, no. 16)

7-9517

NL 0433609 DLC MiU KU CU OU PU NN

---

fl. 1924.
Lochner, Johannes: Das kaufmännische Bestätigungsschreiben, seine Bedeutung und einige Hauptgrundsätze seiner Behandlung. [Maschinenschrift.] v, 79 S. 4°. — Auszug: Oppeln 1924: Raabe. 8 S. 8°
Breslau, R.- u. staatswiss. Diss. v. 20. März 1924 [U 24. 1497

NL 0433610 ICRL

Lochner (Julius Albert) [1835-]. * Ueber Geisteskrankheit im Klimakterium. 19 pp. 8°. *Leipzig, C. G. Naumann,* 1870.

NL 0433611 DNLM

4GV
563
Lochner, Karl E.
Die Entwicklungsphasen der europäischen Fechtkunst. Wien, Selbstverlag des Verfassers, 1953.
40 p.

NL 0433612 DLC-P4

VOLUME 337

Lochner, Louis Paul, 1887–
America's Don Quixote, Henry Ford's attempt to save Europe, by Louis P. Lochner, with a preface by Maxim Gorki. Eight illustrations. London, K. Paul, Trench, Trubner & co., ltd., 1924.
xxii, 10, 240 p. front., plates, ports. 22½cm.

1. Ford, Henry, 1863– 2. European war, 1914–1918—Peace. I. Title.

Library of Congress D613.5.L7 25—7922

NL 0433613 DLC CSt-H CtY NN

LOCHNER, LOUIS PAUL. 1887–
America's Don Quixote; Henry Ford's attempt to save Europe, by Louis P. Lochner; with a preface by Maxim Gorki. London, K. Paul, Trench, Trubner & Co., Ltd., 1924. xxii, 240 p. front.(port.), plates. 8°.

Microfilm.

1. Ford, Henry, 1863-1947. 2. European war, 1914-1918--Peace agitation and mediation. I. Title.

NL 0433614 NN

Lochner, Louis Paul, *1887–*
Amerikanische Berichterstattung. Amerikanisches Nachrichtwesen. [Vortrag gehalten in der Vereinigung Carl Schurz am 29. Januar 1931.]
= Hamburg. Friederichsen, De Gruyter & Co. B.m.b.H. [1931.]
28 pp. 25 cm.
"Sonderheft der Amerika-Post."

N9951 — Reporting. — United States. .ewspapers. — Vereinigung Carl Schurz, Hamburg. Addresses.

NL 0433615 MB NN

Lochner, Louis Paul, 1881–
... La conférence des neutres pour une médiation continue, par Louis P. Lochner ... Stockholm, Neutral conference for continuous mediation, 1916.
30 p. 19cm. (Neutral conference documents. no. 8c)

1. Mediation, International. I. Title.

Library of Congress JX4475.N4 no. 8c 30–6246

NL 0433616 DLC

Lochner, Louis Paul, 1887–
... The Cosmopolitan club movement, by Louis P. Lochner ... New York city, American association for international conciliation, 1912.
14 p. 19½cm. (International conciliation, pub. monthly by the American association for international conciliation ... no. 61)

1. Students' societies. I. Title.

Library of Congress JX1907.A8 no. 61 13—18540

OO PPT MB ICJ NRCR
NL 0433617 DLC OrPR WaS WaU-L CaBVaU DAU MiU OU OCl

DD247 .G6A25 1948a

Lochner, Louis Paul, 1887– ed. and tr.

Goebbels, Joseph, 1897–
The Goebbels diaries, tr. and ed. by Louis P. Lochner. London, H. Hamilton [1948]

Lochner, Louis Paul, 1887– ed. and tr.

DD247 .G6A25

Goebbels, Joseph, 1897–
The Goebbels diaries, 1942–1943. Ed., tr. and with an introd. by Louis P. Lochner. [1st ed.] Garden City, N. Y., Doubleday, 1948.

Lochner, Louis Paul, 1887–
Fritz Kreisler. New York, Macmillan, 1950.
xx, 455 p. illus., ports., music. 21 cm.
"Compositions [including a reprint of the Schott thematic catalog], transcriptions, and arrangements": p. 407–416. "Discography": p. 417–428. Bibliography: p. 429–437.

1. Kreisler, Fritz, 1875–

ML418.K7L6 927.8 50-12787

IdU Or OrCS OrP OrU Wa
NcGU PPFr CaBVa PPL PPD PPA WU CaBViP CaBVaU IdB
WaE WaS MoU MiU MB KyLx MiHM NcU TxU TU KEmT PSt
NL 0433620 DLC OrStbM WaTC WaT IdPI WaSp WaSpG

Lochner, Louis Paul, 1887–
Fritz Kreisler. London, Rockliff [1951, °1950]
xx, 459 p. illus., ports., music. 22 cm.
"Compositions, transcriptions, and arrangements [including a reprint of the thematic catalog published by B. Schotts Söhne, Mainz]": p. 408–412. "Discography": p. 432. Bibliography: p. 433–442.

1. Kreisler, Fritz, 1875– 2. Kreisler, Fritz, 1875– —Discography.
ML418.K9L6 1951a 927.8 52–27127

NL 0433621 DLC CU-S

Lochner, Louis Paul, 1887–
Fritz Kreisler. New York, Macmillan, 1951 [°1950]
xx, 455 p. illus., ports., music. 22 cm.
"Second printing, 1951," with important changes in the text on p. 351.
"Compositions [including a reprint of the Schott thematic catalog], transcriptions, and arrangements": p. 407–416. "Discography": p. 417–428. Bibliography: p. 429–437.

1. Kreisler, Fritz, 1875– 2. Kreisler, Fritz, 1875– —Discography.
ML418.K9L6 1951 927.8 51–6409

NL 0433622 DLC WaWW

Lochner, Louis Paul, 1887–
Fritz Kreisler. New York, Macmillan, 1952 c1950.
xx, 455 p. illus., ports., music. 21 cm.
"Compositions [including a reprint of the Schott thematic catalog], transcriptions, and arrangements": p. 407–416. "Discography": p. 417–428. Bibliography: p. 429–437.

NL 0433623 Or ViU

Lochner, Louis Paul, 1887–
Henry Ford—America's Don Quixote, by Louis P. Lochner, with a preface by Maxim Gorki. Eight illustrations. New York, International publishers, 1925.
xxii, 10, 240 p. front., plates, ports. 22½ cm.
"Printed in Great Britain."
London edition (K. Paul, Trench, Trubner & co. ltd.) has title: America's Don Quixote.

1. Ford, Henry, 1863–1947. 2. European war, 1914–1918—Peace. I. Title.
D613.5.L7 1925 26—2326

NL 0433624 DLC ICN MB NN

Lochner, Louis Paul, 1887–
... Internationalism among universities, by Louis P. Lochner. Boston, World peace foundation, 1913.
12 p. 20½cm. (World peace foundation. Pamphlet series ... vol. III, no. 7, pt. II)

1. Universities and colleges. 2. International cooperation. 3. Students' societies. I. Title.

Library of Congress JX1908.U5 13—20521

MB NRCR
NL 0433625 DLC Or OrU IEN PPT OU MiU OCU OO OCl PPB

Lochner, Louis Paul, 1887– tr.

Luxemburg, Rosa, 1870–1919.
... Letters to Karl and Luise Kautsky from 1896 to 1918. Edited by Luise Kautsky and translated from the German by Louis P. Lochner. New York, R. M. McBride & company, 1925.

HC 286.3 L6215

Lochner, Louis Paul, 1887–
Die Mächtigen und der Tyrann (Tycoons and tyrant) Die deutsche Industrie von Hitler bis Adenauer. [1. Aufl. Einzige, vom Verfasser autorisierte deutsche Ausg. Besorgt von Theodor Büchner unter Mitarbeit von J.K. Thiel] Darmstadt, F. Schneekluth [1955]
343 p. 21cm.

1. Germany - Industry. 2. Industry and state - Germany. I. Title.

NL 0433627 CoFS LU

E183.8 M6L81

Lochner, Louis Paul, 1877–
Mexico - Whose war? New York, Peoples Print [1919?]
24 p. 23cm.
Cover title.

1. Mexico - For. rel. - U.S. 2. U.S. - For. rel. - Mexico. I. Title.

NL 0433628 CSt-H NN

LOCHNER, Louis P[aul], 1887–
The Neutral conference for continuous mediation. Stockholm, Neutral conference for continuous mediation, 1916.

pp.27. 12°.
"Neutral conference documents," 8.

NL 0433629 MH-L

LOCHNER, Louis P[aul], 1887–
Die Neutrale konferenz für ständige vermittlung. Aus dem englischen übersetzt von Ernst Trösch. Stockholm, Neutrale konferenz, 1916.

pp.32. 12°.
"Dokumente der Neutralen konferenz."8b.

NL 0433630 MH-L MiU-L

Lochner, Louis Paul, 1887–
Should there be military training in public schools?
(*In* National education association of the United States. Journal of proceedings and addresses, 1915. p. 217–222)

1. Drill and minor tactics. [1. Military drill—Schools—U. S.]

E 16–735

Library, U. S. Bur. of Education

NL 0433631 DHEW WaS OU

VOLUME 337

D613.5
L715 Lochner, Louis Paul, 1887-
Die Staatsmännischen Experimente des Autokönigs Henry Ford. Mit einigen Gedanken von Maxim Gorki. ⌜Aus dem Englischen Übertr. von Albert Markwitz⌝ München, Verlag für Kulturpolitik, 1923.
xviii, 231 p. 24cm.

1. Ford, Henry, 1863-1947. 2. European War, 1914-1918 - Peace. I. Title.

NL 0433632 GU NN

GERMAN
B
L789s Lochner, Louis Paul, 1887-
Stets das Unerwartete; Erinnerungen aus Deutschland, 1921-1953. ⌜1. Aufl.⌝ Darmstadt, F. Schneekluth ⌜©1955⌝
383 ⌜1⌝ p.

Translation of Always the unexpected.

NL 0433633 MiD NcD CSt-H PPG OCl

DD247
.G6A23 Lochner, Louis Paul, 1887- ed.

Goebbels, Joseph, 1897-
Goebbels Tagebücher aus den Jahren 1942–43, mit andern Dokumenten, hrsg. von Louis P. Lochner. Zürich, Atlantis Verlag ⌜1948⌝

Lochner, Louis Paul, 1887-
Tycoons and tyrant; German industry from Hitler to Adenauer. Chicago, H. Regnery Co., 1954.
304 p. 22 cm.

1. Germany—Indus. 2. Industry and state—Germany. I. Title.

HC286.3.L62 338.943 54—10443 ‡

DAU ODW PRosC PSt GU
CoU CSt KEmT MB NN TxU NcD PPD PP TU OCl OOxM OU OO
NL 0433635 DLC WaE OrU OrPR MtU OClW WaT WaS CaBVaU

Lochner, Louis Paul, 1887-
Wanted: aggressive pacificism, by Louis P. Lochner. Chicago: Chicago Peace Soc. ⌜1915.⌝ 11 p. 12°.

Repr.: The Public (Chicago), Jan. 15, 1915.

1. War and peace. 2. Title.
N. Y. P. L. October 7, 1916.

NL 0433636 NN MH-L

Lochner, Louis Paul, 1887-
What about Germany? By Louis P. Lochner ... New York, Dodd, Mead & company, 1942.
xiv p., 1 l., 395 p. front., plates, ports. 22 cm.

1. Germany—Pol. & govt.—1933-1945. 2. National socialism. 3. World war, 1939-1945—Germany. I. Title.

DD253.L578 943.085 42-24535

OKentU PV ODW OClCC PSC OCl PU OO DAU KU NIC CoU
CaBViP CaBVa OrP PPL PPT OClW NcC NcD OCU CLSU ViU
NL 0433637 DLC WaS WaE Wa Or OrU WaSp MtU WaWW WaT

Lochner, Louis Paul, 1887-
What about Germany? By Louis P. Lochner ... London, Hodder and Stoughton, limited ⌜1943⌝
287 p. plates, ports. 21cm.
"First printed March 1943 ... Reprinted May 1943."

1. Germany—Pol. & govt.—1933- 2. National socialism. 3. World war, 1939- —Germany. I. Title.

43-14612

Library of Congress DD253.L578 1943
⌜3⌝ 943.086

NL 0433638 DLC CtY

Lochner, Louis Paul, 1887-
What about Poland? A radio broadcast over National broadcasting co., by Louis P. Lochner... Beverly Hills, Friends of Poland ⌜1944⌝ 8 p. 15cm.

1. World war, 1939-1945—Poland. I. Friends of Poland, inc.
N. Y. P. L. June 20, 1946

NL 0433639 NN

Lochner (Ludwig). *Zur Casuistik der nervösen Nachkrankheiten der Influenza. 36 pp. 8°. *Würzburg, A. Boegler,* 1896.

NL 0433640 DNLM ICRL

Lochner, Ludwig, 1876-
Pope's literarische beziehungen zu seinen zeitgenossen ... Naumburg a. S., Lippert & co., 1910.
2 p. l., 47, ⌜1⌝ p. 22cm.
Inaug.-diss.—Munich.
Lebenslauf.
Published in full (vii, ⌜1⌝, 118 p.) as Münchener beiträge zur romanischen und englischen philologie, 49.
"Benützte werke": verso of 2d prelim. leaf.

1. Pope, Alexander, 1688-1744.

30-27906

Library of Congress PR3633.L6 821.53

NL 0433641 DLC MH PU OCU

Lochner, Ludwig, 1876-
Pope's literarische beziehungen zu seinen zeitgenossen. Ein beitrag zur geschichte der englischen literatur des 18. jahrhunderts, von dr. Ludwig Lochner. Leipzig, A. Deichert'sche verlagsbuchhandlung nachf., 1910.
vii, ⌜1⌝, 118 p. 23½cm. (*Added t.-p.:* Münchener beiträge zur romanischen und englischen philologie. Hrsg. von H. Breymann und J. Schick. XLIX)

10-20804

OCl OO NN MB
NL 0433642 DLC NjP MiDW OOxM PBm PU OU MiU OCU ViU

Lochner, Martin, 1883-
The organist's handbook: a guide to Lutheran service playing on small pipe-organ, reed-organ, or piano, by Martin Lochner ... St. Louis, Mo., Concordia publishing house, 1937.
36 p. illus. (music) 23cm.
"Music for the pipe-organ": p. 27-35. "Music for the reed-organ and piano": p. 35-36.
"Instructive reading-material": p. 36.

1. Church music—Lutheran church. 2. Musical accompaniment. 3. Organ—Instruction and study. I. Title.

⌜Full name: Martin Gustave Carl Lochner⌝

38-5261

Library of Congress MT191.L8107
——— Copy 2.
Copyright AA 254193 ⌜3⌝ [783 : 284.1] 786.7

NL 0433643 DLC NN

Lochner, Martin Gustave Carl, 1883-
see Lochner, Martin, 1883-

Lochner, Mary Flavia, sister
see Lochner, Flavia, sister.

Lochner, Max.

Grundlagen der Lufttechnik, 1897.

NL 0433646 DAS

Lochner, Max.
Grundlagen der lufttechnik. Gemeinverständliche abhandlungen über eine neue theorie zur lösung der flugfrage und des problems des lenkbaren luftschiffes. Von Max Lochner ... Berlin, W. H. Kühl, 1899.
1 p. l., 33, ⌜1⌝ p. 2 pl. 21½cm.

1. Air-ships.

33-15598

Library of Congress TL654.L6A4
——— Copy 2. 629.13324

NL 0433647 DLC DNW DAS

Lochner, Michael Frederich, 1662-1720.
Commentatio de ananasa, sive Nuce Pinea indica, vulgo Pinhas...
[n.p.] 1716.

YA13187

NL 0433648 DLC MoSB CtY PPAmP

Lochner, Michael Friedrich, 1662-1720
——— De novis et exoticis thee et cafe succedaneis dissertatio epistolica. [Francofurti. 1717.] ⌜1⌝. 4°. Plate.
Ephemerides Academiæ cæsareæ leopoldinæ naturæ curiosorum, 1717, v–vi, appendix, pp. 145–160.

NL 0433649 MH-A

W 4 LOCHNER Michael Friedrich, 1662-1720,
A44 respondent.
1684 ... De nymphomania historiam medicam ... in disputatione
L,1 inaugurali publice defendet ... Mich. Fried. Lochner ...
Altdorffii, Typis Henrici Meyeri [1684]
24 p. 22 cm.
Diss. - Altdorf

NL 0433650 DNLM

⌜Lochner, Michael Friedrich, 1662-1720.
Μηκωνοπαίγνιον; sive, Papaver ex omni antiqvitate ervtvm, gemmis, nvmmis, statvis et marmoribvs aeri incisis illvstratvm. Noribergæ, Typis Melchioris Godefridi Heinii, 1713.
⌜8⌝, 182, ⌜2⌝ p. illus., XXX (i.e.29) plates (part fold.) 20cm

Title vignette.
Dedication signed: Periander ⌜pseud.⌝

1. Plants in art. 2. Mythology, Classical. I. Title. II. Title: Papaver.

NL 0433651 NNC NBu NNBG NBuG

Lochner, Michael Friedrich, 1662–1720.
119776 Memoria Fehriana viri illustris consecrata manibus à Mich. Fried. Lochner, ... [Norimbergæ, Sumptibus W. M. Endteri], 1690.
[2, 129]–182 p. 21cm. (*In* Miscellanea curiosa ... Academiæ Cæsareo-Leopoldinæ, decuriæ II, annus octavus, appendix 8.)
Contains three poems by J. G. Volckamer, L. Schröckius, and J. T. Mœren.

NL 0433652 ICJ

VOLUME 337

Lochner, Michael Friedrich, 1662-1720.
Mvngos animalcvlvm et radix. Noribergae, Sumptibus Wolfgangi Michahelles, 1715.
32p. 22cm.

1 Ophiorrhiza mungos. 2 t.

NL 0433653 NNM PPAN OkU

Lochner, Michael Friedrich, 1662–1720.
Michaelis Friderici Lochneri ... Nerivm sive Rhododaphne vetervm et recentiorvm, qua nerei et nereidvm mythologia, amyci lavrvs, saccharum al-haschar, et ventus ac planta badsamur aliaque explicantur, ac diversis sacrae scripturae locis lux affunditur. Accedit Dafne constantiniana. Norimbergae, apud haeredes, J. Hoffmanni, 1716.
2 p. l., 112 p. VIII pl. (part fold.) 19½ x 15½cm.
Added t.-p., illus.
1. Nerium.
Agr 25-564
Library, U. S. Dept. of Agriculture 452.3L78

NL 0433654 DNAL MH-A MoSB DLC

QH71 .B35B4 Rare bk. coll.

Lochner, Michael Friedrich, 1662-1720, ed.

Besler, Basilius, 1561–1629.
Rariora mvsei Besleriani quae olim Basilivs et Michael Rvpertvs Besleri collegerunt, aeneisqve tabvlis ad vivvm incisa evvlgarvnt: nunc commentariolo illustrata a Johanne Henrico Lochnero ... denvo lvci pvblicae commisit et lavdationem ejvs fvnebrem adjecit maestissimus parens Michael Fridericvs Lochnervs ... ₍Nuremberg₎ 1716.

Lochner, Michael Friedrich, 1662-1770.
——. Schediasma de Parreira brava, novo Americano calculi remedio. 64 pp., 4 pl. sm. 4°. [Norimbergæ, 1712?]

NL 0433656 DNLM

Lochner, Michael Friedrich, 1662-1770.
Schediasma de Parreira brava, novo Americano aliisque recentioribus calculi remediis; * * * editio secunda auctior. Norimbergae, 1719.
Pamphlet. sq. O. (20.5 x 16.9).

NL 0433657 MoSB DNLM

Lochner, Michael Friedrich, 1706-1777, respondent.
... De ivre secvli
see under Hildebrand, Heinrich, 1668-1729, praeses. [Supplement]

Lochner, Michael Friedrich, 1706-1777.
... De reservato imperatoris exigendi avrvm coronarivm a Jvdaeis etiam in aliorvm statvvm imperii terris degentibvs. Von der Juden Cronen-Steuer oder güldnen Opffer-Pfennig ... propvgnata a Michaele Frider. Lochnero ... Altorfii, M. D. Meyer ₍1726₎
40 p. 18½cm.
Diss. - Altdorf.

NL 0433659 MH-L

---

*GC7 L7893 726db

Lochner, Michael Friedrich, 1706-1777.
D. Michaelis Frider. Lochneri ... De reservato imperatoris exigendi avrvm coronarivm a Ivdaeis etiam in aliorvm statvvm imperii terris degentibvs. Von der Juden Cronen=Steuer oder güldnen Opffer=Pfennig, dissertatio inavgvralis ivridica. In norimbergensivm vniversitate d. vii. ivnii MDCCXXVI. solenniter propvgnata.
Altorfii,impensis Stephani Grebneri.1750.
4°. 46p. 20cm.,in case 20.5cm.

NL 0433660 MH NN

Lochner, Oscar von
see Lochner von Hüttenbach, Oscar, Freiherr, 1868-1920.

Lochner, F., tr.

Nowak, Karl Friedrich, 1882–
The collapse of Central Europe, by Karl Friedrich Nowak, with an introduction by Viscount Haldane, O. M. London, K. Paul, Trench, Trubner & co., ltd.; New York, E. P. Dutton & co., 1924.

Lochner, Richard.
The pupil versus the teacher, by Richard Lochner. ₍Philadelphia, Times printing house, °1901₎
5 p. l., 168 p. 16½cm.

1. Teaching. I. Title.
1-10878
Library of Congress LB1025.L8

NL 0433663 DLC PU OClW PPC PPL ICJ

S 352.109747 qL812

Lochner, Robert William, 1906-
Memorandum on constitutional and statutory debt and taxing limitations. [n.p., 194-?]
12, [4] l. 29 cm.

1. Debts, Public. New York (State) 2. Local taxation. New York (State) 1. Title.

NL 0433664 N

Lochner, Robert William, 1906–
The new Patents act. London, National Union of Manufacturers ₍1950₎
29 p. 22 cm.

1. Patent laws and legislation—Gt. Brit.
608 51-23383

NL 0433665 DLC

Lochner, Robert William, 1906–
Lochner's review for New York bar examination; questions—answers—general guide. A manual concisely but comprehensively reviewing the field of substantive law, practice, procedure and evidence, with suggestions, questions and answers. By Robert W. Lochner ... Albany, N. Y., M. Bender & company, incorporated, 1935.
ix, 542 p. 23cm.

1. Law—New York (State)—Examinations, questions, etc. 2. Admission to the bar—New York (State) I. Title. II. Title: New York bar examination.
35-1006
Library of Congress

NL 0433666 DLC

Lochner, Rudolf, 1895–
Deskriptive pädogogik, umrisse einer darstellung der tatsachen und gesetze der erziehung vom soziologischen standpunkt, von Rudolf Lochner. Reichenberg, Gebrüder Stiepel ges. m. b. h., 1927.
xii, 254, ₍1₎ p. 24cm. (Added t.-p.: Schriften der Deutschen wissenschaftlichen gesellschaft in Reichenberg ... Hft. 4)
Bibliography included in "Anmerkungen" (p. ₍238₎-254)

1. Education—Philosophy.
44-17583
Library of Congress LB775.L62
₍2₎ 370.1

NL 0433667 DLC MH NN

Lochner, Rudolf, 1895-
Erziehungswissenschaft im Abriss. Wolfenbüttel,Wolfenbütteler Verlagsanstalt, 1947.
111 p. (Arbeitsbücher für die Lehrerbildung, 2)

NL 0433668 MH

4LB 92

Lochner, Rudolf, 1895-
Erziehungswissenschaft, kurzgefasstes Lehrbuch zum Gebrauch an Hochschulen. München, R. Oldenbourg, 1934.
211 p.

NL 0433669 DLC-P4 ICU

DB 90 .S36 L82

Lochner, Rudolf, 1895-
Georg von Schönerer; ein Erzieher zu Grossdeutschland. Bonn, Scheur, 1942.
19p. 21cm. (Kriegsvorträge der Rheinischen Friedrich-Wilhelms-Universität Bonn a. Rh., Heft 99)

1. Schönerer, Georg, Ritter von, 1842-1921. (Series: Bonn. Universität. Kriegsvorträge. Heft 99)

NL 0433670 IU CU NN

Lochner, Rudolf, 1895-
Geschlechtertrennung und Geschlechtervereinigung im deutschen Schulwesen der Vergangenheit. Von Rudolf Lochner... Langensalza: H. Beyer & Söhne, 1923. 45 p. 8°. (Paedagogisches Magazin. Heft 956.)
"Schriften zur Frauenbildung. Hrsg. von Prof. Dr. Jakob Wychgram... Heft 5."
Bibliography, p. ₍6₎

1. Coeducation, Germany. 2. Series.
N. Y. P. L. September 15, 1924

NL 0433671 NN IU

Lochner, Rudolf, 1895-
Grimmelshausen, ein deutscher mensch im siebzehnten jahrhundert; versuch einer psychologischen persönlichkeitsanalyse unter berücksichtigung literaturgeschichtlicher und kulturgeschichtlicher gesichtspunkte, von Rudolf Lochner ... Reichenberg i. B., F. Kraus, 1924.
xii, 206 p. 25cm. (Added t.-p.: Prager deutsche studien ... 29. hft.)
"Mit unterstützung der Gesellschaft zur förderung deutscher wissenschaft, kunst und literatur in Böhmen."
"Schrifttum": p. ₍201₎-206.
1. Grimmelshausen, Hans Jacob Christoffel von, 1625-1676. I. Gesellschaft zur förderung deutscher wissenschaft, kunst und literatur in Böhmen, Prague.
25-7353
Library of Congress PD25.P7 29. hft.

MH
NL 0433672 DLC CaBVaU CU NcU CLSU OCU MiU PBm PU

Lochner, Rudolf, 1895- ed.
... Der stolze Melcher
see under Grimmelshausen, Hans Jacob Christoffel von, 1625-1676.

VOLUME 337

Lochner, Rudolf, 1895–
Sudetendeutschland; ein Beitrag zur Grenzlanderziehung im ostmitteldeutschen Raum. Langenslza, J. Beltz [1937]
167 p. maps. 19 cm. (Volk und Welt, Arbeitshefte für geschichtliche Gegenwartsfragen, Heft 13)
"Schrifttum zum Sudetendeutschtum in Auswahl": p. 162–167.

1. Germans in the Czechoslovak Republic. I. Title. (Series)

DB200.7.L62 49–35455*

NL 0433674 DLC ICRL IEN NN NNC CU CtY MH

DB215.5 G3L812 ed.2 Hoover Library
Lochner, Rudolf, 1895-
Sudetendeutschland; ein Beitrag zur Grenzland kunde des ostmitteldeutschen Raumes. 2., veränderte und verm. Aufl. Langensalza, J. Belz [1938]
187 p. maps,diagrs. 19cm. (Volk und Welt, Hft. 13)
"Schrifttum zum Sudetendeutschtum in Auswahl": p. [180]-187.

1. Germans in Czechoslovak Republic. Republic. 2. Sudetes. I. Title.

NL 0433675 CSt-H

Lochner, Rudolf, 1895-
Wandlungen des grossdeutschen Gedankens; Rede bei der Feier der nationalen Erhebung und der Reichsgründung am 30.1.1936. Langensalza, Beltz [1937]
28 p. (Erziehungspolitische Reden der Hochschule für Lehrerbildung, Hirschberg (Riesengebirge) 5)

NL 0433676 MH CtY

Lochner, Rudolf, 1895– *ed.*
Zur Neugestaltung der Lehrerbildung; Berichte, Leitsätze, Entwürfe. Reichenberg, F. Kraus, 1930.
64 p. (p. 64 advertisements) 23 cm.
At head of title: Sudetendeutsche Anstalt für Erziehungswissenschaft der Deutschen Wissenschaftlichen Gesellschaft in Reichenberg.
Includes: Die Berichte des Reichenberger Berufserziehertages 1930.
"Das neuere Schrifttum zur Lehrerbildungsfrage in Auswahl": p. 61–63.

1. Education — Congresses. 2. Teachers, Training of — Germany. I. Reichenberger Berufserziehertage, 1930. II. Title.

L106 1930.L6 52–57747

NL 0433677 DLC

Lochner, Stefan, d. 1451.
[Cologne altarpiece; four details] Munich, Hanfstaengel [192-?]
2 col. pl. 70 x 64cm.
In portfolio.
1. Cologne. Cathedral.
2. Altarpieces.

NL 0433678 NNC

Lochner, Stefan, d.1451.
Der Dreikönigsaltar. Berlin, Mann [1948]
30p. plates. 17cm. (Der Kunstbrief, 46)

NL 0433679 MWelC

LOCHNER, Stefan, called Meister Stephan, d.1451.
Five chromolithographs after the triptych in the Cathedral at Cologne
[London.] Arundel society. 1874–75.
191, 192. Exterior panels: The Annunciation.
193. Centre panel: The adoration of the Magi.
194. Left interior panel: St. Ursula and her virgins.
195. Right interior panel: St. Gereon and his warriors.

NL 0433680 MB PP

Lochner, Stefan, *d.* 1451.
Huldigung und Gericht; Einführung von Otto H. Förster. München, Prestel Verlag, 1948.
32 p. (p. 17–32 plates) 32 cm.
An account of the Altar der Stadtpatrone Kölns ("Das Dombild") and of the Weltgerichtsaltar.
"Berichtigung": slip inserted.

I. Förster, Otto Helmut, 1894– II. Title.

ND588.L8F57 759.3 49–18735*

NL 0433681 DLC PPiU

fND588 L8F66 Case B
Lochner, Stefan, d. 1451.
Stefan Lochner, von Otto H. Förster.
[Bremen, Angelsachsen-Verlag, 1936]
[19] p., 13 plates (1 col.) in portfolio.
36cm. (Deutsche Kunst-Sonderhefte)
Caption title.

I. Förster, Otto Helmut, 1894-

NL 0433682 CU

Lochner, Stefan, *d.* 1451.
... Stefan Lochner, ein maler zu Köln. Frankfurt am main, Prestel-verlag, 1938.
204 p. incl. plates (part fold.) facsims. 28½cm.
At head of title: Otto H. Förster.
Edited by Walter Tunk.

I. Förster, Otto Helmut, 1894– II. Tunk, Walter, 1907– ed.

Library of Congress ND588.L8F6 38–37420
[3] 759.3

PU-FA MiU
NL 0433683 DLC WaS NN TU CLSU NcD NcU DAU NIC

ND588 L8F67 1941
Lochner, Stefan, d.1451.
Stefan Lochner, ein Maler zu Köln. [2. Aufl.] München, Prestel-Verlag, 1941.
186 p. (p.9-128 plates, part mounted, incl. facsims.)
"Erklärung der Schriftquellen" [von Dr. Walter Tunk]: p.[141]-148.

1. Lochner, Stefan, d.1451.

NL 0433684 CU MH

Lochner, Stefan, *d.* 1451.
Stefan Lochner, ein Maler zu Köln, [von] Otto H. Förster. [Neuausg.] Bonn, Brüder Auer, 1952.
183 p. plates (part col.) 27 cm.
Includes bibliographical references.

I. Förster, Otto Helmut, 1894–

A 52–10174

Harvard Univ. Library for Library of Congress [2]

NL 0433685 MH ICU TxU OO NN NBuU CU MdBWA

Lochner, Stefan, called Meister Stephan, d.1451
Stephan Lochner und die Kölner malerschule. Acht farbige gemäldewiedergaben. Mit einer einleitung von Karl Schaefer. Leipzig, E. A. Seemann [1924]
[8] p. illus., 8 col. mounted plates. 31 cm. (On cover: E. A. Seemanns künstlermappen 78)
Binder's title: Seemanns künstlermappen 8
Colored mounted plate on cover.
Title vignette.

NL 0433686 MdBP CSmH MWelC OrP

Lochner, Walter O.
Ethics of the secretary. [Springfield, Mass.] 1927. YA 28121
43p.

NL 0433687 DLC

Lochner, Wolfgangus Jacobus.
——. *Casus de phthisi plane funesta ex praegressa hæmoptysi orta; respondente Bened. Audr. Frissio. 26 pp., 3 l. sm. 4°. *Helmstadii, typ. P. D. Schnorrii,* [1743].

NL 0433688 DNLM

Lochner (Wolfgangus Jacobus). *De praecipuis sanguinis qualitatibus ad nutritionem corporis humani facientibus. 32 pp., 1 pl., 1 l. sm. 4°. *Altorfii, typ. J. G. Meyeri,* [1741].

NL 0433689 DNLM

Lochner, Zacharias, d.1608.
Tractätlein / darinnen etliche schöne exempel / auss der geometria / zu dem feldmessen / vnd anderm sehr nützlich vnd dienstlich / durch die edlen regel algebrae, die man sonst coss nennet / mit einem vortheil / dass sie ausser der regel algebrae, oder coss / wol können gemacht werden: durch Zachariam Lochner ... geordnet. Nürnberg / 1583.
4 p.l., 92, [2] p., 1 l. pl. (coat of arms) diagrs. 20cm.
Colophon: Gedruckt zu Nürnberg / durch Valentin Newber / wohnhafft in Obern Wehr; Printer's device; M D LXXXIII.
1. Geometry--Early works to 1800. 2. Algebra--Early works to 1800.

NL 0433690 MiU InU

Lochner von Hüttenbach, Oscar, Freiherr, 1868–1920.
Der gefesselte Genius. Märchenlustspiel in zwei Akten, frei nach Ferdinand Raimund, von Oscar von Lochner. Warendorf in Westf.: Theater-Zentrale für die kathol. Vereinsbühne [1911] 54 p. 18cm.

883417A. 1. Drama, German. I. Raimund, Ferdinand, 1790–1836. Die gefesselte Phantasie. II. Title.
N. Y. P. L. June 11, 1937

NL 0433691 NN

Lochner von Hummelstein, Johann Heinrich
see **Lochner, Johann Heinrich,** 1695–1715.

Lochner von Hummelstein, Michael Friedrich, 1662-1720.
see
Lochner, Michael Friedrich, 1662-1720.

VOLUME 337

Lochner (H. W.) and Company, *Chicago.*
Alexandria, Louisiana, street and highway plan, prepared for the State of Louisiana Department of Highways and the Public Roads Administration, Federal Works Agency. Chicago, 1947.
v, 30 p. illus., map, diagrs., plans (2 fold.) 31 cm.
"The basis of the plan is the origin-destination data obtained from a survey made by the State of Louisiana Department of Highways and the Federal Public Roads Administration."
1. Traffic surveys—Alexandria, La. 2. Alexandria, La.—Streets. I. Louisiana. Dept. of Highways (1942–) II. U. S. Public Roads Administration.
HE372.A5L6 388.3 48-13979*

NL 0433694 DLC NNC IU

q388.2 L78hc Lochner (H. W.) and Company, Chicago.
Highway and transportation plan, Chattanooga, Tennessee, prepared for the Department of Highways and Public Works, state of Tennessee and the Public Roads Administration, Federal Works Agency. [Chicago] 1948.
vii, 44p. illus., maps, plans(part col.) 31cm.
1. Chattanooga, Tenn--Streets. 2. Traffic engineering--Chattanooga, Tenn. I. Tennessee--Dept. of Highways and Public Works. II. U.S.--Public Roads Administration. III. Title.

NL 0433695 IU T

Lochner (H. W.) and Company, *Chicago.*
Highway and transportation plan for Atlanta, Georgia. Prepared for the State Highway Dept. of Georgia and the Public Roads Administration, Federal Works Agency, by H. W. Lochner & Company and De Leuw, Cather & Company. Chicago, 1946.
xiv, 65 p. illus., maps (part fold., part col.) 32 cm.
1. Atlanta—Streets. 2. Traffic surveys—Atlanta. I. De Leuw, Cather and Company, Chicago. II. Georgia. State Highway Dept.
HE372.A7 1946 388.3 48-47628*

NL 0433696 DLC CU ICU IU MdBJ TxU NIC

q388.2 L78he Lochner (H.W.) and Company, Chicago.
Highway and transportation plan, Evanston, Illinois. Prepared for the Plan Commission, Evanston, Ill. [Chicago] 1948.
22p. plans. 31cm.
1. Evanston, Ill.--Streets. 2. Traffic engineering--Evanston, Ill.

NL 0433697 IU

Lochner (H. W.) and Company, *Chicago.*
Highway and transportation plan for Greater Little Rock, Arkansas. Prepared for the Arkansas State Highway Commission in cooperation with the Public Roads Administration, Federal Works Agency, and the city of Little Rock, city of North Little Rock and Pulaski County. Chicago, 1948.
ix, 55 p. illus., plans (part col.) 31 cm.
1. Traffic engineering—Little Rock, Ark. I. Arkansas. State Highway Commission.
HE372.L66L6 388 48-20645*

NL 0433698 DLC

HE372 K74 1948 f Lochner (H.W.) and Company, Chicago.
Highway and transportation plan, Knoxville, Tennessee. Prepared for the Dept. of Highways and Public Works, State of Tennessee and the Public Roads Administration, Federal Works Agency, by H.W. Lochner & Company and De Leuw, Cather & Company. Chicago, 1948.
vii,46 p. illus.,maps(part fold.,part col.) 31cm.
1.Traffic surveys - Knoxville. 2.Automobile parking - Knoxville. I.De Leuw, Cather and Company, Chicago. II.Tennessee. Dept. of Highways and Public Works.

NL 0433699 CSt T

Lochner (H.W.) and Company, Chicago.
Highway and transportation plan, Nashville, Tennessee. Prepared for the Dept. of Highways and Public Works, state of Tennessee, and the Public Roads Administration, Federal Works Agency, by H.W. Lochner & Company and DeLeuw, Cather & Company. Chicago, 1946.
vii,70 p. maps(part fold.),diagrs.
1. Highway engineering - Nashville, Tenn. I. DeLeuw, Cather, and Company, Chicago. II. Tennessee. Dept. of Highways and Public Works. III. U.S. Public Roads Administration.

NL 0433700 CU T

Lochner (H. W.) and Company, *Chicago.*
Highway plan for Baton Rouge, Louisiana, prepared for the State of Louisiana Department of Highways and the Public Roads Administration, Federal Works Agency. [Chicago] 1947.
vi, 44 p. plans. 32 cm.
1. Baton Rouge, La.—Streets. 2. Traffic engineering—Baton Rouge, La. I. Louisiana. Dept. of Highways (1942–) II. U. S. Public Roads Administration.
HE356.5.B3L6 388.1 47-27151*

NL 0433701 DLC Or IU ICJ NNC TxU NIC TU

Lochner (H. W.) and Company, *Chicago.*
Highway plan for Shreveport, Louisiana, prepared for the State of Louisiana Department of Highways and the Public Roads Administration, Federal Works Agency. Chicago, 1947.
vii, 45 p. plans. 32 cm.
1. Shreveport, La.—Streets. 2. Traffic engineering—Shreveport, La. I. Louisiana. Dept. of Highways (1942–) II. U. S. Public Roads Administration.
HE356.5.S5L6 388.1 47-27152*

NL 0433702 DLC OrCS NIC TxU MiU IU ViU LU

HE372 S23 1951 f Lochner (H.W.) and Company, Chicago.
A highway plan for the Illinois portion of the St. Louis metropolitan area. Prepared for the State of Illinois, Dept. of Public Works and Buildings, Division of Highways, and the Bi-State Development Agency, in cooperation with the U.S. Dept. of Commerce, Bureau of Public Roads. Chicago, 1951.
Transportation x,47 p. illus.,maps(part fold.,part col.) 31cm.
1.Traffic surveys - St. Louis. 2.Roads - Illinois. I.Illinois. Dept. of Public Works and Buildings. Division of Highways.

NL 0433703 CSt IU ICarbS CaBVaU

q388.312 L812h Lochner (H.W.) and Company, Chicago.
A highway plan for the tri-city area. Prepared for the State of Illinois Dept. of Public Works and Buildings, Division of Highways, in cooperation with the United States Dept. of Commerce, Bureau of Public Roads. [Chicago] 1952.
35p.
1. Traffic surveys--Rock Island, Ill. 2. Traffic surveys--Moline, Ill. 3. Traffic surveys--East Moline, Ill. 4. Rock Island, Ill.--Streets. 5. Moline, Ill.--Streets. 6. East Moline, Ill.--Streets. I. Illinois. Dept. of Public Works and Buildings. Division of Highways.

NL 0433705 ICarbS IU

q388.2 L78p Lochner (H. W.) and Company, Chicago.
Parking plan for Evanston, Illinois. [Chicago] 1948.
26p. maps. 31cm.
1. Automobile parking--Evanston, Ill.

NL 0433706 IU

Lochner (H. W.) & company, Chicago.
Preliminary engineering report on a highway improvement plan for Brunswick, Georgia. Prepared for the State highway department of Georgia and the Public roads administration, Federal works agency, by H. W. Lochner and company. Chicago, 1945.
26 p. illus. 28cm.
I. Georgia. Highway department. II. United States. Public roads bureau.
N. Y. P. L. March 17, 1949

NL 0433707 NN

Lochner (H. W.) and Company, *Chicago.*
Street and highway plan for Augusta, Georgia. Prepared for the State Highway Dept. of Georgia and the Public Roads Administration, Federal Works Agency. Chicago, 1948.
iii, 29 p. illus., col. maps. 31 cm.
1. Augusta, Ga.—Streets. 2. Traffic surveys—Augusta, Ga. I. Georgia. State Highway Dept.
HE372.A8 1948 388.3 48-47626*

NL 0433708 DLC IU

Lochner (H. W.) and Company, *Chicago.*
Street and highway plan for Columbus, Georgia, and Phenix City, Alabama. Prepared for the State Highway Dept. of Georgia and the Public Roads Administration, Federal Works Agency. Chicago, 1947.
28 p. illus., col. maps. 31 cm.
1. Columbus, Ga.—Streets. 2. Phenix City, Ala.—Streets. 3. Traffic surveys—Columbus, Ga. 4. Traffic surveys—Phenix City, Ala. I. Georgia. State Highway Dept.
HE372.C65 1947 388.3 48-47625*

NL 0433709 DLC IU

Lochner (H. W.) and Company, *Chicago.*
Street and highway plan for Macon, Georgia. Prepared for the State Highway Dept. of Georgia and the Public Roads Administration, Federal Works Agency. Chicago, 1947.
iii, 33 p. illus., maps (part fold., part col.) 32 cm.
1. Macon, Ga.—Streets. 2. Traffic surveys—Macon, Ga. I. Georgia. State Highway Dept.
HE372.M27 1947 388.3 48-47627*

NL 0433710 DLC OCl IU

q388 L812s Lochner (H. W.) and Company, Chicago.
A street and highway plan for the Danville area. Prepared for the State of Illinois Dept. of Public Works and Buildings, Division of Highways, in cooperation with the U. S. Dept. of Commerce, Bureau of Public Roads. Chicago, 1955.
31p. maps (part fold., part col.)
1. Danville, Ill.--Streets. 2. Traffic surveys--Danville, Ill. I. Illinois. Division of Highways. II. Title.

NL 0433711 ICarbS

VOLUME 337

q388.2
L78d Lochner (H. W.) and Company, Chicago.
A street and highway plan for the Decatur area, prepared for the State of Illinois Department of Public Works and Buildings, Division of Highways, in cooperation with the United States Department of Commerce, Bureau of Public Roads. Chicago, 1952.
vii, 27p. col.maps (part fold.) 31cm.

NL 0433712 IU PPCPC

q388
L812sk Lochner (H. W.) and Company, Chicago.
A street and highway plan for the Kankakee area. Prepared for the State of Illinois Dept. of Public Works and Buildings, Division of Highways, in cooperation with the U. S. Dept. of Commerce, Bureau of Public Roads. Chicago, 1954.
37p. maps. (part fold, part col.)

1. Kankakee, Ill.--Streets. 2. Traffic surveys--Kankakee, Ill. I. Illinois. Division of High[illegible]. II. Title.

NL 0433713 ICarbS

q388
L812sm Lochner (H. W.) and Company, Chicago.
A street and highway plan for the Mattoon area. Prepared for the State of Illinois Dept. of Public Works and Buildings, Division of Highways in cooperation with the U. S. Dept. of Commerce, Bureau of Public Roads. Chicago, 1955.
29p. maps (part fold., part col.)

1. Mattoon, Ill.--Streets. 2. Traffic surveys--Mattoon, Ill. I. Illinois. Division of Highways. II. Title.

NL 0433714 ICarbS KMK

388.2
L78pe Lochner (H.W.) and Company, Chicago.
A street and highway plan for the Peoria area. Prepared for the State of Illinois Department of Public Works and Buildings, Division of Highways, in cooperation with the United States Department of Commerce, Bureau of Public Roads. ₍Chicago₎ 1954.
37p. plans(part col., part fold.) 31cm.

1. Peoria--Streets. I. Illinois--Division of Highways.

NL 0433715 IU ICarbS

q388
L812sr Lochner (H. W.) and Company, Chicago.
A street and highway plan for the Rockford area. Prepared for the State of Illinois Dept. of Public Works and Buildings Division of Highways in cooperation with the U. S. Dept. of Commerce, Bureau of Public Roads. Chicago, 1952.
31p. maps (part fold. col.)

1. Rockford, Ill.--Streets. 2. Traffic surveys--Rockford, Ill. I. Illinois. Division of High ways. II. Title.

NL 0433716 ICarbS IU

Lochner (H. W.) and Company, *Chicago.*
A street and highway plan for the Springfield area. Prepared for the State of Illinois Dept. of Public Works and Buildings, Division of Highways, in cooperation with the United States Dept. of Commerce, Bureau of Public Roads. ₍Chicago₎ 1953.
vii, 33 p. col. maps, plans. 31 cm.

1. Springfield, Ill.—Streets. 2. Traffic surveys—Springfield, Ill. I. Illinois. Dept. of Public Works and Buildings. Division of Highways.

HE356.5.S7L6 *625.79 388.4 A 53-10166

Illinois. Univ. Library for Library of Congress ₍2₎†

NL 0433717 IU CU DLC

HE372
L88
1944 Lochner (H.W.) and Company, Chicago.
Traffic analysis and expressway plan for the City of Louisville, Kentucky. Prepared for the Dept. of Highways of the Commonwealth of Kentucky. Chicago ₍1944?₎
36 p. maps(1 fold.) 23 x 29cm.

Transportation

1.Traffic surveys - Louisville, Ky. 2.Express highways - Louisville, Ky. I.Kentucky. Dept. of Highways.

NL 0433718 CSt

LOCHNER (H. W.) AND COMPANY, CHICAGO.
UNION TRUCK TERMINAL PLAN FOR ATLANTA, GEORGIA; SUPPLEMENTING AND TO BE CONSIDERED A PART OF THE PREVIOUSLY ISSUED 'HIGHWAY AND TRANSPORTATION PLAN' PREPARED FOR THE STATE HIGHWAY DEPARTMENT OF GEORGIA AND THE PUBLIC ROADS ADMINISTRATION, FEDERAL WORKS AGENCY. CHICAGO, 1946. 22 P. ILLUS., MAPS.

1. MOTOR-TRUCK TERMINALS.
LOCHNER (H. W.) AND COMPANY, CHICAGO. HIGHWAY AND TRANSPORTATION PLAN FOR ATLANTA, GEORGIA.
TITLE.

NL 0433720 GAT

Lochom, Michel van, 1601-1647, supposed author.
Amoris divini et hvmani antipathia siue effectus varij, e varijs sacrae scripturae...

see under title

Rare Book Room
Mzh200
L789 Lochom, Michel van, 1601-1647.
Images des fondatrices, reformatrices ou principales religieuses de tous les ordres de l'eglise ... A Paris,Chez Michel van Lochom,graueur,& imprimeur du Roy pour les tailles-douces,ruë S.Jacques, à la Rose Blanche.1639.
2p.ℓ.,3-7,14p. 88ports. 22cm.
Signatures: [a]¹A⁴a²-2¹2⁵1.
Added engr. t.-p.: Fvndatrices reformatrices et praecipvae moniales omnivm ordinvm ecclesiae Dei 1639.

NL 0433722 CtY

Lochon, Charles.
Motets en musique ... Sçavois, neuf à voix seule, un à deux voix, deux un à trois voix, avec la B-C. Et un oratorio à six parties. Paris, Ballard, 1701.
(8), 92 p. F°.
Contents. - À une voix: O charitatis Victima; Venite, fideles; Verbum supernum; Quibus sub bina specie; O Salutaris; Ave, bone Jesu; Domine, salvum fac regem; Cur non amatis; Jam quaero sapere. - Tuere nos mortales [T. T.] - Mille voces concinant [T. T. B.] - Thuris odor volet [T. T. B.] - O miraculum! O novitatis prodigium, oratorio à 4 voix.

NL 0433723 MB

4BX
Cath.
663 Lochon, Claudius.
Les Allinges, 14 septembre 1594 - 14 septembre 1836; 2 juillet 1872 - 15 septembre 1873. La politique catholique et L'Association de Pie IX. Annecy, Impr. de C. Burdet, 1873.
75 p.

NL 0433724 DLC-P4

843L789
Oe1715 ₍Lochon, Étienne₎ d.ca.1720.
Entretiens d'un homme de cour, et d'un solitaire, sur la conduite des grands; histoire morale. Où non seulement les grands, mais même tous les peres de famille trouveront d'une maniere nouvelle & familiere, l'explication de leurs principaux devoirs. Par l'auteur du Traité du secret de la confession. Paris, Montalant, 1715.
534p. 17cm.

NL 0433725 IU

[Lochon, Étienne] d. ca 1720.
Traité du secret de la confession. Pour servir d'instruction aux confesseurs, et pour rasseurer les pénitens. Par un docteur de Sorbonne. Paris, Simart, 1708.

331 p.

NL 0433726 MH

₍Lochon, Étienne₎ *d. ca.* 1720.
Le vray devot consideré a l'egard du mariage et des peines qui s'y rencontrent. A Paris, Chez Lambert Roulland. M.DC.LXXIX.
9 p. l., 191 p. 13cm.
"Ex bibliotheca R. Toinet."

1. Marriage. I. Title.

31-25088

Library of Congress HQ731.L6 173.1

NL 0433727 DLC CaQMM

Lochon (Georges) [1871-]. *Étude climatologique, hydrologique et thérapeutique de Thonon-les-Bains. 126 pp. 8°. *Lyon,* 1897, 2. s., no. 64.

NL 0433728 DNLM

F1409
.C8 Lochon, Henri, joint author.

Cornet, Jacques.
Deux hommes, 2 C. V., deux continents ₍par₎ Jacques Cornet ₍et₎ Henri Lochon. Paris, P. Horay ₍1954₎

Lochon, Henri, 1903-
... Contribution à l'étude du chimisme gastrique; ses différentes techniques et sa valeur séméiologique ... Lyon, 1920.
Thèse - Univ. de Lyon.
"Bibliographie": p. 155-161.

NL 0433730 CtY

PR4891
L17P6 Lochore, G.
Poetical recreation, by Gamma. Glasgow, W. G. Blackie, 1870.
viii, 172 p.

NL 0433731 CU

Lochore, Reuel Anson.
From Europe to New Zealand; an account of our continental European settlers. ₍Wellington₎ A. H. & A. W. Reed ₍1951₎
112 p. illus. 23 cm.

1. New Zealand—Foreign population. I. Title.

DU423.L6 325.931 52-31708 ‡

NL 0433732 DLC CaBVaU ICU MH NN ViU

VOLUME 337

Lochore, Reuel Anson.
History of the idea of civilization in France (1830–1870), by R. A. Lochore ... Bonn, L. Röhrscheid, 1935.
3 p. l., 245, [1] p. 24cm. (*Added t.-p.:* Studien zur abendländischen geistes- u. gesellschaftsgeschichte, hrsg. von Hermann Platz ... VII)
"This thesis is a continuation of that by Joachim Moras, which traced the history ... of civilization in France from ... the mid-eighteenth century down to 1830."—Introd.
"Erratum": p. [246]
Bibliography: p. 226–232.

1. Civilization—Philosophy. 2. Philosophy, French. I. Title.
A C 37-194
Northwestern univ. Library for Library of Congress [2]

NL 0433733 IEN CU NcU MdBJ ICU NN

Case Y 1847 .7006 [LOCHORE, ROBERT] 1762-1852.
Margaret and the minister. A true tale... II. A morning walk... Glasgow, Brash & Reid [179-?]
8p. 15cm.

Binder's title: Poems.
By R.Lochore.--cf. Ewing, J.C. Brash and Reid, booksellers in Glasgow.
In verse.

NL 0433734 ICN DLC

Lochore, Robert, 1762–1852.
Patie and Ralph: an elegiac pastoral, on the death of Robert Burns. By Robert Lochore ... Glasgow, Brash & Reid [18—?]
8 p. 15cm.
Chap-book.

I. Title.
8—4302
Library of Congress PR4335.L55

NL 0433735 DLC CtY NjP

Lochot, J. Le chrysanthème; histoire et culture. 12°. pp. ii, 128. il. plate. Paris, [1898]. (Bibliothèque du "Jardin.")

NL 0433736 MBH

Lochot, J.
... Le chrysanthème. 5e édition revue et augmentée ... Paris, Librairie agricole de la Maison rustique [1932]
266 p. incl. front., illus. 19cm.

1. Chrysanthemums.
Agr 33-568
Library, U. S. Dept. of Agriculture 96.519L78

NL 0433737 DNAL

Lochot, J.
... Le chrysanthème. 7e édition revue, remaniée et sensiblement augmentée ... Paris, La Maison rustique [1938]
2 p. l., 301 p. incl. front. (port.) illus. 19cm.

1. Chrysanthemums.
Agr 39-818
U. S. Dept. of agr. Library for Library of Congress 96.519L78 Ed. 7 [SB413.C55] [2]

NL 0433738 DNAL MBH

Lochow, Ferdinand Jost Friedrich von, 1849–1924.
Beiträge über leistungsprüfung und zucht auf leistung beim milchvieh, sowie vererbung der leistung durch mutter- und vatertier, nachgewiesen durch auszüge aus dem zuchtregister des eigenen betriebes, von dr. phil. h. c. F. von Lochow ... Berlin, P. Parey, 1921.
31 p. 26 cm. (*Added t.-p.:* Arbeiten der Deutschen landwirtschafts-gesellschaft ... hft. 309)

1. Cattle—[Breeding] 2. Dairying. [2. Milk—Production]
Agr 22-328 rev
U. S. Dept. of Agr. Libr for Library of Congress 18D48 hft. 309 [r47c1]

NL 0433739 DNAL NN ICJ

Lochow, Hans Juergen von.
China's national railways; historical survey and postwar planning. [1st ed.] Peiping, 1948.
162 p. illus. 23 cm.

1. Railroads—China. I. Title.
HE3285.L6 *385.1 52-23600 ‡

NNC NcU NNUN
NL 0433740 DLC ICU NjP IU MH-BA CtY MH NNC CLSU

NK 7983 .L814 Lochow, Hans Juergen von
Sammlung Lochow: Chinesische Bronzen. Hrsg.von Gustav Ecke. Peking [Fu Jen Press] 1943-44.
2 v. plates. 33 cm.
Added t.p. in Chinese.
Half-title: Sammlung Hans Juergen von Lochow.
Vol.2: Herausgegeben vom Sammler.
Plates printed on double leaves,Chinese style.
Bibliography: v.1,p.63-64;v.2,p.45-46.
In cases.

1.Bronzes,Chinese I.Ecke,Gustav,ed.

NL 0433741 MiU NN NIC CLCM MH OrU

Lochowitz, Anatol.
... Komsomol, die geschichte des allunionsverbandes der Leninschen kommunistischen jugend. Berlin, Verlag Neues Leben [1948]
47 p. illus. 21 cm.

NL 0433742 NcD

LOCHOWITZ, ANATOL.
Komsomol; die Geschichte des Allunionsverbandes der Leninschen kommunistischen Jugend. Berlin, Verlag Neues Leben [c1948] 47 p. illus., ports. 22cm.

Film reproduction. Negative.

1. Youth movement--Russia. I. Title.

NL 0433743 NN

Lochowiz, A B
see
Lokhovits, A B

LOCHRANE, OSBORNE AUGUSTUS, 1829–1887.
Judge O.A.Lochrane's address at West Point, Ga., before the Female College. [Bartow Co., Ga.? 1883.] 21 p. 22½cm.

Cover-title.
Commencement address delivered June 11th, 1875.
Reprinted from The Atlantic Herald.

NL 0433745 NN

RV9 .L6 Toner Coll. Lochrane, Osborne Augustus, 1829-1887.
An address delivered before the Southern reform medical association at their annual meeting in Macon, March 2, 1858, by O. A. Lochrane ... Macon, Georgia telegraph steam power press, 1858.
cover-title, 16 p. 22cm.

1. Medicine, Botanic.

NL 0433746 DLC DNLM

Ga HV5090 G4L6 Lochrane, Osborne Augustus, 1829-1887.
Address of Judge O.A. Lochrane on Prohibition. Atlanta, Jas. P. Harrison, 1885.
16 p. 22cm.

1. Prohibition - Ga.

NL 0433747 GU

Lochrane, Osborne Augustus, 1829-1887.
Georgia Repudiation of the Bonds of the Brunswick & Albany Railroad. Brief of O.A. Lochrane. O.A. Lochrane, E.S. Isham. [no place, 1883?]
[1]-44, 137-150, [45]-138, 153-193 p. 8vo.
Text apparently intact and coherent.
No imprint.
Note: Probably published in 1883, as on p. 145 occurs the date: "Not four months ago ... on the 5th day of March, 1883 ..."

NL 0433748 GU-De DLC

Ga HJ8303 L6 Lochrane, Osborne Augustus, 1829-1887.
Letter from Judge Lochrane to the governor of Georgia, on the legal liabilities of the state. Atlanta, Economical Book and Job Printing House, 1872.
30 p. 21cm.

NL 0433749 GU NN

Lochrane, Osborne Augustus, 1829-1887.
A letter on Fenianism. Macon, Ga., Printed at the Journal & Messenger office, 1866.
cover-title, 7 p. 21cm.

1. Fenians (Society)

NL 0433750 NNC

Ga HJ8303 L62 Lochrane, Osborne Augustus, 1829-1887.
Read and do not be afraid of the truth. Argument of Judge Lochrane on Georgia repudiation, before Hon. W.A. Poste, Asst. Attorney General, N.Y. [n.p., 1885]
63 p. 23cm.

Cover title.

1. State bonds - Georgia. 2. Bonds - Ga. 3. Brunswick and Albany Railroad Company. I. Titl.

NL 0433751 GU DLC

Lochren, William, 1832–1912.

UB373 .A3 1896 d **U. S.** *Congress. House. Committee on appropriations.*
Additional hearings before subcommittee of House Committee on appropriations ... in charge of Pension appropriation bill for 1896. Washington, Govt. print. off., 1894.

VOLUME 337

Lochren, William, 1832-1912.
The First Minnesota at Gettysburg.
(*In* Military Order of the Loyal Legion of the United States. Minnesota Commandery. Glimpses of the nation's struggle. Vol. 3, pp. 42-56. St. Paul. 1893.)

D7176 — Minnesota. Militia. 1st Re... ent. Infantry. — Gettysburg, Pa. Hist. Civil War, 1861-1865. Battle, 1863.

NL 0433753 MB

Lochren, William, 1832-1912.
Minnesota in the Civil and Indian wars, 1861-65
see under Minnesota. Board of commissioners on publication of history of Minnesota in Civil and Indian wars.

Lochridge, Charles, 1905- joint author.
GV1295
.C2R42
Reilly, Ottilie H 1898-
Canasta 1950 ₍by₎ Ottilie H. Reilly and Charles Lochridge. New York, I. Washburn ₍1950₎

Lochridge, E. E.

Biological studies by the pupils of William Thompson Sedgwick. Published in commemoration of the twenty-fifth anniversary of his doctorate. Boston ₍Printed at the University of Chicago press₎ 1906.

664.9
L82
Lochridge, W

"Fairfree", fishing vessel and floating factory development. ₑGlasgow, Scot., Institution of Engineers and Shipbuilders in Scotlandₒ 1950.
ₑ504ₒ-542 p. illus., diagrs.

Reprinted from the Transactions of the Institution of Engineers and Shipbuilders in Scotland, 1950.

NL 0433757 OrP

Lochry, Harry Ream, 1886-
Making American cheddar cheese of uniformly good quality from pasteurized milk ₍by Harry R. Lochry and others. Washington, U. S. Govt. Print. Off., 1951₎
39 p. illus. 24 cm. (U. S. Dept. of Agriculture. Circular no. 880)
"Literature cited": p. 37-39.

1. Cheese₍, Cheddar₎ I. Title. (Series)
[S21.A48 no. 880] Agr 51-405
U. S. Dept. of Agr. Libr. for Library of Congress 1Ag84C no. 880 ₍5*₎

NL 0433758 DNAL

Lochry, Harry Ream, 1886-
The manufacture of low-acid rennet-type cottage cheese. Rev. Apr. 1948. ₍Washington, U. S. Govt. Print. Off., 1948₎
14 p. illus. 24 cm. (U. S. Dept. of Agriculture. Miscellaneous publication no. 119)
Caption title.
Contribution from Bureau of Dairy Industry.
"Revision of a previous edition written by H. L. Wilson ... and C. S. Trimble."

1. Cheese₍, Cottage₎ I. Title: Rennet-type cottage cheese. II. Title: Cottage cheese. (Series)
SF271.L68 637.356 Agr 48-125*
——— Copy 2. S21.A46 no. 119, rev. Apr. 1948
U. S. Dept. of Agr. Libr. for Library of Congress 1Ag84M no. 119 1948 ₍7*₎†

NL 0433759 DNAL WaWW DLC

Lochry, Marie Antonette, 1891-
Corsages of pods and cones; a handbook for the hobbyist. ₍Seattle?₎ Chieftain Press, 1955.
89 p. illus. 24 cm.

1. Corsages. I. Title.
SB449.5.C6L6 635.9664 56-22938 ‡

NL 0433760 DLC WaS Wa Or WaT WaU OCl PP

Lochry's expedition
see under [Linn, John Blair] 1831-1899, ed.

Lochs, Hermann.
... Die antidosis oder der sogenannte vermögenstausch. Eine studie von H. Lochs ... Bielitz, 1897.
32 p. 23 cm. in cover 26 cm.
Programm - K.k. staats-gymnasium, Bielitz (Jahresbericht)
1. Taxation - Greece.

NL 0433762 CU NjP

Lochstein, Veremund von, *pseud.*
see
Osterwald, Peter von, 1718-*ca.* 1776.

Locht Díaz, Guillermo A.
Contabilidad de compañías subsidiarias extranjeras, sistema bi-monetario. ₍Por₎ Guillermo A. Locht Díaz. México, 1934.
36 p. 22cm.

1. Corporations—Accounting. 2. Foreign exchange. I. Title.
35-12972
Library of Congress HF5686.C7L6
₍2₎ ₍657₎ 658.15

NL 0433764 DLC

Lochte, D.
Das gesetz über kleinbahnen und privatanschlussbahnen vom 28. juli 1892. Mit anmerkungen hrsg. von D. Lochte ... Berlin, C. Heymann, 1903.
viii, 199 p. 2 fold. pl. 15½cm. (*On cover:* Taschen-gesetzsammlung 59)

Library of Congress 5-31354

NL 0433765 DLC

Lochte, Edward Heinrich Theodor
see
Lochte, Theodor, 1864-

Lochte, Harry Louis, 1892-
The petroleum acids and bases ₍by₎ H. L. Lochte and E. R. Littmann. New York, Chemical Pub. Co., 1955.
368 p. illus. 23 cm.
Includes bibliography.

1. Petroleum. I. Littmann, Edwin Robert, 1899- joint author. II. Title.
TP690.L6 665.5 55-13809 ‡

IdPI OrU-M IdU MtBuM MtBC OrCS MtU OrP PP PBL TxU DI PU OU DAU Or OrStbM CaBVaU OrSaW IdB WaPS WaE Wa OrPR OrU NcRS CU PSt MB ICJ NN C PPF
NL 0433767 DLC OClW WaT WaTC WaWW WaS WaSp WaSpG

Lochte, Harry Louis, 1892-
Second year chemistry for engineers, by H. L. Lochte ... Ann Arbor, Mich., Edwards brothers, inc., 1934.
1 p. l., ii, 69 numb. l. illus., diagr. 27cm.
Lithoprinted.
"These notes are the outgrowth of laboratory directions and detailed outlines of lectures given ... at the University of Texas."—Pref.
Includes references.

1. Chemistry. 2. Engineering.
CA 34-1215 Unrev'd
Library of Congress QD31.L6
Copyright AA 144037 540

NL 0433768 DLC

Lochte, Harry Louis, 1892-
Symmetrical di-isopropyl hydrazine and related compounds, by Harry Louis Lochte ... ₍Easton, Pa., 1922₎
19, ₍1₎ p. 23½cm.
Thesis (PH. D.)—University of Illinois, 1922.
Vita.
"Reprinted from the Journal of the American chemical society, vol. XLIII, no. 12, December, 1921 and vol. XLIV, no. 11, November, 1922."

1. Isopropyl-hydrazine.
Library of Congress QD305.A8L6 23-17309
Univ. of Illinois Libr.

NL 0433769 IU OU DLC

Lochte, Theodor, 1864- *ed.*
Atlas der menschlichen und tierischen haare ... zum gebrauche für die human- und veterinärmedizin, gerichtliche medizin, zoologie, jagdkunde, züchtungskunde, die organe der rechtspflege sowie die bedürfnisse des pelzhandels und der haarverarbeitenden industrien, bearbeitet von med.-rat dr. med. Th. Lochte ... Leipzig, P. Schöps, 1938.
xii, 306 p. illus. 26½cm.
"Literaturverzeichnis": p. 289-301.

1. Hair.
Agr 38-752
U. S. Dept. of agr. Library for Library of Congress 444L78 [QL942]

NL 0433770 DNAL CU DI NIC NcD

Lochte Theodor) [1864-].
*Beitrag zur modernen Diagnostik der Magenkrankheiten und zur Therapie derselben. 56 pp., 1 l. 8°. Leipzig, G. Fock, 1890.

NL 0433771 DNLM

W 1
BE294
Bd. 2
1938
LOCHTE, Theodor, 1864-
Cuticulastudien am menschlichen Haar. Über die Kopfhaarlänge beim Säugling und Kleinkinde und über Haarwechsel des Kopfhaares des Neugeborenen. Grüngefärbte Haare eines Kupferarbeiters, von K. Feist und Th. Lochte. Leipzig, Schöps, 1938.
59 p. illus. (Beiträge zur Haut-, Haar- und Fellkunde, Bd. 2)
1. Copper 2. Hair I. Feist, K Series

NL 0433772 DNLM

Lochte, Theodor, 1864-

... **Gerichtliche** medizin, von prof. dr. Lochte ... prof. dr. Ziemke ... prof. dr. Müller-Hess ... prof. dr. Hey ... ₍und₎ priv.-doz. dr. Wiethold ... Berlin, C. Heymann, 1930.

Lochte, Theodor, 1864- *ed.*
Gerichtsärztliche und polizeiärztliche technik. Ein handbuch für studierende, ärzte, medizinalbeamte und juristen. Bearbeitet von geh. med.-rat prof. dr. Beumer ₍u. a.₎ ... Herausgegeben von professor dr. Th. Lochte ... Mit 193 abbildungen im text und 1 spektraltafel. Wiesbaden, J. F. Bergmann, 1914.
xiv, 794 p. illus., col. pl. 26cm.
"Literatur" at end of each chapter.
1. Medical jurisprudence. I. Beumer, Friedrich Wilhelm Otto, 1849-1918. II. Title.
₍*Full name:* Edward Heinrich Theodor Lochte₎
14-10543 Revised
Library of Congress RA1051.L7

NL 0433774 DLC ICRL ICJ MiU PPC

VOLUME 337

Lochte, Theodor, 1864–
Grundriss der Entwicklung des menschlichen Haares, dargestellt an Hand neuer Haarmessungen. Zum Gebrauche für Dermatologen, Anthropologen, Gerichtsärzte und Pathologen. Frankfurt/Main, P. Schöp, 1951.
144 p. illus. 25 cm. (Beiträge zur Haut-, Haar- und Fellkunde, Bd. 5)

1. Hair.

QM488.L58 56-31338 ‡

NL 0433775 DLC NIC DNLM

W 1 BE294 Bd. 6 1954
LOCHTE, Theodor, 1864-
Tafeln zur Haarkunde, von Th. Lochte unter Mitarbeit von H. Dathe [et al.] Leipzig, Schöps, 1954.
82 p. illus. (Beiträge zur Haut-, Haar- und Fellkunde, Bd. 6)
1. Hair Series

NL 0433776 DNLM

Lochte, Theodor, 1864–
Über Vorkommen, Bedeutung und Wesen des Gleitphänomens bei menschlichen und tierischen Haaren (Verkürzung gedehnter Haare bei Berührung mit Wasser) von Th. Lochte und Dr. rer. techn. Brauckhoff. Leipzig, P. Schöps, 1942.
23 p. 25 cm. (Arbeit der Reichs-Zentrale für Pelztier- und Rauchwaren-Forschung, Leipzig, Nr. 39)
Cover title.
"Sonderdruck aus 'Der Rauchwarenmarkt' Jahrgang xxx, Nummer 11/12, 13/14 und 15/16."
1. Hair. I. Brauckhoff, Hellmut, joint author. II. Title. (Series: Leipzig. Reichs-Zentrale für Pelztier- und Rauchwaren-Forschung. Arbeit Nr. 39.

QM488.L6 611.781 50-49192

NL 0433777 DLC ICRL NNC-M RPB

Lochte, Theodor, 1864–
... Untersuchungen an erhitzten menschlichen und tierischen haaren (bis 200° C) Mit 22 abbildungen. Von prof. dr. med. Th. Lochte ... Leipzig, P. Schöps, 1940.
2 p. l., 38 p. incl. plates. 24 cm. (Beiträge zur haut-, haar- und fellkunde, bd. III)
"Literatur": p. 38.

1. Hair.

QL942.L8 591.47 A F 47-6218

Columbia univ. Libraries for Library of Congress [1]†

NL 0433778 COU DLC IU NNC DNLM IaU CtY ViU ICRL CtY-M NjP WU

LOCHTE-HOLTGREVEN, Walter, 1903-
Über das intensitatsverhältnis der D-linien. Inaug.-diss., Gottingen. Berlin, J. Springer, 1928.

pp.(21).
"Sonderabdruck aus 'Zeitschrift fur Physik', 47.band, heft 5/6", pp.[362]-378.
"Lebenslauf", at end.

NL 0433779 MH CtY MiU

Lochtin, Stefan.
The Soviet conquest in Central and Eastern Europe. London, Polish Ex-combatants' Association, 1954.
43 p. 22 cm.

1. Russia—For. rel.—Europe, Eastern. 2. Europe, Eastern—Politics. 3. Communism—Europe, Eastern. I. Title.

DR48.5.L63 55-24515 ‡

NL 0433780 DLC NN NBuC NIC

Lochtkemper, ____.
Teleky, Ludwig, 1872–
... Staubgefährdung und staubschädigungen der metallschleifer, insbesondere der des bergischen landes, von landesgewerbearzt dr. Teleky, medizinalrat dr. Lochtkemper, dr. Erika Rosenthal-Deussen und gewerberat Derdack. Berlin, R. Hobbing, 1928.

Lochtkemper, Franz Josef, 1891- Arzt: Über zwei Fälle von Hirntumoren mit eigenartigem Verlauf. [In Maschinenschrift.] 24 S. 4°(2°). — Auszug: Marburg 1921: Hamel. 4 S. 8°
Marburg, Med. Diss. v. 5. Aug. 1921, Ref. Jahrmärker, Müller
[Geb. 5. Dez. 91 Bottrop i. W.; Wohnort: Marburg; Staatsangeh.: Preußen; Vorbildung: OR. Duisburg Reife 12; Studium: Marburg 2, München 1, Marburg 6 S; Coll. 13. Juli 20; Approb. 7. Juli 20.] [U 21. 5011

NL 0433782 ICRL

Loci aliquot difficiliores Trinummi
see under [Fritzsche, Franz Volkmar] 1806-1887.

Loci commvnes ivris civilis. Ex mendis tandem, et barbarie, in gratiam studiosorum utiliter restituti
see under Oldendorp, Johann, 1480-1567.

MS
LOCI communes theologiae. [Germany, 15th cent.] about 300 l. 24cm.

Manuscript. Binder's title.

NL 0433785 ICN

Località internazionale per la pace (Unione lombarda Milan
see Società per la pace e la giustizia internazionale, Milan.

LOCK,
The temple of love. A vision. By Mr. Lock... London: Printed for R. Willoughby, 1717. 60 p. 19cm.

1. Poetry, English. I. Title.

NL 0433787 NN ICN TxU MH ICU

Lock,
The temple of love: a vision. By Mr. Lock ... The second edition. London: Printed for R. Willoughby ... and sold by J. Morphew ... 1717.
5 p.l., 9-60 p. 19½cm.

Signatures: 1 leaf unsigned, A-G⁴, H².
Title in red and black.
Unbound, in cloth case.

NL 0433788 CLU-C CtY

Lock, Alfred George.
Agriculturists their own superphosphate makers ... By Alfred G. Lock... 2d ed. London, New York, E.& F.N.Spon, 1872.
29p. front., 3 pl. 20cm.

1. Phosphates. 2. Fertilizers and manures.

NL 0433789 DP

Lock, Alfred George.
Gold: its occurrence and extraction. Embracing the geographical and geological distribution and the mineralogical characters of gold-bearing rocks; the peculiar features and modes of working shallow placers, rivers, and deep leads; hydraulicing ... a bibliography of the subject; and a glossary of English and foreign technical terms. By Alfred G. Lock ... With six double-page maps, and 185 engravings in the text. London, E. & F. N Spon, 1882.
xxi, 1229 p. front., illus., 6 maps, diagrs. 26½cm.
1. Gold. 2. Gold mines and mining. 3. Gold—Bibl.

6-18204

Library of Congress TN420.L81

NL 0433790 ICRL MiU PPF OCl DLC OrP CaBViPA I ICJ CU MiHM NIC MdBP

TP 215 L813
Lock, Alfred George.
A practical treatise on the manufacture of sulphuric acid. By Alfred G. Lock and Charles G. Lock. London, S. Low, Marston, Searle, and Rivington, 1879.
viii, [1], 247, [1] p. incl. illus., tables, diagrs. 2 fold. pl. (incl. front.)

1. Sulphuric acid. I. Lock, Charles George, joint author.

NL 0433791 DSI MiD RPB PPF MiHM NN ICJ DP

LOCK, Alfred George.
Um jaroraekt og gardyrkju á islandi. Jón A.Hjaltalin íslenzkadi. Kaupmannahofn., prentad hja Valentin og Lund, 1876.

pp.50+. Illus.

NL 0433792 MH NIC NN

Lock, Alfred George.
The true art of Manuring: a Reply to Mr. Spooner's Lectures ... London, 1869.
47 p. 8°. [In College Pamphlets, v. 1735]

NL 0433793 CtY

RM666 .G2L8 (C)
Lock, Archibald C
Aerosols in theory and practice. [2d ed.] London, Aerosols [1947]
59 p.
Bibliography at end of most chapters.

1. Aerosols.

NL 0433794 ICU TxU

Lock, Arnold Charles Cooper.
Destination: Barrier Reef. Photography by author. Melbourne, Georgian House [1955]
227 p. illus. 22 cm.

1. Great Barrier Reef, Australia. I. Title.

DU430.G7L6 919.43 56-34348 ‡

NL 0433795 DLC CaBVa TxU CtY CLU MH NN

VOLUME 337

Lock, Arnold Charles Cooper.
People we met. Illustrated with photos. by the author. Sydney, Angus and Robertson [1951]
355 p. illus. 22 cm.

1. Queensland—Descr. & trav. I. Title.
DU260.L58 919.43 52-22179 ‡

NL 0433796 DLC TxU CaBViP CaBVaU CtY NN

PR 6023 L783s Lock, Arnold Charles Cooper.
Satan's mercy, by Charles Cooper [pseud.] Sydney, Jackson & O'Sullivan, 1934.
269 p.

NL 0433797 CLU

Lock, Arnold Charles Cooper.
Travels across Australia. Photography by the author. Melbourne, Robertson & Mullens [1952]
288 p. illus. 23 cm.

1. Australia—Descr. & trav. I. Title.
DU104.L6 919.4 53-32580 ‡

NL 0433798 DLC TxU CLU NN

Lock, Arnold Charles Cooper.
Tropics and topics. Sydney, Invincible Press [1949]
viii, 285 p. plates. 23 cm.

1. Queensland—Descr. & trav. I. Title.
DU260.L6 919.43 50-25198

NL 0433799 DLC NN TxU

Mann TX 603 L81 Lock, Arthur.
Practical canning. London, Food Trade Press, 1949.
246 p. illus. 22 cm.

1. Canning and preserving. I. Title.

NL 0433800 NIC IU NN MB DNAL

Byzk 28 Lock, Arthur B
... The history of King's Norton and Northfield Wards ... with foreword by C.Raymond Beazley ... Birmingham[Eng.],The Midland educational company,ltd.[19--?]
5p.ℓ.,129p. fold.front.,plates,maps,plans, facsim. 20½cm.
At head of title: Historical association (Birmingham branch)

NL 0433801 CtY IU

LOCK, ARTHUR B.
The story of English industry from the beginnings to the present day, by Arthur B. Lock... London: Univ. of London Press, Ltd., 1935. xiv, 272 p. incl. front. illus. (incl. charts, maps, ports.) 20cm. (The headway histories.)

805616A. 1. Industries—Gt.Br.

NL 0433802 NN

Lock, Bella Sidney (Woolf)
see **Southorn, Bella Sidney (Woolf)** *Lady.*

LOCK B[enjamin] Fossett.
Legal Aid for the Poor. London,1907.
(2)+16 p.

NL 0433804 MH-L

LOCK,Benjamin Fossett.
The opium trade and Sir Rutherford Alcock. London,published for The Society for the Supression of the Opium Trade by Ward,Lock & Co., [1882?].
17 cm. pp.24.
"Reprinted from The Contemporary Review for April,1882."

NL 0433805 MH OO

Lock, Benjamin Fossett.
The three Fs, or, The Irish land question, past, present, and future ... London, Ward, Lock, & co. [1881]
22 p. 21 cm. [Ireland. Pamphlets. Land law. 1876-1881]

NL 0433806 CtY

Lock, Cecil Max
see
Lock, Max.

Lock, Charles George Warnford, 1853–1909.
Coffee: its culture and commerce in all countries. Ed. by C. G. Warnford Lock ... London, New York, E. and F. N. Spon, 1888.
x p., 1 l., 264 p. incl. front., illus. plates. 18½cm.
Bibliography: p. 257–258.

1. Coffee.
Library of Congress SB269.L8 11—32773

NL 0433808 DLC IdU MH-A MdBP CU NNBG OCl PPSteph PPL ICU NIC TNJ

Lock, Charles George Warnford, 1853–1909.
Economic mining; a practical handbook for the miner, the metallurgist, and the merchant, by C. G. Warnford Lock ... London, E. — F. N. Spon; New York, Spon & Chamberlain, 1895.
xiv, 668 p. illus. 22cm.
A leaf of unpaged advertising matter is between p. x and [xi]

1. Mining engineering. I. Title.
G S 15-1082
U. S. Geol. survey. Library for Library of Congress 420 L79 [a37d1-]

NL 0433809 DI-GS OrP IdU MtBuM Wa WaS CU PPF PPSteph MiU OU PP ICJ MiHM

T9 .S76 Lock, Charles George Warnford, 1853-1909, ed.
Spon, Edward.
Spons' encyclopædia of the industrial arts, manufactures, and commercial products ... London, New York, E. & F. N. Spon, 1879–82.

Lock, Charles George Warnford, 1853–1909.
Gold milling, principles and practice ... By C. G. Warnford Lock ... upwards of 200 illustrations. London, E. & F. N. Spon, ltd.; New York, Spon & Chamberlain, 1901.
xix, 823 p. incl. front., illus., diagrs. 22½ cm.

1. Gold—Milling. 2. Gold—Metallurgy.
Library of Congress TN760.L81 3—22847

NL 0433811 DLC MtBuM WaS PPF PPSteph OCl ICJ MH MiHM CU

Lock, Charles George Warnford, 1853-1909.
Gold mining and milling in the Black Hills (S. Dakota). By C.G. Warnford Lock.
[London, J.S. Phillips, 1895]
35 p. illus. 22 cm. [Papers on gold extraction. no. 1]
Caption title.
1. Gold mines and mining - South Dakota - Black Hills.

NL 0433812 CU

Lock, Charles George Warnford, 1853-1909.
The home of the Eddas. By Charles G. Warnford Lock ... With a chapter on the Sprengisandr by Dr. C. Le Neve Foster ... London, S. Low, Marston, Searle, & Rivington, 1879.
xi, 348 p. fold. map. 22½cm.
A journal of a trip through Iceland.
"Across the Bursting Sand in 1876," by Dr. C. L. Foster: p. 263–281.
Appendices: A. Explanation of Icelandic words and names occurring in the journal. B. What the tourist wants to know.

1. Iceland—Descr. & trav. I. Foster, Sir Clement Le Neve.
4—6201
Library of Congress DL312.L81

NL 0433813 DLC NcU NjP CtY MdBP NIC PP OCl MiU OCU NN MH ICU

Lock, Charles George Warnford, 1853-1909.
Miners' pocket-book: a reference book for miners, mine surveyors, geologists, mineralogists, millmen, assayers, metallurgists, and metal merchants, all over the world. By C. G. Warnford Lock ... London, New York, E. & F. N. Spon, 1892.
xiii p., 1 l., 472 p. illus., diagrs. 16½cm.
Leaf of advertising matter between p. [ii] and [iii]

1. Mines and mineral resources—Handbooks, manuals, etc.
G S 16-65
Library, U. S. Geological Survey 420 L79m

NL 0433814 DI-GS CU

LOCK, Charles George Warnford, 1853-1909.
Miners' pocket-book. 2d ed.
London. Spon. 1896. xiii, (1), 472 pp. Illus. Sm. 8°.

NL 0433815 MB

Lock, Charles George Warnford.
Miners' pocket-book; a reference book for miners, mine surveyors, geologists, mineralogists, millmen, assayers, metallurgists, and metal merchants ... by C. G. Warnford Lock ... 3d ed., rev. London, E. & F. N. Spon, limited; New York, Spon & Chamberlain, 1897.
xiii p., 1 l., 472 p. 16½cm.

1. Mining engineering—Handbooks, manuals, etc.
1-18576
Library of Congress TN151.L8

NL 0433816 DLC

VOLUME 337

Lock, Charles George Warnford, 1853-1909.
Miners' pocket-book. A reference book for engineers and others engaged in metalliferous mining. Fourth edition, almost entirely rewritten. viii,424 p. 158 il. S. London: E. & F. N. Spon, 1901.

NL 0433817 ICJ OU PSt MH NjP

Lock, Charles George Warnford, 1853-1909.
The miner's pocket-book; a reference book for engineers and others engaged in metalliferous mining, by C. G. Warnford-Lock ... London: E. & F. N. Spon, Ltd., 1908. viii, 624 p. incl. tables. diagrs., illus. (incl. plans.) 5. ed. [rev.] 16°.

185655A. 1. Mines and mining—Manuals.
N. Y. P. L. November 27, 1925

NL 0433818 NN WaS CU PPSteph

TN505 .L63 Q
Lock, Charles George Warnford, 1853-1909.
Mining and ore-dressing machinery; a comprehensive treatise dealing with the modern practice of winning both metalliferous and non-metalliferous minerals, including all the operations incidental thereto, and preparing the product for the market. By C. G. Warnford Lock ... London, New York, E. & F. N. Spon. 1890.
xii, 466p. incl. illus., tables, diagrs. 32cm.
1. Ore-dressing. 2. Mining machinery. 3. Metallurgy. S

NL 0433819 PPF MiU ICJ PSt NIC DN-Ob ViU MiD MiHM PPSteph

Lock, Charles George Warnford, 1853-1909.
Mining in Malaya for gold and tin. By C. G. Warnford-Lock ... London, Crowther and Goodman, 1907.
xvi, 195 p. illus., 1 pl., fold. map. 22½cm.

1. Gold mines and mining—Malay Peninsula. 2. Tin mines and mining—Malay Peninsula.
G S 8-448 Additions 2
Library, U. S. Geol. survey 431 (630) L79m

NL 0433820 DI-GS OrU ICJ IU MiHM

Lock, Charles George Warnford, 1853–1909.
Practical gold-mining: a comprehensive treatise on the origin and occurrence of gold-bearing gravels, rocks, and ores, and the methods by which the gold is extracted. By C. G. Warnford Lock ... London, New York, E. & F. N. Spon, 1889.
xvi, 788 p. front., illus., plates, diagrs. 26cm.
Bibliography: p. 725–757.

1. Gold mines and mining.
G S 6—1264
U. S. Geol. survey. Library for Library of Congress [a41b1]

NL 0433821 DI-GS CaBVaU NNC DN ICJ MiU OCl PPD PPF

Lock, Charles George Warnford, 1853–1909.
Sugar: a handbook for planters and refiners; being a comprehensive treatise on the culture of sugar-yielding plants, and the manufacture, refining, and analysis of cane, beet, palm, maple, melon, sorghum, milk and starch sugars; with copious statistics of their production and commerce, and a chapter on the distillation of rum. By Charles G. Warnford Lock ... Benjamin E. R. Newlands ... and John A. R. Newlands ... London, New York, E. & F. N. Spon, 1888.
xxiii, [1], 920 p. front., illus., XIII fold. pl., diagrs. 22cm.
An enlarged edition of "Sugar growing and refining", 1882; the chapters by Wigner and Harland in the 1882 ed. have been entirely rewritten for the present edition.
"Literature of sugar": p. xvii–xxiii.
1. Sugar. I. Newlands, Benjamin E. R., joint author. II. Newlands, John A.R., joint author.
Library of Congress TP377.L82 4—9875 [a36b1]

NL 0433822 NN DLC IdU OKentU KEmT CU PP PU ICJ OU MB

Lock, Charles George Warnford, 1853–1909.
Sugar growing and refining: a comprehensive treatise on the culture of sugar yielding plants, and the manufacture, refining, and analysis of cane, beet, maple, melon, milk, palm, sorghum, and starch sugars; with copious statistics of their production and commerce, and a chapter on the distillation of rum. By Charles G. Warnford Lock ... and G. W. Wigner & R. H. Harland ... London, New York, E. & F. N. Spon, 1882.
xxvii, 752 p. illus., 10 fold. pl., diagrs. 22½ cm.

"The chapters on refining, analysis, and patents are wholly written by G. W. Wigner ... in conjunction with his partner, R. H. Harland."—Pref.
"Literature of sugar": p. xv–xx.

1. Sugar. I. Wigner, George William, 1842–1884, joint author. II. Harland, Robert Henry, joint author.

TP377.L8 4—9876

NL 0433824 DLC IdU OKentU CU LU OU MdBP PPF PPL

Lock, Charles George Warnford, 1853-1909.
Sugar growing and refining: a comprehensive treatise on the culture of sugar-yielding plants, and the manufacture, refining, and analysis of cane, beet, maple, melon, milk, palm, sorghum, and starch sugars; with copious statistics of their production and commerce, and a chapter on the distillation of rum. By Charles G. Warnford Lock, ... , and G. W. Wigner & R. H. Harland, ... Second edition, reprinted from the first. Illustrated by 10 plates and 205 engravings. London, New York, E. & F. N. Spon, 1885.
xxvii, 752 p. incl. 205 illus., tables, x fold. pl. 22cm.
"Literature of sugar," p. xv–xx.

NL 0433825 ICJ MdBP

Lock, Charles George Warnford, 1853-1909, ed.
Tobacco: growing, curing, & manufacturing. A handbook for planters in all parts of the world. Ed. by C. G Warnford Lock, F. L. S. London, New York, E. & F. N Spon, 1886.
viii p., 1 l., 285, [1] p. incl. illus., tables. 19cm.
Bibliography: p. 276–280.

1. Tobacco. 2. Tobacco manufacture and trade.
8-27225
Library of Congress SB273.L8

NL 0433826 DLC WaS NcD NcRS CU PPF ICJ

Lock, Charles George Warnford, 1853-1909, ed.
Tobacco: growing, curing and manufacturing; a handbook for planters in all parts of the world. London, Spon, 1903.

285 p.

NL 0433827 PPSteph

FOR OTHER EDITIONS SEE MAIN ENTRY
Lock, Charles George Warnford, 1853-1909.
Workshop receipts ... London, New York, E. & F. N. Spon, 1883-

T49 .W94
Lock, Charles George Warnford, 1853-1909.
Workshop receipts, for manufacturers and scientific amateurs. new and thoroughly revised edition. v. 1-4 ... London, E. & F. N. Spon, ltd.; New York, Spon & Chamberlain, 1909.

Lock, Charles J.
Marquetry and inlaying by Charles J. Lock, with a note on Venetian marquetry by Charles Godfrey Leland. Lond., Dawbarn and Ward, ltd., n. d.
24 p. plates. (Useful arts series, no. 12)

Caption title.

NL 0433830 MiD

Lock, Christopher Noel Hunter.
Airscrew-body interference. London, 1929.

unb. Unacc. Cop. 1 1 April 1929.

NL 0433831 DAL

Lock, Christopher Noel Hunter.
... Airscrew theory; a paper delivered before the fourth International Congress for Applied Mechanics, Cambridge, 1934, by C. N. H. Lock ... London, H. M. Stationery Off. [1936]
cover-title, 11 p. plates, diagrs. 30½cm. ([Great Britain] Aeronautical Research Committee. Reports and memoranda. R. & M. no. 1746. A.R.C. Technical report, 1936)
At head of title: ... Air Ministry.
"List of references": p. 11.

NL 0433832 ICJ

Lock, Christopher Noel Hunter.
... Analysis of experiments on an airscrew in various positions within the nose of a tractor body. By C. N. H. Lock, M.A. September, 1927. London, H. M. Stationery Off., 1928.
cover-title, 20 p. incl. tables. diagrs. 25cm. ([Great Britain] Aeronautical Research Committee. Reports and memoranda, no. 1120 (Ae. 293))
At head of title: Air Ministry. T. 2507.

NL 0433833 ICJ

Lock, Christopher Noel Hunter.
... Application of Goldstein's airscrew theory to design, by C. N. H. Lock, M.A. November 1930 ... London, H. M. Stationery Off., 1932.
cover-title, 24 p. diagrs. 25cm. ([Great Britain] Aeronautical Research Committee. Reports and memoranda no. 1377 (T. 3025))
At head of title: Air Ministry ...

NL 0433834 ICJ

Lock, Christopher Noel Hunter.
... An application of Prandtl theory to an airscrew, by C. N. H. Lock ... August 1932 ... London, H. M. Stationery Off., 1933.
cover-title, v, 41 p. incl. tables. diagrs. 25cm. ([Great Britain] Aeronautical Research Committee. Reports and memoranda no. 1521 (T. 3292))
At head of title: Air Ministry.
"List of references": p. 41.

NL 0433835 ICJ

Lock, Christopher Noel Hunter.
... The application of the theoretical velocity field round a spheroid to calculate the performance of an airscrew near the nose of a streamline body. By C. N. H. Lock, M.A. December, 1928. London, H. M. Stationery Off., 1929.
cover-title, 4 p. diagr. 25cm. ([Great Britain] Aeronautical Research Committee. Reports and memoranda, no. 1239 (Ae. 394))
At head of title: Air Ministry. T. 2703.

NL 0433836 ICJ

VOLUME 337

Lock, Christopher Noel Hunter.

... Calibration of standard pitot-static heads in the high-speed tunnel, by C. N. H. Lock ... and W. F. Hilton ... London, H. M. Stationery Off. [1936]

cover-title, 3 p. 30½cm. ([Great Britain] Aeronautical Research Committee. Reports and memoranda. R. & M. no. 1752. A.R.C. Technical report, 1936)

At head of title: ... Air Ministry.

NL 0433837 ICJ

629.1306
G798r
no.2088 LOCK, Christopher Noel Hunter.
Engin ... Determination of the optimum twist of an
Lib'y airscrew blade by the "calculus of variations", by C.N.H. Lock ... and R.C. Pankhurst ... and R.G. Fowler ... London, H.M. stationery off. [1942]

cover-title, 27p. incl. tables, diagrs. 30½cm. ([Gt. Brit. Air ministry] Aeronautical research council. Reports and memoranda. R. & M. no.2088 (5550, 5564 and 9224) A.R.C. technical report)

At head of title: Ministry of supply.
"References": p.27.

1. Propellers, Aerial. I. Pankhurst, Ronald C., joint author. II. Fowler, R.G., joint author. III. Series (contents)

NL 0433839 TxU

Lock, Christopher Noel Hunter.

... Drag and pressure-distribution experiments on two pairs of streamline bodies, by C. N. H. Lock ... and F. C. Johansen ... March 1933 ... London, H. M. Stationery Off., 1933.

cover-title, 19 p. incl. tables. diagrs. 25cm. ([Great Britain] Aeronautical Research Committee. Reports and memoranda no. 1452 (T. 3126))

At head of title: Air Ministry ...
Bibliographical foot-notes.

NL 0433840 ICJ

Lock, Christopher Noel Hunter.

... The effect of body interference on the efficiency of an airscrew. By C. N. H. Lock, M.A. December, 1928. London, H. M. Stationery Off., 1929.

cover-title, 8 p. diagr. 25cm. ([Great Britain] Aeronautical Research Committee. Reports and memoranda, no. 1238 (Ae. 393))

At head of title: Air Ministry. T. 2702.

NL 0433841 ICJ

Lock, Christopher Noel Hunter.

... The effect of gap between an airscrew and a tractor body. By C. N. H. Lock ... and H. Bateman ... April, 1924. London, H. M. Stationery Off., 1924.

cover-title, 2 p. incl. tables. diagrs. 25cm. (*In* [Great Britain.] Aeronautical Research Committee. Reports and memoranda, no. 921. (Ae. 146.))

At head of title: A. 3. d. Airscrews, 72. (T. 1899.) ...

NL 0433842 ICJ

Lock, Christopher Noel Hunter.

... The effect of wind tunnel interference on a combination of airscrew and tractor body. By C. N. H. Lock ... and H. Bateman ... April 1924. London, H. M. Stationery Off., 1924.

cover-title, 6 p. 1 pl., diagrs. 25cm. (*In* [Great Britain.] Aeronautical Research Committee. Reports and memoranda, no. 919. (Ae. 145.))

At head of title: A. 3. d. Airscrews, 72. (T. 1899.) ...

NL 0433843 ICJ

Lock, Christopher Noel Hunter.

... The equations of motion of a viscous fluid in tensor notation. By C. N. H. Lock, M.A. April, 1929. London, H. M. Stationery Off., 1930.

cover-title, ii, 28 p. 1 diagr. 25cm. ([Great Britain] Aeronautical Research Committee. Reports and memoranda, no. 1290 (Ae. 439))

At head of title: Air Ministry. T. 2798 (revd.)

NL 0433844 ICJ

629.1306
G798r
no.2101 LOCK, CHRISTOPHER NOEL HUNTER
Engin ... Examples of the application of Busemann's
Lib'y formula to evaluate the aerodynamic force coefficients on supersonic aerofoils, by C.N.H. Lock ... London, H.M. stationery off. [1944]

cover-title, 10p. incl. tables. 30½cm. ([Gt. Brit. Air ministry] Aeronautical research council. Reports and memoranda. R. & M. no.2101 (8027) A.R.C. Technical report)

At head of title: Ministry of supply.
"References": p.10.

1. Aerofoils. I. Title. II. Title: Busemann's formula to evaluate the aerodynamic force coefficients on supersonic aerofoils. III. Series (contents)

NL 0433846 TxU

Lock, Christopher Noel Hunter.

... Exploration of the flow near the screw proposed for the N.P.L. compressed air tunnel. By C. N. H. Lock, M.A. and A. R. Collar ... January, 1930. London, H. M. Stationery Off., 1930.

cover-title, 10 p. incl. tables. diagrs. 25cm. ([Great Britain] Aeronautical Research Committee. Reports and memoranda, no. 1293. Ae. 442)

At head of title: Air Ministry. T. 2895.

NL 0433847 ICJ

Lock, Christopher Noel Hunter.

... An extension of the vortex theory of airscrews with applications to airscrews of small pitch, including experimental results. By C. N. H. Lock, M.A., H. Bateman, B.SC., and H. C. H. Townend, B.SC. June, 1926. London, H. M. Stationery Off., 1926.

cover-title, 40 p. incl. tables. diagrs. 25cm. ([Great Britain] Aeronautical Research Committee. Reports and memoranda, no. 1014 (Ae. 217))

At head of title: A. 3. d. Airscrews 71 & 86 (T. 1867. T. 2112)

NL 0433848 ICJ

Lock, Christopher Noel Hunter.

... Graphical method of calculating performance of airscrew, by C. N. H. Lock ... October, 1934 ... London, H. M. Stationery Off., 1935.

cover-title, 30 p. incl. tables. diagrs. 25cm. ([Great Britain] Aeronautical Research Committee. Reports and memoranda no. 1675 (T. 3602))

At head of title: Air Ministry.
"Chart 1" in duplicate on transparent guard sheet.
"List of references": p. 30.

NL 0433849 ICJ

Lock, Christopher Noel Hunter.

... A graphical method of calculating the performance of an airscrew ... by C. N. H. Lock ... [Rev. ed.] London, H. M. Stationery Off. [1938]

70 p. tables, diagrs. 31cm. ([Great Britain] Aeronautical Research Committee. Reports and memoranda. R. & M. no. 1849 <R. & M. no. 1675 rev.> A.R.C. Technical report, 1938)

References: p. 19.
Cover-title.
At head of title: Air Ministry.
Some diagrams in duplicate on transparent guard sheets.

NL 0433850 ICJ

Lock, Christopher Noel Hunter.

... Induced drag due to washout, by C. N. H. Lock ... London, H. M. Stationery Off. [1937]

cover-title, 5 p. diagr. 30½cm. ([Great Britain] Aeronautical Research Committee. Reports and memoranda. R. & M. no. 1769. A.R.C. Technical report, 1937)

At head of title: ... Air Ministry.

NL 0433851 ICJ

629.1306
G798r
no.2043 LOCK, Christopher Noel Hunter.
Engin ... Integrating coefficients for airscrew
Lib'y analysis, by C.N.H. Lock ... and A.E. Knowles ... London, H.M. stationery off. [1941]

cover-title, 12p. incl. tables, diagrs. 30½cm. ([Gt. Brit. Air ministry] Aeronautical research council. Reports and memoranda. R. & M. no. 2043 (5211) A.R.C. Technical report)

At head of title: Ministry of supply.
"References": p.7.

1. Propellers, Aerial. I. Knowles, A.E., joint author. II. Title. III. Series (contents)

NL 0433852 TxU

Lock, Christopher Noel Hunter.

... Interference between bodies and airscrews, pt. 1-2, by C. N. H. Lock ... and H. Bateman ... June 1931-Aug. 1932 ... London, H. M. Stationery Off., 1932-1934.

2 v. tables, diagrs. 25cm. ([Great Britain] Aeronautical Research Committee. Reports and memoranda no. 1445, 1522)

At head of title: Air Ministry ...
Cover-title.
Caption title, pt. 1: Analysis of experiments on the interference between bodies and tractor and pusher airscrews.

NL 0433853 ICJ

629.1306
G798r
no.2084 LOCK, CHRISTOPHER NOEL HUNTER.
Engin ... Interference velocity for a close pair of
Lib'y contra-rotating airscrews, by C.N.H. Lock ... London, H.M. stationery off. [1941]

cover-title, 15p. incl. diagrs. 30½cm. ([Gt. Brit. Air ministry] Aeronautical research council. Reports and memoranda. R. & M. no.2084 (5234) A.R.C. technical report)

At head of title: Ministry of supply.
"References": p.12.

1. Propellers, Aerial. I. Title. II. Series (contents)

NL 0433854 TxU

Lock, Christopher Noel Hunter.

... Periodic flow behind an airscrew, by C. N. H. Lock ... and D. M. Yeatman. February 1932 ... London, H. M. Stationery Off., 1933.

cover-title, 15 p. diagrs. 25cm. ([Great Britain] Aeronautical Research Committee. Reports and memoranda no. 1483 (T. 3223))

At head of title: Air Ministry ...

NL 0433855 ICJ

Lock, Christopher Noel Hunter.

... Photographs of streamers illustrating the flow around an airscrew in the vortex ring state. By C. N. H. Lock, M.A. April, 1928. London, H. M. Stationery Off., 1928.

cover-title, 4 p. 6 pl. on 4 leaves, diagr. 25cm. ([Great Britain] Aeronautical Research Committee. Reports and memoranda, no. 1167 (Ae. 331))

At head of title: Air Ministry. T. 2583.
Each plate accompanied by guard sheet with tracings.

NL 0433856 ICJ

Lock, Christopher Noel Hunter.

... Photographs of the flow round a model screw working in water, especially in the "vortex ring state". By C. N. H. Lock, M.A., and H. C. H. Townend, B.SC. May, 1926. London, H. M. Stationery Off., 1926.

cover-title, 5 p. plates, 1 diagr. 25cm. (*In* [Great Britain.] Aeronautical Research Committee. Reports and memoranda, no. 1043. (Ae. 230.))

At head of title: A. 3. d. Airscrews, 92. (T. 2278.) ...
Errata slip bound in at beginning.

NL 0433857 ICJ

VOLUME 337

Lock, Christopher Noel Hunter.
... Pressure plotting a streamline body with tractor airscrew running, pt. 1–2, by C. N. H. Lock ... and F. C. Johansen ... London, H. M. Stationery Off., 1929–1930.
2 v. plates, tables, diagrs. 25cm. (Great Britain, Aeronautical Research Committee. Reports and memoranda no. 1230, 1284)
Cover-title.
At head of title: Air Ministry ...

NL 0433858 ICJ

Lock, Christopher Noel Hunter.
... Some experiments on airscrews at zero torque, with applications to a helicopter descending with engine "off," and to the design of windmills. By C. N. H. Lock, M.A., and H. Bateman, B.SC. September, 1923. London, H. M. Stationery Off., 1924.
cover-title, 9 p. incl. tables. diagrs. 25cm. (*In* [Great Britain.] Aeronautical Research Committee. Reports and memoranda, no. 885. (Ae. 116.))
At head of title: A. 3. d. Airscrews, 69. (T. 1833.—P. 15.) ...

NL 0433859 ICJ

629.1306
G798r
no.2035
Engin
Lib'y

LOCK, CHRISTOPHER NOEL HUNTER.
... Strip theory method of calculation for airscrews on high-speed aeroplanes, by C.N.H. Lock ... R.C. Pankhurst ... and J.F.C. Conn ... with an appendix, by J.N. Veasey ... London, H.M. stationery off. [1945]
cover-title, 54p. incl. tables. 30½cm. ([Gt. Brit. Air ministry] Aeronautical research council. Reports and memoranda. R. & M. no.2035 (5078, 5233, 5939, 6512, and 8962) A.R.C. Technical report)
At head of title: Ministry of supply.

"References": p.15.

1. Propellers, Aerial. I. Pankhurst, Roland C. joint author. II. Conn, J.F.C., joint author. III. Veasey, J.N. IV. Title. V. Series (contents)

NL 0433861 TxU

Lock, Christopher Noel Hunter.
... Tables for use in an improved method of airscrew strip theory calculation, by C. N. H. Lock ... and D. Yeatman. October 1934 ... London, H. M. Stationery Off., 1935.
cover-title, 27 p. incl. tables. diagrs. 25cm. (Great Britain, Aeronautical Research Committee. Reports and memoranda no. 1674 (T. 3601))
At head of title: Air Ministry.
"List of references": p. 16.

NL 0433862 ICJ

Lock, Christopher Noel Hunter.
... Theory of airscrew body interference, by C. N. H. Lock, M.A. May, 1930 ... London, H. M. Stationery Off., 1932.
cover-title, 23 p. diagrs. 25cm. (Great Britain, Aeronautical Research Committee. Reports and memoranda no. 1378 (T. 2965))
At head of title: Air Ministry ...
Caption title: Theory of airscrew body interference; application to experiments on a body of fineness ratio 3·0 with tractor airscrew.
"List of references": p. 22.

NL 0433863 ICJ

Lock, Christopher Noel Hunter.
... Thrust integrating tubes wind tunnel experiments, by C. N. H. Lock ... F. C. Johansen ... and H. L. Nixon. August, 1931 ... London, H. M. Stationery Off., 1932.
cover-title, 22 p. incl. tables. diagrs. 24½cm. (Great Britain, Aeronautical Research Committee. Reports and memoranda no. 1447 (T. 3152))
At head of title: Air Ministry ...

NL 0433864 ICJ

629.1306
G798r
no.2005
Engin
Lib'y

LOCK, CHRISTOPHER NOEL HUNTER.
... Tunnel interference at compressibility speeds using the flexible walls of the rectangular high-speed tunnel, by C.N.H. Lock ... and J.A. Beavan ... London, H.M. stationery off. [1944]
cover-title, 37p. incl. tables, diagrs. 30½cm. ([Gt. Brit. Air ministry] Aeronautical research committee. Reports and memoranda. R. & M. no.2005 (8073) A.R.C. Technical report)

At head of title: Ministry of aircraft production.
"References": p.18.
1. Aerodynamics. 2. Wind tunnels. I. Beavan, John Allan, joint author. II. Title. III. Series (contents)

NL 0433866 TxU

Lock, Christopher Noel Hunter.
... Wind tunnel experiments on a model autogyro at small angles of incidence. By C. N. H. Lock, M.A., and H. C. H. Townend, B.SC. March, 1928. London, H. M. Stationery Off., 1928.
cover-title, 61 p. incl. tables. 1 pl., diagrs. (1 fold.) 25cm. ([Great Britain] Aeronautical Research Committee. Reports and memoranda, no. 1154 (Ae. 319))
At head of title: Air Ministry. T. 2572.

NL 0433867 ICJ

Lock, Christopher Noel Hunter.
... Wind tunnel experiments on a symmetrical aerofoil (Göttingen 429 section). By C. N. H. Lock, M.A., H. C. H. Townend, B.SC., and A. G. Gadd. November, 1926. London, H. M. Stationery Off., 1927.
cover-title, 20 p. incl. tables. diagrs. 25cm. ([Great Britain] Aeronautical Research Committee. Reports and memoranda, no. 1066 (Ae. 248))
At head of title: A. 3. t. Autogyros, helicopters and rotors, 3. A. 3. a. Aerofoils—General, 169 (T. 2349)

NL 0433868 ICJ

Lock, Christopher Noel Hunter.
... Wind tunnel interference on streamline bodies, by C. N. H. Lock ... and F. C. Johansen ... June 1931 ... London, H. M. Stationery Off., 1933.
cover-title, 21 p. incl. tables. diagrs. 25cm. (Great Britain, Aeronautical Research Committee. Reports and memoranda no. 1451 (T. 3126))
At head of title: Air Ministry ...
Bibliographical foot-notes.

NL 0433869 ICJ

Lock, Christopher Noel Hunter.
... Wind tunnel tests and charts of airscrews at negative thrust, by C. N. H. Lock ... H. Bateman ... and H. L. Nixon ... London, H. M. Stationery Off. [1937]
cover-title, 20 p. incl. tables, diagrs. 30cm. (Great Britain, Aeronautical Research Committee. Reports and memoranda. R. & M. no. 1814. A.R.C. Technical report, 1937)
At head of title: ... Air Ministry.

NL 0433870 ICJ TxU

Lock, Christopher Noel Hunter.
... Wind tunnel tests of high pitch airscrews. Part I–II ... by C. N. H. Lock ... H. Bateman ... and H. L. Nixon ... London, H. M. Stationery Off., 1935–[1936]
2 v. tables, diagrs. (1 fold.) 30½cm. (pt. 1: 25cm.) (Great Britain, Aeronautical Research Committee. Reports and memoranda no. 1673, 1729)
Cover-title.
At head of title: Air Ministry.
Part 2 by C. N. H. Lock and H. Bateman.
Includes bibliographies.

NL 0433871 ICJ

Lock, Dato Tan Cheng
see [Ch'en, Chen-lu] 1893-

Lock, Didericus Jacobus.
Metrisch-diophantische onderzoekingen in K(P) en $K^{(n)}$(P) Amsterdam, 1947.
94 p. 26 cm.
Cover title.
Proefschrift—Vrije Universiteit, Amsterdam.
"Stellingen": [3] p. inserted.
"Preface" in English.
Bibliographical footnotes.

1. Diophantine analysis.

A 52–271

New York. Public Libr.
for Library of Congress [2]

NL 0433873 NN IU NBuU NIC OU NcRS

Lock, Edward G
Nelson's Esperanto course [by] Edward G. Lock ... and Mason Stuttard ... London, New York [etc.] T. Nelson and sons ltd [1946]
xi, 228 p. 18½ cm.
"First published June 1946."
"Books for the student": p. 223.

1. Esperanto—Grammar. I. Stuttard, Mason, joint author. II. Title.

PM8213.L55 408.928242 47–25997

NL 0433874 DLC CaBVa WaS WaSp OrP NN TNJ NcD

408.92
L78n
1952

Lock, Edward G
Nelson's Esperanto course [by] Edward G. Lock – and Mason Stuttard – London, New York [etc.] T. Nelson and sons ltd. [1952]
xi, 228p. 19cm.

"First published June 1946."
"Books for the student": p.223.

1. Esperanto--Grammar. I. Stuttard, Mason, joint author.

NL 0433875 IU

PC2121
L6

Lock, Edward G
La phrase juste, by Edward G. Lock and Marjorie Smith. London, Macdonald [1949]
135 p.

French phrase book, with English form and corresponding French phrases.

1. French language - Conversation and phrase books. I. Smith, Marjorie, joint author.

NL 0433876 CU

Lock, Francis John.
The rapid shorthand writer. Leicester: M. A. Roberts & Co., 1882. 4 p.l., 89 p. 12°.

BEALE SHORTHAND COLL.
1. Shorthand.—Systems (English), 1882.
N. Y. P. L. December 11, 1912.

NL 0433877 NN ICN CtY

LOCK, Frank.
Address, at the annual meeting of the National association of local fire insurance agents at Richmond, Virginia, Sept.26, 1907. [Richmond, Virginia? 1907?]

pp.29.

NL 0433878 MH

VOLUME 337

Lock, Frank.
Address on the causes & prevention of fire waste, delivered by Mr. Frank Lock before the Richmond chamber of commerce, Richmond, Virginia, May 24th, 1909. [Richmond? Va., 1909]
31 p. 22 cm.

Presentation slip attached to t.-p.

1. Fires. 2. Fire prevention. I. Title: Causes & prevention of fire waste.

NL 0433879 Vi MH

LOCK, Frank.
A consideration of the several methods of the fire insurance business; an address given before the fire insurance club of Chicago on March 24, 1914. n.p., [1914?]

pp.16.

NL 0433880 MH-BA

Lock, Frank.
The relation of fire insurance to incendiarism; an address delivered before the International Association of Fire Engineers, September 2, 1913. New York: National Board of Fire Underwriters, 1913. 37 p. 8°.

1. Insurance (Fire). 2. Incendiarism. 3. National Board of Fire Underwriters.
N. Y. P. L. December 10, 1913.

NL 0433881 NN MH MB

Lock, Frank.
The relation of the fire insurance companies to state government and the public.
4°.

NL 0433882 MH-BA

368.1 Lock, Frank.
L78u Uniformity in fire-insurance legislation & in the interpretation of fire insurance contracts. [Wash. 1910]
9p.

NL 0433883 IU

Lock, Frank, fl. 1919.
The nationalisation of credit; the only cure for industrial unrest, by Frank Lock. Sydney, G. B. Philip & son, 1919.
318 p. 19cm.

1. Banks and banking—Australia. 2. Currency question—Australia. 3. Finance—Australia. I. Title.

Library of Congress HG3444.L6 21-752

NL 0433884 DLC NN ICJ

Lock, Fred J.
West African gold mining accounts. London: Gee & Co., 1910. vii p., 1 l., 134 p., 1 table. 8°.

1. Bookkeeping for mines. 2. Mines, etc., Africa (West).
N. Y. P. L. June 6, 1914.

NL 0433885 NN CU NcD

Lock, Frédéric, ed.
La jeunesse de Bachaumont
see under Bachumont, Louis Petit de

Lock, Frédéric, 1813–1876.
La Commune; deuxième siége de Paris, 1871, par Frédéric Lock. Paris: A. Courcier [1871] iii, 6–426 p. 18cm.

J. S. BILLINGS MEM. COLL.
949748A. 1. Paris—Hist.—Commune, 1871.
N. Y. P. L. December 28, 1938

NL 0433887 NN N IU ICN IaU CtY MH

Lock, Frédéric, 1813–1876.
Dictionnaire topographique et historique de l'ancien Paris (avant l'annexion) indiquant la situation, l'origine et l'étymologie des rues, l'historique des monuments, édifices, établissements détruits ou encore existants, l'habitation des personnages célèbres, etc. Avec une notice historique sur Paris et un plan. Par Frédéric Lock. Paris, L. Hachette et cie [1860]
2 p. l., [vii]–lix, 457, [1], 513–516 p. fold. map. 18½cm.
Numbering of p. 513–516 canceled.
Caption title: Guide alphabétique des rues et monuments de Paris.
Caption title and paging (cf. Cat. gén. de la Bibliothèque nationale) indicate that this is the author's "Guide alphabétique des rues et monuments de Paris" (Paris, 1855) with a new t.-p. and with part of the text omitted.
1. Paris—Dict. & encyc. 2. Paris—Streets. 3. Paris—Descr.—Guide-books. 4. Paris—Hist. I. Title.
[Full name: Frédéric Alexandre Auguste Lock]
Library of Congress DC704.L6 35-20206
[2] 914.436

NL 0433888 DLC CtY WaU PU

Lock, Frédéric, 1813-1876.
Guide alphabétique des rues et monuments de Paris a l'usage des voyageurs et des Parisiens, où l'on trouve la situation, l'historie et la description de chaque rue et de chaque monument. Avec un grand nombre de renseignements utiles et une notice historique sur Paris. Par Frédéric Lock ... Paris, L. Hachette et cie., 1855.
lix, 516 p. illus., fold. map. 19 cm.
1860 ed. has title: Dictionnaire topographique et historique de l'ancien Paris.

NL 0433889 CU

Lock, Frédéric, 1813-1876.
Histoire de la restauration, 1814-1830.
Ed. 5. Paris, alcan, [n.d.]

192 p.

NL 0433890 PU

944.06 Lock, Fédéric, 1813-
L789h4 1876.
Histoire de la restauration, 1814-1830. 4.éd. Paris [1861]
192p. (Lettered on cover: Bibliothèque utile. XXVI)

NL 0433891 IU

Lock, Frédéric, 1813-1876.
Histoire des Français.
see Lavalée, Théophile Sébastien, 1804-1866.

DC103 Lock, Frédéric, 1813-1876.
.L81 ... Jeanne d'Arc, 1429-1431 ... 2. éd. Paris, F. Alcan [18--]
207, [1] p. [Bibliothèque utile]
At head of title: Histoire de France.
"Ouvrages a consulter": p. [208]

1. Jeanne d'Arc, Saint, 1412-1431.

NL 0433893 ICU

LOCK, Frédéric, 1813-1876.
Jeanne D'arc. Paris, libr. L. Curmer, 1850.

24°. pp.64.
(Bibliothèque L. Curmer. Enseignement universel, 37-38.)

NL 0433894 MH

Lock, Frédéric, 1813-1876.
WA Jeanne d'Arc, 1429-1431. Paris, Impr. de
29391 Dubuisson, 1866.
207 p. 15 cm. (Bibliothèque utile, 38)
POOR CONDITION At head of title: Histoire de France.

1. Jeanne d'Arc, Saint, 1412-1431.

NL 0433895 CtY

064P
K12
Lock, Frédéric, 1813-1876.
Les prix de vertu fondés par m. de Montyon. Discours prononcés à l'Académie française par mm. Daru, Laya, de la Place, de Ségur [et autres] ... Réunis et publiés avec une notice sur m. de Montyon par mm. Frédéric Lock et J. Couly d'Aragon ... Paris, Garnier frères, 1858.
2 v. 18cm.

Contents.--t. 1. 1819-1838.--t. 2. 1839-1856.

NL 0433896 NNC

Lock, Frédéric Alexandre Auguste, 1813-1876
see Lock, Frédéric, 1813-1876.

530.8 Lock, George Herbert.
L78e Key to J. B. Lock's Elementary dynam-
Key ics. London, 1892.
228p.

NL 0433898 IU

969.82
L813r
Lock, George Winslow.
Report on the Mauritius fibre industry, by G. Winslow Lock [and P.W. Lees. Port Louis, 1948]
45p. 25cm. (Mauritius. Publication, no.44, 1943)

At head of title: Colony of Mauritius. "Development and Welfare."
Cover title: Reports on the Mauritius fibre industry.

NL 0433899 IEN NNC

VOLUME 337

Lock, Gerhard, 1913-
Der höfisch-galante roman des 17. jahrhunderts bei Eberhard Werner Happel ... von Gerhard Lock ... Würzburg-Aumühle, Konrad Triltsch 1939.
2 p. l., 103, [1] p. illus., facsims., diagrs 21cm.

Thesis, Berlin.
"Vorliegende arbeit erscheint gleichzeitig als selbständiges buch im Konrad Triltsch verlag, Würzburg".
"Literaturnach- weis": p. 100-103.

NL 0433900 NNC MiU NcU InU TxU IU NjP CtY NIC MH NN

Lock, Gregory James.
Automomatic speed control for direct current, shunt wound motors... by ... [Cincinnati] 1932.
41 l.

NL 0433901 OCU

Lock, H F
Basic typography; a practical guide for the student typographer to type display and the principles of layout, by H. F. Lock, B. SC. London, Sir I. Pitman & sons, ltd., 1940.
ix, 110 p. illus. 19cm.

1. Printing, Practical. I. Title.
42-51996
Library of Congress Z246.L7
[3] 655.24

NL 0433902 DLC

Lock, Harold F.
Hike-tracks in the West, being detailed descriptions (with maps) of twenty-five rambles in the country round Bristol, Bath, and Weston-super-Mare; in each of which the main roads are as far as possible avoided. By Harold F. Lock. Bristol: H. Hill Ltd. [, 1932.] 111 p. illus. (plans.) 18½cm.

695713A. 1. Somersetshire, Eng.—Guidebooks, 1932. 2. Walking.
N. Y. P. L. April 6, 1934

NL 0433903 NN

Lock, Helen Rosalie, 1883-
... Alfred William Rich, water-colour painter ... by H. R. Lock. London, Walker's galleries, 1922.
32 p. front. (port.) 7 pl. (2 col.) 21½cm. (Walker's quarterly. no. 9)
"List of exhibited work by Alfred W. Rich": p. 21-32.

1. Rich, Alfred William, 1856-1921.
C D 33-139
Library of Congress Card Div. N1.W3 no. 9

NL 0433904 DLC OC1MA MB NN

Lock, Henry
see
Lok, Henry, 1553?-1608?

Lock, Henry Osmond, 1879-
Advice to a young solicitor; worldly wisdom for the tyro, by H. O. Lock ... London, Stevens & sons limited, 1946.
vi, 71 p. 21½cm.
"First published in 1946."

1. Lawyers—Gt. Brit. I. Title.
47-15390

NL 0433906 DLC CtY ICU TxU ViU-L

956.9
L789c
Lock, Henry Osmond, 1879-
The conquerors of Palestine through forty centuries, by Major H. O. Lock ... with an introduction by Field-Marshal Viscount Allenby ... London, R. Scott, 1920.
ix, 121 p. fold. map. 22cm.
"List of books": p. 118.

1. Palestine—Hist. I. Title.
20-4566 Revised
Library of Congress DS118.L7

CtY MiU OCU CU ABS TxU
NL 0433907 DLC NN NcD OrU PU OCH OC1 NNZI PPDrop

Lock, Henry Osmond, 1879-
Dorset, by Major H. O. Lock. Illustrated by Walter Tyndale and A. Heaton Cooper. London, A. & C. Black, ltd. [1925]
xi, 200 p. col. front., illus. (map) col. plates. 21cm. (Half-title: Black's popular series of colour books)

1. Dorset, Eng.—Descr. & trav. I. Tyndale, Walter, illus. II. Cooper, Alfred Heaton, joint illus.
26-14977
Library of Congress DA670.D7L6

NL 0433908 DLC OEac OC1 NN

DA670
D7L6
1934
Lock, Henry Osmond, 1879-
Dorset. 2d ed., with 32 illus. in colour by Walter Tyndale and A. Heaton Cooper. London, A. & C. Black, 1934.
xi, 200 p. illus. (Black's new series of colour books)

1. Dorset, Eng. - Descr. & trav.

NL 0433909 CU

Lock, Henry Osmond, 1879-
With the British army in the Holy Land, by Major H. O. Lock ... London, R. Scott, 1919.
ix, 149 p. maps. 22cm.

1. European war, 1914-1918 — Campaigns — Turkey and the Near East—Palestine. I. Title.
19-16135 Revised
Library of Congress D568.7.L6

NL 0433910 DLC CaBVaU IEG IU NcD NN MiU

Lock, Jean, 1632-1704
see Locke, John, 1632-1704.

Lock, John, 1632-1704.
see
Locke, John, 1632-1704.

Lock, John Bascombe, 1849-1921.
Arithmetic for schools. London, Macmillan, 1886.
312 p.

NL 0433913 PPF

Lock, John Bascombe, 1849-1921.
Arithmetic for schools. By the Rev. J. B. Lock ... American ed., edited and arranged by Charlotte Angas Scott ... London and New York, Macmillan & co., 1891.
viii, 338 p. illus. 17½cm.
Answers: p. 293-338.

1. Arithmetic—1881-1900.
3-29728†
Library of Congress QA103.L81

NL 0433914 DLC KAS DAU NcD OO PPD

LOCK, John Bascombe, 1849-1921.
Arithmetic for schools. American ed. Edited and arranged by Charlotte Angas Scott. New York, etc., Macmillan Co., 1907.

NL 0433915 MH

Lock, John Bascombe, 1849-1921.
Arithmetic for schools, by the Rev. J. B. Lock ... American ed. Ed. and arranged by Charlotte Angas Scott ... New York, The Macmillan company; London, Macmillan & co., ltd., 1915.
viii, 338 p. illus. 17cm.

NL 0433916 ViU

Lock, John Bascombe, 1849-1921.
Arithmetic for schools, by the Rev. J. B. Lock ... American ed., edited and arranged by Charlotte Angas Scott ... New York, The Macmillan company; London, Macmillan & co., ltd., 1916.
viii, 292 p. illus. 17cm.

1. Arithmetic—1901- I. Scott, Charlotte Angas, 1858-
31-1951
Library of Congress QA103.L81 1916 511

NL 0433917 DLC

Lock, J[ohn] B[ascombe], 1849-1921.
Dynamics for beginners. London, etc., Macmillan and Co. 1887.
pp. viii, 178.

Dynamics

NL 0433918 MH ViU OC1W MA CaBVaU

Lock, John Bascombe, 1849-1921.
Elementary dynamics; being a new & enl. ed. of dynamics for beginners. London, Macmillan, 1891.
252 p.

NL 0433919 PPD

VOLUME 337

Lock, John Bascombe, 1849-1921.
Elementary dynamics, being a new and enlarged ed. of Dynamics for beginners, by the Rev.J.B. Lock ... London, New York, Macmillan and co., 1892.
252p. 17½cm.
"Fourth ed. revised and enlarged 1891. Reprinted with corrections 1892."

NL 0433920 MoU NjP CtY

Lock, John Bascombe, 1849-1921.
Elementary statics, by the Rev. J. B. Lock ... London and New York, Macmillan and co., 1888.
viii, 248 p. diagrs. 17½cm.
1. Statics.

NL 0433921 ViU OC1W ViLxW

Lock, John Bascombe, 1849-1921.
Elementary statics, by the Rev. J. B. Lock... London [etc.] Macmillan and co., ltd., 1902. vi, 305 p. 17½cm.
"Second edition."
122250B. 1. Statics.
N. Y. P. L. July 31, 1941

NL 0433922 NN

Lock, John Bascombe, 1849-1921.
Elementary statics, by the Rev. J.B. Lock ... London,Macmillan and co.,1909.
viii,305p. 17½cm.

NL 0433923 PSt MiU

Lock, John Bascombe, 1849-1921.
Elementary trigonometry. 1884.

NL 0433924 DN

Lock, John Bascombe, 1849-1921.
Elementos de trigonometría rectilínea por el rdo. J. B. Lock ... Obra traducida de la última edición inglesa por J. B. Ortega ... Buenos Aires, Á. Estrada y cía., 1904.
4 p. l., [7]-222 p., 1 l. diagrs. 20cm.
1. Trigonometry. I. Ortega, J. B., tr. II. Title. 22-107
Library of Congress QA533.L8

NL 0433925 DLC

Lock, John Bascombe, 1849-1921.
QA103 .L82 Key
Carr, Henry, 1863-1945.
Key to Mr. J. B. Lock's Shilling arithmetic, by Henry Carr ... London and New York, Macmillan and company, 1893.

Lock, John Bascombe, 1849-1921.
Re8.692 Mechanics for beginners. Part I.Dynamics and statics ... London and New York,Macmillan and co.,1891.
viii,264p. diagrs. 17½cm.

NL 0433927 CtY ODW OCU NcD MA RPB MH CU

Lock, John Bascombe, 1849-1921.
New trigonometry for schools & colleges.
London, Macmillan, 1911.
488 p.
By John Bascombe Lock and James Mark Child.

NL 0433928 PU

Lock, John Bascombe, 1849-1921.
A shilling book of arithmetic. L, Macmillan, 1923
Cover title: Elementary arithmetic, without answers.

NL 0433929 MH

Lock, John Bascombe, 1849-1921.
A treatise on elementary trigonometry.
London, Macmillan and co., 1882.

NL 0433930 MH

Lock, John Bascombe, 1849-1921.
A treatise on elementary trigonometry, by the Rev. J. B. Lock ... London, Macmillan & co., 1885.
vi p., 1 l., 274 p., 1 l. diagrs. 17½cm.
Stereotyped edition, revised 1883.
1. Trigonometry.

NL 0433931 MiU

QA533 .L8 Lock, John Bascombe, 1849-1921.
A treatise on elementary trigonometry, by the Rev. J. B. Lock ... Stereotyped ed. London and New York, Macmillan and co., 1887.
vi, [1], 306 p. diagrs. 17½cm.
1. Trigonometry, Plane.

NL 0433932 ICU NNU-W IaU

Lock, John Bascombe, 1849-1921.
Treatise on elementary trigonometry.
Stereotyped ed. London, 1888.

NL 0433933 RPB

QA531 .L63 Lock, John Bascombe, 1849-1921.
A treatise on elementary trigonometry, by the Rev.J.B.Lock... London,Macmillan and co.,1890.
vi,[1],306p. 17cm.
Stereotyped edition.
Bound with this is Fisher,Irving. Essentials of analytical trigonometry. [New York,Macmillan,1890]
1.Trigonometry.

NL 0433934 NNU-W OO

Lock, John Bascombe, 1849-1921.
A Treatise on Elementary Trigonometry.
Stereotyped ed. London [Cambridge] 1891.
16°.

NL 0433935 CtY RPB

Lock, John Bascombe, 1849-1921.
A treatise on elementary trigonometry.
Stereotyped ed. London, Macmillan, 1892.

NL 0433936 MH OC1W CU IU OO

Lock, John Bascombe, 1849-1921.
A treatise on elementary trigonometry; stereotyped ed. London, Macmillan, 1899.
306 p. illus. S.

NL 0433937 PP

Lock, John Bascombe, 1849-1921.
A treatise on elementary trigonometry ...
Stereotyped ed. London, New York, Macmillan and co., 1901.
17.5 cm.

NL 0433938 CtY PPF

Lock, J(ohn) B(ascombe), 1849-1921.
Treatise on elementary trigonometry.
Lond. Macmillan, 1908.

NL 0433939 MA PPSteph

Lock, John Bascombe, 1849-1921.
A treatise on elementary trigonometry.
London. Macmillan & Co. 1912. vi, (1), 306 pp. 17 cm., in 8s.
K259 — Trigonometry.

NL 0433940 MB

Lock, John Bascombe, 1849-1921.
Treatise on elementary trigonometry.
London, 1918.

NL 0433941 RPB

Lock, John Bascombe, 1849-1921.
A treatise on elementary trigonometry and higher trigonometry. By the Rev. J. B. Lock ... London, Macmillan and co., 1884.
vi p., 1 l., 274 p., 1 l., [4], [vii]-viii, 184 p. diagrs. 17 cm.
"A treatise on higher trigonometry": [4], [vii]-viii, 184 p. at end.
Includes "Answers."
1. Trigonometry.
QA531.L8 46-40550 rev

NL 0433942 DLC CaBViP

Lock, John Bascombe, 1849-1921.
Treatise on elementary trigonometry and higher trigonometry. London, 1887.

NL 0433943 NjP

VOLUME 337

Lock, John Bascombe, 1849-1921.
A treatise on elementary trigonometry and higher trigonometry. London, Macmillan, 1889.
199 p. S.

NL 0433944 NcD

514 L78t Lock, John Bascombe, 1849-1921.
A treatise on elementary trigonometry and higher trigonometry. London, 1892.
306, 217p. tables, diagrs.

NL 0433945 IU

Lock, John Bascombe, 1849-1921.
A treatise on elementary trigonometry and higher trigonometry. By the Rev. J.B. Locke ... London, Macmillan and co.; New York, Macmillan [1906]
2 v. in 1. diagrs. 18 cm.
[Volume 2] has special t.-p.: A treatise on the higher trigonometry, by the Rev. J.B. Lock [4th ed., enl.] London, Macmillan and co., ltd.; New York, The Macmillan company, 1906.
Appendix: The vernier, the level, the theodolite, the sextant, the mariner's compass. xvi p. following [v. 1] p. 252.
1. Trigonometry, Plane.

NL 0433946 CU

Lock, John Bascombe, 1849-1921.
A treatise on higher geometry, by the Rev. J.B. Lock ... London, Macmillan and co., limited, 1906.
viii, 217 p. 18 cm.

NL 0433947 CaBVaU

QA531 L813 1884 Lock, John Bascombe, 1849-1921.
A treatise on higher trigonometry, by the Rev. J. B. Lock...London: Macmillan and Co. 1884.
viii, 184 p. 17.5 cm.

NL 0433948 DAU DN-Ob CtY MA CU MH

Lock, John Bascombe, 1849-1921.
A treatise on higher trigonometry. 2d ed., rev. London and New York, Macmillan, 1887.
viii, 199 p. diagrs. 18cm.

1. Trigonometry—Problems, exercises, etc.

NL 0433949 ViU IU NIC RPB

QA535 .L63 Lock, John Bascombe, 1849-1921.
A treatise on higher trigonometry by the Rev. J. B. Lock... 3d edition, revised. London, Macmillan and co., 1889.
viii,199p. 17cm.

1.Geometry.

NL 0433950 NNU-W CaBVaU MH

QA531 .L802 Lock, John Bascombe, 1849-1921.
A treatise on higher trigonometry ... 4th ed., enl. London and New York, Macmillan, 1891.
viii, 217 p. diagrs.

1. Trigonometry.

NL 0433951 ICU

Lock, John Bascombe, 1849-1921.
A treatise on higher trigonometry, by the Rev. J. B. Lock ... 4th ed., enlarged. London, and New York, Macmillan and co., 1893.
viii, 217, [1] p. diagrs. 17cm.
"First edition 1884 ... fourth edition enlarged, 1891. Reprinted, 1893."

1. Trigonometry. 2. Trigonometry—Problems, exercises, etc.

NL 0433952 ViU CU

Lock, John Bascombe, 1849-1921.
A treatise on higher trigonometry, by the Rev. J.B.Lock... 4th ed., enl. London, and N.Y., Macmillan and co., 1895.[c1891]
217 p.

NL 0433953 OCU GEU

Lock, John Bascombe, 1849-1921.
Treatise on higher trigonometry.
Ed. 4, inl. London, Macmillan, 1899.

217 p.

NL 0433954 PPSteph

Lock, John Bascombe, 1849-1921.
A treatise on higher trigonometry; by the Rev. J.B. Lock ... London, Macmillan and Co., Limited, 1920.
viii, 217, [1] p. 17.5 cm.
On verso of title-page: Fourth edition enlarged.

NL 0433955 NcD

Lock, John Bascombe, 1849–1921.
Trigonometry for beginners, by the Rev. J. B. Lock ... Rev. and enl. for use of American schools by John A. Miller ... New York. The Macmillan company: London, Macmillan & co., ltd., 1896.
vii, 147, ix, 63 p. diagrs. 22½cm.
Appended, with separate t.-p. and paging (ix, 63 p.): Tables logarithmic and trigonometric ... by F. L. Sevenoak ... New York, London, 1896. (Issued also separately)
1. Trigonometry. 2. Logarithms. 3. Trigonometry—Tables. I. Miller, John Anthony, 1859– ed. II. Sevenoak, Frank Louis.
2—26620
Library of Congress QA531.L81

NL 0433956 DLC CU PSC OU

LOCK,John Bascombe,1849-1921.
Trigonometry for beginners. Revised and enlarged for the use of American schools by John A.Miller. New York,etc.,Macmillan Co., 1897.

NL 0433957 MH

Lock, John Bascombe, 1849-1921.
Trigonometry for beginners. Revised and enlarged for the use of American schools by John A.Miller. New York, etc., Macmillan co., 1898.

NL 0433958 MH PHC

Lock, John Bascombe, 1849-1921.
Trigonometry for beginners, ... Rev. and enl. for the use of American schools...N.Y. London, The Macmillan co., 1900.
vii,147 p.

NL 0433959 OCU

Lock, John Bascombe, 1849-1921
Trigonometry for beginners.
— London. Macmillan & Co., Limited. 1906. vii, (1), 195 pp. Illus. Plate. Diagrams. Sm. 8°.
By- John Bascombe Lock and James Mark Child.

G4933 — Trigonometry. — Jt. auth.

NL 0433960 MB

Lock, John Bascombe, 1849-1921.
Trigonometry for beginners. Rev & enl. for the use of American schools by John A. Miller. N.Y. Macmillan, 1909.

147 lx 63 p.

NL 0433961 PPF

Lock, John Bascombe, 1849-1921.
Trigonometry for beginners; 2nd ed. rev. & enl. London, Macmillan, 1912.

219 p.

NL 0433962 PP

Lock, John Bascombe, 1849-1921.
Trigonometry for beginners as far as the solution of triangles. London, Macmillan, 1886.

135 p.

NL 0433963 PPF DN-Ob

Lock, John Bascombe, 1849-1921.
Trigonometry for beginners as far as the solution of triangles. Ed. rev. & enl. London., Macmillan, 1888.
144 p.

NL 0433964 OO PPF

Lock, John Bascombe, 1849-1921.
Trigonometry for beginners as far as the solution of triangles. By the Rev. J.B. Lock ... [5th ed.] London and New York, 1890.
4 p.l., 148 p. diagrs. 18 cm.
"The present work is an abridgement of the more complete work on Elementary trigonometry by the same author." Pref.

NL 0433965 CU

VOLUME 337

Lock, John Bascombe, 1849-1921.
Trigonometry for beginners as far as the solution of triangles. ... [6th ed.]
London, Macmillan and co., etc., 1890.
148 p.

NL 0433966 OO

QA533 .L83 Lock, John Bascombe, 1849-1921.
Trigonometry for beginners as far as the solution of triangles. By the Rev. J. B. Lock ... London and New York, Macmillan and co., 1893.
[7], 148 p. diagrs. 17cm.
5th ed.

1. Trigonometry, Plane.

NL 0433967 ICU

Lock, John Bascombe, 1849-1921.
Ventilation of the large examination hall, Cambridge, England.
1910.

NL 0433968 OClW

Lock, John H 1907-1943.
The log of a merchant airman, by Capt. John H. Lock and John Creasey ... With 36 illustrations in half-tone. London, New York [etc.] S. Paul & co., ltd. [1943]
228 p. plates, 2 port. (incl. front.) diagr. 22cm.
Maps on lining-papers.

1. Aeronautics, Commercial—Gt. Brit. I. Creasey, John, joint author. II. Title.
A 43-2108
Harvard univ. Library for Library of Congress [2]

NL 0433969 MH

Lock, Karl: 1888- Untersuchungen über den Gehalt der Blutplasmaproteine an basischen Bestandteilen. Tübingen 1913: Laupp. 34 S. 8°
Tübingen, Naturwiss. Diss. v. 6. März 1913, Ref. Thierfelder
[Geb. 24. Jan. 88 Ellwangen a. Jagst; Wohnort: Tübingen; Staatsangeh.: Württemberg; Vorbildung: G. Ellwangen Reife 06; Studium: Berlin 2, Tübingen 10 S.; Rig. 6. März 13.] [U 13. 4632

NL 0433970 ICRL PU

Lock, Lilian Mary (Gillman)
see
Gillman, Lilian Mary.

Lock, Lucy.
Nursery rhyme singing games. London, Paxton [c1936]
2 v. 28 cm.

NL 0433972 OO

Lock, Ludwig, 1891-
Versuche über das Bis-α-hydrindon-(β,β)-spiran und das β-(Benzyl-o-carbonsäure)-α-hydrindon ... [Berlin, 1915]
52 p., 2 l. 23.5 cm.
Inaug.-Diss. - Berlin.
Lebenslauf.

NL 0433973 CtY

Lock, Mary Land.
Shadows of the swamp; words by Mary Land Lock, illustrations by Jacques de Tarnowsky. Dallas, Tex., The Kaleidograph press [c1940]
x, 1 l., 13-60 p. illus. 20cm.
Illustrated lining-papers.
Poems.

I. Title.
41-141
Library of Congress PS3523.O225S5 1940
——— Copy 2.
Copyright [2] 811.5

NL 0433974 DLC NcD TxU ViU

Lock, Mathias
see Lock, Matthew.

Lock, Matthew.
A book of ornaments, drawn & engrav'd by M. Lock [and others]. Principally adapted for Carvers, but generally usefull for various Decorations in the Present Taste. London, Published by John Weale...M. Lock invt. n. d.
43 pl.

Ornamental t. p.
Includes reproductions of title pages by Thos Pether, Carver and another by Thos Johnson, Carver.

NL 0433976 MiD

NK 9705 L813 Lock, Matthew.
A book of ornaments, drawn & engrave'd by M. Lock, principally adapted for carvers, but generally useful for various decorations in the present taste. London, J. Weale, n.d.
49 pl. (incl. t.-p.) 30 cm.
Added t.-p.: Chippendale's ornaments, and interior decorations in the old French style.

1. Wood-carving. 2. Mantels. 3. Mirrors - Frames. 4. Picture frames and framing. I. Title: Chippendale's ornaments.

NL 0433977 DSI DP

Avery AK 2542 J6 J633 Lock, Matthew.
A book of ornaments, drawn & engrav'd by M. Lock, principally adapted for carvers, but generally usefull for various decorations in the present taste. London, John Weale, 1834.
5 plates (incl. t.-p.) 20cm.

Bound with Johnson, Thomas, carver. A book of ornaments. 1834.
Anonymous engraved plate with caption: Water bound at end.
I. Title.

NL 0433978 NNC

Lock, Matthew.
A collection of ornamental designs, applicable to furniture, frames & the decoration of rooms, in the style of Louis 14th—on 24 plates. London, M. Taylor [1841]
24 pl. 29cm.

1. Decoration and ornament—Louis XIV style. 2. Design, Decorative.
P O 36-62
Library, U. S. Patent Office NK1900.L813

NL 0433979 DP DSI

Lock, Matthew.
A new book of ornaments for looking glass frames, chimney pieces &c., &c., in the Chinese taste by Matt: Lock ... London, Printed for R. Sayer [18—?]
6 plates. 30 cm.
Title-page included in the numbering of the plates.

1. Mirrors - Frames. 2. Decoration and ornament, Chinese.

NL 0433980 MdBP

NK1530 .W3 Lock, Matthew.
Weale, John, 1791-1862, ed.
Old English and French ornament: for the interior embellishment of houses, for carvers and decorators; with designs for doors, windows, fire-places and chimney glasses, ornamental furniture, &c., &c. By Chippendale, Johnson, Inigo Jones, Lock, and others. 220 designs in 100 engravings. London, J. Weale, 1846.

Lock, Matthew, 1630?-1677
See
Locke, Matthew, 1630?-1677.

Lock, Max.
Bedford by the river; a town planning report, by Max Lock, David Grove and Gerald King. London, J. Murray, 1952.
140 p. illus., maps (part fold., part col., 2 in pocket) 20 x 28 cm.

1. Cities and towns—Planning—Bedford, Eng.
Full name: Cecil Max Lock.
NA9187.B4L6 711.0942 52-10107

NL 0433983 DLC CaBVaU NjP CtY NcD NN MH MB TxU

Lock, Max.
The county borough of Middlesbrough survey and plan. Yorkshire, Middlesbrough Corp. [1946]
483 p. plates, maps (part col., part fold.; 2 in pockets) diagrs. 26 x 31 cm.
Cover title: The Middlesbrough survey and plan.

1. Cities and towns—Planning—Middlesbrough, Eng. I. Title: The Middlesbrough survey and plan.
Full name: Cecil Max Lock.
NA9188.M5L58 711.0942 47-27810*

NL 0433984 DLC NNC ICU

Lock, Max.
The county borough of Middlesbrough survey and plan; directed by Max Lock... [Middlesbrough] Middlesbrough corp. [1948]
483 p. illus. 26 x 31cm.

Cover-title: The Middlesbrough survey and plan.

476296B. I. Cities—Plans—Gt. Br.—Eng.—Middlesbrough. I. Middlesbrough, Eng.
N. Y. P. L. April 27, 1949

NL 0433985 NN

VOLUME 337

Lock, Max.
The Hartlepools, a survey and plan, by Max Lock in collaboration with Diana Boyd and others. London, West Hartlepool Corp.; distributed by D. Dobson [1948]
262 p. illus., plans (part col., 2 in pocket) 26 cm.

1. Cities and towns—Planning—Hartlepool, Eng. I. Boyd, Diana Florence, joint author.
Full name: Cecil Max Lock.

NA9188.H3L6 711.0942 49-21616*

NL 0433986 DLC CaBVaU ICU NcD

Lock, Max.
Middlesbrough replanned; the survey and plan for Middlesbrough directed by Max Lock ... and reprinted from the Architects' journal for August 2nd, 1945 ... [London, Printed by Harrison & sons ltd., 1945]
16 p. illus. (incl. maps) 30cm.

1. Cities and towns—Planning—Middlesbrough, Eng.
[*Full name:* Cecil Max Lock]

Library of Congress NA9188.M5L57 46-7337
[2] 711.0942

NL 0433987 DLC

Lock, Max.
Outline plan for the Portsmouth district, by Max Lock...in collaboration with Frank Layfield...Douglas Tookey...and others. Final report, May 1949. [Winchester, 1949] xi,159 p. illus. 23cm.

"Prepared for the Hampshire County and Portsmouth City councils."

1. Cities—Plans—Gt. Br.—Eng.—Portsmouth. I. Hampshire, Eng. County council. II. Portsmouth, Eng. Council.

NL 0433989 NN

Lock, Max.
... A plan for Middlesbrough, the proposals in outline; address to the Council by Max Lock ... [Middlesbrough, Eng., 1945?]
cover-title, 20 p. fold. plates, fold. maps. 25cm.

At head of title: County borough of Middlesbrough survey and plan.
Caption title: The survey and replanning of Middlesbrough; address to the Council by Max Lock ... 25th May, 1945.

1. Cities and towns—Planning—Middlesbrough, Eng. I. Middlesbrough, Eng. Council.
[*Full name:* Cecil Max Lock]

Library of Congress NA9188.M5L6 46-21195
[2] 711.0942

NL 0433990 DLC

Lock, Max.
Reconstruction in the Netherlands, an account of a visit to post-war Holland by members of the Town Planning Institute. [London] Jason Press [1947]
[16] p. illus., maps. 28 cm.

Cover title.
Reprinted from the Journal of the Town Planning Institute.

1. Cities and towns—Planning—Netherlands. 2. Town Planning Institute, London.
Full name: Cecil Max Lock.

NA9207.L6 711.09492 48-20175*

NL 0433991 DLC NN MH

Lock, Michael, fl. 1615.
See
Lok, Michael, fl. 1615.

Lock, Nan K 1906-
No wine for the governor, by N. K. Lock. Cape Town, Pub. by H. B. Timmins for John Lane, ltd., London [1946?]
4 p. l., iii, 241 p. 21cm.

1. Stel, Willem Adriaan van der, 1664-1723—Fiction. I. Title.

PZ3.L785No 47-2228

NL 0433993 DLC TxU

PZ 3 .L785 Th
Lock, Nan K 1906-
Three ships came sailing, by N. K. Lock. Cape Town, H. B. Timmins [1951]
236 p. 22 cm.

Author's name in manuscript on t. p.

NL 0433994 WU NN TxU

823.9 L813t
Lock, Nan K , 1906-
Three ships came sailing. London, Bodley Head [1951]
xii,236p. 22cm.

1. Van Riebeeck, Jan, 1618-1677. Fiction. I. Title.

NL 0433995 IEN NNC

Lock, Otto.
I bunden stil; en samling digte. Patterson, Calif., 1920.

35 p. 20cm.

NL 0433996 MnU

PT9150 .L6
Lock, Otto.
Syndens sold. Eau Claire, Wis., Fremad Pub. Co., 1909.
48 p. 20 cm.

NL 0433997 MnHi

Lock, Otto.
Der var engang; digte. Patterson, Calif. [192-?]

16 p. 18cm.

NL 0433998 MnU

Lock, Peter, supposed author.
An Exmoor scolding ...
see under title

Lock, *Mrs.* Robert Heath
see Southorn, Bella Sidney (Woolf) *Lady.*

Lock, R[obert] H[eath] 1879-1915. and C. O. Macadam.
Ceylon handbook... Colombo: "Times of Ceylon" [1912].
35(1) p., 1 map. illus. nar. 8°.

At head of title: International Rubber and Allied Trades Exposition, New York, 1912.

1. India rubber.—Exhibitions. 2. Macadam, C. O., jt. au.
October 16, 1912.

NL 0434002 NN

Lock, Robert Heath, 1879-1915.
Recent progress in the study of variation, heredity, and evolution, by Robert Heath Lock ... London, J. Murray, 1906.
2 p. l., vii-xv, 299 p. illus., 4 pl., 5 port. (incl. front.) diagrs. 20½cm.
"Glossary": p. 291-294.

1. Variation (Biology) 2. Heredity. 3. Evolution—Hist.

7-12650

PPL PPPD OkU
NL 0434003 DLC OrP CtY DNLM MiU NN OO OCU OC1W

QH366 .L8 1906
Lock, Robert Heath, 1879-1915.
Recent progress in the study of variation, heredity, and evolution, by Robert Heath Lock ... New York, E. P. Dutton and company, 1906.
2 p. l., vii-xv, 299 p. illus., 4 pl., 5 port. (incl. front.) diagrs. 20 1/2cm.
"Glossary": p. 291-294.

1. Variation (Biology) 2. Heredity. 3. Evolution—Hist.

NL 0434004 MB NjP CU ViU

Lock, Robert Heath, 1879-1915.
Recent progress in the study of variation, heredity, and evolution, by Robert Heath Lock ... London, J. Murray, 1907.
2 p. l., vii-xv, 299 p. illus., 4 pl., 5 port. (incl. front.) diagrs. 20½cm.
"Glossary": p. 291-294.

1. Variation (Biology) 2. Heredity. 3. Evolution—Hist.

NL 0434005 ICJ IEdS NcRS PSC IdU

Lock, Robert Heath, 1879-1915.
Recent progress in the study of variation, heredity, and evolution. New York: E. P. Dutton & Co., 1907. 2 p.l., vii-xv, 299 p., 1 port. 8°.

Reprint of first edition.

1. Variation (Biological). 2. Heredity. 3. Evolution (Biological).
July 23, 1913.

NL 0434006 NN

Lock, Robert Heath, 1879-1915.
Recent progress in the study of variation, heredity, and evolution. New York: E. P. Dutton and Co., 1907. 2 p.l., vii-xv, 299 p., 5 port. 12°.

1. Variation (Biological). 2. Heredity. 3. Evolution (Biological).
September 11, 1913.

NL 0434007 NN

Lock, Robert Heath, 1879-1915.
Recent progress in the study of variation, heredity and evolution. New York: E. P. Dutton and Co., 1907. iii-xv, 299 p., 4 pl., 5 port. illus., tables. 8°.

1. Heredity. 2. Evolution. CENTRAL RESERVE.
September 6, 1912.

NL 0434008 NN NjP

VOLUME 337

Lock, Robert Heath, 1879-1915.
Recent progress in the study of variation, heredity, and evolution. New York, Dutton, 1909.
299p. illus.

NL 0434009 ICRL CU NjP

QH 366 L8 1909
Lock, Robert Heath, 1879-1915.
Recent progress in the study of variation, heredity, and evolution. [2d ed.] London, J. Murray, 1909.
xiv, 334 p. illus., plates, ports., diagrs. tables. 21 cm.

Includes bibliographies.

1. Variation (Biology) 2. Heredity. 3. Evolution - History. I. Title.

NL 0434010 NIC OrU-D DNLM OU

Lock, Robert Heath, 1879-1915.
Recent progress in the study of variation, heredity, and evolution, by Robert Heath Lock ... New York, E. P. Dutton and company, 1910.
3 p. l., v-xiv, 334 p. illus., 4 pl., 5 port. (incl. front.) diagrs. 20½cm.
Bibliography at end of each chapter.
CONTENTS.—Evolution.—The theory of natural selection.—Biometry.—The theory of mutation.—The older hybridists.—Mendelism.—Recent cytology.—Eugenics.

1. Variation (Biology) 2. Heredity. 3. Evolution.
10—25850
Library of Congress QH366.L8 1910

NL 0434011 DLC OKentU ViU PPFr

QH 366 L8 1911
Lock, Robert Heath, 1879-1915.
Recent progress in the study of variation, heredity, and evolution. [3d ed.] New York E. P. Dutton, 1911.
xiv, 334 p. illus., plates, ports., diagrs. tables. 21 cm.

Includes bibliographies.

1. Variation (Biology) 2. Heredity. 3. Evolution - History. I. Title.

NL 0434012 NIC PU-BZ PWcS MtU OrPR MH CU NIC

Lock, Robert Heath, 1879-1915.
Recent progress in the study of variation, heredity, and evolution, by Robert Heath Lock ... Rev. by Leonard Doncaster ... Biographical note by Bella Sydney Woolf (Mrs. R. H. Lock) London, J. Murray, 1916.
xxiv, 336 p. front., illus., plates, 5 port. 21 cm.
Fourth edition.

1. Variation (Biology) 2. Heredity. 3. Evolution—Hist. I. Doncaster, Leonard, 1877-1920. II. Woolf, Bella Sidney.
Agr 18—808
U. S. Dept. of Agr. Libr. for Library of Congress 443L78 [QH366.L] [a49f1]

NL 0434013 DNAL WaS CaBVaU WaE NcU MiU NN

LOCK, ROBERT HEATH, 1879-1915.
Recent progress in the study of variation, heredity, and evolution, by Robert Heath Lock... New York, E.P.Dutton and company, 1916.
xxiv,336 p. front.,illus.,plates,ports. 20½cm.

Printed in Great Britain.

597552A. 1. Evolution—Hist. 2. Heredity. 3. Variation, Biological.

NL 0434014 NN CU PP MiU

LOCK,Robert Heath,1879-1915.
Recent progress in the study of variation, heredity,and evolution. Revised by Leonard Doncaster. Biographical note by Bella Sidney Woolf. London,J.Murray,1920.

Ports.,plates and other illustr.
"1st ed.,1906;...5th ed.,1920."
Label pasted over imprint: New York,E.P. Dutton and Co.,Inc.

NL 0434015 MH

QH366 .L8 1920
Lock, Robert Heath, 1879-1915.
Recent progress in the study of variation, heredity, and evolution. Rev. by Leonard Doncaster ... Biographical note by Bella Sidney Woolf (Mrs. R.H. Lock) [5th ed.] London, J. Murray, 1920.
xxiv, 336 p. front., illus., plates, 5 port. 21 cm.

1. Evolution—History. 2. Heredity. 3. Variation (Biology) I. Doncaster, Leonard, 1877- II. Woolf, Bella Sidney.

NL 0434016 TU

Lock, Robert Heath, 1879-1915.
Rubber and rubber planting. By R. H. Lock ... Cambridge, University press, 1913.
xi, [1] p., 1 l., 245 p. illus., x pl. 19½cm.
"Short list of references": p. [xii]

1. India-rubber.
Agr 14-66
Library, U. S. Dept. of Agriculture 77L78

NcD MH-A PU-BZ MiU PPFr ICJ NN MB DPU
NL 0434017 DNAL KEmT CU NIC OrP OrCS CaBVaU OAkU

LOCK,Robert Heath, 1879-1915.
Studies in Plant Breeding in the Tropics. [Colombo],Lechevalier,[1904].

NL 0434018 MH

Lock, Una, pseud.
see [Bailey, Urania Locke (Stoughton), 1820-1882.

CD30 L789b
Lock, Walter, 1846-1933.
The Bible and Christian life. London, Methuen [1905?]
xxiv, 323 p. 20 cm.

Bibliographical footnotes.
Contents.- Thoughts on inspiration.- Thoughts on the study of the New Testament.- Thoughts on the Bible and gentile religion.- Thoughts on the Christian life.

NL 0434020 CtY-D CtY PHC OCl MB PPPD NjNbS MH-AH

Lock, Walter, 1846-1933.
Cfq10 1
Civic duty; a sermon preached before the mayor and corporation of the city of Oxford, in the Church of Saint Martin and all saints, on November 10, 1912 ... Oxford,1912.
Cover-title.
Pamphlet.

Cd.for Madan.

NL 0434021 CtY

Lock, Walter, 1846-1933.
The constructive value of the Bible... Lond., Mowbray, 1921.
31 p.

NL 0434022 OO

Lock, Walter, 1846-1933.
... A critical and exegetical commentary on the Pastoral epistles (I & II Timothy and Titus) by the Rev. Walter Lock ... Edinburgh, T. & T. Clark, 1924.
3 p. l., iii-xliv, 163 p. 21½ cm. (Half-title: The International critical commentary [on the Holy Scriptures of the Old and New Testaments. v. 39])
Series title in part at head of t.-p.
Bibliography: p. ix-xi.

1. Bible. N. T. Pastoral epistles—Commentaries.

BS491.I 6 vol. 39 227.83 24—21704

Wa WaE WaPS WaS WaSp WaSpG WaT WaTC WaWW IdPI MtBuM CaBVaU IdB IdU MtBC MtU OrCS OrP OrPR OrU OCH OOxM PHC KyLxCB KyU PLF ViU MU WaU OClW OClU
NL 0434023 DLC PPEB PPLT NjNbS NcD PPTU OCl OO

BR 2735 L6
Lock, Walter, 1846-1933.
A critical and exegetical commentary on the Pastoral epistles (I & II Timothy and Titus). New York, Scribner, 1924.
xliv, 163 p. 22 cm. (International critical commentary)
1. Bible. N.T. Pastoral epistles--Commentaries. I. Series.

NL 0434025 MBtS DDO NN MWelC MH DCU-H MBrZ MH-AH

BS491 .W4 vol. 45
Lock, Walter, 1846-1933, ed.
Bible. *N. T. Ephesians. English. 1929.*
The Epistle to the Ephesians; with introduction and notes by Walter Lock. London, Methuen & co. [1929]

Lock, Walter, 1846-1933.
The exegesis of the New Testament. An inaugural lecture delivered on Feb. 5, 1896. Oxford, James Parker & co. 1896.
25p. 21 1/2 cm.

NL 0434027 NRCR

Lock, Walter, 1846-1933.
From Robertson's Charles V: Latin prose. n.d.
cover title, 7 p. 21 cm.

NL 0434028 RPB

Lock, Walter, 1846-1933.
John Keble, a biography by Walter Lock ... with a portrait from a painting by George Richmond, R. A. Boston and New York, Houghton, Mifflin and company, 1893.
viii p., 1 l., 245, [1] p. incl. front. (port.) 19½cm.
Appendices: I. The poems of the Christian year, arranged in the order of composition.—II. Published writings.

1. Keble, John, 1792-1866.
BX5199.K3L7 1893 47-33044

NRCR NIC MB KMK OCl CLSU
NL 0434029 DLC MH MeB NcU MdBJ OClW NN DNC MiD PPA

Me65 K234 893l
Lock, Walter, 1846-1933.
John Keble; a biography ... With a portrait from a painting by George Richmond ... London,Methuen & co.,1893.
viiip.,1l.,245,[1]p. front.(port.) 19½cm.
Appendices: I. The poems of the Christian year, arranged in the order of composition. II. Published writings.

1.Keble, John, 1792-1866.

NL 0434030 CtY MsU PPL PPFr OCX NjP NcD

VOLUME 337

283
K25Yℓ.3 Lock, Walter, 1846-1933.
John Keble, a biography. With a port. from a painting by George Richmond, R.A. 3d ed. London, Methuen, 1893;
viii,245p. 20cm.

1. Keble, John, 1792-1866.

NL 0434031 IEN MH

821
K232Bℓ
1893 LOCK, WALTER, 1846-1933.
John Keble, a biography by Walter Lock ... with a portrait from a painting by George Richmond, R.A. 4th ed. London, Methuen & co., 1893.
viiip.,1ℓ.,245,[1]p. front.(port.) 20cm.

Appendices: I. The poems of the Christian year, arranged in the order of composition.—II. Published writings.

1. Keble, John, 1792-1866.

NL 0434032 TxU MU OKentU NRU

821
K232zℓ5 Lock, Walter, 1846-1933.
John Keble, by Walter Lock ... with a portrait from a painting by George Richmond, R. A. 5th ed. London, Methuen & co. 1893.
viii, 248 p. front. (port.) 19 1/2 cm.
(Half-title: Leaders of religion)
Untrimmed.
Appendices: I. The poems of the Christian year, arranged in the order of composition; II. Published writings: p. [239]-245.
Imperfect: Cover soiled.

1. Keble, John, 1792-1866. I. Title.

NL 0434033 MsSM CaBVaU WaSpG AAP

Lock, Walter, 1846-1933.
John Keble, by Walter Lock ... with a portrait from a painting by George Richmond, R. A. 7th. ed. London, Methuen & Co., 1895.
viii p., 2 l., 248 p. front. (port.) 19½cm. (Half-title: Leaders of religion)

Appendices: I. The poems of the Christian year, arranged in the order of composition; II. Published writings: p. [239]-245.

NL 0434034 ICarbS MiU PBm PPPD NBC TU

Lock, Walter, 1846- 1933.
John Keble, by Walter Lock ... with a portrait from a painting by George Richmond, R. A. New and cheaper issue. London, Methuen & co. [1905]
viii p., 2 l., 248 p. front. (port.) 19½cm. (Half-title: Leaders of religion)

Appendices: I. The poems of the Christian year, arranged in the order of composition; II. Published writings: p. [239]-245.

1. Keble, John, 1792-1866.

17-20986

Library of Congress BX5199.K3L7

NL 0434035 DLC PHC IU TNJ-R NNUT

Lock, Walter, 1846-1933.
John Keble, ... with a portrait from a painting by George Richmond, R.A. London, Methuen & co. 8th ed. [1923]

NL 0434036 OO

Lock, Walter, 1846-1933.
John Keble; a biography. Boston, Houghton, 1933.

245 p.

NL 0434037 PPD

Lock, Walter, 1846-1933.
Keble College.
10p.

(Clark, A., Colleges of Oxford, p. 471)

NL 0434038 MdBP

Lock, Walter, 1846-1933.
The Minor prophets, with a commentary, explanatory and practical... London, 1906-07
see under Bible. O. T. Minor prophets. English. 1906-07.

FX35
M67 Lock, Walter, 1846-1933.
Miracles; papers and sermons contributed to the Guardian by W. Lock, W. Sanday, H.S. Holland, H.H. Williams, A.C. Headlam, with a prefatory note by H.S. Holland. London, Longmans, Green, 1911.
vi, 136p.

1. Miracles - Addresses, essays, lectures. I. Sanday, William, 1843-1920, joint author. II. Holland, Henry Scott, 1847-1918, joint author. III. Williams, H H , joint author. IV. Headlam, Arthur Cayley, 1862- joint author. V. Title.

NL 0434040 CSaT PU MH CtY NN DAU

Lock, Walter, 1846-1933.
A morning prayer; a sermon preached by the Rev. Walter Lock...at Westminster Abbey, on October 26th, 1913. London: Soc. for promoting Christian Knowledge, 1913. 16 p. 16°.

1. Prayer.

October 16, 1915.

NL 0434041 NN

LOCK, Walter, 1846-1933.
The Old Testament an essential part of the revelation of God.
(In Oxford house papers. 3d series, pp. 76-104. London, 1897.)

NL 0434042 MB OCl

Lock, Walter, 1846-1933.
Oxford memories, by Walter Lock... London, Oxford university press, H. Milford, 1932.
4 p.l., 120, [2] p. 19 1-2 cm.

NL 0434043 NNG TxDaM PPPD

BS2505 Lock, Walter, 1846- 1933.
.L8 St. Paul the master-builder; being lectures delivered to the clergy of the diocese of St. Asaph in July, 1897 by Walter Lock ... London, Methuen & co., 1899.
[iii]-x, [1], 124 p. 20cm.

NL 0434044 ICJ PHC

BS
2505
.L78 Lock, Walter, 1846-1933.
St. Paul, the master-builder: being lectures delivered to the clergy of the Diocese of St. Asaph in July, 1897. By Walter Lock ... New York, New Amsterdam book company, 1900.
[iii]-x p., 1 l., 124 p. 20cm.

NL 0434045 DNC ICU

Lock, Walter, 1846-1933.
St Paul. the Master-builder... lectures--St. Asaph--1897 ed.2.
Lond. Methuen [c1905]
12-124 p.

NL 0434046 OO PPYH PPPD

Lock, Walter, 1846-1933.
St. Paul the master-builder; being lectures delivered to the clergy of the diocese of St. Asaph in July, 1798, by Walter Lock ... 3d ed. London, Methuen & co., ltd. [1910]
xii, 124 p. 19½cm.

NL 0434047 OrSaWW

Lock, Walter, 1846-1933.
Two lectures on the "Sayings of Jesus" recently discovered at Oxyrhynchus, delivered at Oxford on Oct. 23, 1897, by the Rev. Walter Lock ... and the Rev. William Sanday ... Oxford, The Clarendon press, 1897.
49, [1] p. 21½cm.

CONTENTS.—Bibliography.—Text, with emendations and illustrations.—Interpretation of the text.—History and origin of the Sayings.

1. Bible. N. T. Apocryphal books. Logia Iesou—Criticism, interpretation, etc. 2. Oxyrhynchus papyri. I. Bible. N. T. Apocryphal books. Logia Iesou. Greek. 1897. II. Sanday, William, 1843-1920, joint author.

1-14629

Library of Congress BS2970.L6

PPULC OO NNUT MB
NL 0434048 DLC CaBVaU OrU NIC NcD CtY PPLT PSC

Lock, Walter, 1846-1933, ed.
Westminster commentaries
see under title

Lock, William George.
Askja, Iceland's largest volcano: with a description of the great lava desert in the interior: and a chapter on the genesis of the island. By W. G. Lock... Charlton, Kent, The author, 1881.
106 p. map. 22cm.

AMERICAN ALPINE CLUB COLL.

353098B. 1. Volcanoes—Iceland— Askja.

March 21, 1947

NL 0434050 NN CtY PPAN MnU MA InU ICN

Lock, William George.
Guide to Iceland; a useful handbook for travellers and sportsmen. By Wm. Geo. Lock ... Charlton, The author [1882]
2 p. l., 184 p. front. (fold. map) 18½cm.

1. Iceland—Descr. & trav.—Guide-books. I. Title.

44-18956

Library of Congress DL304.L6

NL 0434051 DLC NIC CtY NjP ViU NN MH

Lock, William George.
... Icelandic Troubles, and Mansion House Muddles. An Exposé of the Famine Story of 1882. [London (Woolwich)] 1883.
40 p. 8°.

NL 0434052 CtY

Lock Wood, *pseud*
see
Lockwood, William L

VOLUME 337

Lock and bell. A monthly paper devoted to the interests of the locksmith, bell-hanger, gunsmith, plater, and electrical worker.

New York, Philadelphia, W. Byrnes, 18

v. illus. 35cm.

1. Locks and keys—Period.

CA 7—71 Unrev'd

Library of Congress TS519.L6

NL 0434054 DLC

YA 23636 The lock and key. [New York, n.d.]
24p.
(American tract society, no. 613)

NL 0434055 DLC

Lock and key: a musical entertainment, in two acts
see under Shield, William, 1748-1829.

The Lock and Key, a musical farce ...
see under Shield, William, 1748-1829.

The lock and key library; the most interesting stories of all nations
see under Hawthorne, Julian, 1846-1934, ed.

Lock collection of hymns
see under London. Lock hospital. Chapel.

B1a80 +B729 The Lock guard.
[Sault Ste Marie,
illus. 28-30½cm. biweekly.

Vol.1 "a publication of the 702d Military police battalion, Fort Brady, Mich.", "published in the interest of the military personnel at Fort Brady"; v. "published for the military personnel of the Sault Ste.Marie Military district."
Caption title.
Vol. processed.

NL 0434060 CtY

Lock Haven (Pa.) Baptist church
Historical sketch ... prepared for the seventieth anniversary, June 1908. [n.p.n.d.]
20p. 21cm.

NL 0434061 NRAB

Lock Haven, Pa. Central State Normal School
see
Pennsylvania. State College, *Lock Haven.*

Lock Haven, Pa. Normal school.
see
Pennsylvania. State normal school, Lock Haven.

Lock Haven, Pa. *Ordinances, etc.*
Code of ordinances of the City of Lock Haven, Pennsylvania, 1947, containing the general and permanent ordinances of the city (to and including May 19, 1947) Pub. by order of City Council. Charlottesville, Va., Michie City Publications Co., 1947.

194 p. 24 cm.

"The first revision and codification of the general ordinances ... since 1883 ... Codified, edited and indexed by the editorial staff of Michie City Publications Company, Charlottesville, Virginia."
To be kept up to date by pocket supplement.

I. Michie City Publications Company, Charlottesville, Va.
JS999.L27A5 1947 352.0748 47-6910*

NL 0434065 DLC

Lock Haven, Pa. State College
see
Pennsylvania. State College, *Lock Haven.*

Lock Haven, Pa. State Teachers College
see
Pennsylvania. State College, *Lock Haven.*

Lock-Haven and Tyrone Railroad Company.
Report of the president and report of engineer.

Philadelphia.

v. 24 cm. annual.

HE2791.L8142 57-51642 ‡

NL 0434068 DLC

Lock Asylum, London
see London. Lock Hospital and Rescue Home

F157 .C6 L63 F The Lock Haven Express.
Clinton county, 1839-1939; centennial edition of the Lock Haven Express, Saturday, December 2, 1939. [Lock Haven, 1939,
[84]p. illus.,ports. 43x58cm. fold to 43x29cm.

1. Lock Haven, Pa. - Hist. 2. Clinton Co., Pa. - Hist. S

NL 0434070 PSt

Lock Haven, Penna., directory, including Mill Hall, Flemington, Castanea, Lockport and Dunnstown ... 19 Binghamton, N. Y., The Calkin-Kelly directory company, °19

v. 24cm.

1. Lock Haven, Pa.—Direct. 2. Mill Hall, Pa.—Direct. 3. Flemington, Pa.—Direct. 4. Castanea, Pa.—Direct. 5. Lockport, Pa.—Direct. 6. Dunnstown, Pa.—Direct.

CA 32-7 Unrev'd

Library of Congress F159.L79A18

NL 0434071 DLC MWA OCl

Lock Hospital, Edinburgh
see Edinburgh. Lock Hospital.

Lock Hospital, London
see London. Lock hospital.

Lock Joint Pipe Company.
Lock joint reinforced concrete pipe; pressure and subaqueous catalogue ... Ampere, N. J.: Lock Joint Pipe Co.[, cop. 1925.]
80 p. incl. diagrs., front., tables. illus. 4°.

Plates printed on both sides.

406331A. 1. Pipe, Cement and concrete.

April 9, 1929

NL 0434074 NN

Lock Joint Pipe Company.
"Lock joint" reinforced concrete pipe; pressure, sewer, culvert, and subaqueous pipe, manufactured by Lock Joint Pipe Company ... [New York, cop. 1918.] 64 p. diagrs. (part col'd), front., illus., plans. 4°.

"Specifications for reinforced concrete pipe," 3 l., inserted.

1. Pipe (Concrete).

September 8, 1922.

NL 0434075 NN

... Lock-step schooling and a remedy
see under [Burk, Frederic Lister] 1862-

.790.5 fL789 LOCK to lock times and river life; the journal of the Thames...
June 9, 1888-

[London, 1888-
v. in illus. 31cm.
weekly, Mar. (or Apr.)- Sept. (1888-Oct.1, 1892, weekly)
Vol. numbering discontinued with v.6, 1892.
Oct.25, 1890-1893 called "new ser."
Title varies slightly.
Absorbed Flood and field Oct.25, 1890, Oct.25, 1890-Jan.1891 having caption title: Flood and field.

1. Thames River. 2. Boats and boating. Periodicals. I. Flood and field.

NL 0434078 MnU

Lockard, Charles Randell, 1900-

SD387 .U62 1937b U. S. *Northeastern forest experiment station, Upper Darby, Pa.*
Centralized management and utilization adapted to farm woodlands in the Northeast, by C. Edward Behre and C. R. Lockard, Northeastern forest experiment station, United States Forest service, in cooperation with the New York state college of forestry. Published by the Charles Lathrop Pack forestry foundation and the New York state college of forestry at Syracuse university. [Syracuse?], 1937.

99.79 L78 Lockard, Charles Randell, 1900-
The future of wood. [n.p., 1947]
21 l.

NL 0434080 DNAL

Lockard, Charles Randell, 1900-
Log defects in southern hardwoods, by C. R. Lockard, J. A. Putnam, and R. D. Carpenter. Washington, U. S. Govt. Print. Off., 1950.

37 p. illus. 27 cm. (Agriculture handbook no. 4)
Contribution from Forest Service.

1. Hard woods. 2. Wood—Defects. I. Title. (Series: U. S. Dept. of Agriculture. Agriculture handbook no. 4)

TA419.L6 620.12 Agr 50-654

U. S. Dept. of Agr. Libr. for Library of Congress 1Ag84Ah no. 4 †

NL 0434081 DNAL NNBG DLC

VOLUME 337

Lockard, Charles Randell, 1900- joint author.
Cline, Albert Collins.
... Mixed white pine and hardwood, by A. C. Cline and C. R. Lockard, with an introduction by R. T. Fisher. Petersham, Mass., Harvard forest, 1925.

Lockard, Charles Randell, 1900-
A rapid forestry control system, especially applicable to farm woodlands, by C. R. Lockard ... [Washington, D.C.] U.S. Department of agriculture, Forest service, 1942.
cover-title, [27] p. 27cm.

Mimeographed.
Appendices paged separately.

NL 0434083 NcD OCl

1.9
F7622T
no.52
Lockard, Charles Randell, 1900-
View-points on farm forestry. New Haven, Conn., 1942.
4 p. (U.S. Forest service. Northeastern forest experiment station. Technical notes. no. 52)

"Radio talk given at Ithaca, N.Y., February 12, 1942."

NL 0434084 DNAL

Lockard, Duane, 1921-
Politics in the Connecticut General Assembly. [New London? Conn.] °1952.
68 l. 29 cm.
Abstract of thesis—Yale.
Thesis presented under title: The role of party in the Connecticut General Assembly.

1. Connecticut—Pol. & govt. 2. Connecticut. General Assembly. I. Title.
Full name: Walter Duane Lockard.

JK3316.L6 328.746 52-66335

NL 0434085 DLC

Lockard, E Kidd.
The influence of New England in denominational colleges in the Northwest, 1830-1860. By E. Kidd Lockard.
(*In* Ohio state archaeological and historical quarterly. Columbus, O., 1944. 23cm. vol. LIII, p. 1-13)
Bibliographical foot-notes.

1. Universities and colleges—Northwest, Old. 2. Church and college in the U. S.
A 45-4981
Ohio state univ. Library for Library of Congress F486.O51 vol. 53
†

NL 0434086 OU DLC

Lockard, E N
Atomic weapons against cancer.
(*In* Smithsonian Institution. Annual report, 1951. Washington, 1952. 24 cm. p. 263-272)
"Reprinted ... from the Yale review, vol. 40, no. 1, autumn 1950 ... with minor revisions by Dr. Seymour Wollman."

1. Cancer. 2. Radioisotopes—Therapeutic use. I. Title.

Q11.S66 1951 54-989

NL 0434087 DLC

Lockard, Earl Norton, 1904-
Technique in the novels of Upton Sinclair. 1947.
287 l.

Typewritten.
Thesis--Univ. of Chicago.

1. Sinclair, Upton Beall, 1878-

NL 0434088 ICU

Lockard, F[rancis] M[arion] 1855-
The history of the early settlement of Norton County, Kansas, by Hon. F. M. Lockard. Norton, Ks., Champion [1894?]
294 p. incl. port. 21cm.

1. Norton Co., Kan.—Hist. 2. Norton Co., Kan.—Biog.
3-5830* Cancel

Library of Congress F687.N8L8

NL 0434089 DLC ICU NN

C636.1
L789bL
Lockard, Frank M
Black Kettle, by Frank M. Lockard. Goodland, Kan., R.G. Wolfe [1924?]
40p. ports. 19cm.

1.Black Kettle (Wild horse)
2.Mustang

NL 0434090 CoD OrU InU ICN CtY NN

Lockard, Frank Parker.
Characteristics of a three-dimensional aerodynamic grid.

Thesis - Harvard, 1951

NL 0434091 MH

Lockard, Gene Kline, 1915-
... A comparative study of the college preparation, teaching combinations, and salaries of Kansas high school administrators and teachers (1946) by Gene K. Lockard ... Topeka, Kan., Printed by F. Voiland, jr., state printer, 1946.
38 p., 1 l. tables. 23cm. (Kansas. State teachers college, Emporia. Bulletin of information, v. 26, no. 11, November, 1946. Studies in education number (thirty-first of the series))
"Literature cited": p. 36. "List of studies in education": p. 37-38.

1. Teachers—Kansas.

LB5.K3 no. 31 371.1 47-32582

NL 0434092 DLC WaTC OU PPT TxU ViU

Lockard, John Ready, 1858-
Bee hunting. A book of valuable information for bee hunters—tells how to line bees to trees, etc. By John R. Lockard. Columbus, O., A. R. Harding publishing co. [°1908]
72 p. 17cm.

1. Bees.
8-29350

Library of Congress SF537.L7

NL 0434093 DLC Or OrCS NcC ICJ

Mann
SF
521
Z99
no. 69
Lockard, John Ready, 1858-
Bee hunting, a book of valuable information for bee hunters - tells how to line bees to trees, etc. Columbus, Ohio [c1936]
72 p.

1. Bees.

NL 0434094 NIC OrCS

Lockard, Lorenzo B 1872-
Tuberculosis of the nose and throat, by Lorenzo B. Lockard ... with eighty-five illustrations, sixty-four of them in colors. St. Louis, C. V. Mosby medical book & publishing co., 1909.
384 p. illus., XXXII col. pl., tab. 25½cm.

1. Nose—Tuberculosis. 2. Throat—Tuberculosis.
9-21837

Library of Congress RF91.L7

OClWH-H
NL 0434095 DLC ViU-M ICRL NcD MiU PPC PPJ ICJ

Lockard, Lorenzo B. 1872-
Tuberculosis of the nose and throat, by ... with eighty-five illustrations, sixty-four of them in colors. St. Louis, C.V.Mosby co., 1913.
384 p. illus. XXXII col.pl.

NL 0434096 OU MiDW PPHa

Lockard, Walter Duane, 1921-
see Lockard, Duane, 1921-

619.096
L78a
Lockard, William H Jr., ed.
The Auburn veterinary handbook; an index to diagnosis and treatment, prepared by sixteen authors. [2d ed.] Auburn, Ala., Auburn Veterinarian, 1952.
177p. illus. 23cm.

"Prepared through the cooperation of the Class of '52, School of Veterinary Medicine, Alabama Polytechnic Institute."
References: p. [79]
1. Veterinary medicine. I. Title.

NL 0434098 IU MiEM DNAL LU

---

q744.424
L81d
Lockard, William Kirby.
Drawing as a means to architecture. [Tucson? Ariz., n.d.]
1v.(unpaged) illus.(part col.) 28x34cm.

1. Architectural drawing. I. Title.

NL 0434099 IU TxHU

Locke,
Local option in taxation. Amendment to the constitution of Ohio. Proposed by Mr. Locke. [Columbus, 1895?]
see under title

Locke, capitaine
see Locke, Victor.

Locke, *pseud.*
An exposition of the Virginia resolutions of 1798; in a series of essays, addressed to Thomas Ritchie, by a distinguished citizen of Virginia, under the signature of "Locke." To which are prefixed the resolutions of 1798, and extracts from the Kentucky resolutions, of the same period, by Thos. Jefferson. Philadelphia, Alexander's general printing office, 1833.
24 p. 20½cm.
Manuscript note at end: "Judge A. P. Upshur is supposed to be th author."
1. Nullification. I. Upshur, Abel Parker, 1790-1844, supposed author. II. Title.
A 12-1102
Title from Univ. of Chicago E384.L81 Printed by L. C.

NL 0434102 ICU ViU Vi PHi PPAmP

PS635
.Z9L827
Locke, A. B.
Peter Williams' will...
Boston, Mass., c1934.
1 pam. 12°

NL 0434103 DLC

Locke, A T
"Hell-bent" Harrison; a Western story. New York, Chelsea house [c.1927]

NL 0434104 MH

VOLUME 337

Locke, Alain Le Roy, 1886-1954.
African art: classic style.
p. 271-278, illus.

NL 0434105 DDO

GN320 .L8 Locke, Alain Le Roy, 1886-1954, ed.
...Culture contacts and conflicts; a study in human group relations, edited by Alain Locke and Bernhard J. Stern. Progressive education association research project in intercultural education. Syllabus outline and abstract with illustrative source materials for P.E.A. workshop discussion and criticism. [New York?] 1939.
359 l. 28cm.
Various pagings.
"Tentative draft for consultation purposes only."
Bibliographical foot-notes.

NL 0434106 ICU

Locke, Alain Le Roy, 1886-1954, comp.
A decade of Negro self-expression, compiled by Alain Locke ... with a foreword by Howard W. Odum ... [Charlottesville, Va.] 1928.
20 p. 22½ cm. (On cover: The Trustees of the John F. Slater fund. Occasional papers, no. 26)
"This pamphlet is little more than an annotated list of books written by Negroes since the outbreak of the world war."—p. [5]
Bibliography: p. [9]-20.
1. Negro literature—U. S.—Hist. & crit. 2. Negro literature—U. S.—Bibl. 3. American literature—Negro authors—Hist. & crit. I. Title.
E185.5.J65 no. 26 016.81 PS153.N5L6 30-31351 rev

OCU OCl OO OU
NL 0434107 DLC PPT PU ViU InU NIC Or NBuG DHU MH

JC433 .N3 Locke, Alain Le Roy, 1886-1954.
National council for the social studies.
Diversity within national unity, a symposium by Alain Locke, presiding ... Carey McWilliams ... Otto Klineberg ... Reverend George B. Ford ... [and] Howard E. Wilson ... Washington, D. C., The National council for the social studies, a dept. of the National education association, 1945.

Locke, Alain Le Roy, 1886-1954.
The drama of negro life.
Extract from Theatre arts monthly, Oct. 1926.

NL 0434109 NcU

[Locke, Alain Le Roy] 1886-1954, ed.
Four negro poets ... New York, Simon & Schuster [c1927]
31 p. 21½cm. (The pamphlet poets)
"Edited by Alain Locke."
Poems by Claude McKay, Jean Toomer, Countee Cullen, and Langston Hughes.
Brief biographies: p. 31.
1. Negro poetry (American) I. Title.
Library of Congress PS591.N4L6 27-12851

NcD OCl MB
NL 0434110 DLC MB MiEM MU WaWW TU ViU NcRR IEN ICN

Film PS 98 LOCKE, ALAIN LeROY, 1886-1954. comp.
Four Negro poets. New York, Simon and Schuster [1927]
31 p. (The Pamphlet poets, new series)
Microfilm (neg.) International Microfilm Press, 3M Co., 1970.
Schomburg Collection, New York Public Library.
Contents: Claude McKay, Jean Toomer, Countee Cullen [and] Langston Hughes.
1. American poetry—Negro authors—Collections. I. Title. [Film ods.

NL 0434111 InU

CJ23 020 Locke, Alain LeRoy, 1886-1954.
Harlem: dark weather-vane ...
"Reprinted from Survey graphic, August, 1936."
1. Negroes - New York (City) 2. Harlem, New York (City)

NL 0434112 CtY

Locke, Alain LeRoy, 1886-1954.
... The Negro and his music, by Alain Locke ... Washington, D. C., The Associates in Negro folk education, 1936.
3 p. l., 142 p. 20½cm. (Bronze booklet no. 2)
"Reading references" at end of each chapter; "Record illustrations" at end of most of the chapters.
1. Negro musicians. 2. Negro songs—Hist. & crit. 3. Music—U. S.—Hist. & crit. 4. Jazz music. 5. Phonograph records. I. Title.
Library of Congress E185.5.B85 no. 2 37-10637
——— Copy 2. ML3556.L6N4
Copyright A 104797 (325.260973) 784.756

PPT PWcS DHU NN OrP Or CaBVa CaBVaU
NL 0434113 DLC IaU MB ICU MiU ViU OCl OO OU OClh

Locke, Alain LeRoy, 1886-1954.
... Negro art: past and present, by Alain Locke ... Washington, D. C., Associates in Negro folk education, 1936.
3 p. l., 122 p. 20½cm. (Bronze booklet no. 3)
"Reading references" at end of each chapter.
1. Negro art. 2. Negroes in literature and art. I. Title.
Library of Congress E185.5.B85 no. 3 E185.82.L74 37-7111
[a44g1] (325.260973) 709.73

MB OClh PSt OrU CaBVa
NL 0434114 DLC MB ViU MiU PP PWcS PPT OCU OCl NN DHU

E185.82 L74 1936a Locke, Alain LeRoy, 1886-1954.
Negro art: past and present, by Alain Locke. Washington, D.C., Associates in Negro Folk Education, 1936.
122p. 21cm. (Bronze booklet, no.3)
"Reading references" at end of each chapter.
Photocopy. Ann Arbor, Mich., University Microfilms, 1969. 20cm.
1. Negro artists. 2. Negroes in literature and art. I. Title.

NL 0434115 IaU

N6538 .N5A4 Locke, Alain LeRoy, 1886-1954.
Albany institute of history and art, Albany.
The Negro artist comes of age; a national survey of contemporary American artists. Albany institute of history and art, January 3rd through February 11th, 1945. [Albany, 1945]

Locke, Alain LeRoy, 1886-1954.
The Negro in art; a pictorial record of the Negro artist and of the Negro theme in art; edited and annotated by Alain Locke ... Washington, D. C., Associates in Negro folk education, 1940.
224 p. incl. illus., plates. col. front., col. double pl. 31½ cm.
"Library edition. First printing, December, 1940."
"Selected bibliography": p. 224.
1. Negro art. 2. Negroes in art. I. Title.
N6538.N5L6 709 41-51637

ViU NcD PSt OrP Or WaS WaSp CaBVa
NL 0434117 DLC NIC OO PU-FA PPFr OClh OCU NBB OU

Locke, Alain Le Roy, 1886-1954.
... The Negro in America, by Alain Locke. Chicago, American library association, 1933.
64 p. 18cm. (Reading with a purpose, no. 68)
Title vignette; tail-piece.
"Books recommended in this course": p. 59.
1. Negroes. 2. Negroes—Bibl. I. American library association. II. Title.
Library of Congress E185.6.L77 33-15520
Copyright A 63281 [5-5-10] 325.260973

OrAshS CaBVa
OEac PV PPT PHC NN MB ViU TU OrP Wa Or WaS OrCS OrU
NL 0434118 DLC CSt KMK AAP ViHaI PU MiU OU OCl OO

Locke, Alain LeRoy, 1886-1954.
The Negro in the three Americas. [Washington, Howard University, College of Education, 1944.
7-18 p. 26 cm.
Cover title.
Original English text of the concluding lecture in a series of six: The rôle of the Negro in the American culture, delivered in Haiti, 1943. Reprinted from the Journal of Negro education, Winter no., 1944.
1. Negroes in America. I. Title.

NL 0434119 MB

Locke, Alain Le Roy, 1886-1954, ed.
The new Negro; an interpretation, edited by Alain Locke; book decoration and portraits by Winold Reiss. New York, A. and C. Boni, 1925.
xviii, 446 p. col. front., illus. (incl. music, facsims.) plates (part col.) col. ports. 24½ cm.
Bibliography: p. 415-446.
1. Negroes. 2. Negro literature (American) 3. American literature—Negro authors. I. Title.
E185.82.L75 25-25228

OrPR IdU-SB WaWW Or OrAshS OrSaW
FMU OU NIC CaBVaU WaE WaS WaTC WaT MtU OrP WaSpG
LNHT OCU ViU NcD PSt ICJ NN MB TNF KEmT PPPrHi
NL 0434120 DLC MWA PHC PSC PU MiU OCl OClW OO

Locke, Alain Le Roy, 1886-1954, ed.
The new Negro; an interpretation, edited by Alain Locke; book decoration and portraits by Winold Reiss. New York, A. and C. Boni, 1925.
xviii, 452p. col.front., illus. (incl.music, facsims.) plates (part.col.) col.ports. 22½cm.
Bibliography: p.421-433.

NL 0434122 MWelC MiD PU

LOCKE, Alain, 1886-1954, editor.
The new Negro; an interpretation. Book decoration and portraits by Winold Reiss. New York, A. and C. Boni, 1925 [c'27].
22.5 cm. Colored ports., plates (part.colored) and other illustr.
"Published, December 1925; 2d printing, March, 1927."
Includes music.

NL 0434123 MH

Locke, Alain Le Roy, 1886-1954, ed.
Plays of Negro life; a source-book of native American drama, selected and edited by Alain Locke ... and Montgomery Gregory ... decorations and illustrations by Aaron Douglas. New York and London, Harper & brothers, 1927.
10 p. l., 3-430 p. front., plates. 22½ cm.
"Bibliography of Negro drama": p. 424-430.
1. Negroes in literature and art. 2. American drama (Collections) 3. Negro literature. I. Gregory, Montgomery, 1887- joint ed. II. Title. III. Title: Negro life, Plays of
Library of Congress PS627.N4L6 27-22553

NcD MU ScU PPAmA WaU
NL 0434124 DLC TNF PP PSC PU OCU MiU OCl OO ViU MB

VOLUME 337

LOCKE, Alain Le Roy, 1886-1954.
The problem of classification in the theory of value, or an outline of a genetic sys tem of values. [Thesis, Harvard University, 1918].

Dated Sept.1,1917.
"Bibliography", ff.261-263.
"Summary outline", ff.7 inserted.

NL 0434125 MH

Locke, Alain Le Roy, 1886-1954.
Le role du Nègre dans la culture des Amériques, conférences. Port-au-Prince, Haïti, Impr. de l'État, 1943.
141 p. 21 cm.
"La traduction française du texte anglais original est due à la précieuse collaboration du docteur et de madame Camille Lhérisson."

1. Negroes. 2. Negroes in America. 3. America—Civilization. I. Title.

E185.6.L78 325.26097 48-37282*‡

NL 0434126 DLC MB FU NN

LOCKE, Alain LeRoy, 1886-1954.
Syllabus of an extension course of lectures on race contacts and inter-racial relations; a study in the theory and practice of race. [Washington, D.C., 1916].

Pamphlet.

NL 0434127 MH

Locke, Alain Le Roy, 1886-1954, *ed.*
When peoples meet; a study in race and culture contacts, edited by Alain Locke ... and Bernhard J. Stern ... New York, Committee on workshops, Progressive education association [°1942]
xii, 756 p. 24½ cm. (*Half-title:* Progressive education association publications. Committee on workshops)

1. Acculturation. 2. Minorities. 3. Race problems. I. Stern, Bernhard Joseph, 1894- joint ed. II. Title.

CB5.L6 901 42—326

OrCS Or OrU MB OrSaW IdU
AU WaS WaSp PU PWcS OrP WaT PPTU OrPR InAndC-T
NL 0434128 DLC PP NcC NcD OO ODW OCl OCU OU ViU CU

Locke, Alain Le Roy, 1886-1954, *ed.*
When peoples meet, a study in race and culture contacts. Rev. ed. Edited by Alain Locke and Bernhard J. Stern. New York, Hinds, Hayden & Eldredge [1946]
xii, 825 p. 24 cm.
"An American Education Fellowship book."

1. Acculturation. 2. Minorities. 3. Race problems. I. Stern, Bernhard Joseph, 1894- joint editor. II. Title.

CB5.L6 1946 901 47—3883*

WaS WaSpG OrCS OrSaW
ICU MB OrPS NIC MiU WaWW CaBVaU MtU OrPR OrU Wa WaE
NL 0434129 DLC CaBViP NcC IaU PPTU PU-Penn NcD ICJ

901
L79w
1946r

Locke, Alain Le Roy, 1886-1954, ed.
When peoples meet, a study in race and culture contacts. Rev. ed. Ed. by Alain Locke and Bernhard J. Stern. New York, Hinds, Hayden & Eldredge [1949, c1946]
xii, 825p. 24cm.

Rev. ed., c1946. Reprinted, 1949.
"An American Education Fellowship book."

1. Acculturation. 2. Minorities. 3. Race problems. I. Stern, Bernhard Joseph, 1894- joint editor. II. Title.

NL 0434130 TxU InU N MH-P DLC

E185
.61
.L6

Locke, Alain LeRoy, 1886-1954.
Whither race relations? A critical commentary. [Lancaster, Pa.] Journal of Negro Education, 1944.
398-406 p. 26 cm.
Reprinted from the Journal of Negro education, summer number, 1944.
Also in

1. Negroes. 2. U. S.—Race question. I. Title.

NL 0434131 MB

Locke, Alain LeRoy, 1886-1954.
World view on race and democracy, a study guide in human group relations, compiled and annotated by Alain Locke ... Chicago, American library association, 1943.
3 p. l., 19 numb. l. 28 x 21½ cm.
Reproduced from type-written copy.

1. Race problems—Bibl. 2. International relations—Bibl. 3. Democracy—Bibl. I. American library association. II. Title.

43-8325

Library of Congress Z7164.R12L6
[a44o½] 016.3231

NL 0434132 DLC Or NN TNF OO OCl PSt

Locke, Alexander Stephen.

Locke decorative co., *Brooklyn.*
Makers of windows, Cathedral chapel, Queen of all saints; Locke decorative co. ... [New York, The De Vinne press] 1913.

Locke, Alton, pseud.
see Kingsley, Charles, 1819-1875.

Locke, Amy Audrey, *d.* 1916.
The Hanbury family, by A. Audrey Locke ... London, A. L. Humphreys, 1916.
2 v. col. front., illus. (incl. map) plates, ports., facsims., coats of arms. 39 cm.
Notes on the parish of Hanbury, Worcs., and Biographical notice of the authoress, by the Rev. Canon Colman.
Heraldic illustrations and notes by the Rev. E. E. Dorling.
"The Bosanquet family": Appendix E; "The Annesley family": Appendix El.

1. Hanbury family. 2. Bosanquet family. 3. Annesley family. I. Colman, Frederick Selincourt, ed. II. Dorling, Edward Earle. III. Title.

21-15204

Library of Congress CS439.H282

NL 0434135 DLC MiU NjP

Keats
*EC8
K2262
Z912l

Locke, Amy Audrey, d.1916, comp.
In praise of Winchester; an anthology in prose and verse, compiled by A. Audrey Locke. London, Constable and company ltd., 10 Orange st., Leicester square W.C.1912.
xiv,295p. 23cm. (Constable's anthologies)
Includes a section on "Keats at Winchester": p.69-77.
Original dark blue cloth; top edges gilt.

NL 0434136 MH

Locke, Amy Audrey, d. 1916, comp.
In praise of Winchester. An anthology in prose and verse, compiled by A. Audrey Locke. London, Constable & co. ltd., 1913.
xiv p., 1 l., 3-295 p. 23 cm.

1. Winchester, Eng. I. Title.

A 13-1898

Title from Peabody Inst., Baltimore. Printed by L. C.

NL 0434137 MdBP CtY OClW WaU

Locke, Amy Audrey, d. 1916.

RS68
.A4C7

Cripps, Ernest Charles, *comp.*
Plough Court, the story of a notable pharmacy, 1715-1927. Compiled by Ernest C. Cripps ... London, Allen & Hanburys limited, 1927.

Locke, Amy Audrey, *d.* 1916.
The Seymour family, history and romance, by A. Audrey Locke ... London, Constable and company, ltd., 1911.
viii, 386 p. front., ports. 21½ cm.

1. Seymour family. 2. Somerset, Dukes of. 3. Hertford, Marquises of.

Library of Congress DA28.35.S5L7 11-29854 Revised

NL 0434139 DLC CaBVa KU NcD CtY OClW OCl ViU ICN

DA
28.35
.S5
L8

Locke, Amy Audrey, d.1916.
The Seymour family, by A. Audrey Locke ... Boston and New York, Houghton Mifflin company, 1914.
viii, 386 p. front., ports. 21½ cm.

1. Seymour family. 2. Somerset, Dukes of. 3. Hertford, Marquises of.

PPFr MeB
NL 0434140 MiU MB MWelC OClWHi IU NN T PP PPL MH

Locke, Amy Audrey, d. 1916, comp.
War and misrule (1307-1399) selected by A. Audrey Locke ... London, G. Bell and sons, ltd., 1913.
viii, 120 p. 19 cm. (Bell's English history source books)

1. Gt. Brit.—Hist.—Sources. I. Title.

A 14-391

Title from Enoch Pratt Free Libr. Printed by L. C.

NL 0434141 MdBE CaBVaU IdU OU OCU OClW

Locke, Amy Audrey, *d.* 1916, *comp.*
War and misrule (1307-1399) selected by A. Audrey Locke ... London, G. Bell and sons, ltd., 1920.
viii, 120 p. 19 cm. (*Half-title:* Bell's English history source books. [no. 6])

1. Gt. Brit.—Hist.—14th cent.—Sources. I. Title.

Library of Congress DA26.B4 no. 6 25-21436

NL 0434142 DLC WaWW PHC NjP

Locke, Anna M.
Everyday grammar and composition [by] Anna M. Locke ... Evanston, Ill., New York [etc.] Row, Peterson and company [°1928]
xi, 392, xiii-xvi p. 19 cm.

1. English language — Grammar — 1870- 2. English language — Composition and exercises. I. Title.

28—5592

Library of Congress PE1111.L54

NL 0434143 DLC NcD PWcS DN

Locke, Anna M., joint author.

Laird, Caroline L.
Everyday English [by] Caroline L. Laird ... Hallie D. Walker ... Anna M. Locke ... Evanston, New York, Row, Peterson and company [°1926]

VOLUME 337

LT
PE1111 Locke, Anna M.
1925 Practice exercises in English ͺbyͺ
.L56 Anna M. Locke... Evanston, Ill., Row, Peterson and company ͺ1925?ͺ
cover-title, 143p. 26cm.

1. English language - Composition and exercises. I. Title.

NL 0434145 NNU-W PPT ODW

Locke, Anna M
The stable door: sketches of child life in northern Nigeria. London, Church Missionary Society, n.d.
vi, 74p. illus. 19cm.

NL 0434146 PPPrHi

Locke, Arthur.
Historical sketch of North Londonderry, N. H., and of the Baptist church therein for 100 years, 1799–1899. By Arthur Locke ... Haverhill, Mass., C. C. Morse & son, 1902.
1 p. l., 11 p. 22cm.

1. North Londonderry, N. H.—Baptist church.

Library of Congress F44.N84L8 3—31545

NL 0434147 DLC MWA MB MoS

Locke, Arthur, 1910–
The tigers of Trengganu; with a foreword by Malcolm MacDonald. London, Museum Press ͺ1954ͺ
191 p. illus. 23 cm.

1. Tigers. 2. Hunting—Trengganu. I. Title.

SK305.T5L6 1954 799.2774428 54–30757 ‡

NL 0434148 DLC FMU CU-S TxU MB MiD NcRS NN

Locke, Arthur, 1910–
The tigers of Trengganu. With a foreword by Malcolm MacDonald. Nͺewͺ Yͺorkͺ Scribner ͺ1954ͺ
191 p. illus. 22 cm.

1. Tigers. 2. Hunting—Trengganu. I. Title.

SK305.T5L6 1954a 799.2774428 54–10372 ‡

NL 0434149 DLC CaBVa Or OrP OKentU CSt CU NcC PP PPA PPL PPAN OCl TxU WaE WaS WaT

Locke, Arthur D'Arcy
see his adopted name **Locke, Bobby.**

Locke, Arthur Horton, 1866–
A history and genealogy of Captain John Locke <1627–1696> of Portsmouth and Rye, N. H., and his descendants; also of Nathaniel Locke of Portsmouth, and a short account of the history of the Lockes in England, by Arthur H. Locke ... ͺConcord, N. H., The Rumford press, 1916ͺ
ix, 720 p. pl., ports., map, coat of arms. 24cm.
"Historical account of the Locke family in England": p. 570–586.

1. Locke family (John Locke, d. 1696) 2. Locke family. I. Title.

Library of Congress CS71.L813 1916 16–24581

NL 0434151 DLC MB MWA PHi OClWHi NN

Locke, Arthur Horton, 1866–
Portsmouth and Newcastle, New Hampshire, cemetery inscriptions; abstracts from some two thousand of the oldest tombstones, by Arthur H. Locke ... Portsmouth, Priv. print., 1907.
44 p. front. (port.) 23cm.

1. Epitaphs—Portsmouth, N. H. 2. Epitaphs—Newcastle, N. H.

Library of Congress F44.P8L8 7—28617

NL 0434152 DLC NN

Locke, Arthur Horton, 1866-
Portsmouth and Newcastle, New Hampshire, cemetery inscriptions. Abstracts from some two thousand of the oldest tombstones. — Portsmouth. Privately printed. 1915. 44 pp. Portrait. 23 cm.

K6627 — New Castle, N. H. Cemeteries. — Portsmouth, N. H. Cemeteries. — Epitaphs.

NL 0434153 MB

Locke, Arthur Preston, 1897–1961.
Arsenical derivatives of phenylacetic acid, with a discussion of a theory of diazotization and of syntheses by means of diazo compounds. The potentiometric estimation of arylamines. 1922.
30 l. illus. 29 cm.
Typescript (carbon copy)
Thesis—University of Chicago.
Includes bibliographical references.

1. Organoarsenic compounds. 2. Phenylacetic acid. 3. Diazo reaction. 4. Amines. 5. Electrochemical analysis. I. Title. II. Title: The potentiometric estimation of arylamines.

QD412.A7L58 76-281242

NL 0434154 DLC ICU

Locke, Arthur S
Guidance ͺbyͺ Arthur S. Locke, in collaboration with Charles H. Dodge ͺand othersͺ Princeton, N. J., Van Nostrand ͺ1955ͺ
xvii, 729 p. illus. 24 cm. (Principles of guided missile design, 1)
Includes bibliographies.

1. Guided missiles—Guidance systems. (Series)

UG630.L64 623.4519 55-9903 rev

NL 0434155 DLC MB PBL NcRS NN OCU MB CoU KEmT OKentU MsSM DSI CaBVa CaBVaU ICJ OrLgE Wa WaE WaS NcD PP ScCleU FTaSU ViU DS PPF TxU NcD PSt PPD OU AU

D780.4
P2
Locke, Arthur Ware, 1883-
The background of the romantic movement in French music, by Arthur W. Locke. ͺNew York, Columbia university bookstore, 1941?ͺ
257-271 p. 25½cm.

Caption-title.
On cover: Music readings. Humanities B.
Reprinted from Musical quarterly, vol. 6, April 1920
Bound with Parker, D. C. Reflections on romanticism. ͺ1941?ͺ

NL 0434156 NNC

Locke, Arthur Ware, 1883–
Music and the romantic movement in France. by Arthur Ware Locke. London, K. Paul, Trench, Trubner & co., ltd.; New York, E. P. Dutton & co., 1920.
viii, 184 p. incl. front. (music) 18½cm. (*Half-title:* Library of music and musicians)
Bibliography: p. ͺ182ͺ–184.
Bibliographical foot-notes.

1. Music—France—Hist. & crit. 2. Music—Hist. & crit.—Modern. 3. Romanticism—France. 4. Romanticism in music. I. Title.

21—8621

NL 0434157 DLC CLSU MsSM PSt PU-FA PBm PSC PPT OCl OClND ODW OU OO ViU MB NN NIC OrPR NcD CaBVa OrP Or OrU WaS

Locke, Arthur Ware, 1883–
....Selected list of choruses for women's voices, compiled by Arthur Ware Locke ... Northampton, Mass., Smith college, 1927.
xi, 103 p. 22½ cm. (Smith college monographs. no. 2)

1. Choral music (Women's voices)—Bibl.

A 40—793

Grosvenor Library for Library of Congress ML128 ͺa56d½ͺ

NL 0434158 NBuG DLC NN KEmT

Music
D784
AL79 Locke, Arthur Ware, 1883-
Selected list of choruses for women's voices. 2d ed., rev. and enl. Northampton, Mass., Smith college, 1946.
x, 237 p. (Smith college monographs, no. 2)

1. Choral music - Bibliog.

NL 0434159 NNC WaS WaT PSt PU-FA PP MB PU CU MH MiD

LOCKE, Augustus, 1883-
The geology of El Oro and Tlalpujahua mining districts, Mexico.

Official copy of the thesis presented for a doctor's degree at Harvard University.

NL 0434160 MH

Locke, Augustus, 1883–
Leached outcrops as guides to copper ore, by Augustus Locke. Baltimore, The Williams & Wilkins company, 1926.
vii, 175 p. xxiv pl. on 12 l., maps (part fold.) diagrs. 23½cm.
"Selected bibliography": p. 10-17.

1. Copper ores. I. Title.

Library of Congress TN440.L6 27-2630

NL 0434161 DLC MtBuM WaS CaBVaU IdU WaTC MtU OrP NIC CU TU PPAN PU OCU OU MiU OO MiHM

Locke, Augustus, 1883- joint author.

Billingsley, Paul, 1887–
Structure of ore districts in the continental framework, by Paul Billingsley and Augustus Locke. New York, N. Y., Pub. by the American institute of mining and metallurgical engineers through the Charles F. Rand foundation fund, 1939.

Locke, Augustus, 1883- joint author.

Billingsley, Paul Raymond, 1887–
... Tectonic position of ore districts in the Rocky mountain region, by Paul Billingsley and Augustus Locke ... New York, American institute of mining and metallurgical engineers, inc., ©1933.

Locke, Augustus W. d. 1893, and others.
[Collection of photographs taken during an investigation into the subject of the gradual abolition of the crossing of highways by railroads at grade. By Augustus W. Locke, William O. Webber and George A. Kimball, engineers.]
[Boston. 1889.] 91 silver prints, pasted into an album. Plans. 4°, obl.
The report of this board, in which some of these photographs are reproduced, is on shelf-number *8011.80.

G329—Massachusetts. R.Rs.— Webber, William O., jt. auth.— Kimball, George Albert, jt. auth. 1850-. — Grade crossings. — Photographs. Colls.

NL 0434164 MB

VOLUME 337

Locke, Augustus W d. 1893.
... Report of an investigation into the subject of the gradual abolition of the crossing of highways by railroads at grade. By Augustus W. Locke, William O. Webber, George A. Kimball ... January 31, 1889. Boston, Wright & Potter printing co., state printers, 1889.
76 p. illus., plates (1 fold.) plans (part fold.) 23cm. ([Massachusetts. General court] House. [Doc.] no. 75)
1. Railroads—Grade crossings. 2. Railroads—Massachusetts. I. Webber, William O., joint author. II. Kimball, George Albert, 1850-1912, joint author.
A 19-54
Title from Bureau of Railway Economics. Printed by L. C.
NL 0434165 DBRE CtY MiU ICJ MB

Locke, B W
Sports car bodywork, construction in timber, metal & plastics. London, Craftsman Publications [1954]
71 p. illus., 6 fold sheets.
In portfolio.
NL 0434166 MiD WaS

Locke, Belle Marshall.
Breezy Point; a comedy in three acts for female characters only, by Belle Marshall Locke ... Boston, W. H. Baker & co., 1899.
50 p. 19cm. (*On cover:* Baker's edition of plays)
I. Title.
Library of Congress PS635.Z9L83 12-36283
NL 0434167 DLC Or NN NcD PU RPB

LOCKE, BELLE MARSHALL.
The great catastrophe: a comedy in two acts. Penn c1895.
30 p.
NL 0434168 Or

Locke, Belle Marshall.
The great catastrophe, a comedy in two acts. By Nellie M. Locke [pseud.] Philadelphia, The Penn publishing company, 1913.
30p. 18cm.
On cover: Belle Marshall Locke
NL 0434169 RPB OCl

Locke, Belle Marshall.
The great catastrophe; a comedy in two acts, by Nellie (sic) M. Locke... Philadelphia: Penn Pub. Co., 1915. 30 p. 12°.
1. Drama (American). 2. Title.
N. Y. P. L. November 10, 1916.
NL 0434170 NN PU

Locke, Belle Marshall.
A heartrending affair; a monologue. by Nelle [sic] M. Locke. Philadelphia: Penn Pub. Co., 1911. 1 p.l., 129-132 p. 12°.
1. Monologues (American). 2. Title.
November 10, 1916.
NL 0434171 NN RPB PU

R.B.R. Locke, Belle Marshall
The Hiartville Shakespeare Club; a farce in one act. Philadelphia, Penn Pub. Co., 1920 [c1896]
149-159 p. 18 cm.
Running title: One hundred choice selections. Number thirty-five.
NL 0434172 NcD InU RPB MiD

Locke, Belle Marshall.
The Hiartville Shakespeare club; a farce in one act, by Belle Marshall Locke... Philadelphia: Penn Pub. Co., 1913. 1 p.l., 149-159 p. 12°.
Forms one of: One hundred choice selections. no. 35.
1. Drama (American). 2. Title.
November 20, 1916
NL 0434173 NN PU

Locke, Belle Marshall.
Humorous monologues and dramatic scenes
see under title

---

812 Locke, Belle Marshall.
L79m Marie's secret, a duologue in one scene
Boston, W. H. Baker & co.[c1894]
8p. (On cover: Baker's edition of plays)
NL 0434175 IU DLC CtY CLSU RPB PU NN

---

812 Locke, Belle Marshall.
L79mi Miss Fearless and co.; a comedy in three acts for female characters only ... Boston, W. H. Baker & co.[c1905]
62p. (On cover: Baker's edition of plays)
NL 0434176 IU RPB Or NN PU

---

812 Locke, Belle Marshall.
L79mr Mr. Easyman's niece, a comedy in four acts ... Boston, W. H. Baker & co.[c1908]
59p. (On cover: Baker's edition of plays)
NL 0434177 IU RPB PU

Locke, Belle Marshall.
Original monologues and sketches.
= Boston. Baker & Co. 1903. 83 pp. 12°.
Contents. — A man, a maid, and a dress-suit case. — How Miss Ceely took the cake. — American beauties. — Polly's surprise party. — Uncle Ned's ring. — His best girl. — Mrs. Follansbee's tramp.
F3453 — Monologues. — Amateur theatricals. — T.r. (7).
NL 0434178 MB MH NN DLC PN

Locke, Belle Marshall.
A victim of woman's rights. A monologue. By Nellie M. Locke ... Clyde, O., Ames' publishing co. [1896]
4 p. 19½cm. (*On cover:* Ames' series of standard and minor drama, no. 371)
1. Woman—Rights of women. I. Title.
Library of Congress JF855.L6 CA 25-1169 Unrev'd
NL 0434179 DLC IU NN CLSU NcD RPB CtY

LD3907 .E3 1941 .L6 Locke, Bernard, 1913-
Intelligence, education, personality, and occupational status as factors in a penal population... New York, 1941.
v,174 typewritten leaves. tables (1 fold.) diagrs. 29cm.
Thesis (Ph.D.) - New York university, School of education, 1941.
Bibliography: p.[170]-174.
NL 0434180 NNU-W

Locke, Bessie.
A kindergarten training for every child.
(*In* National education association of the United States. Addresses and proceedings, 1917. p. 804-807)
1. Kindergarten. I. Title.
E 18-739
Library, U. S. Bur. of Education
NL 0434181 DHEW OU OO

Locke, Bessie.
... Manufacturers indorse the kindergarten. By Bessie Locke ... [Washington, Govt. print. off., 1919]
4 p. 23cm. ([U. S.] Bureau of education. Kindergarten education circular, 1919, no. 4)
Caption title.
At head of title: Department of the interior ...
1. Kindergartens—U. S. I. Title.
E 19-611
Library, U. S. Bur. of Education LB1205.U6A3
NL 0434182 DHEW MiU OU OO

Locke, Bobby.
Bobby Locke on golf. London, Country life [1953]
196 p. illus. 28 cm.
1. Golf. I. Title.
Real name: Arthur D'Arcy Locke
GV965.L6 1953 796.352 54-22749
NL 0434183 DLC PSt

Locke, Bobby.
Bobby Locke on golf. New York, Simon and Schuster. 1954.
196 p. illus. 24 cm.
1. Golf.
Real name: Arthur D'Arcy Locke.
GV965.L6 796.352 54-5807 ‡
OU MB NN OCl PP
NL 0434184 DLC Or CaBVa OrP WaE WaS WaT FU OOxM

[Locke, Bradford H]
Reports, letters, and endorsements of the Bellevue tunnel, Colorado. New York [Cadmus press] 1883.
30 p. 23½cm.
1. Bellevue tunnel, Col. I. Title.
Library of Congress TN423.C7L8 6-18190†
NL 0434185 DLC

[Locke, C A]
[Appeal for the organization of state and local road improvement societies] [Washington, Govt. print. off., 1896]
3 p. 23cm. (U. S. Dept. of agriculture. Office of road inquiry. Circular no. 22)
Signed: C. A. Locke.
1. Roads—Societies. I. Title.
Agr 9-2454
Library, U. S. Dept. of Agriculture 1R53C no. 22
NL 0434186 DNAL CU

VOLUME 337

Locke, Calvin Stoughton, 1829–
Other men have labored: a sermon preached December 7th, 1879, by Rev. Calvin S. Locke ... Pub. by request. Dedham, Mass., Printed by H. H. McQuillen, 1880.
29 p. 23cm.
"Notice of Rev. John White and Mrs. Delia J. H. White. By Rev C. C. Sewall": p. [25]–29.

1. Dedham, Mass. First church. 2. White, John, 1787–1852. I. Sewall, Charles Chauncy, 1802–1886. II. Title.

Library of Congress F74.D3L8 7—27751

NL 0434187 DLC MH-AH MWA Nb

Locke, Calvin Stoughton, 1829–
The patriotic volunteer: a sermon delivered, October 19, 1862, at the funeral of George F. Whiting, who died at Middletown, Maryland, Oct. 5, from a wound received at the battle of South mountain, Sept. 14, 1862. By Calvin S. Locke ... Printed for the family. Boston, Press of J. Wilson and son 1862.
12 p. 19cm.
Whiting served in the 35th Mass. regiment.
1. Whiting, George Francis, 1835–1862. 2. Massachusetts infantry. 35th regt., 1862–1865.

Library of Congress E513.5.35thL 11—31019

NL 0434188 DLC OClWHi

Locke, Calvin Stoughton, 1829–
The powers of the world to come. A Sermon delivered ... May 30, 1858 at the funeral of Mrs. Olive Morse Guild, wife of Deacon Reuben Guild ... Providence, 1858.
8 p. 19 cm.
In Guild, R.A. Pamphlet writings, v. 1.

NL 0434189 RPB ICN MWA MH

Locke, Calvin Stoughton, 1829–
Sermon at the funeral of Newell Fisher, November, 1862. Boston, 1863.
12 p. nar. D.

NL 0434190 RPB

Locke (Carolus Salomo). *De complicationibus dysenteriæ febrilibus. 26 pp. sm. 4°. *Wittenbergæ, lit. Tzschiedrichii,* [1796].

NL 0434191 DNLM

Locke, Carolyn Howe, 1868– *comp.*
Classified commercial correspondence for dictation to shorthand students. Comp. and ed. by Carolyn H. Locke ... [Philadelphia] The Compiler [1903]
144 p., 1 l. 18cm.

1. Shorthand—Exercises for dictation. 2. Commercial correspondence.

Library of Congress Z56.L815 1903 4—1586

NL 0434192 DLC

Locke, Carolyn Howe, 1868– *comp.*
Commercial correspondence for dictation to shorthand students. Comp. and ed. by Carolyn H. Locke ... [Philadelphia] The compiler [1899]
119 p. 17½cm.

1. Shorthand—Exercises for dictation. 2. Commercial correspondence.

Library of Congress Z56.L817 0-1725 Revised

NL 0434193 DLC NN

Locke, Charles E
Lakmé...
see (for libretto) Gondinet, Pierre Edmond Julien, 1828–1888.

Locke, Charles E 1874–
... Mining engineering, by Charles E. Locke ... Boston, Mass., Bellman publishing company, inc. [©1941]
cover-title, 28 p. 23cm. (Vocational and professional monographs. No. 23)
Reproduced from type-written copy.
Bibliography: p. [23]–28.

1. Mining engineering. 2. Mining engineers. 3. Mining schools and education—U. S.

Library of Congress HF5381.V53 no. 23 42-2510
(371.425082) 622.069

NL 0434195 DLC MtBuM OU NNC

Locke, Charles E 1874–
... Mining engineering, by Charles E. Locke ... Boston, Mass., Bellman publishing company, inc. [1945]
cover-title, 23 p. 23cm. (Vocational and professional monographs. No. 23)
Bibliography: p. [19]–23.

1. Mining engineering.

Library of Congress HF5381.V53 no. 23 46–12364
(371.425082) 622.069

NL 0434196 DLC MoU ViU MB

Locke, Charles E., 1874– joint author.
FOR OTHER EDITIONS SEE MAIN ENTRY
Richards, Robert Hallowell, 1844–
Textbook of ore dressing, by Robert H. Richards ... and Charles E. Locke ... assisted by Reinhardt Schuhmann, jr. ... 3d ed., completely rev. and rewritten. New York and London, McGraw-Hill book company, inc., 1940.

Locke, Charles Edward, *jr.*
.... Les tumeurs du cerveau, par docteur Charles-Edward Locke, jr. .... Paris, L. Arnette, 1922.
140, [4] p. 25½cm.
At head of title: Travail fait dans le service de la clinique du professeur A. Depage et le laboratoire du professeur A. Dustin.
Thèse—Univ. de Bruxelles.
"Bibliographie," p. [131]–138.

NL 0434198 ICJ

Locke, Charles Edward, *bp.*, 1858–1940.
Daybreak everywhere, by Charles Edward Locke ... New York, Cincinnati, The Methodist book concern [©1919]
217 p. 19½ cm.

I. Title.
PS3523.O23D3 1919 19—15901

NL 0434199 DLC MiU IEG OO

Locke, Charles Edward, 1858–1940.
Eddyism. Is it Christian? Is it scientific? How long will it last? By Charles Edward Locke ... Los Angeles, Grafton publishing company [©1911]
64 p. 18cm. $0.10
p. 61–64, testimonials.

Library of Congress 11-1322

NL 0434200 DLC

Locke, Charles Edward, 1858–1940.
The eternal masculine, by Charles Edward Locke. New York, Cincinnati, The Methodist book concern [©1924]
294 p. 19½cm.

1. Character. 2. Men. I. Title.

Library of Congress PS3523.O23E8 1924 24-19831

NL 0434201 DLC OrU

Locke, Charles Edward, 1858–1940.
The first Christmas story, "Let us go even unto Bethlehem" [by] Charles Edward Locke ... New York, Dodge publishing company [©1915]
40 p. 18cm. $0.50

I. Title.

Library of Congress 16-4430

NL 0434202 DLC

Locke, Charles Edward, 1858–1940.
Freedom's next war for humanity, by Charles Edward Locke ... Cincinnati, Jennings & Pye; New York, Eaton & Mains [1901]
299, [1] p. 20cm.
"The author believes that the battles will be fought in the field of social disorder."—Foreword, p. 11.

1. Sociology, Christian. 2. U. S.—Pol. & govt. I. Title.

Library of Congress HN64.L83 1-17576

NL 0434203 DLC WaTC OrU NcD OCl

Locke, Charles Edward, *bp.* 1858–1940.
Is the Negro making good? or, Have fifty years of history vindicated the wisdom of Abraham Lincoln in issuing the Emancipation proclamation? By Charles Edward Locke ... Cincinnati, Printed for the author by the Methodist book concern [©1913]
62 p. 18½cm.

1. Negroes. I. Title.

Library of Congress E185.6.L81 13—10968

NL 0434204 DLC ICJ NN

Locke, Charles Edward, 1858–1940.
A man's reach; or, Some character ideals ... by Charles Edward Locke. New York, Eaton & Mains; Cincinnati, Jennings & Graham [©1914]
278 p. 19½cm. $1.00

1. Conduct of life. I. Title.

Library of Congress BJ1581.L55 14-10036

NL 0434205 DLC CLSU OCl NN ICJ

170 Locke, Charles Edward, 1858–1940.
L79m A man's reach; or, Some character ideals New York [etc.] The Methodist book concern [c1914]
278p.

"First edition printed April, 1914. Reprinted August, 1914."

1. Conduct of life. I. Title.

NL 0434206 IU ICRL

VOLUME 337

Locke, Charles Edward, 1858-1940.
... A nineteenth-century crusader, by Charles Edward Locke ... Cincinnati, Jennings & Pye; New York, Eaton & Mains [1902]
37, [1] p. front. (port.) 19cm. (The hero series)
"These two essays, with twenty others of similar character, are published in book form under the title of 'Freedom's next war for humanity, by Charles Edward Locke'."
CONTENTS.—A nineteenth-century crusader [William Ewart Gladstone]—The last Anglo-Saxon invasion.
1. Gladstone, William Ewart, 1809-1898. 2. Anglo-Saxon race. I. Title.
Library of Congress DA563.8.L6 2—13386
NL 0434207 DLC OrU NcD ODW

Locke, Charles Edward, bp., 1858-1940.
Pray; a manual on prayer, by Charles Edward Locke ... New York, Cincinnati [etc.] The Methodist book concern [c1929]
5 p. l., 13-186 p. 17½cm.
1. Prayer. I. Title.
Library of Congress BV210.L6 29-15066
NL 0434208 DLC

Locke, Charles Edward, 1858-1940.
... The typical American, by Charles Edward Locke ... Cincinnati, Jennings & Pye; New York, Eaton & Mains [1902]
28 p., 1 l. front. 19cm. (The hero series [v. 2])
"These two essays, with twenty others, are published in book form under the title of Freedom's next war for humanity, by Charles Edward Locke."
CONTENTS.—The typical American [George Washington]—America's new mission and opportunity.
Subject entries: Washington, George, pres. U. S., 1732-1799. 2-13642
NL 0434209 DLC

Locke, Charles Edward, 1858-1940.
White slavery in Los Angeles ... by Charles Edward Locke ... [Los Angeles, Times mirror co., printer, c1913]
68 p. 18½cm. $0.25
"Published by request."
1. Prostitution—Los Angeles. I. Title.
Library of Congress HQ146.L7L7 13-15348
NL 0434210 DLC NN

Locke, Charles Henry, 1804-1841.
Ps and Qs
see under title

Locke, Charles J. Poems. 4 pp. (Kettell, S., Specimens of Am. poetry, v. 3, p. 319.)
NL 0434212 MdBP

Locke, Charles O
The last princess, a novel of the Incas. [1st ed.] New York, Norton [c1954]
316 p. 22 cm.
I. Title.
PZ4.L814Las 54-6716 ‡
NL 0434213 DLC WaE WaS MoU OOxM NN CU PP TxU OCl ViU WaT CaBVa

Locke, Charles O
A shadow of our own. New York, Scribner, 1951.
326 p. 22 cm.
I. Title.
PZ4.L814Sh 51-1293
NL 0434214 DLC CaBVa OrP WaE WaS

PS3048 .A1 1946 a
Locke, Charles Wheeler, 1899- illus.
Thoreau, Henry David, 1817-1862.
Walden, by Henry David Thoreau, with an introduction by Brooks Atkinson, illustrated by Charles Locke ... New York [Random house, inc., 1946]

Locke, Charlton.
The psychology of speaking to an audience. 1920.
(O.W.U. Thesis.)
NL 0434216 ODW

Locke, Clinton, 1829-1904.
... The age of the great western schism, by Clinton Locke, D. D. New York, The Christian literature co., 1896.
x, 314 p. 20cm. (Ten epochs of church history. [vol. VIII])
1. Schism, The great western, 1378-1417. I. Title.
[Full name: James Dewitt Clinton Locke]
Library of Congress BR141.T4 vol. VIII 28-28080
NL 0434217 DLC InAndC-T KyU KyLxT MU PHC PPL OClW WaU PPPD ViU OCl OO NjNbS ICU MH NRCR WaT WaTC MtU

270.5 L79a 1897
Locke, Clinton, 1829-1904.
... The age of the great western schism, by Clinton Locke, D.D. Edinburgh, T. & T. Clark, 1897.
x, 314p. 21cm. (Eras of the Christian church. [vol. II])
1. Schism, The great western, 1378-1417. I. Title. II. Series.
NL 0434218 TxU NcD Nh MB IU PPT

Locke, Clinton, 1829-1904.
The age of the Great Western Schism. New York, Scribner, 1900 [c1896]
x, 314 p. 20cm. (Ten epochs of church history, v. 8)
1. Schism, The Great Western, 1378-1417. I. Title. II. Series.
NL 0434219 NIC PU

BR141 .T4
Locke, Clinton, 1829-1904.
The age of the Great Western schism. New York, Scribner, 1901 [c1896]
314p. (Ten epochs of church history, v.8)
1. Schism, The Great Western, 1378-1417. I. Title.
NL 0434220 NcU NcGU

Locke, Clinton, 1829-1904.
The defender of the faith. A sermon preached in the Cathedral church of SS. Peter and Paul, Chicago, before the diocesan convention of Illinois, Sept. 15, 1874, in memory of Henry John Whitehouse, second bishop of Illinois. Together with resolutions adopted by the standing committee of the Thirty-seventh annual convention of the diocese of Illinois, and by the standing committee of the diocese of Wisconsin. Also notes of the bishop's last year's work extracted from his private diary, and a list of statistics compiled from the same source. [Chicago] Published by order of the convention [1874?]
45 p.
1. Whitehouse, Henry John, bp., 1803-1874.
NL 0434222 NNC IEG MWA CtY NN MH ICN PHi

Locke, Clinton, 1829-1904.
The example of the president, a memorial sermon. Preached by Rev. Clinton Locke, D. D., rector of Grace church, Chicago, Sunday, September 25th, 1881. Chicago, Cushing, Thomas & Co., printers [1881]
10 p. 26 cm.
NL 0434223 OHi NN

Locke, Clinton, 1829-1904.
Five minute talks, by the Rev. Clinton Locke... Milwaukee, Wis.: The Young Churchman Co.[, cop. 1896.] 252 p. front. (port.) 12°.
29590A. 1. Christianity—Essays and misc. June 8, 1927
NL 0434224 NN NBuU CtY MA OO IMunS DLC

Locke, Clinton, 1829-1904.
Five minute talks. 2d series. By Clinton Locke ... with introduction by the Rev. Morgan Dix ... and biographical sketch by the Rt. Rev. William Edward McLaren ... Milwaukee, The Young churchman co., 1904.
262 p. front. (port.) 19½cm.
"The several 'Talks' are reprinted from the pages of the Living church."
1. Protestant Episcopal church in the U. S. A.—Addresses, essays, lectures. I. Title.
[Full name: James Dewitt Clinton Locke]
BX5937.L6F52 4-13641
NL 0434225 DLC

Locke, Clinton W., pseud.
... Who closed the door; or, Perry Pierce and the old storehouse mystery, by Clinton W. Locke ... illustrated by Russell H. Tandy. Philadelphia, Henry Altemus company [c1931]
iv, 5-212 p. front., plates. 19½cm. (His Perry Pierce mystery stories)
I. Title.
Library of Congress PZ7.L79Pe no. 1 31-15550 Revised 2
NL 0434226 DLC PNt

Locke, Clinton W., pseud.
... Who hid the key; or, Perry Pierce tracing counterfeit money, by Clinton W. Locke ... illustrated by Russell H. Tandy. Philadelphia, Henry Altemus company [c1932]
iv, 5-212 p. front., plates. 19½cm. (His Perry Pierce mystery stories)
I. Title.
Library of Congress PZ7.L79Pe no. 3 32-21439 Revised 2
NL 0434227 DLC MH

VOLUME 337

Locke, Clinton W., *pseud.*
... Who opened the safe; or, Perry Pierce and the secret cipher mystery, by Clinton W. Locke ... illustrated by Russell H. Tandy. Philadelphia, Henry Altemus company [c1931]
iv, 5-216 p. front., plates. 19½cm. (*His* Perry Pierce mystery stories)
I. Title.
31-18069 Revised 2
Library of Congress PZ7.L79Pe no. 2

NL 0434228 DLC MH

Locke, Clinton W *pseud.*
Who took the papers; or, Gathering the printed clues, by Clinton W. Locke; illustrated by C. C. Stevens. Chicago, New York, M. A. Donohue & company [c1934]
2 p. l., 7-222 p. front., plates. 21cm. (*His* Perry Pierce mystery stories for boys. no. 4)
I. Title.
39-10515
Library of Congress PZ7.L79Pe

NL 0434229 DLC

Locke, Cyril L C
A primer of English parsing and analysis, by Cyril L. C. Locke ... London, Rivingtons, 1883.
viii, 96 p. 17 cm.
1. English language - Grammar - 1870-1930.

NL 0434230 NNC

Locke, Cyril L.C.
A primer of English parsing and analysis. New York, Longmans Green, 1898.
viii-96 p.

NL 0434231 WaSpG

Locke, David Millard, 1929–
Aromatization studies on six- and seven-membered heterocyclic rings. Unsaturated amines: diagnosis of double bond position by ultraviolet absorption spectra. Ann Arbor, University Microfilms [1955]
([University Microfilms, Ann Arbor, Mich.] Publication no. 10,508)
Microfilm copy of typescript. Positive.
Collation of the original: viii, 84 l.
Thesis—University of Illinois.
Abstracted in Dissertation abstracts, v. 15 (1955) no. 1, p. 40-41.
Vita.
Bibliography: leaves 66-69, 83-84.
1. Amines. 2. Absorption spectra. 3. Spectrum, Ultra-violet. I. Title.
Microfilm AC-1 no. 10,508 Mic A 55-63
Illinois. Univ. Library for Library of Congress †

NL 0434232 IU DLC

Cd14 269 Locke, David Ross, 1833-1888
Andy's trip to the West, together with a life of its hero, by Petroleum V. Nasby [pseud.] Hinsdale, N.H., Hunter & Co. [c1866]
38p. illus.

NL 0434233 CtY MH

AC85 L7918 866a RARE BOOK COLLECTION [Locke, David Ross], 1833-1888.
Andy's Trip to the West. Together with a Life of its Hero by Petroleum V. Nashby [pseud.] ...
New York: The American News Company, 1866.
p.1-12 plates., [13]-38, [8]p., illus. 18.4cm.
Cf. Sabin - 41721.
Not in Wright.

NL 0434234 PU OClWHi

[**Locke, David Ross**] 1833-1888.
Andy's trip to the West, together with a life of its hero. By Petroleum V. Nasby [*pseud.*] ... New York, J. C. Haney & co., c1866.
2 p. l., [15]-38 p. illus., 6 pl. 19cm.
Title vignette; plates printed on both sides.
1. Johnson, Andrew, pres. U. S., 1808-1875. I. Title.
18-423
Library of Congress E667.L78

NL 0434235 DLC RPB ViU NjP WU PHi PPL OFH MH

Locke, David Ross, 1833-1888.
Beer and the body
see under title

Locke, David Ross, 1833-1888.
The demagogue, a political novel [by] David Ross Locke ("Nasby") ... Boston, Lee and Shepard; New York, C. T. Dillingham, 1891.
iv, 465 p. 19½cm.
I. Title.
7-15162
Library of Congress PZ3.L791D

NL 0434237 DLC MB OFH DCU PPL MtBC CU CoU ViU PPL OFH OCU MB

[**Locke, David Ross**] 1833-1888.
The Democratic John Bunyan, being eleven dreams by Rev. Petroleum V. Nasby [*pseud.*] Showing what is very likely to happen in the event of the election of Hancock and English. Toledo, O., Toledo blade company, 1880.
24 p. illus. 19½cm.
1. Campaign literature, 1880—Republican. 2. U. S.—Pol. & govt.—1881-1885. I. Title.
12-7564
Library of Congress PN6161.L6

NL 0434238 DLC CU-B IU PU

FILM 4274 PR v.3 reel L23 [**Locke, David Ross**] 1833-1888.
The Democratic John Bunyan, being eleven dreams by Rev. Petroleum V. Nasby [*pseud.*] Showing what is very likely to happen in the event of the election of Hancock and English. Toledo, O., Toledo blade company, 1880.
24 p. illus. 19½cm.
(Wright American Fiction. v. III, 1876-1900, no. 3373, Research Publications, Inc. Microfilm, Reel L-23)

NL 0434239 CU

Locke, David Ross, 1833-1888.
The diary of an office seeker; being a record of the experience of Thomas Jefferson Watkins, (who wanted an office, and labored for one, but didn't get it,) in the field of politics. Ed. by D. R. Locke, <Petroleum V. Nasby.> Toledo, O., Blade company, 1881
viii, 9-31 p. 23cm.
1. U. S.—Pol. & govt.—1881-1885. 2. U. S.—Officials and employees—Appointments, qualifications, tenure, etc. I. Title.
12-7563
Library of Congress PN6161.L62

NL 0434240 DLC

PN 6161 L623 Locke, David Ross, 1833-1888.
Divers views, opinions, and prophecies of yoors trooly Petroleum V. Nasby [pseud.] with humorous designs by thee Jones. Cincinnati, R. W. Carroll, 1866.
424p. illus. 20cm.
1. U. S. - Pol. & govt. - Civil war. I. Title.

NL 0434241 MU ViU

[**Locke, David Ross**] 1833-1888.
... Divers views, opinions, and prophecies of yoors trooly Petroleum V Nasby [*pseud.* ... with humorous designs by thee Jones. 6th ed. Cincinnati, R. W. Carroll & co., 1866.
xiv p., 1 l., [25]-424 p. incl. front., illus., plates. 20cm.
Added t.-p., illustrated.
1. U. S.—Pol. & govt.—Civil war. I. Title.
12—7685
Library of Congress PN6161.L623

NL 0434242 DLC OrU CU-B WHi UU PU NcD TU ODW OCl OFH MiU OU

FILM 4274 PR v.2 reel L10 [Locke, David Ross] 1833-1888.
Divers views, opinions, and prophecies of yoors trooly Petroleum V Nasby [pseud.] With humorous designs by Thee Jones. Cincinnati, R. W. Carroll, 1866.
424 p. illus. (Wright American fiction, v.II, 1851-1875, no. 1566, Research Publications Microfilm, Reel L-10)
At head of title: Nasby.
1. U. S. - Pol. & govt. - Civil War - Fiction. I.x.Nasby, Petroleum V.[pseud.] II.Title.

NL 0434243 CU

[**Locke, David Ross**] 1833-1888.
... Divers views, opinions, and prophecies of yoors trooly Petroleum V Nasby [*pseud.*] ... with humorous designs by thee Jones. 6th ed. Cincinnati, R. W. Carroll & co., 1867.
xiv, [25]-424 p. incl. front., illus., plates. 19cm.
Added t.-p., illustrated.

NL 0434244 ViU NjP MWelC PPL PHatU TxU DLC NcU

Locke, David Ross, 1833-1888.
Eastern fruit on western dishes
see his The morals of Abou Ben Adhem.

[**Locke, David Ross**] 1833-1888.
Ekkoes from Kentucky. By Petroleum V. Nasby [*pseud.*] ... Bein a perfect record uv the ups, downs, and experiences uv the Dimocrisy, doorin the eventful year 1867, ez seen by a naturalized Kentuckian. Illustrated by Thomas Nast. Boston, Lee and Shepard, 1867.
324 p. front., plates. 19½ cm.

NL 0434246 ViHaI

[**Locke, David Ross**] 1833-1888.
Ekkoes from Kentucky. By Petroleum V. Nasby [*pseud.*] ... Bein a perfect record uv the ups, downs, and experiences uv the Dimocrisy, doorin the eventful year 1867, ez seen by a naturalized Kentuckian. Illustrated by Thomas Nast. Boston, Lee and Shepard, 1868.
324 p. front., plates. 19½cm.
1. Democratic party. 2. U. S.—Pol. & govt.—1865-1869. I. Nast, Thomas, 1840-1902, illus. II. Title.
12—7561
Library of Congress PN6161.L63

NL 0434247 DLC MdBP KyLx ViU CaOTP CU-B CoU NcD OCl OFH OU MiU OOxM MB CSmH MWA IEN KyHi TU WaS WaTC NIC TxU

FILM 4274 PR v.2 reel L10 [Locke, David Ross] 1833-1888.
Ekkoes from Kentucky. By Petroleum V. Nasby [pseud.]... Bein a perfect record uv the ups, downs, and experiences uv the dimocrisy, doorin the eventful year 1867, ez seen by a naturalized Kentuckian. Illustrated by Thomas Nast. Boston, Lee and Shepard, 1868.
324 p. illus. (Wright American fiction, v.II, 1851-1875, no. 1568, Research Publications Microfilm, Reel L-10)
1. Democratic Party. 2. U. S. - Pol. & govt. - Fiction. I. Nast, Thomas, 1840-1902, illus. II. Title.

NL 0434249 CU KEmT

VOLUME 337

PN6157 Locke, David Ross, 1833-1888.
K6L814e Ekkoes from Kentucky. By Petroleum V. Nasby [pseud.]
1873 Bein a perfect record uv the ups, downs, and experiences uv the
x Dimocrisy, doorin the eventful year 1867, ez seen by a naturalized Kentuckian. Illustrated by Thomas Nast. Boston, Lee and Shepard, 1873.
324 p. front., plates. 20cm. [Koundakjian collection]

1. Democratic Party. 2. U.S. - Politics and government - 1865-1869. I. Nast, Thomas, 1840-1902, illus. II. Title. (Series)

NL 0434250 CU-B

[LOCKE, David Ross, 1833-1888.]
Ekkoes from Kentucky. By Petroleum V. Nasby, [pseud.] Boston, Lee and Shepard, 1888.

Illustr.

NL 0434251 MH MdBP

---

f817 Locke, David Ross, 1833-1888.
L79f Finance and communism. The broadside extra ⌊by⌋ Petroleum V. Nasby ⌊pseud. Toledo, Ohio? Toledo Blade? 1878⌋
sheet. 61x48cm.

1. Campaign literature, 1878--Republican. I. Title.

NL 0434252 IU CtY Nh ViU

[LOCKE, David Loss, 1833-1888.]
Hannah Jane. By Petroleum V. Nasby [pseud.].

Cut from Harper's Monthly Magazine, New York, Oct. 1871, pp. 709-713.
Poem.

NL 0434253 MH

Locke, David Ross, 1833-1888.
PS2248 Hannah Jane, by David Ross Locke
L8H3 (Petroleum V. Nasby) Boston, Lee and
1881 Shepard ⌊c1881⌋
1 v. (unpaged) illus. 21cm.
Poem.
Decorative ivory boards.

NL 0434254 CSt MdBP RPB ViU

Locke, David Ross, 1833-1888.
Hannah Jane, ... Boston, Lee and Shepard; N.Y., C.T. Dillingham [c1881]
[19] p. front., illus., 5 pl. 21cm.

Poem.

NL 0434255 OO

811.4 Locke, David Ross, 1833-1888.
L814h Hannah Jane, by David Ross Locke (Petroleum V. Nasby) Boston, Lee and Shepard, 1882.
19p. illus. 21cm.

Poem.

NL 0434256 IEN ViU OCIW

Locke, David Ross, 1833-1888.
Hannah Jane, by David Ross Locke (Petroleum V. Nasby) ... Boston, Lee and Shepard; New York, C. T. Dillingham, 1882.
⌊19⌋ p. front., illus., 5 pl. 21cm.
Poem.

I. Title.

12—36286

Library of Congress PS2249.L8H3 1882

NL 0434257 DLC IaU CU-B NcU GEU NbU ViU

817
L79h
1882r LOCKE, DAVID ROSS, 1833-1888.
Hannah Jane, by David Ross Locke (Petroleum V. Nasby) ... Boston, Lee and Shepard; New York, T. Dillingham, 1883 [c1881]
[19]p. front., illus., 5 pl. 21cm.

Poem.

NL 0434258 TxU OU MH

Locke, David Ross, 1833-1888.
*AC85 ... High license does not diminish the evil.
L7912 <Extract from an article in the North American
887h review by D. R. Locke, better known as P. V. Nasby [pseud.].>
Published by the National temperance society and publication house, no.58 Reade street, New York, at $3 per thousand. [1887]
4p. 19cm., in folder 20.5cm.
Caption title; imprint on p.4.
At head of title: No.274.

The complete article appeared in the North American review for Sept. 1887.
Unbound, as issued; in cloth folder.

NL 0434260 MH

---

817 ⌊Locke, David Ross⌋ 1833-1888.
L79i ... The impendin crisis uv the dimocracy, bein a breef and concise statement uv the past experience, present condishun and fucher hopes uv the Dimokratic party: incloodin the most prominent reesons why evry Dimokrat who loves his party shood vote for Seemore and Blare, and agin Grant and Colfax. By Petroleum V. Nasby ⌊pseud.⌋ ... New York, American News Co. ⌊1868⌋
23 p. 19½cm.

1. Campaign literature, 1868—Republican. I. Title.

NL 0434261 IU CtY PU ViU

⌊Locke, David Ross⌋ 1833-1888.
... The impendin crisis uv the Dimocracy, bein a breef and concise statement uv the past experience, present condishun and fucher hopes uv the Dimokratic party; incloodin the most prominent reesons why evry Dimokrat who loves his party shood vote for Seemore and Blare, and agin Grant and Colfax. By Petroleum V. Nasby ⌊pseud.⌋ ... Toledo, O., Miller, Locke & co., 1868.
23 p. 19½cm.

1. Campaign literature, 1868—Republican. I. Title.

12—6204

Library of Congress PN6161.L632
E670.L82

NL 0434262 DLC ViU NcU OClWHi PPL

⌊Locke, David Ross⌋ 1833-1888.
Inflation at the Cross Roads, being a history of the rise and fall of the Onlimited trust and confidence company, of Confedrit X Roads. In a series of five letters, by Petroleum V. Nasby ⌊pseud.⌋ ... New York, American news company, 1875.
cover-title, 24 p. illus. 19cm.

1. Campaign literature, 1875—Republican. I. Title.

12-6203

Library of Congress PN6161.L633

NL 0434263 DLC CU CU-B IU ViU

⌊Locke, David Ross⌋ 1833-1888.
Inflation at the Cross Roads, being a history of the rise and fall of the Onlimited trust and confidence company, of Confedrit X Roads. In a series of five letters, by Petroleum V. Nasby ⌊pseud.⌋ ... Toledo, Blade printing & paper co., 1876.
cover-title, 24 p. illus. 19cm.

NL 0434264 MiU

KB ⌊Locke, David Ross⌋ 1833-1888.
H1 Let's laugh, by Petroleum V. Nasby
98 ⌊pseud.⌋ 2d ed. Girard, Kan., Appeal to
G442h Reason ⌊n.d.⌋
127p. 13cm. (People's Pocket Series, no.20)

NL 0434265 KU CtY

PN6157 Locke, David Ross, 1833-1888.
K6L814l Let's laugh, by Petroleum V. Nasby. Girard, Kan.,
1924 Haldeman-Julius Co. [1924?]
x 127 p. 13cm. (Ten cent pocket series no. 20)

Koundakjian collection.
A selection from various newspaper letters.

1. U.S. - History - Civil War - Humor, caricatures, etc. I. Title. (Series. Series: Koundakjian collection)

NL 0434266 CU-B

⌊Locke, David Ross⌋ 1833-1888.
... Let's laugh ⌊by⌋ Petroleum V. Nasby ⌊pseud.⌋ edited, with introduction and notes, by Lloyd E. Smith. Girard, Kan., Haldeman-Julius company ⌊°1924⌋
64 p. 13cm. (Little blue book, no. 20, ed. by E. Haldeman-Julius)
A selection from various newspaper letters.

I. Smith, Lloyd E., ed. II. Title.

CA 26-40 Unrev'd

Library of Congress E647.L73

NL 0434267 DLC IEdS CU-B

[Locke, David Ross] 1833-1888
E667 Nasby's Life of Andy Jonsun, with a true
L8 pictorial history of his great stumping tour
1866 out West, by Petroleum V. Nasby [pseud.] A dimmicrat of thirty years standing, and who allus tuk his licker straight. [N.Y.] J.C. Haney, c1866.
38 p. illus. 20 cm.

Half-title (p.[13]) has title: Androo Johnson, his life...

Also published with two other titles: "Swinging round the circle"; or, Andy's trip to the West; and also with title: Andy's trip to the West.

CU-B
NL 0434269 RPB OClWHi MiDlB MnU ICN MiU-C KyBgW MWA

Locke, David Ross, 1833-1888.
The moral history of America's life-struggle. By D. R. Locke (Petroleum V. Nasby) Illustrated by Th. Nast. Introductory chapter by Hon. Charles Sumner ... Boston, I. N. Richardson and company; ⌊etc., etc., °1874⌋
715 p. front. (port.) 23 pl. 23½cm.
Originally published under title: The Nasby letters.

1. U. S.—Pol. & govt.—Civil war. 2. U. S.—Hist.—Civil war—Personal narratives. I. Sumner, Charles, 1811-1874. II. Nast, Thomas, 1840-1902, illus.

9-8978

Library of Congress E647.L74

NL 0434270 DLC ViU OCU CSmH ODW OCl NjP

VOLUME 337

Locke, David Ross, 1833-1888.
The moral history of America's life-struggle, by D. R. Locke (Petroleum V. Nasby). Illustrated by Th. Nast. Introductory chapter by Hon. Charles Sumner ... Boston, I. N. Richardson and company [1874]
720 p. port. plates, 23cm.

NL 0434271 NNC

Locke, David Ross, 1833-1888.
The morals of Abou Ben Adhem. Edited by D. R. Locke (Petroleum V. Nasby) Boston, Lee and Shepard; New York, Lee, Shephard, and Dillingham, 1875.
231 p. 20 cm.
At head of title: Eastern fruit on western dishes.

I. Title. II. Title: Eastern fruit on western dishes.
PS2248.L8M6 PZ3.L791Mo 12-7562

MB CU-B MdBP MiD-B OClW CoU OU NN MH OCl NjR NN NcU NNU-W LU KyU ViU ICU TU NcD KMK OrU
NL 0434272 DLC NcU ICRL ICN CSmH MiU NcA PPL OEac

Locke, David Ross, 1833-1888.
Nasby in exile; or, Six months of travel in England, Ireland, Scotland, France, Germany, Switzerland and Belgium, with many things not of travel. By David R. Locke (Petroleum V. Nasby) ... Toledo and Boston, Locke publishing company, 1882.
xv, [16]-672 p. incl. front. illus. 23cm.

1. Europe—Descr. & trav.
3-15519
Library of Congress D919.L81

OU ODW MiU NjP MB MdBP WaTC ScU CU-B MU TU OrU C Or
NL 0434273 DLC LU ViU KMK OClW PP PU PPL PV OCl OFH

M-film 810.8 Am35 169-9
Locke, David Ross, 1833-1888.
Nasby in exile; or, Six months of travel in England, Ireland, Scotland, France, Germany, Switzerland and Belgium, with many things not of travel. By David R. Locke (Petroleum V. Nasby) Toledo and Boston, Locke, 1882.
xv, 672 p. illus.

Microfilm (positive) Ann Arbor, Mich., University Microfilms, 1971. 9th title of 9. 35 mm. (American fiction series, reel 169.9)
1. Europe - Descr. & trav. I. Title.

NL 0434274 KEmT CU

---

rare bk. coll. PN 6161 L623 1887
[Locke, David Ross] 1833-1888.
The Nasby letters. [n.p., 1887?]
504? p. 21 cm.

Defective: t.p., p.15-36, and last page lacking.
In very poor condition.
Last letter dated Feb.5, 1887.
First collection of Nasby letters pub. 1864 under title: The Nasby papers.

1. United States - Politics and government - 1865-1900. I. Title.

NL 0434275 NcGU

Locke, David Ross, 1833-1888.
The Nasby letters; being the original Nasby letters as written during his lifetime by David Ross Locke ("Petroleum V. Nasby"). Toledo, Ohio, Toledo Blade Co., (c1893)

NL 0434276 MsU ViU MiD KyBgW OOxM

PN6157 K6L814na x
Locke, David Ross, 1833-1888.
The Nasby letters. Being the original Nasby letters, as written during his lifetime, by David Ross Locke, ("Petroleum V. Nasby."). Toledo, O., The Toledo blade co. [c1893]
510 p. front. (port.) 21cm. [Koundakjian collection]

"The great majority of the Nasby letters were never printed save in the columns of the Toledo blade, in which they originally appeared."--Introd., signed: The Toledo blade co.

1. U. S. - Politics and government - Civil War. 2. U. S. Politics and government - 1865-1898. I. Title. (Series)

NL 0434277 CU-B MiDW WyU PSt ViU IEN MoKU

FILM 4274 PR v.3 reel L23
Locke, David Ross, 1833-1888.
The Nasby letters: Being the original Nasby [pseud.] letters, as written during his lifetime ... Toledo, Ohio, Toledo Blade Co. [c1893]
510 p. front. (Wright American Fiction, v.III, 1876-1900, no.3376, Research Publications, Inc. Microfilm, Reel L-23)

I. Title. II.x. Nasby, Petroleum V., pseud.

NL 0434278 CU

E 647 L81
Locke, David Ross, 1833-1888.
The Nasby letters. Being the original Nasby letters, as written during his lifetime, by David Ross Locke ("Petroleum V. Nasby") Toledo, Ohio, Toledo Blade Co., [c1893]
512 p. 20cm.

"The great majority of the Nasby letters were never printed save in the columns of the Toledo blade, in which they originally appeared."

NL 0434279 NIC DLC OrU Or OrCS MiU ODW IU

PN6157 K6L814nas x
Locke, David Ross, 1833-1888.
... Nasby on inflation. A new comic book by Petroleum V. Nasby. (D. R. Locke) ... Philadelphia, Barclay & co. [1876, c1875]
1 p. l., 19-78 p., 1 l. incl. illus., plates. 23½cm. [Koundakjian collection]

1. U. S.—Pol. & govt.—1873-1877. I. Title. (Series)
Library of Congress PN6161.L6365 12-7560

NL 0434280 DLC NjP CU

FILM 4274 PR v.2 reel L10
[Locke, David Ross] 1833-1888.
Nasby on inflation. A new comic book by Petroleum V. Nasby (D. R. Locke), Mark Twain's only rival... Phila., Barclay [c1875]
78 p. illus. (Wright American fiction, v.II, 1851-1875, no. 1569, Research Publications Microfilm, Reel L-10)

1. U. S. - Pol. & govt. - 1869-1877 - Fiction. I. Title.

NL 0434281 CU KEmT PSt

[Locke, David Ross] 1833-1888.
The Nasby papers. Letters and sermons containing the views on the topics of the day, of Petroleum V. Nasby [*pseud.*] ... Indianapolis, C. O. Perrine & co., 1864.
64 p. 19½cm.

1. U. S.—Pol. & govt.—Civil war.
Library of Congress E647.L75 5-40609

OClWHi OCl PPL MiU IU MB OClWHi
NL 0434282 DLC IaU WU TU OU GU NIC MWA NjP PU

Micro 3
Locke, David Ross, 1833-1888.
The Nasby papers. Letters and sermons containing the views on the topics of the day, of Petroleum V. Nasby [pseud.] Indianapolis, C.O. Perrine & Co., 1864.
64p. 20cm.

Micro-transparency (negative). Louisville, Ky., Lost Cause Press, 1970. 3 cards. 7.5x12.5cm. (L.H. Wright. American fiction, 1851-1875, no.1570)

NL 0434283 PSt CU

[Locke, David Ross] 1833-1888.
The Nasby papers; by Petroleum V. Nasby [*pseud.*] "paster uv sed church in charg." C. O. Perrine & co., Indianapolis, Ind., 1864.
(*In* The Magazine of history with notes and queries. New York, 1912. 26½ x 20cm. Extra number—no. 19, p. [1]-5)
Caption title: Has an interview with the President.

1. Lincoln, Abraham, pres. U. S., 1809-1865—Cartoons, satire, etc. I. Title.
12-8928
Library of Congress E173.M24

NL 0434284 DLC NN TU InHi MH NcD RPB MiU Ct

Locke, David Ross] 1833-1888.
The Nasby papers. By Petroleum V. Nasby [pseud.] . . . London, S. O. Beeton, 1865.
x, [11]-124 pp. 16cm.
2-7300

NL 0434285 DLC ViU

[LOCKE, DAVID ROSS] 1833-1888.
The Nasby papers by Petroleum V. Nasby [pseud.] With an introduction by George Augustus Sala. Original stereotyped edition. London, Ward, Lock, and Tyler, 1865.
viii, 88 p. 12mo

Bound in half leather with original paper wrappers bound in at end.
Bookplate of A. R. Merrill.

NL 0434286 InU

[Locke, David Ross] 1833-1888.
The Nasby papers, by Petroleum V. Nasby [*pseud.*] ... With an introduction by George Augustus Sala. Original stereotyped ed. London, Ward, Lock, and Tyler, 1866.
viii, 88 p. 18cm.

I. Sala, George Augustus Henry, 1828-1896. II. Title.
5-40504
Library of Congress E647.L752

NL 0434287 DLC

PS2248 .L8N45 1870 Lincoln
[Locke, David Ross] 1833-1888.
The Nasby papers. (Southern humour.) By Petroleum V. Nasby [pseud.] ... Author's unabridged ed. London, G. Routledge and sons, 1870?]
viii, 88 p. 18½cm.
Introduction signed: George Augustus Sala. This and the three other works bound with it form part of the collection edited by Sala and issued under the title: Yankee drolleries.

1. U.S.--Pol.& govt.--Civil war.

NL 0434288 ICU ViU

Locke, David Ross, 1833-1888.
A paper city, by D. R. Locke, (Petroleum V. Nasby,) ... Boston, Lee and Shepard; New York, C. T. Dillingham, 1879.
431 p. 20cm.

I. Title.
7-15164
Library of Congress PZ3.L791P
4041.

NL 0434289 DLC NcU TU OU NcD PPL OCU ViU MB OFH MiU

VOLUME 337

FILM 4274 PR v.3 reel L24
Locke, David Ross, 1833-1888.
A paper city, by D. R. Locke, (Petroleum V. Nasby,) ... Boston, Lee and Shepard; New York, C. T. Dillingham, 1879.
431 p. 20cm.
(Wright American fiction, v. III, 1876-1900, no. 3377, Research Publications, Inc. Microfilm, Reel L-24)

NL 0434290 CU OrU KEmT

Locke, David Ross, 1833-1888.
A paper city, by D. R. Locke (Petroleum V. Nasby). Boston, Lee and Shepard, 1888.
431p. 19cm.

NL 0434291 NcU MdBP IaU

Locke, David Ross, 1833-1888.
A paper city, by D. R. Locke (Petroleum V. Nasby) ... Boston, Lothrop, Lee & Shepard co. [1906]
431 p. 18½cm.
First published 1879.

I. Title.

Library of Congress PZ3.L791P4 6-34680

NL 0434292 DLC

MICROFILM Locke, David Ross, 1833-1888.
[Papers. n. p., n. d.]
1 v. (various pagings) illus.
Title supplied.
Partial contents.—Papers and memorabilia of David Ross Locke (Petroleum V. Nasby), 1833-1888, Robinson Locke (Rodney Lee), 1856-1920.—Toledo blade (Nasby's paper) Its rise and progress with some account of its founder, the first Nasby letters, and other matter.
Microfilm (Negative) Fremont, Ohio, Rutherford B. Hayes Library, 1963. 1 reel. 35 mm.

I. Locke, Robinson, 1856-1920.

NL 0434293 IEdS

[Locke, David Ross] 1833-1888.
... Petroleum V. Nasby [pseud.] on silver. New York City, Present problems publ. co. [1896]
6 p. 15cm. (Present problems. v. 1, no. 10. December 15, 1896)
Title-page removed and pasted on pamphlet binder.

1. Currency question—U.S. I. Ser.

NL 0434294 ViU NN PU

Locke, David Ross, 1833-1888.
A pocket book of the early American humorists; selections from the best writings of Washington Irving, William Austin, William T. Thompson, Frederic S. Cozzens, Petroleum V. Nasby [pseud.] The Danbury Newsman [pseud.] Josh Billings [pseud.] Widow Bedott [pseud.] N. P. Willis, and others. Boston, Small, Maynard & company, 1907.

Locke, David Ross, 1833-1888.
The president's policy, being an exposition of the same from the stand-point of the Confedrit X Roads, in the form of six letters from the pen of the philosophical Petroleum V. Nasby [pseud. wich wuz P.M. Toledo, O., Blade company, 1877.
cover-title, 23 p. 20½cm.
"President Lincoln's opinion of Nasby ... by F.B. Carpenter": p.[2] of cover.

1.U.S.—Pol.& govt.—1865-1877.

NL 0434296 MiU

Locke, David Ross, 1833-1888.
Prohibition, by Petroleum V. Nasby (D. R. Locke) New York, National Temperance Society and Publication House, 1886.
22 p. 19cm.

"Reprinted by special permission from the 'North American review.'"

1. Prohibition - U. S. I. Title.

NL 0434297 NNC MH NBuG MB NN CtY ViU

[Locke, David Ross] 1833-1888.
The struggles (social, financial and political) of Petroleum V. Nasby [pseud.] ... Embracing his trials and troubles, ups and downs, rejoicings and wailings; likewise his views of men and things. Together with the lectures "Cussed be Canaan", "The struggles of a conservative with the woman question", and "In search of the man of sin". With an introduction by Hon. Charles Sumner. Illustrated by Thomas Nast ... Boston, I. N. Richardson and company, 1872.
4 p. l., [7]-720 p. front. (port.) plates. 22½cm.
1. U. S.—Pol. & govt.—1865-1869. I. Title.

Library of Congress PN6161.L437 12-6202

MiU OCl PSt NN MB TxFU CoU CLSU
NL 0434298 DLC WU ViU CtY CU-B KEmT NcU UU NcD MWA

FILM 4274 PR v.2 reel L10
[Locke, David Ross] 1833-1888.
The struggles (social, financial and political) of Petroleum V. Nasby [pseud.]... With an introd. by Hon. Charles Sumner... Boston, I. N. Richardson, 1872.
720 p. illus. (Wright American fiction, v.II, 1851-1875, no.1571, Research Publications Microfilm, Reel L-10)

Also published as: The moral history of America's life-struggle.

1. U. S. - Pol. & govt. - 1865-1869 - Fiction. I. Nast. Thomas, 1840-1902. illus. II. Title.

NL 0434300 CU

Locke, David Ross, 1833-1888.
Struggles of Petroleum V. Nasby. Boston, 1873. 8°

NL 0434301 I

Locke, David Ross, 1833-1888.
The struggles, social, financial and political, of Petroleum V. Nasby [pseud.] ... Embracing his trials and troubles, ups and downs, rejoicings and wailings, likewise his views of men and things, embracing the period of American history from 1860 to 1870. With an introd. by Charles Sumner. Illustrated by Thomas Nast. Toledo, Locke Pub. Co., 1880.
627 p. illus. 23 cm.

1. U. S.—Pol. & govt.—1865-1869. I. Title.

PN6161.L6372 56-49692

KyHi NIC NNC WaTC Wa
NL 0434302 DLC CU-B OFH NRU CSmH MH WHi OU MiDW

[Locke, David Ross,] 1833-1888.
The struggles (social, financial and political) of Petroleum V. Nasby [pseud.]...embracing his trials and troubles, ups and downs, rejoicings and wailings; likewise his views of men and things. Together with the lectures "Cussid be Canaan," "The struggles of a conservative with the woman question," and "In search of the man of sin." With an introduction by Hon. Charles Sumner. Illustrated by Thomas Nast. Boston: Lee and Shepard, 1888. 2 p.l., 7-715 p., front. (port.), 23 pl. 8°.

1 plate missing.

1. Wit and humor (American). 2. U. S.—History: Civil war. 3. Sumner, Charles, 1811-74. 4. Nast, Thomas, 1840-1902. 5. Title.
N. Y. P. L. May 27, 1915

ICN OClW CSmH MdBP MH
NL 0434303 NN NcU CtY PU ViU TU IaU ODW OClWHi

PN 6161 L81S9 1893
Locke, David Ross, 1833-1888.
The struggles (social, financial and political) of Petroleum V. Nasby [pseud.] ... Embracing his trials and troubles, ups and downs, rejoicings and wailings; likewise his views of men and things. Together with the lectures "Cussid be Canaan", "The struggles of a conservative with the woman question", and "In search of the man of sin." With an introd. by Hon. Charles Sumner. Illustrated by Thomas Nast. Boston, Lee and Shepard, 1893.
720 p. illus. 23cm.

NL 0434304 NIC NcRS OU PV

Locke, David Ross, 1833-1888.
Swinging round the circle; or, Andy's trip to the West, together with a life of its hero, by Petroleum V. Nasby, a Dimmicrat of thirty years standing, and who allus tuk his licker straight. Hinsdale, N. H., 1866.

Added t. p.: Androo Johnson, his life... by Petroleum V. Nasby.

NL 0434305 WU

[Locke, David Ross] 1833-1888.
"Swinging round the circle"; or, Andy's trip to the West, together with a life of its hero. By Petroleum V. Nasby [pseud.] a Dimmicrat of thirty years standing, and who allus tuck his licker straight. New York, The American news company [1866]
2 p. l., [15]-38 p. illus., 6 pl. 19cm.
Plates printed on both sides.
Added t.-p.: Androo Johnson, his life ... By Petroleum V. Nasby.

1. Johnson, Andrew, pres. U. S., 1808-1875. I. Title.

Library of Congress E667.L8 18-8399

NL 0434306 DLC MWA PHi ViU NBu KyHi MB NN

[Locke, David Ross] 1833-1888.
"Swingin round the cirkle." By Petroleum V. Nasby [pseud.] ... His ideas of men, politics, and things, as set forth in his letters to the public press, during the year 1866. Illustrated by Thomas Nast. Boston, Lee and Shepard, 1867.
299 p. front., plates. 19 cm.

1. Campaign literature, 1866—Republican. I. Title.

PN6161.L638 1867 8—1248

Or WaU-L OrU Wa CaBVaU MtU
ICN NIC CoU WHi ViW TU InU IdPI CU-B MoSW AAP TxHU
PPL PU CSmH MnHi OFH OU OO OCU NcA NcD NNC PBL NcU
NL 0434307 DLC NjP CLSU NNU-W MWA ViU MB MiU PP

FILM 4274 PR v.2 reel L11
[Locke, David Ross] 1833-1888.
"Swingin round the cirkle." By Petroleum V. Nasby [pseud.]... His ideas of men, politics, and things, as set forth in his letters to the public press during the year 1866... Boston, Lee and Shepard, 1867.
299 p. illus. (Wright American fiction, v.II, 1851-1875, no.1572, Research Publications Microfilm, Reel L-11)
Illustrated by Thomas Nast.
Campaign literature, 1866 - Republican.
I. Nast, Thomas, 1840-1902, illus. II.Title.

NL 0434309 CU PSt

[LOCKE, David Ross, 1833-1888.]
"Swingin round the cirkle." By Petroleum V. Nasby, [pseud.] His ideas of men, politics, and things as set forth in his letters to the public press, during the year 1866. Illustrated by Thomas Nast. Boston, Lee and Shepard, etc., etc., 1873.

NL 0434310 MH MiU-C

VOLUME 337

[Locke, David Ross] 1833-1888.
"Swingin round the cirkle", by Petroleum V. Nasby [pseud.] ... His ideas of men, politics, and things as set forth in his letters to the public press. Illustrated by Thomas Nast. Boston, Lee and Shepard, 1888.
299 p. front., plates. 19½cm.

1. Campaign literature. 1866—Republican. I. Nast, Thomas, 1840-1902, illus. II. Title.

24-13982

Library of Congress PN6161.L638 1888

NL 0434311 DLC WaS MdBP

PN6161 .Y2 Locke, David Ross, 1833-1888.
Yankee drolleries. The most celebrated works of the best American humorists. Complete editions, with introductions by George Augustus Sala. London, Ward, Lock, and Tyler, 1866.

T811 L791g Locke, Doris.
A gift of memories. [n.p., c1940]
38p. 23cm.

Poems.

NL 0434313 TxU

PR 6023 .O 237 N6 Locke, Dorothy Mary.
No lords or ladies. London, Grayson & Grayson [1937]
286p.

NL 0434314 ScU

Locke, E W 1818-1900.
Brother, when will you come back? Poetry and music by E. W. Locke. Stephen Berry, printer, foot of Exchange Street, Portland, Me. °1864.
close score ([1] l.) 30 cm.
Caption title.
For voice and chorus (SATB)

1. U. S.—Hist.—Civil War—Songs and music. I. Title.

M1638.L 52-52310

NL 0434315 DLC

Locke, E W 1818-1900.
Hark! To arms! Our country calls us! Army song. [Portland, Me., 18—]
score ([1] l.) 28 cm.
Caption title.
For chorus (TTTB)

1. War-songs, American. 2. U. S.—Hist.—Civil War—Songs and music. I. Title.

M1640.L 52-51190

NL 0434316 DLC

Locke, E. W., 1880-1900.
I feel I'm growing old Lizzie, ballad, words and melody by E. W. Locke. Sinfonies and accompaniments by F. N. Crouch. Boston. Reed & Co. 1854. 5 pp. F°.

G5507 — Crouch, Frederick Nicholls, ed. — T.r. — Songs. With music.

NL 0434317 MB

Locke, E W., 1818-1900.
Three years in camp and hospital. By E. W. Locke ... Boston, G. D. Russell & co. [°1870]
ix, [10]-408 p. 19½cm.

1. U. S.—Hist.—Civil war—Personal narratives. I. Title.

2—17788

Library of Congress E601.L81

MnHi NjP Nh MB NN OU ViU PP Vi IaU TU ICarbS NIC MiU-C CLU NcU MWA
NL 0434318 DLC TNJ NIC NcD CtY-M NNC OO OClWHi

Locke, E. W., 1818-1900.
Three years in camp and hospital. by E. W. Locke ... Boston, G. D. Russell & co., 1871.
ix, (10)-408 p.

1. U.S.-Hist.-Civil war - Personal narratives. I. Title.

NL 0434319 ViN LU

UH22# L79 1872 Locke, E. W., 1818-1900.
Three years in camp and hospital. Boston, Russell, 1872.
ix, 408 p.

1. U. S. - History - Civil war - Personal narratives. I. Title.

NL 0434320 NNC OClWHi MB OU LU CaBVaU

Locke, E. W., 1818-1900.
We are marching down to Dixie's land. Words and music by E.W.Locke ... New York, S.T. Gordon [etc.] c1862.

5 p. 34cm.
Engraved title-page with ornamental border.
Vol.III,no.7: "Music collections."

1.Music-Vocal. 2.Civil war-Music. I.Title. II.Title: Dixie's land.

NL 0434321 MiU-C

Locke, E W 1818-1900.
We are marching on to Richmond; poetry and music by E. W. Locke. [New York, S. T. Gordon] °1862.
score ([1] l.) 29 cm.
Caption title.
For voice and chorus (SATB)

1. U. S.—Hist.—Civil War—Songs and music. 2. War-songs, American. I. Title.

M1640.L 52-52303

NL 0434322 DLC

LOCKE, E. W., 1818-1900.
We're marching down to Dixie's Land. Poetry and Music. Portland, Me., 1861.

Broadside. (2 cop.)

NL 0434323 MH

Locke, E. W., 1818-1900.
We will not retreat any more. [1st edition.] Arranged by G. Ascher [Song, with accompaniment for pianoforte.]
— New York. Gordon. 1863. 5 pp. Decorated cover. [Songs for the Union.] 33½ cm.
The decoration on the cover is two American flags in color.

K7890 — T.r. — Ascher, Gustave, ed.

NL 0434324 MB

Locke, Edna.
Medical seminar discussions, by Edna Locke ... [Berkeley, Cal., Printed by C. W. Calhoun, 1912]
43 p. 19cm. $0.35
Read at the Medical seminar, University of California.
Contents.—Hahnemann.—Florence Nightingale.

1. Hahnemann, Samuel i. e. Christian Friedrich Samuel, 1755-1843. 2. Nightingale, Florence, 1820-1910.

Library of Congress RX85.L7 12-26380

NL 0434325 DLC

Locke, Edna.
... A rapid method of producing bacterial agglutinins, by Edna Locke. Berkeley, University of California press, 1912.
cover-title, p. 91-96. 27cm. (University of California publications in pathology. vol. 2, no. 10)
"From the Hearst laboratory of pathology and bacteriology, University of California."
Also submitted as Thesis (M. S.)—Univ. of California.
"References": p. 96.

1. Serum. 2. Agglutination.

A 13-589

Title from Univ. of Calif. Library of Congress

NL 0434326 CU OrU CaBVaU UU MiU OU OO ICJ

Locke, Edward.
Pause, and other poems. [1st ed.] New York, Exposition Press [1954]
64 p. 21 cm.

I. Title.

PS3523.O2313P3 811.5 54-7044 ‡

NL 0434327 DLC OrU CU NcRR ViU

LOCKE, EDWARD, 1869 or 70-1945.
The case of Becky, by Edward Locke. [New York, 1912?] 44, 36, 28 f. 29cm.

Typewritten.
Original prompt-book.
First New York production at the Belasco theatre, Oct. 1, 1912.

872938A. 1. Drama, American. 2. Prompt-books. I. Title.

NL 0434328 NN

Locke, Edward, 1869 or 70-1945.
Jenks, George C.
The climax, by George C. Jenks; from the celebrated play of the same name by Edward Locke; illustrated by W. W. Fawcett. New York, The H. K. Fly company [1909]

PZ3 .L58584 Cl Locke, Edward, 1869 or 70-1945.
Lewis, Florence Jay.
... The climax, from the screen play by Curt Siodmak and Lynn Starling of the Universal motion picture produced and directed by George Waggner ... adapted by Curt Siodmak from the play by Edward Locke, novelized by Florence Jay Lewis ... New York, Books, inc. [1944]

[Locke, Edward] 1869 or 70-1945.
"The drunkard's daughter;" or, "A mad love;" adapted from "Lady Audley's secret." A drama in three acts, with a prologue. [New York, c1905] 55 f. 32½cm.

Caption-title.
Typewritten.
Imperfect: Prologue wanting.

1. Drama, American. I. Braddon, Mary Elizabeth, 1837-1915. Lady Audley's secret. II. Title. III. Title: A mad love.
December 24, 1941

NL 0434331 NN

VOLUME 337

Locke, Edward, 1869 or 70-1945.

ML96 .R745 Case

Romberg, Sigmund, 1887-1951.
[The love call. Piano-vocal score. English]

The love call. Book and lyrics by Ed. Locke and Harry B. Smith, [192-]

Locke, Edward, 1869 or 70-1945.

The price of ambition. Adapted by Edward Locke from the Hungarian ... [New York? °1919]

LOCKE, EDWARD, 1869 or 70-1945.
Solomon Sly, sleuth; a comedy in three acts. [n.p., 19--] 3 pts in 1 v. 29cm.

1. Drama, American. I. Title.

NL 0434334 NN

[Locke, Edward A]
Facts for consideration of the stamp for distilled spirits. [n. p., 1869?]
cover-title, [1], 16 p. 7 pl. 23½cm.
Plates 2-7 printed on both sides; pl. 1 on verso of page of text.

1. Liquor traffic—U. S.—Taxation. I. Title.

CA 9-4635 Unrev'd

Library of Congress HD9350.8.U5L7

NL 0434335 DLC

[Locke, Edward A]
Letter to the Commissioner of internal revenue regarding the metallic stamp system for collection of the tax on distilled spirits. Washington, Gibson brothers, 1876.
23 p.

Letter signed: Edward A. Locke, D. P. Southworth.

NL 0434336 NNC

Locke, Edward Gibson, 1904-
The fluorination of hexachloroethane and a study of the isomers of dichlorodifluoroethylene... by Edward Gibson Locke ... [Columbus] The Ohio state university, 1932.
2-105 numb.

Thesis (Ph.D.) - The Ohio state university.

NL 0434337 CU

Locke, Edwin, 1857- joint ed.

Methodist Episcopal church.
Doctrines and discipline of the Methodist Episcopal church, 1916. New York, Cincinnati, The Methodist book concern [°1916]

LOCKE, Edwin A.
Hope Hathaway; a drama of the cattle range [in four acts]. Dramatized by E.A.Locke.

4°. Typewritten.
A dramatization of Frances Parker's novel of the same name.

NL 0434339 MH

Locke, Edwin A.
"Hope Hathaway;" a drama of the cattle range. Dramatized by Edwin A. Locke. [Chelsea, Mass., c1906] 69 f. 29cm.

Typewritten.
Copyrighted under the title: The sheepman.

51640B. 1. Drama, American. I. Title.

November 25, 1941

NL 0434340 NN

LOCKE, Edwin A.
"Never say die" schottische composed and arranged for the piano forte. n.p., n.d.

4°.

NL 0434341 MH

Locke, Edwin Allen, 1874-
The blood in scarlet fever
see under Tileston, Wilder, 1875-

Locke, Edwin Allen, 1874-
Boston's hospital school for tuberculous children [by] Edwin A. Locke ... and Timothy J. Murphy ... [Boston? 1911?]
cover-title, 11 p. 24½cm.
Reprinted from the Transactions of the seventh annual meeting of the National association for the study and prevention of tuberculosis.

1. Tuberculosis in schools—Boston. 2. Open-air schools—Boston. I. Murphy, Timothy J., joint author. II. Title.

E 13-283

Library, U. S. Bur. of Education LB3418.T7B7

NL 0434343 DHEW

Locke, Edwin Allen, 1874- *ed.*
Brown university. An illustrated historical souvenir. E. A. Locke ... editor. 1897. [Providence, Preston & Rounds company, °1897]
123 p. illus. (incl. ports.) 17 x 26cm.

1. Brown university.

6-45200

Library of Congress LD638.L8

NL 0434344 DLC DHEW

Locke, Edwin Allen, 1874-
Case of multiple ulcers of the gall bladder, by E.A. Locke ... and S.B. Wolbach. n.d.
Caption-title, 13 p. pl. O.

NL 0434345 RPB

Locke, Edwin Allen, 1874-
The clinical value of the iodine reaction in the leucocytes of the blood. ... Boston, 1902.
22 p. 20 cm.
Cover-title.
Reprinted from the Boston medical and surgical journal, v. 147, Sept. 11, 1902.

NL 0434346 RPB

Locke, Edwin Allen, 1874-
Crusade against tuberculosis in Germany. Boston, 1907.
33 p. il. O.
Repr. from Boston medical and surgical journal, v. 156.

NL 0434347 RPB

Locke, Edwin Allen, 1874-
... Diseases of the bones, by E. A. Locke. [New York, Oxford University Press, 1921]
p. [405]-502. illus., plates. 26cm. ([The Oxford medicine. vol. IV, chap. XVI)
Loose-leaf.
Caption title.
Bibliography: p. 494-502.

NL 0434348 ICJ NNC

Locke, Edwin Allen, 1874-
An economic study of 500 consumptives treated in the Boston consumptives' hospital, by Edwin A. Locke and Cleaveland Floyd. n.p., n.d.
9 p. 24 cm.
Cover-title.

NL 0434349 RPB

Locke, Edwin Allen, 1874-
Food values; practical tables for use in private practice and public institutions, by Edwin A. Locke ... New York and London, D. Appleton and company, 1911.
v, [1] p., 1 l., 110 p. 20½cm. $1.25

1. Food. I. Title.

Library of Congress TX551.L6 11-23711

NL 0434350 DLC MtU OrU-M PPJ PP PU OOxM MiU ICJ NN

Locke, Edwin Allen, 1874-
Food values; practical tables for use in private practice & public institutions. N.Y. Appleton, 1913.
110 p. O.

NL 0434351 OClW

Locke, Edwin Allen, 1874-
Food values; practical tables for use in private practice and public institutions, by Edwin A. Locke ... New York and London, D. Appleton and co., c1911. 1914.

NL 0434352 OCl

Locke, Edwin Allen, 1874-
Food values; practical tables for use in private practice and public institutions, by Edwin A. Locke ... New York, and London, D. Appleton and company, 1916.
v, [1] p., 1 l., 110 p. 20 1/2 cm.

NL 0434353 ViU PPC

Locke, Edwin Allen, 1874-
Food values; practical tables for use in private practice and public institutions. N.Y., Appleton, 1917.

110 p.

NL 0434354 PPD

Locke, Edwin Allen, 1874-
Food values; practical tables for use in private practice and public institutions... New York and London, D. Appleton and co., 1918.

110 p.

NL 0434355 PHC

VOLUME 337

LOCKE,Edwin A[llen],1874-
Food values; practical tables for use in private practice and public institutions. New York,etc.,D.Appleton and Co.,1920.

NL 0434356 MBCo ICRL OU OCU

Locke, Edwin Allen, 1874-
Four unusual cases of aneurism.
n.t.p., 33 p. O.

NL 0434357 RPB

Locke, Edwin Allen, 1874-
Iodophilia, by Edwin A. Locke and Richard C. Cabot ...; a preliminary report. Boston, 1902.
p. 25-42. 24 cm.
Cover-title.
Reprinted from the Journal of medical research, v. 7, Jan., 1902.

NL 0434358 RPB

Locke, Edwin Allen, 1874-
The municipal anti-tuberculosis work in Boston. Boston, n.d.
27 p. 24 cm.
Cover-title.
Reprinted from the Transactions of the fourth annual meeting of the National association for the study and prevention of tuberculosis.

NL 0434359 RPB

Locke, Edwin A[llen] 1874-
The municipal anti-tuberculosis work in Boston. n.p. [1908]
18 p. 8°.
Repr.: Trans. of the 4. ann. meet. of the Nat. Assoc. for the Study and Prev. of Tuberculosis. [1908]

NL 0434360 NN

Locke, Edwin Allen, 1874-
The municipal hospital for advanced consumptives in Boston by Edwin A. Locke ... and Simon F. Cox. [Boston, 1908]
21 p. 23 cm.
Caption-title.
Prepared for the International congress on tuberculosis held in Washington, Sept., Oct., 1908.

NL 0434361 RPB

Locke, Edwin Allen, 1874-
... The nutrition of anemic and tuberculous children. [Boston, 1913]
22 p. 24 cm.
Caption title.
Reprinted from the Boston medical and surgical journal, v. 159, no. 20, p. 701-07, Nov., 1913.

NL 0434362 RPB

Locke, Edwin Allen, 1874-
The nutrition of anaemic and tuberculous children. (In: Internat. Congress on School Hygiene, 4. Buffalo, 1913. Transac. Buffalo, 1914. 8°. v. 5, p. 285-297.)

1. Children.—Nutrition. 2. Anemia. 3. Tuberculosis in children.
August 10, 1917.

NL 0434363 NN

Locke, Edwin Allen, 1874-
Treatment of non-tuberculous chronic arthritis, [by] E.A. Locke and R.B. Osgood. Chicago, 1907.
12 p. O.
Cover-title.
Repr. from Journal of American medical association, v. 48.

NL 0434364 RPB

Locke, Edwin Allen, 1874- ed.
Tuberculosis in Massachusetts
see under Massachusetts. Committee for International Congress on Tuberculosis. 6th, Washington, 1908.

Locke, Edwin Allen, 1910-
Goethe and Napoleon.

Bowdoin prize essay, Harvard university, 1932. Typewritten.

NL 0434366 MH

Locke, Elisha.
I am weary. [Voice & pf.] Boston, 1845.
fol. (In "Music Miscel." 4)

NL 0434367 CtY

RAM4.62
L814
1848
Locke, Elisha.
The school vocalist; containing a thorough system of elementary instruction in vocal music, with practical exercises, songs, hymns, chants, &c., adapted to the use of schools and academies. By E. Locke and S. Nourse. Cincinnati, Wm. H. Moore & Co., 1848.
160p.12cm.
1. School song-books. I. Nourse, S., jt. author. II. Title. III. Moore, William H. and Co. (RA cat. only)

NL 0434368 OC NN

Locke, Elisha, and others, compilers.
The young singer... A collection of school music, original and selected, compiled (at the request of the Board of Trustees,) for the Cincinnati public schools, by Messrs. Locke, Aiken, Mason, and Baldwin... Cincinnati: Wilson, Hinkle & Co., cop. 1860. 2 v. obl. 24°.

Words and music for 4 voices.

1. School music—Song books, etc. 2. Aiken, Charles, 1818-1882, jt. compiler. 3. Mason, Luther Whiting, 1828-1896, jt. compiler. 4. Baldwin, D. H., jt. compiler. 5. Title.
July 13, 1926

NL 0434369 NN NNUT OOxM OO

Locke, Elma Iona, joint ed.

Brown, *Mrs.* Nellie (Clarke) 1862- *ed.*
The Priscilla Hardanger book; a collection of beautiful designs in Hardanger embroidery, with lessons and stitches, ed. by Nellie Clarke Brown and Elma Iona Locke ... Boston, Mass., The Priscilla publishing company, °1909.

Locke, Elsie.
The shepherd and the scullerymaid...1850-1950, Canterbury without laurels. [Christchurch, New Zealand communist party, 1950] 36 p. illus. 21cm.

1. Canterbury, N.Z.—Hist.
February 5, 1952

NL 0434371 NN

Locke, Emma P Boylston, *comp.*
Colonial Amherst; the early history, customs and homes; geography and geology, of Amherst, life and character of General and Lord Jeffery Amherst, reminiscences of "Cricket Corner" and "Pond Parish" districts, by Prof. Warren Upham ... Comp. by Emma P. Boylston Locke. [Milford, N. H., Printed by W. B. & A. B. Rotch] 1916.
1 p. l., [7]-122 p. illus., fold. pl., port. 23½cm.

1. Amherst, N. H.—Hist. I. Upham, Warren, 1850-
16-22667
Library of Congress F44.A5L8

NL 0434372 DLC TU CU MWA MB

MT925
.L62
Locke, Mrs. Flora Elbertine (Huie) 1866-
The foundation of music in rhymes and songs for beginners,...
[Buffalo, N.Y.,] c1908.

NL 0434373 DLC

MT925
.L63
Locke, Mrs. Flora Elbertine (Huie) 1866-
The foundation of music in rhymes and songs for beginners,...
[Buffalo, N.Y.,]c1916.

NL 0434374 DLC

Locke, Frances Sargent
see Osgood, Mrs. Frances Sargent (Locke), 1811-1850.

Locke (F[rank] S[piller]). Of the action of ether on contracture and of positive kathodic polarization of vertebrate voluntary muscle. 26 pp., 4 pl. 8°. *New York*, 1896.
Repr. from: J. Exper. M., N. Y., 1896, i.

0434376 DNLM

Locke, Franklin B. Railway crossings in Europe and America. 16 pp. (*Century Mag.* v. 34, 1898, p. 22.)

NL 0434377 MdBP

Locke, Franklin D.

Thomson, James, *attorney*.
... In the matter of the award against the Republic of Hayti in favor of the United States, upon the claim of A. H. Lazare. Letter addressed to the Hon. Thomas F. Bayard, secretary of state, dated September 20, 1886. James Thomson, J. Hubley Ashton, Franklin D. Locke, of council for Mr. Lazare. New York, B. H. Tyrrel, 1886.

Locke, Franklin D.

[Thomson, James] *attorney*.
In the matter of the award against the Republic of Hayti in favor of the United States, upon the claim of A. H. Lazare. Letter and protest. New-York, B. H. Tyrrel, printer, 1888.

Lilly
PR 4891
.L 15 C5
LOCKE,FRED
"Cinderella." By Fred Locke.
[Greenwich, W. T. Manning, Steam Printing Works, 1893]
64 p. 21.5 cm.

Pagination includes advertising.
Caption title.
On cover: Morton's Theatre, Greenwich ... Mr. Morton's tenth Christmas annual, 1893-4 ... Book of words.
In red printed paper wrappers; portrait mounted on cover.

NL 0434380 InU

VOLUME 337

Lilly
PR 4891
.L 15 D6
LOCKE, FRED
... Dick Whittington. By Fred Locke ... ₍Brixton, "Free Press" Co., Ltd., 1903₎
31 p. ports. 21 cm.

At head of title: Elephant & Castle Theatre. Pantomime, 1903-4.
In pictorial paper wrappers.

NL 0434381 InU

Locke, Fred.
..."Dick Whittington" and his cat...by Mr. Fred Locke. Book of words and songs...written especially for Mr. Walter Hatton... ₍Edinburgh, 1893₎ 50 p. illus. (ports.) 21½cm.

Cover-title.
At head of title: ... Theatre Royal, Edinburgh. The "Royal" grand pantomime.
First produced at the Theatre Royal, Edinburgh, Dec. 16, 1893.
Advertising matter interspersed.

174005B. 1. Pantomimes, Scottish. I. Whittington and his cat. II. Title.
January 19, 19[illegible]

NL 0434382 NN InU

Locke, Fred.
..."Dick Whittington" and his cat...by Mr. Fred Locke. Book of words and songs...written especially for Mr. Walter Hatton... ₍Edinburgh, 1893₎ 50 p. illus. (ports.) 22cm.

Film reproduction. Negative.
Cover-title.
At head of title: ... Theatre Royal, Edinburgh. The "Royal" grand pantomime.
First produced at the Theatre Royal, Edinburgh, Dec. 16, 1893.
Advertising matter interspersed.
Without the music selected and arranged by Thos. C. Povser.

1. Pantomimes, English. 2. Christmas pantomimes. I. Whittington and his cat. II. Title. III. Poyser, Thomas C. Dick Whittington and his cat. IV. Poyser, Thomas C.

NL 0434384 NN

Lilly
PR 4891
.L 15 F7
LOCKE, FRED
Forty thieves. Written by Fred Locke ... ₍London, 1896₎
91 p. illus., ports. 21 cm.

On cover: Shakespeare Theatre, Lavender Hill, Clapham Junction, Battersea ... Grand Christmas pantomime, 1896-7.
In blue printed paper wrappers.

NL 0434385 InU

AW
2
N55
Locke, Fred.
Goody two shoes, with lyrics and topical allusions by Thos. H. Hardman ₍n.d.₎
104p. 17½cm.

Micro-opaque.

NL 0434386 CaBVaU CSt

Lilly
PR 4891
.L 15 L 5
LOCKE, FRED.
... The grand annual comic pantomime, entitled, Little Red Riding Hood. Written expressly for this theatre by Fred. Locke, and produced on Tuesday, December the 26th, 1893 ... ₍Birmingham, 1893₎
36 p. 17 cm.

At head of title: Theatre Royal, Birmingham ...
In printed paper wrappers.

NL 0434387 InU

Lilly
PR 4891
.L 15 R6
LOCKE, FRED.
... The grand annual comic pantomime entitled, Robinson Crusoe. A Christmas story of a "Good Friday." Written expressly for this theatre by Fred. Locke ... ₍Birmingham, Printed at the Theatre Royal Printing Office, 1894.₎
39 p. port. 16 cm.

At head of title: Theatre Royal, Birmingham ...
In printed paper wrappers.

NL 0434388 InU

Lilly
PR 4891
.L 15 S5
LOCKE, FRED
... Mr. W. Morton's Ninth Greenwich pantomime entitled the modern "Sinbad the Sailor Written by Mr. Fred. Locke ... Greenwich, Printed by H. Richardson ₍1892₎
48 p. 21 cm.

At head of title: Morton's Theatre, Greenwich ...
In pink printed paper wrappers.

I. Tc: Locke, Frederick--Sinbad the Sailor

NL 0434389 InU

Locke, Frederic T.
Recollections of an adjutant-general.
(*In* Military Order of the Loyal Legion of the United States. New York Commandery. Personal recollections ... Ser. 1, pp. 42–47. New York. 1891.)

D7135 — United States. Hist. Civil War. Pers. narr.

NL 0434390 MB OFH

Locke, Frederick John, 1829–1903.
Notes from lectures of F. J. Locke, M. D., professor of materia medica and therapeutics, Eclectic medical institute, Cincinnati, Ohio. By students of class 1895. ₍Cincinnati, ©1894₎
170, ₍6₎ p. 30 x 24cm.

1. Materia medica. 2. Therapeutics. 3. Medicine, Eclectic.

Library of Congress RV401.L81
(Copyright 1894: 48726) 7–18667†

NL 0434391 DLC

Locke, Frederick John, 1829–1903.
... Syllabus of eclectic materia medica and therapeutics. Comp. from notes taken from the lectures of Frederick J. Locke ... ed., with pharmacological additions, by Harvey W. Felter ... with notes on specific medicines by John Uri Lloyd. Cincinnati, J. M. Scudders' sons, 1895.
461 p. 20cm. (Eclectic manual. no. 1)

1. Materia medica. 2. Therapeutics. 3. Medicine, Electic. I. Felter, Harvey Wickes, 1865– ed. II. Lloyd, John Uri, 1849–

1–1649 Additions
Library of Congress RV401.L815

NL 0434392 DLC DNLM GAPh

Locke, Frederick John, 1829–1903.
Syllabus of eclectic materia medica and therapeutics. Comp. from notes taken from the lectures of Frederick J. Locke ... ed., with pharmacological additions, by Harvey W. Felter ... with notes on specific medicines, by John Uri Lloyd, PH. M. 2d ed., with appendix. Cincinnati, Scudder brothers co., 1901.
498 p. 20cm. (Eclectic manual, no. 1)

1. Materia medica. 2. Therapeutics. 3. Medicine, Eclectic. I. Felter, Harvey Wickes, 1865– ed. II. Lloyd, John Uri, 1849–

Jan. 31, 1901–139
Library of Congress RV401.L82

NL 0434393 DLC ICJ

Locke, Frederick William.
La queste del Saint Graal; a structural analysis

Thesis - Harvard, 1954

NL 0434394 MH

3781
S78L
Locke, Gardner Lincoln.
Buckling of an initially curved slender prismatic bar under an axially applied impact force... ₍Stanford, Calif.,₎ 1948.

48 numb. l. plates, diagrs.

Thesis (Engineer) - Stanford University, 1948.
"References": numb. leaf 48.

1. Strength of materials. 2. Metals - Fatigue.

Brief cataloging

NL 0434395 CSt

Locke, George Herbert, 1870-1937
A bibliography of secondary education, being a classified index of the School review, volumes I–X. George H. Locke. Chicago, University of Chicago press, 1903.
41 p. 25cm.

4–16187
Library of Congress

NL 0434396 DLC KEmT CoU CU NcD MH ICJ DHEW

Locke, George Herbert, 1870–1937.
Builders of the Canadian commonwealth, by George H. Locke, with an introduction by A. H. U. Colquhoun. Toronto, The Ryerson press ₍©1923₎
xiii p., 1 l., 317 p. 21½cm.

1. Canada—Biog. I. Title.

23–18848
Library of Congress F1005.L81

MtBuM WaT WaTC WaWW Or OrStbM OrCS WaE OEac OCl OrSaW WaPS WaS OrU-M WaSp WaSpG WaU PP CaBVaU IdPI MtU OrP OrU Wa IdB IdU MtBC
NL 0434397 DLC NcD OrU TxU NcU MiU OU NN IU MB

Locke, George Herbert, 1870–1937.
Builders of the Canadian commonwealth, by George H. Locke, with an introduction by A. H. U. Colquhoun. ₍2d ed.₎ Toronto, Ryerson Press ₍1926, c1923₎
xiii p., 1 l., 317 p. 21½ cm.

NL 0434398 NcD CaBVaU CU

Locke, George Herbert, 1870-1937.
A catalogue of the periodicals (in which are included the publications and the transactions of learned societies) to be found in the libraries of the city of Toronto, Canada. Toronto, Printed and pub. by C. W. James, printer to the king's most excellent Majesty, 1924.

Locke, George Herbert, 1870-1937.
The education of a people. The inaugural lecture delivered at Macdonald College. Montreal, The Witness Press, 1908.
12 p. 8°.

NL 0434400 NN RPB CaBVaU

VOLUME 337

Locke, George Herbert, 1870-1937.
... English history, by George H. Locke. Chicago, American library association, 1930.
55 p. 18 cm. (Reading with a purpose, no. 45)
"Books recommended in this course": p. 53-54.

1. Gt. Brit.—Hist. 2. Gt. Brit.—Hist.—Bibl. I. American library association. II. Title.
Library of Congress DA32.7.L6 30—10022

PPT PPFr ViU Or NcD WaE OrP Wa IdU-SB WaS NN MB AAP
NL 0434401 DLC TU PPD PHC PU OU OC1 OCX OO OC1W

Z6945 .T68 1934 Locke, George Herbert, 1870-1937.
A Joint catalogue of the periodicals and serials in the libraries of the city of Toronto. Toronto, Printed and published by the King's printer, 1934.

Locke, George Herbert, 1870-1937, joint ed.
A joint catalogue of the periodicals, publications and transactions of societies and other books published at intervals to be found in the various libraries of the city of Toronto. [2d. ed.] Toronto, University press, 1913.

Locke, George Herbert, 1870-1937.
Commission of enquiry [into the library situation in Canada]
Libraries in Canada, a study of library conditions and needs, by the Commission of enquiry, John Ridington, chairman, Mary J. L. Black, George H. Locke. Toronto, The Ryerson press; Chicago, The American library association, 1933.

UA 602 F5L6 Locke, George Herbert, 1870-1937.
The Queen's Rangers [by George H.Locke and Margaret Ray. Toronto, Toronto Public Library, 1923]
30p. 26cm.

√1.Gt.Brit. Army. First American Loyalist Regiment.√2.U.S. - Hist. - Revolution - British forces.√I.Ray, Margaret, jt.auth.√II. Title.√LC

NL 0434405 CLSU PHi RPJCB MB WaS IU OO

Locke, George Herbert, 1870-1937, ed.
The School review; a journal of secondary education ... v. 1- Jan. 1893-
Chicago, The University of Chicago press; [etc., etc.] 1893-19

q027.271 T6861 Locke, George Herbert, 1870-1937.
The Toronto public libraries. [Montreal? 1925?]
15p. illus., plans.

"Reprinted from the Journal Royal architectural institute of Canada, May-June, 1925."

NL 0434407 IU MH CaBVaU

Locke, George Herbert, 1870-1937.
When Canada was New France, by George H. Locke ... with seven illustrations ... Toronto, J. M. Dent & sons ltd.; [etc., etc.] 1919.
154 p. incl. 6 pl. 20 cm.
"Stories which illustrate references in this book": p. 143-150.

1. Canada—Hist.—To 1763 (New France) I. Title.
Library of Congress F1030.L81 20—3289

CaBVa
NL 0434408 DLC CaNSWA MeB CU PP NN MB CaBVaU Or

F 1030 L81 1919 Locke, George Herbert, 1870-1937.
When Canada was New France; with seven illustrations. Toronto, J.M. Dent, 1920 [c1919]
155 p. illus. 20cm.

"Stories which illustrate references in this book": p. 143-150. "Poems which illustrate references in the book": p. 151-155.
1. Canada - History - To 1763 (New France) I. Title.

NL 0434409 CoU OO DLC ODW OC1 MiU PPYH

Locke, George Herbert, 1870-1937.
When Canada was New France ... New York, E.P. Dutton & co.; London, J. M. Dent & sons ltd. [1923]
127 p. incl. front., pls. 15 cm. (The kings treasures of literature, A.T. Quiller Couch, editor.)
Author's autograph presentation copy.

NL 0434410 MWiW-C CaBVaU

Locke, George Herbert, 1870-1937, ed.
FOR OTHER EDITIONS SEE MAIN ENTRY
The World book encyclopedia; modern, pictorial, comprehensive ... editor-in-chief, M. V. O'Shea ... managing editor, Ellsworth D. Foster, editor for Canada, George H. Locke ... art director, Gordon Saint Clair, assisted by two hundred fifty outstanding leaders in their respective fields ... Chicago, Toronto, W. F. Quarrie & company [c1931]

Locke, George Herbert, 1870-1937, ed.
FOR OTHER EDITIONS SEE MAIN ENTRY
The World book; organized knowledge in story and picture, editor-in-chief, M. V. O'Shea ... editor for Canada, George H. Locke ... assisted by one hundred fifty distinguished scientists, educators, artists and leaders of thought in the United States and Canada ... Chicago, Toronto [etc.] W. F. Quarrie & company, 1929.

Locke, George W
Atlas of Logan Co. Kentucky. From surveys and recorded plans, by George W. Locke, & R.C. Hunt ... Dayton, O., Wight & son, 1877.
n.p. illus. maps. F.

NL 0434413 NcD KyBgW

Locke, Giovanni, 1632-1704
see Locke, John, 1632-1704.

Locke, Gladys Edson, 1887-
The Fenwood murders, by Gladys E. Locke ... London, J. Long, limited [1931]
288 p. 19½cm.

I. Title.
Library of Congress PZ3.L792Fe 31-11202

NL 0434415 DLC MB

Locke, Gladys Edson, 1887-
The golden lotus, by G. E. Locke ... illustrated by Frank T. Merrill. Boston, L. C. Page & company [1927]
4 p. l., 328 p. front., plates. 19½cm.

I. Title.
Library of Congress PZ3.L792Go 27-2310

NL 0434416 DLC PPL MiU MB

Locke, Gladys Edson, 1887-
Grey Gables.
— London. John Long, Ltd. [1929.] 18½ cm., in 8s.
A detective story; the scene is laid in the South Downs, Sussex, England.

D1233 — T.r. — Detective stories.

NL 0434417 MB

Locke, Gladys Edson, 1887-
The house on the downs, by G. E. Locke ... illustrated by Frank T. Merrill. Boston, L. C. Page & company [1925]
4 p. l., 305 p. front., plates. 19½cm.

I. Title.
Library of Congress PZ3.L792Ho 25-9142

NL 0434418 DLC OC1 MB

Locke, Gladys Edson, 1887-
The purple mist, by G. E. Locke ... illustrated by Charles E. Meister. Boston, L. C. Page & company, inc., 1924.
4 p. l., 363 p. front., plates. 19½cm.

I. Title.
Library of Congress PZ3.L792Pu 24-17250

NL 0434419 DLC PP OC1 OC1h MB

Locke, Gladys Edson, 1887-
Queen Elizabeth; various scenes and events in the life of Her Majesty, by Gladys E. Locke, M. A. Boston, Sherman, French & company, 1913.
3 p. l., 295 p. front. (port.) 20½cm. $1.35

1. Elizabeth, queen of England, 1533-1603.
Library of Congress DA355.L6 13-26617

NL 0434420 DLC OC1 PSC MB

Locke, Gladys Edson, 1887-
The Ravensdale mystery, by G. E. Locke ... illustrated by Harold Cue. Boston, L. C. Page & company [c1935]
4 p. l., 405 p. front., plates. 19½cm.
"First impression, September, 1935."

I. Title.
Library of Congress PZ3.L792Rav 35-18239

NL 0434421 DLC CaOTP MB

Locke, Gladys Edson, 1887-
The red cavalier; or, The Twin Turrets mystery, by Gladys Edson Locke, with a frontispiece in full color from a painting by Charles E. Barnes. Boston, The Page company, 1922.
3 p. l., 372 p. col. front. 20cm.

I. Title.
Library of Congress PZ3.L792Re 22-9573

NL 0434422 DLC MB NN

Locke, Gladys Edson, 1887-
The Redmaynes, by G. E. Locke ... illustrated by Dean Freeman. Boston, L. C. Page & company [c1928]
4 p. l., 327 p. front., plates. 19½cm.

I. Title.
Library of Congress PZ3.L792Red 28-18239

NL 0434423 DLC PP ViU MB

VOLUME 337

Locke, Gladys Edson, 1887–
Ronald o' the moors, by Gladys Edson Locke ... with illustrations by Nellie L. Thompson. Boston, The Four seas company, 1919.
332 p. front., plates. 19½cm.

I. Title.
Library of Congress PZ3.L792Ro 20-94

NL 0434424 DLC NcU NcD MB

Locke, Gladys Edson, 1887–
The scarlet macaw, by G. E. Locke ... illustrated by Charles E. Meister. Boston, L. C. Page & company (inc.) 1923.
4 p. l., 315 p. col. front., plates. 19½cm.

I. Title.
Library of Congress PZ3.L792Sc 23-11806

NL 0434425 DLC PP MH NN MB

Locke, Gladys Edson, 1887–
That affair at Portstead manor, by Gladys Edson Locke ... Boston, Sherman, French & company, 1914.
3 p. l., 266 p. 21cm. $1.25

I. Title.
Library of Congress PZ3.L792T 14-13880

NL 0434426 DLC

Locke, Gladys Edson, 1887–
That affair at Portstead Manor, by Gladys Edson Locke.. Boston: Four Seas Co., 1919. 3 p.l., 266 p. 8°.
First published 1914.

1. Fiction (English). 2. Title.
September 4, 1919.

NL 0434427 NN MB

Locke, Harold.
A bibliographical catalogue of the published novels and ballads of William Harrison Ainsworth, by Harold Locke. London, E. Mathews, ltd., 1925.
68 p. 22½cm.
Errata slip inserted.

1. Ainsworth, William Harrison, 1805–1882—Bibl.
Library of Congress Z8020.2.L8 1 26-13965

PBm PSC PP KMK ScU PSt TxU NN
NL 0434428 DLC LU WU NIC NcU InU CtY NcD OO ODW OCl

Locke, Harold.
A bibliographical catalogue of the writings of Sir Arthur Conan Doyle, M. D., LL. D., 1879–1928, by Harold Locke ... Tunbridge Wells, D. Webster, 1928.
84 p. 22½cm.
CONTENTS.—Contributions to magazines.—Pamphlets.—Plays.—Prefaces.—Published works.—Uniform editions.—Index.

1. Doyle, Sir Arthur Conan, 1859– —Bibl.
Library of Congress Z8240.L8 29-16849

NSyU NIC CaBVaU
NL 0434429 DLC MBCo ScU MH NcD CtY ViU OCl PSC NN

LOCKE, HARRY, 1874– , comp.
Automobile local tours: Locke-Rinehart road maps of west Texas and southern New Mexico. [El Paso, H. Locke & R.H. Rinehart, [1912] 48 p. illus., maps. 28cm.

1. Automobiles--Road guides--U.S.--Texas. 2. Automobiles--Road guides--U.S.--New Mexico.

NL 0434430 NN

Locke, Harry, 1874– *comp.*
Automobile local tours; Locke-Rinehart road maps of wes Texas and southern New Mexico ... ₍El Paso, Tex., H. Lock & R. H. Rinehart, 1915₎
cover-title, 48 p. illus. (incl. maps) 26½ x 13cm.
"Compiled by Harry Locke."
Advertising matter included.

1. Automobiles—Road guides—Texas. 2. Automobiles—Road guides—New Mexico. I. Title.
Library of Congress GV1024.L35 15-17674

NL 0434431 DLC

₍**Locke, Harry**₎ 1874– *comp.*
The borderland route; a complete and accurate road map with detailed information required by auto travelers between El Paso-Phoenix, San Diego-Los Angeles. ₍Phoenix, Ariz., H. Locke, ©1915₎
cover-title, 69 p. illus. (incl. maps) 23½ x 12½cm. $0.75
p. 67-69 printed on one side of folded leaf, with map on verso.

1. Automobiles—Road guides. 2. Southwest, New—Descr. & trav.—Guide-books. I. Title.
Library of Congress GV1024.L4 15-10727

NL 0434432 DLC

Map .G 4031 P2 1925 L6

Locke, Harry, 1874-
Good road map of the south central States showing transcontinental routes with principal tributaries. Los Angeles, 19??.
map 53 x 63cm.
Scale 1:2,534,400.
Text on verso.

1. Texas-- Road maps.

NL 0434433 NIC

Locke, Harry, 1874– *comp.*
Locke's good road maps of local and transcontinental automobile routes ... Comp. and pub. by Harry Locke ... Los Angeles, Cal., ©1917.
216 p. illus. (incl. maps) fold. map. 26½cm. $1.25

1. Automobiles—Road guides. 2. U. S.—Descr. & trav.—Guide-books.
Library of Congress GV1024.L3 17-14397

NL 0434434 DLC

GV1024 L6 1920

Locke, Harry, 1874- comp.
Locke's good road maps of local and transcontinental automobile routes. [Los Angeles, c1920]
472 p. illus., maps (1 fold.) 27x14cm.

NL 0434435 CU-B

Locke, Harry, 1874- comp

Arizona good roads association.
... Illustrated road maps and tour book ₍1913₎– ... Los Angeles, Cal., Printed by Frank E. Garbutt company, ©1913–

Locke, Harry, 1874–
Los Angeles, Phoenix route map "the desert classic" race course 1914, including the roads to the Grand Canyon; a complete and accurate road map with detailed information required by travelers. Los Angeles, Cal., Phoenix, Ariz., H. Locke ₍1914₎
cover-title, 29 p. illus. (incl. maps) 24cm. $0.75
p. 27-29 printed on one side of folded leaf, with map on verso.

1. Automobiles—Road guides. 2. Southwest, New—Descr. & trav.—Guide-books. I. Title.
Library of Congress GV1024.L5 15-3411

NL 0434437 DLC CU-B

GV1024 .O 915

Locke, Harry, 1874– comp.
Official guide, the Old Spanish trail. 1st– ed. ₍1916₎– Mobile, Ala., H. Locke, ©1916–

Locke, Harry, 1874– *comp.*
Texas automobile tours including the route to New Orleans ... comp. and pub. by Harry Locke ... Phoenix, Ariz., ©1916.
64 p. illus. (incl. maps) 27 x 13cm. $1.00

1. Automobiles—Road guides. 2. Texas—Descr. & trav.—Guide-books.
Library of Congress GV1024.L57 16-6414

NL 0434439 DLC

HQ728 .B8 1953

Locke, Harvey James, 1900– joint author.
FOR OTHER EDITIONS SEE MAIN ENTRY
Burgess, Ernest Watson, 1886–
The family, from institution to companionship ₍by₎ Ernest W. Burgess ₍and₎ Harvey J. Locke. 2d ed. ₍New York₎ American Book Co. ₍1953₎

Locke, Harvey James, 1900–
A history and critical interpretation of the social gospel of Northern Baptists in the United States, 1930.
xiii, 178 l. illus. 29 cm.
Typescript (carbon copy)
Thesis—University of Chicago.
Bibliography: leaves 165–178.

1. Social gospel. 2. Sociology, Christian (Baptist) I. Title.
BT738.L58 73-172543 MARC

NL 0434441 DLC ICU

Mflm 306

Locke, Harvey James, 1900–
A history and critical interpretation of the social gospel of Northern Baptists in the United States. Chicago, Ill., 1930.
xiii, 178, 13 p. tables, 28 cm.
Thesis (Ph.D.)--University of Chicago.
Bibliography: p. 165-178.
Microfilm. Nashville, Tenn. Microfilmed by the Library Dept. of Photographic Reproduction, University of Chicago for the Historical Commission, Southern Baptist Convention ₍n.d.₎ 1 reel 35 mm.

1. Sociology, Christian. **2. Northern** Baptist Convention. **3. Baptist Congress. 4.** Rauschenbusch, Walter, 1861-1918. **5. Mathews,** Shailer, 1863-1941.

NL 0434443 MNtcA

Locke, Harvey James, 1900–
Predicting adjustment in marriage: a comparison of a divorced and a happily married group. New York, Holt ₍1951₎
xx, 407 p. 22 cm.

1. Marriage. I. Title.
HQ728.L74 392.5 51-4445

Or CU-I
OrU OrSaW WaE WaS WaSpG WaTC CaBVaU AAP TU ViU OrP
NL 0434444 DLC CaOTP CU MiU IdU TxU NcU NN MtU OrCS

VOLUME 337

WC 160 L814s 1938
LOCKE, Harvey James, 1900-
Social aspects of syphilis. ⌈n. p., Indiana State Board of Health, 1938⌉
54 ℓ. illus.
1. Syphilis - prevention & control 2. Syphilis - sociology I. Indiana. State Board of Health

NL 0434445 DNLM

Locke, Harvey James, 1900- joint author.

Sutherland, Edwin Hardin, 1883-
... Twenty thousand homeless men; a study of unemployed men in the Chicago shelters, by Edwin H. Sutherland ... and Harvey J. Locke ... Chicago, Philadelphia, J. B. Lippincott company ⌈°1936⌉

Locke, Helen M.
All due to the management; monologue for a gentleman, by Helen M. Locke ... Chicago, The Dramatic publishing company, °1897.
6 p. 18cm.

I. Title.

Library of Congress PN4305.M6L8 12-36282

NL 0434447 DLC CLSU NN

Locke, Henry
see
Lok, Henry, 1553?-1608?

Locke, Henry Dyer.
An ancient parish; an historical summary of the first parish, Watertown, Mass^tts, by Henry Dyer Locke ... ⌈Watertown, Mass.:⌉ The Tercentenary Committee of the Parish, 1930. 10 p. illus. (incl. plan), plates. 8°.
no. 372 of 1000 copies printed.
"A souvenir of the three hundredth anniversary celebration."

519753A. 1. Watertown, Mass.—Churches—First Church.
N. Y. P. L. April 24, 1931

NL 0434449 NN MH MB MH-AH

HF5549 .L75
Locke, Henry William, 1888-
Fundamentals of personnel management... Aldwych, Institute of Labour Management, 1943.
18p. 21cm.

NL 0434450 NNU-W NIC IaU

658.3 L792f 1943r
Locke, Henry William, 1888-
Fundamentals of personnel management. London, Institute of Personnel Management [1951]
18p. 22cm.

"First edition, 1943. Reprinted, 1951."

1. Employment management. I. Institute of Personnel Management. II. Title.

NL 0434451 TxU NcD

Locke, Henry William, 1888- joint author.

Hall, Patricia.
Incentives and contentment; a study made in a British factory, by Patricia Hall, B. SC., and H. W. Locke, M. A.; with a foreword by B. Seebohm Rowntree, C. H. London, Sir I. Pitman & sons, ltd., 1938.

[LOCKE, Herbert G., compiler].
[Scrapbook of programmes and newspaper clippings relating to the history of Lexington Mass., 1868, '72, '91-1906.]

4°.

NL 0434453 MH

R 388.1 L793D
Locke, J Allan
Development and economic significance of the Tacoma Narrows bridge, 1923-1953.
172 p.

Typescript.
Thesis - College of Puget Sound.

NL 0434454 WaT

Locke, J. Courtenay, 1880-
see Locke, John Courtenay, 1880-

Locke, J.E.
see Locke, James Eagle, 1898-

Locke, J.S.
see Locke, John Staples, 1836-1906.

⌈**Locke, James**⌉
Tweed and Don; or, Recollections and reflections of an angler for the last fifty years ... Edinburgh, W. P. Nimmo; ⌈etc., etc.⌉ 1860.
vii, 152 p. front., illus. 18cm.
Dedication signed: James Locke.

1. Fishing—Scotland. I. Title.

Library of Congress SH439.L81 12-19524

NL 0434458 DLC CaBVaU CtY NIC MB

[LOCKE, James]
Tweed and Don, or Recollections and reflections of an angler for the last fifty years. 2d ed. Edinburgh, W.P. Nimmo, [etc., etc.], 1860.

VIII, 152 p. Front. and other illustr.

NL 0434459 MH

Locke, James, 1869-1928, tr.

QD75 .M43
Menshutkin, Nikolaĭ Aleksandrovich, 1842-1907.
Analytical chemistry, by N. Menschutkin ... translated from the third German edition, under the supervision of the author, by James Locke. London and New York, Macmillan and co., 1895.

Locke, James, 1869-1928
On an isomer of potassium ferricyanide.
(In Wells. Studies from the chemical laboratory. Vol. I, pp 116-129. New York, 1901.)
Reprinted from the American Chemical Journal, vol. 21, 1899 [*7977.1.21].

By James Locke and Gaston Holcomb Edwards

Apr. 16, 1902
E3821 — Isomerism. — Potassium ferricyanide.

NL 0434461 MB

Locke, James, 1869-1928
On some compounds of trivalent vanadium. Illus.
(In Wells. Studies from the chemical laboratory. Vol. I, pp. 103-115. New York, 1901.)
Reprinted from the American Chemical Journal, vol. 20, 1898 [*7977.1.20].

By James Locke and Gaston Holcomb Edwards

Apr. 16, 1902
E3821 — Vanadium. — Jt. auth.

NL 0434462 MB

Locke, James, 1869-1928
On the formation of potassium β-ferricyanide through the action of acids upon the normal ferricyanide. Plate.
(In Wells. Studies from the chemical laboratory. Vol. I, pp 130-135. New York, 1901.)
Reprinted from the American Chemical Journal, vol. 21, 1895 [*7977.1.21].

By James Locke and Gaston Holcomb Edwards

Apr. 16, 1902
F3821 — Potassium ferricyanide. — Jt. auth.

NL 0434463 MB CtY

Locke, James, 1869-1928 **3974.168.1**
On the periodic system and the properties of inorganic compounds. Charts.
(In Wells. Studies from the chemical laboratory. Vol. I, pp. 158-203. New York, 1901.)
Reprinted from the American Chemical Journal, vol. 20, 26, 1898, 1901 [*7977.1.20.26].

Apr. 21, 1902
E3820 — Chemistry, Inorganic. — Atoms.

NL 0434464 MB

Locke, James, 1869-1928
The plotting of Frances Ware, by James Locke ... New York, Moffat, Yard and company, 1909.
4 p. l., 309 p. 19½cm.

9-14414
Library of Congress PZ3.L793P
(Copyright 1909 A 238457)

NL 0434465 DLC

Locke, James, 1869-1928.
The stem of the crimson dahlia, by James Locke; with frontispiece by Ch. Weber-Ditzler. New York, Moffat, Yard & company, 1908.
vii, 3-342 p. col. front. 19½cm.

8-3426
Library of Congress PZ3.L793S

NL 0434466 DLC PPL ViU

Locke, James, 1869-1928
I. Ueber die chemische Konstitution des Topases. II. Ueber Thoriummetaoxyd und dessen Hydrate. Heidelberg, 1896.

30 p.

Inaugural dissertation

NL 0434467 PPC PU ICRL

Locke, James de Witt Clinton.
See
Locke, Clinton, 1829-1904.

VOLUME 337

Locke, James Eagle, 1898–
Practice tests in civil service, advanced clerical, 1947 ⌊by⌋ J. E. Locke and M. Malloy. ⌊Oakland, Calif., 1947⌋
cover-title, 54 numb. l. 28cm.
"First printing March 1947."
1. Civil service—U. S.—Examinations. 2. Clerks—U. S. I. Malloy, Marian Virginia, 1911– joint author.
JK716.L75 351.3 47-20979
Brief cataloging

NL 0434469 DLC

Locke, Jane.
Nothing ever happens, by Jane Locke. London, H. Jenkins, limited ⌊1938⌋
284 p. 19cm.
"First printed 1938."
I. Title.
38-11075
Library of Congress PZ3.L7936No

NL 0434470 DLC PU

⌊**Locke,** *Mrs.* **Jane Ermina (Starkweather)**⌋ 1805–1859.
Boston: a poem ... Boston, W. Crosby and H. P. Nichols, 1846.
46 p., 1 l. 17½cm.
1. Boston—Descr.—Poetry. 2. Poetry of places—Massachusetts—Boston. I. Title.
28-9354
Library of Congress PS2248.L82B6

NL 0434471 DLC MB PU RPB OCl NN

Locke, Mrs. Jane Ermina (Starkweather) 1805–1859.
⌊**Foster,** *Mrs.* **Hannah (Webster)**⌋ 1759–1840.
The coquette; or, The history of Eliza Wharton. A novel: founded on fact. By a lady of Massachusetts. New ed. With an historical preface, and a memoir of the author. Boston, W. P. Fetridge and company, 1855.

Locke, *Mrs.* **Jane Ermina (Starkweather)** 1805–1859.
Daniel Webster; a rhymèd eulogy, by Mrs. J. Ermina Locke. Boston and Cambridge, J. Munroe & company, 1854.
24 p. 21cm.
10—19907
Library of Congress E340.W4L8

NL 0434473 DLC

Locke, Jane Ermina (Starkweather) 1805-1859
Dante. Boston, 1854.
pp. 76-77.
(In her The recalled, in voices of the past and poems of the ideal,)

NL 0434474 NIC

Locke, Jane Ermina (Starkweather) 1805-1859 2395.119
Historical preface including a memoir of the author [Hannah Foster].
(In Foster, Hannah. The coquette . . . Pp. 1-30. Boston, 1855.)
Two copies.
Aug. 13, 1903
F461

NL 0434475 MB

Locke, *Mrs.* **Jane Ermina (Starkweather)** 1805–1859.
Miscellaneous poems. By Mrs. Jane Ermina Locke. Boston, Otis, Broaders & co., 1842.
300 p. 20cm.
28-9721
Library of Congress PS2248.L82M5

NL 0434476 DLC ViU OU NcD NBuG MB

Locke, Jane Erminia (Starkweather) 1805-1859.
Rachael, or, The little mourner. A tale of truth. Lowell [Mass.] Stearns & Taylor, 1844.
16 p. illus. 14 cm.
A poem.
Variant covers.

NL 0434477 RPB CtY

Locke, *Mrs.* **Jane Ermina (Starkweather)** 1805–1859.
The recalled; in voices of the past, and poems of the ideal. By Jane Ermina Locke. Boston and Cambridge, J. Munroe and company, 1854.
vii, 246 p. front. (port.) 18½cm.
I. Title.
28-9722
Library of Congress PS2248.L82R4

NL 0434478 DLC MH NBuG NN MB

LOCKE, Mrs. Jane Ermina (Starkweather) 1805-1859.
The recalled; in voices of the past, and Poems of the ideal. New ed. Boston, etc., 1856 [cop. 1853].
sm. 8°. Port.

NL 0434479 MH

Locke, Jerome George, 1882–
Meritism, a new idea for an economy of equity that will abolish profit and preserve incentive, by Jerome G. Locke. Boston, The Christopher publishing house ⌊©1934⌋
1 p. l., 7–260 p. diagrs. (1 fold.) 20cm.
1. Economics—Miscellanea. I. Title. II. Title: An economy of equity that will abolish profit.
35-124
Library of Congress HB171.7.L55
Copyright A 77428 330.1

NL 0434480 DLC Wa WaS OU NcU NN

Locke, Jerome George, 1882–
Report on Upper Missouri Valley development, by Jerome G. Locke, R. A. Biggs ⌊and⌋ J. V. Bennett, December 12, 1946. Helena, Mont., Printed and distributed by Montana M. V. A. Assn. ⌊1947⌋
29 l. fold. map, diagrs. 28 cm.
Cover title.
1. Missouri River. 2. Missouri Valley. I. Biggs, Raymond A., 1895– joint author. II. Bennett, Joseph V., 1904– joint author. III. Montana Missouri Valley Authority Association.
TC425.M7L6 627.1 48-18869*

NL 0434481 DLC

Locke, John. Commerce of the medial East.
8 pp. 2 maps. (Lancashire and Cheshire Hist. Soc. Trans. v. 9, 1857, p. 119.)

NL 0434482 MdBP

Locke, John.
On polar exploration—Arctic and Antarctic. By John Locke ... Read before the Royal Dublin society, Friday evening, November 19, 1860; and reprinted from the Journal of the society. ⌊Dublin, 1860?⌋
12 p. 2 diagr. 22cm.
Caption title.
1. Arctic regions. 2. Antarctic regions.
5-39700†
Library of Congress G710.L81

NL 0434483 DLC

YA 15969.
Locke, John.
Remarkable discoveries in Central Australia... Dublin, 1863.
13p.

NL 0434484 DLC

WZ 290 L814s 1642F
[LOCKE, John] cleric
A strange and lamentable accident that happened lately at Mears-Ashby in Northamptonshire, 1642. Of one Mary Wilmore, wife to Iohn Wilmore, rough mason, who was delivered of a childe without a head, and credibly reported to have a firme crosse on the brest, as this ensuing story shall relate... London, Harper and Wine, 1642 [Northampton, Eng., Taylor, 1870?]
facsim.: (5 p.) ([Northampton County] tracts [no.] 28, ser. 2)
1. Wilmore, Mary

NL 0434486 DNLM

⌊Locke, John⌋ cleric
A strange and lamentable accident that happened lately at Mears-Ashby in Northamptonshire. 1642. Of one Mary Wilmore, wife to Iohn Wilmore...who was delivered of a childe without a head, and credibly reported to have a firme crosse on the brest, as this ensuing story shall relate... London: Printed for R. Harper and T. Wine, and are to be sold at the Bible and Harpe in Smithfield. 1642. 5 p. 22cm. (Tracts «rare and curious reprints, mss., etc.», relating to Northamptonshire... Second series. London, 1881 ⌊no. 11⌋)
Signed: Iohn Locke, cleric.
301830. 1. Monsters. I. Title.
Revised November 8, 1935

NL 0434487 NN DNLM

⌊**Locke, John**⌋ *cleric.*
A / Strange / And Lamentable accident that happened lately at / Mears-Ashby in Northamptonshire. 1642. / Of one Mary Wilmore, wife of John Wilmore rough Mason, who was / delivered of a Childe without a head, and credibly reported / to have a firme Crosse on the brest, as this en- / suing Story shall relate. / Hor: Miranda cano. / Printed at London for Rich: Harper and Thomas Wine, and are to bee sold / at the Bible and Harpe in Smithfield. 1642. / ⌊East Lansing, 1940⌋
2 p. l., 2–5 numb. l., 2 l. 19½cm. (*Half-title:* Reprints of English books, 1475–1700, ed. by Joseph Arnold Foster. no. 32)
Signed: By Iohn Locke, cleric.
"50 copies printed."
Text reprinted "from the British museum copy, E. 113. (15.)".
1. Wilmore, Mrs. Mary. I. Title.
Virginia. Univ. Library for Library of Congress A 41-256

NL 0434488 ViU CSmH NN

QK 45 L63 1819
Locke, John, Lecturer on Botany
Outlines of botany, taken chiefly from Smith's Introduction; containing an explanation of botanical terms and an illustration of the system of Linnaeus. Also some account of the natural orders, and the anatomy and physiology of vegetables. Boston, Cummings and Hilliard, 1819.
161 p. illus.
1. Botany. I. Smith, Sir James Edward, 1759-1828./ An introduction to physiological and systemical botany. II. Title. rev.

NL 0434489 DNLM

VOLUME 337

Idb75
G7
851ic
Locke, John, of Rathmines, Dublin
Ireland. Emigration, and Valuation and purchase of land in Ireland (Reprinted from the Journal of the Statistical society of London.) ... 2d ed., considerably enlarged. London, J.W. Parker and son, 1853.
19p. 21cm. [Bound with his: Ireland. Observations ... 3d ed. Dublin[etc.]1852]

NL 0434490 CtY IU

[Locke, John] of Rathmines, Dublin
Ireland. Observations on the people, the land, and the law, in 1851...
see under title

330.9415
L793ir
Locke, John, of Rathmines, Dublin.
Ireland's recovery; or, Excessive emigration and its reparative agencies in Ireland. An essay with appendix, containing useful information, and numerous statistical tables, illustrating and substantiating the conclusions deduced. London, 1854.
68p.

NL 0434492 IU NN

Locke, John, of Rathmines, Dublin.
Ireland's recovery; or, Excessive emigration and its reparative agencies in Ireland. An essay, with appendix, containing useful information, and numerous statistical fables, illustrating and substantiating the conclusions deduced... London, J.W. Parker & Son, 1855.
2 p.l., 92 p. 8°.

NL 0434493 NN

Locke, John, Wesleyan minister.
A system of theology. London [William Nichols] 1862.
iv, 506 p.

NL 0434494 CLamB

BT75
L7
Locke, John, Wesleyan minster.
A system of theology. By the Rev. John Locke ... Second edition. Ninth thousand. London, Published by the author, 1867.
viii,556p. 19cm.
1. Theology.
I. Title.

NL 0434495 NBuG

Locke, John, 1632-1704.
Works by this author printed in America before 1801 are available in this library in the Readex Microprint edition of Early American Imprints published by the American Antiquarian Society.
This collection is arranged according to the numbers in Charles Evans' American Bibliography.

NL 0434496 DLC

And.Rm.
B1253*
1714
Locke, John, 1632-1704.
Works. London, Printed for John Churchill and Sam. Manship, 1704.
3 v. 32 cm.

NL 0434497 PPiPT

Locke, John, 1632–1704.
The works of John Locke... London: Printed for J. Churchill, 1714. 3 v. front. (port.) f°.
With bookplate of Wm. S. Johnson.
Vol I includes: An account of the life and writings of John Locke [by J. Le Clerc] The third edition.

1. Philosophy.—Systems and collected works.
October 7, 1924

NNC NIC InU NcGU CLU-C
PP PSC PU NcD NjNbS DFo IU WaU NcU CLSU PPLas WU Scl
NL 0434498 NN CaBVaU Vi NjP NNUT MB MH FU CtY MHi

Locke, John, 1632–1704.
Works. 2d ed. London, Printed for A. Churchill and sold by W. Taylor, 1722.
3 v. port. 33 cm.
Vol. 2 has imprint: Printed for A. Churchill.

1. Philosophy—Collected works.

B1253 1722 51-45985

PU PPPD PPAmP CLU-C CaBVaU
NL 0434499 DLC OGK NjP MiU NcD IU MH OO OClW PHi

Locke, John, 1632–1704.
The works of John Locke ... 3d ed. London, Printed for A. Bettesworth [etc.] 1727.
3 v. fronts. (v. 1: port.) 32½cm.

Library of Congress B1253 1727 10-32044

MH
NL 0434500 DLC NIC ViU IU FTaSU CtY MA MeB PU NcU

Rare
B
1253++
1740
Locke, John, 1632-1704.
Works. 4th ed. London, Printed for E. Parker, E. Symon, C. Hitch and J. Pemberton, 1740.
3 v. front. (port.) 35cm.
Publishers' catalogue: [1] p. at end of v. 1.

NL 0434501 NIC OKentU IEdS CLU-C NcD ViU MWA MiU

B1253
=1751
Locke, John, 1632-1704
The works of John Locke ... with alphabetical tables ... 5th ed. London, Printed for S. Birt, [etc.] 1751.
3 v. 36 cm.
Added t.-p. for v.1, and t.-p. for v.2-3 read: To which is now first added, The life of the author; and a collection of several of his pieces published by Mr. Desmaizeaux.

NL 0434502 RPB N IEN MWiW CtY InU MWA PU ViU

B
1253
1759++
Locke, John, 1632-1704.
Works. The 6th ed. To which is added, the life of the author; and a collection of several of his pieces published by Mr. Desmaizeaux. London, Printed for D. Browne, C. Hitch [etc., etc.] 1759.
3 v. illus. 36cm.

I. Desmaizeaux, Pierre, 1673?-1745.

NL 0434503 NIC ICU CLSU NcD ICN ICJ TxDaM-P IEN

Locke, John, 1632–1704.
The works of John Locke... London: H. Woodfall [and others], 1768. 4 v. front. (port.) 7. ed. f°.

1. Philosophy.—Systems and collected works.
N. Y. P. L. August 2, 1924

NL 0434504 NN NSyU ScU NjP CtY PPL OCl ODW ICJ

B
1253
1777
Locke, John, 1632-1704.
The works of John Locke, in four volumes. 8th ed. London, Printed for W. Strahan [etc.] 1777.
4 v. port., fold chart.

NL 0434505 NBPol ScU IaU OClW PPL MH-L MH IaU

Locke, John, 1632-1704.
The works of ... in four volumes. seventh ed. London, 1788.
4v.

NL 0434506 PPDrop

Locke, John, 1632–1704. Child Mem.
Works. 9th ed. London, printed for T. Longman, etc. 1794.
9 vol. Port. and table.

NL 0434507 MH CtY NcD WaS NjNbS CBPac NhM MeB

192.2
L79X10
Locke, John, 1632-1704.
Works. 10th ed. London, Printed for J. Johnson [etc.] by Bye and Law, 1801.
10 v. 23cm.

1. Philosophy, English.

FMU MH NN MB CtY
NL 0434508 LU NcD PPT PPL PBm MiD MH MWelC NbU DCU

B
1253
1812
Locke, John, 1632-1704.
Works. 11th ed. London, W. Otridge, Leigh and Sotheby [etc.] 1812.
10 v. port. (v. 1) fold. table. 22 cm.
Incomplete set: vols. 5 and 8 wanting
Vol. 1 imperfect: part of folded table torn off.
Errors in paging: v. 2, 40 numbered 322; v. 3, 59 numbered 5; v. 6, 134 and 574 numbered 34 and 274 respectively; v. 7, 188 numbered 138.
Contents. - v. 1. Preface by the editor. Life of the author. Essay concerning human understanding, bk. 1-bk. 2, ch. 22. - v. 2. Essay ... bk. 2, ch. 23-bk. 4, ch. 4. - v. 3. Essay ... (concluded) Defence of Locke's opinion concerning personal identity. Of the conduct of the understanding. Some thoughts concerning reading and study for a gentleman. Elements of natural philosophy. New method of a common-place book. - v. 4. Letters to the Bishop of Worcester relating to the Essay on human understanding. - v. 5. [Three papers relating to the value of money] Two treatises of government. - v. 6. Letters concerning toleration. - v. 7. The reasonableness of Christianity. A vindication of The reasonableness of Christianity from Mr. Edwards's reflections. A second vindication. - v. 8. Paraphrases and notes on the Epistles to the Galatians, Corinthians, Romans, and Ephesians. - v. 9. Some thoughts concerning education. An examination of P. Malebranche's opinion of seeing all things in God. A discourse of miracles. Memoirs of Anthony, first earl of Shaftesbury. Some familiar letters between Mr. Locke and friends. - v. 10. Familiar letters (cont'd) Miscellaneous letters and pieces.

MdBP IU CoU NIC ViU
NL 0434510 Vi CLSU ICN IaU MA NIC NNUT ODW OClW NcU

Locke, John, 1632-1704.
The works of John Locke. A new edition corrected ... London, Printed for Thomas Tegg. W. Sharpe and son [etc.] 1823.
10 v. fold. table. 23 cm.

Contents.--v 1. Preface by the editor. Life of the author. Analysis of Mr. Locke's doctrine of ideas [fold. tab.] Of human understanding. Book I-book II, chap. XXII.--v. 2. Of human understanding. Book II, chapter XXIII-book IV, chap. IV.--v. 3. Of human understanding (concluded) Defense of Mr. Locke's opinion concerning personal identity. Of the conduct of the understanding. Some thoughts concerning reading and study for a gentleman. Elements of natural philosophy. New method of a common-place-book.--v. 4. A letter to the Right Rev. Edward Lord Bishop of Worcester, concerning some passages relating to Mr. Locke's Essay of human understanding

Continued in next column

VOLUME 337

Continued from preceding column

Mr. Locke's Reply. Answer to Remarks upon the Essay concerning human understanding. Mr. Locke's Reply.--v. 5. Some considerations of the consequences of lowering the interest and raising the value of money, in a letter sent to a member of Parliament. 1691. Short observations on a printed paper entitled "For encouraging the coining silver money in England ..." Further considerations concerning raising the

value of money. Two treatises of government.--v. 6. A letter concerning toleration. Second-fourth letter concerning toleration.--v. 7. The reasonableness of Christianity. A vindication of the Reasonableness of Christianity, from Mr. Edward's Reflections. A second vindication.--v. 8. An essay for the understanding of St. Paul's Epistles. A paraphrase and notes on St. Paul's Epistle to the Galatians, first-

second Corinthians, Romans, Ephesians.--v. 9. Some thoughts concerning education. An examination of P. Malebranche's opinion of seeing all things in God. A discourse of miracles. Memoirs relating to the life of Anthony, first earl of Shaftesbury. Some familiar letters between Mr. Locke and several of his friends. --v. 10. Continuation of familiar letters. A collection of several pieces published by Mr. Des Maizeaux

under the direction of Anthony Collins. Observations upon the growth and culture of vines and olives; the production of silk; the preservation of fruits. The whole history of navigation from its original to the year 1704.

NIC
OO OCU OOxM OU PBa OHC TNJ NcD TxFTC InNd PU PPPD
NL 0434516 NSchU TNJ CaBVa CaBVaU MB MH I NN NNC

Locke, John, 1632–1704.
The works of John Locke, in nine volumes. 12th ed. ... London, Printed for C. and J. Rivington [etc.] 1824.
9 v. front. (port.) fold. tab. 23½cm.
CONTENTS.—v. 1. Preface by the editor. Life of the author. Analysis of Mr. Locke's doctrine of ideas (fold. tab.) Essay concerning human understanding. Book I-book III, chap. VI.—v. 2. Essay concerning human understanding (concluded) Defence of Mr. Locke's opinion concerning personal identity. Of the conduct of the understanding. Some thoughts concerning reading and study for a gentleman. Elements of natural philosophy. New method of a common-place-book.—v. 3. Letters to the Right Rev. Edward lord bishop of Worcester, concerning Mr. Locke's Essay of human understanding. Mr. Locke's reply. Answer to Remarks upon an Essay concerning human understanding. Mr. Locke's reply.—v. 4. Some considerations of the consequences of lowering the interest and raising the

value of money (Letter to a member of Parliament. 1691) Short observations on a printed paper entitled, 'For encouraging the coining silver money in England' ... Further considerations concerning raising the value of money. Two treatises of government.—v. 5. A letter concerning toleration. Second-fourth letter for toleration.—v. 6. The reasonableness of Christianity. A vindication of the Reasonableness of Christianity, from Mr. Edward's reflections. A second vindication.—v. 7. Paraphrase and notes on the Epistles of St. Paul to the Galatians, I and II Corinthians, Romans, and Ephesians.—v. 8. Some thoughts concerning education. An examination of P. Malebranche's opinion of seeing all things in God. A discourse of miracles. Memoirs relating to the life of Anthony, first earl of Shaftesbury. Some familiar letters between Mr. Locke and several of his friends.—v. 9. Continuation of familiar letters. (Miscellaneous letters and pieces)

5—31979

Library of Congress B1253 1824

PU ViU
NL 0434518 DLC OrP KEmT MdBP NcU CtY ICN PSC PPDrop

Locke, John, 1632-1704.
The works of John Locke... London, Bell & Daldy, 1871.
v. front. (port.) tabs. 19 cm. (Bohn's standard library)
Contents: v. 1-2. Philosophical works.

NL 0434519 NcU

Locke, John, 1632-1704.
Works. With essay and notes by J.A. St. John. London, Bell, 1876.
2 v. Portr. Table. Sm. 8°.

NL 0434520 MB MH NBuG

Locke, John, 1632–1704.
The works of John Locke ... London, New York, Ward, Lock and co. [1888?]
4 v. front. (port.) fold. tab. 22½cm.
CONTENTS.—An essay on the human understanding (2 v.)—Four letters on toleration.—Some thoughts on education and an essay on the consequences of the lowering of interest and raising the value of money.

12-32775

Library of Congress B1253 1888

NL 0434521 DLC NNUT CtY NNC

Locke, John, 1632–1704.
The works of John Locke, including An essay on the human understanding. Four letters on toleration. Some thoughts on education, and an essay on the value of money. New ed., carefully rev. London, New York, Ward, Lock and co. [1899?]
xvi, 649 p., 1 l., 722 p. front. (port.) 1 fold. tab. 22cm.

4—13552

Library of Congress B1253 1889
[a36b1] -192.2

NL 0434522 DLC IEG

Locke, John, 1632-1704.
Oeuvres philosophiques de Locke. Nouv. éd. rev. par M. Thurot ... Paris, F. Didot, 1821-25.
7 v. 22½cm.
Vol. 3-7 have imprint: Paris, Bossange [etc.]

I. Thurot, Jean François, 1768-1832, ed.

NL 0434523 MiU MH

Z
233
M3L79
1751

Locke, John, 1632-1704.
Abbrégé de l'Essay de Monsieur Locke, sur l'entendement humain, traduit de l'anglois par Mr. Bosset. Nouv. ed. A Londres, Chez Jean Nourse, 1751.
xvi,376,[5] p. port.

Fictitious imprint. Cf. Weller. Die falschen und fingirten Druckorte, II, p. 170.

1. Knowledge, Theory of.

NL 0434524 PHH CLU

LOCKE,John,1632-1704.
Abbrégé de l'essay de Monsieur Locke,sur l'entendement humain. Traduit de l'anglois par Monsieur Bosset. [Colophon: Upsal,chez la veuve du direct. J.Edman,1792.]

Title vign. Phil 2115.48.15

NL 0434525 MH

Locke, John, 1632-1704.
Abregé de l'Essai de Monsieur Locke sur l'entendement humain, tr. de l'anglais par J.P. Bosset. 3. éd. plus exacte que les précedentes. Genève, H.A. Gosse, 1741.
xxiv, 283, [5] p. 20 cm.

NL 0434526 CtY MH

Locke, John, 1632-1704.
Abrege de l' essai... Geneve, 1788.

NL 0434527 NNB

B 1292
1811

Locke, John, 1632-1704.
An abridgment of Locke's essay concerning human understanding/with some conjectures respecting the interference of nature with education, by Louisa Capper. London, Printed by J. Nichols, 1811.
273 p. 28 cm.

1. Knowledge, Theory of, I. Capper, Louisa. II. Title: Human Understanding.

NL 0434528 CaBVaU

Rare
B
1292
1696

Locke, John, 1632-1704.
An abridgment of Mr. Locke's Essay concerning humane [sic] understanding [by John Wynne] London, Printed for A. and J. Churchill and E. Castle, 1696.
310, [10] p. 19cm.

Publishers' catalogue: p. [320]
Wing L 2735.
1. Knowledge, Theory of. I. Locke, John, 1632-1704. Essay concerning human understanding. II. Wynne, John.

CSmH OCU NNUT-Mc
NL 0434529 NIC ICN CtY IEN CLU-C MH NcD InU NjP

17th
Cent.

Locke, John, 1632-1704.
An abridgement of Mr. Locke's Essay concerning humane understanding. The 2d ed., cor. and enl. London, A. &J. Churchil, 1700.
4p. l., 308p., 2l. 19cm.
Title within ruled border.
Abridged by John Wynne.

1. Knowledge, Theory of. I. Wynne, John Bp Bath and Wells, 1667-1743.

NL 0434530 CtY-M MH ICN CU-A CtY CLSU

Locke, John, 1632-1704.
An abridgment of Mr. Locke's Essay concerning human understanding. The fourth edition, corrected. London: Printed for J. and J. Knapton [etc.] 1731.
viii,9-379,[5] p. 17cm.
Dedication signed: John Wynne.
Signatures: A-Q12.
Bound in old sprinkled calf.

NL 0434531 CLU-C MB

121
L814e
1737
LIMITED CIRCULATION

Locke, John, 1632-1704.
An abridgment of Mr. Locke's Essay concerning human understanding. 5th ed. corr. London, Printed for A. Bettesworth [and others] 1737.
379 p. 18cm.

Abridgement by John Wynne.

1. Knowledge, Theory of. I. Wynne, John, bp. of Bath and Wells, 1667-1743. II. Title.

NL 0434532 FU CtY PU-Penn RPB KU

LOCKE,John,1632-1704.
An abridgment of Mr.Locke's essay concerning human understanding [by John Wynne]. 6th ed. corrected. Glasgow,printed and sold by R.Foulis,1744.

NL 0434533 MH

192
L81eh
1767
Abr.

Locke, John, 1632-1704.
An abridgment of Mr. Locke's Essay concernin human understanding. A new ed., with addition carefully rev. and corrected. Edinburgh, printed by A. Donaldson, 1767.
271 p.

KNOWLEDGE, THEORY OF

NL 0434534 KMK RPB

VOLUME 337

B 1272 1770 Locke, John, 1632-1704
An abridgment of Mr. Locke's Essay concerning human understanding. A new ed., with additions, carefully rev. and corr. Edinburgh, Printed by A. Donaldson, 1770.
271p. 18cm.

1. Knowledge, Theory of I. Title: Essay concerning human understanding

NL 0434535 WU

Locke, John, 1632-1704.
An abridgment of Mr. Locke's Essay concerning human understanding. Boston, Printed by Manning & Loring, for J. White, Thomas & Andrews, D. West, E. Larkin, J. West, and the proprietor of the Boston bookstore, 1794.
viii, [9]-250 p. 17½cm.

1. Knowledge, Theory of.

10-32057

Library of Congress B1292 1794

PMA RPJCB NcD
NL 0434536 DLC InU CaBVaU NIC CSt MH MHi MWA NNUT

B 245 .51045 LOCKE, JOHN, 1632-1737.
An abridgment of Mr. Locke's essay concerning human understanding. From the Edinburgh edition. London, Cummings and Hilliard, 1822.
271p. 18cm.

Dedication signed: John Wynne.

NL 0434537 ICN OO OClW NNUT CtY

Locke, John, 1632-1704.
Abstract of Mr. Locke's Essay on human understanding. [Edinburgh, n.d.]
42 p. 22.5 cm.
"Drawn up by no less a man than the late Lord Chief Baron Gilbert..." Advertisement to the Dublin edition.
"The edition used on this occasion was the very elegant one of Edinburgh, 1765." p. 42.
1. Knowledge, Theory of. I. Gilbert, Sir Geoffrey, 1674-1726, ed.

NL 0434538 ViU

Locke, John, 1632-1704.
An Abstract of the Essay of Human Understanding ... Dublin, 1735.

NL 0434539 PU

---

x192 L79e abst. 1752 Locke, John, 1632-1704.
An abstract of Mr. Locke's Essay on human understanding, by Sir Jeffrey Gilbert. Dublin, printed: London, Reprinted for W. Sandby; and sold by J. Hildyard, in York, 1752.
55p. 20cm.

1. Knowledge, Theory of. I. Gilbert, Sir Geoffrey, 1674-1726.

NL 0434540 IU ICN CtY MH

Locke, John, 1632-1704.
Abstract of Mr. Locke's Essay on human understanding ... [Dublin? 1795?]
42 p. 22½cm.
"Drawn up by ... the late Lord Chief Baron Gilbert."
"In re-editing this abstract ... The edition used ... was ... Edinburgh, 1765..." signed: C. L. [i.e. Capel Lofft]
Published also as part of: Gilbert, Sir Geoffrey. The law of evidence ... Considerably enl. by Capel Lofft ... Dublin, 1795-97.
1. Knowledge, Theory of. I. Gilbert, Sir Geoffrey, 1674-1726. II. Lofft, Capel, 1751-1824, ed.

NL 0434541 ViU

Locke, John, 1632-1704.
An account of Mr. Lock's religion, out of his own writings, and in his own words. Together with some observations upon it, and a twofold appendix ... London, J. Nutt, 1700.
2 p. l., 188 p. 19½cm.
Edited by John Milner.

I. Milner, John, 1628-1702, ed.

44-26492

Library of Congress B1298.R4A3

NL 0434542 DLC CtY MH

Locke, John, 1632-1704.
An account of the life and writings of John Locke, esq.
see his Works. London, 1714.

Locke, John, 1632-1704. *3469.26.6
Advantages of the appearance of our Saviour among men.
(In Sparks, Jared, editor. A collection of essays and tracts in theology. Vol. 6, pp. 211-235. Boston, 1823.)

Aug. 7, 1902
E4812

NL 0434544 MB

Locke, John, 1632-1704
An analytical abridgement of Locke's essay concerning human understanding. London, 1808.
xxiv 307 p.

NL 0434545 PPL

B1293 G4K9 Locke, John, 1632-1704.
Anleitung des menschlichen Verstandes zur Erkaentniss der Wahrheit nebst desselben. Abhandlung von den Wunderwerken. Aus dem Englischen übersetzt von George David Kypke. Königsberg, J.H. Hartung, 1755.
176, 16 p.

1. Knowledge, Theory of. I. Kypke, Georg David, 1724-1779.

NL 0434546 CU CaBVaU

[Locke, John] 1632-1705.
An answer to remarks upon an essay concerning humane understanding. [n.p., n.d.]
1 p.l., 7 [1] p. 19.5 cm. [With his A letter to Edward Ld. Bishop of Worcester. 1697]

NL 0434547 CtY-M

Locke, John, 1632-1704.
Beauties of Locke...
London, 1802. 276 p. 24°

NL 0434548 MWA

Locke, John, 1632-1704.
The beauties of Locke, consisting of selections from his philosophical, moral, and theological works. By Alfred Howard, esq. London, Printed by T. Davison, for T. Tegg; [etc., etc., n. d.]
2 p. l., 212 p. front. (port.) 14½cm. (In Howard, Alfred. The beauties of literature ... London, 1833. v. 14 [no. 2])
Also issued separately as v. 18 of series.

I. Title.

28-4316

Library of Congress PN6013.H5 vol. 14

NL 0434549 DLC MH

Locke, John, 1632-1704.
The beauties of Locke, consisting of selections from his philosophical, moral and theological works by Alfred Howard. London, T. Tegg, etc., [1834?]
24°. Engraved port.

NL 0434550 MH

Locke, John, 1632-1704.
Borger og statsmakt, forord av Kåre Foss. [Overs. av Kirsten Pauss Heggdal] Oslo, Dreyer, 1947.
226 p. 21 cm. (Politisk bibliotek; klassikerne)
Translation of Essay concerning the true original extent and end of civil government.

1. Political science. 2. Liberty. I. Title.

JC153.L854 50-31804

NL 0434551 DLC

Locke, John, 1632-1704.
Cateva idei asupra educatiunii... Bucuresti, Vacarescu, 1925.
[2 v.]

NL 0434552 OCl

Lilly Library LOCKE, JOHN, 1632-1704
Le Christianisme raisonnable, tel qu'il nous est representé dans l'ecriture sainte. Traduit de l'Anglois de M. Locke. Troisieme edition ... Amsterdam, Chez Zacharie Chatelain, 1731.
2 v. 8vo

Title in red and black.
Bound in half contemporary vellum, marbled boards.

NL 0434553 InU PPD

Ex 5707 .591 .1740 Locke, John, 1632-1704.
Le christianisme raisonnable, tel qu'il nous est représenté dans l'écriture sainte. Traduit de l'anglois de M. Locke par M. Coste. 4. éd. revue, corrigée & augmentée d'une dissertation... A Amsterdam, Chez Z. Chatelain, 1740.
2 v. in 1. 16 cm.

I. Coste, Pierre, 1668-1747, tr.

NL 0434554 NjP

Locke, John, 1632-1704.
A collection of several pieces of Mr. John Locke, never before printed, or not extant in his works. Pub. by the author of the Life of the ever-memorable Mr. John Hales, &c. London, Printed by J. Bettenham for R. Francklin, 1720.
[35], xxiv, [2], 362, [19] p. diagr. 20cm.
Dedication signed: P. des Maizeaux.
MWiW-C
MiU
I. Desmaizeaux, Pierre, 1672 or 3-1745.
RPJCB

10-28394

Library of Congress B1255.A5 1720

MWiW-C NcD RPJCB NcU
MB ICJ MsM CtY NNNAM CSt TxU ViW CLSU DFo TxHU MiU
NL 0434555 DLC MnU WU ViU PHi PPL NcWsW CLL NcU PU

---

x192 L79co 1724 Locke, John, 1632-1704.
A collection of several pieces of Mr. John Locke, never before printed, or not extant in his works. Publish'd by the author of the life of the ever memorable Mr. John Hales, &c. 2d ed. London, Printed for R. Francklin, 1724.
xxiv, 362p. diagr. 20cm.

Engr. title vignette.
Published by Pierre Desmaizeaux.
I. Desmaizeaux, Pierre, 1673?-1745.

NL 0434556 IU

VOLUME 337

fB1255 1739 Locke, John, 1632-1704.
A collection of several pieces of Mr. John Locke. Publish'd by Mr. Desmaizeaux, under the direction of Anthony Collins, esq. The second edition. London: Printed for R. Francklin... 1739.
5 p. ℓ., x p., 1 ℓ., 118 p. 38cm.
Signatures: [A]-D2, E3, F-Z2, Aa-Ll2, Mm1.
Armorial book-plates of Henry C. Compton esqr. and Scrope Berdmore.
Bound. uncut. in half vellum.

Contents. - The character of Mr. Locke. By Mr. Peter Coste.- The fundamental constitutions of Carolina. - A letter from a person of quality to his friend in the country. - Remarks upon some of Mr. Norris's books. - Elements of natural philosophy. - Some thoughts concerning reading and study. - Several letters to Anth. Collins esq; and other persons. - Rules of a society.

I. Desmaizeaux, Pierre, 1673?-1745, ed. II. Coste, Pierre, 1668-1747.

NSchU CaBVaU
NL 0434558 CU CLU-C NNU-W ICN CtY NcU KEmT NjP

Locke, John, 1632-1704.
Common place-book, on the principles practiced by John Locke, esq. author of An Essay on the human understanding, &c. There is scarce any thing more necessary for the improvement of knowledge ... than for a man to be able to dispose of his own thoughts; and there is scarce any thing more difficult in the whole conduct of the understanding, than to get a full mastery over it. New-Haven, Published and sold by Increase Cooke & co., south corner of the Green. 1804.

[7] p. tables. 24cm.
A description of his method of topical indexing, with the last two pages containing tables illustrating it.

1. Indexing. 2. Commonplace-books. I. t. II. Ptr.

NL 0434560 MiU-C CtY

[Locke, John] 1632-1704, supposed author.
A common-place book to the Holy Bible: or, The Scriptures sufficiency practically demonstrated. Wherein whatsoever is contain'd in Scripture, respecting doctrine, worship, or manners, is reduced to its proper head: weighty cases resolved, truths confirmed, difficult texts illustrated, and explained by others more plain ... London, Printed by E. Jones, for A. and J. Churchill, 1697.
8 p. l., 310, [8] p. 25 x 17cm.
1. Bible—Indexes, Topical. I. Title. II. Title: The Scriptures sufficiency practically demonstrated.
38-30012
Library of Congress BS432.L6 1697

NjR NNUT-Mc GDC CU
NL 0434561 DLC IEN CLU-C CU-A TxDaM-P CtY MH IdU

[Locke, John] 1632-1704, supposed author.
A common place-book to the Holy Bible: or, The Scripture's sufficiency practically demonstrated. Wherein the substance of Scripture, respecting doctrine, worship, and manners, is reduced to its proper head: weighty cases are resolved, truths confirmed, and difficult texts illustrated and explained. The 3d ed.; improved with twelve intire additional chapters; many errors in the former editions are amended, and the whole faithfully collated text by text; together with proper insertions made to connect the sense ... London, Printed for R. and J. Bonwicke, and R. Wilkin [etc.] MDCCXXV.
8 p. l., 440, [12] p. 21 x 17cm.
1. Bible—Indexes, Topical. I. Title. II. Title: The Scripture's sufficiency practically demonstrated.
37-19936
Library of Congress BS432.L6 1725
220.2

NL 0434562 DLC IaU CtY MH RPB

Div.S. 220.2 L814C [Locke, John] 1632-1704, supposed author.
A common place-book to the Holy Bible; or, The Scripture's sufficiency practically demonstrated ... 4th ed. ... London, Printed for A. Bettesworth and C. Hitch, 1738.
309 p. illus. 25 cm.

1. Bible. Indexes, Topical. I. Title.

NL 0434563 NcD PHi MH

BS432 L6 1766 Locke, John, 1632-1704, supposed author.
A commonplace-book to the Holy Bible: or, The Scripture's sufficiency practically demonstrated... 5th ed., rev. and improved...by William Dodd. London, printed for T.Osborne and others, 1766.
360, [10] 27cm.

1. Bible - Indexes, Topical. 2. Commonplace-books. I. Dodd, William, 1729-1777, ed. II. Title. III. Title: The Scripture's sufficiency practically demon strated.

NL 0434564 IaU CtY-D MeWC PPC FU

Locke, John, 1632-1704, supposed author.
Common-place book to the Holy Bible. Revised by W. Dodd. London, 1805.
420 p. 4°

NL 0434565 MWA

BS432 .L81 Locke, John, 1632-1704, supposed author.
A common-place book to the Holy Bible: or, The Scriptures sufficiency practically demonstrated ... By John Locke, esq. Carefully rev. and improved, many errors in former editions cor., and the whole faithfully collated text by text, together with proper insertions made to connect the sense, by William Dodd ... New ed. London, Printed for W. Baynes and son; etc., etc.] 1824.
xvi, 493 p. front. (ports.) 22cm.
1. Bible—Concordances.

NL 0434566 ICU OO

LOCKE, John, 1632-1704, supposed author.
A common place book to the Holy Bible, etc. Revised ed. London, 1828.

NL 0434567 MH-AH

Locke, John, 1632-1704, supposed author. 7424.18
A commonplace-book to the Holy Bible: or, the Scripture's sufficiency practically demonstrated . . . From the 5th London edition, revised by William Dodd.
New York. American Tract Society. [185-?] 413 pp. 22½ cm., in 8s.

L3318 — T.r. — Dodd, William, ed., 1729-1777. — Bible. Commentaries.

NL 0434568 MB ViU NjPT PSt OCl OClW PPPD PPWe NRCR

Locke, John, 1632-1704, supposed author.
A commonplace-book to the Holy Bible: or, The Scripture's sufficiency practically demonstrated. Wherein the substance of Scripture, respecting doctrine, worship, and manners, is reduced to its proper heads: weighty cases are resolved, truths confirmed, and difficult texts illustrated and explained. By the celebrated John Locke ... From the 5th London edition, revised by Rev. William Dodd, LL. D.; with an enlarged index ... New York, Boston, American tract society [1858?]
413 p. 23½cm.
1. Bible—Indexes, Topical. I. Dodd, William, 1729-1777, ed. II. American tract society. III. Title. IV. Title: The Scripture's sufficiency practically demonstrated.
38-12465
Library of Congress BS432.L6
220.2

ViU
NL 0434569 DLC OrCS NN MoU CtY-D MeB IU CU NNUT

Locke, John, 1632-1704, supposed author.
A commonplace-book to the Holy Bible: or, The Scripture's sufficiency practically demonstrated. Wherein the substance of Scripture, respecting doctrine, worship, and manners, is reduced to its proper heads: weighty case are resolved, truths confirmed, and difficult texts illustrated and explained. By the celebrated John Locke, ... from the 5th London ed., revised by Rev. William Dodd ... with an enlarged index ... New York, The American tract society [1899]

413 p. 23½cm.
Locke's connection with this work is questioned by the British museum and Lowndes.

NL 0434571 MiU

B 1270 1718 Locke, John, 1632-1704.
The conduct of The understanding by John Locke, esq., To which is added an abstract of Mr. Locke's essay on human understanding. Cambridge, J. Archdeacon, 1781.
292 p.

KNOWLEDGE, THEORY OF
The conduct of the understanding
An essay concerning human understanding

NL 0434572 KMK MtU ICJ CU NNNAM

Locke, John, 1632-1704.
The conduct of the understanding. A new ed., divided under heads. London, D. Elzevir, 1794.
xv, 195 p. 14 cm.
1. Intellect. 2. Reasoning. 3. Knowledge, Theory of. I. Title.

NL 0434573 MdBP

Locke, John, 1632-1704.
The conduct of the understanding in the search of truth. By John Locke, esq. A new ed. Edinburgh, Printed for W. Creech; [etc., etc.] 1807.
1 p. l., [v]-vii, [1], 141 p. 17cm.
First published in the author's Posthumous works, 1706. Written about 1697 for a new chapter in the Essay concerning human understanding. cf. Stephen, Dict. of nat. biog.

1. Intellect. 2. Reasoning. 3. Knowledge, Theory of.
10-32059
Library of Congress B1270 1807

NL 0434574 DLC

B 1270 1801 Locke, John, 1632-1704.
The conduct of the understanding. By John Locke, esq. A new ed. London, Printed for William Baynes, 1801.
147 p. 18 cm.

1. Intellect. 2. Reasoning. 3. Knowledge, Theory of. I. Title

NL 0434575 OKentU

B1290 1813 Locke, John, 1632-1704.
The conduct of the understanding, by John Locke, esq. [and] Essays, moral, economical and political, by Francis Bacon. With sketches of the lives of Locke and Bacon. London, Printed for J. Walker, 1813.
xii, 262 p. 14cm.

NL 0434576 OrPR

Locke, John, 1632-1704.
The conduct of the understanding. By John Locke, esq. Essays, moral, economical, & political. By Francis Bacon, baron of Verulam, viscount St. Albans ... With sketches of the lives of Locke and Bacon. London: Printed for J. Walker [etc.] 1818.
xii, 262 p. front. 13½cm.
Two added title-pages, one engraved.

30590B. 1. Knowledge. I. Bacon, Francis, viscount St. Albans, 1561-1626.
May 17, 1940

NL 0434577 NN PP OO

Locke, John, 1632-1704.
The conduct of the understanding. By John Locke ... Essays, moral, economical and political. By Lord Bacon. With sketches of the lives of Locke and Bacon. New-York, S. King, 1823.
iv, [5]-295 p. front. (port.) 13½cm.

1. Knowledge, Theory of. I. Bacon, Francis, viscount St. Albans, 1561-1626. II. Title.

NL 0434578 MiU ViU NNC NjR PHi PPA PPL CtY

VOLUME 337

Locke, John, 1632-1704.
The conduct of the understanding. By John Locke. Essays, moral, economical and political by F. Bacon. With sketches of the author's lives. London: Baynes & son, 1825.
Engr. t.p.
240 p., 1 pl. 24°

NL 0434579 NN RPB CtY PHi

Locke, John, 1632-1704.
The conduct of the understanding. By John Locke, Esq. Essays, moral, economical and political. By Lord Bacon. With sketches of the lives of Locke and Bacon. New York, Published by S. King; S. Gould, printer, Caldwell, N.J. 1825.
24 mo. In mottled brown calf; black leather back label.
Brock collection, October 1922.

NL 0434580 CSmH RPB CtY

Locke, John, 1632-1704.
The conduct of the understanding, by John Locke. Essays, moral, economical, and political, by Lord Bacon, with a biographical preface. London, J. Smith, 1828.
2 p.l., [iii]-viii, 256 p. front. (port.) 15cm.
Added t.-p., engr., with vignette.
First published in the author's Posthumous works, 1706. Written about 1697 for a new chapter in the Essay concerning human understanding. cf. Stephen, Dict. of nat. biog.
1. Intellect. 2. Reasoning. 3. Knowledge, Theory of. I. Bacon, Francis, viscount St. Albans, 1561-1626. Essays. II. Title.

NL 0434581 ViU

Locke, John, 1632-1704. 5609a.121
Conduct of the understanding.
(In Locke's Essay on the human understanding. Pp. 371-427. London. 1831.)

NL 0434582 MB

Locke, John, 1632-1704.
Conduct of the Understanding. London, Scott, Webster, Geary, 1838.

NL 0434583 PV

953 C647 bot 1848
Locke, John, 1632-1704.
The conduct of the understanding; also some thoughts concerning education. With a memoir of the author and his writings. Edinburgh, W. and R. Chambers, 1839.
28 p. [Bound with: Clough, A.H. The bothie of Toper-na-fuosich. 1848]
1. Knowledge, Theory of.

NL 0434584 CU MdBJ

Locke, John, 1632-1704.
The conduct of the understanding.
(In Bacon. Essays, moral, economical, and political. Pp. 211-299. New York. [1841.]) 7607.91
Same. (In Same. 1874.) 7607.71

NL 0434585 MB

Locke, John, 1632-1704.
The conduct of the understanding.
Bacon, Francis, viscount St. Albans, 1561-1626.
Essays, moral, economical, and political. By Francis Bacon ... The conduct of the understanding. By John Locke ... With an introductory essay, by A. Potter ... New-York, Harper and brothers, 1844.

001.2 L79c
Locke, John, 1632-1704.
Conduct of the understanding. Edited with introd., notes, etc. by Thomas Fowler. Oxford, Clarendon Press, 1881.
xxiv, 136 p. (Clarendon Press series)
1. Intellect. 2. Reasoning. 3. Knowledge, Theory of. I. Title.

NL 0434587 KEmT WaWW ICJ PSC OU MiU NjP NIC

Locke, John, 1632-1704.
Conduct of the understanding, also some thoughts concerning education. Phil., Lippincott, [c1881]
136 p.

NL 0434588 PU

B1271 .F75 1882
Locke, John, 1632-1704.
... Locke's Conduct of the understanding; edited with introduction, notes, etc. by Thomas Fowler... 2d ed., corrected and revised. Oxford, Clarendon press, 1882.
xxiv, 136 p. 18cm. (Half-title; Clarendon press series)
1. Knowledge, Theory of. I. Fowler, Thomas, 1832-1904, ed.

NL 0434589 DCU OClW

Locke, John, 1632-1704. 153 E3
Conduct of the understanding. By John Locke. [Syracuse, N. Y., C. W. Bardeen, 1882.]
[209]-288 p. 24cm.
Caption title.
Reprinted from American journal of education, vol. 32.

NL 0434590 ICJ

Locke, John, 1632-1704.
The conduct of the understanding... New York, J.B. Alden, 1883.
88 p. (Elzevir library, v. 2, no. 113)

NL 0434591 OO NRCR

B1270 1885
Locke, John, 1632-1704
The conduct of the understanding. New York, J. B. Alden, 1885.
88 p. 16 cm.
1. Intellect. 2. Reasoning. 3. Knowledge, Theory of. I. Title.

NL 0434592 MeB ICJ PBa

B1271 .F75 1892
Locke, John, 1632-1704.
...Locke's Conduct of the understanding; edited with introduction, notes, etc., by Thomas Fowler...4th ed. Oxford, Clarendon press, 1892.
xxiv, 136 p. 18cm. (Half-title: Clarendon press series)
1. Knowledge, Theory of. I. Fowler, Thomas, 1832-1904, ed.

NL 0434593 OCU

B1207 1890
Locke, John, 1632-1704.
Conduct of the understanding; edited with introd., notes, etc. by Thomas Fowler. 3d ed., corr. and rev. Oxford, Clarendon Press, 1890.
xxiv, 136 p. 18 cm. (Clarendon Press series)
1. Intellect. 2. Reasoning. 3. Knowledge, Theory of. I. Title.

NL 0434594 MB PWcS RPB MB OCU ViLxW MWelC CtY ICN

Locke, John, 1632-1704.
The conduct of the understanding, with intro. and notes by J.A. St. John. New York, John B. Alden, 1891.
1 p.l., [5]-92 p.

NL 0434595 OO ODW

B1207 1901
Locke, John, 1632-1704.
Conduct of the understanding; edited with introd., notes, etc. by Thomas Fowler. 5th ed. Oxford, Clarendon Press, 1901.
xxiv, 136 p. 18 cm.
1. Intellect. 2. Reasoning. 3. Knowledge, Theory of. I. Title.
B1207 1901

PU ViU
NL 0434596 MB PP PBm OO OU OCl CU InU MH MiD PBa

192 L79eIc
Locke, John, 1632-1704.
La conoscenza umana; a cura di Armando Carlini. Bari, G. Laterza, 1948.
305p. 21cm. (Piccola biblioteca filosofica)
1. Knowledge, Theory of.

NL 0434597 IU

Locke, John, 1632-1704.
Consequences of the lowering of interest and raising the value of money. By John Locke. London [etc.] Ward, Lock and co. [18--] p. 560-703. 19cm.
211366B. 1. Money, to 1800. 2. Interest, 1691.
January 25, 1943

NL 0434598 NN WaWW

B 1296 A3 1927
Locke, John, 1632-1704.
The correspondence of John Locke and Edward Clarke edited, with a biographical study, by Benjamin Rand .. Cambridge, Harvard University Press, 1927.
xvi, 607, [1] p. front., ports., diagr. 23cm.

NL 0434599 NIC IdU OKentU

Locke, John, 1632-1704.
The correspondence of John Locke and Edward Clarke, edited, with a biographical study, by Benjamin Rand ... London, Oxford university press, H. Milford, 1927.
xvi, 607, [1] p. front., ports., diagrs. 23cm.
I. Clarke, Edward, 1649?-1710. II. Rand, Benjamin, 1856- ed.
28-2130
Library of Congress B1296.A4

WaS WaSpG
OOxM OO OU OCl OCU MiU MH ViU ICN MB MtU WaWW CaBVaU
NL 0434600 DLC NcU TU CU CtY PBm PPT PU-Penn NN

VOLUME 337

Locke, John, 1632-1704.
De intellectu humano. In quatuor libris. Editio quarta aucta & emendata, & nunc primum Latine reddita. Londini, Impensis Aunshami & Johan. Churchil, 1701.
317 p.

1. Intellect. 2. Reasoning. 3. Knowledge, Theory of.

NL 0434601 TxDaM-P MH CLU-C OkU

Ex 6504 .592 .1711 Locke, John, 1632-1704
De l'education des enfans; traduit de l'anglois... par Pierre Coste. Sur la dernière ed. rev., cor., & augm. ... A Paris, Chez J. Musier, 1711
xxii,443,[12] p. 17 cm

I. Coste, Pierre, 1668-1747, tr. II. T

NL 0434602 NjP

---

370 L79sFc 1715 Locke, John, 1632-1704.
De l'education des enfans; traduit de l'anglois de mr. Locke, par Pierre Coste. 6.ed.; rev., corr., & augm. Suivant la copie imprimée a Amsterdam. [n.p.] 1715.
468p.

1. Education. I. Coste, Pierre, 1668-1747, tr

NL 0434603 IU

Locke, John, 1632-1704.
De l'education des enfans; traduit de l'Anglois de M. Locke, par M. Coste. Sur l'edition Angloise publieé après la mort de l'auteur ... Amsterdam, Steenhouwer & Uytwerf, 1721.
xxi, [3] 505 [7] p. front. (port.) 15.5 cm.

NL 0434604 ViW

Locke,John,1632-1704.
De l'education des enfans; tr.de l'anglois de mr.Locke,par mr.Coste. Sur l'edition angloise pub.après la mort de l'auteur,qui l'avoit revuë, corrigée & augmentée. Suivant la copie imprimée a Amsterdam. 1730.
1 p.l.,[4],3-24,468,[8] p.,1 l. front.(port.) 17cm.

1.Education. I.Coste,Pierre,1668-1747,tr.

NL 0434605 MiU IU

Locke, John, 1632-1704.
De l'education des enfants; traduit de l'anglois par M. Coste. Ed. 4. Amsterdam, Uytwerf, 1733.
2 v. in 1.

NL 0434606 OClW

Locke, John, 1632-1704.
De l'education des enfans, traduit de l'anglois par Pierre, Coste... Ed.5 enl.,Amst., Uytwerf, 1737.
2v. in 1.

NL 0434607 PU

Locke, John, 1632-1704.
De l'education des enfans, traduit de l'anglois de Mr. Locke. Par Mr. Coste ... Sixieme edition revüe & corrigée ... A Lausanne: Chez M.-M. Bousquet & comp., 1746. 2 v. in 1. 16½cm.

Paged continuously.

GENET COLLECTION.
75049B. 1. Education—Theory and systems—Locke. I. Coste, Pierre, 1668-1747, tr.
December 27, 1940

NL 0434608 NN

Locke, John, 1632-1740.
De l'education des enfants, traduit del'anglois par Pierre Coste, a laquelle on a joint la methode ovservee pour l'education des enfans de France, revue par J.F. Thurot. New ed. Paris. Bossange, 1821.
2v.

NL 0434609 PU MH

Locke, John, 1632-1704.
... Directions concerning education; being the first draft of his Thoughts concerning education now printed from Additional ms. 38771 in the British museum, with an introduction by Frederic George Kenyon. Oxford, Printed for presentation to the members of the Roxburghe club, 1933.
4 p. l., 84 p. front. (facsim.) 29½cm.

Presented to the Roxburghe club by Frederic George Kenyon.

1. Education. I. Kenyon, Sir Frederic George, 1863- ed. II. Roxburghe club, London. III. Title. IV. Title: Thoughts concerning education.

Library of Congress PR1105.R7 1933 34-16861
(820.82) 370.1

NL 0434610 DLC NN IaU MiU MoU MU IU OU TxU CU

Locke, John, 1632-1704.
Du gouvernement civil, ... Tr. de l'anglois. Amsterdam, A. Wolfgang, 1691.
321 p.

NL 0434611 MiU

J 0 .5105 [LOCKE, JOHN] 1632-1704.
Du gouvernement civil, ou l'on traite de l'origine des fondemens, dela nature, du pouvoir, et des fins des societez politiques. Traduit de l'anglois [par David Mazel] Nouvelle edition. Geneve,Du Villard & Jaquier, 1724.
365p. 15cm.

Unidentified armorial bookplate.

NL 0434612 ICN

J 0 .5106 LOCKE, JOHN, 1632-1704.
Du gouvernement civil, où l'on traite de l'origine, des fondemens, de la nature, du pouvoir, et des fins des sociétez politiques. Traduit de l'anglois de mr. Locke. Nouvelle édition, revüe & corrigée. Bruxelles,1749.
358p. 15cm.

Translated by David Mazel.

NL 0434613 ICN

Locke, John, 1632-1704
Du gouvernement civil, où l'on traite de l'origine, des fondemens, de la nature, du pouvoir, et des fins des sociétés politiques; traduit de l'anglois de M. Locke [par D. Mazel] Nouv. éd., rev. & corr. Bruxelles, 1754.

xii, 358 [2] p. 17 cm.
Translation of the second of Locke's Two treatises on civil government, by D. Mazel.

NL 0434614 PKsL

JC 153 .L7944 (Rare) Locke. John. 1632-1704.
Du gouvernement civil. 5. édition. Amsterdam, Chez J. Schreuder & P. Mortier le jeune, 1755.
328 p.
Traduit de l'Anglois.
Cinquieme édition exactement revüe & corrigée sur la 5. edition de Londres & augmentée de quelques notes, par L.C.R.D.M.A.D.P.

1. Political science. I. L.C.R.D.M.A.D.P. II. Title.

NL 0434615 ICU NjP

LOCKE,[John],1632-1704.
Du gouvernement civil. Traduit de l'anglois. 6e éd.,exactement revue & corrigée sur la derniere edition de Londres & augmentée de quelques notes. Par L.C.R.D.M.A.D.P. Amsterdam,B.Vlam,1780.

NL 0434616 MH

Locke, John, 1632-1704.
Due trattati sul governo, di John Locke. Col Patriarca di Robert Filmer. A cura di Luigi Pareyson. [Torino] Unione tip.-editrice torinese [1948]
555 p. port., facsims. 24 cm. (Classici politici, v. 3)
Classici UTET.

1. Political science. I. Filmer, Sir Robert, d. 1653. Patriarcha. (Series)

JC153.L815 320.1 49-15974*‡

NL 0434617 DLC

Locke, John, 1632-1704.
An early draft of Locke's Essay, together with excerpts from his journals, edited by R. I. Aaron ... and Jocelyn Gibb. Oxford, The Clarendon press, 1936.
xxviii, 132 p. 22½cm.

1. Knowledge, Theory of. I. Aaron, Richard Ithamar, 1901- ed. II. Gibb, Jocelyn, joint ed.

36-29047

Library of Congress B1289.A2

192.2

Wa WaE WaPS IdB IdPS MtBC MtU OrCS OrPS OrU WaSpG WaT PU OCU OU OO NN Or OrStbM OrSaW OrU-M MtBuM CaBVaU
NL 0434618 DLC DFo NNC MoU NBC IEdS NcU NcD CtY InU

Locke, John, 1632-1704.
Educacion de los niños, Obra escrita en ingles por Locke, y traducida al castellano por D.F.A.C.-P.; seguida del tratado de la felicidad en todos los estados de la vida. Nueva edicion ... Burdeos Lawalle, 1825.
2 v. 13.5 cm.
1. Education. I. P., F.A.C. x. P., D.F.-A.C. x. D.F.A.C.P. x. F.A.C.P.

NL 0434620 CtY

Locke, John, 1632-1704.
... The educational writings of John Locke, ed. by John William Adamson ... London, E. Arnold, 1912.
xi, 272 p. 19cm. (Educational classics)

1. Education. I. Adamson, John William, ed.

E13-141

U. S. Off. of educ. Library LB475.L6A25
——— Copy 2.
for Library of Congress [a37f1-]

AU NcD OCU ODW OO MB ICJ OrPR Or WaWW CaBVaU
NL 0434621 DHEW ICJ ViU OU OCX OOxM PPD PCC MWelC

LB 475 .L814 1922 Locke,John,1632-1704.
The educational writings of John Locke. Edited by John William Adamson. [2d ed.] Cambridge, University Press, 1922.
viii,272 p. facsim. 19 cm.
Bibliography: p.20.
CONTENTS.--Introduction.--Some thoughts concerning education.--Of the conduct of the understanding.

1.Education. I.Adamson,John William, 1857- ed.

NL 0434622 MiU TNJ NSyU ICarbS

Locke, John, 1632-1704.
The educational writings of John Locke, ed. by John William Adamson... Cambridge, University press, 1932.
viii, 272 p. facsim. (Front.) 20 cm.

NL 0434623 CaBVaU

VOLUME 337

6106 .333 .9 Locke, John, 1632-1704.
...Einige gedanken über erziehung. Uebersetzt und mit einleitung und anmerkungen versehen von dr.Moritz Schuster. Leipzig, Siegismund [1873]
56,277 p. 21½ cm. (Pädagogische bibliothek; eine sammlung der wichtigsten pädagogischen schriften älterer und neuerer zeit... 9.bd.)

I.Schuster,Moritz,ed.and tr.

NL 0434624 NjP OC1JC MiU

Locke, John, 1632-1704. Educ 112.2.50
Einige gedanken über erziehung. Uebersetzt und mit einleitung und anmerkungen versehen von Moritz Schuster. 2e durchgesehene und verbesserte aufl. Leipzig, M. Hesse, [1881].
pp. lvi, 276. (Pädagogische bibliothek, 9.)

NL 0434625 MH IU OC1

L 110 G776a Locke, John, 1632-1704.
Elemens de physique, avec les pensées du meme auteur sur la lecture & les études qui conviennent à un gentilhomme; ouvrages nouvellement traduits de l'anglois. A Amsterdam, Chez J.Schreuder et P. Mortier, 1757.
x,[2], 98 p. 1 fold. plate. 17cm.
[Bound with: Gravesande,W.J.v. Introduction à la philosophie. Leide, 1748.]
1.Physics - Early works to 1800.

NL 0434626 CSt

Locke, John, 1632-1704.
Elements of natural philosophy. By ... London, 1741

NL 0434627 PPL

B 1280 1750 Cage Locke, John, 1632-1704.
Elements of natural philosophy ... To which are added Some thoughts concerning reading and study for a gentelman ... London, Sold by J. Thomson, S. Dampier, and R. Bland [1750?]
vii [1] 64 p. A-C[12]. 12mo. front.
Imprint date from British Museum Catalogue
Introductory material by P. des Maizeaux, being part of a dedication to some of Locke's works published in 1720

NL 0434628 DFo

192 L79e2 Locke, John, 1632-1704.
Elements of natural philosophy ... To which is added, some thoughts concerning reading and study for a gentleman, by the same author. Berwick upon Tweed, Printed and sold by R. Taylor, 1754.
72p.

1. Science--Early works to 1800. 2. Books and reading.

NL 0434629 IU

B 1280 .1764 Locke,John,1632-1704.
Elements of natural philosophy. By John Locke Esq; To which is added,Some thoughts concerning reading and study for a gentleman, by the same author. Whitehaven, Printed and sold by W.Sheperd, 1764.
vii,72 p. 16 cm.
First published separately in 1750?
"An account of the ... tracts by Monsieur Des Maizeaux,being part of a dedication prefixed to these and some other pieces of Mr.Locke's,when they were first published in ... 1720 [in A collection of several pieces of Mr.John Locke]" p.iii-vii.

Imperfect: p.63-72 mutilated,with slight loss of text.

1.Science--Early works to 1800. 2.Books and reading. I.Desmaizeaux,Pierre,1673?-1745.

NL 0434631 MiU NNNAM CtY

Z834 C6B6 v.20 Library School Locke, John, 1632-1704.
Ensaio philosóphico sobre o entendimento humano. (In Coimbra. Universidade. Biblioteca. Boletin. Coimbra. v. 20 (1951) p. [1]-212)

Also issued as v. 2 in the series Inedita ac rediviva.

1. Knowledge, Theory of.

NL 0434632 CU

Locke, John, 1632-1704.
... Ensayo sobre el gobierno civil; traducción y prefacio de José Carner. México, Fondo de cultura económica [1941]
2 p. l., [vii]-xx, 170, [2] p. 24½cm. (Half-title: Sección de ciencia política [del Fondo de cultura económica; dirigida por Manuel Pedroso. I. Los clásicos)
"Primera edición inglesa, 1690 ... segunda edición española (primera traducción directa), 1941."

1. Political science. 2. Liberty. I. Carner, José, 1884- tr.

Library of Congress JC153.L855 1941 41-19024
320.1

NL 0434633 DLC DPU

LOCKE,John,1632-1704.
Epistola su la tolleranza; traduzion e studio introduttivo del Dr.Francesco A.Ferrari. Lanciano,A.Carabba,[1920].

At head of title: Giovanni Locke.
On cover: Cultura dell'anima.

NL 0434634 MH

261.7 L814 [Locke, John] 1632-1704.
Epistola de tolerantia ad clarissimum virum T.A.R.P.T.O.L.A. Scripta à P.A.P.O.I.L. A. Goudae, Apud J. ab Hoeve, 1689.
96p. 14cm.

Written to Philippus Limborch.

1. Toleration. I. Limborch, Philippus van, 1633-1712. II. Title.

NL 0434635 IEN

RARE BOOK DEPT.
Locke, John, 1632-1704
Essai philosophique concernant l'entendement humain; ou, L'on montre quelle est l'etendue de nos connoissances certaines, et la maniere dont nous y parvenons. Traduit de l'Anglois ... par Pierre Coste, sur la 4e ed., revüe, corrigée, & augm. par l'auteur. Amsterdam, H. Schelte, 1700.
[58] 936p. front. (port.) 26cm.
I. Coste, Pierre, 1688-1747, tr.

NL 0434636 WU DFo FU DLC-P4 MH MWelC PBa

Lilly Library LOCKE,JOHN,1632-1704
Essai philosophique concernant l'entendement humain, ou l'on montre quelle est l'entendue de nos connoissances certaines, et la maniere dont nous y parvenons, traduit de l'anglois de Mr. Locke, par Pierre Coste, sur la quatrième edition, revüe, corrigée, & augmentée par l'auteur ... A La Haye, Pierre Husson, 1714.
[56], 936, [22] p. 4to

Bound in calf; spine designed and lattered in gilt.

NL 0434637 InU MH

B1293 F7C6 in Rare Books Room Locke, John, 1632-1704.
Essai philosophique concernant l'entendement humain, où l'on montre quelle est l'etendue de nos connoissances certaines, & la maniere dont nous y parvenons. Traduit...par Pierre Coste. Nouv. éd., rev., corr., & augm. par l'auteur. Amsterdam, H. Schelte, 1723.
2 v. (936 p.) 21cm.

1. Knowledge, Theory of. I. Coste, Pierre, 1668-1747, tr.

NL 0434638 CoU ICU CtY

RARE BOOK DEPT.
Locke, John, 1632-1704
Essai philosophique concernant l'entendement humain, où l'on montre quelle est l'etendue de nos connoissances certaines, & la maniere dont nous y parvenons. Traduit de l'anglois par Pierre Coste. Nouv. éd., rev., corr., & augm. par l'auteur. Amsterdam, H. Schelte, 1723.
[59] 936 [22]p. front. (port.) 22cm.

I. Coste, Pierre, 1668-1747, tr.

NL 0434639 WU

B1293 F7 1735 Locke, John, 1632-1704.
Essai philosophic concernant l'entendement humain. Tr. de l'anglois par M. Coste. 3. éd., rev., cor., & augm. de quelques additions importantes de l'auteur. A Amsterdam, P. Mortier, 1735.
xlii, 601 p.
"Achevé d'imprimer le 30. novembre 1734."

NL 0434640 CU NcD MH NjP NN

B 1290 1742F Locke, John, 1632-1704.
Essai philosophique concernant l'entendement humain, ou l'on montre quelle est l'entendue de nos connoissances certaines, et la manière dont nous y parvenons. Traduit de l'anglois par M.Coste. 4.éd.,rev.,corr.& augm. de quelques additions importantes de l'auteur qui n'ont paru qu'après sa mort & de plusieurs remarques du traducteur ... Amsterdam, P.Mortier, 1742.
xlii,603p. front.(port.) 26cm.

1. Knowledge, Theory of. I. Coste, Pierre, 1668-1747, tr. II. Title.

NL 0434642 NRU NjP RPB MH ICU

LOCKE,John,1632-1704.
Essai philosophique concernant l'entendement humain,où l'on montre quelle est l'étendue de nos connoissances certaines,et la manier dont nous y parvenons. Traduit de l'Anglois par M. Coste. 5th éd.,revue et corrigée. Amsterdam, etc.,U.Schreuder & P.Mortier le Jeune,1755.
4°. pp.xxxvii,(3),603,(18). Vign.

NL 0434643 MH IU CU-S

Locke, John, 1632-1704.
Essai philosophique concernant l'entendement humain, où l'on montre quelle est l'étendue de nos connoissances certaines, & la maniere dont nous y parvenons. Par M. Locke. Traduit de l'anglois par M. Coste. Nouvelle édition, revue, corrigée & augmentée de quelques additions importantes de l'auteur, qui n'ont paru qu'après sa mort, & de plusieurs remarques du traducteur, dont quelques-unes paroissent pour la premiere fois dans cette edition ... A Amsterdam: Aux dépens de la Compagnie, 1758.
4 v. 17cm.

With heraldic bookplate, probably of Constance de Mailly d'Haucourt, marquise de Voyer.

75007-10B. 1. Knowledge. I. Coste, Pierre, 1668-1747, tr.
December 31, 1940

NL 0434644 NN

VOLUME 337

Locke, John, 1632-1704.
Essai philosophique concernant l'entendement humain ... par M. Locke. Tr. de l'anglois par M. Coste. 4 éd. rev. cor. & augm. ... Paris, Chez Savoye [etc.] 1787.
4 v. front. (port., v. 1) 17cm.

1. Knowledge, Theory of. I. Coste, Pierre, 1668-1747, tr.

NL 0434645 MiU

192
L79eFc
1795
Locke, John, 1632-1704.
Essai philosophique concernant l'entendement humain, où l'on montre quelle est l'étendue de nos connaissances certaines, et la manière dont nous y parvenons. Tr. de l'anglais par M. Coste. Nouv. ed. rev., cor., et augm. .. Paris, 1795.
4v.

NL 0434646 IU

LOCKE, [John], 1632-1704.
Essai philosophique concernant l'entendement humain. Traduit de l'anglois par [P.] Coste. 5e éd. revue, corrigée et augmentée. Paris, Bossange, Masson et Besson, an VII [1799?]

4 vols.

NL 0434647 MH

L814c
1953f
Locke, John, 1632-1704
Essai sur le pouvoir civil. Texte traduit, présenté et annoté par Jean-Louis Fyot. Préf. de B. Mirkine-Guetzévitch et Marcel Prélot. Paris, Presses Universitaires de France, 1953.
xvi, 223 p. 23 cm. (Bibliothèque de la science politique. 2.sér.: Les grandes doctrines politiques)

1. Political science. I. Fyot, Jean Louis, ed. and tr. Series.

NL 0434648 MiU-L CtY MH NNC

---

*fEC65
L7934
689e2
[Locke, John, 1632-1704]
An essay concerning humane understanding. In four books ...
London: Printed by Eliz. Holt, for Thomas Basset, at the George in Fleetstreet, near St. Dunstan's church. MDCXC. [1689]
6p.ℓ., 363, [22] p. 32cm.
Dedication signed: John Locke.
The first issue of the first edition, although widely described as the second issue; in this issue leaf A1 (t.-p.) is conjugate with A4.

For dating see Maurice Cranston (John Locke, p.327).
Inscribed (autograph?) on t.-p.: Henricus Sacheverell. D.D.

NL 0434650 MH

[Locke, John] 1632-1704.
An essay concerning humane understanding. In four books ... London: Printed for Tho. Basset, and sold by Edw. Mory ... 1690.
6 p.l., 362, [22] p. 2 front. (1 port.) 32½cm.
First edition, variant imprint.
Signatures: A^{4}, a^{2}, $B\text{-}Z^{4}$, $Aa\text{-}Zz^{4}$, $Aaa\text{-}Ccc^{4}$.
Pages 76-77, 85, 287, 296, 303 incorrectly numbered 50, 55, 83, 269, 294, 230, respectively.
Fifteen leaves and numerous slips of additions and corrections bound in. The author had them printed for insertion in copies of the first edition while the corrected second edition was being published.
Title within double line border. Marginal notes.
Dedication signed: John Locke.
Newspaper clipping, "An imaginary dialogue between Locke, and Stillingfleet" in verse, tipped in at front.
Bound in red morocco, gilt edges, by F. Bedford.
Cf. Clark, W.A. Early Eng. lit. 1920-25. v.1, p.80-81.

ICU MnU CSt OkU NNC
PBL ICU MnU CSt NNC CtY NbU PU-L NB NNUT-Mc MWiW-C
NL 0434652 CLU-C ViU TxU PU MH NjP CLSU InU MWelC

Locke, John, 1632-1704.
An essay concerning humane understanding. 2d ed., with large additions. London, Printed for Awnsham and J. Churchil, at the Black Swan, 1694.
407 p. port. 32 cm.

1. Knowledge, Theory of.

B1290 1694 50-44479

NCH InU DFo RPJCB NjP CLU-C CSt KMK WU CaBVaU
NL 0434653 DLC NPV TxDaM-P TxU MoSW MH NNUT NcU IEN

Locke, John, 1632-1704.
An essay concerning humane understanding, in four books. Written by John Locke, gent. The 3d ed. ... London, Printed for A. and J. Churchil, and S. Manship, 1695.
20 p. l., 407, [1] p. 33 cm.
On spine: Locke on understanding.
Errors in pagination: 91-92 omitted, 95-96 repeated; 121 numbered 123.
Bookplate covered by bookplate of Virginia state library.
First edition, London, 1690.
1. Knowledge, Theory of. I. Title.
B1290 1695

NL 0434654 Vi MH ICU CLU-C RPB NN NjP CtY

---

*fEC65
L7934
689e2d
Locke, John, 1632-1704.
An essay concerning humane understanding. In four books. Written by John Locke, gent. The fourth edition, with large additions ...
London: Printed for Awnsham and John Churchil, at the Black-Swan in Pater-noster-row; and Samuel Manship, at the Ship in Cornhill, near the Royal-Exchange, MDCC. [1699]
19p.ℓ., 438 (i.e. 432), [12] p. front. (port.) 32cm.
Numbers 227-232 omitted in the paging.

For earlier dating see H.O. Christophersen, A bibliogr. introd. to the study of John Locke, Skrifter utgitt av det Norske videnskaps-akademi i Oslo, II. Hist.-filos. klasse, 1930, no.8.

NL 0434656 MH

Locke, John, 1632-1704.
An essay concerning humane understanding. In four books. Written by John Locke, gent. The fourth edition, with large additions ... London: Printed for Awnsham and John Churchil ... and Samuel Manship ... 1700.
20 p.l., 438 (i.e. 432), [12] p. front. (port.) 33cm.
Signatures: A^{2}, b^{6}, $a\text{-}c^{4}$, $B\text{-}Z^{4}$, $Aa\text{-}Ff^{4}$, Gg^{1}, $Hh\text{-}Zz^{4}$, $Aaa\text{-}Kkk^{4}$, $Lll\text{-}Mmm^{2}$, 1 leaf unsigned.

Pages 91-94, 371, 380-381 incorrectly numbered 93-96, 317, 390-391, respectively; no. 227-232 omitted in the paging.
Title within double line border. Marginal notes.
Armorial book-plate of Francis John Huyshe.
Bound in old paneled calf.

NIC MnU NjP
NL 0434658 CLU-C PPL NRU NNC CSt ICN MH NjP MWelC

Locke, John, 1632-1704.
An essay concerning humane understanding. In four books. Written by John Locke ... The 5th. ed., with large additions. ... London, Printed for A. and J. Churchill ... and S. Manship, 1706.
1 p. l., [32], 604 (*i.e.* 500), [10] p. 35cm.
Many pages incorrectly numbered.

1. Knowledge, Theory of.

OClW ViU ICN OGaK OrU PPFr NN
NL 0434659 MiU MH WU NcGU MoU CLU-C TxDaM NcD OCU

---

*
B1290
1710
Locke, John, 1632-1704.
An essay concerning humane understanding. 6th ed., with large additions. London, Printed for A. and J. Churchill, and S. Manship, 1710.
2 v. 20cm.

1. Knowledge, Theory of.

NL 0434660 ViU NNNAM NjP

Locke, John, 1632-1704.
An essay concerning human understanding. In four books... London, Printed for J. Churchill and S. Manship, 1715-16.
2 v. port. 21cm.

Vol. 1: 7th ed., with large additions, 1716.
Vol. 2 has title: An essay concerning humane understanding; v. 2 printed for A. and J. Churchill and S. Manship.

CaBVaU
NL 0434661 MnU NjP ViU WaSpG CtY CLU-C MH MeB PU

Locke, John, 1632-1704.
An essay concerning human understanding. In four books. Written by John Locke, Gent. The 8th ed., with large additions...London, Printed for A. Churchill and A. Manship, 1721.
2 v.

1. Knowledge, Theory of.

NL 0434662 TxDaM-P PU PU-Penn ICU CLSU CaQMM

Locke, John, 1632-1704.
An essay concerning human understanding. In four books. Written by John Locke, gent. The ninth edition, with large additions ... London, Printed by T.W. for A. Churchill; and Edm. Parker ... 1726.
2 v. front. (port.) 20½cm.
Signatures: v.1. a^{8}, $*a^{8}$, $A\text{-}Z^{8}$, Aa^{2}; v.2. A^{4}, a^{4}, $B\text{-}Y^{8}$, Z^{4}, $Aa\text{-}Cc^{4}$.
Imprint varies; v.2 has imprint: London, Printed by M.J. for A. Churchill: and Edm. Parker.
Titles within double line borders. Marginal notes.
Bound in old calf, rebacked.

NL 0434663 CLU-C CtY RPB MH

153
L814e
1731
Locke, John, 1632-1704.
An essay concerning human understanding. In four books. The 10th ed., with large additions. London, Printed for E. Parker, M.DCC.XXXI. [i.e. 1731]
2v. port. (v.1) 20cm.

1. Knowledge, Theory of. I. Title. LC

NL 0434664 CLSU PPWi IU ViU OU MdBJ

Locke, John, 1632-1704.
An essay concerning human understanding. In four books. Written by John Locke, gent. The eleventh edition ... London: Printed for A. Bettesworth [etc.] 1735.
2 v. front. (port.) 21cm.
Signatures: v.1. A^{8}, $*a^{8}$, $B\text{-}Z^{8}$, Aa^{2}; v.2. $A\text{-}Z^{8}$, Aa^{8}.
Armorial book-plates of John Bennet Lawes.
Bound in old sprinkled calf.

NL 0434665 CLU-C PLatS KEmT PU-Penn MiD MH PU CaBVaU

Locke, John, 1632–1704.
An essay concerning human understanding. By John Locke, Gent. London: C. Hitch, 1741. 2 v. 12. ed. 8°.

t.-p. of v. 1 missing.

FORD COLLECTION.

1. Mind.—Philosophy of.

November 23, 1917.

NL 0434666 NN CaBVaU

VOLUME 337

Locke, John, 1632-1704.
An essay concerning human understanding... 13th ed. London, 1747.

NL 0434667 MH

JGN B 1290 1748 Locke, John, 1632-1704.
An essay concerning human understanding. 13th ed. London, S. Birt, 1748.
2 v. illus.

#Knowledge, Theory of.

NL 0434668 MoU IEG DLC MH PCC OClJC

JX2099 .D7 Jeff. Coll. Locke, John, 1632-1704. An essay concerning human understanding.
[Dodd, William] 1729-1777.
Synopsis compendiaria librorum Hugonis Grotii De jure belli et pacis, Samuelis Clarkii De Dei existentiâ et attributis, et Joannis Lockii De intellectu humano. Cantabrigiæ, typis Academicis excudit J. Bentham, 1751.

K8 L79 F753 Locke, John, 1632-1704.
An essay concerning human understanding; in four books. 14th ed. London, S. Birt, 1753.
2 v. port. 21 cm.

1. Knowledge, Theory of

NL 0434670 CtY NN NNUT MB PPL RPB

B 1290 1759 Locke, John, 1632-1704.
An essay concerning human understanding. In four books. New ed., corr. Glasgow, Printed by R. Urie, 1759.
3 v.

#Knowledge, Theory of.

NL 0434671 MoU MH MB

192.2 L79e15 Locke, John, 1632-1704.
An essay concerning human understanding. In four books. Written by John Locke... 15th ed. London, printed for D. Browne, C. Hitch and L. Hawes [and others] 1760.
2 v. front. 20½cm.

1.Knowledge, Theory of.

NL 0434672 LU MH OU CtY MB OO PSC RPB ViU

BEha L79e 1765 Locke, John, 1632-1704.
An essay concerning human understanding ... New ed., cor., Edinburgh, 1765.
3 v. 18 cm.

NL 0434673 RPB PPL

Yx 808 E5ℓ Locke, John, 1632-1704.
An essay concerning human understanding. In four books. Written by John Locke, gent. The 16th ed. ... London, Printed for H. Woodfall [etc.,etc.]1768.
2v. front.(port.) 21cm.
Inscribed on fly-leaf: James Hillhouse's book. James A.Hillhouse's book. Feb.7,1808. Studied under the instruction of Revd. Timothy Dwight ... in this year of our Lord 1808. Aetat 18.

NL 0434674 CtY MH IEN NN OO RPB

Locke, John, 1632-1704.
An essay concerning human understanding, in four books. A new edition, corrected. Glasgow, Urie, 1769.
3 v.

NL 0434675 OClW

Locke, John, 1632-1704.
An essay concerning human understanding. In four books. Written by John Locke, gent. The 17th ed. ... London, Printed for J. Beecroft [etc.] 1775.
2 v. front. (port.) 21½cm.

1. Knowledge, Theory of.

10-32111

Library of Congress B1270 1775

NL 0434676 DLC WaWW FTaSU PU OO TxU NN

Locke, John, 1632-1704.
An essay concerning human understanding... by John Locke, gent. The 17th edition.. London, Printed for H. Woodfall, A. Millar, J. Beecroft, J. and F. Rivington [etc.] 1786.
2 v. front. (port.) 21 cm.
1. Knowledge, Theory of.

NL 0434677 CtY

Locke, John, 1632-1704.
An essay concerning human understanding. In four books. Written by John Locke, gent. The eighteenth edition. ... London, Printed for J. F. and C. Rivington [etc.] 1788.
2 v. 21½cm.

1. Knowledge, Theory of.

NL 0434678 ViU

Locke, John, 1632-1704.
An essay concerning human understanding... 16th ed. London, 1791.

NL 0434679 MH

XR B1290 1793 Locke, John, 1632-1704.
An essay concerning human understanding. 19th ed. London, Printed for T. Longman [and others] 1793.
2v.

Contents.--v.l. Essay on human understanding. --v.2. Essay on human understanding [continued] A defence of Mr. Locke's opinion concerning personal identity. On the conduct of the understanding. Some thoughts concerning reading and study for a gentleman. Elements of natural philosophy. A new, [ ] method of a common-place-book. Indexes.

NL 0434680 NBC

* B1290 1796 Locke, John, 1632-1704.
An essay concerning human understanding. 20th ed. To which are now added, I. An analysis of Mr. Locke's doctrine of ideas, on a large sheet. II. A defence of Mr. Locke's opinion concerning personal identity, with an appendix. III. A treatise on the conduct of understanding. IV. Some thoughts concerning reading and study for a gentleman. V. Elements of na tural philosophy. VI. A new method of a common-place-book. Extracted from the author's works. London: Printed for T. Longman, B. Law and Son [etc.] 1796.
2 v. 22cm.
Inscribed by Juliana Snow, 1802.
1. Knowledge, Theory of.

NL 0434682 ViU MiU NIC ODW PPPHi

Locke, John, 1632-1704. Phil 2115.32.5
An essay concerning human understanding. Collated with Desmaizeaux's ed. To which is prefixed the life of the author. Edinburgh, printed for Mundell & Son, etc. etc. 1798.
3 vol.

NL 0434683 MH CtY-D CtY OClStM

BEha L79e4 Locke, John, 1632-1704.
Essay concerning human understanding. Edinburgh, 1801. nar. D.
3 v.

NL 0434684 RPB MH CtY MB

N 153 L81a6 Locke, John, 1632-1704.
An essay concerning human understanding ... to which is prefixed the life of the author. 1st American from the 20th London ed. Boston, Printed by D. Carlisle for Thomas & Andrews, 1803.
3 v. 18 cm.

1. Knowledge. Theory of. 2. Amer. impr. Mass. Boston. Carlisle, D. 1803. 3. Amer. impr. Mass. Boston. Thomas & Andrews. 1803.

NL 0434685 N MWA OClW MH InU CU MB

LOCKE, JOHN, 1632-1704.
An essay concerning human understanding. Written by John Locke... The twenty-first edition... London: Printed for J. Johnson [etc.] by Bye and Law, 1805. 2 v. forms, table. 21½cm.

With bookplate of Walter Del Mar.

728194-5A. 1. Knowledge.

NL 0434686 NN NjNbS CSt

Locke, John, 1632-1704.
An essay concerning human understanding. By John Locke, gent. ... To which is prefixed the life of the author ... 2d American ed. Brattleboro, Vt. Printed by William Fessenden, for Thomas & Andrews, and John West, Boston. 1806.
v. 18½cm.

1. Knowledge, Theory of.

42-47687

B1290 1806

OCl OClW NcD OHi OO PHi NjR Vt ViLxW ScNC IaGG LNHT MH MMeT MWA MeBaT MeLB MoSpD NPV NWM PU

NL 0434687 DLC CSt NIC ViU NcD ScU DCU WU GS IaDmD

Locke, John, 1632-1704.
An essay concerning human understanding... 22-ed.... London, Printed for W. Otridge, F.C. and J. Rivington, etc. 1812.
2v.

NL 0434688 PSC ViU

Locke, John, 1632-1704.
An essay concerning human understanding. By John Locke ... With a life of the author ... Boston, Cummings & Hilliard and J. T. Buckingham, 1813.
2 v. 22cm.

1. Knowledge, Theory of.

A 33-2195

Title from Duke Univ. Printed by L. C.

MiU ICU ViU PU

NL 0434689 NcD OrU IEG NcU CSt CU TU MB MH ICU OO

Locke, John, 1632-1704.
Essay concerning human understanding... New ed. Edinburgh, 1815.
3 v.

NL 0434690 NjP

VOLUME 337

PHILOSOPHY
D192L79
Q21 Locke, John, 1632-1704.
An essay concerning human understanding. 23 d ed. To which are now added, I. Analysis of Mr. Locke's doctrine of ideas, on a large sheet. II. A defence of Mr. Locke's opinion concerning personal identity, with an appendix. III. A treatise on the conduct of the understanding. IV. Some thoughts concerning reading and study for a gentleman. V. Elements of natural philosophy. VI. A new method of a common-place-book. Extracted from the author's works. In two volumes. London, Printed for F. C. and J. Rivington, 1817.
2 v. fold. table

NL 0434691 NNC CtY-M MH PPL

SPECIAL COLLECTIONS
B192L79
R
1818 Locke, John, 1632-1704.
An essay concerning human understanding ... With a life of the author ... New-York, Published by Collins and Hannay; J. & J. Harper, printers, 1818.
2 v. in 1. 22cm.

NL 0434692 NNC InU ODW OU PU PSC

*AC85
Al91
Zz818l
Locke, John, 1632-1704.
An essay concerning human understanding. By John Locke .. With a life of the author ... New-York:Published by E.Duyckinck,no.68 Water-street.J.& J.Harper,printers.1818. Price $4.
2v.in 1. fold.table. 22cm.
From the library of Amos Bronson Alcott.

NL 0434693 MH PU

Locke, John, 1632-1704.
An essay concerning human understanding. By John Locke, gent. To which are added, I. An analysis of Mr. Locke's doctrine of ideas, ... II. A defence of Mr. Locke's opinion concerning personal identity, with an appendix. III. A treatise on the conduct of the understanding. IV. Some thoughts concerning reading and study for a gentleman. V. Elements of natural philosophy. VI. A new method of a common place book. Extracted from the author's works. With a life of the author. ... New-York: Published by Richard Scott. J. & J. Harper, printers. 1818.
2 v. in 1. front. (fold. chart) 21 cm.

NL 0434694 CSmH CtY ViLxW PU OCX MWiW

Locke, John, 1632-1704.
An essay concerning human understanding. 2 vol.
London, 1819

NL 0434695 MiD

Locke, John, 1632-1704.
Essay concerning Human understanding...24th ed. with author's last additions and corrections. London, 1823.
14-648 p. 8 3/4 in.

NL 0434696 OO MH PHC

Locke, John, 1632-1704.
An essay concerning human understanding. Written by John Locke, gent. The 24th ed. ... London, Printed for C. and J. Rivington [etc.] 1824.
2 v. fold. tab. 21½cm.
CONTENTS.—v. 1. An analysis of Mr. Locke's doctrine of ideas in his Essay on human understanding. (fold. tab.) Of human understanding.—v. 2. Of human understanding. A defence of Mr. Locke's opinion concerning personal identity. Of the conduct of the understanding. Some thoughts concerning reading and study for a gentleman. Elements of natural philosophy. A new method of a common-place-book.
1. Knowledge, Theory of.
10—32058
Library of Congress B1290 1824

NL 0434697 DLC

Locke, John, 1632-1704.
An essay concerning human understanding, written by John Locke, Gent. Complete, with notes, in one volume. With the author's last additions and corrections. London: J. Bumpus, 1824. 2 p.l., (i)iv-xvi, 668 p., 1 fold. table. 25. ed. 8°.
1. Mind.—Philosophy of.
November 23, 1917

NL 0434698 NN MH FMU PP

Locke, John, 1632-1704.
An essay concerning human understanding, written by John Locke, gent. To which are added, I. An analysis of Mr. Locke's doctrine of ideas, on a large sheet. II. A defence of Mr. Locke's opinion concerning personal identity, with an appendix. III. A treatise on the conduct of the understanding. IV. Some thoughts concerning reading and study for a gentleman. V. Elements of natural philosophy. VI. A new method of a common-place book. Extracted from the author's works. A new ed. ... New-York, V. Seaman, 1824.
2 v. in 1. front. (fold. tab.) 22.5 cm.
On spine: Locke's Essay.
Errors in paging: v. 1: 292, 328 and 430 numbered 293, 264 and 43 respectively; v. 2: 381 numbered 379.
In manuscript on t.-p.: Isaac S. Pennybacker March 9th 1826.
Bookplate: From the library of Gen. John E. Roller ... by his daughter.
"The life of the author": v. 1, p. [17]-30.
1. Knowledge, Theory of. I. Title.

OO ViLxW ICJ AU
NL 0434701 Vi NcU NcD PPDrop PU PHi DHEW MB NN MH

S
B1290
L814e
1825 Locke, John, 1632-1704.
An essay concerning human understanding, by John Locke, to which are added an analysis of Mr. Locke's Doctrine of Ideas on a large sheet, a defence of Mr Locke's opinion concerning personal identity, with an appendix, a treatise on the conduct of the understanding, some thoughts concerning reading and study for a gentleman, elements of natural philosophy, a new Method of a Common Place Book. Extracted from the author's works with a life of the author. A new edition corrected from a late improved London copy. New York, Printed by Samuel Marks, 1825.
2 v. in 1. fold. tab.
1. Knowledge, Theory of I. Title

NL 0434703 PHeM MH OCU OClW MiU PPFr

Locke, John, 1632-1704.
An essay concerning human understanding, with the author's last additions and corrections, and an analysis of the doctrine of ideas. Thoughts concerning reading and study for a gentleman. Of the conduct of the understanding... London, J.F.Dove, 1828.
xii,[12]-590 p. front.(port.) table (fold.)

NL 0434704 OO

B1290
1828
Bur. of
Int. Rel.
Locke, John, 1632-1704.
An essay concerning human understanding, to which are now first added: I. An analysis of Mr. Locke's doctrine of ideas, on a large sheet. II. A defence of Mr. Locke's opinion concerning personal identity, with an appendix. III. A treatise on the conduct of the understanding. IV. Some thoughts concerning reading and study for a gentleman. V. Elements of natural philosophy. VI. A new method of a common-place-book. Extracted from the author's works. A new ed. London, T. Tegg, 1828-32.
3 v.
1. Knowledge, Theory of.

NL 0434705 CU MeWC

Locke, John, 1632-1704.
An essay concerning human understanding. Written by John Locke. Twenty-eighth edition, with the author's last additions and corrections. Complete in one volume. With notes and illustrations, and an analysis of Mr. Locke's doctrine of ideas. London, Printed for T. Tegg and son, 1838.
xii, 566 p. 1 diagr. 23 cm.

NL 0434706 NNUT

Locke, John, 1632-1704.
An essay concerning human understanding. Written by John Locke, gent. 29th ed. with the author's last additions and corrections. With notes and illustrations, and an analysis of Mr. Locke's Doctrine of ideas. Complete in one volume. London,Printed for T.Tegg[etc.] 1841.
xii,548p. front.(port.)fold. tab. 22½cm.
1. Knowledge, Theory of.

NL 0434707 MWelC NN RPB

Locke, John, 1632-1704.
Essay concerning human understanding. Ed. 30. London, Tegg, 1846.
16 + 566 p. por. tab.

NL 0434708 OrP

Locke, John, 1632-1704.
An essay concerning human understanding. With the notes and illustrations of the author, and an analysis of his doctrine of ideas. 3[0]th ed., carefully revised, and compared with the best copies. London, Printed for T.Tegg, 1846.

NL 0434709 MH OrP

Locke, John, 1632-1704.
An essay concerning human understanding; with the notes and illustrations of the author... 30th. ed., carefully revised. London, Tegg, 1849.
564 p.

NL 0434710 PP

B1290
1853a Locke, John, 1632-1704.
An essay concerning human understanding. With the notes and illustrations of the author, and an analysis of his doctrine of ideas. 31st ed. Carefully rev. London, W. Tegg, 1853.
564 p. front.(port.) 23 cm.
1. Knowledge, Theory of.

NL 0434711 T NBC IU MH NN NjP

Locke, John, 1632-1704.
An essay concerning human understanding... With the notes and illustrations of the author, and an analysis of his doctrine of ideas. Also, Questions on Locke's Essay, by A.M. ... 36th ed. Carefully rev., and compared with the best copies. London, W. Tegg, 1869.
xvi, 664 p. in 2 v. front. (port.) fold. tab. 19 cm.
"Questions on Locke", by Thaddeus O'Mahony, p. [611]-649.
Foxwell's copy with his ms. annotations.

NL 0434712 MH-AH

VOLUME 337

Locke, John, 1632-1704.
An essay concerning human understanding... With notes and illustrations of the author, and an analysis of his doctrine of ideas. Also, questions on Locke's essay, by A.M....37th.ed., carefully rev. and compared with the best copies. London, W. Tegg [187-?]

I. O'Mahony, Thaddeus, ed.

NL 0434713 PU IaU

Phil 2115.35.25
Locke, John, 1632-1704.
An essay concerning human understanding. With the notes and illustrations of the author, and an analysis of his doctrine of ideas. Also, questions on Locke's Essay, by A.M. New ed., carefully revised and compared with the best copies. London, W.Tegg and co., 1879.
xvi, 664 p. port., folded table. 19 cm.

NL 0434714 MH MdBJ

Locke, John, 1632-1704.
An essay concerning human understanding. With the notes and illustrations of the author, and an analysis of his doctrine of ideas. Also, Questions of Locke's essay, by A. M. New edition, carefully revised, and compared with the best copies. London, Ward, Lock, & Co. [1880?]
xvi, 664 p. fold. chart. 19 cm.
Published ca. 1880.

NL 0434715 PLatS

B 1290 1689 Locke, John, 1632-1704
An essay concerning human understanding. With the notes and illustrations of the author, and an analysis of his doctrine of ideas. Also, Questions on Lock's Essay, by A. M. New [6th] ed., carefully revised, and compared with the best copies. London, New York, Ward, Lock & Bowden [1880?]
664p. 19cm. (The World library, 31)
Half-title: Locke on the human understanding.

I. M., A. II. Title

NL 0434716 WU RPB NNUT OrPR

B1290 1881 Locke, John, 1632-1704
An essay concerning human understanding, with notes and illustrations of the author and an analysis of his doctrine of ideas, also, Questions on Locke's essay, by A.M. New ed... London, Ward, [1881]
664p. front. (fold. table) 20cm.

The questions sometimes appear as by T. O'M., Thaddeus O'Mahoney
1.Knowledge, Theory of. I.O'Mahony, Thaddeus Questions on Locke's essay.

NL 0434717 IaU CaBVaU NIC IaU

Locke, John, 1632-1704.
An essay concerning human understanding, by John Locke. New ed., carefully revised, and compared with the best copies. London, G. Routledge and sons, limited; New York, E.P. Dutton and co. [189-?]
xvi, 624 p. 19 cm.

NL 0434718 NcRS OCl

Locke, John, 1632-1704. B.H.Ref.940.72 (6250b.72)
An essay concerning human understanding. With the notes and illustrations of the author, and an analysis of his doctrine of ideas. New edition.
— London. Routledge. [189-?] xvi, 624 pp. Table. [Sir John Lubbock's Hundred books.] Sm. 8°.

F6760 — S.r. — Psychology.

NL 0434719 MB

Locke, John, 1632-1704.
An essay concerning human understanding, by John Locke; collated and annotated, with prolegomena, biographical, critical and historical, by Alexander Campbell Fraser ... Oxford, Clarendon press, 1894.
2 v. front. (port.) 23 cm.
"Editions and interpretations of Locke's Essay": v. 1, p. [xi]-xv.

1. Knowledge, Theory of. I. Fraser, Alexander Campbell, 1819-1914, ed.

B1291.F8 1-3469

OCU CtY-D MB NN NcU NjP ICN ICJ M OrPR OrStbM OKentU TxU PU PU-Penn ICRL MiU NcD OO ICJ IU OClU
NL 0434720 DLC OClW ViU PSC PHC PPT PPL DFo CtY NIC

Locke (John) 1632-1704.
An essay concerning human understanding, [Selections from]. (In: Selby-Bigge (L. A.) British moralists . . . Oxford, 1897. 8°. v. 2, pp. 326-347.)

NL 0434722 NN

B1290 19— Locke, John, 1632-1704.
An essay concerning human understanding; with the notes and illustrations of the author, and an analysis of his doctrine of ideas. New ed., carefully rev., and compared with the best copies. London, G. Routledge; New York, E. P. Dutton [19—?]
xvi, 624 p.

1. Knowledge, Theory of.

NL 0434723 ICU

Locke, John, 1632-1704.
Locke's essay concerning human understanding, books II and IV (with omissions) selected by Mary Whiton Calkins ... Chicago, The Open court publishing company; London agents, K. Paul, Trench, Trübner & co., ltd., 1905.
xiii, 342 p. front. (port.) 19½cm. (On cover: Religion of science library, no. 58)
Contains reprint of t.-p. of 2d edition, London, 1694.
"Writings of Locke in order of publication": p. xi-xiii.

1. Knowledge, Theory of. I. Calkins, Mary Whiton, 1863-1930, ed.

Library of Congress B1292 1905 5—4068
Copyright A 106757 [a34h1]

OClND OCU OCX MdBJ
NL 0434724 DLC WaU NcRS OClW MiU WaSpG MH NNF OOxM

Locke, John, 1632-1704. 153 E5
11217 An essay concerning human understanding. By John Locke, ..., with the notes and illustrations of the author, and an analysis of his doctrine of ideas. Also questions on Locke's essay, by A. M., [*pseud.*], ... New edition. Carefully revised, and compared with the best copies. London, Ward, Lock, & Co., [1905].
xvi, 664 p. front. (fold. table). 19cm.
The questions sometimes appear as by T. O'M., Thomas O'Mahony.

NL 0434725 ICJ OrSaW WaT ICRL NNC

Locke, John, 1632-1704.
Essay concerning human understanding. Houghton, 1908. 8°

(Modern classical philosophers.)

NL 0434726 I OrP

B1292 1909 Locke, John, 1632-1704.
An essay concerning human understanding; with the notes and illus. of the author, and an analysis of his doctrine of ideas. New ed., carefully rev., and compared with the best copies. London, Routledge; New York, Dutton [1909]
xvi, 624p. 19cm.

1. Knowledge, Theory of.

NL 0434727 FMU PSC IU-M ViU OU

Locke, John, 1632-1704. 153 E7
121051 Locke's Essay concerning human understanding. Books II and IV, (with omissions). Selected by Mary Whiton Calkins. Second edition revised and corrected. .... Chicago, The Open Court Publishing Company, 1912.
lvii, 348 p. 1 facsim. 20½cm.
"The life and character of Mr. John Locke. By Le Clerc," p. [ix]-lii.
"Writings of Locke in order of publication," p. [lv]-lvii.

NL 0434728 ICJ MWelC PU

B1292 1917 Locke, John, 1632-1704.
Essay concerning human understanding. Books II and IV (with omissions). Selected by Mary Whiton Calkins. 3d ed., rev. and enl. Chicago, Open Court Pub. Co., 1917.
lvii,348p. facsim.,port.

1. Knowledge, Theory of I. Calkins, Mary Whiton, 1863-1930, ed.

NL 0434729 NBC MH

B1292 1920 Locke, John, 1632-1704.
Essay concerning human understanding, books II and IV (with omissions) Selected by Mary Whiton Calkins. Reprint ed., rev. and enl. Chicago, Open Court Pub. Co., 1920.
lvii, 348 p. facsim. 20cm.

1. Knowledge, Theory of. I. Calkins, Mary Whiton, 1863-1930.

NL 0434730 ViU KU CtY

Locke, John, 1632-1704.
An essay concerning human understanding, by John Locke. Abridged and edited by A. S. Pringle-Pattison. Oxford, Clarendon press, 1924.
2 p. l., [iii]-xlviii, 380 p. 20 cm.

1. Knowledge, Theory of. I. Seth Pringle Pattison, Andrew, 1856-1931, ed.

B1292 1924 25—11567

OrU Wa WaE WaPS WaSp WaT WaTC WaWW Or OrStbM OrSaW ICN IU NN IU FU NjP MB CaBVaU IdB IdU MtU OrCS OrPR
NL 0434731 DLC WaS OKentU GU CtY NcU PSC PU MH ICU

Locke, John, 1632-1704.
Essay concerning human understanding...with a life of the author. New ed. from a late improved London copy. N.Y., 1925.
1v.

NL 0434733 PPL

B1292 .C22 Locke,John,1632-1704.
Locke's essay concerning human understanding, books II and IV(with omissions)selected by Mary Whiton Calkins. Reprint edition,revised and enlarged... Chicago,etc.,The Open court publishing company,1927.
lvii,348 p. 19½cm. (On cover:Philosophical classics. Religion of science library,no.58)
Contains reprint of t.-p.of 2d edition,London, 1694.
"Writings of Locke in order of publication":p. [lv]-lvii.

NL 0434734 ICU ICarbS WaSpG TU

Locke, John, 1632-1704.
An essay concerning the human understanding, abridged and edited by A.S. Pringle-Pattison. Oxford, 1928.
380 p.

NL 0434735 PPWe

VOLUME 337

B 1292 1933 Locke, John 1632-1704.
Locke's essay concerning human understanding, books II and IV (with omissions) selected by Mary Whiton Calkins. Reprint ed., rev. and enl.... Chicago, London, The Open court publishing co., 1933.
lvii, 348 p. 19 1/2 cm. (On cover: Religion of science library, n.58)

1. Knowledge, Theory of. I. Calkins, Mary Whiton, 1863-1930, ed.

NL 0434736 IMunS

Locke, John, 1632-1704.
An essay concerning human understanding, ... abridged and ed. by A.S. Pringle-Pattison. Oxford, The Clarendon press [1934]
380 p.

NL 0434737 OU PHC MiU OEac OCl OClW

Locke, John, 1632-1704. An essay concerning human understanding.
Bacon, Francis, *viscount St. Albans*, 1561-1626.
Francis Bacon. The great instauration: proemium, preface, plan of the work, and Novum organum. Thomas Hobbes. Leviathan. John Locke. An essay concerning human understanding. Edited by Gail Kennedy ... Garden City, N. Y., Doubleday, Doran & company, inc. [°1937]

Locke, John, 1632-1704.
An essay concerning human understanding... Abridged and edited by A. S. Pringle-Pattison. Oxford: [1947]

NL 0434739 DFo

Locke, John, 1632-1704.
An essay concerning human understanding. Abridged and ed. by Raymond Wilburn. London, Dent; New York, Dutton [1947]
355 p. 18 cm. (Everyman's library)

1. Knowledge, Theory of. I. Wilburn, Raymond, ed. II. Title: Human understanding.

A48-6331

San Francisco. Public Library for Library of Congress

NL 0434740 MiU OrPR OU NNC DCU MU NBuU WaT OrP WaS OCl Mi CSf ScU WaU ICU MH MiD MiHM TxU PCM OClJC

B1292 1948 Locke, John, 1632-1704.
An essay concerning human understanding. Abridged and edited by Raymond Wilburn. London, Dent; New York, Dutton [1948]
xxv, 355 p. 18 cm. (Everyman's library, no. 984. Science)

1. Knowledge, Theory of. I. Wilburn, Raymond, ed. II. Title: Human understanding. III. Series.

NL 0434741 MB NNC

152L79 R112

Locke, John, 1632-1704.
Locke's Essay concerning human understanding, Books II and IV (with ommissions) Selected by Mary Whiton Calkins. Reprint ed., rev. and enl. Chicago, Open Court Publishing Company, 1949.
lvii, 348 p.

Includes Leclerc's "Life and character of Mr. John Locke".
Bibliography: p. [xlv]-lvii.

NL 0434742 NNC

B1292 1950 Locke, John, 1632-1704.

An essay concerning human understanding. Abridged and edited by A. S. Pringle-Pattison. Oxford, Clarendon Press [1950]
xlviii, 380 p. 20cm.

1. Knowledge, Theory of. I. Seth Pringle Pattison, Andrew, 1856- ed.

NL 0434743 ViU MH

Locke, John, 1632-1704. An essay concerning human understanding.

AC1 .G72 vol. 35 Locke, John, 1632-1704.
A letter concerning toleration. [Translated by William Popple] Concerning civil government, second essay. An essay concerning human understanding. By John Locke. The principles of human knowledge, by George Berkeley. An enquiry concerning human understanding, by David Hume. Chicago, Encyclopædia Britannica [1955, °1952]

Locke, John, 1632-1704.
An essay concerning human understanding; with thoughts on the conduct of the understanding. By John Locke, esq. Collated with Desmaizeaux's edition. To which is prefixed, the life of the author ... London, Printed for Allen & West; Edinburgh, J. Mundell and co. [etc., etc.] 1795.
3 v. 18 cm.
Incomplete set: v. 2-3 wanting.
Errors in pagination, v. 1: xiv numbered vix, xlvi numbered xliv.
1. Knowledge, Theory of. I. Desmaizeaux, Pierre, 1673?-1745. II. Title.

NL 0434745 Vi ICJ NN OO ScU WaWW NjP MH NRCR PWcHi

Locke, John, 1632-1704.
... An essay concerning human understanding. And a treatise on the conduct of the understanding. By John Locke, Gent. Complete in one volume: with the author's last additions and corrections. Philadelphia, James Kay, jun. and brother; Pittsburg, John I. Kay & co. [n. d.]
1 p.l., 4-524 p. 1 fold. analysis. 23 cm.

At head of t.p.: Locke's essays.
On back: University and library edition.

NL 0434746 ViLxW CtY NN NjP ODW OClW

Locke, John, 1632-1704.
Essay concerning human understanding. And a treatise on the Conduct of the Understanding. Complete, in one volume: With the author's last additions and corrections. (Locke's essays) Phila.: J. Kay, Jr. & Bro., 1844.
523 p. 8°.

NL 0434747 NNUT NjP

Locke, John, 1632-1704.
An essay concerning human understanding and a treatise on the conduct of the understanding, by John Locke. Complete, in one volume, with the author's last additions and corrections. Philadelphia, Kay & Troutman, 1846.
523.p. fold. table. 23 cm.
1. Knowledge, Theory of.

NL 0434748 IEG PP OCX

Locke, John, 1632-1704.
An essay concerning human understanding. And A treatise on the conduct of the understanding. Complete, in one volume: with the author's last additions and corrections. Philadelphia, Kay & Troutman, 1847.
523 p. 23 cm.
At head of title: Locke's essays.

NL 0434749 PLatS ViU

LOCKE, John, 1632-1704.
An essay concerning human understanding and A treatise on the conduct of the understanding With the author's last additions and corrections. Philadelphia, Kay & Troutman, etc., etc., 1849.

Folded table.
At head of title-page:-Locke's essays.
Phil 2115.35.15

NL 0434750 MH PPFr NcD

Locke, John, 1632-1704.
... An essay concerning human understanding. And A treatise on the conduct of the understanding. By John Locke, gent. Complete, in one volume: with the author's last additions and corrections. Philadelphia, J. Kay, Jun. and brother; Pittsburgh, J. I. Kay and co. [185-?]
524 p. fold. tab. 23cm.
At head of title: Locke's essays.
On cover: University and library edition.

NL 0434751 ViU MH TxU

Locke, John, 1632-1704.
... An essay concerning human understanding. And a treatise on the conduct of the understanding. By John Locke ... Complete in one volume: with the author's last additions and corrections. Philadelphia, T. E. Zell [185-?]
524 p. 23cm.
At head of title: Locke's essays.

1. Knowledge, Theory of. 17-19452

Library of Congress B1292 1850

NL 0434752 DLC NjP ViU

Locke, John, 1632-1704.
...An essay concerning human understanding. And a treatise on the conduct of the understanding... Complete, in one volume; with the author's last additions and corrections. Philadelphia, Troutman & Hayes; Pittsburgh, Kay & co., 1850.
524 p.

NL 0434753 NRCR

Locke, John, 1632-1704.
... An essay concerning human understanding. And, A treatise on the conduct of the understanding ... Complete, in one volume: with the author's last additions and corrections. Philadelphia, Troutman & Hayes, 1852.
524 p. fold. table. 23 cm.
At head of title: Locke's essays.

NL 0434754 NcD ViU CtY

Locke, John, 1632-1704.
... An essay concerning human understanding. And A treatise on the conduct of the understanding. By John Locke, gent. Complete, in one volume: with the author's last additions and corrections. Philadelphia, Troutman & Hayes; Pittsburgh, Kay & co., 1853.
524 p. fold. tab. 23cm.
At head of title: Locke's essays.

1. Knowledge, Theory of. I. Title: Conduct of the understanding.
15-604

Library of Congress B1290 1853

NL 0434755 DLC PPWe PV OClJC MiU OO ViU

Locke, John, 1632-1704.
... An essay concerning human understanding. And a treatise on the conduct of the understanding. By John Locke, gent. Complete, in one volume: with the author's last additions and corrections. Philadelphia, Hayes & Zell, 1854.
524-p. fold. tab. 23 cm.
At head of title: Locke's essays.

NL 0434756 OCU

VOLUME 337

Locke, John, 1632-1704.
... An essay concerning human understanding. And A treatise on the conduct of the understanding. By John Locke, gent. Complete, in one volume: with the author's last additions and corrections. Philadelphia, Hayes & Zell, 1856.
524 p. 23cm.
At head of title: Locke's essays.

1. Knowledge, Theory of.

NL 0434757 ICU

Locke, John, 1632-1704.
... An essay concerning human understanding. And a treatise on the conduct of the understanding. By John Locke, gent. Complete in one volume: with the author's last additions and corrections. Philadelphia, Hayes & Zell, 1857.
524 p. fold. tab. 23cm.

At head of title: Locke's essays.

NL 0434758 ViU-L PPeSchw PMA

153 L814e 1860a Locke, John, 1632-1704.
An essay concerning human understanding. And a treatise on the conduct of the understanding. Complete in one volume: with the author's last additions and corrections. Philadelphia, Hayes & Zell, 1860.
32,524p. 24cm.
At head of title: Locke's essays.
1. Knowledge, Theory of. I. Title: Human understanding.

NL 0434759 CLSU OCl PHi

Locke, John, 1632-1704.
An essay concerning human understanding, and A treatise on the conduct of the understanding. Phila., 1864.
8°.

NL 0434760 I

Locke, John, 1632-1704.
An essay concerning the true original extent and end of civil government. By the late learned John Locke, esq. Boston, Re-printed and sold by Edes and Gill in Queen-street, 1773.
129 p. 18½cm.
A reprint of the second treatise in Locke's "Two treatises of government," London, 1690.

1. Political science. 2. Liberty.

21-5049

Library of Congress JC153.L85

NL 0434761 DLC CtY ICN CSt N PU

JC336 .B27 1948 Locke, John, 1632-1704. An essay concerning the true original, extent and end of civil government.
FOR OTHER EDITIONS SEE MAIN ENTRY
Barker, *Sir* Ernest, 1874- *ed.*
Social contract; essays by Locke, Hume and Rousseau. New York, Oxford Univ. Press, 1948.

AC1 .G72 vol. 35 Locke, John, 1632-1704. An essay concerning the true original extent and end of civil government. 1955.
Locke, John, 1632-1704.
A letter concerning toleration. [Translated by William Popple] Concerning civil government, second essay. An essay concerning human understanding. By John Locke. The principles of human knowledge, by George Berkeley. An enquiry concerning human understanding, by David Hume. Chicago, Encyclopædia Britannica [1955, °1952]

Locke, John, 1632-1704.
An essay concerning the understanding, knowledge, opinion, and assent, by John Locke; edited with an introduction by Benjamin Rand ... Cambridge, Harvard university press 1931.
lix, [1], 306, [1] p. front. (port.) 3 facsims. on 1 pl. 21½cm.
The hitherto unpublished draft dated 1671, of Locke's Essay concerning human understanding first published in 1690, printed from a photostat copy of the original, with strict adherence to the text, save that the spelling, capitals and punctuation have been modernized. cf. Editor's pref.

1. Knowledge, Theory of. I. Rand, Benjamin, 1856-1934, ed.
31-12985

Library of Congress B1290 1931
[a44j1] 151

NL 0434764 MiU IdU ODW NN KyU CaBVaU WaTC OrU DLC ScU NIC PU PHC PPT OCU MH MB OU OCl

Locke, John, 1632-1704. 5429a.59
Locke's Essay for the understanding of St. Paul's Epistles; and Le Clerc on inspiration.
Boston. Wells & Lilly. 1820. 130 pp. 16°.
The preface is signed A. N. [Andrews Norton].

F8793 — Norton, Andrews, ed. 1786-1853. — Bible. N. T. Epistles of St. Paul. Crit., interp., etc.

NL 0434765 MB PPL MdBJ NIC RPB NNUT MH OO

Locke, John, 1632-1704.
An essay for the understanding of St. Paul's Epistles.
(In Sparks, Jared, editor. A collection of essays and tracts in theology. Vol. 6, pp. 165-195. Boston, 1823.) *3469.26.6

Aug.4, 1902
E5064 — Bible. N. T. Epistles of St. Paul. Crit., interp., &c.

NL 0434766 MB

Locke, John, 1632-1704.
An essay for the understanding of St. Paul's epistles. Boston, Gray & Bowen, 1831.
24 p. 16°. [American unitarian association. Tracts. 1st series, v. 4]

NL 0434767 Nh

BR83 .68 Locke, John, 1632-1704.
An essay on enthusiasm...being the nineteenth chapter of the fourth book of his essay concerning human understanding. London, printed by Stower & Smalfield, Hackney; sold by R. Hunter, 1815.
16 p. 21 cm.

NL 0434768 MB PPFr ICN

LD914 .G8L8 Archives Locke, John, 1632-1704.
An essay on human understanding (Book III) Chicago, Great Books Foundation [1946?]
[223]-254 p.
"This reprint contains only part of a book, the part assigned in the First Course for community groups."

NL 0434769 ICU

Locke, John, 1632-1704. 5609a.121
Locke's Essay on the human understanding. Condensed under the superintendence of A. J. Valpy.
London. Valpy. 1831. (1), xvi, 427 pp. Portrait. 16½ cm., in 8s.
Contains his Conduct of the understanding, catalogued separately.

H6586 — Psychology. — Valpy, Abraham John, ed. 1787-1854.

NL 0434770 MB

192 L81e Locke, John, 1632-1704.
Essays, including Four letters on toleration, Some thoughts concerning education and The value of money. London, New York, Ward Lock [n.d.]
703p. 20cm. (The World library)

NL 0434771 IEN CtY-D MH MdBJ

Locke, John, 1632-1704.
Essays ... London, New York, Ward, Lock and co. [1883]
2 p.l., 400 p., 1 l., [v]-vii, [403]-703 p. 19 cm. (The World library of standard books, v. 67)
Contents. - Four letters on toleration. - Some thoughts concerning education. - Consequences of the lowering of interest and raising the value of money.

NL 0434772 CtY

Locke, John, 1632-1704.

Wynne, Richard, *ed.*
Essays on education, by Milton, Locke, and the authors of the Spectator, &c. to which are added Observations on the ancient and modern languages, by R. Wynne ... London, Printed for J. and R. Tonson, 1761.

Locke, John, 1632-1704.
Essays on the law of nature. The Latin text, with a translation, introd. and notes, together with transcripts of Locke's shorthand in his journal for 1676. Edited by W. von Leyden. Oxford, Clarendon Press, 1954.
xi, 292 p. facsims. 23 cm.
"Three sets of early writings ... published here for the first time from manuscripts in the Lovelace Collection now in the Bodleian Library."
Bibliographical footnotes.

1. Natural law—Addresses, essays, lectures.
B1255.L4 192.2 A55-680
Rochester. Univ. Libr. for Library of Congress [55f5]†

NL 0434775 PSt PP PU MB TU PSC NjPT OU OClW OO OCU PBL IEN NcRS IaU TxU NN CtY MH NNC IU NIC ICN ViU ICU DLC NcD MiU NRU WaSpG OrU OrPR OrCS CaBVaU MoU LU-NO

Locke, John, 1632-1704, supposed author.
The exceptions of Mr. Edwards
see under title

Locke, John, 1632-1704.

Brunt, Jonathan, *b.* 1760.
Extracts, from Locke's Essay on the human understanding; and other writers; containing a defence of natural, judicial, and constitutional rights, on the principles of morality, religion, & equal justice, against the private and public intrigues of artificial society. Together with a short account of the publisher's difficulties, intermixed with some political remarks. To which is added, an universal prayer, for the conversion, to genuine Christianity, of the great family of mankind. Frankfort, Kentucky, Printed and sold by J. Brunt. November 1804.

Locke, John, 1632-1704.
Familiar letters between Mr. John Locke, and several of his friends. In which are explain'd, his notions in his Essay concerning human understanding and in some of his other works. The 4th ed. To which is added, The life and character of Mr. John Locke. London, Printed for F. Noble [etc.] 1742.
1 p.l., 13, [iii]-iv, [5]-424 p. front. (port.) 20cm.

NL 0434778 MnU ICN KyU MiU NNNAM IEN IaU MH IU NcD

Locke, John, 1632-1704.
La filosofia di G. Locke
see under Carlini, Armando, 1878-

Locke, John, 1632-1704.

Carolina.
The first set of the fundamental constitutions of South Carolina: as compiled by Mr. John Locke.
(*In* Carroll, Bartholomew R. Historical collections of South Carolina. New-York, 1836. 22½cm. v. 2, p. [361]-390)

VOLUME 337

Locke, John, 1632-1704.
Five letters concerning the inspiration of the Holy Scriptures
see under [Le Clerc, Jean] 1657-1736.

Locke, John, 1632-1704.
Four letters on toleration. Reprint of seventh edition, 4 to. 1758. [London, A. Murray, 1870.]
400 p. 20 cm.
1. Toleration. I. Title. II. Title: Letters on toleration.

NL 0434782 OCU WaS IEG

BR1610 .L81 1870
Locke, John, 1632–1704.
Four letters on toleration. London, Ward, Lock, and Tyler [1870?]
400 p. 19cm. (The World library of standard works)

1. Toleration.

NL 0434783 ViU MdBJ MH MB

Locke, John, 1632–1704. 172.3 F1
Four letters on toleration. By John Locke. London, Ward, Lock, and Tyler, [1876?].
[6], 400 p. 19cm. (The World library of standard books.)

NL 0434784 ICJ ICU

Locke, John, 1632-1704. FOR OTHER EDITIONS SEE MAIN ENTRY

Carolina.
... The fundamental constitutions of Carolina. 1669. [Boston, Directors of the Old South work, 1906]

[Locke, John] 1632-1704.
Further considerations concerning raising the value of money. Wherein Mr. Lowndes's arguments for it in his late Report concerning an essay for the amendment of the silver coins, are particularly examined. London, Printed for A[wnsham]. and J[ohn]. Churchil, 1695.
8 p.ℓ.,111,[1],24 p. 17cm.

Rare Books Dept.

Includes the author's Short observations on a printed paper, intituled, For encouraging the coining silver money in England, and after for keeping it here (24 p. at end).
Wing L-2745.

NIC NNC PU-R RPB
NL 0434786 CU NjP MH CSmH NN InU MH-BA PU CtY

SPECIAL COLLECTIONS MONTGOMERY

[Locke, John] 1632-1704.
Further considerations concerning raising the value of money. Wherein Mr. Lowndes's arguments for it in his late Report concerning an essay for the amendment of the silver coins, are particularly examined. The second edition corrected. London, Printed for Awnsham and John Churchil, 1696.
[16], 112 p. 19cm. (In his Several papers relating to money, interest and trade. London, 1696)

NL 0434787 NNC MCM CSmH

Locke, John, 1632–1704.
John Lockes Gedanken über die erziehung. Ins deutsche übers. und mit einer einleitung und erklärenden anmerkungen versehen, von prof. dr. Ludwig Wattendorff Mit Lockes bildnis. Paderborn [Prussia] F. Schöningh, 1907.
vi, 292 p. front. (port.) 18½cm. (*Half-title:* Sammlung der bedeutendsten pädagogischen schriften aus alter und neuer zeit. Mit biographien, erläuterungen und erklärenden anmerkungen, hrsg. von dr. J. Gansen ... dr. A. Keller ... dr. B. Schulz ... 32. bd.)

1. Education. I. Wattendorff, Ludwig, tr.

E 10-1494

Library, U. S. Bur. of Education LB475.L6A2

NL 0434788 DHEW ICJ MH

LOCKE, John, 1632-1704.
Gedanken über die erziehung. Ins deutsch übersetzt und mit einer einleitung und erklarenden anmerkungen versehen von Ludwig Wattendorff. 2e aufl. Paderborn, F. Schöningh, 1913.
Port.
(SAMMLUNG der bedeutendsten pädegogischen schriften aus alter und neuer zeit, 32.)
Educ.Lib.

NL 0434789 MH

---

370 L79sGsa
Locke, John, 1632-1704.
John Locke's Gedanken über erziehung. Eingeleitet, übersetzt und erläutert von dr. E. von Sallwürk Langensalza, H. Beyer & söhne, 1883.
lxxii, 235p. (Added t.-p.: H. Beyer's Bibliothek pädagogischer klassiker. Eine sammlung der bedeutendsten pädagogischen schriften älterer und neuerer zeit, hrsg. von Friedrich Mann [22. bd.])
Bibliographical foot-notes.
1. Education. I. Sallwürk, Ernst von, 1839-1926, ed. and tr.

NL 0434790 IU

Locke, John, 1632–1704. 370.4 L791
John Lockes Gedanken über Erziehung. Eingeleitet, übersetzt und erläutert von Dr. E. von Sallwürk, ... Zweite Auflage. Langensalza, H. Beyer & Söhne, 1897.
viii, 310 p. 21cm. (*Added t.-p.:* Bibliothek pädagogischer Klassiker, [Bd. 22].)

NL 0434791 ICJ

Locke, John, 1632–1704.
John Lockes Gedanken über erziehung. Eingeleitet, übers. und erläutert von dr. E. von Sallwürk ... 3. aufl. Langensalza, H. Beyer & söhne (Beyer & Mann) 1910.
viii, 312 p. 21cm. (*Added t.-p.:* Bibliothek pädagogischer klassiker. Eine sammlung der bedeutendsten pädagogischen schriften älterer und neuerer zeit, hrsg. von F. Mann. [22. bd.])

1. Education. I. Sallwürk, Ernst von, 1839– ed. and tr.

A 15-2492

Title from Johns Hopkins Univ. Printed by L. C.

NL 0434792 MdBJ PU

Locke, John, *1632–1704* No. 6 in 4896.50.620
Gedanken über Erziehung. In der Übersetzung Ouvriers mit Einleitung und Anmerkungen herausgegeben von Theodor Fritzsch. — Leipzig. Reclam. [1920.] 319, (1) pp. [Universal-Bibliothek. 6147-6150.] 14 cm., in 8s.

D5008 — S.r.c. — Education. — Fritzsch, Theodor, ed., 1852-

NL 0434793 MB

Locke, John, 1632-1704.
Gleanings from John Locke and other authors
see under [Winans, Ross] 1796-1877, ed.

Locke, John, 1632-1704.
Le gouvernement civil, oder die kunst wohl zu regieren durch den berühmten Engelländer Jean Lock beschrieben ... aus der englischen und frantzös. sprache in die hochteutsche von G. Franckfurth und Leipzig, 1718.

NL 0434795 NNC

[Locke, John] 1632-1704, supposed author.
ΓΡΑΦΑΥΤΑΡΚΕΙΑ, or, the Scriptures sufficiency practically demonstrated... London, Sampson Evans, 1676.
[30], 508 p. 23 1/2 cm.

NL 0434796 MBAt

Locke, John, 1632–1704.
Handbuch der erziehung, aus dem englischen des John Locke übers. von Rudolphi. [Wien und Wolfenbüttel, Bey R. Gräffer und compagnie [etc.] 1787]
xiv p., 1 l., [5]-612 p. 18½cm. (*In* Campe, J. H., ed. Allgemeine revision des gesammten schul- und erziehungswesens. Hamburg [etc.] 1785-92. 9. th.)
Half-title.

1. Education. I. Rudolphi, Ludwig Eberhard Gottlob, d. 1798, tr.

Library of Congress LB14.C2 6-26115†

NL 0434797 DLC

[**Locke, John**] 1632–1704.
Histoire de la navigation, son commencement, son progrè & ses découvertes jusqu'à présent. Tr. de l'anglois ... Paris E. Ganeau, 1722.
2 v. 16cm.
Published anonymously.
"Catalogue de livres de voyage": t. 2, p. 177–274.
"Catalogue général des cartes de géographie": t. 2, p. 275–316.

1. Discoveries (in geography) 2. Voyages and travels. 3. Voyages and travels—Bibl. 4. Maps, Early—Bibl. I. Title.

Library of Congress G80.L79 6—419

NL 0434798 DLC RPJCB CtY MnU MiU-C MiU MH-BA

Locke, John, 1632-1704.

[**Hewatt, Alexander**]
An historical account of the rise and progress of the colonies of South Carolina and Georgia ... London, A. Donaldson, 1779.

Locke, John, 1632-1704, supposed author.
An historical narration of the life and death of our Lord Jesus Christ
see under Woodhead, Abraham, 1609-1678.

Locke, John, 1632-1704. History of Navigation.

[**Churchill, Awnsham**] d. 1728, *comp.*
A collection of voyages and travels, some now first printed from original manuscripts, others now first published in English ... To which is prefixed, an introductory discourse (supposed to be written by the celebrated Mr. Locke) intitled, The whole history of navigation from its original to this time. Illustrated with ... maps and cuts, curiously engraved ... 3d ed. ... London, Printed by assignment from Messrs. Churchill, for H. Lintot [etc.] 1744–46.

LOCKE, John, 1632-1704.
The history of navigation, from its original to the year 1704, with an explanatory catalogue of voyages. (CLARKE, J.S. Progress of maritime Discoveries, 1803, 4°, i. App. 75-202.)

NL 0434802 MH

Locke, John, 1632-1704, supposed ed.
The history of Our Saviour Jesus Christ
see under Bible. N.T. Gospels. English. Harmonies. 1721. Authorized. (also 1724)

Locke, John, 1632–1704.
...How to bring up your children; being Some thoughts on education, by John Locke... London: S. Low, Marston & Co., Ltd., 1902. 115 p. front. (port.) 16°.
At head of title: A book for every parent.
Printed at the Chiswick Press.
Prefatory note signed E. M.

274745A. 1. Education—Theory and systems. 2. M., E., editor. 3. Title. June 16, 1927

NL 0434804 NN NcD

VOLUME 337

B1498 .B3 Locke, John, 1632-1704.

Baratono, Adelchi, 1875- ed.
... Hume e l'illuminismo inglese, a cura di Adelchi Baratono. [Milano, Garzanti [1943]

[Locke, John] 1632-1704.
An introductory discourse, containing the whole history of navigation from its original to this time ...
(In [Churchill, Awnsham] comp. A collection of voyages and travels ... London, 1732. 36cm. vol. I, p. ix-xciv)
"The catalogue and character of most books of travels": p. lxxii-xciv.
Authorship doubtful.

1. Navigation—Hist. I. Title.

CA 7—6562 Unrev'd

Library of Congress G160.C56

NL 0434806 DLC

Locke, John, 1632-1704. *6270.3.1=**Adams 22.6.1
An introductory discourse containing the whole history of navigation from its original to this time. Map.
(In Churchill, O., and J. A collection of voyages and travels. Vol. I, pp. ix-lxxii. London. MDCCXLIV.)
The authorship is doubtful, but has been attributed to John Locke.

NL 0434807 MB

Locke, John, 1632-1704.
Iohannis Lockii armigeri Libri IV de intellectu humano
see his Libri IV de intellectu humano.

Locke, John, 1632-1704.
The Jews' Advocate containing Locke's sentiments respecting their treatment by Christmas
see under title

Locke, John, 1632-1704.

Petzäll, Åke, 1901-
... John Locke, selección de textos precedidos de un estudio de Ake Petzall. Traducción y notas de León Dujovne. Buenos Aires, Editorial sudamericana [1940]

Locke, John, 1632-1704.
John Locke; tercentenary address delivered in the hall at Christ church
see under title

Locke, John, 1632-1704.
John Lockes Gedanken über die erziehung
see his Gedanken über die erziehung.

Lockes, John, 1632-1704.
John Lockes Gedanken über Erziehung
see his Gedanken über Erziehung.

Locke, John, 1632-1704.
John Locke's Reasonableness of Christianity
see his Reasonableness of Christianity.

Locke, John, 1632-1704.
John Locke's Versuch über den menschlichen Verstand...
see his Versuch über den menschlien Verstand...

Locke, John, 1632-1704.
Lectures on Locke; or, The principles of logic...
see under title

B 23 P56 v.93 Locke, John, 1632-1704.
Leitung des Verstandes. Uebers. und mit Einleitung hrsg. von Jürgen Bona Meyer. Heidelberg, G. Weiss, 1883.
x,94 p. 19cm. (Philosophische Bibliothek, Bd. 93)

I. Meyer, Jürgen Bona, 1829-1897, tr.

NL 0434817 NIC MH

Case C 726 .5191 [LOCKE, JOHN] 1632-1704.
A letter concerning toleration... The 2d edition, corrected. London, A. Churchill, 1690.
[4], 87, [5] p. 14cm.

First published in Latin, with title: Epistola de tolerantia, Goudae, 1689. Translated into English by William Popple.
With this is bound [Proast, Jonas] A third letter for toleration. London, 1692.
STC II L 2748.

NjP
NL 0434818 ICN MnU CaBVaU CtY-M MH InU NcD WU NIC

Locke, John, 1632-1704.
A letter concerning toleration. By John Locke... Boston: Printed and sold by Rogers and Fowle, 1743. 77 p. 3. ed. 12°.

Half-title, Mr. Locke on toleration, pasted to front wrapper.

433042A. 1. Liberty, Religious.

September 25, 1929

DLC MWA MeB
NL 0434819 NN CtHT-W MiD-B NNC MB MiU-C CtY RPJCB

Locke, John, 1632-1704.
A letter concerning toleration... Glasgow, 1757.

NL 0434820 NjR RPB

LOCKE, JOHN, 1632-1704.
A letter concerning toleration ... The fourth edition.
Wilmington [Del.], Printed and sold by James Adams, 1764.
vii, 8-77p. 16½cm., in case 18cm.
Ornament of fleurons on t.-p.
Translated by William Popple.
Evans 9712.
Signatures: A-E8 (E8 blank? wanting).
Unbound; in hf. red mor. case.

NL 0434821 PPRF PP PHC PPL DeHi DeWI MWA PHi

SPECIAL COLLECTIONS B192L79 S7 Locke, John, 1632-1704.
A letter concerning toleration. By John Locke, esq. A new edition ... London: Printed for J. Osborne and T. Griffin [etc.] 1784.
vi, [7]-106 p. 13½cm.

First published in Latin, with title: Epistola de tolerantia, Goudae, 1689; tr. into English by William Popple. -cf. L C

NL 0434822 NNC

Locke, John, 1632-1704.
A letter concerning toleration by John Locke, Esq. A new edition, with alterations.
York, Printed by Wilson, Spence, and Mowman; for T. Wilson and R. Spence, High-Ousegate Anno 1788.
205 p. 8.5 x 14 cm.

NL 0434823 NRAB

BR 1610 .L8 1800 [Locke, John] 1632-1704.
A letter concerning toleration. New ed. London, Printed by J. Crowder, 1800.
131 p.

#Toleration.
Popple, William, d. 1708.
A letter concerning toleration.

NL 0434824 MoU NN

[Locke, John] 1632-1704.
A letter concerning toleration: humbly submitted, &c. ... London, Printed for A. Churchill, 1689.
4 p. l., 61 p. 19½cm.
First published in Latin, with title: Epistola de tolerantia, Goudæ, 1689; tr. into English by William Popple.

1. Toleration. I. Popple, William, d. 1708, tr. II. Title.

Library of Congress BR1610.L8 17-19443

NjP IEN NN TxU
NL 0434825 DLC IEN MiU TxDaM DFo CU MH IU CtY MnU

BR 1610 L6 Locke, John, 1632-1704.
A letter concerning toleration. With an introd. by Patrick Romanell. New York, Liberal Arts Press, 1950.
62 p. 20 cm. (The Little library of liberal arts, no. 22)

Bibliography: p. 12.

1. Toleration. I. Title.

NL 0434826 OU ViU NNC AU NcD

Locke, John, 1632-1704.
A letter concerning toleration. [Translated by William Popple] Concerning civil government, second essay. An essay concerning human understanding. By John Locke. The principles of human knowledge, by George Berkeley. An enquiry concerning human understanding, by David Hume. Chicago, Encyclopædia Britannica [1955, °1952]
x, 509 p. 25 cm. (Great books of the Western World, v. 35)
Bibliographical footnotes.
1. Toleration. I. Locke, John, 1632-1704. Concerning civil government, second essay. II. Locke, John, 1632-1704. An essay concerning human understanding. III. Berkeley, George, Bp. of Cloyne, 1685-1753. The principles of human knowledge. IV. Hume, David, 1711-1776. An enquiry concerning human understanding. V. Popple, William, d. 1708, tr. VI. Title. VII. Title: Human understanding.
AC1.G72 vol. 35 *261.73 55-10342

NL 0434827 DLC MnU NIC GU HU MiHM PPPL PSt TxU

BR 1610 L8 1955 Locke, John, 1632-1704.
A letter concerning toleration. With an introduction by Patrick Romanell. Indianapolis, Bobbs-Merrill [1955]
63 p.

Bibliography: p. 63.
Translated from the original Latin by William Popple, first published at London in 1689.-Pref.

1. Toleration. I. Popple, William, d. 1708. II. Title.

NL 0434828 NGenoU LU CU

VOLUME 337

B 1293 E5 .L65 R75
Locke, John 1632-1704.
A letter concerning toleration. With an introduction by Patrick Romanell. 2d ed. Indianapolis, The Bobbs-Merrill Co., (1955)
63 p. 20 cm. (The Library of Liberal Arts)
"Selected bibliography" p. 63.
1. Toleration. I. Title.
CLU MU CaBVaU
NL 0434829 IMunS IU ScU IEN MeB DAU CSt FTaSU NNC

BR1610 L8 1955
Locke, John, 1632-1704.
A letter concerning toleration. With an introd. by Patrick Romanell. 2d ed. New York, Bobbs-Merrill, 1955.
63 p. 21 cm. (Library of liberal arts)
1. Toleration. I. Title.
NL 0434830 OrPR WaSpG

Locke, John, 1632-1704.
Letter from a person of quality to his friend in the country... 1675
see under Shaftesbury, Anthony Ashley Cooper, 1st earl of, 1621-1683.

Locke, John, 1632-1704.
A letter to the Right Reverend Edward Ld Bishop of Worcester, concerning some passages relating to Mr. Locke's essay of humane understanding, in a late discourse of His Lordships, in vindication of the Trinity. London, Printed by H. Clark, for A. and J. Churchill, 1697.
227 p. 20 cm.
Half title: Mr. Locke's letter to the Bishop of Worcester.
Binder's title: A letter to the Bishop of Worcester.
In case.
Bound with the author's Mr. Locke's reply to the Right Reverend the Lord Bishop of Worcester's answer to his letter. London, 1697.
1. Stillingfleet, Edward, Bp. of Worcester, 1635-1699. A discourse in vindication of the doctrine of the Trinity. 2. Locke, John, 1632-1704. An essay concerning humane understanding. I. Title.
B1294.L6 70-20814
OO TxU CtY-M IU NIC CLU-C MWiW-C PU MH NNNAM
NL 0434833 DLC IU MH CtY ICU ICN CSmH CLSU NNUT-Mc

Locke, John, 1632-1704.
Letters concerning toleration. London, Printed for Millar, 1765.
399 p. port. 30 cm.
Edited by Thomas Hollis. Cf. Dict. nat. bibl.
Contains the Latin original of the first letter.
1. Toleration.
BR1610.L82 55-54772
NL 0434834 DLC CtY IU NNUT MeB PPPrHi MH NIC ICN NjP

Locke, John, 1632-1704.
Lettres inédites de John Locke à ses amis Nicolas Thoynard, Philippe van Limborch et Edward Clarke; pub. avec une introduction et des notes explicatives par M. Henry Ollion ... avec la collaboration de M. le professeur Dr. T. J. de Boer ... La Haye, M. Nijhoff, 1912.
x, 258 p. 25cm.
1. Thoynard, Nicolas, 1629-1706. 2. Limborch, Philippus van, 1633-1712. 3. Clarke, Edward, fl. 1681-1701. I. Ollion, Henri, ed. II. Boer, Tjitze J. de.
13-26702
Library of Congress B1296.A2
PBm OC1W NN
NL 0434835 DLC NIC InU NcD FU WaU NcU OU MB CtY ICN

Locke, John, 1632-1704.
Johannis Lockii, Armigeri Libri IV de intellectu humano ... Novissima editio juxta exemplar Londini anno 1701. in fol. editum, expressa, summoque studio a vitiis typographicis in illo occurrentibus purgata. Lipsiae, Sumptibus Theophili Georgi, 1709.
[59], 943 p. port. 17cm.
Translated by Richard Burridge. -Cf. Brit. Mus. Cat.
Title-page mutilated; portrait lacking.
NL 0434836 NNC PMA PU WU

Locke, John, 1632-1704.
Libri IV de intellectu humano, denuo ex novissima editione idiomatis anglicani, longe accuratiori in puriorem stylum latinum translati. Praefixae sunt huic editioni auctoris scripta et vita, nec non elenchus capitum, cura M. Gotthelff Henr. Thiele. Lipsiae, apud Theophilum Georgi, 1741.
[12], 1000 p. 18 cm.
NL 0434837 PLatS NjP CtY PBm MH NjR

Locke, John, 1632-1704.
The life and letters of John Locke, with extracts from his journals and common-place books
see under King, Peter King, 7th baron, 1776-1833.

Locke, John, 1632-1704.
The life of John Locke, with extracts from his correspondence, journals, and common-place books
see under King, Peter King, 7th baron, 1776-1833.

Locke, John, 1632-1704.
Locke, a cura di Armando Carlini. [1. ed. Milano, Garzanti [1949]
300 p. port. 19 cm. (I Filosofi, 19)
"Esposizione e passi scelti delle opere di Locke": p. [113]-298.
"Bibliografia": p. 299-300.
I. Carlini, Armando, 1878- ed. and tr. (Series)
A 49-8101*
Chicago. Univ. Libr. for Library of Congress
NL 0434840 ICU

Locke, John, 1632-1704.

Laboulaye, Édouard René Lefebvre, 1811-1883.
Locke, législateur de la Caroline, par m. Édouard Laboulaye ... Paris, Durand, 1850.

Locke, John, 1632-1704.
Locke on words. An essay concerning human understanding, by John Locke ... Book III.—Of words; with introduction and notes, by F. Ryland ... London, W. S. Sonnenschein & co., 1882.
xv, 324 p. 19cm.
1. Knowledge, Theory of. 2. Language. I. Ryland, Frederick, ed.
10-32056
Library of Congress B1272 1882
NL 0434842 DLC CtY CLU OC1W

Locke, John, 1632-1704.
Locke's Conduct of the understanding...
see his Conduct of the understanding...

Locke, John, 1632-1704.
Locke's essay concerning human understanding, books II and IV...
see his Essay concerning human understanding

Locke, John, 1632-1704.
Locke's Essay for the understanding of St. Paul's Epistles...
see his Essay for the understanding of St. Paul's epistles.

Locke, John, 1632-1704.
Locke's essay on the human understanding
see his Essay on the human understanding.

Locke, John, 1632-1704.
Memoirs of the life and character of Mr. John Locke
see under title

Locke, John, 1632-1704.
Mr. Locke's reply to the Right Reverend the Lord Bishop of Worcester's answer to his letter, concerning some passages relating to Mr. Locke's essay of humane understanding, in a late discourse of His Lordships, in vindication of the Trinity. London, Printed by H. Clark, for A. and J. Churchill, 1697.
174, 7 p. 20 cm.
Bound with the author's A letter to the Right Reverend Edward Ld Bishop of Worcester. London, 1697.
Half title: Mr. Locke's reply to the Bishop of Worcester's answer to his letter.
"An answer to remarks upon An essay concerning humane understanding": 7 p. (2d group)
1. Stillingfleet, Edward, Bp. of Worcester, 1635-1699. The Bishop of Worcester's answer to Mr. Locke's letter concerning some passages relating to his essay of humane understanding. 2. Locke, John, 1632-1704. An essay concerning humane understanding.
B1294.L6 73-20815
MARC
MH InU TxDaM CU MiU NIC
NL 0434848 DLC NjP CtY NNC NIC CLU-C ICN NNUT

---

231 L793m
Locke, John, 1632-1704.
Mr Locke's reply to the Right Reverend the Lord Bishop of Worcester's answer to his second letter: wherein, besides other incident matters, what His Lordship has said concerning certainty by reason, certainty by ideas, and certainty of faith. The resurrection of the same body. The immateriality of the soul. The inconsistency of Mr. Locke's notions with the articles of the Christian faith, and their tendency to sceptism, is examined. London, Printed by H. C. for A. and J. Churchill, at the Black Swan in Pater-Noster-row; and E. Castle, next Scotland-yard by White-hall, 1699.
1 p.l., 452p., 1l. 19½cm.
1. Stillingfleet, Edward, bp. of Worcester, 1635-1699. The Bishop of Worcester's answer to Mr Locke's second letter.

written by ... John Wallis ... London, Printed for J. Greenwood, 1706.
3 p. l., v, 60 p.
1. Commonplace-books. 2. Deaf - Education and institutions. I. Le Clerc, Jean, 1657-1736. II. Wallis, John, 1616-1703.
ICN CU CtY MH CBPac NNUT-Mc PU
NL 0434851 IU NIC NNC InU OrU MnU CLU-C DFo NjP OO

VOLUME 337

Locke, John, 1632-1704.
A new method of making common-place-books; written by ... John Lock, author of the Essay concerning humane understanding. Tr. from the French. To which is added something from Le Clerc, relating to the same subject. A treatise necessary for all gentlemen, especially students of divinity, physick, and law. There are also added two letters containing a useful method for instructing persons that are deaf and dumb, or that labour under any impediments of speech, to speak distinctly; ...

NL 0434852 CtY CLU-C MH NNC ICN DGC

Locke, John, 1632-1704.
A new method of making common-place-books written by ... John Lock. London, Printed by J. Greenwood, 1706.
Microfilm copy.

NL 0434853 NNC

B1296 .O5 Locke, John, 1632-1704.

Ollion, Henri.
... Notes sur la correspondance de John Locke, suivies de trente-deux lettres inédites de Locke à Thoynard (1678-1681) Paris, A. Picard & fils, 1908.

Locke, John, 1632-1704.
Observations upon the growth and culture of vines and olives: the production of silk: the preservation of fruits. Written at the request of the Earl of Shaftesbury: to whom it is inscribed: by Mr. John Locke. Now first printed from the original manuscript in the possession of the present Earl of Shaftesbury. London, Printed for W. Sandby, 1766.
1 p. l., [v]-xv, 73, [1] p. 16½cm.

1. Viticulture—France. [1. France—Viticulture] 2. Canning and preserving. [2. Fruit preservation] 3. Olive-oil. 4. Sericulture—[France] 5. [Olive]

U. S. Dept. of agr. Library for Library of Congress 95L79 SB393.L75 Agr 21-921
[a44c1]†

NL 0434855 DNAL CU NNNAM DFo CU MH CtY MH-A MBH DLC

192.2 L793o Locke, John, 1632-1704.
Oeuvres de Locke et Leibmitz, contenant L'essai sur l'entendement humain, revu, corrigé et accompagné de notes, par M.F. Thurot ... L'éloge de Leibnitz par Fontenelle Le discours sur la conformité de la foi et de la raison, L'essai sur la bonté de Dieu, La liberté de l'homme et l'origine du mal, La controverse réduite à des arguments en forme. Paris, Firmin Didot frères, 1839.
3p.ℓ.,xvii,676p. 27cm.

NL 0434856 OrU MH DLC-P4

B1291 .T38 Locke, John, 1632-1704.
Oeuvres de Locke et Leibnitz contenant l'essai sur l'entendement humain; revu, corrigé et accompagné de notes par M.F. Thurot. Paris, Firmin Didot, 1862.
676 p. 26 cm.

1. Knowledge, Theory of. I. Thurot, F., ed. II. Leibniz, Gottfried Wilhelm, freiherr von, 1646-1716.

NL 0434857 TU MB

---

192 L79Fℓ Locke, John, 1632-1704.
Oeuvres diverses de monsieur Jean Locke. Rotterdam, Fritsch et Böhm, 1710.
xcix, 468p.

"Eloge historique de feu Mr. Locke, par Mr. Jean Le Clerc": p.1-xcix.

I. Le Clerc, Jean, 1657-1736.

NL 0434858 IU OU MH NcU NjP

Locke, John, 1632-1704.
Oeuvres diverses. Nouv.éd. considérablement augm. Amsterdam, J.F.Bernard, 1732.
2v. 17cm.

NL 0434859 CtY NN

Locke, John, 1632-1704.
Of civil government, two treatises. New York: E. P. Dutton and Co. [19—?] 242 p. 16°. (Everyman's library.)

1. Political science. 2. Series. July 15, 1924

NL 0434860 NN

320.1 L79 192- Locke, John, 1632-1704.
Of civil government; two treatises, by John Locke... London, J.M. Dent; New York, E.P. Dutton [192-]
242p. 18cm. (Everyman's library no. 751)

Written in a large part as a reply to Sir Robert Filmer's Patriarcha (320.4 F48)

1. Political science. 2. Filmer, Sir Robert, d.1653. Patriarcha.

NL 0434861 KU

Locke, John, 1632-1704.
Of civil government; two treatises, by John Locke ... London & Toronto, J. M. Dent & sons, ltd.; New York, E. P. Dutton & co. [1924]
xx, 242 p. 17 cm. (*Half-title:* Everyman's library ed. by Ernest Rhys. Philosophy. [No. 751])

Introduction by William S. Carpenter.
"The first treatise ... is a refutation of the doctrine of absolute monarchy founded on divine right ... The adversary selected by Locke for demolition was Sir Robert Filmer, whose Patriarcha was published in 1680."
"List of works of John Locke": p. xviii.

CONTENTS.—book I. An essay concerning certain false principles.—book II. An essay concerning the true original, extent and end of civil government.

1. Political science. 2. Filmer, Sir Robert, d. 1653. Patriarcha. 3. Liberty. I. Title.
JC153.L8 1924 A 25—556
Enoch Pratt Free Libr. for Library of Congress [a48f3]

NL 0434863 OrSaW OrLgE OrU Wa WaSpG OCU OCl MiU ODW NN ViU OCX CaBVaU WaSp OrPR OrIdU-SB MdBE TU OWorP OkU ViU-L PSC PHC PPD OO

Locke, John, 1632-1704.
Of civil government [by] John Locke. London, J. M. Dent & sons, ltd.; New York, E. P. Dutton & co., inc. [193-?]
xx, 242 p. 17½cm. (*Half-title:* Everyman's library, ed. by Ernest Rhys. Philosophy. [no. 751])
"First published in this edition 1924."
Introduction by William S. Carpenter.
"The first treatise ... is a refutation of the doctrine of absolute monarchy founded on divine right ... The adversary selected by Locke for demolition was Sir Robert Filmer, whose Patriarcha was published in 1680."
"List of the works of John Locke": p. xviii.
CONTENTS.—An essay concerning certain false principles.—An essay concerning the true original, extent and end of civil government.
1. Political science. 2. Filmer, Sir Robert, d. 1653. Patriarcha. 3. Liberty.
Library of Congress AC1.E8 no. 751 37-143
320.1

NL 0434864 DLC OrP

320.1 L79 1936 Locke, John, 1632-1704.
Of civil government [two treatises] London, J.M. Dent; New York, E.P. Dutton [1936]
242p. 18cm. (Everyman's library no. 751)

Written in a large part as a reply to Sir Robert Filmer's Patriarcha (320.4 F48)

1. Political Science. 2. Filmer, Sir Robert, d.1653. Patriarcha.

NL 0434865 KU MsU PBm

LOCKE, John, 1632-1704.
Of civil government. London, J.M.Dent & Sons, Ltd., etc., etc., [1940].

17 cm.
Half-title: Everyman's library. Philosophy. [No. 751.]
"Introduction by W.F.Carpenter."
"First published in this edition, 1924; reprinted... 1940."

NL 0434866 MH

JC153 .L8 1943 Locke, John, 1632-1704.
Of civil government [by] John Locke. London, J. M. Dent & sons, ltd.; New York, E. P. Dutton & co., inc. 1943, [1924]
xx, 242 p. 18 cm. (Half-title: Everyman's library, ed. by Ernest Rhys. Philosophy. [no. 751])

"First published in this edition, 1924."
Introduction by William S. Carpenter.

"The first treatise...is a refutation of the doctrine of absolute monarchy founded on divine right...The adversary selected by Locke for demolition was Sir Robert Filmer, whose Patriarcha was published in 1680."
"List of the works of John Locke": p. xviii.

CONTENTS.--An essay concerning certain false principles.--An essay concerning the true original, extent and end of civil government.

1. Political science. 2. Filmer, Sir Robert, d. 1653. Patriarcha. 3. Liberty.

NL 0434869 AAP ViU MH

192.2 L814GA Locke, John, 1632-1704.
Of civil government [by] John Locke. London, J.M. Dent & sons ltd.; New York, E.P. Dutton & co., inc. [1947]
xx, 242 p. 18cm. (Everyman's library, no. 751)

"First published ... 1924."
Contents.-bk. 1. An essay concerning certain false principles.-bk. 2. An essay concerning the true original, extent and end of civil government.

NL 0434870 NcD Mi

Locke, John, 1632-1704.
... Of civil government and toleration, by **John Locke.** London, New York [etc.] Cassell and company, limited, 1901.
192 p. 14½cm. (Cassell's national library. New series)

1. Political science.
A 13-1321
Title from Univ. of Chicago JC153.L76 Printed by L. C.

NL 0434871 ICU OClW

JC 153 L81 1905 Locke, John, 1632-1704.
Of civil government and toleration; with an introd. by H. Morley. London, New York, Cassell, 1905.
192 p. 16cm. (Cassell's national library. New series)

1. Political science.

NL 0434872 NIC MH OCl OOxM

VOLUME 337

321
L79o
1947
Locke, John, 1632-1704.
Of civil government; second essay. Chicago, Great Books Foundation [c1947?]
150p. 18cm.

1. Political science.

NL 0434873 IU MB

JC153
.L85
1948a
Locke, John, 1632-1704.
Of civil government. Second essay. Chicago, H. Regnery Co. for the Great Books Foundation [1948]
150 p. 18cm.
First published as the second essay i[n the] author's Two treatises of government.
1. Political science. I. Title.

NL 0434874 ViU WaT OCl

Locke, John, 1632–1704.
Of civil government, second essay. Introd. by Russell Kirk. Chicago, Gateway Editions, distributed by H. Regnery Co. [1955]
180 p. 18 cm. (A Gateway edition, 6021)
Originally published as the second of two essays in the author's Two treatises of government.
1. Political science. 2. Filmer, Sir Robert, d. 1653. Patriarcha. 3. Liberty. I. Title.
JC153.L8 1955 320.1 55–4199 ‡

NL 0434875 DLC IaU KEmT MU ViU TxU NcU MiU

Locke, John, 1632-1704.
Of the conduct of the understanding... with biography, critical opinions, and explanatory notes by A.Louise M. Gilbert. London, Bell, 1859.
118p.

NL 0434876 MeWC

Locke, John, 1632–1704.
... Of the conduct of the understanding, by John Locke; with biography, critical opinions, and explanatory notes by A. Louise M. Gilbert ... New York, Maynard, Merrill, & co. [1901]
132 p. 16½cm. (Maynard's English classic series, no. 228–229)
Bibliography: p. 14–16.
1. Knowledge, Theory of. I. Gilbert, Anna Louise Myers, ed.
1—24483
Library of Congress B1270 1901

NL 0434877 DLC OClW PU NN

LOCKE, John, 1632-1704.
Oförgripelige tankar om werldslig regerings rätta ursprung, grantsor och andamal; Ofwersatte ifran engelskran al Hans Harmens. Stockholm, uti det Kongl. Tryckeriet, 1726.
pp.(8),382+.
Title in red and black. ~~Phil 2115~~.74.15

NL 0434878 MH

Locke, John, 1632–1704. *3469.26.6
On enthusiasm.
(In Sparks, Jared, editor. A collection of essays and tracts in theology. Vol. 6, pp. 196–210. Boston, 1823.)
Aug. 4, 1902
E5064 — Enthusiasm.

NL 0434879 MB

Locke, John, 1632–1704.
On politics and education. Introd. by Howard R. Penniman. New York, Published for the Classics Club by W. J. Black [1947]
412 p. 20 cm.
1. Political science. 2. Toleration. 3. Liberty. 4. Education. I. Title.
JC153.L79 1947 192.2 48—28*‡

NL 0434880 DLC OrStbM OrPS IdPS MiU MB IU FMU CoU UU FU ICU AU OO TU MH

JC 153
.L 785
1947
Locke, John, 1632-1704.
On politics and education. Edited, with introd. by Howard R. Penniman. New York, D. Van Nostrand [1947]
412 p. 20cm.
"A Classics Club College Edition."
Contents.- A letter concerning toleration.- The second treatise on civil government.- Some thoughts concerning education.
1. Political science. 2. Toleration. 3. Liberty. 4. Education. I. Title.

NL 0434881 MdBJ

JC153
L852
1947
Locke, John, 1632-1904.
On politics and education. Edited, with introduction by Howard R. Penniman. Toronto, New York, Van Nostrand [c1947]
412 p. 20cm.
"A Classics Club College edition."
1.Political science. 2.Toleration. 3.Liberty. 4.Education. I.Title.

NL 0434882 NcRS CaBVaU NBuC DGU NNC InU OCU

Locke, John, 1632-1704
On the conduct of the understanding.
[In the Republic of letters. New York, 1835 30 cm. v. 2, p. 131-142]
AP2
.R374

NL 0434883 DLC

Locke, John, 1632-1704.
On the conduct of the understanding; with other pieces. By John Locke. [London, J. Sharpe] 1820.
2 p. l., [3]-155 p. 13 cm.
Added t.-p., engraved, with portrait: Locke's Conduct of the understanding.
Contents. - Locke on the conduct of the understanding. - Some thoughts concerning reading and study for a gentleman. - Elements of natural philosophy.
1. Knowledge, Theory of. I. Title. II. Title: Conduct of the understanding.

NL 0434884 Vi OClW

Locke, John, 1632-1704.
Forster, Thomas Ignatius Maria, 1789–1860, ed.
Original letters of John Locke, Alg. Sidney, and Lord Shaftesbury, with an analytical sketch of the writings and opinions of Locke and other metaphysicians, by T. Forster ... 2d ed. London, Priv. print., 1847.

Locke, John, 1632-1704.
A paraphrase and notes on the Epistles of St. Paul to the Galatians, I & II Corinthians, Romans, Ephesians. London, 1706-1718
see under Bible. N. T. Epistles of Paul. English. Paraphrases. 1706-1718. Locke.
Also with dates 1706-1707, 1709, 1733, 1742, 1751, 1763, 1812, 1823, and 1832.

Locke, John, 1632–1704.
... Pensées sur l'éducation des enfants, traduction de Coste, revue, abrégée, annotée et précédée d'une introduction, par Louis Fochier ... Paris, C. Delagrave, 1882.
2 p. l., 292 p. 18cm.
At head of title: J. Locke.
1. Education. I. Coste, Pierre, 1668–1747, tr. II. Fochier, Louis, ed.
E 10-1556
Library, U. S. Bur. of Education LB475.L6B2

NL 0434887 DHEW

Locke, John, 1632–1704.
... Pensées sur l'éducation des enfants, traduction de Coste, rev., abrégée, annotée et précédée d'une introduction par Louis Fochier ... 2. éd. Paris, C. Delagrave, 1886.
2 p. l., 292 p. 18½cm. (On cover: Bibliothèque pédagogique)
At head of title: J. Locke.
1. Education. I. Coste, Pierre, 1668–1747, tr. II. Fochier, Louis, ed.
E 13-1498
Library, U. S. Bur. of Education LB475.L6B2 1886

NL 0434888 DHEW

Locke, John, 1632–1704.
Philosophical beauties, selected from the works of John Locke, Esq. To which is prefixed some account of his life. London, Printed by J. Cundee for T. Hurst, 1802.
v, 276 p. port. 15 cm.
1. Philosophy—Collected works. I. Title.
B1255 1802 60–58428

NL 0434889 DLC

Locke, John, 1632–1704.
Philosophical beauties selected from the works of John Locke, Esq. Containing The conduct of the understanding; Elements of natural philosophy; The studies necessary for a gentleman; and A discourse on miracles . . . prefixed, some account of his life. 1st American edition.
New-York. Langdon. 1828. 258 pp. Plate. Engraved title-page. 24°. 7608.180
F7322 — T.r. — Philosophy.

NL 0434890 MB MH CtY MWA NBuC NjR NHi CU NNU-W

190
L8p
K4
Locke, John, 1632-1704.
Philosophical beauties selected from th[e] works of John Locke...containing The conduct of the understanding: Elements of natural philosophy: The studies necessary for a gentleman [etc.,etc.] First American ed. Cooperstown, N.Y., H.& E.Phinney, 1844.
258 p. front 14 cm.
Another t.-p., engraved.

NL 0434891 MiU N OO

192.2
L814
S14
Locke, John, 1632-1704
Philosophical works. With a preliminary essay and notes by J. A. St. John. London, G. Virtue, 1843.
610p. front.(port.) 26cm.
Contents.-On the conduct of the understanding.-An essay concerning human understanding.-An examination of P. Malebranche's opinion on seeing all things in God; with remarks upon some of Mr. Norris's books.-
Elements of natural philosophy.-Some thoughts concerning reading and study for a gentleman.
I. St. John, James Augustus, 1801-1875, ed.

NL 0434893 TNJ MdBP CtY CLSU

VOLUME 337

Locke, John, 1632-1704.
Philosophical works. With a preliminary essay and notes, by J. A. St. John. London: H. G. Bohn, 1854. 2 v. port., fold. table. 12°. (In his: Works. v. 1-2.)
Bohn's standard library.
v. 1. Preliminary discourse by the editor. On the conduct of the human understanding. An essay concerning human understanding. Books 1-2.
v. 2. An essay concerning human understanding. Books 3-4. Appendix. An examination of P. Malebranche's opinion of seeing all things in God. Elements of natural philosophy.
Some thoughts concerning reading and study for a gentleman. Index.

NL 0434894 NN CLU KMK PPPD NIC PPGi PPLT MH ViU

B 1253 1860 Locke, John, 1632-1704.
Philosophical works. With a preliminary essay and notes, by J.A. St. John. London, Henry G. Bohn [186-?]
2 v. illus. 19 cm. (Bohn's standard library)
At head of title: The works of John Locke.
I. St. John, James Augustus, 1801-1875. II. Title

NL 0434895 OKentU

Locke, John, 1632-1704.
... Philosophical works. With a preliminary essay and notes, by J. A. St. John. London, G. Bell and sons, 1868-1877.
2 v. front. (v. 1: port.) 19 cm. (*Half-title:* Bohn's standard library)
At head of title: The works of John Locke.
Vol. 2 has imprint: Bell & Daldy, 1868.
CONTENTS.—v. 1. Preliminary discourse by the editor. On the conduct of the understanding. An essay concerning human understanding, book I-II.—v. 2. An essay concerning human understanding, book III-IV. Controversy with the Bishop of Worcester. An examination of P. Malebranche's opinion of seeing all things in God; with remarks upon some of Mr. Norris's books. Elements of natural philosophy. Some thoughts concerning reading and study for a gentleman. Index.
I. St. John, James Augustus, 1801-1875, ed. II. Title.
[B1253] A 31—1308
Henry E. Huntington Library for Library of Congress [a65c½]

NL 0434896 CSmH NcU OU OClW NjP MH

Locke, John, 1632-1704.
... Philosophical works. With a preliminary essay and notes, by J. A. St. John. London, Bell & Daldy, 1872.
2 v. front. (port.) fold. tab. 18cm. (*Half-title:* Bohn's standard library)
At head of title: The works of John Locke.
CONTENTS.—v. 1. Preliminary discourse by the editor. On the conduct of the understanding. An essay concerning human understanding.—v. 2. An essay concerning human understanding. Controversy with the Bishop of Worcester. An examination of P. Malebranche's opinion of seeing all things in God; with remarks upon some of Mr. Norris's books. Elements of natural philosophy. Some thoughts concerning reading and study for a gentleman. Index.
I. St. John, James Augustus, 1801-1875. II. Title.
8—6816
Library of Congress B1253 1872

NL 0434897 DLC Wa

B 1253 1882 Locke, John, 1632-1704.
Philosophical works. With a preliminary essay and notes, by J. A. St. John. London, G. Bell and sons, 1882-1883 [Vol. 2, 1882]
2 v. illus. 19 cm. (Bohn's standard library.)
At head of title: The works of John Locke.
I. St. John, James Augustus, 1801-1875, ed. II. Title

NL 0434898 OKentU OO PU PPL ViU NN

Locke, John, 1632-1704
Philosophical works. With a preliminary essay and notes, by J. A. St. John. London, G. Bell, 1885.
2 v. front. (port.) fold. tab. 18 1/2 cm. (Half-title: Bohn's standard library)

NL 0434899 MeB MiU MH PU OOxM CtY

Locke, John, 1632-1704.
... Philosophical works. With a preliminary essay and notes, by J. A. St. John. London, G. Bell and sons, 1889.
2 v. front. (port.) fold. tab. 18½cm. (*Half-title:* Bohn's standard library)
At head of title: The works of John Locke.
CONTENTS.—v. 1. Preliminary discourse by the editor. On the conduct of the understanding. An essay concerning human understanding, book I-II.—v. 2. An essay concerning human understanding, book III-IV. Controversy with the Bishop of Worcester. An examination of P. Malebranche's opinion of seeing all things in God; with remarks upon some of Mr. Norris's books. Elements of natural philosophy. Some thoughts concerning reading and study for a gentleman. Index.
I. St. John, James Augustus, 1801-1875, ed. II. Title.
17-4671
Library of Congress B1253 1889 a

PPD PU PPT PV OCl ODW CaBVaU OrCS WaTC
NL 0434900 DLC MtU IdU OrPR WaS GU OKentU NcD ICN

Locke, John, 1632-1704.
The philosophical works of John Locke. Edited, with a preliminary essay and notes, by J.A. St. John. London, etc., G.Bell & sons, 1892.
2 v. port., table. 19 cm.
Half-title: Bohn's standard library.

NL 0434901 MH PU PP PV

Locke, John, 1632-1704.
The philosophical works... Edited with a preliminary essay and notes, by J.A. St. John. London, G. Bell and sons, 1898-1899.
2 v. front. (v. 1: port.) fold. tab. 19 cm. (Half-title: Bohn's standard library)

NL 0434902 ViU

B 1253 1915 Locke, John, 1632-1704.
The philosophical works of John Locke, edited, with a preliminary essay and notes, by J. A. St. John. London, Bell, 19 -
2 v. (Bohn's standard library)

NL 0434903 CLU

B1253 1902a Locke, John, 1632-1704
The philosophical works of John Locke. Edited, with a preliminary essay and notes, by J. A. St. John. London, G. Bell, 1901-02 [v. 1, 1902]
2 v. fold. diagr., port. 19 cm. (Bohn's standard library)
Contents. - v. 1. Preliminary discourse by the editor. On the conduct of the understanding. An essay concerning human understanding.
Book I-II. - v. 2. An essay concerning human understanding. Book III-IV. Controversy with the Bishop of Worcester. An examination of P. Malebranche's opinion of seeing all things in God; with remarks upon some of Mr. Norris's books. Elements of natural philosophy. Some thoughts concerning reading and study for a gentleman. Index.
I. St. John, James Augustus, 1801-1875. ed.

NL 0434905 MeB CtY NN PP-W MiKW

Locke, John, 1632-1704
The philosophical works of John Locke. Edited, with a preliminary essay and notes, by J. A. St. John. v. 1 London: G. Bell & Sons, 1905. v. port. 12°.
1. Philosophy.—Systems, etc. 2. St. John, James Augustus, editor.
March 24, 1914.

NL 0434906 NN NIC

Locke, John, 1632-1704
Philosophical works; edited, with a preliminary essay and notes, by J. A. St. John. London: George Bell and Sons, 1908. 2 v. 1 folded pl., port. 12°. (Bohn's standard library.)
Contents: v. 1. Preliminary discourse by the editor. On the conduct of the understanding. An essay concerning human understanding.
v. 2. Controversy with the bishop of Worcester. An examination of P. Malebranche's opinion of seeing all things in God; with remarks upon some of Mr. Norris's books. Elements of natural philosophy. Some thoughts concerning reading and study for a gentleman.
CENTRAL CIRCULATION.
1. Philosophy. 2. St. John, James Augustus, editor.
May 15, 1911.

NL 0434907 NN

Locke, John, 1632-1704.
... The philosophy of Locke, in extracts from The essay concerning human understanding; arranged, with introductory notes, by John E. Russell ... New York, H. Holt and company, 1891.
iv, 160 p. 20cm. (Series of modern philosophers. [v. 1])
Bibliography: p. 23-26.
1. Knowledge, Theory of. I. Russell, John Edward, 1848-1917, ed.
10—32055
Library of Congress B1292 1891

MiU OO CLSU
NL 0434908 DLC TNJ OKentU KU ICN PBm PSC OU NN MB

B 1292 1906 Locke, John, 1632-1704.
The philosophy of Locke, in extracts from The essay concerning human understanding; arranged with introductory notes, by John E. Russell. New York, H. Holt and Company, 1906.
iv, 160 p. 20 cm. (Series of modern philosophers [v.1])
Bibl.: p. 23-26.
1. Knowledge, Theory of. I. Russell, John Edward, 1848-1917, ed. II. Title. III. Series of modern philosophers v.1.

NL 0434909 NBuU PHC

Locke, John, 1632-1704.
Posthumous works of Mr. John Locke ... London, Printed by W. B. for A. and J. Churchill, 1706.
2 p. l., 336 p. 19½cm.
CONTENTS.—Of the conduct of the understanding.—An examination of P. Malebranche's Opinion of seeing all things in God.—A discourse of miracles.—Part of a fourth letter for toleration, &c.—Memoirs relating to the life of Anthony, first earl of Shaftsbury.—A new method of a common-place-book.
45-34457
Library of Congress B1255 1706

OClW NjP PPL TxU
NcD ViU CtY CSmH CLSU CLU-C ICN IEN IU MH MiU-C NN
NL 0434910 DLC CU-A MoU WU MoSW MnU CaBVaU CU NcU

LOCKE, John, 1632-1704.
I principi dell'illuminismo eclettico; estratti dall "Saggio sull' intelletto umano." Traduzione dall'originale inglese con introduzione e note critiche, a cura di Carlo Mazzantini. Torino, etc., G.B.Paravia & C., [1927].

NL 0434911 MH

Locke, John, 1632-1704.
McCulloch, John Ramsay, 1789-1864.
Principles of political economy: with sketch of the rise and progress of the science. By J. R. M'Culloch. Essay on interest and value of money. By John Locke. London, A. Murray & co., 1872.

Locke, John, 1632-1704.
Clarke, James Stanier, 1765?-1834.
The progress of maritime discovery, from the earliest period to the close of the eighteenth century, forming an extensive system of hydrography. By James Stanier Clarke ... [v. 1] London. T. Cadell, and W. Davies, 1803.

VOLUME 337

Case F 456 .655 Locke, John, 1632-1704.
[Prospectus] Twenty years literary correspondence between John Locke, esq.; Messieurs Limborch, Leibnitz, and the Reverend Mr. King of Exeter, from 1685 to 1705... The third edition. London, 1739. F5.
Binder's title: Pamphlets, 1710-1742.
Preface signed: J.Bancks.
"Extracts of the literary correspondence which passed between Mr. Locke and Monsieur Limborch":

NL 0434914 ICN

Locke, John, 1632-1704.
... Quelques pensées sur l'éducation. Traduction nouvelle avec préface et commentaires par Gabriel Compayré. Paris, Hachette et cie., 1882.
19 cm. (Collection des principaux ouvrages pédagogiques français et étrangers)
Translated also with title: De l'éducation des enfans.

NL 0434915 CtY

Kress Room Locke, John, 1632-1704.
Ragionamenti sopra la moneta, l'interesse del danaro, le finanze e il commercio, scritti e pubblicati in diverse occasioni dal signor Giovanni Locke, tr. la prima volta dall' Inglese, con varie annotazioni ... Firenze, Apresso A. Bonducci, 1751.
2 v. 2 tables (1 fold) 27.5 cm.
Titles in red and black with engraved vignette (vol. 1)

Dedication signed: Gio. Francesco Pagnini, Angelo Tavanti.
Includes also Saggio sopra il giusto pregio della cose by C.F.Pagnini della Ventura and Tavola della bonta peso e valuta ... della monete [adapted from Sir Isaac Newton's considerazione sulla riduzione degl' interessi della moneta.]

NL 0434917 MH-AH

RBS141. Locke, John, 1632-1704.
The reasonableness of Christianity...
7.ed.London: A. Millar..., 1764.

NL 0434918 NNNAM PPL DSI

Ecd 797b [Locke, John]1632-1704.
The reasonableness of Christianity. [London? 184-?]
60p. 24cm. [Bound with: Cleveland, Richard Jeffry, 1773-1860. A narrative of voyages and commercial enterprises ... London,1842]
"A discourse on miracles": p.57-60.

I. Title. (stamped)

NL 0434919 CtY

[Locke, John] 1632-1704.
The reasonableness of Christianity. As delivered in the Scriptures. London: Printed for Awnsham and John Churchil ... 1695.
[4],304 p. 17½cm.
First edition.
Signatures: A^2, $B-U^8$.
Bound in old sprinkled calf.

NcU
NL 0434920 CLU-C CU-A CU NNUT-Mc CSmH MH ICU CtY

[Locke, John] 1632-1704.
The reasonableness of Christianity, as delivered in the Scriptures. The second edition. To which is added, A vindication of the same, from Mr. Edwards's exceptions. London: Printed for Awnsham and John Churchil ... 1696.
2 p.l.,307 p.,2 l.,40 p. 17cm.
Signatures: A^2, $B-V^8$, X^2(X_2, verso, advertisements); A^8, $B-E^4$(E_{3-4}, advertisements)

Title within double line border.
"A vindication of The reasonableness of Christianity, &c. from Mr. Edwards's reflections" has special title-page and separate paging and signaturing.
Bound in old sprinkled calf; with this is bound the author's A second vindication of The reasonableness of Christianity, &c ... London, 1697.

NcD
NL 0434922 CLU-C NNUT-Mc CtY PP MH ICN CU-A PPPD

Locke, John, 1632-1704.
The reasonableness of christianity as delivered in the scriptures, to which is added, A vindication of the same from Mr. Edwards's Exceptions. London, A Bettesworth, & Hitch. 1731.
292p. 20cm.

5th ed.

NL 0434923 RPB PPWe

Locke, John, 1632-1704.
The reasonableness of Christianity as delivered in the Scriptures.
(In Watson, Richard, editor. A collection of theological tracts. Vol. 4, pp. 1-108. London. M.DCC.LXXXV.)
*3454.2.4=**Adams 181.1.4

G7941 — Christianity.

NL 0434924 MB MiD PPL

Locke, John, 1632-1704.
The Reasonableness of Christianity, as delivered in the Scripture.
In Watson's Collection of Theological Tracts, 2d. ed. v. 4. London, 1791. 8°.

NL 0434925 CtY

Locke, John, 1632-1704.
The reasonableness of Christianity as delivered in the Scriptures...To which is added his celebrated essay for the understanding of St. Paul's epistles... London, 1810.
18 cm.

NL 0434925-1 RPB

Locke, John, 1632-1704.
The reasonableness of Christianity, as delivered in the Scriptures. By John Locke, esq. With a preface by the American editor. Boston: Printed By T. B. Wait and company, 1811.
xxx p., 1 l., 256 p. 18 cm.

1. Christianity—17th cent. 2. Philosophy and religion. I. Title.

BR120.L6 230 37—29676

MWA NcD NH ODW OOxM
NL 0434926 DLC ICN PMA CSt ICMcC InU IEG IU Nh ICU

BR 120 L814r 1824 Locke, John, 1632-1704.
The reasonableness of Christianity, as delivered in the Scriptures. A new ed. London, C.&J. Rivington, 1824.
424p. 22cm.

1. Christianity--17th cent. 2. Philosophy and religion. I. Title.

NL 0434927 ICMcC

Locke, John, 1632-1704.
The reasonableness of Christianity as delivered in the Scriptures.
New York, 1835. 8°

(Christian Library, Vol.VI)

NL 0434928 NNUT

Locke, John, 1632-1704.
The reasonableness of Christianity, as delivered in the Scriptures. To which are added, an Essay on the understanding of St. Paul's epistles; and a discourse on miracles. By J. Locke. With a biographical essay, an appendix, and notes, by a layman [i. e., J. A. St. John]. London: J. Hatchard & Son, 1836. lv, 286 p., 1 port. 12°. (The Sacred classics. v. 25.)

1. Apologetics (Christian). 2. Bible.—New Testament: Epistles (Pauline). Introduction. 3. Miracles. 4. Saint John, James Augustus.
January 27, 1912

NL 0434929 NN CtY ICN OO

LOCKE, John, 1632-1704.
The reasonableness of Christianity, as delivered in the Scriptures. To which are added An essay on the understanding of St. Paul's epistles; and A discourse on miracles. New York, T.George, Jr., 1836.

NL 0434930 MH-AH OCl MeB OO

Locke, John, 1632-1704.
... John Locke's Reasonableness of Christianity (Vernünftigkeit des biblischen Christentums) 1695, übers. von prof. dr. C. Winckler ... mit einer einleitung hrsg. von prof. lic. Leopold Zscharnack ... Giessen, A. Töpelmann, 1914.
lxvi p., 1 l., 140 p. 23 cm. (Studien zur geschichte des neueren protestantismus ... 4. quellenhft.)

I. Zscharnack, Leopold, ed. II. Winckler, Carl, tr.

Library of Congress BR45.S82 4. hft. 22-21161

NL 0434931 DLC ICU CU TxU

---

230 L814 Locke, John, 1632-1704.
The reasonableness of Christianity as delivered in the Scriptures ... ed.by A.J.Ferris.
Lond., Marshall press, 1946.
92p. front.(port.) 19cm.

1.Christianity. 17th cent. 2.Philosophy and religion. I.Ferris, Alexander James, ed. II.Title.

NL 0434932 N ICRL

Locke, John, 1632-1704.
The remains of John Locke esq; viz. I. Some memoirs of the life and character of Dr. Edward Pococke. II. Instructions for the conduct of a young gentleman, as to religion and government, &c. III. The best method of studying, and interpreting the Scriptures. IV. Sentiments concerning the Society for promoting Christian knowledg. Publish'd from his original manuscripts. To which are added, three copies of verses formerly written. London, Printed for E. Curll, 1714. iv, 20 p. 35cm. (f°.)
Caption-title: Five letters written by John Locke...
The letters are dated July 23, 1703–Jan. 20, 1704.

265032B. 1. No subject.
N. Y. P. L. May 8, 1944

NL 0434933 NN CtY MeB

Locke, John, 1632-1704.
Remarks upon an essay concerning human understanding
see under [Burnet, Thomas] 1635-1715.

VOLUME 337

Locke, John, 1632-1704, supposed author.
The rights of Protestant dissenters. 1705.
see under Barrington, John Shute Barrington, 1st viscount, 1678-1734.

B1263 .P6 1955
Locke, John, 1632-1704.
Rozwazania dotyczace rozumu ludzkiego. Z oryginału angielskiego przełożył Bolesław J. Gawecki. Przekład przejrzał Czesław Znamierowski. Wyd. 1. W Krakówie, Państwowe Wydawn. Naukowe, 1955.
2 v. port. 20 cm. (Biblioteka klasyków filozofii)
Translation of Essay concerning human understanding and of On the conduct of the understanding.
1. Knowledge, Theory of. I. Title.

NL 0434936 MB

WA 27950
Locke, John, 1632-1704.
Saggio filosofico su l'umano intelletto, compendiato dal Dr. Winne. Tradotto, e commentato da Francesco Soave. Milano, G. Motta, 1775.
3 v. in 1. 18 cm.

NL 0434937 CtY

B1293 .I8S67 Rare Bk
Locke, John, 1632-1704.
Saggio filosofico ... su l'umano intelletto compendiato dal Dr. Winne; tradotto, e commentato da Francesco Soave. 2. ed, veneta. Venezia, Stamperia Baglioni, 1790.
3 v. in 1. 19 cm.
Vol. 3 has title: Guida dell'intelletto nella ricerca della verita' opera postuma.

I. Wynne, John, Bp. of Bath and Wells, 1667-1743. II. Soave, Francesco, 1743-1806, tr.

NL 0434938 ICU CU

B1293 I8G8
Locke, John, 1632-1704.
Saggio su l'intelletto umano, a cura di Augusto Guzzo. Firenze, Vallecchi [1924]
xviii, 278 p. port. (Testi filosofici commentati)

1. Knowledge, Theory of. I. Guzzo, Augusto, 1894-

NL 0434939 CU

Locke, John, 1632-1704.
Saggio sull'intelletto umano; passi, tradotti e commentati da Giuseppe Saitta. Bologna, N. Zanichelli, 1943.
xxv, 318 p. 21 cm.
Includes bibliographical references.

1. Knowledge, Theory of.

B1293.I 8S3 50-48715

NL 0434940 DLC MiD

[Locke, John] 1632-1704, supposed author.
The Scripture's suffiency demonstrated: wherein the substance of Scripture, respecting doctrine, worship, and manners, is reduced to its proper head. To which is added, Dr.Clarke's promises of Scripture, recommended by Dr.Watts, and now corrected, with many improvements. The 2d ed. London, Printed for G.Keith [etc.] 1769.
110 p. 16½ cm.

NL 0434941 NjP PPPrHi

[Locke, John] 1632-1704.
A second letter concerning toleration. Licensed, June 24, 1690. London, A. and J. Churchill, 1690.
1 p. l., 68p. 20cm.
Signed: Philanthropus.
Bound with his A letter concerning toleration.

1. Religious liberty. I. Title.

Printed by the Wesleyan University Library, 1937

MiU-C NNUT-Mc IU ICN MWelC MnU CaBVaU
NL 0434942 CtW NjP PBL NIC MH IEN WU NNG CLU-C CtY

Locke, John, 1632-1704.
The second treatise of civil government and A letter concerning toleration, by John Locke. Edited, with an introduction, by J. W. Gough ... Oxford, B. Blackwell, 1946.
xxxix, 165 p. 20½cm.
"Some books for further reading": p. xxxvii.

1. Political science. 2. Liberty. 3. Toleration. I. Gough, John Wiedhofft, ed. II. Title: Treatise of civil government. III. Title: A letter concerning toleration.

JC153.L85 1946 320.1 47-17325

OCIU ICU PU NNU-W NNC WaE WaU-L WaSpG NcRS
NL 0434943 DLC CaBVaU IdPS OrCS OrP OrSaW OrU OO IaU

Locke, John, 1632-1704.
The second treatise of civil government and A letter concerning toleration, by John Locke. Edited, with an introduction, by J. W. Gough ... Oxford, B. Blackwell; New York, Macmillan Co., 1947.
xxxix, 165 p. 20½ cm.
"Some books for further reading": p. xxxvii.

1. Political science. 2. Liberty. 3. Toleration. I. Gough, John Wiedhofft, ed. II. Title: Treatise of civil government. III. Title: A letter concerning toleration.

NL 0434944 ViU

320.1 L79s 1948
Locke, John, 1632-1704.
The second treatise of civil government and A letter concerning toleration. Edited, with an introd., by J. W. Gough. Oxford, B. Blackwell, 1948.
xl, 165p. 20cm. (Blackwell's political texts)
"Reprinted with revised introduction."
Bibliography: p.xxxix. Bibliographical footnotes.

CU-I IaU NBuU
NL 0434945 IU DFo PPWe ViU-L KEmT CLSU OrSaW NIC

Locke, John, 1632-1704.
The second treatise of government; edited, with an introd., by Thomas P. Peardon. New York, Liberal Arts Press [1952]
xxviii, 139 p. 21 cm. (The Library of liberal arts, no. 31. Political science)
First published in the author's Two treatises of government under title: An essay concerning the true original extent and end of civil government.
Bibliography: p. xxiii-xxv.

1. Political science.

JC153.L85 1952 320.1 52-14648

InU MoU ViU ScU NcD NNC MsU MU WaSpG
NL 0434946 DLC FMU ICarbS NBuU-L AU NBuU CU IU WU

BT1100 .L82
[Locke, John] 1632-1704.
A second vindication of the reasonableness of Christianity, &c. By the author of the Reasonableness of Christianity, etc. London, Printed for A. and J. Churchill [etc.] 1697.
[24], 480 p. 18cm.
Occasioned by John Edward's The Socinian creed, which was a reply to Locke's Reasonableness of Christianity.

1. Edwards, John, 1637-1716. The Socinian creed. 2. Apologetics. 3. Christianity—Evidences.

NL 0434947 ICU NNUT CtY CLU-C CU-A TxDaM-P PPL MH

Locke, John, 1632-1704. *3469.26.6
Selection from [his] works.
(In Sparks. A collection of essays and tracts in theology. Vol. 6, pp. 165-235. Boston, 1826.)
Contents. — An essay for the understanding of St. Paul's Epistles. — On enthusiasm. — Advantages of the appearance of our Saviour among men.

NL 0434948 MB

Locke, John, 1632-1704.
... Selections, edited by Sterling P. Lamprecht ... New York, Chicago [etc.] C. Scribner's sons [°1928]
lv, 349 p. 17cm. (Half-title: The modern student's library. [Philosophy series])
At head of title: Locke.

1. Lamprecht, Sterling Power, 1890- ed.

28-6544

Library of Congress B1255.L3

WaSpG OrPR OrAshS OrP OrPS OrStbM WaWW
MiU PU PHC PSC PV OU ODW OCU OCl OO ViU NN NcD MtU
NL 0434949 DLC KEmT OWorP KyLxCB OKentU NIC AU KU TU

Locke, John, 1632-1704.
... Selections from John Locke's Second treatise of government, 1690. Ed. by S. E. Morison. [Boston, Old South association, 192-]
23 p. 20 cm. (Old South leaflets. [General series. v. 9] no. 208)
Caption title.
These selections are taken "from the edition of the Second treatise most familiar to the American patriots: An essay concerning the true original, extent, and end of civil government, by the late learned John Locke, esq. Boston, Re-printed and sold by Edes and Gill, in Queen-street, 1773. Spelling and punctuation have been modernized, and the chapter and section numbers of the London edition of 1764, upon which this was founded, have been inserted."
1. Liberty. I. Morison, Samuel Eliot, 1887- II. Title: An essay concerning the true original, extent, and end of civil government.
Library of Congress E173.O44 vol. 9 21-2795

NL 0434951 DLC MiU OO WaS NcD

624.97 D59.4hi 1707 cop.1
LOCKE, John, 1632-1704
Sendschreiben von der toleranz, Oder von der Religions- und Gewissens-Freyheit. Aus dem Lateinischen Exemplar übersetzt/ und mit einigen nutzlichen Anmerckungen erläutert. [N.p.] Gedruckt im Jahr Christi 1710.
6p.l., 124p. 17cm.
At head of title: Herrn Johann Lockens.

Translator's preface, dated 6 Jan. 1710.
With 80 footnotes and an added conclusion.
A translation of his Epistila de tolerantia.
No.10 in a bound collection of German theological tract.

NL 0434953 MH-AH

Locke, John, 1632-1704.
Several papers relating to money, interest and trade, &c. Writ upon several occasions, and published at different times. By John Locke, esq. London, Printed for A. and J. Churchill, 1696.
2 p. l., 4, 192, 24, [16], 111, [2] p. 17cm.
Contents.—Some considerations of the consequences of the lowering of interest, and raising the value of money ... 2d ed. cor. London, 1696.—Short observations on a printed paper intituled, For encouraging the coining silver money in England, and after for keeping it here.—Further considerations concerning raising the value of money. Wherein Mr. Lowndes's arguments for it in his late report concerning An essay for the amendment of the silver coins, are particularly examined. 2d ed. cor. London, 1695.
1. Money. 2. Interest and usury.

11-15641

Library of Congress HG937.L74

ICJ NN MB
NL 0434954 DLC PPL InU NjP PU NNC DFo NSyU MH-BA

[Locke, John] 1632-1704.
Short observations on a printed paper, intituled, For encouraging the coining silver money in England, and after for keeping it here. London, Printed for A. and J. Churchill, 1695.
24 p. 16cm.

Bound with the author's Some considerations of the consequences of the lowering of interest and raising the value of money. 1692. cop. 2.
Wing L2758.

NL 0434955 NNC NIC CtY CSmH MH-BA PU RPB

VOLUME 337

[Locke, John] 1632-1704.
Short observations on a printed paper, intituled, For encouraging the coining silver money in England, and after for keeping it here ... [London, 1696]
24 p. 19cm. (In his Several papers relating to money, interest and trade. London, 1696)

NL 0434956 NNC MCM

[Locke, John] 1632-1704.
Some considerations of the consequences of the lowering of interest, and raising the value of money. In a letter to a member of Parliament. London: A. and J. Churchill, 1692. 4, 192 p. 16cm.

232377B. 1. Money, to 1800. 2. Interest, 1692. I. Title. June 25, 1943

NL 0434957 NN CSmH NjP MH-BA PBm NIC IU NNC InU CtY GU OU

[Locke, John] 1632-1704.
Some considerations of the consequences of the lowering of interest, and raising the value of money. In a letter sent to a member of Parliament, 1691. The second edition corrected. London, Printed for Awnsham and John Churchil ... 1696.
1 p.l.,4,192 p. 16½cm.
First edition, 1692; this second edition was published as the first part of the author's Several papers relating to money, interest and trade, &c. ... London, 1696.
Signatures: 3 leaves unsigned, B-M8.
Title within double line border.
Letter at end signed: John Lock.
Armorial book-plates of the Marquis of Stafford and Gower, earl Gower.
Bound in old sprinkled calf, rebacked; coat of arms blind-stamped on cover.

NL 0434959 CLU-C NNC PU CLU MCM

Locke, John, 1632-1704.
Some considerations of the lowering of interest and raising the value of money. [London, Printed for C. and J. Rivington, etc., 1824]
[3]-116 l. 22 cm.
Letter to a member of Parliament, 1691.
Photocopy, from v.4 of The works of John Locke.
1. Finance, Public - Gt. Brit. 2. Interest and usury. 3. Money.

NL 0434960 OrPR

Locke, John, 1632-1704.
Some familiar letters between Mr. Locke, and several of his friends. London, A. and J. Churchill, 1708.
2 p. l., 540 p. 19½cm.
Consists chiefly of correspondence between Locke, William Molyneux, Sir Thomas Molyneux and Philippus van Limborch.
I. Molyneux, William, 1656-1698. II. Molyneux, Sir Thomas, bart., 1661-1733. III. Limborch, Philippus van, 1633-1712. IV. Title.
4-44-10223
Library of Congress B1296.A3 1708

NL 0434961 DLC MH IaU OrU CSmH PU PSC MoSW NjP DFo PSC CtY MiU-C NNUT CLU-C NcU NNNAM NIC MnU KU

Locke, John, 1632-1704.
Some familiar letters between Mr. Locke, and several of his friends. The 3d ed. London, A. Bettesworth and C. Hitch [etc.] 1737.
1v, [5]-424 p. 20cm.
Consists chiefly of correspondence between Locke, William Molyneux, Sir Thomas Molyneux and Philippus van Limborch.
I. Molyneux, William, 1656-1698. II. Molyneux, Sir Thomas, bart., 1661-1733. III. Limborch, Philippus van, 1633-1712. IV. Title.
12-3105
Library of Congress B1296.A3 1737

NL 0434962 DLC NcU NIC PHi PPFr

[Locke, John] 1632-1704.
Some thoughts concerning education. London, Printed for A. and J. Churchill, 1693.
4 p. l., 262, [2] p. 18cm.
1. Education.
E 8-691
Library, U. S. Office of Education LB475.L6 1693

NL 0434963 DHEW PBL NcU GU MH WU NcD-MC MiU OC NcU MnU MBCo CU CtY NjP CSmH NNUT-Mc MWiW-C

LB475 L6 1695 in RareBooks Room
Locke, John, 1632-1704.
Some thoughts concerning education. 3d ed. enl. London, Printed for A. and J. Churchill, 1693.
374 p. 18cm.
1. Education.

NL 0434964 CoU MnU

Locke, John, 1632-1704.
Some thoughts concerning education...The 3d ed., enlarged. London, Printed for A. and J. Churchill, 1695.
374 p.
1. Education. I. Wing L2763.

NL 0434965 TxDaM-P MiU PU NjP DGU MH CLU-C WU

Locke, John, 1632-1704.
Some thoughts concerning education. By John Locke ... the 4th ed. enl. London, Printed for A. and J. Churchill, 1699.
4 p. l., 380, [2] p. 18cm.
1. Education.
E 10-1152
Library, U. S. Bur. of Education LB475.L6 1699

NL 0434966 DHEW OrU MH OU NNC NIC ViY CLU-C CtY ICU DFo PPL MH

618.9 G755
Locke, John, 1632-1704.
Some thoughts concerning education. 5th ed., enl. London, A. and J. Churchill, 1705.
390 p.

NL 0434967 ICJ CtY CSmH

Locke, John, 1632-1704.
Some thoughts concerning education ... By Mr. John Locke. The 6th ed. enl. London, Printed for A. and J. Churchill, 1709.
4 p. l., 390, [2] p. 19½cm.
1. Education.
6-29647†
Library of Congress LB475.L6A3

NL 0434968 DLC OrU PU

Locke, John, 1632-1704.
Some thoughts concerning education ... By Mr. John Locke. London, Printed for a Society of stationers, 1710.
3 p. l., 322, [2] p. 16½cm.
1. Education.
E 10—812
U. S. Off. of educ. Library for Library of Congress LB475.L6 1710 [a40b1]

NL 0434969 DHEW

Locke, John, 1632-1704.
Some thoughts concerning education ... By Mr. John Locke. The seventh edition. London, Printed for A. and J. Churchill, and sold by John Kent ... 1712.
3 p.l.,322,[2] p. 16½cm.
Signatures: A-N12, O6.
Title within double line border.
Armorial book-plate of Edward Duke.
Bound in old paneled calf.

NL 0434970 CLU-C MH

Locke, John, 1632-1704.
Some thoughts concerning education ... By John Lock, esq; The eighth edition. London: Printed by H. P. for A. C. and sold by John Osborn and Tho. Longman ... 1725.
[6],331(i.e.326),[2] p. 17cm.
Signatures: A-N12, O11.
Numbers 163-168 omitted in the paging.
Title within double line border. Paragraph notes.
Armorial book-plate of William Murray of Touchadam.
Bound in old calf.

NL 0434971 CLU-C

LB475 L6 1732 Rare Book
Locke, John, 1632-1704.
Some thoughts concerning education ... 9th ed. London, Printed for A. Bettesworth and C. Hitch, J. Pemberton, and E. Symon, 1732.
[6], 331, [2] p. 17cm.
Armorial bookplate High Legh Library.
I. Education. I. Title.

NL 0434972 GU OU CtY PPL

Locke, John, 1632-1704.
Some thoughts concerning education ... By John Locke ... The tenth edition. London, Printed for A. Bettesworth and C. Hitch ... J. and J. Pemberton ... and E. Symon ... 1738.
3 p.l.,331(i.e.325),[2] p. 17cm.
Signatures: A-O12(O11, verso, O12, advertisements)
Numbers 163-168 omitted in the paging.
Paragraph notes.
Book-plate of Sheppard Frere.
Bound in old sprinkled calf.

NL 0434973 CLU-C OU CU-A PU CtY WaSpG

LB 475 L81s 1752
Locke, John, 1632-1704
Some thoughts concerning education ... The 12th ed. London, Printed for S.Birt, D.Browne [etc.] 1752.
3 p.l.,325,[2]p. 17cm.

NL 0434974 NRU CtY

RBS118. Locke, John, 1632-1704
Some thoughts concerning education. 13.ed. London: A. Millar, H. Woodfall, J. Wiston and B. White... 1764.

NL 0434975 NNNAM MWA

370.1 L814SC
Locke, John, 1632-1704.
Some thoughts concerning education. 13th ed. London, J. and R. Tonson, 1769.
319 p. port. 18 cm.
1. Education. Philosophy.

NL 0434976 NcD OrU MBP

VOLUME 337

*AC85 Ac191 Zz772l Locke, John, 1632-1704.
Some thoughts concerning education ... By John Locke, esq; The fourteenth edition. London: Printed for J.Whiston, W.Strahan, J.and F.Rivington, B.White, L.Davis, Hawes, Clarke and Collins, W.Johnston, W.Owen, T.Caslon, S.Crowder, T.Longman, B.Law, C.Rivington, E.Dilly, J.Wilkie, T.Cadell, S.Baker, T.Payne, T.Davis, G.Robinson, T.Becket, and J.Robson. MDCCLXXII.
12°. 4p.l., 325p. 17.5cm.
From the library of Amos Bronson Alcott.

NL 0434977 MH MiD-B OO PBa CtY-M

Locke, John, 1632-1704.
Some thoughts concerning education; 15. ed. Dublin, 1778.

NL 0434978 NjP OO

Locke, John, 1632-1704.
Some thoughts concerning education ... By John Locke, esq. A new ed. London, J. and R. Tonson, 1779.
4 p. l., 319 p. 18cm.

1. Education.
E 10-1077
Library, U. S. Office of Education LB475.L6 1779

NL 0434979 DHEW KyLx CtY WvFT

Locke, John, 1632-1704.
Some thoughts concerning education. By John Locke. London [etc.] Ward, Lock, and co. [18—] vii, 404-556 p. 19cm.

176775B. 1. Education—Theory and systems.
January 20, 1943

NL 0434980 NN

Locke, John, 1632-1704.
... **Some thoughts concerning education; by John Locke;** and A treatise of education; by John Milton. With an appendix containing Locke's memoranda on study ... Boston, Gray & Bowen, 1830.
viii p., 2 l., [3]-317 p. 18½ cm. (The library of education, v. 1)

1. Education. I. Milton, John, 1608-1674. Tractate on education.
E 10—913
U. S. Office of Education. Library LB475
for Library of Congress [a62b½]

NL 0434981 DHEW MH CtY MeB ViU PPDrop MiU PPT PPF

Locke, John, 1632-1704.
... **Some thoughts concerning education, by John Locke.** 1st ed. New York, J. W. Schermerhorn & co., 1869.
192 p. 13cm. (Library of education, selected from the best writers of all countries (vol. 1))

1. Education.
E 9-1490
Library, U. S. Bur. of Education LB475.L6 1869

NL 0434982 DHEW OO MH

Locke, John, 1632-1704.
Some thoughts concerning education. With introduction and notes by Rev. Canon Daniel. New ed. London, National Society's Depository. [183-7]
364 p. 19 cm.

1. Education. I. Daniel, Evan, 1837-1904, ed.

NL 0434983 CaBVaU

LB475 .L6A3 1880 Locke, John, 1632-1704.
... Some thoughts concerning education, by John Locke. With introduction and notes by the Rev. R. H. Quick ... Edited for the syndics of the University press. Cambridge [Eng.] The University press; [etc., etc.] 1880.
lxiv, 240 p. 17cm. (Pitt press series.)

1. Education. I. Quick, Robert Hebert, 1831-1891, ed.

MiU ViU
NL 0434984 DLC OrCS NBC NIC MHi ViU PPL PPPD PU

LOCKE, John, 1632-1704.
Some thoughts concerning education. With an introduction by J.S.Blackie. London, etc., Watd, Lock and co., [1883].

(Ward, Lock & co's popular library of literary treasures.)

NL 0434985 MH NcD

Locke, John, 1632-1704.
Some thoughts concerning education... London, New York [etc.] Ward, Lock, Bowden, & co. [1886]
19 cm. (Books for all time)

NL 0434986 CtY

Locke, John, 1632-1704. 370.4 L79
Some thoughts concerning education. With introduction and notes by the Rev. R. H. Quick. Second edition. .... lxiv, 240 p. S. (Pitt Press series.) Cambridge: University Press, 1889. pref. 1884.

NL 0434987 ICJ PPD OCU OC1W WaWW NIC ICarbS

---

370 L79s 189- Locke, John, 1632-1704.
Some thoughts concerning education London [etc.] Ward, Lock & co., limited [189-?]
vii, [403]-556p. (On cover: Books for all time)

1. Education. I. Title.

NL 0434988 IU

LB 475 .L6 1892 Locke, John, 1632-1704.
Some thoughts concerning education. With introduction and notes by the Rev. R. H. Quick. New ed. Cambridge, Univ. Press; London, C. J. Clay and sons, 1892.
lxiv, 240 p. 17cm. (Pitt press series)

1. Education. I. Quick, Robert Hebert, 1831-1891, ed.

NL 0434989 DCU PSC PP OC1W

Locke, John, 1632-1704.
Some thoughts concerning education. With introduction and notes, by R.H.Quick. Edited for the syndics of the University press. Cambridge [Eng.]. The University press, etc., etc. 1895.
lxiv, 240 p. (Pitt press series)

NL 0434990 MH OC1

Locke, John, 1632-1704.
Some thoughts concerning education, by John Locke. With introduction and notes, by the Rev. R. H. Quick. Cambridge: University Press, 1899. lxiv, 240 p. 16°. (Pitt Press series.)

1. Education.—Theory, etc. 2. Quick, Rev. Robert Hebert.
August 15, 1913.

NL 0434991 NN PSC

Locke, John, 1632-1704.
... **Some thoughts concerning education, by John Locke. With introduction and notes by the Rev. R. H. Quick ... Stereotyped ed. Cambridge, University press, 1902.**
lxiv, 240 p. 17cm. (Pitt press series)
"Introduction, biographical and critical": p. xix-lix.

1. Education. I. Quick, Robert Hebert, 1831-1891, ed.
4—16243
Library of Congress LB475.L6O6
[s27l2] Ik

CaBVa PPHPI
MiU OC1CC OOxM ViU PV Wa KU OrPR NNC WaS OrSaW CaBVaU
NL 0434992 DLC MtU OrP WaT ICU ICRL MsSM CtY PBm

Locke, John, 1632-1704.
Some thoughts concerning education.
... **English** philosophers of the seventeenth and eighteenth centuries: Locke, Berkeley, Hume, with introductions, notes and illustrations. New York, P. F. Collier & son [c1910]

Locke, John, 1632-1704.
... Some thoughts concerning education, by John Locke. With introduction and notes by the Rev. R.H. Quick... Cambridge, University Press, 1913.

NL 0434994 OrSaW PPT PCC PU OC1 OU

Locke, John, 1632-1704.
... Some thoughts concerning education, ... With intro. and notes by R.H. Quick... Cambridge University press, 1927.

NL 0434995 OO PU PPSteph

U 192.2 L814S Locke, John, 1632-1704.
... Some thoughts concerning education, by John Locke. With introduction and notes by R. H. Quick. [Rev. ed.] Cambridge, University Press, 1934.
lxiv, 240 p. 17 cm. (Pitt press series)
This edition first published 1884.
"Introduction, biographical and critical": p. xix-lix.

1. Education. I. Quick, Robert Hebert, 1831-1891, ed. II. Title.

NL 0434996 NcD

Locke, John, 1632-1704.
Some thoughts on education. By John Locke. With notes, and an historical account of the progress of education in Egypt, Persia, Crete...by J. A. St. John. London: J. Hatchard and Son, 1836. lxiii, 333 p., 1 port. 12°. (Masterpieces of English prose literature. v. 3.)

1. Education.—Theory, etc. 2. St. John, James Augustus, 1801-1875.
January 22, 1914

NL 0434997 NN CtY MeWC OO MH

Locke, John, 1632-1704
Some thoughts on the conduct of the understanding in the search of truth. By ..., Esq. London, 1741.

NL 0434998 PPL

VOLUME 337

Locke, John, 1632–1704.
Some thoughts on the conduct of the understanding in the search of truth. By John Locke ... Glasgow, Printed for the booksellers, MDCCLXIII.
183, [1] p. 14½cm.
First published in the author's Posthumous works, 1706. Written about 1697 for a new chapter in the Essay concerning human understanding. *cf.* Dict. of nat. biog.
1. Intellect. 2. Reasoning. 3. Knowledge, Theory of. 39-17847
Library of Congress B1270 1763

NL 0435000 DLC

Ocal0
1
1808L
Locke, John, 1632-1704.
The spirit of John Locke on civil government revived by the Constitutional Society of Sheffield. Sheffield, Printed by J. Gales [1800]
42p.
Contains extracts of the second treatise of civil government.
I. Constitutional Society of Sheffield. II. Title.

NL 0435001 CtY MiU

Locke, John, 1632-1704.
A syllabus of Locke's Essay on the human understanding... 3d. ed. Cambridge, 1802.
45 p. 21 cm. [College pamphlets, v. 302]

NL 0435002 CtY

LOCKE, John, 1632–1704. No. 4 in Pph. vol. 35
A syllabus of Locke's Essay on the human understanding. 4th edition. Harlow. Deighton & Nicholson. 1807. 44 pp. 8°.

NL 0435003 MB CtY

Locke, John, 1632-1704.
A syllabus of Locke's Essay on the human understanding...5th ed. Harlow, 1809.
43 p. 22.5 cm.

NL 0435004 CtY

Locke, John, 1632-1704.
A syllabus of Locke's Essay on the human understanding. 6th ed. Harlow, Printed by B. Flower, 1812.
43 p. 21 cm.

NL 0435005 MWiW

Locke, [John], 1632-1704.
A syllabus of Locke's Essay on the human understanding, in the way of question and answer; for the use of students in the universities. Cambridge: R. Newby and G. B. Whittaker, 1824. 1 p.l., 262 p. nar. 12°.
1. Mind.—Philosophy of.
N. Y. P. L. January 4, 1912.

NL 0435006 NN

Locke, John, 1632-1704.
[Dodd, William] 1729–1777.
Synopsis compendiaria librorum Hugonis Grotii De jure belli et pacis, Samuelis Clarkii De Dei existentiâ et attributis, et Joannis Lockii De intellectu humano. Cantabrigiæ, typis Academicis excudit J. Bentham, 1751.

[Locke, John] 1632-1704.
A third letter for toleration, to the author of the third letter concerning toleration. London, Printed for Awnsham and John Churchill, at the Black Swan in Pater-Noster-Row. MDCXCII [1692]
2 p.ℓ., 350, [2] p. 21.5cm.
Errata and publisher's advertisement: [2] p. at end.
Signed at end: Philanthropus.
Bound with his A second letter concerning toleration.
1. Toleration. I. t. II. Assn. III. Philanthropus, pseud.

NL 0435008 MiU-C CaBVaU MnU NIC IU NjP MH CtY WU

Locke, John, 1632–1704.
Travels in France, 1675–1679, as related in his Journals, correspondence and other papers. Edited with an introd. and notes by John Lough. Cambridge [Eng.] University Press, 1953.
lxvi, 308 p. illus., port., map, facsim. 23 cm.
1. France—Descr. & trav. I. Title.
DC24.L6 914.4 53—10435

WaSpG WaT WaTC WaWW
IdU IdPI MtBC MtU OrCS OrP OrU Wa WaE WaSp WaS
PBm CaBViP Or OrStbM OrSaW OrU-M MtBuM CaBVaU
OCl OU PSt IEN MiU IaU OClW OOxM OO IU NcD PP
ViU ICU NcU TU NN LU MB CtY NIC NNC WU NBuU MH
NL 0435009 DLC AU TU MsSM CoU AAP KyLoU GU TxU

Locke, John, 1632–1704.
Treatise of civil government and A letter concerning toleration, by John Locke; edited by Charles L. Sherman ... New York, London, D. Appleton-Century company; incorporated [°1937]
xv, 224 p. 19½ cm. (*Half-title:* Appleton-Century philosophy source-books; S. P. Lamprecht, editor)
"A letter concerning toleration" was first published in 1689 and "An essay concerning the true original, extent and end of civil government" in 1690. *cf.* Introd.
1. Political science. 2. Liberty. 3. Toleration. I. Sherman, Charles Lawton, 1894– ed. II. Title. III. Title: A letter concerning toleration.
JC153.L85 1937 320.1 37—997

Wa OrU OrPR OrP
IdU MtBC OrCS WaWW WaTC WaT WaSp WaS WaPS WaE
MiU NjR Or OrStbM OrSaW OrU-M MtBuM IdB CaBVaU
TU ODW OU OCl OO PPT PBm PV FTaSU ScU LU AU
NL 0435011 DLC KEmT IEN NSyU OkU NIC NBuC CtY-D

HG937
L15
Locke, J[ohn] 1632–1704.
A treatise of raising our coin, taken out of a book written by Mr. J. Lock, entituled, Some considerations of the consequences of lowering of interest, and raising the value of money. Printed in the second volume of his works, in folio. London, Printed for W. Churchill, 1718.
47 p. 20½cm.
4-36540†
Library of Congress

NL 0435013 DLC

Locke, John, 1632–1704.
A treatise on the conduct of the understanding.
= Boston. Williams. 1825. 132 pp. 24°. 7608.140
F4803

NL 0435014 MB MH MWA

Locke, John, 1632-1704.
Treatise on the conduct of the understanding. Boston, Bedlington, 1828.
132 p.

NL 0435015 PU-Penn MH IU

192
L79tr
1831
Locke, John, 1632-1704.
A treatise on the conduct of the understanding ... Boston, T. Bedlington, 1831.
132p. 14½cm.
First published in the author's Posthumous works, 1706. Written about 1697 for a new chapter in the Essay concerning human understanding. cf. Dict. nat. biog.
With this is bound: Bacon, Francis. Essays, moral, economical and political. Boston, 1831.
1. Intellect. 2. Reasoning. 3. Knowledge, Theory of.

NL 0435016 IU CSt MH PHi

Locke, John, 1632–1704.
A treatise on the conduct of the understanding. By John Locke ... To which is now added a sketch of his life. A new ed. Boston, Water street bookstore, 1833.
xiv, [3]–132 p. 17½cm.
First published in the author's Posthumous works, 1706. Written about 1697 for a new chapter in the Essay concerning human understanding. *cf.* Dict. nat. biog.
1. Intellect. 2. Reasoning. 3. Knowledge, Theory of. 35—31681
Library of Congress B1270 1833
[a39c1] [159.921] 151

NL 0435017 DLC PPLT

Locke, John, 1632-1704.
A treatise on the conduct of the understanding by John Locke...to which is now added a sketch of his life. A new ed. Boston, T.H. Carter, 1837.
[3]-132 p.

NL 0435018 MiU

Locke, John, 1632-1704.
A Treatise on the conduct of the Understadding. By ..., Gent. to whibh is added a sketch of his life. New ed. Boston, Weeks, Jordan & co., 1839.
132 p.

NL 0435019 PV

Locke, John, 1632-1704.
A treatise on the conduct of the understanding. To which is now added a sketch of his life. New ed. Andrus, 1847.
216 p.

NL 0435020 PPPD

Locke, John, 1632-1704.
A treatise on the conduct of the understanding; added, a sketch of his life. New ed. Hartford, 1849.
16°

NL 0435021 NN

VOLUME 337

Locke, John, 1632–1704.
A treatise on the conduct of the understanding, by John Locke, gent. To which is added a sketch of his life. A new ed. Hartford, S. Andrus & son, 1851.
xiv, [3]–132 p. 15½cm.
First published in the author's Posthumous works, 1706. Written about 1697 for a new chapter in the Essay concerning human understanding. cf. Dict. of nat. biog.

1. Intellect. 2. Reasoning. 3. Knowledge, Theory of.
19—713†
Library of Congress B1270 1851

NL 0435022 DLC ViU PV

Locke, John, 1632-1704.
The two charters granted by King Charles IId. to the proprietors of Carolina
see under Carolina.

JC153 .L78 1949
Locke, John, 1632-1704.
Two treatises of civil government. London, J. M. Dent; New York, Dutton [1949]
xx, 242 p. 18cm. (Everyman's library, no. 751. Philosophy)

1. Political science. 2. Liberty. I. Series.

NL 0435024 MB

Locke, John, 1632–1704.
Two treatises of civil government. Introd. by W. S. Carpenter. London, Dent; New York, Dutton [1953]
xvi, 242 p. 19 cm. (Everyman's library, 751. Philosophy)
First ed. published in 1690 under title: Two treatises of government. "A list of the works of John Locke": p. xv–xvi.

1. Political science. 2. Filmer, Sir Robert, d. 1653. Patriarcha.
JC153.L8 1953 320.1 53–11660

MB OC1
NL 0435025 DLC WaS OrPS OrP CaBVaU NIC OO MnU NN

Locke, John, 1632–1704.
Two treatises of civil government. Introd. by W. S. Carpenter. London, Dent; New York, Dutton [1955]
xvi, 242 p. 19 cm. (Everyman's library, 751. Philosophy)
First ed. published in 1690 under title: Two treatises of government. "A list of the works of John Locke": p. xv–xvi.

NL 0435026 FU WaU NcU MB

[Locke, John] 1632–1704.
Two treatises of government: in the former, the false principles, and foundation of Sir Robert Filmer, and his followers, are detected and overthrown. The latter is an essay concerning the true original, extent, and end of civil government. London, A. Churchill, 1690.
6 p. l., 271 (i. e. 467) p. 18cm.
Pages 465–467 incorrectly numbered 269–271.

1. Political science. 2. Filmer, Sir Robert, d. 1653. Patriarcha.
44–48351
Library of Congress JC153.L8 1690

NNUT-Mc
NL 0435027 DLC MH NIC CoU N NjR InU PBm CtY IU NcD

Cincinnati RA320.1 L81td 1694
Locke, John, 1632-1704.
Two treatises of government: in the former, the false principles and foundation of Sir Robert Filmer, and his followers, are detected and everthrown. The latter is an essay concerning the true original, extent, and end of civil-government. The second edition corrected. London, Printed for Awnsham and John Churchill, 1694.
[8],358,[2]p.18cm.

NL 0435028 OC PU N DLC-P4 ViU ICN NNC TxU CtY OGaK

Case J 0 .5109
[LOCKE, JOHN] 1632-1704.
Two treatises of government: in the former, the false principles and foundation of Sir Robert Filmer, and his followers, are detected and overthrown. The latter is an essay concerning the true original, extent, and end of civil-government. London,Printed for A.and J.Churchill, 1698.
[6],358p.

Armorial bookplate: Leeds.

ViU NIC DLC-P4 NNC CLU-C
CLSU RPJCB ICU DCU MnU OU CU-A TxDaM-P MiU-C KyU MH
NL 0435029 ICN PHatU ICN MH MB MiU-L ODW PPM CLL

Locke, John, 1632–1704.
Two treatises of government: in the former, the false principles and foundation of Sir Robert Filmer, and his followers are detected and overthrown. The latter, is an essay concerning the true original, extent, and end of civil-government. By John Locke, esq; The 4th ed. ... London, J. Churchill, 1713.
379, [2] p. 17½cm.

1. Political science. 2. Filmer, Sir Robert, d. 1653. Patriarcha. 3. Liberty.
43–27697
Library of Congress JC153.L8 1713

NL 0435030 DLC NIC WU DFo NjP

Locke, John, 1632-1704.
WILLIAM ANDREWS CLARK MEMORIAL LIBRARY
Two treatises of government: in the former, the false principles and foundation of Sir Robert Filmer, and his followers, are detected and overthrown. The latter, is an essay concerning the true original, extent, and end of civil government. By John Locke esq; The fifth edition ... London: Printed for A. Bettesworth ... J. Pemberton ... and E. Symon ... 1728.
[8],308,[2] p. 19½cm.

Signatures: A^4, $B-U^8$, X^4 (A_1, title-page, cancel; X_4, advertisement)
Title within double line border.
Book-plate of Inverness Subscription Library.
Bound in old half calf.

ViW
NL 0435032 CLU-C CU CtY PU PP NN ICU NcU MH CU-A

Ocg55 L793 690f
Locke, John, 1632-1704.
Two treatises of government, by Iohn Locke ... London,Printed 1689,reprinted by A.Millar [etc.]1764.
6p.l.,416p. front.(port.) 21cm.
Edited by Thomas Hollis, F.R.S. - cf.British museum catalogue.

NjP
NL 0435033 CtY IU NjP CSmH MH RPJCB MA OO PPL PNt

Locke, John, 1632–1704.
Two treatises of government, by John Locke... London, 1689; repr. the seventh time by J. Whiston, 1772. x, 376 p. 19½cm.
"Two treatises of government. In the former the false principles and foundation of Sir Robert Filmer and his followers are detected and overthrown. The latter is an essay concerning the true original extent and end of civil government."—p. [iii.]

630977A. 1. Government.
September 18, 1933

NL 0435034 NN NcD ViU MH

Locke, John, 1632-1704.
Two treatises of government. In the former, the false principles and foundation of Sir Robert Filmer, and his followers are detected and overthrown. The latter, is an essay concerning the true original extent and end of civil government. Dublin, Printed for J. Sheppard and G. Nugent, 1779.
1 p. l., iii p., 1 l., 331 p. 17cm.
Armorial bookplates of Crawford and Balcarres.
1. Political science. 2. Filmer, Sir Robert, d. 1653. Patriarcha. 3. Liberty.

NL 0435035 ViU CtY

JC153 L8 1796
Locke, John, 1632-1704.
Two treatises of government: in the former, the false principles and foundation of Sir Robert Filmer, and his followers, are detected and overthrown. The latter is an essay concerning the true original, extent and end of civil government. By John Locke. 6th ed. Glasgow, Printed by W. Paton for R. Smith, and D. Boag, 1796.
431 p. 17 cm.

NL 0435036 OU MH

Locke, John, 1632–1704.
Two treatises of government. A new ed. London, Printed for C. and J. Rivington, 1824.
277 p. 22 cm.

1. Political science. 2. Filmer, Sir Robert, d. 1653. Patriarcha. 3. Liberty.
JC153.L8 1824 51–51458

NL 0435037 DLC NN MH

Locke, John, 1632–1704.
Two treatises of government. With a supplement, Patriarcha, by Robert Filmer. Ed. with an introd. by Thomas I. Cook. New York, Hafner Pub. Co., 1947.
xlii, 311 p. 21 cm. (The Hafner library of classics, no. 2)
"Selected bibliography": p. xl–xli.

1. Political science. I. Filmer, Sir Robert, d. 1653. Patriarcha. II. Cook, Thomas Ira, 1907– ed.
JC153.L8 1947 320.1 48–5372*

ICU TxU MH PU MiU MiEM
OrU CaBVa WaSp AU KyLxT MiU NIC OKentU ViU OU NcD
NL 0435038 DLC NNUN CaBViP MtU WaTC WaS OrCS OrSaW

Locke, John, 1632–1704.
Two treatises on civil government, by John Locke, preceded by Sir Robert Filmer's "Patriarcha"; with an introduction by Henry Morley ... London, G. Routledge and sons, limited; New York, E. P. Dutton and co. [pref. 1884]
320 p. 20cm.
"In the former the false principles and foundation of Sir Robert Filmer and his followers are detected and overthrown. The latter is an essay concerning the true original, extent, and end of civil government."—p. [75]

1. Political science. 2. Filmer, Sir Robert, d. 1653. Patriarcha. 3. Liberty. I. Filmer, Sir Robert, d. 1653.
38–570
Library of Congress JC153.L8 1884 a
320.1

OU CaBVaU MiU OCU MB
NL 0435039 DLC TxU WaU-L IdU-L CaBViP CoFS OKentU

VOLUME 337

Locke, John, 1632–1704.
Two treatises on civil government, by John Locke, preceded by Sir Robert Filmer's "Patriarcha"; with an introduction by Henry Morley ... London, New York, G. Routledge and sons, 1884.
320 p. 20 cm. (*Half-title:* Morley's universal library)
"In the former the false principles and foundation of Sir Robert Filmer and his followers are detected and overthrown. The latter is an essay concerning the true original, extent, and end of civil government."—p. [75]
1. Political science. 2. Filmer, Sir Robert, d. 1653. Patriarcha. 3. Liberty.
A 13—1322
Chicago. Univ. Libr. for Library of Congress JC153 [66m½]

NRCR PSC PHC PU
NL 0435040 ICU WaWW WaSpG OrPS GU-L ViU NN MH MB

JC 153 L82 1887 Locke, John, 1632-1704.
Two treatises on civil government, preceded by Sir Robert Filmer's "Patriarcha". With an introd. by Henry Morley. 2d ed. London, George Routledge, 1887.
320p. (Morley's universal library)
1. Political science - Early works to 1700. 2. Filmer, Sir Robert, d. 1653. / Patriarcha. 3. Liberty. I. Filmer, Sir Robert, d. 1653. Patriarcha. II. Title.

PPFr OCU MiU PU PBm PP OClW
NL 0435041 CU-AL ViU TxU ICMcC OU TU MH OO NjP NN

Locke, John, 1632-1704.
Two treatises on civil government...introd. by H. Morley. London, [189?]

NL 0435042 NjP

---

321 L79 1903 Locke, John, 1632-1704.
Two treatises on civil government ... preceded by Sir Robert Filmer's "Patriarcha", with an introduction by Henry Morley ... London, G. Routledge and sons, 1903.
320p. [Morley's universal library. 9]
1. Political science. I. Filmer, Sir Robert, b.1653. Patriarcha.

NL 0435043 IU OClW PU NN NjP

Locke, John, 1632–1704.
Two treatises on government. By John Locke ... London, Printed for R. Butler [etc.] 1821.
xii, 401, [1] p. front. (port.) 22 cm.
"Two treatises on government. In the former the false principles and foundation of Sir Robert Filmer and his followers are detected and overthrown. The latter is an essay concerning the true original extent and end of civil government."—p. [v]
1. Political science. 2. Filmer, Sir Robert, d. 1653. Patriarcha. 3. Liberty.
9—20097
Library of Congress JC153.L8

NL 0435044 DLC ICJ OU ViLxW

LOCKE, John, 1632-1704.
Über den menschlichen verstand; eine abhandlung. Aus dem englischen übersetzt von Th. Schultze. Leipzig, P. Reclam jun., [1897].
2 vol. 24°.

NL 0435045 MH

Locke, John, 1632–1704.
Über den menschlichen verstand; eine abhandlung von John Locke, aus dem englischen übersetzt von Th. Schultze ... Leipzig, P. Reclam [1898]
2 v. 15cm. [Universal-bibliothek. nr. 3816-25a]
"Für die ... übersetzung ist die englische ausgabe von Lockes Philosophical works in two volumes by J. A. St. John, London, George Bell and sons, 1875, benutzt worden, die anmerkungen des englischen herausgebers sind jedoch nicht mit übersetzt."—Vorbemerkung.
I. Schultze, Theodor, 1824-1898, tr. II. Title.
31-34276
Library of Congress B1260.S3 151

NL 0435046 DLC MB CU

Locke, John, 1632-1704.
Über den richtigen Gebrauch des Verstandes, neu übers. von Otto Martin. Leipzig, F. Meiner, 1920. viii,109 p. 18cm. (Philosophische Bibliothek; oder, Sammlung der Hauptwerke der Philosophie alter und neuer Zeit. Bd. 79)
1. Knowledge. I. Martin, Otto, tr. II. Ser. III. Martin, Otto.

NL 0435047 NN DLC-P4

LB 475 L6B2 1698 Rare Book Locke, John, 1632-1704.
Verhandeling over de opvoeding der kinderen, behelzende verscheydene nutte Aenmerkingen die de ouders ten opzigt van 't Lichaam, doch voornamentlijk van de Ziel hunner Kinderen in de Opvoeding hebben waar te nemen. Door Dr. Johannes Lock ... Te Rotterdam, by Barent Bos, 1698.
352 p. 15cm.
Title in red and black.
Added t.-p., engr.
1. Education. I. Title.

NL 0435048 ViW

Locke, John, 1632-1704.
Vernunftmässiges Christenthum, wie es in der heiligen Schrift enthalten ist, von Johann Loke. Berlin und Leipzig, Günther, 1758.
2 v.

NL 0435048-1 PPG

B 23 P568 v.50-51 Locke, John, 1632-1704.
Versuch über den menschlichen Verstand. Uebers. und erläutert von J.H.v. Kirchmann. Berlin, L. Heimann, 1872-73.
2v. 19cm. (Philosophische Bibliothek. 50-51 Bd.)
Bound with Kirchmann, J.H.v. Erläuterungen zu John Locke's Versuch über den menschlichen Verstand. Berlin, 1873-74.
1. Knowledge, Theory of I. Kirchmann, Julius Hermann von, 1802-1884. II. Title. (Series)

NL 0435049 ICMcC InU

B 23 P56 v.50-51 Locke, John, 1632-1704.
Versuch über den menschlichen Verstand. Uebers. und erläutert von J. H. v. Kirchmann. 2. Aufl. Berlin, Philos.-Histor. Verlag, 1873-94 [v.2, 1873]
2 v. 19cm. (Philosophische Bibliothek, Bd. 50-51)
Vol. 2, without edition statement, has imprint: Berlin, L. Heimann.
I. Kirchmann, Julius Hermann von, 1802-188[4].

NL 0435050 NIC

Locke, John, 1632–1704.
John Locke's Versuch über den menschlichen Verstand... übersetzt von Carl Winckler... Leipzig, F. Meiner, 1911–13. 2 v. 19cm. (Philosophische Bibliothek. Bd. 75–76)
Vol. 1, 1913.
550384–5B. I. Winckler, Carl, tr. II. Title. III. Ser. April 30, 1951

NL 0435051 NN NcD MH

[Locke, John] 1632-1704.
A vindication of The reasonableness of Christianity, &c. from Mr. Edwards's reflections. London: Printed for Awnsham and John Churchil ... 1695.
2 p.l.,40 p. 17cm. (In his The reasonableness of Christianity ... London, 1696)
Signatures: A8, B-E4(E3-4, advertisements)
Title within double line border.

NL 0435052 CLU-C NSyU MH

[Locke, John,] 1632–1704, supposed author.
The whole history of navigation from its original to this time. (1704.) Prefixed to Churchill's Collection of voyages. [London: T. Tegg, 1823.] 357–564 p. 22cm.
Excerpt from his: Works. London, 1823. new ed. v. 10.
"A catalogue and character of most books of voyages and travels," p. 513–564.
FORD COLLECTION.
165486. 1. Navigation—Hist. 2. Voyages and travels. 3. Voyages and travels—Bibl. I. Title. Revised November 21, 1932

NL 0435053 NN

320.1 L81XG Locke, John, 1632-1704.
Zwei Abhandlungen über Regierung. Nebst Patriarcha von Robert Filmer. Deutsch von Hilmar Wilmanns. Halle, M. Niemeyer, 1906.
viii,383p. 22cm.
1. Political science. 2. Filmer, Sir Robert, d. 1653. Patriarcha. 3. Liberty. 4. Monarchy. I. Filmer, Sir Robert, d. 1653. Patriarcha. II. Title.

NL 0435054 IEN NNC MH

Locke, John, 1792-1856.
An address on the subject of agricultural chemistry...delivered at the fifth annual Fair of the Warren Co., Ohio, Agricultural society - September, 1854... Lebanon, O., Western Star office, 1854.
28 p.

NL 0435055 OClWHi

Locke, John, 1792–1856.
Analyses of the waters in the vicinity of Cincinnati; reported to the trustees of the city water works, by John Locke ... and Joseph Morris Locke ... Cincinnati, Printed at the job rooms of the Cincinnati daily enquirer, 1853.
1 p. l., 16 p. 24cm.
[Mineralogical pamphlets, v. 3, no. 23]
1. Cincinnati—Water-supply. I. Locke, Joseph Morris, joint author.
5-30823†
Library of Congress QE353.M7
Library of Congress [Technological pamphlets, v. 13, no. 11] T7.T25

NL 0435056 DLC NN OClWHi

VOLUME 337

Locke, John, 1792-1856.
Smithsonian institution.
Catalogue of rocks, minerals, ores and fossils, collected by Dr. John Locke.
(*In* Smithsonian institution. Annual report, 1854. Washington, 1855. 23½cm. p. 367-383)

NL 0435058 PPAN

Locke, John, 1792-1856.
Catalogue of specimens [and report of field work in Lake Superior region] forwarded to Dr. Jackson by John Locke, December, 1847.
U.S. 31st Cong., 1st sess., S. Ex. doc. 1, pt. 3, p. 563-605, 1849.
Bd. with C.T. Jackson's Report on the geol. & mineralogical survey ... Michigan.

NL 0435058 PPAN

Locke, John, 1792-1856.
An English grammar for children; according to the elementary method of Pestalozzi; containing easy lessons in composition, whereby young persons may acquire the habit of speaking and writing correctly ... By John Locke ... Cincinnati, W. M. & O. Farnsworth, jr., printers, 1827.
xvii, [3], 21-228 p. front. (fold. tab.) 15cm.
1. English language—Grammar—1800-1870.
D' C Old Off 10-25555†
Library of Congress PE1109.L75

NL 0435059 DLC

Locke, John, 1792-1856.
[Geological map of Adams Co., Ohio, and other geological charts of south western Ohio.] n.d.

NL 0435060 OClWHi

Locke, John, 1792-1856.
An introductory lecture on chemistry and geology: delivered November 6, 1838, before the class of the Medical college of Ohio, by John Locke... Published at the request of the class. Cincinnati, 1839.
18 p., 1 l. 21 cm.

NL 0435061 OU DNLM OClW-H MoSHi

Locke, John, 1792-1856.
A lecture on toxicology: delivered before the chemical class of the University of the state of Missouri, Fifth of March, 1854... Columbia, Mo., Printed at the Statesman office, 1854.
23 p. 21 cm.

NL 0435062 NcD

Locke, John, 1792-1856. 615.9 K100
A lecture on toxicology, delivered January 15, 1841, before the class of the Medical College of Ohio, by John Locke ... Cincinnati, The Class, 1841.
24 p. front. (fold. tab.) 21cm.
With this is bound his An introductory lecture on chemistry and geology ... Cincinnati, 1839. 18, [1] p.

NL 0435063 ICJ OClW-H MBCo

RA1213 .L6 1843 Toner Coll.
Locke, John, 1792-1856.
A lecture on toxicology, delivered before the class, of the Medical college of Ohio, January 15, 1841. By John Locke ... 2d ed. Published by the class. Cincinnati, Printed by R. P. Donogh, 1843.
15 p. 22½cm.
"Professor Locke's Table of poisons and their antidotes": 1 fold. leaf inserted at end.

Toner Coll. --- ---- Copy 2.

NL 0435064 DLC TU NcD-MC

Locke, John, 1792-1856.
——. A lecture on toxicology; delivered before the class of the Medical College of Ohio. 3. ed. 14 pp., 1 l. 8°. Cincinnati, J. A. Robinson & Co., 1842.

NL 0435065 DNLM OC

Locke, John, 1792-1856.
Natural theology. A valedictory lecture, delivered to the class of students in the medical college of Ohio, in the department of chemistry on February 25, 1853, by John Locke. Cincinnati, Printed by T. Wrightson, 1853.
30 p. 22 cm.
Bound with Conclin's new river guide. Cincinnati, J.A. and U.P. James, 1851.
1. Natural theology.

NL 0435066 PLatS Nh OClWHi

Locke, John, 1792-1856.
Observations made in the years, 1838, '39, '40, '41, '42, and '43, to determine the magnetical dip and the intensity of magnetical force, in several parts of the United States. Read April 19, 1844.
(In American Philosophical Society. Transactions. Philadelphia, 1846. 30cm. n. s. v. 9, p. [283]-328. illus.)
1. Magnetism, Terrestrial--U. S.

NL 0435067 NIC OCU

Locke, John, 1792-1856.
... Observations on terrestrial magnetism. By John Locke ... [Washington, Smithsonian institution, 1852]
29, [1] p. 32½cm. (Smithsonian contributions to knowledge. vol. III, art. 1)
Smithsonian institution publication 35.
1. Magnetism, Terrestrial—Observations.
S 13-13
Library, Smithsonian Institution Q11.S68
Library of Congress [Q11.S68 vol. 3]

NL 0435068 OrP MU NcU OU OO MiU OCU OCl ICJ NN PP PSC PPL DSI MnHi MdBP OClW DAS CaBVaU OrU WaS

Locke, John, 1792-1856.
Observations on the terrestrial magnetism of several parts of the United States: by John Locke ... Philadelphia, Printed by W. S. Young, 1846.
1 p. l., [283]-328 p. 1 pl., 3 maps (1 fold.) tables, diagrs. 29½ x 23½cm.
"Extracted from the Transactions of the American philosophical society."
1. Magnetism, Terrestrial—U. S.
5-31405†
Library of Congress QC825.1.L8
[Physical pamphlets, v. 1, no. 6]
Library of Congress QC3.P5

NL 0435069 DLC PU NN

Q 11 P53T7++ n.s. v.7 pt.17
Locke, John, 1792-1856.
Observations to determine the horizontal magnetic intensity and dip at Louisville, Kentucky, and at Cincinnati, Ohio. Read May 15, 1840.
(In American Philosophical Society. Transactions. Philadelphia, 1841. 30cm. n. s. v. 7, p. [261]-264)
1. Magnetism, Terrestrial--Ohio--Cincinnati. 2. Magnetism, Terrestrial--Kentucky--Louisville.

NL 0435070 NIC

College Pamphlets v.1540
Locke, John, 1792-1856.
On the invention of the electro-chronograph. A letter to Nicholas Longworth, esq. ... Cincinnati, Office of the "Great West", 1850.
75p. 21½cm.

NL 0435071 CtY MH PU

Q 11 P53T7++ v.6 pt.6
Locke, John, 1792-1856.
On the magnetic dip at several places in the State of Ohio, and on the relative horizontal magnetic intensities of Cincinnati and London. In a letter to John Vaughan, Esq., librarian of the Am. Philos. Soc. Read June 15, 1838.
(In American Philosophical Society. Transactions. Philadelphia, 1839. 30cm. n.s., v.6, p. [267]-273)
1. Magnetism, Terrestrial--Ohio.

NL 0435072 NIC DN-Ob

x580 793o
Locke, John, 1792-1856.
Outlines of botany, taken chiefly from Smith's Introduction; containing an explanation of botanical terms and an illustration of the system of Linnæus. Also some account of natural orders, and the anatomy and physiology of vegetables. Illustrated by engravings. For the use of schools and students. Boston, Pub. by Cummings and Hilliard, for the author, 1819.
xiii, 161p. plates. 19cm.

NL 0435073 CtY OkU MBHo IU MnU CaBVaU InU CU NN CLSU MH OOxM

Locke, J[ohn] 1792-1856.
Problems to illustrate the most important principles of geography and astronomy, performed by the inclinable orrery, an instrument invented by J. Locke, M. D. and made by A. Willard, jr. Cincinnati, Morgan, Fisher and L'Hommedieu, 1828.
14 p. front. 24cm.
1. Astronomical models.
Library of Congress QB67.L8 5-2142†

NL 0435074 DLC

Locke, John, 1792-1856. 522.52 L001
Report of Professor John Locke, of Cincinnati, Ohio, on the invention and construction of his electro-chronograph for the National Observatory, in pursuance of the act of Congress, approved March 3, 1849 ... Cincinnati, Printed by Wright, Ferris and Co., 1850.
3 p. l., xi, 67 p. illus., XVII fold. pl., diagrs. 24cm.

NL 0435075 ICJ DN-Ob PPAmP CtY NN

Locke, John, 1792-1856.
Guyandotte land company.
Reports and letters relating to the Guyandotte land company, 1853. London, W. Penney [1853?]

VOLUME 337

4K Locke, John, 1805-1880, ed.
Gt.Brit.
407 The game laws, comprising all the acts now in force on the subject; brought down to the end of the session of Parliament of the 3 & 4 Vict., with explanatory notes and an index. 2d ed. by John Locke. London, Shaw, 1840.
200 p.

NL 0435077 DLC-P4

Locke, John, 1805–1880, *ed.*
The game laws, comprising the whole of the law now in force on the subject, brought down to the present time, with introduction, explanatory notes, cases, and index. 4th ed. By John Locke ... London, Shaw and sons, 1856.
xxxvi, xcii, [93]–328, [36] p. 18cm.

1. Game-laws—Gt. Brit. I. Gt. Brit. Laws, statutes, etc.
33-13231

NL 0435078 DLC

Locke, John, 1805–1880.
The law and practice of foreign attachment in the Lord Mayor's court, under the new rules of practice. With an appendix of the forms of proceeding in attachment, and in ordinary actions. By John Locke ... London, S. Sweet, 1853.
xxvi, 130 p. 19½cm.

1. Attachment and garnishment—Gt. Brit. 2. London. Lord Mayor's court. 3. Forms (Law)—Gt. Brit. I. Title: Foreign attachment, The law and practice of.
39-31224

NL 0435079 DLC CSt PU-L

Locke, John, 1805–1880.
The law and practice of foreign attachment in the Lord Mayor's court, under the new rules of practice. With an appendix, of the forms of proceeding in attachment, and in ordinary actions. By John Locke ... Philadelphia, T. & J. W. Johnson, 1854.
xviii, [19]–84 p. 23½cm. (*In* The Law library. Philadelphia, 1853. [v. 79, July/Sept. 1853, no. 2)

1. Attachment and garnishment—Gt. Brit. 2. London. Lord Mayor's court. 3. Forms (Law)—Gt. Brit. I. Title: Foreign attachment, The law and practice of.
40-20481

NL 0435080 DLC WaU-L PU-L ViU-L MiU-L PP

Locke, John, 1805–1880.
The law and practice of foreign attachment in the Lord mayor's court, under the new rules of practice. By John Locke.
(*In* Drake, Charles Daniel, 1811-1892. A treatise on the law of suits by attachment, in the United States ... 2d ed., rev. and enl. ... Boston, Little, Brown and company, 1858. 24cm. p. [691]–746)
First published in 1853 under title: Law and practice of foreign attachment in the Lord mayor's court, under the new rules of practice, with appendix of forms. (xxvi, 130 p.)

1. Attachment and garnishment—Gt. Brit. [2. Foreign attachment]
14-16521

Library of Congress

NL 0435081 DLC

Locke, John, 1805–1880, *ed.*
A treatise on the game laws of England and Wales; including introduction, statutes, explanatory notes, cases and index. By John Locke ... 5th ed., in which are introduced the game laws of Scotland and Ireland, by Gilmore Evans ... London, H. Sweet [etc.] 1866.
xxxi, [1], 390 p. 18cm.

1. Game-laws—Gt. Brit. 2. Game-laws—Scotland. 3. Game-laws—Ireland. I. Evans, Gilmore. II. Gt. Brit. Laws, statutes, etc. III. Scotland. Laws, statutes, etc. IV. Ireland. Laws, statutes, etc.
33-13230

NL 0435082 DLC

Locke, John, 1805-1880.

Drake, Charles Daniel, 1811–1892.
A treatise on the law of suits by attachment, in the United States. By Charles D. Drake ... 2d ed., rev. and enl.: with an appendix, containing the leading statutory provisions of the several states and territories of the United States, in relation to suits by attachment; and a treatise on foreign attachment in the Lord mayor's court of London, by John Locke. Boston, Little, Brown and company, 1858.

---

*C-3 p.v.563
Locke, John, 1847-1889.
Dawn on the Irish coast. Poems...with memoir and guide to Callan by James Maher. Mullinahone, Kilkenny Journal, 1952. 24 p. illus.,port. 21cm.

1. Callan, Ire. I. Maher, James, ed. II. Title.

NL 0435084 NN MH

M-R747.C7
C73
1952 **Locke, John C**
Experimental studies with antibiotics and antibiotic mixtures in vitro and in the treatment of intraocular infections. [New York] 1952.
96 l. illus., tables. (Columbia University. College of Physicians and Surgeons. Thesis for the degree of Doctor of medical science.)

Bibliography: p. 83-96.

NL 0435085 NNC

Locke, John Courtenay, 1880– *ed.*
... The first Englishmen in India; letters and narratives of sundry Elizabethans written by themselves and edited with an introduction and notes by J. Courtenay Locke. London, G. Routledge & sons, ltd. [1930]
xvi, 229 p. front. (port.) plates, maps (part fold.) 22½ cm. (The Broadway travellers, edited by Sir E. Denison Ross and Eileen Power)
The text is from the 1903 MacLehose edition of Hakluyt and the 1905 MacLehose edition of "Purchas his pilgrimes." *cf.* p. v.
1. Voyages and travels. 2. India—Descr. & trav.—1498–1761. 3. Asia, Western—Descr. & trav. I. Hakluyt, Richard, 1552?–1616. Principal navigations, voyages, traffiques & discoveries of the English nation. II. Purchas, Samuel, 1577?–1626. Purchas his pilgrimes. III. Title.
DS411.L6 915.4 32—5967

PHC PU-F OCU OO OC1 MiEM CU
NL 0435086 DLC WaSpG NcU CaBVaU TxU NN ICN MH DFo

Locke, John Courtenay, tr.

Grillot de Givry, Émile Angelo, 1870–
Witchcraft, magic & alchemy, by Grillot de Givry, translated by J. Courtenay Locke; with 10 plates in colour and 366 illustrations in the text. Boston and New York, Houghton Mifflin company, 1931.

Locke, John F
Apprenticeship course for printing apprentices, copyrighted and written by John F. Locke ... [Cincinnati, Printing trade school of the Cincinnati public schools] °1923.
1 v. 25cm.
Loose-leaf.
Cover-title.

1. Printing, Practical. I. Cincinnati. Printing high school. II. Title.
24-1613 Revised
Library of Congress Z122.5.U6L8

NL 0435088 DLC

Locke, John F
Apprenticeship course for printing apprentices, copyrighted and written by John F. Locke ... [Cincinnati, Printing trade school of the Cincinnati public schools] 1924.
1 v. 25cm.
Loose-leaf.
Cover-title.

1. Printing, Practical. I. Cincinnati. Printing high school. II. Title.
24-6453 Revised
Library of Congress Z122.5.U6L8 1924

NL 0435089 DLC

Locke, John F.
A hand book for electrotypers, by John F. Locke. [Cincinnati, Printing trade school] 1922.
35 p. 18cm.

1. Electrotyping.
Library of Congress Z252.L82 22-17778

NL 0435090 DLC

Locke, John F.
Punctuation for printing apprentices; a textbook for the apprentices of the Printing Trade School and a reference book for the graduates, by John F. Locke... [Cincinnati: Prtg. Trade School, cop. 1923.] 44 p. 8°.

1. English language.—Punctuation.
July 1, 1924

NL 0435091 NN OC1

Locke, John Fillmore.
Wheat market fundamentals... [Cincinnati, 1936.
91 l.

NL 0435092 OCU

Locke, John Flowers, 1908–
... Microsporogenesis and cytokinesis in *Asimina triloba* ... by John Flowers Locke ... [Chicago, 1936]
1 p. l., p. 159–168. pl. 24cm.
Thesis (PH. D.)—University of Chicago, 1934.
"Contributions from the Hull botanical laboratory 474."
"Private edition, distributed by the University of Chicago libraries, Chicago, Illinois."
"Reprinted from the Botanical gazette, vol. 98, no. 1, 1936."
"Literature cited": p. 167–168.

1. Papaw. 2. Karyokinesis. I. Title.
37-5145
Library of Congress QH605.L56 1934
Univ. of Chicago Lib.
[583.115] 581.87623

NL 0435093 ICU ViU OCU DLC

VOLUME 337

Locke, John Francis, 1844-1924. *"20th".32.93
[A collection of circulars, clippings, etc., relating to the celebration of the fiftieth anniversary of the Battle of Gettysburg, at Gettysburg, July 1-4, 1913.]
= Scrap-book. [Dorchester, Mass. 1913.] 1 v. 28 cm.

D9233 — Scrap-books. Gettysburg, Pa. .. Battle, 1863. — Gettysburg, Pa. Hist. Battle, 1863. — Gettysburg, Pa. Centennial celebrations, etc.

NL 0435094 MB

Locke, John Francis, 1844-1924. *"20th".40c.39.2
John F. Locke's Recollections.
(In Roe, Alfred S. The Thirty-ninth Regiment, Massachusetts Volunteers, 1862-1865. Pp. 308-317. Worcester. 1914.)
Recollections of the Confederate prisons at Belle Isle, Va., and Salisbury, N. C.

M7107 — Belle Isle, Va. Military Prison. — Salisbury, N. C. Military Prison.

NL 0435095 MB

Locke, John Franklin, 1903-
Repeated sums of certain functions, by John Franklin Locke ... [Sendai, Japan, 1935]
1 p. l., p. [128]-141, 1 l. 23cm.
Summary of thesis (PH. D.)—University of Illinois, 1933.
Vita.
"Reprinted from the Tohoku mathematical journal, vol. 40, part 1."

1. Difference equations. I. Title.

35-20322
Library of Congress QA431.L67 1933
517.6

NL 0435096 DLC CtY

Locke, John Goodwin.
The social genesis and character of universals. 1923.
139 l. 29 cm.
Typescript (carbon copy)
Thesis—University of Chicago.
Includes bibliographical references.

1. Universals (Philosophy) I. Title.

B105.U5L62 72-275928

NL 0435097 DLC ICU

Locke, John Goodwin, 1803-1869.
Book of the Lockes. A genealogical and historical record of the descendants of William Locke, of Woburn. With an appendix containing a history of the Lockes in England, also of the family of John Locke, of Hampton, N. H., and kindred families and individuals. By John Goodwin Locke ... Boston, J. Munroe & co., 1853.
406 p. front., illus., ports., facsims., coat of arms. 24½cm.

1. Locke family (William Locke, 1628-1720) 2. Locke family (John Locke, d. 1696)

9-11610
Library of Congress CS71.L813 1853

NL 0435098 DLC MeB C-S PHi PPL MB NN MWA MnHi

Locke, John Goodwin, 1803-1869.
The Munroe genealogy. By John G. Locke. Boston and Cambridge, J. Munroe and company, 1853.
15 p. 25½cm.
Reprinted from his "Book of the Lockes ..." Boston, 1853, p. 302-313.

1. Monroe family (William Munroe, 1625-1717)

9-12324
Library of Congress CS71.M753 1853

NL 0435099 DLC NIC OO PHi MWA MnHi

LOCKE, John Lymburner, 1832-1876.
History of Phoenix Lodge. No.24. of Belfast, Maine. Belfast, 1863.

..pp.25.

NL 0435100 MH Nh

Locke, John Lymburner, 1832-1876
Sketches of the history of the town of Camden, Maine; including incidental references to the neighboring places and adjacent waters. By John L. Locke ... Hallowell, Masters, Smith & company, 1859.
xii, [7]-267 p., 1 l. incl. plates. 20cm.

1. Camden, Me.—Hist.

1-8947
Library of Congress F29.C2L8

PHi PPPrHi Nh MdBP CtY MWA MeB
NL 0435101 DLC CU NcD MU NIC MB KMK MdBP OU MnHi NN

Locke, John Lymburner, 1832-1876.

Waldo, Samuel, 1696-1759.
Translation of Gen. Waldo's circular—1753; with an introduction by John L. Locke.
(In Collections of the Maine historical society. Portland, 1859. 23cm. [1st ser.] v. 6, p. [319]-332)

Locke, John R
Highlights of color television. [1st ed.] New York, J. F. Rider [1954]
44 p. illus. 22 cm. (A Rider publication, no. 157)

1. Color television. I. Title.

TK6670.L6 621.388 54-7346 ‡

NL 0435103 DLC MtU IdPI DAU MB PPD PU-EI NN

Locke, John Staples, 1836-1906.
The art of correspondence: how to construct and write letters according to approved usage. Containing model business, social, and love letters by distinguished writers, with the etiquette for using wedding and calling cards. By John S. Locke. Boston, De Wolfe, Fiske and company, 1883.
vi p., 1 l., 9-243 p. 18cm.

1. Letter-writing. 2. Visiting-cards.

11-6208
Library of Congress PE1483.L6

NL 0435104 DLC NIC MiU

LOCKE, JOHN STAPLES, 1836-1906.
A brave struggle; or, The orphans' inheritance.
New York, Cassell [c1886] vi,304 p. illus. 23cm.

NL 0435105 NN NjP OKentU

Locke, John Staples, 1836-1906.
Historical sketches of Old Orchard and the shores of Saco Bay; Biddeford Pool, Old Orchard Beach, Pine Point, Prout's Neck. By J. S. Locke. Enl. ed. Boston, C. H. Woodman & co., 1884.
103 p. col. front., illus., plates (1 fold.) ports. 19½cm.

1. Saco Bay, Me. 2. Biddeford Pool, Me. 3. Old Orchard, Me.

1-8916
Library of Congress F27.Y6L82

NL 0435106 DLC MnHi Nh MeB OClWHi PHi NN

[Locke, John Staples] 1836-1906.
Old Orchard beach, Maine. Portland, Me., G. W. Morris [1900]
81 p. incl. front., illus., pl. obl. 12°.

1. Old Orchard, Me.—Descr.

0-4883
Library of Congress F29.O4L81

NL 0435107 DLC WHi

Locke, John Staples, 1836-1906.
Old Orchard, Maine. Pen and pencil sketches. By J. S. Locke. Boston, Graves, Locke & co. [1879]
2 p. l., 7-48 p. illus., fold. col. pl., double plan. 19½ cm.

1. Old Orchard Beach, Me.—Hist. 2. Old Orchard Beach, Me.—Descr.

F29.O4L8 1-8991

NL 0435108 DLC OClW OClWHi MWA MeB NIC DSI

PZ
8.3
.L82

Locke, John Staples, 1836-1906.
Picture rhymes for happy times. New York, Cassell [1886]
172 p. illus.

NL 0435109 MiU

Locke, John Staples, 1836-1906
Pictures and rhymes for our pets, by John S. Locke. New York, Cassell publishing co. [c1895]
160 p. incl. front., illus. 28 cm.

1. Children's poetry I. Title.

NL 0435110 RPB

Locke, John Staples, 1836-1906.
Shores of Saco Bay. A historical guide to Biddeford Pool, Old Orchard beach, Pine Point, Prout's Neck. By J. S. Locke. Boston, J. S. Locke and company, 1880.
105 p. fold. front., illus., plates, ports. 19½cm.

1. Saco Bay, Me. 2. Biddeford Pool, Me. 3. Old Orchard, Me.

1-8915
Library of Congress F27.Y6L8

NL 0435111 DLC MWA MeB

847
1

Locke, Joseph
An oration, pronounced at Billerica, July 5, 1802, in commemoration of the Declaration of American independence ... Boston, Young and Minns, printers[1802]
20p. 20cm.
Pamphlet.

NL 0435112 CtY N MH

Locke, Joseph, 1805-1860.
Railway gauge. A letter to the Right Hon. Lord John Russell, M.P., on the best mode of avoiding the evils of mixed gauge railways and the break of gauge ... London, J.Ridgway [1848]
15, [1] p. fold.diagr. 21.5 cm.

NL 0435113 MH-BA

VOLUME 337

TF
258
.L82

Locke, Joseph, 1805-1860.
Report of Joseph Locke, chief engineer of the Grand junction railway between Birmingham and Liverpool, England. To the directors of the Grand junction railway company ... [Liverpool?, 1835?]
20 p. illus. 22cm.
Caption title.
A report on rails and chairs.
1. Railroads--Rails. I. Grand junction railway company (England)

NL 0435114 MiU NN

Locke, Joseph, 1805-1860.
Report ... of the Grand junction railroad between Birmingham and Liverpool, (Eng.) June 3, 1835. New-York, The New-York and Erie railroad company, 1835.
cover-title, 20 p. illus., tables, fold. chart. 22.5 cm.

NL 0435115 MH-BA NjP NN-P MWA MB CSmH NN

Locke, Joseph, 1805-1860.

Walker, James, 1781-1862.
Report to the directors of the Liverpool and Manchester railway, on the comparative merits of locomotive and fixed engines, as a moving power. By James Walker ... Observations on the comparative merits of locomotive and fixed engines, as applied to railways. By Robert Stephenson and Joseph Locke ... An account of the Liverpool and Manchester railway. By Henry Booth ... Philadelphia, Carey & Lea, 1831.

Locke, Joseph A., tr.
Life of St. Clare of Montefalco, 1884
see under Tardy, Laurence.

Locke, Joseph Morris, joint author.

Locke, John, 1792-1856.
Analyses of the waters in the vicinity of Cincinnati; reported to the trustees of the city water works, by John Locke ... and Joseph Morris Locke ... Cincinnati, Printed at the job rooms of the Cincinnati daily enquirer, 1853.

Locke, Joseph M[orris].
A monograph upon the preservation of organic substances, by the means of a current of dry air. To which is added the practical results as obtained from Schooley's patented process. Cincinnati, Moore, Wilstach, Keys & Co. 1856.
pp. 60. Illus.

Food preservation||.

NL 0435119 MH-C MB N

Locke, Joseph Morris.
Report on the analyses of three specimens of milk, made at the request of the Health officer of the city of Cincinnati, by Joseph M. Locke ... Cincinnati, Bloch & co., city printers, 1870.
19 p. fold. tab. 22cm.

1. Milk—Analysis and examination. I. Cincinnati. Health dept.
Agr 7-1138
U. S. Dept. of agr. Library for Library of Congress 44L79 SF253.L65

NL 0435120 DNAL

Locke, Joseph M[orris]
Smelting plants (for gold, copper, lead, and silver) The selection of their site and adaptation and equalization of their parts. By Joseph M. Locke ... Cincinnati, O., The Lane & Bodley co. [1883]
26 p. illus., double pl. 25cm.

1. Smelting.

Library of Congress TN673.L8 6-18899†

NL 0435121 DLC

Locke, Josephine C., joint author.

Hicks, *Mrs.* **Mary (Dana)** 1836-
The Prang primary course in art education; suggestions for the use of form study, drawing, and color in their relation to art education and also in their relation to general education in primary schools, by Mary Dana Hicks ... and Josephine C. Locke ... Pt. 1[-2] first-second] primary year. Boston, The Prang educational company, 1892-93.

Locke, Katharine Mary
see Hewett, Katharine Mary (Locke) 1869-1920.

Locke, Leslie Leland, 1875-
The ancient quipu or Peruvian knot record, by L. Leland Locke. [New York] The American museum of natural history, 1923.
2 p. l., 84 p. front., illus., LIX (i. e. 61) pl. (1 fold.; incl. facsims.) 27½cm.

1. Quipu. I. Title. II. Title: Peruvian knot record. III. Title: Knot record.

Library of Congress F3429.3.Q6L8 23-8614

CU CLSU MU NIC PSt PSC PBm PU OCl OU MiU OClMN ViU
NL 0435124 DLC PPAN OrU CU TxU MWA OrP MtU CaBVaU

Locke, Leslie Leland, 1875-
... A Peruvian quipu, by L. Leland Locke. New York, Museum of the American Indian, Heye foundation, 1927.
11 p. pl. LXII-LXIII (1 fold.) 25cm. (Contribution from the Museum of the American Indian, Heye foundation. vol. VII, no. 5)

1. Quipu. I. Title.

Library of Congress E51.N42 vol. 7 27-5611

WaWW OrU Wa WaE WaS WaSp WaT WaTC
OrSaW OrU-M MtBuM CaBVaU IdB IdPI OrCS OrP OrPR
PP PPAmP OCl MiU OClMA MB NN MtU MtBC Or OrStbM
NL 0435125 DLC KMK ICarbS MoU ViU GU PU-Mus

Locke, Leslie Leland, 1875-
...Pure mathematics, by L. Leland Locke; Foundations of mathematics, by Professor Cassius J. Keyser; Mathematical applications, by Dr. Franz Bellinger; introduction, by Professor Cassius J. Keyser. [New York: Current Literature Pub. Co., cop. 1909.] xii, 324 p. front., illus. (incl. diagrs., facsim.), plates. 16°. (The science-history of the universe. v. 8.)

51723A. 1. Mathematics, 1909. 2. Keyser, Cassius Jackson, 1862- 3. Bellinger, Franz.
May 13, 1924.

NL 0435127 NN PBa

Locke, Leslie Leland, 1875-
...Pure mathematics, by L.L. Locke. Foundations of mathematics, by C.J. Keyser. Mathematical applications, by F. Bellinger... N.Y., Current literature publ. co., 1910.
324 p. illus. 18 cm. (The science histor of the universe. v. 8)

NL 0435128 IdU CaBVa

Locke, Leslie Leland, 1875-
Pure mathematics... N.Y., Current literature publishing co., 1912.
324 p. (The science-history of the universe, v. 8.)

NL 0435129 OCl

Locke, Leslie Leland, 1875-
... Supplementary notes on the quipus in the American museum of natural history, by L. Leland Locke. New York city, The Trustees, 1928.
1 p. l., p. 39-73. illus. 24½cm. (Anthropological papers of the American museum of natural history. vol. XXX, pt. II)

1. Quipu. 28-13678
Library of Congress GN2.A27 vol. XXX, pt. II
F3429.3.Q6L85

OCU MiU OClMN ViU
NL 0435130 DLC CaBVaU OrU OrP DAU NBuU OrPS PU-Mu

Locke, *Leslie Leland, 1875-*
Synchronism and anachronism... n.p., Scripta mathematica, 1932.
5 p.

NL 0435131 PPD

Locke, Lillian H.
Outline for a course of study in clothing for high school
see under Baldt, Laura Irene.

Locke, Louis Glenn, 1912- *ed.*
Literature of western civilization, selected and edited by Louis G. Locke, John Pendy Kirby [and] M. E. Porter. New York, Ronald Press Co. [1952]
2 v. illus. 26 cm.

1. Literature — Collections. 2. English literature — Translations from foreign literature. I. Title.

PN6014.L663 808.8 52-6204 ‡
Library of Congress [56r53x1]

WaSp WaSpG WaT WaTC WaWW
IdU MtBC MtU OrCS OrP OrPR OrU Wa WaE WaS WaPS
AU NcU Or OrStbM OrSaW OrU-M MtBuM CaBVaU IdB IdPI
NL 0435133 DLC AAP ViU NcD OU GU NBuU MB CaOTP FMU

Locke, Louis Glenn, 1912- *ed.*
Reading for liberal education, ed. by Louis G. Locke, William M. Gibson [and] George Arms. New York, Rinehart [1948]
2 v. illus. 24 cm.
CONTENTS.—1. Toward liberal education.—2. Introduction to literature.

1. Literature—Collections. I. Gibson, William Merriam, 1912- joint ed. II. Arms, George Warren, 1912- joint ed. III. Title.

PN6014.L664 808.8 48-3214 rev 2*

LU PCM PPT PHC PP ViU MiU
NL 0435135 DLC CaBVaU IdU OrStbM OrPS NIC CoU NN

VOLUME 337

808.8 L814 **Locke, Louis Glenn,** 1912- ed.
Reading for liberal education, ed. by Louis G. Locke, William M. Gibson [and] George Arms. New York, Rinehart [1950]
2 v. illus. 24 cm.
CONTENTS.—1. Toward liberal education.—2. Introduction to literature.

NL 0435136 CSt

Locke, Louis Glenn, 1912- ed.
Readings for liberal education, ed. by Louis G. Locke, William M. Gibson [and] George Arms. New York, Rinehart [1948]
2 v. in 1. 24 cm.
CONTENTS.—1. Toward liberal education.—2. Introduction to literature.
1. Literature—Collections. I. Gibson, William Merriam, 1912- joint ed. II. Arms, George Warren, 1912- joint ed. III. Title.
PN6014.L664 1948a 808.8 48-11613*

NL 0435137 DLC ICU OU PPT WaE MtBC CU OrAshS Or

C 808. L793R Locke, Louis Glenn, 1912-
Readings for liberal education. Edited by Louis G. Locke, William M. Gibson, and George Arms. New York, Rinehart & Company c1951, c1948.
2v. illus.
Contents.-Toward liberal education.- Introduction to literature.
Each vol. has also special t.p.
1. Literature - Collections I. ta Toward liberal education

NL 0435138 OCl

Locke, Louis Glenn, 1912- ed.
Readings for liberal education. [Edited by Louis G. Locke, William M. Gibson, and George Arms. Rev. ed. New York, Rinehart, 1952]
2 v. 24 cm.
Each vol. has also special t. p.
CONTENTS.—1. Toward liberal education.—2. Introduction to literature.
1. Literature—Collections. I. Title.
PN6014.L664 1952 808.8 52-5591 rev

NL 0435139 NcRS LU OCIW PPTU-P PSt PPT MB NcD OO MiU NcGU DLC OkU IdPI OrCS OrSaW WaWW AAP FTaSU

Locke, Louis Glenn, 1912- ed.
Readings for liberal education, edited by Louis G. Locke, William M. Gibson [and] George Arms. Rev. ed. New York, Rinehart [1952]
830, 749 p. illus. 24 cm.
1. Literature—Collections. I. Title.
PN6014.L664 1952 808.8 52-5593 ‡

NL 0435140 DLC Wa

PN 6014 L664 1954 **Locke, Louis Glenn,** 1912- ed.
Readings for liberal education. [Edited by Louis G. Locke, William M. Gibson, and George Arms. Rev. ed. New York, Rinehart, 1954 [c1952]
2 v. 24 cm.
Each vol. has also special t. p.
CONTENTS.—1. Toward liberal education.—2. Introduction to literature.

NL 0435141 NSyU

AC5 .A7 Locke, Louis Glenn, 1912- joint ed.
Arms, George Warren, 1912- ed.
Symposium [edited by] George Arms [and] Louis Locke. New York, Rinehart [1954]

Locke, Louis Glenn, 1912-
Tillotson; a study in seventeenth-century literature. Copenhagen, Rosenkilde and Bagger, 1954.
187 p. 25 cm. (Anglistica, v. 4)
Bibliography: p. [176]-183.
1. Tillotson, John, Abp. of Canterbury, 1630-1694. 2. English literature—Early modern (to 1700)—Hist. & crit. (Series)
BX5199.T6L6 55-325

NL 0435143 WaT WaTC WaWW IdPI IdU MtBC MtU OrCS OrP OrPR WaPS OrU WaS WaSp PPT Or OrStbM OrSaW OrU-M MtBuM CaBVaU Wa WaE IdB MB NBC OO OCU OU OCIW PBm OOxM PPWe NcD PU PBL MsU GU MoU MH NIC ICU MoSU NN CtY ViU IaU TxU DCU DLC AAP OrPS OrU IU ScU OO MB PPD

---

* PN6014 .L588 1955 Locke, Louis Glenn, 1912- , ed.
Toward a liberal education. Edited by Louis G. Locke, William M. Gibson, [and] George Arms. Rev. ed. New York, Rinehart [1955]
830 p. 24cm.
1. Literature—Collections. I. Gibson, William M., joint ed. II. Arms, George Warren, 1912- , joint ed. III. Title.

NL 0435145 ViU

SB186 .L6 **Locke, Lowell Francis,** 1894-
Cultural practices for sorghums and miscellaneous field crops at the Southern Great Plains Field Station, Woodward, Okla. By L. F. Locke and O. R. Mathews. Washington [U. S. Govt. Print. Off.] 1955.
iii, 63 p. illus. 23 cm. (U. S. Dept. of Agriculture. Circular no. 959)
"Literature cited": p. 44.
1. Field crops—Research. 2. Sorghum—Research. 3. U. S. Southern Great Plains Field Station, Woodward, Okla. I. Mathews, Oscar Roland, 1890- joint author. (Series)
Agr 55-245
U. S. Dept. of Agr. Libr. for Library of Congress 1Ag84C no. 959

NL 0435146 DNAL DLC

Locke, Lowell Francis, 1894-
Growing fruits and nuts in the southern Great Plains. [Washington, U. S. Govt. Print. Off., 1955]
ii, 28 p. illus., map. 23 cm. (U. S. Dept. of Agriculture. Farmers' bulletin no. 2087)
1. Fruit-culture—Great Plains. [1. Great Plains—Pomology] 2. Nuts. (Series)
S21.A6 no. 2087 Agr 55-366
U. S. Dept. of Agr. Libr. for Library of Congress 1Ag84F no. 2087

NL 0435147 DNAL DLC CaBViP

SB191 .W5L6 **Locke, Lowell Francis,** 1894-
Relation of cultural practices to winter wheat production, Southern Great Plains Field Station, Woodward, Okla., by L. F. Locke and O. R. Mathews, in cooperation with the Oklahoma Agricultural Experiment Station. Washington [U. S. Govt. Print. Off.] 1953.
54 p. illus., tables. 24 cm. (U. S. Dept. of Agriculture. Circular no. 917)
Cover title.
1. Wheat—Oklahoma. [2. Wheat—Research] 3. U. S. Southern Great Plains Field Station, Woodward, Okla. I. Mathews, Oscar Roland, 1890- joint author. II. Title: Winter wheat production, Southern Great Plains Field Station, Woodward, Okla. (Series)
[S21.A48 no. 917] Agr 53-199
U. S. Dept. of Agr. Libr. for Library of Congress 1Ag84C no. 917 [5*]

NL 0435148 DNAL DLC

Locke, Lucie H 1904-
Naturally yours, Texas; nature in Texas. Verses and illus. by Lucie H. Locke. San Antonio, Naylor Co. [1949]
60 p. illus., map (on lining-papers) 22 cm.
1. Texas—Descr. & trav.—Poetry. 2. Poetry of places—Texas. 3. Nature in poetry. I. Title.
PS3523.O232N3 811.5 49-9436*

NL 0435149 DLC TxU

1926 L01566m **Locke, Margaret.**
Meditations of glory ... [n.p.] [1941?] cover-title, 2p.l., 40, [3]p. port. 20 cm.

NL 0435150 RPB

Locke, Maria Bayne
see Bell, Maria Bayne (Locke) 1881-

[**Locke, Marshall P** W]
The hunting of the snark; or, The professor's dream. In a prologue and five acts ... [Indianapolis, Andrew & Moore, 1883]
2 p. l., 108 p. 18cm.
Copyrighted by Marshall Locke.
I. Title.
42-44961
Library of Congress PS2248.L83H8

NL 0435152 DLC

AS36 M75 v. 14 p. 37-58 **Locke, Martha**
A framework for understanding.
(In Missouri. Northwest Missouri State College, Maryville. Studies. Maryville, 1950. 26 cm. v. 14, p. [37]-58.)
1. Social psychology. I. Title. (Series: Missouri. Northwest Missouri State College, Maryville. Studies, v. 14, p. 37-58.)

NL 0435153 MeB

Locke, *Mrs.* **Mary.**
In far Dakota. By Mrs. Mary Locke. London, [etc.] W. H. Allen & co., 1890.
3 p. l., 152 p. 16cm.
I. Title.
4-8641
Library of Congress PZ3.L794 I

NL 0435154 DLC CtY PPL

VOLUME 337

*EC75 L7941 791e
Locke, Mary, fl.1791.
Eugenius; or, Virtue in retirement. A poem. By Mary Locke.
London:Printed for T.Hookham,New Bond street. 1791.
4°. 2p.ℓ.,19p. 25.5cm.
Tribute to Edward Taylor, the author's uncle.

NL 0435155 MH

Locke, Mary Stoughton.
... Anti-slavery in America from the introduction of African slaves to the prohibition of the slave trade (1619–1808) By Mary Stoughton Locke, A. M. Boston, Ginn & company, 1901.
xv, 255 p. 23cm. (Radcliffe college monographs, no. 11)
Bibliography: p. [199]–231.

1. Slavery in the U. S.—Anti-slavery movements. I. Title.
1—25849
Library of Congress [E446.L81]

PBm PU PHC UU MsSM NSyU KEmT DAU IdU WaS OrCS
NL 0435156 MB NN MiU ViU OO OC1W OU OCU PPAmP PSC

Microfilm 8150 E
Locke, Mary Stoughton.
... Anti-slavery in America from the introduction of African slaves to the prohibition of the slave trade (1619–1808) By Mary Stoughton Locke, A. M. Boston, Ginn & company, 1901.
xv, 255 p. 23 cm. (Radcliffe college monographs, no. 11)
Bibliography: p. [199]–231.
C. Copy Replaced by Microfilm

1. Slavery in the U. S.—Anti-slavery movements. I. Title.
[E446.L81] 1—25849

NL 0435157 DLC

Locke, Matthew, writer on ornament
see Lock, Matthew.

FILM A969 M
Locke, Matthew, 1630?-1677.
[Works, instrumental. Selections]
Compositions for broken and whole consorts, of two, three, ffower, ffiuv, and six parts. [1672]
score(65 ℓ.) port. On film(positive)

Microfilm copy of autograph MS., Additional 17801, in the British Museum.

I. British Museum. MSS. (Additional 17801)

NL 0435159 CU

---

m782.614 L814c
Locke, Matthew, 1630?-1677.
[Consort of three parts]
Consort [for three recorders]: descant, treble and tenor. [Arranged by Elli] McMullen. London, Schott [c1953]
score (8p.) 31cm. (Schott's Archive of recorder consorts, no.9)

Cover title.

1.Suites (3 recorders) - To 1800.
*

NL 0435160 CLSU

Locke, Matthew, 1630?-1677.
[Consort of four parts]

Consort zu 4 Stimmen (um 1660) für alte Instrumente (Violenchor, Blockflötenchor) oder moderne Instrumente (Streichquartett, Streichorchester) bearb. und hrsg. von F. J. Giesbert. Mainz, B. Schott's Söhne; New York, Associated Music Publishers [°1935]
score (2 v.) and parts. 31 cm. (Antiqua, eine Sammlung alter Musik)
Edition Schott, No. 2311a–2311b.

Six suites for viols or string quartet; may be performed by recorder quartet or string orchestra. Originally for 4 unspecified instruments.
CONTENTS.—Heft 1. D moll. D dur. F dur.—Heft 2. F dur. G moll. G dur.

1. Suites (String quartet)—To 1800. I. Giesbert, Franz Julius, 1896– ed. II. Title. (Series)

M451.L6C63 M 53–1904

NL 0435162 DLC NcD NN IaU MiU

Film 10630
[Locke, Matthew] 1630?-1677.
[Cupid and Death. Libretto. English]
Cupid and Death; a private entertainment, represented with scenes and musick, vocall and instrumentall, by J.S. London, Printed for J.Crooke and J.Playford, 1659.
27p.
Libretto by James Shirley. Music by Matthew Locke and Christopher Gibbons.
Microfilm (negative) London, British Museum (644.c.66), 1967. 1 reel. 35mm.

NL 0435163 IaU

Locke, Matthew, 1630?-1677.
[Cupid and Death. English]

Cupid and Death. [Masque by James Shirley, music by] Matthew Locke and Christopher Gibbons, edited by Edward J. Dent. Published for the Royal Musical Association. London, Stainer & Bell, 1951.
xxii, score (79 p.) facsims. 33 cm. (Musica Britannica, 2)
With unfigured bass realized for harpsichord or piano. Parts for second violin and viola have been supplied by the editor.
"For the music the ... source is Matthew Locke's autograph manuscript in the British Museum (Add. MS 17799)"
1. Masques with music—To 1800—Scores. I. Gibbons, Christopher, 1615–1676. Cupid and Death. II. Shirley, James, 1596–1666. Cupid and Death. III. Dent, Edward Joseph, 1876– ed. IV. Title.
M2.M638 vol. 2 52—23632

WaE WaS WaPS WaSp WaT WaTC WaWW
MtBuM OrU OrPR OrP OrCS MtU MtBC IdPI IdB Wa
NIC ICN WU CaBVa CaBVaU Or OrStbM OrSaW OrU-M
NL 0435164 DLC NN MeB CLU AAP CLSU OU MB MiU

Locke, Matthew, 1630?-1677.
[Suites, strings]

... Eight suites in 4 parts, from consort music by Matthew Locke; edited by Sydney Beck. [New York] The New York public library, 1942.
[46] p. 36½ x 29½cm. and 4 pts. 30 x 28cm. (English instrumental music of the 16th and 17th centuries from manuscripts in the New York public library. No. 6)
Black-line print.
Printed on double leaves in Chinese style.
Publisher's plate no.: NN24.
Score (violin 1, violin 2, viola and violoncello) and parts.
1. Suites (2 violins, viola, violoncello)—To 1800. I. Beck, Sydney, ed.
44-10535
Library of Congress M2.E63 no. 6

NL 0435166 DLC OCl NN

Locke, Matthew, 1630?-1667
The English opera; or the vocal musick in Psyche, with the instrumental therein intermix'd. To which is adjoyned the instrumental musick in The tempest. By Matthew Lock. London. Printed by T. Ratcliff, and N. Thompson for the Author ... MDCLXXV. (8), 76 pp. 23 cm., in 2s.
The words are from Shadwell's tragedy, Psyche.
Manuscript emendations have been made in the music.
This copy once belonged to J. O. Halliwell-Phillipps and contains a manuscript note by him, on the fly-leaf.
Pp. 75, 76 are incorrectly numbered 71, 72.
The music for the tempest is catalogued separately.
M1500.L82P6

K2715 — Double main card. — Locke, Matthew. (M1) — Shadwell, Thomas, 1640?-1692. (M2) — T.r. (1)

NL 0435167 MB MWiW-C CtY CSmH MH DLC ICN DFo

Locke, Matthew, 1630?-1667.
[Suites, strings. Selections]

Four suites made from consort music. Ed. by Sydney Beck. New York, New York Public Library, 1947.
score (26 p.) 31 cm. (English instrumental music of the 16th and 17th centuries from manuscripts in the New York Public Library, no. 7)
For 2 violins, viola and violoncello.
First issued in 1942 as suites 1, 7, 3 and 8 of his Eight suites in 4 parts (no. 6 of the black-line print series)
1. Suites (String quartet)—To 1800. I. Beck, Sydney, ed. (Series)
M2.E628 no. 7 48—20284*

NIC KU
NL 0435168 DLC OrU OrP MtU CaBVa CoU NBC MH PPT

785.74 .L79s
Locke, Matthew, 1630?-1667.
[Suites, strings. Selections]
Four suites made from consort music. Edited by Sydney Beck. New York, Published for the New York Public Library by C.F. Peters, °1954.
score and parts. 31 cm. (English instrumental music of the 16th and 17th centuries from manuscripts in the New York Public Library, no. 7)
Edition Peters, no. 6176.
For 2 violins, viola and violoncello.

1. Suites (2 violins, viola, violoncello)-- To 1800. I. Beck, Sydney, ed. II. Series.

NL 0435170 LU LN

Locke, Matthew, 1630?-1677
Lord, let me know mine end. Anthem. [Accomp. for organ.]
(In Boyce. Cathedral Music. Ed. Novello. London. [182-?])
No. 51 in *8054.3

April 11, 1902.
E3687 — T.r. — Church music. Anthems, &c.

NL 0435171 MB

Locke, Matthew, 1630?-1677.
[Macbeth]
Macbeth, by Dr. Boyce. [175-?] 7 parts.

Microfilm of ms., mostly in William Boyce's hand, in the British Museum. MSS. 47860. Incidental music for Shakespeare's play. For orchestra, chorus, and solo voices. English words. TOSCANINI MEMORIAL ARCHIVES.

1. Music - Manuscripts - Facsimiles. (1) Boyce, William. 1710-1779. (TITLE)

NL 0435173 NN

KEPT IN BROWN MUSIC COLLECTION
*M1510 .L6M3
Locke, Matthew, 1630?-1677.
... Macbeth in complete score, with accompaniment for the pianoforte, by E. J. Loder. London, Augener & co. [1934?]
1 p. l., 32 p. 31cm. (Augener's edition. no. 9100)
Vocal score.

1. Music, Incidental. I. Shakespeare, William. Music. Macbeth. II. Loder, Edward James, ed.

NL 0435174 MB CtY

VOLUME 337

Locke, Matthew, 1630?-1677.
Melothesia: or, Certain general rules for playing upon a continued-bass. With a choice collection of lessons for the harpsicord and organ of all sorts: never before published. All carefully reviewed by M. Locke ... The first part. London, Printed for J. Carr, 1673.
9 p., [2] p. (music), [1] p., 84 p. (music) 12 x 23cm.
Only pt. 1 was published.

1. Thorough-bass. 2. Harpsichord music—Collections.
17-31238
Library of Congress MT49.A2L6

NL 0435175 DLC InU WaU IaU

Microfilm
R2103 Locke, Matthew, 1630?-1677.
Melothesia; or, Certain general rules for playing upon a continued-bass. With a choice collection of lessons for the harpsichord and organ of all sorts: never before published. All carefully reviewed by Mr. Locke. The first part. London, J. Carr, 1673.
1 reel
Only pt. 1 published.
1. Thorough bass. 2. Harpsichord - Studies and exercises. 3. Organ - Studies and exercises. I. Title.

NL 0435176 CaBVaU

Locke, Matthew, 1630-1677.
Melothesia: or, Certain general rules for playing upon a continued-bass. With A choice collection of lessons for the harpsicord and organ of all sorts, never before published. All carefully reviewed by M.Locke. The first part. London, F.Carr, 1673.
9, 84 p. 13 x 27 cm.
Photostat reproduction (positive) of a copy in the British Museum.

NL 0435177 MH-I

LOCKE, MATTHEW, 1630?-1677.
Music for His Majesty's sackbuts and cornetts (1661)... Transcribed for woodwind or brass ensemble by Anthony Baines... London, New York, Oxford university press [c1951] 8 p. 26cm.

Score: trumpet I-II, trombone I-III and piano reduction.
Edited from the manuscript part-books in the Fitzwilliam museum, having the title "5-part things for the cornetts."

Movements. —Air. —Courante. —Allemande. —Courante. —Allemande. —Sarabande.

1. Trumpet in quintets (2 trumpets, 3 trombones)—To 1800. 2. Suites (Quintets)—To 1800. 3. Instumental music, 5-part—To 1800. 4. Cornett in quintets. 5. Coronations—Gt. Br., 1661. I. Locke, Matthew, 1630?-1677. Five-part things for the cornetts. II. Baines, Anthony, ed.

NL 0435179 NN ICU WaU CLU NBC NIC IU IaU OrP OrU

M788
L79m Locke, Matthew, 1630?-1677.
Music for King Charles II. Edited by Robert King. North Easton, Mass., Robert King Music Co. [195-?]
score (4p.) and 9 parts. 28cm.

Caption title.
For horn, 3 cornets, trombone, baritone and tuba.
Includes alternate parts: horn for 3d cornet, and trombone for horn.
Duration: 5 min., 30 sec.

NL 0435180 IU CLSU

Locke, Matthew, 1630?-1677
[Macbeth.] Locke's music for Macbeth. Boosey & Son's complete edition. [Accomp. for pianoforte.]
London. Boosey. [1860.] 24 pp. 4°. No. 3 in **G.4060.6

F3524 — Music. Incidental. — Shakespeare, William. Macbeth.

NL 0435181 MB

Locke, Matthew, 1630?-1677.
Ne'er trouble thyself. Glee [T. T. B.].
(In Social Harmony. Pp. 156, 157. London. [1818.]) No. 135 in **M.215.21

NL 0435182 MB

Locke, Matthew, 1630?-1677.
Observations upon a late book, entituled, An essay to the advancement of musick, &c. Written by Thomas Salmon ... By Matthew Locke ... London, Printed by W. G. and are to be sold by J. Playford, 1672.
2 p. l., 39 p. illus. (music) 16½cm.
Salmon replied to this criticism with his Vindication of An essay to the advancement of musick.

1. Salmon, Thomas, 1648-1706. An essay to the advancement of music. 2. Musical notation.
19-7359
Library of Congress ML432.A2S27

NL 0435183 DLC OC CSmH

VM
1513
L 81m LOCKE, MATTHEW, 1630?-1677, supposed composer.
The original music in Macbeth as composed by Matthew Locke, arranged from the score and adapted for the piano forte by B.Jacobs... London,Linley,n.d.
18p.

English words, chiefly taken from Middleton's tragi-comedy The witch.--cf. British museum. Catalogue of printed music.
Written for Davenant's version of Shakespeare's Macbeth produced in 1672. Authorship still in dispute. Attributed to Purcell. ICN

NL 0435184 ICN MB

Locke, Matthew, 1630?-1677.
The original music in Macbeth as composed by M. Locke [1673] Arranged from the score and adapted for the piano-forte by B. Jacobs. London, G. Walker, n.d.
1 l., 18 p. f°.
Containing also: The opening symphony, the furies and the witches dance for piano solo.

NL 0435185 NN

Locke, Matthew, 1630?-1677.
The original music, introduced in the tragedy of Macbeth, composed by Matthew Locke... Arranged with a separate accompaniment for the piano forte, by John Clarke... London: Birchall & Co.[, 1822.] Publ. pl. no. 1219. iv, 40 p. f°.
Vocal score. English words.
First performed in 1672.
"The words chiefly taken from Middleton's tragi-comedy 'The witches.'"—*Brit. Mus. cat. of printed music.*
Music ascribed also to Henry Purcell.

1. Incidental music. 2. Clarke, John, afterwards Clarke-Whitfield, 1770-1836, editor. 3. Shakespeare, William: Macbeth. 4. Middleton, Thomas, d. 1627: The witch. 5. Purcell, Henry, 1658?-1695, supposed author. 6. Title: Macbeth.
October 31, 1927

NL 0435186 NN

LOCKE, MATTHEW, 1630?-1677.
The original music, introduced in the tragedy of Macbeth, composed by Matthew Locke. Arranged with a separate accompaniment for the piano forte, by John Clarke. London, Birchall & co. [1822]
Pl. no. 1219. iv, 40 p.

Film reproduction. Master negative.

Vocal score. English words.
Music ascribed also to Henry Purcell.
First performed in 1672.
"The words chiefly taken from Middleton's tragi-comedy 'The witches.' "--Brit. Mus. cat. of printed music.

NL 0435188 NN

M1513
L58M2
1824
Case
X Locke, Matthew, 1630?-1677.
[Macbeth; acc. arr. piano]
The original music introduced in the tragedy of Macbeth, composed by Matthew Locke. Arranged with a separate accompaniment for the piano forte by John Clarke. London, Printed & sold by Birchall [ca. 1824] Pl. no. 1219.
iv, 40 p.

Vocal score with piano accompaniment. English words.
"The Original music in the Witches Scene, in Middleton's Comedy of the Witch, from a M.S. of that Age": iv p. at beginning.

NL 0435189 CU

PR2823
f.L8 Locke, Matthew, 1630?-1677.
The original songs, airs, & chorusses, which were introduced in the tragedy of Macbeth, in score. Composed by Matthew Locke... Rev. & cor., by Dr. Boyce... London, Printed by J.M.Clementi & co. [17 -]
29 p. (music) 36cm.
T.-p.engr.

NL 0435190 ICU

Locke, Matthew, 1630?-1677.
[Macbeth]
The original songs, airs & chorusses which were introduced in the tragedy of Macbeth, in score. Rev. & corrected by Boyce. London, Longman & Broderip [ca. 1780]
score (29 p.) 34 cm.
With string orchestra acc.
Words principally from The witch by Middleton: cf. British Union Catalogue of Early Music.
1. Music, Incidental—To 1800—Scores. I. Shakespeare, William, 1564-1616. Macbeth. II. Middleton, Thomas, d. 1627. The witch. III. Title: Macbeth.
M1510.L82M28 79-295339

NL 0435191 DLC CaBVaU MH ICN MiU MB

Vm27
C8 Locke, Matthew, 1630?-1677, attributed composer.
[Macbeth]
The original songs, airs & choruses, which were introduced in the Tragedy of Macbeth, in score. Composed by Matthew Locke ... Revised & corrected by Dr. Boyce ... London, Printed & sold by Preston [ca. 1785]
1p.l.,29p. 31½cm.
English words, chiefly taken from Middleton's tragi-comedy The witch. - cf. British museum. Catalogue of printed music.

Written for D'Avenant's version of Shakespeare's Macbeth produced in 1672. Authorship still in dispute. Attributed to Purcell.
Full score. Printed from Johnston's plates.

NL 0435193 CtY DFo

VOLUME 337

Locke, Matthew, 1630?-1677.
The original songs, airs & choruses which were introduced in the tragedy of Macbeth ... Revised & corrected by Dr. Boyce... London, Printed & sold at Bland & Wellers [ca. 1795]
29 p. f°.
Full score.
Oliphant-Cummings copy, annotated.

NL 0435194 DFo

Locke, Matthew, 1630?-1677.
The original songs, airs, & chorusses, which were introduced in the tragedy of Macbeth ... Revised & corrected by Dr. Boyce... London, Printed by Broderip & Wilkinson [ca. 1798]
29 p. f°.
Full score. Printed from Johnston's plates.

NL 0435195 DFo

Locke, Matthew, 1630?-1677.
The present practice of musick vindicated against the exceptions and new way of attaining musick lately publish'd by Thomas Salmon, M. A. &c.; by Matthew Locke ... To which is added Dvellvm mvsicvm by John Phillips gent., together with a letter from John Playford to Mr. T. Salmon by way of confutation of his Essay, &c. ... London, N. Brooke [etc.] 1673.
2 p. l., 96 p. 17cm.

"In 1672 an extraordinary controversy commenced between Locke and Thomas Salmon, who had published An essay to the advancement of musick by casting away the perplexity of different cliffs ... Locke attacked the work in Observations upon a late book entitled An essay, etc. ... to which Salmon replied in A vindication of his essay ... and Locke in 167. retorted in The present practice of music vindicated."—Grove, Dict. of music and musicians.

1. Salmon, Thomas, 1648-1706. A vindication of An essay to the advancement of musick. 2. Musical notation. I. Phillips, John, 1631-1706. II. Playford, John, 1623-1686?

8-16367

Library of Congress ML432.A2S22

NL 0435197 DLC CtY CaBVaU CSmH MiU

Film 1607 Locke, Matthew, 1630?-1677.
The present practice of musick vindicated against the exceptions and new way of attaining musick lately publish'd by Thomas Salmon, M. A. &c.; by Matthew Locke ... To which is added Dvellvm mvsicvm by John Phillips, gent., together with a letter from John Playford to Mr. T. Salmon by way of confutation of his Essay, &c. ... London, N. Brooke [etc.] 1673.
2 p. l., 96 p. 17cm.
Microfilm.

NL 0435198 OU

Locke, Matthew, 1630?-1677.

Shadwell, Thomas, 1642?-1692.
Psyche: a tragedy, acted at the Duke's theatre. Written by Tho. Shadwell. London, Printed by T. N. for Henry Herringman, at the Anchor in the lower Walk of the New Exchange. 1675.

Locke, Matthew, 1630?-1677.

Shadwell, Thomas, 1642?-1692.
Psyche: a tragedy, as it is now acted at Their Majesties theatre in Dorset-Garden. Written by Tho. Shadwell, laur. London, Printed by J. M. for H. Herringman, and sold by R. Bentley, 1690.

Locke, Matthew, 1630?-1677.
The rare theatrical, and other compositions... transcribed in score from various manuscripts... overtures, symphonies, [etc.] n.p., n.d.
117 p. f°.
Ms.

NL 0435201 NN

LOCKE, MATTHEW, 1630?-1677.
[WORKS. SELECTIONS]
The rare theatrical, & other compositions, by Mr. Mathew Lock, transcribed in score from various M.S. --viz. Overtures [etc.] [n.p., n.d.] score (117 p.)

Microfilm (master Negative)
Positive in *ZB-310.
Microfilm of manuscript in the New York public library (Drexel 3976)

NL 0435202 NN

LOCKE, MATTHEW, 1630?-1677, supposed composer.
[MACBETH. SELECTIONS. ARR. FOR PIANO, 4 HANDS]
Simphonies & choruses from the tragedy of Macbeth. Composed by Matthew Locke. Arr. for two performers on the piano forte by T. Haigh. London, W. Mitchell [18--] Pl. no. 103 13 p. 33cm.

Of doubtful authorship. Also ascribed to Purcell or Leveridge.--cf. Dent, E.J. Foundations of English opera.
Incidental music to Davenant's alteration of Shakespeare's Macbeth.
1. Piano, 4 hands--Arr. 2. Incidental music. I. Haigh, Thomas, 1769-1808, arr. II. Shakespeare, William. Macbeth.

NL 0435203 NN

Locke, Matthew, 1630?-1677.
[Quartets. Strings.]
Six string quartets, by Matthew Locke... Transcribed for two violins, viola, and violoncello, by Peter Warlock [pseud.]; edited by André Mangeot... [London: J. & W. Chester Ltd., 1932.] Publ. pl. no. J. W. C. 252. 4 parts in 1 v. 33½cm. (Chester library.)

Parts only.
"These quartets for four viols are copied from Locke's autograph score, in a volume (now at the British Museum [Add. 17801, ff. 48-61b]) which the composer is said to have presented to King Charles II in 1672."

Each quartet contains a fantasia, courante (or galliard), ayre and saraband.

Carnegie Corporation of New York.
1. Chamber music, 17th cent.—Quartets. 2. Violin—Quartets—Two violins, viola and violoncello. I. Heseltine, Philip, 1894-1930. II. Mangeot, André, editor.
August 14, 1934

NL 0435205 NN NjR ICU MB CaBVaU MiU OO ICN ViU NcD

M 287 .L82 S9 194- Locke, Matthew, 1630?-1677.
[Suite, 2 viols, G minor]
Suite for treble and bass viols "ffor severall ffriends." [London? 194-?]
score (4 p.) 36 cm. (Viola da Gamba Society. Publication, no.1)
Reproduction of MS.
CONTENTS.--Fantasie.--Pavan.--Ayre.--Coranto.--Sarabande.--Jigg.
1.Suites (2 viols)

NL 0435206 MiU

Locke, Matthew, 1630?-77 (2)
[The broken consort, pt.1. Suite no.4]
Suite in C for string trio (violin I, violin II & violoncello)/ Arr. by P.Warlock [pseud.] L, Augener [c1929] Pl.no.17783
Score (4 p.) & 3 pts.

NL 0435207 MH

M787.4243 L79s 1949 Locke, Matthew, 1630?-1677.
[Suite, 3 viols, F major]
Suite [in F major, from "The little consort." Edited by Cecily Arnold and Marshall Johnson] London, Stainer & Bell [c1949]
score(4p.) and 3 parts. 26cm. (The Consort player. Three part, [5])
Transcribed from the manuscript in the British Museum.

Score (violin, or treble viol; viola, or tenor viol; and violoncello, or bass viol) with 3 parts (treble, tenor and bass)
Contents.- Pavan.- Ayre.- Courante.- Saraband.

NL 0435209 IU CSt MH

Locke, Matthew, 1630?-1677.
[Consort of four parts. Suite no. 1; arranged]
... Suite nº 1, in D minor, from the Consort of foure parts, by Matthew Locke ... London, Stainer & Bell, ltd [c1931]
15 p. 31 x 24½cm. (The Polychordia string library ... arranged and ed. by James Brown. Nº 132)
At head of title: ... Middle grade.
Publisher's plate no.: S. & B. 4080.
Score: violin 1, violin 2, viola, violoncello, double-bass and piano reduction. "Originally composed for four viols."
Contents.—Fantazie.—Courante.—Ayre.—Saraband.
1. Suites (2 violins, viola, violoncello, double-bass), Arranged.
I. Brown, James, 1863- ed. and arr.
45-44256
Library of Congress M554.L

NL 0435210 DLC

Locke, Matthew, 1630?-1677.
[Consort of four parts. Suite no. 2; arranged]
... Suite nº 2, in D, from the Consort of foure parts, by Matthew Locke ... London, Stainer & Bell ltd [c1931]
15 p. 31 x 24½cm. (The Polychordia string library ... arranged and ed. by James Brown. Nº 133)
At head of title: ... Middle grade.
Publisher's plate no.: S. & B. 4081.
Score: violin 1, violin 2, viola, violoncello, double-bass and piano reduction. "Originally composed for four viols."
Contents.—Fantazie.—Courante.—Ayre.—Saraband.
1. Suites (2 violins, viola, violoncello, double-bass), Arranged.
I. Brown, James, 1863- ed. and arr.
45-45093
Library of Congress M554.L

NL 0435211 DLC

M1103 .L81T2 Locke, Matthew, 1630?-1677.
[The tempest; arr.]
The tempest music, arr. in two suites for string orchestra with optional pianoforte or harpsichord by W. Gillies Whittaker. London, Oxford University Press [1934]
score (2 v. in 1) (Oxford orchestral series, edited by W. Gillies Whittaker, no.0103-4)

1. Suites (String orchestra) I. Title: The tempest.

NL 0435212 ICU

Locke, Matthew, 1630?-1677.
... Three songs, edited by Anthony Lewis. Paris, The Lyrebird press, Louise B. M. Dyer [c1938]
4 p. l., 16 p. 16½ x 12½cm. (Miniature song series. The Lyrebird books, 8)
Publisher's plate no.: O. L. 79.
With piano accompaniment.
Contents.—Vulcan's song.—To a lady singing to herself by the Thames' side.—The witches' song.
I. Lewis, Anthony, ed.
43-37759
Library of Congress M1620.L79
784.81

NL 0435213 DLC NBC NcD

VOLUME 337

Locke, Matthew, 1630?-1677.
'Tis love and harmony (SATB) by Matthew Lock [London] Oxford University Press [c1937]
score (3 p.) 26 cm. (The John Playford collection of vocal part-music, no. XXX)
Cover title.
Sung a cappella.
English text.
1. Choruses, Secular (Mixed voices, 4 pts.), Unaccompanied. I. Title.

NL 0435214 IEdS

Locke, Michael, ed.

Society for Developmental Biology.
Symposium. [Papers presented] 11th- 1952-
New York, London [etc.] Academic Press [etc.]

Locke, Milo W
Communication to the Joint standing committee on the harbor. Baltimore, March 27, 1875. [Baltimore, 1875]
10p. maps.

NL 0435216 IU

Locke, Miriam Austin, 1907- ed.
An edition of The true patriot by Henry Fielding
see under The true patriot.

Locke (N[ATHANAEL] C.)
"Watch, therefore." A discourse, occasioned by the death of Mrs. Margaretta Willoughby: delivered January 28, 1849. With the address at the funeral, [Jan. 22.] *New York: Leavitt, Trow & Co.* 1849. 48 pp. 8°.
In: *C p. v. 1193.
Gift of Mrs. Henry R. Hoyt.

NL 0435218 NN MB MH MnHi PHi PPPrHi CtY

Locke, Nellie M. [pseud.]
see Locke, Belle Marshall.

Locke, Norman Malcolm, 1908-
Color constancy in the rhesus monkey and in man, by Norman Malcolm Locke ... New York, 1935.
38 p. illus. 25cm.
Thesis (PH. D.)—Columbia university, 1935.
Vita.
Published also as Archives of psychology, no. 193.
"References": p. 37-38.

1. Color-sense. 2. Optics, Physiological. 3. Psychology, Comparative. 4. Monkeys. I. Title.
37-620
Library of Congress QP481.L75 1935
Columbia Univ. Libr. [2] [159.93133] [152.133] 612.8433

NL 0435220 NNC DLC

Locke, Norman Malcolm, 1908-
Color constancy in the rhesus monkey and in man, by Norman Malcolm Locke ... New York, 1935.
38 p. illus. 25cm. (Archives of psychology ... no. 193)
Issued also as thesis (PH. D.) Columbia university.
"References": p. 37-38.

1. Color-sense. 2. Optics, Physiological. 3. Psychology, Comparative. 4. Monkeys. I. Title.
37-619
Library of Congress BF21.A7 no. 193
[(159.9082)] (150.82) [159.93133] [152.133] 612.8433

NL 0435221 DLC WaTC DNLM ViU OCU OU PBm PU

Locke, Norman Malcolm, 1908-
Some factors in size-constancy, by Norman M. Locke ... [1938]
514-520 p. 23 cm.
Caption title.
Reprinted from the American journal of psychology, vol. LI, July 1938.
1. Perception. I. Title: Size-constancy, Some factors in.

NL 0435222 NNC

Locke, Norman Malcolm, 1908- joint author.

Peatman, John Gray, 1904-
Studies in the methodology of the digit-span test, by John Gray Peatman ... and Norman M. Locke ... New York. 1934.

Locke, O E
Eureka schottisch, composed and dedicated to his friends, Stephen P. and Charles R. Simpson, by O. E. Locke. Figure 2½ in five pointed star. New York, Cook & Brother, 463 Broadway, ©1856.
5 p. 35cm. [Sheet music collection, v. 81, no. 42]
Decorated cover: Stackpole, N. Y., lithographer.
1. Schottisches (Piano) I. Title.

NL 0435224 ViU

Locke, Prescott, *pseud.*
... The conversion of Hamilton Wheeler; a novelette of religion and love, introducing studies in religious psychology and pathology, by Prescott Locke ... Bloomington, Ill., The Pandect publishing company, 1917.
3 p. l., 5-285 p. diagr. 20cm.
At head of title: A voluntary contribution to the National mental hygiene movement.
Bibliography: p. 26.

I. Title.
17-23954 Revised
Library of Congress BR110.L6

NL 0435225 DLC PPC PHC

Locke, Putnam F b.1791.
Four short sermons, on Sabbath breaking, and profane swearing, covetousness, &c. By Putnam F. Locke, Ira, Vermont....a youth thirteen years of age.
Montpelier, Vt. Printed for the purchaser. [1804?]
14p. 21.5cm.

NL 0435226 MH

Locke, Putnam F., b. 1791.
Sermons written by Putnam F. Locke, of Ira, Vermont, in...1804, a youth only thirteen years of age. Rutland [Vt.] Printed for the author [1804?]
24 p. 21 cm.

NL 0435227 PBL

Locke, R.J.
see Locke, Roscoe Janvrin, 1877-

Locke, Richard.
Letters of Rev. Richard Locke and Rev. George Craig, missionaries in Pennsylvania of the "Society for propagating the gospel in foreign parts," London. 1746-1752. By Benjamin F. Owen. [Philadelphia, 1901.
cover-title, 12 p. 25cm.
"Reprinted from the Pennsylvania magazine for January, 1901."

1. Pennsylvania—History—Colonial period. I. Craig, George, joint author. II. Owen, Benjamin F., ed. III. Society for the propagation of the gospel in foreign parts, London.
1-13624
Library of Congress BV2803.P4L8

NL 0435229 DLC

Locke, Richard, mathematician.
The longitude. bound with The Touchstone. London, 1732.

NL 0435230 CoD

Locke, Richard, mathematician
A miscellany of mathematicks. In two parts. By Richard Locke ... London: Printed and sold by Mess. Innys and Manby ... Mr. Lewis ... and Mr. Meighan ... 1736.
[8],155 p. diagrs. (1 fold.) 18cm.

Armorial book-plate of John, earl of Bute; bookmark of Kenney collection.
Bound in old sprinkled calf.

NL 0435231 CLU-C

Locke, Richard, mathematician.
A new problem to discover the longitude at sea by the same observation, and with the same certainty, as the latitude is: together with the translation of the problem into Latin. London, R. Baldwin, 1751.
24 p., 1 diag. 8°.

NL 0435232 NN

Locke (RICHARD) 1737-1806
The customs of the manor of Taunton and Taunton Deane, agreeably to the ancient rolls and customaries of the said manor. *Taunton: J. Savage,* 1816. 2 p.l., v-vii, 8-65 pp. 16°.
In: **CBF** p. v. 1.

NL 0435233 NN

Locke, Richard, 1737-1806.
Supplement to Collinson's History of Somerset. Richard Locke, 18th century antiquary, surveyor and agriculturist. Extracts from Locke's survey, with a short biography by F. Madeline Ward, M. A. Foreword by Prof. R. B. Mowat ... Taunton, Barnicotts ltd. (formerly Barnicott and Pearce) 1939.
175, [1] p. incl. front. (coat of arms) illus. (plans) geneal. tab. 30cm.
Bibliography: p. [169]-170.

1. Somerset, Eng.—Hist. I. Collinson, John, 1757?-1793. The history and antiquities of the county of Somerset. II. Ward, Frances Madeline.
41-12944
Library of Congress DA670.S5C72
942.38

NL 0435234 DLC MH CSmH NjP OCl ICU ICN

Locke, Richard, 1737-1806
The western rebellion, by Richard Locke. Reprinted for the Somerset archaeological and natural history society. Taunton, Printed by Barnicott and son, 1888.
iv, 26 p. 22½cm.
Facsimile t.-p. of 1782 edition.
"A chronological register of events relating to the town of Taunton": p. 23-26.

1. Bloody assizes, 1685. 2. Gt. Brit.—History—Monmouth's rebellion, 1685. 3. Taunton, Eng.—History. I. Title.
A 19-81
Title from California State Libr. Printed by L. C.

NL 0435235 C

VOLUME 337

F 4555 .51 LOCKE, RICHARD, 1737-1806.
The western rebellion... Taunton, Reprinted by Barnicott and Pearce, 1912.
26p.

Facsimile t.-p. of 1792 edition.
"A chronological register of events relating to the town of Taunton": p.[23]-26.

NL 0435236 ICN IU

Locke, Richard Adams, 1800-1871.

Verne, Jules, 1828-1905.
All around the moon; from the French of Jules Verne, freely translated by Edward Roth ... with a map of the moon ... and ... an appendix containing the famous Moon hoax by R. Adams Locke. New York, The Catholic publication society, 1876.

[Locke, Richard Adams] 1800-1871.
The celebrated "moon story," its origin and incidents; with a memoir of the author, and an appendix, containing, I. An authentic description of the moon; II. A new theory of the lunar surface in relation to that of the earth. By William N. Griggs. New York, Bunnell and Price, 1852.
143 p. 15cm.

A series of articles by Richard Adams Locke originally published in the Sun, August, 1835, under title, "Great astronomical discoveries," which purported to be an account of the discoveries of Sir John Herschel at the cape of Good Hope, and which pretended to be reprinted from a supplement to the Edinburgh journal of science (then defunct)

Has been ascribed on insufficient evidence to Joseph Nicolas Nicollet. cf. Dict. Amer. biog.; F. M. O'Brien, The story of the Sun (1918) p. 64-102.

1. Moon hoax. 2. Herschel, Sir John Frederick William, bart., 1792-1871. I. Griggs, William N., ed. II. Nicollet, Joseph Nicolas, 1786-1843, supposed author. III. Title.

7-14295

Library of Congress PZ3.L7953G4

NL 0435239 ViU OU MB NN NjR PU PPPrHi DLC MiU OO NIC IaU PSt MdBP CtY TU NjP

[Locke, Richard Adams] 1800-1871.
A complete account of the late discoveries in the moon. From a supplement to the Edinburgh journal ... [New York? 1835?]
11 p. 24cm.
Published anonymously.
Caption title.
A hoax.

1. Moon hoax.

7-14296†

Library of Congress PZ3.L7953G

NL 0435240 DLC MdPB KMK

Micro 3 Locke, Richard Adams, 1800-1871
A complete account of the late discoveries in the moon. From a supplement to the Edinburgh journal ... [New York? 1835?]
2 cards. 7.5x12.5cm. (L.H. Wright. American fiction, 1851-1875. no.1704a)
Micro-transparency (negative). Louisville, Ky., Lost Cause Press, 1970.
Collation of the original: 11p. 24cm

1. Moon hoax. I. Title.

NL 0435241 PSt

[LOCKE, Richard Adams] 1800-1871.
Découvertes dans la lune, faites au Cap de Bonne-Espérance par Herschel fils. Traduit de l'Américain de New York, septembre, 1835. Paris, L. Babeuf, etc., etc., 1835.

pp. viii, 56.
The preface is signed "A.A.", probably Auguste César Raymond Amic.

NL 0435242 MH

Gimbel QB 52 L81 1836b [Locke, Richard Adams] 1800-1871.
Découvertes dans la lune, faites au Cap de Bonne-Espérance par Herschel fils ... Traduit de l'Américain de New-York, Septembre 1835... Lausanne, G. Rouiller et M. Ducloux, 1836.
41 p. 20cm.
Includes in manuscript (half-title and 2 leaves at end) quotations and reflections signed A. Baron, archiviste d'Etat, 1864.

I. Baron, A II. Title.

NL 0435243 CoCA

PS2248 .L831 M64 1836 [Locke, Richard Adams] 1800-1871.
Découvertes dans la lune, faites au Cap de Bonne-Espérance. Par Herschel fils, astronome anglais, traduit de l'américain de New York. 2. éd. Paris, L. Babeuf, 1836.
vi, [7]-48p. 22cm.
First published in the New York Sun, Aug. 1835, under title: Great astronomical discoveries lately made by Sir John Herschel at the Cape of Good Hope.
1. Moon hoax. I. Herschel, Sir John Frederick, William, bart., 1792-1871. II. Title.

NL 0435244 PSt

B 8625 .512 [LOCKE, RICHARD ADAMS] 1800-1871.
Découvertes dans la lune, faites au Cap de Bonne-Espérance, par Herschel fils, astronome anglais. Traduit de l'américain de New-York. 3. éd. Paris, L. Bareuf, 1836.
45p. 22cm.

Has been ascribed on insufficient evidence to Joseph Nicolas Nicollet.—cf. Nouv. biog. gén.

NL 0435245 ICN MH

Bla 223

[Locke, Richard Adams] 1800-1871
Découvertes dans la lune, faites au Cap de Bonne-Espérance par Sir John Herschel. Strasbourg, G. Silbermann, 1836.
55 p.
Notorious moon-hoax, first published by Nicollet in the New York Sun, nos.615 to 619, 1835; purports to relate the astronomical discoveries of Sir John Herschel during his S. African expedition, including animal and plant life on the moon.

I. Herschel, Sir John Frederick William, bart., 1792-1871. II. New York Sun, 1835, no.615-619.
523.3 520.9262 520.94028
ICJ57 0
327962

NL 0435247 ICJ

Gimbel QB 52 L81 1836e [Locke, Richard Adams] 1800-1871.
Delle scoperte fatte nella luna dal Sig. Herschel. [n.p., 1836]
29 p. 20cm.
At head of title: Estratto dalla Gazzetta di Francia del di 27 febbraio 1836.

NL 0435248 CoCA

4N 629 [Locke, Richard Adams] 1800-1871.
Delle scoperte fatte nella luna dal dottore Herschel. Firenze, Presso G. Formigli, 1836.
24 p.

NL 0435249 DLC-P4 PU

PS2248 .L831 M66 [Locke, Richard Adams] 1800-1871.
Delle scoperte fatte nella luna dal Dottor Herschel. Livorno, P. Meucci, 1836.
24p. 20cm.
First published in the New York Sun, Aug. 1835, under title: Great astronomical discoveries lately made by Sir John Herschel at the Cape of Good Hope.
1. Moon hoax. I. Herschel, Sir John Frederick William, bart., 1792-1871. II. Title.

NL 0435250 PSt CoCA

[Locke, Richard Adams] 1800-1871.
Delle scoperte fatte nella luna del dottor Giovanni Herschel. Traduzione dal francese sulla 104 edizione fatta in Parigi nel marzo 1836, del Sig. E. P. con una figura rappresentante gli abitatori di essa, e disegnata al Capo di Buona Speranza dal Sig. Kelk. Napoli: G. Nobile, 1836. 23 p. front. 21cm.

1. Moon hoax. 2. Eccentric literature. I. P., E., tr. II. Title.
June 12, 1942

NL 0435251 NN CU

[Locke, Richard Adams] 1800-1871.
Grandes descubrimientos astronómicos hechos recientemente por Sir John Herschel en el Cabo de Buena-Esperanza. Traducido del ingles por Francisco de Carrion. Habana, Imprenta del gobierno y de la Real sociedad patriótica por S. M., 1835.
1 p. l., ix, 52 p., 1 l. 15 cm.

A series of articles originally published in the Sun, August, 1835, under title, "Great astronomical discoveries", which purported to be an account of the discoveries of Sir John Herschel at the Cape of Good Hope, and which pretended to be reprinted from a supplement to the Edinburgh journal of science (then defunct) Has been ascribed on insufficient evidence to Joseph Nicolas Nicollet. cf. Dict. Amer. Biog.
1. Moon hoax. 2. Herschel, Sir John Frederick William, bart., 1792-1871. I. Nicollet, Joseph Nicolas, 1786-1843, supposed author. II. Title.

NL 0435253 NSchU CoCA MH

[Locke, Richard Adams] 1800-1871.
Grandes descubrimientos astronómicos, hechos últimamente en el Cabo de Buena Esperanza, por Sir Juan Herschell [!] Suplemento al periódico científico de Edimburgo. Traducido del inglés al español por J.R. Pacheco. 2. ed. México. Impreso por I. Cumplido, 1835.
26 p. 20cm. [Papeles varios. v.179, no.1]

F1203 P16 v.179:1 x

NL 0435254 CU-B

523.3 L795g [Locke, Richard Adams] 1800-1871.
Great astronomical discoveries lately made by Sir John Herschel at the Cape of Good Hope. [n.p., n.d.]
16+ p. 22 cm.

Caption title.
"First published in the New York Sun, from the supplement to the Edinburgh Journal of Science"
Copy imperfect: all after p.16 wanting.

NL 0435255 KyU

VOLUME 337

[Locke, Richard Adams] 1800-1871.
Great astronomical discoveries, lately made, by Sir John Herschel...at the Cape of Good Hope. By R.A. Locke. New York, 18-?
28p. 8°.

NL 0435256 NN MH MdBJ

Gimbel QB 52 L81 1835g [Locke, Richard Adams], 1800-1871.
Great astronomical discoveries lately made by Sir John Herschel ... at the Cape of Good Hope. [n.p., 1835]
28p. 25cm.
"First published in the New-York Sun, from the Supplement to the Edinburgh Journal of Science."
Caption title.
Detached gatherings, uncut.
1. Herschel, Sir John Frederick William, 1792-1871. I. Title.

NL 0435257 CoCA MB MH CtY

828 L8139g Locke,Richard Adams,1800-1871.
Great astronomical discoveries lately made by Sir John Herschel ... at the Cape of Good Hope. [New York, 1835]
28 p. 21½cm.
Caption title.
"<First published in the New-York Sun,from the Supplement to the Edinburgh journal of science.>"
Purports to be an account of human beings found to be living on the moon. The Edinburgh journal of science,from which it pretends to have been reprinted,was then defunct. Has been ascribed to Joseph Nicolas Nicollet. cf.Dict. Amer.biog.; F.M.O'Brien,The story of the Sun (1918) p.64-102.
1.Moon hoax. 2. Herschel,Sir John Frederick William,bart.,1792-1871. I.Nicollet,Joseph Nicolas,1786-1843,supposed author.

NL 0435258 MiU CtY

[Locke, Richard Adams] 1800-1871.
Great astronomical discoveries lately made by Sir John Herschel...at the Cape of Good Hope. [London? 1836?]
28 p. 24 cm.
Published anonymously.
Caption title.
A hoax.
"First published in the New York Sun, from the Supplement to the Edinburgh journal of science."
1. Moon hoax. I. Title.

NL 0435259 CU

PZ3 .L7953Gr 1841 Locke, Richard Adams, 1800-1871.
Great astronomical discoveries lately made by Sir John Herschel at the Cape of Good Hope. Rev. and corr. by the author. New York, Craighead, 1841.
44 p. illus.
Cover title: Locke's moon story.
1. Moon hoax. 2. Herschel, Sir John Frederick William, bart., 1792-1871. I. Nicollet, Joseph Nicolas, 1786-1843, supposed auth. II. Title. III. Title: Locke's moon story. IV. Title: Moon story.

NL 0435260 NbU NN MH

Locke, Richard Adams, 1800-1871.
The great moon hoax of Richard Adams Locke. Arranged as a reading book for students in phonetic shorthand. By William W. Osgoodby ... Rochester, N. Y., W. W. Osgoodby [1886]
67 p. 17½cm.
1. Shorthand—Texts. 2. Moon hoax. I. Osgoodby, William Wesley, 1834-1916. II. Title.
Library of Congress Z57.L81 11-16203

NL 0435261 DLC NN

[Locke, Richard Adams] 1800-1871.
Interesting astronomical discoveries, made in the moon, by Sir John Herschel at the Cape of Good Hope... Pawtucket, R.I., 1835.
9 p. 20 cm.
"An authentic account from the Edinburgh journal of science."
A hoax.

NL 0435262 RPB

Gimbel QB 52 L81 1836i [Locke, Richard Adams] 1800-1871.
Intorno alle scoperte fatte nella luna dal Signor Herschel. [Ravenna, Tip. Roveri, 1836]
16 p. 20cm.
Caption title. "Estratto dalla Gazzette de France delli 27 Febbrajo 1836."
First Italian ed.? cf Caproni.
1. Herschel, Sir John Frederick William, bart., 1792-1871. I. Title.

NL 0435263 CoCA

Locke, Richard Adams, 1800-1871.
Lecture on magnetism and astronomy. Reported for the New York Tribune. n.p., Greeley & McElrath [1842?]
8 p. 22.5 cm.
Cover-title.

NL 0435264 MH

Locke (Richard Adams) 1800-1871.
Magnetism and astronomy. A lecture. *New York,* 184?]
8 pp. 8°.
In: *C p. v. 1192.
Gift of Mrs. Henry R. Hoyt.

NL 0435265 NN

Locke, Richard Adams, 1800-1871.
The moon hoax; or, A discovery that the moon has a vast population of human beings. By Richard Adams Locke ... New York, W. Gowans, 1859.
vi, [7]-63 p. incl. front. 24½cm.
A series of articles originally published in the Sun, August, 1835, under title, "Great astronomical discoveries", which purported to be an account of the discoveries of Sir John Herschel at the cape of Good Hope, and which pretended to be reprinted from a supplement to the Edinburgh journal of science (then defunct) Has been ascribed on insufficient evidence to Joseph Nicolas Nicollet. cf. Dict. Amer. biog.; F. M. O'Brien, The story of the Sun (1918) p. 64-102.
1. Moon hoax. 2. Herschel, Sir John Frederick William, bart., 1792-1871. I. Nicollet, Joseph Nicolas, 1786-1843, supposed author. II. Title.
Library of Congress PZ3.L7953G6 40-37532

MWA OU MdBP CtY NcD OKentU MB ICN ICJ ViU PU PPL PP PHC NcU InU IU PSt
NL 0435266 DLC CtY NjR MiU OCl NNQ RPB NN MdBP

Locke, Richard Adams, 1800-1871.
The moon hoax; or, A discovery that the moon has a vast population of human beings. By Richard Adams Locke.
(*In* Verne, Jules. All around the moon. New York, 1876. 18½cm. p. 431-484)
"First published in the New York sun, in ... 1835, from the Supplement to the Edinburgh journal of science."—Caption title.
I. Title: The moon hoax.
Library of Congress PZ3.V594Aro 1-14614

NL 0435267 DLC

Gimbel QB 52 L81 1836g [Locke, Richard Adams] 1800-1871.
Neuste Berichte vom Cap der guten Hoffnung über Sir John Herschel's höchst merkwürdige astronomische Entdeckungen, den Mond und seine Bewohner betreffend ... Hamburg, J. P. Erie, 1836.
116 p. 17cm.
A hoax. Published anonymously.

NL 0435268 CoCA MH CSmH

Gimbel QB 52 L81 1836p [Locke, Richard Adams] 1800-1871.
Publication complète des nouvelles découvertes de Sir John Herschel, dans le ciel austral et dans la lune, traduit de l'Anglais... Paris, Masson et Duprey, 1836.
160 p. 21cm.
A hoax.

NL 0435269 CoCA MnU CtY MH

[Locke, Richard Adams], 1800-1871
Some account of the great astronomical discoveries lately made by Sir John Herschel at the Cape of Good Hope. London, Effingham Wilson, 1936.
1p.l.,85p.
First published in the New York Sun from the Supplement to the Edinburgh Journal of science under title: "Great astronomical discoveries lately made by Sir John Herschel...at the Cape of Good Hope.

NL 0435270 OCl CtY

Locke, Robert Henry, 1874-
Latin forms and syntax, by Robert H. Locke, B. A. Philadelphia, Allen, Lane & Scott, 1908.
206 p. 20½cm.
Library of Congress (Copyright 1908 A 216946) 8-27520

NL 0435271 DLC PBa PV OClJC-U

Locke, Robert Henry, 1874-
Latin forms and syntax, by Robert H. Locke ... 4th ed. New York, Latin forms and syntax company [1927]
2 p. l., 344 p. 21cm.
1. Latin language—Grammar—1870- I. Title.
Library of Congress PA2087.L823 1927 27-25335

NL 0435272 DLC

VOLUME 337

Locke, Robert Henry, 1874–
Latin forms and syntax, by Robert H. Locke ... American ed., 4th rev. Philadelphia, San Francisco [etc.] Latin forms and syntax co. [°1928]
2 p. l., xi, 349 p. 20½cm.

1. Latin language—Grammar—1870– I. Title.

Library of Congress PA2087.L823 1928 28-30946

NL 0435273 DLC Or TxU

Locke, Robert H[enry] 1874–
The Latin method of thought and expression; an introductory Latin book, for schools and colleges, containing grammar and syntax, with explanations of the rules of syntax, and exercises in Latin-English and English-Latin taken from Caesar, Bellum Gallicum I. By Robert H. Locke, B. A. Philadelphia, Press of Allen, Lane & Scott [°1905]
201 p. 24cm.

7-3093
Library of Congress (Copyright A 124912)

NL 0435274 DLC PU

Locke, Robinson, 1856–1920, joint ed.

Freemasons. *U. S. A. a. Scottish rite. Supreme council. Northern jurisdiction.*
... The jubilee year of the Supreme council of sovereign grand inspectors-general of the thirty-third and last degree of the Ancient accepted Scottish rite of freemasonry for the Northern masonic jurisdiction of the United States of America ... comp. and ed. by James Hodge Codding, 33°, grand secretary general ... and Robinson Locke, 33°, marshal of the camp, by the direction and under the authority of the Supreme council. [Toledo, Press of the B. F. Wade & sons co.] 1918.

Locke, Robinson, 1856–1920.
The Robinson Locke collection of dramatic scrap books. [Toledo, 1920?] 491 v. f°.
Contents: Lina Abarbanell. Maude Adams. 8 v. Maude & Annie Adams. Frances Alda. Viola Allen. 3 v. Viola Allen & C. Leslie. Pasquale Amato. Mary Anderson. Margaret Anglin. 4 v. Maclyn Arbuckle. Belle Archer, Caroline Miskel. Edwin Arden. George Arliss. Julia Arthur. 2 v. Minnie Ashley. Frank Bacon. Fay Bainter. Theda Bara. 2 v. Lawrence Barrett. Ethel Barrymore. 5 v. Ethel Barrymore, Maurice & Georgie D. John Barrymore. 2 v. Lionel Barrymore. Blanche Bates. 3 v. Nora Bayes. 2 v. Janet Beecher. David Belasco. 5 v. Kyrle Bellew. 2 v. Richard C. Bennett. Valerie Bergere. Sam Bernard. Sarah Bernhardt. 11 v. Amelia Bingham. 2 v. David Bispham. Lillian Blauvelt. Holbrook Blinn. Clara Bloodgood. Alessandro Bonci. Jessie Bonstelle. Edwin Booth. Boucicault, Roland Reed. Alice Brady. 2 v. William A. Brady. Edmund Breese. Elizabeth Brice. May Buckley. Billie Burke. 5 v. Billie Burke, Cherie Watson & Flo Ziegfeld. Ferruccio Busoni. Marie Cahill. Marie Cahill & D. V. Arthur. Emma Calvé. 2 v. Mrs. Patrick Campbell. 2 v. Mrs. Pat. Campbell, Stella & Alan. Richard Carle. Mrs. Leslie Carter. 4 v. Enrico Caruso. 3 v. Lina Cavalieri. 2 v. Charles Chaplin. Sid & Chas. Chaplin. Pauline Chase. Ruth Chatterton. Kitty Cheatham. Ina Claire. 2 v. Marguerite Clark. 2 v. Charles & Gertrude Coghlan. Rose Coghlan. Rose Coghlan & Rosalind. George M. Cohan. 3 v. Constance Collier. Louise Allen Collier. William Collier 3 v. Ida Conquest. Jane Cowl. 2 v. William H. Crane. 2 v. Laura Hope Crews. Henrietta Crosman. 3 v. Charlotte Cushman. Alan Dale. 2 v. Arnold Daly. Augustin Daly. Walter Damrosch. Frank Daniels. E. L. Davenport. Dazie. Julia Dean. Gaby Deslys. Emmy Destinn. Elsie De Wolfe. Leo Ditrichstein. Henry Dixey. 2 v. J. E. Dodson. Dorothy Donnelly. Marie Doro. Louise Dresser. Marie Dressler. 2 v. John Drew. 3 v. John Drew & parents. Emma Dunn. Minnie Dupree. Eleanora Duse. 2 v. Emma Eames. Virginia & Maud Earl. Robert Edeson. 2 v. Gertrude Elliott. Maxine Elliott. 2 v. Maxine Elliott & Gertrude. Mischa Elman. Julian Eltinge. Geraldine Farrar. 6 v. Lotta Faust. William Faversham. 4 v. Wm. Faversham & Julie Opp. Maude Fealy. Elsie Ferguson. 2 v. Lew Fields. 2 v. Alice Fischer. Sallie Fisher. Mrs. Fiske. 8 v. Mrs. Fiske & husband. Clyde Fitch. Forbes-Robertson. 2 v. Edwin Forrest. Eddie Foy. Eddie Foy & family. Irene Franklin. Pauline Frederick. Olive Fremstad. Trixie Friganza. Charles Frohman. 2 v. Ossip Gabrilowitsch. Johanna Gadski. Bertha Galland. Amelita Galli-Curci. Mary Garden. 5 v. Adeline Genée. Grace George. 3 v. Idah McGlone Gibson, "Mac." 5 v. Mrs. G. H. Gilbert. William Gillette. 2 v. Mabelle Gilman. Mabelle Gilman & sisters. Lulu Glaser. 2 v. Alma Gluck. Nat Goodwin. 3 v. Katherine Clemmons Gould. Katherine Grey. Yvette Guilbert. Louise Gunning. James K. Hackett. 2 v. James K. Hackett & J. H. Oscar Hammerstein. 3 v. Virginia Harned. 2 v. Anna Held. 3 v. Frieda Hempel. Victor Herbert. Selma Herman. Robert Hilliard. Raymond Hitchcock. Will T. Hodge. Gertrude Hoffman. 2 v. Josef Hofmann. E. M. Holland. Mildred Holland. Louise Homer. De Wolfe Hopper. 2 v. De Wolfe Hopper & Hedda. Edna Wallace Hopper. 2 v. Edna Hunter. Henrik Ibsen. 2 v. Margaret Illington. 3 v. H. B. Irving & wife, L. Irving & wife. Henry Irving. 6 v. May Irwin. 2 v. May Irwin & Flo. Elsie Janis. Joseph Jefferson. 2 v. Bertha Kalich. Doris Keane. Frank Keenan & daughters. Fritz Kreisler. Jan Kubelik. Wilton Lackaye. Lillie Langtry. 2 v. Harry Lauder. Cecilia Loftus. 2 v. John McCormack. Christie MacDonald. Francis Macmillen. Louis Mann. Louis Mann & Clara Lipman. Mary Mannering. 2 v. Richard Mansfield. 8 v. Richard Mansfield

Continued in next column

Continued from preceding column

& family. Robert Mantell. 2 v. Julia Marlowe. 6 v. Sadie Martinot. John Mason. Wynne Matthison. Cyril Maude. Edna May. Edna, Jane & Marguerite May. Nellie Melba. 3 v. Rose Melville. Henry Miller. 2 v. Modjeska. Clara Morris. 3 v. Alla Nazimova. 4 v. Evelyn Nesbit. 3 v. Olga Nethersole. 4 v. Alice Nielsen. 2 v. Lillian Nordica. 3 v. James O'Neill. Nance O'Neill. 2 v. Julie Opp. Kathryn Osterman. Jan Paderewski. 2 v. Nan Patterson. 2 v. Adelina Patti. 2 v. Anna Pavlowa. 4 v. Olga Petrova. Mary Pickford. 3 v. Mary Pickford, Lottie & Jack. Guy Bates Post. Maud Powell. James T. Powers. Gabrielle Rejane. Gertrude Rennyson. Corinne Rider-Kelsey. Blanche Ring. 3 v. Adele Ritchie. Eleanor Robson. 3 v. May Robson. 2 v. Stuart Robson. Edmond Rostand. Annie Russell. 2 v. Annie Russell & Oswald Yorke. Lillian Russell. 6 v. Sol Smith Russell. Ruth St. Denis. Tomaso Salvini. Julia Sanderson. Fritzi Scheff. 2 v. Fritzi Scheff & Aurelia Jaeger. Schumann-Heink. Marcella Sembrich. Mary Servoss. Effie Shannon. Truly Shattuck. George Bernard Shaw. 3 v. Mary Shaw. Otis Skinner. 3 v. E. H. Sothern. 6 v. E. H. Sothern & E. A. Hilda Spong. Rose Stahl. Frances Starr. Emily Stevens. J. H. Stoddart. Marguerite Sylva. Mabel Taliaferro. Norma Talmadge. Eva Tanguay. Laurette Taylor. 2 v. Fay Templeton. Ellen Terry. 3 v. Ellen Terry & Kate. Luisa Tetrazzini. 2 v. Maggie Teyte. Augustus Thomas. Toole; Florence. Charlotte Townsend. Emma Trentini. Dorothy Usner. Richard Wagner. 4 v. Charlotte Walker. Lester Wallack. Blanche Walsh. 3 v. Helen Ware. David Warfield. 3 v. H. B. Warner. Rebecca Warren. Joseph Weber. 2 v. Walker Whiteside. E. S. Willard. Hattie Williams. Francis Wilson. 2 v. William Winter. 3 v. Thomas A. Wise & Gertrude Whitty. May Yohé. 2 v. Fannie Bloomfield Zeisler.

1. Stage.

NL 0435283 NN

Locke, Robinson, 1856-1920.

New York. Public library. *Robinson Locke collection.*
The Robinson Locke dramatic collection in the New York public library. On exhibition in the New York public library May 13 to September 30, 1925. [New York, 1925]

Locke, Rudolf, 1888-
Die Darlehnsgewährung eines Stellvertreters an sich selbst. Breslau, 1930.
59 p.
Inaug. Diss. Auszug.

NL 0435285 ICRL

Locke, Roscoe Janvrin, 1877–
Strangers and other poems, by R. J. Locke. Boston, Mass., The Stratford company [°1933]
2 p. l., iv p., 2 l., 91 p. 19½cm.

I. Title.

Library of Congress PS3523.O23388 1933 33-32752
Copyright A 65793 811.5

NL 0435286 DLC

Locke, S.B.
see
Locke, Samuel Barron.
Locke, Seth Barton, 1906-

Locke, S.D.
see Locke, Sylvanus Dyer, 1833-1898?.

Locke (Salomo Christoph. Jacob.) *De celeri corporum incremento caussa debilitatis in morbis. 30 pp. sm. 4°. *Lipsiæ, ex off. Langenhemia,* [1760]. [*Also, in:* P., v. 59.]

NL 0435289 DNLM PPC

Locke, Samuel.

The stronger sex. New York [Columbia Broadcasting System, n.d.]

21 l.

NL 0435290 CaBVaU

Locke, Samuel, 1737–1777.
Works by this author printed in America before 1801 are available in this library in the Readex Microprint edition of Early American Imprints published by the American Antiquarian Society.
This collection is arranged according to the numbers in Charles Evans' American Bibliography.

NL 0435291 DLC

C LOCKE, SAMUEL, 1732-1778.
6519 A sermon preached before the ministers of
.185 the province of the Massachusetts-Bay, in New-England, at their annual convention in Boston,
v.2 May 28, 1772... Boston, Draper, 1772.
51p.

Binder's title: Congregationalism. Sermons v.2.

NN ICN RPJCB MWA NjR MH DLC
NL 0435292 ICN CtY NcD PHi MiU-C MHi MBAt MB MH MA

Locke, Samuel Barron.
... Whitefish, grayling, trout, and salmon of the inter-mountain region. By S. B. Locke ... Washington, U. S. Govt. print. off., 1929.
1 p. l., p. 173–190. illus. 23cm. (U. S. Bureau of fisheries. Report of the commissioner [with appendices] 1929. Appendix v)

At head of title: Department of commerce ...
Bureau of fisheries document no. 1062.

1. Whitefishes. 2. Grayling. 3. Trout. 4. Salmon. I. Title.

F 29-39 Revised

Library, U. S. Bur. of Fisheries SH11.A15
Library of Congress QL627.L6

NL 0435293 DI OrU OrCS PP OO OCl PPT

Locke, Seth Barton, 1906–
Growth substance and the development of crown gall. By S. B. Locke ... A. J. Riker ... and B. M. Duggar ...
(*In* **U. S. Dept. of agriculture. Journal of agricultural research. v. 57, no. 1, July 1, 1938, p. 21–39. illus. 23½cm. Washington, 1938)**

Contribution from Wisconsin Agricultural experiment station (Wis.—94)
Published July 27, 1938.
"Literature cited": p. 37–39.

1. Crown-gall (disease) I. Duggar, Benjamin Minge, 1872– joint author. II. Riker, Albert Joyce, 1894– joint author.

Agr 38-557

U. S. Dept. of agr. Library 1Ag84J vol. 57, no. 1
for Library of Congress [S21.A75 vol. 57, no. 1]

(630.72)

NL 0435294 DNAL DLC OU

Locke, Seth Barton, 1906–
The nature of growth substance originating in crown gall tissue. By S. B. Locke ... A. J. Riker ... and B. M. Duggar ...
(*In* **U. S. Dept. of agriculture. Journal of agricultural research. v. 59, no. 7, Oct. 1, 1939, p. 535–539. 23cm. Washington, 1939)**

Contribution from Wisconsin Agricultural experiment station (Wis.—104)
Published Dec. 6, 1939.
"Literature cited": p. 538–539.

1. Crown-gall (disease) I. Duggar, Benjamin Minge, 1872– joint author. II. Riker, Albert Joyce, 1894– joint author.

Agr 39-788

U. S. Dept. of agr. Library 1Ag84J vol. 59, no. 7
for Library of Congress [S21.A75 vol. 59, no. 7]

(630.72)

NL 0435295 DNAL OU DLC

VOLUME 337

Locke, Seth Barton, 1906–
Production of growth substance on peptone broth by crown gall bacteria (*Phytomonas tumefaciens* (Smith and Town.) Bergey et al.) and related nongall-forming organisms. By S. B. Locke ... and A. J. Riker ... and B. M. Duggar ...
(*In* U. S. Dept. of agriculture. Journal of agricultural research. v. 59, no. 7, Oct. 1, 1939, p. 519–525. diagr. 23cm. Washington, 1939)
Contribution from Wisconsin Agricultural experiment station (Wis.—105)
Published Dec. 6, 1939.
Literature cited": p. 524–525.
1. Phytomonas tumefaciens. (1. Bacterium tumefaciens) 2. Crown-gall (disease) I. Duggar, Benjamin Minge, 1872– joint author. II. Riker, Albert Joyce, 1894– joint author.
Agr 39-786
U. S. Dept. of agr. Library 1Ag84J vol. 59, no. 7
for Library of Congress [S21.A75 vol. 59, no. 7]
(5*) (630.72)

NL 0435296 DNAL DLC OU

[Locke, Seymour E]
Official programme of the music festival held in the Mechanics' Pavilion...
see under Thomas, Theodore, 1835-1905.

SF521 .A4
Locke, Silas M., ed.
The American apiculturist: a journal devoted to scientific and practical beekeeping.
Wenham, Mass. (etc.) S. M. Locke & co., 18

Pam E469.8 .L6
Locke, Stephen
English sympathies & opinions regarding the late American Civil War. London, Thomas Bosworth, 1866.
26 p. 20 cm.

1. U.S.--Hist.--Civil War--Foreign public opinion. I. Title.

NL 0435299 T MnU CtY

Locke, Sumner.
Samaritan Mary, by Sumner Locke; illustrations by James O. Chapin. New York, H. Holt and company, 1916.
1 p. l., 340 p. front. 19½cm. $1.25

I. Title.
Library of Congress PZ3.L7955S 16—5619

NL 0435300 DLC

Locke, S(ylvanus) D(yer) 1833–1898?
The Battle of Bennington should be called the battle of Walloomsac. By Hon. S. D. Locke ... (Troy, N. Y., 1892?)
cover-title, 16 p. 23½cm.
"Published in Troy daily times, January 2, 1892."

Subject entries: Bennington, Battle of, 1777.
3-9542
Library of Congress, no. E241.B4L8.

NL 0435301 DLC MB OClWHi NBuHi PHi MWA NIC

Locke, Una, *pseud.*
see
Bailey, Urania Locke (Stoughton) 1820–1882.

Locke, Victor.
Catalogue des mammifères et des oiseaux observés en Algérie par le Capitaine Locke ... Rédigé d'après la classification de S.A. le Prince Charles Lucien Bonaparte. Paris, 1858.

NL 0435303 PPAN

Locke, W. J.
see Locke, William John, 1863-1930.

Locke, W. S.
see Locke, Warren S.

Locke, Walter, 1875-
A cash transaction and divers other slips of an editorial pen. Yellow Springs, Ohio, Antioch Press, 1928.
62 p. 21 cm.

NL 0435306 WaTC

Locke, Walter, 1875–
Halcyon days and The year at the whistling post. (Essays. Yellow Springs, Ohio) Antioch Press (1949)
171 p. 21 cm.

I. Title.
PS3523.O234H3 814.5 49-9232*

NL 0435307 DLC ICU

Locke, Walter, 1875–
John Halcyon's father (by) Walter Locke. Yellow Springs, O., The Antioch press, 1945.
4 p. l., 3–97 p. front. 20cm.

I. Title.
46–350
Library of Congress * PS3523.O234J6
818.5

NL 0435308 DLC MoU

Locke, Walter, 1875–
Whistling post, Ohio, by Walter Locke ... (Yellow Springs, O., The Antioch press company, °1934)
4 p. l., 110 p. 20cm. $1.50
Illustrated t.-p.
Essays.

I. Title.
Library of Congress PS3523.O234W5 1934 34-42026
Copyright A 77544 814.5

NL 0435309 DLC

Locke, Warren Andrew, 1847-

The University hymn book, for use in the chapel of Harvard university. Cambridge, The University, 1895.

Locke, Warren S.
The five orders of architecture
see under Vignola, Giacomo Barozzio, called, 1507-1573.

Locke, W(arren) S.
An outline course in mechanical drawing for evening drawing classes, by W. S. Locke ... Providence, R. I. (Prov. press co., printers 1888)
74 p. incl. illus., diagrs. (partly fold.) 19½ x 10½cm.

1. Mechanical drawing.
Library of Congress T353.L81 5-27318†

NL 0435312 DLC

Locke, W(arren) S.
An outline course in mechanical drawing for evening classes, by W. S. Locke ... Providence, R. I., 1891.
iv p., 1 l., (7)–124 p. incl. illus., tables, diagrs. 20cm.

1. Mechanical drawing.
Library of Congress T353.L82 5-27316†

NL 0435313 DLC

Locke, W(arren) S.
An outline course in mechanical drawing for evenin classes. By W. S. Locke ... 2d ed. Providence, R. I. (Press of E. L. Freeman & son) 1896.
iv p., 1 l., (7)–124 p. incl. illus., tables, diagrs. 20cm.

1. Mechanical drawing.
Library of Congress T353.L83 5-27317†

NL 0435314 DLC

Locke, Warren S.
An outline course in mechanical drawing, with various plates, diagrams, and kindred printed matter. By Warren S. Locke ... 3d ed. Providence, R. I., °1903.
iv p., 1 l., (7)–128 p. illus., tables, diagrs. 20cm.

1. Mechanical drawing.
Library of Congress T353.L85 8—17560

NL 0435315 DLC ICJ

Locke, Warren S. 4068.71
An outline course in mechanical drawing with various plates, diagrams and kindred printed matter. 4th edition.
— Providence, R. I. The Author. 1908. 137 pp. Diagrams. Charts. 20 cm., in 6s.

H2384 — Mechanical drawing.

NL 0435316 MB OU

Locke, William.
The land we live in; or, England's history in simple language. 4th ed. London, Nisbet, 1862.
144 p. Pls. 32°.

NL 0435317 MB

VOLUME 337

Locke, William. 6519a.98
Stories of the land we live in; or, England's history in simple language.
London. Nisbet. 1878. viii, 189 pp. Plates. Sm. 8°.
An earlier edition with the title "The land we live in; or, England's history in simple language," may be found on shelf-number 6519.84

Aug. 24, 1903
E8694 — T.r. — Great Britain. Hist.

NL 0435318 MB

Locke, William E.
Advantages of earth; sermon, funeral of John B. Osborn, containing portraiture of life, preached Dec. 3, 1848. New York, 1849.
16 p. O.

NL 0435319 RPB

Locke, Rev. William E.
Brief historical sketch of the Congregational church, East Alstead, N.H. n.p.n.d.

NL 0435320 Nh

Locke, William E.
A centennial discourse, containing a history of the Scotch Plains Baptist Church, New Jersey, during the first century of its ecclesiastical existence. By William E. Locke, the pastor. Preached August 8th, 1847. New York: G. B. Maigne, 1847.
36 p. 8°.

1. Scotch Plains, N. J.—Churches (Baptist). November 30, 1921.

NL 0435321 NN NjR RPB ICN NRCR

Locke, William E
The perpetuity of Christian baptism; a sermon, preached in Perry, Tompkins co., N. Y., June 20, 1841, in reply to the sentiments of the Quakers. By Rev. W. E. Locke ... Ithaca, N. Y., Mack, Andrus, and Woodruff, printers, 1841.
23 p. 21 cm.

1. Baptism. 2. Friends, Society of—Doctrinal and controversial works. I. Title.

NL 0435322 CSmH RPB N PPPrHi

Locke, William Henry.
The story of the regiment. By William Henry Locke, A. M., chaplain. Philadelphia, J. B. Lippincott & co., 1868.
xii, 401 p. front. 19½cm.

1. Pennsylvania infantry. 11th regt., 1861-1865. 2. U. S.—Hist.—Civil war—Regimental histories—Pa. inf.—11th.
2-15900
Library of Congress E527.5.11th

NL 0435323 DLC NjP PHi PPL PP OCl OClWHi TxU

Locke, William Henry.
The story of the regiment. By William Henry Locke ... New York, J. Miller, 1872.
xii, [13]-401 p. 19cm.

1. Pennsylvania infantry. 11th regt., 1861-1865. 2. U. S.—Hist.—Civil war—Regimental histories—Pa. inf.—11th.
45-51948
Library of Congress E527.5 11th 1872

NL 0435324 DLC OClWHi OCl MH NjP MWA NcD

Locke, William James, 1868-
A handbook for city officials of the fifth and sixth class cities of California
see under League of California Cities.

[Locke, William James] 1868- comp.
Crocker's blue book on principal city street improvement laws of California, containing "Improvement act of 1911" as amended, with annotations, "Improvement bond act of 1915", as amended, with annotations, "Change of grade act of 1909", as amended, "Street opening act of 1889", as amended, Act of 1921, providing for bonds in relation to Street opening act of 1889, "Vrooman act" of 1885, as amended, Act of 1893, providing for issuance of bonds for street improvements, as amended, "Local improvement act of 1901", as amended; appendix, setting forth, for reference, specifications for various kinds of street work. 1923 ed., rev. and annotated by H. C. Symonds ... San Francisco, Los Angeles [etc.] H. S. Crocker co., inc. [c1923]
369 p. illus. (plan) 18cm.
Published also under titles: 1913-1917, Improvement act of 1911; 1919-1921, Locke's blue book; 1921 Street improvement act of California.

1. Highway law—California. I. Symonds, H. C. II. California. Laws, statutes, etc. III. Title. IV. Title: Improvement act of 1911.
24-520
Library of Congress TE324.C2 1923

NL 0435326 DLC CU

[Locke, William James] 1868- comp.
Crocker's blue book on principal city street improvement laws of California, containing "Improvement act of 1911", as amended, with annotations, "Improvement bond act of 1915", as amended, with annotations, "Change of grade act of 1909" as amended, "Street opening act of 1889", as amended, Act of 1921, providing for bonds in relation to Street opening act of 1889, "Vrooman act" of 1885, as amended, Act of 1893, providing for issuance of bonds for street improvements, as amended, "Local improvement act of 1901", as amended, "Acquisition and improvement act of 1925", Public work revolving fund act of 1925, City boundary line act of 1911, as amended. Appendix setting forth, for reference, specifications for various kinds of street work. 1925 ed., rev. and annotated by H. C. Symonds ... San Francisco, Los Angeles [etc.] H. S. Crocker co., inc. [c1925]
480 p. illus. (plan) 18cm.

1. Highway law—California. I. Symonds, Harry Clinton, 1872- II. California. Laws, statutes, etc. III. Title. IV. Title: Improvement act of 1911.
25-18786
Library of Congress TE324.C2 1925 a

NL 0435328 DLC

Locke, William James, 1868- comp.
Improvement act of 1911 as amended in 1913, 1915 and 1917, with citations, notes, model forms and model specifications, Improvement bond act of 1915 as amended in 1917, also Vrooman act; comp. by Wm. J. Locke. San Francisco, Ingrim stationery company [c1917]
220 p. illus. (plan) 18½cm.

1. Highway law—California. I. California. Laws, statutes, etc. II. Title.
17-27936
Library of Congress TE324.C2 1917

NL 0435329 DLC ICRL

Locke, William James, 1868- comp.
Improvement act of 1911 (with amendments of 1913) annotated and containing citations; comp. by Wm. J. Locke. San Francisco, A. Carlisle & co. [c1913]
cover-title, 3 p. l., 55 p. 23cm. $2.00
Includes advertising matter.

1. Streets. 2. Highway law—California. I. California. Laws, statutes, etc. II. Title.
13-22259 Revised
Library of Congress TE324.C2 1913

NL 0435330 DLC

[Locke, William James] 1868- comp.
... "Locke's blue book"; containing "Improvement act of 1911", as amended, with annotations, "Improvement bond act of 1915", as amended, with annotations, "Change of grade act of 1909", as amended, "Street opening act of 1889", as amended, Act of 1921, providing for bonds in relation to Street opening act of 1889, "Vrooman act" of 1885, as amended, Act of 1893, providing for issuance of bonds for street improvements, as amended, "Local improvement act of 1901", as amended; appendix, setting forth, for reference, specifications for various kinds of street work. 1921 ed., enl. and rev. by H. C. Symonds. San Francisco, Los Angeles [etc.] H. S. Crocker co., inc. [c1921]
337, [27] p. illus. (plan) 18cm.
At head of title: City street improvement laws of California.

1. Highway law—California. I. Symonds, H. C. II. California. Laws, statutes, etc. III. Title. IV. Title: Improvement act of 1911.
21-17209
Library of Congress TE324.C2 1921

NL 0435332 DLC

Locke, William James, 1868- comp.
"Locke's blue book"; Improvement act of 1911 as amended in 1913, 1915, 1917 and 1919, with citations, notes, model forms and model specifications, Improvement bond act of 1915, with amendments, and Vrooman act. 1919 ed., comp. by Wm. J. Locke. San Francisco, Ingrim-Rutledge company, 1919.
197, [25] p. illus. (plan) 19cm.
Blank pages for "Notes" ([15] at end)

1. Highway law—California. I. California. Laws, statutes, etc. II. Title. III. Title: Improvement act of 1911.
20-721
Library of Congress TE324.C2 1919

NL 0435333 DLC

Locke, William James, 1898-
Municipal hand book for city officials of California
see under League of California Cities.

Locke, William James, 1868- ed.
Pacific municipalities. v. 1-46; Aug. 1899-Sept. 1932. San Francisco, Calif. [etc.] 1899-1932.

[Locke, William James] 1868-
The road laws of California, embracing the provisions of the constitution, the codes and special statutory acts relating to highways, bridges and the condemnation of lands for public use. San Francisco, A. Carlisle & co., 1907.
1 p.l., xxix, [5]-236 p. 16cm.

1. Highway law - California. 2. Roads - California.

NL 0435336 CU-B

[Locke, William James] 1868-
The road laws of California, embracing the provisions of the constitution, the codes, and special statutory acts relating to highways, bridges and the condemnation of lands for public use. San Francisco, A. Carlisle, 1911.
1 p.l., xxxvip., 2 l., [7]-318 p. 18 cm.

NL 0435337 CU

VOLUME 337

[Locke, William James] 1868- comp.
The road laws of California, 1925, embracing the provisions of the constitution, the codes, and special statutory acts relating to highways, bridges and the condemnation of lands for public use. San Francisco, A. Carlisle & co., 1925.
2 p. l., l, [3]-549 p. 15½cm.
"Enlarged and revised edition of the Street improvement acts of California, compiled by Wm. J. Locke."
1. Highway law—California. 2. Streets. I. California. Laws, statutes, etc. II. Title. III. Title: The road laws of California.
Library of Congress TE324.C2 1925 b 25-25520

NL 0435338 DLC

[Locke, William James] 1868- comp.
The road laws of California, 1929, embracing the provisions of the constitution, the codes, and special statutory acts relating to highways, bridges and the condemnation of lands for public use. San Francisco, A. Carlisle & co., 1929.
2 p. l., liii, [3]-679 p. 16cm.
"Enlarged and revised edition of the Street improvement acts of California, compiled by Wm. J. Locke ... and H. A. Postlethwaite."
1. Highway law—California. 2. Streets. I. California. Laws, statutes, etc. II. Postlethwaite, H. A., joint comp. III. Title.
Library of Congress TE324.C2 1929 29-22210

NL 0435339 DLC

Locke, William James, 1868- comp.
... Street improvement acts of California (including amendments of 1921) comp. by Wm. J. Locke. [Rev. ed.] San Francisco, A. Carlisle & co. [c1921]
2 p. l., vi, 3-161 p. 20½cm.
Advertising matter: p. 160-161.
1. Streets. 2. Highway law—California. I. California. Laws, statutes, etc. II. Title.
Library of Congress TE324.C2 1921 a 22-14590

NL 0435340 DLC ICJ

Locke, William James, 1868- comp.
Street improvement acts of California (including amendments of 1923) compiled by Wm. J. Locke. Enl. and rev. ed. San Francisco, A. Carlisle & co., [1923]
ix, 220 p. 21 cm.
Provenance: Joseph M. Gleason (with his bookplate): San Francisco College for Women Library.
1. Streets - California. 2. Highway law - California. I. California. Laws, statutes, etc. II. Title.

NL 0435341 CU-B

Locke, William James, 1868- comp.
... Street improvement acts of California (including amendments of 1925) compiled by Wm. J. Locke ... San Francisco, A. Carlisle & co. [c1925]
2 p. l., ix, 5-233 p. 21½cm. $3.50
At head of title: Enlarged and revised edition.
Advertising matter: p. 230-233.
1. Highway law—California. 2. Streets. I. California. Laws, statutes, etc. II. Title.
Library of Congress TE324.C2 1925 25-15979

NL 0435342 DLC

Locke, William James, 1868- comp.
... Street improvement acts of California (including amendments of 1929) compiled by Wm. J. Locke ... and H. A. Postlethwaite. San Francisco, A. Carlisle & co. [c1929]
2 p. l., xiv, [3]-390 p. front. 21 cm.
At head of title: Enlarged and revised edition.
Advertising matter: p. 386-390.
1. Streets. 2. Highway law—California. I. California. Laws, statutes, etc. II. Postlethwaite, H. A., joint comp. III. Title.
TE324.C2 1929a 29—22209

NL 0435343 DLC

[Locke, William James] 1868- comp.
... Street improvement acts of California (including amendments of 1931) compiled and edited by H. A. Postlethwaite. San Francisco, A. Carlisle & co., Upham & Rutledge, inc. [c1931]
2 p. l., [1], xvi, 470 p. fold. form. 21cm.
At head of title: Enlarged and revised edition.
Earlier editions compiled by W. J. Locke and H. A. Postlethwaite.
Advertising matter: p. 466-470.
1. Streets. 2. Highway law—California. I. California. Laws, statutes, etc. II. Postlethwaite, Hartley Albert, 1901- joint comp. III. Title.
Library of Congress TE324.C2 1931 31-25008
Copyright A 42512 625.709794

NL 0435344 DLC

[Locke, William James] 1868- comp.
... Street improvement acts of California (including amendments of 1933) compiled and edited by H. A. Postlethwaite. San Francisco, A. Carlisle & co., Upham & Rutledge, inc. [c1933]
2 p. l., [1], xii, 2-387 p. 20½cm.
At head of title: Enlarged and revised edition.
Earlier editions compiled by W. J. Locke and H. A. Postlethwaite.
Advertising matter: p. 384-387.
1. Streets. 2. Highway law—California. I. California. Laws, statutes, etc. II. Postlethwaite, Hartley Albert, 1901- joint comp. III. Title.
Library of Congress TE324.C2 1933 34-3501
Copyright A 69519 625.709794

NL 0435345 DLC

Locke, William John, 1863-1930.
... El amado vagabundo, novela traducida del inglés por Alejandro Frías Giraud. Barcelona, Madrid. Sociedad general de publicaciones, s. a. [c1926]
300 p. plates. 20cm.
At head of title: William J. Locke.
I. Frías Giraud, Alejandro, tr. II. Title.
Library of Congress PR6023.O15B4 1926 27-10076
Copyright A—Foreign 32852

NL 0435346 DLC

Locke, William John, 1863-1930
Ancestor Jorico, by William J. Locke. London, John Lane [1929]
3 p. l., 312 p. 19½cm.
I. Title.
Library of Congress PZ3.L796An 2 29-29981

NL 0435347 DLC MH TxU CaBVaU

Locke, William John, 1863-1930
Ancestor Jorico, by William J. Locke. New York, Dodd, Mead & company, 1929.
3 p. l., 339 p. 19½cm.
I. Title.
Library of Congress PZ3.L796An 29-24373

NL 0435348 DLC CaOTP Wa CaBVa WaS WaSp MsU NBuU FMU TxU PU PPL PHC OCU OO OCl MiU OClh MB

Locke, William John, 1863-1930.
The apostle, by William J. Locke. New York, John Lane company; London, John Lane, 1921.
32 p. 18½cm.
I. Title.
Library of Congress PZ3.L796Ap 21-13414

NL 0435349 DLC

Locke, William John, 1863-1930.
At the gate of Samaria, a novel, by William John Locke. New York, D. Appleton and company, 1894.
2 p. l., 322 p. 18½cm.
I. Title.
Library of Congress PZ3.L796At 7—15165

NL 0435350 DLC Wa NN NcU PPL MB

823 Locke, William John, 1863-1930.
L79a At the gate of Samaria. A novel. London, W. Heinemann, 1895.
1895 322p. 20cm.

NL 0435351 IU CtY

Locke, William John, 1863-1930 66.27
At the gate of Samaria. A novel.
London. Lane. 1906. (4), 322 pp. 19½ cm., in 8s.
M3727 — T.r.

NL 0435352 MB

Locke, William John, 1863-1930.
At the gate of Samaria, by W. J. Locke. London, J. Lane; New York, J. Lane company, 1907.
2 p. l., 322 p. 19½cm.
First published 1894.
I. Title.
Library of Congress PZ3.L796At 2 7—15540

NL 0435353 DLC ViU NjP PP PPRCl

PZ 3 .L796 .AT3 Locke, William John, 1863-1930.
At the gate of Samaria, by W. J. Locke. London, J. Lane; New York, J. Lane company, 1909.
322 p.
First published 1894.

NL 0435354 MoU

Locke, William John, 1863-1930.
At the gate of Samaria. London, Lane, 1910.
322 p.

NL 0435355 OClW OCl OClh NcD PHC PU

VOLUME 337

Locke, W[illiam] J[ohn], 1863-1930.
At the gate of Samaria. New York: John Lane Co., 1910.
3 p.l., 322 p. 12°.

NL 0435356 NN

Locke, William John, 1863-1930.
The belovéd vagabond. New York, A. L. Burt [19--]
303 p. 20cm. (Burt's library of the world's best books)

NL 0435357 ViU

Locke, William John, 1863-1930.
The beloved vagabond. London, Lane, c1900.
303 p.

NL 0435358 OClW PWcS PHC PU

LOCKE, William J[ohn], 1863-1930.
The beloved vagabond. New York, A.L. Burt Co., [cop. 1900].
22418.15.70

NL 0435359 MH IaU OO OCl OClh OLak

PR 6023 O 15B4 1905a
Locke, William John, 1863-1930.
The belovéd vagabond. New York, A.L. Burt [c1905]
303 p. 20cm.

NL 0435360 CoU FU MB PPPCPh

Locke, William John, 1863-1930.
The belovéd vagabond, by William J. Locke. New York, J. Lane company; [etc., etc.] 1906.
303 p. 19½cm.

I. Title.

6-37606

Library of Congress PZ3.L796Be

WaSp OEac ViU TxU WaE OO OrP MoU Or OrU WaS IdPI CaBVa
NL 0435361 DLC NjP OKentU NN PPT PBa PPL OClW OO ODW

Locke, William John, 1863-
The belovéd vagabond, by William J. Locke. New York, J. Lane company; [etc., etc.] 1907.
303 p. 19cm.

9-32302

Library of Congress PZ3.L796Be 2

NL 0435362 DLC NBuU TNJ MH IU MtU CaBVa ViU MB

Locke, William John, 1863-1930.
The belovéd vagabond, by William J. Locke. New York, J. Lane company; [etc., etc.] 1908.
303 p. 19½cm.

I. Title.

9-8815

Library of Congress PZ3.L796Be 3

NL 0435363 DLC CaBVaU IdU MiU

Locke, William J[ohn], 1863-1930.
The belovéd vagabond. New York: J. Lane Co., 1909.
303 p. 12°.

1. Fiction (English). 2. Title.

May 15, 1914.

NL 0435364 NN

Locke, William John, 1863-1930.
The belovéd vagabond, by William J. Locke. ..New York, A. L. Burt company, [1910]
303 p. 19½cm.

NL 0435365 ViU

Locke, William John, 1863-1930.
The beloved vagabond, ... New York, J. Lane co., : [etc., etc., 1911]
303 p.

NL 0435366 MiU

PR 6023 023 B4 1915
Locke, William John, 1863-1930.
The beloved vagabond, New York, John Lane, 1915.
303 p.

NL 0435367 KMK

Locke, William John, 1863-1930.
The beloved vagabond... N.Y., J. Lane co., [etc., etc.] 1918.
303 p.

NL 0435368 OU

Locke, William John, 1863-1930.
The belovéd vagabond, by William J. Locke. Illustrated by Jean Dulac. London, John Lane [1922]
4 p. l., 267 p. col. front., illus., 15 col. pl. 22 x 17½cm.

I. Dulac, Jean, illus. II. Title.

23-11681

Library of Congress PZ3.L796Be 7

NL 0435369 DLC CaBVaU TxU FMU

Locke, William John, 1863-1930.
The belovéd vagabond, by William J. Locke ... New York, A. L. Burt company [1928]
303 p. 19½cm.

I. Title.

32-19514

Library of Congress PZ3.L796Be 9

NL 0435370 DLC OrU PV

Locke, William John, 1863-1930.
The beloved vagabond. N.Y., Dodd, 1929.
303 p.

NL 0435371 OClW

823 L79b 1930
Locke, William John, 1863-1930.
The beloved vagabond. New York, Dood, Mead, 1930.
303p. 20cm.

NL 0435372 IU PU

Locke, William John, 1863-1930.
... William J. Locke's The belovèd vagabond, edited by R. L. Lyman ... [Boston] Ginn and company [°1931]
xvii, 290 p. 19cm. (Modern literature series)

I. Lyman, Rollo La Verne, 1879- ed. II. Title: The belovèd vagabond.

31-14184

Library of Congress PZ3.L796Be 12

—— Copy 2.

Copyright A 38472

823.91

NL 0435373 DLC NIC OClW OCl OU MB

Locke, William John, 1863-1930, ed.

A book of Belgium's gratitude; comprising literary articles by representative Belgians, together with their translations by various hands, and illustrated throughout in colour and black and white by Belgian artists. London, John Lane; New York, John Lane company; [etc., etc.] 1916.

823.9 L314boXG
Locke, William John, 1363-1930.
Carlotta. Autorisierte Übersetzung aus dem Englischen von Pauline Klaiber. Stuttgart, J. Engelhorn, 1909.
2 v. in 1. 18cm. (Engelhorns allgemeine Roman-Bibliothek, 25 Jahrg., Bd 21/22)

I. Klaiber, Paulina. tr.
II. Title.

NL 0435375 IEN OCl

Locke, William John, 1863-1930
A Christmas mystery. The story of the three wise men. [c1909]

NL 0435376 PWcS

VOLUME 337

Locke, William John, 1863-1930.
A Christmas mystery; the story of three wise men, by William J. Locke; illustrated by Blendon Campbell. New York, John Lane company, 1910.
54 p. front., plates. 21cm.
Ornamental borders.

I. Title.
Library of Congress PZ3.L796Ch 10—23938
Copyright A 273791 [n37d1]

WaSpG WaT WaTC WaWW
Wa WaE IdB WaPS IdPI WaS MtB MtU OrCS OrPR OrU
OCl PJA PU Or OrStbM OrSaW OrU-M MtBuM CaBVaU
NL 0435377 DLC KU ViU MU MB OCU TxU PP NN OEac

Locke, William John, 1863-1930
A Christmas mystery; the story of three wise men, by William J. Locke. Illustrated by W. W. Lendon. London: J. Lane, 1922. vii, 35 p. col'd front., illus., col'd plates. 8°.

390800A. 1. Christmas—Fiction. 2. Lendon, W. W., illustrator. 3. Title.
December 31, 1928

NL 0435379 NN CtY CSmH

Locke, William John, 1863-1930.
A Christmas mystery; the story of three wise men. Illus. by W. W. Lendon. [2d ed.] London, John Lane, 1922.
vii, 35 p. illus.

NL 0435380 WaU

AC-L
L796co
1924
Locke, William John, 1863-1930.
The coming of Amos, by William J. Locke. London, John Lane [1924]
3p.ℓ., 328p. 20cm.

NL 0435381 TxU UU OCl CSmH

Locke, William John, 1863-1930.
The coming of Amos, by William J. Locke ... New York, Dodd, Mead and company, 1924.
3 p. l., 370 p. 19½ cm.

I. Title.
PZ3.L796Co 24-20558

PPL OO OCl OClh OLak MiU NN MB TxU FU MsU MU ViU
NL 0435382 DLC IdU Wa WaS OrU OrCS CaBVaU PP PU

Locke, William John, 1863-1930.
The coming of Amos. 1929.

NL 0435383 PHatU

Locke, William John, 1863-1930.
The demagogue and Lady Phayre, by William J. Locke ... New York, E. Arnold [1895]
2 p. l., 155 p. 18½cm. (*On cover:* The Pioneer series)

Library of Congress PZ3.L796De 7-15166†

NL 0435384 DLC MB RPB

PR
6023
L79d
Locke, William John, 1863-1930.
The demagogue and Lady Phayre. London, W. Heinemann, 1896.
155 p. (Pioneer series)

NL 0435385 CLU FTaSU PU

Locke, William John, 1863-1930.
The demagogue and Lady Phayre. London, 1903.

NL 0435386 PPL

PR
6023
015D4
1908
Locke, William John, 1863-1930
The demagogue and Lady Phaydre. London, J. Lane, The Bodley Head; New York, J. Lane, 1908.
155p. 20cm.

NL 0435387 MU NjP OrU

Locke, William John, 1863-1930.
The demagogue and Lady Phayre...
London, Lane [1911]
155 p. 19cm.

NL 0435388 NjP

823.91
L814d
1911
Locke, William John, 1863-1930.
The demagogue and Lady Phayre. [3d ed.]
London, New York, J. Lane [1911]
3p.ℓ., 155p.

NL 0435389 ICarbS NN

KD 12562
Locke, William John, 1863-1930.
Derelicts. London, etc., J.Lane, n.d.

[Cheap ed.]

NL 0435390 MH

Locke, William John, 1863-1930.
Derelicts, by William J. Locke ... London and New York, J. Lane, 1897.
3 p. l., 414 p., 1 l. 20cm.

I. Title.
Library of Congress PZ3.L796Der —15172

OrCS OrP OrPR WaT WaSpG OrU WaSp Wa WaS WaE WaPS
OrSaW OrU-M MtBuM CaBVaU IdB IdU MB MtBC WaWW WaTC
NL 0435391 DLC MU LU NBuU FU TxU IdPS Or OrStbM

22418.15.6.2
LOCKE, William John, 1863-1930.
Derelicts. London and New York, J.Lane, 1898.

20 cm.
"Second edition."

NL 0435392 MH

Locke, William John, 1863-1930
Derelicts. London, Lane, 1904 [c1897]
413 p

NL 0435393 PU

Locke, William John, 1863-1930
Derelicts. London, 1907.

NL 0435394 PPL

Locke, William John, 1863-1930.
Derelicts, by William J. Locke. London, J. Lane; New York, J. Lane co., 1908.
2 p. l., 413, [1] p. 19 cm.
"Sixth edition."

NL 0435395 Vi ViU MH

LOCKE, WILLIAM JOHN, 1863-1930.
Derelicts, by William J. Locke. New York [etc.] J. Lane Co., 1911. 413 p. 19cm.

NL 0435396 NN MH

Locke, William John, 1863-1930.
Derelicts, by William J. Locke ... New York, A. L. Burt company [1912]
1 p.l., 413, [1] p. 19½cm.

NL 0435397 ViU

22418.15.6.15
Locke, William John, 1863-1930.
Derelicts. New York, Dodd, Mead & co., 1922.
413 p. 19 cm.

NL 0435398 MH

Locke, William John, 1863-1930.
...Divas sievietes; romāns; tulkojusi Zelma Kroders. Rīgā: "Grāmatu draugs," 1930. 246 p. 20½cm. (Vērtīgu grāmatu virkne. Sējums 89.)
At head of title: ...Viljams Džons Loks.

571562A. I. Fiction, English. I. Kroder, Zelma, translator. II. Title. III. Ser.
May 16, 1933

NL 0435399 NN

VOLUME 337

Locke, William John, 1863–
... Las divertidas aventuras de Aristides Pujol, novela traducida del inglés por Alejandro Frías Giraud, cubierta en colores y láminas de Szathmary. Barcelona, Madrid, Sociedad general de publicaciones, s. a. [1925]
306 p., 1 l. plates. 20½cm.
At head of title: William J. Locke.
I. Frias Giraud, Alejandro, tr. II. Title.
Library of Congress PR6023.O15J64 1925 26-7161

NL 0435400 DLC

Locke, William John, 1863–
Far-away stories, by William J. Locke. London, John Lane; New York, John Lane company, 1916.
5 p. l., 3-334 p. 19cm.
Second edition.
CONTENTS.—The song of life.—Ladies in lavender.—Studies in blindness: I. An old-world episode. II. The conqueror. III. A lover's dilemma.—A Christmas mystery.—The princess's kingdom.—The heart at twenty.—The scourge.—Viviette.
I. Title.
Library of Congress PZ3.L796Fa 2 19-14480

NL 0435401 DLC MiU CSmH PPL NN

Locke, William John, 1863–1930.
Far-away stories, by William J. Locke ... New York, John Lane company; London, John Lane; [etc., etc.] 1919.
265 p. 19½ cm.
CONTENTS.—The song of life.—Ladies in lavender.—Studies in blindness: I. An Old-world episode. II. The conqueror. III. A lover's dilemma. IV. A woman of the war.—The princess's kingdom.—The heart at twenty.—The scourge.—My shadow friends.
I. Title.
Library of Congress PZ3.L796Fa 19—11562

WaSp WaS WaSpG WaT WaTC WaWW
CaBVaU IdB IdPI IdU MtU OrCS OrPR OrU Wa WaE WaPS
OClh OCl OLak ViU Or OrStbM OrU-M OrSaW MtBuM
NL 0435402 DLC MB TxU NBuU MU PU PPGi PPL OO MiU

Locke, William John, 1863–1930.
Flower o' the rose; a romantic play, by William J. Locke. London, Printed by Ralph Straus at the Sign of the ostrich, 1909. 4 p.l., 24 p., 1 l. 22cm.
No. 24 of 50 copies printed for private circulation. "Each copy...signed by the author."
Author's autographed presentation copy to John Lane.
459300B. I. Drama, English. I. Title. November 29, 1948

NL 0435404 NN CoU

Locke, William John, 1863–1930.
The fortunate youth, by William J. Locke; illustrations by Arthur I. Keller. New York, John Lane company; London, John Lane; [etc., etc.] 1914.
352 p. front., plates. 19cm.
I. Title.
Library of Congress PZ3.L796Fo 14—5512
Copyright A 369514 [a35b1]

CaBVaU OrStbM WaWW
FTaSU NjP PP PPL PBm OO OCl OClh MiU ViU MB NN IdPI
NL 0435405 DLC TxU ICU CaOTP LU MB FMU NcD MoU TNJ

Locke, William John, 1863-1930
The fortunate youth... New York, John Lane company ; London, John Lane, 1921.
352 p.

NL 0435406 PPT PSC

Locke, William John, 1863-1930
Fortunate youth. N.Y., Dodd, 1927. c1913-

NL 0435407 PU CaBVa

Locke, William John, 1863–1930.
... Der geliebte vagabund, roman. Wien [etc.] W. Frick, 1937.
302, [1] p. 20cm.
"Aus dem englischen original übertragen von Norbert Lynkke [pseud.]"
I. Fischer, Oskar, 1885– tr. II. Title.
Library of Congress PR6023.O15B38 42-51853
823.91

NL 0435408 DLC

Locke, William John, 1863–1930.
... La gloria de Clementina; novela traducida del inglés por Alejandro Frias Giraud, cubierta en colores y láminas en negro de Longoria. Barcelona, Madrid, Sociedad general de publicaciones, s. a. [1925?]
384 p. plates. 20½cm.
At head of title: William J. Locke.
I. Frias Giraud, Alejandro, tr. II. Title.
Library of Congress PR6023.O15G6 1925 26-9414

NL 0435409 DLC

Locke, William John, 1863–1930.
The glory of Clementina, by William J. Locke ... illustrations by Arthur I. Keller. New York, John Lane co., 1911.
4 p. l., 367 p. front., plates. 19½cm.
I. Title.
Library of Congress PZ3.L796G1 11—18970
[a41b1]

NL 0435410 DLC OEac MiU OCl OO OLak

Locke, William John, 1863–1930.
The glory of Clementina, by William J. Locke; illustrations by Arthur I. Keller. New York, John Lane company, 1911.
4 p. l., 367 p. front., plates. 19½cm.
I. Title.
Library of Congress PZ3.L796G1 2 11—19661

PU OrP PPT PPL PPHa MB NN NjP TxU
NL 0435411 DLC IdPI WaWW WaS MeB FU TNJ GU LU MsU

PR6025 .O2G53 1911a
Locke, William John, 1863–1930.
The glory of Clementina, by William J. Locke; illustrations by Arthur I. Keller. Toronto, H. Frowde, 1911.
4 p. l., 367 p. front., plates. 19½cm.
Imperfect: Original t.-p. and 1 p.l., wanting, (rebound).

NL 0435412 ViU

Locke, William John, 1863-1930.
Glory of Clementina. N.Y., Dodd, 1912.
367 p.

NL 0435413 PU

Locke, William J[ohn], 1863-1930.
The glory of Clementina Wing. London: John Lane [19—?] 314 p. 16°.

NL 0435414 NN

Locke, William John, 1863–
The glory of Clementina Wing, by William J. Locke. London, John Lane; New York, John Lane company, 1911.
3 p. l., 375 p. 19½cm. 6/-
Published in the United States under title: The glory of Clementina.
Library of Congress PZ3.L796Gl 3 11-20592

NL 0435415 DLC CaBVaU NcD TxU

PR 6023 O15 G64 1924
Locke, William John, 1863-1930.
The golden journey of Mr. Paradyne, illustrated in colour and black and white by Marcia Lane Foster. London, J. Lane, 1924.
4 p. l., 46 p. col. front., illus., col. plates. 20 cm.

NL 0435416 CaBVaU

AC-L L796go 1924
Locke, William John, 1863-1930.
The golden journey of Mr. Paradyne, by William J. Locke, illustrated in colour and black and white by Marcia Lane Foster. London, John Lane, 1924.
4p.ℓ.,53p. col. front.,illus.,col. plates. 20cm.
"First published in 1924."
I. Title. A.F.: Bond, J.S.

NL 0435417 TxU FMU KU CSmH MH CLU-C

Locke, William John, 1863– 1930.
The golden journey of Mr. Paradyne, by William J. Locke, illustrated in colour and black and White by Marcia Lane Foster. New York, Dodd, Mead and company, 1924.
4 p. l., 46 p. col. front., illus., col. plates. 20cm.
I. Title.
Library of Congress PZ3.L796Go 24—25646

CaBVa
NL 0435418 DLC MB OEac PPD OCl PU OLak OClh OrP

823.91 L814GR
Locke, Willian John, 1863-1930.
The great Pandolfo. London, J. Lane [1925]
306 p. 20 cm.

NL 0435419 NcD CaBVaU CoU CSmH MoU TxU

VOLUME 337

Locke, William John, 1863–
The great Pandolfo, by William J. Locke ... New York, Dodd, Mead and company, 1925.
3 p. l., 366 p. 19½cm.

I. Title.
Library of Congress PZ3.L796Gr 25—17123

NL 0435420 OO ViU PRosC PPT PU NN MB OClh OLak MtU WaSp DLC IdU WaT FU TNJ TxU FMU NBuU PHC OCl

---

Locke, William John, 1863–1930
The great Pandolfo... London, J. Lane, The Bodley head limited, 1928.
[3]-306 p.

"First published in 1925... popular ed. 1928."

NL 0435421 MiU

Locke, William John, 1863-1930.
The great wheel: a comedy, by William Locke.
[n.p., 19--] 26,36,39 f.

Typescript.
Prompt-book.

1. Drama, English. 2. Prompt-books. I. Title.

NL 0435422 NN

PR6023 .02G83 Locke, William John, 1863-1930.
Der grosse Pandolfo; roman von W. J. Locke. Berlin, J.Singer [1927?] 328p. 19cm. (Half-title: Erdkreis-bücher)
"Aus dem englischen übersetzt von Ludwig Goldscheider."

I.Goldscheider, Ludwig, 1896- tr. II.Title.

NL 0435423 NNU-W

Locke, William John, 1863–1930.
The house of Baltazar, by William J. Locke ... New York, John Lane company; London, John Lane; [etc., etc.] 1920.
3 p. l., 9-312 p. 19½cm.

I. Title.
Library of Congress PZ3.L796Ho 20—26105

NL 0435424 PPAp PV MB IdPI MtU Or WaS WaSp NcD FU NjP NBuU TxU WaS MiU OCl OClW-H OO OCH PPGi DLC Or TxU KU WaU LU MB NN MH ICarbS AAP

Locke, William John, 1863-1930.
The house of Baltazer. Toronto, Ryerson Press, 1920.
312 p. 20 cm.

NL 0435425 CaBVaU

PR 6023 .O1513 1898 Locke, William John, 1863–1930.
Idols, by William J. Locke. New York, John Lane company, London, John Lane, 1898.
366 p. 20 cm.

NL 0435426 OKentU OCl OClh

Locke, William John, 1863–1930.
Idols, by William J. Locke. London: J. Lane, 1899. 366 p. 12°.

302881A. 1. Fiction, English. 2. Jews in fiction. 3. Title.
June 17, 1927

NL 0435427 NN PPL MH

Locke, William John, 1863–1930.
Idols, by William J. Locke. [3d ed.] New York & London, J. Lane, 1904.
3 p. l., 365, [2] p. 20cm. (Half-title: Canvasback library of popular fiction, vol. xx)

I. Title.
Library of Congress (✱) (PZ3.L796I 3) 5—9718

NL 0435428 DLC OClJC

LOCKE, William J[ohn], 1863–1930.
Idols. London, J.Lane, etc., etc., [cop.1905].

NL 0435429 MH NjP OO

PR6023 L814 I 2 Locke, William John, 1863-1930.
Idols. New York, A.L. Burt [1905]
365 p. 20cm.

NL 0435430 GU NRU KU PP IdU

Locke, William John, 1863-1930.
Idols, by William J. Locke. London, J. Lane, Bodley Head; New York, J. Lane, 1908 [c1905]
365 p. 20 cm.

NL 0435431 CSt MH

Locke, William John, 1863–1930.
Idols, by William J. Locke...New York, A. L. Burt, company, [1910]
3 p. l., 365[3] p. 20cm.

NL 0435432 ViU IdPI

Locke, William John, 1863–1930
Idols, by William J. Locke. New York, John Lane company; London, John Lane, 1911.
3 p. l., 365, [1] p. 19cm.

I. Title.
Library of Congress PZ3.L796I 7 20-15617

NL 0435433 DLC CaOTP NN

Locke, William John, 1863–1930.
Idols. London, Lane, 1913. c1898.
365 p.

NL 0435434 PU

---

823 L814i Locke, William John, 1863-1930.
Idols. New York, John Lane company; London, John Lane, the Bodley head, 1921.
365p. 19cm.

NL 0435435 NcU

Locke, William John, 1863-1930.
Idols. [London] John Lane [1925]
309 p. 17.5 cm.
Half-title: The works of William J.Locke. Autograph edition, vol.4.

NL 0435436 MH

Locke, William John, 1863–1930.
Jaffery. c1914.

NL 0435437 OClh OCl OLak PPAp

Locke, William John, 1863–1930.
Jaffery, by William J. Locke; illustrations by F. Matania. New York, Grosset & Dunlap [©1915]
352 p. front., plates. 19½cm.

NL 0435438 LU

Locke, William John, 1863–1930.
Jaffery, by William J. Locke; illustrations by F. Matania. New York, John Lane company; London, John Lane, 1915.
352 p. front., plates. 19½cm.

I. Title.
Library of Congress PZ3.L796Ja [a42m1] 15—26351

NL 0435439 IdPI CaBVaU OU OEac MiU NN MB PPT WaWW TxU OCX OClW WaS OrU DLC KU MB ICarbS CoU TxU MU FU PP MH PPGi

---

823.91 L814jo Locke, William John, 1863-1930.
Joshua's vision. London, J. Lane [1928]
3p.l., 337p.

NL 0435440 ICarbS CaBVaU MtU CSt NcD MH

Locke, William John, 1863–
Joshua's vision, by William J. Locke. New York, Dodd Mead and company, 1928.
3 p. l., 353 p. 19½cm.

I. Title.
Library of Congress PZ3.L796Je 28-29080

NL 0435441 MiU OCU PPL PU ViU WaSp CaBVa IdPI OrU Or DLC LU KU IdU CoU TxU NBuU OO OCl OClh

VOLUME 337

Locke, William John, 1863-1930.
... Un joven afortunado; novela traducida del inglés por Alejandro Frías Giraud. Cubierta en colores e ilustraciones en negro de J. Longoria. Barcelona, Madrid, Sociedad de publicaciones, s. a. [°1926]
373 p. plates. 20cm.
At head of title: William J. Locke.

I. Frías Giraud, Alejandro, tr. II. Title.
Library of Congress PR6023.O15F64 1926 26-15985

NL 0435442 DLC

Locke, William John, 1863-1930. *A.5287K.1
The joyous adventures of Aristide Pujol. [Fiction.]
— London. John Lane the Bodley Head. 1912. 325 pp. Plates. 19 cm.

N5149 — T.r.

NL 0435443 MB KMK PPAp

Locke, William John, 1863-1930
The joyous adventures of Aristide Pujol, by William J. Locke; illustrations by Alec Ball. New York, John Lane company, 1912.
325 p. front., plates 19cm. $1.30

I. Title.
Library of Congress PZ3.L796J 12-22809

TxU PU PPT OC1 OO OC1JC ViU OC1W NN MB
NL 0435444 DLC MH IdB CaBVaU WaS MoU ICU NBuU PPL

H+SS A-6616 Brief listing
Locke, William John, 1863-1930
The joyous adventures of Aristide Pujol. Illus. by Alec Ball. Toronto, H. Frowde, 1912.

NL 0435445 CaOTU

LOCKE, William J[ohn], 1863-1930.
The joyous adventures of Aristide Pujol. New York, J.Lane company, 1919, [cop.1912].

NL 0435446 MH PHC

823.91 L565.2
Locke, William John, 1863-1930.
The joyous adventures of Aristide Pujol. London, Bodley Head [1926]
325 p.

NL 0435447 CaOTP

Locke, William John, 1863-1930.
Juhras swaigsne; Uiljama Dsch. Lokka romans; tulk. A. Gk.
Stella Marie.

Lettish.

NL 0435448 OC1

823.91 L814k 1927r2
Locke, William John, 1863-1930.
The Kingdom of Theophilus. London, J. Lane [1927]
3p.l., 3-342p.

NL 0435449 ICarbS CaBVaU MH CtY NcD

Locke, William John, 1863-1930.
The kingdom of Theophilus, by William J. Locke ... New York, Dodd, Mead and company, 1927.
3 p. l., 370 p. 19½cm.

I. Title.
Library of Congress PZ3.L796K1 27-19222
——— Copy 2.
Copyright A 1004263 [n41k1]

OEac OO OU MiU ViU NN MB PP PU CaBVa OC1W
NL 0435450 DLC LU WaSp TxU MsU CaOTP FU NBuU WaS

Locke, William John, 1863-1930.
The lengthened shadow, by William J. Locke ... New York, Dodd, Mead and company, 1923.
3 p. l., 372 p. 19½ cm.

I. Title.
PZ3.L796Le 23-12872

MiU ViU MB NN TxU IdU WaWW WaSp WaS
NL 0435451 DLC KU NBuU TxU PP PU NRCR OO OCU OU OEac

PR 6023 O15L4
Locke, William John, 1863-1930.
The lengthened shadow, by William J. Locke.
New York, Grosset & Dunlap [°1923]
372 p. 20 cm.

NL 0435452 LU OKentU

Locke, William John, 1863-1930.
Die lustigen Abenteuer des Aristide Pujol. Einzige autorisierte übersetzung von Gertrud Tiktin. Berlin, Volksverband der Bücherfreunde, Wegweiser [192-?]
310 p. 19 cm.

NL 0435453 CLSU WaS

Locke, William John, 1863-1930.
... **Mon neveu d'Australie, traduit de l'anglais par Théo. Varlet.** [Paris] Hachette [°1929]
2 p. l., 408 p. 19cm. (On cover: Les meilleurs romans étrangers)
At head of title: William J. Locke.

I. Varlet, Théo., 1878- tr. II. Title. *Translation of* The coming of Amos.
Library of Congress PR6023.O15C62 29-17809

NL 0435454 DLC

823.91 L814mo
Locke, William John, 1863-1930.
Moordius & co. London, J. Lane [1923]
324p.

"...Published in the United States under the title 'The lengthened shadow.'"

I. Title. II. Locke, William John, 1863-1930. The lengthened shadow.

NL 0435455 ICarbS IU TxU CSt KU CSmH

---

828 L796moo
Locke, William John, 1863-1930.
Moordius & Co. Toronto, Longmans, Green [1923]
324 p. 19 cm.

NL 0435456 LU

Locke, William John, 1863-1930.
Moordius i ska; przełożył Wanda Peszkowa.

NL 0435457 OC1

Locke, William John, 1863-1930.
... **Moordius y compañía, novela; traducida del inglés por Th. Scheppelmann, cubierta en colores e ilustraciones en negro de Szathmáry. Barcelona, Madrid, Sociedad general de publicaciones, s. a.** [°1925]
355 p. plates. 20cm.
At head of title: William J. Locke.

I. Scheppelmann, Th., tr. II. Title.
Library of Congress PR6023.O15M64 1925 26-7156

NL 0435458 DLC

PZ 8.3 L68 Mr 1915
Locke, William John, 1863-1930.
Morals for the young by Marcus [pseud.] Illustrated by George Morrow with a foreword by William J. Locke. London, J. Lane, 1915.
1 v. (unpaged) illus.

NL 0435459 CaBVaU MH

Locke, William John, 1863-1930.
The morals of Marcus Ordeyne; a play...by William J. Locke. [New York? 19—] 1 v. 29cm.
Prompt-book, typewritten.

1. Drama, English. 2. Prompt-books. I. Title. May 12, 1944

NL 0435460 NN

LOCKE, WILLIAM JOHN, 1863-1930.
The morals of Marcus Ordeyne; a play in four acts. [New York, Rosenfield, 190-] 4 pts. in 1 v. 28cm.

Typescript.
Includes property, light and costume plots and original cast.
Produced as "The morals of Marcus" at the Criterion theatre, New York, Nov. 18, 1907.

1. Drama, English. I. Title.

NL 0435461 NN

Locke, William John, 1863-1930.
The morals of Marcus Ordeyne; a novel, by William J. Locke. New York and London, J. Lane, 1905.
5 p. l., 3-303 p. 19cm.

I. Title.
Library of Congress PZ3.L796Mo 5-11070

MtBuM
MtBC MtU OrCS OrPR OrP WaTC WaT WaTC OrStbM OrSaW IdPI IdU IdB AAP KU MiU OEac OC1h PPL OrU-M OrU
NL 0435462 DLC WaSpG WaSp WaE WaS Wa WaPS CaBVaU

VOLUME 337

Locke, William John, 1863-
... The morals of Marcus Ordeyne. A play in four acts, by William J. Locke. London, Printed by W. T. Haycock & sons, ltd., 1906.
80 p. 21½cm.
"For private circulation only."

I. Title.

NL 0435463 MiU MH

Locke, William John, 1863-1930.
The morals of Marcus Ordeyne, a novel, by William J. Locke. London, John Lane; New York, John Lane company [°1906]
3 p. l., 3-303 p. 19 cm.

I. Title.

Library of Congress PZ3.L796Mo 3 20—15618

NL 0435464 DLC MU OU OCl IdPI

Locke, William John, 1863-1930.
The morals of Marcus Ordeyne, a novel, by William J. Locke. New York, Grosset & Dunlap [°1906]
5 p. l., 3-303 p. 19½cm.

I. Title.

Library of Congress PZ3.L796Mo+ 43-37795

WaSpG WaS WaT WaWW WaTC
MH ViU NjP PU OrStbM MtBuM OrU OrPR WaE OrCS Wa
NL 0435465 DLC IdB WaPS OrSaW OrU-M Or NcU CoU NN

Locke, William John, 1863-1930.
The morals of Marcus Ordeyne; a novel, by William J. Locke. New York, J. Lane company; [etc., etc.] 1907.
5 p. l., 3-303 p. 19½cm.

I. Title.

Library of Congress PZ3.L796Mo 2 7—32442

NL 0435466 DLC OrU WaS OOxM MoU PBm

PZ 3 .L796 .MO5 Locke, William John, 1863-1930.
The morals of Marcus Ordeyne, a novel, by William J. Locke. London, John Lane; New York, John Lane company, 1908.
303 p.

The morals of Marcus Ordeyne.

NL 0435467 MoU

Locke, William John, 1863-
The morals of Marcus Ordeyne; a novel, by William J. Locke. New York, J. Lane company; [etc., etc.] 1909.
5 p. l., 3-303 p. 19½cm.

I. Title.

Library of Congress PZ3.L796Mo 4 9—7339

NL 0435468 DLC WaSp NcD OO OCl PBa PU

LOCKE, William John, 1863-1930.
The morals of Marcus Ordeyne; a novel. London, J. Lane, The Bodley Head, etc., etc., 1910, [cop.1906].

19 cm.

NL 0435469 MH PHC PPT PU

PR6023 O81M8 1910 Locke, William John, 1863-1930.
The morals of Marcus Ordeyne; a novel. New York, Grosset & Dunlap [1910?]
5 p.l., 3-303 p., 4 l. 19cm
Copyright date on cover illus.: 1910.
Publisher's advertisements (4 l.) at end.
Beige cloth, with col. illustrated label mounted on front cover.

NL 0435470 CSt

Locke, William John, 1863-1930.
The morals of Marcus Ordeyne; a novel, by William J. Locke. New York, Dodd, Mead and company, 1927.
4 p. l., 3-303 p. 19½cm.

NL 0435471 ViU PU

Locke, William John, 1863-1930
Mountebank. Grosset, Lane, 1920-21.

NL 0435472 PPAp

Locke, William John, 1863-
The mountebank, by William J. Locke ... New York, John Lane company; London, John Lane, 1921.
320 p. 19½cm.

I. Title.

Library of Congress PZ3.L796Mou 21—2970

CaBVaU
LU IdU PU PCC PPT OCl OO MiU OEac ViU TxU MB NN
NL 0435473 DLC IdPI WaS ICarbS NcD TxU IEN NBuU MoU

823.89 L79 Oo 1926 Locke, William John, 1863-1930.
The old bridge. London, John Lane [1926]
347p. 19cm.

NL 0435474 KU CaBVaU TxU ICarbS ICN CSmH MH PPSCI

Locke, William John, 1863-
Perella, by William J. Locke ... New York, Dodd, Mead and company, 1926.
3 p. l., 378 p. 19½cm.

I. Title.

Library of Congress PZ3.L796Pe 26—15180

OC1W OEac OLak MB NN Or CaBVa CaBVaU
NL 0435475 DLC LU IdPI NcD CoU TxU PPT PHC PPL OO

Locke, William John, 1863-1930.
The red planet, by William J. Locke ... New York, John Lane company; London, John Lane; [etc., etc.] 1917.
349 p. 19cm.

I. Title.

Library of Congress PZ3.L796Re 17—26481

WaSpG Or
PPGi OC1W OClh OLak OO CSmH MB NN TxU CaBVaU WaWW
NL 0435476 DLC LU FU TxU CaOTP NcD NjP PHC PSC OU

Locke, William John, 1863-1930.
Rough road. N.Y., Grosset, [c1917]

NL 0435477 PU

PR6023 O 2R6 in RareBooks Room Locke, William John, 1862-1930.
The rough road. London, New York, Lane, 1918.
308 p. 20cm.
Author's autograph presentation copy.

1. European War, 1914-1918 - Fiction.
I. Title.

NL 0435478 CoU

Locke, William John, 1863-
The rough road, by William J. Locke ... New York, John Lane company; London, John Lane; [etc., etc.] 1918.
346 p. 19½cm.

1. European war, 1914-1918—Fiction. I. Title.

Library of Congress PZ3.L796Ro 18-15263

CaOTP LU MU NcU ViU NcD NjP
OC1JC PHC PPGi TxU WaS OrP IdU WaTC CaBVaU UU
NL 0435479 DLC OC1W MB NN PU OO OCl OClh MiU

PR6023 .O 15R6 1927 Locke, William John, 1863-1930.
The rough road. New York, Dodd, Mead, 1927.
346 p. 19 cm.

1. European war, 1914-1918--Fiction.
I. Title.

NL 0435480 PU

Locke, William John, 1863-
... Séptimo, novela traducida del inglés por Alejandro Frías Giraud, cubierta en colores y láminas en negro de P. Clapera. Barcelona, Madrid, Sociedad general de publicaciones, s. a. [°1925]
358 p. plates. 20cm.

I. Frías Giraud, Alejandro, tr. II. Title.

Library of Congress PR6023.O15S4 1925 26-10521

NL 0435481 DLC

VOLUME 337

ar V
92
Locke, William John, 1863-
Septimus. With four illustrations by James Montgomery Flagg. New York, A.L. Burt Company ⌐1908⌐
315 p. 20cm.

NL 0435482 NIC OrSaW IdU WaWW PU

Locke, William John, 1863–1930.
Septimus, by William J. Locke; illustrations by James Montgomery Flagg. New York, J. Lane company, 1909.
4 p. l., 315 p. front., 7 pl. 19½cm.

I. Title.

Library of Congress PZ3.L796Se 9—562

NL 0435483 DLC WaSp OO IdPI TxU OClW PBa PP OCl OClJC OEac NN PPL NcU OKentU PPGi TxU OrP WaS

PR6023
.O 15S4
1909
Locke, William John, 1863-1920.
Septimus. Toronto, H. Frowde, 1909.
360 p. 20 cm.

NL 0435484 MB ICarbS CaBVaU IU OClW PU

Locke, William John, 1863–1930.
Septimus, by William J. Locke. Illustrations by James Montgomery Flagg. New York, John Lane company, 1910.
4 p. l., 315 p. front., plates. 19cm.

I. Title.

Library of Congress (✱) (PZ3.L796Se 2) 12—31343
[a37g1]

NL 0435485 DLC Wa PHC PU PPT MB NN

823
L79se
1912
Locke, William John, 1863-
Septimus, by William J. Locke ... with four illustrations by James Montgomery Flagg. New York, A. L. Burt company [1912]
315p. front., plates.

NL 0435486 IU

Locke, William John, 1863-1930.
Septimus. [London] John Lane [1925]
310 p. 17.5 cm.
Half-title: The works of William J.Locke. Autographed ed., vol.X.

NL 0435487 MH

Locke, William John, 1863–
Septimus, by William J. Locke. New York. Dodd, Mead and company, 1927.
3 p. l., 315 p. 19½cm.

I. Title.

Library of Congress PZ3.L796Se 6 29-25271

NL 0435488 DLC PPD PSt

Locke, William John, 1863–1930.
The shorn lamb, by William J. Locke. New York, Dodd, Mead & company, 1930.
3 p. l., 321 p. 19½cm.

I. Title.

Library of Congress PZ3.L796Sh 30-27068

NL 0435489 DLC WaE LU PPL PHC PU OO MiU OCl OClh OLak Or WaS NN WaT

Locke, William John, 1863-1930.
The shorn lamb, by William J. Locke. London, J. Lane [1931]
3 p.l.,326 p. 19cm.

"First published in 1931."
Advertisements, ⌐10⌐ p., at end.

NL 0435490 CLU-C TxU CtY MH

Locke, William John, 1863–
Simon the jester, by William J. Locke. London, J. Lane; New York, John Lane company, 1910.
3 p. l., 348 p. 20cm. $1.50

Library of Congress PZ3.L796Si 2 10-15396

NL 0435491 DLC NcD PU PBa PBm OEac OO OCl OCX MiU CSmH MB NRCR

Locke, William John, 1863–1930.
Simon the jester, by William J. Locke; illustrations by James Montgomery Flagg. New York, John Lane company, 1910.
3 p. l., 332 p. front., plates. 19cm.

I. Title.

Library of Congress PZ3.L796Si 10—14369

NL 0435492 DLC MtBC WaE OrPR OrP OrCS MtU Wa WaT WaSpG WaS OrSaW OrU-M WaWW MtBuM OrStbM OrU MsU CaOTP MB NN GU CaBVaU WaTC OrU WaSp WaPS IdU NjP Wa IdB IdPI ViU TxU MU OU NBuU MoU OClW

Locke, William John, 1863–
Simon the jester, by William J. Locke. London, John Lane; New York, John Lane company, 1911.
3 p. l., 348 p. 20cm.
On verso of t.-p.: Fourth edition.

I. Title.

Library of Congress PZ3.L796Si 4 16-19164

NL 0435493 DLC

PR6023
.01585
1913
Locke, William John, 1863–1930.
Simon the jester; with illus. by James Montgomery Flagg. New York, A. L. Burt Co. ⌐1913⌐
332 p. plates. 20cm.

NL 0435494 ViU

Locke, William John, 1863-1930
Simon the jester... N.Y., Dodd, Mead and co., 1922.
332 p.

NL 0435495 PPT

Locke, William John, 1863-1930
Simon the jester. N.Y., Dodd, 1925 ⌐c1909⌐

NL 0435496 PU

Locke, William John, 1863–
Some women and a man; a comedy of contrasts, by William J. Locke ... New York, F. T. Neely, 1896.
vi, 285 p. plates. 20½cm. (Publisher's lettering: Neely's library of choice literature. no. 59)

Library of Congress PZ3.L796So 7-15171†

NL 0435497 DLC

Locke, William John, 1863–
Stella Maris, by William J. Locke, illustrations by Frank Wiles. New York: Grosset & Dunlap [cop. 1912]. 2 p.l., 357 p., 4 pl. (incl. front.) 12°.

1. Fiction (English). 2. Title. 3. Wiles, Frank, illustrator.
December 19, 1917

NL 0435498 NN

Locke, William John, 1863–1930.
Stella Maris, by William J. Locke; illustrations by Frank Wiles. New York, John Lane company; London, John Lane; [etc., etc.] 1913.
3 p. l., 357 p. front., plates. 19½cm.

I. Title.

Library of Congress PZ3.L796St 13—35200

NL 0435499 DLC WaWW WaTC WaS WaT WaPS WaSpG Or OrPR OrSaW CaBVaU IdB IdPI IdU OrP OrCS MtU MtBC Wa NjP MU MiU TxU OrU WaE ICarbS WaSp MtBuM OrU-M OrStbM PBm PBa PPT PPL OO OCl OClh OClW ViU NN

Locke, William John, 1863-1930.
Stella Maris; illustrations by Frank Miles. N.Y., 1918.
357 p.

NL 0435500 PHC

Locke, William John, 1863-
Stella Maris ...N.Y., Dodd, Mead 1924.
357 p.

NL 0435501 PSC

VOLUME 337

Locke, William John, 1863-1930.
Stella Maris... N.Y., Dodd, Mead & co., 1936.

NL 0435502 PU

823.91 L814ST
Locke, William John, 1863- 1930.
Stories near and far, by William J. Locke. London, J. Lane [1926]
302 p. 19 cm.
CONTENTS.—The song of Oo-oo.—A moonlight effect.—A spartan of the hills.—Pontifex.—An echo of the past.—The apostle.—Ridet Olympus.—The golden journey of Mr. Paradyne.

NL 0435503 NcD TxU CtY CSmH

Locke, William John, 1863-
Stories near and far, by William J. Locke. New York, Dodd, Mead & company, 1927.
4 p. l., 253 p. 19cm.
CONTENTS.—The song of Oo-oo.—A moonlight effect.—A spartan of the hills.—Pontifex.—An echo of the past.—The apostle.—Ridet Olympus.—The golden journey of Mr. Paradyne.—Roses.

I. Title.
Library of Congress PZ3.L7968to 27—4322

WaPS WaSp
CaBVaU WaE IdU OrP OrPR MtBC IdPI Wa IdB MtU WaS
OrStbM OrSaW Or ViU OCl OLak OClW MiU PP PPL MB
NL 0435504 DLC WaSpG WaT WaTC WaWW MtBuM OrU-M

823.89 L79 Ost
Locke, William John, 1863-1930.
A study in shadows. London & New York, J. Lane [n.d.]
285p. 20cm.

NL 0435505 KU

Locke, William John, 1863-1930.
Study in shadows. London, Ward, 1896.
285 p.

NL 0435506 PU IU

Locke, William John, 1863-1930.
A study in shadows. London, 1899.

NL 0435507 PPL

PR 6023. 015S87 1907
Locke, William John, 1863-
A study in shadows. London, J. Lane; New York, J. Lane, 1907.
285p. 19cm.

NL 0435508 MU PPRCl NjP

Locke, William John, 1863-1930.
A study in shadows, by William J. Locke. London, J. Lane; New York, J. Lane company, 1908.
4 p. l., 285 p. 19cm.

W 10-102
Washington, D. C. Public Library

NL 0435509 DWP IdPI PBa OCl

LOCKE, William J[ohn], 1863-1930.
A study in shadows. London, J.Lane, etc., etc., [1913].

NL 0435510 MH

PZ 3 .L796 Stu
Locke, William John, 1863-1930.
A study in shadows, and The demagogue and Lady Phayre, by William J. Locke. [London] John Lane [1920]
viii, 326 p. 18cm.

I. Title. II. Title: The demagogue and Lady Phayre.

NL 0435511 KyLoU

Locke, William John, *1863-1930.* 3066.271
Tajemnica Mateusza Lanyona. [Powieść.] Z upoważnienia autora przełożył Dr. J. P. Zajączkowski. [Przy] W. J. Locke. — Warszawa. 1935. 263 pp. [Biblioteka tygodnika ilustrowanego.] 19.5 cm., in 8s.
Translated title: Mystery of Mateusza Lanyona.

D9832 — T.r. — S.r. — Poland. Lan...ge. Works in Polish. — Zajączkowski, J. P., tr.

NL 0435512 MB OCl PP

PR 6023 015T3
Locke, William John, 1863-1930
The tale of Triona. Toronto, McClelland and Stewart [n.d.]
312 p.

NL 0435513 CaOTU

823.91 L814TE
Locke, William John, 1863-1930.
The tale of Triona. London, J. Lane, 1922.
312 p. 19 cm.

NL 0435514 NcD CaOTP PSt CtY CsmH TxU CaBVaU

Locke, William John, 1863-1930.
The tale of Triona, by William J. Locke ... New York, Dodd, Mead and company, 1922.
3 p. l., 397 p. 19½cm.

I. Title.
Library of Congress PZ3.L796Ta 22—18470

PU PP OCU OEac MiU OClJC OCl OO NN MB
NL 0435515 DLC MoU MU NBuG TxU WaE WaS ViU NRCR

Locke, William John, 1863-1930.
The town of Tombarel. c1926.

NL 0435516 OClh

Locke, William John, 1863-1930.
Town of Tombarel. N.Y., Dodd. Mead & co., 1926.

NL 0435517 PPYH

823.91 L814TA
Locke, William John, 1863-1930.
The town of Tombarel. London, J. Lane [1930]
311 p. 19 cm.

NL 0435518 NcD TxU CoU MU CLU-C

Locke, William John, 1863-1930.
The town of Tombarel [by] William J. Locke. New York Dodd, Mead & company, 1930.
3 p. l., 297 p. 19½cm.

I. Title.
Library of Congress PZ3.L796To 30—8603
——— Copy 2.
Copyright A 20601 [a41b1]

OO MiU ODW PPL ViU NN PU GU NBuU NcD LU
NL 0435519 DLC MB WaE WaWW WaS MoU PPAp OCU OClW

Locke, William John, 1863-
The usurper, by William J. Locke. London and New York, J. Lane, 1902 [1901]
2 p. l., 356 p. 20½cm.

I. Title. 1—23427
Library of Congress PZ3.L796Us

OO GU
NL 0435520 DLC PPT PU NjP PPL MiU OEac OCl OClh NN

Locke, William John, 1863-1930.
The usurper. New York, Grosset & Dunlap, 1902 [c1901]
356 p. 20 cm.

NL 0435521 LU

Locke, William John, 1863-1930.
The usurper, by William J. Locke. New York & London, J. Lane, 1904.
2 p. l., 356 p. 20½cm. (Half-title: Canvasback library of popular fiction. vol. VIII)

NL 0435522 ViU

Locke, William John, 1863-1930.
The ursurper. N.Y., Lane, 1908.
356 p.

NL 0435523 PPRCI

VOLUME 337

Locke, William J[ohn]. 1863-1930. 2
The usurper. New York: J. Lane Company, 1909. 2 p.l., 356 p. 12°.

NL 0435524 NN

LOCKE, William J[ohn], 1863-
The usurper. London, J. Lane, etc., etc., 1910.

NL 0435525 MH

Locke, William John, 1863-
The usurper, ... London, and N.Y., J. Lane, 1911. 356 p.

NL 0435526 OClW

Locke, William John, 1863-
The usurper. London, 1920.

NL 0435527 NjP

Locke, William John, 1863-
El vendedor de felicidades, novela traducida del inglés por Alejandro Frías Giraud, cubierta en colores y láminas en negro de Longoria. Barcelona, Madrid, Sociedad general de publicaciones, s. a. [1926]
375 p. plates. 20cm.
At head of title: William J. Locke.

I. Frías Giraud, Alejandro, tr. II. Title.
Library of Congress PR6023.O15W65 1926 26-11406

NL 0435528 DLC

PZ3 .L796Vi Locke, William John, 1863-1930.
Viviette, ... [New York, c1910]

NL 0435529 DLC

Locke, William John, 1863-
Viviette, by William J. Locke ... with illustrations in colour by Earl Stetson Crawford. New York, John Lane company; London, John Lane, 1916.
198 p. col. front., col. plates. 19½cm. $1.00

I. Title.
Library of Congress PZ3.L796Vi 2 16—10123

NL 0435530 DLC IdU MB NN PP PPL PBa MiU OCl

Locke, William J[ohn], 1863-1930. 2
Where love is. New York: Grosset & Dunlap [cop. 1903]. vi p., 1 l., 358 p. 12°.

I. Title. CENTRAL CIRCULATION.
N. Y. P. L. June 16, 1911.

NL 0435531 NN GU ViU PPL

Locke, William John, 1863-1930.
Where love is, a novel, by William J. Locke ... New York and London, J. Lane, 1903.
vi p., 1 l., 358 p. 20cm.

I. Title.
Library of Congress (PZ3.L796W) 3—22818

NL 0435532 DLC CaBVaU WaWW

Locke, William John, 1863-1930.
Where love is. New York, 1907.

NL 0435533 NjP

Locke, William John, 1863-1930
Where love is, a novel. N.Y., Lane, 1908. 358 p.

NL 0435534 PPRCI

Locke, William John, 1863-1930.
Where love is, a novel, by William J. Locke ... New York and London, J. Lane, 1909.
vi p., 1 l., 358 p. 20cm.

NL 0435535 ViU

Locke, William John, 1863-1930
Where love is. N.Y., Lane, 1910. 358 p.

NL 0435536 PU IdPI

22418.15.8.10
Locke, William John, 1863-1930.
Where love is. London, etc., John Lane, 1917.
358 p. 19 cm.

NL 0435537 MH

Locke, William John, 1863-1930.
Where love is. [London] John Lane, ltd. [1925]
viii, 358 p. 18.5 cm.
"The works of William J. Locke. Autograph edition. Vol. VII." - p.[iii]

NL 0435538 MH

PR 6023 .O15W45 1899 Locke, William John, 1863-
The white dove. [3d ed.] New York, J. Lane[1899]
391p. 20cm.

NL 0435539 MU ViU OClh OCl PPRCl OO

Locke, William John, 1863-
The white dove [a novel] by William J. Locke ... London and New York, J. Lane, 1900 [1899]
4 p. l., 391 p. 19½cm.

Jan. 25, 1900-133
Library of Congress PZ3.L796Wh

NL 0435540 DLC IU PPL PU

PR6023 .O81W58 1907 Locke, William John, 1863-1930.
The white dove. [3d ed.] New York, J. Lane, 1907, [c1899]
4 p.l., 391 p. 19cm
Green cloth.

NL 0435541 CSt NjP

Locke, William J[ohn], 1863-1930. 2
The white dove. New York: John Lane Co., 1911. 4 p.l., 391 p. 12°.

NL 0435542 NN

Locke, William John, 1863-
The white dove, by William J. Locke ... London, John Lane; New York, John Lane company, 1912.
4 p. l., 391 p. 20cm.

I. Title.
Library of Congress PZ3.L796Wh 4 16-19165

NL 0435543 DLC IdPI

Locke, William John, 1863-
The William J. Locke calendar, comp. by Emma M. Pope. London, John Lane; New York, John Lane company; [etc., etc.] 1914.
3 p. l., 3-122 p. 19½cm. $1.00

I. Pope, Emma M., comp. II. Title.
Library of Congress PR6023.O15W5 1914 14-18373

NL 0435544 DLC NN OCl

AC-L L796wo 1916 Locke, William John, 1863-1930.
The wonderful year, by William J. Locke ... London, John Lane; New York, John Lane company, 1916.
345p. 20cm.

Bookplate of Charles Dexter Allen, Montclair, N.J.

I. Title. A.F.: Allen, Charles Dexter.

NL 0435545 TxU MH NcD IU

VOLUME 337

Locke, William John, 1863–1930.
The wonderful year, by William J. Locke ... New York, John Lane company; London, John Lane, 1916.
364 p. 20½cm.

I. Title.
Library of Congress PZ3.L796Wo 16—20111

KMK MU LU
OClh MH MB NN CSmH NIC CoFS MoU Or OrP TxU NSyU
NL 0435546 DLC WaWW WaS PPL PU PSC PBm OClW OO OCl

823
L796w
1917 LOCKE, WILLIAM JOHN, 1863-1930.
The wonderful year, by William J. Locke ... New York, John Lane company; London, John Lane, 1917.
364p. 20½cm.

NL 0435547 TxU IdU PHC NjP

Locke, William John, 1863-1930
The wonderful year. Lane. N.Y., 1918.
364 p

NL 0435548 OClW-H

F29
B916 Locke, William Nash, 1909-
The French colony at Brunswick, Maine; a historical sketch, par William N. Locke. [n. p., n. d.]
97-111 l. map, tables. 25 cm.

Caption title.
Reprinted from Archives de folklore.

1. French in Brunswick, Me. I. Title.

NL 0435549 MeB

Locke, William Nash, 1909- joint comp.

Sullivan, Edward Daniel, 1913– *comp.*
Glossary of technical terms for La guerre moderne [by] Edward D. Sullivan and William N. Locke. With a comparative table of ranks in the army, navy, and air force of the United States, Great Britain, and France. Cambridge, Mass., Harvard university press, 1942.

Locke, William Nash, 1909- joint comp.

Sullivan, Edward Daniel, 1913– *comp.*
La guerre moderne; recueil d'articles choisis par Edward D. Sullivan et William N. Locke ... Cambridge, Mass., Harvard university press, 1942.

Locke, William Nash, 1909- ed.

MT. Mechanical translation; devoted to the translation of languages with the aid of machines. v. 1-
Mar. 1954–
[Cambridge, Mass.] Massachusetts Institute of Technology.

Locke, William Nash, 1909– *ed.*
Machine translation of languages; fourteen essays, edited by William N. Locke and A. Donald Booth. [Cambridge] Published jointly by Technology Press of the Massachusetts Institute of Technology and Wiley, New York [1955]
xii, 243 p. 24 cm.
Includes bibliographies.

1. Machine translating. 2. Translating machines. I. Booth, Andrew Donald, joint ed. II. Title.

PN242.L6 808 55-8750

WaTC AU NBuC DAU DSI MU
PPSKF PP CaBVaU OCU OCl OU NN PSt DNLM IdU MoSW
IaU TU NN MB TxU OClW ICJ OO OrCS Or OrPR OrU WaS
NL 0435553 DLC IdPI NcRS NcD PBL PPT PPF ViU

Locke, William Nash, 1909–
Pronunciation of the French spoken at Brunswick, Maine. With a pref. by J. M. Carrière. Greensboro, N. C., American Dialect Society, 1949.
201 p. diagrs. 23 cm. (Publication of the American Dialect Society, no. 12)
Bibliography: p. 21-22.

1. French language—Dialects—Brunswick, Me. (Series: American Dialect Society. Publication no. 12)

PC3680.U7M3 447.9 51-39554

UU CoU OrPS
NL 0435554 DLC TxU OrU MoU NNC ViU MH NIC MU NN

Locke, William Nash, 1909–
Scientific French; a concise description of the structural elements of scientific and technical French. Cambridge [Mass.] Technology Press of M. I. T., 1954.
63 p. 28 cm.

1. French language— Technical French. I. Title.

[Q211] 448.242 55-14653 ‡
Printed for U. S. Q. B. R. by Library of Congress

NL 0435555 ScCleU

Locke, W[illiam] O[scar]
Locke's platinum dog-heads; photographed from life. Cincinnati, O., W. O. Locke [1900]
41 numb. l. incl. plates. 18 x 21½cm.

1. Dog—Pictorial works. Nov. 15, 1900–132

Library of Congress QL795.D6L7 Copyright

NL 0435556 DLC ViW

Locke, William S 1904–
Connecticut probate practice, by William S. Locke and P. Corbin Kohn. Boston, Little, Brown, 1950–51 [v. 1, 1951; v. 3, 1950]
3 v. 24 cm.
Kept up to date by pocket part service.
"A revision of ... Probate law and practice of Connecticut by Cleaveland, Hewitt and Clark, published in 1915."
CONTENTS.—v. 1. The probate court.—v. 2. Settlement of decedents' estates. Commitment, conservatorship, guardianship, adoption.—v. 3. Connecticut death taxes.
1. Probate law and practice — Connecticut. 2. Inheritance and transfer tax—Connecticut. I. Kohn, P. Corbin, 1909– joint author. II. Cleaveland, Livingston Warner, 1860–1929. Probate law and practice of Connecticut.

347.6 50-7612 rev
[r51c2]

NL 0435557 DLC NBuU-L GU-L CU-I

LOCKE, William Ware.
"Lead, kindly light". Evening, night morning. Boston, 1907.

1 pam.

NL 0435558 MH

LOCKE, William Ware.
On the voyage; [a gift-book for my fellow-travellers]. Boston, cop. 1915.

pp. (2), 45.

NL 0435559 MH RPB

Locke, William Ware.
On the voyage, and other poems, by William Ware Locke. Boston, Manthorne & Burack, inc. [©1941]
195 p. 20½cm.

I. Title.
Library of Congress PS3523.O234O5 1941 42-1334
811.5

NL 0435560 DLC NN

Locke, William Willard.
1897 Reports on: I. Garbage disposal in the outlying wards. II. History of the garbage contract. III. Refuse disposal of cities. 120 p. il. O. [Brooklyn 1897.]
Reprinted from *Report of the Department of Health of the City of Brooklyn, 1896.*
By William Willard Locke & Joseph B. Taylor.

NL 0435561 ICJ

Locke-Elliott, Sumner.
Buy me blue ribbons, comedy in three acts. Acting ed. [New York] Dramatists Play Service [1952]
78 p. illus. 19 cm.

I. Title.
PR6023.O2B9 822.91 52-39333 ‡

WaSpG WaT WaTC WaWW Or OrStbM OrSaW OrU-M MtBuM
MtU OrCS RPB OrP OrPR OrU Wa WaE WaPS WaS WaSp
NL 0435562 DLC IdU IdPI IdB CaBVaU PU NN MtBC

Locke-Elliott, Sumner.
Interval, a play in three acts, by Sumner Locke-Elliott Melbourne and London, Melbourne university press in association with Oxford university press, 1942.
105, [1] p. 19cm.

I. Title.
Library of Congress PR6023.O2 I 5 43-48335
822.91

NL 0435563 DLC OU CtY TxU

LOCKE-ELLIOTT, SUMNER.
Interval; a play in three acts. [2. ed.] [Melbourne]
Melbourne university press, 1947. 107 p. 19cm.

1. Drama, English. I. Title.

NL 0435564 NN NcU ICarbS CaBVaU

VOLUME 337

Locke Amsden, or The schoolmaster
see under Thompson, Daniel, 1795-1868.

Locke & Locke, *Dallas.*
Discussion before the Texas welfare commission of the Robertson insurance act requiring life insurance companies to invest their Texas reserves in Texas securities and imposing certain taxes and other requirements. By Locke & Locke, Dallas, Texas. Dallas, Egan printing company [1912]
cover-title, iv, 74 p. 24cm.

1. Insurance, Life—Finance. 2. Insurance law—Texas. I. Texas welfare commission.
13-26027
Library of Congress HG8846.L6

NL 0435566 DLC ICJ IU

Locke & Locke, Dallas, Texas.
The Robertson bill, ... Dallas, J.F. Worley ptg co. n.d.
34 p.

At head of t.p.- House bill no.112 in the Texas legislature.

NL 0435567 OO

F863 .6 L48 Locke & Montague, plaintiffs-appellants.
(Porter Gold and Silver Mining Company, et al., defendants-respondents)
Action in equity to foreclose a mortgage.
George Rowe and F.L. Hatch, attorneys for plaintiffs-appellants; Charles E. Filkins, attorneys for defendants-respondents.
No. [unnumbered] in the Supreme Court of the State of California.
Contents.
[1] Respondents' brief. Marysville, Calif., 1869. (17 p.)

1. Foreclosure - California. I. Porter Gold and Silver Mining Company, defendant-respondent. II. Rowe, George, lawyer. III. Hatch, F L IV. Filkins, Charles E V. California. Supreme Court.

NL 0435568 CU-B

Locke decorative co., *Brooklyn.*
Makers of windows, Cathedral chapel, Queen of all saints; Locke decorative co. ... [New York, The De Vinne press] 1913.
[63] p. col. front., illus. 19½cm. $0.75

1. Brooklyn. Cathedral of the Immaculate conception. I. Locke, Alexander Stephen.
14-2880
Library of Congress NK5312.B8C3

NL 0435569 DLC NBLiHi

Locke Richardson's tour around the world with Shakespeare—some information as to his remarkable career in many lands... [New York, 1889?] 48 p. port. 15cm.

1. Richardson, Locke. 2. Shakespeare, William—Stage history—Indiv. actors—Richardson.

NL 0435570 NN

Locke Township, Ingham Co., Michigan
[lists. n.p., n.d.]
[6] ℓ. typescript

Contents.-Landowners listed on map published 1859.-Some of the earliest residents... including 1840 census and/or resident taxpayers in 1844.

NL 0435571 MiD

Locked doors
see under Beranger, Clara.

LOCKEFEER, LOUIS.
"Springtij", spel van de watersnood in drie bedrijven. Zaandijk, J. Heijnis [1953] 88 p. 18cm. (Toneelfonds J. Heijnis Tsz. 401)

Film reproduction. Negative.

1. Drama, Dutch. I. Title.

NL 0435573 NN

Lockefeer, Louis.
Zondvloed; een spel van het land... 2. druk. Zaandijk, J. Heijnis Tsz. [n.d.] 119 p. 17cm.

On cover: no. 366.

1. Drama, Dutch.

NL 0435574 NN

Lockemann (C. A. Adolph). * Ueber die akute Gehirnhöhlen-Wassersucht. 38 pp. 8°. *Würzburg, C. A. Zürn,* 1835.

NL 0435575 DNLM

Lockemann, Fritz.
Das Gedicht und seine Klanggestalt. Emsdetten (Westf.) Verlag Lechte [1952]
xii, 232 p. diagrs. 24 cm.

Bibliography included in "Anmerkungen" (p. 211-225) "Quellen der Beispiele": p. 226-227.

1. Poetics. 2. Accents and accentuation. 3. Versification. 4. German poetry - Hist. & crit. I. Title.
A 53-4241
Illinois. Univ. Library for Library of Congress

NL 0435576 NN TxU UU CU-S GU OrU IU PPiU CtY OO CU IaU OU PPT OkU CLSU

808.5 L814s **Lockemann, Fritz.**
Sprecherziehung als Menschenbildung. Heidelberg, F.H. Kerle [1954]
99p. 21cm. (Werkheft zur Sprecherziehung)

1.Speech. I.Title.

NL 0435577 IEN

Lockemann, Fritz.
Zur aesthetik des reproduktiven kunstschaffens. Goettingen. Diss 1932.

NL 0435578 PU

Lockemann, Georg, 1871- ed.

Archiv für geschichte der mathematik, der naturwissenschaften und der technik ... 1.-9. bd., [nov. 1908]-aug. 1922; 10.-13. bd. (neue folge 1-4), juli 1927-feb. 1931. Leipzig [etc.] F. C. W. Vogel, 1909-31.

Lockemann, Georg, 1871–
Aschenanalyse. Von Georg Lockemann ...
(*In* Abderhalden, Emil, ed. Handbuch der biologischen arbeitsmethoden ... Berlin, 1920– 25cm. abt. I, Chemische methoden. t. 3 (1921) p. [657]-844. illus., pl. I-II (1 col.))
Bibliographical foot-notes.

1. Chemistry, Analytic. I. Title.
A C 36-4222
Title from Ohio State Univ. Library of Congress [QH324.A3 1920 abt. 1, t. 3]
(574.072)

NL 0435580 OU DNLM

Lockemann, Georg, 1871–
Die Beziehungen der Chemie zur Biologie und Medizin, von Dr. Georg Lockemann, ... Heidelberg, C. Winter, 1909.
29, [1] p. 24cm.

NL 0435581 ICJ OCU CU DNLM

Lockemann, Georg, 1871–
Einführung in die analytische Chemie. [2. völlig umbearb. Aufl.] Heidelberg, C. Winter, 1946.
178 p. illus., tables. 23 cm.

1. Chemistry, Analytic. I. Title.
QD75.L62 1946 A F 48-5227*
Iowa. State Coll. Libr. for Library of Congress †

NL 0435582 IaAS DLC NcU TxU MH ViU InU

Lockemann, Georg, 1871–
Die Entwicklung und der gegenwärtige Stand der Atomtheorie, in Umrissen skizziert von Dr. Georg Lockemann, ... Heidelberg, C. Winter, 1905.
viii, 48 p. 1 fold. table. 23½cm.
"Literatur," p. [42]-44.

NL 0435583 ICJ WU MiU OCU

Lockemann, Georg, 1871-
Ernst Beckmann (1853-1923) sein leben und wirken dargestellt von Georg Lockemann. Berlin, Verlag Chemie g. m. b. h., 1927.
3 p. l., [5]-65 p. front. (port.) 23½cm.
"Druckfehlerberichtigung" slip inserted before p. 31.
"Verzeichnis der wissenschaftlichen abhandlungen von Ernst Beckmann": p. 53-60.
"Verzeichnis der doktoranden von Ernst Beckmann und der title ihrer dissertationen": p. 60-65.

1. Beckmann, Ernst Otto, 1853-1923.

NL 0435584 MiU CU NN OCU

VOLUME 337

Lockemann, Georg, 1871-
Geschichte der Chemie, in kurzgefasster Darstellung. Berlin, W. de Gruyter, 1950-55.
2 v. illus. 16 cm. (Sammlung Göschen, Bd. 264-265/265a)

1. Chemistry—Hist.
QD11.L55 52-41026 rev ‡
Library of Congress ⌐r56b2¬

NL 0435585 DLC NN CLU ICJ

Lockemann, Georg, 1871-
Quantitative faecesaschenanalyse. Von Georg Lockemann ...
(*In* Abderhalden, Emil, ed. Handbuch der biologischen arbeitsmethoden ... Berlin, 1920- 25cm. abt. IV, Angewandte chemische und physikalische methoden. t. 6, 1. hälfte (1926) p. ⌐357⌐-396. illus.)
Bibliographical foot-notes.

1. Feces—Analysis. A C 36-2670
Title from Ohio State Univ.
Library of Congress [QH324.A3 1920 abt. 4, t. 6] (574.072)

NL 0435586 OU

Lockemann, Georg, 1871-
Robert Wilhelm Bunsen, Lebensbild eines deutschen Naturforschers. Stuttgart, Wissenschaftliche Verlagsgesellschaft, 1949.
262 p. ports., geneal. tables. 22 cm. (Grosse Naturforscher, Bd. 6)
Bibliography: p. 231-240.

1. Bunsen, Robert Wilhelm Eberhard, 1811-1899. (Series)
QD22.B9L6 925.4 50-26718

MnU OCU ICJ IU
NL 0435587 DLC DNLM ViU CtY CaBVaU ICU IEN PU CU

QD341 .A9L8 Lockemann, Georg, 1871-
Ueber amido- und jod-derivate von homologen des azobenzols.
Heidelberg, 1896.
51p.
Inaug. diss. Heidelberg.

NL 0435588 DLC PU PPC

QD299 .A8L7 Lockemann, Georg, 1871-
I. Ueber die akroleindarstellung nach dem borsaureverfahren und beitraege zur kenntnis des aethylidenphenylhydrazins. II. Ueber den arsennachweis mit dem Marsh'schen apparate und die katalytische zersetzung von arsenwasserstoff.
Weida i. Thur. 1904.
104p.
Habilitationsschrift, Leipzig.

NL 0435588-1 CtY

Lockemann, Hans Hermann, 1900-
... Ein Adenomyom im hinteren Scheidengewölbe mit dezidualer Reaction ... Königsberg i. Pr., 1929.
Inaug.-Diss. - Würzburg.
Lebenslauf.
"Literatur": p. 37-44.

NL 0435589 CtY

Lockemann, Theodor, 1885-
Bibliothek und studium, von dr. Theodor Lockemann ... Jena, Frommannsche buchhandlung (W. Biedermann) 1931.
22 p. 18cm. (On cover: Student und leben hft.1.)

NL 0435590 MdBJ-W

Lockemann, Theodor, 1885- ed.
Claves Jenenses; Veroeffentlichungen der Universitätsbibliothek Jena
see under Jena. Universität. Bibliothek.

PA72 .G6 LOCKEMANN, THEODOR, 1885-
Die Danzsche sammlung von briefen an Carl Wilhelm Goettling, bearb. von Theodor Lockemann. Jena, G. Fischer, 1928.
[205]-281, [1]p. 21½cm. (Zeitschrift des Vereins für thüringische geschichte und altertumskunde...n.f., 12.beiheft. Beiträge zur geschichte der Universität Jena. hft.1[nr.]2)
With Goetz, Georg. Geschichte der klassischen studien an der Universität Jena von ihrer gründung bis zur gegenwart. Jena, 1928.

NL 0435592 ICU MnU ICN

Lockemann, Theodor, 1885-
Ein Jenaer Universitäts-Bibliothekar des achtzehnten Jahrhunderts im Kampf um Besoldung und Amt. (In: Beitraege zur thüringischen und sächsischen Geschichte. Jena, 1929. 8°. p. ⌐385⌐-408. tables.)
Bibliographical footnotes.

441018A. 1. Libraries—Germany— Jena. January 18, 1930

NL 0435593 NN

Lockemann, Theodor, 1885- ed.
Die Matrikel der Akademie zu Jena 1548/1557
see under Jena. Universität.

BR332 .L69L82 **Lockemann, Theodor, 1885-**
... Technische studien zu Luthers briefen an Friedrich den Weisen, von Theodor Lockemann. Leipzig, R. Voigtländer, 1913.
viii, 208 p. 22½cm. (Probefahrten; erstlingsarbeiten aus dem deutschen seminar in Leipzig ... 22. bd.)
"Diese arbeit erscheint gleichzeitig als dissertation."

1. Luther, Martin, 1483-1546.

NL 0435595 ICU MiU MH CtY OU CU IU MH MH-AH ICRL PU

Lockemann, Theodor, 1885-
...Thüringischer Zeitschriftenkatalog; alphabetisches Verzeichnis der in der Universitätsbibliothek Jena, der Landesbibliothek Weimar, der Herzoglichen Bibliothek Gotha, den Landesbüchereien Altenburg und Rudolstadt, der Öffentlichen Bücherei des Landes Thüringen und des herzoglichen Hauses Meiningen, der Carl-Alexander-Bibliothek zu Eisenach und den Landesbüchereien Sondershausen und Gera laufend gehaltenen Zeitschriften und Reihen, bearbeitet von Dr. Th. Lockemann ⌐und⌐ Dr. W.

Continued in next column

Continued from preceding column

Schmitz. Jena: Frommannsche Buchhandlung, 1931. vii, 179 p. 24½cm. (Jena. Univ. Bibliothek. Claves Jeneses; Veröffentlichungen. Heft 1.)

600292A. 1. Periodicals—Bibl. 2. Societies, Learned—Bibl. 3. Libraries—Germany—Thuringia. I. Schmitz, Wilhelm, 1878– jt. au. II. Title. III. Ser. May 13, 1933

NL 0435597 NN CU MH PU

M(055) G373m Nr.5 **Lockemann, W**
Das Rundschreibnetz des Deutschen Wetterdienstes in den Jahren 1936-1945. Von W. Lockemann und P. Wüsthoff. Bad Kissingen, 1950.
12 p. diagrs. 21cm. (Germany. (Territory under Allied Occupation, 1945- U.S. Zone. Wetterdienst. Mitteilungen Nr.5)

Translation: The communications network of the German Weather Bureau in the years 1936-1945.

NL 0435598 DAS

Lockenberg, Ernst
Ein beitrag zur lehre von den athembewegungen.
Inaug. Diss. Wuerzburg, 1973

NL 0435599 ICRL DNLM

Lockenberg, W.
Einfache Möbel im modernen Stil; Sammlung praktischer Möbel zur Ausstattung von Wohnräumen des Mittelstandes... Entworfen und für den unmittelbaren Gebrauch bearbeitet von W. Lockenberg. Leipzig: F. Voigt, 1913. 8 p., 56 pl. in portfolio. 4°.

1. Furniture (German). January 15, 1913.

NL 0435600 NN

Lockenour, Roy Merle, 1889-
The Oregon law of family relations, by Roy M. Lockenour .. ⌐Portland, Or., Binsford and Mort, °1941⌐
207 p. 20½cm.
All Oregon statutes and Supreme court decisions to August 1, 1941, have been examined. As the law is modified and expanded by subsequent acts and decisions, a supplement will be issued in March of each year, showing such changes. cf. Notice to readers.

1. Domestic relations—Oregon. I. Title.
41-19178

NL 0435601 DLC DI

Lockenour, Roy Merle, 1889-
Outline-digest of Oregon law, pertaining to contracts, negotiable instruments, sales, principal and agent, real property; with a brief outline of the Oregon court system; answers to a thousand and one legal questions, by Roy M. Lockenour ... ⌐Salem, Or., The author, 1935⌐
8 p. l., 139 numb. l. 27½ x 21cm.
Mimeographed on one side of leaf only.

1. Contracts—Oregon. 2. Negotiable instruments—Oregon. 3. Sales—Oregon. 4. Agency (Law) — Oregon. 5. Real property — Oregon. 6. Courts—Oregon. I. Title.
35-18810

NL 0435602 DLC

VOLUME 337

823 L796s **Locker, Arthur, 1828-1893.**
Sir Goodwin's folly; a story of the year 1795. London, Chapman and Hall, 1864.
3v. 21cm.

NL 0435603 IU

Locker, Arthur, 1828-1893.
Stephen Scudamore the younger; or, The fifteen-year olds. London, New York, G. Routledge & sons, 1871.
339 p. front., plates. 18 cm.

NL 0435604 MB

Locker, Arthur, 1828-1893.
... What the shepherd saw: a tale of four moonlight nights
see under Hardy, Thomas, 1840-

Locker, Berl, 1887-
Covenant everlasting; Palestine in Jewish history. New York, Sharon Books, 1947 [°1946]
125 p. maps (on lining-papers) 20 cm.
London ed. pub. under title: A stiff-necked people.
Bibliographical footnotes.

1. Jews—Hist. 2. Jews in Palestine. I. Title.

DS119.L6 1947 956.9 48-352*

NL 0435606 PSC NIC ViU TxU OFH MiU OrSaW OrU WaS WaT WaTC IdU DLC CaBViP IdB Or OrP MB CU Mi MH OCH

Locker, Berl, 1887-
היסטארישע פארבינדונג און היסטארישע רעכט. תל-אביב, וועלט-פאריייניקונג פועלי-ציון (צ. ס.)-התאחדות, תרצ"ח.
[Tel-Aviv] 1938.
40 p. 22 cm.
On verso of t. p.: Historical connection and historical right.

1. Zionism—Addresses, essays, lectures. 2. Jews in Palestine.
Title transliterated: Historishe farbindung un historishe rekht.

DS149.L58 55-49563

NL 0435607 DLC OC1

Locker, Berl.
Palestine and the Jewish future, by Berl Locker. [London] Jewish socialist labour party [1942] 55 p. 15cm.
"This pamphlet is a revised and enlarged reprint of an article published in 'Left news' for March 1942."

1. Zionism. 2. Jews—Territorialism. I. Poale Zion.
July 5, 1945

NL 0435608 NN CtY

DS 119 L6.14 Locker, Berl, 1887-
Le peuple à la nuque roide; la Palestine dans l'histoire Juive version française de Ruth Schatzman. Paris, "Les Editions de la Terre Retrouvee," 1947.
98 p. 22 cm.
Translation of A stiff-necked people Palestine in Jewish history.

1. Jews--History. I. Title

NL 0435609 OCH

Locker, Berl, 1887- ed.
Po'ale Tsyion shriften.
Borochov, Ber, 1881-1917.
פועלי ציון שריפטען ... ניו יארק, פועלי ציון פארלאג.
[New York] 1920-28.

Locker, Berl, 1887-
A stiff-necked people; Palestine in Jewish history, by Berl Locker ... London, V. Gollancz ltd, 1946.
79 p. 19 cm.
American ed. (New York, Sharon Books) pub. under title: Covenant everlasting.

1. Jews—Hist. 2. Jews in Palestine. I. Title.

DS119.L6 1946 956.9 46-22633 rev

NL 0435611 DLC ICU NNZi NcU

Locker, Berl, 1887-
Was ist Poale-Zionismus? [Brünn] Jüdisch-Sozialdemokratische Arbeiterpartei Poale Zion in der Tschechoslowakei vereinigt mit Zionistisch-Sozialistischen Gruppen. [Brünn, 19]
7 p. (Schriftenreihe "Der neue Weg", 1)

NL 0435612 MH

TL620 .G25A6 Rare Bk. Coll. Locker, Edward Hawke, 1777-1849.
Air balloon. A full and accurate account of the two aërial voyages made by Mons'. Garnerin, on Monday, June 28, and Monday, July 5, 1802; including the interesting particulars communicated by Captain Sowden and Mr. Locker, who accompanied M. Garnerin. As written by themselves. To which is prefixed, The origin of balloons; the method of constructing, filling, and directing them through the atmosphere; and an account of the several aerial adventures, to the present period; together with A sketch of the life of M. Garnerin. [Sommers Town, Eng.] A. Neil [1802]

Locker, Edward Hawke, 1777-1849, ed.
The Englishman's library
see under title

Locker, Edward Hawke, 1777-1849.
Memoirs of celebrated naval commanders, illustrated by engravings from original pictures in the Naval gallery of Greenwich hospital, by Edward Hawke Locker ... [London, Harding and Lepard, 1832.
4 p.ℓ., [284] p. ports. 27cm.
CONTENTS:--Charles Howard.--Robert Blake.--George Monk.--Edward Montague.--Sir George Rooke. John Benbow.--Edward Russell.--George Byng.--Edward, Lord Hawke.--Sir Charles Saunders,--John Kempenfelt.--Viscount Bridport.--James Cook.--Samuel Barrington.-- Lord Collingwood.--William Locker.
Book-plate of Lord Queenborough.

NL 0435615 CtNlCG RPB DN NN ICN OU

Locker, Edward Hawke, 1777-1849.
The naval gallery of Greenwich hospital; comprising a series of portraits and memoirs of celebrated naval commanders. By Edward Hawke Locker ... [London] Harding and Lepard, 1831.
6 p. l., [286] p. plates, ports. 31 x 24cm.
Various pagings.
Added t.-p.: Memoirs of celebrated naval commanders, illustrated by engravings from original pictures in the naval gallery of Greenwich hospital, by Edward Hawke Locker ... 1832.
Issued in 4 parts, 1831-32.
1. Gt. Brit.—Navy—Biog. 2. Admirals—Portraits. 3. Naval battles—Gt. Brit. I. Greenwich royal hospital, Greenwich, Eng. II. Title. III. Title: Memoirs of celebrated naval commanders.

27-795

Library of Congress DA74.L6

NL 0435616 DLC CtY PU

Locker, Edward Hawke, 1777-1849, ed.
The Plain Englishman: comprehending original compositions, and selections from the best writers, under the heads of the Christian monitor; the British patriot; the Fireside companion ...
London, Hatchard and son etc. 18

Locker, Edward Hawke, 1777-1849.
Views in Spain, by Edward Hawke Locker ... London, J. Murray, 1824.
[138] p. 60 pl. 30cm.
Engr. t.-p.

1. Spain—Descr. & trav.—Views.

4-26626

Library of Congress DP38.L81

NL 0435618 DLC TxHU TNJ NjP IU OClSA OClRC NNH

---

ar W 52379 no.6 Locker, Emil.
Die Anfechtbarkeit der Ehe wegen Irrtums nach B.G.B. Colmar, Colmarer Druckerei, 1909.
55 p. 22cm.
Inaug.-Diss.--Erlangen.

NL 0435619 NIC MH ICRL MH-L NN

Locker, Ernst.
Nominales und Verbales Adjektivum.
Wien, A. Sexl, 1951.
50 p. 24 cm. (Beihefte zur Zeitschrift für Sprachwissenschaft "Die Sprache," Hft. 1)
Habilitationsschrift--Wien, under title: Beiträge zur Lehre vom Adjektivum."
Bibliographical footnotes.
1. Grammar, Comparatice and general. Adjective. I. Title.

NL 0435620 NcD ViU MH RPB CLSU OU NjP TxU

Locker, Ernst.
Rückläufiges Wörterbuch der griechischen Sprache, im Auftrage der Wiener Akademie der Wissenschaften unter Leitung ihres ordentlichen Mitgliedes Paul Kretschmer. Göttingen, Vandenhoeck & Ruprecht, 1944.
vii, 688 p. 24 cm.

1. Greek language—Glossaries, vocabularies, etc. I. Title.

PA459.L6 54-51529

NL 0435621 DLC NBuC ICU NNC MH MiU NN CU IaU

Locker, Frederick
see
Locker-Lampson, Frederick, 1821-1895.

Locker, Mrs. Frederick
see Locker-Lampson, Hannah Jane (Lampson)

Locker, Godfrey Lampson
see
Locker-Lampson, Godfrey Tennyson Lampson, 1875-

VOLUME 337

Locker, Hermann, 1884-
Der Pfarrzwang nach katholischem und evangelischem Kirchenrecht ... von Hermann Locker ... Borna-Leipzig, R. Noske, 1908.
xi, 82, ⌊1⌋ p. 22½cm.
Inaug.-diss. - Breslau.
"Lebenslauf": p.⌊83⌋
"Literaturverzeichnis": p.⌊ix⌋-xi.

NL 0435625 MH-L NN MH ICRL

Locker, John.
Address to the king, the ministry, and the people of Great Britain and Ireland, on the present state of the money system of the united kingdoms. With an appendix, containing letters of His Majesty's ministers to the author, and some important documents farther explanatory of the system, and the means of amendment. By John Locker, esq. London, Printed by W. Flint, for S. Tipper, 1809.
xvii, 65 p. 22cm.
1. Currency question—Gt. Brit.
Library of Congress HG938.L7 6-40913†

NL 0435626 DLC MH-BA CtY PU

Kress Room Locker, John
Timely application to the people of Ireland: or, remarks on the necessity of a most effectual reformation in the state of the coin, being essential to the completion of national prosperity, wealth, trade, commerce, peace, and independence of Ireland ... Also extracts from a pamphlet published in the year 1729, entitled, A scheme of the money-matters of Ireland. Dublin, Printed by W.Porter, 1799.
1 p.*l*., ii, [5]-35 p. 21.5 cm.

NL 0435627 MH-BA CtY

Locker, John A.
Combination or competition, which? By John A. Locker. New York, The Independent retail tobacconist association ⌊°1914⌋
36 p. 23cm.
1. American tobacco company. I. Independent retail tobacconist association, New York. II. Title.
Library of Congress HD2769.T6L6 14-2282

NL 0435628 DLC ICJ

Locker, Mabel Elsie, 1890-
God's heroes; teacher's and pupil's book; under the auspices of the Parish and Church school board of the United Lutheran Church in America. Phila., U.L.P.H.,⌊c1931-32.⌋
328 p.

NL 0435629 PPLT

Locker, Mabel Elsie.
God's book; teacher's and pupil's book; prepared under the auspices of the Parish and Church School Board of the United Lutheran Church in America. Phila., U.L.P.H., c1933-34.
391 p.

NL 0435630 PPLT

Locker, Mabel Elsie, 1890–
Human nature, by Mabel Elsie Locker and Paul J. Hoh. Prepared under the auspices of the Parish and church school board of the United Lutheran church in America. Philadelphia, Pa., The United Lutheran publication house ⌊1935⌋
144 p. 19½cm.
"Helpful books for further study" at end of each chapter.

——— A study of Christian growth ... Leader's guide ... Philadelphia, Pa., The United Lutheran publication house ⌊1936⌋
15, ⌊1⌋ p. 19½cm. (The Lutheran leadership course; P. J. Hoh, editor)
1. Educational psychology. 2. Religious education. I. Hoh, Paul Jacob, 1893– joint author. II. United Lutheran church in America. Parish and church school board. III. Title.
35-10729 Revised
Library of Congress BV1533.L55 Guide
⌊r44d2⌋ 268.372

NL 0435632 DLC ICU PPLT

Locker, Mabel Elsie, 1890–
Patriarchs and leaders, by Mabel Elsie Locker ... Philadelphia, Columbus ⌊etc.⌋ Christian growth press ⌊1944⌋
84 p. illus. (part col., incl. maps) 22cm. (⌊The Christian growth series of Sunday school lessons⌋ Study book. Junior I, 1st quarter)
"Books to read": p. 6.
1. Religious education—Text-books for children—Lutheran. I. Title.
44-37024
Library of Congress BX8015.L57
268.432

NL 0435633 DLC

Locker, Mabel Elsie, 1890–
... What difference does it make? ⌊By⌋ Mabel Elsie Locker. A junior unit, ages 9, 10, 11. Leader's book. ⌊Philadelphia, The United Lutheran publication house, °1939⌋
63 p. 21½cm. (The children of the church series)
"Prepared under the auspices of the Parish and church school board of the United Lutheran church in America."
Includes bibliographies.
1. Religious education—Text-books for children. I. United Lutheran church in America. Parish and church school board. II. Title.
40-35632
Library of Congress BX8015.L6
Copyright AA 309334 268

NL 0435634 DLC

Locker, Mabel Elsie, 1890–
... World Christians worshiping ⌊by⌋ Mabel Elsie Locker. A junior unit, ages 9, 10, 11. Leader's book. ⌊Philadelphia, The United Lutheran publication house, °1941⌋
62 p., 1 l. 21½cm. (The children of the church series)
Illustrated t.-p.
"Prepared under the auspices of the Parish and church school board of the United Lutheran church in America."
Bibliography: p. 6-7.
1. Religious education—Text-books for children. I. United Lutheran church in America. Parish and church school board. II. Title.
42-478
Library of Congress BV1546.L57
268.62

NL 0435635 DLC

Locker, Malka, 1887–
די. לידער. תל־אביב. פארלאג "ים." ⌊Tel-Aviv⌋ 1932.
80 p. 21 cm.
I. Title. *Title transliterated:* Du.
PJ5129.L587D8 57-53884 ‡

NL 0435636 DLC MH

PJ 5129 L5.87 G4 Locker, Malka, 1887-
Gedichte [von] Malkah Locker. Wien, Fiba-Verlag [1937]
62 p. 20 cm.

NL 0435637 OCH

Locker, Malka, 1887–
די וועלט איז אן א היטער. ניו־יארק, "אידישער קעמפער."
⌊New York⌋ 1947.
122 p. 22 cm.
1. World War, 1939–1945—Poetry. I. Title.
Title transliterated: Di velt iz on a hiter.
A 51-3706
New York. Public Libr. for Library of Congress

NL 0435638 NN DLC

Locker, Malka, 1887–
זשאן ארטור רעמבא (Jean Arthur Rimbaud) ⌊פון⌋ מלכה לאקער. ניו־יארק, אידישער קעמפער, 1950.
219 p. port. 19 cm.
1. Rimbaud, Jean Nicolas Arthur, 1854–1891.
Title transliterated: Zshan Artur Rembo.
PQ2387.R5Z6965 HE 67-978

NL 0435639 DLC

4K 9904 Locker, Max, 1888-
Die Kriegsgefangenschaft insbesondere nach römischem und heutigem Recht. Breslau, 1913.
71 p.

NL 0435640 DLC-P4 MH PU-L ICRL

Locker, Willis Clyde.
Teacher's guide; Locker easy method writing, by W. C. Locker ... ⌊Richmond, The William Byrd press⌋ 1919.
42 p. illus. 24cm.
1. Penmanship. I. Title.
Library of Congress Z43.L72 19-16471

NL 0435641 DLC ViU

LOCKER-LAMPSON, Frederick, 1821-1895.
[" A collection of autograph letters mostly addressed to Frederick Locker, by the leaders of literary and artistic thought of the mid-Victorian era.]

Bookplate of Frederick Locker.
Label in MS."Artists,writers, philosophers, My friends and acquaintance."

NL 0435642 MH

[Locker-Lampson, Frederick] 1821-1895, ed.
PR1175 L62a [A collection of poetical pieces in the autograph of Frederick Locker Lampson, being poems which he had selected for the "Lyra Elegantiarum," but not used. London?, 186-?-90]
1 v. 22 cm.
Mss. in portfolio.
Author's A.L.S. to Ward & Lock inserted.

NL 0435643 RPB

VOLUME 337

Locker-Lampson, Frederick, 1821-1894.
[Leechiana from the Frederick Locker-Lampson collection. London, 1864-1872]
see under title

MAY MSS 103
Locker-Lampson, Frederick, 1821-1895.
Letter [?] Feb.24 [London] to [?]
[2]p.on 1l. 18cm.
Holograph signed.
Inviting addressee for dinner.

NL 0435645 NSyU

MAY MSS 21
Locker-Lampson, Frederick, 1821-1895.
Letter, 1871 Nov.21 [London] to [Algernon] Swinburne [Holmwood]
2p.on 1l. 18cm.
Holograph, signed with initials.
Concerning Sestina and a poem in French by Swinburne.
Tipped in The complete works of Algernon Charles Swinburne, edited by E.Gosse & T.Wise, MAY PR5501 F25 v.3.
1.Swinburne, Algernon Charles, 1837-1909. Sestina. I.Swinburne, Algernon Charles, 1837-1909.

NL 0435646 NSyU

LOCKER - LAMPSON, Frederick, 1821-1895.
Letter to Mr. Stoddard. Oct. 29, 1880.

NL 0435647 MH

Locker-Lampson, Frederick, 1821-1895.
London lyrics. by Frederick Locker. London, Chapman and Hall, 1857.
90 p. illus. 15 cm.

NL 0435648 WU ICN NN PPRCl MH CLU-C CSmH TxU CU-I ICN IU ScU NjP CaBVaU OC1RC

Locker-Lampson, Frederick, 1821-1895.
London lyrics, by Frederick Locker. London, B. M. Pickering, 1862.
viii, 143 p. 18 cm.
Photo. mounted on fly leaf.

I. Title.
PR4891.L2A7 1862 821'.8 73-176724 MARC

NL 0435649 DLC TxU NN ICN IU CSmH MH CaBVaU CtY

Widener Coll.
Locker-Lampson, Frederick, 1821-1895.
London lyrics. By Frederick Locker.
<Not published.>
London:John Wilson, 93, Great Russell street. 1868.
viii, 134p., 1l. 19.5cm.
Device of the Chiswick press on recto of last leaf.
One of about 150 copies on ordinary paper. Cohn (1924: 497) quotes a record of the edition in Locker's autograph: "Poems, 1868, bound in roxburgh. Illustrated

Continued in next column

Continued from preceding column

by G[eorge]. C[ruikshank]. ... Not published, 100, and 20 large paper, and on ordinary paper without illustration, about 150 copies." The copies with front. by Cruikshank were published under the title: Poems.
In this copy leaf containing p.95 & 96 is original, the last stanza on p.95 beginning "One hundred years! They soon will leak"; in later copies the leaf is a cancel, p.95

reading "One hundred years, like one short week,".
Original half brown morocco & maroon cloth; top edges gilt; press notices of the author's poems, the 1st from The Times, June 6, 1865 (20p.) inserted at back cover.
Inserted is A.N.s. (F[rederick] L[ocker] to Bard [i.e. Lord Tennyson]; [London] undated; ls. (1p.); inviting Tennyson to tea to meet Swinburne and Arnold.

Contains the bookplates of Sir William A. Fraser (The Knight of Morar) and Clarence S. Bement.

*EC85 L7968 857ℓd
Another copy. 19.5cm.
In this copy leaf containing p.95 & 96 is present in both states; the cancel leaf has been wrongly inserted in place of p.79 & 80, which have been canceled.

NL 0435653 MH CaBVaU CSmH PPL NN IU CLSU TxFTC NSyU TxU IEN NNC

Ap L797ℓ 1870 Stark Lib'y
Locker-Lampson, Frederick, 1821-1895.
London lyrics, by Frederick Locker. London, Strahan & Co., 1870.
ix, 194, 4p. 18cm.
"List of books published by Strahan and Co.": 4p. at end.
First published in 1857; this edition adds six new poems. Cf. CBEL.
TxU copy imperfect? Half title wanting?
Autograph of F.E. Dawe.

NL 0435654 TxU MH NcU ScU PHC PPC OCl NBuG T CtY

Y 185 .L 8094
LOCKER-LAMPSON, FREDERICK, 1821-1895.
London lyrics. 5th ed. London, Strahan & Co., 1872.
ix, 200p. 18cm.

Author's autograph presentation copy; autographs of John Drinkwater and Holbrook Jackson.
Bookplate of John Drinkwater.

NL 0435655 ICN CSmH MH PPD GEU

LOCKER - Lampson, Frederick, 1821-1895.
London lyrics. By Frederick Locker. 6th ed., London, Strahan, & co., 1872.

NL 0435656 MH

Locker-Lampson, Frederick, 1821-1895.
London lyrics, by Frederick Locker. 7th ed. London, W. Isbister & co., 1874.
x, 203 p. 17½cm.

I. Title.
Library of Congress PR4891.L2A7 1874 12-36288

NL 0435657 DLC CaBVaU OrU CtY ScU RPB CtY MB MH PU

Ap L797ℓ 1876 Stark Lib'y
Locker-Lampson, Frederick, 1821-1895.
London lyrics, by Frederick Locker. A new ed., enlarged and finally revised. London, H.S. King & Co., 1876.
x, 199, 48p. front.(port.) 18½cm.
"An alphabetical list of Henry S. King & Co.'s publications. June, 1876": 48p. at end.
First published in 1857; this edition adds six poems. Cf. CBEL.
Inscribed on title page: G.S. Ritchie, December 1877.

NL 0435658 TxU CaBVaU MB OC1RC CtY NN

Ap L797ℓ 1878 Stark Lib'y
Locker-Lampson, Frederick, 1821-1895.
London lyrics, by Frederick Locker. London, C.K. Paul & Co., 1878.
x, 199p. 17cm.
First published in 1857. Cf. CBEL.
Manuscript note on front free end paper: Re-issue of King's 8th edn.

NL 0435659 TxU CaBVaU MH OCl MB

Locker-Lampson, Frederick, 1821-1895.
London lyrics, by Frederick Locker. London [Chiswick press: C. Whittingham and co.] 1881.
x, 108 p. incl. front. pl. 23½cm.
Plates on India paper, mounted.
Privately printed.
Large paper copy with the frontispiece by Caldecott, in original state and a proof in the altered state inserted.
Bound in vellum.

I. Title. 15-17090
Library of Congress PR4891.L2A7 1881

NL 0435660 DLC CaBVaU MH NN NSyU OC1RC TxU MB MH NjP

PR 4891 L2 A7 1883
Locker-Lampson, Frederick, 1821-1895.
London lyrics. London, Kegan Paul, Trench, 1883.
x, 199 p. 17cm.

NL 0435661 CU-I MH CSmH

Locker-Lampson, Frederick, 1821-1895.
London lyrics, by Frederick Locker. New York: Printed for the Book fellow's club, 1883. viii, 104 p., 1 l. front. (port.), illus. 18cm.
"One hundred and four copies printed... Four on vellum...of which this is no. 1."
"Press of Theo. L. De Vinne & co., New-York."
Extra illustrated with an impression of the frontispiece, on paper, with a couplet of doggerel, in ms., signed and dated, by the author.
Illustrations are after drawings by Caldecott, Kate Greenaway, and G. B. Bowlend.

Binding, by R. W. Smith, of full blue crushed levant morocco, gilt, doublures of brown morocco. In slip case. Original front cover bound in.
With bookplate of the author.
Holograph letter from the author to V. A. Blacque, 2 l., tipped in.
Two clippings inserted.

152582B. 1. Poetry, English. I. Book fellow's club, New York. II. Title.
January 29, 1942

NL 0435663 NN NjP MB

LOCKER-[LAMPSON], Frederick, 1821-1895.
London lyrics. New York, White, Stokes & Allen, 1884.

Port.
"Author's ed."
Title page printed in red.

NL 0435664 MH NjP OC1RC OU

VOLUME 337

Locker-Lampson, Frederick, 1821–1895.
London lyrics, by Frederick Locker. London: K. Paul, Trench & co., 1885. xi p., 146 p., 1 l. front. (port.) 20cm.
"Tenth edition published in England."
"Fifty copies... were printed on large paper... All are numbered and signed. This is no. 41. Charles Whittingham & co."
Printed at the Chiswick press.
Extra illustrated throughout the text, and with plates, part inlaid, with sketches, part hand colored, by various artists: with two original drawings for the author's bookplate, one by Kate Greenaway, and one by George Bowlend; and with holograph letters, inlaid, from the author, George Du Maurier, E. A. Abbey and Linley Sambourne. An "Index to illustrations and illustrators," one printed leaf bound in at end.

Binding, by the Club bindery, Leon Maillard finisher, of full green crushed levant morocco, gilt, with doublures of green morocco, with inlays of red and tan morocco. In slip case.
With bookplate of the author.

CU-A CaOTP TxU
NL 0435666 NN PU ViU ICN MH CtY OO CSmH WaTC IU TU

828 L797L Locker-Lampson, Frederick, 1821-1895.
London lyrics, by Frederick Locker. New York, White, Stokes, & Allen, 1886.
108p. 16cm.

1. English poetry. I. Title.

NL 0435667 LU NcU MB NjP OrU

PR4891 L2L7 1889 Locker-Lampson, Frederick, 1821-1895.
London lyrics, by Frederick Locker. London, Kegan Paul, Trench & co., 1889.
3p.ℓ.,[ix]-xi,146p. front.(port.) 16½cm.
"The present is the eleventh edition published in England. There have been also three American editions, and a fourth privately printed by the Bookfellows' club, New York. The portrait by Mr. J. E. Millais first appeared in the edition of 1868".
Printed at the Chiswick press.
I. Title. II. Chiswick press.

NL 0435668 NBuG ODW MiD ViU CtY OClJC

Locker-Lampson, Frederick, 1821–1895.
London lyrics, by Frederick Locker. London: Kegan Paul, Trench & Co., 1891. 3 p.l., (i)x–xi, 170 p. front. (port.) 16°.

1. Poetry (English). 2. Title.
October 19, 1920.

NL 0435669 NN OClW

Locker-Lampson, Frederick, 1821-1895.
London lyrics, by Frederick Locker. New York, Stokes, 1891.
x, 108 p.

NL 0435670 NNC PP NSyU

Locker-Lampson, Frederick, 1821–1895.
London lyrics, by Frederick Locker. New York, Frederick A. Stokes company, 1893.
3 p. l., [ix]–x, 113 p. 16 cm.

I. Title.
4—13916
Library of Congress PR4891.L2A7 1893
[a37g1] -821.89

NL 0435671 DLC OrP WaS CaBVaU OClRC MB NN

PR 10 R6 G6 1904 Locker-Lampson, Frederick, 1821-1895.
London lyrics; with an introd. and notes by A.D. Godley. Methuen, 1904.
87 p.

NL 0435672 CaBVaU NjR MH ViU NBuG GU

PR 4891 L2L3 1904 Locker-Lampson, Frederick, 1821-1895.
London lyrics. With introd. and notes by Austin Dobson. London, Macmillan [1904]
xxv,196 p. port. 17cm. (Golden treasury series)
"Based upon ... 'the twelfth [1893] edition published in England,' and ... printed from a copy of that edition in which the author had made some later corrections."

NL 0435673 NIC MiU CtY IdU CaBVaU CLSU InU NN

Locker-Lampson, Frederick, 1821- 1895.
London lyrics; with introduction and notes by Austin Dobson. London: Macmillan and Co., Ltd., 1908. xxv, 196 p., 1 port. 16°. (Golden treasury series.)

NL 0435674 NN

Locker-Lampson, Frederick, 1821-95
London lyrics. Edinburgh, Foulis [1909]
32 p. illus. (London booklets, 2)

NL 0435675 MH

Locker-Lampson, Frederick, 1821–1895.
London lyrics, by Frederick Locker Lampson, with introduction and notes by Austin Dobson. London, Macmillan and co., 1909.
xxv, 196 p. front. (port.) 16½cm.
Title vignette.

I. *Dobson, Austin, 1840-1921, ed. II. Title.
A 10-1189
Title from Stanford Univ. Printed by L. C.

NL 0435676 CSt OOxM

S73 1882 Locker-Lampson, Frederick, 1821-1895.
London rhymes. London [Chiswick Press] 1882
vi, 98 p. 17cm.

Contains author's inscription and signature.

NL 0435677 NNC CaBVaU OClRC NN PP TxU CSmH MH NcU

Locker-Lampson, Frederick, 1821-1895.
London rhymes. [Author's ed., selected and revised by him] New York, White, Stokes, & Allen, 1884.
98 p. illus. 16 cm.

I. Title.
PR4891.L2A6 1884 52-46764 ‡

NL 0435678 DLC TxU NcU IEdS ICN PU MA OClW OU NN

Locker-Lampson, Frederick, 1821–1895.
London rhymes. By Frederick Locker. Author's edition. — New York. White, Stokes, & Allen. 1886. vi, 98 pp. Decorated title-page. 16 cm.

NL 0435679 MB MH OCl PP CU NcD N

828 L815Lr5 Locker-Lampson, Frederick, 1821-1895.
London rhymes. Fifth American edition. New York, Frederick A. Stokes company, 1890.
vi, 98p. 16cm.

NL 0435680 LNHT MdBP

Locker-Lampson, Frederick, 1821-1895.
London rhymes, by ... 6th. American ed. N.Y., F.A. Stokes company, 1892.
96 p.

NL 0435681 PU

LOCKER-LAMPSON, FREDERICK, 1821-1895.
London rhymes, by Frederick Locker. Seventh American edition. New York: F. A. Stokes co., 1893. vi, 96 p. 16cm.

31457B. 1. Poetry, English. I. Title.

NL 0435682 NN ICRL RPB IU

821 L791 1894 Locker-Lampson, Frederick, 1821-1895.
London rhymes. New York, White, Stokes, & Allen, 1894.
98p. front.
Title in red with title vignette in red and white.
"This edition is the author's edition."

NL 0435683 IU

Locker-Lampson, Frederick, 1821–1895, *ed.*
Lyra elegantiarum; a collection of some of the best specimens of vers de société and vers d'occasion in the English language by deceased authors. Ed. by Frederick Locker ... London, E. Moxon & co., 1867.
xx, 360 p. 16½cm.

1. Society verse. 2. English poetry (Collections) I. Title.
23—1517
Library of Congress PR1195.V3L6 1867

OClRC OrPR AU CaBVaU
NL 0435684 DLC AU NcU PP PPL OO NN CtY MB TxU NjP

Locker-Lampson, Frederick, 1821–1895, *ed.*
Lyra elegantiarum: a collection of some of the best specimens of vers de société and vers d'occasion in the English language by deceased authors. Ed. by Frederick Locker. A new and rev. ed. ... London, E. Moxon & co., 1867.
3 p. l., [ix]–xx, 345 p. 16cm.

1. Society verse. 2. English poetry (Collections) I. Title.
27-9684
Library of Congress PR1195.V3L6 1867

NL 0435685 DLC MtU CaBVaU CLSU PU PP OClW

PR1195 .V3L6 1886 Locker-Lampson, Frederick, 1821-1895, ed.
Lyra elegantiarum; a collection of some of the best specimens of vers de société and vers d'occasion in the English language by deceased authors. Edited by Frederick Locker. New York, White, Stokes, and Allen, 1886.
xvi, 360 p. 20 cm.

1. Society verse. 2. English poetry--Collections. I. Kernahan, Coulson, 1858- ed. II. Title.

NL 0435686 TU CtY OCU MH PP OCl ODW OClRC MeB MA

VOLUME 337

Locker-Lampson, Frederick, 1821-1895, *ed.*
... Lyra elegantiarum; a collection of some of the best social and occasional verse by deceased English authors. Rev. and enl. ed. Edited by Frederick Locker-Lampson, assisted by Coulson Kernahan. London, New York ₍etc.₎ Ward, Lock, and co., 1891.
xx, 425 p. front. (port.) 19cm. (The Minerva library of famous books. Ed. by G. T. Bettany. ₍v. 21₎)
1. Society verse. 2. English poetry (Collections) I. Kernahan, Coulson, 1858- joint ed. II. Title.
27-20166
Library of Congress PR1195.V3L6 1891
NL 0435687 NcGU NjP NBuG MH NN CSmH CoU NIC WaU MH TxHU CaBVaU CU-S DLC PP LU PBm PPL PU OClW OU MiU OClRC

Locker-Lampson, Frederick, 1821-1895. ed.
Lyra elegantiarum. a collection of some of the best specimens of vers de societe and vers d'occasion in the English language, by deceased authors. Ed. by ... N.Y., Stokes, 1891.
360 p.
NL 0435688 PSC PV ICRL NcD

PR1175 .L527 1889 Locker-Lampson, Frederick, 1821-1895, ed.
Lyris elegantiarum; a collection of some of the best specimens of vers de société and vers d'occasion in the English language by deceased authors. New York, F. A. Stokes, 1889.
xvi, 360 p. 16cm.
1. Society verse. 2. English poetry (Collections) I. Title.
NL 0435689 ViU MB OOxM ICU

₍**Locker-Lampson, Frederick**₎ 1821-1895.
Memories of men, places, and things, belonging to past times ... ₍London, C. Whittingham and co., 1894?₎
27, ₍1₎ p. 20½cm.
"50 copies printed."
1. Art—Private collections. I. Title.
42-10813
Library of Congress N5245.L75
NL 0435690 DLC

[Locker-Lampson, Frederick, 1821-1895]
My confidences. An autobiographical sketch. Addressed to my descendants ...
[London? ca.1892]
[ca.385]p. mounted port. 26cm., in case 27.5cm.
Author's private trial edition; one of two(?) copies printed for his use in revision. First published posthumously with the above title, edited with omissions by Augustine Birrell, in 1896.
The first two words of the title are on a mounted printed slip; the next three words are scored through as though to be omitted.
Begun in 1888 and worked on during the last years of his life, some of the leaves as first printed have been cancelled; other newly printed leaves have been supplied; many pages have mounted printed slips with corrections or additions; profusely revised in ms. throughout.
NL 0435692 MH OClRC

PR 4891 L2A83 1896a Locker-Lampson, Frederick, 1821-1895.
My confidences. An autobiographical sketch addressed to my descendants. New York, Scribner, 1896.
440p. ports. 23cm.
NL 0435693 MH MB MU TxDaM KU NIC CoU RPB MiU-C PU PPL PBa

Locker-Lampson, Frederick, 1821-1895.
My confidences. An autobiographical sketch addressed to my descendants. By Frederick Locker-Lampson ... 2d ed. London. Smith. Elder. & co., 1896.
x p., 1 l., 440 p. 2 port. (incl. front.) 23cm.
Edited by Augustine Birrell.
1. Locker family. I. Birrell, Augustine, 1850-1933. ed.
4-22765
Library of Congress PR4891.L2A83 1896.
NL 0435694 NcU TU CtY GU CaBVaU MiU-C LU WaWW WaS OClRC MiU-C OrU OrCS PP PPL WaU TxU NIC DLC MH NjP PBL NcU OCU OO OCl MiU OU OClW

821 L796 L 1910 Locker-Lampson, Frederick, 1821-1895.
My confidences. An autobiographical sketch addressed to my descendants. London, New York, T. Nelson ₍1910₎
377p. port. 16cm.
Edited by Augustine Birrell.
1. Locker family. 2. Locker-Lampson, Frederick, 1821-1895. I. Birrell, Augustine, 1850-1933, ed.
NL 0435695 OrU

Locker-Lampson, Frederick, 1821-1895.
Patchwork, by Frederick Locker. London, Smith, Elder & co., 1879.
viii, 234 p. 18cm.
Title vignette and tail-piece.
A common place-book, prose and verse original and selected.
First printed in quarto for the Philobiblon society. *cf.* Dict. nat. biog.
1. Commonplace-books. I. Title.
22-4818
Library of Congress PR4891.L2A73
NL 0435696 ScU CtY NcD OClRC PP TU MB NjP DLC KyLoU NIC OClJC KU CaBVaU MoSW MdBP

Locker-Lampson, Frederick, 1821-1895.
Patchwork. Second series. By Frederick Locker; with note by Rt. Hon. Augustine Birrell, M. P., preface by Philip Darrell Sherman, F. R. C. Cleveland, The Rowfant club, 1927.
xx, 113 p., 1 l. 20½cm.
"Of this volume, two hundred copies have been printed, of which this is number 197."
In slide case.
1. Commonplace-books. I. Birrell, Augustine, 1850- II. Sherman, Philip Darrell. III. Title.
29-3196
Library of Congress PR4891.L2A73 2d ser.
NL 0435697 OClRC OCl MnU NN DLC OKentU MH NjR OU NIC ViU OClW OO MH

LOCKER-LAMPSON, Frederick, 1821-1895.
[Poem beginning:] Oh for the poet-voice that swells...
Manuscript. 1 page.
4 line stanza, signed and dated: Frederick Locker, July 1873.
NL 0435698 MH

Locker-Lampson, Frederick, 1821-1895.
Poems by Frederick Locker. ⟨Not published.⟩ London, J. Wilson, 1868.
viii, 134 p., 1 l. front. 19½cm.
Cancel of p. 95-96 inserted by author's request (*cf.* ms. note prefixed) "Only one hundred copies printed, including twenty copies on large paper."
Mounted autotype copy of author's portrait inserted in front has inscription: A' mon ami F. Locker, George du Maurier. Mars 1872 ...
Press notices, 20 pages at end (16cm)
Author's book plate and autograph.
15-4337
Library of Congress PR4891.L2A75
NL 0435699 DLC NjP NcU TxU CSt MH CaBVaU NNC WU

PR4891 L815A17 1883 Locker-Lampson, Frederick, 1821-1895.
The poems of Frederick Locker. New York, White, Stokes, and Allen, 1883.
244 p. illus., ports. 17cm.
Author's presentation copy "to Charles Coburn."
NL 0435700 GU IU NcU I CtY PRosC ODW NBuG MH

820 L815 rp.9 Locker-Lampson, Frederick, 1821-1895.
The poems of Frederick Locker. New York, White, Stokes and Allen, 1884.
vi, 244p. 17cm.
NL 0435701 CLSU CtY OClRC PHC MB MeB

PR4891 .L2 A7 1885 Locker-Lampson, Frederick, 1821-1895.
Poems. Authorized ed. New York, White, Stokes & Allen, 1885.
262p. front.
NL 0435702 NcU OO NjP MB MH

821.89 L81p Locker-Lampson, Frederick, 1821-1895.
The poems of Frederick Locker. Authorized ed. New York, White, Stokes & Allen, 1885.
vii, 261 p. port. 20 cm.
Title vignette (author's bookplate)
NL 0435703 N

Locker-Lampson, Frederick, 1821-1895.
The poems of Frederick Locker. Authorized ed. ... New York, F. A. Stokes & brother, 1889.
vii, ₍7₎-262 p. 19cm.
Title vignette (author's book-plate)
18-22072
Library of Congress PR4891.L2A7
NL 0435704 DLC NN InU

LOCKER-LAMPSON, Frederick, 1821-1895.
The Rowfant autographs; Frederick Locker's great album containing his choicest specimens of the very rarest autographs, among them many of the world's most famous names. Now offered for sale as a collection by Dodd, Mead & company New York, [New York? 1909.]
NL 0435705 MH ICN NNC OClRC

VOLUME 337

Locker-Lampson, Frederick, 1821-1895.
... The Rowfant books; a selection of one hundred titles from the collection of Frederick Locker-Lampson, offered for sale by Dodd, Mead & company ... New York city. [New York, 1906]
87 p. illus., facsims. 21cm.

1. Bibliography—Rare books. 2. Catalogs, Booksellers'—U. S. I. Dodd, Mead and co., firm, booksellers, New York.
6-22883
Library of Congress Z997.L815

NL 0435706 DLC NNC PP OC1JC NN

Locker-Lampson, Frederick, 1821-1895.
The Rowfant library. A catalogue of the printed books, manuscripts, autograph letters, drawings and pictures, collected by Frederick Locker-Lampson. London, B. Quaritch, 1886.
xii p., 2 l., 232 p. front., pl., port. 26½cm.
"150 copies printed for sale."
—— An appendix to the Rowfant library. A catalogue of the printed books, manuscripts, autograph letters etc. collected since the printing of the first catalogue in 1886 by the late Frederick Locker Lampson. London, Chiswick press, 1900.
xvi p., 2 l., 181 p. 2 front. 26cm.
"Three hundred and fifty copies were printed ... of which one hundred are in the possession of the Rowfant club, Cleveland, Ohio."
Comp. by Godfrey Locker-Lampson. Pref. by Augustine Birrell; poems by Austin Dobson, Andrew Lang, Earl of Crewe, Wilfrid Scawen Blunt.
1. English poetry—Bibl.—First editions. 2. Bibliography—Rare books. I. Locker-Lampson, Godfrey Tennyson Lampson. II. Birrell, Augustine, 1850- III. Rowfant library.
5-20375
Library of Congress Z997.L81

OC1WHi MiU PP OC1W OrP MnU PU
OC1 NcU MoSW MdBWA CtY CSt NcD PSC PU MH TxU NjP
NL 0435708 DLC PP OC1RC KU NN OU OC1W NIC MiU-C MB

Locker-Lampson, Frederick, 1821-1895.
Rowfant rhymes, by Frederick Locker; with an introduction by Austin Dobson. Cleveland, The Rowfant club, 1895.
143, [1] p. front. (port.) 17cm. [Rowfant club publication]
Title vignette; head and tail-piece.
"One hundred and twenty-seven copies printed in the month of September, 1895." This copy not numbered.
13-24203 Revised
Library of Congress PR4891.L2A75

OC1 NIC CLU MH NcU OKentU
NL 0435709 DLC NBu OU NN MB MH OC1WHi ViU OC1RC TxU

Locker-Lampson, Frederick, 1821-1895.
... A selection from the works of Frederick Locker. With illustrations by Richard Doyle. London, E. Moxon & co., 1865.
ix p., 1 l., 180 p. front. (port.) illus. 17 x 13cm. (Moxon's miniature poets)
"Some of these pieces appeared in ... 'London lyrics,' of which there have been two editions, the first in 1857, and the second in 1862; a few of the pieces have been restored to the reading of the first edition."
44-50421
Library of Congress PR4891.L2A7 1865

OC1RC
NL 0435710 DLC CaBVaU MH MoSW MiU NN MB NBuG CSmH

953 Locker-Lampson, Frederick, 1821-1895.
L815 A selection from the works of Frederick
1868 Locker. With illustrations by Richard Doyle. London, E. Moxon, 1868.
ix,180 p. illus.,port. (Moxon's miniature poets)

NL 0435711 CU CaBVaU OC1RC PU WU

Locker-Lampson, Frederick, 1821-1895.
To Johna[?] Marshall, dated "Weyland Cromer, Sunday [Aug. ?, 1881.]
Autograph letter signed 1p. 18x11cm.
With envelope.
Re: Regrets.

I. Marshall, Johan[?]

NL 0435712 NSyU

Ms.L Locker[-Lampson] Frederick, 1821-1895
L81h To Leigh Hunt. [London] 25 Nov. 1858. Concerning his gift of tea and a volume of verses to Hunt. Mounted and bound. Typed copy follows.
Leigh Hunt Coll. A.L.S. [1] l. 0.

NL 0435713 IaU

[LOCKER-LAMPSON, Frederick] 1821-1895.
Unanimity. My wife. My neighbor's wife. n.p., n. d.
pp.(3).
Without title-page. Caption title.
Signed: Frederick Locker.

NL 0435714 MH

Locker Lampson, Mrs. Godfrey
see Locker-Lampson, Sophie Felicite (De Rodes) "Mrs. G.L.T. Locker-Lampson"

Locker-Lampson, Godfrey Tennyson Lampson, 1875-1946.
Catalogue of ancient Greek coins collected by Godfrey Locker Lampson, compiled by E. S. G. Robinson ... London, A. L. Humphreys, 1923.
3 p. l., v-xx, 126 p., 1 l. front., xxvi pl. 26½ x 20½cm.
Errata slip inserted.

1. Coins, Greek. I. Robinson, Edward Stanley Gotch, comp.
26-14480
Library of Congress CJ317.L6

NL 0435716 DLC CU OCU MiU PU ViU NN MB

Locker-Lampson, Godfrey Tennyson Lampson, 1875-
A consideration of the state of Ireland in the nineteenth century, by G. Locker Lampson ... London, A. Constable & co., ltd., 1907.
viii, 699, [1] p. 23cm.

1. Ireland—Pol. & govt.—19th cent. 2. Ireland—Econ. condit.
8-3615
Library of Congress DA950.L7

OO OC1 MiU PPL PP PHC ICU ICJ NN NjP MB
NL 0435717 DLC CaBVaU OrP CU PSt NSyU ODaU NcD CtY

Locker-Lampson, Godfrey Tennyson Lampson, 1875-
The country gentleman and other essays, by Godfrey Locker Lampson. London, J. Cape [1932]
2 p. l., 7-251 p. 20½cm.
Contents.—The premiership.—The political careerist.—The country gentleman.—The agricultural show.—The Leger.—Old retainers.—Trials.—The cow-pasture.—Hay-making.—Poachers.—Feast week.—The point-to-point.—The birds.—The river.—Holidays.—First editions.—The country doctor.—Ghosts.—Spirits of the air.—On biking.—The philosophy of beauty.—The law of compensation.—The duties of citizenship.

1. Country life—England. I. Title.
33-8296
Library of Congress PR6023.O25C6 1932
824.91

NL 0435718 DLC CtY NIC FMU OC1RC NIC

Locker-Lampson, Godfrey Tennyson Lampson, 1875-
A few Italian pictures collected by Godfrey Locker-Lampson, with an introduction by R. Langton Douglas. [London, Chiswick press ltd., 1937?]
47, [1] p. incl. front., xix pl. 30cm.
Descriptive letterpress on versos facing plates.

1. Paintings, Italian. 2. Paintings—Private collections. I. Douglas, Robert Langton, 1864-
43-35671
Library of Congress ND615.L6
759.5

NL 0435719 DLC OC1RC OC1MA MWiCA NBB

Locker-Lampson, Godfrey Tennyson Lampson, 1875-

Gt. Brit. *Home dept. Committee on compensation for silicosis.*
... First report of the departmental committee on compensation for silicosis dealing with the refractories industries (silicosis) scheme, 1919. London, Printed & pub. by H. M. Stationery off., 1924.

Locker-Lampson, Godfrey Tennyson Lampson, 1875-1946.
Life in the country. London, F. Muller [1948]
viii, 188 p. plates (part col.) 23 cm.

1. Country life—England. I. Title.
S521.L58 630.1 49-1929*

NL 0435721 DLC FMU CtY MH

Locker-Lampson, Godfrey Tennyson Lampson, 1875-
Love lyrics, and other melic numbers by Godfrey Locker Lampson. London, F. Muller ltd [1943]
3 p. l., 33 p. 17½cm.
"First published ... in 1943."

I. Title.
44-25830
Library of Congress PR6023.O25L6
821.91

NL 0435722 DLC

Locker-Lampson, Godfrey Tennyson Lampson, 1875-
Mellow notes, by Godfrey Locker Lampson. London, F. Muller ltd [1944]
4 p. l., 35 p. 17½cm.
Poems.
"First published ... in 1944."

I. Title.
A 45-3632
Harvard univ. Library for Library of Congress PR6023.O25M4
†
821.91

NL 0435723 MH CtY DLC

VOLUME 337

Locker-Lampson, Godfrey Tennyson Lampson, 1875–
On freedom, by G. Locker Lampson. ... London, Smith, Elder, & Co., 1911.
x, 294 p. 21cm.

NL 0435724 ICJ NN NCH ICN

Locker-Lampson, Godfrey Tennyson Lampson, 1875-1946, ed.
Oratory, British and Irish; the great age from the accession of George the Third to the Reform Bill - 1832.) Edited with notes by Godfrey Locker Lampson. London, Humphreys, 1918.
xvi, 599 p. 24cm.

1. Orations. 2. English orations. I. Title.

NL 0435725 FU WaS IEN IU NN MH MB MiU TU TxU OU

Locker-Lampson, Godfrey Tennyson Lampson, 1875–
An outline of financial procedure in the House of Commons, by Godfrey Locker Lampson ... London: Hatchards, 1924. 39 p. incl. tables. 2. ed., rev. 12°.

1. Finance—Gt. Br. 2. Parliamentary practice—Gt. Br. April 6, 1925

NL 0435726 NN MH

Locker-Lampson, Godfrey Tennyson Lampson, 1875–
Peep show, by Godfrey Locker Lampson. [London] P. Davies, limited, 1937.
223 p. 20½cm.
CONTENTS.—Sidelights.—E'en such is time.—Incidents.—The candid journalist.—Characters.—Disillusion.—Egypt.—Atonement.—As-will-with.—King of beasts.—Talk.—The nun.—Our little life.—Combustion.—Atalanta.—A queer thing.

I. Title.

Library of Congress PR6023.O25P4 1937 38-14115 828.91

NL 0435727 DLC NN OCLRC

Locker-Lampson, Godfrey Tennyson Lampson, 1875–
Poems to Baa, by Godfrey Locker Lampson. New ed., rev. London, Hatchards, 1939.
51 p. 20cm.
Printed on one side of leaf only.
A sonnet sequence.

I. Title.

Michigan. Univ. Library for Library of Congress A 41-3947

NL 0435728 MiU MtU NBuU CU

Locker-Lampson, Godfrey Tennyson Lampson, 1875–
Poems to Baa, by Godfrey Locker Lampson. Rev. ed. London, J. Murray, 1941.
51 p., 1 l. 19½cm.

I. Title.

Library of Congress PR6023.O25P6 1941 42-22314 821.91

NL 0435729 DLC

Locker-Lampson, Godfrey Tennyson Lampson, 1875-
Gt. Brit. *Home dept. Committee on accidents in shipbuilding and ship repairing.*
... Report of the departmental committee on accidents in shipbuilding and ship repairing. London, Printed & pub. by H. M. Stationery off., 1924.

Locker-Lampson, Godfrey Tennyson Lampson, 1875-
Locker-Lampson, Frederick, 1821–1895.
The Rowfant library. A catalogue of the printed books, manuscripts, autograph letters, drawings and pictures, collected by Frederick Locker-Lampson. London, B. Quaritch, 1886.

Locker-Lampson, Godfrey Tennyson Lampson, 1875–
A soldier's book of love poems, arranged by Godfrey Locker Lampson. London, A. L. Humphreys, 1917.
xi, 187 p. 17½cm.

1. English poetry (Collections) I. Title.

Title from Forbes Libr. Printed by L. C. A 19-379

NL 0435732 MNF OrP NN

Locker-Lampson, Godfrey Tennyson Lampson, 1875–
Songs of the heart, by Godfrey Locker Lampson ... London, J. Murray, 1942.
35, [1] p. 17½cm.

I. Title.

Harvard univ. Library for Library of Congress A 42-3613

NL 0435733 MH WaS MB OU OCl OCLRC NN PP

Locker-Lampson, Godfrey Tennyson Lampson, 1875–
Sun and shadow; collected love lyrics and other poems by Godfrey Locker Lampson. London, F. Muller ltd. [1945]
139, [1] p. 18cm.
"First published ... in 1945."

I. Title.

Library of Congress PR6023.O25S8 46-2788 821.91

NL 0435734 DLC FU

Locker-Lampson, Godfrey Tennyson Lampson, 1875-
Sun and shadow; collected love lyrics and other poems. [2d ed. (rev. and with additions)] London, Muller [1946]
147 p.

NL 0435735 NNC

Locker-Lampson, Godfrey Tennyson Lampson, 1875-
A tale in everything. Lond. Davies, 1934.
220 p.

NL 0435736 OCLRC CaBVaU

Locker-Lampson, Godfrey Tennyson Lampson, 1875-
Thoughts in middle life, by Godfrey Locker Lampson. [London] A. L. Humphreys, 1919.
3 p. l., 136, [1] p. 20cm.
"Second impression."
Essays.

I. Title.

Library of Congress PR6023.O25T5 1919 20-17686

NL 0435737 DLC CtY CU

Locker-Lampson, Godfrey Tennyson Lampson, 1875-
Verses. Lond. Daview, 1936.
63 p.

NL 0435738 OCLRC

Locker-Lampson, Hannah Jane (Lampson)
What the blackbird said; a story in four chirps, by Mrs. Frederick Locker. Illustrated by Randolph Caldecott. London, New York, G. Routledge, 1881.
87 p. illus.

I. Caldecott, Randolph, 1846-1886. II. Title.

NL 0435739 NNC MiD ICU MH OO OClW WU

[Locker-Lampson, Oliver Stillingfleet] 1880–
Recollections of Frederick Locker Lampson, by his son, O. L. L. [Peterborough, Priv. print. by the Peterborough press, ltd., 19—]
48, [1] p. 23cm.
"Only 50 copies."

1. Locker-Lampson, Frederick, 1821–1895. I. Title.

Library of Congress PR4891.L2L6 44-27679

NL 0435740 DLC OClW

Locker-Lampson, Sophie Felicité (De Rodes) *"Mrs. G. L. T. Locker-Lampson."*
A Quaker post-bag; letters to Sir John Rodes of Barlbrough hall, in the county of Derby, baronet, and to John Gratton of Monyash, 1693–1742; selected and edited by Mrs. Godfrey Locker Lampson. With a preface by Augustine Birrell ... London, New York [etc.] Longmans, Green and co., 1910.
xii p., 3 l., 3-202 p. pl., 2 port. (incl. front.) 3 facsim. (2 fold.) 22½cm.
CONTENTS.—Preface.—Introductory note.—Letters of William Penn to Sir John Rodes, 1693, 1694, to John Gratton, 1695: to Sir John Rodes, 1697, to John Gratton, 1699.—Letters of Martha Rodes to her son, 1690–1713.—Letters of Henry Gouldney, 1690–1725.—Letters of John Tomkins, 1694–1703.—Letters of Silvanus Bevan, 1719–1742.
1. Friends, Society of. England. I. Rodes, Sir John, bart., 1670 (ca.)–1743. II. Gratton, John, 1641–1712. III. Penn, William, 1644–1718. IV. Title.
Library of Congress BX7615.L7 10-30410 Rev

CU NNUT
CaBVaU NcGU MB MBr-Z PP PU PHC PPL CSmH PPFr OCl NN
NL 0435741 DLC CaBVaU PHC NcU CSt CBBP CBPac GU

Locker guide book
see Guide book of the frozen food locker industry.

Locker management. v. 1–
Aug. 1947–
[St. Louis, J. L. Hoppe]
v. in illus., ports. 29 cm. monthly.
Absorbed Locker operator in Oct. 1950.

1. Food, Frozen—Period. 2. Cold-storage lockers—Period.

TP493.5.A1L63 *664.8505 52-33133

NL 0435743 DLC DNAL TU OCl IU

VOLUME 337

The Locker operator.

[Des Moines, 19
v. illus. 28cm. monthly.

Official organ of the National frozen food locker association and, June 1943- the Frozen food locker manufacturers and suppliers association.
Publication began Aug. 1939.

1. Cold storage lockers—Period. 2. Food, Frozen—Period. I. National frozen food locker association. II. Frozen food locker manufacturers and suppliers association.

Library of Congress TP490.L6 45-17037 664.8

NL 0435744 DLC MnSJ OCl TU IU NN TxU

Locker plants and frosted foods. Gardenvale,Quebec,National business publications,1946-

Quarterly.

NL 0435745 CaBVa DNAL

Lockerbie, George Murray, *1771-1856*.
Lockerbie's Assessment list of Indianapolis, 1835. [Edited by] Eliza G. Browning.
(*In* Indiana Historical Society. Publications. Vol. 4, pp. 397-434. Indianapolis. 1909.)

M9673 — Indianapolis. Ind. Real estate. — Browning, Eliza Gordon, ed. — Indianapolis, Ind. Taxation.

NL 0435746 MB

Lockerbie, Leslie.
The games of Ao-tea-roa. Dunedin, A. H. and A. W. Reed [193-?] 27 p. illus. 19cm. (The Raupo series of school readers. no. 22)

1. Games. Maori.

NL 0435747 NN

Lockerby, Daniel F.
Acrostical pen portraits of the eighteen presidents of the United States, by D. F. Lockerby. Biographical, historical, descriptive and eulogistic ... Philadelphia, J. L. Sibole, 1876.
ix, 3-104 p. 17 x 13½cm.
Eulogies of the presidents, from George Washington to Ulysses S. Grant.

1. Acrostics. 2. Presidents—U. S. I. Title.

Library of Congress E176.1.L81 13-11871

NL 0435748 DLC OClWHi CSmH PPL

Lockerby, Elisabeth N
see Bacon, Elizabeth N (Lockerby)

Lockerby, Florence.
... Banking, by Florence Lockerby. Developed in grade VIII, Hurley public schools, Hurley, Wisconsin. Principal—Georgiana Boyington. Superintendent—J. E. Murphy. New York city, Bureau of publications, Teachers college, Columbia university [°1932]
1 p. l., 21 p. 23cm. ([Columbia university. Teachers college. Teachers' lesson unit series. no. 28)
Blank pages for notes at end.
Bibliography: p. 18-19.

1. Banks and banking. I. Title.

Library, U. S. Office of Education LB1027.C7 no. 28 E 33-11
Library of Congress [HG1616.L55]

NL 0435750 DHEW OrMonO AAP PPT OCU

Lockerby, William, 1782-1853.
The journal of William Lockerby, sandalwood trader in the Fijian Islands during the years 1808-1809: with an introduction & other papers connected with the earliest European visitors to the islands. Edited by Sir Everard im Thurn ... and Leonard C. Wharton. London, Printed for the Hakluyt society, 1925.
cxi, 250 p., 1 l. 3 pl. (incl. front.) fold. maps (in pocket) 23cm. (*Half-title:* Works issued by the Hakluyt society ... 2d ser., no. LII)
"Issued for 1922."

CONTENTS.—Introduction.—Journal of William Lockerby (1808-9)—Samuel Patterson's narrative of the wreck of the "Eliza" in 1808.—Journal of the missionaries put ashore from the "Hibernia" on an islet in the Fiji group in 1809.—Captain Richard Siddon's experience in Fiji in 1809-1815.—Appendix: Extracts from periodical publications. Mbuli Ndama, Tradition as to, Tristan d'Acunha Island in 1811.—List of books consulted (p. [225]-231)

1. Fiji Islands. I. Im Thurn, Sir Everard Ferdinand, 1852- ed. II. Wharton, Leonard Cyril, joint ed.

Library of Congress G161.H2 2d ser., no. LII 25-10555

CaBViPA
OrU MoU ViU PBm PP PPL PU OCU MiU OU CU OClWHi MB MH
NL 0435752 DLC CaBVaU RPJCB KMK WaSpG MU OrCS WaS

Lockert, Charles Lacy, 1888- ed.

Massinger, Philip, 1583-1640.
The fatal dowry, by Philip Massinger and Nathaniel Field, ed., from the original quarto, with introduction and notes ... by Charles Lacy Lockert, jr. ... Lancaster, Pa., Press of the New era printing company, 1918.

Lockert, Édouard.
La vapeur et ses merveilles, par Édouard Lockert ... Ouvrage illustré de 76 gravures. P. Brunet, éditeur. Paris, A. Rigaud [1870?]
216 p. incl. illus., plates. 21cm. (*Half-title:* Bibliothèque de la science pittoresque)

1. Steam. 2. Steam-engines. I. Title.

Library of Congress TJ275.L7 17-31611

NL 0435754 DLC

Lockert,Else,1910-
... Ueber den einfluss der krampfgifte auf die dehydrierungsvorgänge im gewebe ... Bottrop i.W., 1933.

Münster
diss.
1933

NL 0435755 MiU DNLM OClW

WC 17005

Lockert, Eugène
Le prophète Amos. Paris, Impr. Coueslant [n.d.]
173 p.

1. Amos, the prophet.

NL 0435756 CtY

Lockert, George, fl. 1520
see Lokert, Georgus, fl. 1520.

Lockert, Juliette, ed.
Agenda-buvard du chauffeur et de l'alcool
see under title

Lockert, Juliette, ed.
Anatomie de l'automobile. [Sectional and working plates] [Paris, The Author, 1906]
6 col. pl. 38 1/2 cm.

Title from cover.

NL 0435759 MiD

Lockert, Lacy, tr.

Racine, Jean Baptiste, 1639-1699.
The best plays of Racine; translated into English rhyming verse with introductions and notes by Lacy Lockert ... Princeton, Princeton university press, 1936.

Lockert, Lacy, ed. and tr.

PQ1745
.E5L6

Corneille, Pierre, 1606-1684.
The chief plays of Corneille; translated into English blank verse, with an introductory study of Corneille, by Lacy Lockert. Princeton, Princeton University Press, 1952.

Lockert, Lacy, tr.

Dante, Alighieri, 1265-1321.
The Inferno of Dante, translated into English terza rima verse with introduction and notes by Lacy Lockert ... Princeton, Princeton university press, 1931.

Lockert, Lacy.
World drama and world dramatists, an address, by Professor Lacy Lockert ... delivered under the auspices of the Phi beta kappa society at Saint Lawrence university, May 12, 1922. Canton, N. Y., Commercial advertiser press, 1922.
16 p. 22cm.

1. Drama—Hist. & crit. I. Title.

[Full name: Charles Lacy Lockert]

Library of Congress PN1657.L6 22-16607

NL 0435763 DLC ODW

Lockert, Louis.
Petroleum motor-cars.
London. Sampson Low, Marston & Co. 1898. xv, 218 pp. Illus. Plans. 17½ cm., in 8s.
Contains chapters on motor-cycles.

K4321 — Automobiles. — Motor cycles.

NL 0435764 MB MiD MiU PPF OCl ICJ

VOLUME 337

ar V Lockert, Louis.
21833 Petroleum motor-cars. New York, D. Van Nostrand, 1899.
xv, 218 p. illus. 19cm.

NL 0435765 NIC MH CtY

Lockert, Louis.
Traité des véhicules automobiles. [Premier volume.] Les vélocipèdes. 287 p. 105 il. D. (Bibliothèque scientifique et technique du Touring-Club de France.) Paris: Touring-Club de France, 1896.

NL 0435766 ICJ CtY ICRL PPF MiD

Lockert, Louis.
Traité des véhicules automobiles. Second volume. Les voitures à vapeur. 247 p. 48 il. D. (Bibliothèque scientifique et technique du Touring-Club de France.) Paris: L. Lockert, 1896.

NL 0435767 ICJ MiD CtY

Lockert, Louis.
Traité des véhicules automobiles sur routes. Les voitures à pétrole. 295 p. 92 il. D. (Bibliothèque scientifique et technique du Touring-Club de France.) Paris: Touring-Club de France, 1896.

NL 0435768 ICJ MiD CtY

Lockert, Louis.
Traité des véhicules automobiles sur routes. Les voitures électriques avec supplément aux voitures à pétrole et note sur les moteurs à acétylène et à alcool. 330 p. 85 il. D. (Bibliothèque scientifique et technique du Touring-Club de France.) Paris: Touring-Club de France, 1897.

NL 0435769 ICJ NIC MiD

Lockert, Tore.
Modning. Dikt. Oslo, Dreyer, 1947.
47 p. 20 cm.

I. Title.

PT8950.L667M6 48-27400*

NL 0435770 DLC

Lockert, Wilbur H
The study of a bastian recording wattmeter. 1907.
Wilbur H. Lockert.

NL 0435771 OClW

942058
L815
Locke's annual register of births, marriages and deaths.
[London?] Published for the proprietor by C. Dickens and Evans.
v. 22cm.

1. Registers of births, etc. - England.

NL 0435772 FU

... "Locke's blue book"
see under [Locke, William James] 1868- comp.

AP2
.L42 Locke's national monthly,...
Toledo, O.,[18-

NL 0435774 DLC ViU N OClWHi

Locket, George Hazlewood.
British spiders, by G. H. Locket & A. F. Millidge. [London, Ray Society, 1951-53]
2 v. illus. 22 cm. (Ray Society, London. [Publications] no. 135, 137)
Includes bibliographies.

1. Spiders—Gt. Brit. I. Millidge, Alfred Frank, joint author. II. Title. (Series: Ray Society, London. Publications, no. 135 [etc.])

QL457.4.L58 595.44 51-6521 rev

NL 0435775 DLC CaBVaU DNAL GU CU NcD NN NIC MiD MB TxU NNC OrU OrCS ICJ IdU

Locket, George Hazlewood, joint author.

Bishop, Arthur Henry Burdick.
An elementary chemistry, by A. H. B. Bishop ... and G. H. Locket ... Oxford, The Clarendon press, 1936.

Locket, Sidney
Medical cases described for nurses, an introduction to clinical medicine for nurses. Edinburgh, Livingstone, 1948.
vii, 88 p. diagrs.

1. Medicine, Clinical. I. Nurses and nursing - Medicine - Texts.

NL 0435777 NNC-M DNLM

*EC75 The locket; or, The history of Mr. Singleton.
A100 A novel. In two volumes. By the author of
774l Emily ...
London:Printed for R.Snagg,no.29,Pater-noster-row.M,DCC,LXXIV.
12°. 2v.in 1. 19.5cm.

NL 0435778 MH ICN

Map Lockett, Colonel
G Carte générale de L'Afrique.
8200 Cairo, 1877. Cairo, 1934.
1877 col. map on 4 sheets 83 x 80 cm.
L6
Scale 1:2,988,691.
"Sa reproduction à mi-grandeur de l'original a été exécutée en 1934 sur l'ordre de S.M. Fouad 1er, Roi d'Egypte par l'Administration de l'Arpentage du Gouvernement Egyptien."

NL 0435779 NIC

Lockett, Abraham, ed. and tr.

PJ6101
.J82E5 al-Jurjānī, 'Abd al-Qāhir ibn 'Abd al-Raḥmān, d. 1078?
1814 The Miut ąmil, and Shurhoo Miut ąmil; two elementary treatises on Arabic syntax, translated from the original Arabic with annotations, philological and explanatory, in the form of a perpetual commentary. The rules exemplified by a series of stories and citations from various Arabian authors, with an appendix containing the original text. By A. Lockett. Calcutta, Printed by P. Pereira at the Hindoostanee Press, 1814.

Z LOCKETT, Allan B.
201 Lockett's shorthand instructor. 2d ed.
.516 London, Shorthand Institute, 1885.
16p. 16cm.

Cover title.

NL 0435781 ICN NN CtY

Z LOCKETT, Allan B.
201 Lockett's shorthand instructor, complete
.516a for schools, business, reporting.. 4th ed.
London, Lockett's Shorthand Institute, 1887.
24p. 21cm.

Cover title.

NL 0435782 ICN NN CtY

Lockett, Allan B
Lockett's shorthand instructor ... 5th ed.
... London, Lockett's shorthand institute, 1888.
42 cover-title, 19p. 16½cm.
L81 "A modification and adaptation of Duployé."
1888 cf. N.Y. Public library. The shorthand collection, p.286.

NL 0435783 CtY NN

Lockett, Andrew M jr.
Chess players of New Orleans, a record of their achievements in tournament and match play from 1830 to 1931. [10]p. 87 numb.l. [New Orleans] Author, 1931.

Mimeographed.

NL 0435784 OCl

Lockett, Andrew M jr.
Chess players of New Orleans; a record of their achievements in tournament and match play from 1830 to 1935. Enl. ed. combining part I and part II. [New Orleans?] 1935.
[14]p. 154 numb. l. front.

Reproduced from typewritten copy.

NL 0435785 OCl

Lockett, Annie
A power sewing machine work project; its development and evaluation, ... National youth administration in Ohio, 1939.
49 p. illus. (National youth administration in Ohio - Division of research in program evaluation. Evaluation studies, Report no.7)

NL 0435786 OClCC

VOLUME 337

Lockett, Arthur.
Camera lenses; a useful handbook for amateur and professional photographers, by Arthur Lockett ... with one hundred illustrations and diagrams. London, H. Greenwood & co. ltd.; New York [etc.] Sir I. Pitman & sons, ltd., 1925.
xi, 111 p. illus., diagrs. 18½cm.

1. Lenses, Photographic. I. Title.

Library of Congress TR270.L6 25-15604

NL 0435787 DLC CU OCl OO NN MB

Lockett, Arthur.
Camera lenses; a useful handbook for amateur and professional photographers, with 100 illus. and diagrs. London, H. Greenwood; New York, Pitman, 1928.
xi, 111 p. illus. 19cm.

1. Lenses, Photographic. I. Title.

NL 0435788 MB

Lockett, Arthur.
Camera lenses; a useful handbook for amateur and professional photographers, with 100 illus. and diagrs. London, H. Greenwood; New York, Pitman, 1932.
xiii, 111 p. illus. 19cm.

1. Lenses, Photographic. I. Title.

NL 0435789 MB

Lockett, Arthur.
Camera lenses; a useful handbook for amateur and professional photographers, by Arthur Lockett ... With one hundred illustrations and diagrams. New York, Pitman publishing corporation, 1935.
xiii, 111 p. illus., diagrs. 18cm.
"Made in Great Britain."

1. Lenses, Photographic. I. Title.

NL 0435790 ViU

Lockett, Arthur.
Camera lenses; a useful handbook for amateur and professional photographers, by Arthur Lockett ... Revised by H. W. Lee. 2d ed. London, Sir I. Pitman & sons, ltd. [etc.] 1937.
ix, 113 p. illus., diagrs. 18½cm.

1. Lenses, Photographic. I. Lee, H. W. II. Title.

Library of Congress TR270.L6 1937 37-30384
771

NL 0435791 DLC WaSp WaT Or NN MB NcD OClh CU NcU PPGi

Lockett, Arthur.
Camera lenses; a useful handbook for amateur and professional photographers, by Arthur Lockett ... Revised by H.W.Lee. 2d ed. N.Y. Pitman publishing corporation, 1938.
113p.

NL 0435792 NcRS

Lockett, Arthur.
Camera lenses... 2d ed. N.Y., Chicago, Pitman publishing co., 1940.
113 p.

NL 0435793 OU

Lockett, Arthur.
Camera lenses... N.Y., Chicago, Pitman, 1944.
113 p.

NL 0435794 OClW NcD

535.85
L79c
1947

Lockett, Arthur.
Camera lenses; a useful handbook for amateur and professional photographers. Revised by H. W. Lee. 2d ed. New York, Pitman Publishing Corporation, 1947.
ix, 113p. illus. 19cm.

1. Lenses, Photographic. I. Lee, H. W. II. Title.

NL 0435795 IU NRU

Lockett, Arthur.
Camera lenses; a handbook to lenses and accessories for amateur and professional photographers. Completely rev. by H. W. Lee. 3d ed. London, Pitman [1952]
142 p. illus. 20 cm.

1. Lenses, Photographic. I. Title.

TR270.L6 1952 771.35 52—2957 ‡

NL 0435796 DLC WaT WaS ICJ NN MB PPT

Lockett, Arthur

Orford, Henry.
Lens-work for amateurs, by Henry Orford ... revised by A. Lockett ... 5th ed. London, New York [etc.] Sir I. Pitman & sons, ltd., 1931.

Lockett, B.L.,
Diary, 1911 - 1920

TNSB has this on 1 roll of negative microfilm.

NL 0435798 TNSB

Lockett, *Mrs.* Elkin (Lightfoot) 1887–
Basil Lee Lockett; a beloved physician, by Elkin Lightfoot Lockett. Richmond, Va., Foreign mission board, Southern Baptist convention, 1936.
xii, 206 p. front., plates, ports., double map. 19cm.

1. Lockett, Basil Lee, 1879–1933. 2. Missions—Nigeria. 3. Baptists—Missions. 4. Missions, Medical. I. Southern Baptist convention. Foreign mission board.

Library of Congress BV3625.N5L65 36-16559
Copyright A 96218 922.6669

NL 0435799 DLC TxU

Lockett, H Claiborne.
Along the Beale trail. A photographic account of wasted range land based on the diary of Lieutenant Edward F. Beale, 1857. Text by H. C. Lockett. Photographs by Milton Snow. A publication of the Education division, U. S. Office of Indian affairs. Edited by Willard W. Beatty, director of education. [Lawrence, Kan., Printing dept., Haskell institute, 1940]
56 p. illus. 11 x 16cm. (U. S. Office of Indian affairs. [Materials on cooperatives, conservation, etc.])
"First ed.: November 21, 1939. Second ed.: June 5, 1940."—p. [2] of cover.
Also issued without the phrase "Based on the diary of Lieutenant Edward F. Beale, 1857," on t.-p.

1. Southwest, New—Descr. & trav.—Views. I. Beale, Edward Fitzgerald, 1822–1893. II. Snow, Milton. III. Beatty, Willard Walcott, 1891– ed. IV. Title.

Library of Congress F786.L78 1940 41-15607
917.91

NL 0435800 DLC KU WHi UU DI-GS CU OkU CU-B NN

Lockett, H Claiborne.
Woodchuck Cave, a Basketmaker II site in Tsegi Canyon, Arizona, by H. Claiborne Lockett and Lyndon L. Hargrave. Edited by Harold S. Colton and Robert C. Euler. Flagstaff, Northern Arizona Society of Science and Art, 1953.
v, 33 p. illus., map. 26 cm. (Museum of Northern Arizona. Bulletin 26)
Bibliography: p. 32.

1. Arizona—Antiq. 2. Basket-maker Indians. I. Hargrave, Lyndon Lane, 1896– joint author. II. Title. (Series: Flagstaff, Ariz. Museum of Northern Arizona. Bulletin 26)

F806.M95 no. 26 *979.1 913.791 53—11187

NL 0435801 DLC GU NBuC TxU DI CU MU ScU CoU OU CSt

Lockett, Hattie Greene.
... The unwritten literature of the Hopi, by Hattie Greene Lockett. Tucson, Ariz., University of Arizona [1933]
102 p. illus. (incl. ports.) 22½cm. ([Arizona. University] Social science bulletin. no. 2)
University of Arizona bulletin. vol. IV, no. 4.

1. Hopi Indians. 2. Hopi Indians—Legends. I. Title.

Library of Congress E99.H7L84 33-28293
970.3

NL 0435802 DLC WaTC CoU NcD PP PBm PU OU OO OCl MiU OrU WaSp MeB DI WHi CU UU MU NcGI ScCleU

Lockett, Jack, 1884-
Blind Jack's book of jokes and rhymes ... Dallas, Texas, J. Lockett [1925?]
15 p. 17 cm.
Text within folder, with port. on front cover.

NL 0435803 RPB

[LOCKETT, JACK] 1884-
A blind man's experiences and adventures in crossing the country; 3000 miles on a bicycle. [Dallas, Tex., 192-] 32 p. 19cm.

Cover-title.
Author's port. on cover.
Signed: Jack Lockett.

1. United States—Descr. and trav., 1910- . 2. Blind—U.S., 1922. I. Title.

NL 0435804 NN

Lockett, James.
Great Pearl Robbery of 1913
see under Humphreys, Christmas, 1901-

Lockett, Mamie
see Dodson, Mamie(Lockett)

VOLUME 337

Lockett, Mary F.
Christopher ⌜a novel⌝ by "the Princess" Mary F. Lockett. New York, London ⌜etc.⌝ The Abbey press ⌜1902⌝
iv p., 1 l., 328 p. front., pl. 20cm. 2-11132

NL 0435807 DLC

Lockett, Myrta
see Avary, Mrs. Myrta Lockett.

Lockett, Richard Cyril, 1873-1950
Catalogue of the celebrated collection of coins formed by R.C.Lockett. L, Glendining. 1955-
v. 1 illus.

NL 0435809 MH-FA PBm

NJ 47 .S 7 1927 a
Lockett, Richard Cyril, 1873-1950.
Catalogue of the valuable collection of English milled coins from Cromwell to Victoria, the property of R. Cyril Lockett, esq. ... Which will be sold by auction, by Messrs. Sotheby and co. ... auctioneers ... at their ... galleries ... on ... the 28th of April, 1927 ... London, Printed by J. Davy & sons, ltd. [1927]
19 p. II pl. 25½cm.
192 items.

NL 0435810 MdBJ

Lockett, Richard Cyril, 1873-1950.
... The Lockett collection. London, Pub. for the British academy by H. Milford, Oxford university press ⌜etc.⌝ 1938-
v. plates. 39½cm. (Sylloge nummorum graecorum. vol. III)
Preface signed: E. S. G. Robinson.

1. Coins, Greek. I. Robinson, Edward Stanley Gotch. II. Title.
Library of Congress CJ314.S9 vol. 3 40-33403 (737.0938) 737.0938

NL 0435811 DLC NIC ViU

Lockett, Samuel Henry, d 1891
Louisiana state university and agricultural and mechanical college.
... Annual report of the topographical survey of Louisiana, by Colonel Samuel H. Lockett ... ⌜1st⌝-3d; 1869-1871. New Orleans, 1870-72.

L976.3 (526.9) L813cX
Lockett, Samuel Henry, d 1891.
The coast of Louisiana ...
70,3 numb.l. 28cm.
Typewritten.
Transcribed from manuscript.
Includes information on navigable Louisiana rivers and bayous: 3l. at end.

1. Louisiana - Coasts. I. Title.

NL 0435813 LNHT

Ms. 976.3 (526.9) L813c
Lockett, Samuel Henry, d.1891.
The coast of Louisiana ... n.p., n.p., ⌜18 ?⌝
76,4 numb.l. 25cm.
Caption title.
In manuscript.
Includes information on navigable Louisiana rivers and bayous: 4l.at end.

1. Louisiana - Coasts. I. Title.

NL 0435814 LNHT

Ms. L976.3 (917) L813L
Lockett, Samuel Henry, d.1891.
Louisiana as it is; a geographical and topographical description of the state, copiously illustrated by original sketches and accompanied by a map ... The results of an actual and official survey of the state ... 1873.
xv,354 numb.l. illus., photos. 32cm.
In manuscript.

1. Louisiana - Descr. & trav. I. Title.

NL 0435815 LNHT

Lockett, Samuel Henry, d.1891.
Louisiana. *Topographical survey.*
The Louisiana state university topographical map of Louisiana, showing the characteristic features of the surface of the state in symbols and colors, comp. from the latest and most authentic sources with many additions and corrections from actual reconnaisance, by S. H. Lockett ... assisted in the draughting by D. M. Brosnan ... New York, Engraved, printed and manufactured by G. W. & C. B. Colton & co., ©1873.

Lockett, Samuel Henry, d.1891.
Mounds in Louisiana. By Prof. Samuel H. Lockett ...
(*In* Smithsonian institution. Annual report. 1872. Washington, 1873. 23½ cm. p. 429-430)

1. Mounds—Louisiana.
[Q11.S66 1872] S 15-356
Smithsonian Institution. Library for Library of Congress ⌜r70b2⌝ rev

NL 0435817 DSI OO OU OClMN MiU

Lockett, Samuel Henry, d. 1891.
Louisiana state university and agricultural and mechanical college.
Report of topographical survey of part of Louisiana, made during the months of July and August, 1869, by Colonel Samuel H. Lockett ... Topographical memoir.
(*In its* Annual report of the Board of supervisors ... 1869 ... New Orleans, 1870. 23cm. p. ⌜49⌝-76)

Lockett, S⌜amuel⌝ H⌜obart⌝ 1870-
... Continental insurance co. of N. Y. Instructions to inspectors. ⌜New York, 1898⌝
50, ⌜2⌝ p. 16°. Dec. 21, 98-55

NL 0435819 DLC

Lockett, Samuel Hobart, 1870-
... Instructions to inspectors. By S. H. Lockett, manager. Chicago, G. E. Marshall & co., 1899.
23 p. 22½cm.
At head of title: Information bureau.

1. Insurance, Fire—Inspectors. I. Continental insurance company, New York.
Library of Congress HG9715.L82 99-1447 Revised

NL 0435820 DLC

Lockett, Samuel Hobart, 1870-
... Special hazards. Extracts from letters and reports prepared by S. H. Lockett, special agent, under the supervision of the Continental insurance co. ⌜New York?⌝ ©1897.
146 p. 17cm.
At head of title: Confidential. Continental ins. co. of N. Y.

1. Insurance, Fire—Inspectors. 2. Insurance, Fire—Risks. I. Continental insurance company, New York. 7-17789†
Library of Congress HG9715.L84

NL 0435821 DLC

Lockett, Samuel Hobart, 1870-
Wood-workers, their processes and hazards. Being a brief description, from a fire insurance standpoint, of the processes peculiar to wood-working establishments as well as their hazardous features ... Chicago, Rollins publishing company, 1903.
1 p. l., 103, ⌜2⌝ p. 17 cm.

1. Woodworking industries. 2. Insurance, Fire—Risks. I. Title.
HG9731.W6L7 3—10761

NL 0435822 DLC ICJ

Lockett, William George, tr.
The Courier.
Davos ⌜Switzerland, Verkehrsverein Davos, etc.⌝

Lockett, William George, tr.
Davos as health-resort; a handbook containing contributions by A. F. Bill, M. D.; A. Brecke ⌜and others⌝ ... and introduction by W. R. Huggard ... With 6 chromotype reproductions of water colour paintings and 44 other illustrations. Davos (Switzerland) Davos printing company, ltd., 1906.

Lockett, William George.
"Davoseries." Illustrated by W.J.Urquhart. Davos-Platz [Davos printing co., ltd.] 1904.
80 p. 23 cm.

NL 0435825 MH

Lockett, William George.
Robert Louis Stevenson at Davos, by W. G. Lockett ... with 28 illustrations. London, Hurst & Blackett, ltd. ⌜1934⌝
2 p. l., 7-304 p. front., plates, ports. 22½cm.
"List of exhibits in the museum at the Robert Louis Stevenson memorial house": p. 289-291.
"Principal authorities consulted": p. 293-295.

1. Stevenson, Robert Louis, 1850-1894. 2. Davos, Switzerland. I. Title.
Library of Congress PR5495.L6 1934 35-1393
Copyright A ad int. 19811 928.2

NL 0435826 DLC NIC CtY NBuU MsU OU NN

VOLUME 337

PR5495
L6
1934 Lockett, William George
Robert Louis Stevenson at Davos. London, Hurst & Blackett ⌐1934⌐
304 p. illus.

Photocopy. Ann Arbor, University Microfilms, 1973. 18cm.

1. Stevenson, Robert Louis, 1850-1894. 2. Davos, Switzerland. I. Title.

NL 0435827 GU

Lockett (W[illiam] R.) The use of gloves in surgery; with a report of an investigation as to the efficacy of cotton gloves. 7 pp. 8°. *Philadelphia*, 1899.
Repr. from: Phila. M. J., 1899. iii.

NL 0435828 DNLM

Lockette, Henry Wilson.
An inaugural dissertation on the warm bath ... By Henry Wilson Lockette ... Philadelphia: Printed by Carr & Smith. 1801.
3 p. l., 53, ⌐1⌐ p. incl. tables. pl. 20cm.
Thesis (M. D.)—University of Pennsylvania, 1801.
Imperfect: plate wanting.

1. Baths, Warm. I. Title. II. Title: Warm bath, An inaugural dissertation on the.

A 30-553

Title from Virginia State Libr. RM822.W2L8 Printed by L. C.

PPC PU
NL 0435829 Vi PPL RPB DNLM NcD-MC NRCR PHi PPAmP

Locketus, E respondent.
Disputatio juridica de jure ventorum ...
see under Lincke, Heinrich, 1642-1692, praeses.

Lockey, Bernard.
The interpretation of ordnance survey maps and geographical pictures, by B. Lockey ... London, G. Philip & son; Liverpool, Philip, son & nephew, 1937.
31, ⌐1⌐ p., 1 l. incl. illus., diagrs. 7 col. maps. 24cm.

1. Geography—Study and teaching. 2. Maps. I. Title.

A 42-4108

Wisconsin. Univ. Libr. for Library of Congress

NL 0435831 WU MH NNC ICU PPD TxU

910.7
L79i
1950 Lockey, Bernard.
The interpretation of Ordnance Survey maps and geographical pictures ⌐with answers⌐ 4th ed. London, G. Philip, 1950.
31,6p. illus., col.maps, diagrs. 25cm.

1. Geography--Study and teaching. 2. Maps.

NL 0435832 IU

Lockey, J Florence
Elementary typewriting and office practice, including keyboard mastery (touch system) and hints on English. 3d ed. Lond.,Pitman,1948. 123p.

NL 0435833 CaBVa

Lockey, Joseph Byrne, 1877-1946.
East Florida, 1783-1785; a file of documents assembled and many of them translated by Joseph Byrne Lockey; edited with a foreword by John Walton Caughey. Berkeley, University of California Press, 1949.
xxiv, 764 p. 24 cm.
"Authorities cited": p. 751-754.

1. Florida—Hist.—English colony, 1763-1784—Sources. 2. Florida—Hist.—Spanish colony, 1784-1821—Sources. I. Title.

F314.L85 975.9 49-47287*

OKentU MB NcU OrU
NL 0435834 DLC WaTC ICU ViU CU CU-B NcD PPAmP TxU

Lockey, Joseph Byrne, 1877-1946.
La enseñanza de la aritmética en la escuela primaria, por Joseph B. Lockey... Lima: Libreria é imprenta Gil, 1911.
viii, 84 p., 1 l. 12°.

1. Arithmetic.—Study and teaching.

December 17, 1917.

NL 0435835 NN DPU

Lockey, Joseph Byrne, 1877–
Essays in Pan-Americanism, by Joseph Byrne Lockey. Berkeley, University of California press, 1939.
4 p. l., 174 p. 23cm.

1. American republics. 2. U. S.—For. rel.—Spanish America. 3. Spanish America—For. rel.—U. S. I. Title: Pan-Americanism, Essays in.

40-849

Library of Congress F1418.L65

Copyright A 134604 327.7098

OO OClW OCU MH DNAL
NL 0435836 DLC WHi KEmT OrU NcD ViU PP PU PPT OU

Lockey, Joseph Byrne, 1877-1946.
Estudios sobre la instrucción primaria en el departamento de Lima y la provincia constitucional del Callao, por Joseph Byrne Lockey ... Lima, Perú, Gil, 1914.
xiii, ⌐2⌐, 290, ⌐1⌐ p. VIII pl., tables (1 fold.) plans. 20½ cm.

1. Education—Peru—Lima (Dept.) 2. Education—Peru—Callao (Province) 3. Education, Primary. ⌐3. Elementary education—Lima, Peru⌐ I. Title.

LA599.L5L7 E 14-451

U. S. Office of Education. Library for Library of Congress ⌐a52b1⌐†

NL 0435837 DHEW NN DLC

Lockey, Joseph Byrne, 1877–
The meaning of Pan-Americanism, by Joseph B. Lockey ...
(*In* American journal of international law. Concord, N. H., 1925. v. 19, p. 104-117)

1. American republics. 2. U. S.—Foreign relations—Spanish America. 3. Spanish America—Foreign relations—U. S. I. Title. II. Title: Pan-Americanism.

A 25-445

Carnegie endow. int. peace. Library for Library of Congress [JX1.A6 vol. 19] ⌐a37c1⌐ (341.05)

NL 0435838 NNCE OCl OO

Lockey, Joseph Byrne, 1877–
Orígenes del panamericanismo, por Joseph Byrne Lockey ... Versión castellana, con anotaciones, dispuesta por la Camara de comercio de Caracas en conmemoración del primer centenario del Congreso de Panama. Caracas, Empresa El Cojo, 1927.
vi, 512 p. 23cm.
Also published in English with title: Pan-Americanism: its beginnings.
"Bibliografía": p. 499-512.

1. American republics. I. Caracas. Cámara de comercio. II. Title.

28-23887

Library of Congres F1404.L83

NL 0435839 DLC PSt NcU

Lockey, Joseph Byrne, 1877-1946.
Pan-Americanism and imperialism, by Joseph B. Lockey ...
(*In* American journal of international law. Concord, N. H., 1938. v. 32, p. 233-243)

1. American republics. ⌐1. Pan Americanism⌐ 2. Imperialism. 3. U. S.—Foreign relations. I. Title.

A 38-1135

Carnegie endow. int. peace. Library for Library of Congress [JX1.A6 vol. 32] (341.05)

NL 0435840 NNCE DLC DPU CaBVaU

Lockey, Joseph Byrne, 1877–
Pan-Americanism: its beginnings, by Joseph Byrne Lockey ... New York, The Macmillan company, 1920.
5 p. l., 503 p., 1 l. 21cm.
Thesis (PH. D.)—Columbia university, 1920.
Vita.
Published also without thesis note.
Bibliography: p. 468-486.

1. American republics. I. Title.

20-11652

Library of Congress F1404.L82
Columbia Univ. Libr. ⌐s21c2⌐

NL 0435841 NNC DAU DLC OrStbM OrSaW WaS MtU OrP

Lockey, Joseph Byrne, 1877–
Pan-Americanism: its beginnings, by Joseph Byrne Lockey. New York, The Macmillan company, 1920.
5 p. l., 503 p. 23cm.
Issued also as thesis (Ph. D.) Columbia university.
Bibliography: p. 468-486.

1. American republics. I. Title.

20-7062

Library of Congress F1404.L8

PHC PU OO OU ODW OCU MiU ICJ MB NN CU
NL 0435842 DLC Or CtY MWA DAU MeB MiU OrPR ViU PBm

LOCKEY,Joseph Byrne, 1877-1946.
Pan-Americanism,its beginnings. New York, Macmillan Co.,1926.
"Bibliography",pp.468-486.

NL 0435843 MH OCl OClW PU-W

Lockeyear, J. R.
Mr. Bunyip; an Australian story for children. Melb., 1891.
24 p.

NL 0435844 CSt

VOLUME 337

Lockformer Company

Procedures and practices in the fabrication of ducts and connectors. [Chicago] Author [n.d.]
unpaged. illus.

1.Air-pipes. 2.Heating-pipes. I.Title: Fabrication of du cts and connectors.

NL 0435845 OrP

Lockhard, Leonard, *pseud.*
see Harness, Charles Leonard, 1915–

Lockhart, Agnes Helen.

Gems from Scotia's crown. Boston, American Printing and Engraving Company [c1867]

47 p. illus. 16 x 23.5 cm.

1. NovaScotia - Descr. & trav. I. Title.

NL 0435847 CaBVaU

Lockhart, Agnes Helen.
Gems from Scotia's crown. Boston, American printing and engraving co. [c.1897]

NL 0435848 MH

Lockhart, Agnes Helen.
Told in the garden [by] Agnes Helen Lockhart. Boston, Mass., 1902.
1 p. l., iii, 3–119 p. front. (port.) 19½cm.
2-24260

NL 0435849 DLC WaS

Lockhart, Agnes Ruth
see
Sengstacken, *Mrs.* Agnes Ruth (Lockhart) 1859–

Lockhart, Aileene Simpson, 1911-
Modern dance: building and teaching lessons. With music by Jessie B. Flood, and illus. by Elizabeth Quinton. Dubuque, W. C. Brown Co. [1951]
v, 136 p. illus. 29 cm.
"Dance accompaniment for movement fundamentals": p. 99–133.
"Suggested music for movement fundamentals and composition" (bibliography) : p. 134–136.

1. Dancing. I. Title. *Full name:* Jeanne Aileene Lockhart.

GV1751.L58 793.307 51–5055 rev

NcU TxU OrP WaS OrU
NL 0435851 DLC CaBVaU CaBViP MtBC KyLx KMK NN Or

Lockhart, Aileene Simpson, 1911-
Selected volleyball articles...1937-1953...
see under American Association for Health, Physical Education, and Recreation. Division for Girls and Women's Sports.

791.7
L81t

Lockhart, Aileene Simpson, 1911-
Teams and tournaments, by Aileene Lockhart and Jane A. Mott. Fond du Lac, Wis., National Sports Equipment Co., °1954.
60 p. illus. 28 cm.

Title on cover: "How to organize teams and tournaments."

1. Tournaments. I. Mott, Jane A joint author. II. Title.

NL 0435853 LU IU NcD

AW
.L8112
Cutter

Lockhart, Aileene Simpson, 1911-
The value of the motion picture as an instructional device in learning a motor skill, by Jeanne Aileene Lockhart ... 1942.
7 p. ℓ., 107 numb. ℓ., 1 ℓ., 99 numb. ℓ. incl. tables (part fold.) diagrs. fold. table. 28cm.
Typewritten.
Thesis (Ph. D.) - University of Wisconsin, 1942.
Bibliography: numb. ℓ. 99-107.
1. Moving pic- tures in education
2. Physical ed- ucation & training

NL 0435854 WU

LB3999 Lockhart, Albert Victor, 1892-
The popularization of public secondary education in Illinois, 1885-1944. 1948.
176 l.

Typewritten.
Thesis--Univ. of Chicago.

1. Education, Secondary. 2. Education--Illinois.

NL 0435855 ICU

Lockhart, Alexander, lord Covington
see
Covington, Alexander Lockhart, lord

Lockhart, Andrew Francis.
At the bars of memory, and other poems, by Andrew Francis Lockhart. Milan, Ill., Truth and light publishing house, 1918.
cover-title, 23 p. 19½cm. $0.25

I. Title.
Library of Congress PS3523.O236A9 1918 19-831

NL 0435857 DLC

Lockhart, Arthur John, 1850-1926.
Beside the Narraguagus, and other poems, by Arthur John Lockhart. Buffalo, The Peter Paul book company, 1895.
1 p. l., vi, 9–112 p. 15½cm. (*Half-title:* ... The tenth volume of the Lotus series ...)
"... Issued in a limited edition of six hundred copies, of which this is no. 71." Signed.
"The poems 'By the Gaspereau' and 'Love and song' are by my brother, Rev. Burton W. Lockhart."—p. 112.

I. Lockhart, Burton Wellesley, 1855– II. Title.
Library of Congress PS2249.L83B4 1895 14-22062

NL 0435858 DLC CaBVaU ViU MeB NBuG MiU NN NBuHi

Lockhart, Arthur John, 1850-1926.
The birds of the cross, and other poems, by Arthur John Lockhart ... Winterport, Me., C. R. Lougee, 1909.
6 p. l., [9]–239 p. 16cm. $1.00

10-1370
Library of Congress

NL 0435859 DLC NNC MeB

Lockhart, Arthur John, 1850-1926.
Burns and Clarinda [poems]
(In- Ross, John D., comp. Burns' Clarinda, N.Y., [c1897] 20 cm. p. [236]-250.)

NL 0435860 RPB

[Lockhart, Arthur John] 1850-1926.
[Manuscripts. Loose sheets in notebook cover]
1 v. (various pagings) 21x13cm.

Largely holograph manuscripts, with a few mounted clippings. At end: "Longfellow, a reminiscence" ([1], 33 l.)
Letter from Lockhart's daughter inserted.

NL 0435861 NNC

[**Lockhart, Arthur John**] 1850-1926.
The masque of minstrels and other pieces, chiefly in verse. By two brothers. Bangor [Me.] B. A. Burr, printer, 1887.
2 p. l., iii-iv, [5]–361 p. 2 port. (incl. front.) 18cm.

I. Lockhart, Burton Wellesley, 1855– joint author. II. Title.
Library of Congress PS2248.L85M3 1887 28-9355

NL 0435862 DLC NBuG ICRL ICU

[Lockhart, Arthur John] 1850-1926.
The muses of Ville Marè [manuscript poem, signed Pastor Felix]
(In- Weir, Arthur. The romance of Sir Richard. Montreal, 1890. p. [123])

NL 0435863 RPB

Lockhart, Arthur John, 1850 - 1926.
The papers of Pastor Felix [Arthur John Lockhart] Cincinnati, Jennings and Pye; New York, Eaton and Mains [1903]
388 p. 20cm.
CONTENTS.—Memory and bells.—'Phemie; the story of a child.—Vernal notes.—The minister's Saturday evening; a symposium.—Winter on the Penobscot.—Our doctor at Grand-Pré.—The grace of death.—Wave-songs.—Autumnal notes.—L'envoy.
3-14279

NL 0435864 DLC CaBVaU NN RPB TxU ODW

Lockhart, Arthur William.
Christ's Hospital exhibitioners to the Universities of Oxford and Cambridge, 1566-1923
see under Allan, George A T ed.

VOLUME 337

1230 .502 .59 Lockhart, Arthur William
Gabriel Jones (1724-1806); sometime a scholar of Christ's hospital, an American citizen and friend of George Washington.. London, The school press, 1918.
cover-title,12 p. port. 24 cm.

1.Jones,Gabriel,1724-1806.

NL 0435866 NjP NNC CtY CSmH MH

516.5 L811c Lockhart, Brooks Javins, 1920-
Covariant correspondences and covariant sets of points defined by a given correspondence on an algebraic curve ... Urbana, Ill. 1943.
27 numb.l.
Thesis (Ph.D.)--University of Illinois, 1943.
Typewritten.
Vita.
1943 L811 ——— ——— Thesis copy.

1. Geometry, Algebraic. 2. Curves, Algebraic. I. Title.

NL 0435867 IU

Lockhart, Brooks Javins, 1920–
Covariant correspondences and covariant sets of points defined by a given correspondence on an algebraic curve, by Brooks Javins Lockhart ... Urbana, Ill., 1943.
1 p. l., 8 p., 1 l. 23cm.
Abstract of thesis (PH. D.)—University of Illinois, 1943.
Reproduced from type-written copy.
Vita.

1. Geometry, Algebraic. 2. Curves, Algebraic. I. Title.
A 44-803
Illinois. Univ. Library for Library of Congress QA564.L6
†

NL 0435868 IU NIC DLC

Lockhart, Bruce
see Lockhart, Robert Hamilton Bruce, 1887-

Lockhart, Burton Wellesley, 1855-

Lockhart, Arthur John, 1850–
Beside the Narraguagus, and other poems, by Arthur John Lockhart. Buffalo, The Peter Paul book company, 1895.

Lockhart, Burton Wellesley, 1855-
The closing address. Delivered November 14, 1898. The Church and the modern world.
(In The First Church in Exeter, New Hampshire. 1638–1888—1698–1898. Pp. 122–129. Exeter. 1898.)

G1647 — Church, The.

NL 0435871 MB

Lockhart, Burton Wellesley, 1855- joint author.

[Lockhart, Arthur John] 1850–1926.
The masque of minstrels and other pieces, chiefly in verse. By two brothers. Bangor [Me.] B. A. Burr, printer, 1887.

Lockhart, Burton Wellesley, 1855-
Semi-centennial hymn, set to music by E.T. Baldwin ...
(In Manchester, N.H. Semi-centennial of the city of Manchester, N.H., Sept. 6-9, 1896. Manchester, N.H., 1897. 26 cm. p. 77)
Hymn without music.

NL 0435873 RPB

Lockhart, Burton Wellesley, 1855-
Victory of faith. Manch., 1901.

NL 0435874 Nh

Lockhart, Caroline, 1875-
The dude wrangler, by Caroline Lockhart; frontispiece by Dudley Glyne Summers. Garden City, N. Y., and Toronto, Doubleday, Page & company, 1921.
vi, 319, [1] p. front. 19½cm.

I. Title.
Library of Congress PZ3.L81Du 21—8308

NL 0435875 DLC CoU PPL

---

818 L816d Lockhart, Caroline, 1875-
The dude wrangler; frontispiece by Dudley Glyne Summers. New York, Burt [1923]
319p. front. D.

NL 0435876 IaU

Lockhart, Caroline.
The fighting shepherdess, by Caroline Lockhart ... with a frontispiece by M. Leone Bracker. Boston, Small, Maynard & company [1919]
4 p. l., 373 p. col. front. 19½cm. $1.50
"Third printing, March, 1919."

I. Title.
Library of Congress PZ3.L81Fi 19–5695

NL 0435877 DLC MH PP NjP ViU NN OClW MB PU

Lockhart, Caroline.
The full of the moon, by Caroline Lockhart ... with illustrations by Charles H. Stephens. Philadelphia & London, J. B. Lippincott company, 1914.
4 p. l., 7–267 p. col. front., col. plates. 19½cm. $1.25

I. Title.
Library of Congress PZ3.L81Fu 14–7279

NL 0435878 DLC OClW PP PPL

Lockhart, Caroline.
The lady doc, by Caroline Lockhart ... with illustrations by Gayle Hoskins. Philadelphia & London, J. B. Lippincott company, 1912.
339 p. col. front., plates. 19½cm. $1.25

I. Title.
Library of Congress PZ3.L81La 12-23065

NL 0435879 DLC CtY ViU OClW

Lockhart, Caroline.
The man from the Bitter Roots, by Caroline Lockhart ... frontispiece by Gayle Hoskins. New York, A. L. Burt company [1915]
327 p. incl. col. front. 19½cm.
"Third edition."

I. Title.
37-32815
Library of Congress PZ3.L81Ma 2

NL 0435880 DLC PPL

Lockhart, Caroline.
The man from the Bitter Roots, by Caroline Lockhart ... with illustrations in color by Gayle Hoskins. Philadelphia & London, J. B. Lippincott company, 1915.
327 p. col. front., col. plates. 20cm. $1.25

I. Title.
Library of Congress PZ3.L81Ma 15—24004

NL 0435881 DLC IdU IdB CtY

Lockhart, Caroline.
"Me—Smith", by Caroline Lockhart; with illustrations by Gayle Hoskins. Philadelphia & London, J. B. Lippincott company, 1911.
315 p. incl. col. front. plates. 19½cm. $1.20

I. Title.
Library of Congress PZ3.L81M 11—2073

NL 0435882 DLC PU PP PPT PPL ViU

Lockhart, Caroline.
"Me-Smith". With illustrations by Gayle Hoskins. New York, Grosset & Dunlap [1913]

NL 0435883 MH

Lockhart, Caroline, 1875-
Old West—and new, a novel [by] Caroline Lockhart. Garden City, N. Y., Doubleday, Doran & company, inc., 1933.
3 p. l., v–vii, 357 p. 19½cm.
"First edition."

I. Title.
Library of Congress PZ3.L81Ol 33–9681

NL 0435884 DLC MtU OClh OEac

Lockhart, Charles, 1745–1815.
[Songs. Selected]

Four songs and a hunting cantata, set to music for the voice and harpsichord by Charles Lockhart ... London, The author [1775?]
2 p. l., 17 p. 35cm.
CONTENTS.—The slighted lover.—The habitation.—Cordelia.—Nancy.—The Staffordshire fox chace.
1. Songs (High voice) with harpsichord—To 1800. 2. Solo cantatas, Secular (High voice)—To 1800—Vocal scores with piano. 3. Hunting music. I. Lockhart, Charles, 1745–1815. The Staffordshire fox chace. II. Title: The Staffordshire fox chace.
46–42033
Library of Congress M1620.L794S6

NL 0435885 DLC OClW

VOLUME 337

Lockhart, Charles, 1745-1815.
A set of hymn tunes, and an anthem. (The whole original, and never before published) for three voices, and properly adapted for the piano forte, organ, &c. with the chords inserted in small notes, instead of figures, for the accommodation of juvenile performers. Composed...by C. Lockhart... London: the composer [1810]. 1 p.l., 4, 49(1) p. ob. 8°.
Ms. music, 1 l., inserted at end.
Words with music for S. A. and B. with organ or piano acc.

1. Hymns.
January 14, 1920.

NL 0435886 NN

Microfilm 11359 PR Lockhart, Charles D
Poems on various subjects, in which are blended the humourous and pathetic. 3d ed., enl. Ayr, Printed for the author by F. M'Bain, 1836.
178 p. 19 cm.

L. C. Copy Replaced by Microfilm

[PR4891.L35P6 1836] 48-40027*

NL 0435887 DLC

554.452 L81a Lockhart, Charles François.
Aperçu de la constitution géologique et de la paléontologie du département du Loiret, par M. Lockhart. Orléans, Impr. de Pagnerre, 1851.
16p. 22cm.
"Extrait du tome IX des Mémoires de la Société [de sciences, belles-lettres et arts d'Orléans]"

NL 0435888 IU

554.45 L81g Lockhart, Charles François.
Géologie de la Sologne, considérée dans ses rapports avec l'agriculture de cette contrée, par M. Lockhart. Orléans, Impr. de Pagnerre, 1850.
19p. 22cm.
"Lu a la seance du 19 mars 1849 de la Société des science, belles-lettres et arts d'Orléans."
"Extrait du tome IX des Mémoires de [la Société de sciences, belles-lettres et arts d'Orléans]"

NL 0435889 IU

Lockhart, Charles Fulton, 1872-
Lockhart's book of instructions for locomotive fireman.
180 p.
[Cleveland, Author, c1908]

NL 0435890 OC1

Lockhart, Charles Fulton, 1872-
Practical instructor and reference book for locomotive firemen and engineers: a practical treatise... By Charles F. Lockhart ... Over eight hundred examination questions with their answers are included. These cover the examinations required by the different railroads. New York, The Norman W. Henley publishing co., 1911.
362 p. incl. front., illus. 17½cm. $1.50

1. Locomotives—Handbooks, manuals, etc.
11—15022
Library of Congress TJ607.L6

NL 0435891 DLC ICJ NN OC1

Lockhart, Charles Fulton, 1872-
Practical instructor and reference book for locomotive firemen and engineers; a practical treatise... by Charles F. Lockhart ... over eight hundred examination questions with their answers are included. These cover the examinations required by the different railroads and the interstate commerce requirements. New York, The Norman W. Henley publishing co., 1916.
362 p. incl. front., illus., diagrs. 16½cm. $1.50

1. Locomotives—Handbooks, manuals, etc.
16-22885
Library of Congress TJ607.L6 1916

NL 0435892 DLC

Lockhart, Charles Stewart Montgomerie, ed.
The centenary memorial of Sir Walter Scott, bart. By C. S. M. Lockhart ... London, Virtue & co., 1871.
xxii p., 1 l., 171 p. xv pl. (incl. front., plans (1 fold.) facsims.) 19½cm.
"What little I may have to say myself, will be found as connecting links which unite the contributions."—Pref.
"List of contributors": p. [xvii]-xx.

1. Scott, Sir Walter, bart., 1771-1832. I. Title.
28-19037
Library of Congress PR5339.1871.L6

NL 0435893 DLC KyLoU IdU CtY ICU MdBP MiU MB

Lockhart, Charles Stewart Montgomerie, jt. author.
A general history of Hampshire, or the county of Southampton including the Isle of Wight
see under Woodward, B[ernard] B[olingbroke] 1816-1869.

[Lockhart, Mrs. Charlotte Sophia (Scott)] 1799-1837.
Letters, hitherto unpublished, written by members of Sir Walter Scott's family to their old governess; ed., with an introduction and notes, by the warden of Wadham college, Oxford. London, E. G. Richards, 1905.
2 p. l., 164 p. front. (fold. facsim.) 20cm.
"Of the forty-seven letters [to Miss Millar] twenty-eight were written by Charlotte Sophia Scott ... twelve by Anne Scott."—p. 16-17.

1. Scott family. I. Scott, Anne, 1803-1833. II. Wright-Henderson, Patrick Arkley, 1841-1922, ed. III. Millar, Miss, d. 1860? IV. Title.
6-24914 Revised
Library of Congress PR5332.L5

NL 0435895 DLC FMU CtY OC1

Lockhart, Clinton, 1858-1951.
Apostolic Christianity. Edited by Harry C. Munro. St. Louis, Christian Board of Publication [c1925]
72p. (Young people's handbook for the pupil, international graded ser., 2d year course [summer quarter])

1. Church history - Primitive and early church. 2. Bible. N. T. - Study - Text-books. I. Munro, Harry Clyde, 1890-1962, ed. II. Title. (Series)

NL 0435896 TNDC

Lockhart, Clinton, 1858-
The laws of interpretation; axioms and rules of interpretation, with references to passages by which they are illustrated. Lexington, Ky., Press of the Worker Pub. Co. [1890]
27p.

1. Bible--Hermeneutics. I. Title.

NL 0435897 TxFTC

Lockhart, Clinton, 1858-
The Messianic message of the Old Testament. By Clinton Lockhart ... [Des Moines? Ia., c1905]
2 p. l., [7]-428 p., 1 l. 20½cm.

1. Messiah — Prophecies. 2. Bible. O. T. — Prophecies. 3. Bible — Prophecies—O. T. I. Title.
5-34003
Library of Congress BT235.L8

NL 0435898 DLC NN

Lockhart, Clinton, 1858-
Principles of interpretation; the laws of interpretation treated as a science, derived inductively from an exegesis of many important passages of Scripture. By Clinton Lockhart ... Des Moines, Ia., The Christian index publishing co., 1901.
306 p. 20cm.

1. Bible—Criticism, interpretation, etc. I. Title. II. Title: Interpretation, Principles of.
1-31553 Revised
Library of Congress BS476.L6

NL 0435899 DLC KyLxCB NRCR KyWnS

Lockhart, Clinton, 1858-1951.
Principles of interpretation, as recognized generally by biblical scholars, treated as a science, derived inductively from an exegesis of many passages of Scripture. 2d ed., rev. Fort Worth, Tex., S. H. Taylor, 1915 [c1901]
260p.

1. Bible - Criticism, interpretation, etc. I. Title. II. Title: Interpretation, Principles of.

NL 0435900 TNDC

[Lockhart, Douglas]
Seeds of war: a political study of Austria, Hungary, Czecho-Slovakia, Roumania and Jugo-Slavia, 1922. By Robert Birkhill [pseud.] London, W. Gandy, 1923.
xiii, 164 p. front., plates, 2 maps (1 fold.) 23cm.

1. European war, 1914-1918—Territorial questions. 2. Reconstruction (1914-1939) 3. Minorities—Europe. I. Title.
23—10924
Library of Congress D653.L65
[a45r26c1]

NL 0435901 OC1BHS DLC NNC CtY PPL NjN OOxM OC1W ICJ NN

D653 .L8 Lockhart, Douglas.
Seeds of war: a political study of Austria, Hungary, Czecho Slovakia, Roumania and Jugo-Slavia. By Douglas Lockhart (Robert Birkhill) With an introduction by the late Lt.-Col. the Hon. Aubrey Herbert ... London, W. Gandy, 1925.
xvi, 164 p. front., plates, 2 maps (1 fold.) 23cm.
2d ed.

1. European war, 1914-1918—Territorial questions. 2. Reconstruction (1914-)

NL 0435902 ICU CSt-H NN NIC

Lockhart, Earl Granger, 1879-
... The attitudes of children toward law, by Earl G. Lockhart, PH. D. Iowa City, Ia., The University [1930]
61 p. diagrs. 23½cm. (University of Iowa. Studies in character. vol. III, no. 1)
On cover: University of Iowa studies. First series, no. 185.
Thesis (PH. D.)—University of Iowa, 1929.
Without thesis note.
Bibliography: p. 38.

1. Character tests. 2. Moral education. 3. Mental tests. I. Title. II. Title: Law, The attitudes of children toward.
31-27336
Library of Congress LC268.L58 1929
Univ. of Iowa Libr.
Thesis note on label mounted on t.-p.
136.7434

NL 0435903 OU NcD PBm ODW OCH MiU OC1 OC1W PU PPT IaU OrPR NIC MB OrCS WaTC OrU MH DLC NcU

VOLUME 337

Lockhart, Earl Granger, 1879-
Child training, the pathway to happiness, prepared by Earl G. Lockhart [and] Glenda X. Mabrey. A course in the scientific training of children. [Parent's guide. Kansas City, Mo.] National Educational & Research Institute [19
v. illus. 28 cm.
Includes bibliographies.

1. Children—Management. I. Mabrey, Glenda X., joint author.
HQ769.L6 649.1 48-1757*

NL 0435904 DLC

Lockhart, Earl Granger, 1879-
How to improve your personality, by Earl G. Lockhart ... Chicago, Ill., Walton publishing company [c1941]
xx, 453 p. 23cm.

1. Personality. I. Title.
41-24000
Library of Congress BF698.L59
[159.9235] 137.5

NL 0435905 DLC LU NcU PP PSt

137
L811h
1943
Lockhart, Earl Granger, 1879-
How to improve your personality, by Earl G. Lockhart ... [Chicago] Wilcox & Follett co.; Grosset & Dunlap, trade distributors, 1943 [c1941]
3p.ℓ.,v-xxp.,1ℓ.,453p. 21cm.

1. Personality. I. Title.

NL 0435906 TxU FTaSU Mi

Lockhart, Earl Granger, 1879-
Improving your personality, by Earl G. Lockhart ... Chicago, Ill., Walton publishing company [c1939]
xx, 512 p. 23cm.
"References" at end of each chapter.

1. Personality. I. Title.
39-23878
Library of Congress BF698.L6
Copyright A 132268 [159.923] 137

NL 0435907 DLC IdU OrU ICRL NN PWcS OU OClW OOxM PPT

Lockhart, Earl Granger, 1879- *ed.*
My vocation, by eminent Americans; or, What eminent Americans think of their callings, selected and arranged by Earl G. Lockhart ... New York, H. W. Wilson company, 1938.
334 p. incl. ports. 20cm.

1. Vocational guidance. 2. Occupations. I. Title.
38—27164
Library of Congress HF5381.L6
[a45m2] 371.425

WaHW OrSaW WaE OrMonO OrLgE CaBVa
PWcS OU OClU OClCC NN ICJ PPT PU PSC NcD NcRS PP PV
NL 0435908 DLC DAU KEmT ODW Or IdU OLak OClND OClW

Lockhart, Earl Granger, 1879-
Power through personality, by Earl G. Lockhart ... Des Moines, Ia., National research institute [c1941]
1 v. 29 x 25cm.
Loose leaf; variously paged.
Reproduced from type-written copy.

1. Personality. 2. Psychology, Applied. I. Title.
41-15066
Library of Congress BF636.L6
[159.9235] 137.5

NL 0435909 DLC

Lockhart, Earl Granger, 1879-
The psychology of personality, by Earl G. Lockhart ... [Des Moines, Ia., c1935]
5 p. l., 3-470 p. 23½cm.
"References" at end of each chapter.

1. Personality. I. Title.
35-2270
Library of Congress BF698.L6
Copyright A 80231 [159.923] 137

NL 0435910 DLC

Lockhart, Edgar Henry, 1839?-1868.

Six essays on commons preservation: written in competition for prizes offered by Henry W. Peek ... Containing a legal and historical examination of manorial rights and customs, with a view to the preservation of commons near great towns ... London, S. Low, son, and Marston, 1867.

Lockhart, Elizabeth, 1812-1870, tr.

BX4700
.F65E5
1898
Bonaventura, *Saint, Cardinal,* 1221-1274.
The life of St. Francis of Assisi. [Translated] from the "Legenda Sancti Francisci" of St. Bonaventure, by Miss Lockhart. Edited, with a pref., by His Grace the Cardinal-Archbishop of Westminster. 4th ed. London, R. Washbourne; New York, Benziger Bros., 1898.

[Lockhart, Elizabeth] 1812-1870.
Lifeof saint Teresa. Edited with a preface, by Henry Edward Manning. London, Hurst & Blackett, 1865.

NL 0435913 NjNbT

PQ6437
.T328L8
[Lockhart, Elizabeth] 1812-1870.
The life of Saint Teresa of the Order of Our Lady of Mount Carmel. Ed. with a pref. by His Grace the Cardinal Archbishop of Westminster. 4th ed. Dublin, J. Duffy [1865]
xxx, 300 p.

1. Teresa, Saint, 1515-1582.

NL 0435914 ICU

929.72
L816D
[Lockhart, Ephraim]
A disquisition on the right of jurisdiction in peerage successions, particularly the peerage of Scotland; contained in letters to the Right Honourable the Lord K________: with an Appendix [by Thomas Christopher Banks] 2d ed. ... London, James Ridgway, 1830.
118 p. 21 cm.
1. Gt. Brit. Peerage. 2. Scotland. Peerage.
I. Title: Letters to the Right Honourable the Lord K II. Title. III. Banks, Thomas Christopher, 1765-1854.

NL 0435915 NcD MH NN

Lockhart, Ephraim.
Genealogical account of the family of Alexander, in Scotland, Earls of Stirling and Dovan, &c. 77 pp. Genealogical table.
(In Humphrys, Alexander. Narrative of the oppressive law proceedings . . . resorted to by the British Government . . . to overpower the Earl of Stirling. Edinburgh. 1836.)

H1080 — Alexander family. — Genealogy. Alexander.

NL 0435916 MB

Lockhart, Ephraim.
An historical view of the Province of Nova Scotia, and other territories in America; and account of the grants of those territories, with their dependencies, &c., in favour of Sir William Alexander, Earl of Stirling, &c. . . . in the reign of Charles the First: with proofs . . . vi, 77 pp.
(In Humphrys, Alexander. Narrative of the oppressive law proceedings . . . resorted to by the British government . . . to overpower the Earl of Stirling. Edinburgh. 1836.)

H5968 — Nova Scotia. Hist.

NL 0435917 MB

Lockhart, Ephraim.
Humphrys-Alexander, Alexander, *calling himself earl of Stirling,* 1783-1859.
Narrative of the oppressive law proceedings, and other measures, resorted to by the British government, and numerous private individuals, to overpower the Earl of Stirling and subvert his lawful rights. Written by himself. Also A genealogical account of the family of Alexander, earls of Stirling, &c. ... followed by An historical view of their hereditary possessions in Nova Scotia, Canada, &c. by Ephraim Lockhart, esq. With a copious Appendix of royal charters and other documents. Edinburgh [J. Walker, printer] 1836.

[**Lockhart, Ephraim**]
Statement with reference to the knights baronets of Nova Scotia, their creations, privileges, and territorial rights of property in that colony, &c. ... with an appendix. Edinburgh, W. Tait; [etc., etc.] 1831.
36 p. 23cm.
"Advertisement" signed: E. Lockhart.

1. Nova Scotia. 2. Scotland—Baronetage. I. Title.
20-2102
Library of Congress F1038.L81

NL 0435919 DLC MH NN

Lockhart, Ernest E., ed.
Coffee Brewing Institute, ***New York.***
A survey of world literature on coffee.

New York.

Lockhart, Eugene, 1891-
...A modest little thing. Words and music by Eugene Lockhart. New York, Chappell-Harms inc. [c1919]
First line: You've heard of the maid of Quaker town.
Chorus: I do not paint or powder.
From the musical revue at the Hecksher theatre, Bunk of 1926.

NL 0435921 NN

LOCKHART, EUGENE, 1891-
On the road to Jericho. Words and music by Gene Lockhart. New York, Chappell [c1953]
First line: A man went down to Jericho.
1. Songs, Popular--1890- 2. Jericho 3. Good Samaritan

NL 0435922 NN

VOLUME 337

D1962
Lockhart, Eugene, 1891-
Sumurun, synopsis of scenes. ⌐Los Angeles Federal Theatre Project⌐ 1939.

Mimeographed synopsis of the play.

I. Federal Theatre Project. II. Title.

NL 0435923 KU

Lockhart, Eugene, 1891-
...The way to your heart... Words and music by Eugene Lockhart. New York, Chappell-Harms inc. [c1919]

First line: The beauty of the morn.
Chorus: In your eyes, dear.
From the musical revue at the Heckshar theatre, Bunk of 1926.

NL 0435924 NN

Lockhart, Frank Jones, 1916- joint author.

QD543 .B4
Bergelin, Olaf Preysz, 1911–
... Liquid-liquid extraction across a known interfacial area, by Olaf Bergelin ... Philadelphia, Pa., American institute of chemical engineers ⌐1943⌐

Lockhart, Fred T
... Bible biographies from Adam the first man ... by Fred T. Lockhart ... ⌐Augusta, Ga., Richard & Shaver, c1892⌐

NL 0435926 GEU

Lockhart (F[rederick] A[lbert] L[awton]).
Artificial dilatation of the non-pregnant uterine canal. 7 pp. 8°. *New York*, 1896.
Repr. from: Am. Gynæc. & Obst. J., N. Y.. 1896, viii.

NL 0435927 DNLM

Lockhart, Frederick Albert Lawton.
... The operative treatment of uterine fibroids. By F. A. Lockhart ... ⌐New York⌐ 1899.

11 p. tab. 24½cm. ⌐Papers by the staff of the medical faculty, McGill university. 1899⌐

"Reprinted from the American gynæcological and obstetrical journal for December, 1899."
Bibliography: p. 10–11.

1. Uterus—Tumors.

Library of Congress R111.M14 7-25014†

NL 0435928 DLC MB

Lockhart, Gene
see Lockhart, Eugene, 1891-

Lockhart, George.
Grey titan; the book of elephants, by George Lockhart and W. G. Bosworth ... London, B. Oates & Washbourne ltd. ⌐1938⌐

3 p. l., ix–xii, 113 p. front. (ports.) illus., plates. 19cm.

1. Elephants. 2. Elephants—Legends and stories. I. Bosworth, William George, 1904– joint author. II. Title.

Library of Congress QL795.E4L85 39-20141
599.61

NL 0435930 DLC CU INS

Lockhart, George, fl. 1520
see Lokert, Georgius, fl. 1520.

⌐**Lockhart, George**⌐ 1673–1731.
Histoire secrete des intrigues de la France en diverses cours de l'Europe: où l'on voit que l'accroissement du pouvoir de cette couronne est dû au succès de ces intrigues, plûtôt qu'à ses propres forces & à l'habileté de ses ministres d'état, &c..... On a joint à la tête de l'ouvrage la lettre d'un Wigg à un Tory sur la conjoncture presente ... Traduit de l'Anglois. Londres, 1713–14.
3 v. in 1. 20cm.

201081B. 1. France—For. rel., 1492– 1715. I. Title.
October 19, 1942

NL 0435932 NN CLU ICU NIC

Lockhart, George, 1673-1731, supposed author.
A key to the Memoirs of the affairs of Scotland
see under title

---

*EC7 L8113 710l
[Lockhart, George, 1673-1731]
A letter to a L-d of the s-ss-n[i.e. Lord of the session].
London:Printed in the year, MDCCX.
12p. 20.5cm.

NL 0435934 MH

Lockhart, George, 1673–1731.
The Lockhart papers: containing memoirs and commentaries upon the affairs of Scotland from 1702 to 1715, by George Lockhart ... his secret correspondence with the son of King James the Second from 1718 to 1728, and his other political writings; also, journals and memoirs of the Young Pretender's expedition in 1745, by Highland officers in his army. Pub. from original manuscripts in the possession of Anthony Aufrere ... London, Printed by R. and A. Taylor, for W. Anderson, 1817.
2 v. 28½cm.
1. Scotland—Hist.—Anne, 1702-1714. I. Aufrere, Anthony, 1756-1833, ed.

3-28445

Library of Congress DA805.L83

TU NcGU CaBVaU
MdBP MBAt MB NcD Vi NcU OU MdBP KU CSt ODaU OC LU
NL 0435935 DLC OCl NN MiDU NjP CtY MnU PPL PU MiU

⌐**Lockhart, George**⌐ 1673–1731.
Memoirs concerning the affairs of Scotland, from Queen Anne's accession to the throne, to the commencement of the union of the two kingdoms of Scotland and England, in May, 1707. With an account of the origine and progress of the design'd invasion from France, in March, 1708. And some reflections on the ancient state of Scotland ... London, J. Baker, 1714.
xxx, 420 p. 20½ cm.
"Published ananymously, without Lockhart's consent."—Dict. nat. biog.
Appended: A key to the Memoirs of the affairs of Scotland. London, Printed for J. Moor, 1714 (23 p.)
1. Scotland—Hist.— 1689–1745. I. Title.

DA805.L81 3—29495

ICU NRU MH ICN CtY NjP OO MoU CaBVaU OrU
MdBP N NjR DFo ICRL OCl NNUT CLU-C IaU TxU MB ViU
NL 0435936 DLC PPL InU Vi CU-A NcD CU ViW PU TU MsU

---

*EC7 L8113 714m
[Lockhart, George, 1673-1731]
Memoirs concerning the affairs of Scotland, from Queen Anne's accession to the throne, to the commencement of the union of the two kingdoms of Scotland and England, in May, 1707. With an account of the origine and progress of the design'd invasion from France, in March, 1708. And some reflections on the ancient state of Scotland. To which is prefix'd an introduction, shewing the reason for publishing these memoirs at this juncture.

London, Printed: and sold by the booksellers of London and Westminster. 1714.
8°. xxx,403(i.e.387)p. 20cm.
Numbers 305-320 omitted in the paging.
According to ms. note on fly-leaf at front, this copy belonged to George Colman the younger.

NL 0435938 MH MB ViU NRU ICN DLC DFo MdBP MoU FU

⌐**Lockhart, George**⌐ *fl.* 1683.
A further account of East-New-Jarsey by a letter write to one of the proprietors thereof, by a countrey-man, who has a great plantation there. Together with the discription of the said province, as it is in Ogilbies atlas, printed in the year, 1671. Edinburgh, Printed by John Reid, Anno Dom. 1683. ⌐Boston, 1941⌐
facsim: 7 p. 23cm. ⌐Photostat Americana. Second series ... Photostated at the Massachusetts historical society. No. 133⌐
Signed: Geo: Lockhart.
One of 14 copies from the original in the John Carter Brown library, July 1, 1941.
1. New Jersey—Descr. & trav. I. Ogilby, John, 1600–1676. America. 1671. II. Title.

Library of Congress F137.L6 1671 a 41-16440
917.49

NL 0435939 DLC MiU-C NjP ViW ViU RPJCB NcD

Lockhart, George L 1883–
Public schools; their construction, heating, ventilation, sanitation, lighting and equipment, by G. L. Lockhart ... St. Paul, Minn., H. W. Kingston company ©1918
211 p. illus., plans. 31½cm.

1. School-houses. I. Title.

Library, U. S. Bur. of Education LB3221.L8 E 22-514

PP
NL 0435940 DHEW CU OrU WaS KEmT MiU NN IU ICJ PU-FA

---

*E611 .L82
Lockhart, H C
An incident in the rebellion ...
Boston, 1862.
2l. 25cm.

Caption title.
Letter from H. C. Lockhart, Lieutenant-Colonel, prisoner of war, to Aaron Goodrich, St. Paul, Minnesota.

NL 0435941 MnHi

Lockhart, Haines Boots, 1920–
Quantitative experiments on the nutritive value of amino acids ⌐by⌐ Haines Boots Lockhart ... Urbana, Ill., 1945.
1 p. l., 5, ⌐1⌐ p. 22½cm.
Abstract of thesis (PH. D.)—University of Illinois, 1945.
Vita.
Bibliography: p. 2, 5.

1. Amino acids.

Illinois. Univ. Library for Library of Congress QP801.A5L6 A 46-302

NL 0435942 IU DLC NIC

VOLUME 337

Lockhart, Helen S 1918- *ed.*
Nutrition education in elementary and secondary schools, edited by Helen S. Lockhart and F. Eugenia Whitehead. ⌊Boston, Dept. of Nutrition, Harvard University School of Public Health⌋ distributed by the Nutrition Foundation, New York ⌊1952⌋
43 p. illus. 28 cm.

1. Nutrition—Study and teaching. I. Whitehead, Floy Eugenia, 1913- joint ed. II. Title.

LB1587.N8L6 371.716 53—1226 ‡

NL 0435943 DLC ICarbS MB PSt TxU OCU OrCS MBCo

Lockhart, Howard M
Consequences; a family game in three acts. Glasgow, Brown, Son & Ferguson ⌊19--⌋
88p. 18cm.

NL 0435944 ScU NN

Lockhart, Howard M
The story of Madeleine Smith, a dramatic fiction founded on fact. A play in three acts. London, H. F. W. Deane; Boston, W. H. Baker Co. ⌊1949⌋
72 p. 22 cm. (Deane's series of plays)

1. Smith, Madeleine Hamilton, 1835-1893?—Drama. I. Title.

PN6120.A5L524 822.91 49-54912*

NL 0435945 DLC

Lockhart, Hugh, comp.
Extracts from various Greek authors...
see under [Sandford, Sir Daniel Keyte] 1799-1838, ed.

Lockhart, I. E., tr.

Werkmann von Hohensalzburg, Karl Martin, *freiherr*, 1878–
The tragedy of Charles of Habsburg, by Baron Charles von Werkmann ... London, P. Allan & co. ⌊1924⌋

Lockhart, J G.
Notes on the habits of the moose in the far north of British America in 1865. By J. G. Lockhart.
(*In* U. S. National museum. Proceedings. Washington, 1891. 23½cm. v. 13, 1890, p. 305–308)
Issued November 15, 1890.

1. Moose.

S 33-220

Library, Smithsonian Institution
Library of Congress [Q11.U55 vol. 13]

NL 0435948 DSI OU

Lockhart, Jack H.
Thirty. [A play in one act]
(From- The Cue, Jan. 1930. 23 cm. p. 10-22.)

NL 0435949 RPB

LOCKHART, JACK H.
Thirty, by Jack Lockhart... (In: Cloetingh, A.C., editor. Prayers for Passel, and other prize plays. New York[, cop. 1931]. 19cm. p. 73-94.)

In one act.

599305A. 1. Drama, American. I. Title.

NL 0435950 NN

Lockhart, Jacques
...Le marché des changes de Paris. Fonctionnement. Réglementation. Technique des opérations...par Jacques Lockhart ... Paris: Les Presses universitaires de France⌊, 1927⌋. 410 p. incl. tables. 8°.
Dissertation, Paris.
Bibliography, one page following t.-p.

355403A. 1. Money market—France—Paris. May 7, 1928

NL 0435951 NN CtY

L[ockhart], J[ames]
The Salutation. By J--- L---. 16 April, 1859. London.
3 l. 4°. (In "Poems", 43)

NL 0435952 CtY

[Lockhart, James]
Sonnet, dedicated to the Poles. [Signed: J. L.]
2 l. (incl. half-title) 4°. (In "Poems," 43.)

NL 0435953 CtY

Lockhart, James, M.A.
Aglaia, Choric, Evviva. For the name day of Her Royal Highness Margherita, princess of Piedmont. Roma, Tip. romana di C. Bartoli, 1871.
(8) p. f°.
Verse.

NL 0435954 MH

LOCKHART, James, M.A.
The Benison April 22,1868. A lay of troth-plight. [Florence, 1868]
pp. 23.

NL 0435955 MH CtY

Lockhart, James, M.A.
Cavour. Patria e gloria, poem dedicated to the sons of Italia, by James Lockhart ... November VIII, MDCCCLXXIII. [Firenze, Tip. dei successori Le Monnier, 1873]
19 p. 30 cm.

NL 0435956 CtY

Lockhart, James, *M. A.*
Dante Alighieri; the festal day, May MDCCCLXV. Italia amans concors venerans. By James Lockhart ... ⌊Firenze, Tip. dei successori Le Monnier, 1865⌋
34 p. 24cm.
A poem.

3-25146

NL 0435957 DLC NIC

Lockhart, James., M.A.
Jupiter the balancer, or The mysteries of gold and paper. A legend of the nineteenth century, by James Lockhart, ... [Firenze, Tip. dei successori Le Monnier], 1874.
17 p. 30½cm.

NL 0435958 ICJ CtY

Lockhart, James, M.A.
The patriot's grave, April XXVIII, MDCCCLXVII, an elegy, by James Lockhart ... [Firenze, Tip. dei successori Le Monnier, 1867]
13 p. 28 cm.
1. Poerio, Carlo, 1803-1867 - Poetry.

NL 0435959 CtY

Lockhart, James, M.A.
Venetia of the roseate dawn. June MDCCCLXVI. ... By James Lockhart ... [Firenze, Tip. dei successori Le Monnier, 1866]
12 p. 25.5 cm.
In verse.

NL 0435960 CtY

QA218 L58 Lockhart, James, 1763-1852.
Extension of the celebrated theorem of C. Sturm, whereby the roots of numeral equations may be separated from each other, with copious examples. Oxford, Printed for the author by D.A. Talboys, 1839.
19 p.
"Addenda" slip inserted at p.19.

1. Equations, Roots of

NL 0435961 CU

Lockhart, James, 1763–1852.
A method of approximating towards the roots of cubic equations belonging to the irreducible case, by James Lockhart ... London, Printed for the author, 1813.
vi, ⌊7⌋–87 p. diagr. 24½cm.

Subject entries: 1. Equations—Numerical solutions. 2. Equations, Cubic.

3-12741

Library of Congress, no. QA218.L8.

NL 0435962 DLC CU NWM

Lockhart, James, 1763–1852.
The nature of the roots of numerical equations. By James Lockhart ... London, Printed by C. and J. Adlard, 1850.
iv, ⌊5⌋–20 p. 21cm.

Subject entries: Equations, Roots of.

3-12742

Library of Congress, no. QA218.L82.

NL 0435963 DLC CU

Lockhart, James, 1763–1852.
Resolution of equations. By James Lockhart ... Part the first. Oxford, Printed for the author, 1837.
vi, 46 p. 27½ x 21½cm.
Title vignette.

Subject entries: Equations—Numerical solutions.

3-22978

Library of Congress, no. QA218.L84.

NL 0435964 DLC

VOLUME 337

QA218 L8 Lockhart, James, 1763-1852.
Resolution of equations by means of inferior and superior limits ... By James Lockhart ... London, T. & C. Lockhart, 1842.
24 p. 29cm.

---- ------ Appendix ... London, Sold by T. & C. Lockhart, 1843.
15 p. 29cm. ₍With the above₎

1.Equations - Numerical solutions.

NL 0435965 CU

Lockhart, James, 1763–1852.
Resolution of two equations. By James Lockhart ... Being a homage to the memory of the founders and benefactors of the University of Oxford, at the commemoration held on the 12th of June, 1839. Oxford, Printed for the author, 1839.
10 p., 1 l. 27½ x 21½cm. ₍With his Resolution of equations. Oxford, 1837₎

Subject entries: Equations—Numerical solutions. 3-20447

Library of Congress, no. QA218.L84.

NL 0435966 DLC

Lockhart, Sir James Haldane Stewart, 1858–1937.
The currency of the Farther East from the earliest times up to the present day. By J. H. Stewart Lockhart ... Hongkong, Noronha & co., 1895–98.
3 v. plates. 22 x 29cm.
Title of vol. 2 reads: The plates of the Chinese, Annamese, Japanese, Corean coins; of the coins used as amulets, and of the Chinese government and private notes. Collected by the late Mr. G. B. Glover ... and now in the possession of Mrs. Glover ...; title of vol. 3: A guide to the inscriptions on the Coins of the Farther East, with special reference to the Glover collection and a chronology of the dynasties and emperors of China, Annam, and Japan ...
Vol. 2 has half-title: The currency of the Farther East. vol. II.
Plates (vol. 2) printed on both sides.
"List of works consulted": vol. 1, p. ₍217₎–223.
1. Coins, Oriental. 2. Amulets. 3. Paper money—China. 4. East (Far East)—Hist. I. Glover, G. B. II. Title.
Library of Congress CJ3525.L8 10—27946 ₍a42e1₎

NL 0435967 DLC ICU MSaE NN MH CtY OCl PP

Lockhart, James Haldane Stewart, 1858–
The currency of the Farther East from the earliest times up to 1895. By J. H. Stewart Lockhart, ... Vol. I–[III]. Hongkong, Noronha and Co., 1895–1907.
3 vol. 204 (*i.e.* 102) pl. 21½ x 27cm.–25½cm.
The plates (vol. 2) have illustrations on both sides.
Vol. 2 title reads: The plates of the Chinese, Annamese, Japanese, Corean coins; of the coins used as amulets and of the Chinese government and private notes. Collected by the late Mr. G. B. Glover . . . , and now in the possession of Mrs. Glover; vol. 3: A guide to the inscriptions on the coins of the Farther East, with special reference to the Glover collection and a chronology of the dynasties and emperors of China, Annam, and Japan.
Vol. 2 has half-title: The currency of the Farther East. Vol. II.
Vol. I: 1907.
"List of works consulted," vol. I, p. [217]–223.

NL 0435968 ICJ MB OClWHi

Lockhart, Sir James Haldane Stewart, 1858- ed.
Fraser, Sir Everard Duncan Home, 1859–1922.
Index to the Tso chuan ... compiled by Everard D. H. Fraser ... revised and prepared for the press by James Haldane Stewart Lockhart ... London, New York ₍etc.₎ Oxford university press, H. Milford. 1930.

Lockhart, Sir James Haldene Stewart, 1858- tr.
Ch'êng yü k'ao.
A manual of Chinese quotations, being a translation of the Ch'êng yü k'ao ... With the Chinese text, notes, explanations and English and Chinese indices for easy reference, by J. H. Stewart Lockhart ... ₍2d ed.₎ Hongkong ₍etc.₎ Kelly & Walsh, limited, 1903.

DSI CtY
NL 0435977 IEN DLC NN ICU ViU MH OCl OClMA DDO WaTC

Lockhart, James Haldane Stewart, 1858-
Hongkong. *Commission on Tung Wa hospital.*
... Report of the Commission appointed by His Excellency Sir William Robinson ... to enquire into the working and organization of the Tung Wa hospital, together with the evidence taken before the Commission, and other appendices. Hongkong, Printed by Noronha & co., government printers, 1896.

Lockhart, Sir James Haldane Stewart, 1858-1937.
... Report of the Commission appointed by His Excellency Sir William Robinson ... to inquire into the existence of insanitary properties in the colony, ...
see under Hongkong. Commission on insanitary properties.

Lockhart, Sir James Haldane Stewart, 1858-
Hongkong. *Committee on British trade in Hongkong.*
... Report of the Committee appointed by His Excellency Sir William Robinson ... to enquire into the condition of British trade in Hongkong, together with the evidence taken before the Committee. Hongkong, Printed by Noronha & co., government printers, 1896.

Lockhart, James Haldane Stewart, 1858-
Hongkong. *Public works commission.*
Report of the Public works commission. Hongkong, Noronha & co., government printers, 1902.

Lockhart, Sir James Haldane, Stewart, 1858-
Hongkong. *Special committee on the Pó Léung Kuk.*
... Reports of the Special committee appointed by His Excellency Sir William Robinson ... to investigate and report on certain points connected with the bill for the incorporation of the Pó Léung Kuk, or Society for the protection of women and girls, together with the evidence taken before the Committee, and an appendix containing correspondence, reports, returns, &c. Hongkong, Printed by Noronha & co., government printers, 1893.

Lockhart, Sir James Haldane Stewart, 1858–1937.
... The Stewart Lockhart collection of Chinese copper coins, by Sir James H. Stewart Lockhart ... Shanghai ₍etc.₎ Kelly & Walsh, limited, 1915.
2 p. l., xv, 174, 36 p. illus. 31½cm. (Royal Asiatic society, North China branch. Extra volume, no. 1)
The illustrations (referred to as "plates" in the Introduction) comprise p. 1–174, and are followed by descriptive letterpress (36 p.)

1. Coins, Chinese. 2. Numismatics—China. I. Title. 16—23859

Library of Congress CJ3500.L7

NL 0435976 DLC Or MSaE NcD NjP NN OO CU

Lockhart, James Henry.
An exhibition of 100 prints and drawings from the collection of James H. Lockhart, jr. With a foreword and notes by Robert McDonald. May 4th to June 30th, 1939. Pittsburgh, Pa., Carnegie institute ₍1939₎
3 p. l., 217 p., 1 l. illus. 23½ cm.
"General books on prints": p. 217.

1. Engravings — Private collections. 2. Engravings — Exhibitions. I. McDonald, Robert, 1912– II. Pittsburgh. Carnegie institute.
NE57.L6 A 40–1983 rev 2
Northwestern Univ. Library for Library of Congress ₍r48f1₎†

Lockhart, James L.
Porkey, an Arkansas razorback; story and pictures by James L. Lockhart ... Chicago, A. Whitman & co., 1939.
64 p. illus. 22½cm.
Illustrated t.-p.
"Junior press books."

I. Title. 39–23298

Library of Congress PZ10.3.L83Po

NL 0435978 DLC

Lockhart, Jeanne Aileene Simpson
see
Lockhart, Aileene Simpson, 1911–

Lockhart, Jeffrey Garald, 1923–
Coal deposits of New Brunswick; location, description and future possibilities, by J. G. Lockhart for New Brunswick Resources Development Board. Fredericton, 1946.
iii, 104 l. maps. 28 cm.
"References": leaves 96–98.

1. Coal—New Brunswick. 2. Coal mines and mining—New Brunswick. I. New Brunswick. Resources Development Board.
TN806.C2L6 553.2 G S 47–198 rev*
U. S. Geol. Survey. Library for Library of Congress ₍r47d2₎†

NL 0435980 DI-GS DLC

Lockhart, Jeffrey Garald, 1923-
Coal deposits of New Brunswick; location, description and future possibilities, by J. G. Lockhart and K. O. J. Sidwell. New Brunswick resources development board, Fredericton, N. B. February, 1950. ₍Fredericton, N. B., 1950₎
iiii, 116 l. maps.

"References": l. 108-110.

NL 0435981 NNC NN

Lockhart, Mrs. Jennie Clare (Fagen) *d.* 1938.
Dramas for church services, by Jennie Clare Lockhart. Cincinnati, O., The Standard publishing company ₍°1939₎
128 p. 23½cm.

1. Religious drama. I. Title. 40-6167
Library of Congress PN6120.R4L56

Copyright D pub. 67929 792.1

NL 0435982 DLC Or

LOCKHART, John.
The covenant of God the hope of man; a sermon, preached before the Society in Scotland. for propagating Christian knowledge, in Edinburgh, June 6, 1811. Edinburgh, 1812.

NL 0435983 MH-AH

BS605 .L8 LOCKHART, JOHN, LL.D.
The Bible manual: a hand-book, historical, and biographical, of the leading facts of the Bible. With an epitome of ancient history. By John Lockhart, LL.D. London[etc.]T.Nelson and sons, 1870.
viii, [9]-252 p. 18½cm.

1.Bible--Study.

NL 0435984 ICU

VOLUME 337

Lockhart (JOHN) 1794-1870.
Exposure of the Rev. James Pringle's attempt at defence from the charge of slander...with an appendix... *Newcastle upon-Tyne: M. A. Richardson,* 1835. 44 pp. 12°.
In: ZWGM p. v. 5.

NL 0435985 NN

[LOCKHART, JOHN,] 1794-1870.
A further exposure of the Reverend Dr. Ralph Wardlaw, his meeting house, and his voluntary associates; in a letter addressed to him, by Anglo-Scotus [pseud.]... Newcastle upon Tyne: M.A.Richardson[, etc., etc.], 1834. 16 p. 21½cm.

252022. 1. Wardlaw, Ralph, 1779-1853: Exposure exposed. 2. Voluntary church system—Gt.Br.—Scotland.

NL 0435986 NN

[Lockhart, John,] 1794-1870.
A new exposure of the reverend leaders of the voluntary church associations, lately organized to oppose the established churches of the empire, and particularly the Church of Scotland; in a letter, containing eight demonstrations that they are a degenerate body of professing Christian ministers, addressed to them by Anglo-Scotus [pseud.]. Newcastle upon Tyne: M. A. Richardson[, etc., etc.], 1833. 58 p. 23cm.

191006A. 1. Voluntary church system—Gt. Br.—Scotland. *Revised* January 8, 1935

NL 0435987 NN

[Lockhart, John,] 1794-1870.
A new exposure of the reverend leaders of the voluntary church associations, lately organized to oppose the established churches of the empire, and particularly the Church of Scotland; in a letter, containing eight demonstrations that they are a degenerate body of professing Christian ministers, addressed to them by Anglo-Scotus [pseud.]. Third edition, much enlarged, with an appendix, containing, besides other matter, a reply to the Rev. Dr. Wardlaw's "Exposure exposed." Newcastle upon Tyne: M. A. Richardson[, etc., etc.], 1834. iv, 5-69 p. 21cm.
*** C p.v.1140, no.2** —— Second copy.

1. Voluntary church system—Gt. Br.—Scotland. 2. Wardlaw, Ralph, 1779-1853: Exposure exposed. *Revised* January 14, 1935

NL 0435989 NN

[Lockhart, John,] 1794-1870.
The West-of-Scotland arch-voluntary; or, The Rev. Andrew Marshall, the anti-burgher minister at Kirkintilloch, called to account for his mendacious, dishonest, and impertinent lucubrations in the 24th number of the United secession magazine, by Anglo-Scotus [pseud.]... Newcastle-upon-Tyne: M. A. Richardson, 1835. 26 p. 21cm.

553217A. 1. Marshall, Andrew, 1779-1854. 2. Voluntary church system—Gt. Br.—Scotland. September 19, 1934

NL 0435990 NN

Lockhart, John Gibson, 1794-1854, *tr.*
Ancient Spanish ballads, historical and romantic. With Hallam's "View of Spain during the Middle Ages." London, Murray [18—]
119 p. 19 cm. (Murray's people's classics, no. 3)

1. Spanish ballads and songs—Translations into English. 2. English ballads and songs—Translations from Spanish. I. Title.

PQ6267.E4B26 52-57010

NL 0436001 DLC ICU

860.81 Lockhart, John Gibson, 1794-1854, tr.
L81a Ancient Spanish ballads: historical and
1823 romantic. Edinburgh, W. Blackwood, 1823.
xxvii, 209p. 25cm.

Contents.- Historical ballads.- Moorish ballads.- Romantic ballads.

1. Spanish ballads and songs. 2. Spanish poetry--Translations into English. 3. English poetry--Translations from Spanish. I. Title.

NNH MB MH ICN OC1W PPL PV MiU
NL 0436002 IU CaBVaU ODaU KU InU CSt NIC CU CSmH

PQ Lockhart, John Gibson, 1794-1854, tr.
6267 Ancient Spanish ballads, historical and
E4B26 romantic. Translated, with notes, by
1823b J.G.Lockhart. New York, G.Routledge [introd.1823]
xxxiii,320p. 14cm. [Routledge's pocket library]

Published also under title: The Spanish ballads.

NL 0436003 CLSU

C-L Lockhart, John Gibson, 1794-1854, tr.
357L Ancient Spanish ballads; historical and
811a romantic. Tr., with notes, by J.G. Lockhart,
841 esq. A new ed., rev. With numerous illustrations from drawings by William Allan, R.A., David Roberts, R.A., William Simson, Henry Warren, C.E. Aubrey, and William Harvey. The borders and ornamental vignettes by Owen Jones ... London, J. Murray, 1841.
1v.(unpaged) illus.,col. plates. 26cm.

Added t.p., in colors.

Ornamental borders, part colored; half-titles illus. in colors.
Publisher's advertisements ([8]p.) dated [May?] 1841, bound in at end.
In ms. on free front end paper: J.E. Gough.
Bookplate of Evelyn Waugh.

I. Jones, Owen, 1809-1874, illus. II. Title.
A.F.: Gough, J.E.

KMK CU OU IdU KyU PP PPT OCU VtY MH
NL 0436005 TxU ViU WU PPRF MdBP CSmH ICN MH NcD

Lockhart, John Gibson, 1794-1854, *tr.*
Ancient Spanish ballads; historical and romantic. Tr., with notes, by J. G. Lockhart, esq. A new ed., rev. With numerous illustrations from drawings by William Allan, R. A., David Roberts, R. A., William Simson, Henry Warren, C. E. Aubrey, and William Harvey. The borders and ornamental vignettes by Owen Jones ... London, J. Murray; [etc., etc.] 1842.
[242] p. illus., plates. 25cm.
Ornamental borders, part colored; half-titles illus. in colors.
I. Jones, Owen, 1809-1874, illus. II. Title.
12—36284

DCU-IA
NL 0436006 DLC OrU FMU IU WU MnU TU OU NNH NN

Lockhart, John Gibson, 1794-1854, *tr.*
Ancient Spanish ballads; historical and romantic. Translated, with notes, by J. G. Lockhart, esq. A new ed., rev. With an introductory essay on the origin, antiquity, character, and influence of the ancient ballads of Spain: and an analytical account, with specimens, of the romance of the Cid. New-York, Wiley and Putnam, 1842.
vi p., 1 l., 272 p. 21cm.
Bibliography: p. [270]-272.

1. Spanish ballads and songs. 2. Spanish poetry—Translations into English. 3. English poetry — Translations from Spanish. 4. El Cid Campeador. I. Title.
32-35242

Library of Congress PQ6267.E4B26 1842 a **861.04**

ViU MH MeB NNJ NWM CSmH
NL 0436007 DLC Wa NjP MsSM NcU ViU CtY PHi PP OC1W

Lockhart, John Gibson, 1794-1854, tr.
Ancient Spanish ballads; historical and romantic. Translated by J. G. Lockhart. 4th ed. London, J. Murray, 1853.
xviii, 127 p. 18 cm.

NL 0436008 CU-S ViLxW MH KU

Lockhart, John Gibson, 1794-1854, tr.
Ancient Spanish ballads; historical and romantic. Translated by J. G. Lockhart. 5th ed. London, John Murray, 1854.
xviii, 127 p.

NL 0436009 WaU PPL OO OU KyU CU

Lockhart, John Gibson, 1794-1854, *tr.*
Ancient Spanish ballads; historical and romantic. Tr. by J. G. Lockhart, esq. A new rev. ed., with a biographical notice. Boston, Whittemore, Niles, and Hall; Milwaukie, A. Whittemore & co., 1856.
xxiv p., 1 l., [27]-151 p. front. (port.) 19cm.
Biographical notice signed: C. C. S. [i. e. Charles C. Smith]

1. Spanish ballads and songs. I. Smith, Charles Card, 1827-1918, ed. II. Title.
12-36285

Library of Congress PQ6267.E4B26 1856

OC1W MB
NL 0436010 DLC NcD MtU NcU NcD PP PPGi IaU OO

He38 **Lockhart, John Gibson, 1794-1854, tr.**
078 **Ancient Spanish ballads; historical and romantic. Translated, with notes, by J.G.Lockhart ... With numerous illustrations from drawings by William Allan ... David Roberts ... Henry Warren, C.E.Aubrey, and William Harvey. The borders and ornamental vignettes by Owen Jones. A new edition, revised. London,J.Murray,1856.**
[242]p. illus.,plate,port. 27cm.
The half-titles illustrated in colors are not included in pagination.

NL 0436011 CtY OOxM MH WU NBuG ICU

Lockhart, John Gibson, 1794-1854, *tr.*
Ancient Spanish ballads; historical and romantic. Tr., with an introduction and notes, by J. G. Lockhart, esq. A new ed., rev., with a biographical sketch of the author. New York, C. S. Francis & co., 1856.
xxxviii, 154 p. 19cm.

1. Spanish ballads and songs. I. Title.
16-12447

Library of Congress PQ6267.E4B26 1856 a

NL 0436012 DLC OrU PBm PV MB

Lockhart, John Gibson, 1794-1854.
Ancient Spanish Ballads ... Boston, 1857.

NL 0436013 NjR MiU OC1 OCU

AC-L Lockhart, John Gibson, 1794-1854, tr.
#357L Ancient Spanish ballads; historical and
L811a romantic. Tr., with notes, by J.G. Lockhart,
1859 esq. With numerous illustrations from drawings by William Allan, R.A., David Roberts, R.A., Henry Warren, C.E. Aubrey, and William Harvey. The borders and ornamental vignettes by Owen Jones. A new ed., rev. London, J. Murray, 1859.
1v.(unpaged) illus.,plates, port. 27cm.

Ornamental borders, part colored; half-titles illus in colors.

Continued in next column

VOLUME 337

Continued from preceding column

In ms. on front end paper: R.H. Milward, June 1st, 1866.
From the library of Evelyn Waugh.

I. Jones, Owen, 1809-1874, illus. II. Title.
A.F.: Milward, R.H.

NL 0436015 TxU IaU IU MH NN ICN TU NcD

Lockhart, John Gibson, 1794-1854, *tr.*
Ancient Spanish ballads; historical and romantic. Tr., with an introduction and notes, by J. G. Lockhart, esq. A new ed., rev., with a biographical sketch of the author. Boston, T. O. H. P. Burnham, 1861.
xxxviii, 154 p. front. (port.) 22½cm.

1. Spanish ballads and songs. 2. Spanish poetry—Translations into English. 3. English poetry—Translations from Spanish. I. Title.

16-5271

Library of Congress PQ6267.E4B26 1861

NL 0436016 DLC NjR FMU NjP MB NN

He38.79 Lockhart, John Gibson, 1794-1854, tr.
Ancient Spanish ballads; historical and romantic. Tr. by J.G.Lockhart, Esq. A new rev. ed. with a biographical notice.
Boston,Ticknor & Fields,1861. 18½cm.

NL 0436017 CtY CSmH OClW PU PPL TxU OrP

Lockhart, John Gibson, 1794-1854, tr.
Ancient Spanish ballads; historical and romantic. Translated by J. G. Lockhart. New edition. With portrait and illustrations. London: J. Murray, 1870. xxii, 127 p. front. (port.), illus., plates. 19½cm.

Astor 1440. 1. Ballads, Spanish. Revised
N. Y. P. L. October 15, 1937

NL 0436018 NN CtY PU MWelC ODW NcD I NBuG MH

861.25
N
1873
Lockhart, John Gibson, 1794-1854, tr.
[Ancient spanish ballads, historical and romantic, including the chronicle of the Cid. London, 1873]
466p. 18cm. (Chandos classics)

Title page lacking. Information supplied by the British Museum catalog, v. 32.

NL 0436019 KU

Lockhart, John Gibson, 1794-1854, *tr.*
Ancient Spanish ballads, historical and romantic, tr. by J. G. Lockhart, with a biographical notice. New ed., rev. New York, H. Holt and company, 1877.
xxiv p., 1 l., [27]-151 p. 17½cm.

1. Spanish ballads and songs. 2. Spanish poetry—Translations into English. 3. English poetry—Translations from Spanish. I. Title.

17-16108

Library of Congress PQ6267.E4B26 1877

NL 0436020 DLC NcD PV OO NjP

861.08
L81a
1889
Lockhart, John Gibson, 1794-1854, tr.
Ancient Spanish ballads; historical and romantic. Tr. with notes by J.G. Lockhart. Reprinted from the rev. ed. of 1841, with numerous illustrations by William Allen, David Roberts [and others] New York, Putnam [1889?]
299p. front.,illus. T. (Knickerbocker nuggets)

NL 0436021 IaU OClW PHC FU PP OCl PV NcU NNC

Lockhart, John Gibson, 1794-1854, *tr.*
Ancient Spanish ballads, historical and romantic, tr., with notes, by J. G. Lockhart. London, G. Routledge & sons, ltd.; New York, E. P. Dutton & co. [1890?]
xxxiii p., 1 l., 37-320 p. 13½cm.

1. Spanish ballads and songs. 2. Spanish poetry—Translations into English. 3. Spanish poetry—Translations from Spanish. I. Title.

4-19745

Library of Congress PQ6267.E4B26 1890
[a41b1] 861.04

NL 0436022 DLC CtY KU IdB WaS NRCR

PQ6267
.E3L8
(Ed)
Lockhart, John Gibson, 1794-1854, *tr.*
Ancient Spanish ballads; historical and romantic. Tr. with notes by J. G. Lockhart. Reprinted from the rev. ed. of 1841. With numerous illustrations by William Allen, R. A., David Roberts, R. A. William Simson, Henry Warren, C. E. Aubrey, and William Harvey. New York and London, C. P. Putnam's sons [1895]
ix, 299 p. front., illus. 16½cm. [Ballads of the nations]

1. Spanish ballads and songs. 2. Spanish poetry—Translations into English. 3. English poetry—Translations from Spanish.

NL 0436023 ICU ViU

Lockhart, J[ohn] G[ibson], 1794-1854
Ancient Spanish ballads: historical and romantic, translated with notes by J. G. Lockhart, reprinted from the revised edition of 1841, with...illustrations by William Allen, R.A., David Roberts, R.A., William Simson, Henry Warren, C. E. Aubrey, and William Harvey. New York: G. P. Putnam's Sons [190-?]. ix, 299 p., 1 pl. illus. 16°.

NL 0436024 NN

Lockhart, John Gibson, 1794-1854, compiler and translator.
Ancient Spanish ballads, historical and romantic, translated with notes by J. G. Lockhart. Reprinted from the revised edition of 1841, with numerous illustrations by William Allen...David Roberts...William Simson...[and others.] New York: G. P. Putnam's Sons[, 1912?]. ix, 299 p. front., illus. 16½cm. (Ballads of the nations.)

653318A. 1. Ballads, Spanish. I. Title.
N. Y. P. L. February 2, 1934

NL 0436025 NN

[Lockhart, John Gibson] 1794-1854.
Answers to Mr. Macaulay's criticism in the Edinburgh Review on Mr. Croker's edition of Boswell's life of Johnson... 2.ed. 16 pp. London: J. Murray, 1856. 8 .

NL 0436026 NN

[Lockhart, John Gibson,] 1794-1854
Answers to the Edinburgh Reviewer of Crocker's Boswell, selected from Blackwood's Magazine. [London, Printed by William Clowes, 1831?].
12 p. 21 1/2cm.

NL 0436027 NNC

[**Lockhart, John Gibson**] 1794-1854.
The Ballantyne-humbug handled, in a letter to Sir Adam Fergusson. By the author of Memoirs of the life of Sir Walter Scott. Edinburgh, R. Cadell; [etc., etc.] 1839.
2 p. l., 122 p. 20cm.
Signed: J. G. Lockhart.
A reply to the "Refutation of the misstatements and calumnies contained in Mr. Lockhart's Life of Sir Walter Scott, bart., respecting the Messrs. Ballantyne. By the trustees and son of the late Mr. James Ballantyne", 1838.

1. Ballantyne, James, 1772-1833. 2. Ballantyne, John, 1774-1821. 3. Ferguson, Sir Adam, 1771-1855. I. Title.

28-21674

Library of Congress PR5338.B3

MH MB IU
NL 0436028 DLC MH InU OCl CtY MdBJ NcU PU MiU PPL

Lockhart, John Gibson, 1794-1854.
Captain Paton's lament.
(In Tales from Blackwood. Vol. 5 Edinburgh. [187-?])

NL 0436029 MB

Lockhart, John Gibson, 1794-1854.
A defence of the missions in the South Sea and Sandwich Islands, against the misrepresentations contained in a late number of the Quarterly review, in a letter to the editor of that journal
see under Orme, William, 1787-1830.

Lockhart, John Gibson, 1794-1854, supposed author.
The domestic manners of the Americans; or, Sketches of the people of the United States
see under title

Lockhart, John Gibson, 1794-1854, ed.

Cervantes Saavedra, Miguel de, 1547-1616.
Don Quixote ... [by] Miguel de Cervantes Saavedra. London, J. M. Dent & sons, ltd.; New York, E. P. Dutton & co., inc. [1930-32]

Lockhart, John Gibson, 1794-1854.
Epitome of Lockhart's Life of Scott, by Henry Irwin Jenkinson ... Edinburgh, A. and C. Black, 1873.
19 cm.
I. Jenkinson, Henry Irwin, d. 1891.

NL 0436033 CtY

Lockhart, John Gibson, 1794-1854.

Cervantes Saavedra, Miguel de, 1547-1616.
The history of Don Quixote de La Mancha, by Miguel de Cervantes Saavedra ... London, J. M. Dent & co.; New York, E. P. Dutton & co. [1909]

---

xPR4891
L4A62
[Lockhart, John Gibson] 1794-1854.
The history of Matthew Wald. Edinburgh, William Blackwood; London T.Cadell, 1824.
382p. 20cm.

ViW ICN MiU OU MH MA MdBP PU MB
NL 0436035 IaU OCU NNC MdBP CtY CU CaBVaU ICU IU

PR
4891
.L4H4
Lockhart, John Gibson, 1794-1854.
The history of Matthew Wald. Edinburgh, W. Blackwood. London, T. Cadell, 1824.
382 p.
Xerox-reprint by SUNY at Buffalo, 1967.

NL 0436036 NBuU

VOLUME 337

[LOCKHART, JOHN GIBSON] 1794-1854.
The history of Matthew Wald. By the author of Valerius ...&c. ... New York: E. Duyckinck, Collins & Hannay [etc.] 1824. 223 p. 18½cm.

118447B. 1. Fiction, Scottish. I. Title.

NL 0436037 NN MdBP MB NjP

W823 L8157h Lockhart, John Gibson, 1794-1854.
The history of Matthew Wald. Edinburgh, William Blackwood; London, T. Cadell, 1840.
382 p. 21 cm.
According to slip tipped in, this is 1st ed.

NL 0436038 NcU

*EC8 C8885 829l2 [Lockhart, John Gibson, 1794-1854]
The history of Napoleon Buonaparte. With engravings on steel and wood ...
London:John Murray,Albemarle street. MDCCCXXIX.
2v. fronts.,plates,ports. 15.5cm. (On cover: Murray's Family library, i-ii)
Cohn (1924): 589, 1st issue.
Includes 8 wood engravings by George Cruikshank.
First edition, first issue: in v.1 the plate to p.71 is numbered 68 & included in the paging as p.[67]-68; also the plate to p.123, unnumbered, is included in the paging as p.[121-122].
Wrappers & advts. not preserved; bound in half green calf & marbled boards; maroon morocco labels on spine; top edges gilt.

NL 0436040 CtY MH NN NjR IU CSmH MiD-B OU PPL CLU-C ICN

*EC8 C8885 829l2b [Lockhart, John Gibson, 1794-1854]
The history of Napoleon Buonaparte. With engravings on steel and wood ...
London:John Murray,Albemarle street. MDCCCXXX.
2v. fronts.,plates,ports. 15cm.
Includes 8 wood engravings by George Cruikshank.

NL 0436041 MH PPA MH NN DLC NjR PHa TU MdBP PSC C ViU

Lockhart, John Gibson, 1794-1854
... The history of Napoleon Buonaparte. By J. G. Lockhart, esq. With copperplate engravings ... New York, J. & J. Harper, 1830.
2 v. front. (ports.) 16 cm.

NL 0436042 MeB

ar V 3451 Lockhart, John Gibson, 1794-1854.
The history of Napoleon Buonaparte. Harper's stereotype ed. New-York, J. & J. Harper, 1831.
2 v. illus. 16cm. (Harper's family library, no. 4-5)

1. Napoleon I, Emperor of the French, 1769-1821.

NL 0436043 NIC IdU NN PPT

Lockhart, John Gibson, 1794-1854.
... The history of Napoleon Buonaparte. By J. G. Lockhart, esq. With copperplate engravings ... New York, J. & J. Harper, 1832.
2 v. front. (ports.) 16cm. (On cover: Harper's family library. no. IV-V)
At head of title: Harper's stereotype edition.

NL 0436044 ViU OClWHi NBuG

Lockhart, John Gibson, 1794-1854.
... The history of Napoleon Buonaparte. By J. G. Lockhart, esq. With copperplate engravings ... New York, J. & J. Harper, 1833.
2 v. front. (ports.) 16cm. (On cover: Harper's family library. no. IV-V)
At head of title: Harper's stereotype edition.

1. Napoléon I, emperor of the French, 1769-1821. I. Title.

Library of Congress DC203.L79 6-38464

NL 0436045 DLC MiEM

Lockhart, John Gibson N.Y. 1834
History of Napoleon Buonaparte 2v...

NL 0436046 NjNbS

Lockhart, John Gibson, 1794-1854.
The history of Napoleon Buonaparte, with engravings on steel and wood. 3d ed. London, Murray,1835. 2v.front.(ports.) plates. 15cm.

NL 0436047 MWelC DLC NjP MB OrCS CaBViP MiU LU

Lockhart, John Gibson, 1794-1854.
The history of Napoleon Buonaparte,... New York, 1836.
2 v.

NL 0436048 NWM

Lockhart, John Gibson, 1794-1854.
...The history of Napoleon Buonaparte... With copperplate engravings... N.Y., Harper, 1837.
2 v. front.(ports.) (Harper's family library)
At head of title: Harper's stereotype edition.

NL 0436049 PMA

LOCKHART,John Gibson,1794-1854.
The history of Napoleon Buonaparte. New York,Harper & Brothers,1840-41.
2 vol. 16 cm. Ports.
At head of title: Harper's stereotype edition.

NL 0436050 MH CU DLC

Lockhart, John Gibson, 1794-1854.
... The history of Napoleon Buonaparte... 1843.
2 v. (On cover: Harper's family library. no.IV-V)

NL 0436051 OCX MB ODW MeB

Lockhart, John Gibson, 1794-1854.
History of Napoleon Buonaparte. New York, 1855.
2 v.

NL 0436052 NWM

DC 203 L79 1858 Lockhart,John Gibson,1794-1854.
... The history of Napoleon Buonaparte. By J.G.Lockhart,esq. With two portraits on steel. New York, Harper & Bros., 1858.
2 v. front.(ports.)

1.Napoléon I,emperor of the French,1769-1821. I.Title.

NL 0436053 NSyU

Lockhart, John Gibson, 1794-1854.
The history of Napoleon Buonaparte. London, W. Tegg, 1861.
2v.

NL 0436054 PU

B N16Loch5 Lockhart, John Gibson 1794-1854
The history of Napoleon Buonaparte. Illus. by G. Cruikshank. Reprinted from The Family library, with considerable additions. London, W. Tegg [1867]
xxii, 655p. plates. 20cm.

NL 0436055 CoD CtY

[Lockhart, John Gibson] 1794-1854.
The history of Napoleon Buonaparte. Illustrated by G. Cruikshank. Reprinted from the Family library with considerable additions. London, William Tegg [1869]
xxii, 655 p. incl.front. plates. 18½cm.
Title vignette (port.)

1. Napoléon I, emperor of the French, 1769-1821. I. Cruikshank, George, 1792-1878, illus. II. Title.

NL 0436056 ViU NN

DC 203 L79 Lockhart, John Gibson, 1794-1854.
The history of Napoleon Buonaparte. New York, Harper, 1875.
2 v. ports. 16cm.

1. Napoléon I, Emperor of the French, 1769-1821. I. Title.

NL 0436057 CoU I

Lockhart, John Gibson, 1794-1854.
The history of Napoleon Buonaparte, reprinted from The family library. Illustrated by George Cruikshank. With an appendix. London, Ward, Lock [1881] xxii, 653p.

NL 0436058 OClW

944.04 N216.Lo Lockhart, John Gibson, 1794-1854
The history of Napoleon Bonaparte... New York, Fowle, 1900.
2v. front.(port.) S. (On cover: Criterion library)

NL 0436059 IaU PPAmSwM PPT OO

DC 203 L8 1906 Lockhart, John Gibson, 1794-1854.
The history of Napoleon Buonaparte. London, J. M. Dent,1906.
511p. illus. 18cm. (Everyman's Library, edited by Ernest Rhys. Biography)

1. Napoleon I, emperor of the French, 1769-1821.

NL 0436060 MU OrPR MH

VOLUME 337

Lockhart, John Gibson, 1794–1854.
The history of Napoleon Buonaparte, by John Gibson Lockhart. London, J. M. Dent & co.; New York, E. P. Dutton & co. [1907]
3 p. l., ix–xi, 511, [1] p. 17½cm. (*Half-title:* Everyman's library, ed. by Ernest Rhys. Biography)
Title within ornamental border: illustrated lining-papers. "First edition, February 1906; reprinted, April 1906; May 1907."
Bibliography: p. xi.

NL 0436061 ViU MiU

Lockhart, John Gibson, 1794–1854.
The history of Napoleon Buonaparte, by John Gibson Lockhart. London, J. M. Dent & co.; New York, E. P. Dutton & co. [1909]
3 p. l., ix–xi, 511, [1] p. 17½ cm. (*Half-title:* Everyman's library, ed. by Ernest Rhys. Biography)
Title within ornamental border; illustrated lining-papers. "First edition, February 1906; reprinted, April 1906; May 1907; July 1909."
Bibliography: p. xi.
1. Napoléon I, emperor of the French, 1769–1821.
[DC203.L] A 10--2358
Enoch Pratt Free Libr. for Library of Congress [a54n1]

NL 0436062 MdBE OClND OClJC OCl NN AU

UGL DC 203 .L6 1910 Lockhart, John Gibson, 1794-1854.
The history of Napoleon Buonaparte. London, J. M. Dent; New York, E. P. Dutton [1910] 511 p. (Everyman's library. Biography)
First published 1906.
#Napoléon I, emperor of the French, 1769-1821.

NL 0436063 MoU

944.04 N216.Lo 1916 Lockhart, John Gibson, 1794-1854
...The history of Napoleon Buonaparte, with an introd. by J. Holland Rose. London, Milford, 1916.
539p. D.
At head of t.-p.: Oxford edition.

NL 0436064 IaU FTaSU MiD CaBVaU NcRS PP

Lockhart, John Gibson, 1794–1854.
The history of Napoleon Buonaparte [by] John Gibson Lockhart. London, J. M. Dent & sons, ltd.; New York, E. P. Dutton & co., inc. [1930]
3 p. l., ix–xi, 511, [1] p. 17½cm. (*Half-title:* Everyman's library, ed. by Ernest Rhys. Biography. [no. 3])
"First published in this edition 1906. Reprinted ... 1930." "Works of John Gibson Lockhart": p. xi.
1. Napoléon I, emperor of the French, 1769–1821. 36–37660
Library of Congress AC1.E8 no. 3 [2] 923.144

NL 0436065 DLC KyLx

Lockhart, John Gibson, 1794-1854.
The history of Napoleon Buonaparte [by] John Gibson Lockhart. London, J. M. Dent and sons, ltd.; New York, E. P. Dutton [1947] 3 p. l., ix-xi, 511 [1] p. 18cm. (Half-title: Everyman's library, ed. by Ernest Rhys. Biography [no.3]
"First published in the ed. in 1906. Reprinted ... 1947."

NL 0436066 OrPS

Lockhart, John Gibson, 1794-1854.
Cervantes Saavedra, Miguel de, 1547–1616.
The history of the ingenious gentleman, Don Quixote of La Mancha; tr. from the Spanish, by Motteux. A new ed., with copious notes; and an essay on the life and writings of Cervantes ... Edinburgh, A. Constable and co.: London, Hurst, Robinson, and co., 1822.

Lockhart, John Gibson, 1794-1854.
Janus; or, The Edinburgh literary almanack. [Edinburgh] Oliver & Boyd, 1826.

[**Lockhart, John Gibson**] 1794–1854.
John Bull's letter to Lord Byron, ed. by Alan Lang Strout. [1st ed.] Norman, Univ. of Oklahoma Press, 1947.
xiii, 170 p. ports., facsims. 22 cm.
With facsimile reproduction of original t.-p.: Letter to the Right Hon. Lord Byron, by John Bull [pseud.] London, 1821. "A bibliographical baker's dozen": p. 3–5. Bibliographical footnotes.
1. Byron, George Gordon Nöel Byron, 6th baron, 1788–1824. I. Strout, Alan Lang, 1895– ed. II. Title.
PR4891.L4A84 821.76 47-11671*

NL 0436069 MB ICU TxU NcD CaBVaU MtU OrU DLC FTaSU KMK NSyU NjP Or OO MiU-C ViU

Lockhart, John Gibson, 1794-1854, tr.
Schlegel, Friedrich von, 1772–1829.
Lectures on the history of literature, ancient and modern. From the German of Frederick Schlegel ... Philadelphia, T. Dobson and son, 1818.

[Lockhart, John Gibson] 1794–1854.
Letter to the Right Hon. Lord Byron. By John Bull [pseud.] ... London, Printed by and for William Wright, 1821.
64 p. 22cm. [With Plays. London, 182–?]
1. English poetry—19th cent.—Hist. & crit. I. Byron, George Gordon Noël Byron, 6th baron, 1788-1824.

NL 0436071 ViU NN ICN CtY MH NN

Lockhart, John Gibson, 1794-1854.
The life and letters of John Gibson Lockhart
see under Lang, Andrew, 1844-1912.

944.05 N162 Lo **Lockhart, John Gibson, 1794-1854.**
The life of Napoleon Bonaparte, Emperor of France. Philadelphia, Porter & Coates [185-?]
392p. illus., ports. 20cm.
1. Napoléon I, Emperor of the French, 1769-1821.

NL 0436073 OrU WaSpG OO OU

Lockhart, John Gibson, 1794–1854.
Life of Napoleon Bonaparte, emperor of France. By J. G. Lockhart. A new ed., rev. and cor. Auburn [N. Y.] Derby and Miller, 1851.
viii, [9]–392 p. front. (port.) 19cm.
"Mainly an abridgment of Lockhart's Napoleon."—Introd.
1. Napoléon I, emperor of the French, 1769–1821. 4–13180
Library of Congress DC203.L81

NL 0436074 DLC

DC203 .L81 1852 **Lockhart, John Gibson, 1794-1854.**
Life of Napoleon Buonaparte. Rev. and abridged from the larger work. Edinburgh, W. P. Nimmo, Hay & Mitchell [1852?] 316 p. col. illus. (port.) 20 cm.

NL 0436075 MB DNW

Lockhart, John Gibson, 1794–1854.
Life of Napoleon Bonaparte, emperor of France. By J. G. Lockhart. A new ed., rev. and cor. Auburn [N. Y.] Derby and Miller; **Buffalo, Derby, Orton and Mulligan, 1854.**
viii, [9]–392 p. front. (port.) 19cm.
"Mainly an abridgment of Lockhart's Napoleon."—Introd.
Front wanting.
At head of title: Sixth thousand.

NL 0436076 ViU CU

DC203 L81 Lockhart, John Gibson, 1794-1854.
Life of Napoleon Bonaparte, emperor of France, By J. G. Lockhart. A new edition, revised and corrected. New York and Auburn, Miller, Orton & Mulligan, 1856 [c1851]
viii [9]-392p. front. (port.) 20cm.
1. Napoléon I, emperor of the French, 1769-1821. I. Title.

NL 0436077 NBuG NcD OO OCU

Lockhart, John Gibson, *1794-1854.*
Life of Napolean Buonaparte. N.Y. 1857.

NL 0436078 OClStM

Lockhart, J[ohn] G[ibson], *1794-1854.*
Life of Napoleon Bonaparte, emperor of France. New York: C. M. Saxton, Barker & Co., 1860. viii, (1)10-392 p., 1 port. new ed. 12°.
1. Napoleon I., emperor of the French. N. Y. P. L. December 5, 1911.

NL 0436079 NN OrP

DC203 .L81 1879 **Lockhart, John Gibson, 1794-1854.**
The life of Napoleon Bonaparte, Emperor of France. Philadelphia, Porter & Coates [1879?] 392 p. 20cm.
Mainly an abridgment of the author's Napoleon.
1. Napoléon I, Emperor of the French, 1769-1821.

NL 0436080 ViU

Lockhart, John Gibson, *1794-1854.*
The life of Napoleon Buonaparte. Illustrated by George Cruikshank. London, etc., Ward, Lock & Co. [1881].
pp. xxii, 653. Plates.

NL 0436081 MH

Lockhart, J[ohn] G[ibson], *1794-1854.*
The life of Napoleon Buonaparte. New ed. London, Bickers & Son, 1883.
pp. xii, (1), 496. Port., photographs, and other illus.

NL 0436082 MH PP

VOLUME 337

Lockhart, John Gibson, 1794-1854.
The life of Napoleon Buonaparte. New ed. ...
London, 1891.
21 cm.

NL 0436083 CtY

Lockhart, John Gibson, 1794-1854.
Life of Napoleon Buonaparte; rev. and abridged from the larger work; illus. Edinburgh, 1894.

NL 0436084 ODW

AC-L
W357L
L811ℓ
Lockhart, John Gibson, 1794-1854.
Life of Napoleon Buonaparte, by John Gibson Lockhart ... Rev. and abridged from the larger work. Edinburgh, W.P. Nimmo, Hay, & Mitchell, 1895.
2p.ℓ.,316p. front.,plates. 20cm.
Head and tail pieces.
Bookplate of Henry Foster, Malvern College.
From the library of Evelyn Waugh.
1. Napoléon I, Emperor of the French, 1769-1821. A.F.: Foster, Henry.

NL 0436085 TxU

Lockhart, John Gibson, 1794-1854.
Life of Napoleon Buonaparte. Rev. and abridged from the larger work. Edin.,Nimmo,1898. 316p.illus.

NL 0436086 CaBVa

PR
4331
L6
1828b:1
Lockhart, John Gibson, 1794-1854.
The life of Robert Burns, by J.G. Lockhart.
(In The Edinburgh review. Edinburgh. 22 cm. v. 96 (1828), p. [267]-312)
1. Burns, Robert, 1759-1796. I. Title.

NL 0436087 CaBVaU MdBP

Lockhart, John Gibson, 1794-1854.
Life of Robert Burns. By J. G. Lockhart ... Edinburgh, Constable and co.; ⌊etc., etc.⌋ 1828.
vi, 446 p. illus. (port.) 22cm.
1. Burns, Robert, 1759-1796.
4-6628
Library of Congress PR4331.L6 1828

NL 0436088 DLC ViW PPRF CtY NcU ViU OU

Lockhart, J⌊ohn⌋ G⌊ibson⌋ 1794-1854.
Life of Robert Burns. By J. G. Lockhart ... Edinburgh, Printed for Constable and co.; ⌊etc., etc.⌋ 1828.
1 p. l., vii, ⌊9⌋-310 p. 16cm. (*Added t.-p.:* Constable's miscellany. vol. XXIII)
The added t.-p. is engraved.
Subject entries: Burns, Robert, 1759-1796.
3-29684

NL 0436089 DLC CaBVaU MiU PPRF PPL MB TxU NjP

⌊Lockhart, John Gibson⌋ 1794-1854.
... Life of Robert Burns ... Edinburgh, Printed for the booksellers, 1828.
24 p. 15½cm. (A selection of amusing and instructive pamphlets ... No. 1)
Title vignette (port.)
An abstract only.
1. Burns, Robert, 1759-1796.
2-28618
Library of Congress PR4331.L63 1828

NL 0436090 DLC

⌊Lockhart, John Gibson⌋ 1794-1854.
... Life of Robert Burns. Edinburgh, Printed for Constable & co.; ⌊etc., etc.⌋ 1830.
1 p. l., ⌊v⌋-viii, ⌊vi⌋-vii, ⌊9⌋-328 p. 15½cm. (Constable's miscellany of original and selected publications in the various departments of literature, science & the arts. vol. XXIII)
Engraved t.-p., with vignette (portrait)
1. Burns, Robert, 1759-1796. I. Title.
4-6627
Library of Congress PR4331.L63 1830

NL 0436091 DLC CaBVaU MiU

PR4331
.L6
1830
Lockhart, John Gibson, 1794-1854.
Life of Robert Burns. By J. G. Lockhart ... 3d ed., cor. Edinburgh, Printed for Constable and co.; [etc., etc.] 1830.
1 p. l., viii, [9]-328 p. 15cm.
1. Burns, Robert, 1759-1796.

NL 0436092 MB MH

Lockhart, J⌊ohn⌋ G⌊ibson⌋ 1794-1854.
Life of Robert Burns. By J. G. Lockhart ... With an essay on his writings, prepared for this edition. New York, W. Stodart ⌊etc.⌋ 1831.
2 p. l., ⌊iii⌋-xxii, ⌊19⌋-320 p. front. (port.) 15cm.
Added t.-p., engr.
5-25316

NL 0436093 DLC WaSpG CaBVaU MeB OO OClW PP

Lockhart, John Gibson, 1794-1854.
Life of Robert Burns. By J. G. Lockhart ... With an essay on his writings, prepared for this edition. New York, W. Stodart ⌊etc.⌋ 1831.
2 p. l., ⌊iii⌋-xxii, ⌊19⌋-318 p. front. (port.) 14½ cm.
Added t.-p., engraved, with vignette.
1. Burns, Robert, 1759-1796.
PR4331.L6 1831a 48-40636

NL 0436094 DLC

Lockhart, J⌊ohn⌋ G⌊ibson⌋ 1794-1854.
Life of Robert Burns. By J. G. Lockhart ... 4th ed. London, J. Murray, 1838.
vii, 348 p. front. (port.) 18cm.
Subject entries: Burns, Robert, 1759-1796.
3-6284

NL 0436095 DLC CaBVaU

Lockhart, John Gibson, 1794-1854.
Life of Robert Burns. By J.G. Lockhart. 5th ed. London, J. Murray, 1847.
vii, 348 p. 17.5 cm.
1. Burns, Robert, 1759-1796.

NL 0436096 NcD MA

PR4300
1849
.N3
Lockhart, John Gibson, 1794-1854. Life of Robert Burns.
Burns, Robert, 1759-1796.
Works. New York, Leavitt, Trow, 1849.

Lockhart, John Gibson, 1794-1854.
The life of Robert Buns. Enl. ed. Rev. and cor. from the latest text of the author, with new annotations and appendices by William Scott Douglas. London, G.Bell, 1882.
349 p. front. (port.) 19 cm. (Bohn's standard library)
"Memoir of Lo ckhart": p. [vii]-xii.

NL 0436098 CaBVaU MiU RP

Lockhart, John Gibson, 1794-1854.
... The life of Robert Burns. By John Gibson Lockhart. Rev. ed. With new notes, appendices, and literary illustrations, by John H. Ingram ... London, New York, and Melbourne, Ward, Lock and co., 1890.
xx, 390 p. front., plates, ports. 18½cm. (The Minerva library of famous books ⌊v. 19⌋)
1. Burns, Robert, 1759-1796. I. Ingram, John H., 1849- ed.
4-6629

NL 0436099 DLC WaT WaSpG CaBVaU ViU TxU

Lockhart, John Gibson, 1794-1854.
The life of Robert Burns, by J. G. Lockhart, D. C. L. Enl. ed. Rev. and cor. from the latest text of the author, with new annotations and appendices, by William Scott Douglas ... London and New York, G. Bell & sons, 1892.
xvi p., 1 l., 349 p. front. (port.) 19 cm. (*Half-title:* Bohn's standard library)
"Memoir of Lockhart": p. ⌊vii⌋-xii.
1. Burns, Robert, 1759-1796. I. Douglas, William Scott, 1815-1883, ed.
PR4331.L6 1892 4-17164

NL 0436100 DLC CaBViP CaBVaU WaT PU PPGi PSC OOxM OClW PBm

Lockhart, John Gibson, 1794-1854.
... The life of Robert Burns; with new notes, ... by John H. Ingram. Ed.2. London, Ward, Lock, Bowden and co.[etc.] 1892.
xx,390 p. illus. ports. (Minerva library of famous books)

NL 0436101 OCl

Lockhart, John Gibson, 1794-1854
The life of Robert Burns, ... with new annotations and appendices, by William Scott Douglas... London G. Bell and sons, 1898.
349 p. (Bohn's standard library)

NL 0436102 OU

VOLUME 337

Lockhart, John Gibson, 1794-1854.
The life of Robert Burns. To which is adde Thomas Carlyle's review-essay. Newly edited with notes, etc. London, Hutchinson, 1904.
315 p. front. (port.) 17 cm. (Library of standard biographies)
1. Burns, Robert, 1759-1796, 1759-1796. I. Carlyle Thomas, 1795-1881.
NL 0436103 CaBVaU

---

821 B93 L 1892 Lockhart, John Gibson, 1794-1854.
The life of Robert Burns. Edited with notes and appendices, by William Scott Douglas. London, G.Bell, 1905[c1892]
xvi,349p. port. 19cm. (Bohn's standard library)
"Memoir of Lockhart": p.[vii]-xii.
1. Burns, Robert, 1759-1796. I. Douglas, William Scott, 1815-1883, ed. II. Series.
NL 0436104 OrU CaBVaU IdU OKentU NCH

B B9671o 1905 Lockhart, John Gibson, 1794-1854.
The life of Robert Burns ... to which is added Thomas Carlyle's review-essay. Newly edited with notes, etc. London, Hutchinson & co.; [etc. etc.] 1905.
315p. front.(port.) (Half-title: The library of standard biographies: Lockhart's Life of Robert Burns, ed. by J. M. Sloan)
1. Burns, Robert, 1759-1796. I. Sloan, John MacGavin, 1854-1926, ed. II. Carlyle, Thomas, 1795-1881. Essay on Burns.
NL 0436105 IU OrU

Lockhart, John Gibson, 1794–1854.
Life of Robert Burns, by J. G. Lockhart. London, J. M. Dent & co.; New York, E. P. Dutton & co. [1907]
xv, [1], 322 p., 1 l. 17½cm. (*Half-title:* Everyman's library, ed. by E. Rhys. Biography)
Title within ornamental border. Illustrated end-papers.
1. Burns, Robert, 1759–1796.
Library of Congress PR4331.L6 1907 7—15536
NL 0436106 PRosC MiU ODW OCl OO OClh NN WaTC WaT NcRS CaBVaU DLC OCU MoU OrSaW OrU MtU OKentU NIC

PR 4331 L6 1914 Lockhart, John Gibson, 1794-1854.
Life of Robert Burns, by J. G. Lockhart. Edited with notes and appendices by William Scott Douglas and an essay on Robert Burns by Walter Raleigh. Liverpool, H. Young, 1914.
2 v. illus. 24 cm.
"This edition is limited to 500 copies for sale, and 20 copies for presentation, of which this is no. 162.
1. Burns, Robert, 1759-1796.
NL 0436107 MH PPRF IEdS NcU N OCU MiU PP CaBVaU CtY ICN

Lockhart, John Gibson, 1794-1854.
The life of Robert Burns. London, J.M. Dent [1916]
322 p. 18 cm. (Everyman's library)
This ed. first published 1907.
Contains also Select letters and journals of Burns and his Border tour and Highland tour.
NL 0436108 CaBVaU NN

Lockhart, John Gibson, 1794–1854.
Life of Robert Burns, by J. G. Lockhart. London & Toronto, J. M. Dent & sons, ltd.; New York, E. P. Dutton & co. [1933]
xv, [1], 322 p., 1 l. 17½ cm. (*Half-title:* Everyman's library, ed. by Ernest Rhys. Biography. [no. 156])
"First published in this edition, 1907; reprinted ... 1933."
Contains also Select letters and journals of Burns and his Border tour and Highland tour.
1. Burns, Robert, 1759–1796.
AC1.E8 no. 156 928.2 36—37021
NL 0436109 DLC WaU CaBVa ViU

Lockhart, John Gibson, 1794-1854.
Life of Scott. London, Marrill & Baker.[1836]
4 v. fronts.,illus.,facsims.
Preface dated 1836.
NL 0436110 OCl MiD OClW

Lockhart, John Gibson, 1794–1854.
Lockhart's Life of Scott, abridged and edited with introduction and notes, by O. Leon Reid ... New York, The Macmillan company, 1914.
xiii, 262 p. front. (port.) 14½cm. (Macmillan's pocket American and English classics)
Lockhart's abridgement of his "Memoirs of Sir Walter Scott" (10 v.) (first published in two volumes in 1848 under title: Narrative of the life of Sir Walter Scott) further abridged by the present editor.
1. Scott, Sir Walter, bart., 1771–1832. I. Reid, Ohio Leon, 1875– ed.
Library of Congress PR5332.L62 1914 14—4333
NL 0436111 DLC TU OClh OClND OClW PCM PRosC ViU

Lockhart, John Gibson, 1794-1854.
The life of Sir Walter Scott, bart., by J. G. Lockhart. Edinburgh, T. C. & E. C. Jack, n.d. (Waverley novels v. XXVI & XXVII)
2v. illus. 22cm.
NL 0436112 PPLas

Lockhart, John Gibson, 1794-1854.
The life of Sir Walter Scott, complete, by his literary executor (Lockhart). Edinburgh, 1842.
1v.
NL 0436113 PPL

B 843111 Lockhart, John Gibson, 1794-1854.
Life of Sir Walter Scott ... With prefatory letter by J. R. Hope Scott. New York [1848?]
652p. front.
NL 0436114 IU OCl

Lockhart, John Gibson, 1794-1854.
Life of Sir Walter Scott...N.Y., Crowell, 1848.
2v.
Facsimile.
NL 0436115 PPPL MH OrP

LOCKHART, John Gibson, 1794-1854.
Life of Sir Walter Scott. 2d ed. Edinburgh, 1853.
ff.(2). ff. iv,837.
8 portraits and 4 engravings.
Also with an engraved title-page.
NL 0436116 MH

Lockhart, John Gibson, 1794–1854.
Life of Sir Walter Scott, bart., begun by himself and continued by J. G. Lockhart. 3d ed. Edinburgh, A. and C. Black, 1853.
2 p. l., iv, 837 p. front., plates, ports. 19cm.
Added t.-p., engr.
1. Scott, Sir Walter, bart., 1771–1832.
S D 19-114
Library, U. S. Dept. of State CT.Sco86.L82
NL 0436117 DS

Lockhart, John Gibson, 1794–1854.
Life of Sir Walter Scott, by J. G. Lockhart; with prefatory letter by J. R. Hope Scott. New York, Boston, T. Y. Crowell & company [187–]
xiv, 652 p. 2 pl., 2 port. (incl. front.) 19½cm.
Reprint of an abridgment by Lockhart of his "Memoirs of Sir Walter Scott" (in 10 vols.) published in 1848 in 2 vols. under title: Narrative of the life of Sir Walter Scott.
"Memoir of Sir Walter Scott's early years, written by himself": p. [1]–43.
1. Scott, Sir Walter, bart., 1771–1832. I. Hope-Scott, James Robert, 1812–1873, ed.
29-24973
Library of Congress PR5332.L62 1870
NL 0436118 DLC FMU MtU OEac CoU MsU NjR OrCS TU

In Sco86 W837Le Lockhart, John Gibson, 1794-1854.
The life of Sir Walter Scott, bart. abridged from the larger work by J.G.Lockhart. With a prefatory letter by James R.Hope Scott, Q.C. Edinburgh,A.& C.Black,1871.
xx,837p. front.(port.) 17½cm.
Added t.-p., engr. with vignette(port.)
Reprint of an abridgment by Lockhart of his "Memoirs of Sir Walter Scott" (in 10 vols.) published in 1848 in 2 vols. under title: Narrative of the life of Sir Walter Scott.
NL 0436119 CtY NRCR OU OClW PU OCU NcD ViW

Lockhart, John Gibson, 1794-1854.
Life of Sir Walter Scott, bart. Edinburgh, A. and C. Black c1872.
2v.
"Centenary edition."
NL 0436120 PPT MsU

PR 5332 L62 1884 Lockhart, John Gibson, 1794-1854.
The life of Sir Walter Scott, Bart. Abridged from the larger work. With a prefatory letter by James R. Hope Scott. Edinburgh,Black,1884.
837p. 20cm.
1. Scott, Sir Walter, bart., 1771-1832.
NL 0436121 MU

Lockhart, John Gibson, 1794-1854
Life of Sir Walter Scott. With prefatory letter by J.R.Hope Scott. New York, Crowell [189- ?]
2 v. fronts.
NL 0436122 MH

Lockhart, John Gibson, 1794-1854.
Life of Sir Walter Scott. [London] A. & C. Black, 1892.
2 v.
NL 0436123 WaSpG

VOLUME 337

Lockhart, John Gibson, 1794-1854.
The life of Sir Walter Scott, bart. [4th series] 1822 to 1826. London, Black, 1893.

NL 0436124 MH

Lockhart, John Gibson, 1794–1854.
The life of Sir Walter Scott, bart. New popular edition. By J. G. Lockhart. 1771–1832. London, A. & C. Black, 1893.
2 p. l., [iii]–xii, 806 p. 23½cm.

NL 0436125 CaBVaU

Microfilm 11507 PR
Lockhart, John Gibson, 1794–1854.
The life of Sir Walter Scott, bart. New popular edition. By J. G. Lockhart, 1771–1832. London, A. & C. Black, 1893.
2 p. l., [iii]–xii, 806 p. 23½cm.
L. C. Copy Replaced by Microfilm.
1. Scott, Sir Walter, bart., 1771–1832.
28—20089
Library of Congress [PR5332.L6 1893]

NL 0436126 DLC

PR5332 .L6 1896
Lockhart, John Gibson, 1794-1854.
The life of Sir Walter Scott, bart., 1771-1832. New popular ed., with seventeen illustrations. London, A. & C. Black, 1896.
806p. ports.

NL 0436127 NBC OCl

Lockhart, John Gibson, 1794–1854.
The life of Sir Walter Scott, bart. Abridged from the larger work by J. G. Lockhart. London, A. and C. Black, 1898.
xx, 837 p. incl. front. (port.) 19½cm.
1. Scott, Sir Walter, bart., 1771–1832.

NL 0436128 ICU WaWW ICarbS OCl OO

LOCKHART, JOHN GIBSON, 1794–1854.
The life of Sir Walter Scott, by John Gibson Lockhart ... Boston: Dana, Estes & Co. [190-?] 10 v. facsim., fronts., plan, plates, ports. 23cm.
Printed in Great Britain.
"New Abbotsford edition."
No. 86 of 1000 copies printed.
811403-12A. 1. Scott, Sir Walter, bart., 1771–1832.

NL 0436129 NN RPB

Lockhart, John Gibson, 1794-1854.
The life of Sir Walter Scott. Edinburgh, T. and A. Constable for T.C. and E.C. Jack Causewayside, 1902-03.
10 v. plates, ports. 23 cm.
"The text of this Edinburgh Edition is that of the 1839 edition, and the alterations and additions of the abridged Life, which were never incorporated in the larger work, are added in footnotes."--Note.
1040 copies; unnumbered set.
"Chronological list of the publications of Sir Walter Scott:" v.10, p. 241-247.
Index: v. 10, p. 249-328.
1. Scott, Sir Walter, bart, 1771-1832. I. Title

NL 0436130 VtU ICN ViU MH NjP IU PPL ICU

828 S431Bl 1903
Lockhart, John Gibson, 1794-1854
The life of Sir Walter Scott...
London, Millet [1903?]
10v. fronts.,plates, ports.,double map, double facsim. O.

NL 0436131 IaU ViU OrPR WaTC

Lockhart, John Gibson, 1794–1854.
The life of Sir Walter Scott, by John Gibson Lockhart, abridged and newly ed., with notes, etc. London, Hutchinson & co., 1904.
1 p. l., viii, 376 p. front. (port.) 17 cm. (*Half-title:* The library of standard biographies; Lockhart's Life of ... Scott, abridged and ed. by J. M. Sloan)
An abridgment of the Memoirs of the life of Sir Walter Scott, further abridged from that by Lockhart himself which appeared in 1848 in two volumes under title: Narrative of the life of Sir Walter Scott ...
1. Scott, Sir Walter, bart., 1771–1832. I. Sloan, John MacGavin, 1880– ed.
PR5332.L62 1904 928.2 4—17999

NL 0436132 DLC CaBVaU

PR 5332 L62 1906
Lockhart, John Gibson, 1794-1854.
The life of Sir Walter Scott [by] J.G. Lockhart. London, Dent [1906]
viii,675p. 18cm. (Everyman's library, 55)

NL 0436133 CLSU PPGi ScU

Lockhart, John Gibson, 1794–1854.

Hutton, Richard Holt, 1826–1897.
The life of Sir Walter Scott, abridged from Lockhart's Life of Scott, by Richard H. Hutton ... with an introductory appreciation by the late secretary of state, John Hay. Philadelphia, J. D. Morris & company [1905]

B S4311 1912
Lockhart, John Gibson, 1794-1854.
The life of Sir Walter Scott, bart. (abridged from the larger work) ... London, 1912.
837p. col.front.(port.) col.plates.

NL 0436135 ICU MiD MH PU OClND OEac OCl NjP

Lockhart, John Gibson, 1794-1854.
Life of Sir Walter Scott. Macmillan, 1922.

NL 0436136 OCX PHC

PR5332 .L62 1931
Lockhart, John Gibson, 1794-1854.
The life of Sir Walter Scott [by] J. G. Lockhart. London, J. M. Dent & sons, ltd.; New York, E. P. Dutton & co., inc. [1931]
viii, 675, [1] p. 17½cm. (Half-title: Everyman's library, ed. by Ernest Rhys. Biography. No.55.)
Bibliography: p. viii.
1. Scott, Sir Walter, bart., 1771-1832. I. Ser.

NL 0436137 ViU IU

PR5332 .L62 1937
Lockhart, John Gibson, 1794-1854.
The life of Sir Walter Scott. London, J. M. Dent; New York, E. P. Dutton [1937]
viii, 675 p. 18cm. (Everyman's library. Biography. No. 55)
1. Scott, Sir Walter, bart., 1771-1832.

NL 0436138 ViU NcD NcRS

Lockhart, John Gibson, 1794–1854.
Lockhart's literary criticism, with introduction and bibliography, by M. Clive Hildyard. Oxford, B. Blackwell, 1931.
5 p. l., 168 p. front. (port.) 22½cm.
"The more important critical judgments of Lockhart ... extending over a period of nearly forty years."—Pref. note.
"Bibliography of Lockhart's critical writings": p. 153–164.
1. Criticism. 2. Literature—Hist. & crit. 3. Lockhart, John Gibson, 1794–1854—Bibl. I. Hildyard, Margaret Clive, ed.
31-30434
Library of Congress PR4891.L4A6 1931
[3] 820.4

NL 0436139 MiU OU IU NN MB WaU ViU DLC OrPR KMK NIC PPT NcD CtY PU OCl OCU

Lockhart, John Gibson, 1794-1854.
Memoirs of Sir Walter Scott. Edinburgh, A.and C.Black, 1853. 10v. fronts(ports.,v.1-7) 17cm.
Added t.p. engraved with vignette.
Memoir of the early life of Sir Walter Scott, written by himself: v.1,p.1-84.
Chronological list of the publications of Sir Walter Scott: v.10, [p.269]-276.
Index: v.10, [p.277]-359.
1. Scott, Sir Walter, bart., 1771-1832.

NL 0436140 MWelC PU

Lockhart, John Gibson, 1794-1854.
Memoirs of Sir Walter Scott, by J. G. Lockhart ... Edinburgh, A. and C. Black, 1869.
10 v.
1. Scott, Sir Walter, bart., 1771-1832.

NL 0436141 WaU ViU ICN

Lockhart, John Gibson, 1794–1854.
Memoirs of Sir Walter Scott, by J. G. Lockhart ... Edinburgh, A. and C. Black, 1882.
10 v. fronts. (ports., v. 1–7) fold. facsim. 18cm.
Added t.-p., engr., with vignette.
Illus. by J. M. W. Turner.
On back of cover: Author's edition with Turner's plates.
CONTENTS.—v. 1. 1771–1797.—v. 2. 1798–1806.—v. 3. 1806–1812.—v. 4. 1812–1814.—v. 5. 1814–1818.—v. 6. 1818–1821.—v. 7. 1822–1825.—v. 8. 1825–1826.—v. 9. 1826–1830.—v. 10. 1830–1832.
1. Scott, Sir Walter, bart., 1771–1832. I. Turner, Joseph Mallord William, 1775–1851, illus.
1-24132
Library of Congress PR5332.L6 1882

NL 0436142 DLC NcU WaS FTaSU PPD PPULC MH

Lockhart, John Gibson, 1794–1854.
Memoirs of Sir Walter Scott, by J. G. Lockhart... London [etc.] Macmillan and co., ltd., 1900. 5 v. 23cm. (Half-title: Library of English classics.)
"Chronological list of the publications of Sir Walter Scott," v. 5, p. [467]–472.
836024-8A. N. Y. P. L. 1. Scott, Sir Walter, bart., 1771–1832. June 16, 1937

NL 0436143 PP PPRCl MiD MsSM WaU CU-I MiU NcD WaWW CaBVaU OClW NN OrPR OClW TxU MiU OO OCU CtY MH PSC

Lockhart, John Gibson, 1794-1854.
Memoirs of the life of Sir Walter Scott, bart. By J.G. Lockhart ... London, Warne, n.d.
2 v.
New ed. ... condensed and rev.

NL 0436144 NcRS

VOLUME 337

Lockhart, John Gibson, 1794-1854.
Memoirs of the life of Sir Walter Scott, bart. Reprinted from the celebrated Edinburgh edition. With a portrait of Sir Walter Scott. Philadelphia, T.B. Peterson, 1836.
590 p. front. port.

NL 0436145 WaSpG PU

LOCKHART, J[ohn] G[ibson], 1794-1854.
Memoirs of the life of Sir Walter Scott, bart. Boston, Otis, Broaders & co., 1837.
4 vol.

NL 0436146 MH MB

Lockhart, John Gibson, 1794-1854.
Memoirs of the life of Sir Walter Scott, Bart. By J. G. Lockhart. v. New York: W. Lewer, 1837. v. front. (port.) 12°. (Foster's cabinet miscellany. v.)
v. 5 with book-plate of John Bigelow.

4858A. 1. Scott, Sir Walter, bart., 1771-1832.
N. Y. P. L. May 16, 1921.

NL 0436147 NN CtY

Lockhart, John Gibson, 1794-1854.
Memoirs of the life of Sir Walter Scott, bart. Par., Baudry, 1837.
3 v.

NL 0436148 PU NcD

Lockhart, John Gibson, 1794-1854.
Memoirs of the life of Sir Walter Scott, bart. By J. G. Lockhart ... Philadelphia, Carey, Lea, & Blanchard, 1837.
2 v. front. (port.: v. 2) 24cm.

1. Scott, Sir Walter, bart., 1771-1832.

17-21088

Library of Congress PR5332.L6 1837

NL 0436149 DLC OU NcU PPL PU PWcS PHat PPA NjP NjR CSmH NN MeB CtHT-W

LOCKHART, JOHN GIBSON, 1794-1854.
Memoirs of the life of Sir Walter Scott, bart., by J.G. Lockhart... Boston: Otis, Broaders, and Co., 1837-38.
7 v. front. (port., v. 5.) 19½cm.

Vols. 5-7 have imprint: Philadelphia, Carey, Lea, & Blanchard.

792540-6A. 1. Scott, Sir Walter, bart., 1771-1832.

NL 0436150 NN CU MWA CtY Nh OO MB MH

[Lockhart, John Gibson] 1794-1854.
Memoirs of the life of Sir Walter Scott, bart. ... Edinburgh, R. Cadell; [etc., etc.] 1837-38.
7 v. front. (port.) fold. facsim. 20cm.
Preface signed: J. G. Lockhart.
Memoir of the early life of Sir Walter Scott written by himself: v. 1, p. 1-60.
"Chronological list of the publications of Sir Walter Scott": v. 7, p. [433]-439.

1. Scott, Sir Walter, bart., 1771-1832. I. Title.

17-25965

Library of Congress PR5332.L6 1837

NL 0436151 DLC PU OrU TxU NjP OCl PPL PP PV FTaSU DGU NcRS OU MiD OrU CaBVaU WaS InStme WaS CtY InU CaBVa OrCS IdU

PR5332 .L755 Lockhart, John Gibson, 1794-1854.
Memoirs of the life of Sir Walter Scott. Paris, A. and W. Galignani, 1837-38.
4 v.
Memoir of the early life of Sir Walter Scott written by himself: v.1, p.1-34.

1. Scott, Sir Walter, bart., 1771-1832. I. Title.

NL 0436152 ICU NjNbS MH

R5332 L6 837 Lockhart, John Gibson, 1794-1854.
Memoirs of the life of Sir Walter Scott, bart. by J. G. Lockhart ... Philadelphia, Carey, Lea, & Blanchard, 1837-38.
2 v. 23cm.

1. Scott, Sir Walter, bart., 1771-1832.

NL 0436153 ViU ODW

Lockhart, John Gibson, 1794-1854.
Memoirs of the life of Sir Walter Scott, bart. Boston [etc.] Otis, Broaders [etc.] 1837-39.
7 v. 19 cm.

NL 0436154 MB

Lockhart, John Gibson, 1794-1854.
Memoirs of the life of Sir Walter Scott. By J. G. Lockhart ... Paris, Baudry [etc.] 1838.
4 v. 22cm.

1. Scott, Sir Walter, bart., 1771-1832.

4-19477

Library of Congress PR5332.L6 1838

NL 0436155 DLC NcD NcU OCl PSC NN

Lockhart, John Gibson, 1794-1854.
Memoirs of the life of Sir Walter Scott, bart., by J. G. Lockhart ... Philadelphia, Carey, Lea, & Blanchard, 1838.
2 v. front. (port.) 23½cm.
"Chronological list of the publications of Sir Walter Scott": v. 2, p. 761-765.

1. Scott, Sir Walter, bart., 1771-1832.

29-23522

Library of Congress PR5332.L6 1838 a

NL 0436156 DLC CLSU FTaSU KMK NcD PP PPLT OOxM OClh MH NjP

Scott PR 5332 L6 1838 Lockhart, John Gibson, 1794-1854.
Memoirs of the life of Sir Walter Scott, bart. Philadelphia, Carey, Lea, and Blanchard, 1838.
7 v. front. (port.) 19cm.

Memoir of the early life of Sir Walter Scott written by himself: v.1, p. 1-45.
Appendix, "Chronological list of the publications of Sir Walter Scott": v. 7, p. [329]-335.

NL 0436157 IdU ViU

Y 12 .S 4283 [LOCKHART, JOHN GIBSON] 1794-1854.
Memoirs of the life of Sir Walter Scott, bart.... 2d edition. Edinburgh, R.Cadell, 1839.
10v.

Preface signed: J.G.Lockhart.
Bookplate of Walter William Bainbridge in v.7.
Added title-pages, engraved, with title: Life of Sir Walter Scott...
"Memoir of the early life of Sir Walter Scott written by himself": v.1, p.1-84.
"Chronological list of the publications of Sir Walter Scott" v.10, p.[269]-276.

NL 0436158 ICN ViU PU PP MB ICU MH CU-B MWelC PPL I

[Lockhart, John Gibson] 1794-1854.
Memoirs of the life of Sir Walter Scott.
2nd ed. Edin.,J.Murray & Whittaker & co.,1839.
10v. fronts.,ports.,facsim. 17cm.

Added t.-p.,engraved.

NL 0436159 OrU GU CaBVaU IdU

Lockhart, John Gibson, 1794-1854.
Memoirs of the life of Sir Walter Scott. Philadelphia, Lea and Blanchard, 1839. 7 v. front.,(port.v.1) 20cm.

Memoir of the early life of Sir Walter Scott, written by himself: v.1,p.1-45.
Chronological list of the publications of Sir Walter Scott: v.7,p.329-335.

1. Scott, Sir Walter,bart., 1771-1832.

NL 0436160 MWelC MB OU

PR 5332 L6 1840 Lockhart, John Gibson, 1794-1854.
Memoirs of the life of Sir Walter Scott, bart., by J. G. Lockhart. Philadelphia, Carey and Hart, 1840.
590 p. port. 24 cm.

1. Scott, Sir Walter, bart., 1771-1832.

NL 0436161 OU PU

Lockhart, John Gibson, 1794-1854
Memoirs of the life of Sir Walter Scott. N.Y., Francis, 1841.
6 v. in 3. 19 1/2 cm.

NL 0436162 PPT MB

Lockhart, John Gibson, 1794-1854.
Memoirs of the life of Sir Walter Scott...
N.Y., Philadelphia, Conner, Carey, 1838, 1842.
590 p.

NL 0436163 OClW

Lockhart, John Gibson, 1794-1854.
Memoirs of the life of Sir Walter Scott, bart. N.Y., C.S. Francis & co., Boston, J.H. Francis [etc.] 1843.
8 v. in 4.

NL 0436164 OClW

VOLUME 337

[Lockhart, John Gibson,] 1794-1854.
Memoirs of the life of Sir Walter Scott, bart. [Edinburgh? 1845?] 590 p. 8°.
In double columns.
Half-title; t.-p. wanting.

1. Scott, Sir Walter, bart., 1771-1832.
N. Y. P. L. August 17, 1917.

NL 0436165 NN

Lockhart, John Gibson, 1794-1854.
Memoirs of the life of Sir Walter Scott, bart. By J. G. Lockhart, esq. ... A new ed. ... Edinburgh, R. Cadell, 1845.
xii, 806 p. 2 front. (port., fold. facsim.) 24½cm.
"Chronological list of the publications of Sir Walter Scott": p. 764-765.

1. Scott, Sir Walter, bart., 1771-1832.
42-35523
Library of Congress PR5332.L6 1845

NL 0436166 DLC OrPR CU MiU MB NjP

ar W
11881
Lockhart, John Gibson, 1794-1854.
Memoirs of the life of Sir Walter Scott, bart. A new ed., complete in one volume. Edinburgh, R. Cadell, 1847.
xii,806 p. illus. 25cm.
Added t.-p. with port.

1. Scott, Sir Walter, bart., 1771-1832.

NL 0436167 NIC

Lockhart, John Gibson, 1794-1854.
Memoirs of the life of Sir Walter Scott, bart., by J. G. Lockhart ... Edinburgh, R. Cadell; [etc., etc.] 1848.
10 v. fronts. (v. 1-7: ports.) 16½cm.
Added title-pages, engr., dated 1839.

1. Scott, Sir Walter, bart., 1771-1832.
12-36287
Library of Congress PR5332.L6 1848

NL 0436168 DLC MB DGU

Lockhart, John Gibson, 1794-1854.
Memoirs of the life of Sir Walter Scott, bart.. A new ed., complete in one volume.
xii,806,front.(port.) facsim. Edinburgh. A. and C. Black 1851.

NL 0436169 OCl KyLx ViU NjP

Lockhart, John Gibson, 1794-1854.
Memoirs of the life of Sir Walter Scott, bart. By J. G. Lockhart ... New York, C. S. Francis & co.; Boston, J. H. Francis [etc.] 1851.
8 v. in 4. 19cm.
Imprint varies slightly.
On cover: Parker's revised edition.

1. Scott, Sir Walter, bart., 1771-1832.
14-21153
Library of Congress PR5332.L6 1851

NL 0436170 DLC NjP NcU OCl PHC

Lockhart, John Gibson, 1794-1854.
Memoirs of the life of Sir Walter Scott, bart. ... A new ed., complete in one volume. Edinburgh, A. & C. Black, 1852.
25.5 cm.
Added engraved t.-p.

NL 0436171 CtY

Lockhart, John Gibson, 1794-1854.
Memoirs of the life of Sir Walter Scott, bart. Edinburgh, Black, 1856.
10 vol.

NL 0436172 PP

Lockhart, John Gibson, 1794-1854.
Memoirs of the life of Sir Walter Scott ... New ed. New York, 1857.
8 v. in 4.
Chronological list of the publications of Sir Walter Scott, v. 8, p. [241]-247.
1. Scott, Sir Walter, bart. 2. Bibliography - Scott, Sir Walter, bart.

NL 0436173 NjP PBa

Lockhart, John Gibson, 1794-1854.
Memoirs of the life of Sir Walter Scott. Boston, 1859.
9 vol.

NL 0436174 PHi

PR5332
L6
1861
Lockhart, John Gibson, 1794-1854
Memoirs of the life of Sir Walter Scott, bart. New ed. Boston, Ticknor and Fields, 1861.
9 v. illus., ports. 18 cm.
Added t.-p.
Biographical sketch of John Gibson Lockhart: v. 1, p. [vii]-xix.
"Memoir of Sir Walter Scott's early years written by himself": v. 1, p. [31]-86.

"Chronological list of the publications of Sir Walter Scott": v. 9, p. 274-280.

1. Scott, Sir Walter, bart., 1771-1832

NL 0436176 MeB NcA-S MH PPSteph

Lockhart, John Gibson, 1794-1854.
Memoirs of the life of Sir Walter Scott, bart. A new edition, complete in one volume. Edinburgh, A.& C. Black, 1861. xii, 806 p. port., facsim. 26 cm.

NL 0436177 MBC

Lockhart, John Gibson, 1794-1854
Memoirs of the life of Sir Walter Scott. Boston, 1861-1862.
9 v.

New ed.

NL 0436178 MiU NRU CtY MiD PP

Lockhart, John Gibson, 1794-1854.
Memoirs of the life of Sir Walter Scott, bart. New ed. Boston, Ticknor and Fields, etc. 1861-71.
9 vol. Ports. and plate.
Cover: "Household edition."
Added title-pages engraved.

NL 0436179 MH IU NjP

Lockhart, John Gibson, 1794-1854.
Memoirs of the life of Sir Walter Scott, bart. Edinburgh, A. & C. Black, 1862.
10 v.

v.10 lacking.

NL 0436180 MiD OClW MB MdBP MiD TU

B
S4311
1873
Lockhart, John Gibson, 1794-1854.
... Memoirs of the life of Sir Walter Scott, bart. ... Boston, J. R. Osgood & co., 1873.
9v. in 3. fronts., plates, ports.

At head of title: Illustrated library edition.
"Biographical sketch of the author": v.1, p. [vii]-xix.
"Chronological list of the publications of Sir Walter Scott": v.1, p.274-280.

1. Scott, Sir Walter, 1771-1832.

NL 0436181 IU OClW MH KyLx PPFr PWcS PU

Lockhart, John Gibson, 1794-1854.
Memoirs of the life of Sir Walter Scott, bart. Boston, Houghton Mifflin, 1881.
9 v. in 3. (Illustrated library edition)

NL 0436182 OFH OCl

PR
5332
.L6
1888
Lockhart, John Gibson, 1794-1854.
Memoirs of the life of Sir Walter Scott, bart A new ed , condensed and rev. London and New York, F. Warne, 1888
749 p. (The Chandos classics)

#Scott, Sir Walter, bart, 1771-1832
(A)Memoirs of the life of Sir Walter Scott, bart.

NL 0436183 MoU CLU PPAN NcD WaT

Lockhart, John Gibson, 1794-1854.
Memoirs of the life of Sir Walter Scott, by John Gibson Lockhart... [Cambridge ed.] Boston and N.Y., Houghton, Mifflin and company, 1901.
5 v.

NL 0436184 OClCC OClU PP PV MtU IdU WaWW

Lockhart, John Gibson, 1794-1854.
Memoirs of the life of Sir Walter Scott, bart., by John Gibson Lockhart ... [Large paper ed.] Boston and New York, Houghton, Mifflin and company, 1901.
10 v. fronts., plates, ports. 23cm.
Added t.-p., engraved, with coat of arms in gilt and colors.
"Six hundred copies printed." This copy not numbered.
Edited by Susan M. Francis.
"Biographical sketch of John Gibson Lockhart": v. 1, p. [xiii]-xxxvi.
Appendix (v. 10) includes additional genealogical data and a bibliography of Scott's works (p. 208-214)
1. Scott, Sir Walter, bart., 1771-1832. 2. Scott family. I. Francis, Susan M., ed.
2—202
Library of Congress PR5332.L6 1901
Copyright A 22643- 22646, 23270-23274

NL 0436185 DLC WaT NcGU NRCR OU DAU

VOLUME 337

Lockhart, John Gibson, 1794–1854.
Memoirs of the life of Sir Walter Scott, by John Gibson Lockhart ... [Cambridge ed.] Boston and New York, Houghton, Mifflin and company, 1902.
5 v. fronts., ports. 21½cm.
Edited by Susan M. Francis.
"Biographical sketch of John Gibson Lockhart": v. 1, p. [xiii]-xxxvi.

1. Scott, Sir Walter, bart., 1771–1832. I. Francis, Susan M., ed.
4—17391
Library of Congress PR5332.L6 1902

PPFr OC1W OO
NL 0436186 DLC WaSpG OEac ICN TU PP PPT PPLas

Lockhart, John Gibson, 1794-1854.
Memoirs of the life of Sir Walter Scott. Fireside ed. Boston, etc., [Houghton, Mifflin and co., 1910.
5 v.

NL 0436187 MH WaS PHC MeB MiD

Lockhart, John Gibson, 1794-1854, tr.
FOR OTHER EDITIONS SEE MAIN ENTRY
Moorish literature: comprising romantic ballads, tales of the Berbers, stories of the Kabylie, folk-lore and national traditions; translated into English for the first time, with a special introduction by Epiphanius Wilson, A. M. Rev. ed. New York, The Colonial press [°1901]

Lockhart, John Gibson, 1794-1854.
Napoleon. [Verse.] 102-104 pp.
(In Tales from Blackwood. Vol. 1. Edinburgh. [1861.])

NL 0436189 MB

944.05 N16b Lockhart, John Gibson, 1794-1854.
Napoleon Bonapartes historia. Öfversättning från 4. original-uppl. Landskrona, J.L. Törnqvist, 1871.
xvi, 518 p. illus., port. 20cm.
(Familje-bibliotek. 9)

1. Napoléon I, Emperor of the French, 1769-1821. 2. France. Hist. 1799-1815.

NL 0436190 MnU

Lockhart, John Gibson, 1794–1854.
Narrative of the life of Sir Walter Scott, bart. Begun by himself and continued by J. G. Lockhart, esq. In two volumes ... Edinburgh, R. Cadell; [etc., etc.] 1848.
2 v. fronts. (v. 2: port.) 20cm.
Added t.-p., engraved, with vignette.
"An abridgment of the Memoirs of the author, originally comprised in seven volumes ... Embracing only what may be called more strictly narrative."—Pref.
"Memoir of Sir Walter Scott's early years, written by himself": v. 1, p. 1-56.

1. Scott, Sir Walter, bart., 1771–1832.
28—20090
Library of Congress PR5332.L6 1848 a

NL 0436191 DLC CtY

Lockhart, John Gibson, 1794–1854.
Narrative of the life of Sir Walter Scott, bart., begun by himself and continued by J. G. Lockhart. London, J. M. Dent & co.; New York, E. P. Dutton & co. [1906]
viii, 675, [1] p. 17½ cm. (*Half-title:* Everyman's library, ed. by Ernest Rhys. Biography)
Title within ornamental border; illustrated lining-papers.
Bibliography: p. viii.

1. Scott, Sir Walter, bart., 1771–1832.
A 10—2222
Enoch Pratt Free Libr. for Library of Congress [PR5332.L]

WaU NmU OCl MeB MH
NL 0436192 MdBE NRCR OCU OLak PSC NN CaBVa Or WaT

PR 5332 L81 1909 Lockhart, John Gibson, 1794-1854.
Narrative of the life of Sir Walter Scott, begun by himself and continued by J. G. Lockhart. [3d ed.] London, J. M. Dent; New York, E. P. Dutton [1909]
viii, 675 p. 18cm. (Everyman's library. Biography [no. 55])

An abridgment of the author's Memoirs of the life of Sir Walter Scott, bart., originally published in seven volumes, 1837-1838.

1. Scott, Sir Walter, bart., 1771-1832.

NL 0436193 NIC MH OOxM

Lockhart, John Gibson, 1794 - 1854.
Narrative of the life of Sir Walter Scott, bart., begun by himself and continued by J.G. Lochart. London, Dent, 1912.
676 p. S.

NL 0436194 PP MtU

LOCKHART, John Gibson,1794-1854.
Narrative of the life of Sir Walter Scott, begun by himself and continued by J.G. Lockhart. London, & Toronto, J.M.Dent & sons Ltd., etc., etc., [1915].
pp. viii, 675.
(Everyman's library)
Bibliography, p. viii.

NL 0436195 MH ViU Wa LU NjP

Lockhart, John Gibson, 1794-1834.
Narrative of the life of Sir Walter Scott, ... London, J.M. Dent & co.; N.Y., E.P. Dutton & co. 1922.

NL 0436196 OC1W

Lockhart, John Gibson, 1794–1854.
Narrative of the life of Sir Walter Scott, bart., begun by himself and continued by J. G. Lockhart. London & Toronto, J. M. Dent & sons, ltd.; New York, E. P. Dutton & co. [1931]
viii, 675, [1] p. 17½cm. (*Half-title:* Everyman's library, ed. by Ernest Rhys. Biography. [no. 55])
Title within ornamental border.
"First published in this edition, 1906; reprinted ... 1931."
An abridgment of the author's Memoirs of the life of Sir Walter Scott, bart., originally published in seven volumes, 1837–38.
Bibliography: p. viii.

1. Scott, Sir Walter, bart., 1771–1832.
36—37065
Library of Congress AC1.E8 no. 55
[2] 928.2

NL 0436197 DLC CaBVaU MiU

Lockhart, John Gibson, 1794-1854.
FOR OTHER EDITIONS SEE MAIN ENTRY
Wilson, John, 1785–1854.
Noctes Ambrosianae, by the late John Wilson ... and Wm. Maginn, LL. D., J. G. Lockhart, James Hogg, &c; with memoirs and notes by R. Shelton Mackenzie ... New York, Redfield, 1857.

[Lockhart, John Gibson] 1794-1854.
Notice on the Savoy Chapel, built by King Henry VII. and recently restored by Queen Victoria, 1844.
20 p. 8°.

NL 0436199 CtY

[Lockhart, John Gibson] 1794–1854.
Peter's letters to his kinsfolk. The 2d ed. Edinburgh, W. Blackwood; [etc., etc.] 1819.
3 v. front., ports. 21cm.
Title vignettes.
"Dedication" and "Epistle liminary": signed: Peter Morris (*pseud.*)

1. Scotland—Soc. life & cust. 2. Edinburgh—Soc. life & cust. 3. Glasgow—Soc. life & cust. 4. Scotland—Descr. & trav. I. Title.
15—10874
Library of Congress DA772.L6

OCU PPL NN IU NjP CSmH NNC ICN CoU NcU TU
NL 0436200 DLC OrP WU NIC TxU TNJ NcD CtY TxU OO

[Lockhart, John Gibson] 1794–1854.
Peter's letters to his kinsfolk. 3d ed. ... Edinburgh, W. Blackwood; [etc., etc.] 1819.
3 v. front., 1 illus., ports. 22cm.
Title vignettes.
"Dedication" and "Epistle luminary" signed: Peter Morris (*pseud.*)

1. Scotland—Soc. life & cust. 2. Edinburgh—Soc. life & cust. 3. Glasgow—Soc. life & cust. 4. Scotland—Descr. & trav. I. Title.
34—18446
Library of Congress DA772.L6 1819 a [a41]

NcU ViU OOxM IU CU NcD-MC ILfC NcD-MC
NL 0436201 DLC CaBVaU ICU MH NN NjNbS MdBP CtY

[Lockhart, John Gibson] 1794–1854.
Peter's letters to his kinsfolk. 1st American, from the 2d Edinburgh ed. New-York: Printed by C. S. Van Winkle, 101 Greenwich street, for A. T. Goodrich & co. Kirk & Mercein, C. Wiley & co. W. B. Gilley, and James Olmstead, 1820.
vii, 575 p. 22cm.
"Dedication" signed: Peter Morris (*pseud.*)

1. Scotland—Soc. life & cust. 2. Edinburgh—Soc. life & cust. 3. Glasgow—Soc. life & cust. 4. Scotland—Descr. & trav. I. Title.
35—36532
Library of Congress DA772.L6 1820

PPFr NjR KyLx MWA CtHT-W
NL 0436202 DLC MsSM InU CtY PPA PU MiU NN NNUT

Lockhart, John Gibson, 1794–1854.
Peter's letters to his kinsfolk. To which is added, Postscript, addressed to Samuel T. Coleridge, esq. 2d American ed. New-York: Printed by James and John Harper, no. 138 Fulton-street, for E. Duyckinck, Collins & co., Collins & Hannay, S. Campbell & son, and G. Long. 1820.
viii, [9]-520 p. 23½cm.
"Dedication" signed: Peter Morris (*pseud.*)

1. Scotland—Soc. life & cust. 2. Edinburgh—Soc. life & cust. 3. Glasgow—Soc. life & cust. 4. Scotland—Descr. & trav. I. Title.
17—31123
Library of Congress DA772.L6 1820

NL 0436203 DLC FTaSU InU NN TNJ NBu MnU OU NjP

VOLUME 337

LOCKHART, JOHN GIBSON, 1794-1854.
Peter's letters to his kinsfold. London, New York, T. Nelson [1952]

xvii, 364p. 17cm. (Nelson classics)

"Excepting an unauthorized American ed. of 1820, this is the first reissue, in part or in full... since Lockhart supervised the 'third' edition of 1819. It represents about half of the original work... [and] follows the 'third' ed."-Introd., signed C. P. H.

NL 0436204 MH PPT PU ICN

Lockhart, John Gibson, 1794-1854, ed.

Scott, *Sir* Walter, *bart.*, 1771-1832.
The poetical works of Sir Walter Scott, bart. ... With all his introductions and notes; also various readings, and the editor's notes. Edinburgh, R. Cadell; [etc., etc.] 1847.

LOCKHART, John Gibson, 1794-1854.
Postscript to Peter's letters. Addressed to S. T. Coleridge. [Anon] N. Y. Van Winkle. 1820. 23 pp. 8°.
May be found also in his Peter's letters to his kinsfolk [4574.72].

NL 0436206 MB DGU

941.58 [Lockhart, John Gibson] 1794-1854.
C692 Postscript to the third edition of
v.74 Peter's letters. [Edinburgh, 1819]
no.1 24p.

[Collins pamphlets. v.74, no.1]

NL 0436207 IU

Lockhart, John Gibson, 1794-1854, ed.
The Quarterly review
see under title

[Lockhart, John Gibson] 1794-1854.
Reginald Dalton. By the author of Valerius, and Adam Blair ... Edinburgh, W. Blackwood; London, T. Cadell, 1823.
3 v. 19½cm.

I. Title.

41-33244

Library of Congress PZ3.L811R3

MB MH
NL 0436209 DLC MH LU FU NcU CtY PSC PU OC1W MiU

[Lockhart, John Gibson] 1794-1854.
Reginald Dalton. By the author of Valerius, and Adam Blair ... New-York, E. Duyckinck [etc.] 1823.
2 v. in 1. 19½cm.

I. Title.

7-15170

Library of Congress PZ3.L811R

NL 0436210 DLC CtY NN NIC

In [Lockhart, John Gibson] 1794-1854.
L811 Reginald Dalton, by the author of Valerius.
823c A new edition. Edinburgh and London, W. Blackwood and sons, 1847.
2p.l.,505p. 17cm.

1. Oxford. University-Fiction. I. Title.

NL 0436211 CtY NjP

[Lockhart, John Gibson] 1794-1854.
Reginald Dalton. By the author of Valerius. New ed. Edinburgh and London, W. Blackwood and sons, 1849.
2 p. l., 505 p. 17cm.

I. Title.

7-15169

Library of Congress PZ3.L811R3

NL 0436212 DLC CtY

[Lockhart, John Gibson] 1794-1854.
Reginald Dalton, by the author of 'Valerius.' New ed. Edinburgh and London, W. Blackwood and sons, 1868.
3 p. l., 505 p. 18cm. (*Half-title:* Blackwood's standard novels)

I. Title.

42-29942

Library of Congress PZ3.L811R5

NL 0436213 DLC

Lockhart, John Gibson, 1794-1854.
Selections from Lockhart's Life of Scott; ed. by A. Barter. Lond., 1910.

142 p.

NL 0436214 PHC

Lockhart, John Gibson, 1794-1854.
FOR OTHER EDITIONS SEE MAIN ENTRY
Hutton, Richard Holt, 1826-1897.
Sir Walter Scott, by Richard H. Hutton. London & New York, Macmillan, 1903.

[LOCKHART, JOHN GIBSON] 1794-1854.
Some passages in the life of Mr. Adam Blair, minister of the gospel at Cross-Meikle. Boston: Wells and Lilly, 1822. 251 p. 17½cm.

118442B. 1. Fiction, Scottish. I. Title.

NL 0436216 NN MWeT MH T CtY MiU OCU

Lockhart, John Gibson, 1794-1854.
Some passages in the life of Mr. Adam Blair, minister of the Gospel at Cross-Meikle. Edinburgh, W. Blackwood; London, T. Cadell, 1822.
337,12 p. 21 cm.

"Books printed for William Blackwood": 12 p. at end.

NL 0436217 NjP MH IU AAP CaBVaU

Lockhart, John Gibson, 1794-1854.
Some passages in the life of Mr. Adam Blair, minister of the gospel at Cross-Meikle. 2nd ed. Edinburgh, Blackwood, 1824.
367 p.

NL 0436218 NNC

[Lockhart, John Gibson] 1794-1854.
Some passages in the life of Mr. Adam Blair. And The history of Matthew Wald. By the author of Valerius and Reginald Dalton. Edinburgh and London, W. Blackwood and sons, 1843.
379 p. front. 17cm.

Library of Congress PZ3.L811S 7-15168†

NL 0436219 DLC MB

[Lockhart, John Gibson] 1794-1854.
Some passages in the life of Mr. Adam Blair. The history of Matthew Wald. Edinburgh, Blackwood, 1846.
379 p. 17½ cm.

NL 0436220 NjP MB

---

823 [Lockhart, John Gibson] 1794-1854.
L811s Some passages in the life of Mr. Adam Blair,
1855 and The history of Matthew Wald, by the author of Valerius and Reginald Dalton. Edinburgh, W. Blackwood, 1855.
379p. 17cm.

NL 0436221 TxU

PZ3
.L811 Lockhart, John Gibson, 1794-1854.
S 2 Some passages in the life of Mr. Blair. And The history of Matthew Wald. By the author of Valerius and Reginald Dalton. Edinburgh and London, W. Blackwood and sons, 1849.
2 p. l., [3]-379 p. front. 16cm.

NL 0436222 MB

Lockjart, John Gibson, 1794-1854, tr.
... The Spanish ballads. Tr. by J.G. Lockhart. ... and the Chronicle of the Cid. By Robert Southey. London and N.Y., F. Warne & co., n.d.
466 p.

NL 0436223 OC1W PWcS NjP NNH PRosC PP PPD PBa NcU

LOCKHART, John Gibson, 1794-1854, tr.
The Spanish ballads, translated by J.G. Lockhart and the Chronicle of the Cid, by Robert Southey. New York, T.Y.Crowell & Co., [18- ?].

19 cm.
Originally issued under the title "Ancient Spanish ballads."

NL 0436224 MH NjP OC1

VOLUME 337

Lockhart, John Gibson, 1794–1854, tr.
... The Spanish ballads. Translated by J. G. Lockhart ... and the Chronicle of the Cid. By Robert Southey. London and New York, F. Warne and co. [1823]
viii, 466 p. 19½ cm. (The Chandos classics)
Published also under title: Ancient Spanish ballads.
"Lockhart's translations of the Spanish ballads appeared originally in Blackwood's magazine, and were published in a separate form in 1822, from which edition this volume has been printed. It contains two or three more ballads than the later edition."—Pref.
"This Chronicle of the Cid is wholly translation, but it is not the translation of any single work."—Pref to the Chronicle.
CONTENTS.—Historical ballads.—Moorish ballads.—Romantic ballads.—Chronicle of the Cid, Rodrigo Diaz de Bivar, the campeador, by Robert Southey.
1. Spanish ballads and songs. 2. Spanish poetry—Translations into English. 3. English poetry—Translations from Spanish. 4. El Cid Campeador. I. Southey, Robert, 1774–1843, tr.
A 35—1813
Virginia. Univ. Libr. for Library of Congress [PQ6267.E]

NcU FTaSU IU
NL 0436226 ViU OrP OkU MsU TU MoSW PSC IEdS OKentU

LOCKHART, John Gibson, 1794-1854, tr.
The Spanish ballads, translated by J.G.Lockhart, and the Chronicle of the Cid, by Robert Southey. London, F.Warne and Co., etc., etc., [187-?].
18 cm. Plates.
At head of title: The "Chandos classics".
Originally issued under the title "Ancient Spanish ballads".

NL 0436227 MH OO CU

Lockhart, John Gibson, 1794–1854, translator.
The Spanish ballads, translated by J. G. Lockhart ... and the Chronicle of the Cid, [translated] by Robert Southey. New York: Scribner, Welford and Armstrong [187–?]. viii, 466 p. 4 pl. (incl. front.) 12°.
1. Ballads (Spanish). 2. Cid, El, Rodrigo Diaz de Bivar. 3. Southey, Robert, 1774–1843, translator. 4. Title.
N. Y. P. L. August 9, 1915

NL 0436228 NN

PQ6267 .E3L85 Lockhart, John Gibson, 1794–1854, tr.
... The Spanish ballads. Tr. by J. G. Lockhart, LL. B. and the Chronicle of the Cid. By Robert Southey. London and New York, F. Warne and co. [1873–75]
viii, 466 p. 20cm. (The "Chandos classics")
1. Spanish ballads and songs—Translations into English. 2. English ballads and songs—Translations from Spanish.

NL 0436229 ICU IaU ViU NN MB CU

Lockhart, John Gibson, 1794-1854, tr.
The Spanish ballads. Tr.by J.G.Lockhart, LL.B. And the Chronicle of the Cid. By Robert Southey. New York, T.Y.Crowell & co. [188-?]
463 p. 18½cm.
"Lockhart's translations of the Spanish ballads appeared originally in Blackwood's Magazine, and were published in a separate form in 1822, from which edition this volume has been printed."--Pref.
1.Spanish ballads and songs--Translations into English. 2.English ballads and songs--Translations from Spanish. I.Southey, Robert, 1774-1843, tr. II.El Cid Campeador. III.Title: Chronicle of the Cid.

NL 0436230 MiU OCU OU

Lockhart, John Gibson, 1794-1854, tr.
... The Spanish ballads. Translated by J.G. Lockhart ... and the Chronicle of the Cid. By Robert Southey. London and New York, F. Warne and co. [1886?]
viii, 466 p. 19.5 cm. (The Chandos classics)
Published also under title: Ancient Spanish ballads
"Lockhart's translations of the Spanish ballads appeared originally in Blackwood's magazine, and were published in separate form in 1822, from which edition this volume has been printed. It contains two or three more ballads than the later edition." - Pref.
"This Chronicle of the Cid is wholly translation, but it is not the translation of any single work." - Pref. to the Chronicle.

NL 0436232 CtY

PQ6267.E4 L72 Lockhart, John Gibson, 1794-1854, tr.
The Spanish ballads. Translated by J. G. Lockhart ... and the Chronicle of the Cid. By Robert Southey. New York, Thomas Y. Crowell & co. [1890?]
463p. 18½cm.
Published also under title: Ancient Spanish ballads.
"Lockhart's translations of the Spanish ballads appeared originally in Blackwood's magazine, and were published in a separate form in 1822, from which edition this volume has been printed. It contains two or three more ballads than the later edition".-Pref.
"This Chronicle of the Cid is wholly translation, but it is not the translation of any single work".-Pref. to the Chronicle.
Contents.-Historical ballads.-Moorish ballads.-Romantic ballads.-Chronicle of the Cid, Rodrigo Diaz de Bivar, the campeador, by Robert Southey.

NL 0436234 NBuG

860.81 L81s 1907 Lockhart, John Gibson, 1784-1854, tr.
The Spanish ballads, translated by J. G. Lockhart ... and the Chronicle of the Cid, translated by Robert Southey. New York, The Century co., 1907.
463p. front., illus. (On cover: Old Spanish romances, vol.VI)
Contents.- Historical ballads.- Moorish ballads.- Romantic ballads.- Chronicle of the Cid, Rodrigo Diaz de Bivar, the Campeador, by Robert Southey.

NL 0436235 IU MdBP OOxM NN PP MoSW GU

PQ 6267.2 L81a 1908 Lockhart, John Gibson, 1794-1854, tr.
The Spanish ballads, translated by J.G. Lockhart ... and the Chronicle of the Cid, translated by Robert Southey. New York, The Century co., 1908.
463p. front., plates. 20½cm. (On cover: Old Spanish romances, vol.VI)

NL 0436236 NRU MH NBuU OKentU

*EC8 L8112 821s [Lockhart, John Gibson, 1794-1854]
Statement.
[Edinburgh, 1821]
8p. 20.5cm., in case 21.5cm.
Caption title.
Dated at foot of p.2: Edinburgh, February 8, 1821.
In reply to an attack on Lockhart by John Scott.

NL 0436237 MH

[LOCKHART, John Gibson] 1794-1854.
Theodore Hook; a sketch. 3d ed. London, 1852.
sm.8°.

NL 0436238 MH PPL MiU

828 H763ZL [Lockhart, John Gibson] 1794-1854.
Theodore Hook. A sketch. 4th ed. London, J. Murray, 1853.
102 p. 17 cm.
1. Hook, Theodore Edward, 1788-1841.

NL 0436239 LU MB

[Lockhart, John Gibson 1794–1854.
Valerius; a Roman story ... Boston, Wells and Lilly, 1821.
2 v. 18cm.
1. Rome—Hist.—Trajan, 98-117—Fiction. I. Title.
Library of Congress PZ3.L811V 7—15167

NL 0436240 DLC MiU TxU CtY ScU ViU OCl MB

[Lockhart, John Gibson,] 1794-1854.
Valerius; a Roman story... Edinburgh: W. Blackwood, 1821. 3 v. 12°.
1. Fiction (Scottish). 2. Title.
N. Y. P. L. May 1, 1915

MiU FU CtY ICU
NL 0436241 NN TxU MH TxFTC NIC CSt ICN NcU OClW

[Lockhart, John Gibson] 1794-1854.
Valerius; a Roman story... New York, Pub.by Harper & brothers, 1835.
2 v. 19½ cm.

NL 0436242 NjP PPG PPL

[Lockhart, John Gibson, 1794-1854]
Valerius; a Roman story. A new ed., revised. Edinburgh and London, W.Blackwood and sons, 1842.
Added title-page: Blackwood's standard novels

NL 0436243 MH NN NjP

[Lockhart, John Gibson] 1794-1854.
Valerius; a Roman story. A new rev. ed. Edinburgh, W. Blackwood, 1849.
361 p. 18 cm.
1. Rome - Hist. - Trajan, 98-117 - Fiction. I. Title.

NL 0436244 MdBP

[Lockhart, John Gibson, 1794-1854.]
Valerius; a Roman story. New ed., revised. Edinburgh and London, W.Blackwood and sons, 1856.
18 cm.

NL 0436245 MH IU

VOLUME 337

[Lockhart, John Gibson] 1794-1854.
Valerius; a Roman story. New ed. Edinburgh and London, W. Blackwood and sons, 1869.
2 p. l., 361 p. 17cm. (Half-title: Blackwood's standard novels)

1. Rome—Hist.—Trajan, 98-117—Fiction. I. Title. II. Series.

NL 0436246 MB PU

Lockhart, John Gibson, 1794-1854.
Valerius. A Roman story. [Anon.] New edition. Edinburgh. Blackwood. [187-?] Sm. 8°.
The persecutions of the Christians under Trajan.

A1081 — Anon ref. — Early Christians. Hist. Fict.

NL 0436247 MB

Lockhart, John Gibson, 1794-1854.

Beckford, William, 1760-1844.
Vathek, by William Beckford, esq. [London] P. Allan & co. [1923]

Lockhart, John Gibson, 1794-1854.
FOR OTHER EDITIONS SEE MAIN ENTRY
Burns, Robert, 1759-1796.
The works of Robert Burns. With a series of authentic pictorial illustrations, marginal glossary, numerous notes, and appendixes: also the life of Burns, by J. G. Lockhart; and essays on the genius, character, and writings of Burns, by Thomas Carlyle and Professor Wilson. Edited by Charles Annandale ... London [etc.] Blackie & son, limited [pref. 1887]

Lockhart, John Gilbert, 1891-
Babel visited; a churchman in soviet Russia, by J. G. Lockhart (the janitor) London, The Centenary press [1933]
128 p. front., plates. 19cm.
"This book expands a series of articles which I was asked to contribute last autumn [1932] to the Church times."—p. [5]

1. Russia—Descr. & trav.—1917- 2. Russia—Soc. condit. I. Title. II. Title: A churchman in soviet Russia.

Library of Congress DK267.L55 41-19000
[2] 914.7

NL 0436250 DLC CtW

Lockhart, John Gilbert, 1891-
Babel visited; a churchman in Soviet Russia. Milwaukee, Morehouse [1933]
128 p. illus. 19 cm.

1. Russia--Church history--1917- I. Title.

NL 0436251 KyLxCB NN CU

Lockhart, John Gilbert.
Blenden hall; the true story of a shipwreck, a casting away and life on a desert island, by J. G. Lockhart. London, P. Allan, 1930.
4 p. l., 232 p. front., plates, fold. map. 22½cm.
Based upon a book by Alexander M. Greig published in New York in 1847 under title: Fate of the Blenden hall. cf. Introd.

1. Blenden hall (Ship) I. Greig, Alexander M. Fate of the Blenden hall.

Library of Congress G530.B65 31-8084
910.4

NL 0436252 DLC WaS OrU TU OCl PU NN

Lockhart, *Captain* John Gilbert.
Blenden Hall; the true story of a shipwreck, a casting away and life on a desert island. By J. G. Lockhart.
— New York. Appleton & Co. 1930. (7), 232 pp. Plates. Map. 22 cm., in 8s.
Based on Alexander M. Greig's Fate of the Blenden Hall.

N8189 — Blenden Hall, ship. — Shipwrecks. — Greig, Alexander M.

NL 0436253 MB IdU MU OO NN TxU

Lockhart, John Gilbert.
Cecil Rhodes, by J. G. Lockhart ... London. Duckworth [1933]
135, [1] p. illus. (map) 19cm. (Great lives. [6])
"First published January 1933; reprinted January 1933."
Bibliography: p. [136]

1. Rhodes, Cecil John, 1853-1902. 2. Africa, South—Pol. & govt.

Library of Congress DT776.R4L6 1933 a 33-14310
923.242

OCl PPD NN CtY IU OrU
NL 0436254 DLC WaWW OrSaW GU IaU ScU IEN CtY CU

Lockhart, John Gilbert.

Cecil Rhodes, by J. G. Lockhart ... New York, The Macmillan co., 1933.
135, [1] illus. (map) 19cm. (Great lives [6])
"Printed in Great Britain."
Bibliography: p. [136]

1. Rhodes, Cecil John, 1853-1902. 2. Africa, South—Pol. & govt. I. Ser.

NL 0436255 ViU IdU KEmT MB ViU PSt OO

Lockhart, John Gilbert.
Charles Lindley, viscount Halifax ... by J. G. Lockhart London, G. Bles: The Centenary press [1935-
v. front., plates, ports., fold. geneal. tab. 23½cm.

1. Halifax, Charles Lindley Wood, 2d viscount, 1839-1934.

Library of Congress DA565.H155L6 36-3492
923.242

OCU OCl
NL 0436256 DLC MU CaBVaU TU NN IEG MdBP PPYH CtY

Lockhart, John Gilbert, 1891-
Cosmo Gordon Lang. [London] Hodder and Stoughton [1949]
xi, 481 p. plates, ports. 23 cm.

1. Lang, Cosmo Gordon Lang, baron, Abp. of Canterbury, 1864-1945.

BX5199.L17L6 922.342 50-1846

KyLxCB OKentU
NjR MsU OrU FTaSU ILfC NBC CaBViP CaBVa KMK ScU PPL
NL 0436257 DLC WaS ICU TU MH TxU PPWe NcD PP MB

Lockhart, John Gilbert.
... Curses, lucks and talismans. London, G. Bles [1938]
viii, 184 p. front., plates, group port. 22cm.
At head of title: J. G. Lockhart.
"First published in 1938."

1. Blessing and cursing. 2. Talismans. 3. Superstition. 4. Legends—Gt. Brit. I. Title.

Library of Congress GR141.L57 39-31660
[159.961409421] 133.40942

NL 0436258 DLC CaBVaU OOxM TU CLSU NcU OCl

Lockhart, John Gilbert.
East all the way [by] J. G. Lockhart. London. E. Benn limited [1928]
317, [1] p. 19cm.

I. Title.

Library of Congress PZ3.L8112Ea 28-16289

NL 0436259 DLC

Lockhart, John Gilbert.
East all the way, by J. G. Lockhart. New York, D. Appleton & company, 1928.
vi, 301, [1] p. 19½cm.

I. Title.

Library of Congress PZ3.L8112Ea 2 28-21968

NL 0436260 DLC

Lockhart, John Gilbert
The feet of the young men
see under Janitor, pseud.

Lockhart, John Gilbert.
A great sea mystery; the true story of the "Mary Celeste," by J. G. Lockhart. London: P. Allan & Co., Ltd. [, 1927.] 143 p. front. 8°.

342290A. 1. Ships, Derelict—Mary Celeste.
N. Y. P. L. January 20, 1928

NL 0436262 NN NNC OCl MH ICN CtY PP

Lockhart, John Gilbert.
A great sea mystery; the true story of the "Mary Celeste," by J. G. Lockhart. 2d. ed. London, P. Allan [1930]
3p., *l.*, [9]-173p. fold. map. 17cm. (Nautilus Library)

1. Mary Celeste (Brig) I. Title.

NL 0436263 KU CU

Lockhart, John Gilbert.
A great sea mystery; the true story of the "Mary Celeste", by J. G. Lockhart. New York, W. F. Payson [1931]
3 p. l., [9]-173 p. fold. map. 17cm. (*Half-title:* The deep sea library)
Printed in Great Britain.

1. Mary Celeste (Brig) I. Title.

Library of Congress G530.M34 31-27011
[5] 910.4

NL 0436264 DLC FMU

VOLUME 337

Lockhart, John Gilbert.
Here are mysteries, by J. G. Lockhart ... London, P. Allan & co., ltd. [1927]
5 p. l., 3-250, [1] p. front., plates, ports. 22½cm.
CONTENTS.—The heart of great Montrose.—The disappearance of John Orth.—The mystery of the dauphin.—The emperor and the hermit.—The mystery of the 'Maine'.—The foundling of Nuremberg.—The mystery of Lord Kitchener's death.

I. Title. II. Title: Mysteries.
27-20132
Library of Congress D24.L6 1927

NL 0436265 DLC CLSU NcD PPGi PPL NN

Lockhart, J[ohn] G[ilbert].
Here are mysteries. New York: Frederick A. Stokes Co.[, 1927.] 251 p. pl., port. 8°.
Contents: The heart of great Montrose. The disappearance of John Orth. The mystery of the dauphin. The emperor and the hermit. The mystery of the Maine. The foundling of Nuremberg. The mystery of Lord Kitchener's death.

1. Title. 2. History—General. 3. Seven anal.
N. Y. P. L. June 3, 1927

NL 0436266 NN FTaSU PP

Lockhart, John Gilbert, 1891–
The "Mary Celeste," and other strange tales of the sea. London, R. Hart-Davis, 1952.
191 p. 19 cm. (The Mariners library, 20)

1. Sea stories. 2. Adventure and adventurers.
G525.L67 *910.45 53-1069 ‡

NL 0436267 OOxM MB NN NcU DLC CaBViP CaBVa Or OrP WaS WaT CSt PP

Lockhart, J[ohn] G[ilbert].
Mysteries of the sea; a book of strange tales. New York: Frederick A. Stokes Co.[, 19—?] 254 p. illus. 12°. (The nautilus library.)
Contents: Who discovered America? The finding of Madeira. The Flying Dutchman. The hanging of Captain Green. Jenkins's ear. The lost ships of La Pérouse. The sea-monster. The great sea-serpent. The sinking of H. M. S. "Victoria." The mystery of the "Maine." The disappearance of the "Waratah." Lord Kitchener's last journey.

1. Ocean. 2. Shipwrecks. 3. Pirates. 4. Title.
N. Y. P. L. June 28, 1929

NL 0436268 NN

Lockhart, John Gilbert.
Mysteries of the sea; a book of strange tales, by J. G. Lockhart. London: P. Allan & Co., 1924. 265 p. front., illus., plates, ports. 8°.
Contents: Who discovered America? The finding of Madeira. The flying Dutchman. The hanging of Captain Green. Jenkins' ear. The lost ships of La Pérouse. The sea-monster. The great sea-sepent. The mystery of the 'Mary Celeste.' The sinking of H. M. S. 'Victoria.' The disappearance of the 'Waratah.' Lord Kitchener's last journey.

181953A. 1. Geography—Discoveries. 2. Piracy. 3. English West Indian expedition, 1739–1742. 4. Shipwrecks. 5. Lapérouse, Jean François de Galaup, comte de, 1741–1788. 6. Sea serpent. 7. Ships—Derelict. 8. Kitchener of Khartoum, Horatio Herbert Kitchener, 1st earl, 1850–1916. 9. Title.
N. Y. P. L. May 13, 1925

NL 0436269 NN MH

Lockhart, John Gilbert.
Mysteries of the sea, a book of strange tales, by J. G. Lockhart. London, P. Allan & co. [1925]
5 p. l., 265 p. front., illus., plates, ports. 22½cm.
"First published in 1924; second edition, 1925."
CONTENTS.—Who discovered America?—The finding of Madeira.—The Flying Dutchman.—The hanging of Captain Green.—Jenkins' ear.—The lost ships of La Pérouse.—The sea-monster.—The great sea-serpent.—The mystery of the 'Mary Celeste'.—The sinking of H. M. S. 'Victoria'.—The disappearance of the 'Waratah'.—Lord Kitchener's last journey.

I. Title.
25—14958
Library of Congress G525.L68 1925

NL 0436270 DLC WaS IdB OrP OCl PPA

910.4
L81m
Lockhart, John Gilbert, 1891-
Mysteries of the sea, a book of strange tales. New York, F. A. Stokes Co. [1925] 265 p. illus. 23 cm.

Contents:- Who discovered America?- The finding of Madeira.- The Flying Dutchman.- The hanging of Captain Green.- Jenkins' ear.- The lost ships of La Pérouse.- The sea-monster.- The great sea-serpent.- The mystery of the 'Mary Celeste'.-The sinking of H. M. S. 'Victoria'.-

Contents cont'd:-The disappearance of the 'Waratah'.- Lord Kitchener's last journey.

NL 0436272 LU PPULC NcRS PPL

LOCKHART, JOHN GILBERT
Mysteries of the sea, a book of strange tales. New York, 1926.

NL 0436273 MChB

Ech
924Lc
Lockhart, John Gilbert
Mysteries of the sea; a book of strange tales. [3d ed.] London,P.Allan[1928]
254p. illus. 18cm. (Nautilus Library. I)
"First published, 1924."
Bibliographic footnotes.
Contents. - Who discovered America? - The finding of Madeira. - The Flying Dutchman. - The hanging of Captain Green. - Jenkins' ear. - The lost ships of La Pérouse. - The sea-monster. - The great sea-serpent. - The

sinking of H. M. S. 'Victoria'. - The disappearance of the 'Waratah'. - Lord Kitchener's last journey.

NL 0436275 CtY NN

Lockhart, John Gilbert.
Mysteries of the sea; a book of strange tales, by J. G. Lockhart. New York, F.A. Stokes company [1929]
254 p. illus. 19 cm.
Contents. - Who discovered America? - The finding of Madeira. - The Flying Dutchman. - The hanging of Captain Green. - Jenkin's ear. - The lost ships of La Perouse. - The sea-monster. - The great sea-serpent. - The sinking of H. M. S. "Victoria". - The mystery of the "Maine". - The disappearance of the "Waratah". - Lord

Kitchener's last journey.
1. Sea stories. I. Title.

NL 0436277 CU

Lockhart, John Gilbert.
Palestine days and nights; sketches of the campaign in the Holy Land, by Captain J. G. Lockhart. London, R. Scott [1920]
x, 140 p. 19½cm.

1. European war, 1914–1918—Campaigns—Turkey and the Near East—Palestine. I. Title.
21-18327 Revised
Library of Congress D568.7.L63

NL 0436278 DLC MB

Lockhart, John Gilbert.
The peacemakers, 1814–1815, by J. G. Lockhart ... London, Duckworth, 1932.
376 p. front., ports. 22½cm.
"Some books consulted": p. 367-368.
CONTENTS.—"Le Congrès danse."—World crisis. 1814.—Talleyrand.—Metternich.—Alexander I.—William Pitt.—Castlereagh.—Canning.—William Wilberforce.

1. Vienna. Congress, 1814–1815. 2. Statesmen. I. Title.
32-20741
Library of Congress DC249.L6
Copyright A ad int. 16634 940.27

NL 0436279 NN NNC DLC CaBVaU CaBVa NcGU ViU MiU OCl PPD

Lockhart, John Gilbert.
The peacemakers, 1814–1815, by J. G. Lockhart ... New York, G. P. Putnam's sons, 1934.
376 p. front., ports. 23cm.
Printed in Great Britain.
"Some books consulted": p. 367-368.
CONTENTS.—"Le Congrès danse."—World crisis, 1814.—Talleyrand.—Metternich.—Alexander I. — William Pitt. — Castlereagh. — Canning. — William Wilberforce.

1. Vienna. Congress, 1814–1815. 2. Statesmen. I. Title.
34-17686
Library of Congress DC249.L6 1934
940.27

NL 0436280 OClW MoU OKentU WaS FTaSU OrP OrU WaSp WaE MB DLC MtU NcU PV PPT PPA PPPL OClh OO OU

Lockhart, John Gilbert.
Peril of the sea, a book of shipwrecks and escapes, by J. G. Lockhart. London, P. Allan & co. [1924]
294 p. front., plates, ports. 22½cm.

1. Shipwrecks. I. Title.
25—1664
Library of Congress G525.L7

NL 0436281 DLC CaBVa NN PPGi

Lockhart, J[ohn] G[ilbert].
Peril of the sea; a book of shipwrecks and escapes. New York: Frederick A. Stokes Co. [1925?] 294 p. pl., port. 8°.
The White ship. The strange voyage of Pietro Quirini. The last voyage of Sir Humfrey Gilbert. The casting away of the Tobie. The wreck and redemption of Sir Thomas Gates. The shipwreck of King James II. The story of Occum Chamnam. The wreck of the Wager. The wreck of H. M. S. Phœnix. The loss of the Royal George. The shipwreck and slavery of Saugnier. The loss of the Halsewell, East Indiaman. The loss of H. M. S. La Tribune. The Medusa. The burning of the Kent, East Indiaman. The wreck of the Rothsay Castle, steam packet. The story of the Birkenhead. The loss of the Titanic.

1. Shipwrecks. 2. Title.
N. Y. P. L. November 27, 1925

NL 0436282 NN LU MH WaTC OClh OCl NcD PPL WaS

Lockhart, *Captain* John Gilbert.
Peril of the sea. A book of shipwrecks and escapes.
— New York. Frederick A. Stokes Co. [1929.] 254 pp. [The nautilus library. 3.] 19 cm., in 8s.
Contents. — The "White Ship," 1120. — The last voyage of Sir Humfrey Gilbert, 1583. — The casting away of the "Tobie," 1593. — The shipwreck of King James II., 1682. — The story of Occum Chamnam, 1686. — The wreck of the "Wager," 1740. — The wreck of H. M. S. "Phœnix," 1780. — The loss of the "Royal George," 1782. — The loss of the "Halsewell" East Indiaman, 1786. — The "Medusa," 1816. — The burning of the "Kent" East Indiaman, 1825. — The wreck of the "Rothsay Castle," steam packet, 1830. — The story of the "Birkenhead," 1852. — The loss of the "Titanic," 1912.

N6421 — T.r. — S.r. — Shipwrecks.

NL 0436283 MB NcRS FMU

Lockhart, John Gilbert.
Pulpits and personalities
see under Janitor, pseud.

Lockhart, John Gilbert, 1891–
The sea, our heritage, by J. G. Lockhart. London, G. Bles [1940]
vii, 257 p. front., illus. (maps) plates, group port. 23cm.
"First published February 1940; enlarged edition October 1940."
"Books consulted": p. 257.

1. European war, 1914–1918—Naval operations. 2. Gt. Brit.—Navy. 3. Sea stories. I. Title.
41-16473
Library of Congress D581.L6 1940 a
940.459

NL 0436285 DLC CaBVa

VOLUME 337

Lockhart, *Captain* John Gilbert.
Strange adventures of the sea. A book of murders, maroonings, treasure-hunts, piracies, mutinies and tales of horror on the high seas.
— New York. Frederick A. Stokes Co. [1925?] (8), 279 pp. Portraits. Plates. Maps. 21½ cm., in 8s.
Contents. — The escape of John Fox. — The end of Blackbeard. — The adventures of Philip Ashton. — Marooned. — The story of the 'Grosvenor'. — The adventures of Mary Ann Talbot. — The misfortunes of Aaron Smith. — The terrible story of the 'Mary Russell'. — Sea messages and mysteries. — The tragedy of the Seven Hunters. — Of the company of the privateers. — Strange stories of today.

N2885 — T.r. — Adventures. — Stories of the sea. — Pirates.

NL 0436286 MB

Lockhart, *Captain* John Gilbert.
Strange adventures of the sea. By J. G. Lockhart.
— New York. Payson. [1925?] 255 pp. [The deep sea library.] 17 cm., in 8s.
Contents. — The escape of John Fox. — The end of Blackbeard. — The adventures of Philip Ashton. — Marooned. — The story of the "Grosvenor." — The adventures of Mary Ann Talbot. — The misfortunes of Aaron Smith. — The terrible story of the "Mary Russell." — Sea messages and mysteries. — The tragedy of the seven hunters. — Of the company of the privateers. — Strange stories of to-day.

D8026 — T.r. — S.r. — Stories of the sea. — Pirates. — Adventures.

NL 0436287 MB

Lockhart, John Gilbert.
Strange adventures of the sea; a book of murders, maroonings, treasure-hunts, piracies, mutinies and tales of horror on the high seas. By J. G. Lockhart... London: P. Allan and Co., [1925]. 279 p. plans, plates, ports. 8°.
Contents: The escape of John Fox. The end of Blackbeard. The adventures of Philip Ashton. Marooned. The story of the 'Grosvenor.' The adventures of Mary Ann Talbot. The misfortunes of Aaron Smith. The terrible story of the 'Mary Russell.' Sea messages and mysteries. The tragedy of the seven hunters. Of the company of the privateers. Strange stories of to-day.

242016A. 1. Shipwrecks. 2. Piracy. 3. Sea life. 4. Title.
N. Y. P. L. June 24, 1926

NL 0436288 NN CU

Lockhart, John Gilbert.
Strange adventures of the sea; a book of murders, maroonings, treasure-hunts, piracies, mutinies and tales of horror on the high seas. By J. G. Lockhart ... New York, Frederick A. Stokes company [1926]
5 p. l., 3-279 p. front., plates, ports., map. 22cm.
"Printed in Great Britain."

1. Adventure and adventurers. I. Title.

Library of Congress G525.L75 26—7772

NL 0436289 DLC OrP GU LU PPL MiU OCl OEac MChB

Lockhart, John Gilbert.
Strange adventures of the sea, by J. G. Lockhart. London, P. Allan & Co. Ltd. [1929] 255 p. 17cm. (Half-title: The Nautilus library [no. 8])
"Printed in Great Britain."
"Second edition."

1. Adventure and adventurers. I. Title.

NL 0436290 AU CaBVa CaBViP

Lockhart, John Gilbert.
Strange adventures of the sea, by J. G. Lockhart. New York, W. F. Payson [1931]
255 p. 17cm. (*Half-title:* The deep sea library)
"Printed in Great Britain."

1. Adventure and adventurers. I. Title.

Library of Congress G525.L75 1931 32-6780
910.4

NL 0436291 DLC ICU

Lockhart, John Gilbert, 1891–
Strange tales of the seven seas, by J. G. Lockhart ... London, P. Allan & co. ltd. [1929]
xi, 210 p. incl. map. front., plates, ports. 22½ cm.

1. Sea stories. I. Title.

G525.L76 910.4 30—20993

NL 0436292 DLC OEac OCl DN MH

Lockhart, John Gilbert.
Strange tales of the seven seas, by J. G. Lockhart... New York: D. Appleton and Co., 1930. xi, 210 p. front., plates. 8°.
Printed in Great Britain.
Contents: Introduction. The murder of George Glass. The story of the 'Flowery Land.' The man who walked the plank. The steward of the 'Lennie.' The 'Caswell' barque. Last thoughts on the 'Mary Celeste.' The running amok in the 'Frank N. Thayer.' The 'crook ship.' The Filipinos of the 'Ethel.' The strange affray in the 'Leicester Castle.' The negro of the 'Veronica.' More about the 'Waratah.' The mystery of the 'White Rose.' When thieves fell out. The pilongs of the 'Tai On.'

492750A. 1. Sea life. I. Title.
N. Y. P. L.

NL 0436293 NN WaS ViU PP

Lockhart, John Gilbert.
That followed after [by] J. G. Lockhart. London, E. Benn limited [1929]
vii p., 1 l., 11-288 p. 19cm.

I. Title.

Library of Congress PZ3.L8112Th 29-25032

NL 0436294 DLC

Lockhart,John Gilbert,1891-
True tales of the sea,by J.G.Lockhart. London, Quality press,ltd. [1939]
510 p. illus. 22cm.
"First published,1939."

1. Shipwrecks. 2. Adventure and adventurers. 3. Sea stories. I. Title.

NL 0436295 CtNlCG

Lockhart, John Gilbert, 1891–
Winston Churchill. Front. by Osbert Lancaster. London, G. Duckworth [1951]
158 p. illus. 19 cm.

1. Churchill, Winston Leonard Spencer, 1874–

DA566.9.C5L6 923.242 52–2589 ‡

NL 0436296 DLC CaBViP MtU FMU NN LU IEN MH

Lockhart, John Ingram, tr.

Müller, Karl Otfried, 1797–1840.
Attica and Athens: an inquiry into the civil, moral, and religious institutions, of the inhabitants, the rise and decline of Athenian power, and the topography and chorography of ancient Attica and Athens ... Tr. from the German of K. O. Müller, Grotefend, and others. By John Ingram Lockhart ... London, R. Groombridge; [etc., etc.] 1842.

Lockhart, John Ingram, tr.

Díaz del Castillo, Bernal, 1492–1581?
The memoirs of the conquistador Bernal Diaz del Castillo written by himself, containing a true and full account of the discovery and conquest of Mexico and New Spain; translated from the original Spanish by John Ingram Lockhart ... London, J. Hatchard and son, 1844.

Nva95 Lockhart, John Ingram.
G6 Report of the Fulham charities ... [London]
1 Printed for the Fulham rate-payers' association
1846 by G.Barclay,1846.

1.Charities - Fulham, Eng.

NL 0436299 CtY

Lockhart, John Ingram.
Speeches of Lockhart, and Charles Adams, Sir Charles Burrell ...
see under Morice, Burton.

Lilly
PR 4891
L 3 T8
[LOCKHART,JOHN INGRAM]
The treble angel and two maidens, with the last battle. Tragedy and comedy, by Ovidius Naso, junior [pseud.] ... [London, E. W. Allen, 1882]
89 p. 18.5 cm.
Inscribed presentation copy to Algernon Charles Swinburne.
In brown printed paper wrappers.

NL 0436301 InU

Lockhart, John Moses
The memorial volume of the Hyde Park Baptist church of Hyde Park, Cincinnati, Ohio. Cincinnati, Highlands & Highlands. [1908]
34 p.

NL 0436302 OClWHi

W 6
P3
LOCKHART, John Washington, 1824-1900
Medical monopoly exposed and medical laws unconstitutional. [Portland, Or.] 1898.
31 p.
Title

NL 0436303 DNLM

Lockhart, John Washington, 1824–1900.
Sixty years on the Brazos; the life and letters of Dr. John Washington Lockhart, 1824–1900, by Mrs. Jonnie Lockhart Wallis in association with Laurance L. Hill. Los Angeles, Calif., Priv. print. [Press of Dunn bros.] 1930.
7 p. l., 336 p. front., plates, ports, coat of arms, facsims. 24½cm.
"Two hundred copies ... have been printed for the relatives, descendants and friends of Dr. John Washington Lockhart." This copy not numbered.

1. Frontier and pioneer life—Texas. 2. Texas—Hist.—To 1846. 3. Houston, Samuel, 1793–1863. I. Wallis, Mrs. Jonnie (Lockhart) comp. II. Hill, Laurance Landreth, comp. III. Title. IV. Title: Brazos, Sixty years on the.

Library of Congress F389.L81 31-206
——— Copy 2.
Copyright A 31807 976.4

NL 0436304 DLC TxH OkU CU

VOLUME 337

Lockhart, Jorge, joint author.

Surraco, Luis A 1884–
Las algias del talón en los urinarios; síndrome de pies calientes dolorosos, por Luis A. Surraco ... y Jorge Lockhart ... Montevideo, Rosgal, 1945.

Lockhart, Jorge, joint author.

RC941 .S9 Surraco, Luis A 1884–
Los ángulos colo-esplénico y colo-gástrico en el diagnóstico de las tumefacciones del flanco-hipocondrio, por los doctores Luis A. Surraco ... y Jorge Lockhart ... Montevideo, Imprenta Rosgal, de H. Rosillo, 1943.

Lockhart, Jorge, joint author.

Surraco, Luis A 1884–
Procesos del ligamento suspensor (escroto-pene-perineales) ... por Luis A. Surraco ... y Jorge Lockhart ... Montevideo, "Rosgal," 1946–

Lockhart, Jorge, joint author.

RC899 .S8 Surraco, Luis A 1884–
La próstata y la fiebre de los viejos, las falsas gripes, por Luis A. Surraco ... y Jorge Lockhart ... Montevideo, Imprenta Rosgal, de H. Rosillo, 1943.

Lockhart, L.
see
Lockhart, Laurence.

---

823 L78r Lockhart, Langton.
Raised to the woolsack. London, T. C. Newby, 1864.
3v. 21cm.

NL 0436310 IU

Lockhart, Laurence.
Famous cities of Iran, by Laurence Lockhart ... With a foreword by Lord Cadman of Silverdale. Brentford, Middlesex, W. Pearce & co., 1939.
115, [1] p. illus. (map) plates. 25½cm.
Map on lining-papers.
"Selected bibliography": p. 113.

1. Persia — Hist. 2. Persia — Descr. & trav. 3. Cities and towns — Persia. I. Title.
40-8887
Library of Congress DS325.A2L6
955

NL 0436311 DLC TxU CU-S CU IU N NBuU MH ICU OCl WaU

HD9576 I6L814 Lockhart, Laurence.
Histoire du pétrole en Perse jusqu'au début du XX-e siècle. [Paris, Impr. Revue pétrolifère, 1938]
[10] p. map. 31cm. (Études historiques)
"Extraits de 'La Revue pétrolifère', nos. 810, du 4 novembre et 811, du 11 novembre 1938."

1. Petroleum - Iran. I. Title.

NL 0436312 CSt-H

Lockhart, Laurence.
Nadir Shah; a critical study based mainly upon contemporary sources, by L. Lockhart ... With a foreword by Sir E. Denison Ross ... London, Luzac & co., 1938.
xv, 344 p. incl. geneal. tab. front. (port.) plates, maps (1 fold.) 25½cm.
Errata slip inserted.
"Bibliographical particulars": p. 292-313. Bibliography: p. 314-328.

1. Nādir Shāh, shah of Persia, 1688-1747. 2. Persia—Hist.—Medieval and modern, 640– 3. India—Hist.—European settlements, 1500-1765.
39-33551
Library of Congress DS294.L6
955

NL 0436313 DLC CU NcU RPB WaU ICN OCU WU CtY InU MB OCl ICU MH

---

955 Ir175 no.1 Lockhart, Laurence.
The navy of Nadir Shah. London, 1936.
19 p. (The proceedings of the Iran Society vol. 1, pt. 1)

NL 0436314 NNC MH

[Lockhart, Laurence,] 1796-1876.
An answer to the protest of the Free Church, prepared in consequence of a challenge from an elder of that church. By a minister of the Establishment... Edinburgh: M. Macphail, 1846. 31 p. 8°.

1. Free Church of Scotland: Protest. 2. Church and state—Gt. Br.—Scotland. 3. Title.
N. Y. P. L. April 25, 1928

NL 0436315 NN CtY

Lockhart, Laurence, 1796-1876.
Facts for the times; or, The recent schism and the present position ... of the church ... Glasgow, Murray & Stewart, 1843.
8 p. 8°.

NL 0436316 NN

[Lockhart, Lawrence] 1796-1876.
Facts, not Falsehoods, or a plain Defence of the Church of Scotland, suited to the Times. By a Parish Minister. Edinb., 1845.
vi, 55 p. 8°. [In vol. , "Foreign Pamphlets."]

NL 0436317 NN CtY

W823 L816d Lockhart, Laurence William Maxwell, 1831-1882.
Doubles and quits. With twelve illustrations by Sylvestris. Edinburgh, W. Blackwood, 1869.
2 v. 20 cm.
According to dealer's slip tipped in, this is a 1st edition.

NL 0436318 NcU NjP

---

823 L812f Lockhart, Laurence William Maxwell, 1831-1882.
Fair to see, a novel. Edinburgh, W. Blackwood, 1871.
3v. 20cm.
"Originally published in Blackwood's magazine."

NL 0436319 IU NcU

3830 .9 .333 Lockhart, Laurence William Maxwell, 1831-1882.
Fair to see; a novel.. New York, Harper, 1872.
163 p. 23½ cm.

NL 0436320 NjP PPL NjP MH MB

Lockhart, Lawrence W[illiam] M[axwell], 1831-1882.
Fair to see. New York: Harper & Brothers, 1873. 163 p. 8°. (Library of select novels. no. 370.)

1. Fiction (English). 2. Title.
N. Y. P. L. August 5, 1912.

NL 0436321 NN

Lockhart, Laurence William Maxwell, 1831-1882.
... Fair to see. A novel. By Lawrence W. M. Lockhart ... New York, G. Munro, 1882.
79 p. 32½cm. (The seaside library. v. 60, no. 1211)

I. Title.
CA 9—1994 Unrev'd
Library of Congress PZ1.S44 vol. 60

NL 0436322 DLC

LOCKHART, Laurence William Maxwell, 1831-1882.
Fair to see. New edition.
Edinburgh. Blackwood. [189-?] Sm. 8°.

NL 0436323 MB

Lockhart, Laurence William Maxwell, 1831-1882.
Mine is thine, a novel... New edition. Edinburgh and London, William Blackwood & sons. n.d. 465 p.

NL 0436324 OClW

---

823 L812m Lockhart, Laurence William Maxwell, 1831-1882.
Mine is thine, a novel. Edinburgh, W. Blackwood, 1878.
3v. 21cm.

NL 0436325 IU MH

PZ3 .L81123 Mi Lockhart, Laurence William Maxwell, 1831-1882.
Mine is thine; a novel, by Laurence W. M. Lockhart. Copyright ed. ... Leipzig, Bernhard Tauchnitz, 1878.
2 v. in 1. 15cm. (Half-title: Collection of British authors. Tauchnitz edition. v. 1776-1777)

NL 0436326 MB NjP NIC

Lockhart, Laurence William Maxwell, 1831-1882.
... Mine is thine. A novel. By L. W. M. Lockhart. New York, G. Munro, 1878.
59 p. illus. 32½cm. (The seaside library. v. 19, no. 376)
Caption title.

I. Title.
CA 9—1993 Unrev'd
Library of Congress PZ3.L8114M

NL 0436327 DLC

VOLUME 337

PR4891 .L43 M5 Lockhart, Laurence William Maxwell, 1831-1882.
Mine is thine; a novel. New York, Harper, 1878.
186p.

With this is bound Payn, James. By Proxy. New York, 1878; and Besant, Sir Walter. By Celia's arbour. Toronto, 1878.

NL 0436328 NcU PPL NN MH MB

Lockhart, Laurence William Maxwell, 1831-1882.
A night with the volunteers of Strathkinahan.
(In Tales from Blackwood. New series. No. 2. Edinburgh. [1879.])

K4765 — T.r.

NL 0436329 MB

Lockhart, Laurence William Maxwell, 1831-1882.
A night with the volunteers of Strathkinahan.
(In Tales from Blackwood. New series No. 2. Leipzig. 1880.)

NL 0436330 MB

Lockhart, Laurence William Maxwell, 1831-1882.
A night with the volunteers of Strathkinahan.
(In Tales from Blackwood. Series I, vol. 2. New York. 1905)

NL 0436331 MB

Lockhart, Laurence William Maxwell, 1831-1882.
Unlucky Tim Griffin, his love and his luck.
(In Tales from "Blackwood." New series. No. 8, pp. 56-137. Edinburgh. [1879.])

Δ1082 — T.r.

NL 0436332 MB

---

qM788 L811b Lockhart, Lee M.
The Lockhart band-class method, by Lee M. Lockhart & Edmund M. Goehring. New York, M. Witmark c1933-
v. 31cm.

NL 0436333 IU

Lockhart, Lee M.
Bugles and drums; a class method for these instruments combined... New York, M. Witmark & sons [c1938] 32 p. illus. 26cm.

1. Bugle and drum—Studies and exercises.
2. Drum—Studies and exercises.

NL 0436334 NN OO OCl

Lockhart, Lee M.
From timpette to drum, by Lee M. Lockhart ... Los Angeles, Calif., L. M. Lockhart [1943]
16 p. illus. (incl. music) 11½ x 15½cm.
Instructions for playing the timpette.

1. Drum—Methods. I. Title.

44-31521

Library of Congress MT662.L85

NL 0436335 DLC

Lockhart, Lee M., arr.
Sarabande from Oboe concerto
see under Händel, Georg Friedrich, 1685-1759.

787.07 L816l

Lockhart, Lee M.
The Lockhart string-class method. Teacher's score. New York, Witmark [c1938]

score (111 p.) 31cm.

1. Stringed instruments - Instruction and study. 2. Stringed instruments - Methods.

NL 0436337 FU CoU

Lockhart, Lee M.
Valse fantaisie, arranged for band
see under Glinka, Mikhail Ivanovich, 1804-1857.

Lockhart, Leonard Phipps.
A short manual of industrial hygiene for managers, foremen, forewomen and industrial supervisors generally, by Leonard P. Lockhart... With a foreword by the Rt. Hon. Lord Invernairn. London: J. Murray [, 1927]. xiv, 114 p. illus. 12°.
Contains bibliographies.

340810A. 1. Hygiene, Industrial.
N. Y. P. L. December 28, 1927

NL 0436339 NN CLU ICRL DNLM NcU PPC OU ICU

Lockhart, Leonora Wilhelmina.
Der Basic English Lehrer; ein Lehrbuch für Europäer, von L. W. Lockhart... Übers. von W. Repton. Bilder von James Forsyth. London, Basic English pub. co., 1951. xx,370 p. illus.,maps. 21cm.

1. Basic English.

NL 0436340 NN

Lockhart, Leonora Wilhelmina.

Ogden, Charles Kay, 1889-
Basic English versus the artificial languages, by C. K. Ogden; with contributions by Paul D. Hugon ... and L. W. Lockhart ... London, K. Paul, Trench, Trubner & co. ltd., 1935.

Lockhart, Leonora Wilhelmina.
Basic for economics, by L. W. Lockhart ... London, K. Paul, Trench, Trubner & co., ltd., 1933.
139 p. front. (fold. tab.) 15½cm. (*Half-title:* Psyche miniatures. General series, no. 57)
Consists of examples from the writings of noted economists put into Basic, selected by Prof. Sargant Florence. *cf.* p. 7.

1. Basic English. 2. English language—Text-books for foreigners. 3. Language, Universal. 4. Economics. I. Title.

34-551

Library of Congress PE1073.5.Z9L58
[a41d1] [330.1] 428.2

NL 0436342 DLC PHC ViU MB OCl

Lockhart, Leonora Wilhelmina.
Basic picture talks, by L. W. Lockhart ... Pictures by James Forsyth. Cambridge [Eng.] The Basic English publishing company, 1942.
viii, 116 p. illus. 25cm.
"Put into Basic from The shape of things to come."

1. Basic English. 2. English language—Conversation and phrase books. 3. English language—Text-books for foreigners. I. Title.

44-4313

Library of Congress PE1073.5.L6
428.25

NL 0436343 DLC OCl OClW

Lockhart, Leonora Wilhelmina, 1906-
The Basic teacher, a course for European students. Pictures by James Forsyth. London, Basic English Pub. Co., 1950.
xiv, 374 p. illus. 21 cm.

1. Basic English. I. Title.
PE1073.5.L62 1950 428.25 50-54613

NL 0436344 DLC NN

Lockhart, Leonora Wilhelmina.
The Basic traveller and other examples of Basic English, by L. W. Lockhart ... with an introduction by C. K. Ogden ... London, K. Paul, Trench, Trubner & co. ltd., 1931.
119 p. fold. front. 15½ cm. (*Half-title:* Psyche miniatures. General series, no. 34)
Using a limited vocabulary selected to form an international auxiliary language for all who do not already speak English.

1. English language—Text-books for foreigners. 2. Language, Universal. 3. Basic English. I. Title.

PE1073.5.Z9L6 428.25 33—22421

NL 0436345 DLC OrPR OCl CU NIC

Lockhart, Leonora Wilhelmina.
The Basic way reading books. London, Evans brothers ltd. [193- ?]

2 pt. illus. 19.5 cm.
"The Basic books; with the authority of the Orthological institute.

NL 0436346 MH

428.25 L81ba Lockhart, Leonora Wilhelmina.
The Basic way reading books, authorized by the Orthological institute... London, Evans [1940-41]
2v. illus. D.

For use with The Basic way to English.

NL 0436347 IaU

Lockhart, Leonora Wilhelmina.

Frank, Leonhard, 1882-
Carl and Anna, by Leonhard Frank; translated into Basic English by L. W. Lockhart. London, K. Paul, Trench, Trubner, & co. ltd., 1930.

VOLUME 337

408.9
L811e LOCKHART, Leonora Wilhelmina.
Everyday Basic ("The Basic traveller"). Examples of Basic English... London, K. Paul, Trench, Trubner & co. ltd., 1934.

133 p. fold. front. 16cm. (Half-title: Psyche miniatures. General series, no.34)

1931 ed. has title: The Basic traveller.
1. English language. Text-books for foreigners. 2. Language, Universal 3. Basic English. I. Title.

NL 0436349 MnU ViU CU MB

Lockhart, Leonora Wilhelmina.
Everday Basic ("The Basic traveller") Examples of Basic English. London, Kegan Paul, 1939.

133 p. fold. table. (Psyche miniatures. General series, 34)

NL 0436350 MH MiU

Lockhart, Leonora Wilhelmina.

Stevenson, Robert Louis, 1850–1894.
Keäwe's bottle, by Robert Louis Stevenson: being "The bottle imp" put into Basic English by L. W. Lockhart ... London, K. Paul, Trench, Trubner & co. ltd., 1935.

Lockhart, Leonora Wilhelmina.

Garnett, James Clerk Maxwell, 1880–
The organization of peace, by Maxwell Garnett ... put into Basic by L. W. Lockhart ... London, K. Paul, Trench, Trubner & co. ltd., 1933.

Lockhart, Leonora Wilhelmina.
Word economy, a study in applied linguistics, by L. W. Lockhart. London, K. Paul, Trench, Trubner & co., ltd., 1931.

94 p. 15½cm. (*Half-title:* Psyche miniatures. General series. no. 38)

1. Vocabulary. 2. Language and languages. 3. English language—Word formation. I. Title.

Library of Congress P305.L6 34–2683
413

NL 0436353 DLC OrPR CLU CU OC1 OO OU NN

Lockhart, Louise, 1910–
A born nurse, by Lucile Yarbrough [pseud.] Macon, Ga., Printed by the J. W. Burke Co. [1950]

142 p. 23 cm.

I. Title.

PZ3.L811413Bo 50–39076

NL 0436354 DLC

Lockhart, Lovine.
Number helps, including number games, number rimes, number songs, sense-training exercises, and speed and accuracy tests, by Lovine Lockhart ... A. C. Eldredge ... J. C. Brown ... Chicago, New York, Rand, McNally & company [©1924]

xxii, 120 p. illus. 19½cm.

1. Arithmetic—Study and teaching. I. Eldredge, Albert C., joint author. II. Brown, Joseph Clifton, 1879– joint author. III. Title.

Library of Congress QA135.L65 24—5597

NL 0436355 DLC Or PPI PPPL OC1 OO OOxM OC1BE ODW

Lockhart, Luther Bynum, 1881–
American lubricants, from the standpoint of the consumer, by L. B. Lockhart ... Easton, Pa., The Chemical publishing company; [etc., etc.] 1918.

3 p. l., v–ix, [1], 236 p. illus., diagrs. 23cm.
"References" at end of some of the chapters.

1. Lubrication and lubricants. I. Title.

Library of Congress TJ1077.L6 18—5522

NL 0436356 DLC MB NN ICJ PPF MiU DAL PP Nc IdU-SB Or IdU

Lockhart, Luther Bynum, 1881–
American lubricants from the standpoint of the consumer, by L. B. Lockhart ... 2d ed., rev. and enl. Easton, Pa., The Chemical publishing company; [etc., etc.] 1920.

3 p. l., v–xi, [1], 341 p. incl. illus., tables, diagrs. 23cm.
References at end of some of the chapters.

1. Lubrication and lubricants. I. Title.

Library of Congress TJ1077.L6 1920 20—17377

NL 0436357 DLC CU ICRL OrPR NcRS PPEFH OU MiU OO ICJ MB MiHM

Lockhart, Luther Bynum, 1881–
American lubricants from the standpoint of the consumer, by L. B. Lockhart ... 3d ed. Easton, Pa., The Chemical publishing co., 1927.

3 p. l., v–x p., 1 l., 408 p. incl. illus., tables, diagrs. 24cm.
References at end of some of the chapters.

1. Lubrication and lubricants. I. Title.

Library of Congress TJ1077.L6 1927 27–19135

NL 0436358 DLC WaE NIC PPSOPR NcRS OCU OLak OC1 OC1W PPEFH

Lockhart, Luther Bynum, 1881–
Oil bulletin. Inspection of illuminating oils. [Raleigh, 1910.] 23 p. 8°. (North Carolina. Agriculture Dept. Bull. v. 31, no. 8. Whole no. 140, supplement.)

1. Oils (Illuminating), U. S.: N. C.
N. Y. P. L. April 21, 1913.

NL 0436359 NN

Lockhart, Marion.
Standard cook book for all occasions, by Marion Lockhart; what to cook, how to cook, what to serve. New York, J. H. Sears & company, inc. [©1925]

iv, 115 p. 16½cm.

1. Cookery, American. I. Title.

Library of Congress TX715.L78 25–19774

NL 0436360 DLC OC1

[Lockhart, *Mrs.* Mary Jane (Freeman)]
W. P. Lockhart, merchant and preacher: a life story, comp. by his wife. With a preface by the Rev. Alexander Maclaren, D. D. London, Hodder and Stoughton, 1895.

xi, 263, [1] p. front. (port.) 21cm.
Subject entries: Lockhart, William Peddie, 1835–1893.
2–6142

NL 0436361 DLC

Lockhart, Myra R.
The basis of character, by Myra Lockhart. [In Essays of the Philosophy discussion club, University of British Columbia, 1929/32]
1 p.l., 11 p. 28.5 cm.
Typewritten on one side of page only.

NL 0436362 CaBVaU

Lockhart, Ninian.
The means of Christian edification, as taught and exemplified in the New Testament. 2d ed. Kirkcaldy, Birrell, 1843.
(4), 50 p. 8°.

NL 0436363 MB

Lockhart, Oliver Cary, 1879–
The assessment of intangible property in Ohio under the uniform rule, ... Madison, Wis., National tax association, 1914.
10 p.

Reprinted from Proceedings of the 7th annual conference of the National tax association.

NL 0436364 OU

Lockhart, Oliver Cary, 1879–
The development of interbank borrowing in the national system: 1869–1914 ... by Oliver Cary Lockhart ... [Chicago, 1921]

1 p. l., 42 p. 24½cm.
Thesis (PH. D.)--Cornell university, 1917.
"Reprinted from the Journal of political economy, vol. XXIX, nos. 2 and 3. February, March, 1921."

1. National banks—U. S. I. Title. II. Title: Interbank borrowing.

22–522
Library of Congress HG2557.L6
Cornell Univ. Libr.

NL 0436365 NIC OU NN DLC

Lockhart, Oliver Cary, 1879–
... The oölitic limestone industry of Indiana. By Oliver C. Lockhart ...

(*In* Indiana university studies. Bloomington, Ind., 1910. 22½cm. vol. I, no. 9, p. 71–110)
Caption title.

1. Limestone. 2. Quarries and quarrying—Indiana.

17–15031
Library of Congress AS36.I4 vol. 1, no. 9

NL 0436366 DLC ViU UU RPB OrU OC1 OO MiU OCU OU

Lockhart, Percy Clare Eliott-
see
Eliott-Lockhart, Percy Clare, 1867–1915.

VOLUME 337

LD3907 .E3 1950 .L6 Lockhart, Raymond John, 1896-
A comparative study to determine the merits of the Union Free School District and the Central School District plans of organization for the area now included in the Massapequa, Seaford, and Wantagh School districts. New York, 1949.
xi,208 typewritten leaves. fold. maps,tables,diagrs. 29cm.

Final document (Ed.D.) - New York University, School of Education, 195
Bibliography: p.207-208.

NL 0436369 NNU-W

Lockhart, Robert.
Today's method of the prevention of scarlet fever; comp. by Robert Lockhart, with the collaboration of Roger G. Perkins. n.d.

NL 0436370 OCl

Lockhart, Robert Douglas, 1894-
Living anatomy, a photographic atlas of muscles in action and surface contours. London, Faber and Faber [1948]
71 p. illus. 26 cm.

1. Muscles. 2. Anatomy, Human. I. Title.

QM151.L6 1948 612.74 48-23680*

NL 0436371 OrU-M DNLM DLC PPT OOxM NcU NcD CtY PSt CU CaBVaU

QM151 .L8 Lockhart, Robert Douglas, 1894-
Living anatomy, a photographic atlas of muscles in action and surface contours. New York, Oxford University Press, 1948.
71 p. illus.

1. Muscles. 2. Anatomy, Human.

NL 0436372 ICU OrAshS ViU OClSA OU

Lockhart, Robert Douglas, 1894-
Living anatomy, a photographic atlas of muscles in action and surface contours. [2d ed.] London, Faber and Faber [1950]
71 p. illus. 26 cm.

1. Muscles. 2. Anatomy, Human. I. Title.

[QM151.L] 612.74 A 51-8935
Wisconsin. Univ. Libr. for Library of Congress [5]

NL 0436373 WU DNLM

Lockhart, Robert Douglas, 1894-
Living anatomy, a photographic atlas of muscles in action and surface contours. [3d ed.] London, Faber and Faber [1952]
76 p., illus.

NL 0436374 ICJ PSt NNC-M PPJ DNLM CaBVa CaBVaU

612.74 L816L4 Lockhart, Robert Douglas, 1894-
Living anatomy; a photographic atlas of muscles in action and surface contours. [4th ed.] London, Faber and Faber [1955]
79p. (chiefly illus.) 25cm.

1. Muscle 2. Anatomy, Human I. Title.

NL 0436375 NBC OO NIC FU-HC CtY-M CU MiU

Lockhart, Robert Hamilton Bruce, 1887-
Als Diplomat, Bankmann und Journalist im Nachkriegseuropa. «Berechtigte Übersetzung aus dem Englischen von Franz Arens» Stuttgart Deutsche Verlags-Anstalt, 1935.
424 p.

1. Europe - Politics - 1918-1945. 2. Czechoslovak Republic - History. 3. Balkan Peninsula - History. 4. Central Europe. I. Title.

NL 0436376 WaU NN GA

Lockhart, Robert Hamilton Bruce, 1887-
Als Diplomat, Bankmann und Journalist im Nachkriegseuropa. [Berechtigte Übersetzung aus dem Englischen von Franz Arens] Stuttgart, Deutsche Verlags-Anstalt [1938]
424 p. 21 cm.
Translation of Retreat from glory.

1. Europe—Politics—1918-1945. 2. Czechoslovak Republic—Hist. 3. Balkan Peninsula—Hist. I. Title.

D443.L5515 940.5 50-50958

NL 0436377 DLC

Lockhart, *Sir* Robert Hamilton Bruce, 1887-
Britain and Europe. Copenhagen, Langkjærs bogtr., 1951.
29 p. illus. 21 cm.

1. Gt. Brit.—Pol. & govt.—1945- —Addresses, essays, lectures. 2. Gt. Brit.—For. rel.—1936- —Addresses, essays, lectures. I. Title.

DA588.L6 *942.085 942.084 52-35432 ‡

NL 0436378 DLC NN

Lockhart, Robert Hamilton Bruce, 1887-
British agent, by R. H. Bruce Lockhart: New York and London, G. P. Putnam's sons, 1932.
7 p. l., 3-354 p. facsims. 22½cm.
Two of the facsimiles accompanied by guard sheets with translations. London edition (Putnam) has title: Memoirs of a British agent.

1. Gt. Brit.—For. rel.—Russia. 2. Russia—For. rel.—Gt. Brit. 3. European war, 1914-1918—Russia. 4. Bolshevism—Russia. I. Title.

NL 0436379 ViU IU PPD

942.083 L811B1 1933 LOCKHART, ROBERT HAMILTON BRUCE, 1887-
British agent, by R.H. Bruce Lockhart; with an introduction by Hugh Walpole. Garden City, N.Y., Garden City publishing co., inc. [c1933]
7p.ℓ.,3-354p. facsims. 21cm.
London edition (Putnam) has title: Memoirs of a British agent.
1. Gt. Brit. - For. rel. - Russia. 2. Russia - For. rel. - Gt. Brit. 3. European war, 1914-1918 - Russia. 4. Bolshevism - Russia. I. Title. II. Lockhart, Robert Hamilton Bruce, 1887- Memoirs of a British agent.

NL 0436380 MH TxU DLC WaWW OrP CaBVa MtBC OkU MnCS

B L816 Lockhart, Robert Hamilton Bruce, 1887-
British agent. N.Y., Putnam, 1933.

NL 0436381 KyU-A KyLxT KyLx

Lockhart, Robert Hamilton Bruce, 1887-
British agent, by R. H. Bruce Lockhart; with an introduction by Hugh Walpole. New York and London, G. P. Putnam's sons, 1933.
7 p. l., 3-354 p. facsims. 22½cm.
Two of the facsimiles accompanied by guard sheets with translations. London edition (Putnam) has title: Memoirs of a British agent.

1. Gt. Brit.—For. rel.—Russia. 2. Russia—For. rel.—Gt. Brit. 3. European war, 1914-1918—Russia. 4. Bolshevism—Russia. I. Title.

Library of Congress DA47.65.L6 1933 33—4369
——— Copy 2.
Copyright A 59645 [33p5] 923.242

NL 0436382 UU TU OrSaW NcD NcRS CoU KyU KyLx FTaSU PBm PPA PU OO OCU OCl MiU OOxM OClU PJA MB NN Or WaTC OrPR WaSp IdB IdU WaT WaE MeB ViU NjR PPGi DLC WaS OrU OrMonO OrStbM MtU Wa OrCS

Lockhart, Robert Hamilton Bruce, 1887-
British agent, by R. H. Bruce Lockhart; with an introduction by Hugh Walpole. New York and London, G. P. Putnam's sons, 1933. [i.e. 1934]
7 p. l., 3-354 p. facsims. 22½cm.
Two of the facsimiles accompanied by guard sheets with translations. London edition (Putnam) has title: Memoirs of a British agent.

1. Gt. Brit.—For. rel.—Russia. 2. Russia—For. rel.—Gt. Brit. 3. European war, 1914-1918—Russia. 4. Bolshevism—Russia. I. Title.

NL 0436383 ViU

Lockhart, Robert Hamilton Bruce, 1887-
British agent, by R. H. Bruce Lockhart; with an introduction by Hugh Walpole. Garden City, N. Y., Garden City publishing co., inc. [1936]
7 p. l., 3-354 p. facsims. 21cm. [Star books]

1. Gt. Brit.—For. rel.—Russia. 2. Russia—For. rel.—Gt. Brit. 3. European war, 1914-1918—Russia. 4. Bolshevism—Russia. I. Title.

Library of Congress DA47.65.L6 1936 36-10047
——— Copy 2. 923.242

NL 0436384 DLC OClCC KU

Lockhart, Robert Hamilton Bruce, 1887-
"British agent" screen play
see under Doyle, Laird.

Lockhart, Robert Hamilton Bruce.1887-
Cestou ke slave; vzpominky britskeho diplomata. Praha, Borovy, 1936.
400,[1] p.

Memoirs of a British agent.
Bohemian.

NL 0436386 OCl

Lockhart, Robert Hamilton Bruce, 1887-
Comes the reckoning. London, Putnam [1947]
384 p. 22 cm.

1. World War, 1939-1945—Personal narratives, English. 2. World War, 1939-1945—Propaganda. 3. World War, 1939-1945—Diplomatic history. I. Title.

D811.5.L563 940.548142 48-2739*

NL 0436387 OO OU MB NN MH CtY NcU NcRS CLSU OrU NBuU TU NIC DLC CaBVaU CaBViP WaSpG CaBVa GU IaU PU

VOLUME 337

Lockhart, Robert Hamilton Bruce, 1887-
(Egy brit diplomata emlekei; forditotta Juhasz Andor. [Budapest] Revai, n.d.
398 [1] p

British agent.
Hungarina.

NL 0436388 OCl

Lockhart, Robert Hamilton Bruce, 1887-
Guns or butter, by R. H. Bruce Lockhart ... Boston, Little, Brown and company, 1938.
4 p. l., [3]-439 p. 23cm.
"First edition."

1. Europe—Politics—1914- I. Title.
Library of Congress D443.L54 38-27942
——— Copy 2.
Copyright A 122534 [15-10] 940.5

PBm PPFr PP PPL
NcD IdU OrP WaE WaS DAU MB MH NIC OrU Or Wa WaSp NN
NL 0436389 DLC ILfC MiEM OCU OO OEac OCl OLak OU

Lockhart, Robert Hamilton Bruce, 1887-
... Guns or butter; war countries and peace countries of Europe revisited. London, Putnam [1938]
5 p. l., 3-382 p., 1 l. 23cm.
At head of title: R. H. Bruce Lockhart.
Map on lining-papers.
"First published October, 1938."

1. Europe—Politics—1914- I. Title.
39-51
Library of Congress D443.L54 1938 a
Copyright A ad int. 24378 940.5

NL 0436390 DLC PPT GU CaBVa CtY CaBVaU

940.5
L816g
Lockhart, Robert Hamilton Bruce, 1887-
Guns of butter; war countries and peace countries of Europe revisited. Toronto, McClelland & Stewart [c1938]
382 p. maps (on lin ing-papers)

1. Europe - Politics - 1914-
I. Title.

NL 0436391 CaQML

Lockhart, *Sir* Robert Hamilton Bruce, 1887-
Jan Masaryk, a personal memoir. [London] Dropmore Press [1951]
80 p. plate. 26 cm.
"500 copies have been printed and numbered 1-500 of which 100 copies have been specially bound and signed by the author ... Number 135."

1. Masaryk, Jan Garrigue, 1886-1948.
DB217.M29L6 923.2437 51-6819

NL 0436392 DLC NN MH CaBVa Wa

DB217
.M29L6
Lockhart, Sir Robert Hamilton Bruce, 1887-
Jan Masaryk, a personal memoir. [New York] Philosophical Library [1951]
80 p. plate. 26 cm.

1. Masaryk, Jan Garrigue, 1886-1948.

Wa WaT IdPI CaBVaU
NL 0436393 TU PSt MU ViU N NcU NNC MB OrU OrP Or

DB 217
.M33 L 85
LOCKHART,Sir ROBERT HAMILTON BRUCE,1887-
Jan Masaryk; osobní vzpomínky. V Londýně, Ústav Dra Edvarda Beneše [c1952]
73 p. illus.

Translation by Milan Smutný of Jan Masaryk a personal memoir.

1. Masaryk,Jan Garrigue,1886-1948.

NL 0436394 InU

Lockhart, *Sir* Robert Hamilton Bruce, 1887-
The marines were there; the story of the Royal Marines in the Second World War. London, Putnam [1950]
229 p. maps (part col.) 23 cm.

1. Gt. Brit. Royal Marine Forces. 2. World War, 1939-1945—Regimental histories—Gt. Brit.—Royal Marine Forces. I. Title.
D770.L6 940.545942 50-9822

NL 0436395 DLC KU MiU CaBVa CaBViP NcD

DA
47.65
L81bF
Lockhart, Robert Hamilton Bruce, 1887-
Mémoires d'un agent Britannique en Russie (1912-1918) Traduit de l'anglais par Lucien Thomas. Paris, Payot, 1933.
365,[2] p. (Collection de mémoires, études et documents pour servir a l'histoire de la guerre mondiale)

Translation of Memoirs of a British agent.

1. Gt.Brit. - For. rel. - Russia. 2. Russia - For. rel. - Gt.Brit. 3. European war, 1914-1918 - Russia. 4. Communism - Russia. I.Title.

NL 0436396 CLU

940.48642 L57 1932
Lockhart, Robert Hamilton Bruce, 1887-
... Memoirs of a British agent; being an account of the author's early life in many lands and of his official mission to Moscow in 1918. London, Putnam [1932]
355 p. facsims.

American edition has title: British agent.

NL 0436397 CaOTP

Lockhart, Robert Hamilton Bruce, 1887-
... Memoirs of a British agent; being an account of the author's early life in many lands and of his official mission to Moscow in 1918. London and New York, Putnam [1932]
2 p. l., vii-xi, 355 p. facsims. 22½cm.
At head of title: R. H. Bruce Lockhart.
"First published November 1932. Reprinted November 1932."
American edition (New York and London, G. P. Putnam's sons) has title: British agent.

1. Gt. Brit.—For. rel.—Russia. 2. Russia—For. rel.—Gt. Brit. 3. European war, 1914-1918—Russia. 4. Communism—Russia. I. Title.
33-2057 Revised
Library of Congress DA47.65.L6 1932 a
[r41n2] 923.242

NL 0436398 DLC OrP CaBVa CaBVaU LU MiU DN NN PPL

Lockhart, Robert Hamilton Bruce, 1887-
Memoirs of a British agent; being an account of the author's early life in many lands, and of his official mission to Moscow in 1918. Toronto, McClelland & Stewart [1934]
xi, 355 p.

NL 0436399 CaBVaU

Lockhart, *Sir* Robert Hamilton Bruce, 1887-
My Europe. London, Putnam [1952]
273 p. 22 cm.

1. Europe—Politics—1918-1945. 2. Communism—Russia. 3. Europe—Politics—1945- I. Title.
D443.L545 940.5 53-455 ‡

MH NN MB OrU FTaSU CaBVa CaBVaU Or CaBViP OrP
NL 0436400 DLC ILfC WaT WaS NcU NcD OO ViU CtY MiD

Lockhart, Robert Hamilton Bruce, 1887-
My rod my comfort; with wood engravings by J. Gaastra. London, Dropmore Press, 1949.
75 p. plates. 29 cm.

1. Fishing—Europe. I. Title.
SH439.L84 799.12 49-29518*

NL 0436401 DLC NjP CtY CaBVaU

Lockhart, Robert Hamilton Bruce, 1887-
... My Scottish youth. London, Putnam [1937]
5 p. l., 3-372 p., 1 l. 23 cm.
At head of title: R. H. Bruce Lockhart.
Map on lining-papers.
American edition (New York, G. P. Putnam's sons) has title: A son of Scotland.

I. Title.
PR6023.O3Z5 1937 923.242 38-4296

TxU LU NcD
NL 0436402 DLC ILfC CaBVaU CLSU ScU TU PPC PP CtY

Lockhart, Robert Hamilton Bruce, 1887-
Navrat do Malajska. Praha, Borovy, 1937.
435,[1] p. map.

Return to Malaya.
Z anglickeho originalu prelozil Jaroslav Kolarik.
Bohemian.

NL 0436403 OCl

LOCKHART, ROBERT HAMILTON BRUCE, 1887-
...Retreat from glory. London: Putnam [1934] 372 p. 22½cm.

Map on end papers.

754345A. 1. No subject. I. Title.

NL 0436404 NN NjP PPJ

Lockhart, Robert Hamilton Bruce, 1887-
Retreat from glory, by R. H. Bruce Lockhart. New York, G. P. Putnam's sons, 1934.
5 p. l., 3-348 p. front. (port.) 23cm

1. Europe—Politics—1914- 2. Czechoslovak republic—Hist. 3. Balkan peninsula—Hist. I. Title.
34-32697
Library of Congress D443.L55
——— Copy 2.
[5-5-5]

NcRS OClUr FTaSU WaE OrP WaT IdU WaSp IdB Or WaWW
MiU OO MB NN OU OCl OEac OCU DN ViU PSC PPL MeB PP
NL 0436405 DLC WaTC IdPI WaSpG OrU NcD OrCS NIC AAP

VOLUME 337

D
443
L55
1934

Lockhart, Sir Robert Hamilton Bruce, 1887-
Retreat from glory ⌊by⌋ R.H. Bruce Lockhart. Toronto, McClelland & Stewart ⌊1934⌋
367 p. 23 cm.

1. Europe--Politics--1918-1945. 2. Czechoslovak Republic--Hist.--1918-1938. 3. Balkan Peninsula--Hist. I. Title.

NL 0436406 LU CaBVa

940.5
L81r
1935

Lockhart, Robert Hamilton Bruce, 1887-
Retreat from glory. ⌊2d ed.⌋ London, Putnam ⌊1935⌋
372p. 23cm.

Map on lining papers.

1. Europe--Politics--1914- 2. Czechoslovak Republic--Hist. 3. Balkan peninsula--Hist. I. Title.

NL 0436407 IU

Lockhart, Robert Hamilton Bruce, 1887-
Retreat from glory. [2d ed.] London, Putnam ⌊1937]
372 p. map. 21 cm.

This ed. first published 1935.

1. Europe - Politics - 1914- 2. Czechoslovak republic - Hist. 3. Balkan peninsula - Hist. I. Title.

NL 0436408 CaBVaU

D
443
L55
1938

Lockhart, Robert Hamilton Bruce, 1887-
Retreat from glory. New York, Garden City Pub. Co., 1938.
348 p. 21cm.

1. Europe - Politics - 1914- 2. Czechoslovak Republic - Hist. 3. Balkan peninsula - Hist. I. Title.

NL 0436409 CoU KU KyLx OkU

Lockhart, Robert Hamilton Bruce, 1887-
Retreat from glory. New York, Putnam ⌊194-⌋
348 p. illus. O.

NL 0436410 KyLx

Lockhart, Robert Hamilton Bruce, 1887-
... Return to Malaya. London, Putnam ⌊1936⌋
5 p. l., 3-426 p., 1 l. 23cm.
At head of title: R. H. Bruce Lockhart.
Maps on lining-papers.

1. Malay archipelago—Descr. & trav. I. Title.
37-2510
Library of Congress DS601.L6 1936 a
919.1

NL 0436411 DLC NN IdU NcD CaBVaU CaBVa Wa WaE CoU CaQML TxU KyLoU

Lockhart, Robert Hamilton Bruce, 1887-
... Return to Malaya. New York, G. P. Putnam's sons, 1936.
4 p. l., 3-376 p. 23cm.
At head of title: R. H. Bruce Lockhart.
Maps on lining-papers.

1. Malay archipelago—Descr. & trav. I. Title.
36-35173
Library of Congress DS601.L6
——— Copy 2.
Copyright A 100771 919.1

NL 0436412 DLC ILfC NcU CoU NN ViU MB OClND OO OCl OCU OU PBa PPA PP PV VU NIC IEN GU NSyU WaSp OrP Or IdB OrU WaS WaT OrCS OrStbM

Lockhart, *Sir* Robert Hamilton Bruce, 1887-
Scotch, the whisky of Scotland in fact and story. London, Putnam ⌊1951⌋
184 p. illus. 23 cm.

1. Whiskey. I. Title.
TP605.L6 663.5 51-14860 ‡

NL 0436413 DLC OrP WaS CaBVa CaBViP CU OKentU ScU MB FMU CaBVaU NN MH

4A
9953

LOCKHART, Sir ROBERT HAMILTON BRUCE, 1887-
Scotch; the whiskey of Scotland in fact and story. London, Putnam [1952]
184p. 23cm.

Illus. end-papers.

NL 0436414 ICN MB

DB 217
.B3 L 8

LOCKHART, ROBERT HAMILTON BRUCE, 1887-
The second exile of Eduard Beneš. ⌊n.p. n.d.⌋
35-59 p.

Detached from Slavonic Review.

1. Beneš, Edvard, pres. Czechoslovak Republic, 1884-1948. I. Tc.

NL 0436415 InU

Lockhart, Robert Hamilton Bruce, 1887-
A son of Scotland ⌊by⌋ R. H. Bruce Lockhart. New York, G. P. Putnam's sons, 1938.
5 p. l., 3-325 p. 23cm.
London edition (Putnam) has title: My Scottish youth.

I. Title.
38-27153
Library of Congress PR6023.O325 1938
——— Copy 2.
Copyright A 114276

NL 0436416 DLC ILfC NN PPFr PU PBa OClh OU OCU OCl OO GU KyLx NIC WaE OrP OrU WaSp OrCS OrSaW WaWW WaS WaT CaBVa

---

Lockhart, Robert Hamilton Bruce, 1887-
Ustup ze slavy. Druhe vydani. Praha, F. Borovy, 1935.
411, [1]p. front.

Retreat from glory.
Prelozil Jaroslav Kolarik.

NL 0436417 OCl

Lockhart, Robert Hamilton Bruce, 1887-
Vom Wirbel erfasst, Bekenntnisse eines britischen Diplomaten. Übersetzt von A. Dombrowsky. Stuttgart, Deutsche Verlags-Anstalt ⌊19—⌋
335 p. 21 cm.
Translation of British agent.

1. Gt. Brit.—For. rel.—Russia. 2. Russia—For. rel.—Gt. Brit. 3. European War, 1914-1918—Russia. 4. Communism—Russia. I. Title.
DA47.65.L614 923.242 50-33252

NL 0436418 DLC

Lockhart, Robert Hamilton Bruce, 1887-
Vom Wirbel erfasst; Bekenntnisse eines britischen Diplomaten; übersetzt von A. Dombrowsky. Stuttgart: Deutsche Verlags-Anstalt, 1933. 336 p. 8°.
Translation of Memoirs of a British agent.

1. Lockhart, Robert H. Bruce. 2. Russia—Hist., 20th cent. 3. Title.
N. Y. P. L. August 22, 1933

NL 0436419 NN

Lockhart, *Sir* Robert Hamilton Bruce, 1887-
What happened to the Czechs? London, Batchworth Press ⌊1953⌋
48 p. illus. 18 cm. (Background books)

1. Czechoslovak Republic—Hist. I. Title.
DB215.L65 943.7 54-17755 ‡

NL 0436420 DLC CaBVaU MH NN NcU IU OU

Lockhart, Robert Hamilton Bruce, 1887-
Wieder in Malaya. ⌊Aus dem Englischen übertragen von Rudolf von Scholtz und W. E. Süskind⌋ Stuttgart, Deutsche Verlags-Anstalt, 1937.
423 p. map (on lining paper) 21 cm.

1. Malay Archipelago—Descr. & trav. I. Title.
DS601.L614 919.1 50-46115

NL 0436421 DLC CaBVaU

Lockhart, *Sir* Robert Hamilton Bruce, 1887-
Your England. London, Putnam, 1955.
303 p. 22 cm.

1. Gt. Brit.—Descr. & trav. I. Title.
DA630.L57 914.2 55-4342 ‡

NL 0436422 DLC CaBVa CaBViP OrMonO OrU KU OrU CU MB NN MH PP ILfC WaWW

Lockhart, *Sir* Robert Hamilton Bruce, 1887-
Your England. New York, Putnam ⌊1955⌋
303 p. 22 cm.

1. Gt. Brit.—Descr. & trav. I. Title.
[DA630] 914.2 56-3124 ‡
Printed for A. B. P. by Library of Congress ⌊20⌋

NL 0436423 ViU FMU ICU MiU OOxM OCl PPL WaS Wa OrP Or

Lockhart, Theodore F.

Dominica. *Registrar-general's office.*
Dominica. Census taken November 1871, tables. Roseau, Printed at the New Dominican office for the contractor for the public printing, 1872.

VOLUME 337

Lockhart, Thomas.

[Ashburton, John Dunning, *baron*] 1731-1783.
Archibald James Edward Stewart, alias Douglas, under the assumed character of son of the deceased Lady Jane Douglas, appellant. His Grace George James duke of Hamilton and Brandon, marquis of Douglas, &c. and Lord Douglas Hamilton, and their guardians, Sir Hew Dalrymple, baronet, &c., respondents. Case of the respondents, the Duke of Hamilton, &c. [Edinburgh? 1768?]

Lockhart, Thomas E., joint author.

Vincent, Harry Dunham, 1877-
Twentieth century guide to correct pronunciation. A careful selection of over 1000 common words frequently mispronounced, with brief definitions and diacritical markings. For use in homes, grammar schools, high schools, normal schools, and colleges. By H. D. Vincent ... and T. E. Lockhart ... New York, Chicago, Atkinson, Mentzer & company [c1922]

Ga
CT275
B434L8 Lockhart, V. D.
Madison Bell: a biographical sketch of his early life and education, with a brief account of his military and official career. Atlanta, Byrd & Pattillo [1887]
75 p. port. 21cm.

1. Bell, Madison, 1836-1896.

NL 0436427 GU

369.17
C748 Lockhart, W.G.
Lee at Orange Court-House.
Confederate Veteran Vol.XI, p. 268 (Prose)

NL 0436428 ViLxW

Lockhart, Mrs. N. P.
see
Lockhart, Mrs. Mary Jane (Freeman)

Lockhart, Walter S
The Guidherts of Moat Brae; being some old-time echoes of a Lowland town, by Walter S. Lockhart... London: H. Cranton, Ltd., 1925. 227 p. 12°.

229467A. 1. Fiction, Scottish. 2. Title.
N. Y. P. L. March 30, 1926

NL 0436430 NN

Lockhart, Walter Samuel, 1874-
A handbook of the law of evidence for North Carolina, by Walter S. Lockhart ... Cincinnati, The W. H. Anderson company [c1915]
1 p. l., v-xli, 384 p. 18½cm. $5.00
Interleaved.

1. Evidence (Law)—North Carolina. I. Title.
Library of Congress 15-15349

NL 0436431 DLC NcD

Lockhart, Walter Samuel, 1874-
A handbook of the law of evidence for North Carolina, by Walter S. Lockhart ... 2d ed., rev., extended and enl. by the author, with the assistance of Richmond Rucker ... Cincinnati, The W. H. Anderson company [c1931]
xvii, 540 p. 20cm.
"Table of cases": p. 413-438.

1. Evidence (Law)—North Carolina. I. Rucker, Richmond, ed. II. Title.
Library of Congress 31-3412

NL 0436432 DLC NcD TU NcRS MH-L

M(055)
U585n
50-1R-4 Lockhart, Wilbur M.
Offshore winds along the west coast of the United States. Washington, D.C., 1946.
12p. illus., charts. 27cm. (U.S. Office of Naval Operations. NAVAER 50-1R-4)

Mimeographed.
Revised ed.

NL 0436433 DAS

M(055)
U585n
50-1R-125 Lockhart, Wilbur M.
Practical aids in weather map analysis. Washington, D.C., Govt.print.off., 1944.
v, 50p. illus., charts, diagrs. 27cm. (U.S. Office of Naval Operations. NAVAER 50-1r-125)

Reprinted by U.S. Office of Naval Operations as its NAVAER 50-1R-125.

NL 0436434 DAS

Lockhart, Wilfred Cornett, 1906- *ed.*
In such an age; younger voices in the Canadian church. Toronto, McClelland & Stewart [1951]
215 p. 22 cm.

1. Theology—Addresses, essays, lectures. I. Title.
BR123.L67 1951 230.04 51-8949 ‡

NL 0436435 DLC CaBViP

Lockhart, Wilfred Cornett, 1906-
John Fletcher, evangelist, by Wilfred C. Lockhart ... London, The Epworth press (E. C. Barton) [1939]
27, [1] p. 18½ cm. (*Half-title:* Wesley bicentenary manuals, no. 11)
"First published in 1939."

1. Fletcher, John William, 1729-1785.
BX8495.F6L6 922.742 40-332 rev

NL 0436436 DLC

4
Rare
Book Lockhart, Will.
The secrets of advanced prestidigitation. Plaistow, E., Printed by W. Bull, 1894.
29 p.

NL 0436437 DLC-P4

Lockhart, Will P
see Lockhart, William Pemberton, 1863-

Lockhart, Sir William, 1621-1676.
A letter sent from Col. Will. Lockhart, dated at Dunkirk, Decemb.31. 1659. Superscribed, for ... William Lenthall ... Speaker of the Parliament of the common-wealth of England ... Read in Parliament, January 3. 1659. London, Printed by J. Streater, and J. Macock, 1659.
8 p. 19cm.

Describes the author's procedure as Commander of Dunkirk.
From the Isaac Foot collection.
Wing L-2779

NL 0436439 CLU-C MH CtY

Lockhart, William, 1811-1896.
The medical missionary in China: a narrative of twenty years' experience. By William Lockhart ... London, Hurst and Blackett, 1861.
xi, 404 p. col. front. 22½cm.

1. Missions, Medical. 2. China—Soc. life & cust. 3. Medicine—China.
4-22418
Library of Congress R722.L81

WaU ViU MSaE OCl MnU ICJ
NL 0436440 DLC NIC ICRL MBCo CU CtY PU PPL PPC

Lockhart, William, 1811-1896.
The medical missionary in China: a narrative of twenty years' experience. By William Lockhart ... 2d ed. London, Hurst and Blackett, 1861.
xi, 404 p. col. front. 22½cm. 2-25832

Library of Congress, no.

NL 0436441 DLC DNLM MB

Wason
DS703
Z109 Lockhart, William, 1811-1896.
On the importance of opening the navigation of the Yang-tse-kiang, and the changes that have lately taken place in the bed of the Yellow river, &c. [London, 1858]
[201]-209 p. 22cm.
Detached from the Proceedings of the Royal Geographical Society of London, vol. 2, no. 4, July, 1858.
In vol. lettered: Pamphlets relating to China. Vol. IX.
1. Yangtze River. 2. Hwang ho.

NL 0436442 NIC

Lockhart, William, 1820-1892.
Cardinal Newman; reminiscences of 50 years since, by one of his oldest living disciples... London, 1891.

NL 0436443 PPL

LOCKHART, William, 1820-1892.
The chasuble. Its genuine form and size.
Lond. Burns & O. 1891. 20 pp. Pls. Sm. 8°.

NL 0436444 DCU-H PPL MB

Lockhart, William, 1820-1892, ed.

Bussierre, Marie Théodore Renouard, *vicomte* de, 1802-1865.
The conversion of Marie-Alphonse Ratisbonne: original narrative of Baron Théodore de Bussières [!], followed by a letter from Mr. Ratisbonne to Rev. Mr. Dufriche-Desgenettes ... Edited by the Rev. W. Lockhart ... New York, T. W. Strong [1876?]

VOLUME 337

Lockhart, William, 1820-1892.
B3646
.M3
1886
[Macwalter, Gabriel Stuart]
Life of Antonio Rosmini Serbati, founder of the Institute of Charity; ed. by William Lockhart. 2d ed. London, K. Paul, Trench, 1886.

Lockhart, William 1820-1892.
Non Possumus. London, 1868.

NL 0436447 OClStM

Lockhart, William, 1820-1892.
The old religion; or, How shall we find primitive Christianity? Edited by William Lockhart. London, Burns and Oates, n.d.
504p. 19cm.
Reprinted from "Catholic opinion."

NL 0436448 PV

283
P987eY
L
1866
Theol.
Lockhart, William, 1820-1892.
Possibilities and difficulties of reunion. A review of Dr. Pusey's Eirenicon ... 2nd ed., with a preface. London, Longmans, Green, and co., 1866.
xvii, 63p. 21cm.

1. Pusey, Edward Bouverie, 1800-1882. An eirenicon. 2. Church of England--Relations--Catholic church. I. Title.

NL 0436449 TxDaM

Lockhart, William, 1820-1892.
Possibilities and difficulties of reunion. A review of Dr. Pusey's Eirenicon. 2d ed. Longmans, Green, 1886.
63 p.

NL 0436450 WaSpG

BX
2141
.L8
L8
1890
Lockhart, William, 1820-1892.
S. Etheldreda's and old London. 2d ed. London, Burns & Oates; New York, Catholic Publication co., 1890.
64 p. 19 cm.

1. London. St. Etheldreda (Church) I. Title.

NL 0436451 DCU

Lockhart, William, 1820-1892.
Vie d'Antonio Rosmini Serbati...
tr. de L'anglais par E. Segond. Paris, 1889.

NL 0436452 PPL

B
3646
L811Ql
Lockhart, William, 1820-1892.
Vita di Antonio Rosmini, prete roveretano; versione dall'inglese, con modificazioni ed aggiunte di Luigi Sernagiotto. Venezia, Tip. di M. S. fra compositori-impressori tipografi, 1888.
xxx,673 p. ports.

Translation of Life of Antonio Rosmini-Serbati, begun by G. S. MacWalter, finished by Lockhart and issued in 1886 without MacWalter's name.

NL 0436453 CLU CU

LX44
D28
X481
Lockhart, William, 1825-1902.
The Church of Scotland in the thirteenth century; the life and times of David de Bernham of St. Andrews (Bishop) A.D. 1239 to 1253, with list of churches dedicated by him, and dates. 2d ed. Edinburgh, W. Blackwood, 1892.
x, 152 p. 24 cm.

Bibliographical footnotes.

NL 0436454 CtY-D NjPT NN ICU NcD PPEB

Lockhart, William, 1825-1902.
Sorrowing for the departed. A Memorial Sermon. Edinburgh, 1875.
30 p. 8°. [In "College Pamphlets," v. 2007]

NL 0436455 CtY

Z
659
.L82
Lockhart, William B.
Literature, the law of obscenity and the constitution [by] William B. Lockhart and Robert C. McClure. [Minneapolis, Minnesota Law Review Foundation, 1954]
[295]-395 p. 26 cm.
Caption title.
Detached from Minnesota law review, v.38, no.4, March, 1954.
1. Literature, Immoral--Laws and legislation. I. McClure, Robert C., joint author.

NL 0436456 MiU IU ICU MiD Wa IdPI

Lockhart, William Edgar.
Good, Milt, 1889-
Twelve years in a Texas prison, by Milt Good as told to W. E. Lockhart. (Illustrations drawn by Isabel Robinson) ... Amarillo, Tex., Printed by Russell stationery company, °1935.

Lockhart, William Ewart, 1846-1900, illus.
PR4327
.I 55
Rare bk. coll.
Illustrations to the works of Robert Burns from original drawings by Alex. Nasmyth, Sam Bough, R. S. A., Wm. E. Lockhart, R. S. A., Clark Stanton, A. R. S. A. Engraved by William Forrest, H. R. S. A., & Robert Anderson, A. R. S. A. Edinburgh. W. Paterson, 1880.

Lockhart, William F.
How to make forms for concrete buildings. Concrete-Cement Age Publishing Co., c1923.
104 p. illus.

NL 0436459 WaE

ILR
TJ
607
L6
1908
Lockhart, William Fulton, 1872-
Lockhart's book of instructions for locomotive firemen. [Cleveland, c1908]
180 p. illus. 18 cm.

O
NIC-I
1/70
[1. Railroads - Locomotives] 1. Locomotives - Handbooks, manuals, etc. [2. Railroads - Trainmen's manuals] I. Title.

NL 0436460 NIC

LOCKHART, William Peddie.
The Gospel wall; or, lessons from Nehemiah.
Lond. Nisbet & co. 1879. 220 pp. Sm. 8°.

NL 0436461 MB

Lockhart, William Pemberton, 1863-
Lone Star lyrics [by] Will P. Lockhart. Boston, R. G. Badger [1912]
7 p., 1 l., 9-90 p. 19½cm. $1.00
Partly reprinted from various periodicals.

I. Title.

Library of Congress PS3523.O24L6 1912 12-14121

NL 0436462 DLC NcD OO MiU

Lockhart, William Raymond, 1925-
Factors limiting total growth in bacterial cultures. Ann Arbor, University Microfilms [1955]
([University Microfilms, Ann Arbor, Mich.] Publication no. 10,697)
Microfilm copy of typescript. Positive.
Collation of the original as determined from the film: ii, 65 l. diagrs., tables.
Thesis—Purdue University.
Abstracted in Dissertation abstracts, v. 15 (1955) no. 2, p. 190-191.
Vita.
Bibliography: leaves 62-65.
1. Bacteriology—Cultures and culture media. I. Title.
Microfilm AC-1 no. 10,697 Mic 57-5006

NL 0436463 DLC

Lockhart, William S.
The ministry of worship; a study of the need, psychology and technique of worship, by W. S. Lockhart ... St. Louis, Mo., Christian board of publication, 1927.
212 p. 1 illus. 19½cm.
Bibliography: p. 209-212.

1. Worship. 2. Disciples of Christ. I. Title.

Library of Congress BV10.L6 27-18906

NL 0436464 DLC TNJ-R NcD OO PCC

Lockhart, William S.
Orders of worship,...
St. Louis, Mo., 1927

BX7325
.L6

NL 0436465 DLC

WO
L815a
LOCKHART-MUMMERY, John Percy, 1875-
The after-treatment of operations; a manual for practitioners and house surgeons. [1st] ed. London, Baillière, Tindall and Cox, 1903-
v. illus.

NL 0436466 DNLM

VOLUME 337

Lockhart-Mummery, John Percy, 1875-
The after-treatment of operations. A manual for practitioners and house surgeons by P. Lockhart Mummery, ... Second edition. London, Baillière, Tindall and Cox, 1904.
ix, 240 p. 37 illus. 19cm.
"References" at ends of chapters.

NL 0436467 ICJ PPC DNLM MtU MB

Lockhart-Mummery, John Percy, 1875-
The after-treatment of operations. A manual for practitioners and house surgeons by P. Lockhart Mummery, ... Third edition. London, Baillière, Tindall and Cox, 1909.
viii, [2], 251 p. 38 illus. incl. diagrs. 19cm.

NL 0436468 ICJ DNLM

Lookhart-Mummery, John Percy, 1875-
The after-treatment of operations; a manual for practitioners and house surgeons, by P. Lockhart Mummery ... 3d ed. New York, W. Wood & company, 1909.
ix, 251 p. illus., diagrs. 19cm.
"References" at end of some of the chapters.

1. Operations, Surgical. I. Title.

NL 0436469 MiU

Lockhart-Mummery, John Percy, 1875-
The after-treatment of operations. A manual for practitioners and house surgeons by P. Lockhart-Mummery, ... Fourth edition. New York, W. Wood & Co., 1916.
ix, 275 p. 39 illus. (incl. diagrs.) 19cm.
"References" with special subjects.

NL 0436470 ICJ PPC DNLM

WO 183 L816a 1929
LOCKHART-MUMMERY, John Percy, 1875-
The after-treatment of operations; a manual for practitioners and house surgeons. 5th ed. London, Baillière, Tindall and Cox, 1929.
ix, 281 p. illus.
1. Surgery - Complications & sequels 2. Surgery - Pre- & postoperative care

NL 0436471 DNLM

617.9 L816a5
Lockhart-Mummery, John Percy, 1875-
The after-treatment of operations. A manual for practitioners and house surgeons 5th ed. New York, W. Wood and co., 1929.
281p. illus., diagrs.

"Printed in Great Britain."

1. Surgery--Preoperative and postoperative care. 2. Surgery--Postoperative complications.

NL 0436472 IU-M OrU-M

Lockhart-Mummery, John Percy, 1875-
The after-treatment of operations; a manual for practitioners and house surgeons. 5th ed. Toronto, Macmillan, 1930.
281 p. illus. 20 cm.

1. Surgery - Complications. 2. Postoperative care. I. Title.

NL 0436473 CaBVaU

Lockhart-Mummery, John Percy, 1875-
After us; or, The world as it might be, by J. P. Lockhart-Mummery ... with foreword by the Rt. Hon. Lord Horder of Ashford ... London, S. Paul & co. ltd. [1936]
2 p. l., 11-287 p. front. 24cm.

1. Utopias. 2. Civilization. I. Title.

37-11423

Library of Congress HX811.1936.L56

321.07

NL 0436474 DLC DNLM GU NN

WI L816d 1910
LOCKHART-MUMMERY, John Percy, 1875-
Diseases of the colon and their surgical treatment. Bristol, Wright, 1910.
vi, 322 p. illus.
Based on the Jacksonian essay for 1909.

NL 0436475 DNLM ICRL

Lockhart, Mummery, John Percy, 1875-
Diseases of the colon and their surgical treatment, ... By P. Lockhart Mummery, ... Illustrated by coloured and other plates, and numerous figures in the text, many of which are reproduced from the author's sketches. New York, W. Wood and Co., 1910.
vi, [2], 322 p. illus., 6 pl. (partly col.) 22cm.
"Founded on the Jacksonian essay for 1909."
"References" at ends of chapters.

NL 0436476 ICJ PPC

WI 600 L816d 1914
LOCKHART-MUMMERY, John Percy, 1875-
Diseases of the rectum and anus; a practical handbook. London, Baillière, Tindall and Cox, 1914.
vii, 348 p. illus.

NL 0436477 DNLM

Lockhart-Mummery, John Percy, 1875-
Diseases of the rectum and anus. A practical handbook by P. Lockhart-Mummery, ... New York, W. Wood & Co., 1914.
vii, 348 p. 102 illus. 21½cm.

NL 0436478 ICJ CtY PPC PPJ MiU

Lockhart-Mummery, John Percy, 1875-
Diseases of the rectum & colon and their surgical treatment; by P. Lockhart-Mummery ... London, Baillière, Tindall & Cox, 1923.
x, 872 p. illus. (part col.) v pl. (incl. front.: part col.) 22cm.
"References" at end of most of the chapters.
"My previous book on diseases of the rectum, and also that on diseases of the colon, required revision, and it appeared to me wiser to combine the two volumes into one rather than to revise them separately."—Pref.

1. Rectum—Diseases. 2. Rectum—Surgery. 3. Colon [(Anatomy)]—Diseases. 4. [Colon—Surgery]

[Full name: John Percy Lockhart-Mummery]

S G 24-16

Library, U. S. Surgeon-General's Office

PPT-M MBCo
NL 0436479 DI-GS DNLM OrU-M ICJ ICRL TxDaS NIC CU

Lockhart-Mummery, John Percy, 1875-
Diseases of the rectum & colon and their surgical treatment, by P. Lockhart-Mummery ... New York, W. Wood and Co., 1923.
x, 872 p. illus., v pl. (incl. front., part col.) 22½cm.
Printed in Great Britain.
"References" at end of chapters.

NL 0436480 ICJ OClW-H CaBVaU

Lockhart-Mummery, John Percy, 1875-
Diseases of the rectum and colon and their surgical treatment, by J. P. Lockhart-Mummery ... 2d ed. Baltimore, W. Wood and company, 1934.
xii, 605 p. illus. 25½cm.
Printed in Great Britain.
"A large part of the book has been entirely rewritten and several new chapters have been added."—p. vii.
"References": p. 595-598.

1. Rectum—Diseases. 2. Rectum—Surgery. 3. Colon (Anatomy)—Diseases. 4. Colon (Anatomy)—Surgery.

35-11871

Library of Congress RC860.L6 1934

616.34

PU-Med PPWM
NL 0436481 DLC DNLM ICU CtY-M MiU NcD PPC PPJ

QH311 .L68
Lockhart-Mummery, John Percy, 1875-
Nothing new under the sun. Illus. by William Wood. London, New York, A. Melrose [1947] [treated]
x, 178 p. illus. 22 cm.

1. Biology. 2. Physiology. 3. Natural history. I. Title.

A 49-3798*

Harvard Univ. Library for Library of Congress

NL 0436482 MH CaBVa TxU CU

Lockhart-Mummery, John Percy, 1875-
The origin of cancer, by J. P. Lockhart-Mummery ... with 29 illustrations. London, J. & A. Churchill, 1934.
ix, 150 p. illus., plates, diagrs. 21cm.
"References": p. 145-147.

1. Cancer. I. Title.

34-39891

Library of Congress RC261.L8

616.994

NL 0436483 DLC CtY-M OCl ICJ DNLM ViU

WIB L816s 1906
LOCKHART-MUMMERY, John Percy, 1875-
The sigmoidoscope; a clinical handbook on the examination of the rectum and pelvic colon. London, Baillière, Tindall and Cox, 1906.
x, 88 p. illus.

NL 0436484 DNLM

Lockhart-Mummery, John Percy, 1875-
Sigmoidoscope. A clinical handbook on the examination of the rectum and pelvic color. London, Bailliere, 1908.

88 p.

NL 0436485 PPC

Lockhart-Smith, William James, ed.

Law

Nyasaland. *Laws, statutes, etc.*
The laws of Nyasaland in force on 31st December, 1946. Rev. ed. Prepared under the authority of the Revised edition of the laws ordinance, 1946, by Charles Mathew and William Edward Lardner Jennings. London, Printed by C. F. Roworth, 1947-49.

Lockhart the Brave; and the Base Pamphleteer. [London]
4 p. 8°. [In vol. labeled "Political Tracts."]
2d ed.

NL 0436487 CtY

VOLUME 337

The Lockheed "?"
see its later titles
Lockheed Vega aircraftsman;
Lockheed aircraftsman.

Lockheed Aircraft Corporation, Burbank, Calif.
Air cargo trends
see under
Hackney, L. R.

Lockheed aircraft corporation, *Burbank, Calif.*
Aircraft design sketch book. Burbank, Calif., Lockheed aircraft corporation [©1940]
cover-title, 2 p. l., [130] p. of illus. 28½ x 23cm.
Various pagings.

1. Aeroplanes—Design and construction. I. Title.
41-6281
Library of Congress TL671.2.L555

NL 0436490 DLC WaS NIC NcRS PP PSt OLak OCl OU ViU

Lockheed aircraft corporation, *Burbank, Calif.*
Annual report of the president.
[Burbank, 19
v. illus. (part col.) 22-28½cm.
Title varies: -1937, Report of the president.
1938- Annual report of the president.

44-29755
Library of Congress TL724.5.L6A3

NL 0436491 DLC OrCS NN

Lockheed aircraft corporation, Burbank, Calif.
Approved factory jobs for the physically handicapped. [n.p.] Industrial relations research department [1934].
93 l. tables 29 cm.

NL 0436492 PBm

Lockheed Aircraft Corporation, Burbank, Calif.
Catalog of parts, Lockheed "14". Burbank, Calif. [1939]
1 v. (various paging) illus., diagrs.

NL 0436493 MH-BA

Lockheed Aircraft Corporation, Burbank, Calif.
Comparison of model 649 and model 749, improved performance. Burbank, Calif., 1947.
13, 8, iv, 68 p. charts. (SLR/746, March 21, 1947)

NL 0436494 MH-BA

Lockheed Aircraft Corporation, *Burbank, Calif.*
Crew operating instructions for Lockheed airplanes, models 649 and 749. Burbank, Calif., 1948 [©1947]
1 v. (loose-leaf) diagrs. 28 cm. (*Its* Lockheed report no. 6027)
On cover: Crew operating manual for the Constellation, models 649-749.

1. Aeroplanes. I. Title. (Series)
TL686.L6L6 629.13334 48-18868*

NL 0436495 DLC

Lockheed aircraft corporation, *Burbank, Calif.*
Design handbook. [Burbank, Calif., Lockheed aircraft corporation, ©1940]
2 p. l., 14, [305] p. incl. illus., tables, diagrs. 29½cm.
Title from cover.

1. Aeroplanes—Design and construction. I. Title.
40-32866
Library of Congress TL671.2.L56
——— Copy 2.
Copyright 629.1341

NL 0436496 DLC

Lockheed aircraft corporation, Burbank, Calif.
Development of the Lockheed P-80A jet fighter airplane
see under Johnson, Clarence L.

[Lockheed aircraft corporation, *Burbank, Calif.*]
Drafting practice manual. [Burbank, 1944]
1 v. illus. 29cm.
Loose-leaf; reproduced from type-written copy.

1. Aeronautics—Design and construction. 2. Drawing-room practice. I. Title.
45-2505
Brief cataloging
Library of Congress TL671.25.L6
629.1341

NL 0436498 DLC

Lockheed Aircraft Corporation, *Burbank, Calif.*
Engineering design handbook.
Burbank.
v. illus. 30 cm. annual.

1. Aeroplanes—Materials. 2. Aeroplanes—Design and construction. 3. Aeroplanes—Apparatus and supplies.
TL688.L63 52-37732

NL 0436499 DLC

TL671 .2 .L558 1954 Lockheed Aircraft Corporation, Burbank, Calif.
Engineering elements in aircraft development. [Burbank?, Lockheed Aircraft Corp., California Division ,1954?]
[36, p. illus. 28cm.
Cover title.

1. Aeroplanes—Design and construction. I. Title.

NL 0436500 ViU

Lockheed aircraft corporation, Burbank, California.
. . . Engineering standards manual. [Burbank, Calif., 1945?]
1 v. illus. 29cm.

333972B. 1. Aeroplanes—Type—Lockheed, 1945. 2. Aeroplanes—Specifications.
N. Y. P. L. April 9, 1946

NL 0436501 NN

[Lockheed aircraft corporation, Burbank, Calif.]
Lockheed's estimates of air cargo market. [Burbank?, 1946]
15 numb.l. fold.chart.

Caption title.
Manifold copy.

NL 0436502 MH-BA

Lockheed Aircraft Corporation, Burbank, Calif.
Flight manual, Lockheed model 10 "Electra". Burbank, Calif. [194-]
43, 11 p. illus., diagrs.

NL 0436503 MH-BA

Lockheed aircraft corporation, Burbank, Calif.
Hangar flying
see under title

620.18 L81h Lockheed Aircraft Corporation, Burbank, Calif.
High energy rate metal forming. Interim engineering report. no.1-
[Washington, D.C.] U.S. Dept. of Commerce, Office of Technical Services [19--]
v.1 v.2 v.3 v. illus. 28 cm. ([Lockheed] Report 12970, 13350, 13435
"AF 33(600)35543."
PB 161271-
Contents.-no.1 Period of October 18, 1957 to February 28, 1958.-no.2. Reporting period July 1 to September 30, 1958.-no.3. October 1 to December 31, 1958.

NL 0436506 KMK

Lockheed Aircraft Corporation, Burbank, Calif.
Human factors index. Marietta, Georgia, no date.
4p. processed.

Added to collection 1961.

NL 0436507 OClW

Lockheed aircraft corporation, *Burbank, Calif.*
Industrial relations code. 1st- ed.; June 15, 1944-
Burbank, Calif. [1944-
v. 18½cm.
On cover, 1944- : A reference handbook of industrial relations; policies, programs & regulations.
Compiler: 1944- C. J. Dexter.

1. Industrial relations — Handbooks, manuals, etc. I. Dexter, Charles J.
44-7172 Revised
Library of Congress HD6975.L6
[r45b2] 658.3

NL 0436508 DLC OCl

VOLUME 337

Lockheed aircraft corporation, *Burbank, Calif.*
Interim letter report to stockholders.
[Burbank, 19
v. 23–28cm.
Covers the six month's period, Jan.–June.
Title varies: –1941, Semi-annual statement.
1942– Interim letter report to stockholders.
45-25408
Library of Congress TL724.5.L6A32

NL 0436509 DLC

Lockheed Aircraft Corporation, Burbank, Calif.
Lockheed aircraftsman
see under title

Lockheed Aircraft Corporation, Burbank, Calif.
The Lockheed constellation. [Burbank, Calif., 1949?]
1 v. (unpaged) col. illus.

NL 0436511 MH-BA

[Lockheed Aircraft Corporation, Burbank, Calif.]
[The] Lockheed Constitution development story.
[Burbank, Calif.] 1950.
54 p. illus.

NL 0436512 MH-BA

Lockheed aircraft corporation, Burbank, Calif.
The Lockheed 14-F62 transport airplane; two engine monoplane; specification. Burbank, Calif., 1938.
9 p.
"Report no. 964, Oct. 1, 1938."

NL 0436513 MH-BA

Lockheed aircraft corporation, Burbank, Calif.
The Lockheed 14-G3B transport airplane; two engine monoplane; specification. Burbank, Calif., 1938.
9 *l.*
"Report no. 966, Oct. 1, 1938."

NL 0436514 MH-BA

Lockheed aircraft corporation, Burbank, Calif.
The Lockheed 14-H2 transport airplane; two engine monoplane; specification. Burbank, Calif., 1938.
9 *l.*
"Report no. 965, Oct. 1, 1938."

NL 0436515 MH-BA

Lockheed Aircraft Corporation, Burbank, Calif.
TL724 .5 .L6A36 Lockheed log. v. 1–
May 1943–
[Burbank, Calif., Lockheed Aircraft Corp., etc.]

Lockheed aircraft corporation, *Burbank, Calif.*
Lockheed paper[s] no. 1–
[Burbank] 1939–
nos. in illus., tables, diagrs. 30cm. irregular.
Loose-leaf; many numbers reproduced from type-written copy.
Chiefly reprints from various periodicals.
1. Aeronautics—Collected works.
45-49242
Library of Congress TL507.L6

NL 0436517 DLC

Lockheed aircraft corporation, Burbank, California.
Lockheed process specification manual; revision August 1, 1945.
[Burbank, Calif., 1945] 1 v. illus. 29cm.
333971B. 1. Aeroplanes—Type—Lockheed, 1945. 2. Aeroplanes—Specifications.
N. Y. P. L. April 9, 1946

NL 0436518 NN

Lockheed Aircraft Corporation, Burbank, Calif.
TL724 .5 .L6A4 Lockheed star.
Burbank, Calif.

Lockheed Aircraft Corporation, Burbank, Calif.
The Lockheed Super Constellation; model 1049 series. [Burbank, 1950?]
Cover-title, 32 p. illus.

NL 0436520 MH-BA

Lockheed Aircraft Corporation, Burbank, Calif.
Lockheed 12 service instructions. [Burbank, Calif., 194-]
vii, 103 p. illus., diagrs.

NL 0436521 MH-BA

Lockheed aircraft corporation, Burbank, Calif.
Lockheed Vega aircraftsman. v. 1–
Nov. 1935–
[Burbank, Calif., Employees of Lockheed and Vega corporations, etc., 1935–

[Lockheed aircraft corporation, *Burbank, Calif.*]
Loft handbook. [Burbank, 1940?]
1 v. diagrs. 29cm.
Loose-leaf; reproduced from type-written copy.
1. Aeroplanes—Design and construction. I. Title.
45-46779
Brief cataloging
Library of Congress TL671.2.L563
[2] 629.1341

NL 0436523 DLC

Lockheed aircraft corporation, Burbank, Calif.
Manufacturing standards manual. [Burbank] Lockheed aircraft corp. [1945] 1 v. illus. 30cm.
Loose-leaf.
333499B. 1. Aeroplanes—Type—Lockheed. 2. Aeroplanes—Manufacture.
N. Y. P. L. January 8, 1947

NL 0436524 NN

Lockheed Aircraft Corporation, Burbank, Calif.
Operating instructions, Lockheed Lodestar.
Burbank, Calif. [194-]
iv, 75 p. illus., diagrs.
On cover: Model 18 operating instructions.

NL 0436525 MH-BA

Lockheed aircraft corporation, Burbank, Calif.
Ndy61 U2 +L81m [Pamphlets. Economic aspects]
28cm.

NL 0436526 CtY

Lockheed aircraft corporation, Burbank, Calif.
... Performance characteristics of commercial airplanes and their influence on airport requirements ... Burbank, California, 1944.
2 p.*l.*, iii, 24 numb.*l.* figures (2 fold.) charts. (Report no. 4846, July 13, 1944)
Report prepared by Clarence L.Johnson and Philip A.Colman.

NL 0436527 MH-BA MiD

Lockheed aircraft corporation, Burbank, Calif.
Pictorial review of Lockheed air cargo developments. Burbank, Calif., 1951. 1 v. (chiefly illus.) 28cm. (ITS: Report. SLR/1018)
1. Aeroplanes--Type--Lockheed, 1951. 2. Aeroplanes-Stowage. t. 1951.

NL 0436528 NN

Lockheed aircraft corporation,Burbank, Calif.
Portfolio series [pictorial portfolios of Lockheed history making airplanes] nos. illus. Author,[1946?-

NL 0436529 OrP

Lockheed Aircraft Corporation, Burbank, Calif.
GC2 .I48 Interindustrial Oceanographic Symposium.
Proceedings.
[Burbank? Calif., Lockheed Aircraft Corp.]

Lockheed aircraft corporation, *Burbank, Calif.*
Semi-annual statement
see its
Interim letter report to stockholders.

VOLUME 337

Lockheed Aircraft Corporation, *Burbank, Calif.*
Special model 18s. Burbank [1941?]
1 v. (loose-leaf) diagrs., tables. 30 cm. (*Its* Report no. 1670)

1. Aeroplanes—Apparatus and supplies. (Series: Lockheed Aircraft Corporation, Burbank, Calif. Lockheed report no. 1670)
TL686.L6L63 50-40068

NL 0436532 DLC

f658.5 L816s Lockheed Aircraft Corporation, Burbank, Calif.
Standard production manual. [Burbank, 1940]
1v.(loose-leaf) 29cm.

Cover title. On spine: Standard practice manual. In Foreword: Leader's manual.

NL 0436533 CLSU

Lockheed aircraft corporation, *Burbank, Calif.*
Structural repair handbook ... for Constellation airplanes, model 049 ... Burbank, Calif., Lockheed aircraft corporation, 1946.
1 p. l., iv, 322 p. incl. illus., tables, diagrs. 29 x 23ᶜᵐ. (LAC report no. 5886)
"Use of this handbook authorized by Civil aeronautics administration."
1. Aeroplanes—Maintenance and repair. I. Title: Constellation airplanes, model 049.
TL703.L6A3 629.134 47-20652

NL 0436534 DLC

D620.7 L81 Lockheed aircraft corporation, Burbank, Calif.
Suggestions for engineering training ... distributed by the Education department, Lockheed aircraft corporation and Vega airplane company. [194-?]
9 l. 28ᶜᵐ.

Reproduced from type-written copy.
"Comments ... made in response to inquiries by Professor F. C. Hockema ... conducting a survey for the Carnegie corporation, with the purpose of gathering information which will aid colleges and universities engaged in teaching engineers."

NL 0436535 NNC

Lockheed aircraft corporation, *Burbank, Calif.*
Supervisory development (Course 1-) [Burbank] Lockheed aircraft corporation, Vega airplane company [1941-
v. illus. (incl. plans) diagrs., forms. 29 x 22ᶜᵐ.
Title from cover.
Reproduced from type-written copy.
Introduction signed: The Supervisory development section, Lockheed-Vega education department.
Includes "Sources."
1. Aeronautics—Study and teaching. 2. Employees, Training of. I. Vega aircraft corporation, Burbank, Calif. II. Title.
42-19711 Revised
Library of Congress TL560.25.L6A4 [r43c2] 629.130714

NL 0436536 DLC

Lockheed aircraft corporation, *Burbank, Calif.*
... Supervisory development, on-the-job training [by the] Education department, Industrial relations office, in collaboration with the manufacturing departments. [Burbank, Calif.] 1941.
1 v. 1 illus., forms. 29 x 22ᶜᵐ.
At head of title: Lockheed aircraft corporation [and] Vega airplane company.
Reproduced from type-written copy; variously paged.
1. Aeronautics—Study and teaching. 2. Employees, Training of. I. Vega airplane company, Burbank, Calif. II. Title.
42-19712
Library of Congress TL560.25.L6A5 629.130714

NL 0436537 DLC

Lockheed aircraft corporation, Burbank, Calif.
... Time study job manual, compiled by Robert A. Trumpis ... [Burbank, Lockheed aircraft corporation] 1944.
1 v. tables, forms, diagrs. 29 cm.
Loose-leaf.
1. Time study. I. Trumpis. Robert A., comp.

NL 0436538 CU

Lockheed aircraft corporation, Burbank, Calif.
Tool design standards manual. [Burbank] Lockheed aircraft corp. [1945] 1 v. 30cm.
Loose-leaf.

333498B. 1. Machine-tools. 2. Aeroplanes—Manufacture.
N. Y. P. L. January 8, 1947

NL 0436540 NN

Lockheed Aircraft Corporation, Burbank, Calif.
Wing loading, icing and associated aspects of modern transport design
see under Johnson, Clarence L.

TL686 .L6L67 Lockheed Aircraft Corporation. Lockheed-California Company.
Lockheed field service digest. v. 1-
July/Aug. 1954-
[Burbank, Calif., Lockheed-California Co.]

Lockheed aircraftsman.
v.

[Burbank, Calif.] 19 v. illus. 30cm.
Monthly (slightly irregular).
Published by employees of Lockheed and Vega corporations, -Nov. 1943; by Lockheed employees recreation club, Dec. 1943-
Title varies: v. -Nov. 1943), Lockheed-Vega aircraftsman.
v. 9- Lockheed aircraftsman (Dec. 1943 has cover-title: The Aircraftsman).

1. House organs. I. Lockheed aircraft corporation, Burbank, Calif. II. Vega aircraft corporation, Burbank, Calif. III. Lockheed-Vega aircraftsman. IV. Title: The Aircraftsman.
N. Y. P. L. September 17, 1945

NL 0436543 NN WaS

Lockheed aircraftsman
see also its earlier title Lockheed Vega aircraftsman.

Lockheed-California Company
see Lockheed Aircraft Corporation. Lockheed-California Company.

[The] Lockheed Constitution development story
see under [Lockheed Aircraft Corporation, Burbank, Calif.]

Lockheed field service digest. v. 1-
July/Aug. 1954-
[Burbank, Calif., Lockheed-California Co.]
v. in illus. 28 cm.
Frequency varies.
Vols. for 1954- issued by the company under its earlier name: Lockheed Aircraft Corporation, California Division.
INDEXES:
Vols. 1-5, 1954-May/June 1959, *with* v. 5, no. 6.

1. Aeroplanes—Maintenance and repair—Period. I. Lockheed Aircraft Corporation. Lockheed-California Company.
TL686.L6L67 67-6439

NL 0436547 DLC OrCS NN

Lockheed log. v. 1-
May 1943-
[Burbank, Calif., Lockheed Aircraft Corp., etc.]
v. illus. (part col.) ports. 31-35 cm. quarterly (irregular)
Title varies: May 1943- Global service log.

1. Aeroplanes—Period. I. Lockheed Aircraft Corporation, Burbank, Calif.
TL724.5.L6A36 629.1305 49-40779*

NL 0436548 DLC WaS NN MH-Ba

Lockheed Overseas Corporation.
Report. -2d; -July 1, 1943/May 1, 1944.
[n. p.]
v. illus., ports. 23 x 27 cm.

TL724.5.L62A3 55-52960 ‡

NL 0436549 DLC

Lockheed star.

Burbank, Calif.
v. in illus., ports. 28-42cm.
Weekly, biweekly,
Began publication in 1934.
Vol. numbers irregular: issues for -May 19, 1944 called v. -v. 11, no. 23; May 26, 1944- called v. 1, no. 1- called v. (some issues called v. no.

Official publication of the Lockheed Aircraft Corporation (Mar. 28, 1941-Nov. 26, 1943, of the Lockheed and Vega Aircraft Corporations)
Title varies: Mar. 21, 1941-Nov. 26, 1943, The Lockheed-Vega star.

I. Lockheed Aircraft Corporation, Burbank, Calif. II. Vega Aircraft Corporation, Burbank, Calif.
TL724.5.L6A4 629.13065 49-17946 rev*

NL 0436551 DLC WaS

Lockheed Vega aircraftsman. v. 1-
Nov. 1935-
[Burbank, Calif., Employees of Lockheed and Vega corporations, etc., 1935-
v. in illus. 30ᶜᵐ. monthly (irregular)
Vol. 2, no. 7; v. 4, nos. 2 and 8 were not published.
Title varies: Nov. 1935, The Lockheed "7"
Dec. 1935-June 1942, Lockheed aircraftsman.
July 1942- Lockheed Vega aircraftsman.
1. Aeronautics—Period. I. Lockheed aircraft corporation, Burbank, Calif. II. Vega airplane company, Burbank, Calif.
43-38812
Library of Congress TL501.L6 629.1305

NL 0436552 DLC

Lockheed Vega aircraftsman
see also its later title Lockheed aircraftsman.

VOLUME 337

The Lockheed-Vega star
see Lockheed star.

Lockheed's estimates of air cargo market...Burbank, 1946.

see

[Lockheed aircraft corporation, Burbank, Calif.]
Estimates of air cargo market.

Lockhorn, J. O. M., 1889- ed.

TL272
.M27
1944

Maltha, Th E
... Handleiding accumulatoren, lood, ijzer-nikkel, cadmium-nikkel (voornamelijk automobiel- en andere transportabe e accumulatoren) Herzien door ir J. O. M. Lockhorn ... 2. druk. Amsterdam, H. Stam [1944]

Lockhorst, van.
État de Guatémala. (Amérique centrale.) D'après les croquis de M. van Lockhorst. Lith. par M. Dupressoir. [Paris, 184-?] 16 plates. f°.

Title from plates.
Two of the sketches by Francisco Cisnéros.

49751A. 1. Guatemala.—Views.
N. Y. P. L. September 6, 1922.

NL 0436557 NN

van Lockhorst (W[outerus] C[ornelis]). Praktische opmerkingen ontleend aan eene in de jaren 1863 en 1864 in Dieren en omstreken geheerscht hebbende croup-epidemie. 24 pp. 8°. *Utrecht, P. W. van der Weijer,* [1865].
Repr. from: Nederl. Tijdschr. v. Heel- en Verlosk., Utrecht, 1865, n. s., x.

NL 0436558 DNLM

van Lockhorst (Wouterus Cornelis). * Quaedam de resectionibus ossium. 2 p. l., 40 pp. 8°. *Trai. ad Rhenum, H. A. Banning,* 1851.

NL 0436559 DNLM

Lockhorst van Vryenhoeven, Didericus van
... De praescriptione ... defendet Didericus van Lockhorst van Vryenhoeven ... Lugduni Batavorum, apud viduam M. Cyfveer, 1820.
3 p.l., 92 p. 27½cm.
Diss. - Leiden.

NL 0436560 MH-L

Lockie, John.
Lockie's Marine engineers' drawing book. Adapted to the requirements of the Board of Trade examinations. London. Crosby Lockwood & Son. 1892. 22 plates, with descriptive text. 17½ × 26½ cm.

L8989 — Marine engines. — Great Britain. Board of Trade.

NL 0436561 MB

Lockie, John, ed.
The Steamship: an illustrated monthly review of shipping, shipbuilding, and marine engineering ... v. 1- July 1889-

Leith, J. Lockie, 1890-

Lockie, John, Inspector.
Topography of London, giving a concise local description of and accurate direction to every square, street, lane, court, dock, wharf, inn, public office, &c. in the metropolis and its environs ... The whole alphabetically arranged ... Taken from actual survey by John Lockie. London, 1810.
1 v. (unpaged) 23 cm.
1. London - Streets. 2. London - Descr. - Gazetteers. I. Title.

NL 0436563 CtY MdBP OKentU

Lockie, John, Inspector.
Lockie's topography of London; giving a concise local description of, and accurate direction to, every square, street, lane, court, dock, wharf, inn, public office, etc. in the metropolis and its environs... London, Nicol, 1810.
1v. 22cm.

1. London--Description--Gazetteers

NL 0436564 AAP NjP MnU

Lockie, John, Inspector.
Topography of London; giving a concise local description of, and accurate direction to, every square, street, lane, court, dock, wharf, inn, public office, &c. in the metropolis and its environs ... The whole alphabetically arranged ... Taken from actual survey, by John Lockie ... 2d ed., cor. and rev. by the author ... accompanied by a new map of London. London, Printed for Sherwood, Neely, and Jones [etc.] 1813.
[327] p. 16 cm.
"The new Map of London ... the author hopes shortly to publish."—Pref.
1. London—Descr.—Gazetteers.

DA683.L81 3—3332

NL 0436565 DLC AAP OCU

914.21
L816T

Lockie, John, Inspector.
Topography of London; or, Street directory. Giving a concise local description of, and accurate direction to every square, street, lane, court, dock ... &c., in the metropolis and its environs; including the new buildings to the present time ... 2d ed., corr. and rev. ... accompanied with a new map of London. London, Printed for Sherwood, Neely, & Jones, 1816.
1 v. (unpaged) 17½cm.
"The new Map of London ... the author hopes shortly to publish" - cf. Preface.

1. London. Description. Gazetteers. 2. London. Streets. I. Topography of London.

NL 0436567 NcD CtY

914.1445
L81p

Lockie, Katharine F.
Picturesque Edinburgh. With 500 illus. Edinburgh, J. Lockie, 1899.
437p. illus., ports., plates, maps. 20cm.

Bibliography: p.[8]

1. Edinburgh--Descr.

NL 0436568 IU OClRC PP ScU OrU WaU

Lockie, Laurence Dagenais.
From potions to pills to penicillin; a condensed story of the profession of pharmacy. [Buffalo? 1954]
119 p. 22 cm.

1. Pharmacy—Hist. I. Title.

RS61.L6 615.09 54-42610 ‡

NL 0436569 DLC OrCS MtU IdPI PPT-D PPSKF TxU DNLM

Lockie (Stewart). On some anomalies in disease; an inaugural address, read at the annual meeting of the border counties branch of the British Medical Association. 16 pp. 8°. *Edinburgh, Maclachlan & Stewart,* 1877.

NL 0436570 DNLM

286.81
L81

Lockie, Pemberton & co.
Course of broken rice prices [annual chart]
[London,
Chart also gives Course of freights.

1. Rice. Prices.

NL 0436571 DNAL

286.81
L81C

Lockie, Pemberton & co.
Course of eastern rice prices [annual chart]
[London,
Chart also gives Course of freights.

1. Rice. Prices.

NL 0436572 DNAL

286.81
L81Cr

Lockie, Pemberton & co.
Course of rice bran prices [annual chart]
[London,

1. Rice bran. Prices.

NL 0436573 DNAL

286.81
L81D

Lockie, Pemberton & co.
Direct imports of rice at undermentioned places [annual]
London,

Each issue gives comparative statistics for several years, as 1928 gives also 1923-1927.
1933-1934 have title: Direct imports of rice and broken rice at undermentioned places; 1935 has title: Direct imports of eastern rice and broken rice at undermentioned places; 1936- : Direct shipments of eastern rice and broken rice to the undermentioned places.

NL 0436574 DNAL

VOLUME 337

286.81
L81W Lockie, Pemberton & co.
Weekly rice report.

London,

Includes occasional supplementary issues giving Rice forecast.
Includes supplementary issues giving annual Rice statistics for various countries, exports, imports, crop yield (acres, tons). Each gives comparative figures for several years.

NL 0436575 DNAL

LOCKIER, FRANCIS, 1667-1740.
A sermon preach'd before the Honourable House of Commons, at St. Margaret's Westminster, on Monday, January 31, 1725. Being the anniversary-fast for the martyrdom of King Charles I. By Francis Lockier ... London, Printed for J. Tonson and J. Watts, 1726.
26 p. 4to

NL 0436576 InU RPB DFo

Lockier, Lionel
see Lockyer, Lionel, 1600?-1672.

Lockier, Nicholas
see Lockyer, Nicholas, 1611-1685.

Locking, John.

Au soleil et sur les monts; scènes de la vie des soldats alliés internés en Suisse. Texte de MM. G. Jaccottet, Marcel de Fourmestraux, D. Baud-Bovy et Locking ... [Genève, Administration Sadag, 1918?]

Locking, John E. Old Boston. 8 pp. (Blackwood's Mag. v. 147, 1890, p. 242.)

NL 0436580 MdBP

---

ar W
9122 Lockinge, Henry.
Historical gleanings on the memorable field of Naseby. London, Longman, Reese, Orme, Brown, and Green, 1830.
xiv, 130 p. illus., facsim. 21cm.

1. Naseby, Eng.--Descr. 2. Naseby, Battle of, 1645.

NL 0436581 NIC MdBP NjP ICN MH CtY

Lockington, Charles, *petitioner.*

The case of alien enemies, considered and decided upon a writ of habeas corpus, allowed on the petition of Charles Lockington, an alien enemy, by the Hon. William Tilghman, chief justice of the Supreme court of Pennsylvania, the 22d day of November, 1813. Reported by Richard Bache, esq. Philadelphia: Printed by John Binns, no. 70, Chesnut-street. 1813.

45, viii p. 23½cm.

Continued in next column

Continued from preceding column

Appendix: Containing the acts of Congress, and the public acts and regulations of the President of the United States, respecting alien enemies, with extracts from the official instructions to the marshals of the districts and territories of the United States, which were referred to in Lockington's case: viii p. at end.

1. Aliens—U. S. 2. U. S.—Pol. & govt.—War of 1812. I. Pennsylvania. Supreme court. II. Tilghman, William, 1756-1827. III. Bache, Richard, 1784-1848. IV. Title: Alien enemies, The case of.

20—16040

Library of Congress E358.L81

NL 0436583 DLC DS MB MH NNJ PPAmP PPB

LOCKINGTON, JOHN.
Book of ornamented crests, engraved on 12 copper plates, as a cabinet for the gentleman and curious fancy worker, or pattern-book for the coach painter, engraver, jeweller, sadler, plater, embroider, modeller, &c. London, Laurie & Whittle, 1812.
12 plates (incl. t. p.) 24 x 32cm.

Engraved t. p.
A companion vol. to his Book of cyphers.
1. Engravings, British, 19th cent. 2. Heraldry in decorative art. 3. Ornament, Engraved. 4. Animals in art.

NL 0436584 NN NcGU

Lockington, John.
Bowles's new and complete book of cyphers; designed and engraved on 24 copper-plates, by John Lockington. Including a curious print of the Emperor Charlemagne's Crown. London, printed for and sold by Carington Bowles... 1777.

20 x 26 cm. ff.(1),25.
Engraved throughout.

NL 0436585 MH PU

Wing
ZW
15
.516 LOCKINGTON, JOHN.
Bowles's new and complete book of cyphers... including a curious print of the Emperor Charlemagne's crown, &c. London, Bowles & Carver [ca.1785]
25 pl.incl.t.-p. 21x26cm.

NL 0436586 ICN

Lockington, W. J.
Bodily health and spiritual vigour; a book for preachers and teachers. London: Longmans, Green, and Co., 1913. 128 p. illus. 12°.

1. Hygiene. 2. Physical education. 3. Title.
CENTRAL CIRCULATION.
N. Y. P. L. August 19, 1913.

NL 0436587 NN MBtS OClND

RA
775
L62 Lockington, W. J.
Bodily health and spiritual vigour; a book for preachers and teachers, by William J. Lockington. London, New York, Longmans, Green [1913]
126p. illus. 20cm.

1. Hygiene. I. Title.

NL 0436588 MU

RA781
.L5 Lockington, W. J.
Bodily health and spiritual vigour; a book for preachers and teachers, with diagrams. London, Longmans, Green, 1914
x,126p. illus. 19cm.

NL 0436589 NNU-W PRosC KAS DGU MiD NNU-W OCX

Lockington, W. J.
Bodily health and spiritual vigour. A book for preachers and teachers. 3d impression.
— London. Longmans, Green & Co. 1919. x, 126 pp. Illus. 18½ cm., in 8s.

M1199 — T.r. — Body and mind. — Health and hygiene.

NL 0436590 MB NNF

Lockington, W J.
The soul of Ireland, by W. J. Lockington, S. J.; with an introduction by G. K. Chesterton. London, Harding & More, ltd., 1919.
8 p. l., 167, [1] p. 20 cm.

1. Ireland. 2. Catholic church in Ireland. I. Title.

DA925.L6 20—283

NL 0436591 DLC NcU

274.15
L812s Lockington, W. J.
The soul of Ireland, by W. J. Lockington, S. J.; with an introduction by G. K. Chesterton. London, Harding & More, ltd., 1920.
8 p. l., 167, [1] p. 20 cm. 6/3

1. Ireland. 2. Catholic church--Ireland. I. Jesuits (Works by) II. Title.

NL 0436592 MoSU

Lockington, W J.
The soul of Ireland, by W. J. Lockington, S. J.; with an introduction by G. K. Chesterton. New York, The Macmillan company, 1920.
xv, 182 p. 20cm.

1. Ireland. 2. Catholic church in Ireland. I. Title.
20—824
Library of Congress DA925.L6 1920

MiU OCX OU OClJC NcRS NN MB
NL 0436593 DLC WaSpG OrStbM AAP NIC IU PCC PV PSC

Lockington, W. J.
The Soul of Ireland. N.Y., 1922.

NL 0436594 OClStM

Lockington, W. J.
The soul of Ireland. With an introduction, by G.K.Chesterton. New York, Macmillan co., 1927.

NL 0436595 MH OClW PRosC

VOLUME 337

Lockington, W.N. , ed.
Architecture
see under Essenwein, August Ottomar.

Lockington, Wm. J., S. J.,
SEE
Lockington, W. J.

Lockington, William N.
Day-dreams. By W. N. Lockington ... San Francisco, Cal., Pub. for the author, 1880.
viii, [9]-131 p. 15½cm.

I. Title.

A 22—147

H. E. Huntington library for Library of Congress PS2248.L86D3 [a41r28d1]

NL 0436598 CSmH PPM OO MH

Lockington, William N.
Description of a new chiroid fish, *Myriolepis zonifer*, from Monterey bay, California. By W. N. Lockington.
(*In* U. S. National museum. Proceedings. Washington, 1881. 23½cm. v. 3, 1880, p. 248–251)
Issued September 4, 1880.

1. [Myriolepis zonifer]

S 32-150

Library, Smithsonian Institution
Library of Congress [Q11.U55 vol. 3]

NL 0436599 DSI OU

Lockington, William N.
Description of a new fish from Alaska (*Uranidea microstoma*). By W. N. Lockington.
(*In* U. S. National museum. Proceedings. Washington, 1881. 23½cm. v. 3, 1880, p. 58–59)
Issued May 6, 1880.

1. [Uranidea microstoma]

S 32-131

Library, Smithsonian Institution
Library of Congress [Q11.U55 vol. 3]

NL 0436600 DSI OU

Lockington, William N.
Descriptions of new genera and species of fishes from the coast of California. By W. N. Lockington.
(*In* U. S. National museum. Proceedings. Washington, 1880. 23½cm. v. 2, 1879, p. 326–332)
Issued March 25, 1880.

1. Fishes—California.

S 32-107

Smithsonian inst. Library for Library of Congress [Q11.U55 vol. 2]

NL 0436601 DSI OU CaBVaU

Lockington, William N.
Description of a new genus and some new species of California fishes (*Icosteus ænigmaticus* and *Osmerus attenuatus*). By W. N. Lockington.
(*In* U. S. National museum. Proceedings. Washington, 1881. 23½cm. v. 3, 1880, p. 63–68)
Issued May 24, 1880.

1. Fishes—California.

S 32-133

Library, Smithsonian Institution
Library of Congress [Q11.U55 vol. 3]

NL 0436602 DSI OU

Lockington, William N.
Description of a new genus and species of *Cottidæ*. By W. N. Lockington.
(*In* U. S. National museum. Proceedings. Washington, 1882. 23½cm. v. 4, 1881, p. 141–144)
Issued June 22, 1881.

1. Cottidae.

S 32-216

Library, Smithsonian Institution
Library of Congress [Q11.U55 vol. 4]

NL 0436603 DSI OU CaBVaU

Lockington, William N.
Description of a new sparoid fish (*Sparus brachysomus*), from Lower California. By W. N. Lockington.
(*In* U. S. National museum. Proceedings. Washington, 1881. 23½cm. v. 3, 1880, p. 284–286)
Issued September 28, 1880.

1. [Sparus brachysomus]

S 32-159

Library, Smithsonian Institution
Library of Congress [Q11.U55 vol. 3]

NL 0436604 DSI OU

Lockington, William N.
Description of a new species of *Agonidæ* (*Brachyopsis verrucosus*), from the coast of California. By W. N. Lockington.
(*In* U. S. National museum. Proceedings. Washington, 1881. 23½cm. v. 3, 1880, p. 60–63)
Issued May 6, 1880.

1. [Brachyopsis verrucosus]

S 32-132

Library, Smithsonian Institution
Library of Congress [Q11.U55 vol. 3]

NL 0436605 DSI OU

Lockington, William N.
Description of a new species of *Prionotus* (*Prionotus stephanophrys*), from the coast of California. By W. N. Lockington.
(*In* U. S. National museum. Proceedings. Washington, 1881. 23½cm. v. 3, 1880, p. 529–532)
Issued April 18, 1881.

1. Prionotus.

S 32-189

Library, Smithsonian Institution
Library of Congress [Q11.U55 vol. 3]

NL 0436606 DSI OU

Lockington, William N.
Note on a new flat-fish (*Lepidopsetta isolepis*) found in the markets of San Francisco. By W. N. Lockington.
(*In* U. S. National museum. Proceedings. Washington, 1881. 23½cm. v. 3, 1880, p. 325)
Issued October 27, 1880.

1. [Lepidopsetta isolepis]

S 32-168

Library, Smithsonian Institution
Library of Congress [Q11.U55 vol. 3]

NL 0436607 DSI OU

Lockington, William N.
Remarks on the species of the genus *Chirus* found in San Francisco market, including one hitherto undescribed. By W. N. Lockington.
(*In* U. S. National museum. Proceedings. Washington, 1881. 23½cm. v. 3, 1880, p. 53–57)
Issued May 6, 1880.

1. Rays (Fishes)

S 32-130

Library, Smithsonian Institution
Library of Congress [Q11.U55 vol. 3]

NL 0436608 DSI OU

Lockington, William N.
Review of the *Pleuronectidæ* of San Francisco. By W. N. Lockington.
(*In* U. S. National museum. Proceedings. Washington, 1880. 23½cm. v. 2, 1879, p. 69–108)
Issued July 1–September 19, 1879.

1. Flounders. I. Title.

S 32-83

Library, Smithsonian Institution
Library of Congress [Q11.U55 vol. 2]

NL 0436609 DSI OU CaBVaU

Lockitt, Charles Henry, 1877- *ed.*
The adventure of travel. Australian ed. London, New York, Longmans, Green [1943]
159 p. illus. 19 cm. (The Heritage of literature series, section A, no. 7)

1. Voyages and travels—Collections. I. Title.

G170.L6 910.8 53-51772 ‡

NL 0436610 DLC

Lockitt, Charles Henry, 1877- *ed.*
The art of the essayist. London, New York, Longmans, Green [1949]
255 p. front. 18 cm. [The Clifford library]

1. English essays. I. Title.

PR1363.L73 824.082 50-13426

NL 0436611 DLC CU

808.3 L81i Lockitt, Charles Henry, 1877- ed.
The imaginary eye-witness, edited by C. H. Lockitt ... London [etc.] Longmans, Green and co. [1937]
191p. (Half-title: The heritage of literature series. Section A, no.15)

1. History--Fiction. I. Title.

NL 0436612 IU

Lockitt, Charles Henry, 1877- *ed.*
More one-act plays. London, New York, Longmans, Green [1946]
xii, 207 p. 18 cm.
CONTENTS.—They went forth, by H. F. Rubinstein.—Hyacinth Halvey, by Lady Gregory.—Fours into seven won't go, by Val Gielgud and Stephen King-Hall.—Prelude to massacre, by Evan John.—An interlude of war, by G. P. Preedy.—Valley of a dream, by Mary Pakington.—Simon, by L. J. Hines.

1. English drama (Collections)

A 49-2644*

New York. Public Libr. for Library of Congress

NL 0436613 NN NcD

VOLUME 337

Lockitt, Charles Henry, 1877-
The relations of French and English society (1763 — 1793)... by C. H. Lockitt... London: Longmans, Green and Co., 1920. x, 136 p. 8°.

Thesis, London University, 1911.
Bibliography, p. 126-132.

1. France.—Relations (General), with Gt. Br. 2. Gt. Br.—Relations (General), with France. 3. Culture (British), France. 4. Culture (French), Gt. Br. 5. France.—Social life, 1763-93. 6. Gt. Br.—Social life, 1763-93.
N. Y. P. L. February 23, 1921.

NL 0436614 NN MB MH

Lockitt, Charles Henry, 1877-
The relations of French and English society (1763-1793) ... by C. H. Lockitt ... London, New York ₍etc.₎ Longmans, Green and co., 1920.
x, 136 p. 22cm. $2.50
"List of works consulted": p. 126-132.

1. France—Soc. life & cust. 2. England—Soc. life & cust. 3. Émigrés. I. Title.
20-17099
Library of Congress DC33.4.L6

NL 0436615 DLC CaBVaU PPL PU MiU OU OO OCl IaU NjP

PN 3321 L62 1949
Lockitt, Charles Henry, 1877-
Short stories of the past. Edited by C.H. Lockitt. London, Longmans, Green, 1950, c1949.
243 p. front. (Heritage of literature series, Section B, no. 27)

1. Short stories - Collections. I. Title.

NL 0436616 CaBVaU

RA917.7199 L816
Lockland, Ohio. Board of Trade.
The town of Lockland, offering decided advantages to manufacturers seeking a better location. ₍Lockland₎ 1895.
39p.illus.ports.22cm.

1. Lockland, Ohio.

NL 0436617 OC

Locklar, Henry Clay, 1878- joint comp.

White, Samuel Laurie, 1885- *comp.*
Citations to the Supreme court reports of Arkansas, volumes 1 to 100 inclusive, by S. L. White and H. C. Locklar. ₍Little Rock, Democrat print. & litho. co., 1913₎

Lockley, Mrs. Doris (Shellard) illus.

Lockley, Ronald Mathias, 1903-
Birds of the Green Belt and the country around London, by R. M. Lockley ... With plates and sketches by Doris Lockley. London, H. F. & G. Witherby, ltd. ₍1936₎

DA740 .S55L55
Lockley, Doris (Shellard) illus.

Lockley, Ronald Mathias, 1903- FOR OTHER EDITIONS SEE MAIN ENTRY
Dream island days; a record of the simple life, by R. M. Lockley. With sketches by Doris Lockley and eight plates from photographs. London, H. F. & G. Witherby, ltd. ₍1943₎

Lockley, Fred, 1871-1958. FOR OTHER EDITIONS SEE MAIN ENTRY

Bonney, Benjamin Franklin, 1838-
Across the plains by prairie schooner; personal narrative of B. F. Bonney of his trip to Sutter's fort, California, in 1846, and of his pioneer experiences in Oregon during the days of Oregon's provisional government, by Fred Lockley. Eugene, Ore., Koke-Tiffany co. ₍192-₎

₍**Lockley, Fred**₎ 1871-1958.
As one thief to another. ₍Salem, Or., 194-₎ 24 p. 16cm.
"To the reader" signed: Fred Lockley...C. H. Gram...₍and 6 others₎

1. No subject. I. Title.
N. Y. P. L. July 10, 1947

NL 0436622 NN OrU

₍LOCKLEY, FRED₎ 1871-1958.
₍Biographical material collected for the Who's who of Oregon department of the Oregon Journal₎
2 filing cases.

This material was furnished in response to requests from Mr. Lockley. Most of it is typewritten or written by hand, but there are some newspaper clippings.

NL 0436623 Or

Lockley, Fred, 1871-1958.
Captain Sol. Tetherow, wagon train master; personal narrative of his son, Sam. Tetherow, who crossed the plains to Oregon, in 1845, and personal narrative of Jack McNemee, who was born in Portland, Oregon, in 1848, and whose father built the fourth house in Portland. By Fred Lockley. Portland, Or., F. Lockley ₍1925?₎
27 p. 23cm.

1. Frontier and pioneer life—Oregon. 2. Overland journeys to the Pacific. 3. Tetherow, Solomon, b. 1800. I. Title.
37-10000
Library of Congress F880.L815
916.95

Or WaU PPT IdU MB ICU MWA WaSpG IdB OrSaW Wa OrCS CaBViPA MH ICN UU NBuU N CU CU-A TxU NjP ICN MH MtHi
NL 0436624 DLC OCl CSmH ODW CtY NjP MtU OrP WaSp NN

LOCKLEY, FRED, 1871-1958, comp.
A catalog of Americana, Oregon, Washington, California, British Columbia, Montana, Idaho; Indian wars, genealogy, overland expeditions, travel and exploration, biography, law, and some rare items relative to the far West. Portland, Fred Lockley ₍1936₎
31 p.

NL 0436625 Or

Lockley, Fred, 1871-1958.

Fred Lockley, republican candidate for Secretary of state; election card and letter. Author, 1920.

NL 0436626 OrP

Lockley, Fred, 1871-1958.
History of the Columbia river valley from The Dalles to the sea, by Fred Lockley ... Chicago, The S. J. Clarke publishing company, 1928.
3 v. front., illus., plates, ports. 27cm.
Vols. 2-3, biographical.

1. Columbia river valley. 2. Columbia river valley—Biog.
29-13349
Library of Congress F853.L82

Or WaSp Wa OrP WaTC WaS OrPR OrStbM OrU WaWW TxU WaU ICN OrP Or WaSpG MtU IdU OrU OrCS OrSaW OrHi
NL 0436627 DLC MtBC CaBVa CaBViP CaBVaU CU-B OCl NN

LOCKLEY, Fred, 1871-1958.
History of the first free delivery service of mail in Alaska at Nome, Alaska in 1900.
Portland, Ore. [n. pub. 1955?] 12p.

CaBViPA
NL 0436628 WaS IEdS Or OrP Wa CU-B OrU WaSpG

Lockley, Fred, 1871-1958, ed.
Impressions and observations of the Journal man. ₍Portland, Or., 1925-28₎
5 v. 27 cm.

Clippings relating the experiences of pioneer settlers in the Northwest as told to F.Lockley and pub.by him in the Portland, Oregon, Journal.

NL 0436629 NjP

LOCKLEY, FRED, 1871-1958.
₍Interview with Mrs. Lucretia (Perkins) Walker₎ (copied from the Oregon daily journal, 170'30)
₍2₎ l.

NL 0436630 Or

LOCKLEY, FRED, 1871-1958.
Journal man abroad ₍clippings from the Oregon daily journal, Jan. 30, - Nov. 2, 1918₎

NL 0436631 Or

[Lockley, Fred] 1871-1958.
Know your Oregon, by F.L. n. pub., n.d.
Typewritten notes of articles pub. in the Oregon Journal.

NL 0436632 OrP

₍Lockley, Fred₎ 1871-1958.

Know your Portland, by F.L. n.pub.n.d.

Typewritten notes of articles pub. in the Oregon Journal.

NL 0436633 OrP

Lockley, Fred, 1871-1958.
Life, civilization, the way of peace...
₍Portland, Author, n.d.₎

NL 0436634 OrCS

VOLUME 337

Lockley, Fred, 1871-1958.
"More power to you," by Fred Lockley and Marshall N. Dana. Portland, Or., The Oregon journal, 1934.
5 p. l., 112 p. illus. 30½cm.
Illustrated lining-papers.
A short sketch of the development of the Oregon country and the story of the Bonneville power and navigation project.
On cover: Oregon journal edition.
CONTENTS.—Bonneville, its background in history, by Fred Lockley.—Bonneville, its promise for the future, by M. N. Dana.
1. Bonneville dam. 2. Columbia river—Power utilization. 3. Northwest, Pacific. 4. Bonneville, Benjamin Louis Eulalie de, 1796-1878. I. Dana, Marshall Newport, 1885- II. Oregon journal, Portland. III. Title.
35—540
Library of Congress TC425.C7L6
[a41e1] 627.809795
WaS OrU-L OrLgE CaBViP OrHi
NL 0436635 DLC OrP WaTC IdU Wa WaSp MtHi Or OrU

LOCKLEY, FRED, 1871-1958.
Observations and impressions of the Journal man. (from the Oregon Journal, 1918-1923)
4 v. illus.
Incomplete.
v.1 has title: Journal man abroad.
Indexed in Oregon index.
NL 0436636 Or

F852 M5IL6 Lockley, Fred, 1871-1958.
The old emigrant trail, the story of Ezra Meeker and his ox-team.
[12]-22 p. port., illus. 26cm.
Extract from The Pacific monthly.
1. Meeker, Ezra, 1830-1928. I. Title.
NL 0436637 CU-B

Lockley, Fred,1871-1958.
Oregon folks. 7v. Author,n.d.
Typewritten notes including unpublished material.
NL 0436638 OrP

Lockley, Fred, 1871-1958.
Oregon folks, by Fred Lockley. "Oregon journal" ed. New York, The Knickerbocker press, 1927.
vii, 220 p. 19½cm.
1. Oregon—Hist. 2. Oregon—Biog. I. Title.
28—3821
Library of Congress F876.L82
WaWW Or OrSaW WaS WaU OrHi IdU CaBVaU CaBViPA LU
NL 0436639 DLC CBPac NjP WaTC OrP WaT Wa WaSp MtHi

Lockley, Fred, 1871-1958.
Oregon trail blazers, by Fred Lockley. New York, The Knickerbocker press, 1929.
v, 369 p. 20cm.
1. Frontier and pioneer life—Oregon. 2. Oregon—Biog. I. Title.
29—30534
Library of Congress F880.L82
CaBViPA CaBVa OrLgE OrStbM WaWW
OrU MiU MWA WaU IdU OrU-L OrCS OrAshS OrSaW CaBVaU
NL 0436640 DLC WaS WaTC MtU OrP Wa MtHi Or CaOTP PP

Lockley, Fred, 1871-1958.
Oregon's yesterdays, by Fred Lockley. New York, The Knickerbocker press, 1928.
v, 350 p. 20cm.
1. Frontier and pioneer life—Oregon. 2. Oregon—Biog. I. Title.
28—31187
Library of Congress F864.L8
CaBVa CaBVaU CaBViPA MtBC WaWW OrStbM IdPI
MWA WaU OrP WaS OrHi WaTC IdB WaSp MtHi Or IdU Wa
NL 0436641 DLC CoU N NBuU UU WaU TxU NjP OCl OClW

PNC Z071.953 L812p **[Lockley, Fred] 1871-1958.**
A picture story of how a great newspaper is made ... and a bit of its history. Portland, Ore. The Journal [192-?]
48 p. front., illus.
Cover title: The story of the Journal.
OrP InU MH ODW NcD GU WaSpG WaS MtU
NL 0436642 WaSp CaBViPA Wa NBuG WaU OrHi ICN OrMonO

Lockley, Fred, 1871-1958.
A picture story of how a great newspaper is made...and a bit of its history. The Journal, afternoon — Sunday. Portland, Ore. [193-] 48 p. illus. (incl. ports.) 19½cm.
Cover-title: The story of the Journal, by Fred Lockley.
1. Newspapers—U. S.—Oregon —Portland—Journal.
N. Y. P. L. March 16, 1942
NL 0436643 NN

[LOCKLEY, FRED] 1871-1958.
A picture story of how a great newspaper is made, and a bit of its history. Portland, Ore.: The Journal [1933?] 48 p. illus. (incl. ports.) 19½cm.
Cover-title: The story of the Journal, by Fred Lockley. Today's news today.
839925A. 1. Newspapers—U.S.—Ore.—Portland—Oregon Journal.
NL 0436644 NN IU MBrigStJ

---

308 Z Box 811 Lockley, Fred, 1871-1958.
Recollections of Benjamin Franklin Bonney. Eugene, Or., Koke-Tiffany co., 1923.
cover-title, 19 p.
"Reprinted from Oregon historical quarterly, Vol. XXIV, no. 1."
1. Overland journeys to the Pacific.
2. Bonney, Benjamin Franklin, b. 1838.
NL 0436645 NNC InU Wa OrP

Lockley, Fred, 1871-1958.
Reminiscences of Captain William P. Gray; Reminiscences of J.E.R.Harrell; Reminiscences of Colonel Henry Ernst Dosch; The McNemees and Tetherows with the migration of 1845. (see Oregon historical society Pioneer life in Oregon; extracts from the Quarterly Dec.1913, June 1923, Mar., Dec.1934. v.14 p.321-54; v.24, p.186-92; v.25, p.53-71, 353 377)
NL 0436646 OrP

Lockley, Fred, 1871-1958.
Reminiscences of Mrs. Frank Collins, neé Martha Elizabeth Gilliam. (see Oregon historical society Pioneer women of Oregon; extracts from the Quarterly Dec.1916 v.17, p.358-72)
NL 0436647 OrP

[LOCKLEY, FRED] 1871-1958.
Rev. William Wallace Youngson, D.D. [Clarke] 1928]
p.698-704, port.
Reprinted from the author's History of the Columbia river, v.3.
NL 0436648 Or

SPECIAL COLL. CA L812 **Lockley, Fred, 1871-1958.**
Scrapbook of mementos concerning services as Y.M.C.A. secretary with the American Expeditionary Force, 1917-1918.
1v.
Lockley was also a correspondent for the Portland, Ore. Journal.
1. European War, 1914-1918.
NL 0436649 OrU

SPECIAL COLL. CB L812 Lockley, Fred, 1871-1958, comp.
[Scrapbooks of biographies and reminiscences published by Fred Lockley in the Oregon Journal column, "Impressions and observations of a Journal man." Portland, Ore., n.d.]
58v.
1. Oregon. Biography.
NL 0436650 OrU

Lockley, Fred, 1871-1958.
The sheep industry in eastern Oregon. [N.p.n.pub.1907].
Illus.Q.
NL 0436651 CaBViP

Lockley, Fred, 1871-1958.
A talk with Edwin Markham, by Fred Lockley. [n. p., 192-]
[12] p. incl. port. 17½cm.
1. Markham, Edwin, 1852- 2. Death. 3. Immortality. I. Title.
24-16305
Library of Congress PS2363.L6
NL 0436652 DLC OU Or ViU PPRF NN NBuG

Lockley, Fred, 1871-1958.
To Oregon by ox-team in '47: the story of the coming of the Hunt family to the Oregon country and the experiences of G. W. Hunt in the gold diggings of California in 1849, by Fred Lockley. Portland, Or., F. Lockley [1924?]
cover-title, 15, [1] p. 23cm.
Condensed from the account furnished by Jeptha T. Hunt of Marion co., Or.
1. Hunt family. 2. Oregon. I. Hunt, Jeptha T., 1862- II. Title.
24—15726
Library of Congress F881.L82
CaBViPA CaBVaU OrHi OrSaW
TxU ODW OCl OClWHi PPT MWA MB WaU MtU IdU WaSp CaBVa
NL 0436653 DLC WaT Wa WaSpG UU MH ViU CU NcD IdIf

VOLUME 337

Microcard
PS 563 LOCKLEY, FRED, 1871-1958.
Ser.C To Oregon by ox-team in '47; the story of
no.242 the coming of the Hunt family to the Oregon country and the experiences of G.W. Hunt in the gold diggings of California in 1849. Portland, Or., The author, [1924?]
15 p. (Nineteenth century American literature on microcards, Ser. C [no. 242])

Title-page wanting.

Condensed from the account furnished by Jeptha T. Hunt of Marion Co., Oregon.

1. Oregon—Descr. 2. Overland journeys to the Pacific. 3. Hunt family. I. Hunt, Jeptha T., 1862- . II. Title. Microcd. ed.

NL 0436655 InU MsU MoU

Lockley, Fred, 1871-1958, ed. FOR OTHER EDITIONS SEE MAIN ENTRY

Dosch, Henry Ernst, 1841-
Vigilante days at Virginia City; personal narrative of Col. Henry E. Dosch, member of Fremonts body guard and one-time pony express rider. By Fred Lockley. Portland, Or., F. Lockley [1924]

Lockley, Frederick.
A Kansas settler.
11 p. (Overld. Monthly, v. 7, 1871, p. 22)

NL 0436657 MdBP

Lockley, Frederick.
The "Labor reform party."
[Chicago. Lakeside Publishing Co. 1870.] 356-364 pp. 23 cm.
Cut from the Western Monthly, vol. 4, December, 1870 [*5400a.1.4].
Contains an account of the National Labor Union.

K1265 — Labor Reform Party. United States. — National Labor Union.

NL 0436658 MB

Lockley, John G.
Dahlia growing made easy, by John G. Lockley ... Sydney, "The Amateur gardener" proprietary [1908]
128 p. incl. front., illus. 18cm.

1. Dahlia.

Agr 9-2508

Library, U. S. Dept. of Agriculture 97L81

NL 0436659 DNAL ICJ

Lockley, John G.
Rose growing made easy, by John G. Lockley ... (2d ed.) Sydney, "Amateur gardener" [190-]
153, [14] p. incl. front., illus. 18½cm.
Advertisements interspersed.

1. Rose.

Agr 9-2807

Library, U. S. Dept. of Agriculture 97L81R

NL 0436660 DNAL

Lockley, John G.
Rose growing made easy, by John G. Lockley ... Cornstalk pub. co., 1927.
153, [14] p. incl. front., illus. 18.5 cm.
Advertisements interspersed.

NL 0436661 OrP

Lockley, Lawrence Campbell, 1899- joint author.
Haase, Albert Ericssen, 1896-
Advertising agency compensation; theory, law, practice, by Albert E. Haase, in collaboration with Lawrence C. Lockley; with legal opinion by Isaac W. Digges ... A study made for Lee H. Bristol ... Allyn B. McIntire ... [and] Stuart Peabody ... as trustees for the Association of national advertisers, inc. [New York, National process company, inc., °1934]

Lockley, Lawrence Campbell, 1899-
Cases in marketing [by] Lawrence C. Lockley [and] Charles J. Dirksen. New York, Allyn and Bacon, 1954.
332 p. 22 cm.

1. Marketing. I. Dirksen, Charles J., joint author. II. Title.

HF5415.L56 658.8 54-8754 ‡

WaS
OrLgE GAT OC1U OU OCU PPT PU-W OC1 OC1W TU OrPS
NL 0436663 DLC IdPI CaBVa FTaSU ICU MiU PPT OrCS

Lockley, Lawrence Campbell, 1899-
Direct mail advertising for life insurance, by Lawrence C. Lockley ... Los Angeles, 1926.
cover-title, 3-19 p. 23 cm.
1. Insurance, Life. 2. Advertising - Insurance, Life.

NL 0436664 CU NN

Lockley, Lawrence Campbell, 1899-
Faulty paragraphs for composition classes, by Lawrence Campbell Lockley... and Phyllis Harrington Lockley... San Francisco, Cal.: Harr Wagner Pub. Co. [1923.] 132 p. 12°.

1. Composition (Literary), English. 2. Lockley, Phyllis Harrington, jt. au.

March 24, 1924.

NL 0436665 NN

Lockley, Lawrence Campbell, 1899-
Instructional notes to accompany Principles of effective letter writing, by Lawrence Campbell Lockley ... (Rev. 2d ed.) New York and London, McGraw-Hill book company, inc., 1933.
1 p. l., iii-v, 114 numb. l. 27½cm.
Lithoprinted.
"References for further assignments on correct English": leaves 4 and 5.

1. Commercial correspondence—Study and teaching. I. Title.
CA 33-944 Unrev'd
Library of Congress HF5721.L632 1933
——— Copy 2.
Copyright A 66639 651.75

NL 0436666 DLC OC1W

Lockley, Lawrence Campbell, 1899-
Making letters build business, by Lawrence C. Lockley ... [Los Angeles, °1925]
127 p. 22½cm.

1. Commercial correspondence. I. Title.
26-3177
Library of Congress HF5721.L6

NL 0436667 DLC NcD

Lockley, Lawrence Campbell, 1899-
Principles of effective letter-writing, by Lawrence Campbell Lockley ... 1st ed. New York [etc.] McGraw-Hill book company, inc., 1927.
x, 344 p. illus., plates, facsims. 21cm. $3.00
Bibliography: p. 330-337.

1. Commercial correspondence. I. Title.

27-11053 Revised
Library of Congress HF5721.L63

ICJ PPGi PPT OC1W OC1ND OC1 MiU OU NcRS
NL 0436668 DLC MH MtU Or OC1h WaPS CU KEmT NN MB

Lockley, Lawrence Campbell, 1899-
Principles of effective letter writing, by Lawrence Campbell Lockley ... 2d ed. New York and London, McGraw-Hill book company, inc., 1933.
x, 440 p. illus., plates (1 double) 23½cm.
Bibliography: p. 432-434.

1. Commercial correspondence. I. Title.
33-13053
Library of Congress HF5721.L63 1933

Copyright A 61838 651.75

NL 0436669 DLC TU ViU OC1JC OC1 OU MiU OC1W ICRL NN

Lockley, Lawrence Campbell, 1899-
... A road-map to literature; good books to read. Lawrence Campbell Lockley and Percy Hazen Houston. Girard, Kansas, Haldeman-Julius company [c1926]
89 p. 22 cm. (Big blue book no. B-22. Ed. by E. Haldeman-Julius)
1. Bibliography - Best books. 2. Books and reading. I. Houston, Percy Hazen, jt. auth. II. Title.

NL 0436670 CU

Lockley, Lawrence Campbell, 1899-
The value of intra-store television as a sales promotion medium
see under Jonas, Hilda.

LOCKLEY, Lawrence Campbell, 1899-
Vertical cooperative advertising. Thesis, Harvard University, [Graduate School of Business Administration], 1930, [1931].

Typewritten. 4°. Tables.
"Bibliography", ff. 223-226.

NL 0436672 MH

Lockley, Lawrence Campbell, 1899-
Vertical cooperative advertising, by Lawrence Campbell Lockley ... a study undertaken at the suggestion of and in conjunction with the Association of national advertisers, inc. New York and London, McGraw-Hill book company, inc., 1931.
xiii, 267 p. 21cm. [Harvard business studies]
Bibliography: p. 257-259.

1. Advertising. I. Association of national advertisers. II. Title.
31-5661
Library of Congress HF5823.L73

Copyright A 34410 [a36f1] 659.1

ICJ MB NN PPT PP
NL 0436673 DLC OrCS WaS MtU CoU ScU CU OLak MiU OC1

Lockley, Lawrence Campbell, 1899-
Writing to-day's business letters ...
Los Angeles, First national trust & savings bank [192-?]
cover-title, [14] p. 22.5 cm.

NL 0436674 MH

VOLUME 337

Lockley, Ronald Mathias, 1903–
Bird-ringing; the art of bird study by individual marking, by R. M. Lockley and Rosemary Russell. London, Lockwood, 1953.
119 p. illus. 19 cm.
Includes bibliography.

1. Bird-banding. I. Russell, Rosemary, joint author. II. Title.

QL677.5.L6 598.2 54—16897 ‡

MB NN NIC DSI CaBVaU MtU Or OrP
NL 0436675 DLC KEmT WaU NcD CtY TxU PSt MiD PP DI

QL 690 .G7 L83 Lockley,Ronald Mathias,1903-
The birds of Pembrokeshire,compiled for the West Wales field society by R.M.Lockley in collaboration with Geoffrey C.S.Ingram and H. Morrey Salmon. [Cardiff, Western mail & echo ltd., 1949?]
71 p. plates,map (on lining papers) 21½ cm.
"Bibliographical": p.37-38.
1.Aves--Wales--Pembrokeshire. I.Ingram, Geoffrey C S. II.Salmon,H Morrey. III.West Wales field society.

NL 0436676 MiU

Lockley, Ronald Mathias, 1903–
Birds of the Green Belt and the country around London, by R. M. Lockley ... With plates and sketches by Doris Lockley. London, H. F. & G. Witherby, ltd. [1936]
xix, 236 p. front., illus., plates. 18cm. (Birdlovers' manuals)
"Transport guide": p. 213-236.

1. Birds—England—London. I. Lockley, Mrs. Doris (Shellard) illus. II. Title.

A 38-558

Iowa. State coll. Library for Library of Congress

NL 0436677 IaAS NIC

Lockley, Ronald Mathias, 1903–
Birds of the sea. Colour plates by R. B. Talbot Kelly. London, New York, Penguin Books, 1945.
32, 24 p. illus. 19 cm. (The King penguin books, K2)
Includes bibliography.

1. Sea birds. 2. Birds—Gt. Brit. I. Title.

QL690.G7L59 63-721 ‡

NL 0436678 DLC CaBViP NcD

Lockley, Ronald Mathias, 1903–
The charm of the Channel Islands. London, Evans Bros. [1950]
136 p. plates, map (on lining papers) 23 cm.
Bibliography: p. 132.

1. Channel Islands—Descr. & trav. I. Title.

DA670.C4L6 914.234 51-3487

NL 0436679 DLC MH NN Wa CaBVa CaBViP

914.234 L816C Lockley, Ronald Mathias, 1903–
The charm of the Channel Islands. London, Evans Bros. [1952]
136 p. plates, map (on lining papers) 23 cm.
Bibliography: p. 132.
"First published 1950."

1. Channel Islands—Descr. & trav. I. Title.

NL 0436680 NcD MB

914.23 L118C Lockley, Ronald Mathias, 1903-
The Charm of the Channel Islands. Bentley, 1953.
136 p. illus.

NL 0436681 WaT

Lockley, Ronald Mathias, 1903–
The cinnamon bird. Illus. by C. F. Tunnicliffe. London, New York, Staples Press [1948]
79 p. col. plates. 22 cm.

1. Birds—Legends and stories. I. Title.

QL795.B57L6 598.81 49-22726*

NL 0436682 DLC CaBViP

Lockley, Ronald Mathias, 1903–
Dream island, a record of the simple life, by R. M. Lockley; with sketches by D. Lockley. London, H. F. & G. Witherby [1930]
192 p. front., illus., plates. 22½cm.
Description of visits to islands along the coast of Pembroke, Wales.

1. Skokholm island. 2. Natural history—Outdoor books. 3. Pembrokeshire, Wales—Descr. & trav. I. Lockley, D., illus. II. Title.

31-22041 Revised

Library of Congress DA740.S55L54
[r44c2] [570.7] 914.299

NL 0436683 DLC NN MB

Lockley, Ronald Mathias, 1903–
Dream island days; a record of the simple life, by R. M. Lockley. With sketches by Doris Lockley and eight plates from photographs. London, H. F. & G. Witherby, ltd. [1943]
144 p. front., illus. (incl. map) plates. 22cm.
Map on lining-paper.
"First published separately as 'Dream island' in 1930 and 'Island days' in 1934. Revised and published, in one volume, 1943."

1. Skokholm island. 2. Natural history—Outdoor books. 3. Pembrokeshire, Wales—Descr. & trav. I. Lockley, Doris (Shellard) illus. II. Title.

A 43-2891

Harvard univ. Library for Library of Congress DA740.S55L55
† 914.299

NL 0436684 MH CtY DLC

Lockley, R[onald] M[athias], 1903-
Dream island days; a record of the simple life ... Lond.Witherby[1946].
144p.illus.plates,map,O.

NL 0436685 CaBViP

Lockley, Ronald Mathias, 1903–
Early morning island; or, A dish of sprats, written down and photographed by R. M. Lockley ... London [etc.] G. G. Harrap & co., ltd. [1939]
2 p. l., 7-122, [1] p. front., plates, ports. 20½cm.
Eight year old Ann Lockley's account of her summer on Skokholm as told to her father. cf. Foreword.
"First published 1939."

1. Lockley, Ann. 2. Skokholm island. I. Title.

40-1149

Library of Congress DA740.S55L56 1939
Copyright A ad int. 25494 914.299

NL 0436686 DLC

Lockley, Ronald Mathias, 1903–
Gilbert White. London, H. F. & G. Witherby [1954]
127 p. illus. 21 cm. (Great naturalists series)

1. White, Gilbert, 1720-1793.

QH31.W58L6 925.74 54-33283 ‡

WaE CaBViP
NL 0436687 DLC NN PU MB OU IU MH-L MdU CtY CaBVaU

[S]52 [L]G Lockley, Ronald Mathias, 1903-
The golden year. London, Witherby, 1948.
183 p.

1. Wales. Agriculture. 2. Wales. Natural history. I. Title.

NL 0436688 DNAL CaBViP

S 521 L624 1950 Lockley, Ronald Mathias, 1903-
The golden year [by] R. M. Lockley. With drawings by Phyllida Lumsden. London, Readers Union, Witherby, 1950.
183 p. illus. 21 cm.

1. Country life - Gt. Brit. I. Title.

NL 0436689 CaBVaU CaBVa CaBViP

W.C.L. 914.2 L816I Lockley, Ronald Mathias, 1903–
I know an island, by R. M. Lockley. London, G. G. Harrap [1938]
3 p. l., 5-299, [1] p. front., illus. (maps) plates, ports. 22½cm.

CONTENTS.—Skokholm.—Grassholm.—Ramsey.—Bardsey.—The Blaskets.—Heligoland.—Fair isle.—North Ronaldshay.—The Faeroes.—The Westmann islands.—Skokholm again.

1. Skokholm island. 2. Birds—Islands of the Atlantic. 3. Islands of the Atlantic—Descr. & trav. I. Title.

NL 0436690 NcD PPL

QH81 .L8 Lockley, Ronald Mathias, 1903-
I know an island. New York, D. Appleton-Century, 1939.
299 p. illus., maps. 20cm.
CONTENTS.—Skokholm.—Grassholm.—Ramsey.—Bardsey.—The Blaskets.—Heligoland.—Fair Isle.—North Ronaldshay.—The Faeroes.—The Westmann Islands.—Skokholm again.
1. Skokholm Island. 2. Birds—Islands of the Atlantic. 3. Island of the Atlantic—Descr. & trav. I. Title.

NL 0436691 MB NN

Lockley, Ronald Mathias, 1903–
I know an island, by R. M. Lockley. New York, London, D. Appleton-Century company incorporated, 1939.
3 p. l., 5-299, [1] p. front., illus. (maps) plates, ports. 22½cm.
Printed in Great Britain.
CONTENTS.—Skokholm.—Grassholm.—Ramsey.—Bardsey.—The Blaskets.—Heligoland.—Fair isle.—North Ronaldshay.—The Faeroes.—The Westmann islands.—Skokholm again.

1. Skokholm island. 2. Birds—Islands of the Atlantic. 3. Islands of the Atlantic—Descr. & trav. I. Title.

39-27554

Library of Congress DA740.S55L6
914.2

OCIW PHC PU PP
NL 0436692 DLC WaS WaT Or OrCS Wa NcRS OCl OU OOxM

VOLUME 337

Lockley, Ronald Mathias, 1903–
I know an island. With illus. by James Lucas. ⌈London, 1947⌉
242 p. illus., maps. 20 cm. (Harrap's country-lovers library)
CONTENTS.—Skokholm.—Grassholm.—Ramsey.—Bardsey.—The Blaskets.—Heligoland.—Fair Isle.—North Ronaldshay.—The Faeroes.—The Westmann Islands.—Skokholm again.

1. Skokholm Island. 2. Birds—Islands of the Atlantic. 3. Islands of the Atlantic—Descr. & trav. I. Title.
DA740.S55L6 1947 914.2 47-29448*

NL 0436693 DLC CaBViP CLSU

Lockley, Ronald Mathias, 1903–
Inland farm, by R. M. Lockley. London, H. F. & G. Witherby ⌈1943⌉
191 p. illus. (incl. plans) plates. 20cm.
"First published 1943."

1. Agriculture — Wales — Pembrokeshire. 2. Agriculture—Skokholm Island. I. Title.
Library of Congress S521.L6 44-21936
630.942

NL 0436694 DLC MtU

LOCKLEY, Ronald Mathias, 1903–
Island days; a sequel to "Dream island," by R.M.Lockley, with sketches by Doris Lockley, and fourteen plates from photographs. London: H.F. & G.Witherby[, 1934]. 120 p. incl. map. front., illus., plates. 23cm.
Map on end papers.

730093A. 1. Skokholm island, Wales. I. Title.

NL 0436695 NN MB

HD1491 W26P4 Lockley, Ronald Mathias, 1903-
The island farmers, with sketches by Phyllida Lumsden. London, H.F. & G. Witherby, Ltd. ⌈1946⌉
174 p. illus.,plates,maps. 20cm.

1. Agriculture, Cooperative - Wales - Pembrokeshire. 2. Agriculture - Wales - Pembrokeshire. I. Title.

NL 0436696 CU IU INS CU-A

Lockley, Ronald Mathias, 1903– joint ed.

QH144 .B8
Buxton, John, ed.
Island of Skomer, a preliminary survey of the natural history of Skomer Island, Pembrokeshire, undertaken for the West Wales Field Society and edited by John Buxton and R. M. Lockley. London, New York, Staples Press ⌈1950⌉

Lockley, Ronald Mathias, 1903–
Islands round Britain ⌈by⌉ R. M. Lockley. With 8 plates in colour and 27 illustrations in black & white. London, Collins, 1945.
47, ⌈1⌉ p. illus., col. plates, maps. 23 cm. (*Half-title:* Britain in pictures)
The British people in pictures.
"A short bibliography": p. ⌈48⌉

1. Gt. Brit.—Descr. & trav. 2. Islands—Gt. Brit. I. Title.
DA668.L6 914.2 45-11380

NL 0436698 DLC OCl CaBVa CaBViP OrStbM KMK OU FMU

DA668 L8161 Lockley, Ronald Mathias, 1903-
Islands round Britain. London, Collins, 1946.
47 p. illus., col. plates, maps. 23cm. (Britain in pictures)

The British people in pictures.
First pub. 1945.

1. Gt. Brit. - Descr. & trav. 2. Islands - Gt. Brit. I. Title. II. Series: Britain in pictures.

NL 0436699 GU

Lockley, Ronald Mathias, 1903–
Letters from Skokholm, illus. by Charles Tunnicliffe. London, J. M. Dent, 1947.
ix, 243 p. illus., maps. 22 cm.

1. Natural history—Skokholm Island. 2. Birds—Skokholm Island. I. Title.
QH144.L6 574.942 48-5054*

NL 0436700 DLC CtY TxU NN

Lockley, Ronald Mathias, 1903– *ed.*
The nature-lovers' anthology. With illus. by Phyllida Lumsden. London, H. F. & G. Witherby, 1951.
309 p. illus. 21 cm.

1. Nature in literature. I. Title.
PN6071.N3L52 808.8 52-21534 ‡

NL 0436701 DLC MB

Lockley, Ronald Mathias, 1903–
Puffins; illustrated with a coloured front. by C. F. Tunnicliffe, drawings in the text by Nancy Catford, and 16 pages of photos., and maps. London, Dent ⌈1953⌉
186 p. illus. 23 cm.

1. Puffins.
QL696.A3L6 1953 *598.2 598.44 53—39489 ‡

NL 0436702 DLC CtY NIC NcRS NN MB PPAN OCl TxU MtU CaBVaU CaBViP

Lockley, Ronald Mathias, 1903–
Puffins. Illustrated with a coloured front. by C. F. Tunnicliffe; drawings in the text by Nancy Catford; and 16 pages of photos. and maps. New York, Devin-Adair Co. ⌈1953⌉
186 p. illus. 22 cm.

1. Puffins.
[QL696] *598.2 598.44 54-4972 ‡
Printed for U. S. Q. B. R. by Library of Congress

NL 0436703 WaS Or WaTC NBuU KEmT NBuC FU TU PSt NcD N

Lockley, Ronald Mathias, 1903–
The saga of the grey seal. Introducing the natural history of the grey seal of the North Atlantic. With photos. & maps by the author. Black-and-white drawings by Phillida and John Mead. ⌈1st American ed.⌉ New York, Devin-Adair ⌈1955⌉
149 p. illus. 22 cm.
First published in London in 1954 under title: The seals and the curragh.

1. Seals (Animals) I. Title.
QL737.P6L65 1955 *599.745 599.748 55-7741 ‡

NL 0436704 DLC WaS Wa Or OrLgE OrCS MtU DSI CSt KEmT FU LU MB NN IU CtY OCl PP PPAN ICJ CaBVaU

Lockley, Ronald Mathias, 1903–
The sea bird as an individual: results of ringing experiments, by R. M. Lockley ...
(*In* Smithsonian institution. Annual report, 1939. Washington, 1940. 23½cm. p. 341-353)
"Reprinted ... from Proceedings of the Royal institution, vol. 30, pt. 3, 1938."
"References": p. 353.

1. Water-birds. 2. Puffinidae. I. Title.
Library of Congress Q11.S66 1939 41-4154

NL 0436705 DLC OU OC1MN WaS

Lockley, Ronald Mathias, 1903– joint author.
FOR OTHER EDITIONS SEE MAIN ENTRY
QL679 .F5 1954
Fisher, James, 1912–
Sea-birds; an introduction to the natural history of the sea-birds of the North Atlantic, by James Fisher and R. M. Lockley. Boston, Houghton, Mifflin, 1954.

Lockley, Ronald Mathias, 1903–
The seals and the curragh; introducing the natural history of the grey seal of the North Atlantic. With photos. & maps by the author. Black-and-white drawings by Phillida and John Mead. London, J. M. Dent ⌈1954⌉
149 p. illus. 22 cm.
Includes bibliography.

1. Seals (Animals) I. Title.
QL737.P6L65 1954 *599.745 599.748 54-44369 ‡

NL 0436707 DLC PU PBL NN NcD OrU CaBVaU CaBViP

Lockley, Ronald Mathias, 1903–
The sea's a thief, a novel by Ronald M. Lockley. London New York ⌈etc.⌉ Longmans, Green and co. ⌈1936⌉
viii, 316 p. 19½cm.

I. Title.
Library of Congress PZ3.L81142Se 36-27490

NL 0436708 DLC ViU PPSCI

Lockley, Ronald Mathias, 1903–
Shearwaters ⌈by⌉ R. M. Lockley. London, J. M. Dent & sons ltd ⌈1942⌉
xi, ⌈1⌉, 238 p. front., illus. (incl. maps) plates. 22cm.
"First published 1942."

1. Puffinidae.
Library of Congress QL696.P8L6 42-16700
598.44

NL 0436709 DLC PP OCl OU NcD CaBVaU CtY CU MtU WaS Or MtBC

Lockley, Ronald Mathias, 1903–
Shearwaters. New York, Devin-Adair Co.
238 p. illus. 22 cm.

1. Water-birds. 2. Manx shearwater.
[QL696] *598.2 598.44 54-4971 ‡
Printed for U. S. Q. B. R. by Library of Congress

NL 0436710 TU

VOLUME 337

Biology
QL696
P665L6 Lockley, Ronald Mathias, 1903-
Shearwaters, by R. M. Lockley. New York, Devin-Adair Co. [1947, 1942]
xi, 238 p. illus., plates, maps. 22 cm.

NL 0436711 FMU NBuC LU MeB

QL696
P8L6
1947 Lockley, Ronald Mathias, 1903-
Shearwaters. New York, Devin-Adair, [1949,c1942]
238 p. illus.
1. Puffinidae. I. T.

NL 0436712 NBuU

Lockley, Ronald Mathias, 1903-
Shearwaters. New York, Devin-Adair Co. [1954?]
238 p. illus. 22 cm.

1. Water-birds. 2. Manx shearwater.
[QL696] 54—4971 ‡/CD
*598.2 598.44
Printed for Card Div. Library of Congress [a66f½]

NL 0436713 MB NcU CaBVaU

Lockley, Ronald Mathias, 1903-
Travels with a tent in western Europe. London, Odhams Press [1953]
240 p. illus. 22 cm.

1. Europe—Descr. & trav.—1945- I. Title.
D967.L6 914 54-27358 ‡

NL 0436714 DLC CaBViP CaBVa CaBVaU CLSU TxU MH NN

Lockley, Ronald Mathias, 1903-
The way to an island, by R. M. Lockley. Illustrated with 19 photographs and a map. London, J. M. Dent & sons ltd. [1941]
xi, 208 p. front. (port.) plates. 22cm. (*Half-title: Travellers' tales*)
Map on t-p.
"First published 1941."

1. Skokholm island. 2. Natural history—Outdoor books. 3. Outdoor life. I. Title.
A 42-17
New York. Public library for Library of Congress

NL 0436715 NN CaBViP INS PPL

Forestry Library
Lockley, Ronald Mathias, 1903-
The way to an island, by R. M. Lockley. Illustrated with 19 photographs and a map. London, J. M. Dent & sons ltd. [1947]
xi, 208 p. front. (port.) plates. 22cm. (*Half-title: Travellers' tales*)
Map on t-p.
"First published 1941."

1. Skokholm island. 2. Natural history—Outdoor books. 3. Outdoor life. I. Title.

NL 0436716 CtY

R.Rm.
BY568
.S86L8 Lockley, Walter H., d. 1934.
1909 The story of Stockport Circuit of the United Methodist Church; a series of lectures.
in: Stockport, T. Hooley and Co., 1909.
GTS vii, 200p. frontis., illus. 20cm.

1. United Methodist Church in Gt. Brit.—Southport circuit. 2. Methodist church in Southport. I. Title.

NL 0436717 IEG NcD

Locklin, Anne Littlefield.
Tidewater tales [by] Anne Littlefield Locklin, illustrated by Rafaello Busoni. New York, The Viking press, 1942.
2 p. l., 7-222 p. illus. 21cm.
"First published October 1942."

I. Busoni, Rafaello, illus. II. Title. 42-24040
Library of Congress PZ7.L812Ti

NL 0436718 DLC Or NN PP OCl PPI

Locklin, Curtis Brockway.
A handy book on assaying, comprising fire assay, wet assay, occurence [!] and description of the principal metals, tables of rock classification, etc. Comp. and pub. by Curtis Brockway Locklin ... Rev. to date, January 1914 ... [Bodie, Cal.] °1914.
2 p. l., [3]-51 p. port., fold. tab. 17½cm.

1. Assaying. 16-1078
Library of Congress TN550.L76

NL 0436719 DLC

385.2312 [Locklin, David Philip, 1897-]
L812d Discrimination between places under section 3 of the Interstate commerce act. [Chicago] 1934.
p.613-640.

Caption title.
Signed: D. Philip Locklin.
"Reprinted for private circulation from the Journal of political economy, vol.XLII, no.5, October, 1934."

NL 0436720 IU

Locklin, David Philip, 1897-
Economics of transportation, by D. Philip Locklin ... Chicago, Business publications, inc., 1935.
xii, 788 p. illus. (maps) diagrs. 23½cm.
"Selected references" at end of each chapter.

1. Transportation—U. S. 2. Railroads—U. S. 3. Railroads—U. S.—Rates. I. Title.
35-10137
Library of Congress HE2741.L7
Copyright A 84061 385.1320973

NL 0436721 DLC CoU CU FU OrU OrCS PPD PU-W PSC OCU OU MiU NcRS NcD OClCC NcU ViU MB

Locklin, David Philip, 1897-
Economics of transportation... Chicago, Business publications, inc., 1935 [i.e., 1936]

"Fourth printing, December, 1936."

NL 0436722 OO

Locklin, David Philip, 1897-
Economics of transportation, by D. Philip Locklin ... Rev. ed. Chicago, Business publications, inc., 1938.
x, 863 p. illus. (maps) diagrs. 23½cm.
"First printing, August, 1938."
"Selected references" at end of each chapter.

1. Transportation—U. S. 2. Railroads—U. S. 3. Railroads—U. S.—Rates. I. Title.
38-23534
Library of Congress HE2741.L7 1938
Copyright A 120148 385.1320973

NL 0436723 DLC CaBVaU Or WaS PV ICJ OClU OU OCl OEac PU-W PHC NcRS PLF ViU CoU CU ICRL

Locklin, David Philip, 1897-
Economics of transportation, by D. Philip Locklin ... Rev. ed. Chicago, Business publications, inc., 1938. [i.e. 1939]
x, 863 p. illus. (maps) diagrs. 23½cm.
"First printing, August, 1938, Second printing, February, 1939."
"Selected references" at end of each chapter.
On spine: A business publications text.

1. Transportation—U. S. 2. Railroads—U. S. 3. Railroads—U. S.—Rates. I. Title.

NL 0436724 ViU OU

Locklin, David Philip, 1897-
Economics of transportation, by D. Philip Locklin ... 3d ed. Chicago, R. D. Irwin, inc., 1947.
x, 885 p. illus. (maps) diagrs. 23½cm.
"First printing, February, 1947."
"Selected references" at end of each chapter.

1. Transportation—U. S. 2. Railroads—U. S. 3. Railroads—U. S.—Rates. I. Title.
HE2741.L7 1947 385.132 47-21026

NL 0436725 DLC OU CU AU MiU WaTC MiHM ICU ICJ ViU OrCS WaSpG WaE WaSp

---

Locklin, David Philip, 1897-
Economics of transportation, by D. Philip Locklin ... 3d ed. Chicago, R. D. Irwin, inc., 1949
x, 885 p. illus. (maps) diagrs. 23½ cm.
"First printing, February, 1947."
"Selected references" at end of each chapter.

1. Transportation—U. S. 2. Railroads—U. S. 3. Railroads—U. S.—Rates. I. Title.

NL 0436726 OClJC

Locklin, David Philip, 1897- 9385.973A272R
Economics of transportation. 3d ed. Chicago, R. D. Irwin, 1951.
x, 885 p. illus., maps. 24cm.
Includes bibliographies.

1. Transportation—U. S. 2. Railroads—U. S. 3. Railroads—U. S.—Rates. I. Title.

NL 0436727 MB WaS OrPS CaBVa

Locklin, David Philip, 1897-
Economics of transportation. 4th ed. Homewood, Ill., R. D. Irwin, 1954.
916 p. illus. 24 cm. (The Irwin series in economics)

1. Transportation — U. S. 2. Railroads — U. S. 3. Railroads — U. S.—Rates. I. Title.
HE2741.L7 1954 385.132 54—587 ‡

NL 0436728 DLC CaBVa CaBVaU TxU ViU IEN PU-W PSC PP PPD IU TU OOxM CU NcGU Or OrU WaS WaWW MtU PPT PSt OU OCl OU OCU MiHM

VOLUME 337

385.2312 Locklin, David Philip, 1897-
L812f Freight rates and the Hoch-Smith resolution.
p.[361]-370.
Caption title.

"Reprinted from the journal of land & public utility economics, November, 1927."

NL 0436729 IU

A385.231 Locklin, David Philip, 1897-
L811 The literature on railway rate theory. [Boston] 1933.
cover-title, p.167-230.

"Reprinted from the Quarterly journal of economics, vol.XLVII, February, 1933."

NL 0436730 IU

---

q385.11 Locklin, David Philip, 1897-
L812ra Railroad legislation of 1933. [Chicago, 1934]
p.[13]-21.

Caption title.
"Reprinted from The Journal of land & public utility economics, February 1934."

NL 0436731 IU

Locklin, David Philip, 1897–
Railroad regulation since 1920, by D. Philip Locklin ... Chicago & New York, A. W. Shaw and company; London, A. W. Shaw and company, limited, 1928.
vii, 211 p. diagr. 21½cm.
Bibliography: p. [199]–206.
ViU HE2757.1928.L6
—— —— Copy 2.
Copyright A 674
—— 1931 Supplement, by D. Philip Locklin ... New York and London, McGraw-Hill book company, inc., 1931.
vii, 31 p. 20cm.
1. Railroads—U. S. 2. Transportation act, 1920. I. Title.
28-28988 Revised
Library of Congress HE2757.1928.L6 Suppl.
—— —— Copy 2.
Copyright A 36204 [r31k2]

MB ViU
FMU NIC CU PPD PHC PPT PU MH-BA OO MiU OU OCl ICJ
NL 0436732 DLC NcD WaS WaTC WaWW OrP OrPR Or PSt

Locklin, David Philip, 1897–
Railroad regulation since 1920, by D. Philip Locklin ... New York, London, McGraw-Hill book company, inc., 1928.
vii, 211 p. diagr. 21cm.
Bibliography: p. [199]–206.

1. Railroads—U. S. 2. Transportation act, 1920. I. Title.
30-27860
Library of Congress HE2757.1928.L62 385.0973

NL 0436733 DLC PSC PPB

HE2757
1928
.L63 Locklin, David Philip, 1897-
Railroad regulation since 1920.
N.Y., Lond., 1928
211p. 21 cm.
With this is issued the author's... 1931 supplement... N.Y. and Lond., 1931. (31p. bd at front of vol.)

NL 0436734 DLC

Locklin, David Philip, 1897–
Regulation of security issues by the Interstate commerce commission, by David Philip Locklin ... [Urbana, Ill., 1927]
189, [1] p. 24cm.
Thesis (PH. D.)—University of Illinois, 1926.
Vita.
"Reprinted from the University of Illinois studies in the social sciences, vol. XIII, no. 4."
Bibliography: p. 181–186.

1. Railroads—U. S.—Finance. 2. Securities—U. S. 3. U. S. Interstate commerce commission. I. Title.
27-13546
Library of Congress HE2236.L65 1926
Univ. of Illinois Libr.

DLC
NL 0436735 IU NcD PU-W PBm PU OU MiU OCU OOxM MH

Locklin, David Philip, 1897–
Regulation of security issues by the Interstate commerce commission, by David Philip Locklin ... Urbana, University of Illinois [1927]
189 p. 24cm. (*Added t.-p.:* University of Illinois studies in the social sciences, vol. XIII, no. 4)
Published also as thesis (PH. D.) University of Illinois, 1926.
Bibliography: p. 181–186.

1. Railroads—U. S.—Finance. 2. Securities—U. S. 3. U. S. Interstate commerce commission. I. Title.
27-27141
H31.I4 vol. XIII, no. 4
HE2236.L65 1927

PU ViU-L OCl OO NcU ICJ ViU
NL 0436736 DLC GU-L MU CoU NBuU-L OrPR PU-L PPB

Locklin, David Philip, 1897-
HE2123
.A52
1943 j U. S. *Transportation investigation and research board.*
... Report on interterritorial freight rates. [Washington] 1943.

Locklin, David Philip, 1897-
HE2123
.A52
1943 k U. S. *Transportation investigation and research board.*
... Report on interterritorial freight rates. Letter from the Board of investigation and research transmitting Report on interterritorial freight rates ... Washington, U. S. Govt. print. off., 1943.

385.73 Locklin, David Philip, 1897-
L81s ... Statistical analysis of 31 reorganizations of class I railways, 1914-1933 inclusive. Prepared ... in the Bureau of statistics of the Interstate commerce commission but not considered or adopted by the commission. [Washington? 1934?]
14p. XXIV tab.

At head of title: Interstate commerce commission. Bureau of statistics.
Caption title.
Revised issue.
Mimeographed.

NL 0436739 IU

Locklin, David Philip, 1897-

U. S. *Transportation investigation and research board.*
... Summary report on study of interterritorial freight rates. [Washington, 1943]

Locklin, David Philip, 1897-

U. S. *Transportation investigation and research board.*
... Summary report on study of interterritorial freight rates. Letter from the Board of investigation and research transmitting a summary report on its study of interterritorial freight rates ... Washington, U. S. Govt. print. off., 1943.

385.231 Locklin, David Philip, 1897-
L81t Transport coordination and rate policy ... [Chicago] 1937.
cover-title, p.417-428.

"Reprinted from Harvard business review, summer, 1937."

1. Railroads--U.S.--Rates. 2. Transportation--Rates. I. Title.

NL 0436742 IU

385.2 Locklin, David Philip, 1897-
L81w The weak-and-strong-road problem. [Chicago, 1934]
p.[337]-349.

Caption title.
"Reprinted from the Journal of land & public utility economics, Nov., 1934."

NL 0436743 IU

E 639.73 Locklin, Harrison Duane, 1891-
W27bpw ... Berry cultivation in Western Washington
no.16 ... Pullman, State college, 1930.
22 [1]p. illus., tables. (Western Washington experiment station, Puyallup. Bulletin no. 16)

1. State college of Washington authors, Works of. 2. Berries. 3. Fruit - Washington (State).

NL 0436744 WaPS

E639.73 Locklin, Harrison Duane, 1891-
W27bpw ... Culture of Christmas holly ... Pullman,
no.7 State college, 1928.
25p. illus. (Western Washington experiment station, Puyallup. Bulletin no. 7)

1. State college of Washington authors, Works of. 2. Holly.

NL 0436745 WaPS PP

E639.73 Locklin, Harrison Duane, 1891-
W27bm ... Fertilizers for berries. Why sweet
v.11,no.6 cherries do not set fruit ...

(In Western Washington experiment station. Bi-monthly bulletin, v. 11, no. 6, March, 1924)

1. State college of Washington authors, Works of. 2. Fertilizers and manures. 3. Cherry. 4. Fertilization of plants.

NL 0436746 WaPS

E639.73 Locklin, Harrison Duane, 1891-
W27bpw ... Filbert culture ... Pullman, State
no.6 college, 1927.
32p. illus., table, diagr. (Western Washington experiment station, Puyallup. Popular bulletin no. 6)

1. State college of Washington authors, Works of. Filbert.

NL 0436747 WaPS

VOLUME 337

E630.73 W27eb no.170 Locklin, Harrison Duane, 1891-
... Filbert culture [by] H. D. Locklin ... Pullman, Wash., State college, 1932.
8 p. illus. (State college of Washington. Extension service. Bulletin no. 170)

"The State college of Washington and U. S. Department of agriculture co-operating."

1. State college of Washington authors, Works of. 2. Filbert. I. Title.

NL 0436748 WaPS

634.54 L812f Locklin, Harrison Duane, 1891-
Filberts in western Washington. Pullman, Wash. State College of Washington, 1922?
4 p. illus.

1. State college of Washington authors, Works of 2. Nuts. 3. Filbert. I. Title.

NL 0436749 WaPS

E639.73 W27bm v.12,no.1 Locklin, Harrison Duane, 1891-
... Filberts in Western Washington ...

(In Western Washington experiment station. Bi-monthly bulletin, v. 12, no. 1, May, 1924)

1. State college of Washington authors, Works of. 2. Filbert.

NL 0436750 WaPS

E639.73 W27bm v.11,no.5 Locklin, Harrison Duane, 1891-
... Grapes in Western Washington ...

(In Western Washington experiment station. Bi-monthly bulletin, v. 11, no. 5, January, 1924)

1. State college of Washington authors, Works of. 2. Grapes - Washington (State).

NL 0436751 WaPS

E639.73 W27bm v.12,no.2 Locklin, Harrison Duane, 1891-
... Handling berries for greater profits ..

(In Western Washington experiment station. Bi-monthly bulletin, v. 12, no. 2, July, 1924)

1. State college of Washington authors, Works of. 2. Fruit - Marketing. 3. Fruit - Cost of production.

NL 0436752 WaPS

E639.73 W27bpw no.19 Locklin, Harrison Duane, 1891-
... Head lettuce in Western Washington, by H. D. Locklin and Geo. A. Newton ... Pullman, State college, 1931.
37p. illus., tables. (Western Washington experiment station, Puyallup. Bulletin no. 19)

"References": p. 36-37.

1. State college of Washington authors, Works of. (2 cds., one for each author) 2. Lettuce - Diseases. 3. Farm produce - Washington (State). I. Title. II. Newton, George Albert, 1879- joint author.

NL 0436753 WaPS

E630.73 W27eb no.174 Locklin, Harrison Duane, 1891-
... Home storage of fruits and vegetables, by H. D. Locklin ... Pullman, Wash., State college, 1932.
12 p. illus., diagrs. (State college of Washington. Extension service. Extension bulletin no. 174)

"The State college of Washington and U. S. Department of agriculture co-operating."

1. State college of Washington authors, Works of. 2. Farm produce - Storage. I. Title.

NL 0436754 WaPS

E630.73 W27eb no.179 Locklin, Harrison Duane, 1891-
... Home storage of fruits and vegetables, by H. D. Locklin ... Pullman, Wash., State college, 1933.
8 p. diagrs. (State college of Washington. Extension service. Extension bulletin no. 179)

"The State college of Washington and U. S. Department of agriculture co-operating."

1. State college of Washington authors, Works of. 2. Farm produce - Storage. I. Title.

NL 0436755 WaPS

E639.73 W27bm v.11,no.4 Locklin, Harrison Duane, 1891-
... Making sauerkraut. Fall work in the berry field. Are you considering planting more fruit? ...

(In Western Washington experiment station. Bi-monthly bulletin, v. 11, no. 4, November, 1923)

1. State college of Washington authors, Works of. 2. Sauerkraut. 3. Fruit-culture. 4. Berries. 5. Tree planting.

NL 0436756 WaPS

Z 634.211 L81 Thesis Locklin, Harrison Duane, 1891-
Promising varieties of apples that have originated in Washington.

NL 0436757 WaPS

E639.73 W27bm v.12,no.5 Locklin, Harrison Duane, 1891-
... Pruning ornamental plants ...

(In Western Washington experiment station. Bi-monthly bulletin, v. 12, no. 5, January, 1925)

1. State college of Washington authors, Works of. 2. Pruning.

NL 0436758 WaPS

E639.73 W27bpw no.13 Locklin, Harrison Duane, 1891-
... Recommended dates for application of standard hot water treatment to hardy narcissus by H. D. Locklin and Geo. A. Newton ... Pullman, State college, 1929.
32p. illus., tables, diagrs. (Western Washington experiment station, Puyallup. Bulletin no. 13)

"References": p. 32

1. State college of Washington authors, Works of. (2 cds., one for each author) 2. Narcissus. I. Newton, George Albert, 1879- joint author.

NL 0436759 WaPS

E630.73 W27eb no.172 Locklin, Harrison Duane, 1891-
... Red raspberry growing in Washington [by] H. D. Locklin and C. L. Vincent ... Pullman, Wash., State college, 1932.
7 p. diagr. (State college of Washington. Extension service. Bulletin no. 172)

"The State college of Washington and U. S. Department of agriculture c-operating."

1. State college of Washington authors, Works of (2 cards, one for each author) 2. Raspberries. 3. Fruit-culture - Washington (State). I. Vincent, Chester Leon, 1894- joint author. II. Title.

NL 0436760 WaPS

E639.73 W27bpw no.9 Locklin, Harrison Duane, 1891-
... The relation of season of pruning out old cuthbert raspberry canes to amount of winter injury ... Pullman, State college, 1928.
12p. tables. (Western Washington experiment station, Puyallup. Bulletin no. 9)

1. State college of Washington authors, Works of. 2. Pruning. 3. Fruit culture. 4. Raspberries. I. Title.

NL 0436761 WaPS

E639.73 W27bm v.11,no.3 Locklin, Harrison Duane, 1891-
... Select seed potatoes now ...

(In Western Washington experiment station. Bi-monthly bulletin, v. 11, no. 3, September, 1923)

1. State college of Washington authors, Works of. 2. Potatoes, Seed.

NL 0436762 WaPS

E639.73 W27bm v.12,no.3 Locklin, Harrison Duane, 1891-
... Sour cherry growing in Western Washington ...

(In Western Washington experiment station. Bi-monthly bulletin, v. 12, no. 3, September, 1924)

1. State college of Washington authors, Works of. 2. Cherry. 3. Fruit-culture - Washington (State).

NL 0436763 WaPS

E639.73 W27bm v.11,no.2 Locklin, Harrison Duane, 1891-
... Thinning fruits ...

(In Western Washington experiment station. Bi-monthly bulletin, v. 11, no. 2, July, 1923)

1. State college of Washington authors, Works of. 2. Fruit-culture. 3. Fruit - Thinning.

NL 0436764 WaPS

E639.73 W27bm v.12,no.4 Locklin, Harrison Duane, 1891-
... Tree surgery ...

(In Western Washington experiment station. Bi-monthly bulletin, v. 12, no. 4, November, 1924)

1. State college of Washington authors, Works of. 2. Tree surgery.

NL 0436765 WaPS

VOLUME 337

E639.73 W27bm v.11,no.1 Locklin, Harrison Duane, 1891-
... Where do new varieties of fruits come from? ...

(In Western Washington experiment station. Bi-monthly bulletin, v. 11, no. 1, May, 1923)

1. State college of Washington authors, Works of. 2. Fruit-culture - Varieties.

NL 0436766 WaPS

Tzz 976.41 M589l Locklin, Sam.
The story of Milam County. [Sinton, Tex., Printed by San Patricio County news, 1940]
38p. 23cm.

1. Milam Co., Tex. - Hist.

NL 0436767 TxU

Lockling, Lydia Waldo.
... The adventures of Polly and Gilbert in Washington, D. C. By Lydia Waldo Lockling ... New York, The Cosmopolitan press, 1912.
130 p. front., plates. 19cm. $1.00

1. Washington, D. C.—Descr. I. Title.

Library of Congress F199.L79 12-7880

NL 0436768 DLC

---

q332.45 L81r Lockling, William Bruce, 1905-
Recent developments in the theory of the foreign exchanges. Urbana, Ill. [1933]
267 numb.l. tables, fold.diagrs.

Thesis (Ph.D.)--University of Illinois, 1933.
Typewritten (carbon copy)
Vita.
Bibliography: leaves 243-267.

NL 0436769 IU

Lockling, William Bruce, 1905-
Recent developments in the theory of the foreign exchanges, by William Bruce Lockling ... Urbana, Ill., 1933.
1 p. l., 8 p., 1 l. 23cm.
Abstract of thesis (PH. D.)—University of Illinois, 1933.
Vita.

1. Foreign exchange. I. Title.

Library of Congress HG3821.L6 1933 33-31143
Univ. of Illinois Libr
332.77

NL 0436770 IU OU PPT DLC

S.1946 [Lockman, John] 1698-1771.
The all-devouring monster; or New five per c-t. A ballad by Trojanus Laocoon [pseud.] Pandaemonium [i.e. London] 1748. 8 p.

NL 0436771 MH

---

*EC7 L8126 748a [Lockman, John, 1698-1771, ascribed author]
The all-devouring monster; or New five per c------t. A ballad. By Trojanus Laocoon [pseud.] ...
Pandaemonium[i.e.London],Printed for venerable Merlin,at the Memento Mori, MDCCXLVIII.
7p. 27cm.
Fictitious imprint.

NL 0436772 MH

---

xq821 L812b Lockman, John, 1698-1771.
Business, pleasure, and prudence: a fable. Inscribed to The Right Honourable William, Lord Boston. London, Printed for the author, and sold by J. Dodsley, 1769.
6p. 34cm.

A poem.

NL 0436773 IU MH :

---

*fEC7 L8126 761cc Lockman, John, 1698-1771.
Charity and pleasure. A fable. By Mr. Lockman. On occasion of the assembly and ball at Ranelagh-house, Tuesday 9th June, 1761. for the benefit of the Middlesex hospital. Presented to His Majesty at St. James's ... The third edition, corrected and enlarged.
London:Printed for Mess.Dodsley,in Pall-Mall. MDCCLXI.
f°. 7p. 33.5cm.
In verse.

Contemporary blue wrappers (mutilated) preserved; bound in cloth.
Inscribed inside front cover (part of inscription missing): ... his dear Niece:— Mrs Dor.y Boucher:—from the Author.

NL 0436775 MH

[Lockman, John] 1698-1771.
The entertaining instructor: in French and English. Being a collection of judicious sayings, smart repartees, short stories, &c. extracted from the most celebrated French authors, and particularly the books in ana ... By the author of the History of England by question and answer; the Roman history, &c. Intended chiefly for the use of schools. London, A. Millar, 1765.
2 p. l., iii-xx, 287, [1] p. 17cm.
French and English on opposite pages.
1. Commonplace-books. 2. French literature (Selections: Extracts, etc.) 3. French literature—Translations into English. 4. English literature—Translations from French. I. Title.

Library of Congress PN6246.F5L6 42-35446

NL 0436776 DLC NjP MH CtY ICU

Lockman, John, 1698-1771.
A faithful narrative of the late pretended gun-powder plot: in a letter to the Right Honourable Stephen Theodore Janssen, esq; lord-mayor of London. By Mr. Lockman... London: The author [etc.] 1755. 27 p. 23cm.

1. May, Benjamin, 1700?-1759. January 20, 1944

NL 0436777 NN DFo TxU

Lockman, John, 1698-1771.

Bayle, Pierre, 1647-1706.
A general dictionary, historical and critical: in which a new and accurate translation of that of the celebrated Mr. Bayle, with the corrections and observations printed in the late edition at Paris, is included: and interspersed with several thousand lives never before published. The whole containing the history of the most illustrious persons of all ages and nations particularly those of Great Britain and Ireland, distinguished by their rank, actions, learning and other accomplishments. With reflections on such passages of Bayle, as seem to favor scepticism and the Manichee system. By the Reverend Mr. John Peter Bernard, F. R. S., the Reverend Mr. Thomas Birch... Mr. John Lockman; and other hands. London, Printed by J. Bettenham, 1734-41.

Lockman, John, 1698-1771, tr.

[Voltaire, François Marie Arouet de] 1694-1778.
Henriade. An epick poem. In ten canto's. Tr. from the French into English blank verse. To which are now added, the argument to each canto, and large notes historical and critical. London, Printed for C. Davis, 1732.

Rare BR 1600 L81 Lockman, John, 1698-1771, comp.
A history of the cruel sufferings of the Protestants, and others, by popish persecutions, in various countries. Together with a view of the reformations from the church of Rome interspersed with the barbarities of the Inquisition ... Comp. from a great number of authors in different languages... London, Printed for J. Clarke, 1760.
xii,345 p. 17cm.

1. Persecution. 2. Inquisition.

NL 0436780 NIC PMA OO DLC NjP PPL

Lockman, John, 1698-1771.
A history of the cruel sufferings of the Protestants, and others, by Popish persecutions, in various countries: Together with a view of the reformations from the church of Rome. Interspersed with the barbarities of the Inquisition. By question and answer. Faithfully compiled from a great number of authors in different languages, by John Lockman...writ principally for schools: and being intended as a preservative from popery and arbitrary power, may be of use in all Protestant families... London: Printed. And, Dublin: Reprinted by J. Potts, 1763. xii, 343 p., 13 l., 12 p. 16½cm.

"The memorial of Mr. Donatus Calas, addressed to the chancellor and council of state of France, concerning the execution of his father, Mr. John Calas," 12 p. at end.

19728B. 1. Persecutions against Protestants. I. Calas, Donat.
September 3, 1940

NL 0436782 NN WaU RPJCB

Lockman, John, 1698-1771, tr. FOR OTHER EDITIONS SEE MAIN ENTRY

Voltaire, François Marie Arouet de, 1694-1778.
... Letters concerning the English nation. With an introduction by Charles Whibley. London, P. Davies, 1926.

Lockman, John, 1698-1771, tr.

La Fontaine, Jean de, 1621-1695.
The loves of Cupid and Psyche; in verse and prose. From the French of La Fontaine ... To which are prefix'd, a version of the same story from the Latin of Apuleius. With a new life of La Fontaine, extracted from a great variety of authors. The whole illustrated with notes. By Mr. Lockman. London, H. Chapelle, 1744.

Lockman, John, 1698-1771.
A new history of England by question and answer
see under Rapin-Thoyras, Paul de, 1661-1725.

[Lockman, John] 1698 1771.
A new history of Greece. By way of question and answer. In three parts. I. A geographical description ... II. A short historical account of the kingdoms of Sicyonia, Argos, Thebes ... III. Of the religion, laws, customs and manners of the Grecians ... London: Printed for T. Astley; and sold by R. Baldwin ... 1750.
[6],219 p. 17cm.
Bound in old sprinkled calf.

NL 0436786 CLU-C ICU

VOLUME 337

Lockman, John, 1698-1771, tr.

Lambert, Anne Thérèse de Marguenat de Courcelles, *marquise* de, 1647-1733.
New reflexions on the fair sex. Written originally in French, by the celebrated Marchioness de Lambert, (and by her suppress'd) ... Tr. into English by J. Lockman. London, Printed and sold by N. Prevost [etc.] 1729.

---

937 L816n [Lockman, John] 1698-1771.
A new Roman history, by question and answer. In a new method much more comprehensive than any of the kind extant. Extracted from ancient authors, and the most celebrated among the modern. And intersper'd with such customs as serve to illustrate the history. With a complete index. Designed principally for schools. By the author of the History of England by question and answer. London, Printed for T. Astley, 1737.
viii, 342, [14, 4] p. 17cm.

At head of title: Wm. W. Cole.
Errata: p. 342.
Publisher's list at end of volume.

1. Rome - Hist. 2. Rome - Civilization.

NL 0436789 FU

---

937 L812n 1749 [Lockman, John] 1698-1771.
A new Roman history, by question and answer./ In a method much more comprehensive than any of the kind extant. Extracted from ancient authors, and the most celebrated among the modern. And intersper'd with such customs as serve to illustrate the history. With a complete index. Designed principally for schools. By the author of the History of England by question and answer. The 3d ed., cor. ... London, Printed for T. Astley and sold by R. Baldwin, 1749.
342p. front., plates.
Dedication signed: John Lockman.

NL 0436790 IU CaBVaU

Lockman, John, 1698-1771.
A new Roman history, by question and answer. The 5ed corr. London, Printed for T. Astley, 1759.
xii,342,[17]p.

NL 0436791 OU

---

x973 L812n 1778 Lockman, John, 1698-1771.
A new Roman history, by question and answer; in a method much more comprehensive than any of the kind extant. Extracted from ancient authors, and the most celebrated among the modern; and interspersed with such customs as serve to illustrate the history ... By the author of the History of England by question and answer. 9th ed., corr. London, Printed for J. Rivington, 1778.
xii, 342p. 16 plates. 18cm.
Dedication signed: John Lockman.

NL 0436792 IU OCU

Lockman, John, 1698-1771.
A new Roman history, extracted from ancient authors, and the most celebrated among the modern... London, 1791.

NL 0436793 PPL

---

*EC7 L8126 739o Lockman, John, 1698-1771.
An ode for St. Cecilia's-day. The words by Mr. Lockman. The musick by Mr. Boyce. [London]Printed in the year M.DCC.XXXIX.
8°. 8p. 20.5cm.
Without the music.

NL 0436794 MH

---

*fEC7 L8126 730o Lockman, John, 1698-1771.
An ode: inscrib'd to His Grace the Duke of Buckingham, on his embarking for France. By John Lockman ...
London:Printed for L.Gilliver,at Homer's Head, over against St.Dunstan's church,in Fleet-street.M.DCC.XXX. (Price four-pence.)
f°. 6p. 33cm.

NL 0436795 MH

---

*fEC7 L8126 760o Lockman, John, 1698-1771.
An ode on the birth-day of His Royal Highness George, prince of Wales. 4th June, 1760. By John Lockman. Secretary to the Society of the free British fishery. Presented to His Royal Highness at Savile-house ...
London:Printed for Mess.Dodsley,at Tully's Head,in Pallmall;and sold by M.Cooper,in Pater-noster row.MDCCLX.
f°. 7p. 32.5cm.

NL 0436796 MH CtY

---

*EC7 L8126 741v Lockman, John, 1698-1771.
An ode, on the crushing of the rebellion, anno MDCCXLVI. Presented to his Majesty at Kensington and humbly inscrib'd to his Royal Highness the Duke. By J. Lockman ...
London:Printed for the author;and sold by M. Cooper,at the Globe in Pater-noster-row: likewise by H.Chapelle,Grosvenor-street;G.Woodfall,at the King's Arms,Charing-cross;P.Russell, stationer,in Panton-street near Leicester square; and at the several pamphlet-shops.MDCCXLVI.
<Price six pence.> MH66-2347
4°. 18p. 26.5cm.
No.3 in a volume of Lockman's poems.

NL 0436797 MH NjP

Lockman, John, 1698-1771.
An ode, to His Eminence Cardinal de Fleury, by Mr Lockman... Presented to His Eminence, in his cabinet, at Versailles. Paris: Printed for Piget, 1761 [really 1741?]. 5, 5 p. 4°.

Approbations, p. 5 and p. 5, dated: 21. novembre 1741.
"De l'Imprimerie de Prault pere."
"Imitation de l'ode angloise. Par Monsieur l'abbé Dromgold," 5 p. at end.
With inscription on fly-leaf: Francis Barrell(?) esq' is requested to accept of these poems, from J. Lockman.
"Epilogue to the Miser. Writ by Mr. Lockman." [London, 1750?] small broadside pasted on fly-leaf.

582189A. 1. Poetry, English. 2. Poetry, French. 3. Fleury, André Hercule de, cardinal, 1653-1743. I. Dromgold, Jean, 1720-1780.
July 29, 1932

NL 0436798 NN CSmH MH

Lockman, John, 1698-1771.
An ode: to the memory of His Grace the Duke of Buckinghamshire ... [London?1735?]
8p. 19½cm.

1.Buckingham, Edmund Sheffield, duke of, 1716-1735.

NL 0436799 CtY MH

---

*fEC7 L8126 735o Lockman, John, 1698-1771.
An ode: to the memory of His Grace the Duke of Buckinghamshire. By J. Lockman ...
London:Printed for R.Dodsley,at Tully's Head in Pallmall.[1735?] (Price six-pence.)
f°. 8p. 35cm.

NL 0436800 MH

LOCKMAN,John,1698-1711.
An ode to the right honourable,the Earl of Middlesex,writ,on a particular occasion,in December,1747;and presented to his Lordship on his birth-day,February 6,1750-1. London, [1751].
1.8°. pp.7.
Imprint cropped.

NL 0436801 MH

LOCKMAN (John]) 1698-1771.
Ode to the Right Honourable, the Earl of Middlesex. Writ, on a particular occasion, in December, 1747; and presented to His Lordship on his birthday Feb. 6. 1750-1. London, Printed for W. Owen, 1751. 7 p. 26cm.
Microfilm.
1. Dorset, Lionel Cranfield Sackville, 1st duke of, 1688-1765—Poetry.

NL 0436802 NN

---

*EC7 L8126 743p Lockman, John, 1698-1771.
Pastoral stanzas. Written on occasion of the marriage of C. Phipps, esquire, with the Honourable Miss Lepel Hervey. By Mr. Lockman ...
London,MDCCXLIII.
4°. 6p. 27cm.

NL 0436803 MH TxU

Lockman, John, 1698-1771, tr.

Marivaux, Pierre Carlet de Chamblain de, 1688-1763.
Pharsamond: or, The new knight-errant. In which is introduced the story of the fair anchoret, with that of Tarmiana and her unfortunate daughter. Written originally in French, by Monsieur de Marivaux ... Tr. by Mr. Lockman ... London, Printed for C. Davis [etc.] 1750.

[Lockman, John] 1698-1771.
A proper answer to a vile, anonymous libel written by L. D. N. chiefly against John Lockman ... in a letter to Slingsby Bethell ... London, Printed and sold by the booksellers of London, 1753.
28 p. 20 cm.

NL 0436805 NcD

Lockman, John, 1698-1771.
Rosalinda. Musical drama, 1 pt.

Application "18 Decr. 1739 This piece is to be represented at my House. Jas. Hugford." Prod. Hickman's Room, Jan. 4, 1740.
MS: some corrections in hand of author(?); included are: "Imitations. Argument, to ye. following Sonnet"; and account of the circumstances attendant upon the composition of a sonnet "by Henault, who speaks to ye Eabrio in ye Person of Madlle de Guerchi"; and the sonnet, in French. Comp. 1740 (K-D 46): virtually idectical.

NL 0436806 CSmH

VOLUME 337

Lockman, John, 1698-1771.
Rosalinda, a musical drama. As it is performed at Hickford's Great Room, in Brewer's Street. By Mr. Lockman. Set to music by Mr. John Christopher Smith. . . . Prefixed, An enquiry into the rise and progress of operas and oratorios, with some reflections on lyric poetry and music.
London: Printed by W. Strahan for the author; and sold by C. Corbett . . . MDCCXL. 19 pp. 23½ cm., in 2s.
Words only.
An enquiry into the rise and progress of operas and oratorios . . . is missing in the copy on shelf-number **T.35.24.
The title-page of the copy on shelf-number No. 7 in **G.3824.2 is missing and the margins have been too closely trimmed.

K4500 — T.r. — Opera. Hist. and crit.

NL 0436807 MB PPL DFo ICU CtY MH CSmH

Lockman, John, 1698-1771.
Rosalinda. London, 1740.
(In Three centuries of drama: English, 1701-1750)

Microprint.

I. Title.

NL 0436808 MoU

Lockman, John, 1698-1771.
The Shetland herring, and Peruvian gold-mine: a fable ... By John Lockman ... London, W. Owen, 1751.
7 p. 36cm.
In verse.

1. Fisheries—Gt. Brit. I. Title.

12-28151

Library of Congress SH255.L8

NL 0436809 DLC MH CtY

[LOCKMAN, John, 1698-1771]
Some reflexions concerning operas, lyric poetry, music, &c., [London, 1740]

pp. xxiv.
Extracted from his Rosalinda, 1740, pp. i-xxiv.

NL 0436810 MH

---

*EB7 L8126 759t

Lockman, John, 1698-1771.
To the Honourable General Townshend, on his arrival from Quebec. By Mr. Lockman. [London, 1759]

broadside. 22.5x16cm.
In verse.
Inscribed: To the rvrend, & very learned Dr Macro: London 28th Decr 1759. from the Author.

NL 0436811 MH

821.6 L816t

Lockman, John, 1698-1771.
To the long-conceal'd first promoter of the Cambrick and tea-bills; an epistle writ at the close of last session of Parliament. London, Printed for the author, and sold by M. Cooper, 1746.
34p. 24cm.

A poem.

NL 0436812 IEN MH

---

*fEC7 L8126 763t

Lockman, John, 1698-1771.
To the Right Honourable the Lord Warkworth, on his return from his travels, Tuesday, July 26, 1763. A lyrical epistle. By John Lockman. Presented to his Lordship at Northumberland-house ...
London: Printed for the author. MDCCLXIII.

f°. 6p. 32.5cm.

NL 0436813 MH

Lockman, John, 1698-1771, tr.
The travels of Mr. John Gulliver
see under Desfontaines, Pierre François Guyot, 1685-1745.

Lockman, John, 1698-1771, tr. FOR OTHER EDITIONS SEE MAIN ENTRY
Travels of the Jesuits, into various parts of the world; compiled from their letters. Now first attempted in English. Intermix'd with an account of the manners, government, religion, &c. of the several nations visited by those fathers: with extracts from other travellers, and miscellaneous notes. By Mr. Lockman. Illustrated with maps and sculptures ... London, J. Noon, 1743.

Lockman, John, 1698-1771.

Sarpi, Paolo, 1552-1623.
A treatise of ecclesiastical benefices and revenues ... Written originally in Italian, by the learned Father Paul ... Translated by Tobias Jenkins ... and illustrated with notes by him, and from the ingenious Amelot de La Houssaye. 3d ed. To which is prefixed, (never before printed) The life of Father Paul, by Mr. Lockman. And a preface, giving an account of the work. [London] Printed for O. Payne and J. Fox, M.DCC.XXXVI.

---

*fEC7 L8126 758t

Lockman, John, 1698-1771.
Truth: a vision. Most humbly addressed to the Prince of Wales: on His Royal Highness's birth-day, June 4, 1758. By John Lockman, secretary to the Society of the free British fishery. Presented to His Royal Highness at Savile house ...
London, Printed for R. and J. Dodsley, at Tully's Head, in Pall-Mall; and sold by M. Cooper, in Pater-noster row. MDCCLVIII. <Price sixpence.
f°. 1p.l., ii, [3]-12p. 30cm.
In verse.

NL 0436817 MH

HD9461 .L78 Rare Bk

Lockman, John, 1698-1771.
The vast importance of the herring fishery, &c. to these kingdoms: as respecting the national wealth, our naval strength, and the Highlanders. In three letters, addressed to a member of Parliament. London, W. Owen [1750]
39 p.

1. Fisheries--Gt. Brit. 2. Herring-fisheries. I. Title.

NL 0436818 ICU MH-BA NIC MH

[Lockman, John] 1698-1771.
The vast importance of the herring fishery, &c. to these kingdoms: as respecting the national wealth, our naval strength, and the Highlanders. In three letters, addressed to a member of Parliament. 2d ed. ... London, Printed for W. Owen, 1750.
1 p. l., [4]-5, [7]-39 p. 20cm.
Dedication signed: J. Lockman.

1. Fisheries—Gt. Brit. 2. Herring-fisheries. I. Title.

A 18-1513

Harvard univ. Library for Library of Congress [a39b1]

NL 0436819 MH MnU CtY NN

---

*fEC7 L8126 758v

Lockman, John, 1698-1771.
Verses most humbly addressed to the Princess Dowager of Wales: on Her Royal Highness's birth-day, Nov. 30, 1757. By John Lockman, secretary to the Society of the free British fishery. Presented to Her Royal Highness at Leicester-house ...
London, Printed for the author, and sold at the pamphlet shops. MDCCLVIII.
f°. 7p. 29.5cm.

NL 0436820 MH

---

*fEC7 L8126 760v

Lockman, John, 1698-1771.
Verses on the demise of the late King, and the accession of His Present Majesty. Most humbly addressed, and presented to His Majesty, at St. James's. By John Lockman, secretary to the Society of the free British fishery. To which is prefix'd, an epistle to the Most Noble the Marquis of Caernarvon, on the above occasion ...
London: Printed for R. and J. Dodsley, at Tully's Head, Pallmall; and sold by M. Cooper, in Pater-noster-row. MDCCLX.
f°. 8p. 30cm.

NL 0436821 MH CSmH

---

*EC7 L8126 741v

[Lockman, John, 1698-1771]
Verses to a lady of quality, insulted by the rabble of writers ...
London: Printed for the author. MDCCXLI.
4°. 7p. 26.5cm.
Tribute to the Duchess of Buckingham.
No.1 in a volume of Lockman's poems.

NL 0436822 MH TxU NN

---

*fEC7 L8126 743v

Lockman, John, 1698-1771.
Verses to His Royal Highness the Duke of Cumberland: on his being wounded, at the repulse of the French, near Dettingen. By Mr. Lockman ...
London: Printed for H. Chapelle, in Grosvenor street, and sold by J. Robinson, at the Golden Lion, in Ludgate street. 1743. <Price three-pence.>
f°. 5p. 32cm.

NL 0436823 MH

Lockman, John, 1698-1771.
Verses to Their Royal Highnesses the Prince and Princess of Wales: presented at Leicester-house: on waiting upon them, with early Shetland herrings, from the council of the Free British fishery ... London, Printed for J. Brindley, 1757.
7 p. 25 x 20 cm.

NL 0436824 MH-BA CSmH

TL 555 L81+

Lockman, Robert F.
The predictive use of the linear discriminant function in naval aviation cadet selection. [Pensacola, Fla.] 1953.
11 p. tables. 26cm.

"U. S. Naval School of Aviation Medicine, Naval Air Station, Pensacola, Florida. Research report, report no. NM 001 057.16.02."

NL 0436825 NIC

VOLUME 337

Lockman, William T.
Structural behavior of Grand Coulee Dam; 15-year report. Denver, U. S. Dept. of the Interior, Bureau of Reclamation [1955]
20, [46] p. illus., diagrs., tables. 27 cm. (U. S. Bureau of Reclamation. Technical memorandum 652)

1. Grand Coulee Dam. (Series)

TC7.U55 no. 652 627.8 55-61238

NL 0436826 DLC DI

Lockmann, the fabulist
see Lokman.

Lockmann, Jean Jacques.

Schweizerische geodätische kommission.
... Astronomisch-geodätische arbeiten in der Schweiz (Fortsetzung der publikation: "Das schweizerische dreiecknetz") hrsg. von der Schweizerischen geodätischen kommission, organ der Schweizerischen naturforschenden gesellschaft. 10.– bd. ... Zürich, Kommissionsverlag von Fäsi & Beer (vorm. S. Höhr) 1907–

Cuba K7 .L5
Lockmiller, David Alexander, 1906–
The advisory law commission of Cuba, by David A. Lockmiller. [Durham, N.C., 1937]
29 p. 25 cm.
Cover-title.
"Reprinted from the Hispanic American historical review, volume xvii, number 1, February, 1937."
Bibliographical footnotes.

NL 0436829 DPU MH-L

Cuba S 471 .L6
Lockmiller, David Alexander, 1906–
Agriculture in Cuba during the second United States intervention, 1906-1909, by David A. Lockmiller.
cover-title, p. 181-188. 25.5 cm.
"Reprinted from Agricultural history, 11: 181-188 (July 1937)"

NL 0436830 DPU

Lockmiller, David Alexander, 1906–
The consolidation of the University of North Carolina, by David A. Lockmiller; with foreword by Fred J. Kelly. Raleigh, Chapel Hill [etc.] The University of North Carolina, 1942.
xiv, [2], 160 p. front., illus., plates, ports. 23½cm.
"Selected bibliography": p. [146]-152.

1. North Carolina. University. 2. North Carolina. University. State college of agriculture and engineering. 3. North Carolina. University. Woman's college, Greensboro. I. Title.

42-22131 Revised

Library of Congress LD3943.L6 [r43e3]

PSt AAP OrCS OrU IdU NIC
NL 0436831 DLC Or NcGU NcRS PU-Penn OU OCl ViU

Lockmiller, David Alexander, 1906–
Enoch H. Crowder: soldier, lawyer, and statesman. Columbia, University of Missouri Studies, 1955.
286 p. illus., ports. 28 cm. (The University of Missouri studies, v. 27)
Bibliography: p. [263]-274.

1. Crowder, Enoch Herbert, 1859-1932. (Series: Missouri. University. The University of Missouri studies, v. 27)

E181.C94L6 923.273 55-62560
AS36.M82 vol. 27

MoU MU NjR MdBP OrU
ViU WHi NIC PBm TxU PSt PP OU OCU CaBVaU OrCS OrPR
NL 0436832 DLC OrU CU AAP FTaSU NcRS NcD OO TxU DS

Lockmiller, David Alexander, 1906–
History of the North Carolina state college of agriculture and engineering of the University of North Carolina, 1889-1939, by David A. Lockmiller, with a foreword by Frank P. Graham. Raleigh [Printed by Edwards & Broughton] 1939.
xvii, [1], 310 p. front., illus., plates, ports. 23½cm.
Illustrated lining-papers.
"Selected bibliography": p. [291]-294.

1. North Carolina. University. State college of agriculture and engineering.

39-30809 Revised

Library of Congress S537.N87L6 [r43d2] 630.711

NL 0436833 DLC NcRS NcD OCU ViU TxU MsSM

Lockmiller, David Alexander, 1906–
Magoon in Cuba: a history of the second intervention, 1906-1909, by David A. Lockmiller. Chapel Hill, The University of North Carolina press, 1938.
xiii, 252 p. front. (port.) illus. (map) 22½cm.
"Selected bibliography": p. 225-239.

1. Cuba—Hist.—American occupation, 1906-1909. 2. Cuba—Pol. & govt.—1906-1909. 3. Magoon, Charles Edward, 1861-1920. I. Title.

38-9138 Revised

Library of Congress F1787.L82 [r43j3] 972.91

OCl OCU OU DPU WaSpG WaTC OrCS OrU
NL 0436834 DLC GU CU AAP NcRS PPT PSC PU ViU KU

Lockmiller, David Alexander, 1906–
The second United States intervention in Cuba, 1906-1909. Chapel Hill, 1935. 343(i.e.344)p. Q.
p.26 followed by p.26A.
Thesis (Ph.D.) - University of North Carolina, 1935.
Carbon copy of typewritten manuscript.
Bibliography: p.326-343.

NL 0436835 NcU

Cuba BR 645 .L6
Lockmiller, David Alexander, 1906–
The settlement of the church property questions in Cuba, by David A. Lockmiller. [Durham, N.C., 1937]
p. [488]-498. 25.5 cm.
Reprinted from The Hispanic American Historical review, vol. xvii, no. 4, November, 1937.
Bibliographical foot-notes.

NL 0436836 DPU

Lockmiller, David Alexander, 1906–
Sir William Blackstone, by David A. Lockmiller ... Chapel Hill, The University of North Carolina press, 1938.
xiii p., 1 l., 308 p. front., illus., plates, ports., facsims., tables (1 fold. geneal.) 23cm.
"Selected bibliography": p. [283]-294.

1. Blackstone, Sir William, 1723-1780.

38-37894 Revised

WaU-L OrU WaSpG
OCl OO OClW NN TU NcRS WaU MiU CaBVaU WaS OrU-L
NL 0436837 DLC FTaSU PV PP PPT PU ViU-L OU OClh

K B55L6x 1967
Lockmiller, David Alexander, 1906-
Sir William Blackstone. Chapel Hill, University of North Carolina Press, 1938.
xvii,308p.(on double leaves) illus.(1 fold.) 21cm.
"This is an authorized facsimile of the original book, and was produced in 1967 by microfilm-xerography by University Microfilms, A Xerox Company, Ann Arbor, Mich., U.S.A."
"Selected bibliography": p.[283]-294.

NL 0436838 ViBlbV NBuU-L

---

32 10116
Locknane, Clement.
In dreamland; or, the little sleeper. A cantata for ladies' voices. Words by James Strang. Music by Clement Locknane. London, Houghton, & co., 1896.
lv, 62 p. 4°.

NL 0436839 DLC

W 4 F82 1955
LOCKNER, Dieter Bernhard Wilhelm, 1928-
Das Verhalten der Thrombozyten nach verschiedenen gynäkologischen Operationen. [Frankfurt? a. M. 1955?]
29 *l*. illus.
Inaug.-Diss. - Frankfurt.
1. Blood platelets 2. Gynecology - Operative

NL 0436840 DNLM

CPA VF 939
Lockner, Karl, 1909?-
"Feed the hungry" for jobs or cash relief. For passage of the "Workers Unemployment and Social Insurance Bill." Speech of Karl Lockner before Governor Horner and the Illinois Emergency Relief Commission on June 29, 1934. [Chicago, Ill., Unemployment Council of Cook County, 1934?]
23 p.
"[Published] jointly with the Election Campaign Committee of the Communist Party."

1. Unemployed - Illinois. 2. Labor and laboring classes - Illinois. 3. Insurance, Social - Illinois. I. Title.

NL 0436841 MiEM

Lockney, John F tr.
The month of St. Joseph, a series of daily prayers translated from the French by Rev. J. F. Lockney. New York, W. H. Young & co., 1900.
40 p. 12°.

1. Joseph, Saint—Prayer-books and devotions—English. 2. Catholic church—Prayer-books and devotions—English. I. Title.

0-8501

Library of Congress BX2164.L6

NL 0436842 DLC

Locko Park.

Richter, Jean Paul, 1847-1937.
Catalogue of pictures at Locko Park. By Jean Paul Richter. London, Bemrose & sons, limited [1901]

VOLUME 337

977.325 Lockport, Ill.
L81l Lockport has a birthday, 1830-1930. Prepared and published by the Publicity Committee of the centennial celebration, October 17-18, 1930. [n.p.] c1930.
[40]p. 19cm.

"Introductory and explanatory" signed: Bruce D. Cheadle, chairman.

1. Lockport, Ill.--Hist.

NL 0436844 IU ICN

Lockport, Ill. Lewis College
see Lewis College, Lockport, Ill.

Ofv54 Lockport, Ill. Ordinances, etc.
1 Lawful regulations for the conduct of elec-
1900 tions under the Myers' ballot system [Lockport, Ill., Lockport Union Print, 19--?]
folder (8 p.) illus. 23 cm.

Caption title.

1. Voting - Lockport, Ill. I. Title. II. Title: Myers' ballot system.

NL 0436846 CtY

Lockport, Ill. Ordinances, etc.
Municipal code of Lockport containing the general ordinances of the city of Lockport, Illinois, as revised, codified and amended, passed by the City Council of the city of Lockport as Ordinance no. 429, December 30, 1940. Rev., compiled and edited by Glenn E. Miller, city attorney. Lockport, 1940.
1 v. (unpaged) 23 cm.

I. Miller, Glenn E.

352.0773 51-46616

NL 0436847 DLC

Lockport, N.Y.
Decoration day. Floral tributes...
see under title

Lockport, N.Y. Baptist church.
The articles of faith, covenant, and rules and regulations, of the Second Baptist church in Lockport, N.Y. Lockport, 1853.
16 p. 18.5 cm.

NL 0436849 CtY

Lockport, N. Y. Baptist church.
125th anniversary year, 1941, the Baptist church of Lockport, New York ... [Lockport, N. Y.] 1941.
[24] p. plates, port. 25cm.
"Anniversary edition."

I. Title.

Library of Congress BX6480.L64A5 41-18792
286.174798

NL 0436850 DLC

Lockport, N. Y. Board of commerce.
Work ... of the Lockport Board of commerce. 1st-1916/17-
[Lockport] 1916-
v. 24-28cm.

Title varies slightly.
Report year ends in February.

I. Title.

Library of Congress HF296.L8 20-12036

NL 0436851 DLC

Lockport, N.Y. Board of education.
Directory of the board of education and the public schools 1912; 14/15; 18/19 - (Lockport, N.Y., 1912 - 18)
3 v. 14½ cm.

NL 0436852 DHEW

YLA Lockport, N.Y. Board of Education
339 100 years of education, 1847-1947.
.L81 [Editor, Ralph L. Shattuck] Lockport [1948]
A110 184p. illus.,ports. 32cm.

1. Education - New York (State) - Lockport. I. Shattuck, Ralph L., ed. II. Title.

NL 0436853 NRU N NIC

Lockport, N.Y. Board of trade.
[New York short ballot organization]
... A suggestion for an optional third class cities law (The "Board of directors" plan) [New York? 1910?]

LOCKPORT, N.Y. Charters.
The charter of the city of Lockport. (Laws of 1911, chapter 870, as amended) [Albany, 1949] 105,12 p. 29cm. [IN: New York (State). Audit and control dept. Municipal affairs division. Charters of the cities of New York state. Albany, 1949. v.5]

Caption title.

NL 0436855 NN NIC

LOCKPORT, N.Y. Charters.
Revised charter and ordinances of the city of Lockport ... Lockport, N.Y.: Union Prtg. and Pub. Co., 1886. 469 p. 23½cm.

657752A. 1. Municipal charters and ordinances—U.S.—N.Y.—Lockport. I. Lockport, N.Y. Ordinances.

NL 0436856 NN

Lockport, N. Y. Charters.
Revised charter and ordinances of the city of Lockport ... Lockport, N. Y. [Press of Roberts brothers co.] 1913.
[686] p. 23cm.
Various pagings.

I. Lockport, N. Y. Ordinances, etc.

Library of Congress JS999.L8A5 1913 45-53512

NL 0436857 DLC NN

S
352.0747 Lockport, N. Y. Common Council.
L8163 Proceedings of the Common Council and municipal boards. [Lockport]
v. in 25 cm. annual.

1. Lockport, N. Y. Pol. & govt.

NL 0436858 N

Lockport, N.Y. Evangelical Lutheran Church.
Summary of Faith & Rules of Discipline. Albany, 1851.
8 p. 12°. [In v. 28, Library of Americana-Pamphlets.]

NL 0436859 CtY

MF4 Lockport, N.Y. First Free Congregational church
5 Constitution, confession of faith, list of members and officers of the First Free Congregational church of Lockport. [n.p., 1838?]
10 p. 21 cm. (Binder's title: Congregational church manuals, vol. 5 [no. 14])

Caption title.

NL 0436860 CtY-D

Lockport, N. Y. First free Congregational church.
A manual of the First free Congregational church of Lockport. Lockport [N. Y.] Printed by S. Wright, 1849.
16 p. 14 cm. Original white paper covers.

NL 0436861 CSmH

MF64 Lockport, N.Y. First Free Congregational Church.
L812m A manual of the First Congregational Church in Lockport. Lockport [N.Y.] Printed by S. Wright, 1870.
32 p. 15 cm.

"List of members": p. 13-32.

NL 0436862 CtY-D

Lockport, N.Y. First Free Congregational Church.
Manual of the First Free Congregational Church of Lockport, N. Y. 1885. Lockport, N. Y.: Jour. Book and Job Prtg. House, 1885. 125 p., 1 l. 12°.

1. Lockport. N. Y.—Churches (Congregational): First Free Congregational.
April 25, 1917.

NL 0436863 NN

Lockport, N.Y. First Presbyterian Church.
A memorial record of the proceedings at the jubilee re-union of the First Presbyterian Society, Lockport, N. Y., Wednesday, May 15th, 1872, on the thirtieth anniversary of Rev. Dr. William C. Wisner's pastorate with that people; also, An anniversary discourse, preached by the pastor, Sunday, May 12th, 1872. Lockport, N. Y.: M. C. Richardson & Co., 1872. 66 p. 8°.

HANFORD COLLECTION.
516124A. 1. Lockport, N. Y.—Churches, Presbyterian—First. I. Wisner, William Carpenter, 1808-1880.
April 6, 1931

NL 0436864 NN Nh

VOLUME 337

Lockport, N.Y. Free Congregational Church
see Lockport, N.Y. First Free Congregational Church.

Lockport, N. Y. Free public library.
Catalogue of the Public library of the city of Lockport, N. Y. As revised in May, 1893 ... Prepared ... by Emmet Belknap. Lockport, J. H. Murphy, steam book and job printer, 1893.
179 p. 23cm.
Pt. I: Title of books by sections; pt. II: Catalogue of authors, in alphabetic order.
—— Supplement catalogue ... Books added to the library from May 1st, 1893, to March 1st, 1898 ... Lockport, J. H. Murphy, book and job printer, 1898.
cover-title, 32 p. 23cm.
I. Belknap, Emmet.
4-8139-0
Library of Congress Z881.L816

NL 0436866 DLC

Lockport, N. Y. Free public library.
Lockport, N. Y. Union school district library.
Catalogue of Union school district library. Lockport, Skeels & Boyce, printers, 1872.

Lockport, N.Y. Free Public Library
see also Lockport, N.Y. Union School District Library.

Lockport, *N. Y. Mayor.*
Annual message ...
[Lockport,
v. port., tables. 23cm.

1. Lockport, N. Y.—Pol. & govt.
CA 34-2394 Unrev'd
Library of Congress JS13.L8a 352.074798

NL 0436869 DLC NBuG

Lockport, N. Y. Old Home Week Committee.
Old Home Week, celebrating the hundredth anniversary of the Erie Canal. July 19th to 25th, 1925. Lockport, N. Y. [Corson Manufacturing Company, 1925]
32p. illus. 28cm.

NL 0436870 NBu

Lockport, N. Y. Ordinances, etc.
JS999 .L3A5 1913
Lockport, *N. Y. Charters.*
Revised charter and ordinances of the city of Lockport ... Lockport, N. Y. [Press of Roberts brothers co.] 1913.

Lockport, N.Y. Second Baptist Church
see Lockport, N.Y. Baptist Church.

Lockport, N.Y. Union school.
Annual catalogue and circular of the officers and students of the Lockport union school, for the year 1852
Lockport, C.L.Skeels printer, 1852.
1v. 21cm.

NL 0436873 NRU

Lockport, N. Y. Union school district library.
Catalogue of Union school district library. Lockport, N. Y., Richardson & Freeman, printers, 1860.
28 p. 23½cm.
"Index": p. [2] of cover.
40-25085
Library of Congress Z881.L816 017.1

NL 0436874 DLC

Lockport, N. Y. Union school district library.
Catalogue of Union school district library. Lockport, Skeels & Boyce, printers, 1872.
30 p. 23cm.
Incorporated as Free public library Feb. 9, 1893.

I. Lockport, N. Y. Free public library.
4-8140
Library of Congress Z881.L816

NL 0436875 DLC

Lockport and Niagara Falls Railroad Company.
Map of the several routes from Rochester to Buffalo. Compiled from county maps and actual surveys in the office of the Co. [Signed] Julius W. Adams, Engr.
[Boston?] 1841. Size, 21⅞ × 34 inches. Scale (computed), 2⅔ miles to 1 inch. Profiles.

G7887 — New York, State. R.Rs.

NL 0436876 MB

Lockport and Niagara Falls railroad company.
Report of the engineer to the directors of the Lockport and Niagara Falls railroad company, on the proposed extension of their road eastward. With an appendix. Sept. 30, 1841. Boston, Printed by S. N. Dickinson, 1841.
cover-title, 66, [2] p. 22cm.
Signed: Julius W. Adams, engineer.

I. Adams, Julius Walker, 1812-1899.
A 28-883
Title from Bureau of Railway Economics. Printed by L. C.

NL 0436877 DBRE NN

Lockport and Niagara Falls Railroad Company.
Report on the Lockport and Niagara Falls Railroad, to the president and directors
see under Stuart, Charles Beebee, 1814-1881.

Lockport Bank investigation. To the public ...
see under [Field, George]

The Lockport city and Niagara County directory for the year
see under Kirwin, William H comp.

The **Lockport** city directory ...
1867/68, 1874/75
Rochester, N. Y., E. R. Andrews, printer [1867–
v. 21-23cm.
Publishers: 1867/68, Webb & Fitzgerald.—1874/75– Fitzgerald & Dillon.

1. Lockport, N. Y.—Direct.
7-40100 Revised
Library of Congress F129.L75A18

NL 0436881 DLC MWA

Lockport city directory for [1892]– ... Lockport, N. Y., Roberts brothers co. [1892]–
v. fold. map, fold. plan. 24cm.
Title varies: 1892-99, Waite's Lockport city directory.
1900– Lockport city directory; L. P. Waite & co., pub., 1900-04, Roberts brothers co., pub., 1905–
The 1892 number is a continuation of the Lockport city directory comp. by W. H. Kirwin.

1. Lockport, N. Y.—Direct.
7-40101
Library of Congress F129.L75A18

NL 0436882 DLC NBuG NN

Lockport Journal and Courier.
18

Lockport, N. Y., 18 f°.
v.
Daily.

1. Newspapers, U. S.: N. Y.: Lockport.
March 14, 1923.

NL 0436883 NN

The **Lockport** leader...
v. 1–
Lockport, N. Y.: Lockport Board of Commerce, 1916– 4°.
v. illus.

Monthly.

1. Commerce, U. S.: N. Y.: Lockport. 2. Lockport Board of Commerce, Lockport, N. Y.
August 11, 1922.

NL 0436884 NN

A 6 .516
Lockport telegraph.
v.1,no.3-6,11,13-14,16,18,21,25, 27-30 (May 6-Nov.6,1850)
Lockport,Ill.,1850.
J.F.Daggett, M.D., editor.
"Published every Wednesday."

NL 0436885 ICN

Lockport Typographical Union.
see International Typographical Union of North America. Union no. 67, Lockport.

VOLUME 337

Lockport Water and Electric Company, Lockport, N. Y.
Charter of Lockport Water and Electric Company. Being chapter 106 of the laws of the state of New York passed in 1886, as amended by chapter 438 of the laws of 1890. ₍Lockport, 1890?₎ 8 p. 8°.
Caption-title.

651778. 1. Corporations, Public service—U. S.—N. Y.—Lockport. Revised June 17, 1931

NL 0436887 NN

LOCKQUELL, CLEMENT
Les élus que vous êtes. Montréal, Les Éditions variétés [1949] 197 p. 19cm.

1. Fiction, Canadian--French. I. Title.

NL 0436888 NN CaOTU CaQML

Lockrey, Andrew Jules, 1897–
Half-tone processes, by A. J. Lockrey; a practical working-treatise for the amateur or professional, describing methods and materials for all types of photo-mechanical reproduction. New York city, Fotocolor laboratories, ©1939.
66 numb. l. 22½ᶜᵐ.
Reproduced from type-written copy.

1. Photo-engraving—Half-tone process. I. Title.
44-50722
Library of Congress TR975.L6 1939
777.2

NL 0436889 DLC NN

777
L816h **Lockrey, Andrew Jules**, 1897–
Halftone processes. 2d ed., rev. and enl. By A. J. Lockrey ... New York city, The J. J. Tepper corporation, ©1941.
61 p. illus., diagrs. 23ᶜᵐ.

1. Photo-engraving—Half-tone process. I. Title.
41-12623
Library of Congress TR975.L6 1941
777

TxU DN
NL 0436890 DLC IdU WaSp OrP NcC NcGU Or OCl OO

Lockrey, Andrew Jules, 1897–
"Plastics" in the school and home workshop, by A. J. Lockrey. New York city, Governor publishing corporation ₍1937₎
228 p. incl. illus., plates. 22ᶜᵐ.
"First printing, June, 1937."

1. Handicraft. 2. Gums and resins. 3. Plastic materials. I. Title.
37-28552
Library of Congress NK8595.L6
Copyright A 111375 ₍10-5₎ ₍731₎ 668.4

OClND OO OU OCU FMU NN
NL 0436891 DLC OrCS WaE WaS PP PPD PPGi OCl OEac

Lockrey, Andrew Jules, 1897–
Plastics in the school and home workshop ₍by₎ A. J. Lockrey. New York city, D. Van Nostrand company, inc., 1940.
xiii, 233 p. col. front., illus., diagrs. 23½ᶜᵐ.
Second edition. cf. p. v.

1. Handicraft. 2. Gums and resins. 3. Plastic materials. I. Title.
40-29573
Library of Congress NK8595.L6 1940
——— Copy 2.
Copyright 668.4

WaS KEmT CaOTP ICJ
NL 0436892 DLC NcRS OU OEac OCl OU CaBVaU WaSp

Lockrey, Andrew Jules, 1897-
Plastics in the school and home workshop... New York city, D. Van Nostrand ₍1943, c1940₎
xiii, 233 p. illus., diagrs. 24 cm.

NL 0436893 TU

Lockrey, Andrew Jules, 1897–
Plastics in the school and home workshop ₍by₎ A. J. Lockrey. 3d ed. New York city, D. Van Nostrand company, inc. ₍1946₎
xv, 289 p. col. front., illus., diagrs. 23½ᶜᵐ.

1. Handicraft. 2. Gums and resins. 3. Plastic materials. I. Title.
46-5629
Library of Congress NK8595.L6 1946
668.4

PP PPPL OCl PSt TxU WaT WaSp
NL 0436894 DLC CaBViP CaBVa CaBVaU OrP Wa WaS KEmT

Lockridge, Frances Louise (Davis)
Adopting a child, by Frances Lockridge, with the assistance of Sophie van S. Theis. New York, Greenberg ₍1947₎
vi, 216 p. 21 cm.
Bibliography: p. 210-212.

1. Adoption—U. S. I. Theis, Sophie van Senden, 1886– joint author. II. Title.
HV875.L56 362.73 47-11003*

OrCS NcC NcGU Or OrP WaOB Wa MB
NL 0436895 DLC WaT WaS OrPS IdB NSyU CU CaBVa

HV875
.L8 Lockridge, Frances Louise (Davis)
Adopting a child, by Frances Lockridge, with the assistance of Sophie van S. Theis. ₍n.p., Reader Service, 1948₎
40 p. illus. (Reader Service booklet no.205)
"Condensed from the book of the same title published by Greenberg, New York."

1. Adoption.

NL 0436896 ICU

Lockridge, Frances Louise (Davis)
Adopting a child, by Frances Lockridge, with the assistance of Sophie van S. Theis. ₍Rev. and enl. ed.₎ New York, Greenberg ₍1948₎
vi, 229 p. 21 cm.
Bibliography: p. 223-225.

1. Adoption—U. S. I. Theis, Sophie van Senden, 1886– joint author. II. Title.
HV875.L56 1948 362.73 48-20622*

NL 0436897 DLC OrU TxU NcRS NcD OrU WaT CaBViP

Lockridge, Frances Louise (Davis) joint author.

Lockridge, Richard, 1898–
Burnt offering; a Captain Heimrich mystery, by Richard and Frances Lockridge. ₍1st ed.₎ Philadelphia, Lippincott ₍1955₎

Lockridge, Frances Louise (Davis)
The cat who rode cows, by Frances and Richard Lockridge. Pictures by Peggy Bacon. Philadelphia, Lippincott ₍1955₎
36 p. illus. 21 cm.

I. Lockridge, Richard, 1898– joint author. II. Title.
PZ10.3.L836Cat 55-7988 ‡

NL 0436899 DLC PP OCl OOxM OrU OrP Or CaBVaU

Lockridge, Frances Louise (Davis)
Cats and people ₍by₎ Frances and Richard Lockridge; with drawings by Helen Stone. ₍1st ed.₎ Philadelphia, Lippincott ₍1950₎
286 p. illus. 22 cm.
Bibliography: p. 277-280.

1. Cats. I. Lockridge, Richard, 1898– joint author.
SF447.L6 636.8 50-8836
Library of Congress

OrP Wa WaS
NcGU CU-A MoU NcU CaBVa CaBVaU IdB Or WaT IdU OrCS
NL 0436900 DLC CaBViP MiU NN TxU ScU OCl DNAL MB

Lockridge, Frances Louise (Davis) ed.

PZ1
.M9995
Cq **Mystery Writers of America.**
Crime for two, by members of the Mystery Writers of America. Edited by Frances and Richard Lockridge. ₍1st ed.₎ Philadelphia, Lippincott ₍1955₎

Lockridge, Frances Louise (Davis)
Curtain for a jester, by Frances and Richard Lockridge. New York, Avon ₍1953₎
161p. 17cm. (Avon, 608)

NL 0436902 OrU

Lockridge, Frances Louise (Davis)
Curtain for a jester; a Mr. and Mrs. North mystery, by Frances and Richard Lockridge. ₍1st ed.₎ Philadelphia, Lippincott ₍1953₎
222 p. 22 cm. (Main Line mysteries)

I. Lockridge, Richard, 1898– joint author. II. Title.
PZ3.L81143Cu 53—12291 ‡

OOxM PPL PP PLF OCl ViU CaOTP FMU FTaSU NjP PSt
NL 0436903 DLC NcD WaE WaSp WaT OrP OrCS CaBVa

Lockridge, Frances Louise (Davis)
Dead as a dinosaur; a Mr. and Mrs. North mystery, by Frances and Richard Lockridge. ₍1st ed.₎ Philadelphia, Lippincott ₍1952₎
185 p. 22 cm. (Main line mysteries)

I. Title.
PZ3.L81143Db 52-5631 ‡

OEac NN ICU
NL 0436904 DLC KyLx WaT WaSp WaE OrP CaBVa ViU

Lockridge, Frances Louise (Davis) joint author.

PZ3
.L81144
Db **Lockridge, Richard**, 1898–
Death and the gentle bull, a Captain Heimrich mystery, by Richard and Frances Lockridge. ₍1st ed.₎ Philadelphia, Lippincott ₍1954₎

VOLUME 337

Lockridge, Frances Louise (Davis)
Death has a small voice; a Mr. and Mrs. North mystery, by Frances and Richard Lockridge. [1st ed.] Philadelphia, Lippincott [1953]
186 p. 22 cm. (Main line mysteries)

I. Lockridge, Richard, 1898- joint author. II. Title.
PZ3.L81143Dbj 52-13739 ‡

NL 0436906 DLC NcD OU OOxM PP FTaSU NjP ICU CaOTP CaBVa OrP WaE WaSp WaT

---

*
AC8 .A6 no.1231 1946
Lockridge, Frances Louise (Davis)
Death of a tall man [by] Frances and Richard Lockridge. New York, Editions for the Armed Services [1946]
256 p. 16cm. (Armed Services ed. 1231)

NL 0436907 ViU

Lockridge, Frances Louise (Davis)
... Death of a tall man, by Frances & Richard Lockridge. Philadelphia, New York, J. B. Lippincott company [1946]
247, [1] p. 19½cm.
At head of title: A Mr. and Mrs. North mystery.
"First edition."

I. *Lockridge, Richard, 1898- joint author. II. Title.
PZ3.L81143Dc 46-7663

NL 0436908 DLC CaBVa OrP WaE WaS WaT NBuU PP PPL TxU

Lockridge, Frances Louise (Davis)
Death of an angel, by Frances and Richard Lockridge. [1st ed.] Philadelphia, Lippincott [1955]
192 p. 22 cm. (*Their* A Mr. and Mrs. North mystery)
Main line mysteries.

I. Lockridge, Richard, 1898- joint author. II. Title.
PZ3.L81143Dd 55—6720 ‡

NL 0436909 DLC CaBVa WaSp OrP OCl OCU OClW PP PPL TxU OOxM OU WaT MsU MsSM

---

*
AC8 .A6 no.747 1942
Lockridge, Frances Louise (Davis)
Death on the aisle, a Mr. and Mrs. North mystery. New York, Editions for the Armed Services, ©1942.
255 p. 10 x 15cm. (Armed Services ed. 747)

NL 0436910 ViU

813.0872
L816d
Lockridge, Frances Louise (Davis)
Death on the aisle; a Mr. and Mrs. North mystery, by Frances and Richard Lockridge. New York, P. F. Collier & Son ©c1942.
288p. (Front page mysteries, 6th series)

NL 0436911 OClUr

Lockridge, Frances Louise (Davis)
Death on the aisle, a Mr. and Mrs. North mystery, by Frances and Richard Lockridge. New York, Grosset & Dunlap [c1942]
288p. 20cm.

NL 0436912 PSt

Lockridge, *Mrs.* Frances Louise (Davis)
Death on the aisle, a Mr. and Mrs. North mystery, by Frances and Richard Lockridge. Philadelphia and New York, J. B. Lippincott company [1942]
288 p. 19½cm.
"First edition."

I. Lockridge, Richard, 1898- joint author. II. Title. 42-10088
Library of Congress PZ3.L81143De

NL 0436913 DLC WaT WaS OrCS WaE OrU OCU OCl OClh OEac PP PPL

Lockridge, Frances Louise (Davis)
Death takes a bow, by Frances and Richard Lockridge; a Mr. and Mrs. North mystery. Philadelphia and New York, J. B. Lippincott company, 1943.
276 p. 19cm.
"First printing."

I. *Lockridge, Richard, 1898- joint author. II. Title. 43-4641
Library of Congress PZ3.L81143Dh

NL 0436914 DLC CaBVa WaS WaT WaE PPL PBa PU OCU OCl OEac OOxM

Lockridge, Frances Louise (Davis)
Death takes a bow, by Frances and Richard Lockridge; a Mr. and Mrs. North mystery. New York, Avon Book Co. [1948]
253 p. 17 cm. (New Avon library, 131)

I. Lockridge, Richard, 1898- joint author. II. Title.
PZ3.L81143Dh 3 48-20688*

NL 0436915 DLC

Lockridge, Frances Louise (Davis)
The dishonest murderer [by] Frances and Richard Lockridge. [1st ed.] Philadelphia, Lippincott Co. [1949]
223 p. 20 cm. (Main line mysteries)
At head of title: A Mr. and Mrs. North mystery.

I. Lockridge, Richard, 1898- joint author. II. Title.
PZ3.L81143Di 49-48150*

NL 0436916 DLC CaBVa OrCS Or OrP CaOTP CoU MsU ViU OEac PP PPA WaE WaSp WaT NN OCl OrU KyLx

---

Lockridge, Frances Louise (Davis) joint author.

PZ3 .L81144 Fo
Lockridge, Richard, 1898-
Foggy, foggy death; a Captain Heimrich mystery [by] Richard and Frances Lockridge. [1st ed.] Philadelphia, Lippincott [1950]

PS3523 .O248H3 942
Lockridge, Frances Louise (Davis)
Hanged for a sheep, by Frances & Richard Lockridge. Bats fly at dusk, by A. A. Fair [pseud.] Cue for murder, by Helen McCloy. New York, Detective Book Club [1942?]
3 v. in 1. 19cm.
I. Lockridge, Richard, 1898- jt. author. II. Gardner, Erle Stanley, 1889- Bats fly at dusk. III. McCloy, Helen. Cue for murder. IV. Title. V. Title: Bats fly at dusk. VI. Title: Cue for murder.

NL 0436918 ViU

Lockridge, Frances Louise (Davis)
Hanged for a sheep, a Mr. and Mrs. North mystery, by Frances and Richard Lockridge. Philadelphia, New York, J. B. Lippincott company [1942]
301 p. 19½cm.

I. *Lockridge, Richard, 1898- joint author. II. Title.
Library of Congress PZ3.L81143Han 42-22725

NL 0436919 DLC OrPR WaE WaS WaT PP PPL PBa OCU OCl OLak OEac OOxM

Lockridge, Frances Louise (Davis)
How to adopt a child, with a list of reliable agencies through which children may be adopted, and valuable information on the rearing of adopted children...New York, N. Y. Children, the magazine for parents. 1928
22½. 23 x 10 cm.

NL 0436920 DL

Lockridge, Frances Louise (Davis) joint author.

PZ3 .L81144 I
Lockridge, Richard, 1898- FOR OTHER EDITIONS SEE MAIN ENTRY
I want to go home; a Captain Heimrich mystery [by] Richard and Frances Lockridge. [1st ed.] Philadelphia, J. B. Lippincott Co. [1948]

Lockridge, Frances Louise (Davis)
A key to death, by Frances and Richard Lockridge. [1st ed.] Philadelphia, Lippincott [1954]
224 p. 22 cm. (*Their* A Mr. and Mrs. North mystery)
Mainline mysteries.

I. Lockridge, Richard, 1898- joint author. II. Title.
PZ3.L81143Ke 54-9427 ‡

NL 0436922 DLC NcD WaT FU TxU OCl PP PPL OCU CaOTP CaBVa OrP WaSp

---

*
AC8 .A6 no.950 1944
Lockridge, Frances Louise (Davis)
Killing the goose, by Frances and Richard Lockridge. New York, Editions for the Armed Services, ©1944.
287 p. 10 x 15cm. (Armed Services ed. 950)

NL 0436923 ViU

VOLUME 337

Lockridge, Frances Louise (Davis)
L & B
blo
21f
Killing the goose, by Frances and Richard Lockridge. New York, Grosset & Dunlap [1944]
254 p. 20 cm.

At head of title: A Mr. and Mrs. North mystery.

I. Lockridge, Richard, 1898- joint author. I. Title

NL 0436924 CtY

Lockridge, Frances Louise (Davis)
... Killing the goose, by Frances and Richard Lockridge Philadelphia, New York, J. B. Lippincott company [1944]
254 p. 19cm.
At head of title: A Mr. and Mrs. North mystery.
"First edition."

I. *Lockridge, Richard, 1898- joint author. II. Title.
44-1216
Library of Congress PZ3.L81143Ki

NL 0436925 DLC CaBVa WaE WaS WaT PP PSt PBa PPL OCU OLak OCl OClh ViU TxU

Lockridge, Frances Louise (Davis)
Killing the goose, by Frances and Richard Lockridge. New York, Avon Pub. Co. [1948]
214 p. 17 cm. (Their A Mr. and Mrs. North mystery)
[New Avon library] 142.

I. Lockridge, Richard, 1898- joint author. II. Title.
PZ3.L81143Ki 4 48-10779*

NL 0436926 DLC

Lockridge, Frances Louise (Davis)
Let dead enough alone; a Captain Heimrich mystery, by Richard and Frances Lockridge. Philadelphia, Lippincott [c1955]
191 p. (Main line mysteries)

NL 0436927 MH

Lockridge, Frances Louise (Davis)
The lucky cat, by Frances and Richard Lockridge; with illus. by Zhenya Gay. [1st ed.] Philadelphia, Lippincott [1953]
89 p. illus. 22 cm.

I. Lockridge, Richard, 1898- joint author. II. Title.
PZ10.3.L836Lu 52-12909 ‡

NL 0436928 DLC OCl OOxM Or WaS OrLgE

Lockridge, Mrs. Frances Louise (Davis)

Davis, Owen, 1874-
Mr. and Mrs. North, a comedy in three acts, by Owen Davis. From the "Mr. and Mrs. North" stories by Frances and Richard Lockridge. New York, Los Angeles, S. French; [etc., etc.] 1941.

Lockridge, Frances Louise (Davis)
Murder comes first. New York, Lippincott, c1951.
192 p.

NL 0436930 KyLx

Lockridge, Frances Louise (Davis)
Murder comes first; a Mr. and Mrs. North mystery, by Frances and Richard Lockridge. [1st ed.] Philadelphia, Lippincott [1951]
192 p. 22 cm. (Main line mysteries)

I. Lockridge, Richard, 1898- joint author. II. Title.
PZ3.L81143Mo 51-10617

NL 0436931 DLC CaBVa WaT WaE WaSp Or OrP TxU MB

Lockridge, Frances Louise (Davis)
Murder in a hurry [by] Frances and Richard Lockridge. [1st ed.] Philadelphia, Lippincott [1950]
223 p. 20 cm. (Their A Mr. and Mrs. North mystery)
Main line mysteries.

I. Lockridge, Richard, 1898- joint author. II. Title.
PZ3.L81143Mq 50-6996

NL 0436932 DLC NN OEac NcD ViU TxU OrU NcGU KMK NcU CaOTP CaBVa OrU WaT WaE OrP

Lockridge, Frances Louise (Davis) and Richard.
Murder is served. New York, Detective book club, c1948.
187 p.
Bound with this are: The witness for prosecution and Three blind mice by Christie, and Dark abyss by Knight.

NL 0436933 PBa

Lockridge, Frances Louise (Davis)
Murder is served, by Frances and Richard Lockridge. Abridged ed. NY, Spivak [c1948]
128 p. (Mercury mystery, 145)

NL 0436934 MH

Lockridge, Frances Louise (Davis)
Murder is served; a Mr. and Mrs. North mystery, by Frances and Richard Lockridge. [1st ed.] Philadelphia, J. B. Lippincott Co. [1948]
240 p. 20 cm. (Main line mysteries)

I. Lockridge, Richard, 1898- joint author. II. Title.
PZ3.L81143Mr 48-8046*

NL 0436935 DLC CaBVa OrP WaE WaS WaT TxU OOxM OEac ViU

Lockridge, Frances Louise (Davis)
Murder is served, by Frances & Richard Lockridge. The witness for the prosecution, and, Three blind mice, by Agatha Christie. Dark abyss, by Clifford Knight. [1950?]

NL 0436936 OCl

Lockridge, Mrs. Frances Louise (Davis)
Murder out of turn; a Mr. and Mrs. North mystery, by Frances and Richard Lockridge ... New York, Frederick A. Stokes company, 1941.
5 p. l., 3-294 p. 19½cm.
Map on lining-papers.

I. *Lockridge, Richard, 1898- joint author. II. Title.
41-528 Revised
Library of Congress PZ3.L81143Mu

NL 0436937 DLC WaT WaE OrU PP PPL PU OLak OEac OCl OOxM OCU

Lockridge, Frances Louise (Davis)
... Murder within murder, by Frances & Richard Lockridge. Philadelphia & New York, J. B. Lippincott company [1946]
240 p. 19½cm.
At head of title: A Mr. and Mrs. North mystery.
"First edition."

I. *Lockridge, Richard, 1898- joint author. II. Title.
46-402
Library of Congress * PZ3.L81143Mw

NL 0436938 DLC CaBVa OrP WaE WaS WaT PP PPL OCl OEac

Lockridge, Frances Louise (Davis)
The nameless cat, by Frances and Richard Lockridge. Pictures by Peggy Bacon. Philadelphia, Lippincott [1954]
78 p. illus. 22 cm.

I. Lockridge, Richard, 1898- joint author. II. Title.
PZ10.3.L836Nam 53-12836 ‡

NL 0436939 DLC OOxM OCl WaSp WaS OrP Or

Lockridge, Frances Louise (Davis)
(The North Stories)

See also

Lockridge, Richard, 1898-

Lockridge, Frances Louise (Davis)
The Norths meet murder, by Frances and Richard Lockridge. Grosset & Dunlap, c1940.

NL 0436941 WaE

Lockridge, Mrs. Frances Louise (Davis)
The Norths meet murder, by Frances and Richard Lockridge. New York, Frederick A. Stokes company, 1940.
5 p. l., 309 p. 19cm.

I. *Lockridge, Richard, 1898- joint author. II. Title.
40-27108 Revised
Library of Congress PZ3.L81143No

NL 0436942 DLC WaT Or WaS OrP PP PPL ViU OCU OOxM OClh OCl

*
AC8
.A6
no.789
1945
Lockridge, Frances Louise (Davis)
Payoff for the banker, by Frances and Richard Lockridge. New York, Editions for the Armed Services, ©1945.
287 p. 10 x 14cm. (Armed Services ed. 789)

NL 0436943 ViU

VOLUME 337

Lockridge, Frances Louise (Davis)
Payoff for the banker ... a Mr. and Mrs. North mystery ₍by₎ Frances and Richard Lockridge. Philadelphia and New York, J. B. Lippincott company ₍1945₎
214 p. 19cm.

I. *Lockridge, Richard, 1898- joint author. II. Title.
45-3115
Library of Congress PZ3.L81143Pay

NL 0436944 CaBVa DLC TxU PP PPL OCl OCU OEac WaS WaE

Lockridge, Frances Louise (Davis)
A pinch of poison, a Mr. and Mrs. North mystery, by Frances and Richard Lockridge ... New York, Frederick A. Stokes company, 1941.
5 p. l., 3-302 p. 19½cm.

I. *Lockridge, Richard, 1898- joint author. II. Title.
41-20727 Revised
Library of Congress PZ3.L81143Pi

NL 0436945 OCl DLC CaBVa WaT WaS PP TxU PPL OCU OOxM

Lockridge, Frances Louise (Davis)
A pinch of poison, by Frances & Richard Lockridge.
302 p
(In Gardner, E.S. The case of the empty tin. [1942. pt.3])

NL 0436946 MH

Lockridge, Frances Louise (Davis) A pinch of poison.
Gardner, Erle Stanley, 1889-
The case of the empty tin, by Erle Stanley Gardner. Evil under the sun, by Agatha Christie. A pinch of poison, by Frances & Richard Lockridge. New York, Detective book club ₍1942₎

Lockridge, Frances Louise (Davis)
The proud cat, by Frances and Richard Lockridge, with drawings by Elinore Blaisdell. ₍1st ed.₎ Philadelphia, Lippincott ₍1951₎
94 p. illus. 22 cm.

I. Title.
PZ10.3.L836Pr 51-11172 ‡

NL 0436948 DLC NN Or WaS WaSp

PZ3 .L81144 Sp
Lockridge, Frances Louise (Davis) joint author.
FOR OTHER EDITIONS SEE MAIN ENTRY
Lockridge, Richard, 1898-
Spin your web, lady! A Captain Heimrich mystery, by Richard and Frances Lockridge. ₍1st ed.₎ Philadelphia, J. B. Lippincott Co. ₍1949₎

Lockridge, Frances Louise (Davis) joint author.
Spin your web, lady
see also under Allingham, Margery, 1904-
More work for the undertaker.

PZ3 .L81144 St
Lockridge, Frances Louise (Davis) joint author.
Lockridge, Richard, 1898-
Stand up and die, a Captain Heimrich mystery, by Richard and Frances Lockridge. ₍1st ed.₎ Philadelphia, Lippincott ₍1953₎

PZ3 .L81144 Th
Lockridge, Frances Louise (Davis) joint author.
Lockridge, Richard, 1898-
Think of death ₍by₎ Richard and Frances Lockridge ... Philadelphia, New York, J. B. Lippincott company ₍1947₎

Lockridge, Frances Louise (Davis)
Untidy murder, a Mr. & Mrs. North mystery ₍by₎ Frances and Richard Lockridge. ₍1st ed.₎ Philadelphia, J. B. Lippincott Co. ₍1947₎
254 p. 20 cm. (Main line mysteries)

I. *Lockridge, Richard, 1898- joint author. II. Title.
PZ3.L81143Un 47-12327*

NL 0436953 DLC CaBVa WaE WaT TxU ViU OOxM

Lockridge, Norman, ed.
Bachelor's quarters; stories from two worlds, edited by Norman Lockridge, with an introduction by John Cournos. New York, Biltmore publishing company, 1944.
xv, 17-764 p., 1 l. 21½cm.

1. Short stories. I. Title.
45-2289
Library of Congress PZ1.L82Bac

NL 0436954 ViU OU PP DLC OrSaW CaBVa IdPI WaE CoU NcD MiHM

PN6014 .L667
Lockridge, Norman, ed.
Bachelor's quarters; stories from two worlds; with an introd. by John Cournos. New York, Herald Pub. Co. [c1946]
xv, 764 p. 21cm.

1. Short stories. I. Title.

NL 0436955 MB FTaSU

Lockridge, Norman, ed.
A golden treasury of the world's wit and wisdom: edited by Norman Lockridge. New York, The Black hawk press, 1936.
3 p. l., 9-564 p. 23½cm.
"Only 1,545 copies have been printed of this first edition ... 1,500 are for sale, 20 for our favorite reviewers, and 25, in a special paper and binding, have been numbered and signed by the editor."

1. Epigrams. 2. Wit and humor. I. Title.
36-9289
Library of Congress PN6281.L56
808.8

NL 0436956 DLC FTaSU OClU Wa

Lockridge, Norman, ed.
The golden treasury of the world's wit and wisdom, edited by Norman Lockridge. New York, Halcyon house, °1936.
585 p. 22cm.

1. Epigrams. 2. Wit and humor. I. Title.
A 38-501
Western Res. univ. Library for Library of Congress [PN6281.L]
808.8

NL 0436957 OClWHi LU OCl MB

Lockridge, Norman.
Lese majesty; the private lives of the Duke & Duchess of Windsor. New York, Boar's Head Books, 1952.
190 p. ports. 22 cm.

1. Edward VIII, King of Great Britain, 1894- I. Title.
DA580.L6 923.142 52-3507

NL 0436958 DLC FU WaTC CLSU CtY NN MoU CoU

HQ31 .L81
Lockridge, Norman.
The sexual conduct of men & women, a minority report; with a preface by S. Klein, and a minority report on Prof. Kinsey by G. Legman. New York, Hogarth House, 1950 ₍°1948₎
256 p. 22 cm.

1. Sexual ethics. 2. Kinsey, Alfred Charles, 1894-1956. Sexual behavior in the human male. I. Title. GTS-64

NL 0436959 IEG NcGU MH WaE NmU

Lockridge, Norman.
Waggish tales of the Czechs, originally entitled Gesta Czechorum
see under title

R 808.8 L81w
Lockridge, Norman, ed.
World's wit and wisdom, edited by Norman Lockridge. New York, Herald publishing company [1936]
3 p. l., 9-585 p. 22cm.

NL 0436961 OrSaW

PN6281 .L56 1945
Lockridge, Norman, ed.
World's wit and wisdom; edited by Norman Lockridge. New York, Biltmore Pub. Co. ₍1945₎
564 p. 21cm.
First edition published under title: A golden treasury of the world's wit and wisdom.
1. Epigrams. 2. Wit and humor. I. Title.

NL 0436962 ViU

R 808.8 L813g 1945
Lockridge, Norman, ed.
World's wit and wisdom. New York, Biltmore Publishing House ₍°1945₎
585 p. 22cm.
First published, 1936, with title The golden treasury of the world's wit and wisdom.

1. Epigrams. 2. Wit and humor. I. Title.

NL 0436963 AU

PN6281 L56 1945
Lockridge, Norman, ed.
World's wit and wisdom, edited by Norman Lockridge. New York, Dorene Pub. Co. [c1945]
585 p. 21cm.

1. Epigrams. 2. Wit and humor. I. Title.

NL 0436964 CoU

VOLUME 337

Lockridge, Richard, 1898–
Burnt offering; a Captain Heimrich mystery, by Richard and Frances Lockridge. [1st ed.] Philadelphia, Lippincott [1955]
189 p. illus. 22 cm. (Main line mysteries)

I. Lockridge, Frances Louise (Davis) joint author. II. Title.
Full name: Richard Orson Lockridge.
PZ3.L81144Bu 55-6311 ‡

NL 0436965 DLC CaOTP OrPS OrP FU OU TxU OOxM TU ViU OCl PPL PP OCU CaBVa WaE NcD WaSp WaT KyLx

---

PZ10 .3 .L836 Cat
Lockridge, Richard, 1898– joint author.
Lockridge, Frances Louise (Davis)
The cat who rode cows, by Frances and Richard Lockridge. Pictures by Peggy Bacon. Philadelphia, Lippincott [1955]

SF447 .L6
Lockridge, Richard, 1898– joint author.
Lockridge, Frances Louise (Davis)
Cats and people [by] Frances and Richard Lockridge; with drawings by Helen Stone. [1st ed.] Philadelphia, Lippincott [1950]

Lockridge, Richard, 1898–
A client is canceled; a Captain Heimrich mystery, by Richard and Frances Lockridge. [1st ed.] Philadelphia, Lippincott [1951]
185 p. 22 cm. (Main line mysteries)

I. Title.
PZ3.L81144Cl 51-11206 ‡

NL 0436968 DLC ViU CaOTP Or WaT WaE CaBVa

PZ3 .L81143 Cu
Lockridge, Richard, 1898– joint author.
Lockridge, Frances Louise (Davis)
Curtain for a jester; a Mr. and Mrs. North mystery, by Frances and Richard Lockridge. [1st ed.] Philadelphia, Lippincott [1953]

LOCKRIDGE, RICHARD, 1898-
Darling of misfortune: Edwin Booth: 1833-1893. New York, The Century co. [c1932] xi, 358 p. illus., ports. 22cm.

1. Booth, Edwin, 1833-1893. I. Title. i. subs. for *R-MWES.

NL 0436970 NN TU GU MoU MB

Lockridge, Richard, 1898–
Darling of misfortune: Edwin Booth: 1833–1893, by Richard Lockridge ... New York, London, The Century co. [°1932]
xi, 358 p. front., pl., ports. 21½ cm. $3.50
"First printing."

1. Booth, Edwin, 1833–1893. I. Title.
Library of Congress PN2287.B5L6 32-26998
Copyright A 54718 927.92

NL 0436971 DLC OKentU WaU OClJC PBm PP PPGi PPD OOxM ODW OCl OO OClW NN FMU MiU OU NIC MoU Or MtBC CaBVa OrP IdU OrU WaSpG WaS

Lockridge, Richard, 1898–
Death and the gentle bull, a Captain Heimrich mystery, by Richard and Frances Lockridge. [1st ed.] Philadelphia, Lippincott [1954]
224 p. 22 cm. (Main line mysteries)

I. Lockridge, Frances Louise (Davis) joint author. II. Title.
Full name: Richard Orson Lockridge.
PZ3.L81144Db 54-6111 ‡

NL 0436972 DLC CaOTP OrU NcD NIC NcGU WaE OrCS PP CaBVa OU PLF TxU OOxM WaSp WaT FTaSU

Lockridge, Richard, 1898–
Death by association; a Captain Heimrich mystery, by Richard and Frances Lockridge. [1st ed.] Philadelphia, Lippincott [1952]
192 p. 22 cm. (Main line mysteries)

I. Title.
Full name: Richard Orson Lockridge.
PZ3.L81144Dc 52-10933 ‡

NL 0436973 DLC MB NBuC TxU ViU OOxM FMU FTaSU CoU KyLx ICU IdB OrP OrU WaE WaS WaSp WaT

PZ3 .L81143 Dbj
Lockridge, Richard, 1898– joint author.
Lockridge, Frances Louise (Davis)
Death has a small voice; a Mr. and Mrs. North mystery, by Frances and Richard Lockridge. [1st ed.] Philadelphia, Lippincott [1953]

Lockridge, Richard, 1898–
Death in the mind [by] Richard Lockridge & G. H. Estabrooks. New York, E. P. Dutton & company, inc., 1945.
251 p. 19½ cm.
"First edition."

I. Estabrooks, George Hoben, 1895– joint author. II. Title.
45-6321
Library of Congress PZ3.L81144De

NL 0436975 DLC TxU PPL PP OEac OCU OO OCl NcU WaS WaT

Lockridge, Richard, 1898–
Death in the mind [by] Richard Lockridge & G. H. Estabrooks. Cleveland, World Pub. Co. [1947]
251 p. 19½ cm.

I. Estabrooks, George Hoben, 1895– joint author. II. Title.
45-6321

NL 0436976 ViU

PZ3 .L81143 De
Lockridge, Richard, 1898– joint author.
Lockridge, Frances Louise (Davis)
... Death of a tall man, by Frances & Richard Lockridge. Philadelphia, New York, J. B. Lippincott company [1946]

PZ3 .L81143 Dd
Lockridge, Richard, 1898– joint author.
Lockridge, Frances Louise (Davis)
Death of an angel, by Frances and Richard Lockridge. [1st ed.] Philadelphia, Lippincott [1955]

Lockridge, Richard, 1898– joint author.
Lockridge, *Mrs.* Frances Louise (Davis)
Death on the aisle, a Mr. and Mrs. North mystery, by Frances and Richard Lockridge. Philadelphia and New York, J. B. Lippincott company [1942]

Lockridge, Richard, 1898– joint author.
Lockridge, Frances Louise (Davis)
Death takes a bow, by Frances and Richard Lockridge; a Mr. and Mrs. North mystery. Philadelphia and New York, J. B. Lippincott company, 1943.

PZ3 .L81143 Di
Lockridge, Richard, 1898– joint author.
Lockridge, Frances Louise (Davis)
The dishonest murderer [by] Frances and Richard Lockridge. [1st ed.] Philadelphia, Lippincott Co. [1949]

Lockridge, Richard, 1898–
Foggy, foggy death; a Captain Heimrich mystery [by] Richard and Frances Lockridge. [1st ed.] Philadelphia, Lippincott [1950]
223 p. 22 cm. (Main line mysteries)

I. Lockridge, Frances Louise (Davis) joint author. II. Title.
PZ3.L81144Fo 50—10759

NL 0436982 DLC CaBVa OrP Or WaE WaSp WaT NcD ViU TxU

Lockridge, Richard, 1898– joint author.
Lockridge, Frances Louise (Davis)
Hanged for a sheep, a Mr. and Mrs. North mystery, by Frances and Richard Lockridge. Philadelphia, New York, J. B. Lippincott company [1942]

Lockridge, Richard, 1898–
I want to go home; a Captain Heimrich mystery [by] Richard and Frances Lockridge. [1st ed.] Philadelphia, J. B. Lippincott Co. [1948]
249 p. 20 cm. (Main line mysteries)

I. Lockridge, Frances Louise (Davis) joint author. II. Title.
Full name: Richard Orson Lockridge.
PZ3.L81144 I 48-1419*

NL 0436984 DLC OOxM TxU OEac WaT WaE OrP CaBVa

PZ3 .L81143 Ki 4
Lockridge, Richard, 1898– joint author.
FOR OTHER EDITIONS SEE MAIN ENTRY
Lockridge, Frances Louise (Davis)
Killing the goose, by Frances and Richard Lockridge. New York, Avon Pub. Co. [1948]

VOLUME 337

813.54
L816L
Lockridge, Richard, 1898-
Let dead enough alone; a Captain Heimrich mystery, by Richard and Frances Lockridge. Philadelphia, Lippincott [c1955]
191 p. 22 cm. (Main line mysteries)
"Book Club edition."-Dust jacket.
I. Lockridge, Frances Louise (Davis) joint author. II. Title.
NL 0436986 CaOTP OEac FU NcD

PZ10 .3 .L836 Lu
Lockridge, Richard, 1898- joint author.
Lockridge, Frances Louise (Davis)
The lucky cat, by Frances and Richard Lockridge; with illus. by Zhenya Gay. [1st ed.] Philadelphia, Lippincott [1953]

Lockridge, Richard, 1898-
A matter of taste. [1st ed.] Philadelphia, J. B. Lippincott Co. [1949]
250 p. 21 cm.
I. Title.
Full name: Richard Orson Lockridge.
PZ3.L81144Mat 49-10005*
NL 0436988 DLC CaBVaU CaBVa WaSp WaE WaT NcD OEac PP

Lockridge, Richard, 1898-
Mr. and Mrs. North; a novel by Richard Lockridge. New York, Frederick A. Stokes company, 1936.
viii p., 1 l., 265 p. illus. 21½cm.
I. Title. 36-27436
Library of Congress PZ3.L81144M1
NL 0436989 DLC OrCS Or PP PPL CtY OClW OLak OEac OClh OCl ViU NN

Lockridge, Richard, 1898-
Davis, Owen, 1874-
Mr. and Mrs. North, a comedy in three acts, by Owen Davis. From the "Mr. and Mrs. North" stories by Frances and Richard Lockridge. New York, Los Angeles, S. French; [etc., etc.] 1941.

PZ3 .L81143 Mo
Lockridge, Richard, 1898- joint author.
Lockridge, Frances Louise (Davis)
Murder comes first; a Mr. and Mrs. North mystery, by Frances and Richard Lockridge. [1st ed.] Philadelphia, Lippincott [1951]

PZ3 .L81143 Mq
Lockridge, Richard, 1898- joint author.
Lockridge, Frances Louise (Davis)
Murder in a hurry [by] Frances and Richard Lockridge. [1st ed.] Philadelphia, Lippincott [1950]

PZ3 .L81143 Mr
Lockridge, Richard, 1898- joint author.
Lockridge, Frances Louise (Davis)
Murder is served; a Mr. and Mrs. North mystery, by Frances and Richard Lockridge. [1st ed.] Philadelphia, J. B. Lippincott Co. [1948]

Lockridge, Richard, joint author.
FOR OTHER EDITIONS SEE MAIN ENTRY
Lockridge, Frances Louise (Davis)
Murder out of turn; a Mr. and Mrs. North mystery, by Frances and Richard Lockridge ... New York, Frederick A. Stokes company, 1941.

PZ3 .L81143 Mw
Lockridge, Richard, 1898- joint author.
Lockridge, Frances Louise (Davis)
... Murder within murder, by Frances & Richard Lockridge. Philadelphia & New York, J. B. Lippincott company [1946]

PZ10 .3 .L836 Nam
Lockridge, Richard, 1898- joint author.
Lockridge, Frances Louise (Davis)
The nameless cat, by Frances and Richard Lockridge. Pictures by Peggy Bacon. Philadelphia, Lippincott [1954]

Lockridge, Richard, 1898- joint author.
Lockridge, Frances Louise (Davis)
The Norths meet murder, by Frances and Richard Lockridge. New York, Frederick A. Stokes company, 1940.

PZ3 .L81143 Pay
Lockridge, Richard, 1898- joint author.
Lockridge, Frances Louise (Davis)
Payoff for the banker ... a Mr. and Mrs. North mystery [by] Frances and Richard Lockridge. Philadelphia and New York, J. B. Lippincott company [1945]

Lockridge, Richard, 1898- joint author.
Lockridge, Frances Louise (Davis)
A pinch of poison, a Mr. and Mrs. North mystery, by Frances and Richard Lockridge ... New York, Frederick A. Stokes company, 1941.

D811 .M24
Lockridge, Richard, 1898- joint author.
McKeogh, Michael James.
Sgt. Mickey and General Ike, by Michael J. McKeogh and Richard Lockridge. New York, G. P. Putnam's sons [1946]

Lockridge, Richard, 1898-
Spin your web, lady! By Richard & Frances Lockridge. NY, Mercury Publications, Spivak [c1949]
127 p. (A Mercury mystery, 154)
NL 0437001 MH

Lockridge, Richard, 1898-
Spin your web, lady! A Captain Heimrich mystery, by Richard and Frances Lockridge. [1st ed.] Philadelphia, J. B. Lippincott Co. [1949]
218 p. 20 cm. (Main line mysteries)
I. Lockridge, Frances Louise (Davis) joint author. II. Title.
Full name: Richard Orson Lockridge.
PZ3.L81144Sp 49-7468*
NL 0437002 DLC TxU ViU OEac PSt WaS WaE WaT Or CaBVa

Lockridge, Richard, 1898-
Spin your web, lady
see also
Allingham, Margery, 1904-
More work for the undertaker.

Lockridge, Richard, 1898-
Stand up and die, a Captain Heimrich mystery, by Richard and Frances Lockridge. [1st ed.] Philadelphia, Lippincott [1953]
219 p. 22 cm. (Mainline mysteries)
I. Lockridge, Frances Louise (Davis) joint author. II. Title.
Full name: Richard Orson Lockridge.
PZ3.L81144St 53-8928 ‡
NL 0437004 DLC OrU FMU OrP OrU CaBVa ICU NcD PP OU OCl PLFM PPLas OOxM WaS WaT WaSp

---

*
AC8 .A6 no.1293 1947
Lockridge, Richard, 1898-
Think of death, by Richard and Frances Lockridge. New York, Editions for the Armed Services [1947]
256 p. 16cm. (Armed Services ed. 1293)
NL 0437005 ViU

Lockridge, Richard, 1898-
Think of death [by] Richard and Frances Lockridge ... Philadelphia, New York, J. B. Lippincott company [1947]
272 p. 19cm.
"Main line mysteries."
"First edition."
I. Lockridge, Frances Louise (Davis) joint author. II. Title.
[Full name: Richard Orson Lockridge]
PZ3.L81144Th 47-2226
NL 0437006 DLC TxU NBuU CaBVa WaS PP OCU PPL

PZ3 .L81143 Un
Lockridge, Richard, 1898- joint author.
FOR OTHER EDITIONS SEE MAIN ENTRY
Lockridge, Frances Louise (Davis)
Untidy murder, a Mr. & Mrs. North mystery [by] Frances and Richard Lockridge. [1st ed.] Philadelphia, J. B. Lippincott Co. [1947]

VOLUME 337

Lockridge, Ross Franklin, 1877-1952.
A. Lincoln, by Ross F. Lockridge ... Yonkers-on-Hudson, N. Y., World book company, 1930.
xiv, 320 p. incl. front., illus. (incl. ports.) 20½cm.

1. Lincoln, Abraham, pres. U. S., 1809-1865. I. Title.
30-11880
Library of Congress E457.L82
——— Copy 2.
Copyright A 22458 [38c2] 923.1

NL 0437008 DLC NIC InU WaS WaSp Or WaT OLak MiU-C

E 457 L82 1931 **Lockridge, Ross Franklin,** 1877-1952.
A. Lincoln, by Ross F. Lockridge ... Yonkers-on-Hudson, N. Y., World book company, 1931. [c1930]
xiv, 320 p. incl. front., illus. (incl. ports.) 20½cm.

NL 0437009 NSyU NIC

Lockridge, Ross Franklin, 1877-1952, ed.
The Citizen; organ of the movement for a new constitution for the state of Indiana. v. 1 (no. 1-10); July 1915-Apr. 1916. Indianapolis, Ind. [etc.] Citizens league of Indiana, 1915-16

Lockridge, Ross Franklin, 1877-1952.
Debating and public discussion. Manual for civic discussion clubs
see Indiana. University. Bureau of Public discussion.
Manual for civic discussion clubs.

Lockridge, Ross Franklin, 1877-1952.
George Rogers Clark, pioneer hero of the Old Northwest, by Ross F. Lockridge ... Yonkers-on-Hudson, N. Y. and Chicago, Ill., World book company [c1927]
xxi, [1], 210 p. incl. front., illus. 20½cm.

1. Clark, George Rogers, 1752-1818. 2. Northwest, Old—Hist.—Revolution.
Library of Congress E207.C5L7 27-23470

KyBgW TU
OLak OEac OCl OO TxU ViU NN Or AU ICRL WaSp IdPI OrP
NL 0437012 DLC KyHi KyLx KyU-A InU PP PWcS PSC OU

Lockridge, Ross Franklin, 1877-1952.
How government functions in Indiana, by Ross F. Lockridge ... an Indiana supplement to Thomas Harrison Reed's Form and functions of American government. Yonkers-on-Hudson, N. Y., World book company, 1918.
101 p. 19cm.
Bibliography: p. 91-92.

1. Indiana—Pol. & govt. I. Reed, Thomas Harrison, 1881- Form and functions of American government. II. Title.
Library of Congress JK5625.1918.L6 l 18-14397

NL 0437013 DLC

JK5625 1918 .L65 **Lockridge, Ross Franklin,** 1877-1952.
How government functions in Indiana, by Ross F. Lockridge ... an Indiana supplement to Thomas Harrison Reed's Form and functions of American government. Yonkers-on-Hudson, N. Y., World book company, 1918.
120p. 19cm.
Bibliography: p. 85-86.

NL 0437014 FMU ICJ

Lockridge, Ross Franklin, 1877-1952.
The labyrinth, a history of the New Harmony labyrinth, including some special study of the spiritual and mystical life of its builders, the Rappites, and a brief survey of labyrinths generally. By Ross F. Lockridge, director of the New Harmony memorial commission, in collaboration with other members of the commission. [New Harmony, Ind.] The New Harmony memorial commission, 1941.
94 p. incl. front., illus. (incl. port.) 23 cm.
Bibliography included in preface.
1. Labyrinths. 2. Harmony society. I. Indiana. New Harmony memorial commission. II. Title.
HX656.N5L78 335.9772 43-1673

NL 0437015 DLC OU NcD MnHi IEdS MoU

Lockridge, Ross Franklin, 1877-1952.
La Salle, by Ross F. Lockridge ... Yonkers-on-Hudson, N. Y., World book company, 1931.
xvi, 312 p. incl. front., illus. 20cm.

1. La Salle, Robert Cavelier, sieur de, 1643-1687?
31-2113
Library of Congress F1030.5.L81
Copyright A 33260 [2] 923.944

NL 0437016 DLC OClND MiU OEac CU Or MtU WaTC

PN4185 .I5A3 Lockridge, Ross Franklin, 1877-1952.
Indiana. University. *Bureau of public discussion.*
... Manual for civic discussion clubs. [Bloomington? Ind., 1913]

Lockridge, Ross Franklin, 1877-1952.
The Old Fauntleroy home, by Ross F. Lockridge ... Published for the New Harmony memorial commission by courtesy of Mrs. Edmund Burke Ball. [New Harmony, Ind.] 1939.
xii, 219 p. front., illus., plates. 20½cm.
Map on lining-papers.
"A panoramic view of New Harmony from the portals and windows of the Old Fauntleroy home."—Pref.

1. New Harmony, Ind.—Hist. 2. Fauntleroy family. 3. Harmonists. I. New Harmony (Ind.) memorial commission. II. Title.
40-12939
Library of Congress F534.N5L6
[a47d1] 977.234

NL 0437018 DLC WaS

Lockridge, Ross Franklin, 1877-1952.
Our great hoosier memorials: I. Our hoosier Lincoln memorial. Indiana university alumni quarterly, vol. XVII, no. 2, April, 1930, p. 133-108.

NL 0437019 MiKW

Lockridge, Ross Franklin, 1877-1952.
The story of Indiana. Oklahoma City, Harlow Pub. Corp., 1951.
v, 406 p. illus., ports. 24 cm.
"Bibliography, references, teaching aids on Indiana": p. 390-400.

1. Indiana—Hist.
F526.L78 977.2 51-48262

NL 0437020 DLC

Lockridge, Ross Franklin, 1877-1952.
The story of Indiana; with additions by Herbert L. Heller. [2d ed.] Oklahoma City, Harlow Pub. Corp., 1955.
417 p. illus. 24 cm.
Includes bibliography.

1. Indiana—Hist.
F526.L78 1955 977.2 55-12691 ‡

NL 0437021 DLC OO MiU

Lockridge, Ross Franklin, 1877-1952.
Theodore F. Thieme, a man and his times, by Ross F. Lockridge ... [Los Angeles, Printed by Haynes corporation] 1942.
xix, 211 p. front., illus., plates, ports. 21½cm.

1. Thieme, Theodore Frederick, 1857- 2. Hosiery. 3. Wayne knitting mills.
Library of Congress HD9969.H8U7 42-14055
[2] 923.373

NL 0437022 DLC InGo

Lockridge, Ross Franklin, 1877-1952.
What we owe to George Rogers Clark, by Ross F. Lockridge...(In Cooperative school bulletin, May 1928 p. 5-6, 15, 20)

NL 0437023 MiU-C

Film 2117 Lockridge,Ross Franklin,1914-1948.
The dream of the flesh of iron. [n.p., 1941. 19,vii,399 p.
Microfilm of the original ms in the Lockridge ms collection in the Lilly Library,Indiana University. Bloomington,Ind., Lilly Library,University of Indiana, n.d. 1 reel.

I. Indiana. University. Lilly Library. II. Title.

NL 0437024 NSyU

Lockridge, Ross Franklin, 1914-1948.
Raintree County ... which had no boundaries in time and space, where lurked musical and strange names and mythical and lost peoples, and which was itself only a name musical and strange. Boston, Houghton Mifflin Co., 1948.
xiv, 1066 p. maps. 22 cm.

I. Title.
PZ3.L81146Rai 48-245*

WaT WaS OrP IdU IdB CaBVaU
OrPS WaWW WaSpG KyU-H MtBC WaTC CaBVa OrCS WaE WaSp
FTaSU MoU KyLx NcGU ICU MH MB FMU MiU MiEM OU NcD Or
NL 0437025 DLC TxU OrLgE MtU IdPI OrU OrStbM ICU InU

PS3523 .O25R3 1948 Lockridge, Ross Franklin, 1914-1948.
Raintree County ... which had no boundaries in time and space, where lurked musical and strange names and mythical and lost peoples, and which was itself only a name musical and strange.
New York, Popular Library [c1948]
990 p. (Eagle books edition, 220)

NL 0437026 ICU TxU OCU MiU OU CaOTP WaU

Lockroi, Joseph Philippe Simon
see Lockroy, Joseph Philippe Simon, 1803-1891.

VOLUME 337

Lockrow, Laurice Laird, 1896-
Critical potentials and spectra of oxygen ... by L. L. Lockrow ... [Chicago, 1926]
cover-title, p. 205-217. illus., pl. XIII, diagrs. 24cm.
Thesis (PH. D.)—University of Michigan, 1926.
"Reprinted from the Astrophysical journal, vol. LXIII, no. 4, May 1926."

1. Oxygen. 2. Ionization of gases. 3. Spectrum analysis. I. Title.
27-3543
Library of Congress QC462.O8L6 1926
Univ. of Michigan Libr.

NL 0437028 MiU OrU OrCS NIC OU OO DLC

LOCKROY, pseud.

See LOCKROY, Joseph Philippe Simon, called, 1803-1891.

DS 97.6 C4 L55
Lockroy, Édouard Étienne Antoine Simon, called 1840-1913.
Ahmed le Boucher; la Syrie et l'Égypte au XVIIIe siecle [par] Edouard Lockroy. Paris, P. Ollendorff, 1888.
293p. 19cm.

1. Cezzâr, Ahmed, paşa, d. 1804. 2. Syria--Hist. 3. Egypt--Hist.--19th century. I. Title.

NL 0437030 UU NjP WaPS

956.9 L816a
Lockroy, Édouard Étienne Antoine Simon, called, 1840-1913.
Ahmed le Boucher; la Syrie et l'Egypte au XVIIIe siècle. 2.éd. Paris, P. Ollendorff, 1888.
x,293p. 19cm.

1. Syria - Hist. I. Title.

NL 0437031 NcU

DS 97.5 .L82 1882
Lockroy, Édouard Étienne Antoine Simon, called, 1840-1913.
Ahmed le boucher; la Syrie et l'Égypte au XVIIIe siècle. 4.éd. Paris, P.Ollendorff, 1888.
x,293 p. 19 cm.

1.Cazzâr, Ahmed, paşa, d.1804. 2.Egypt--Hist.--640-1882. 3.Syria-- Hist.

NL 0437032 MiU MH

Lockroy, Édouard Étienne Antoine *Simon, Called, 1840-*
... Au hasard de la vie, notes et souvenirs; préface de Jules Claretie. Paris, B. Grasset, 1913.
xv, 294 p., 1 l. 19cm. fr. 3.50
"L'épopée de 1861, les souvenirs de Tripoli de Syrie, les journées d'angoisse autour de Metz, les nuits de garde autour de Paris."—Préf.

I. Title.
13-12346
Library of Congress PQ2338.L7A2 1913

NL 0437033 DLC MB CtY NcD NN

4DC 1410
Lockroy, Édouard Étienne Antoine Simon, called, 1840-1913.
La Commune et l'Assemblée. Paris, A. Le Chevalier, 1871.
48 p.

NL 0437034 DLC-P4 NN IaU

Lockroy, Édouard Étienne Antoine Simon, *called*, 1840-1913.
Comptoir d'echantillons des fabricants bijoutiers, joailliers & orfèvres. France—exportation. Compte rendu in-extenso de l'inauguration solennelle faite le 29 juillet 1886 sous la présidence de m. Lockroy ... Paris, Impr. typ. Mayer et c^e, 1886.
47, [1] p. 23cm.

1. Jewelry trade—France. I. Title.
G S 34-459
Libr., U. S. Geol. Surv.. Geo. F. Kunz Collection K480.5 L81

NL 0437035 DI-GS

Soc VA 503 L63
Lockroy, Édouard Étienne Antoine Simon, called, 1840-1913.
La défense navale. Paris, Berger-Levrault, 1900.
548p.

1. France. Marine. 2. France - Defenses. I. Title.

NL 0437036 FTaSU DN MH NcD

Lockroy, Édouard Étienne Antoine Simon, *Called 1840-* 1913.
Du Weser à la Vistule: lettres sur la marine allemande, par Édouard Lockroy ... Paris, Nancy, Berger-Levrault & c^ie, 1901.
xii, 300 p. 19cm.

1. Germany—Navy. I. Title.
2-14822
Library of Congress YA513.L81

NL 0437037 DLC DN ICJ NN

Lockroy, Édouard Étienne Antoine Simon, called, 1840-1913, *ed.*
[**Jullien,** *Mme.* **Rosalie (Ducrolay)**]
The great French revolution, 1785-1793. Narrated in the letters of Madame J——, of the Jacobin party. Ed. by her grandson, M. Édouard Lockroy. From the French by Miss Martin, and an American collaborateur. London, S. Low, Marston, Searle, & Rivington, 1881.

Lockroy, Édouard Étienne Antoine Simon, called, 1840-1913.
L'île révoltée. Paris, Marpon et Flammarion [1891].
pp. (4), 221 +. (Auteurs célèbres.)
Treats of Garibaldi's expedition against Sicily in 1860.

Italy-Hist. 1860-61 [Garibaldi]

NL 0437039 MH NjP CU

Lockroy, Édouard Étienne Antoine Simon, called, 1840-1913.
Journal d'une bourgeoise pendant la révolution. 1881
see under Jullien, Rosalie (Ducrolay)

Soc VA 503 L6 1897
Lockroy, Edouard Etienne Antoine Simon, called, 1840-1913.
La marine de guerre. Six mois rue Royale. 2. éd. Paris, Berger-Levrault, 1897.
385p.

1. France. Marine. 2. France - Defenses. I. Title. II. Title: Six mois rue Royale.

NL 0437041 FTaSU NN MH DN CtY

Lockroy, Édouard Étienne Antoine Simon, called, 1840-1913.
.... Les marines française et allemande. Paris, H. Charles-Lavauzelle, 1904.
267 p. 19½cm.
At head of title: Édouard Lockroy. . . . .

NL 0437042 ICJ DN DNW MH NN

Lockroy, Édouard Étienne Antoine Simon, called, 1840-1913.
Une mission en Vendée, 1793
see under Jullien, Marc Antoine, 1775-1848.

Lockroy, Édouard Étienne Antoine Simon, called, 1840-1913.
M. de Moltke, ses mémoires et la guerre future. Paris, E. Dentu, 1892.
pp. (3), 258.

Moltke[].

NL 0437044 MH CtY

Lockroy, Édouard Étienne Antoine Simon, called, 1840-1913.
Sarraut, Maurice.
Le problème de la marine marchande, par Maurice Sarraut ... Préface de m. Édouard Lockroy ... Paris [etc.] Berger-Levrault et cie., 1901.

Lockroy, Édouard Étienne Antoine Simon, called, 1840-1913.
Le programme naval. Paris, H. Charles-Lavauzelle, 1906.
262 p. 12°.

NL 0437046 NN DN

Lockroy, Édouard Étienne Antoine Simon, called, 1840-1913.
Bernard, Albert.
... Résumé chronologique de l'histoire des Français depuis les origines jusqu'à nos jours à l'usage des écoles primaires, par Albert Bernard ... avec une lettre-préface de Édouard Lockroy. Cours supérieur. Paris, Dentu [189-?]

G6 1 L81
Lockroy, Édouard Étienne Antoine Simon, called, 1840-1913.
Ueber die Zukunft des classischen Unterrichts in Frankreich. Rede, gehalten am 30. Juli 1888 an der Sorbonne zu Paris ... Mit Autorisation des Verfassers aus dem Französischen übersetzt von J. Singer. Wien, 1888.

NL 0437048 CtY

VOLUME 337

Lockroy, Édouard Étienne Antoine Simon, called, 1840-1913.
Ueber die Zukunft des classischen Unterrichts in Frankreich. n.p., 1889.

NL 0437049 NjP

844L813
JA LOCKROY, Joseph Philippe Simon, 1803-1891.
Al pie de la escalera. Comedia en un acto. Escrita en francés por mm. Lockroi y Anicet-Bourgeois. (Traducida por d. J.G. Doncél.)... ⌐Madrid, Imprenta de la viuda de Jordan é hijos, 1844⌐
16 p. 26cm.
Caption title.
I. Anicet-Bourgeois, Auguste, 1806-1871, jt.auth. II. García Doncel, Juan, tr. III. Title.

NL 0437050 MnU

⌐Lockroy, Joseph Philippe Simon⌐ 1803-1891.
... Al pie de la escalera. Comedia en un acto, nuevamente arreglada y corregida por D.J.G. Doncel, para representarse en Madrid el año de 1856. 2. ed. [Madrid, V. de Lalama, 1856]
8 p. 4°. (Biblioteca dramática. Coleccion de comedias representados con éxito en los teatros de Madrid)
Caption-title.
1. Drama (Spanish) 2. Title.

NL 0437051 CtY NN

⌐Lockroy, Joseph Philippe Simon, called⌐ 1803-1891.
Les amours de Faublas, ballet-panto-mime en trois actes et quatre tableaux, de M. M.*******et Léon. Musique de M. Piccini. ⌐Paris, Imprimerie de Mme. de Lacombe, 1835?⌐
16p.
Microcard edition.

NL 0437052 ICRL AU

ar X
911
v.2 Lockroy, Joseph Philippe Simon, called, 1803-1891.
Les amours de Faublas, ballet-pantomime en trois actes et quatre tableaux, de M.M.******* et Léon, maître de ballets du Théâtre de Marseille ... Musique de M. Piccini ... ⌐Paris, Marchant, 1835⌐
16 p. 26cm.
Caption title.
Without music.

No. 6 in vol. lettered: Magasin théatral. II.

I. Léon, master of ballets at the Théâtre du Marseille. II. Title.

NL 0437054 NIC MH CU

⌐Lockroy, Joseph Philippe Simon, called, 1803-1891⌐
Les amours de Faublas, ballet-pantomime en trois actes et quatre tableaux, de M. M***** et Léon, maître de ballets du Theatre de Marseille. ⌐Paris, Marchant, 1835⌐
16p.
Microcard edition.

NL 0437055 ICRL

Lockroy, Joseph Philippe Simon, 1803-1891.
Un ange tutélaire; comédie-vaudeville en un acte, par MM. Lockroy [pseud.], Jaime [pseud.] et Marc-Michel, ... [Paris, 1844]
16 p. l. 8°. [In Bibl. dram., 3e sér., t. 90]
I. Michel, Marc Antoine Amédée.

NL 0437056 CtY

Lockroy, Joseph Philippe Simon, called, 1803-
Arturo; ó, Los remordimientos
see under Coll, Gaspar Fernando, 1826-1855.

Lockroy, Joseph Philippe Simon, called, 1803-1891.
Bonsoir, Mr. Pantalon! Opéra comique en 1 acte
see under Grisar, Albert, 1808-1869.

Lockroy, Joseph Philippe Simon, called, 1803-1891. Bonsoir, monsieur Pantalon.

M1503
.O 93B8 **Oudrid y Segura, Cristóbal,** 1825-1877.
... Buenas noches, sor d Simon. Musica de C. Oudrid ... ⌐Madrid, Unión musical española, 1852?⌐

Lockroy, Joseph Philippe Simon, called, 1803-1891, joint author.
C'est encore du bonheur...
see under Arnould, Auguste Jean François, 1803-1854.

Lockroy, Joseph Philippe Simon, called, 1803-1891.
Planché, James Robinson, 1796-1880. FOR OTHER EDITIONS SEE MAIN ENTRY
The captain of the watch. A comedietta, in one act. By J. R. Planche. <Freely rendered from the French piece, entitled, "Le chevalier du guet", by M. Lockroy.> As performed at Covent Garden theatre, London, in 1841. To which are added, a description of the costumes ... and the whole of the stage business. New York, R. M. De Witt, ©1876.

Lockroy, Joseph Philippe Simon, called, 1803-1891, joint author.
Catherine II...
see under Arnould, Auguste Jean François, 1803-1854.

Lockroy, Joseph Philippe Simon, called, 1803-1891.
Charlot, comédie en trois actes, par MM. Lockroy, Anicet-Bourgeois et Vanderburch. ⌐Paris, Impr. de Mme. de Lacombe, n.d.⌐
24p.
Microcard edition.

NL 0437063 ICRL AU

PQ1222
M32
v.2 Lockroy, Joseph Philippe Simon, called, 1803-1891.
Charlot, comédie en trois actes, par MM. Lockroy, Anicet-Bourgeois et Vanderburch. ⌐Paris? 1840?⌐
24 p. (Magasin théâtral ⌐selections. v.2⌐)
Caption title.

NL 0437064 CU

Lockroy, Joseph Philippe Simon, 1803-1891.
Charlot; comédie en trois actes, par MM. Lockroy [pseud.], A. Bourgeois et Vanderburch, ... Bruxelles, 1841.
86 p. 16°. [In Bibl. dram., 4e sér., t. 67]
I. Vanderburch, Louis Émile.

NL 0437065 CtY

Lockroy, Joseph Philippe Simon, called, 1803-1891.
Le chevalier du guet, comédie en deux actes. ⌐Paris, Impr. de Mme. de Lacombe, n.d.⌐
23p.
Microcard edition.

NL 0437066 ICRL AU

[LOCKROY, Joseph Philippe Simon, called, 1803-1891]
Le chevalier du guet, comédie en deux actes. Par M. Lockroy. [Paris, 18..]
1.8°. pp. 23.

NL 0437067 MH

Lockroy, Joseph Philippe Simon, 1803-1891.
Le chevalier du Guet, comédie en deux actes, par m. Lockroy, représentée, pour la première fois à Paris, sur le théâtre des Variétés, le 9 septembre 1840. ⌐Paris, Henriot, 1840?⌐
23p. 25cm. (In ⌐Théâtre. (Bound pamphlet collection) v. 2, no. 19⌐)
Caption title.

I. Title.

Printed by Wesleyan University Library

NL 0437068 CtW

Lockroy, Joseph Philippe Simon, *called*, 1803-1891.
Le chevalier du guet, comédie en deux actes ... ⌐Paris, 1840⌐
23 p. 25cm. ⌐Répertoire dramatique des auteurs contemporains, n. 129⌐
Caption title.

I. Title.

Library of Congress PQ2338.L72C5 44-18244 Brief cataloging

NL 0437069 DLC CtY

Lockroy, Joseph Philippe Simon, called, 1803-1891.
La chien du jardinier
see under Grisar, Albert, 1808-1869.

Lockroy, Joseph Philippe Simon, called, 1803-1891.
La croix de Marie
see under Maillart, Louis, 1817-1871.

VOLUME 337

Lockroy, Joseph Philippe Simon, called, 1803-1891.
Deux compagnons du tour de France, comédie-vaudeville en deux actes, par MM. Lockroy et Jules de Wailly. ₍Paris, n.d.₎
32p.
Microcard edition.

NL 0437072 ICRL OrU AU

Lockroy, Joseph Philippe Simon, 1803-1891.
Deux compagnons du tour de France, comédie-vaudeville en deux actes, par mm. Lockroy et Jules de Wailly, représentée pour la première fois, sur le théatre des Variétés, le 10 novembre 1845. ₍Paris, C. Tresse, 1845?₎
32p. 25cm. (In ₍Théâtre. (Bound pamphlet collection) v. 3, no. 29₎)
Caption title.

I. Wailly, Jules de, 1806-1866, joint author. II. Title.

NL 0437073 CtW

Lockroy, Joseph Philippe Simon 1803-1891.
Deux compagnons du tour de France, comedie-vaudeville en deux actes, par MM. Lockroy et Jules de Wailly, representée pour la première fois, sur le theatre des Variétes le 10 novembre 1845.

NL 0437074 NN

ML50 .M219 D74 1940

Lockroy, Joseph Philippe Simon, called, 1803-1891. Les dragons de Villars.

Maillart, Louis, 1817-1871.
₍Les dragons de Villars. Libretto. German₎

Das Glöckchen des Eremiten, komische Oper in drei Aufzügen von Aimé Maillart. Dichtung von Lockroy und Cormon. Hrsg. und eingeleitet von Georg Richard Kruse. Leipzig ₍194–₎

Hrl Lo25

Lockroy, Joseph Philippe Simon, 1803-1891.
Un duel sous le cardinal de Richelieu, drame en trois actes, mêlé de couplets, par MM. Lockroy et Edmond Badon. Représenté pour la première fois, sur le théâtre national du Vaudeville, le 9 avril 1832. [Paris,18--?]
20p. 25½cm.
Caption title.

NL 0437076 CtY

PQ1222 M32 v.1

Lockroy, Joseph Philippe Simon, called, 1803-1891.
Un duel sous le cardinal de Richelieu, drame en trois actes, mêlé de couplets, par MM. Lockroy et Edmond Badon. ₍Paris? 1832?₎
20 p. (Magasin théâtral ₍selections. v.1₎)

Caption title.
Without music; tunes indicated by title.

NL 0437077 CU

[LOCKROY, Joseph Philippe Simon, called, 1803-1891]
Un duel sous le cardinal de Richelieu; drama en trois actes, mêlé de couplets. Par MM. Lockroy, [pseud.] et Edmond Baron. Paris, J.N. Barba,1832.

pp.48,
"Représenté pour la première fois, le 9 avril 1852".

NL 0437078 MH

Lockroy, Joseph Philippe Simon, called, 1803-1891.
Un duel sous le Cardinal de Richelieu, drame en trois actes, mêlé de couplets, par MM. Lockroy et Edmond Badon. Paris, Barba, 1832.
50p.

Microcard edition.

NL 0437079 ICRL

[LOCKROY, Joseph Philippe Simon,called , 1803-1891]
Une duel sous le cardinal de Richelieu, drame en trois actes, mêle de couplets, par MM. Lockroy et Edmond Badon. [Paris,1834]

1.8°. pp.20.
(La France dramatique, au XIXe siecle)

NL 0437080 MH CtY

---

ar X 698 v. 1

Lockroy, Joseph Philippe Simon, called, 1803-1891.
Un duel sous le cardinal de Richelieu, drame en trois actes, mêlé de couplets, par MM. Lockroy et Edmond Badon. ... ₍Paris, Barba, Pollet et Bezou, 184-₎
20 p. 26cm.

Caption title.
Without music.
No. 10 in vol. lettered: France dramatique. I.

NL 0437081 NIC

LOCKROY,[Joseph Philippe Simon,called,1803-1891
Un duel sous le Cardinal de Richelieu;drame en trois actes,mêlé de couplets,par MM.Lockroy et Edmond Badon. [Paris,C.Tresse,1842.]

1.8°. pp.20.
Without title-page. Caption title.
"La France dramatique au dix-neuvième siècle, choix de pièces modernes. Vaudeville."

NL 0437082 MH

[LOCKROY, Joseph Philippe Simon, called,1803-1891]
Un duel sous le cardinal de Richelieu; drame en trois actes, mêle de couplets, par MM.Lockroy [pseud.] for J.P.Simon], et Edmond Badon. [Paris, Tresse,1876].

1.8°. pp.20.

(LA FRANCE dramatique au dix-neuvième siècle.")

NL 0437083 MH

Lockroy, Joseph Philippe Simon, 1803-1891.
...Un duel sous le cardinal de Richelieu; drame... Paris: Calmann Lévy, 1892. 20 p. 26cm.

Cover-title.
At head of title: Lockroy & Edmond Badon.

1. Drama, French. I. Badon, Edmond, 1808-1849, jt. au. II. Title.
N. Y. P. L. April 9, 1943

NL 0437084 NN

Lockroy, Joseph Philippe Simon, called, 1803-1891, joint author.
El espectro de Herbesheim
see under Arnould, Auguste Jean François, 1803-1854.

Lockroy, Joseph Philippe Simon, 1803-1891.
L'extase, comédie en trois actes, mêlée de chant, par MM. Lockroy et Arnould, musique nouvelle de M. Doche, représentée pour la première fois sur le théâtre du Vaudeville, le 23 janvier 1843. ₍Paris: Marchant, 1843₎ 31 p. 25cm. (Magasin théatral. Tome 34 ₍no. 2₎)

Caption-title.
Without the music.

78602B. 1. Drama, French. I. Arnould, Auguste Jean François, 1803-1854, jt. au. II. Title. III. Ser.
N. Y. P. L. May 13, 1941

NL 0437086 NN PU CtY

Lockroy, Joseph Philippe Simon, 1803-1891.
La fée Carabosse
see under Massé, Victor, 1822-1884.

PQ2153 .A73F7

Lockroy, Joseph Philippe Simon, called, 1803-1891, joint author.

Arnould, Auguste Jean François, 1803-1854.
Le frère de Piron; comédie-vaudeville en un acte, par MM. Arnould et Lockroy. Représentée pour la première fois, à Paris, sur le Théâtre national du Vaudeville, le 13 septembre 1836. ₍Paris, Impr. de Vᵉ Dondey-Dupré, 1836?₎

Lockroy, Joseph Philippe Simon, called, 1803-1891.
Good night, Signor Pantaloon
see under Grisar, Albert, 1808-1869.

Lockroy, Joseph Philippe Simon, called, 1803-1891.
Gute Nacht, Herr Pantalon!
see under Grisar, Albert, 1808-1869.

Lockroy, Joseph Philippe Simon, 1803-1891.
Der Hauptmann der Schaarwache. Lustspiel in zwei Akten, frei nach Lockvoy ₍sic₎ von Th. Rose. ₍Berlin, A. W. Hayn, 1852?₎ 19 p. 26cm. (Bühnen-Repertoir des Auslandes. Bd. 20. No. 154)

1. Drama, French—Translations into German. I. Rose, Th., tr. II. Rose, Th.

NL 0437091 NN

Lockroy, Joseph Philippe Simon, called, 1803-1891.
Un homme qui a perdu son do. Vaudeville en un acte.[par] Lockroy et Michel. Paris, M. Levy Frères, 1855.
46 p. 12°.
I. Michel, M.[A. A.], called Marc Michel.

NL 0437092 NN CtY

VOLUME 337

Lockroy, Joseph Philippe Simon, 1803-1891.
L'Impératrice et la juive; drame ... par MM. Lockroy et Anicet. Bruxelles, 1834.
131 p. 16°. [In v. 14, Bibliothèque Dramatique, 4e sér.]

NL 0437093 CtY

Lockroy, Joseph Philippe Simon, 1803-1891.
L'impératrice et la Juive, drame en cinq actes et en prose, par mm. Lockroy et Anicet ... Paris, Marchant [etc.] 1834.
86 p. 21cm.

I. Anicet-Bourgeois, Auguste, 1806-1871, joint author. II. Title.
PQ2338.L6I3

NL 0437094 MiU NN CU

Lockroy, Joseph Philippe Simon, called, 1803-1891.
L'impératrice et la juive, drame en cinq actes et en prose, par MM. Lockroy et Anicet. [Paris, Marchant, 1834]
32p.
Microcard edition.

NL 0437095 ICRL AU

Lockroy, Joseph Philippe Simon, called, 1803-1891, joint author.
Scribe, Augustin Eugène, 1791-1861.
... Irène; ou, Le magnétisme; comédie-vaudeville en deux actes, par mm. Scribe et Lockroy; représenté pour la première fois, à Paris, sur le théâtre du Gymnase dramatique, le 2 février 1847 ... [Paris, Michel Lévy frères, 1854]

PQ 6296 .T4 v.58
Lockroy, Joseph Philippe Simon, called, 1803-1891.
Isabel de Baviera, ó París en 1418; drama histórico en cinco actos [de Lockroy y Anicet-Bourgeois] traducido del francés por Narciso de la Escosura. Madrid, Imp. de J. M. Repullés, 1838.
92 p. (In Teatro español. [Madrid, etc., 1787-1935] v. 58, [1])
Translation of Perinet Leclerc.

NL 0437097 MiEM

Micro-card 57-11 ser.2 no.1502
Lockroy, Joseph Philippe Simon, called, 1803-1891.
Job et Jean, vaudeville en deux actes, par MM. Lockroy et Anicet Bourgeois. [Paris, n. d. Louisville, Ky., Falls City Press, 1960]
1 card. [Three centuries of French drama. ser.2: 17th, 18th and 19th centuries, no.1502]
Microcard edition.
Collation of original: 21 p.
I. Anicet-Bourgeois, Auguste, 1806-1871, joint author. II. Title.

NL 0437098 AU ICRL OrU

Lockroy, Joseph Philippe Simon, 1803-1891.
Job et Jean; vaudeville en deux actes. Bruxelles, 1841.
71 p. 16°. [In v. 74, Bibliothèque Dramatique, 4e sér.]

NL 0437099 CtY

ar X 911 v. 3
Lockroy, Joseph Philippe Simon, called, 1803-1891.
Les jours gras sous Charles IX, drame historique en trois actes, par MM. Lockroy et Arnould ... [Paris, Marchant, 18]
27 p. 26cm.
Caption title.
No. 34 in vol. lettered: Magasin théatral. III.

NL 0437100 NIC

Lockroy, Joseph Philippe Simon, 1803-1891.
Les jours gras sous Charles IX; drame historique en trois actes, par MM. Lockroy [pseud.] et Arnould, ... [Paris, 1832]
27 p. l. 8°. [In Bibl. dram., 3e sér., t. 9]

NL 0437101 CtY

Lockroy, Joseph Philippe Simon, 1803-1891.
Les jours gras sous Charles IX, drame historique en trois actes, par MM. Lockroy et Arnould, représenté pour la première fois, à Paris sur le théâtre national du Vaudeville, le 8 novembre 1832. [Paris: Marchant, 1835] 27 p. 25cm. (Magasin théatral. Tome 6 [no. 14])
Caption-title.

78575B. 1. Drama, French. 2. Charles IX, king of France, 1550-1574—Drama. 3. Henry IV, king of France, 1553-1610—Drama. I. Arnould, Auguste Jean François, 1803-1854, jt. au. II. Title. III. Ser.
N. Y. P. L. April 30, 1941

NL 0437102 NN

Lockroy, Joseph Philippe Simon, 1803-1891.
Les jours gras sous Charles IX, drame historique en trois actes, par mm. Lockroy et Arnould, représenté pour la première fois, à Paris, sur le théâtre national du Vaudeville, le 8 novembre 1832 [Paris, Marchant, 1835]
27 p. 25cm. [Magasin théâtral [t.10]]
Caption title.

NL 0437103 CU

Lockroy, Joseph Philippe Simon, called, 1803-1891.
Les jours gras sous Charles IX, drame historique en trois actes, par MM. Lockroy et Arnould. [Paris, Marchant, 1835]
27p.
Microcard edition.

NL 0437104 ICRL AU

Lockroy, Joseph Philippe Simon, 1803-1891.
Karl, conde de Richter, ou O castigo. Drama em 3 actos e 1 prologo. (Archivo theatral. Lisboa, 1839. 12°. v. 2, p. 1-22)
By Lockroy and Anicet-Bourgeois.
I. Anicet-Bourgeois, A.

NL 0437105 NN

Lockroy, Joseph Philippe Simon, called, 1803-1891, and A. Anicet-Bourgeois.
Karl, ou, Le chantiment, drame en quatre actes, par MM. Lockroy, et Anicet Bourgeois, musique de M. Piccini... [Paris: Marchant, 1835.] 20 p. 4°. (Le Magasin théatral. Année 2, tome 2.)
Caption-title.
Without music.

53166A. 1. Drama (French). 2. Anicet-Bourgeois, Auguste, 1806-71, jt. au. 3. Title. 4. Series.
N. Y. P. L. October 24, 1922

NL 0437106 NN CU CtY

Lockroy, Joseph Philippe Simon, called, 1803-1891.
Karl, ou Le châtiment, drame en quatre actes, par MM. Lockroy et Anicet Bourgeois, musique de M. Piccini. [Paris, Marchant, 1835]
20p.
Microcard edition.

NL 0437107 ICRL AU

Lockroy, Joseph Philippe Simon, called, 1803-1891.
Le lansquenet, comédie-vaudeville en un acte, par MM. Lockroy et Ferdinand Langlé. [Paris, n.d.]
27p.
Microcard edition.

NL 0437108 ICRL OrU AU

Lockroy, Joseph Philippe Simon, 1803-1891.
Le lansquenet, comédie-vaudeville en un acte, par mm. Lockroy et Ferdinand Langlé [pseud.], représentée pour la première fois sur le théâtre des Variétés, le 27 mai 1845. [Paris, Tresse, 1845?]
27p. 25cm. (In [Théâtre. (Bound pamphlet collection) v. 7, no. 22])
Caption title.

I. Langlois, Joseph Adolphe Ferdinand, 1798-1867, joint author. II. Title.

Printed by Wesleyan University Library

NL 0437109 CtW CtY

Lockroy, Joseph Philippe Simon, 1803-1891.
Madame Barbe-Bleue; comédie-vaudeville en deux actes, par MM. Lockroy [pseud.] et Choquart, ... Paris [1843]
25 p. l. 8°. [In Bibl. dram., 3e sér., t. 75]

NL 0437110 CtY

LOCKROY, JOSEPH PHILIPPE SIMON, 1803-1891.
Madame Barbe-Bleue; comédie-vaudeville en deux actes, par Lockroy et Choquart. [Paris C. Tresse, 1843] 25 p. 25cm. (La France dramatique au dix-neuvième siècle)
Micro-opaque. Louisville, Ky., Falls City microcard, 1958. 1 card. 7.5 x 12.5cm. (Three centuries of French drama)

Caption-title.

1. Drama, French. I. Choquart, Adolphe, joint author. II. Title.

NL 0437112 NN OrU ICRL AU

VOLUME 337

He77 026 9 [Lockroy, Joseph Philippe Simon] 1803-1891.
... El maestro de escuela. Caricatura literaria en un acto, arreglada á la escena española por D. Juan del Peral, representada ... en el teatro de la Cruz, el 26 de mayo de 1846, y en el teatro Español el año de 1850. (2.ed.) [Madrid, Impr. de V. de Lalama, 1851]
10p. 25½cm. (Biblioteca dramática)
Binder's title: Teatro español, 9.
Caption title.
From the French of Lockroy and Anicet-Bourgeois
Marked copy; torn and mended.

NL 0437113 CtY

[Lockroy, Jospeh Philippe Simon] 1801-1891.
El Maestro de Escuela. Caricatura literaria en un acto, arreglada á la escena española por D. Juan del Peral, representada con grande aplauso en el teatro de la Cruz el 26 de mayo de 1846, y en el teatro Español el año de 1850.
[At end]: Barcelona, 1864.
[Biblioteca dramática]

NL 0437114 NNH

PQ1222 M32 v.3 Lockroy, Joseph Philippe Simon, called, 1803-1891.
Le maître d'école, vaudeville en un acte, par MM. Lockroy et Anicet-Bourgeois. [Paris? 1841?]
18 p. (Magasin théâtral [selections. v.3])
Caption title.
Without music; tunes indicated by title.

NL 0437115 CU

Lockroy, Joseph Philippe Simon, called, 1803-1891.
Le maître d'école, vaudeville en un acte, par MM. Lockroy et Anicet-Bourgeois. [Paris, Impr. de Mme. de Lacombe, n.d.]
18p. illus.
Microcard edition.

NL 0437116 ICRL AU OrU

Lockroy, Joseph Philippe Simon, 1803-1891.
Le maître d'école, vaudeville en un acte, par mm. Lockroy et Anicet-Bourgeois, représenté pour la première fois, à Paris, sur le théâtre des Variétés, le 20 mars 1841. [Paris, Impr. de mme. de Lacombe, 1841?]
16p. 25cm. (In [Théâtre. (Bound pamphlet collection) v. 8, no. 18])
Caption title.

I. Anicet-Bourgeois, Auguste, 1806-1871, joint author. II. Title.

NL 0437117 CtW CtY

Lockroy, Joseph Philippe Simon, 1803-1891.
Le mari de sa cuisinière; comédie en deux actes, mélée de chant, par M. Lockroy [pseud.] ... [Paris, 1841]
24 p. l. 8°. [In Bibl. dram., 3e sér., t. 76]

NL 0437118 CtY

Lockroy, Joseph Philippe Simon, called, 1803-1891.
Le mari de sa cuisinière, comédie en deux actes, mêlée de chant. [Paris, 1841?]
24p.
Microcard edition.

NL 0437119 ICRL OrU AU

[Lockroy, Joseph Philippe Simon, called] 1803-1891.
Maria Remond. Madrid, 1839.

NL 0437120 MH

PQ 6226 .T4 v.28 Lockroy, Joseph Philippe Simon, called, 1803-1891.
María Rémond; drama en tres actos, traducido del francés por Juan del Peral. Madrid, Imp. de I. Boix, 1839.
46 p. (In Teatro español. [Madrid, etc., 1787-1935] v. 28, [8])
Translation of Marie Rémond.

I. Anicet-Bourgeois, Auguste, 1806-1871, joint author. II. Peral Richart, Juan del, d. 1888, tr. III. Title.

NL 0437121 MiEM

848 L817ma [Lockroy, Joseph Philippe Simon, called, 1893-1891]
Maria Remond, drama en tres actos. Traducido por Gregorio Romero Larrañaga. Madrid, En la Impr. de Yenes, 1839.
31 p. (Galería dramatica; colección de las mejores obras del teatro antiguo y moderno español, y del teatro estrangero: teatro moderno estrangero)
By Joseph Lockroy and Auguste Anicet-Bourgeois. Cf. Bibl. de la France.
I. Anicet-Bourgeois, Auguste, 1806-1871, joint author. II. Romero y Larrañaga, Gregorio, 1815-1872, tr. III. Title.

NL 0437122 MiU MH

He77 027 10 Lockroy, Joseph Philippe Simon, 1803-1891.
Maria Rémond, drama en tres actos, tr. libremente del francés por D. Juan del Peral. 2.ed. [Madrid, 1852]
14p. 27cm. (Biblioteca dramatica)
Binder's title: Teatro español. 3.ser., v.10.
Caption title.

NL 0437123 CtY

Lockroy, Joseph Philippe Simon, 1803-1891.
Marie de Rohan; ou, Un duel sous Richelieu; opéra sérieux en trois actes, paroles de MM. Lockroy [pseud.] et Edmond Badon, ... Paris [1843]
13 p. l. 8°. [In Bibl. dram., 3e sér., t. 76]
Based upon their drama, Un duel sous le cardinal de Richelieu.

NL 0437124 CtY

Lockroy, Joseph Philippe Simon, *called*, 1803-1891.
Marie Rémond, drame en trois actes, par mm. Lockroy et Anicet-Bourgeois ... [Paris, 1839]
20 p. 1 illus. 25cm. [Magasin théâtral]
Caption title.

I. Anicet-Bourgeois, Auguste, 1806-1871, joint author. II. Title.
44-18245 Brief cataloging
Library of Congress PQ2338.L72M3

NL 0437125 DLC CtY NN

Lockroy, Joseph Philippe Simon, called, 1803-1891.
Marie Rémond, drame en trois actes, par MM. Lockroy et Anicet-Bourgeois. [Paris, Marchant, 1839]
20p. illus.
Microcard edition.

NL 0437126 ICRL

Lockroy, Joseph Philippe-Simon, 1803-1891.
En Nattegjaest. Vaudeville-Spøg, i een Act ... omarbejdet af T. Overskou ...
11 p.
(In: Det Kongelige Theaters Repertoire. Kjøbenhavn, 1828-45? nar. 8°. v. 6)
I. Anicet-Bourgeois, A.

NL 0437127 NN

Lockroy, Joseph Philippe Simon, called, 1803-1891.
On demande des professeurs, vaudeville en un acte, par MM. Lockroi [!] et Jaime. [Paris, n.d.]
18p.
Microcard edition.

NL 0437128 ICRL NN OrU AU

Lockroy, Joseph Philippe Simon, *called*, 1803-1891.
Passé minuit, vaudeville en un acte, par mm. Lockroy et Anicet-Bourgeois ... [Paris, n. d.]
12 p. 25cm.
Caption title.
Without music.

I. Anicet-Bourgeois, Auguste, 1806-1871, joint author. II. Title.
44-18100 Brief cataloging
Library of Congress PQ2338.L72P3

NL 0437129 DLC

Lockroy, Joseph Philippe Simon, called, 1803-1891.
Passé minuit, vaudeville en un acte, par MM. Lockroy et Anicet-Bourgeois. [Paris, n.d.]
10, [1]p.
Microcard edition.

NL 0437130 ICRL AU OrU

PQ1222 M32 v.3 Lockroy, Joseph Philippe Simon, called, 1803-1891.
Passé minuit, vaudeville en un acte, par MM. Lockroy et Anicet-Bourgeois. [Paris? 1839?]
12 p. (Magasin théâtral [selections. v.3])
Caption title.
Without music; tunes indicated by title.
I. Anicet-Bourgeois, Auguste, 1806-1871, joint author. II. Title.

NL 0437131 CU

LOCKROY, JOSEPH PHILIPPE SIMON, 1803-1891.
Passé minuit; vaudeville en un acte, par Lockroy et Anicet-Bourgeois. Représenté pour la première fois, à Paris, sur le théâtre du Vaudeville, le 10 juin 1839. [Paris? n.d. Louisville, Ky., Falls City microcards, 1958] 1 card 7.5 x 12.5cm.
Microprint copy.
Collation of original: 12 p. 25cm.

Continued in next column

VOLUME 337

Continued from preceding column

Words only; tunes indicated by title.

1. Drama, French. 2. Vaudevilles--Librettos. Passé minuit. I. Anicet-Bourgeois, Auguste, 1806-1871, joint author. II. Title.

NL 0437133 NN

Lockroy, Joseph Philippe Simon, called, 1803-1891.
Passé minuit; vaudeville en un acte, par mm. Lockroy et Anicet-Bourgeois. Représenté pour la première fois, à Paris, sur le Théâtre du vaudeville, le 10 juin 1839. ₍Paris, Impr. de Boulé et c^e, 1839?₎
12 p. 26cm.
Caption title.
₍No. 7₎ in a volume with binder's title: Théâtre moderne. v.2.

NL 0437134 NcD CtY

[LOCKROY, Joseph Philippe Simon, called, 1803-1891]
Passe´ minuit, vaudeville en un acte par MM. Lockroy et Anicet-Bourgeois. Paris,1839.
pp.28. 41581.33
The same. Paris,1839.
1.8°. pp.12.
(LaFrance dramatique au XIXe siecle)

NL 0437135 MH

Lockroy, Joseph Philippe Simon, 1803-1891.
... Passé minuit, vaudeville en un acte Paris, Tresse, 1872.
cover-title,12p. 26cm. (La France dramatique au dix-neuvième siècle)
"Par mm.Lockroy et Anicet Bourgeois."
With this is bound Un tigre du Bengale, par mm. Édouard Brisebarre et Marc Michel. [1849]
I. Bourgeois, Anicet, joint auth. II. Title.

NL 0437136 NRU

Lockroy, Joseph Philippe Simon, called, 1803-1891, joint author.
Périnet Leclerc
see under Anicet-Bourgeois, Auguste, 1806-1871.

[LOCKROY, Joseph Philippe Simon, called,1803-1891]
Pourquoi? Comedie-vaudeville un acte, par M. Lockroy et Anicet. [Paris,-18-]
1.8°. pp.(16)
La France dramatique au XIXe siecle)
By Joseph Philippe Simon and Auguste Anicet Bourgeois called Anicet-Bourgeois.

NL 0437138 MH

Lockroy, Joseph Philippe Simon, *called*, 1803-1891.
Pourquoi? Comédie-vaudeville en un acte, par MM. Lockroy et Anicet. Représentée pour la première fois, à Paris, sur le Théâtre du Vaudeville, le 14 juin 1833. Paris, J.-N. Barba, 1833.
37 p. 22 cm.
Without the music; tunes indicated by title.
I. Anicet-Bourgeois, Auguste, 1806-1871, joint author. II. Title.
PQ2338.L72P6 53-53784

NL 0437139 DLC

Micro-card 57-11 ser.2 no.1504
Lockroy, Joseph Philippe Simon, called, 1803-1891.
Pourquoi? comédie-vaudeville en un acte, par MM. Lockroy et Anicet. ₍Paris, Barba, 1838. Louisville, Ky., Falls City Press, 1960₎
1 card. ₍Three centuries of French drama. ser.2: 17th, 18th and 19th centuries, no.1504₎
Microcard edition.
Collation of original: 53-68 p.
I. Anicet-Bourgeois, Auguste, 1806-1871, joint author. II. Title.

NL 0437140 AU ICRL OrU

---

ar X 698 v. 5
Lockroy, Joseph Philippe Simon, called, 1803-1891.
Pourquoi? Comédie-vaudeville en un acte, par MM. Lockroy et Anicet ... ₍Paris, Barba, Pollet et Bezou, 184-₎
₍53₎-68 p. 26cm.
Caption title.
No. 20 in vol. lettered: France dramatique. V.
I. Anicet-Bourgeois, Auguste, 1806-1871, joint author. II. Title.

NL 0437141 NIC

Lockroy, Joseph Philippe Simon, 1803-1891.
...Pourquoi? Par Lockroy et Anicet. La suite d'un bal masqué, par Madame de Bawr. Bielefeld ₍etc.₎ Velhagen & Klasing, 1881. 95 p. (Théâtre français. sér. 4., livr. 4.)
Film reproduction. 35mm. Reduction 12. Positive.
F4180. 1. Drama, French. I. Anicet-Bourgeois, Auguste, 1806-1871, jt. au. II. Bawr, Alexandrine Sophie (Goury de Champgrand) baronne de, 1773-1860. La suite d'un bal masqué. III. Title. IV. Title: La suite d'un bal masqué.
N.Y.P.L. September 30, 1946

NL 0437142 NN

Lockroy, Joseph Philippe Simon, called, 1803-1891.
La première ride, comédie-vaudeville en un acte, par MM. Lockroy et Anicet Bourgeois. ₍Paris, Impr. de Mme. de Lacombe, n.d.₎
18p.
Microcard edition.

NL 0437143 ICRL OrU AU

[LOCKROY, Joseph Philippe Simon, called,1803-1891]
La premiere ride, comedie-vaudeville en un acte, par MM. Lockroy et Anicet Bourgeois [Paris, 18-]
1.8°. pp.18.

NL 0437144 MH

Lockroy, Joseph Philippe Simon, called, 1803-1891.
Le premiere ride, comedie-vaudeville en un acte, par MM. Lockroy et Anicet Bourgeois, representee pour la premiere fois ... le 24 de decembre 1839. Paris, Tresse, 1840.
45 p. (In Theatre francais, v. 271. no. 5)

NL 0437145 PU

Lockroy, Joseph Philippe Simon, called, 1803-1891.
La reine Topaze
see under Massé, Victor, 1822-1884.

Lockroy, Joseph Philippe Simon, 1803-1891.
Sous une porte cochère; vaudeville en un acte ... Brux., 1840.
62 p. 16°. [In v. 61, Bibliothèque Dramatique, 4e sér.]

NL 0437147 CtY

Micro-card 57-11 ser.2 no.1506
Lockroy, Joseph Philippe Simon, called, 1803-1891
Sous une porte cochère, vaudeville en un acte par MM. Lockroy et Anicet-Bourgeois. ₍Paris, n. d. Louisville, Ky., Falls City Press, 1960₎
1 card. ₍Three centuries of French drama. ser.2: 17th, 18th and 19th centuries, no.1506₎
Microcard edition.
Collation of original: 16 p.
I. Anicet-Bourgeois, Auguste, 1806-1871, joint author. II. Title.

NL 0437148 AU ICRL OrU

Lockroy, Joseph Philippe Simon, 1803-1891.
Tomkins the troubadour. (L'homme qui a perdu son do.) A farce, in one act. By Messrs. Lockroy and Marc Michel. As first produced at the Varieties théâtre, Paris, and, in English, at the Queen's theatre, London...on...Aug. 31, 1868. To which is added a description of the costumes...and the whole of the stage business. New York: R. M. De Witt ₍1868?₎ 15 p. 19cm. (De Witt's acting plays. no. 134.)
1. Drama, French—Translations into English. I. Michel, Marc Antoine Amédée, 1812-1868, jt. au. II. Title. III. Ser.
N.Y.P.L. April 9, 1943

NL 0437149 NN MH IU OU CLSU

PQ1222 C6 v.190
Lockroy, Joseph Philippe Simon, called, 1803-1891.
Les trois coups de pied, comédie-vaudeville en deux actes, par MM. Lockroy et A. de Comberousse. ₍Paris? 1851?₎
55 p. (In Collection of French plays and librettos ₍v.190₎)
Caption title.
Without music; tunes indicated by title.

NL 0437150 CU

Lockroy, Joseph Philippe Simon, called, 1803-1891.
Les trois coups de pied. Comédie-vaudeville en deux actes ... par mm. Lockroy et A. de Comberousse. [Poissy, Arbieu, 1851?]
55 p. 12°.
In NKM. p.v. 56, no. 2.
I. Comberousse, A.[B.B.] de.

NL 0437151 CtW NN

VOLUME 337

Lockroy, Joseph Philippe Simon, 1803-1891.
Les trois coups de pied; comédie-vaudeville en deux actes, par MM. Lockroy [pseud.] et A. de Comberousse ... [Paris, 1851]
55 p. 12°. [In Bibl. dram., t. 36]

NL 0437152 CtY

Micro-card 57-11 ser.2 no.1507

Lockroy, Joseph Philippe Simon, called, 1803-1891.
Trois épiciers, vaudeville en trois actes, par MM. Lockroy et Anicet-Bourgeois. [Paris, n. d. Louisville, Ky., Falls City Press, 1960]
1 card. [Three centuries of French drama. ser.2: 17th, 18th and 19th centuries, no.1507]

Microcard edition.
Collation of original: 27 p.

I. Anicet-Bourgeois, Auguste, 1806-1871, joint author. II. Title.

NL 0437153 AU ICRL OrU

Lockroy, Joseph Philippe Simon, 1803-1891.
Trois épiciers; vaudeville en trois actes, par MM. Lockroy [sic] et A. Bourgeois ... [Paris, 1840]
27 p. 1. 8°. [In Bibl. dram., 3e sér., t. 47]

NL 0437154 CtY

Lockroy, Joseph Philippe Simon, 1803-1891.
Trois épiciers; vaudeville en trois actes, par MM. Lokcroy [sic] et A. Bourgeois ... Bruxelles, 1840.
96 p. 16°. [In Bibl. dram., 4e sér., t. 60]

NL 0437155 CtY

Lockroy, Joseph Philippe Simon, called, 1803-1891.
Les trois sultanes; comédie de Favart en trois actes, et en vers
see under Favart, Charles Simon, 1710-1792.

[LOCKROY, Joseph Philippe Simon, called, 1803-1891]
La vieillesse d'un grand roi, drame en trois actes et en prose, par MM. Lockroy et Arnould. [Paris, 18..]

1.8°. pp.30. Vign.

(Magasin theatrale).

NL 0437157 MH ICRL

Lockroy, Joseph Philippe Simon, called, 1803-1891.
La vieillesse d'un grand roi, drame en trois actes et en prose, par MM. Lockroy et Arnould. [Paris, n.d.]
30p.

Microcard edition.

NL 0437158 ICRL AU OrU

Lockroy, Joseph Philippe Simon, called, 1803-1891.

La vieillesse d'un grand roi; drame en trois actes et en prose, par mm. Lockroy et Arnould, représenté pour la première fois, à Paris, sur le Théâtre-Français, par les comédiens ordinaires du Roi, le 28 mars 1837. [Paris, Impr. de Dondey-Dupré, 1837?]
30 p. 1 illus. 26cm.

Caption title.
[No. 15] in a volume with binder's title:

Théatre moderne. v.3.

NL 0437160 NcD

PQ1222 M3 v.17

Lockroy, Joseph Philippe Simon, called, 1803-1891.
La vieillese d'un grand roi, drame en trois actes et en prose, par MM. Lockroy et Arnould. [Paris, Marchant, 1837]
30 p. (Magasin théâtral, t.17)

Caption title.

I. Arnould, Auguste Jean François, 1803-1854, joint author. II. Title.

NL 0437161 CU

Lockroy, Joseph Philippe Simon, 1803-1891.
La vieillesse d'un grand roi, drame en trois actes et en prose, par mm. Lockroy et Arnould ... Paris, Marchant, 1837.
106 p. 20½cm.

I. Arnould, Auguste Jean François, 1803-1854, joint author. II. Title.

PQ2338.L6V7

NL 0437162 MiU CtY

Lockroy, Stéphanie.
Fées de la famille. Paris.

NL 0437163 NjP

HD10000

Locks, Mitchell O., 1922-
The influence of unions on wages in the Cleveland, Ohio labor market from 1945 to 1950. 1953.
122 l.

Thesis--Univ. of Chicago.

1. Wages--Cleveland. 2. Trade-unions--U.S.

NL 0437164 ICU

Locks, Mitchell O., 1922 -
The influence of unions on wages in the Cleveland, Ohio, labor market from 1945 to 1950. Chicago, 1953. iv, 122 l. tables.

Film reproduction. Positive.
Thesis—University of Chicago.
Bibliography, leaves 118-122.

1. Trade unions—U. S.—O.—Cleveland. 2. Wages—U. S.—O.—Cleveland.

NL 0437165 NN MiD CSt

---

271 L81b

Locks, Walter Alexander.
Barking Abbey in the Middle Ages. With an introd. by the Right Rev. the Bishop of Barking. London, E. Stock, 1913.
85, iii p. illus. 22cm.

1. Barking Abbey.

NL 0437166 IU

Locks, Walter Alexander, ed.
East London antiquities. Some record of East London in the days of old, its history, legends, folk-lore and topography. Ed. by Walter A. Locks. With an introduction by Sir Walter Besant. London, "East London advertiser" office, 1902.
vi p., 1 l., 192 p. 25½cm.

1. London—Antiq.

Library of Congress DA685.E1L8 5-15988

NL 0437167 DLC InU

Locks and Canals Company
see
Proprietors of the Locks and Canals on Merrimack River.

Locks and Canals on Merrimack River, Proprietors of the
see
Proprietors of the Locks and Canals on Merrimack River.

Lockshin, N.
Elimination of slum areas in large cities.

NL 0437170 OClW

Lockshin, Samuel D.
A comparative study of incentive wage systems ... [Columbus] The Ohio state university, 1930.
46 numb. l.
Thesis (B. I. E.) - The Ohio state university.

NL 0437171 OU

Locksley hall sixty years after, etc. ... 1887
see under Tennyson, Alfred Tennyson, 1st baron, 1809-1892.

Locksmith ledger; technical news of the lock and key industry.
[Jersey City]
v. in illus., ports. 24 cm. monthly.
Subtitle varies slightly.

1. Locks and keys—Period.

TS519.L63 683 50-20048

NL 0437173 DLC ICJ NN OCl DSI

VOLUME 337

LOCKSMITH LEDGER.
[Compilation of tricks of the trade for locksmiths]
Little Falls, N.J. [etc.] no. diagrs. 22cm.

Vol. 7 in VBA p.v. 1715.

1. Locks and keys.

NL 0437174 NN

LOCKSMITH LEDGER.
Exploded lock views and service information on key-in-the-knob locks.
Little Falls, N.J. v. diagrs. 22cm.

1. Locks and keys--Per. and soc. publ.

NL 0437175 NN

Locksmith ledger.
Helpful hints for locksmiths. [Jersey City, 1954]
64 p. illus.

NL 0437176 ICJ NN

Locksmith ledger.
Locksmith's index and directory. [Jersey City] 1948.
105 p. illus.

NL 0437177 ICJ

Locksmith ledger.
Jiffy jobs for locksmiths. [Wood-Ridge, N.J., 1952] 64 p. illus. 22cm.

1.Locks and keys. 2.Locks and keys,1952.

NL 0437178 NN ICJ

Locksmith ledger.
Locksmiths' notebook. [Jersey City, 1953?]
64 p. illus.

NL 0437179 ICJ

LOCKSMITH LEDGER.
Safe man's guide.
Little Falls, N.J. v. diagrs. 22cm.

1, Safes.

NL 0437180 NN

Locksmith ledger.
Short cuts for lock shops. Jersey City [1951]
64 p. illus. 22cm.

1. Locks and keys. 2. Locks and keys, 1952.

NL 0437181 NN ICJ

Locksmith ledger.
Time savers for locksmiths. [Jersey City. 1951]
64 p. illus.

NL 0437182 ICJ

Locksmith ledger.
Tricks of the trade. Jersey City [1949?]
44 p. illus.
Short cuts and helpful hints selected from the Locksmith ledger over a period of months.

1. Locks and keys. 683

NL 0437183 ICJ

The locksmith of Philadelphia. Revised by the editors. New York: Published by T. Mason and G. Lane, for the Sunday School Union of the Methodist Episcopal Church, 1839. 28 p. 14cm.
Title vignette.
In original covers.

734350A. 1. Juvenile literature—Fiction, American. I. Methodist Episcopal Church. Board of Sunday Schools.
N. Y. P. L. August 23, 1933

NL 0437184 NN

Lockspeiser, Ben.
... Reduction of draughtiness of open cockpits, by B. Lockspeiser ... and A. Graham ... July, 1934 ... London, H. M. Stationery Off., 1935.
cover-title, 12 p. incl. tables. plates, diagrs. 25cm. ([Great Britain] Aeronautical Research Committee. Reports and memoranda no. 1633 (T. 3563))
At head of title: Air Ministry.
"References": p. 12.

NL 0437185 ICJ

Lockspeiser, Ben.
... Ventilation of 24-ft. wind tunnel. By B. Lockspeiser, M.A. February, 1931. ... London, H.M. Stationery Off., 1931.
cover-title, 10 p. diagrs. 25cm. ([Great Britain] Aeronautical Research Committee. Reports and memoranda, no. 1372 (Ae. 499—T. 3096))
At head of title: Air Ministry ...

NL 0437186 ICJ

Lockspeiser, Ben.
... Wind tunnel tests of recommendations for prevention of wing flutter, by B. Lockspeiser ... and C. Callen ... February 1932. ... London, H. M. Stationery Off., 1932.
cover-title, 32 p. incl. tables. diagrs. 25cm. ([Great Britain] Aeronautical Research Committee. Reports and memoranda no. 1464 (T. 3216))
At head of title: Air Ministry ...
"References": p. 30.

NL 0437187 ICJ

ML 410 D28 L8
Lockspeiser, Edward, 1905-
... Berlioz, by Edward Lockspeiser. London, Novello & co., ltd. [1937]
16 p. 18½cm. (Novello's biographies of great musicians. General editor: W. McNaught)
"A summary of Berlioz's chief works": p. 16.

NL 0437188 WU

Lockspeiser, Edward, 1905-
... Berlioz, by Edward Lockspeiser. London, Novello & co., ltd. [1939]
16 p. 18½cm. (Novello's biographies of great musicians. General editor: W. McNaught)
"A summary of Berlioz's chief works": p. 16.

1. *Berlioz, Hector, 1803-1869. 40-13716
Library of Congress ML410.B5L7
927.8

NL 0437189 DLC KMK NcU OO ICU

Lockspeiser, Edward, 1905-
Bizet. London, Novello [195-]
16 p. 19 cm. (Biographies of great musicians)

1. Bizet, Georges, 1838-1875.
ML410.B62L7 927.8 52-43529 rev ‡

NL 0437190 DLC

Lockspeiser, Edward, 1905-
Debussy.
— London. J. M. Dent & Sons, Ltd. [1936.] xi, 291, (1) pp. Portraits. Facsimiles. Music. Illustrated end-papers. [The master musicians.] 18 cm., in 8s.
Bibliography, pp. 267-273.

E2401 — S.r. — Debussy, Achille Claude, 1862-1918.

NL 0437191 MB

Lockspeiser, Edward, 1905-
... Debussy, by Edward Lockspeiser ... London, J. M. Dent and sons, ltd.; New York, E. P. Dutton and co., inc. [1936]
xi, 291, [1] p. front., illus. (music) ports., facsims. (incl. music) 18½cm. (Half-title: The master musicians, new series, ed. by E. Blom)
Series title in part also at head of t.-p.
"Catalogue of works": p. 247-259.
Bibliography: p. 267-273.

1. *Debussy, Claude, 1862-1918. 37-21495
Library of Congress ML410.D28L6
[10-5] 927.8

NL 0437192 NcD PRosC OClCC OCl OO OU OClh PP PPT NN DLC Or WaWW OrPR CaBVa OrP WaT WaSp PSt

---

ML 410 D28 L81
Lockspeiser, Edward, 1905-
... Debussy, by Edward Lockspeiser ... London, J. M. Dent and sons, ltd.; New York. E. P. Dutton and co., inc. [1937]
xi, 291, [1] p. front., illus. (music) ports., facsims. (incl. music) 18½cm. (Half-title: The master musicians, new series, ed. by E. Blom)
Series title in part also at head of t.-p.
"Catalogue of works": p. 247-259.
Bibliography: p. 267-273.

1. *Debussy, Claude, 1862-1918. I. Series: Master musicians. New series.

NL 0437193 NIC

Lockspeiser, Edward, 1905-
Debussy. [3d ed.] New York, Pellegrini and Cudahy, 1949 [i. e. 1951]
xv, 304 p. ports., music. 18 cm. (The Master musicians)
Preface to third edition, p. v-vii, dated 1951.

1. Debussy, Claude, 1862-1918. (Series: The Master musicians. New series)
A 53-9831
North Carolina. Univ. Library for Library of Congress [5]

NL 0437194 NcU MiD N NN MH NNC MB WU MeB KyWA DLC Wa IdU

VOLUME 337

780.92 D289L 1951 Under-grad. lib.
Lockspeiser, Edward, 1905-
Debussy. London, J. M. Dent; New York, Pellegrini and Cudahy [1951]
304p. front., illus.(music) ports., facsims. (incl. music) 19cm. (Half-title: The Master Musicians, new series, ed. by E. Blom)
"First published 1936. Revised and reset 1951."
"Catalogue of works": p.259-271.
Bibliography: p.277-282.
1. Debussy, Claude, 1862-1918.

NL 0437195 NcD NcU

780.92 D354ZLo 1951
Lockspeiser, Edward, 1905-
Debussy. [3d ed.] London, Dent; New York, Pellegrini and Cudahy [1951]
xv, 304 p. illus. 19 cm. (Master musicians)

1. Debussy, Claude, 1862-1918. I. Series.

NL 0437196 LU CaBVaU CaBViP CLSU CU KU MiU NIC PSt

Lockspeiser, Edward, 1905- tr.

Prunières, Henry, 1886-
A new history of music; the middle ages to Mozart, by Henry Prunières, with an introduction by Romain Rolland. Translated from the French and edited by Edward Lockspeiser. New York, The Macmillan company, 1943.

Lockstaedt, Alexander von.
Die zwangsvollstreckung in das grundstueckszubehoer, insbes. die behandlung des mehreren grundstuecken gemeinschaftl. zubehoers in der zwangsversteigerung.
Inaug. diss. - Erlangen, 1929.
Bibl.

NL 0437198 DLC

Lockstaedt, Paul von, 1874-
Ueber Vorkommen und Bedeutung von Druesenschlaeuchen in den Myomen des Uterus. Berlin, 1898.
50 p.
Inaug.-Diss. - Königsberg.

NL 0437199 ICRL PPC CtY DNLM

BS3555 .L78
LOCKTON, WILLIAM, 1878-
Certain alleged Gospel sources, a study of Q, Proto-Luke and M, by W. Lockton... London[etc.] Longmans, Green and co., 1927.
vii, [2], 74 p. 18cm.

1. Bible. N.T. Gospels--Criticism, interpretation, etc.

NL 0437200 ICU NjPT MWelC MH

BS 2555 .L81
Lockton, William, 1878-
Certain alleged gospel sources; a study of Q, Proto-Luke and M. New York, Longmans, 1927.
vii, 74 p. 19 cm.

1. Bible. N. T. Gospels - Evidences, authority, etc. I. Title.

NL 0437201 DCU

Lockton, William, 1878-
Divers orders of ministers; an inquiry into the origins and early history of the ministry of the Christian church, by W. Lockton ... London, New York [etc.] Longmans, Green and co., 1930.
viii, 254 p. 22½cm.

1. Church history—Primitive and early church. 2. Clergy. I. Title.
Library of Congress BV660.L6 30-22342
[3] 262.1

NL 0437202 DLC KyLxCB MB PPPD NcD

Lockton, William, 1878-
The resurrection and other Gospel narratives and the narratives of the virgin birth; two essays by W. Lockton ... London, New York [etc.] Longmans, Green and co., 1924.
x, 184 p. 19½ cm.

1. Bible. N. T. Gospels—Criticism, interpretation, etc. 2. Jesus Christ—Resurrection. 3. Jesus Christ—Nativity. 4. Bible—Criticism, interpretation, etc.—N. T. Gospels. I. Title.
BS2555.L55 24—16780

NL 0437203 DLC MBrZ NjNbS CU

Lockton, William, 1878-
The three traditions in the Gospels, an essay by W. Lockton ... London, New York [etc.] Longmans, Green and co., ltd., 1926.
ix, [2], 306, [2] p. 19½cm.

1. Bible. N. T. Gospels—Criticism, interpretation, etc. 2. Bible—Criticism, interpretation, etc.—N. T. Gospels. I. Title.
26—24502
Library of Congress BS2555.L56

NL 0437204 DLC IEG MB

Lockton, William, 1878-
The treatment of the remains at the eucharist after holy communion and the time of the ablutions, by W. Lockton ... Cambridge, University press, 1920.
vi p., 1 l., 280 p. 22½cm.

1. Lord's supper. I. Title.
A 20-1309
Title from General Theol. Sem. Printed by L. C.

NL 0437205 NNUT NjPT CPFT KyLxCB IaU PPPD MoSU-D

Der Lockvögel Warnungsgesang
see filed under the article in the genitive Der followed by the rest of the title. [Supplement]

W 4 M961 1953
LOCKWALD, Horst Erich, 1927-
Über 105 Oberschenkelhalsbrüche bei Unfallversicherten. München, 1953.
46 ℓ.
Inaug.-Diss. - Munich.
Typewritten copy.
1. Femur - Fracture

NL 0437207 DNLM

Lockward, Clemente A
La cita del fauno. Ciudad Trujillo, Editora Montalvo, 1940.
93, 2 p. 20 cm.
Poems.

I. Title.
PQ7409.L57C5 861.6 48-41119*

NL 0437208 ViU MH DLC

Lockward, Lynn Grover, 1878-
A Puritan heritage; the First Presbyterian Church in Horse-Neck (Caldwell, N. J.) Illus. by the author. [Caldwell? N. J., 1955]
488 p. illus. 24 cm.

1. Caldwell, N. J. First Presbyterian Church. I. Title.
BX9211.C146L6 285.1749 56-19293 ‡

NL 0437209 DLC PPPrHi NN NjN NjPT MH-AH

Lockward, Yoryi.
Acúcheme uté [por] Yoryi Lockward. Cuentos típicos dominicanos. [Puerto Plata, R. D., Imp. El Porvenir, A. Rodríguez D., 1941]
cover-title, 47 p. 21½cm.

1. Tales, Dominican. I. Title.
45-45544
Library of Congress PQ7409.L6A66
[2] 863.6

NL 0437210 DLC DPU CtY

Lockwine, Alexandra Agusta Guttman, 1863-
Camping, by Biddy, known in real life as Alexandra G. Lockwine, R. N. New York, The Advertisers printing co. [1911]
182 p. incl. illus., plates. 19½cm. $1.00

1. Camping.
11-11333
Library of Congress SK601.L7

NL 0437212 DLC NN

NK550 .L7
Lockwood,
Appartamento Lockwood. Parte prima: Collezione di oggetti antichi: porcellane europee ed orientali; majoliche italiane; vetri di Murano ... ecc. Le vendito all' asta pubblica avranno luogo in Roma nella casa D. Corvisieri ... 17 ... 18 ... 19 ... 20 ... 22 maggio 1899. [Roma, Tip. editr. rom., 1899]
55 p. 4 plates. 33 cm.

NL 0437213 DLC NN

VOLUME 337

Lockwood,
The disputed parables of Jesus Christ
see under Lockwood, William Maynard, 1835-

Lockwood,
Fundamental principles of psychological phenomena
see under Lockwood, William Maynard, 1835-

HE2791
N4
L7
Lockwood, A. J.
An act to grant the Nevada and Oregon Railroad Company the right of way ... from Virginia City, Nevada, to the northern boundary of this state, and to encourage the construction ... to Umatilla, Oregon. [Carson City? 1875]
19 p. 30cm. (State of Nevada. Senate bill. No. 80.)

1. Nevada and Oregon Railroad Company. I. Nevada. Legislature. Senate.

NL 0437216 CSt

Lockwood, A. M., ed.
History of the 7th Canadian medium regiment, R. C. A.
see under Canada. Army. 7th medium regiment.

Lockwood, Adolphus N., comp.
Accident agent's manual, Provident fund society, New York city ...
see under Provident fund society, New York.

Lockwood, Adolphus N., comp.

National accident society, *New York.*
Agent's manual of the National accident society of the city of New York ... Adopted August 1, 1887. Arranged ... by A. N. Lockwood ... N. Y., G. W. Burnham & co., printers, °1887.

Lockwood, Adolphus Newman.
The morning breath of June; a poem. Illustrated by C. J. Taylor and E. J. Meeker. New York, 1884.
sm. 4°. pp. (60). Illus.
Added title-page illustrated.

NL 0437220 MH

ML128
P3L3
Lockwood, Albert Lewis, 1871-1933.
Notes on the literature of the piano. Ann Arbor, University of Michigan Press, 1940.
xx, 235 p. 27cm.

1. Piano music - Bibl. I. Lockwood, Samuel Pierson, 1879- ed. II. Title.

NL 0437221 CoU

Lockwood, Albert Lewis, 1871–1933.
Notes on the literature of the piano, by Albert Lockwood. Ann Arbor, University of Michigan press; London, H. Milford, Oxford university press, 1940.
5 p. l., xiii-xx, 235 p. 26cm.
"Note" signed: Samuel P. Lockwood.
"References": p. 218-225.

1. Pianoforte music—Bibl. I. Lockwood, Samuel Pierson, 1879– ed. II. Title.

Library of Congress ML128.P3L3 40-28503
——— Copy 2.
Copyright [4] [781.97] 786.4

NL 0437222 DLC OrSaW OrStbM WaS OkU PWcS PP PJB PU OO OCl OLak OU OClW NcGU OrU OrP

Law
Lockwood, Alfred Collins, 1875– comp.

Arizona. *Laws, statutes, etc.*
Arizona code, 1939; containing the General laws of Arizona, annotated. Published by authority of Laws 1939, chapter 89; compiled under the supervision of the members of the Supreme Court of Arizona: Chief Justice Henry D. Ross; associate justices, Alfred C. Lockwood [and] Archibald G. McAlister. [Official ed.] Indianapolis, Bobbs-Merrill [°1940–

Lockwood, Mrs. Alice Gardner (Burnell) 1874– ed.

Garden club of America.
Gardens of colony and state; gardens and gardeners of the American colonies and of the republic before 1840 ... Compiled and edited for the Garden club of America by Alice G. B. Lockwood, chairman, Special publications committee. [New York] Pub. for the Garden club of America by C. Scribner's sons, 1931–34.

Lockwood, Anthony.
A brief description of Nova Scotia, with plates of the principal harbors: including a particular account of the island of Grand Manan. By Anthony Lockwood ... London, Printed for the author, by G. Hayden and sold by Cadell and Davies, 1818.
2 p. l., 134 p. fold. front., maps. 27½cm.

1. Nova Scotia—Descr. & trav. 2. Pilots and pilotage—Nova Scotia.

Library of Congress F1037.L81 1-21546

NL 0437225 DLC CaNSWA CaOTP CtY CaBVaU RPJCB PPL NN

Lockwood, Anthony.
A brief description of Nova Scotia, with plates of the principal harbors; including a particular account of the Island of Grand Manan. London, Printed for the author by G. Hayden and sold by Cadell and Davies, 1818.
102, ii p. maps. 27 cm.

1. Nova Scotia—Descr. & trav. 2. Pilots and pilotage—Nova Scotia.

F1037.L81 1818a 63-57095

NL 0437226 DLC

Lockwood, Anthony. Brief description of Nova Scotia. 12 pp. (Rev. of in *Westm. Rev.* v. 19, 1833, p. 300.)

NL 0437227 MdBP

BJ4337
.B35
1952
Lockwood, Arthur, joint author.

FOR OTHER EDITIONS SEE MAIN ENTRY

Bean, Philip R
Rating valuation practice, by Philip R. Bean and Arthur Lockwood. 3d ed. London, Stevens, 1952.

Lockwood, August G
How to finish your attic and basement yourself [by] August G. Lockwood and Norman E. Stanton. Drawings by Louis A. D'Amelio. New York, M. Barrows [1953]
279 p. illus. 22 cm.

1. Attics. 2. Basements. 3. Dwellings—Remodeling. I. Stanton, Norman E., joint author. II. Title.

TH3000.L55 694 53—8221 ‡

NL 0437229 DLC CaBVa CaBViP Or OCl NcDur NcC MB NN PPD PP OrP Wa WaE WaS WaSp WaT

308
Z
Box 719
Lockwood, Belva Ann (Bennett) 1830-1917.
An appeal for woman suffrage, made by Mrs. James Bennett, in the Legislative hall, Frankfort, Kentucky, January, 1884. Lafayette, Ind. Our herald [1884]
15 p.

1. Woman - Suffrage - U. S.

NL 0437230 NNC

Lockwood, Belva Ann (Bennett) 1830-1917.
Arbitration and the treaties. no t.p. [Washington, 1897]
8p.
YA 13097

NL 0437231 DLC Nh DS

Lockwood, *Mrs.* Belva Ann (Bennett) 1830–1917.
The Central American peace congress and an international arbitration court for the five Central American republics. Paper presented by Belva A. Lockwood, of Washington, D. C., to the 17th International peace congress, in Caxton hall, London, England, July 31, 1908 ... [Washington?] 1908.
15 p. 21½cm.

1. Central American peace conference, Washington, 1907.

YA 10363
Library of Congress F1438.L8 18-4501

NL 0437232 DLC

Lockwood, Belva Ann (Bennett) 1830–1917.
A complete list of all the treaties entered into by the United States with the various nations of the world from the foundation of the republic until July 15, 1893. Compiled for the Universal peace union by Belva A. Lockwood. Washington, D. C., July 15, 1893. Phila.: Off. of the Universal peace union [1893] 27 p. 23cm.

1. United States—For. rel.—Treaties—Bibl. I. Universal peace union, Philadelphia.
N. Y. P. L. December 29, 1939

NL 0437233 NN Nh

Lockwood, Mrs. Belva Ann (Bennett) 1830-1917.
Congrès internationale de la paix, Nov. 1891. La creation d'un internationale de la paix. Wash., 1891.

NL 0437234 Nh

Lockwood, Mrs. Belva Ann (Bennett) 1830-1917.
Discours. Paris, 1889.

NL 0437235 Nh

VOLUME 337

Lockwood, Belva Ann (Bennett) 1830-1917.
The growth of peace principles and methods of propagating them. Paper...triennial woman's council. Washington, D.C., 1895. YA 10365
12p.

NL 0437236 DLC Nh

Lockwood, *Mrs.* Belva Ann (Bennett) 1830-1917.
The Hague arbitration court, a supplement to "Peace and the outlook," by Belva A. Lockwood ... Washington, D. C. [M. Tibbetts, printer] 1901.
13 p. front. (port.) 22cm.

1. Title.

16-7159

Library of Congress JX1963.L472

NL 0437237 DLC

Lockwood, Mrs. Belva Ann (Bennett) 1830-1917.
International arbitration court and a congress of nations. Wash., 1893.

NL 0437238 Nh

Lockwood, *Mrs.* Belva Ann (Bennett) 1830-1917.
Peace and the outlook: an American view, by Belva A. Lockwood ... Washington, D. C. [T. W. Cadick, pr.] 1899.
20 p. 23cm.

1. Peace.

YA 8377 16-18134 Revised

Library of Congress JX1963.L47

NL 0437239 DLC

Lockwood, Belva Ann (Bennett) 1830-1917.
A resume of international arbitration and the national conference at Washington April 22d and 23d, 1896. Parkesburg, Pa., 1896. YA 10364
16p.

NL 0437240 DLC Nh

YA 8483 Lockwood, Belva Ann (Bennett) 1830-1917.
The right of women to vote guaranteed by the constitution. Memorial of Belva A. Lockwood and others, with the moral and constitutional argument in support of the same... Washington, 1871.
8p.

NL 0437241 DLC MnHi

Lockwood, Bonnie Allen, 1917-
A study of the characteristics and duties of certified professional secretaries. Ann Arbor, University Microfilms [1954]
([University Microfilms, Ann Arbor, Mich.] Publication no. 9980)
Microfilm copy of typescript. Positive.
Collation of the original: viii, 120 l. tables.
Thesis—University of Pittsburgh.
Abstracted in Dissertation abstracts, v. 14 (1954) no. 12, p. 2241-2242.
Vita.
Bibliography: leaves 93-94.
1. Secretaries, Private. 2. Office practice.

Microfilm AC-1 no. 9980 Mic A 54-3343

Pittsburgh. Univ. Libr. for Library of Congress [1]†

NL 0437242 PPiU IaU MsU DLC

Lockwood, C B.
Philosophic reminiscences, by C. B. Lockwood ... memories of Emerson and others; and personal thoughts on the destiny of the soul; delivered as an address before the Unitarian club of Washington, D. C., May 10, 1916. [Washington, D. C., The Unitarian club of Washington, 1916]
cover-title, 16 p. 23cm.

1. Emerson, Ralph Waldo, 1803-1882. 2. Transcendentalism. I. Title.

16-18037

Library of Congress B905.L6

NL 0437243 DLC OClWHi

TN872 T4L6 Lockwood, C.D., firm.
Reference report, Texas upper gulf coast, 1939. Science Houston, 1939.
Various paging. Maps, tables, diagrs. 28cm.

A supplement prepared for and presented complimentary to our subscribers. C.D. Lockwood's Texas oil report.

1. Petroleum--Texas. I. Title.

NL 0437244 TxDaM

sVM 1621 L 81a LOCKWOOD, C. T.
...And he's got the money too... Chicago, Root & Cady, c1869.
5p. 33cm.

Vocal solo with piano accompaniment.
Plate no.: 5504.

NL 0437245 ICN

Lockwood, C. T.
Don't you go, Tommy. Arr. for guitar by Charles Harris. Detroit, Whittemore & Stephens [1870]
M780 M62 no.251 Vault
5p. music. 36cm. ([Michigan sheet music collection, no. 251])
For voice, chorus (SATB) and guitar.
At head of title: To the boys of America.
"Echoes of the serenade"
I.Harris, Charles. II.Whittemore & Stephens, Detroit. III.Title. IV.Series.

NL 0437246 Mi

q784.3 Sh37 v.4 no.24 Lockwood, C. T.
... Gathering home, song and chorus. Words by H. M. Look. Music by C. T. Lockwood ... Chicago, Root & Cady, c1868.
5p.

[Sheet music printed in Chicago prior to 1871. v.4,no.24]

I. Look, H. M. II. Title.

NL 0437247 IU

q784.3 Sh37 v.14 no.34 Lockwood, C. T.
... Gathering home. Song and chorus. Composed by C. T. Lockwood Chicago, Root & Cady, c1868.
5p.

[Sheet music printed in Chicago prior to 1871. v.14,no.34]
"Words by N.[!] M. L[ook]"

I. Look, Henry M. II. Title.

NL 0437248 IU

q784.3 Sh37 v.14 no.35 Lockwood, C. T.
Give the boy a chance, song & chorus. Words by C. Ernst Fahnestock. Music by C. T. Lockwood. Chicago, Root & Cady, c1870.
7p.

[Sheet music printed in Chicago prior to 1871. v.14,no.35]
Illustrated t.-p.
Plate no.: 5787.

I. Fahnestock, C. Ernst. II. Title.

NL 0437249 IU

q784.3 Sh37 v.8 no.20 Lockwood, C. T.
... Little stub toe polka ... Chicago, Root & Cady, c1868.
5p.

[Sheet music printed in Chicago prior to 1871. v.8, no.20]
Plate no.: 4837.

1. Pianoforte music. I. Title.

NL 0437250 IU

Lockwood, C. T.
On the far off shore. Music by C.T. Lockwood. [Words by C. Ernst Fahnestock] Pontiac, Mich., Published for the benefit of the family of the deceased by Mrs. C.T. Lockwood, 1874.
M780 M62 no.261 Vault
5p. music. 36cm. ([Michigan sheet music collection, no. 261])
For voice, chorus (SATB) and piano.
"In memoriam"
I.Fahnestock, C. Ernst. II.Title. III. Series.

NL 0437251 Mi

q784.3 Sh37 v.4 no.25 Lockwood, C. T.
Starry waves, song & chorus. Words by C. Ernst Fahnestock. Music by C. T. Lockwood. Chicago, Root & Cady, c1869.
5p.
[Sheet music printed in Chicago prior to 1871. v.4,no.25]
At head of title of cop.2: To my very dear friend Miss Hattie Draper.
Plate no.: 5625.

I. Fahnestock, C. Ernst. II. Title.

NL 0437252 IU

q784.3 Sh37 v.4 no.26 Lockwood, C. T.
Tommy's return. Composed by C. T. Lockwood ... Chicago, Root & Cady, c1868.
5p.

[Sheet music printed in Chicago prior to 1871. v.4,no.26]
Plate no.: 4921.

NL 0437253 IU

Lockwood, C. T.
Vive vale (Farewel] and be happy) schottisch, by C.T. Lockwood. Pontiac, Mich., Lockwood & Hoyt, 1867.
M780 M62 no.260 Vault
5p. music. 34cm. ([Michigan sheet music collection, no. 260])
For piano.
"To J. Henry Whittemore"
I.Whittemore, J. Henry. II.Lockwood & Hoyt, Pontiac, Mich. III.Title. IV. Series.

NL 0437254 Mi

VOLUME 337

Lockwood, Charles A., 1890–
Hellcats of the sea, by Charles A. Lockwood and Hans Christian Adamson. With a foreword by Chester W. Nimitz. New York, Greenberg [1955]
335 p. illus. 23 cm.

1. World War, 1939–1945—Naval operations—Submarine. 2. World War, 1939–1945—Japan Sea. I. Adamson, Hans Christian, joint author. II. Title.

D780.L6 940.5451 55—10961 ‡

NL 0437255 NcD NcC CU OCl OCU WHi Or OrP Wa WaE WaS WaSp WaT DLC CaBVa MtBC TxU PP OOxM PPL TxU MB NN

Lockwood, Charles A., 1890–
Hellcats of the sea. Philadelphia, New York, Chilton [1955]

NL 0437256 IdB

Lockwood, Charles A., 1890–
Sink 'em all; submarine warfare in the Pacific. With a foreword by Chester W. Nimitz. [1st ed.] New York, Dutton, 1951.
416 p. ports., map (on lining papers) 22 cm.

1. World War, 1939–1945—Naval operations—Submarine. 2. World War, 1939–1945—Pacific Ocean. 3. World War, 1939–1945—Personal narratives, American. I. Title.

D783.L6 940.5451 51-9835

NL 0437257 ICU MB NcRS WaE WaS WaT DLC CaBVa Or OrP Wa KMK OEac TU MiU NNC

Lockwood, Charles A., 1890–
Sink 'em all; submarine warfare in the Pacific. With a foreword by Chester W. Nimitz. New York, Dutton [1953, c1951] 416 p. ports. 22cm.

Map on lining-papers.

1. World war, 1939-1945—Naval history and operations, Submarine—Pacific. I. Title.

NL 0437258 NN

WI L817a 1901 LOCKWOOD, Charles Barrett, 1856-1914.
Appendicitis; its pathology and surgery. London, Macmillan, 1901.
xii, 287 p. illus.

NL 0437259 DNLM WaU MiDW-M IU-M

Lockwood, Charles Barrett, 1856-1914.

Appendicitis; its pathology and surgery. London, Macmillan and co., limited; New York, The Macmillan company, 1901.

xii, 287p. illus., diagrs. 22½cm.

NL 0437260 NBuG PPC OC1W-H

Lockwood, Charles Barrett, 1856-1914.
47233 Appendicitis; its pathology and surgery. By Charles Barrett Lockwood, ... Second edition. London, New York, Macmillan and Co., ltd., 1906.
xiv, 342 p. 62 illus. 22½cm.

NL 0437261 ICJ PPC

WO L817a 1896 LOCKWOOD, Charles Barrett, 1856-1914.
Aseptic surgery. Edinburgh, Pentland, 1896.
xiv, 233 p.

NL 0437262 DNLM PPC

WO L817a 1899 LOCKWOOD, Charles Barrett, 1856-1914.
Aseptic surgery. 2d ed. Edinburgh, Pentland, 1899.
xiv, 264 p.

NL 0437263 DNLM PPC MiDW-M

Lockwood, Charles Barrett, 1856-1914.
... Aseptic surgery, by Charles Barrett Lockwood ... 3d ed. London, H. Frowde; Hodder & Stoughton, 1909.
2 p. l., vii–xii, 275 p. 18½cm. (Oxford medical publications)

1. Surgery, Aseptic and antiseptic.

A 20—313

Stanford univ. Library for Library of Congress [a41b1]

NL 0437264 CSt DNLM ICJ PPC

WPA L817c 1913 LOCKWOOD, Charles Barrett, 1856-1914.
Cancer of the breast; an experience of a series of operations and their results. London, Frowde, 1913.
ix, 234 p. illus.

NL 0437265 DNLM OC1W-H ICJ OU PPC CtY

WO L817c 1907 LOCKWOOD, Charles Barrett, 1856-1914.
Clinical lectures and addresses on surgery. London, Frowde, 1907.
viii, 276 p. (Oxford medical publications)
Previously published in the British medical journal and the Clinical journal.

NL 0437266 DNLM

LOCKWOOD, CHARLES BARRETT, 1856-1914.
...Clinical lectures and addresses on surgery, by C. B. Lockwood... London, H. Frowde [etc.] 1907.
viii, 307, [1]p. plates (part col.) 18½cm. (Oxford medical publications)
Second ed.

1. Surgery. I. Title.

Printed by Wesleyan University Library

NL 0437267 ICJ CtW CtY-M DNLM N PPC PU MiU OC1W-H ViU

Lockwood, Charles Barrett, 1856-1914.
... Clinical surgery ... London, H. Frowde, Hodder & Stoughton [1911]
viii, 389, [1] p. plates (1 col.) 19 cm. (Oxford medical publications)
2d ed.
Former title: Clinical lectures and addresses on surgery.

NL 0437268 CtY DNLM

Lockwood (Charles Barrett) [1856–1914]. Drill, tactics, and strategy in surgery. 6 pp. 4°. London & Dorking, Allard & Son, 1906.
Forms Suppl. to St. Barth. Hosp. J., Lond., 1905-6, xiii, No. 11.

NL 0437269 DNLM

WJA L817h 1888 LOCKWOOD, Charles Barrett, 1856-1914.
Hunterian lectures on the development & transition of the testis; normal and abnormal. London, Williams & Norgate, 1888.
122 p. illus.
Reprinted from the Journal of anatomy and physiology.
Title: Hunterian lectures, 1887

NL 0437270 DNLM PPC

WI L817h 1889 LOCKWOOD, Charles Barrett, 1856-1914.
Hunterian lectures on the morbid anatomy, pathology, and treatment of hernia. London, Lewis, 1889.
168 p. illus.
Reprinted from the Illustrated medical news.
Title: Hunterian lectures, 1889

NL 0437271 DNLM KU-M

Lockwood, Charles Barrett, 1856-1914.
[1]On abnormalities of the cæcum and colon, with reference to development: and [2]abnormality of the colon a cause of unsuccessful colotomy. 27 pp. 8°. *Edinburgh, Neill & Co.*, 1884.
Repr. from: [1]Brit. M. J., Lond., 1882, ii. [2]St. Barth. Hosp. Rep., Lond., 1883, xix.

NL 0437272 DNLM

WI L817r 1898 LOCKWOOD, Charles Barrett, 1856-1914.
The radical cure of hernia, hydrocele, and varicocele. Edinburgh, Pentland, 1898.
x, 279 p. illus.

NL 0437273 DNLM PPC

Film 1121 no. 29 LOCKWOOD, Charles Barrett, 1856-1914.
Statistical tables of two hundred cases of operation for appendicitis. [London, 1906?]
20 p.
Film copy.
Unrevised proof.

NL 0437274 DNLM

QWA L817t 1896 LOCKWOOD, Charles Barrett, 1856-1914.
Traumatic infection. Edinburgh, Pentland, 1896.
138 p. illus. (Hunterian lectures, 1895)
Reprinted from Lancet.
Series

NL 0437275 DNLM MnU

Lockwood, Charles Barrett, 1856-1914.
——. Traumatic infection. Hunterian lectures delivered at the Royal College of Surgeons in England. 5 p. l., 138 pp. 12°. *Edinburgh & London, Y. J. Pentland*, 1896.

NL 0437276 DNLM PPC

VOLUME 337

Lockwood, Charles C., 1877-

New York (*State*) *Legislature. Joint committee on housing.*
... Final report of the Joint legislative committee on housing ... Albany, J. B. Lyon company, printers, 1923.

Lockwood, Charles C., 1877-

New York (*State*) *Legislature. Joint committee on housing.*
... Intermediate report of the Joint legislative committee on housing ... Albany, J. B. Lyon company, printers, 1922.

Lockwood, Charles C., 1877-

New York (*State*) *Committee on housing and ice conditions.*
... Preliminary report of the Committee appointed to investigate housing and ice conditions of the state. Albany, J. B. Lyon company, printers, 1920.

Lockwood, Charles C., 1877-

New York (*State*) *Legislature. Joint committee on housing.*
... Report of the Joint legislative committee on housing. Transmitted September 20, 1920. Albany, J. B. Lyon company, printers, 1920.

Lockwood, Charles Daniel, 1868–1932.
The principles and practice of surgical nursing, by Charles D. Lockwood ... in collaboration with Mildred E. Newton ... New York, The Macmillan company, 1932.
xiii, 344 p. incl. front. (port.) illus., diagr. 22½cm.
"This book is based upon a series of lectures which have been delivered annually for twenty-five years to student nurses."—Pref.

1. Nurses and nursing. 2. Operations, Surgical. I. Newton, Mildred E. II. Title: Surgical nursing.

Library of Congress RD99.L6 32—10055
Copyright A 50554 [a41g1] 617.073

NL 0437281 DLC ICRL ViU WaS MB

Lockwood, Charles Daniel, 1868–1932.
The principles and practice of surgical nursing, by Charles D. Lockwood ... and John A. Wolfer ... in collaboration with Mildred E. Newton ... 2d ed., rev. New York, The Macmillan company, 1935.
xv p., 1 l., 371 p. incl. front. (port.) illus., diagr. 22cm.

1. Nurses and nursing. 2. Operations, Surgical. I. Wolfer, John Adam, 1880– II. Newton, Mildred E. III. Title: Surgical nursing.

Library of Congress RD99.L6 1935 35-11591
——— Copy 2
Copyright A 84736 [5] 617.073

NL 0437282 DLC CaBVaU ICRL OCl OU ViU

Lockwood (Charles E.) A study of alcohol, tobacco, coffee, and tea as causative factors in the production of nervous disorders. 36 pp. 12°. *New York, D. Appleton & Co.,* 1898.
Repr. from: N. York M. J., 1898, lxviii.

NL 0437283 DNLM

Lockwood, Charles N., comp.

Meadows manufacturing company, *Bloomington, Ill.*
How Meadowasher is built; second division of Meadow-salesmanship, compiled by Chas. N. Lockwood; illustrations by E. A. Erlandson. Bloomington, Ill., The Meadows manufacturing company, Sales development department, °1929.

Lockwood, Charlotte Daniels, 1905–
Church on Main Street; a history of First Methodist Church, Jackson, Michigan, 1830–1943. [Jackson, 1947]
51 p. illus. 23 cm.

1. Jackson, Mich. First Methodist Church. I. Title.
BX8481.J3F5 287.6774 48-12690*‡

NL 0437285 DLC

---

ar W 3733 Lockwood (Crosby) & Son, publ.
Catalogue of scientific and technical books including a list of Weale's rudimentary scientific series. London, 1893.
72 p. 23cm.

NL 0437286 NIC MdBP

Lockwood (Crosby) & Son.
Lockwood's Builder's, architect's, contractor's & engineer's price book...
see under title

Lockwood, (Crosby) & son, publ.
Lockwood's dictionary of terms used in the practice of mechanical engineering...
see under Horner, Joseph Gregory, 1847-1927, ed.

25Xd E68sa **Lockwood, Daniel Newton, 1798-1858.**
[Biography]

(In The savings accounts of successful Buffalonians, Erie Co. Savings Bank, Buffalo, 1937. p.7)

NL 0437289 NBuHi

Lockwood, Daniel Newton, 1844–1906.
Investigation of the electoral frauds. Speech of Hon. Daniel N. Lockwood, of New York, on investigation of the electoral frauds. In the House of representatives ... May 1, 1878 ... Washington, Printed by Darby & Duvall, 1878.
8 p. 22cm.

1. Presidents—U. S.—Election—1876.

9-24848†
Library of Congress JK526.1876.L7

NL 0437290 DLC NN

LOCKWOOD, DANIEL NEWTON, 1844-1906.
Investigation of the electoral frauds; speech on investigation of the electoral frauds, in the House of representatives, May 1, 1878. Washington. Printed by Darby & Duvall, 1878. 8 p. 23cm.

Film reproduction. Negation.

1. United States. President--Election, 1876.

NL 0437291 NN

TC225 .C73A3 1907 Lockwood, Daniel Wright, 1845-1931.

U. S. *Army. Corps of engineers.*
... Coney island channel and Rockaway inlet, New York. Letter from the secretary of war, transmitting, with a letter from the chief of engineers, report of examination and survey of Coney island channel and Rockaway inlet, New York ... [Washington, Govt. print. off., 1907]

Lockwood, Daniel Wright, 1845–1931.
The great pyramid. By Colonel D. W. Lockwood ...
(*In* Professional memoirs, Engineer bureau, United States army. Washington, 1909. 23cm. v. 1, p. 149-163 incl. diagrs.)

1. Pyramids.

War 11-166
Title from U. S. Engineer School Libr. Printed by L. C.

NL 0437293 DES

Lockwood, Daniel Wright, 1845-1931.

U. S. *Engineer dept.*
... Harbors on the Great Lakes and elsewhere. Letter from the secretary of war, transmitting, with a letter from the chief of engineers, report on examination of the harbors on the Great Lakes and elsewhere in which the whole or a part of the harbor is improved at local expense, with a view to determining whether the improvements so made by the local authorities should be undertaken or maintained by the general government and to establishing uniform rules in making harbor improvements ... [Washington, Govt. print. off., 1910?]

TC425 .H8A4 1907 Lockwood, Daniel Wright, 1845-1931.

U. S. *Army. Corps of engineers.*
... Hudson river from Troy to Waterford, N. Y. Letter from the acting secretary of war, transmitting, with a letter from the chief of engineers, reports of examination and survey of the Hudson river, with a view to extending the existing project to Waterford, N. Y. ... [Washington, Govt. print. off., 1907]

Lockwood, Daniel Wright, 1845-1931.

U. S. *Engineer dept.*
Preliminary report of the general features of the military reconnaissance through southern Nevada, conducted under direction of Lieutenant George M. Wheeler ... assisted by Lieutenant D. W. Lockwood ... [San Francisco? 1870?]

F841 .U53 Lockwood, Daniel Wright, 1845-1931.

U. S. *Army. Corps of Engineers.*
Preliminary report upon a reconnaissance through southern and southeastern Nevada, made in 1869, by Geo. M. Wheeler, Corps of Engineers, U. S. Army, assisted by D. W. Lockwood, Corps of Engineers, U. S. Army. Washington, Govt. Print. Off., 1875.

VOLUME 337

Lockwood, Daniel Wright, 1845-1931.
U. S. *Engineer dept.*
... Report of examination of Ohio river with a view to obtaining channel depths of 6 and 9 feet, respectively, made by a board of engineers, transmitted by the chief of engineers. War department. Washington, Govt. print. off., 1908.

NL 0437298 ...

LOCKWOOD, DAVID.
Night & green ginger. London, Hodder and Stoughton [1951] 256 p. 20cm.

I. Title.

NL 0437299 NN

Yzk 1 917b Lockwood, Dean Putnam, 1883-
Classical and Biblical scholarship in the age of the renaissance and reformation ... [by] Dean P. Lockwood ... and Roland H. Bainton ... (In Church history ... New York, 1941. 26cm. v.X, no.2. p.125-143)

NL 0437300 CtY

Lockwood, Dean Putnam, 1883-
De Rinucio Aretino Græcarum litterarum interprete.
(In Harvard studies in classical philology. Vol. 24, pp. 51-110. Cambridge. 1913.)

K1107 — Greece. Lit. Ancient Greek. Crit., interp., etc. — Castiglione, Rinucci da.

NL 0437301 MB MH OO

Lockwood, Dean Putnam, 1883-
...The Haverford plan... Columbus, O., Ohio State University Press, 1930.
314 p.

NL 0437302 PHC

Lockwood, Dean Putnam, 1883-
Leonardo Bruni's translation of Act 1 of the Plutus of Aristophanes, [by] Dean Putnam Lockwood. (In: Classical studies in honor of John C. Rolfe. Philadelphia, 1931. 8°. p. 163-172.)

569656A. 1. Aristophanes. Plutus (Latin). 2. Bruni, Leonardo, called Aretino, 1369-1444.
N. Y. P. L. May 12, 1932

NL 0437303 NN

Lockwood, Dean Putnam, 1883-
A survey of classical Roman literature, by Dean Putnam Lockwood ... New York, Prentice-Hall, inc., 1934-
v. 21cm.

1. Latin literature (Selections: Extracts, etc.) 2. Latin language—Chrestomathies and readers. I. Title.
Library of Congress PA6116.L6 34-40316
——— Copy 2.
Copyright [3] 870.822

NL 0437304 OCX PV PU OrU PRosC OrU MtU OrCS OrSaW OrStbM WaTC DLC CU NcU WaU NcGU NcD OU OCl OO OCU ODW

Lockwood, Dean Putnam, 1883-
A survey of classical Roman literature. Vol.I New York, Prentice-Hall, inc., 1937.

NL 0437305 MH

Lockwood, Dean Putnam, 1883-
A survey of classical Roman literature. N.Y., Prentice -Hall, Inc., 1946.
2 v.

NL 0437306 OClUr

Lockwood, Dean Putnam, 1883-
A survey of classical Roman literature, by Dean Putnam Lockwood. New York, Prentice-Hall, 1954, c1934.
2 v.

NL 0437307 OClND PBL

Lockwood, Dean Putnam, 1883-
Ugo Benzi, medieval philosopher and physician, 1376-1439. [Chicago] University of Chicago Press [1951]
xvi, 441 p. 24 cm.
Bibliographical footnotes.

1. Benzi, Ugo, 1376-1439.
R147.B4L6 926.1 51-10990

NL 0437308 TU ViU ICJ DDO TxU NIC CtY MB MtU CaBVaU WaSpG DLC KU-M NcD-MC MU OKentU NcU NN DNLM

Lockwood, Dorothy Frink.
A study of "The Federal Orrery." [Thesis] . . . Columbia University. By Dorothy Frink Patton.
— *Typewritten manuscript.* [Madeira, South India.] 1928. (1), 65, (6) ff. 28 cm.
Bibliography, f. (6).
Typed on one side of the leaf only.

D9788 — Federal Orrery, newspaper.

NL 0437309 MB

Lockwood, E., & co., pub.
... Godey's illustrated souvenir guide to Chicago, World's fair and New York. The most complete, comprehensive directory of information of both cities ... [Chicago & New York, E. Lockwood & co., °1893]

Lockwood, E. H. Steam from a samovar.
16 pp. (*Harper's Mag.* v. 80, 1890, p. 931.)

NL 0437311 MdBP

Z 347.1 L81 Thesis Lockwood, E. S.
State laws pertaining to the construction & operation of electrical equipment.

NL 0437312 WaPS

Lockwood, Edna, ed.
The Home monthly.
Boston, The Home monthly publishing company 1900; New York The Home monthly company 1900-

Lockwood, Edna K
see Bowman, Edna Katherine (Lockwood) 1887-

Lockwood, Edward Dowdeswell.
The early days of Marlborough college; or, Public school life between forty and fifty years ago. To which is added A glimpse of old Haileybury; Patna during the mutiny; A sketch of the natural history of the Riviera; and, Life in an Oxfordshire village. By Edward Lockwood ... London, Simpkin, Marshall, Hamilton, Kent & co., limited; [etc., etc.] 1893.
xi p., 2 l., 234 p. incl. front., illus., pl. 21½ x 17cm.
"A sketch of the natural history of the Riviera" first appeared in the Field.
1. Marlborough college, Marlborough, Eng. 2. Haileybury East India college. 3. India—Hist.—Sepoy rebellion, 1857-1858. 4. Natural history—Riviera.
Library of Congress LF795.M35L6 2—16342

NL 0437315 PU MB DLC MdBP ICU OrU OrU-M CtY OCl MiU PPL

Lockwood, Edward Dowdeswell.
Natural history, sport, and travel.
London. Allen & Co. 1878. xii, 284 pp. Illus. Sm. 8°.
Relates chiefly to India.

Jan. 8, 1904
F2601 — India. Geog. — India. Nat. hist.

NL 0437316 MB CtY KMK CU MH

Lockwood, Edward Harrington.
Algebra for science and engineering students. Cambridge, Univ.pr., 1940. 102p.

NL 0437317 CaBVa

512 L817a Lockwood, Edward Harrington.
Algebra for science and engineering students. Cambridge [Eng.] University Press, 1950.
ix,102p. illus.,tables. 23cm.

"First edition, 1940; reprinted, 1950."

1.Algebra. LC

NL 0437318 CLSU

Lockwood, Edwin H., 1904-
Roth, Willard, 1903-
Electric heating, by Willard Roth ... E. H. Lockwood ... and J. C. Woodson ... Scranton, Pa., International textbook company [1939]

Lockwood, Edwin Hoyt, joint author.
Tracy, John Clayton, 1869-
Introductory course in mechanical drawing, by J. C. Tracy ... With chapter on perspective by E. H. Lockwood ... New York and London, Harper & brothers, 1898.

VOLUME 337

Lockwood, Edwin Hoyt.
Notes on mechanical drawing ...
New Haven, 1893.
48 p. 6 fold. pl. 22 cm.

NL 0437321 CtY

Lockwood, Edwin Hoyt.
Perspective. Illus.
(In Tracy. Introductory course in mechanical drawing. p. 87-92. New York, 1898)

NL 0437322 MB

Lockwood, Eleanor Stanley.
Chum, Judith Anne [by] Eleanor Stanley Lockwood; drawings by Frank Marasco. Milwaukee, The Bruce publishing company [c1939]
262 p. incl. front., plates. 19½cm.

I. Title.
39-23299
Library of Congress PZ7.L813Ch

NL 0437323 DLC OC1ND

Lockwood, Eleanor Stanley.
Fatal shadows. Boston, Humphries [1949, c1948]
225 p. 21 cm.

I. Title.
PZ3.L812Fat 49-10541*

NL 0437324 DLC DLC-P4

Lockwood, Elisabeth M., tr.
Laurent, Lea.
Our lady of Belgium (Notre dame de Belgique) by Lea Laurent; tr. from the French by Elisabeth M. Lockwood. 2d impression. London, Iris publishing company [c1916]

LB1587 .N8H3
Lockwood, Elizabeth Anne, 1907-
Harvard University. *School of Public Health. Dept. of Nutrition.*
Activities in nutrition education for kindergarten through sixth grade [by] Elizabeth A. Lockwood, Dept. of Nutrition, Harvard School of Public Health. [New York, Distributed by the Nutrition Foundation] c1948.

Lockwood, Elizabeth Anne, 1907-
Film bibliography to aid a program in nutrition education
see under Harvard University. School of Public Health. Dept. of Nutrition.

Lockwood, Elon Dunbar, 1838-
Holden, Frederic Augustus.
Descendants of Robert Lockwood. Colonial and revolutionary history of the Lockwood family in America, from A. D. 1630. Comp. by Frederic A. Holden and E. Dunbar Lockwood. Philadelphia, Print. priv. by the family, 1889.

Lockwood, Emily Helene (Bedford) 1847-1871.
In memoriam Emily H. (Bedford) Lockwood
see under Lockwood, Joseph S.

LOCKWOOD, ERNEST, 1879-
Colne Valley folk; the romance and enterprise of a textile stronghold, by Ernest Lockwood. With a foreword by the Rt.Hon. the Viscount Snowden. London: Heath, Cranton Ltd., 1936. 189 p. 19½cm.

854265A. 1. Industries—Gt.Br.—Eng.—Yorkshire. 2. Yorkshire, Eng.—Hist. I. Title

NL 0437329 NN CU ICU

Lockwood, Ernest Lapham.
Episodes in Warwick history, by Ernest L. Lockwood ... [Warwick, R. I.] City of Warwick historical committee of the Rhode Island tercentenary celebration, 1937.
5 p. l., [7]-40 p. illus. (map) plates. 19½cm.
Bibliography included in foreword.

1. Warwick, R. I.—Hist. I. Title.
37-4578
Library of Congress F89.W2L6
——— Copy 2.
Copyright A 105017 [3] 974.54

NL 0437330 DLC

Lockwood, Ethel K
Side roads calling; traveling the unbeaten paths from California to Florida. Illus. by the author. New York, Exposition Press [1949]
185 p. illus., maps (on lining-papers) 23 cm.

1. U. S.—Descr. & trav. I. Title.
E169.L8 917.3 49-10366*

NL 0437331 DLC WaT

Lockwood, Ethel Keifer.
Katherine gets the cup. A comedy in one act. [Tujunga, Cal.] c1932.
12 p. 21 cm.

NL 0437332 RPB

Lockwood, Ezra, 1777-1853.
Sketches of Poundridge, N. Y., and genealogy of the Lockwood family, by Hon. Ezra Lockwood ... To which is added notes by the copyist. Copied from an original manuscript of the late author's, by Joseph B. Lockwood ... September 1878. [New York? 1878] iv p., 74 f. front. (mounted port.) 28½cm.
In ms.

115425B. 1. Lockwood family. 2. Poundridge, N. Y.—Hist. I. Lockwood, Joseph B.
N. Y. P. L. May 6, 1941

NL 0437333 NN

Lockwood, F.
The home handyman, dealing with cleaning, renovating, repair, care and maintenance of domestic articles and appliances. London, C. A. Pearson [1950]
156 p. (p. 151-156 advertisements) illus. 19 cm. (Home mechanic series)

1. Workshop receipts. I. Title. (Series)
T49.L57 680 51-18110

NL 0437334 DLC CaBViP

Lockwood, Ferris.
Mr. Lowell on art-principles ...
From- Scribners Magazine, Feb. 1894.
24 cm. p. 186-189.

NL 0437335 RPB

[Lockwood, Ferris]
... The nature of poetry. [n.p., 1888 ?]
cover-title, [3]-35 p. 17.5 x 14.5 cm.
At head of cover-title: Class studies in English literature.
Signed: Ferris Lockwood.
1. Poetry - Addresses, essays, lectures.

NL 0437336 CtY MH

[**Lockwood,** Mrs. **Florence Bayard.**]
Suggestions for the use of visitors to the insane. Being a brief essay on the cure and care of insane patients. New York, 1880. 38 p. 8°. (State Charities Aid Association. New York. Publication 22.)

1. Insane.—Care and treatment.
N. Y. P. L. August 12, 1912.

NL 0437337 NN MH

Lockwood, Florence Bayard.
The training of children. By Florence Bayard Lockwood. Philadelphia, E. Stern & co., 1879.
41 p. 17½ cm.

1. Education, Primary. I. Title.
LB1507.L81 6-39637

NL 0437338 DLC MH PPL

Lockwood, Francis Cummins, 1864-
The Apache Indians, by Frank C. Lockwood ... New York, The Macmillan company, 1938.
xvi p., 1 l., 348 p. front., plates, ports., 2 maps (1 fold.) 22cm.
"First printing."
Bibliography at end of each chapter.

1. Apache Indians. 2. Apache Indians—Government relations.
38-6746
Library of Congress E99.A6L6
—— Copy 2.
Copyright A 114677 [5] 970.3

WaSp MtBuM OOxM
OCU OC1 ODW OFH PP PPL NN OrP IU WaS OrU CaBVaU Or
NL 0437339 DLC WaTC IEN NIC MoU UU TxU DI NcD PU

Lockwood, Francis Cummins, 1864- ed.
Barnes, William Croft, 1858-1936.
Apaches & longhorns; the reminiscences of Will C. Barnes, edited and with an introduction by Frank C. Lockwood ... with a decoration by Cas Duchow. Los Angeles, The Ward Ritchie press, 1941.

Lockwood, Francis Cummins, 1864-
Arizona characters, by Frank C. Lockwood ... Los Angeles, The Times-mirror press, 1928.
xiv p., 1 l., 230 p. front., plates, ports. 20½cm. $2.50

1. Arizona—Biog. 2. Frontier and pioneer life—Arizona. I. Title.
28-23777
Library of Congress F810.L82

NL 0437341 DLC NjP TxU IEN RU NNC OU PP

VOLUME 337

Lockwood, Francis Cummins, 1864-
Emerson as a philosopher. A thesis presented to the Northwestern University.
= [Evanston?] 1896. 23 pp. 8°.

E2905 — Emerson, Ralph Waldo.

NL 0437342 MB PMA MiU RPB ICN OU

LOCKWOOD FRANCIS CUMMINS, 1864-
*Emerson as a philosopher. [Evanston, Ill.?, 1896] 23 p. 20cm.

Microfiche (neg.) 1 sheet. 11 x 15cm. (NYPL FSN 11,755)
Thesis--Northwestern University.

1. Emerson, Ralph Waldo, 1803-1882.

NL 0437343 NN

Lockwood, Francis Cummins, 1864- comp.
The freshman and his college; a college manual, by Francis Cummins Lockwood ... Boston, New York [etc.] D. C. Heath & co. [1913]
vi p., 1 l., 156 p. 17cm. $0.80
Bibliography: p. [155]-156.
CONTENTS.—Introduction.—The afterself, by D. S. Jordan.—An address to freshmen, by W. D. Hyde.—Habit, by W. James.—How to study, by F. C. Lockwood.—Recent tendencies in college education, by D. S. Jordan.—The new definition of the cultivated man, by C. W. Eliot.—Two kinds of education for engineers, by J. B. Johnson.—A poisonous phrase, by W. D. Hyde.—An inaugural address, by A. Meiklejohn.—The philosophy of education, by J. G. Hibben.—New wine in old bottles, by W. W. Thoburn.—The description of a gentleman, by J. H. Newman.
1. Students—U. S. 2. Education—Addresses, essays, lectures. I. Title.
Library of Congress LB2321.L7 13-19169

DAU NN ICJ NjP
ODW PMA NcD NcRS OrP Or MtBuM WaS OrCS WaSpG OrSaW
NL 0437344 DLC FU CU PPGi PHC PPT PV OU OCU OCl OO

Lockwood, Francis Cummins, 1864- joint comp.

Jameson, Kate W comp.
The freshman girl, a guide to college life, by Kate W. Jameson ... and Frank C. Lockwood ... Boston, New York [etc.] D. C. Heath and company [c1925]

Typ 970H B948p2
Lockwood, Francis Cummins, 1864-
Life as a fine art, by Frank C. Lockwood. Ysleta [Tex.], Edwin B. Hill, 1943.
2p.l., 11p., 1l. 19.5cm.
Title vignette.
"Ninety copies ... have been printed by Edwin B. Hill on his private press at Ysleta, Texas, during October, 1943."
Original printed white wrappers; in half morocco case labeled: Pamphlets printed by Edwin B. Hill of Ysleta, Texas.

NL 0437346 MH CtY

Lockwood, Francis Cummins, 1864-
... Life in old Tucson, 1854-1864, as remembered by the little maid, Atanacia Santa Cruz, by Frank C. Lockwood ... [Tucson, Ariz., The Tucson civic committee, 1943]
xx, 255 p. front., plates, ports. 21½cm.

1. Tucson, Ariz.—Biog. 2. Tucson, Ariz.—Hist. 3. Hughes, Atanacia (Santa Cruz) 1850-1934. I. Tucson, Ariz. Civic committee.
43-14327
Library of Congress F819.T9L6
[5] 979.1

NL 0437347 DLC MiU CLU TxU UU NmU CaBVaU ViU ODW ICU

Lockwood, Francis Cummins, 1864-
The life of Edward E. Ayer, by Frank C. Lockwood ... Chicago, A. C. McClurg & company, 1929.
xii, 300 p. front., plates, ports. (1 col.) 23½cm.
Illustrated lining-papers.

1. Ayer, Edward Everett, 1841-1927.
Library of Congress CT275.A953L6 29-29952

WaSp OrPR WaTC WaS OrU OrCS OrP IdU
ViU MiU-C NcD ICJ MH MB CU PMA TU FMU MtU
NL 0437348 DLC PPRF MeB PP PSC PHC PU ODW OO OCl OU

Lockwood, Francis Cummins, 1864-
The Life of Edward E. Ayer ...
New York, 1934.

NL 0437349 RPJCB

Lockwood, Francis Cummins, 1864-
... More Arizona characters, by Frank C. Lockwood ... Tucson, Ariz., University of Arizona, 1943.
79 p. illus. (ports.) 23cm. [Arizona. University. General bulletin no. 6]
University of Arizona bulletin. Vol. XIII, no. 3. July 1, 1942.

1. Arizona—Biog. 2. Frontier and pioneer life—Arizona. I. Title.
43-53060
Library of Congress F810.L84
[4] 917.91

OCIW RPB OkU WaTC MtU
NL 0437350 DLC MU NcGU C NIC PPT PBm PHC PU PSt OU

Lockwood, Francis Cummins, 1864-
Pioneer days in Arizona, from the Spanish occupation to statehood, by Frank C. Lockwood ... New York, The Macmillan company, 1932.
xiv p., 1 l., 387 p. incl. front., illus. (incl. ports., maps) 24cm.
"Newspapers, books, and libraries": p. 345-367.

1. Arizona—Hist. 2. Pioneers—Arizona. 3. Frontier and pioneer life—Arizona. I. Title.
Library of Congress F811.L75 32-29213
——— Copy 2.
Copyright A 56456 [5] 979.1

TxU MiU NjP UU CoU NIC Or OrCS NN MB
OCl ODW ViU CU MtU IdB OrPR WaS OrU Wa CaBVaU WaU
NL 0437351 DLC FTaSU DSI PMA NcD PU PPL OO MiU OFH

Lockwood, Francis Cummins, 1864-
Public speaking today; a high school manual, by Francis Cummins Lockwood ... and Clarence De Witt Thorpe ... Chicago, New York [etc.] B. H. Sanborn & co. [c1921]
xxiv, 264 p. 19½cm.
Bibliography: p. 223-237.

1. Oratory. I. Thorpe, Clarence De Witt, joint author. II. Title.
21-16015
Library of Congress PN4121.L6

PWcS OCl MiU OrCS OrU-D
NL 0437352 DLC WaE WaTC MtU Or OrU OrAshS PPGi OO

Lockwood, Francis Cummins, 1864-
Public speaking today; a high school manual, by Francis Cummins Lockwood... and Clarence De Witt Thorpe... Chicago, New York [etc.] B.H. Sanborn & co. [c1922]
xxiv, 264 p.
Bibliography: p.223-237.

NL 0437353 PMA OrU

Lockwood, Francis Cummins, 1864-
Public speaking today; a high school manual, by Francis Cummins Lockwood ... and Clarence De Witt Thorpe ... Chicago, New York [etc.] B. H. Sanborn & co., 1925.
xxiv, 264 p. 19½cm.
Bibliography: p. 223-237.

NL 0437354 ViU OU ODW

808.5 L81p
Lockwood, Francis Cummins, 1864-
Public speaking today, a high school manual, by Francis Cummins Lockwood and Clarence De Witt Thorpe. Chicago, B. H. Sanborn, 1927 [c1921]
xxiv, 264 p. 20 cm.
Bibliography: p. 223-237.

1. Oratory. I. Thorpe, Clarence De Witt, 1887- joint author. II. Title.

NL 0437355 LU

Lockwood, Francis Cummins, 1864-
Public speaking today, a high school manual, by Francis Cummins Lockwood ... and Clarence De Witt Thorpe ... Rev. ed. Chicago, New York [etc.] B. H. Sanborn & co., 1931.
xxviii, 420 p. illus. 20 cm.
Contains bibliographies.

1. Public speaking. I. Thorpe, Clarence De Witt, 1887- joint author. II. Title.
PN4121.L6 1931 808.5 31-15296 rev

NL 0437356 DLC Or LU

Lockwood, Francis Cummins, 1864-
... Robert Browning, by Frank C. Lockwood. New York, Eaton & Mains; Cincinnati, Jennings & Graham [1906]
146 p. front. (port.) 20cm. (Modern poets and Christian teaching)

1. Browning, Robert, 1812-1889.
Library of Congress 6-45153

NL 0437357 DLC WaT OrSaW PPM ODW PMA MB

Lockwood, Francis Cummins, 1864-
Story of the Spanish missions of the middle Southwest; being a complete survey of the missions founded by Padre Eusebio Francisco Kino in the seventeenth century and later enlarged and beautified by the Franciscan fathers during the last part of the eighteenth century, by Frank C. Lockwood ... Santa Ana, Calif., The Fine arts press, 1934.
4 p. l., vi, 78 p. xxx pl. on 16 l. (incl. front.) double map. 25cm.
1. Spanish missions of Arizona. 2. Spanish missions of Sonora, Mexico. 3. Kino, Eusebio Francisco, 1644-1711. 4. Missions—Arizona. 5. Missions—Sonora, Mexico. I. Title. II. Title: Spanish missions of the middle Southwest.
35-246
Library of Congress F799.L74
——— Copy 2.
Copyright A 78667 [5] 917.91

OCIW PP
NL 0437358 DLC UU DSI TxU CU WaSp OrP WaS NcD OCl

Lockwood, Francis Cummins, 1864-
Three remarkable southwestern libraries, by Frank C. Lockwood ... [Tucson, Ariz., 1940]
18 numb. l. 28 x 22cm.
Type-written (carbon copy)
"Address ... before the foundation meeting of the Friends of the University of Arizona library [April 30, 1940]"—Leaf 18.

1. Los Angeles. Southwest museum. Munk library of Arizoniana. 2. Newberry library, Chicago. Edward E. Ayer collection. 3. Henry E. Huntington library and art gallery, San Marino, Calif. 4. Libraries—Special collections—Americana. I. Title.
41-23335
Library of Congress Z731.L8

NL 0437359 DLC ICN IU

VOLUME 337

Lockwood, Francis Cummins, 1864–
... Thumbnail sketches of famous Arizona desert riders, 1538–1946, by Frank C. Lockwood ... Tucson, Ariz., University of Arizona, °1946.
30 p. 23cm. (Arizona. University; General bulletin no. 11)
University of Arizona bulletin, vol. XVII, no. 2.
"Additional references": p. 30.

1. Arizona—Biog. I. Title.
F810.L85 920.0791 46-27506

NL 0437360 MH PBm PU PP NNC NIC C MtU WaS WaTC MU DLC NcGU CU-B DSI OkU PSt Mo OClW TxU

Lockwood, Francis Cummins, 1864–
Tucson - - - the old pueblo, by Dean Frank C. Lockwood and Captain Donald W. Page ... Phoenix, Ariz., The Manufacturing stationers, inc. [1930]
94 p. front., plates, maps, coat of arms. 23½cm.
"Sources of information": p. 93–94.

1. Tucson, Ariz.—Hist. I. Page, Donald W. II. Title.
30-28491
Library of Congress F819.T9L81
—— Copy 2.
Copyright A 29100 [2] 979.1

NL 0437361 ICU OCl ODW PHi TU MWA DLC OrP MtHi WaSp OrU CaBVaU PMA TxU NjP

SPEC COLL
F
799
K63
1934
Lockwood, Francis Cummins, 1864-
With Padre Kino on the trail, and, A guide to his mission chain, by Frank C. Lockwood. [n.p., n.d.]
162 l. 28cm.
Typewritten manuscript (carbon copy) presented to the library by the author, March 15, 1934.
Leaves numbered in manuscript.
1.Kino, Eusebio Francisco, 1644–1711. 2.Spanish missions of California. I.Title. LC

NL 0437362 CLSU

Lockwood, Francis Cummins, 1864–
... With Padre Kino on the trail, by Frank C. Lockwood. Tucson, Ariz., University of Arizona [1934]
142 p. illus. (incl. facsims.) maps (1 fold.) 23cm. ([Arizona. University] Social science bulletin. no. 5)
University of Arizona bulletin. vol. V, no. 2.

1. Kino, Eusebio Francisco, 1644–1711. I. Title.
34-27435
Library of Congress F799.K63
—— Copy 2. [3] 922.273

NL 0437363 OCU MiU ODW OU OO WaSpG WaTC OrU WaSp CaBViPA DLC OKentU NcGU CoU LNHT UU C NcD PBm PU

Lockwood, Francis Cummins, 1864-
With Padre Kino on the Trail. University of Arizona Bulletin, 1935.

NL 0437364 OCX

Lockwood, *Sir* Frank, 1846–1897.
The law and lawyers of Pickwick. A lecture. With an original drawing of "Mr. Serjeant Buzfuz". By Frank Lockwood ... London, The Roxburghe press [1894]
108 p. front. 17½cm.
A lecture "delivered ... at Morley hall, Hackney, on December 13th, 1893".—Prefatory note.

1. Dickens, Charles, 1812–1870. Posthumous papers of the Pickwick club. 2. Lawyers in literature. I. Title.
20-3639
Library of Congress PR4569.L6

NL 0437365 CaBVaU ViU-L CSmH OCU MB PU PPL DLC AAP FMU CU-AL NcU FU FTaSU WaU CtY

823.83
L817L
Lockwood, *Sir* Frank, 1846–1897.
The law and lawyers of Pickwick. A lecture. With an original drawing of "Mr. Serjeant Buzfuz."
2d ed. London, The Roxburghe press [1902?]
108 p. front. 17½ cm.
A lecture "delivered ... at Morley hall, Hackney, on December 13th, 1893."—Prefatory note.

NL 0437366 NcD TxU OCl

Lockwood, Sir Frank, 1846–1897.
The Frank Lockwood sketch book, being a selection from the pen and ink drawings of the late Sir Frank Lockwood... London, E. Arnold, 1898. 80 p. illus. 24 x 32cm.

311808B. 1. No subject.
N. Y. P. L. March 29, 1946

NL 0437367 NN WaSpG PPL NcD TxU NBuG

Lockwood, *Sir* Frank, 1846–1897.
The Frank Lockwood Sketch book. Being a selection from the pen and ink drawings of the late Sir Frank Lockwood. 2d edition.
— London. Arnold. 1898. 80 pp. 23½ × 31½ cm.
Cartoons and caricatures.

K8754 — Caricatures.

NL 0437368 MB

Lockwood, Sir Frank, 1846–1897.
The Frank Lockwood sketch book, being a selection from the pen and ink drawings of the late Sir Frank Lockwood. 3d ed. London, E. Arnold, 1898.
obl. 8°. pp. 80.

NL 0437369 MH AAP NBuG

Lockwood, Sir Frank, 1846–1897.
Party prospects
see under title

Lockwood, Frank Cummins
See
Lockwood, Francis Cummins, 1864-

Lockwood, G. H., firm, publisher, Kalamazoo, Mich.
see Lockwood Publishing Co., Kalamazoo, Mich.

Lockwood, George.
How to find employment, or better one's self in New York or elsewhere. A hand-book of direction and information, showing how to secure a position for 5, 10, 15 or 20 cents. By George Lockwood. New York, G. Lockwood, °1888.
71 p. 15½cm.

1. Applications for position.
Library of Congress HF5383.L8 7-5951†

NL 0437373 DLC

Lockwood, George, 1874–

U. S. *Immigration and naturalization service.*
... Manual of immigration Spanish, by inspector George Lockwood ... interpreter George N. Vanson ... [and] clerk Josephine Ortiz ... William E. Knickerbocker ... editor ... [Washington?] 1936.

Lockwood, George Browning, 1872–
Americanism, by George B. Lockwood, with a compilation, by John T. Adams, of utterances on Americanism by great Americans. Washington, The National republican publishing co., 1921.
vii, 223 p. 23½cm.

1. U. S.—Pol. & govt.—1913–1921. 2. U. S.—For. rel.—1913–1921. 3. European war, 1914–1918—U. S. I. Adams, John Taylor, 1862– II. Title.
21-12987
Library of Congress E766.L8

NL 0437375 DLC OCl PPComm

Lockwood, George Browning, 1872 -
Americanism; with a compilation, by John T. Adams, of utterances on Americanism by great Americans. Washington: The National Republican Pub. Co., 1921. 223 p. 2. ed. 8°.

CENTRAL CIRCULATION.
1. Republican Party. 2. Title. 3. U. S.—Government and politics. 4. U. S.—Foreign relations. 5. European war.—U. S. 6. Adams, John Taylor, compiler.
N. Y. P. L.

NL 0437376 NN Wa OClWHi

Lockwood, George Browning, 1872-
Lincoln. [Poem] (In, The National Republican, Feb. 2, 1924. p. 3)

NL 0437377 RPB

Lockwood, George Browning, 1872-
Lincoln. Washington, D.C., 1925]
folder [3]p. port. 30cm.
A poem.

NL 0437378 IHi RPB

Lockwood, George Browning, 1872-
The New Harmony communities. [Prospectus]
Marion, The Chronicle co., 1902.
[12] p. pl.

NL 0437379 OO

Lockwood, George Browning, 1872–
The New Harmony communities. [By] George Browning Lockwood. Marion, Ind., The Chronicle company, 1902.
3 p. l., [11]–282 p. incl. pl., port., facsim. front. 24½cm.
Bibliography: p. 280–282.

1. New Harmony, Ind.—Hist. 2. Harmonists.
Library of Congress HX656.N5L9 2-18595

NL 0437380 NIC OOxM OCl MiU PBm PPAN PPT MB ICJ NN InNhW DLC DL WaTC CaBVaU MtU KyBgW InU MnHi

VOLUME 337

Lockwood, George Browning, 1872- Soc. Ethics Lib.
The New Harmony communities. 2d ed. Marion, Ind., the Chronicle Co., 1902.
pp. 282. Ports. and plates.

NL 0437381 MH IEN NcU InU

Lockwood, George Browning, 1872-
The New Harmony movement, by George B. Lockwood, with the collaboration of Charles A. Prosser in the preparation of the educational chapters. New York, D. Appleton and company, 1905.
xvi, 404 p. front., plates, ports., facsims. 19½cm.
"Sources": p. 379-385.
Enlarged from his "The New Harmony communities", 1902.
1. Harmonists. 2. New Harmony, Ind.—Hist. I. Prosser, Charles Allen, 1871- II. Title.
5—16517
Library of Congress HX656.N5L8

PHC WaTC OrP WaSpG OrCS CaBVaU OrPR OrU WaU InU IEG MnHi PCC NcD ODW OU OCl OO MB ViU ICJ NN PU
NL 0437382 DLC AAP KU IU FTaSU KyLxCB TxU NIC Wa

Lockwood, George Browning, 1872- ed.
Outdoors pictorial. v. 1-5; Sept. 1924-Nov. 1926. Washington, D. C. [National Republican publishing co.] 1924-26.

HX15 .P3 vol. 7 no. 30
Lockwood, George Browning, 1872-
Red radicalism - menace or myth? Assaults of communism and socialism upon government, religion and the home are only a small part of a general perversive movement ... Washington, D.C., Issued by the National republic [192-?]
[7] p. [Pamphlets on socialism, communism, bolshevism, etc., v. 7, no. 30]

NL 0437384 DLC

Lockwood, George Browning, 1872-
The strength that was Lincoln's. An address delivered at the Lincoln Day dinner of the Clark county Republican club, Memorial Hall, Springfield, Ohio, Feb. 12, 1923. Washington, The National Republican, [1923]
[8]p. 21x8 1/2cm.
Portrait on title page.

NL 0437385 IHi

Lockwood, George Browning, 1872-
Thoughts on Americanism, by George B. Lockwood ... Washington, D. C., The National republic [1927?]
cover-title, 56 p. 18½cm.
1. U. S.—Civilization. I. Title.
28-8556
Library of Congress E169.1.L81

NL 0437386 DLC

HD 5706 .L63S5x SPEC. COLL.
Lockwood, George D.
Shakin' 'em down: Cause and cure for unemployment as told by Rastus Sucker, Peter Simple, and others of the Black Man's Federated Club. Ypsilanti, Michigan [1931]
132 p. 19 cm.
1. Unemployment. I. Title.

NL 0437387 MiAlbC DLC

TT520 .L81
Lockwood, George E.
The centre system for drafting garments for all the various forms of the human body, defined by direct lines from the center and bottom of scye. New York, 1863.

NL 0437388 DLC

Lockwood, George H.
The priest and the billy goat
see under Lockwood Publishing Co., Kalamazoo, Mich.

Lockwood, George H.
The soldier and the billy goat
see under Lockwood Publishing Co., Kalamazoo, Mich.

Lockwood, George P.
An address, delivered before the Young Men's Christian Association at the Second Presbyterian church, Wheeling, Va., February 7th, 1860 ...
cover-title, 12 p. 21 cm.

NL 0437391 NcD NjP

Lockwood, George R.
Catalogo de los libros espanoles,... Nueva York, 1870
[With Vingut, Francisco J. Key to the spanish teacher. New York, 1871]

NL 0437392 DLC

[Lockwood, George R.]
John James Audubon. (Caption title). [New York, George R Lockwood, 1870]
xv, (i) p. (last p. is ad. of Audubon's Works). 8vo. Bound in blue cloth.
Dated and signed: G.R.L. - 1870.
With inscription at end: George R. Lockwood, Nov. 22, 1878. Presented to Mr. Samuel H. Hunt.
From Anderson Galleries, 2-3 April 1923, No. 42.
1. Audubon, John James, 1780- I. Title.

NL 0437393 CSmH

Lockwood, George R.
John James Audubon
see also in Audubon, John James, 1785-1851. The Birds of America. 1871.

Lockwood, George R., & son, New York, ed.
A complete course of ladies' angular handwriting
see under title

Lockwood, George R., & son, New York, ed.
Glad tidings. New York, 1886
see under title

Lockwood, George R. & son, New York, ed.
Saint Nicholas and Christmas eve. New-York, Geo. R. Lockwood & son, 1885.
15, [1] p. 13½cm.
CONTENTS.—A visit from Saint Nicholas, by Clement C. Moore.—Merry Christmas, by Louise Alcott.—Stocking song on Christmas eve.—Once a year.—A song of Saint Nicholas.
1. Santa Claus. I. Title.
CA 19-324 Unrev'd
Library of Congress PN6110.C5L66

NL 0437397 DLC

Lockwood, George R., trustee.
Ithaca, Auburn and western railway company.
...Income second mortgage. New York, Morison & Bisland, printers [1877?]

Lockwood, George Robinson, 1853-
Lockwood on trusts: Apprehension versus progress and The tools to him who can handle them, with an afterword, by George R. Lockwood ... [St. Louis, 1906]
cover-title, 31, [1] p. 22½cm.
1. Trusts, Industrial.
CA 8—140 Unrev'd
Library of Congress HD2795.L82

NL 0437399 DLC

Lockwood, George Robinson, 1853-
Some facts and figures against the unlimited coinage of silver, with comments thereon. By Geo. R. Lockwood ... [St. Louis, 1900]
16 p. 23½cm.
Caption title.
"First published in September, 1896."
1. Silver question.
CA 7—6868 Unrev'd
Library of Congress HG529.L8

NL 0437400 DLC

Lockwood, George Robinson, 1853-
"The tools to him who can handle them"; or, A protest against the anti-trust crusade. By Geo. R. Lockwood ... [St. Louis, Mo., 1903]
13 p. 23½cm.
Caption title.
1. Trusts, Industrial.
CA 8-141 Unrev'd
Library of Congress HD2795.L8

NL 0437401 DLC

Lockwood, George Robinson, 1853-
Why I oppose woman suffrage; a pamphlet, not an essay, by George R. Lockwood ... [St. Louis? 1912?]
cover-title, 20 p. 23cm.
1. Woman—Suffrage. I. Title.
41-35470
Library of Congress JF853.L6
[2] 324.3

NL 0437402 DLC

VOLUME 337

Lockwood, George Roe.
Diseases of the stomach, including dietetic and medicinal treatment, by George Roe Lockwood ... illustrated with 126 engravings and 15 plates. Philadelphia and New York, Lea & Febiger, 1913.
vi, [17]-624 p. illus., xv pl. 24½cm. $5.50

1. Stomach—Diseases.
Library of Congress RC816.L7 13-13947

NL 0437403 ICJ DLC OrU-M PU-M PPC PV ICRL DNLM OClW-H

Lockwood, George Roe.
A manual of the practice of medicine, by George Roe Lockwood ... Philadelphia, W. B. Saunders, 1896.
935 p. illus., plates (partly col.) charts (partly fold.) 21cm.

1. Medicine—Practice.
Library of Congress RC46.L818 6-27077

NL 0437404 ICJ OClW-H DLC PU PPC OU IdPI PPT ICRL DNLM MiU

Lockwood, George Roe.
A manual of the practice of medicine, by George Roe Lockwood ... 2d ed., rev. ... Philadelphia and London, W. B. Saunders & co., 1901.
847 p. illus., plates (partly col.) charts (partly fold.) 23½cm.

1. Medicine—Practice.
Library of Congress RC46.L82 1-25561

NL 0437405 ICRL DLC OrU-M PPJ OClW-H DNLM ICJ PU PPC

Lockwood (George Roe). Purpura hæmorrhagica. 16 pp. 12°. New York, Trow, 1891.
Repr. from: Med. Rec., N. Y., 1891, xxxix.

NL 0437406 DNLM

Lockwood, Gertrude M.
The keg and I. [1st ed.] New York, Pageant Press [1955]
225 p. illus. 21 cm.

I. Title.
PZ4.L82Ke 55-10673 ‡

NL 0437407 DLC Wa WaE WaS

Lockwood, Guy H.

Duggar, Ben.
Figure techniques; a revised edition of the Lockwood technique plates, edited and compiled by Ben Duggar and Guy Lockwood; drawings by the French artist, La Lire. Madison, Wis., Art headquarters, °1939–

Lockwood, Guy H.
How to live 100 years; dedicated to my best chum, comrade and sweetheart, my wife, by G. H. Lockwood... Kalamazoo, Mich.: Lockwood Pub. Co.[, 1912?] 158 p. illus. (incl. port.) 12°.

278295A. 1. Hygiene, Personal. 2. Longevity. 3. Title.
N. Y. P. L. April 22, 1927

NL 0437409 NN IU

---

811 Lockwood, Guy H.
L81m Mastership or mediumship, which? A timely warning; a new viewpoint on the subject of communicating with the dead. Guy Lockwood, visible author. Kalamazoo, Mich., The author, 1920.
43p.

Poems.

NL 0437410 IU

Lockwood, Guy H.
The story of the giants and their tools, by G. H. Lockwood ... [Kalamazoo, Mich.: Lockwood Pub. Co., 191–?] 47 p. illus. 16°.
Cover-title.

1. Civilization—Hist. 2. Socialism.
N. Y. P. L. June 14, 1927

NL 0437411 NN

Lockwood, Guy H., ed.

The Student's art magazine.
Kalamazoo, Mich., Student's art magazine publishing company, 19

J LOCKWOOD, GUY H.
27 Wagon mission souvenir, '97-1900. [Nash-
335.04 ville, Tenn., 1900]
L 81 22p. illus. 19x25cm.

Cover title.
A traveling, socialist mission conducted by G.H.Lockwood and his wife, Annie T.Grigsby Lockwood.

NL 0437413 ICN ICJ

Lockwood, H.G.
... Accurate and dependable prospector's and traveller's guide ot Barkerville of to-day ...
N.p.,n.pub.[Pref.1933].
32p.,fold.map,24x11cm.

NL 0437414 CaBViPA

Lockwood, H. T., & bro.
Values of square and special-sized tinplates. Computed and pub. by H. T. Lockwood & bro. ... Chicago, Press of Shea, Smith & co., 1885.
62 p. 17cm.

1. Tin-plate—Tables and ready-reckoners.
Library of Congress HF5716.T4L7 8-33880†

NL 0437415 DLC

Lockwood, Hamilton D.
... In equity. Hamilton D. Lockwood vs. James J. Essex ... Boston, 1868.
26, [2] p. 22 cm.
At head of title: Circuit court of The U.S. District of R.I.
Causten Browne, for complainant.
Wm. P. Sheffield, for respondent.
In Rhode Island law cases, v.[4]

NL 0437416 RPB

Lockwood, Hamilton D
Philip Case Lockwood memorial collection of civil war portraits and autographs
see under Lockwood, Philip Case.

Lockwood, Harriet R
Exercises in English grammar with Tests and key, by Harriet R. Lockwood ... New York, Chicago [etc.] American book company [1943–
v. 24 x 19cm.
"Based on Practice sheets in English grammar and punctuation."

1. English language—Grammar—1870– I. Lockwood, Harriet R. Practice sheets in English grammar and punctuation.
Library of Congress PE1111.L548 44-9027
[3] 425

NL 0437417 DLC OCU ODW

PE1111 Lockwood, Harriet R. Practice sheets in Eng-
.L548 lish grammar and punctuation.
Lockwood, Harriet R
Exercises in English grammar with Tests and key, by Harriet R. Lockwood ... New York, Chicago [etc.] American book company [1943–

Ed Lockwood, Harriet R.
428.1 A workbook in vocabulary building ... New York,
L814w The Macmillan co., 1932.
ii, 46 p.

1.Vocabulary. 2.English language - Study and teachings. I.Title. II.Ed. sh. cd.

NL 0437419 WaPS CaBViP MH

Lockwood, Harry Albert, 1861–
Are our municipalities to become business corporations? By Hon. Harry A. Lockwood ... [Lansing? Mich., 1907?]
[7] p. 23cm.
"An address delivered before the State association of circuit judges at Lansing, Mich., December 28, 1907."

1. Municipal ownership—U. S. I. Title.
Library of Congress HD4605.L6 16-11084

NL 0437420 DLC

Lockwood, Harry Albert, 1861–
Are our municipalities to become business corporations? By Hon. Harry A. Lockwood ... [n.p., 1908?]
[7] p. 23 cm.
An address delivered before the State association of circuit judges at Lansing, Mich., December 28, 1907.

NL 0437421 CU

VOLUME 337

Lockwood, Harry Albert, 1861-
Soft coal conditions, their cause and suggestions as to remedies. 1917.

NL 0437422 MiU

Lockwood, Hazel.
The golden book of birds, by Hazel Lockwood, illustrated by Feodor Rojankovsky. New York, Simon and Schuster, 1943.
[42] p. illus. (part col.) 20 x 17cm. (On cover: The Little golden library, 13)
"First printing, April, 1943."
1. Birds—Juvenile literature. I. Rojankovsky, Feodor, 1891- illus. II. Title.
Library of Congress PZ10.3.L84Go 43-13706

NL 0437423 DLC WaSp WaS OO PP

Lockwood, Helen Drusilla.
The meaning of euthenics; an essay on action as a tool of knowledge, by Helen Drusilla Lockwood. Poughkeepsie, N. Y., Vassar college, 1929.
34 p., 1 l. illus. 26cm.
1. Euthenics. 2. Vassar college. Blodgett hall of euthenics. I. Title.
Library of Congress HN64.L845 29-17082

NL 0437424 DLC CU MiU OCU OClW IU NN MB PU

Lockwood, Helen Drusilla.
Tools and the man: a comparative study of the French workingman and the English chartists in the literature of 1830-1848, by Helen Drusilla Lockwood ... New York, Columbia university press, 1927.
244, [2] p. illus. (music) 23½cm. (Half-title: Columbia university studies in English and comparative literature)
Thesis (PH. D.)—Columbia university, 1927.
Vita.
Published also without thesis note.
Bibliography: p. [233]-234.
1. Authors, Laboring class. 2. French literature—19th cent.—Hist. & crit. 3. English literature—19th cent.—Hist. & crit. 4. Chartism. 5. Literature, Comparative—English and French. 6. Literature, Comparative—French and English. I. Title.
Library of Congress PN171.L3L6 1927 a 27-15814
Columbia Univ. Libr. [2]

NL 0437425 NNC DLC NIC PBm

Lockwood, Helen Drusilla.
Tools and the man; a comparative study of the French workingman and English chartists in the literature of 1830-1848, by Helen Drusilla Lockwood, PH. D. New York, Columbia university press, 1927.
244 p., 1 l. illus. (music) 23½cm. (Half-title: Columbia university studies in English and comparative literature)
Issued also as thesis (PH. D.) Columbia university.
Bibliography: p. [233]-234.
1. Authors, Laboring class. 2. French literature—19th cent.—Hist. & crit. 3. English literature—19th cent.—Hist. & crit. 4. Chartism. 5. Literature, Comparative—English and French. 6. Literature, Comparative—French and English. I. Title.
Library of Congress PN171.L3L6 1927 27—12534

OO OCl OClW MB PU PPD WaS MtU
NL 0437426 DLC WaWW OrPR CaBVaU OrU NcD MiU OU OCU

Lockwood, Helen Virginia.
A study of the St. Nicholas day nursery for negro children, an institution for social welfare... Philadelphia, Pa., 1934.
52 p.

NL 0437427 PPT

VT33 L81 1874
Lockwood, Henry.
Sacred lyrics. By Henry Lockwood...
London, Kerby & Endean, 1874.
iv, 92 p. 18 cm.
Title-page and text within red borders.
Initials and tail pieces.

NL 0437428 NNUT

Lockwood, Henry C.
The abolition of the presidency. By Henry C. Lockwood ... New York, R. Worthington, 1884.
viii, [2], [9]-331 p. 21½cm.
"Works of reference": p. [329]-331.
1. Presidents—U. S.
Library of Congress JK516.L8 9-23143

MiU-C MH ICJ PPFr PP PHC PPL PU MdBP
NL 0437429 DLC MWA NjP AU ViU OClWHi OFH OO MiU

JK 516 .L82 1884a
Lockwood, Henry C.
The abolition of the presidency. By Henry C. Lockwood ... New York, R. Worthington, 1884.
viii, [2], [9]-331 p. 21½cm.
"Works of reference": p. [329]-331.
Photocopy. Ann Arbor, Mich., University Microfilms. 1968. 331 p. (on double leaves)

NL 0437430 DLC FTaSU MiU

[Lockwood, Henry C.]
The Capture of Fort Fisher. First Expedition. [caption-title] [Boston, 1871]
8vo. In 1/2 dark blue calf, light blue boards.
Excerpt: Atlantic Monthly. Vol. 28, May-June 1871; p. 622-636, and (1), 685-690.
Both signed at end: "H.C. Lockwood".
With ms. title-page bound in.
Nicholson collection, September 1922.

NL 0437431 CSmH NcU OClWHi

342.44 L81c
Lockwood, Henry C.
Constitutional history of France. By Henry C. Lockwood ... Supplemented by full and precise translations of the text of the various constitutions and constitutional laws in operation at different times, from 1789 to 1889. Illustrated with 32 portraits and a map of Paris. Chicago and New York, Rand, McNally & company, c1889.
x, 11-424 p. incl. front. ports., fold. plan., 22½cm.

NL 0437432 KEmT

Lockwood, Henry C.
Constitutional history of France. By Henry C. Lockwood ... Supplemented by full and precise translations of the text of the various constitutions and constitutional laws in operation at different times, from 1789 to 1889. Illustrated with 32 portraits and a map of Paris. Chicago and New York, Rand, McNally & company, 1890.
x, 11-424 p. incl. front. ports., fold. plan. 22½cm.
1. France—Constitutional history. I. France. Constitution.
Library of Congress JN2453.L8 9—33344

ViU-L OClW OCl DNW ViU ICJ MB MH
NL 0437433 DLC CaBVaU PPL PP MiU NjP OKentU NcU

Lockwood, Henry C.
The constitutional history of France, supplemented by a full and precise trans. of the various constitutions and constitutional laws in operation at different times from 1789-1889. N.Y., Rand. McNally, 1897.
423 p.

NL 0437434 OCX WaS

Im55 tl
[Lockwood, Henry C.]
Greetynge. [n.p.,1887?]
Pamphlet
Signed: H.C.L.

NL 0437435 CtY

PS2248 L83L3
Lockwood, Henry C.
A legacy in verse, from Henry C. Lockwood. Troy, N. Y., Aims and Knight, 1891.
59p. 17½cm.

NL 0437436 NBuG NcD RPB CtY

973.738 L817m
Lockwood, Henry C.
A man from Maine; a true history of the Army at Fort Fisher. [Rockland, Me., The Maine Bugle, ca. 1894-98]
[29]-71 p. front., illus. 24 cm.
1. U. S.--Hist.--Civil War--Campaigns and battles. 2. Ames, Adelbert, Brevet Major General, U. S. Army. 3. Fort Fisher, North Carolina. I. Title.

NL 0437437 ICarbS CSmH

Lockwood, Henry C
Our president-king. [New York, 1895?] 1 p.l., viii, 329 f., 1 port. 4°.
Typewritten.
1. United States.—Presidents and presidency.
N. Y. P. L. March 1, 1912.

NL 0437438 NN

Lockwood, Henry Francis.
...Report on working of southern group of railways in England, by Mr. H. F. Lockwood... Calcutta: Gov. of India Central Publ. Branch, 1925. 13 p. 8°. (India. Railway Board. Technical paper. no. 241.)
1. Railways—Operation and management—Gt. Br. 2. Ser.
N. Y. P. L. February 17, 1926

NL 0437439 NN DLC

Folio J 453
Lockwood, Henry Francis, 1811-1878.
Design for the concentration of the law courts, by Henry F. Lockwood. [n.p. 1867?]
1 v. of illus. 44 cm.
"Questions under the consideration of the joint sub-committees of the bar and of solicitors" (5 p.) and "[Letter] to George Pownall, Esq. and John Shaw, Esq." (3 p.) inserted.
1. Architecture - Designs and plans.
2. Court-houses - London. I. Title. (1)

NL 0437440 CtY

VOLUME 337

LOCKWOOD, Henry Francis, 1811-1878.
Design for the concentration of the law courts. [London, 1867]

f°. pp.(2). Plates and plans.
Inserted in the bakc is his Report on a design, etc. consisting of 31 pages of text.

NL 0437441 MH

Lockwood, Henry Francis, 1811–1878.
The history and antiquities of the fortifications to the city of York, by Henry F. Lockwood, and Adolphus H. Cates ... London, J. Weale; [etc., etc.] 1834.
viii, 48 p. front. (fold. map) illus., plates. 32 x 24½cm.

1. York, Eng.—Fortifications. 2. York, Eng.—Hist. I. Cates, Adolphus H., joint author.
Library of Congress DA690.Y6L6 43-36124

NL 0437442 DLC MdBP ICN CSmH OCl

Lockwood, Henry Francis, 1811-1878.
History and antiquities of the fortifications to the city of York. [Illustr.] London, 1836. fo. 2531

NL 0437443 MdBP

Lockwood, Henry Hayes, 1814-1899.
U. S. *Bureau of ordnance (Navy dept.)*
Exercises in small-arms and field artillery: arranged for the naval service, under an order of the Bureau of ordnance and hydrography of the Navy department ... Philadelphia, Printed by T. K. and P. G. Collins, 1852.

974.766 Lockwood, Henry R.
L817 A sermon preached in St. Paul's Church Syracuse, N.Y., on the twenty-fifth anniversary of his rectorship, January 16, 1898. Syracuse, N.Y., E.M. Grover, printer and binder, 1898.
15 p. 23 cm.

1. Syracuse, N.Y. St. Paul's Church. H. 1. New York (State) Syracuse.

NL 0437445 N

LOCKWOOD, Hiland.
[Memorial.]
[Cambridge. Wilson. 1874?] 30 pp. Portr. 12°.

NL 0437446 MB

Lockwood, Hilliard L.
Homœopathic hints. A simplified arrangement of the principal remedies, with definite instructions for their selection and administration adapted to the treatment of those more ordinary ills in which professional advice is not always necessary. With especial reference to the diseases of infancy and childhood. By Hilliard L. Lockwood ... New York, J. Medole & son, 1887.
71 p. 17 x 9cm.

1. Homeopathy—Popular works.
Library of Congress RX76.L81 7-13817†

NL 0437447 DLC

Lockwood, Howard, 1846-1892.
Commerce of South America, and exposition of the commercial intercourse of South American states with other countries, with suggestions as to increasing trade between the United States and South America Addressed to the Boston Chamber of Commerce. New York [Lockwood Press] 1880.
32 p. 8°.

NL 0437448 NN

AA
735
N4
L81
Lockwood, Howard, 1846-1892.
Lockwood's illustrated guide to New York City. New York, 1872.
cover-title, 32 p. plates. 24cm.

1. New York (City) - Description - Guide-books. I. Title.

NL 0437449 NNC-A MWA PPL

Lockwood, Howard, 1846-1892, ed.
The Millers' journal and flour and grain reporter.
New York [H. Lockwood, etc.] 18

15
9412
Lockwood, Howard, 1846-1892.
The stationers' price book and illustrated and descriptive catalogue, Embracing a comprehensive finding list. New York, H. Lockwood, 1879.
4°.

NL 0437451 DLC

Lockwood, Howard, 1846-1892.
The stationer's price book for the use of the wholesale and retail sale trade and for the commercial travelers
see under Geyer, Andrew, 1842-1919, comp.

Lockwood, Howard, 1846–1892.
Tariffs of foreign nations importing United States goods. Tr., rev., and cor. from latest official documents ... New York, H. Lockwood [c1878
v. 22½cm.

1. Tariff—Law.
Library of Congress HJ6043.L8 8-32438†

NL 0437453 DLC

Lockwood, (Howard) & Co.:
American dictionary of printing and bookmaking.... New York, 1894.
frontisp. ill. 1 f. + 4 + 592 p. 28½cm.

Frontisp. is a por. of Franklin.....

NL 0437454 DN-Ob

Lockwood, Howard, & co.
Hofmann, Karl, 1836-1916.
... Hofmann's treatise on paper-making, by Carl Hofmann, Berlin, Germany ... Tr. from the German, and printed and published by Howard Lockwood & co. ... New York city, H. Lockwood & co., 1895–

Lockwood, Howard & co., translators.
A practical treatise on the manufacture of paper. 1894
see under Hofmann, Karl, 1836-1916.

LOCKWOOD, Ina.
Problem geography; Latin America. Rochester, Minn. n.d. 75p.

NL 0437457 WaS

PZ
8
.L8Bar
Lockwood, Ingersoll, 1841-1918.
Baron Trump's marvellous underground journey, by Ingersoll Lockwood...illustrated by Charles Howard Johnson. Boston, Lee and Shepard, 1892.
xiv p., 1 l., 235 p. illus 21 cm.

NL 0437458 OKentU

Lockwood, Ingersoll, 1841-1918.
Baron Trump's marvellous underground journey, by Ingersoll Lockwood ... illustrated by Charles Howard Johnson. Boston, Lee and Shepard, 1893.
xiv p., 1 l., 235 p. incl. front., plates. 21cm.

I. Title.
Library of Congress PZ8.L8Bar 44-33373

NL 0437459 DLC CoU MB PPL

Lockwood, Ingersoll, 1841-1918, ed.
The Book lover, a monthly journal ... For those interested in rare & standard books, portraits & views for extra-illustration, autograph letters, historical documents. Ed. by Ingersoll Lockwood <Phil Biblion> v. 1; Nov. 1888–Jan. 1890. New York, W. E. Benjamin, 1888–90.

PZ
8
.L82
Lockwood, Ingersoll, 1841-1918.
Extraordinary experiences of Little Captain Doppelkop on the shores of Bubbleland. [Illustrated by Clifton Johnson] Boston, Lee and Shepard, 1892.
287 p. illus.

I. Title. II. Title: Little Captain Doppelkop.

NL 0437461 MiU NNU-W PPL DLC

PN 6161 Lockwood, Ingersoll, 1841-1918.
L843 How to be witty; or, Old saws with new teeth ... By Irwin Longman. Illustrated by W. T. Longman. New York [G. W. Dillingham, 1887] c1886.
viii, 117 p. incl. front., illus. 17 cm.

NL 0437462 OU PPL

VOLUME 337

Lockwood, Ingersoll, 1841-1918.
In varying mood; or, jetsam, flotsam and ligan. Saratoga Springs, N. Y.: the author, 1912. vii, 75 p. 8°.

1. Poetry (American). 2. Title.
N. Y. P. L. April 11, 1913

NL 0437463 NN MiU

Lockwood, Ingersoll, 1841-1918, tr.
Letters on wine [translated from the French by Ingersoll Lockwood]. n.t.p. [London, 1865]
47 p. 8°.
Translator's name from binder's title.
Presentation copy.

NL 0437464 NN

Lockwood, Ingersoll, 1841-1918.
1900; or, The last President, by Ingersoll Lockwood ... New York, The American news company, ©1896.
48 p. 19cm.

Library of Congress PZ3.L813N 7-22741†
(Copyright 1896: 53530)

NL 0437465 DLC CU NN

Lockwood, Ingersoll, 1841-1918.
1000 legal don'ts, or The lawyer's occupation gone; a legal remembrancer, instructor and adviser for those who have no time to read big books. New York, G.W.Dillingham, etc., etc., 1887.

NL 0437466 NH PPL

Lockwood, Ingersoll, 1841-1918.
1000 legal don'ts; or, The lawyer's occupation gone. A legal remembrancer, instructor and adviser for those who have no time to read big books. By Ingersoll Lockwood ... New York, G. W. Dillingham; [etc., etc., 1889]
143 p. 18½cm.
On cover: A lawyer's don'ts.

1. Business law—U. S. I. Title. II. Title: A lawyer's don'ts.
44-27725
Library of Congress HF1241.L6

NL 0437467

Microfilm
12985
HF
Lockwood, Ingersoll, b. 1841.
1000 legal don'ts; or, The lawyer's occupation gone. A legal remembrancer, instructor and adviser for those who have no time to read big books. By Ingersoll Lockwood ... New York, G. W. Dillingham; [etc., etc., 1889]
143 p. 18½cm.
On cover: A lawyer's don'ts.

L. C. Copy Replaced by Microfilm

1. Business law—U. S. I. Title. II. Title: A lawyer's don'ts.
44-27725
Library of Congress HF1241.L6

NL 0437468 DLC

Lockwood, Ingersoll, 1841-1918.
The P. G., or, perfect gentleman. By Ingersoll Lockwood ... New York, G. W. Dillingham, successor to G. W. Carleton & co.; [etc., etc.] 1887.
230 p. 19cm.

1. Etiquette.
9-32558†
Library of Congress BJ1855.L7

NL 0437469 DLC PU MH

Lockwood, Ingersoll, 1841-1918, tr.
Renan, Ernest, 1823-1892. FOR OTHER EDITIONS SEE MAIN ENTRY
Saint Paul. By Ernest Renan ... Translated from the original French by Ingersoll Lockwood. New York, G. W. Dillingham; Paris, Michel Lévy frères, 1887.

Lockwood, Ingersoll, 1841-1918.
Sammy and Burchy at the Union school. By Ingersoll Lockwood ... New York, 1876.
20 p. 23cm.

I. Title.
Library of Congress PN6161.L6385 12-6201

NL 0437471 DLC OFH MB

Lockwood, Ingersoll, 1841-1918.
Superstition. Saratoga Springs, 1910. 82 p., 2 port. 12°.
Title-page missing

1. Superstition.
N. Y. P. L. January 22, 1914

NL 0437472 NN

PZ
8
.L8Tr
Lockwood, Ingersoll, 1841-1918.
Travels and adventures of Little Baron Trump and his wonderful dog Bulger. Illus. by George Wharton Edwards. Boston, Lee and Shepard [1889]
287 p. illus. 22 cm.

NL 0437473 OKentU

Lockwood, Ingersoll, 1841-1918.
Travels and adventures of little Baron Trump and his wonderful dog Bulger, by Ingersoll Lockwood; illustrated by George Wharton Edwards. Boston: Lee and Shepard [etc., etc.] 1890.
287 p. illus. 22cm.

237657B. 1. No subject. I. Title.
N. Y. P. L. July 8, 1943

NL 0437474 NN ViW CtU NNU-W MB

PZ7
.L797
Tr 2
Lockwood, Ingersoll, 1841-1918.
Travels and adventures of little Baron Trump and his wonderful dog Bulger, by Ingersoll Lockwood; illustrated by George Wharton Edwards. Boston, Lee and Shepard; New York, C. T. Dillingham, 1894.
287 p. incl. front., illus., pl. 21 1/2cm.

NL 0437475 MB

Lockwood, Ingersoll, 1841-1918.
Washington: a heroic drama of the revolution, in five acts, by Ingersoll Lockwood ... New York, The author [©1875]
67 p. 19½cm.

1. Washington, George, pres. U. S.—Drama. I. Title.
17-8410
Library of Congress E312.65.L8

NL 0437476 DLC TU PU PBL

Lockwood, Ingersoll, 1841-1918.
Wonderful deeds and doings of little giant Boab and his talking raven Tabib, by Ingersoll Lockwood ... profusely illustrated by Clifton Johnson. Boston, Lee and Shepard; New York, C. T. Dillingham, 1891.
302 p. incl. front., illus. 21½cm.

I. Johnson, Clifton, 1865-1940, illus. II. Title.
44-36610
Library of Congress PZ8.L8Wo

NL 0437477 DLC IU NN MB

[Lockwood, Isaac Ferris]
A few steps in philosophy. [By I. F. Lockwood.] New York, G. P. Putnam's Sons, 1880.
1 p.l., 72 p. sq. 16°.

NL 0437478 NN

Lockwood, Isabel Ingersoll.
Oriental brasses and other objects for temple and household use; two hundred and forty-five specimens selected from the Lockwood collection, illustrated and described by Israel Ingersoll Lockwood. Glendale, Calif., The Arthur H. Clark company, 1935.
339 p. incl. front., 75 pl. 25cm.
"Of this volume five hundred copies have been printed, each numbered, this being number 109."
Bibliography: p. [335]-339.
1. Art objects, Oriental. 2. Oriental antiquities. 3. Art objects—Private collections. 4. Metal work, Oriental. 5. Brasses. 6. Implements, utensils, etc. I. Title.
[Full name: Mrs. Isabel Dwight Ingersoll Lockwood]
34-36805
Library of Congress NK1037.L6
[a45g1] 739

NL 0437479 DLC NSyU MdBWA NIC OrP MB

559.7
N552s
no.1
Lockwood, J A
On the temperature dependence of BF_3 proportional neutron counters, by J.A. Lockwood, F.R. Woods and E.F. Bennett. [Durham, N.H.] 1953.
12 l. diagrs. 28cm. (New Hampshire. University. Dept. of Physics. Scientific report no.1, contract AF19(604)-75)

1. Neutrons. I. t. II. Woods, F.R., joint author. III. Bennett, E.F., joint author. IV. Contract AF19(604)-75. ser.

NL 0437480 DAS

LOCKWOOD, J. [Dalby.
The midnight review, or Apotheosis of Napoleon. A dream. St.Helena, printed at the Free Press, by James Bennett, 1852.

pp.12.
The "Note", on verso of title-page and the poem are both dated: June 1849.
In verse.

NL 0437481 MH

VOLUME 337

Lockwood, J. Traviss
see
Lockwood, John Traviss.

Lockwood, James, 1714–1772.
Works by this author printed in America before 1801 are available in this library in the Readex Microprint edition of Early American Imprints published by the American Antiquarian Society.
This collection is arranged according to the numbers in Charles Evans' American Bibliography.

NL 0437483 DLC

Lockwood, James, 1714–1772.
Descendants of Robert Lockwood
see under Holden, Frederic Augustus.

Lockwood, James, 1714–1772.
The duty and privilege of gospel-ministers, to preach among mankind the unsearchable riches of Christ. A sermon, delivered at the ordination of the Reverend Mr. Eleazer May, at Haddam, June 30, 1756. By James Lockwood... New-Haven: Printed by J. Parker and Co.[, 1756.] 2 p.l., 34 p. 8°.
Evans 7699.

90938. 1. May, Eleazer.
N. Y. P. L. November 18, 1929

NL 0437485 NN CtY CtHi MB RPJCB

Lockwood, James, 1714–1772.
Man mortal: God everlasting, and the sure, unfailing refuge and felicity of his faithful people, in all generations. Illustrated in a discourse delivered at Weathersfield, July 27, 1755; being the next Lord's Day, after the death of the Hon. Col. Williams, of that place. To which is added, by another hand, an appendix containing some brief memoirs of the life of Col. Williams. New-Haven, Printed by J. Parker, 1756.
48, xv p. 23 cm.

1. Sermons, American. 2. Williams, Elisha, 1694–1755. I. Title.
BX7233.L59M2 58–54687

NL 0437486 DLC RPJCB NN CtY PSC NIC MBAt MWA ICMcC

Lockwood, James, 1714–1772.
Religion the highest interest of a civil community, and the surest means of its prosperity. A sermon preached before the General Assembly of the colony of Connecticut, at Hartford, on the day of the anniversary election, May 9th, 1754. By James Lockwood... New-London: Printed and sold by T. Green, 1754. 2 p.l., 50 p., 1 l. 8°.
Evans 7230.
Printed by order of the General Assembly.
List of "election sermons preach'd at Hartford, printed by T. Green of N. London," one leaf at end.

1. Elections—Sermons—U. S.—Conn., 1754. 2. Connecticut (colony). General Assembly.
N. Y. P. L. March 7, 1930

NL 0437487 NN CtHi CtY IU ICN MH

Lockwood, James, 1714–1772.
Religion the highest interest of a civil community, and the surest means of its prosperity. A sermon preached before the General Assembly of the colony of Connecticut, at Hartford, on the day of the anniversary election, May 9th, 1754. By James Lockwood... New-London, Printed and sold by Timothy Green, printer to the Governour & company, 1754. [Philadelphia, Printed privately by the [Lockwood] family, 1889]
2 p.l., 50 p. 26 cm. (In Holden, F.A. Descendants of Robert Lockwood. Philadelphia, 1889)
Facsimile- reprint.

NL 0437488 CtY DLC

Lockwood, James, 1714–1772.
A sermon preached at Weathersfield, July 6, 1763. Being the day appointed by authority for a public thanksgiving, on account of the peace, concluded with France and Spain. By James Lockwood... New Haven: Printed ay [sic] J. Parker and Co.[, 1763.] 35 p. 8°.
Evans 9417.

1. United States—Hist.—French and Indian war, 1755–1763—Addresses, sermons, etc.
N. Y. P. L. July 17, 1929

InU ICN MWiW-C
NL 0437489 NN CtY PPL CtHi DLC NNUT PPL-R MiU-C

Pequot Z93
Lockwood, James, 1714-1772.
The tears of an affectionate, bereaved people, wept over their faithful, deceased minister. A sermon, preached (the substance of it) at Glassenbury, August 7, 1758. Being the day of the interment of the Reverend Mr. Ashbel Woodbride [!] ... By James Lockwood ... New-Haven:Printed by J.Parker and company,at the Post-office.[1758]
31p. 19cm. [Bound pamphlets]
Signatures: [A]-D⁴.
Imperfect: p.[1-2] (half-title?) wanting.

NL 0437490 CtY CtHi MBAt

Lockwood, James, 1714–1772.
The worth and excellence of civil freedom and liberty illustrated, and a public spirit and the love of our country recommended. A sermon delivered before the General assembly of the colony of Connecticut, at Hartford, on the day of the anniversary election. May 10th. 1759. By James Lockwood... New London: Printed and sold by Timothy Green, printer to the governor & company, 1759. 36 p. 16cm. (8°.)

Sabin 41749, note. Evans 8386. Trumbull 1010.
Printed by order of the General assembly.

57R0418. 1. Connecticut—Elections—Sermons, 1759. I. Connecticut. General assembly. t. 1759.

NL 0437492 NN MWA CtY CtHi NN MH MiU-C ICN PPPrHi

Cb4a 1775
Lockwood, James, 1746-1795.
New-York, Tuesday, April 25, 1775. This Day, about Noon, arrived a second Express from New-England, with the following important Advices. Wallingford, Monday, April 24, 1775. Dear Sir, Colonel Wadsworth was over in this place, most of yesterday, and has ordered 20 men out of each company in his regiment ... [signed] James Lockwood. N.B. Col. Gardner took 9 prisoners ... [signed and dated] Isaac Beers, Pierpont Edwards. New-Haven,April 24, half past 9

Forenoon. The above copy, came authenticated from the several towns through which it passed, by the following gentlemen, viz. ... [New York] Printed from the attested Original, by John Holt[1775]
broadside. 27x21cm.
Printed in two columns.
In connection with the battles of Lexington and Concord.

NL 0437494 CtY

Lockwood, James B
Cotton and miniature golf.
Wash., 1930.
unp.

NL 0437495 PP

Lockwood, James D.
Life and adventures of a drummer-boy; or, Seven years a soldier. By James D. Lockwood ... A true story ... Albany, N. Y., J. Skinner, 1893.
191 p. front. 20cm.

1. U. S.—Hist.—Civil war—Personal narratives. I. Title.
Library of Congress E601.L85 14—5958

NL 0437496 DLC MB NcD NcU ICN CtY NjP PHC PPL

Lockwood, James H.
... Early times and events in Wisconsin. By James H. Lockwood ...
(In Wisconsin. State historical society. Collections. Madison, 1856. 21½cm. vol. II, p. 98-196)
Appendix no. 6.

1. Wisconsin—Hist. 10-23164
Library of Congress F576.W81
——— Copy 2, detached. F584.L81

NL 0437497 DLC OClWHi OFH MiU OCl

Lockwood, James Harry, 1864–
The creation of wealth; modern efficiency methods analyzed and applied, by J. H. Lockwood. Cincinnati, The Standard publishing company [©1915]
225 p. illus. 20½cm.

1. Economics. 2. Efficiency, Industrial. I. Title.
Library of Congress HB171.7.L6 15—2803

OCU MiU OO OClU PBm NN MB
NL 0437498 DLC WaSpG ICarbS FU OCU NjP ICRL PSt

Lockwood, James Harry, 1864–
110533 The creation of wealth. Modern efficiency methods analyzed and applied, by J. H. Lockwood. Indianapolis, The Bobbs-Merrill Co., [1915].
[2], 225 p. illus. 19½cm.

NL 0437499 ICJ NjP OClW PPT

Lockwood, Jeremiah, 1891–
... Accounting, by Jeremiah Lockwood ... and Calvin H. Rankin ... Boston, Mass., Bellman publishing company, inc. [©1940]
cover-title, 39 p. 23cm. (Vocational and professional monographs. no. 7)
Reproduced from type-written copy.
Bibliography: p. [35]-39.

1. Accounting. I. Rankin, Calvin Hagan, joint author. II. Title.
Library of Congress HF5381.V53 no. 7 41-4942
——— Copy 2.
Copyright [2] (371.425082) 657.069

NL 0437500 DLC MoU NNC OrU ViU OO PU

Lockwood, Jeremiah, 1891- joint author.
FOR OTHER EDITIONS SEE MAIN ENTRY
Gordon, William Duncan, 1892–
Modern accounting systems, by William D. Gordon ... and Jeremiah Lockwood ... 2d ed., 2d printing revised. New York, J. Wiley & sons, inc.; London, Chapman & Hall, limited, 1937.

VOLUME 337

Lockwood, Jeremiah, 1891–
Textile costing; an aid to management, by Jeremiah Lockwood ... and Arthur D. Maxwell ... Washington, The Textile foundation, 1938.
xiv p., 1 l., 282 p. incl. forms. 23½cm. (Half-title: Textile economics series)
Prepared for the foundation. cf. Foreword.
1. Textile industry and fabrics—Accounting. 2. Cost—Accounting. I. Maxwell, Arthur Dewey, joint author. II. Textile foundation, inc. III. Title.
Library of Congress HF5686.T4L56 38–17473
[42r39n2] 338.4

PU-W PPT PP DFT
NL 0437502 DLC OrP CU NcRS OC1U OU OC1 ViU NN ICJ

304 L81 1945
Lockwood, Jeremiah, 1891–
Textile costing, and aid to management. Washington, Textile foundation, 1945.
282 p. (Textile economics series)

NL 0437503 DNLM NcD NcGU

Lockwood, John.
Religious healing and the truth about doctors [by] John Lockwood. Buffalo, N. Y., Beaver book company [1923]
263 p. 19½cm.
1. Medicine. 2. Therapeutics, Physiological. I. Title.
Library of Congress R710.L6 24-896

NL 0437504 DLC

Lockwood, John, 1825 or 6-1901.
[Russel, William Channing]
Address [by William C. Russel] and poem [Palermo ... 1860, by John Lockwood] before the Association of the alumni of Columbia college. New-York, The Association, 1861.

Lockwood, John, 1825 or 6–1901.
An aid-book in elementary English grammar ... New York, 1885.
vi, 86 p. 13 cm.
1. English language—Grammar—1870–1950. I. Title.
PE1111.L55 11–5837 rev

NL 0437506 DLC

Lockwood, John, 1825 or 6–1901.
Hi-Li, the moon-man; or, Free-silver in America; being a diverting contribution to the McKinley-Bryan Presidential campaign, by a member of the Society for the Prevention of Humanity to Mongolians. Brooklyn, 1896.
52 p. 24 cm.
1. Campaign literature, 1896—Republican. I. A member of the Society for the Prevention of Humanity to Mongolians. II. Title.
PZ3.L8133H 7–34696 rev

NL 0437507 DLC

Lockwood, John, 1825 or 6-1901.
Learning by doing. Elementary language-book in graded lessons; or, learning to make english. [anon] [Brooklyn, N.Y., printed by Lain & Robertson, 1885]
vi, 190 p. 16°.

NL 0437508 DLC

[Lockwood, John] 1825 or 6–1901.
Our campaign around Gettysburg; being a memorial of what was endured, suffered, and accomplished by the Twenty-third regiment (N. Y. S. N. G.) and other regiments associated with them, in their Pennsylvania and Maryland campaign, during the rebel invasion of the loyal States in June–July, 1863. Brooklyn, A. H. Rome, 1864.
168 p. 20 cm.
1. Gettysburg Campaign, 1863. 2. U. S.—Hist.—Civil War—Regimental histories—N. Y. infantry—23d reg't—1862– 3. New York infantry—23d reg't—1862– I. Title.
E475.51.L81 2–10559 rev

NL 0437509 DLC NcU NIC TxU NcD ViU NjP

Lockwood, John, 1825 or 6-1901.
Palermo . . . 1860: a broken ballad. Recited before the Association of the alumni of Columbia College, November 13th, 1860. [New York. 1860.] 3-36 pp. 22½ cm., in 4s.
K3362 — Columbia University. Association of the Alumni. Addresses. — Palermo, Sicily. Hist.

NL 0437510 MB RPB

*PS3233 .L63 1871
[Lockwood, John] 1825 or 6-1901.
Poems of earlier years. Brooklyn, Rome Brothers, Printers, 1871.
6 l., [13]-127 p. 24½cm.
Printed for private circulation.
Rome Brothers were friends and publishers of Walt Whitman's first edition of Leaves of grass. cf. Winwar, Frances, American giant, Walt Whitman and his times, Harper, 1941.
Inscription: "Presented to Wm. A. Lockwood with the love of Aunt Amy, second month, 3rd 1874."
1. Whitman, Walt, 1819-1892.

NL 0437511 ViU PSC-Hi

[Lockwood, John, 1825 or 6–1901.
A primer of language; or, First steps in composition and grammar, by a teacher. Brooklyn, Rome Bros., printers, 1881.
282 p. 20 cm.
"Printed for private circulation only."
1. English language—Grammar—1870–1950. I. A teacher. II. Title.
PE1111.L553 11–5838 rev

NL 0437512 DLC

Lockwood, John, 1825 or 6–1901.
The river; a song of human life, by Ala. Brooklyn, 1890.
45 p. 18 cm.
"Privately printed in honor of our mother's ninety-fourth birthday."
I. Title.
PS2248.L88R5 20–14048

NL 0437513 DLC NN RPB

Lockwood, John, 1825 or 6–1901.
The silent dormitory, and other poems, by Ala. New York, 1887.
112 p. 20 cm.
"For private circulation."
I. Title.
PS2248.L88S5 28–9343

NL 0437514 DLC CtY NN NjP MH PSC-Hi

Lockwood, John, 1825 or 6–1901.
Topical brief of Swinton's Outlines of history; a suggestive analysis for the use of pupils in the preparation and recitation of lessons. New York, Ivison, Blakeman, Taylor, 1877.
xv, 128 p. 17 cm.
1. History—Outlines, syllabi, etc. I. Swinton, William, 1833–1892. Outlines of the world's history. II. Title.
D21.S977 3–2891 rev 2

NL 0437515 DLC OO

[Lockwood, John A]
An essay on flogging in the navy; containing strictures upon existing naval laws, and suggesting substitutes for the discipline of the lash. New-York, Pudney & Russell, printers, 1849.
2 p. l., 56, 23 p. 22½cm.
"This essay appeared in the Democratic review, for August, September, and October."—page following t.-p.
1. Corporal punishment. 2. U. S.—Navy—Crimes and misdemeanors. I. Title: Flogging in the navy, Essay on.
Library of Congress VB910.L8 13–20672

NL 0437516 DLC MB ICN MH RPB PHi CtY

Lockwood, John Alexander, 1856–
Cadet's handbook. A manual for military students at colleges and academies. By Captain John A. Lockwood ... Kansas City, Mo., Press of Hudson-Kimberly publishing co. [1903]
373 p., 1 l. illus., diagrs., 13 forms. 19cm.
1. Military art and science. 2. Tactics. I. Title.
Library of Congress U113.L8 4–822

NL 0437517 DLC CU DNW OC1 ICJ

Lockwood, John D., 1908?- ed.
The Courier. v. 1-3: Dec. 1, 1920–Apr. 29, 1922. Washington, D. C. [The National printing company, etc.] 1920–22.

Lockwood, John Edwards, 1904–
The Economic agreement of Bogotá.
(In American journal of international law. Lancaster, Pa., 1948. 26 cm. v. 42, p. 611–620)
Bibliographical footnotes.
1. International American Conference. 9th, Bogotá, 1948. 2. Spanish America—Economic policy. I. Title.
JX1.A6 vol. 42 A 49–1414*
Carnegie Endow. for Int. Peace. Library for Library of Congress [1]†

NL 0437519 NNCE DLC

VOLUME 337

Lockwood, John Edwards, 1904–
Proposed international legislation with respect to business practices.
(*In* American journal of international law. Lancaster, Pa., 1947. 26 cm. v. 41, p. 616–621)
Bibliographical footnotes.

1. International Trade Organization (Proposed) 2. Commercial policy. I. Title.
JX1.A6 vol. 41 A 47–5240*
Carnegie Endow. Int. Peace. Library for Library of Congress [2]†

NL 0437520 NNCE CaBVaU DLC

Lockwood, John Francis, ed.

Smith, *Sir* **William,** 1813–1893.
A smaller Latin-English dictionary, by Sir William Smith ... Rev. ed. by J. F. Lockwood ... London, J. Murray [1933]

Lockwood, John Francis.
The tradition of scholarship; an inaugural address delivered at University College, London, on May 24th, 1946. London, H. K. Lewis, 1947.
18 p. 22 cm.

1. Learning and scholarship. I. Title.
AZ103.L6 001 51–28692

NL 0437522 DLC ICU NN

Lockwood, John Hoyt, 1848-
Fort Hoosac, address at the unveiling of a memorial boulder at Williamstown, Massachusetts June 19, 1916, together with other material relating to the West Hoosac block house, 1756.
"Privately printed by the author."

NL 0437523 NN

Lockwood, John Hoyt, 1848-
Memorial sketch of Rev. George H. C. Viney, assistant pastor of the First Church of Christ, Pittsfield, Mass., by John H. Lockwood... Westfield, Mass. [1897?]
3p.ℓ., [9]-60p. front. (port.), port., illus. 19cm.
Poetry and prose.

NL 0437524 RPB

Lockwood, John H[oyt]
A sermon commemorative of the two-hundredth anniversary of the First Congregational church of Westfield, Mass., delivered by the pastor, Rev. John H. Lockwood, Sunday, October 5, 1879, to which an appendix is added ... Westfield, Mass., Clark & Story, printers, 1879.
55 p. 24cm.
Published by request.

1. Westfield, Mass. First Congregational church.
Library of Congress F74.W56L8 6–38847

NL 0437525 DLC MH-AH

Lockwood, John Hoyt, 1848– *ed.*
Western Massachusetts; a history, 1636–1925, board of editors: Rev. John H. Lockwood, D. D., Ernest Newton Bagg, Walter S. Carson, Herbert E. Riley, Edward Boltwood, Will L. Clark, staff historian ... New York and Chicago, Lewis historical publishing company, inc., 1926.
4 v. fronts., plates, ports., facsims., coats of arms. 27½cm.
Vols. 3–4 contain biographical material.

1. Massachusetts—Hist. 2. Massachusetts—Biog. I. Bagg, Ernest Newton, joint ed. II. Carson, Walter Scott, 1851– joint ed. III. Riley, Herbert Ellihu, 1873– joint ed. IV. Boltwood, Edward, 1870–1924, joint ed. V. Clark, Will Leach, 1853– VI. Title.
Library of Congress F64.L76 27—6635

NL 0437526 DLC MH OrU TxU C-S MB NIC

Lockwood, John Hoyt, 1848–
Westfield and its historic influences, 1669–1919; the life of an early town, with a survey of events in New England and bordering regions to which it was related in colonial and revolutionary times, by Rev. John H. Lockwood ... [Westfield, Mass. Printed and sold by the author [1922]
2 v. fronts., plates, ports., maps (1 fold.) 22½cm.

1. Westfield, Mass.—Hist.
Library of Congress F74.W68L82 22–25234

NL 0437527 DLC MH MB MWA IaU IU Or OClMA OClWHi MoSW

Lockwood, John Palmer, *d.* 1910.
Darkey sermons from Charleston County, composed and delivered by John Palmer Lockwood alias Rebrin Isrel Manigo. Columbia, S. C., The State company, 1925.
45 p., 2 l. front. (port.) 19cm.

I. Title.
Library of Congress PN6231.N5L6 26–15411

NL 0437528 DLC IU NcD GU ViU

284.6
B633Bℓ
Lockwood, John Prior, 1813-1887.
Memorials of the life of Peter Böhler, Bishop of the Church of the United Brethren. With an introd. by Thomas Jackson. London, Wesleyan Conference Office, 1868.
vii, 142p. port. 18cm.

1. Böhler, Peter, 1712-1775. 2. Wesley, John, 1703-1791.

NL 0437529 TxU GU-De NcD NNUT

BY1542
.B66L8
Lockwood, John Prior, 1813-1887.
The western pioneers; or, Memorials of the lives and labours of the Rev. Richard Boardman and the Rev. Joseph Pilmoor, the first preachers appointed by John Wesley to labour in North America, with brief notices on contemporary persons and events. London, Wesleyan Conference Office, 1881.
xii, 211 p. front. (port.), plates. 19 cm.

1. Boardman, R[ich]ard, 1738-1782. 2. Pilmoor, Jose[ph], d. 1821. I. Title.

NL 0437530 IEG MBU ICN NcD CtY

Lockwood, John Salem, 1907–

Pennsylvania. University. *Bicentennial conference.*
... Chemotherapy, by E. K. Marshall, jr., John S. Lockwood [and] René J. Dubos. Philadelphia, University of Pennsylvania press, 1941.

Lockwood, John Salem, 1907–
... Chimiothérapie des infections chirurgicales, par le docteur J. S. Lockwood ... Traduit de l'anglais par le docteur Julien P. Maes. New York, N. Y., Pub. par la Belgian American educational foundation, inc., et par la Fondation Francqui, Bruxelles, 1945.
50 p. 23cm. (Actualités médico-chirurgicales ... No. VII)
"Rédigé sur les bases du chapitre ... préparé pour le traité de chirurgie de Christopher."—Introd.

1. Wounds—Treatment. 2. Chemotherapy. I. Maes, Julien Peter, 1911– tr. II. Belgian American educational foundation, inc. III. Fondation Francqui, France.
S G 46–155
U. S. Surg.-gen. off. Libr. for Library of Congress RM663.L6 [2]† 615.1

NL 0437532 DNLM DLC

Lockwood, John Traviss.
John Eliot. A sketch read at the dedication of the Eliot memorial window in Widford church, Herts, May 21st, 1894. By J. Traviss Lockwood ... Hertford, Printed by S. Austin and sons, 1894.
20 p. 18½cm.
"Printed for private circulation."
"To the descendants of John Eliot 'apostle to the Indians'" ([4] p., signed: Ellsworth Eliot, New York, N.Y., September 25, 1893) laid in.
"Widford church. Dedication of the Eliot memorial window 21st May, 1894. Order of service" ([4] p.) laid in.
1. Eliot, John, 1604-1690.

NL 0437533 MiU PP NN ICN CtY

G
265
.516
LOCKWOOD, JOSEPH.
A guide to St. Helena, descriptive and historical, with a visit to Longwood, and Napoleon's tomb. St. Helena, G. Gibb, 1851.
iv, 106, 42p. 21cm.

NL 0437534 ICN CU

Lockwood, *Sir* **Joseph Flawith,** 1904–
Flour milling, by J. F. Lockwood ... (assisted by Anthony Simon) First impression June, 1945. Second impression January, 1946. Liverpool, New York [etc.] The Northern publishing co. ltd., 1945.
511 p. illus., diagrs. 22½ cm.
"Works of reference": p. 495–498.

1. Flour-mills. I. Simon, Anthony, joint author. II. Title.
A 46–4827 rev
New York. Public Libr. for Library of Congress [r61c2]

NL 0437535 NN CaBVa OrP WaS DNAL IU PSt CU

298
L81F
Ed.2
Lockwood, Sir Joseph Flawith, 1904-
Flour milling. 2d ed. Liverpool, Northern Publishing Co., 1948.
543 p.

NL 0437536 DNAL

TS
2145
L6
1949
Lockwood, Sir Joseph Flawith, 1904-
Flour milling, by J.F. Lockwood... (assisted by Anthony Simon) 2d ed. Second impression, 1949. Liverpool, New York [etc.] The Northern publishing co. ltd., 1949.
543 p. illus. diagrs.

FLOUR-MILLS
Simon, Anthony, joint author
Title

NL 0437537 KMK PSt MiD ICJ

VOLUME 337

TS 2145 .L82 1952 Lockwood, Sir Joseph Flawith, 1904-
Flour milling, by J.F.Lockwood (assisted by Anthony Simon) 3d ed. Liverpool, New York, Northern Publishing Co., 1952.
557 p. illus. (part col.) 23 cm.
Bibliography: p.539-543.
1.Flour-mills. I.Simon,Anthony,joint author. II.Title.

NL 0437538 MiU CaBVaU

Lockwood, *Sir* Joseph Flawith, 1904-
Provender milling; manufacture of feeding stuffs for live stock, by J. F. Lockwood ... (Assisted by Anthony Simon) Liverpool and London, Northern publishing co. ltd., 1939.
1 p. l., 438 p. illus., tables. 22½ cm.
"Works of reference": p. 438.
1. Flour and feed trade. 2. Feeds. [2. Milling products as feeding stuffs] 3. Milling machinery. I. Simon, Anthony, joint author. II. Title.
Agr 40-619 rev
U. S. Dept. of Agr. Libr. 298L81
for Library of Congress [r61c2]

NL 0437539 DNAL OrP WaS KMK CSt

---

298 L81 Ed.2 Lockwood, Sir Joseph Flawith, 1904-
Provender milling; manufacture of feeding stuff for live stock. Liverpool, Northern publishing co., 1945.
372 p.
"Second edition."

NL 0437540 DNAL NcD

Lockwood, Sir Joseph Flawith, 1904-
Provender milling; manufacture of feeding stuffs for live stock, by J.F. Lockwood... (Assisted by Anthony Simon) Liverpool and London, Northern publishing co., ltd., 1946.
372 p. illus., tables, diagrs. 23 cm.
"Second edition."
"Works of reference": p. 366.
1. Flour and feed trade. 2. Feeding and feeding stuffs. 3. Milling machinery. I. Simon, Anthony, joint author. II. Title.

NL 0437541 CU

Lockwood, Sir Joseph Flawith, 1904-
Provender milling; manufacture of feeding stuffs for live stock, by J. F. Lockwood (assisted by Anthony Simon) [2d ed.] London, New York, Northern Pub. Co., 1947.
372 p. illus., diagrs., tables. 22cm.
"Works of reference": p. 366.
1. Flour and food trade. 2. Feeding and feeding stuffs. 3. Milling machinery. I. Simon, Anthony, joint author. II. Title.

NL 0437542 MB

635.3 L81p 1949 Lockwood, Sir Joseph Flawith, 1904-
Provender milling; manufacture of feeding stuffs for live stock, by J. F. Lockwood, assisted by Anthony Simon. (3d ed.) London, New York, Northern Pub. Co., 1949.
435p. illus., tables. 23cm.
Bibliography: p.428.
1. Flour and feed trade. 2. Feeding and feed stuffs. 3. Milling machinery. I. Simon, Anthony, joint author. II. Title.

NL 0437543 IU DNAL

Lockwood, Sir Joseph Flawith, 1904-
The tradition of scholarship; an inaugural address delivered at University College, London, May 24th, 1946. L, H.K.Lewis, 1947

NL 0437544 MH

LOCKWOOD, JOSEPH S.
In memoriam Emily H. (Bedford) Lockwood. New York, E. O'Keefe, printer [1874] lxxviii p. port. 19cm.
1. Lockwood, Emily Helene (Bedford), 1847-1871.

NL 0437545 NN

---

he QP 6 Z991 no.1 Lockwood, Julia Etta, 1901-
The relation of the adrenal cortex to vitamins A, B_1 and C. Buffalo, 1933.
21 p.
1. Vitamins. 2. Suprarenal bodies. I. Title.

NL 0437546 NIC

---

*QP187 L7 1936 Lockwood, Julia Etta, 1901-
The relation of the adrenal cortex to vitamins A, B_1 and C, by Julia E. Lockwood. A thesis submitted to the Committee on graduate study and degrees of the University of Buffalo in partial fulfillment of the requirements for the degree of Doctor of philosophy. [Buffalo, N. Y., The University of Buffalo] 1936.
4p.ℓ.,103 numb.ℓ. illus.(mounted charts) 28cm. (Buffalo. University. Doctors' theses)
Typewritten copy (carbon)

NL 0437547 NBuG

Lockwood, Karl Lee, 1929-
Part I: The attempted synthesis of 2,2,8,8-tetramethylcyclononanone. Part II: Studies in the 1,4-polymethylenebenzene series. A. Synthesis and attempted resolution of 2-(ω-carboxypropionyl)-1,4-nonamethylenebenzene. B. Attempted synthesis of 1,4-octamethylenebenzene. [Ithaca, N.Y.] 1955.
vi, 33, iv, 57 l. illus. 29cm.
Thesis (Ph. D.)--Cornell Univ., Sept. 1955.

NL 0437548 NIC

Lockwood, Katharine Read.
Viola; a novel by Katharine Read Lockwood. Boston, B. Humphries, inc. [c1935]
204 p. 20cm.
I. Title.
Library of Congress PZ3.L8138Vi 36-6807

NL 0437549 DLC

Lockwood, Laufa M
Star in the night, by Laufa M. Lockwood. [Francisco, Ind., 1943]
87 p., 1 l. 20½cm.
Poems.
I. Title.
Library of Congress PS3523.O25S8 43-9053
[2] 811.5

NL 0437550 DLC

Lockwood, Laufa M
The way the winter came. [Poems] Columbus, Ohio, F. J. Heer Print. Co. [1949]
86 p. illus. 21 cm.
I. Title.
PS3523.O25W3 811.5 49-26744*

NL 0437551 DLC

Lockwood, Laura Emma, 1863- ed.
Letters that live, selected and ed. by Laura E. Lockwood and Amy R. Kelly. New York, H. Holt and company, 1911.
xiii, 253 p. 16cm. $1.50
Illustrated end-papers.
I. Kelly, Amy Ruth, 1878- joint ed. II. Title.
Library of Congress PR1348.L6 11-12667

NL 0437552 DLC Wa Or WaS OEac ViU MB

Lockwood, Laura Emma, 1863-
Lexicon to the English poetical works of John Milton, by Laura E. Lockwood ... New York, London, The Macmillan company, 1907.
xii, 671 p. 22½cm.
"The first one hundred and seventy pages [of the book] were in 1898 presented to the Philosophical faculty of Yale university as a doctoral thesis. These pages were also, during the ... [same] year, put through the press."—Pref.
1. Milton, John—Dictionaries, indexes, etc. 2. Milton, John—Concordances.
Library of Congress PR3580.L7 7—37515

OrP WaT OrCS WaSp OrPR CaBVaU CaBVa WaSpG OO OCl PBm PPT PP PPL MB NN WaU ViU NjNbS MeB WaS
NL 0437553 DLC CtY PCM TU NcD NjP ODW OU MiU OCU

Lockwood, Laura Emma, 1863- ed.
Shakespeare, William, 1564-1616.
... A midsummer-night's dream, by William Shakespeare; from the Riverside ed., edited by Richard Grant White, with introduction, notes, and a study of the play by Laura Emma Lockwood ... Boston [etc.] Houghton, Mifflin and company [1903]

Lockwood, Laura Emma, 1863-
Milton's corrections to the Minor poems... Baltimore [1910]
cover-title. 5 p. 28 cm.
"Reprinted from Modern language notes, November, 1910."

NL 0437555 CtY

VOLUME 337

Lockwood, Laura Emma, 1863- ed.
FOR OTHER EDITIONS SEE MAIN ENTRY
Milton, John, 1608–1674.
... Of education; Areopagitica; The commonwealth, by John Milton; with early biographies of Milton, introduction, and notes, ed. by Laura E. Lockwood ... Boston, New York [etc.] Houghton Mifflin company [c1911]

PS 2248 .L857 **Lockwood,** Laura Emma, 1863-
Poems. Wellesley, Mass. [n.p.] 1955.
30p. 23cm.

NL 0437557 TNJ KyU KU MWelC

Lockwood, Laura Emma, 1863- *ed.*
... Sonnets, selected from English and American authors, by Laura E. Lockwood ... Boston, New York [etc.] Houghton Mifflin company [c1916]
xiii, [1], 113, [1] p. 18cm. (The Riverside literature series) $0.35

1. Sonnets, English.

Library of Congress PR1195.S5L6 16-2243

NL 0437558 DLC AAP WaU WaS NcU OClND OCX MiU OCl OClJC OCU NN MB WaSpG IdU PU PHC

Lockwood, Laura Emma, 1863- *ed.*
Specimens of letter-writing, selected and ed. by Laura E. Lockwood ... and Amy R. Kelly ... New York, H. Holt and company, 1911.
xii, 274 p. 17cm. (*On cover:* English readings)

1. Letter-writing. I. Kelly, Amy Ruth, 1878- joint ed. II. Title.

Library of Congress PE1497.L6 11-14415

NL 0437559 DLC IdU NjP OClW MiU MB

Lockwood, Le Grand, 1820–1872.
... The entire collection of important modern paintings, statuary, bronze, articles of vertu, etc., belonging to the late Mr. Le Grand Lockwood, will be sold by auction ... April 18th and 19th [1872] ... Geo. A. Leavitt & co., auctioneers. New York, 1872.
29 p. 1 illus. 26cm.
93 items.
Priced in manuscript.

1. Art—Private collections. I. Leavitt, firm, auctioneers, New York. (1872. Geo. A. Leavitt & co.)

Library of Congress N5220.L6 43-26783

NL 0437560 DLC NNMM

Lockwood, Lewis Byford, 1908–
The physiology of *Rhizopus oryzae.* By. L. B. Lockwood ... G. E. Ward ... and O. E. May ...
(*In* U. S. Dept. of agriculture. Journal of agricultural research. v. 53, no. 11, Dec. 1, 1936, p. 849-857. 23½cm. Washington, 1936)
Contribution from Bureau of chemistry and soils (E—68)
Published Feb. 3, 1937.
"Literature cited": p. 857.

1. [Rhizopus oryzae] I. May, Orville Edward, 1901- joint author. II. Ward, George Edward, 1908- joint author.

U. S. Dept. of agr. Library for Library of Congress 1Ag84J vol. 53, no. 11 [S21.A75 vol. 53, no. 11] Agr 37-97

NL 0437561 DNAL OCl

Lockwood, Lewis Byford, 1908–
... A study of the physiology of *Penicillium javanicum* van Beijma with special reference to the production of fat, by Lewis Byford Lockwood ... Washington, D. C., The Catholic university of America, 1933.
4 p. l., 35 p., 1 l. pl. 23cm. (The Catholic university of America. Biological series. no. 13)
Thesis (PH. D.)—Catholic university of America, 1934.
Vitae.
"Literature cited": p. 31-35.

1. Penicillium. 2. Plants—Metabolism. 3. Botany—Physiology. 4. Fat.

Library of Congress QK623.P4L6 34—392
——— ——— Copy 2.
Copyright A 68476 [a36d1] 581.1337

NL 0437562 DLC CU NcU NcD OU MiU OCl PV PU-B

C 895 .817 LOCKWOOD, LEWIS C.
Gospel hymnal, volume first, for public and social worship and gospel meetings, containing one hundred hymns, mostly original. To be used in connection with Gospel hymns and tunes, for the sake of variety... Jamaica, N.Y., Standard print, 1886.
cover-title, 97p.

Without music.
No more published?

NL 0437563 ICN

C 89 .517 LOCKWOOD, LEWIS C.
Gospel hymnal. 2d edition, containing two hundred hymns, to be used in connection with Gospel hymns and choir, for the sake of variety... Jamaica, N.Y., Long Island farmer print, 1888.
cover-title, 54p.

Without music.

NL 0437564 ICN

Lockwood, Lewis C
Historical discourse on the rise and progress of the Presbyterian church of Melville, delivered September 10th, 1876, by Rev. L.C. Lockwood... [n.p., n.d.]
11 p. 20.5 cm.
Cover title.

NL 0437565 NjPT PPPrHi

LOCKWOOD, LEWIS C.
Mary S. Peake, the colored teacher at Fortress Monroe. By Rev. Lewis C. Lockwood... With an appendix. Boston: American Tract Soc. [186-?] 64 p. front. (port.), plates. 15½cm.

779248A. 1. Peake, Mary Smith (Kelsey), 1823-1862.

NL 0437566 NN ViHarT TNF OClWHi OO DHU MWiW NjP MShM

BP595 .S824 Lockwood, Loni, joint tr.

Steiner, Rudolf, 1861–1925.
... Anthroposophy and the human gemüt; reflections on the Michael thought in its true aspect [and] the regeneration of the Michael festival. Four lectures delivered in Vienna, September 27–October 1, 1923, published from a stenographic report not edited by the lecturer with permission of Marie Steiner. Translated from the original by Samuel and Loni Lockwood. New York, Anthroposophic press, inc., 1946.

427 1924b Lockwood, Louisa C
Locating a forgotten Washington headquarters ...
(In Daughters of the American revolution magazine. Albany, N.Y., 1924. 26cm. v.58, p.15-18. illus.)

NL 0437568 CtY

940.3747 qW589L **Lockwood,** Louisa C.
The world war history of the city of White Plains, 1917-1918, together with a concise historical sketch of White Plains from the first settlement, 1683, to the incorporation of the city, 1916 ... White Plains, 1926.
53p. plates, ports. 27cm.

1. European war, 1914-1918. White Plains, N.Y. 2. New York (State) White Plains.

NL 0437569 N NN

BX5937 .L814 **Lockwood, Luke A**
Address delivered at the laying of the corner stone of the school chapel of St. Paul's Episcopal Society, at Riverside, September 9, 1876. Port Chester [N. Y.?] Journal Power Press Print, 1876.
8 p.

1. Protestant Episcopal Church - Sermons. 2. Sermons, American - 19th cent. I. Title. II. St. Paul's Episcopal Society, Riverside, N. Y.

NL 0437570 CtHC

Lockwood, Luke A.
Masonic law and practice, with forms. By Luke A. Lockwood ... New York, Masonic publishing and manufacturing co., 1867.
144 p. 19½cm.

1. Freemasons—Laws, decisions, etc.

Library of Congress HS440.L8 9—20950

NL 0437571 DLC

Lockwood, Luke A.
Masonic law and practice, with forms. By Luke A. Lockwood ... New York, Masonic publishing and manufacturing co., 1869 [c1897]
144 p. 19½cm.

NL 0437572 NcD

Lockwood, Luke A
Masonic law and practice, with forms.. ... N.Y., Macoy publishing and Masonic supply co. (Inc.) 1905.

NL 0437573 OCl

NK 2406 .L813 Lockwood, Luke Vincent, 1872-1951.
Amerikanische Möbel der Kolonialzeit, hrsg. von L. V. Lockwood. Deutsche Ausgabe besorgt von Karl Pullich. Stuttgart, J. Hoffmann [1915]
192 p. (chiefly illus.) (Bauformen-Bibliothek, Bd. 10)

Dieses Werk is eine gekürzte ... Ausgabe von Colonial furniture in America ...

Continued in next column

VOLUME 337

Continued from preceding column

two volumes.

≠Furniture--U.S.
Amerikanische Möbel der Kolonialzeit.
Bauformen-Bibliothek. Bd. 10.

NL 0437575 MoU PP OClSA PPT

Jka52 +901Ln
Lockwood, Luke Vincent, 1872- ed.
Amerikanische Möbel der Kolonialzeit, hrsg. von L. V. Lockwood. Deutsche Ausgabe besorgt von Karl Pullich. Stuttgart, J. Hoffmann [1917]
xiii p., 192 p. of illus. 29 cm. (Amerikanische Möbel der Kolonialzeit. Bauformen-Bibliothek, Bd. 10)
"Dieses Werk ist eine gekürzte und nur für Deutschland bestimmte Ausgabe von: Colonial Furniture in America by Luke Vincent Lock[wood]"

NL 0437576 CtY PSt CU

Lockwood, Luke Vincent, 1872-
Amerikanische möbel der kolonialzeit herausgegeben von L.V. Lockwood. Deutsche ausgabe besorgt von Karl Pullich. Stuttgart, Julius Hoffman, c1926?.
xiv p., 1 l., 192 p. illus. 30 cm.

NL 0437577 Wa CaBVaU

Lockwood, Luke Vincent, 1872–
A collection of English furniture of the XVII & XVIII centuries, by Luke Vincent Lockwood. New York, Tiffany studios, 1907.
6 p. l., 17–18 p., 2 l., 19–479 p. illus. 30cm.
"This volume is no. 474 of 500 copies published by Robert Grier Cooke, incorporated, for the Tiffany studios."
"The collection of antique furniture which is described in this catalogue was made by Thomas B. Clarke."—Foreword.
1. Furniture, English. I. Tiffany, studios, New York. II. Clarke, Thomas Benedict, 1848–1931.
8—33823
Library of Congress NK2529.L8

MdBWA
NL 0437578 DLC MB PBm ICJ OCl DDO NN MB PHC PP

Lockwood, Luke Vincent, 1872–
Colonial furniture in America, by Luke Vincent Lockwood. New York, C. Scribner's sons, 1901.
xix, 352 p. incl. plates. front., 11 pl. 29 cm.
Plates, not included in paging, accompanied by guard sheet with descriptive letterpress.
1. Furniture—U. S. I. Title.
1—28164
Library of Congress NK2406.L8 1901

PPFr PHC PP MB WaWW WaT WaS OrP MiGR
NL 0437579 DLC CU KyLx NBuT PPD OClRC OO OCl MB PHi

Lockwood, Luke Vincent. 749
Colonial furniture in America. London: B. T. Batsford, 1902. xix, 352 p., 12 pl. illus. sq. 4°.

NL 0437580 NN MiU

Lockwood, Luke Vincent. 1872–
Colonial furniture in America.
New York. Scribner. 1902. xix, 352 pp. Illus. Plates. 27cm.

NL 0437581 MB TxU PPL

Lockwood, Luke Vincent, 1872–
Colonial furniture in America, by Luke Vincent Lockwood. New and greatly enl. ed., with eight hundred and sixty-seven illustrations of representative pieces. New York, C. Scribner's sons, 1913.
2 v. fronts., illus. 34cm. $25.00
1. Furniture—U. S. I. Title.
13—21117
Library of Congress NK2406.L8 1913

NN
OClMA DDP PPPM ViU MtU OCl PU-FA PPL PPL PP MB CU
NL 0437582 DLC NBuU WaSp MU OClWHi OClW MiGr OO

Lockwood, Luke Vincent.
Colonial furniture in America. New York: Charles Scribner's Sons, 1921. 2 v. front., illus. new enl. ed. f°.
1. Title. 2. Furniture.
N. Y. P. L. May 15, 1928

NL 0437583 NN InU KMK NcD OOxM OU

Lockwood, Luke Vincent, 1872–1951.
Colonial furniture in America, by Luke Vincent Lockwood. 3d ed. Supplementary chapters and one hundred and thirty-six plates of new subjects have been added to this edition, which now includes over a thousand illustrations of representative pieces ... New York, C. Scribner's sons, 1926.
2 v. fronts., illus. 31½ cm.
1. Furniture—U. S. I. Title.
NK2406.L8 1926 26—22375

PPT OEac ViU MB IdU OrP WaT OrU
NL 0437584 DLC KEmT MiFR TNJ WaU PSt IaU NIC OCl

Lockwood, Luke Vincent, 1872-
Colonial furniture in America; 3d ed.
N.Y., Scribner, 1927.
2 v.

NL 0437585 PP

NK 2406 L8 1951
Lockwood, Luke Vincent, 1872-
Colonial furniture in America, by Luke Vincent Lockwood. 3d ed. Supplementary chapters and one hundred and thirty-six plates of new subjects have been added to this edition, which now includes over a thousand illustrations of representative pieces ... New York, C. Scribner's sons, 1951 [c1926]
2 v. fronts., illus. 28½ cm.
1. Furniture - U. S. I. Title.

NL 0437586 Vi MiU CaOTP MH N MB IdPI WaE

Lockwood, Luke Vincent, 1872–
... The furniture collectors' glossary, by Luke Vincent Lockwood. New York, Printed for the Society, 1913.
viii, 55, [1] p. illus. 25cm. $5.00
At head of title: The Walpole society.
"Compiled with the idea of bringing together in convenient form the words used in the cabinetmaker's art."—Pref.
"Of this book there have been printed at the Gilliss press, twenty-five copies on Nordeling hand-made paper for the members of the Walpole society, and one hundred and seventy-five copies on Cheltenham deckel-edge paper for general distribution."
1. Furniture—Dictionaries. I. Walpole society. II. Title.
13-12624
Library of Congress NK2240.L75

ICJ MB MiU PP MWA PPPM MiGr
NL 0437587 DLC ICRL MeB RPJCB MH OClMA NNC NN

Lockwood, Luke Vincent, 1872-
Tiffany studios, *New York.*
Illustrated catalogue of a notable collection of beautiful English furniture of the XVII and XVIII centuries, the collection formed by Mr. Thomas B. Clarke and acquired by the Tiffany studios, for whose account the collection will be sold at unrestricted public sale on the dates herein stated [December 1st, 2nd and 3rd, 1910] catalogued by Luke Vincent Lockwood; the sale will be conducted by Mr. Thomas E. Kirby, of the American art association, managers. New York [Press of the Lent & Graff company] 1910.

Lockwood, Luke Vincent, 1872-
Pendleton, Charles Leonard.
The Pendleton collection [by] Luke Vincent Lockwood. [Providence] The Rhode Island school of design, 1904.

Lockwood, Luke Vincent, 1872-
Prospectus of a Book on eighteenth Century Furniture Descriptive of the Pendleton Collection.
[Providence] 1904.

NL 0437590 RPJCB

Lockwood, Luke Vincent, 1872-1951.
The St. Memin Indian portraits.
N.Y., 1928.
26 p. 8°
(R'p't. N.Y. Hist. Soc. Quar. Bull. Apr. 1928)

NL 0437591 MWA PPAmP

Lockwood, Luke Vincent, 1872-1951.
Connecticut. *Tercentenary commission.*
Three centuries of Connecticut furniture. 1635. 1935; an exhibition at the Morgan memorial, Hartford, as a part of the celebration of the tercentenary of Connecticut, June 15–October 15, 1935. [Hartford, Printed by the Case, Lockwood & Brainard company, °1935]

Lockwood, Lyn.
It's not cricket
see under It's not cricket (Motion picture script)

Lockwood, M. C.
Addresses incidental to the dedication of the crematory of Cincinnati
see under Cincinnati Cremation Company.

Lockwood, M C.
... Baccalaureate sermon, Religion and childhood. (1892)

NL 0437595 DHEW

Lockwood, M.C.
Eulogy on the death of James A. Garfield, assassinated July 2d, 1881. Died September 19th, 1881. Pronounced in the First Baptist Church, Albany, September 26th. Albany, N.Y., Burdick& Taylor, [1881]
18 p. 12°.
In AN Garfield p. v. 14, no. 3.

NL 0437596 NN

VOLUME 337

Lockwood, M.C.
Profit or plunder, which? A question of the day
see under Thompson, Ralph Seymour.

Lockwood, M. L.
Remarks of Hon. M. L. Lockwood on the Free Pipe Line Bill, in the House, [Pennsylvania] Wednesday, March 23d, 1881. n. p., 1881. 8 p. 8°.

Cover-title.
In: * C p. v. 1540, no. 17.

1. Pipe lines, U. S.: Pa. 2. Pennsylvania.—House of Representatives.
N. Y. P. L. March 8, 1917.

NL 0437598 NN

Lockwood, M P
The hot lunch for rural schools.
Tucson, 1918.
30 p.

NL 0437599 PP

Lockwood, Margaret, 1916–
Lucky star; the autobiography of Margaret Lockwood. London, Odhams Press [1955]
191 p. illus. 22 cm.

I. Title.

PN2598.L59A3 927.92 56-23985 ‡

NL 0437600 DLC OrCS CaBVa NN MH PP MiD NIC

Lockwood, Margaret, 1916–
My life and films, by Margaret Lockwood. Ed. by Eric Warman. London, World film publ., 1948. 78 p. illus. 19cm.

I. Warman, Erik, 1904– , ed.
N. Y. P. L. December 22, 1950

NL 0437601 NN IaU CLSU

Lockwood, Marian, 1899- joint author.

Fisher, George Clyde, 1878–
Astronomy, by Clyde Fisher ... and Marian Lockwood ... New York, J. Wiley & sons, inc.; London, Chapman & Hall, limited, 1940.

Lockwood, Marian.
The earth among the stars [by] Marian Lockwood [and] Arthur L. Draper. [New York, Basic books, inc., °1935]
3 p. l., 3-91 p. illus. 19½cm.
"Edited by Paul Grabbe."
"Suggested reading": p. 88-89.

1. Astronomy. I. Draper, Arthur L., joint author. II. Grabbe, Paul, 1902– ed. III. Title.

35-33570

Library of Congress QB44.L75
——— ——— Copy 2.
Copyright A 88113 [3] 523

NL 0437603 DLC KEmT Or WaS OrCS OrMonO CaBVa OCl NN PPFr PPT PP

Lockwood, Marian, 1899- joint author.

Draper, Arthur L.
The story of astronomy [by] Arthur L. Draper and Marian Lockwood ... New York, The Dial press, 1939.

Lockwood, Mary, tr.

Lenormant, François, 1837–1883.
The beginnings of history according to the Bible and the traditions of Oriental peoples. From the creation of man to the deluge. By François Lenormant ... (Tr. from the 2d French ed.) With an introduction by Francis Brown ... New York, C. Scribner's sons, 1882.

Lockwood, Mary Jane.
Philip Case Lockwood memorial collection of civil war portraits and autographs
see under Lockwood, Philip Case.

Lockwood, *Mrs.* Mary (Smith) 1831–1922.
Afoot and awheel in Europe, by Mrs. Mary S. Lockwood; colored frontispiece and sixteen half-tones. Garden City, N. Y., The Country life press, 1916.
viii p., 2 l., 3-233, [1] p. col. front., plates, port. 24½cm. $1.50

1. Europe—Descr. & trav. I. Title.

Library of Congress D921.L6 16-6794

NL 0437607 DLC NN

Lockwood, Mrs. Mary (Smith) 1831-1922, ed.

The American monthly magazine ... v. 1-42; July 1892–June 1913. Washington, D. C., National society, D. A. R. [1892-1910]; New York [1911-13]

Lockwood, *Mrs.* Mary (Smith) 1831–
Art embroidery: a treatise on the revived practice of decorative needlework. By M. S. Lockwood and E. Glaister. With nineteen plates printed in colours from designs by Thomas Crane. London, M. Ward & co., 1878.
83 p. 19 col. pl. 32½cm.

1. Needlework. I. Glaister, Elizabeth, joint author. II. Crane, Thomas, 1843?– illus. III. Title.

8—23947

Library of Congress TT750.L82

NL 0437609 DLC CaOTP MdBP PPD PU PPL PP ICJ MB OCl OClWHi

Lockwood, Mrs. Mary (Smith) 1831-1922.

Augusta co., *Va.*
Chronicles of the Scotch-Irish settlement in Virginia: extracted from the original court records of Augusta county, 1745–1800, by Lyman Chalkley ... pub. by Mary S. Lockwood ... Rosslyn, Va., Printers: The Commonwealth printing co. [°1912–13]

Lockwood, *Mrs.* Mary Smith, 1831–
Columbia guide to historic and modern Washington, by Mary S. Lockwood ... Harrisburg, Pa., Harrisburg publishing co., 1897.
1 p. l., iv, 66 p. front., illus. (incl. plan) fold. map. 19½cm.

1. Washington, D. C.—Descr.—Guide-books.

10-19541

Library of Congress F199.L81

NL 0437611 DLC NN

Lockwood, *Mrs.* Mary (Smith) 1831–1922.
Hand-book of ceramic art, by M. S. Lockwood. New York, G. P. Putnam's sons, 1878.
137 p. front. 17½cm.
Bibliography: p. [135]–137.

1. Pottery—Hist.

12—7115

Library of Congress NK4225.L7

NL 0437612 DLC IU NjP NcRS NN

Lockwood, *Mrs.* Mary Smith, 1831–1922.
Historic homes in Washington: its noted men and women, by Mary S. Lockwood ... New York, Belford company [°1889]
304 p. front., plates. 24cm.

1. Washington, D. C.—Historic houses, etc. I. Title.

29-12032

Library of Congress F195.L79

NL 0437613 DLC WaE DI IEN MB PPL PPFr

Lockwood, *Mrs.* Mary Smith, 1831–1922.
Historic homes in Washington: its noted men and women, by Mary S. Lockwood ... New York, Belford company [°1890]
304 p. front., plates. 23 x 19cm.

1. Washington, D. C.—Historic houses, etc. I. Title.

6-34770

Library of Congress F195.L8

NL 0437614 DLC OClWHi

Lockwood, Mary S[mith] 1831-
Historic homes in Washington; its noted men and women and a century in the White House. ... Washington, D.C., The national tribune, 1899.
336 p. plates., 21.5cm.

NL 0437615 OClWHi

Lockwood, Mary (Smith)
Lineage book of the charter members of the Daughters of the American Revolution
see Daughters of the American revolution. Lineage book, National society of the Daughters of the American revolution
Daughters of the American revolution. Lineage book of the charter members.

VOLUME 337

Lockwood, *Mrs.* Mary (S[mith]) 1831–
Story of the records, D. A. R., by Mary S. Lockwood and Emily Lee Sherwood (Mrs. W. H. Ragan) ... Washington, D. C. [G. E. Howard] 1906.
326 p. plates, ports., facsims. 23cm.

1. Daughters of the American revolution. I. Ragan, Emily Lee (Sherwood) "Mrs. W. H. Ragan," joint author.
6-43548
Library of Congress E202.5.A21 (Copyright A 136830)

NL 0437617 DLC Or WHi CoU NcD MdBP OC1W PHi NN MB PPiU

Lockwood, *Mrs.* Mary (Smith) 1831–1922.
Yesterdays in Washington, by Mary Smith Lockwood ... Rosslyn, Va., The Commonwealth company [c1915]
2 v. fronts. (v. 1, port.) plates. 20½cm.

1. Washington, D. C.—Hist. I. Title.
Library of Congress F194.L8 15-9231

NL 0437618 DLC NN

624.151 L814s Geol Lib'y
Lockwood, Mason G
Subsidence from declining artesian pressure can no longer be ignored in Houston area, Texas. Presented at spring meeting, Texas Section, ASCE, April 9, 1954, Midland, Texas. [n.p., 1954?]
19p. illus. 23cm.

1. Subsidences (Earth movements) 2. Geology - Texas - Houston.

NL 0437619 TxU

Lockwood, Matilda Devenport.
In memoriam; Matilda Devenport Lockwood
see under title

Ix L815 893b
[Lockwood, Melancthon Clarence]
The new minister, by Kenneth Paul [pseud.]
New-York, A.S. Barnes & company[c1893]
vi, 342p. 19cm.

NL 0437621 CtY

FILM 4274 PR v.3 reel L24
[Lockwood, Melancthon Clarence]
The new minister. By Kenneth Paul [pseud.]
New York, A. S. Barnes [c1893]
342 p. (Wright American fiction, v.III, 1876-1900, no.3379, Research Publications, Inc. Microfilm, Reel L-24)

NL 0437622 CU

Lockwood, Myna.
Beckoning star, a story of old Texas, written and illustrated by Myna Lockwood. New York, E. P. Dutton and company, inc., 1943.
242 p. incl. front., illus. 21cm.
"First edition."

1. Texas—Hist.—Fiction. I. Title.
43-5781
Library of Congress PZ7.L817Be
[5]

NL 0437623 DLC Or PP WaSp OC1 OEac

Lockwood, Myna.
The dagger and the cup [by] Myna Lockwood ... Indianapolis, New York, The Bobbs-Merrill company [1947]
404 p. 21cm.
"First edition."

I. Title.
PZ3.L8139Dag 47-2542
Library of Congress

NL 0437624 DLC WaE

Lockwood, Myna.
Delecta Ann, the circuit rider's daughter, written and illustrated by Myna Lockwood. New York, E. P. Dutton and company, inc., 1941.
335 p. incl. front., illus. 21cm.
Illustrated lining-papers.
"First edition."

I. Title. 41-3675
Library of Congress PZ7.L817De

NL 0437625 DLC WaSp OrP Or WaS OEac OC1 OC1h OOxM PP PWcS

Lockwood, Myna.
Free river, a story of old New Orleans, written and illustrated by Myna Lockwood. New York, E. P. Dutton and company, inc., 1942.
255 p. incl. front., illus. 21cm.
"First edition."

1. New Orleans—Hist.—Fiction. I. Title.
42-16135
Library of Congress PZ7.L817Fr

NL 0437626 DLC WaWW PP WaSpG NcD OC1 OEac

Lockwood, Myna.
Indian chief; the story of Keokuk, by Myna Lockwood; decorations by the author. London, New York [etc.] Oxford university press [1943]
320 p. illus. 21cm.

1. Keokuk, Sauk chief, 1780?-1848. I. Title.
43-2042
Library of Congress E99.S23K45
970.2

NL 0437627 DLC INS Or OC1 PP

Lockwood, Myna.
Lo and behold! By Myna Lockwood; pictures by the author. London, New York [etc.] Oxford university press [1945]
213 p. illus. 21cm.
On cover: A cape Cod mystery.

I. Title.
45-1873
Library of Congress PZ7.L817Lo

NL 0437628 DLC Or WaSp PP

Lockwood, Myna.
Macaroni, an American tune, by Myna Lockwood; pictures by the author. London, New York [etc.] Oxford university press [c1939]
44, [2] p. illus. (part col.) 22cm.
"Printed in the United States of America."

I. Title.
39-25145
Library of Congress PZ7.L817Mac

NL 0437629 DLC Or OC1 PPT

Lockwood, Myna.
The mysterious box, by Myna Lockwood; pictures by the author. London, New York [etc.] Oxford university press [c1941]
47, [1] p. illus. (part col.) 22 x 19cm.

I. Title.
41-18619
Library of Congress PZ7.L817My

NL 0437630 DLC OC1 PP

Lockwood, Myna.
Mystery at Lonesome End, by Myna Lockwood. New York, Oxford university press, 1946.
219 p. 21cm.

I. Title.
PZ3.L8139My 46-8238

NL 0437631 DLC PP

Lockwood, Myna. Now listen to me.

PN6120 .A5P476 1948
Phillips, Irving Walter.
Now and forever, a comedy in three acts; based on the Saturday evening post story [Now listen to me] by Myna Lockwood. Chicago, Dramatic Pub. Co. [1948]

Lockwood, Myna.
Up with your banner, written and illustrated by Myna Lockwood. New York, E. P. Dutton and company, inc., 1945.
256 p. illus. 19½cm.
"First edition."

1. Texas—Hist.—Fiction. I. Title.
45-6795
Library of Congress * PZ7.L817Up

NL 0437633 DLC WaSp OrU Or PP OC1 OEac

Lockwood, Myna.
The violin detectives, by Myna Lockwood, pictures by the author. London, New York [etc.] Oxford university press [c1940]
48 p. col. illus. 22 x 19cm.
Illustrated t.-p. in color.

I. Title.
40-32437
Library of Congress PZ7.L817Vi

NL 0437634 DLC MoU OrU Or OC1

Lockwood, Normand, 1906–
...Benedictus (6-pt.)... New York: G. Schirmer [c1939] Publ. pl. no. 38612. 7 p. 26cm. (G. Schirmer's choral church music... no. 8390.)
Score: S. S. A. T. T. B. and piano reduction. Latin words.

1. Choral music, Sacred—Mixed —6 pt.—Unacc. 2. Benedictus qui venit.
N. Y. P. L. February 9, 1943

NL 0437635 NN

VOLUME 337

Lockwood, Normand, 1906–
[The birth of Moses]

The birth of Moses, for women's voices, SSA, with piano and flute. New York, Mercury Music Corp. [1949]
score (22 p.) 27 cm.
"A Merrymount Music Press Publication."
"Text from Exodus."

1. Choruses, Sacred (Women's voices, 3 pts.) with flute and piano.

M2074.3.L 49-51958*

NL 0437636 DLC

Lockwood, Normand, 1906–
[Carol fantasy. Piano-vocal score. English]

Carol fantasy, for chorus and orchestra. New York, Associated Music Publishers [1952]
58 p. and parts. 30 cm.
For chorus (SSAATTBarBarBB), 2 optional trumpets, optional kettle drums, and piano or organ.
The parts are for the optional acc.
CONTENTS.—Deck the hall.—We three kings.—Away in a manger.—Once, long ago.—O Tannenbaum.—When the winter sun.
1. Choruses, Sacred (Mixed voices, 10 pts.) with orchestra—Vocal scores with piano. 2. Carols. 3. Christmas music. I. Title.

M2023.L814C3 M 54-2351 rev

NL 0437637 DLC FTaSU NcU MB NN ViU

[Lockwood, Normand] 1906–
[Children of God. Libretto. English]

Children of God; an oratorio on the brotherhood of man, with libretto compiled from the Revised standard version of the Holy Bible. Libretto compiled and edited by Clara Chassell Cooper [and others] Berea, Ky., Berea College, °1953.
18 l. 28 cm.

1. Oratorios—Librettos. I. Chassell, Clara Frances, 1893– Children of God. II. Title.

ML53.L62C5 1953 M 57-1298

NL 0437638 DLC

784.86
L81c

Lockwood, Normand, 1906–

Choral selections for mixed voices. [v.p., v.pub.] c1937-40.
v.p. Q.

Typewritten t.-p. supplied.
Part of selections have piano or organ accompaniment.
Contents: David mourneth for Absalom.- Dirge for two veterans.- Four songs: 1. Forever be my song of songs. 2. Be not disconsolate. 3. Omen. 4. Tinmouth town.- A lullaby

Contents (cont.) for Christmas.- Monotone.- Out of the cradle endlessly rocking.- Psalm 114.- Psalm 123.- Psalms 117,63,134.- Three choruses for peace: no.1. Exhortation. no.2. Psalm. no.3. Laud.

NL 0437640 IaU

LOCKWOOD, NORMAND, 1906-
[THE CLOSING DOXOLOGY. VOCAL SCORE. ENGLISH]
The closing doxology (Psalm 150) For mixed chorus and band. New York, Broude bros. [c1952] 28 p. 28cm. (Masterworks of the choral art by composers of the 19th and 20th centuries)

Score: SSAATTBB and piano (for rehearsal only), with instrumental cues.

1. Choral music, Sacred (Mixed, 8 pt.)--Keyboard acc. I. Masterworks of the choral art, by composers of the 19th and 20th centuries. II. Bible. O.T. Psalms. CL. English.

NL 0437641 NN IU

M1205
.L6C6
1953

Lockwood, Normand, 1906–

Concerto for organ & brasses. New York, Associated Music Publishers [1953.
score (48 p.) and 4 parts. 31cm.
Cover title.

Score and parts: trumpet I in B^b, trumpet II in B^b, trombone I, trombone II.

1. Concertos (Organ with band)—Scores and parts.

NL 0437642 ViU FTaSU KEmT OO NBC MB CLSU IU OCl LU NIC NcD OCU

Lockwood, Normand, 1906–

...David mourneth for Absalom [by] Normand Lockwood... Chicago, Ill.: N. A. Kjos [c1937] 12 p. 26cm. (Oberlin choral series... Choruses for mixed voices. 12.)

Score: S. S. A. A. T. T. B. B. and piano reduction. English words.

1. Choral music, Sacred—Mixed —8 pt.—Unacc.
N. Y. P. L. February 9, 1943

NL 0437643 NN OO

Lockwood, Normand, 1906-

Dirge for two veterans, S.A.T.B., a cappella, musical setting by Normand Lockwood, poem by Walt Whitman. New York, M. Witmark & sons [c1936]
13 p. 27 cm. (Witmark choral library. No. 2879)

Publisher's plate no. 19705-11

NL 0437644 RPB

M1548
.L6D5

Lockwood, Normand, 1906-

Dirge for two veterans, by Walt Whitman, set to music. New York, M. Witmark [c1937]
12, 13 p. 26cm. (No. 2926)
Cover title.
"S.A.T.B. a cappella."
"This ed. contains a special foreword and analysis of the poem and music and rehearsal suggestions by Jacob Evanson."
1. Choruses, Secular (Mixed voices, 4 pts.), Unaccompanied. I. Whitman, Walt, 1819-1892. Dirge for two veterans. II. Evanson, Jacob, ed. III. Title.

NL 0437645 MB OO

Lockwood, Normand, 1906–

..."Exhortation;" no. 1 from "Three choruses for peace." Anthem for mixed voices, a cappella... New York [etc.] C. Fischer, inc. [c1938] Publ. pl. no. 28339. 5 p. 26cm. (Carl Fischer's choir music edition. ser. 7. 523.)

Score: S. A. T. B. and piano reduction.
First line: Hear ye the voice of the Spirit.
"Words and music by Normand Lockwood."

HENRY HADLEY MEM. LIB.

1. Choral music, Sacred—Mixed —4 pt.—Unacc. 2. Anthems.
N. Y. P. L. September 25, 1941

NL 0437646 NN

Music
Score
M
2092.6
L62F67
1939

Lockwood, Normand, 1906–

Four choral responses to the words of Christ; mixed voices (SATB) divided [a cappella] Philadelphia, O. Ditson [c1939]
score (12 p.) 27 cm.
Cover title.
For chorus (SAATTBB) a cappella.
English text.
Contents.—Tell the vision to no man.—Why callest thou me good?—Suffer little children.—Arise, and be not afraid.
1. Choruses, Sacred (Mixed voices, 8 pts.), Unaccompanied.
I. Title: Choral responses to the word of Christ.

NL 0437647 IEdS

Lockwood, Normand, 1906–

...Four songs [by] Normand Lockwood... Chicago, Ill.: N. A. Kjos [c1938] 8 p. 26cm. (Oberlin choral series... Choruses for mixed voices. 16.)

Score: S. S. A. A. T. Bar.
Words by Grant Loomis.
CONTENTS.—Forever be my song of songs.—Be not disconsolate.—Omen.—Tinmouth Town.

1. Choral music, Secular—Mixed —6 pt.—Unacc. I. Loomis, Grant.
N. Y. P. L. February 9, 1943

NL 0437648 NN IEdS OO

Lockwood, Normand, 1906–

...Hosanna... New York: G. Schirmer [c1939] Publ. pl. no. 38613. 12 p. 26cm. (G. Schirmer's choral church music. no. 8391.)

Score: S. A. T. B. and piano reduction. Latin words.

1. Choral music, Sacred—Mixed —4 pt.—Unacc. 2. Hosanna.
N. Y. P. L. February [illegible]

NL 0437649 NN IEdS

Lockwood, Normand, 1906-

I hear America singing, composed by Normand Lockwood (for mixed voices); poems by Walt Whitman. Delaware Water Gap, Pa., Shawnee Press, c1954.
30 p. 27 cm. (Waring Contemporary Choral series)

Publisher's plate no.: I hear, etc.- 28 S.A.T.B.

NL 0437650 RPB

Lockwood, Normand, 1906–

..."Laud;" no. 3 from "Three choruses for peace." Anthem for mixed voices, a cappella... New York [etc.] C. Fischer, inc. [c1938] Publ. pl. no. 28340. 5 p. 26cm. (Carl Fischer's choir music edition. ser. 7. 525.)

Score: S. A. T. B. and piano reduction.
First line: Lord, we are each Thy vassal.
"Words and music by Normand Lockwood."

HENRY HADLEY MEM. LIB.

1. Choral music, Sacred—Mixed —4 pt.—Unacc. 2. Anthems.
N. Y. P. L. September 25, 1941

NL 0437651 NN

Lockwood, Normand, 1906–

...The Lord reigneth <psalm 93> (7 part) [by] Normand Lockwood... New York: Galaxy music corp., c1938. 8 p. 27cm. (Galaxy music for the church. no. 891.)

Score: S. S. A. T. Bar. Bar. B. and piano reduction.
Performance: 3½ minutes.

1. Choral music, Sacred—Mixed —7 pt.—Unacc. I. Bible. O. T. Psalms. XCIII. English.
N. Y. P. L. October 2, 1942

NL 0437652 NN IU OO

Lockwood, Normand, 1906–

...A lullaby for Christmas [by] Normand Lockwood... Chicago, Ill.: N. A. Kjos [c1937] 5 p. 26cm. (Oberlin choral series... Choruses for mixed voices. 11.)

Score: S. S. A. A. T. T. B.
Words by J. A. Symonds. First line: Sleep, baby.

1. Choral music, Sacred—Mixed —7 pt.—Unacc. 2. Christmas—Choral music. 3. Lullabies, U. S. I. Symonds, John Addington, 1840-1893.
N. Y. P. L. February 9, 1943

NL 0437653 NN OO

VOLUME 337

Lockwood, Normand, 1906–

...Monotone [by] Normand Lockwood... Chicago, Ill.: N. A. Kjos music co. [c1937] 3 p. 26cm. (Oberlin choral series... Choruses for mixed voices... 8.)

Open score: S. A. T. B. English words.
Words from the poem Monotone by Carl Sandburg.

1. Choral music, Secular—Mixed —4 pt.—Unacc. I. Sandburg, Carl, 1878–
N. Y. P. L. October 3, 1941

NL 0437654 NN OO

Lockwood, Normand, 1906–

...O Our Father, Who art in Heaven (The Lord's prayer according to Dante) [by] Normand Lockwood... New York: Galaxy music corporation [c1938] Publ. pl. no. G. M. 889. 12 p. 27cm. (Galaxy choruses for mixed voices. no. 889.)

Score: S. A. T. B. and piano reduction. English words.
"English version by Charles Eliot Norton."

Henry Hadley Mem. Lib.

1. Choral music, Sacred—Mixed —4 pt.—Unacc. 2. Lord's prayer. I. Dante Alighieri.
N. Y. P. L. September 25, 1941

NL 0437655 NN OO

MUSIC M 1621 L64 O3 Lockwood, Normand, 1906-
[Oh, lady, let the sad tears fall]
Oh, lady, let the sad tears fall; for medium voice and piano. (g-d) New York, Music Press [c1947]
score (5p.) 31cm. (The Music Press cont contemporary song series)

1.Songs (Medium voice) with piano. I. Title.

NL 0437656 CLSU

Lockwood, Normand, 1906–
...Out of the cradle endlessly rocking...for four-part chorus of mixed voices a cappella, by Normand Lockwood. To words by Walt Whitman... New York: G. Schirmer, inc. [1939] Publ. pl. no. 38466. 23 p. 26cm. (G. Schirmer octavo. no. 8316.)

Score: S. A. T. B. and piano reduction. English words.

Henry Hadley Mem. Lib.

1. Choral music, Secular—Mixed —4 pt.—Unacc. I. Whitman, Walt, 1819–1892.
N. Y. P. L. June 10, 1940

NL 0437657 NN OO

qM784 L81p Lockwood, Normand, 1906-

Pacific lament. [Words by] Charles Olson. [Princeton, January 1,1949] [Urbana, Ill., 1949]
9p.(on double leaves) 35cm.

Black-line print from composer's(?) ms. copy. For chorus (SSAATTBaB)

1. Choruses, Secular (Mixed voices, 8 pts), Unaccompanied. I. Olson, Charles. II. Title.

NL 0437658 IU

Lockwood, Normand, 1906–

Prairie; for chorus and orchestra. Text by Carl Sandburg. A special festival ed. printed for the University Musical Society of the University of Michigan. [Ann Arbor, 1953]

score (68 p.) 31 cm.
"From the composer's original manuscript."
1. Choruses, Secular (Mixed voices, 8 pts.) with orchestra—Vocal scores with piano. 2. Lockwood, Normand—Manuscripts—Facsimiles. I. Sandburg, Carl, 1878– II. Title.
M1533.L808P7 1953 M 54–1687 rev

NL 0437659 DLC NN

Lockwood, Normand, 1906–

..."Psalm;" no. 2 from "Three choruses for peace." Anthem for mixed voices, a cappella... New York [etc.] C. Fischer, inc. [c1938] Publ. pl. no. 28341. 5 p. 26cm. (Carl Fischer's choir music edition. ser. 7. 524.)

Score: S. A. T. B. and piano reduction.
First line: We entreat thee, O Lord.
"Words and music by Normand Lockwood."

Henry Hadley Mem. Lib.

1. Choral music, Sacred—Mixed —4 pt.—Unacc. 2. Anthems.
N. Y. P. L. September 25, 1941

NL 0437660 NN

M783.4 L81ps Lockwood, Normand, 1906-

Psalm 114, an exhortation to fear God in His power; for full chorus of mixed voices with organ acc. [New York, G. Schirmer] c1940.
7p. 27cm. (G. Schirmer's choral church music, octavo no.8484)

Caption title.

1. Choruses, Sacred (Mixed voices, 4 pts.) with organ. 2. Psalms (Music)--114th Psalm. I. Title.

NL 0437661 IU OO

Lockwood, Normand, 1906–

...Psalm[s] 117 [63, 134]... Chicago, Ill.: N. A. Kjos music co. [c1938] Publ. pl. no. Ed. 18. 6 p. 26cm. (Oberlin choral series... Choruses for mixed voices... 18.)

Open score: S. A. T. B. English words.
Contents.—Psalm 117 "O praise the Lord, all ye nations."—Psalm 63 "O God, Thou art my God."—Psalm 134 "Behold, bless ye the Lord."

1. Choral music, Sacred—Mixed —4 pt.—Unacc. I. Bible. O. T. Psalms. Selections. English. 1938.
N. Y. P. L. September 25, 1941

NL 0437662 NN OO

Lockwood, Normand, 1906–

...Psalm 123; the godly profess their confidence in God. A song of degrees... New York: Arrow music press [c1939] 4 p. 26cm.

Score: S. A. T. B.
First line: Unto Thee lift I up mine eyes.

1. Choral music, Sacred—Mixed —4 pt.—Unacc. I. Bible. O. T. Psalms. CXXIII. English. 1939.
N. Y. P. L. February 9, 1943

NL 0437663 NN MB IU OO

MUSIC m780.3 L817r Lockwood, Normand, 1906-
[River magic]
River magic, for medium voice and piano (d-f) New York, Music Press [c1947]
score (7p.) 31cm. (The Music press contemporary song series)

Words by Eva Byron.

1.Songs (Medium voice) with piano. I.Title.

NL 0437664 CLSU NBC

M783.4 L817s Lockwood, Normand, 1906-
[Sing unto the Lord a new song]
Sing unto the Lord a new song. For mixed voices (S.A.T.B.) Delaware Water Gap, Pa., Shawnee Press [1952]
score (7p.) 27cm. (Waring choir series)

Cover title.

NL 0437665 IEN

Lockwood, Normand, 1906–
[Serenades, strings]

Six serenades for string quartet. New York, Music Press [1947]
score (8 p.) 31 cm.
Cover title.

1. String quartets—Scores.

M452.L778S4 48-14746*

NL 0437666 DLC LU NcU OrU NBC FMU

Lockwood, Normand, 1906–

...Sweet and low; lullaby... [By] Normand Lockwood. [New York] Galaxy music corp., c1937. Publ. pl. no. G. M. 747. 16 p. 26cm. (Galaxy octavo.)

Score: S. S. A. A. T. T. B. B. and piano reduction.
Words by Tennyson.
Caption-title.

1. Choral music, Secular—Mixed —8 pt.—Unacc. 2. Lullabies, U. S. I. Tennyson, Alfred Tennyson, 1st baron, 1809–1892.
N. Y. P. L. February 9, 1943

NL 0437667 NN OO

Lockwood, Normand, 1906–
[Quartet, strings, no. 3]

Third string quartet. New York, G. Schirmer [1948]
score (36 p.) and parts. 31 cm. (Society for the Publication of American Music. [Publication] 27th season, 1945/46, [no.] 55)
Cover title.

1. String quartets—Scores and parts. (Series)
M2.S69A5 1945/46 48-22090 rev*
——— Copy 2. M452.L778Q3

NL 0437668 DLC NcGU OkU MtU OCIW INS ICN MB LU OrU

Lockwood, Normand. 1906-
... Three choruses for peace... [by] Normand Lockwood. N.Y., Boston [etc.] Carl Fischer, inc. [c1938]
3 pts. in 1. 25.5 cm. (Carl Fischer's choir music edition. Series VII, 523-525)

NL 0437669 OO

Lockwood, Normand, 1906–
[Trio, flute, viola & harp]

Trio, for flute, viola & harp. [1939]
score (42 p.) and 2 parts. 35 cm. holograph.
In ink.
On p. 1: To Mrs. Elizabeth Sprague Coolidge. Normand Lockwood.
The composer acknowledges his indebtedness for the helpful suggestions of Miss Lucy Lewis and to "L'étude moderne de la harpe" by Carlos Salzedo.
Parts: Flute, viola.
Commissioned by Mrs. Coolidge.
Gift of Mrs. Coolidge, Dec. 29, 1941.

——— Photocopy (positive)
Score only. ML29e.L815
——— Photocopy (negative)
Score only. ML29e.L815

1. Trios (Harp, flute, viola) I. Lockwood, Normand, 1906– MSS.
ML29c.L815 M 55-1717

NL 0437671 DLC

VOLUME 337

Lockwood, Peter, 1798-1882.
Memoir of John D. Lockwood, being reminiscences of a son, by his father. N.Y., R. Carter, 1845.
252 p. port. 16cm.

1 Lockwood, John Davenport, 1825-1844

NL 0437672 NjPT OO CtY PPPrHi

Lockwood, Peter, 1798-1882.

CT275 L73L7 Memoir of John D. Lockwood. By Rev. Peter Lockwood, Binghamton, N. Y. Second edition revised by the author. New York, The American tract society [c1852]

231p. front.(port.) 16cm.

1. Lockwood, John Davenport, 1825-1844. I. Title.

NL 0437673 NBuG MiU PPPrHi NjNbS

Lockwood, Peter, 1798-1882.
Remarks of Rev. P. Lockwood at the fiftieth anniversary of the First Presbyterian Church in Binghamton (N.Y.) Nov. 26, 1867. Binghamton, N.Y., Mallette, 1870.
(pam.)

NL 0437674 CtY PPPrHi

Lockwood, Philip Case.
Philip Case Lockwood memorial collection of civil war portraits and autographs. Presented to Harvard University by Mary Jane Lockwood in the name of her nephew, Hamilton De Forest Lockwood, A.B., Harvard College, 1890.
4°. pp. xii, 637.

U. S.-Army-Portraits [Manuscripts (c)-English Lockwood, Philip Case]

NL 0437675 MH

Lockwood, Preston.
Graphic presentation of court system and appeal procedure in New York County. [By] Preston Lockwood and Kenneth B. Low. [New York] Columbia law review, 1922.
broadside. 28 x 43cm.

1. Courts—New York (County) 2. Appellate procedure—New York (County) I. Low, Kenneth Brooks, 1897- joint author.

Library of Congress 22-24054

NL 0437676 DLC

Lockwood, Preston.
The sun never sets on the British Empire. Some collected notes [by] Preston Lockwood and Allen McCarty... N[ew] Y[ork] c[ity] The Court press, 1941. 12 p. 23cm.

Cover-title.
Bibliographical footnotes.

1. Colonies and colonization, British—Govt. I. McCarty, Allen, jt. au.
N. Y. P. L. April 27, 1942

NL 0437677 NN

Lockwood, Preston.
Underwriting contracts, within purview of Securities act of 1933, with certain suggested provisions, by Preston Lockwood... and Sidney A. Anderson... Reprinted from the George Washington law review, November, 1939.
34 p. 25 cm.

NL 0437678 ViU-L

Lockwood, Preston, dramatist.
Sham; a playlet of two scenes... by Preston Lockwood and Lincoln Eyre. St. Louis, c1914.
12 p. 23 cm.

NL 0437679 RPB

Lockwood, R.L.
Moving gear for electric ore handling bridge. 1900.

NL 0437680 OCIW

Lockwood, R.M.
Characteristic curves of materials most used in engineering.

NL 0437681 OCIW

Lockwood, Ralph Ingersoll, 1798-1855.
Address, delivered before the American institute of the city of New-York, July 4, 1829. By Ralph Lockwood, esq. Published at the request of the Institute. New York, Printed by Elliott & Palmer, 1829.
24 p. 21cm.

1. Fourth of July orations. 2. Tariff—U. S. I. American institute of the city of New York.

37-9987
Library of Congress E286.N6 1829
[2] 337.30973

NL 0437682 DLC

Lockwood, Ralph Ingersoll, 1798-1855.
An analytical and practical synopsis of all the cases argued and reversed in law and equity, in the Court for the correction of errors of the state of New York, from 1799 to 1847: with the names of the cases and a table of the titles, &c.; by Ralph Lockwood ... New York, Banks, Gould & co.; Albany, Gould, Banks & Gould, 1848.
xlvii, 567, 567a-567j, 569-693 p. 24½cm.
Binder's title: Lockwood's reversed cases in law & equity.
1. Law reports, digests, etc.—New York (State) I. New York (State) Court for the trial of impeachments and correction of errors. II. Title: Reversed cases in law & equity.

34-10548

NL 0437683 DLC IU NcU NcD CtY NN ViU-L

Lockwood, Ralph Ingersoll, 1798-1855.
Essay on a national bankrupt law. By Ralph Lockwood ... New York, Printed and sold by G. F. Hopkins, 1825.
32 p. 23cm.
Appendix (p. [29]-32): Abstract of the bankrupt bill which was introduced into the Senate of the United States, January 2d, 1821, and into the House of representatives at the subsequent session, in December, 1822.

1. Bankruptcy—U. S.

20-16590
Library of Congress HG3766.L6

NL 0437684 DLC Nh

[Lockwood, Ralph Ingersoll] 1798-1855.
The insurgents: an historical novel ... Philadelphia, Carey, Lea & Blanchard, 1835.
2 v. 19cm.
Published anonymously.

1. Shay's rebellion, 1786-1787—Fiction.

Library of Congress PZ3.L814 I 7-15846†

NL 0437685 DLC CU ViU InU NN PU

[Lockwood, Ralph Ingersoll] 1798-1855.
Rosine Laval: a novel. By Mr. Smith [pseud.] ... Philadelphia, Carey, Lea & Blanchard, 1833.
v, 300 p. 19½cm.

I. Title. 7-15161

Library of Congress PZ3.L814R

NL 0437686 DLC NcA-S ViU N MdBP MH NjP PU OU ViW

FILM 4274 PR v.1 reel L8
[Lockwood, Ralph Ingersoll] 1798-1855.
Rosine Laval: a novel. By Mr. Smith [pseud.] Philadelphia, Lea & Blanchard, 1833.
300 p. (Wright American fiction, v.1, 1774-1850, no.1706, Research Publications Microfilm, Reel L-8)

NL 0437687 CU

Lockwood, Ralph Ingersoll, 1798-1855, ed.

Bright, John Edward, b. 1811.
A treatise on the law of husband and wife, as respects property. Partly founded upon Roper's treatise, and comprising Jacob's notes and additions thereto. By John Edward Bright ... with copious notes and references to the American decisions, by Ralph Lockwood ... New York, Banks, Gould & co.; Albany, Gould, Banks and Gould, 1850.

Lockwood, Richard Bigelow, 1882-
Industrial advertising copy, by R. Bigelow Lockwood ... 1st ed. New York [etc.] McGraw-Hill book company, inc., 1929.
xiii, 328 p. illus. (part col.) diagrs. 21cm. $3.00

1. Advertising. 2. Printing, Practical. I. Title.

Library of Congress HF5825.L6 29-6423

NL 0437689 DLC CU NN MB PPT PP OCU OU MiU OCl ICJ

Lockwood, Richard Bigelow, 1882-
Productive advertising copy; a series of articles on trade and technical advertising copy, reprinted from Class. Chic., G. D. Crain, ©1923.
95 p. illus.

NL 0437690 MiD

VOLUME 337

Lockwood, R[obert] M[inturn] 1857-
Frames and lenses, a practical treatise for optometrists ... by R. M. Lockwood ... New York, F. Boger pub. co. [1905]
87 p. illus. 17cm.

1. Spectacles.

Library of Congress RE951.L78 Copyright 5-14469

NL 0437691 DLC DSI ICRL ICJ

Lockwood, R[obert] M[inturn] 1857-
The human eye. With two dissected sectional models in colors, containing fifteen separate plates, with a clear and detailed explanation of the various parts of the eye and their functions. Translated and adapted from the German of Dr. Securio by R. M. Lockwood. New York, F. Boger publishing company [1905]
16 p. col. plates. 26cm.

1. Eye. I. Securio, Dr.

5-17948

Library of Congress QM511.L81 Copyright

NL 0437692 DLC CaBVaU CU

Lockwood, Robert Minturn, 1857-
The human eye... N.Y., Optical publishing co[c1910]
16 p.

"Second ed."

NL 0437693 OU

Lockwood, Robert Minturn, 1857-
The human eye, with two dissected sectional models in colors, containing fifteen separate plates, with a clear and detailed explanation of the various parts of the eye and their functions. Tr. and adapted from the German of Dr. Securio, by R. M. Lockwood. New York. Optical publishing company [c1914]
16 p. 2 mounted col. pl. 26cm. $1.00
Plates superimposed; 1 included in paging, the other mounted on inside of back cover.
1. Eye. I. Securio, Dr.

Library of Congress QM511.L81 1914 14-12824

NL 0437694 DLC DNLM

Lockwood, Robert Minturn, 1857-
The principles of optometry; an illustrated text book with questions, for use in optical schools and for private students ... By R. M. Lockwood ... New York, F. Boger pub. co. [1903]
144 p. diagrs. 17½ x 14cm.

1. Lenses. I. Title: Optometry.

Library of Congress RE961.L7 3-29600 Revised

NL 0437695 DLC OU ICJ

Lockwood, Robert Minturn, 1857-
The principles of optometry; an illustrated text book with questions, by R. M. Lockwood. 2d ed. New York, F. Boger pub. co. [c1906]
125 p. diagrs.

1. Lenses. 2. Optometry.

NL 0437696 NNC InU

RE 928 .L82 LOCKWOOD, ROBERT MINTERN, 1857-
Skiascopy without the use of drugs; a practical treatise for optometrists. New York, F. Boger [c1906]
112 p. illus.

1. Skiascopy.

NL 0437697 InU CU

Lockwood, R[obert] M[inturn] 1857-
Subjective tests for difficult cases, a practical treatise for optometrists ... by R. M. Lockwood ... New York, F. Boger pub. co. [1904]
84 p. illus. 17cm.

1. Eye—Examination.

Library of Congress RE91.L82 Copyright 4-27668

NL 0437698 DLC PPC

Lockwood, Robert Minturn, 1857-
Transpositions; a practical treatise for optometrists and opticians, by R. M. Lockwood ... New York, F. Boger pub. co. [c1907]
32 p. diagrs. 17½ x 13½ cm.

1. Spectacles. 2. Lenses.

7—29700

Library of Congress RE961.L73

NL 0437699 DLC ICJ

Lockwood, Robert Minturn, 1857-
Transpositions; a practical treatise for optometrists and opticians, by R. M. Lockwood. New York, The Optical publishing co., 1916.
32 p. diagrs. 16cm.

1. [Optometry] 2. Lenses. 3. [Spectacles] I. Title.

S G 17-60

Library, U. S. Surgeon-General's Office

NL 0437700 DNLM

Lockwood, R[obert] M[inturn] 1857-
The trial case and how to use it; a practical treatise for optometrists ... by R. M. Lockwood ... New York, F. Boger pub. co. [1904]
1 p. l., 69, [2] p. illus., diagrs. 17 x 13½cm. 4-9227

NL 0437701 DLC

Lockwood, R[obert] M[inturn] 1857-
The trial case and how to use it; a practical treatise for optometrists. Illustrated 2d ed. By R. M. Lockwood ... New York, F. Boger pub. co. [1904]
78, [2] p. illus., diagrs. 17 x 13½cm.

1. Spectacles.

Library of Congress RE961.L812 Copyright 5-611

NL 0437702 DLC DNLM CU

Lockwood, Robert Minturn, 1857-
The trial case and how to use it; a practical treatise for optometrists. 4th ed., enl. and rev. New York, Optical Pub. Co. [1906?]

NL 0437703 MH

RE 961 .L817 **LOCKWOOD, ROBERT MINTURN, 1857-**
The trial case and how to use it. A practical treatise for optometrists, by R.M. Lockwood. 4th ed., enl. and rev. New York, Optical Pub. Co. [1916?]
85 p. illus.

1. Eyeglasses. I. Title.

NL 0437704 InU

F869 S3 .76 L6 x Lockwood, Rufus A 1811-1857.
Argument of R. A. Lockwood, Esq., delivered in Supreme Court of the United States, in the case of Edward Field, plaintiff in error, vs. Pardon G. Seabury, et als., defendants in error. Appeal from the Circuit Court of U. S. for the Districts of California. San Francisco, O'Meara & Painter, Printers, 1857.
37 p. 24cm.

Cover title.

1. Land titles - San Francisco. 2. San Francisco Beach and Water Lots.

NL 0437705 CU-B MH

Lockwood, Rufus A 1811-1857.
Speech of R. A. Lockwood, esq., delivered in defence of J. H. W. Frank, at the October term of the Tippecanoe Circuit court, 1837. Indianapolis, Bolton and Livingston, 1837.
76 p. 22½cm.
Frank was tried for the murder of John Woods.

1. Woods, John, d. 1836 or 7. I. Frank, John H. W., defendant.

39-11337

NL 0437706 DLC MH CSmH In NN MH-L NBLiHi

[Lockwood, Rufus A] 1811-1857.
Supreme Court of the United States, December Term, 1855. Field v. Seabury et al, No. 113,... Argument [by R.A. Lockwood] for the plaintiff in Error. [caption-title] [Washington, D.C.? 1856?]
8vo.
At end of text on p. 37: Delivered in Supreme Court, Friday, May 9, 1856.
Bound (3) with: Lockwood, Rufus A (1811-1857) Speech of... Delivered in Defence of J. H. W. Frank, ... 1837. Indianapolis, 1837.

NL 0437707 CSmH

Lockwood, Rufus A 1811-1857.
The Vigilance committee of San Francisco. Metcalf *vs.* Argenti et al. Speeches of R. A. Lockwood, esq. San Francisco, Cal., 1852.
47, [1] p. 22cm.
Speeches before the Superior court of San Francisco and the District court of Santa Clara in a suit against members of the Vigilance committee.

1. San Francisco. Committee of vigilance.

14-19555

Library of Congress F865.L8

NL 0437708 DLC MdBP ICN MH NN

VOLUME 337

Lockwood, Rupert.
America invades Australia. [Sydney, Current Book Distributors, 1955?]
93 p. 22 cm.

1. Australia—Indus. 2. Investments, American—Australia. I. Title.
HC605.L6 57-21994 ‡

NL 0437709 DLC NN

LOCKWOOD, RUPERT.
Bankers backed Hitler. Sydney, Current book distributors, 1948. 16 p. illus. 21cm.

Film reproduction. Positive.

1. Banks and banking--Govt. ownership. 2. Finance--Germany, 1933-1945.

NL 0437710 NN CSt-H

Lockwood, Rupert.
Crisis in Egypt. Sydney, Current book distributors, 1952. 16 p. 18cm.

1. Egypt—Govt., 1922-

NL 0437711 NN

Lockwood, Rupert.
Guerrilla paths to freedom, by Rupert Lockwood. Sydney, London, Angus and Robertson ltd., 1942.
ix p., 1 l., 83, [1] p. 18½cm.

1. Guerrillas. I. Title.
42-17674
Library of Congress D431.L6
[3] 355.42

NL 0437712 DLC

Lockwood, Rupert.
Japan's heart of wood, by Rupert Lockwood ... Sydney, Current book distributors, 1943.
32 p. 21½cm.

1. Japan. 2. World war, 1939- —Japan. I. Title.
43-14982
Library of Congress DS889.L6
[3] 915.2

NL 0437713 DLC

DS596.5 L62
Lockwood, Rupert
Malaya must cost no more Australian blood. [Sydney, Printed by Newsletter Printery, 1951]
16 p. 20 cm. (Leave them alone, no. 2)
Cover title.
Photocopy. New Haven, Yale University. Library. 1972. 16 p. (on double leaves) 21 cm.
1. Malaya - Hist. 2. Malaya - Foreign population. 3. World War, 1939-1945 - Malaya. I. Title (1)

NL 0437714 CtY NIC

Lockwood, Rupert.
Persian oil... Sydney, Current book distributors, 1951. 16 p. 18cm.

1. Petroleum—Political and economic aspects—Persia.

NL 0437715 NN

Lockwood, Ryland Leonard, 1878-

U. S. *Office of federal coordinator of transportation. Section of property and equipment.*
Report on consolidation or joint use of railroad major repair shops and modernization of repair shop facilities. Federal coordinator of transportation, Section of property and equipment, June, 1936. [Washington, 1936]

Lockwood, Ryland Leonard, 1878-
U. S. *Office of federal coordinator of transportation. Section of purchases.*
Report on handling and disposition of scrap, based on returns to Scrap survey inquiry, S. P. 1. Prepared by Section of purchases, Federal coordinator of transportation. [Washington, 1935]

Lockwood, S Bruce, ed.
South Euclid becomes a city; official program of the South Euclid says "Howdy neighbor" celebration, June 7th to 11th. South Euclid, Ohio, 1941.
32 p.

NL 0437718 OClND

Lockwood, Samuel, 1721-1791.
Works by this author printed in America before 1801 are available in this library in the Readex Microprint edition of Early American Imprints published by the American Antiquarian Society.
This collection is arranged according to the numbers in Charles Evans' American Bibliography.

NL 0437719 DLC

Lockwood, Samuel, 1721-1791.
Civil rulers an ordinance of God, for good to mankind. A sermon, preached before the General assembly, of the colony of Connecticut, at Hartford; on the day of their anniversary election, May 12th, 1774. By Samuel Lockwood, A. M., pastor of the church in Andover ... New-London: Printed by Timothy Green, printer to the governor and company. M,DCC,LXXIV.
39 p. 21 x 16½cm.

1. Election sermons—Connecticut. I. Title.
40-17550
Library of Congress BV4260.C9 1774
[2] 252.6

NL 0437720 DLC CtHi CtY NN MHi MWA MiU-C MB RPJCB N MdBP InU M

Lockwood (Samuel), 1819-1894. Abnormal entozoa in man. 4 pp. 8°. [n. p., 1881.]
Repr. from: Am. J. Micr., N. Y., 1881, vi.

NL 0437721 DNLM

LOCKWOOD, Samuel, 1819-1894.
The American oyster; its natural history, and the oyster industry in New Jersey. n.p., 1883.

Plates.
"Being a part of the 5th annual report of the Bureau of Statistics of Labor and Industries of the State of New Jersey,1883".
pp.217-350.
With German translation.

NL 0437722 MH OO

---

920 Zs29l
Lockwood, Samuel, 1819-1894
Manly old age, An obituary sermon, in relation to the late De La Fayette Schanck, preached in the Reformed Dutch Church of Keyport, N.J., Sept. 21st, 1862. New York G.A. Whitehorne, steam printer, 1863.
24 p. coat of arms. 24 cm.

1. Schanck, De La Fayette, 1781-1862.
H 1. Geneal. Schenck family (Roelof Martense Schenck, 1619-1704) 2. Schenck family (Roelof Martense Schenck, 1619-1704)

NL 0437723 N NjP IU NjNbS

739.27 L817m Sutro
[Lockwood, Samuel] 1819-1894, supposed author
The most famous diamonds of the world. [N.Y.? 188-?]
6p. 25cm.

Caption title.

NL 0437724 C-S

LOCKWOOD, Samuel, 1819-1894.
The natural history of the oyster. n.p., 1874.

Illustr.
Cut from the Popular Science Monthly, Nov. Dec. 1874, pp.1-20, 157-173.

NL 0437725 MH

589.3 L817r Sutro
Lockwood, Samuel, 1819-1894.
Raising diatoms in the laboratory. N.Y., 1886.
11p. 2pl. 24cm.

"Reprinted from the Journal of the New York Microscopical Society."

NL 0437726 C-S CtY

Lockwood, Samuel, 1819-1894.
Readings in natural history. Animal memoirs. Pt. I-II ... By Samuel Lockwood, PH. D. New York and Chicago, Ivison, Blakeman, and company [1888]
2 v. fronts. 18cm.
CONTENTS.—pt. I. Mammals.—pt. II. Birds.

1. Zoology—Juvenile and popular literature.
Library of Congress QL50.L81 4-31502

NL 0437727 DLC MiU CU OClW

VOLUME 337

Lockwood, Samuel, 1819-1894.
Some phenomena in exuviation, by the reptiles. New York, Stettiner, Lambert & Co., 1893.
11 p. 8°.
Title from cover.
n.t.-p.
Repr.: N.Y. Microscop. Soc. v. 9, no. 3. 1015.

NL 0437728 NN PU-Z

Lockwood, Samuel Drake, 1789-1874.

Illinois. *Laws, statutes, etc.*
The revised code of laws, of Illinois, enacted by the Fifth General assembly, at their session held at Vandalia, commencing on the fourth day of December, 1826, and ending the nineteenth of February, 1827. Published in pursuance of law. Vandalia, Printed by R. Blackwell, printer to the state, 1827.

Lockwood, Samuel M.
Lockwood's greenback and specie payment commentary ... ⌜New York, cop. 1878.⌝ 16 p. 8°.
Cover-title.

1. Money (Paper), U. S., 1878. December 6, 1916.
N. Y. P. L.

NL 0437730 NN

Lockwood, Samuel M.
The white slaves. By Samuel M. Lockwood. ⌜New York⌝ 1884.
29 p. 15cm.

1. Currency question—U. S. I. Title.
CA 7—5659 Unrev'd
Library of Congress HG527.L81

NL 0437731 DLC

BP595 .S824 Lockwood, Samuel P., tr.

Steiner, Rudolf, 1861-1925.
... Anthroposophy and the human gemüt; reflections on the Michael thought in its true aspect ⌜and⌝ the regeneration of the Michael festival. Four lectures delivered in Vienna, September 27-October 1, 1923, published from a stenographic report not edited by the lecturer with permission of Marie Steiner. Translated from the original by Samuel and Loni Lockwood. New York, Anthroposophic press, inc., 1946.

BP595 .S86615 Lockwood, Samuel P., tr.

Steiner, Rudolf, 1861-1925.
... Easter as a chapter in the mystery wisdom of man; four lectures delivered at Dornach, April 19-22, 1924. Published from a stenographic report not edited by the lecturer with permission of Marie Steiner. Translated from the original by S. P. Lockwood. New York, Anthroposophic press, inc., 1947.

LB41 .S783 Lockwood, Samuel P., tr.

Steiner, Rudolf, 1861-1925.
The three fundamental forces in education ⌜by⌝ Rudolf Steiner. A lecture delivered in Stuttgart, September 16, 1920. Published from a stenographic report not edited by the lecturer with permission of Marie Steiner, translated from the original by S. P. Lockwood. New York, Anthroposophic press, inc.; London, Rudolf Steiner publishing co., 1944.

Lockwood, Samuel Pierson, 1879-
Elementary orchestration, by Samuel Pierson Lockwood ... Ann Arbor, Mich., G. Wahr ⌜c1926⌝
125 p. illus. (music) 23½cm.

1. Instrumentation and orchestration. I. Title.
Library of Congress MT70.L817E5 27-14230

NL 0437735 DLC OrSaW MtU Or FU CLSU MB OCl OClL

781.6 L817e.2 Lockwood, Samuel Pierson, 1879-
Elementary orchestration. 2d ed., rev. and enl. Ann Arbor, Mich., G. Wahr [1929]
123p. illus.(music) 24cm.

1. Instrumentation and orchestration. I. Title.

NL 0437736 IEN OU OCl TU CU MiU OrU TxU PPT

Lockwood, Samuel Pierson, 1879- ed.

Lockwood, Albert Lewis, 1871-1933.
Notes on the literature of the piano, by Albert Lockwood. Ann Arbor, University of Michigan press; London, H. Milford, Oxford university press, 1940.

PZ8 .L887 Ad Lockwood, Sara Elizabeth (Husted) 1854- ed.

⌜**Lorenzini, Carlo**⌝ 1826-1890.
The adventures of Pinocchio, by C. Collodi ⌜*pseud.*⌝ translated from the Italian by Walter S. Cramp, with editorial revision by Sara E. H. Lockwood, and many original drawings by Charles Copeland. Boston ⌜etc.⌝ Ginn and company ⌜1904⌝

PE1408 .L6 1901a Lockwood, Sara Elizabeth (Husted) 1854-
Composition and rhetoric, by J.W. Sewell. Abridged and revised for use in the schools of Tennessee, from "Composition and rhetoric for higher schools," by Sara E.H. Lockwood and Mary Alice Emerson. Boston, Ginn ⌜c1901⌝
354 p. 19 cm.

1. English language--Rhetoric. I. Emerson, Mary Alice, jt. author. II. Sewell, James Witt, ed.

NL 0437739 T

Lockwood, *Mrs.* **Sara Elizabeth (Husted)** 1854-
Composition and rhetoric, by Sara E. H. Lockwood ... and Mary Alice Emerson ... Rev. ed. Boston, New York ⌜etc.⌝ Ginn and company ⌜1912⌝
x, 390 p. front., 9 pl., 2 port. 19½cm.

1. English language—Rhetoric. I. Emerson, Mary Alice, joint author.
Library of Congress PE1408.L6 1912 12-18517

NL 0437740 DLC OCX

Lockwood, *Mrs.* **Sara Elizabeth (Husted)** 1854-
Composition and rhetoric for higher schools, by Sara E. H. Lockwood ... and Mary Alice Emerson ... Boston, Ginn & company, 1901.
ix, 470 p. illus. 19½cm.

1. English language—Rhetoric. I. Emerson, Mary Alice, joint author.
Library of Congress PE1408.L6 1—21932

OClJC Or OrCS PPT PV PBa PP PU NN
NL 0437741 DLC T MH NIC ViU MB OrP Wa ODW MiU OO

Lockwood, Sara Elizabeth (Husted) 1854-
Composition and rhetoric for higher schools. By Sara E. H. Lockwood and Mary Alice Emerson. Boston, Ginn & Co., 1902.
470p. illus.

NL 0437742 ICRL OU OCl MtU

Lockwood, Sara Elizabeth Husted, 1854-
Composition and rhetoric. For higher schools. By Sara E.H.Lockwood and Mary Alice Emerson. Boston, Ginn & co., 1903.

NL 0437743 MH

Lockwood, Sara Elizabeth Husted, 1854-
Composition and rhetoric for higher schools. By Sara E.H.Lockwood and Mary Alice Emerson. Boston, Ginn & co., 1904.

NL 0437744 MH

Lockwood, Mrs. Sara Elizabeth (Husted) 1854-

Whitney, William Dwight, 1827-1894.
An English grammar for higher grades in grammar schools. Adopted from "Essentials of English grammar", by Professor W. D. Whitney ... With new arrangement and additional exercises suitable for younger pupils. By Mrs. Sara E. H. Lockwood ... Boston, Ginn & company, 1892.

Lockwood, Sara Elizabeth Husted, 1854-
Lessons in English, adapted to the study of American classics; a text-book for high schools and academies. Boston, Ginn & co., 1888.

NL 0437746 MH OCU OO MiU OCl PPL

EDUC-T PE 1111 .L57 Lockwood, Sara Elizabeth (Husted) 1854-
Lessons in English, adapted to the study of American classics. A text-book for high schools and academies. By Sara E. Husted Lockwood ... Boston, Ginn & company, 1889.
403 p. illus.

#English language--Grammar--1870-

NL 0437747 MoU PP PPT OO ODW MH

VOLUME 337

Lockwood, *Mrs.* Sara Elizabeth (Husted) 1854–
Lessons in English, adapted to the study of American classics. A text-book for high schools and academies. By Sara E. Husted Lockwood ... Boston, Ginn & company, 1890.
xix, 403 p. 7 port. 19cm.

1. English language—Grammar—1870–

Library of Congress PE1111.L57 11—5839

NL 0437748 DLC MtU OCU

EDUC-T PE 1111 .L57 1891 Lockwood, Sara Elizabeth (Husted) 1854–
Lessons in English, adapted to the study of American classics. A text-book for high schools and academics. By Sara E. Husted Lockwood ... Boston, Ginn & company, 1891.
403 p. illus.

NL 0437749 MoU MH

Lockwood, *Mrs.* Sara Elizabeth (Husted) 1854–
Lessons in English, adapted to the study of American classics. A text-book for high schools and academies. By Sara E. Husted Lockwood ... Boston, Ginn & company, 1892.
xix, 403 p. ports. 19cm.
Contains numerous lists of references.

1. English language—Teaching.

E 11-136

Library, U. S. Bur. of Education

NL 0437750 DHEW NIC NN

Lockwood, Sara Elizabeth (Husted) 1854–
Lessons in English, adapted to the study of American classics. Boston. Ginn & Co. 1893. xix, 403 pp. Portraits. 12°.

NL 0437751 MB MH

EDUC-T PE 1111 .L57 1894 Lockwood, Mrs. Sara Elizabeth (Husted) 1854–
Lessons in English, adapted to the study of American classics. A text-book for high schools and academies. By Sara E. Husted Lockwood. Boston, Ginn & company, 1894.
xix, 403 p. 19 cm.
#English language--Grammar--1870–

NL 0437752 MoU OClW MH

Lockwood, Sara Elizabeth (Husted) 1854–
Lessons in English, adapted to the study of American classics. Boston, Ginn & Co., 1895.
403p.

NL 0437753 ICRL OCl NjP MH ViU PP

Lockwood, Sara Elizabeth (Husted) 1854–
Lessons in English, adapted to the study of American classics. A text-book for high schools and academies. Boston, Ginn & co., 1897.

NL 0437754 MH ViU

Lockwood, Sara Elizabeth Husted, 1854–
Lessons in English, adapted to the study of American classics; a text-book for high schools and academies. Boston, Ginn & co., 1899.

NL 0437755 MH

Lockwood, Sara Elizabeth Husted.
Lessons in English; adapted to the study of American classics; a text-book for high schools and academies. Boston: Ginn & Co., 1900. 403 p. 12°.

NL 0437756 NN OClW MH

Lockwood, Sara Elisabeth Husted.
Lessons in English; language, composition, rhetoric, literature. Boston: Ginn & Co. [pref. 1887.] (i)vi-xix, 403 p. 12°.
Title-page lacking. Title from cover.

1. Rhetoric (English). 2. Composition (Literary) English.
N. Y. P. L. January 8, 1913.

NL 0437757 NN

Lockwood, *Mrs.* Sara Elizabeth (Husted) 1854–
Teachers' manual to accompany Lockwood and Emerson's Composition and rhetoric. Boston, Ginn & company, 1902.
xv, 66 p. 19cm.

1. English language—Rhetoric. I. Emerson, Mary Alice, joint author.

Library of Congress PE1408.L61 2-15996

NL 0437758 DLC

Lockwood, Sara Lawrence
see
Williams, *Mrs.* Sara Lawrence (Lockwood)

Lockwood, Sarah (McNeil) 1882–
Antiques, by Sarah M. Lockwood; text illustrations by Ernest Stock; wrapper and lining drawings by Ilonka Karasz. Garden City, N. Y., Doubleday, Page & company, 1925.
3 p. l., 161 p. illus. 25½cm.
Bibliography: p. 152–[153]

1. Art industries and trade—U. S. 2. Furniture—U. S. 3. Art objects—U. S. I. Title.

Library of Congress NK806.L6 26—1146

NL 0437760 NN OCl OClh PPA PU DLC OrU NcD MoSW Wa CaBVa TU MdBWA MB

NK2406 .L81 Lockwood, Mrs. Sarah (McNeil) 1882–
Antiques. Text illustrations by Ernes Stock. Wrapper and lining drawings by Ilonka Karasz. Garden City, Doubleday, Page, 1926.
161 p. illus.

1. Furniture--U. S. 2. Art objects--U. S.

NL 0437761 ICU WaT NcRS OrP OOxM MB MiGr ViU

Lockwood, Sarah M.
Antiques; text illustrations by Ernst Stock; wrapper and lining drawings by Ilonka Karasz. Garden City, N. Y.: Doubleday, Doran & Co., Inc., 1928. 161 p. illus. sq. 4°.
Bibliography, p. 152-153.

1. Furniture.
N. Y. P. L. March 14, 1929

NL 0437762 NN WaS WU NcU OO

Lockwood, Mrs. Sarah (McNeil), 1882–
Antiques; text illustrations by Ernest Stock...
Garden City, N.Y., Doubleday, 1930.
161 p.

NL 0437763 PP OrPR

Lockwood, *Mrs.* Sarah McNeil, 1882–
Antiques, by Sarah M. Lockwood; text illustrations by Ernest Stock; wrapper and lining drawings by Ilonka Karasz. Garden City, N. Y., Doubleday, Doran & company, inc., 1936.
3 p. l., 161 p. incl. illus., plates. 25½ x 20cm.
Illustrated lining-papers.
Bibliography: p. 152–153.

1. Art industries and trade—U. S. 2. Furniture—U. S. 3. Art objects—U. S. I. Title.

36-33950

Library of Congress NK806.L6 1936
—— Copy 2. [5] 749

NL 0437764 DLC MB OU OClMA PPPL

Lockwood, Sarah (McNeil) 1882–
Decoration, past, present & future, by Sarah M. Lockwood. Garden City, N. Y., Doubleday, Doran & company, inc., 1934.
xi, 198 p. illus. 25½ cm.
"First edition."
Bibliography: p. 191.

1. Art, Decorative—Hist. 2. Decoration and ornament—Hist. 3. Interior decoration. 4. Furniture—Hist. 5. Architecture, Domestic—Hist. I. Title.

NK1175.L6 747 35—930

NL 0437765 PU-FA OEac OLak OClL PPD PP DLC NN WaSp MB CaBVa WaE Or OrSaW NcRS

Lockwood, Mrs. Sarah (McNeil) 1882–
Decoration, past, present & future, by Sarah M. Lockwood. New York, The Literary Guild [1934]
xi, 198 p. illus. 26 cm.
Bibliography: p. 191.

1. Art, Decorative--Hist. 2. Decoration and ornament--Hist. 3. House decoration. 4. Furniture--Hist. 5. Architecture, Domestic--Hist. I. Title.

NL 0437766 ViU WaTC OrCS NcU CaBVaU

Lockwood, Sarah (McNeil) 1882–
A fistful of stars. New York, D. Appleton-Century Co. [1947]
335 p. 21 cm.

I. Title.
PZ3.L8143Fi 47-31413*
Library of Congress

NL 0437767 DLC CaBVa OrP Or Wa WaE WaS WaT

VOLUME 337

Lockwood, Sarah (McNeil) 1882-
The man from Mesabi. [1st ed.] Garden City, N. Y., Doubleday, 1955.
287 p. 22 cm.

I. Title.

PZ3.L8143Man 55—6481 ‡

IdPT Or OrP WaE WaS WaT WaSp IdB AAP
NL 0437768 DLC CoU PP ViU OCl OOxM NN FMU CaBVa

Lockwood, Sarah (McNeil) 1882-
New York, not so little and not so old, by Sarah M. Lockwood; illustrations by Ilonka Karasz. Garden City, N. Y., Doubleday, Page & company, 1926.
viii p., 1 l., 197 p. incl. illus., maps. 25½cm.
"First edition after the printing of 200 de luxe copies."
Maps on lining-papers.
Bibliography: p. 189.

1. New York (City)—Hist. 2. New York (City)—Descr. I. Title.
27-1284 Revised
Library of Congress F128.3.L82
[r43d2]

OCl PHi MB OClJC PU
NL 0437769 DLC MB NIC WaS WaSp WaTC CaBVaU OEac NN

Lockwood, Theodore.
Mountaineers. [Denver, Artcraft Press, 1950?]
65 p. illus., port., maps. 23 cm.
Cover title.

1. U. S. Army. 10th Division. 2. World War, 1939-1945—Regimental histories—U. S.—10th Division. 3. World War, 1939-1945—Campaigns—Italy. I. Title.

D769.3 10th.L6 940.542 52-16388
[1]

NL 0437770 DLC WaS

Microfilm
HX 266 .L6
Lockwood, Theodore Davidge.
French socialists and political responsibilities, 1898-1905. [Princeton, N.J.] 1952.
333,86 l. illus.

Microfilm (positive)
Thesis- Princeton University.
Bibliography: l.52-74 at end.

1. Socialism in France. 2. France. Pol. & govt. 1870-1940. I. Title.

NL 0437771 OrU

Lockwood, Thomas Dixon, 1848-1927.
Electrical measurement and the galvanometer; its construction and uses. By T. D. Lockwood. New York, J. H. Bunnell & co., 1883.
1 p. l., iii, 137 p. incl. illus., tables, diagrs. 19cm.

1. Electric measurements. 2. Galvanometer.
Library of Congress QC535.L7 17—11049

NL 0437772 DLC PPFr CU OClJC

Lockwood, Thomas D
Electrical measurement and the galvanometer; its construction and uses. 2nd ed.
N.Y., Bunnell, 1887.
137 p.

NL 0437773 PPL DN

Lockwood, Thomas Dixon, 1848-
Electrical measurement and the galvanometer; its construction and uses. ...N.Y., J.H. Bunnell & co., 1890. Ed.2.
133 p.

NL 0437774 OCl CU

Lockwood, Thomas Dixon
Electrical measurement and the galvanometer; its construction and uses. By T. D. Lockwood. 3d ed. New York, J.H. Brunnell & co., 1898.
137p. incl. illus., tables, diagrs.

NL 0437775 MiEM

Lockwood, Thomas Dixon, 1848-1927.
Electricity, magnetism, and electric telegraphy; a practical guide and hand-book of general information for electrical students, operators, and inspectors. By Thomas D. Lockwood. New York, D. Van Nostrand, 1883.
317 p. incl. illus., tables. 23cm.

1. Electric engineering. 2. Telegraph.
8—1316
Library of Congress TK145.L8

NL 0437776 DLC CU NcRS ICJ MH MB OClJC

Lockwood, Thomas Dixon, 1848-1927.
Electricity, magnetism, and electric telegraphy, a practical guide and hand-book of general information for electrical students, operators, and inspectors. By Thomas D. Lockwood. 3d ed. New York, D. Van Nostrand company, 1890.
377 p. illus. 23cm.

1. Electric engineering. 2. Telegraph.
42-27932
Library of Congress TK145.L8 1890
[2]

NL 0437777 DLC CtY NN OCl

Lockwood, Thomas D.
Electricity, magnetism, and electric telegraphy. A practical guide and hand-book of general information for electrical students, operators, and inspectors. Fourth edition. 375 p. 152 il. O. New York: D. Van Nostrand Co., 1894. c. 1883.

NL 0437778 ICJ CSt PPHa NN

Lockwood, Thomas Dixon, 1848- ed.

Ohm, Georg Simon, 1787-1854.
The galvanic circuit investigated mathematically. By Dr. G. S. Ohm. Berlin, 1827. Tr. by William Francis ... with a preface by the editor Thomas D. Lockwood ... New York, D. Van Nostrand company, 1891.

Lockwood, Thomas Dixon, 1848-
Practical information for telephonists, by T. D. Lockwood ... New York, W. J. Johnston, 1882.
192 p. 18cm.

1. Telephone—Operators' manuals.
8-1059†
Library of Congress TK6163.L8

NL 0437780 DLC InU NjP OKentU

Lockwood, Thomas D
Practical information for telephonists
N.Y., Johnston, 1884.
192 p.

NL 0437781 PPF

Lockwood, Thomas Dixon
Practical information for telephonists
N.Y., Johnston, 1887.
192 p.

NL 0437782 PPF

Lockwood, Thomas Dixon, 1848-
Practical information for telephonists, by T. D. Lockwood ... New York, W. J. Johnston, 1888.
192 p. 18cm.

1. Telephone—Operators' manuals.
17-18391
Library of Congress TK6163.L8 1888

NL 0437783 DLC PU

LOCKWOOD, Thomas Dixon.
Practical information for telephonists.
New York, W.J.Johnson Co., 1891.

NL 0437784 MH CtY

Lockwood, Thomas Dixon, 1848-1927.
Practical information for telephonists, by T. D. Lockwood ... New York, The W. J. Johnston co., ltd 1893.
192 p. 18cm.

1. Telephone—Operators' manuals.

NL 0437785 ViU PP

Lockwood, Thomas Meakin.
The book of the house of Coleport, which lieth by the sea: the burden of the architects, and the troubles of them who were minded to build. Chester [Eng.] Imprinted by E. Thomas [1883]
lviii p., 1 l. 22 x 17½cm.
Preface signed: T. M. L.; in ms. on cover: Thos. M. Lockwood, architect, Chester.
"For private circulation only."
Half-title: The house of Coleport.
"The following pages were written ... as a relaxation during a troublesome and harassing period of professional business (of which it is a record) ... This has been printed ... as a harmless joke."—Pref.
1. Architecture—Anecdotes, facetiae, satire, etc. I. Title. II. Title: The house of Coleport.
Library of Congress NA2599.L6 15-14351

NL 0437786 DLC

[Lockwood, Thomas Meakin]
A tale of seven widowers, told by another [Thomas Meakin Lockwood] [Chester, Eng., Printed by Edward Thomas, 1885?]

7, [1] p. 21cm.
Half-title.
Signed & dated at end: "T. M. L., Chester, March, 1885."
Last line of p. [2] crossed out in ms., & printed slip with this line mounted at foot of p. 3.
Apparently by the author of "The book of the House of Coleport ...": Thomas M. Lockwood.

NL 0437787 CSmH

VOLUME 337

Lockwood, Thomas P.
A geography of South-Carolina, adapted to the use of schools and families. Comprising a distinct chorographical account of each district, interspersed with historical anecdotes. A general view of the state; embracing its natural features, government, inhabitants, towns and villages, spas, minerals, the state of education and religion; with a sketch of its agricultural, commercial and natural history. By Thomas P. Lockwood. With a new map of the state ... Charleston, J. S. Burges, 1832.
viii, 135, [1] p. front. (fold. map) 15cm.
1. South Carolina—Descr. & trav.
11-6079
Library of Congress F273.L81

NL 0437788 DLC

Lockwood, V
Synopsis of patent and trademark law. Law school lectures, by V.H. Lockwood. Indianapolis, Indiana, 1902.
41p.
Cover title.

NL 0437789 NcD-L

Lockwood, Van Buren, 1829-1905.
Sweet-briar petals; poems by Van Buren Lockwood, with a brief memoir by C. R. Hathaway [Stamford, Conn., Press of the Gillespie bros., inc., 1907?]
102 p. front. (port.), plate. 14½ x 12cm.
I. Hathaway, C R II. Title.

NL 0437790 ViU RPB

Wason PR6023 O16R8
Lockwood, Vere, 1906-
Ruby fire. London, H. Jenkins [1931]
311 p. 18cm. (A Herbert Jenkins' book)

NL 0437791 NIC

WO 240 L817 1905
Lockwood (W. A.) Dental supplier
Illustrated catalogue ... , Washington, D. C., [1905].
808 p., illus., 23 cm.
Cover title: Dental furniture, instruments and materials.
Xerox copy of anesthesiological items (p. 503-527) from original catalog in Chicago Historical Society.
1. Apparatus and supplies.

NL 0437792 IParkA

RC359 .S75
Lockwood, Wallace Victor, 1915-
Studies in electroconvulsive shock: Electroconvulsive shock and memory; the effect of shocks administered in rapid succession [by] Philip Worchel and George Gentry. Some relations between response to frustration (punishment) and outcome of electric convulsive therapy; an experimental study in psychiatric theory [by] Wallace Lockwood. Berkeley, University of California Press, 1950.

Lockwood, Walter Thomas
Religious renaissance; a series of sermons. Strawn. 1925.

NL 0437794 IdB

Lockwood, Ward.
A more or less inaccurate map of Taos, New Mexico, and a guide to the land of mañana in a state of peace. [Santa Fé, Chamber of Commerce, 1949]
map 29 x 22 cm.
Not drawn to scale.
1. Taos, N. M.—Maps, Pictorial.
G4324.T171 1949.L6 Map 50-181

NL 0437795 DLC

HD9161 .A1L6
Lockwood, Warren S.
Lockwood's monthly rubber report.
-Dec. 15, 1949. Washington, W. S. Lockwood.

Lockwood, William, 1753-1828.
Works by this author printed in America before 1801 are available in this library in the Readex Microprint edition of Early American Imprints published by the American Antiquarian Society.
This collection is arranged according to the numbers in Charles Evans' American Bibliography.

NL 0437797 DLC

Lockwood, William, 1753-1828.
A sermon, delivered at the funeral of Mrs. Jerusha Woodbridge, relict of the late Rev. Ashbel Woodbridge, of Glastenbury, August 1st, 1799. By William Lockwood, A. M. pastor of the First church in Glastenbury. Middletown:—Printed by Tertius Dunning. 1799.
23, [1] p. 20cm.
Half-title: Mr. Lockwood's sermon, at the funeral of Madam Woodbridge.
1. Woodbridge, Mrs. Jerusha (Pitkin) 1710-1799. 2. Funeral sermons.
A 33-3427
Title from H. E. Huntington Libr. Printed by L. C.

NL 0437798 CSmH NIC ICMcC OClWHi MHi MBAt MWA CtY MH NN RPJCB

Lockwood, William Burley.
An introduction to modern Faroese. København, E. Munksgaard, 1955.
xii, 244 p. 25 cm. (Færoensia; textus & investigationes, v. 4)
1. Faroese dialect—Grammar. (Series: Færoensia, v. 4)
A 55-4357
Harvard Univ. Library for Library of Congress [1]

NL 0437799 MH IEN CSt OU LU ICU ICN PU NN ViU MiU TxU NcU GU

Lockwood, William Burley.
A manuscript in the Rylands Library, and Flemish-Dutch and Low German accounts of the life and miracles of Saint Barbara.
(In John Rylands Library, Manchester. Bulletin. Manchester. 27 cm. v. 36 (1953/54) p. 23-37)
Bibliographical footnotes.
1. Barbara, Saint. I. John Rylands Library, Manchester. Mss. (Dutch 9)
Z921.M18B vol. 36 A 55-10746
New York Univ. Wash. Sq. Library for Library of Congress [2]†

NL 0437800 NNU-W DLC

Lockwood, William E
Address on Shaw Locomotive. Franklin Institute, Sept. 20, 1882.
Phila., Shaw Locomotive co., 1882.
29 p.

NL 0437801 PPF PPL

Lockwood, William E.
Circular Letter of William E. Lockwood to the shareholders of the Pennsylvania Railroad Company February 8th, 1886. ... [Philadelphia, 1886]
12 p. sm. 12mo. Stitched.

NL 0437802 CSmH

Lockwood, William E
Discussions on hammer-blow of a locomotive's driving wheel. (Repr. Locomotive Engineer's Monthly Journal. Oct. 1889)
n.p., n.d.
812-817 p.

NL 0437803 PPF

Lockwood, William E
Pioneer locomotives
Terra Haute, Indiana, 1890.
3 p.

NL 0437804 PPF

Lockwood, William E
Pioneer Locomotives
Terra Haute, 1891.
3 p.

NL 0437805 PPF

---

707 L81i
Lockwood, William F
Improvement of instruction in art education in Louisiana, by William F. Lockwood... Louisiana state university, Baton Rouge, La. [1941]
90p. 29cm.
Reproduced from typewritten copy.
"A selected bibliography: p.82-84."
1. Art--Study and teaching--Louisiana. I. Title.

NL 0437806 LU

Lockwood, William H., comp.
The American standard of excellence, as revised by the poultry fanciers of America, at their convention held in New York, Feb., 1871, giving a complete description of all the known varieties of fowls. Also containing an essay on breeding prize birds for exhibition. Comp. by Wm. H. Lockwood ... Hartford, Conn., W. H. Lockwood, 1871.

VOLUME 337

Lockwood, William Howard, 1905–
Catalytic oxidation ... by William H. Lockwood. Baltimore, 1933.
15 p., 1 l. diagrs. 25½cm.
Imprint date changed in manuscript to 1934.
Thesis (PH. D.)—Johns Hopkins university, 1933.
Biography.
Caption title: High temperature catalysts for carbon monoxide oxidation.
"Reprinted from the Journal of physical chemistry, vol. XXXVIII, no. 6, June, 1934."
"References": p. 15.
1. Catalysis. 2. Oxidation. 3. Carbon monoxide.
Library of Congress QD501.L8135 1933 35-1966
Johns Hopkins Univ. Libr.
[2] 541.39

NL 0437808 MdBJ OU DLC

Lockwood, W[illiam] L.
In memory of Emma Gertrude Bailey.
Boston, 1875.
11 p. 8°

NL 0437809 MWA

25013
PZ
[Lockwood, William L]
The lord or the doctor? A story. By Lock Wood [pseud.] ... [Brooklyn, N. Y., 1892]
200 p. 19½cm.
LC copy replaced by microfilm
Library of Congress [PZ3.L8126L] 7-22740†

NL 0437810 DLC

FILM 4274 PR v.3 reel L24
[Lockwood, William L]
The lord or the doctor? A story. By Lock Wood [pseud.] ... [Brooklyn, N. Y., 1892]
200 p. 19½cm.
(Wright American fiction, v. III, 1876-1900, no. 3380, Research Publications, Inc. Microfilm, Reel L-24)

NL 0437811 CU

Lockwood, William Lewis.
In love and war. By W. L. Lockwood ... [Saratoga, N. Y., 190–] 21 f. 29cm.
Caption-title.
Typewritten; cover-title in ms.
In one act.
——— 19 f.
Typewritten.
Bound with the above.
I. Drama, American. I. Title.
N. Y. P. L. September 16, 1940

NL 0437812 NN

LOCKWOOD, WILLIAM LEWIS.
In the captain's room. Saratoga, N.Y. [c1913] 19 l. 30cm.
Typescript.
1. Drama, American. I. Title.

NL 0437813 NN

Lockwood, William Lewis.
Trailers of the North ... by William Lewis Lockwood. New York, Broadway publishing company [1905]
3 p. l., 197 p. front., 5 pl. 20cm.
CONTENTS.—In the great silence.—Fanshaw of the Northwest mounted.—A kronikle of the trale.—The golden cache.—Fool gold.—Skookum Jim.—Shipmates of the trail.
6-1905
Library of Congress PZ3.L8148T (Copyright A 123590)

NL 0437814 DLC

Lockwood, W[illiam] M[aynard] 1835–
Continuity of life a cosmic truth. Based upon the principles of natural philosophy and the co-relations of nature's elements, energies and forces. By Prof. W. M. Lockwood ... Chicago? 1902.
210 p. pl. 20cm.
3-714

NL 0437815 DLC ICJ PP CtY-M

Lockwood, William Maynard, 1835–
The disputed parables of Jesus Christ [by] Lockwood. [Buffalo, Queen City printing co., °1913]
27 p. 19½cm. $0.25
I. Title.
13-17006
Library of Congress

NL 0437816 DLC NBuG

BF1272 L8
Lockwood, William Maynard, 1835-
Fundamental principles of psychological phenomena [by] Lockwood. [No imprint, c1910]
44p. 19½cm. (Bound with: Lockwood, William Maynard. The molecular hypothesis of nature. [c1895])
1. Metaphysics. 2. Science.-Philosophy.

NL 0437817 NBuG

Lockwood, William Maynard, 1835–
Historical, logical, and philosophical objections to the dogmas of reincarnation and re-embodiment; an address before the Philadelphia spiritualists' society ... Feb. 20, 1898. By Prof. W. M. Lockwood ... [n. p., 1898]
47 p. 19½cm.
Portrait on cover.
1. Reincarnation.
Library of Congress BP573.R5L6 99-64 Revised
[r41b2]

NL 0437818 DLC NBuG

BF1272 L8
Lockwood, William Maynard, 1835-
The infidelity of ecclesiasticism; a menace to American civilization. By Prof. W. M. Lockwood ... Chicago, Ill. [n.p.] 1897c.
1p.l.,53p. 19½cm. (Bound with: Lockwood, William Maynard. The molecular hypothesis of nature. [c1895])
1. Religion and science. I. Title.

NL 0437819 NBuG IEN

BF1272 L8
Lockwood, William Maynard, 1835-
An inquiry into the reality, amplitude & dynamics of the fourth dimension of space by Prof, W. M. Lockwood. Buffalo, N. Y. [n.p.] 1909.
13p. illus. 19½cm. (Bound with: Lockwood, William Maynard. The molecular hypothesis of nature. [c1895])
1. Spiritualism. 2. Fourth dimension. I. Title.

NL 0437820 NBuG

Lockwood, William Maynard, 1835–
The molecular hypothesis of nature; the relation of its principles to continued existence and to the philosophy of spiritualism. By Prof. W. M. Lockwood ... [Chicago? °1895]
57 p. 19½cm.
1. Spiritualism. CA 11-1766 Unrev'd
Library of Congress BF1272.L8

NL 0437821 DLC CLSU

BF1272 L8
Lockwood, William Maynard, 1835-
Scientific analysis of spirit photography and spirit materialization [by] Lockwood. [Buffalo? n. p., 1895?]
1p.l.[5]-35p. 19½cm. (Bound with: Lockwood, William Maynard. The molecular hypothesis of nature. [c1895])
1. Spiritualism. 2. Psychical research. I. Title.

NL 0437822 NBuG

Lockwood, William Maynard, 1835-
Scientific analysis of spirit photography and spirit materialization... [Buffalo, c1912] 35 p. 20cm.
1. Spirit photography.

NL 0437823 NN

SPECIAL COLL. G 1922 L814
Lockwood, William Maynard, 1835-
Scientific lecture. Thought transference and psychic projection explained by an analysis of the principles of the telegraph, telephone, phonograph, and photographic action ... Portland, Ore., W.E. Spurrier [1922] broadside. 17½x13cm.
1. Spiritualism.

NL 0437824 OrU

Lockwood, William Maynard, 1835–
The spiritualism of nature; the formula and fact of the invisible co-relations of nature's elements, energies, and forces, discover and demonstrate life and intelligence beyond the grave. By Prof. W. M. Lockwood ... [Chicago? °1899]
43 p. 19cm.
1. Title.
Library of Congress BF1272.L83 0-1034 Revised

NL 0437825 DLC

VOLUME 337

Lockwood, William V
The handling of desegregation in the Baltimore public schools. The school administrator and public policy. Baltimore, 1955.
69 p. 28cm.
1. Negroes - Segregation. 2. Segregation in education. 3. Baltimore, Md. - Public schools. I. Title.

NL 0437826 FU

Lockwood, William Wirt, 1906–
America and the Far Eastern war [by] Wm. W. Lockwood, jr. San Francisco, New York [etc.] American council, Institute of Pacific relations [c1937]
20 p. 23cm.
1. U. S.—For. rel.—1933– 2. U. S.—Neutrality. 3. Eastern question (Far East) I. Institute of Pacific relations. American council. II. Title.
38-1561
Library of Congress E806.L635
——— Copy 2.
Copyright A 112628 [5] 327.73095

NL 0437827 DLC PPT Or CaBVaU NcD OC1W

Lockwood, William Wirt, 1906–
British and American relations in the Far East, by William W. Lockwood, jr. ... New York, N. Y., American council, Institute of Pacific relations [c1938]
15 p. 22cm.
"From American foreign policy: The twelfth annual Debate handbook."
1. East (Far East) 2. Eastern question (Far East) 3. U. S.—Foreign relations. 4. Gt. Brit.—Foreign relations. I. Institute of Pacific relations. American council. II. Title.
A 41-793
Northwestern univ. Libr. for Library of Congress [2]

NL 0437828 IEN CaBVaU OrU NN CtY OC1CC

Lockwood, William Wirt, 1906–
The economic development of Japan: growth and structural change, 1868–1938. Princeton, N. J., Princeton University Press, 1954.
xv, 603 p. illus., map, tables. 25 cm.
Bibliographical footnotes.
1. Japan—Econ. condit. 2. Japan—Indus. I. Title.
HC462.L77 330.952 54—6077

OCU PU OU WaS OrP
PU-W PPD PP PBm MtU WaT PSC OrCS IdPI WaSpG IdU MiU
TU MB AAP TxU CaBVa OrPR OrU OO CaBVaU OrLgE WaWW
NL 0437829 DLC CoU MH GU ViU NN OC1W NcGU PBL NcD

Lockwood, William Wirt, 1906–
The foreign trade policy of the United States [by] William W. Lockwood, jr. ... Prepared for the sixth international conference of the Institute of Pacific relations, to be held at Yosemite, California, August 15 to 29, 1936 ... New York, American council, Institute of Pacific relations, 1936.
58 p. 23 cm. ([Institute of Pacific relations] American council data papers, no. 5)
1. U. S.—Commercial policy. 2. Tariff—U. S. 3. U. S.—Economic policy. I. Institute of Pacific relations. 6th conference, Yosemite, Calif., 1936. II. Title.
HF1456 1936.L6 382.0973 36—23847

NL 0437830 DLC CU OU OCU OrP CaBVaU OrPR WaS

LOCKWOOD, William Wirt, 1906-
The International Settlement at Shanghai. [Baltimore, 1934].
25 cm. pp.(18).
"Reprinted from The American Political Science Review, vol.28, no.6, December, 1934," pp.1030-1046.

NL 0437831 MH

Lockwood, William W[irt] 1906-
Japanese cotton goods in the American market. N.Y., Institute of Pacific relations, 1935.
p.57-64. 31cm. (Far Eastern survey, v.4, no.8)

NL 0437832 OrU

Lockwood, William Wirt, 1906-
Japan's response to the West. A paper prepared for a program of the American Historical Association, December 30, 1955, on "Sino-Japanese Response to the West: the Nineteenth Century." [c1955]
17 l.
1. Japan - Relations (general) with Europe. 2. Japan - Civilization - Occidental influences

NL 0437833 NNC-EA

DS518 .8 .A86

Lockwood, William Wirt, 1906– ed.
FOR OTHER EDITIONS SEE MAIN ENTRY
American Institute of Pacific relations.
Our Far Eastern record, a reference digest on American policy ... [New York, San Francisco, etc.] American council, Institute of Pacific relations [1945]

Lockwood, William Wirt, 1906–
Showdown at Singapore? An analysis based on a group discussion of the possibilities of international coöperation in the Pacific, edited by W. W. Lockwood and Michael Greenberg. New York, San Francisco [etc.] American council, Institute of Pacific relations, 1941.
31 p. illus. (map) 19½cm.
1. Pan-Pacific relations. 2. Singapore. 3. Japan—For. rel. 4. International cooperation. I. Greenberg, Michael, joint ed. II. Institute of Pacific relations. American council. III. Title.
41-19215
Library of Congress DU29.L57
[10] 950

TxU PSt
NL 0437835 DLC CaBVaU IU CtY Or NcD OU OC1 OC1h

Lockwood, William Wirt, 1906–
Trade and trade rivalry between the United States and Japan [by] William Lockwood, jr. ... Prepared for the sixth international conference of the Institute of Pacific relations, to be held at Yosemite, California, August 15 to 29, 1936 ... New York, American council, Institute of Pacific relations, 1936.
66 p. incl. map, tables, diagrs. 23 cm. (American council papers, no. 6)
1. U. S.—Comm.—Japan. 2. Japan—Comm.—U. S. 3. U. S.—Commercial policy. 4. Japan—Commercial policy. 5. Competition, International. I. Institute of Pacific relations. 6th conference, Yosemite national park, Calif., 1936. II. Title.
HF3127.L6 382.0973 36—17677

NL 0437836 DLC CU WaS OrPR CaBVaU

Lockwood, William Wirt, 1906-
War and economic welfare in Japan [by] William W. Lockwood ... (In American historical association. War as a social institution; the historian's perspective. 1941. p. 212-223)
1. Japan - Economic conditions. I. Title.

NL 0437837 NNC

Lockwood academy, Brooklyn, N.Y.
Annuals. np., n.d.

NL 0437838 NjP

Lockwood & Everett, *New York.*
Description of the recent improvements of Lockwood & Everett in steam rendering apparatus; a discussion of the sanitary questions involved in rendering animal matter; reports of Metropolitan board of health upon the New York rendering co.; table of relative pressure and temperature of steam, &c., &c. New York, Lockwood & Everett [1871]
cover-title, 28 p. 2 fold. pl. 22½cm.
1. Rendering apparatus. 2. Refuse and refuse disposal. 3. New York rendering company.
8-21198†
Library of Congress TP438.L8

NL 0437839 DLC

Lockwood & Hendrie's. California pictorial for 1860. San Francisco, Lockwood & Hendrie, [1860]
2 leaves (21 x 27.5 inches) Lg. fol.
Illustrated.

NL 0437840 CSmH

Lockwood, Brooks, and company, *Boston.*
List of books published by Lockwood, Brooks, and company. Trade list of inks, mucilage, and other articles manufactured by Lockwood, Brooks, and company ... Boston. [Boston, 1881]
8 p. 25cm.
1. Catalogs, Publishers'—U. S.
CA 17-2307 Unrev'd
Library of Congress Z1217.L82

NL 0437841 DLC

Lockwood Clinic, Toronto.
Collected papers of the Lockwood clinic.
v. 1- n.p., 1929- Toronto, 1929-

NL 0437842 PPC CaBVaU

Lockwood, Crosby & Son
SEE
Lockwood (Crosby) & Son.

Lockwood, Goldsmith and Galt.
Hand book on patent and trade-mark law, unfair competition, copyrights ... Indianapolis, Washington, D. C., Lockwood, Goldsmith and Galt, c1933.
2 p. l., 59 p. 25½cm.
1. Patent laws and legislation—U. S. 2. Patent laws and legislation. 3. Trade-marks—U. S. 4. Trade-marks. 5. Copyright—U. S. 6. Competition, Unfair—U. S. I. Title.
33-35694
Library of Congress

NL 0437844 DLC

VOLUME 337

Lockwood, Greene & company, inc.
Annual conference Lockwood, Greene & company. 1st- 1912-
[Boston, C. A. Pinkham, Pinkham press, °1912-
v. plates, ports. 22½cm.

Library of Congress TA217.L7 13-839

NL 0437845 DLC

Lockwood, Greene & Company, inc.
Builders. "Building with foresight."
v. 1, no. 1-
Boston, v. illus. (incl. map, plans, ports.), tables. 4°.

1. House organs. 2. Title.
N. Y. P. L.

NL 0437846 NN

GT :708 L81
Lockwood, Greene & Co., Inc.
Directory of work. 8th ed. Boston [1928]
176 p.

---- Supplement. 9th ed. Boston, 1928.
11 p. [Bounc in]

NL 0437847 MH-BA

GT :867 L81a
Lockwood, Greene & Co., Inc.
Fourscore years; a record of Lockwood, Greene & Co.'s contribution to industrial engineering. Boston [1912]
36 p. illus.

NL 0437848 MH-BA MH

Lockwood, Greene & Co., Inc.
How many values has your property? ... Boston, Lockwood, Greene & Co. [°1924]
12 p. 25cm.

NL 0437849 ICJ

Lockwood, Greene & Co., inc.
Industrial plants illustrating building with foresight; Lockwood Greene, founded 1832. Boston, Lockwood Greene & Co. [1921]
42 p. illus.

NL 0437850 MH-BA

Lockwood, Greene & Co., Inc.
Industrial power plants. Boston, Lockwood, Greene & Co. [°1924]
40 p. illus., diagrs. (1 fold.) 29cm.
Slip pasted over imprint reads: Lockwood, Greene Engineers, Inc.
"This booklet has been written for the men in charge of industrial plants ... its purpose is to sell the services of Lockwood, Greene & Co."

NL 0437851 ICJ

Lockwood, Greene & Co., inc.
Industrial survey of Bloomington and Normal, Illinois. [Chicago],
157918 Lockwood, Greene & Co., [1926].
cover-title, [1], A-C, 1-8, [1], 9-22, [1], 23-69 leaves. incl. maps (1 fold.), tables, diagrs. 1 fold. plan. 30½ x 23cm.
Multigraphed.

NL 0437852 ICJ

Lockwood, Greene & Co., inc.
Industrial survey of Centralia, Illinois. [Chicago], Lockwood,
156726 Greene & Co., engineers, [1926].
cover-title, [4], 55 leaves incl. fold. maps, tables, diagrs. 29cm.
Mimeographed.

NL 0437853 ICJ

Lockwood, Greene & co., inc.
Industrial survey of Decatur, Illinois. [By] Lockwood, Greene
157250 & Co., engineers. [New York, 1926.]
cover-title, [4], 65 leaves incl. tables, diagrs. 28½cm.
Submitted to the Illinois Power and Light Corporation, Decatur, Illinois.
Mimeographed.

NL 0437854 ICJ

Lockwood, Greene & Co., Inc.
Industrial survey of Okmulgee, Oklahoma. (2d ed. - August 15, 1929) [Boston] Lockwood, Greene & Co., Inc. [1929]
58 l. illus.

Mimeographed.

NL 0437855 ICRL

Lockwood, Greene & Co. Inc.
Industrial survey of territory served by the Tennessee Electric Power Company, Chattanooga, Tenn., Sept. 15, 1927. Atlanta, Ga., Lockwood, Greene & Co. Inc. [1927]
109 (*i.e.* 108) numb. leaves, 16 leaves incl. 1 illus., tables, diagrs. maps (part fold.) 28cm. (Commission no. 1712)

Mimeographed.
Error in paging: p. 67 omitted in numbering.
"A brief industrial survey of Chattanooga": 16 leaves at end.

NL 0437856 ICJ CU ICRL

Lockwood, Greene & Co., Inc.
Industrial survey of Troy, New York [by] Lockwood, Greene & Co., Inc. Troy, N. Y. [1926]
3 leaves, 94 numb. leaves. 28½cm.

Mimeographed.

NL 0437857 ICJ ICRL

Lockwood, Greene & Co., inc.
Industrial survey of Weldon, North Carolina. Atlanta, 1924.
[14], xxxi p. maps, tables. 28cm.

1. Weldon, N.C.

NL 0437858 NcU

Lockwood, Greene & co., inc.
Industrial survey of Wichita, Kansas. No pub. [1927].
161 l. maps.

Typewritten copy, duplicated.

NL 0437859 MiD

Lockwood, Greene & Co., Inc.
Knitting mills and some problems that are presented in knitting mill design ... Boston, New York [etc.] Lockwood, Greene & Co., Inc. [°1926]
27, [1] p. incl. illus., plans. 27cm. *bound* 29½cm.

Slip pasted over imprint reads: Atlanta, Boston [etc.] Lockwood Greene Engineers, Inc.

NL 0437860 ICJ

Lockwood, Greene & co. inc.
Report on the industrial resources of the state of Oklahoma, for Hon. W. B. Pine, February 1, 1928. [New York] Lockwood, Greene & co. inc. [1928]
120 p. 2 maps (incl. double front.) 23cm.
Bibliography: p. 120.

1. Oklahoma—Econ. condit. 2. Natural resources. I. Title: Industrial resources of the state of Oklahoma.

Library of Congress HC107.O5L6 33-15726
330.9766

NL 0437861 DLC WaS CU OU OC1 PBL NN ICJ

LOCKWOOD, GREENE & COMPANY, INC.
Report on the industrial resources of the state of Oklahoma for W. B. Pine, February 1, 1928. [New York, 1928] 120 p. illus., map. 24cm.

Microfiche (neg.) 3 sheets. 11 x 15cm. (NYPL FSN 11,103)
Bibliography, p. 120.

1. Economic history--U. S.--Oklahoma. 2. Natural resources--U. S.--Oklahoma. I. Pine, William Bliss, 1877- . t. 1928.

NL 0437862 NN

Lockwood, Greene & Co., inc.
Retrospective appraisals. Boston, Lockwood, Greene & Co. [1931?]
14 p. 24cm.

Includes Income tax mimeograph, Collectors no. 3209, Treasury Department, Washington, D. C.

NL 0437863 ICJ

Lockwood, Greene & Co., inc.
Sanford, North Carolina industrial facts. Extracts from industrial survey by Lockwood, Greene & Co. Sanford, Lee County Chamber of Commerce [1924]
16 p. 15cm.

1. Sanford, N.C.

NL 0437864 NcU

Lockwood, Greene & Company, inc.
see also Lockwood Greene Engineers, Inc.

VOLUME 337

Lockwood, Greene & Co. of Canada, ltd.
Building with foresight.
Montreal [c1920]
27 p. illus., plans.

Page 27 in French.

NL 0437866 CaOTP

Lockwood Greene Engineers, Inc.
Appraisal reports. New York: Lockwood Greene Engineers, Inc.[, 1930.] 12 p. nar. 12°.

535800A. 1. Valuation, Industrial.
N. Y. P. L. July 17, 1931

NL 0437867 NN

Lockwood Greene engineers, inc.
Building with foresight; a partial list of clients and illustrations of typical industrial buildings. New York city, Boston [etc.] Lockwood Greene engineers, inc. [©1929]
63, [1] p. incl. front., illus. 27½cm.
Cover-title: Industrial plants illustrating Building with foresight.

1. Mill and factory buildings. 2. Mercantile buildings. 3. Office buildings. I. Title.
30-20612
Library of Congress TH4511.L65
——— Copy 2.
Copyright A 16398 [3] 692.4

NL 0437868 DLC

Lockwood Greene Engineers, Inc.
Facts about fire insurance.

[New York, cop. 19 8°.
v. diagrs.

1. Insurance, Fire.
N. Y. P. L. July 11, 1931

NL 0437869 NN ICJ

Lockwood Greene Engineers, Inc.
Industrial survey of Huntington, W.Va. April 1942. New York, 1942.
8 p.ℓ., 169 ℓ.incl.plans, tables. maps.

Manifold copy.

NL 0437870 MH-BA NcC

Lockwood Greene Engineers, Inc.
Industrial survey of the Wyoming Valley, Pennsylvania. [New York, Lockwood Greene Engineers, Inc., 1930]
9 l., 269 numb. l. incl. front., maps (1 fold.) tables, diagrs. 28cm.
A survey made by Lockwood Greene Engineers, Inc.
Mimeographed.

NL 0437871 ICJ

Lockwood Greene Engineers, Inc.
[Minor publications]
Some publications issued by the earlier firm: Lockwood, Greene & Co., Boston.

NL 0437872 ICJ

Lockwood Greene Engineers, Inc.
Oklahoma City business and its trade territory
see under Oklahoma City. Chamber of commerce.

711.411
L62 Lockwood Greene Engineers, inc.
Proposed industrial and residential community known as Ricwilville. Engineering report. Cleveland, Ric-Wil Co., 1950.
12p.
"This comprehensive engineering report presents a comparison between central power plant operation and individual plant operation for serving the development with heating, air conditioning, hot water, and industriel process steam."
1. Planned communities.

NL 0437874 DHUD

Lockwood Greene engineers, inc.
Report on cotton textile manufacturing in California for the San Joaquin valley association of commercial organization secretaries, May 1, 1945. New York, N. Y., Boston [etc.] Lockwood Greene engineers, inc., ©1945.
1 p. l., [1], ii, [1], 49 p. incl. 2 maps on 1 l., fold. plan. 28 x 21½cm.
Cover-title: Cotton textile manufacturing in California.

1. Cotton growing and manufacture—California. I. San Joaquin valley association of commercial organization secretaries.
45-19882
Library of Congress HD9877.C2L6
[3] 338.4767721

NL 0437875 DLC

Lockwood Greene engineers, inc.
Report on the industrial resources of the part of Maine served by companies affiliated with New England public service company. [New York] Lockwood Greene engineers, inc. [1929]
cover-title, 8 p. l., 2-318 numb. l. incl. maps, diagrs. 27½cm.
A study made by Lockwood Greene engineers, inc. for the New England public service company. cf. 2d prelim. leaf.

1. Maine—Indus. 2. Maine—Econ. condit. 3. Maine. I. New England public service company.
34-10889
Library of Congress HC107.M2L6 330.9741

NL 0437876 DLC OC1 NN ICRL ICJ

Lockwood Greene Engineers, Inc.
see also Lockwood, Greene & Company, inc.

[Lockwood hardware manufacturing company, *Fitchburg, Mass.*]
Build good hardware business. Let's work it out together! [Fitchburg, 1944]
cover-title, [17] p., 1 l., [iii]-ix, 212 p., 1 l., [18] p. incl. illus., forms, diagrs. plans (1 fold.) tables (part fold.) 30 x 22½cm.
"Copyright ... [by] Lockwood hardware mfg. co."
Includes Taking the mystery out of builders' hardware, by Adon H. Brownell. 2d ed. (1 l., [iii]-ix, 212 p., 1 l.)

1. Hardware. 2. Building fittings. I. Brownell, Adon H. Taking the mystery out of builders' hardware. II. Title.
44-40306
Library of Congress TS400.L6
[3] 658.971

NL 0437878 DLC

---

ffF869
S3
.7
M34
no.18
x
Lockwood House, San Francisco.
Dinner bill of fare. [San Francisco] O'Meara & Painter, printers [between 1854 and 1859]
menu 33x15cm. [Menus of early San Francisco hotels and restaurants, no.18]

In portfolio.
Ornamental borders.
"Lockwood House, 93 Pine Street, between Montgomery and Sansome. Mr. & Mrs. John L. Bills, Proprietors."

1. Menus. 2. Early printing - California - San Francisco. I. Bills, John L. (Series)

NL 0437879 CU-B

---

ffF869
S3
.7
M34
no.19
x
Lockwood House, San Francisco.
Dinner bill of fare. [San Francisco] O'Meara & Painter, printers [between 1854 and 1859]
menu 33x15cm. [Menus of early San Francisco hotels and restaurants, no.19]

In portfolio.
Printed on blue paper with selections in upper case. Ornamental borders.
"Lockwood House, 93 Pine Street, between Montgomery and Sansome. Mr. & Mrs. John L. Bills, Proprietors."

1. Menus. 2. Early printing - California - San Francisco. I. Bills, John L. (Series)

NL 0437880 CU-B

---

q
HE
2947
L635
LAC
Lockwood, Kessler & Bartlett, inc.
Informe sobre los estudios del ferrocarril del Río Magdalena. Bogotá, Imp. Deptal. [1952]
42p. illus. 30cm.

1. Railroads - Colombia. I. Title.

NL 0437881 TxU

670.85
~~.L81~~
Lockwood manufacturing company.
Lockwood hardware. South Norwalk, Conn., 1914.
688 p. illus., 30 cm.

1. Hardware - Catalogs.

NL 0437882 DSI

Lockwood Memorial Library, *Buffalo*
see New York (State) State University, *Buffalo*. Lockwood Memorial Library.

Lockwood Publishing Co., Kalamazoo, Mich.
Human heads rendered in many ways. [Kalamazoo, G. H. Lockwood, 1923?] 48 p. illus. 29cm. (Lockwood art technique plates. no. 8.)

1. Head.
N. Y. P. L. January 31, 1946

NL 0437884 NN

Lockwood Publishing Co., Kalamazoo, Mich.
The priest and the billy goat [by] G.H. Lockwood. Kalamazoo, Mich. [1913?]
32p. illus. 16cm. (Its Publications, no.1)

Cover title.

1.Catholic Church-Clergy. 2.Socialism and Catholic Church. I.Lockwood, G.H. II.Title.

NL 0437885 Mi NBu

VOLUME 337

Lockwood Publishing Co., Kalamazoo, Mich.
The soldier and the billy goat ₍by₎ G.H. Lockwood. Kalamazoo, Mich. ₍1913?₎
32p. illus. 16cm. (Its Publications, no.2)

Cover title.

1.Government, Resistance to. 2.War and socialism. I.Lockwood, G.H. II.Title.

NL 0437886 Mi NBu

Lockwood Trade journal co., inc., New York.
Lockwood's directory of the paper, and allied trades
see under title

Lockwood trade journal co., inc., New York.
The progress of paper, with particular emphasis on the remarkable industrial development in the past 75 years and the part that Paper trade journal has been privileged to share in that development. New York₍1947₎

NL 0437888 CaBVa

Lockwood trade journal co., inc., *New York.*
1690–1940, 250 years of papermaking in America. New York, N. Y., Lockwood trade journal co., inc. ₍©1940₎
1 p. l., 180 p. illus. (incl. ports.) diagr. 29½ x 22½ᶜᵐ.
Pages 136–180, advertising matter.

1. Paper making and trade—U. S.—Hist. I. Title. II. Title: 250 years of papermaking in America.

Library of Congress TS1095.U6L6 41-6919
₍7₎ 676.0973

PP PU
NL 0437889 DLC WaSp WaS OrP MtU NcD ICJ OCl NcRS

Lockwood's builder's, architect's, ₍contractor's & engineer's price book ... A comprehensive hand-book of the latest prices of every kind of material and labour in trades connected with building, including many useful memoranda and tables ... With a supplement containing the London building acts, 18 to 19 and other enactments relating to buildings in the metropolis with the by-laws and other regulations now in force, notes of all important decisions in the superior courts and an index to the acts and regulations ... London, C. Lockwood and son,
v. 19ᶜᵐ.
Editors: F. T. W. Miller.—19 R. S. Ayling.
1. Building—Estimates. I. Miller, Francis T. W., ed. II. Ayling, R. Stephen, ed.
Library of Congress TH435.L8 CA 8-2967 Unrev'd

NL 0437890 DLC CaBVaU MB

Lockwood's dictionary of terms used in the practice of mechanical engineering
see under Horner, Joseph Gregory, 1847-1927.

Lockwood's directory of the paper, and allied trades. ₍1st₎– ed.; 1873/74–
New York, Lockwood trade journal co., inc. ₍etc.₎ 1873–₍19
v. 24½ᶜᵐ. annual.
Title varies slightly.

1. Paper making and trade—Direct.

Library of Congress TS1088.L82 1-12840 Revised
₍r43b2₎

OCl FTaSU ICJ TxDaM PPFr PU AAP
NL 0437892 DLC TxU CLU NcG ICRL TxU DFT NN CU PSt

Lockwood's directory of the paper, and allied trades ... Special traveler's ed. ...
New York, Lockwood trade journal co., inc. ₍©19
v. 19½ᶜᵐ.

1. Paper making and trade—Direct.

Library of Congress TS1088.L83 CA 28-8 Unrev'd

NL 0437893 DLC TxU NcRS

Lockwood's monthly rubber report.
-Dec. 15, 1949. Washington, W. S. Lockwood.
3 v. illus. 29 cm.
Began publication with Jan. 1947 issue? Cf. Union list of serials.

1. Rubber industry and trade—Period. I. Lockwood, Warren S.

HD9161.A1L6 338.47678 52-20959

NL 0437894 DLC MH

Lockyear, Fred W
The practical ventriloquist: an unerring guide to ... ventriloquism ... together with complete information necessary for the successful manipulation of mechanical talking figures. London, Hart & Co.
vi, (1) 8-56 p. 24°.

NL 0437895 NN

Lockyear, M H.
The book-keeper's friend ... Safeguards, or how to prevent and locate errors, and labor-saving methods of addition, concluding with proofs of multiplication and labor-saving rules for calculating interest. Copyrighted and published by M. H. Lockyear ... Evansville, Ind., 1898.
ii, ₍3₎–31 p. front. (port.) 22ᶜᵐ.

1. Bookkeeping.

Library of Congress HF5659.L8 6-33003†

NL 0437896 DLC

Lockyear, M H.
An introductory course; Lockyear's bookkeeping, by M. H. Lockyear ... script illustrations, by F. B. Courtney. New York, Chicago, The Gregg publishing company ₍©1911₎
iv, 105 p. incl. forms. 22½ᶜᵐ. $0.75

1. Bookkeeping.

Library of Congress HF5635.L82 11-31179

NL 0437897 DLC CU

PZ7 .L62 Lockyer, A M
Bubbles. London, New York, Marcus Ward & co. ₍1887₎
1 v. illus. 17 x 21½ cm.

NL 0437898 NjR

Lockyer, Carel
see Lockyer, Charles.

Lockyer, Charles.
An account of the trade in India: containing rules for good government in trade, price courants, and tables: with descriptions of Fort St. George, Acheen, Malacca, Condore, Canton, Anjengo, Muskat, Gombroon, Surat, Goa, Carwar, Telichery, Panola, Calicut, the Cape of Good-Hope, and St. Helena... To which is added, An account of the management of the Dutch in their affairs in India... London, Printed for the author, and sold by S. Crouch, 1711.
6 p. l., 340 p. 20ᶜᵐ.
1. India—Comm.

Library of Congress HF3785.L8 6-26623

NN MH-BA
NL 0437900 DLC CSt MnU NIC CU PU NcD CtY InU

MICROFORMS CENTER FILM 3221 Lockyer, Charles
An account of the trade in India. London, Printed for the author, and sold by S. Crouch, 1711.
340p. 20cm.
Microfilm (negative) London, British Museum, 1969. 1 reel.
Filmed with Terpstra, Heert. De opkomst der westerkwartieren van de Oost-Indische Compagnie. 's-Gravenhage, 1918.
1. India - Comm. I. Title

NL 0437901 WU

Wason Film 3160 no.1 Lockyer, Charles.
Beschryvinge van den koophandel in Oost-indien ... door Carel Lockyer. In 't Engels beschreven, A°. 1711. Nieuwlyks vertaald door Arnout Schuyt. Amsterdam, A. Douci, 1753.
3, 139 l.

Microfilm. 1 reel. 35mm.
With this are filmed: Hemmelmann, F. A., defendant. Het rechtsgeding. Batavia, 1866; Mossel, J. Memorien. ₍Batavia?₎ 1753, 1755;

Zamenspraak wegens de oorzaaken van het bederf der Nederl. O. I. Compagnie. Rotterdam ₍1773?₎; Tweede zamenspraak. Rotterdam ₍1773₎; Les vrais intérêts du commerce de l'état. Londres, 1773; Hofhout, J. Bataviasche almanach. Rotterdam ₍n.d. and₎ Oost-en West-Indische post. Utrecht, 1784.
1. Asia, South eastern--Comm. 2. India--Comm. I. Title.

NL 0437903 NIC

Lockyer, Charles R
Kentucky taxes affecting life insurance. Lexington, University of Kentucky, 1950.
vi, 68 p. 22 cm. (Bulletin of the Bureau of Business Research, College of Commerce, no. 22)
Bibliographical footnotes.

1. Insurance, Life—Kentucky—Taxation. I. Title. (Series: Kentucky. University. Bureau of Business Research. Bulletin no. 22)

HG8913.K4L6 368.3 50-62931

NL 0437904 DLC WaU-L ViU OOxM TxU MiU

Lockyer, Cuthbert Henry Jones, 1867-
Adenomyoma. Prior. Hagertown; Md.
pp.1-36. 8°

NL 0437905 OCIW-H

VOLUME 337

Lockyer, Cuthbert Henry Jones, 1867–
Fibroids and allied tumours (myoma and adenomyoma); their pathology, clinical features and surgical treatment, by Cuthbert Lockyer ... with an introductory notice by Alban Doran ... with 316 illustrations including 37 coloured plates. London, Macmillan and co., ltd., 1918.
xix, [1], 603 p. illus., xxxvii col. pl.
Bibliographical foot-notes.
1. Tumors. 2. [Fibroma] 3. [Myoma] 4. [Adenomyoma] 5. Abdomen—Surgery.
S G 18 350
U. S. Surg.-gen. off. Libr. for Library of Congress [a40b1]

NL 0437906 DI-GS NBuU DNLM OU MiU ICJ PPC

Lockyer, Cuthbert Henry Jones, 1867-
The Lockyer collection of obstetric and gynaecological specimens
see under Charing Cross Hospital Medical School. Museum.

B610.24 Ed4 1805 v.1
Lockyer, Edmund.
De chorea ... Edinburgi, Excudebat J. Ballantyne, 1805.
[8], 43 p. 21 cm. (In Edinburgh. University. Dissertationes medicae, 1805, v.1)
Inaug. Diss. - Edinburgh.

NL 0437908 MnU-B DNLM

Lockyer, Edmund B.
National impeachment. To mankind, especially capitalists and shareholders. By Edmund B. Lockyer ... Edinburgh: D. Mathers [etc., etc.] 1866. 71 p. 22cm.
1. Railways—Social and economic relations—Gt. Br. 2. Harbors—Gt. Br. 3. Commerce—Gt. Br.
N. Y. P. L. November 20, 1942

NL 0437909 NN

Lockyer, Florence
The garland alphabet. London, Society for Promoting Christian Knowledge [1891]
[30] p. illus.

NL 0437910 NNC

Lockyer, George J
The strangers' illustrated guide through Lincoln
see under title

R383.22 L815
Lockyer, Gilbert E , comp.
Colonial stamps: also those of Great Britain; comprising lists of the various postal issues, watermarks, and perforations, with geographical and other notes. London, Stanley Gibbons and co., [pl887]. illus.

NL 0437912 WaSp MB CtY

Lockyer, Herbert.
Are these the last days? Grand Rapids, Zondervan Pub. House [1951]
29 p. 20 cm.
1. End of the world. I. Title.
Full name: Herbert Henry John Lockyer.
BT875.L75 54-30478

NL 0437913 DLC

Lockyer, Herbert
The art of praying and speaking in public; practical hints for Christians who desire to witness. Grand Rapids, Zondervan [c1952]
61 p. 20 cm.
Bibliography: p. 60-61.
1. Oratory. I. Title.

NL 0437914 KyWAT

BV4235 .L3L82
Lockyer, Herbert.
The art of praying and speaking in public. London, P. Jackman [1955]
63 p. 19 cm.
1. Preaching, Lay.

NL 0437915 IEG

Lockyer, Herbert
The breath of God. Cleveland, Ohio, Union Gospel Press [c1949]
257 p.

NL 0437916 CLamB CMIG

Lockyer, Herbert.
Cameos of prophecy; are these the last days? By Herbert Lockyer ... Grand Rapids, Mich., Zondervan publishing house [1942]
128 p. 20cm.
1. End of the world. I. Title.
43-194
Library of Congress BT875.L76
[2] 236

NL 0437917 DLC

RR46 L818C
Lockyer, Herbert.
The Christ of Christmas. New York, Loizeaux Brothers [c1942]
93 p.
1. Jesus Christ - Person and offices. 2. Incarnation. 3. Christmas. I. Title.

NL 0437918 TxFS

Lockyer, Herbert, ed.
Commentary on the whole Bible... (Introd. by Dr. H. Lockyer) Grand Rapids, Zondervan [1954]
see under Bible. English. 1954.

Lockyer, Herbert.
The double name, by Herbert Lockyer. Grand Rapids, Mich., Zondervan publishing house [c1936]
28 p. 20cm. (*His* Unique Bible study series)
1. Bible—Language, style. I. Title.
37-2977
Library of Congress BS537.L6
——— Copy 2.
Copyright A 103004 [2] 220.8808

NL 0437920 DLC

Lockyer, Herbert.
... Earthquakes! The prophetic significance of physical upheavals. [Chicago: The Bible institute colportage ass'n. c1935]
15 p. 18½cm.
Cover-title.
At head of title: Herbert Lockyer writes on.
1. Earthquakes. 2. Prophecies. I. The Bible institute colportage association, Chicago.
N. Y. P. L. March 20, 1943

NL 0437921 NN

Lockyer, Herbert.
Evangelize or fossilize, a stirring call to evangelism, by Herbert Lockyer ... Chicago, The Bible institute colportage ass'n. [c1938]
92 p. 19½cm.
1. Evangelistic work. 2. Sermons, English. I. Title.
38-25912
Library of Congress BV3790.L56
——— Copy 2.
Copyright A 119089 [3] 253

NL 0437922 DLC

Lockyer, Herbert.
Fairest of all, and other sermons, by Dr. Herbert Lockyer. Grand Rapids, Mich., W. B. Eerdmans publishing co. [c1936]
157 p. 20cm.
1. Sermons, English. I. Title.
37-12795
Library of Congress BV4253.L6
——— Copy 2.
Copyright A 105950 [3] 252

NL 0437923 DLC NRCR

Lockyer, Herbert.
Give us this day; daily portions for pilgrims, by Herbert Lockyer ... Grand Rapids, Mich., Zondervan publishing house [1942]
126 p. 19½cm.
"Appeared in Revelation during 1941."—Pref.
1. Devotional exercises. 2. Calendars. I. Title.
42-16415
Library of Congress BV4832.L55
[2] 242

NL 0437924 DLC

Lockyer, Herbert.
The gospel in the Pentateuch ... by Herbert Lockyer ... Chicago, The Bible institute colportage ass'n [c1939]
125 p. illus. (map) diagr. 19cm.
1. Bible. O. T. Pentateuch—Study—Text-books. 2. Bible—Study—Text-books—O. T. Pentateuch. I. Title.
39-9927
Library of Congress BS1227.L6
——— Copy 2.
Copyright A 126854 [2] 222.1

NL 0437925 DLC

VOLUME 337

Lockyer, Herbert.
The H-bomb and the end of the age. Grand Rapids, Zondervan, °1950.
32 p. 20 cm.

1. Atomic bomb—Moral and religious aspects. 2. End of the world. I. Title.
Full name: Herbert Henry John Lockyer.

BR115.A85L56 236 50-11934

NL 0437926 DLC

Lockyer, Herbert.
Herbert Lockyer writes on the triads of Scripture ... [Chicago, The Bible institute colportage ass'n. °1935]
16 p. 18½cm.

1. Symbolism. 2. Three (The number) I. Title: The triads of Scripture.

Library of Congress BS477.L6 35-9015
Copyright AA 172505 [2] 220.6

NL 0437927 DLC

Lockyer, Herbert.
The heritage of saints; or, Studies in the Holy Spirit... Chicago, Bible inst. colportage assn. of Chic., n.d.
127 p.

NL 0437928 PPEB

Lockyer, Herbert.
How I can make prayer more effective. Grand Rapids, Zondervan Pub. House [1953]
125 p. 19 cm.

1. Prayer. I. Title.
Full name: Herbert Henry John Lockyer.

BV220.L6 264.1 53-13072 ‡

NL 0437929 DLC KyU KyLxCB PPRETS

Lockyer, Herbert.
Is there healing for all?... Oklahoma City, Okla., Western network radio church of the air [n.d.]
74 p., ports., 22cm.

NL 0437930 NjPT

Lockyer, Herbert.
The love story of Ruth; the book of books—and how to read it, by Herbert Lockyer. [Philadelphia, American Bible conference association, inc., °1935]
12 p. 19½cm. (*On cover:* Revelation series. [no. 2])
"Foreword" on p. [2] of cover.

1. Bible. O. T. Ruth—Criticism, interpretation, etc. 2. Bible—Criticism, interpretation, etc.—O. T. Ruth. I. Title.

Library of Congress BS1315.L6 35-13953
Copyright AA 181586 [3] 222.3

NL 0437931 DLC

Lockyer, Herbert
The mulberry trees; or, When revival comes. Grand Rapids, Wm. B. Eerdmans Publishing Co., [c1936]

91 p.

1. Revivals. I. Title.

NL 0437932 CLamB

Lockyer, Herbert.
The mystery of godliness; of, The virgin birth; or, Was Christ virgin horn? Grand Rapids, W.B. Eerdmans [1935]
68 p. 20cm.

"Books that have helped me": p. 68.

NL 0437933 NjPT

Lockyer, Herbert.
A panorama of prophecy, by Herbert Lockyer. Philadelphia, Pa., The American Bible conference association [°1936]
43 p. 19½cm.

1. End of the world. I. Title.

Library of Congress BT875.L77 36-12300
——— Copy 2.
Copyright A 94320 [3] 236

NL 0437934 DLC

Lockyer, Herbert.
Russians & Romans; or, Will the European crisis result in the end of the age? By Dr. Herbert Lockyer ... Grand Rapids, Mich., Zondervan publishing house [°1940]
28, [1] p. illus. (incl. map) 19½cm.
"Reprinted ... from 'Grace and truth', the publication of the Denver Bible institute, Denver, Colorado."
"The Man in yonder glory" (words and music) : p. [29]

1. End of the world. I. Title.

Library of Congress BT875.L78 1940 40-35355
——— Copy 2.
Copyright [2] 236

NL 0437935 DLC

Lockyer, Herbert.
... Satan and the spider, by Dr. Herbert Lockyer. Grand Rapids, Mich., Wm. B. Eerdmans publishing co., 1945.
87 p. 1 l. 20cm. (Home devotional library)

1. Devotional literature. I. Title.

Library of Congress BV4832.L56 45-9870
[2] 242

NL 0437936 DLC

Lockyer, Herbert.
Satan the Anti-Christ, by Herbert Lockyer ... Grand Rapids, Mich., Zondervan publishing house [°1936]
74 p. 20cm.

1. Devil. 2. Antichrist. I. Title.

Library of Congress BT980.L6 37-1548
——— Copy 2.
Copyright A 103001 [2] 235

NL 0437937 DLC

Lockyer, Herbert.
Sorrows and stars, by Herbert Lockyer, D. D. Grand Rapids, Mich., Wm. B. Eerdmans publishing company, 1938.
135 p. 20cm.
"First edition."

1. Evangelistic sermons. 2. Sermons, English. I. Title.

Library of Congress BV3797.L6 38-30216
——— Copy 2.
Copyright A 119955 [3] 252

NL 0437938 DLC

Lockyer, Herbert, and H. Lockyer.
The two Herberts, father and son; two radio dialogues by Rev. Herbert Lockyer...and Herbert Lockyer, jr. ...broadcast over WMCA and affiliated stations... January 1, 1936 and... January 5, 1936... [New York? 1936] 15 p. 20cm.

1. No subject. I. Lockyer, Herbert, 1914?–
N. Y. P. L. July 29, 1938

NL 0437939 NN

Lockyer, Herbert.
"V" for victory; sermons on the Christian's victories, by Herbert Lockyer ... Grand Rapids, Mich., Zondervan publishing house [°1941]
3 p. l., 11-99 p. 19½cm.

1. Sermons, American. I. Title.

Library of Congress BV4253.L63 42-3777
[2] 241

NL 0437940 DLC

BV85
.L81 Lockyer, Herbert
When God died, a series of meditations for Lent, including descriptive messages on the seven sayings on the cross. Grand Rapids, Wm. B. Eerdmans, 1939.
118p.

1. Lenten sermons. 2. Sermons - American. 3. Jesus Christ - Seven last words. I. Title.

NL 0437941 TNJ-R

BV4277
L6 Lockyer, Herbert
When God died; a series of meditations for Lent, including descriptive messages on the seven last words of Jesus from the cross. 2d ed. Grand Rapids, Eerdmans, 1942.
118 p. 20 cm.

1. Lenten sermons. I. Title.

NL 0437942 PPiPT

Lockyer, Herbert Henry John
see Lockyer, Herbert.

SYMBOLS MOST FREQUENTLY USED IN THE NATIONAL UNION CATALOG

MISSISSIPPI

MsG William Alexander Percy Memorial Library, Greenville.
MsSC* Mississippi State University, State College.
MsSM Mississippi State University, State College.
MsU University of Mississippi, University.

MONTANA

MtBC Montana State University, Bozeman.
MtBozC* Montana State University at Bozeman.
MtU University of Montana, Missoula.

NEW YORK

N New York State Library, Albany.
NAlU State University of New York at Albany.
NAurW Wells College, Aurora.
NB Brooklyn Public Library, Brooklyn.
NBB Brooklyn Museum Libraries, Brooklyn.
NBC Brooklyn College, Brooklyn.
NBM Medical Research Library of Brooklyn.
NBPol Polytechnic Institute of Brooklyn, Brooklyn.
NBSU-M State University of New York, Downstate Medical Center Library, Brooklyn.
NBiSU-H State University of New York, Harpur College, Binghamton.
NBronSL Sarah Lawrence College, Bronxville.
NBu Buffalo and Erie County Public Library, Buffalo.
NBuC State University of New York, College at Buffalo.
NBuG Grosvenor Reference Division, Buffalo and Erie County Public Library, Buffalo.
NBuU State University of New York at Buffalo.
NCH Hamilton College, Clinton.
NCaS St. Lawrence University, Canton.
NCorniC Corning Glass Works Library, Corning. (Includes Corning Museum of Glass Library)
NCoxHi Greene County Historical Society, Inc., Coxsackie.
NFQC Queens College Library, Flushing.
NGrnUN* United Nations Library.
NHC Colgate University, Hamilton.
NHi New York Historical Society, New York.
NIC Cornell University, Ithaca.
NJQ Queens Borough Public Library, Jamaica.
NL* Newberry Library, Chicago.
NLC Not a library symbol.
NN New York Public Library.
NNAB American Bible Society, New York.
NNAHI Augustinian Historical Institute, New York.
NNAJHi American Jewish Historical Society, New York.
NNB Association of the Bar of the City of New York, New York.
NNBG New York Botanical Garden, Bronx Park, New York.
NNC Columbia University, New York.
NNC-T — Teachers College Library.
NNCFR Council on Foreign Relations, New York.
NNCoCi City College of New York, New York.
NNE Engineering Societies Library, New York.
NNF Fordham University, New York.
NNFI French Institute in the United States, New York.
NNG General Theological Seminary of the Protestant Episcopal Church. New York.
NNGr Grolier Club Library, New York.
NNH Hispanic Society of America, New York.
NNHeb Hebrew Union College, Jewish Institute of Religion Library, New York.
NNHi New York Historical Society.
NNJ Jewish Theological Seminary of America, New York.
NNJIR* Jewish Institute of Religion, New York.
NNJef Jefferson School of Social Science, New York. (Library no longer in existence)
NNM American Museum of Natural History, New York.
NNMM Metropolitan Museum of Art Library, New York.
NNMor* Pierpont Morgan Library.
NNNAM New York Academy of Medicine, New York.
NNNM New York Medical College, Flower & Fifth Avenue Hospitals, New York.
NNNPsan New York Psychoanalytic Institute, New York.
NNPM Pierpont Morgan Library, New York.
NNQ* Queens Borough Public Library, New York.
NNQC* Queens College Library, Flushing.
NNRI Rockefeller Institute for Medical Research, New York.
NNSU-M* State University of New York College of Medicine at New York City.

NEW YORK *continued*

NNU New York University Libraries, New York.
NNU-W — Washington Square Library.
NNUN United Nations Library, New York.
NNUN-W — Woodrow Wilson Memorial Library.
NNUT Union Theological Seminary, New York.
NNUT-Mc — McAlpin Collection.
NNWML Wagner College Library, Staten Island.
NNYI Yivo Institute for Jewish Research, New York.
NNZI Zionist Archives and Library of Palestine Foundation, New York.
NNerC College of New Rochelle, New Rochelle.
NNiaU Niagara University, Niagara University.
NPV Vassar College, Poughkeepsie,
NRAB Samuel Colgate Baptist Historical Library of the American Baptist Historical Society, Rochester.
NRU University of Rochester, Rochester.
NSchU Union College, Schenectady.
NSyU Syracuse University, Syracuse.
NUt Utica Public Library.
NWM U.S. Military Academy, West Point.
NYPL* New York Public Library.
NYhI International Business Machines Corporation, Thomas J. Watson Research Center, Yorktown Heights.

NEBRASKA

NbOC Creighton University, Omaha.
NbU University of Nebraska, Lincoln.

NORTH CAROLINA

Nc North Carolina State Library, Raleigh.
Nc-Ar North Carolina State Department of Archives and History, Raleigh.
NcA Pack Memorial Public Library, Asheville.
NcA-S — Sondley Reference Library.
NcAS* Sondley Reference Library, Asheville.
NcC Public Library of Charlotte & Mecklenburg County, Charlotte.
NcCC Charlotte College Library, Charlotte.
NcCJ Johnson C. Smith University, Charlotte.
NcCU University of North Carolina at Charlotte.
NcD Duke University, Durham.
NcDurC North Carolina College at Durham, Durham.
NcGU* University of North Carolina at Greensboro.
NcGW University of North Carolina at Greensboro.
NcGuG Guilford College, Guilford.
NcR Olivia Raney Public Library, Raleigh.
NcRR Richard B. Harrison Public Library, Raleigh.
NcRS North Carolina State University at Raleigh.
NcU University of North Carolina, Chapel Hill.
NcWfC* Wake Forest College, Winston-Salem.
NcWfSB Southeastern Baptist Theological Seminary Library, Wake Forest.
NcWilA Atlantic Christian College, Wilson.
NcWilC Carolina Discipliniana Library, Wilson.
NcWsW Wake Forest College, Winston-Salem.

NORTH DAKOTA

NdFA North Dakota State University, Fargo. (Formerly North Dakota Agricultural College)
NdHi State Historical Society of North Dakota, Bismarck.
NdU University of North Dakota Library, Grand Forks.

NEW HAMPSHIRE

Nh New Hampshire State Library, Concord.
NhD Dartmouth College, Hanover.
NhU University of New Hampshire, Durham.

NEW JERSEY

NjGbS Glassboro State College, Glassboro.
NjHi New Jersey Historical Society, Newark.
NjMD Drew University, Madison.
NjN Newark Public Library.
NjNBR* Rutgers–The State University, New Brunswick.
NjNbS New Brunswick Theological Seminary, New Brunswick.
NjNbT* New Brunswick Theological Seminary.
NjP Princeton University, Princeton.
NjPT Princeton Theological Seminary, Princeton.
NjR Rutgers–The State University, New Brunswick.
NjT Trenton Free Library, Trenton.

NEW MEXICO

NmA Albuquerque Public Library, New Mexico.
NmU University of New Mexico, Albuquerque.
NmUpU New Mexico State University, University Park.

NEVADA

NvU University of Nevada, Reno.

OHIO

O Ohio State Library, Columbus.
OAU Ohio University, Athens.
OAkU University of Akron, Akron.
OBerB Baldwin-Wallace College, Berea.
OBlC Bluffton College, Bluffton.
OC Public Library of Cincinnati and Hamilton County, Cincinnati.
OCH Hebrew Union College, Cincinnati.
OCHP Historical and Philosophical Society of Ohio, Cincinnati.
OCLloyd Lloyd Library and Museum, Cincinnati.
OCU University of Cincinnati, Cincinnati.
OCX Xavier University, Cincinnati.
OCl Cleveland Public Library.
OClCS Case Institute of Technology, Cleveland.
OClFC Cleveland State University, Cleveland. (Formerly Fenn College)
OClJC John Carroll University, Cleveland.
OClMA Cleveland Museum of Art, Cleveland.
OClSA Cleveland Institute of Art, Cleveland.
OClW Case Western Reserve University, Cleveland.
OClWHi Western Reserve Historical Society, Cleveland.
ODW Ohio Wesleyan University, Delaware.
ODa Dayton and Montgomery County Library, Dayton.
ODaStL St. Leonard College Library, Dayton.
ODaU University of Dayton, Dayton.
OEac East Cleveland Public Library.
OFH Rutherford B. Hayes Library, Fremont.
OGK Kenyon College, Gambier.
OHi Ohio State Historical Society, Columbus.
OKentC Kent State University, Kent.
OO Oberlin College, Oberlin.
OOxM Miami University, Oxford.
OSW Wittenberg University, Springfield.
OTU University of Toledo, Toledo.
OU Ohio State University, Columbus.
OWibfU Wilberforce University, Carnegie Library, Wilberforce.
OWicB Borromeo Seminary, Wickliffe.
OWoC College of Wooster, Wooster.
OWorP Pontifical College Josephinum, Worthington.
OYesA Antioch College, Yellow Springs.

OKLAHOMA

Ok Oklahoma State Library, Oklahoma City.
OkEG Graduate Seminary Library, Enid.
OkS Oklahoma State University, Stillwater.
OkT Tulsa Public Library.
OkU University of Oklahoma, Norman.

OREGON

Or Oregon State Library, Salem.
OrCS Oregon State University Library, Corvallis.
OrHi Oregon Historical Society, Portland.
OrP Library Association of Portland, Portland.
OrPR Reed College, Portland.
OrPS Portland State College, Portland.
OrSaW Willamette University, Salem.
OrStbM Mount Angel College, Mount Angel Abbey, Saint Benedict.
OrU University of Oregon, Eugene.

PENNSYLVANIA

PBL Lehigh University, Bethlehem.
PBa Academy of the New Church, Bryn Athyn.
PBm Bryn Mawr College, Bryn Mawr.
PCA* Samuel Colgate Baptist Historical Library of the American Baptist Historical Society, Rochester, N. Y.
PCC Crozer Theological Seminary, Chester.
PCamA Alliance College, Cambridge Springs.
PCarlD Dickinson College, Carlisle.
PHC Haverford College, Haverford.
PHi Historical Society of Pennsylvania, Philadelphia.
PJA Abington Library Society, Jenkintown.
PJAlG Alverthorpe Gallery, Rosenwald Collection, Jenkintown.
PJB Beaver College, Jenkintown.